W9-BVP-108

Symbolic Logic

$p \wedge q$	Conjunction (p **and** q)
$p \vee q$	Disjunction (p **or** q)
$\sim p$	Negation (**not** p)
$p \Leftrightarrow q$	The statements p and q are **equivalent;** that is, they have identical truth tables.
$p \to q$	Conditional (**If** p **then** q)
$p \leftrightarrow q$	Biconditional (p **if and only if** q)
$q \to p$	Converse of $p \to q$
$\sim p \to \sim q$	Inverse of $p \to q$
$\sim q \to \sim p$	Contrapositive of $p \to q$
Modus ponens	$\begin{array}{l} p \to q \\ \underline{p \qquad} \\ \therefore q \end{array}$
Modus tollens	$\begin{array}{l} p \to q \\ \underline{\sim q \qquad} \\ \therefore \sim p \end{array}$
Hypothetical syllogism	$\begin{array}{l} p \to q \\ \underline{q \to r} \\ \therefore p \to r \end{array}$
Disjunctive syllogism	$\begin{array}{l} p \vee q \\ \underline{\sim p \qquad} \\ \therefore q \end{array}$

Algebra

If $a \geq 0$, then:

$|x| < a$ is equivalent to $-a < x < a$

$|x| > a$ is equivalent to $x > a$ or $x < -a$

Quadratic formula, $x = \dfrac{-b \pm \sqrt{b^2 - 4ac}}{2a}$	Gives the solution(s) of a quadratic equation $ax^2 + bx + c = 0$.
Linear equation	An equation that can be written in the form $ax + by = c$.
Distance formula, $d = \sqrt{(x_2 - x_1)^2 + (y_2 - y_1)^2}$	The distance between two points (x_1, y_1) and (x_2, y_2).
Slope of a line	$m = \dfrac{y_2 - y_1}{x_2 - x_1}$
Point-slope equation	$y - y_1 = m(x - x_1)$
Slope-intercept equation	$y = mx + b$
General equation of a line	$Ax + By = C$

Geometry

$S = (n - 2) \cdot 180°$	Sum of the measures of the angles of a polygon of n sides.
Circumference, $C = \pi d = 2\pi r$	The perimeter of a circle of diameter d (radius r).
$A = bh$	The area of a rectangle (or, more generally, a parallelogram) of base b and height h.
$A = \dfrac{1}{2}bh$	The area of a triangle of base b and height h.
$A = \pi r^2$	The area of a circle of radius r.
Pythagorean theorem, $c^2 = a^2 + b^2$	The square of the hypotenuse c of a right triangle equals the sum of the squares of the other two sides (a and b).
$V = a^3$ $S = 6a^2$	The volume V and surface area S of a cube of edge a.
$V = lwh$ $S = 2(lw + lh + wh)$	Volume V and surface area S of a rectangular box of length l, width w, and height h.
$V = \pi r^2 h$ $S = 2\pi rh + 2\pi r^2$	Volume V and surface area S of a circular cylinder of radius r and height h.
$V = \frac{1}{3}\pi r^2 h$ $S = \pi r^2 + \pi rs$	Volume V and surface area S of a circular cone of radius r, height h, and slant height s.
$V = \frac{4}{3}\pi r^3$ $S = 4\pi r^2$	Volume V and surface area S of a sphere of radius r.

Consumer Mathematics

$I = Prt$	Simple interest I when P is the principal and r the annual rate for time t.
$A = P(1 + i)^n$	Compound interest A when P is the principal, i is the rate per period, and n is the number of periods.
$\dfrac{r(r + 1)}{n(n + 1)} \cdot F$	The unearned interest on a loan of n periods with r remaining periods when F is the finance charge.

Counting and Probability

Sequential Counting Principle (SCP)	If one event can occur in m ways, a second event can occur in n ways, a third event can occur in p ways, and so on, then the sequence of events can occur in $m \times n \times p \ldots$ ways.
$P(n, r) = \dfrac{n!}{(n-r)!}$	The number of permutations of n objects taken r at a time.
$C(n, r) = \dfrac{n!}{r!(n-r)!}$	The number of combinations of n objects taken r at a time.
$P(T') = 1 - P(T)$	The probability of the complement of an event.
$P(A \cup B) = P(A) + P(B) - P(A \cap B)$	The probability of event A **or** event B.
$P(A \mid B) = \dfrac{P(A \cap B)}{P(B)}$	The probability of event A **given** event B.
$P(A \cap B) = P(A) \cdot P(B)$	The probability of event A **and** event B where A and B are independent.
Odds f: u in favor of an event	Where f and u, respectively, represent the number of favorable and unfavorable ways that an event can occur.
$E = a_1p_1 + a_2p_2 + \cdots + a_np_n$	The expected value E for an event where $a_1, a_2, \ldots, a_n$ are the values that occur with probability $p_1, p_2, \ldots, p_n$.

Statistics

Mean $\overline{x}$	The sum of a set of data values divided by the number of values.
Median	The middle value when data values are ranked in order of magnitude. If there is an even number of values, it is the mean of the two middle values.
Mode	The value(s) that occur most often in a set of data.
Range	The difference between the greatest and least values in a set of data.

$$s = \sqrt{\frac{(x_1 - \overline{x})^2 + (x_2 - \overline{x})^2 + \cdots + (x_n - \overline{x})^2}{n-1}}$$

The standard deviation of a set of data values $x_1, x_2, \ldots, x_n$.

$$z = \frac{x - \mu}{\sigma}$$

The z-score associated with the raw data value x where μ is the mean and σ is the standard deviation.

EDITION 10

Topics in Contemporary Mathematics

Ignacio Bello
University of South Florida

Anton Kaul
Cal Poly, San Luis Obispo

Jack R. Britton
University of South Florida

BROOKS/COLE
CENGAGE Learning™

Australia • Brazil • Japan • Korea • Mexico • Singapore • Spain • United Kingdom • United States

BROOKS/COLE
CENGAGE Learning™

Topics in Contemporary Mathematics, 10th Edition
Ignacio Bello, Anton Kaul, Jack R. Britton

Senior Acquisitions Editor: Marc Bove
Developmental Editor: Stefanie Beeck
Assistant Editor: Lauren Crosby
Editorial Assistant: Ryan Furtkamp
Media Editor: Bryon Spencer
Senior +Brand Manager: Gordon Lee
Senior Market Development Manager: Danae April
Senior Content Project Manager: Tanya Nigh
Art Director: Vernon Boes
Manufacturing Planner: Rebecca Cross
Rights Acquisitions Specialist: Tom McDonough
Production Service and Compositor: Cenveo Publisher Services
Photo Researcher: Jeremy Glover, Q2A/Bill Smith
Text Researcher: Pablo D'Stair
Copy Editor: Betty Passagno
Text Designer: Terri Wright
Cover Designer: Irene Morris
Cover Image: BrendaStarrArt/Getty Images

Library of Congress Control Number: 2012949528

ISBN-13: 978-1-133-10742-2

ISBN-10: 1-133-10742-7

Brooks/Cole
20 Davis Drive
Belmont, CA 94002-3098
USA

Cengage Learning is a leading provider of customized learning solutions with office locations around the globe, including Singapore, the United Kingdom, Australia, Mexico, Brazil, and Japan. Locate your local office at **www.cengage.com/global.**

Cengage Learning products are represented in Canada by Nelson Education, Ltd.

To learn more about Brooks/Cole, visit **www.cengage.com/brooks/cole**

Purchase any of our products at your local college store or at our preferred online store **www.CengageBrain.com.**

Printed in the United States of America
1 2 3 4 5 6 7 16 15 14 13 12

CONTENTS

PREFACE

In this tenth edition we continue with our goal of introducing students to the many interesting mathematical concepts used in our contemporary world. We bring out the basic ideas and techniques as simply and clearly as possible and relate these ideas to other areas—such as sociology, psychology, business, and technology—that will be attractive to the reader. Elementary applications are given whenever feasible. These applications can be found at the beginning of each section, throughout the text discussions and examples, and in the lesson problem sets. As suggested by the *Crossroads in Mathematics: Standards for Introductory College of Mathematics of AMATYC,* we deemphasized the more abstract and theoretical aspects of the subject matter and, instead, placed emphasis on promoting the understanding and use of the various concepts introduced. Important aids to reaching this goal are the **exercise sets,** which include problems ranging from routine drills to more challenging problems for advanced students, and the Using Your Knowledge and Discovery sections appearing at the end of the exercises in most sections. Readers will find considerable support and explanation in the worked-out examples.

A WORD ABOUT PROBLEM SOLVING

Problem solving has become a fixture in mathematics textbooks. Inspired by the teachings of George Polya, and following the recommendations of the NCTM and the MAA, most mathematics books at this level cover the topic. Many texts front-load much of the presentation in the first chapter. We have chosen to integrate problem solving where it is needed and, consequently, where it can be taught and learned most effectively.

For example, a few of the strategies suggested by Polya himself call for making a table, writing an equation, making a diagram, and accounting for all possibilities.

As an ongoing theme of this text, problem solving is presented purposefully not only in Chapter 1 but in meaningful and appropriate contexts when dealing with sets, truth tables, algebra, geometry, probability, finances, and counting, where students can best understand and appreciate its methods. Above all, we hope that this integrated approach will help students learn how to apply problem-solving techniques in the real world once they have completed the course.

NEW TO THE TENTH EDITION

At the request of the reviewers, we have updated the data in most of the applications problems throughout the textbook. In addition we have made the following changes:

- A list of objectives that correspond to the objective heads in the exposition and in the end-of-section exercise sets has been added at the beginning of each section to provide students with a map to navigate each chapter.
- In response to feedback from reviewers, Chapter 5 on Number Theory and the Real Numbers has been extensively revised and condensed creating a more comprehensive chapter.
- Throughout the text, applications have been replaced and revised for currency and student interest.

- The following topics are now more easily accessible in the printed book rather than being available online only: the section on linear programming, right triangle trigonometry, chaos and fractals, as well as the chapters on voting and apportionment, and graph theory.

- An Instructor's Edition is available for the tenth edition providing instructors with an appendix in the book containing answers to all exercises and an appendix that outlines the exercises that are available through Enhanced WebAssign.

SPECIFIC CHAPTER CHANGES

Chapter 1

Section 1.1 now includes Deductive Reasoning, and Section 1.2 has an updated tax table. New exercises dealing with topics such as text messaging, saving water and electricity, and hacked passwords as well as new examples on interpreting pie charts, line graphs, environmental topics and the dangers of texting and driving are included.

Chapter 2

A new introduction and clarification of the concept of set complementation is now in Section 2.2, which also contains 50 new exercises covering hours slept, credit reports, web sites visited, average earning of persons with associate degrees, health care expenses, life expectancy, college costs, and the most populated twitter cities as well as new examples involving diabetes, health care expenses and talking, texting and e-mailing while driving.

Chapter 3

A new technique for doing truth tables is introduced in Sections 3.2-3.4 and Section 3.6 has a new objective to illustrate how to supply a valid conclusion to an argument. Sections 3.1-3.6 have new exercises dealing with social networks, graphs about salaries and ethnicity, statement you can make when asking for a loan, and analyzing online statements. We also added new examples covering negations of conjunctions and disjunctions, implications, and valid conclusions regarding iPhones and smart phones.

Chapter 4

In Section 4.1 we clarify the procedure for multiplication using successive duplications while Sections 4.4 and 4.5 have been combined into a new section dealing with binary, octal and decimal systems and now has a completely revised exercise set. Section 4.2 has new exercises discussing food consumption and national garbage output as well as 2 new examples about writing numbers in Egyptian numerals and as decimals. The Practice Test has been updated to reflect the changes made in Sections 4.1 and 4.4.

Chapter 5

The chapter has been condensed to 6 sections instead of 8. Section 5.1 has new exercises dealing with medication dosages and frequencies, while section 5.2 contains 10 new examples and 86 brand new exercises including applications to graph interpretation for SAT scores and the environmental lapse.

The material in Section 5.3 now includes decimals in expanded form, scientific notation and operations with decimals. New exercises covering per capita garbage production, octane ratings, pulse and cell phone rates, global warming and nutrition have been added. Section 5.4 now includes rational and irrational numbers, the Trichotomy Law and the density of the rational numbers. New Using Your Knowledge Exercises are included. The last two sections cover radicals and real numbers and number sequences. There are new exercises dealing with Prednisone dosages and computer sales. We updated the Summary and the Chapter test for this chapter.

Chapter 6

Section 6.1 has a new example: Saving Lives with Angioplasty or TPA and new exercises on improving gas mileage and first-class mail costs. Section 6.2 has a new example about laptops, desktops and inequalities and new exercises covering the inequalities involved in CAFE regulations. Section 6.3 has new exercises on budgets, expenses, variances and absolute values. The last three sections, 6.4-6.5 cover quadratic equations, modeling and problem solving and ratio, proportion and variation are supported by new examples dealing with factoring, national health insurance, auto stopping distances, and car air pollution and new exercises which cover endangered species, suspension bridges, oil supply-demand and variation and a new Using Your Knowledge topic: Sun Protection Factor and variation. The Summary and Practice Test have been revised.

Chapter 7

We added many new exercises and examples covering topics such as the Deepwater Horizon disaster, tobacco use, Twitter followers and friends, life expectancy, the Kyoto protocol, NFL salaries, credit card debt and smart phone sales. Section 7.8 is a completely new section dealing with linear programming. The Summary and Practice Test have been updated to include linear programming.

Chapter 8

Section 8.1 has a new definition and discussion of parallel and intersecting lines and new exercises covering angles in Hawaiin carvings, solar eclipses, and energy sources for electric power. Section 8.3 has new exercises dealing with compost bins. Section 8.4 has 8 new exercises about EPA approved stadiums, bridges and conveyor belts. In Section 8.5 we discuss the volume of pyramids and 8.6 has new exercises involving efficient travel. Chapter 8 now includes Sections 8.7 (Right Triangle Trigonometry) and 8.8 (Chaos and Fractals) with 9 new examples and 66 new exercises. The Practice Test had been updated to include trigonometry problems.

Chapter 9

We revised the Introduction in 9.1 added a new exercise dealing with the prediction of the day of the week in the future. Section 9.2 has a new topic, Tropical Mathematics, in the Using your Knowledge and is accompanied by 4 new exercises. A new diagram illustrating the smoking and non-smoking states in the U.S. is now in Section 9.3. We revised the Summary and the Practice Test for this chapter.

Chapter 10

We clarified the construction of tree diagrams in Sections 10.1-10.3 with applications to topics including household expenses, Nascar Sprint Cup standings, and smartphones. We also have new exercises dealing with ordering at a restaurant, bottled water, back pain medicine, scanning items at the supermarket, saving the environment and congressional delegations.

Chapter 11

We revised the chapter introduction and added new exercises discussing the probability of hitting a home run. Section 11.2 has a new tree diagram for oil drilling probabilities and new exercises on the NFL draft, defective Katrina housing and shuttle crews. The conditional probability section (11.4) has new examples and exercises involving the workforce. Section 11.5 has new examples and exercises on topics such as baseball and Atlantic hurricanes. Section 11.6 has new examples illustrating how to determine insurance premiums and expected and fair values and new exercises discussing fair prices for life insurance premiums and expected values in baseball.

Chapter 12

Section 12.1 has new exercises on sampling, with applications to Nielsen ratings, best U.S. Presidents, population, household income, education and obesity, and professional hockey and baseball players' salaries. Section 12.2 has new exercises dealing with gas prices, the best-paying jobs in America, attendance at amusement parks and unique visitors at the top ten websites. In Section 12.3 we have new exercises involving educational activities and the response time for firefighters. We present the normal distribution as problem-solving tool in section 12.4 and include new examples and exercises on topics such as car prices and SAT scores. Section 12.5, covering graphs, is viewed as a problem solving tool as well and includes new graphing problems discussing social networks, major food commodities, purchases by gender and "friends" on Facebook. We use linear regression in Section 12.6 to make predictions about the Olympics. New exercises cover topics like age conversions for cats and dogs, least square lines for Olympic events and marriage rates.

Chapter 13

In this chapter we cover many of the financial matters that everyone should know about: interest, taxes and discounts (Section 13.1) with updated exercises on credit cards and consumer credit (Section 13.2), APR and the Rule of 78, how to calculate car payments, and compare buying versus leasing a car. The chapter ends with the information you need about investing in stocks, bonds, and mutual funds (Section 13.5) which uses a Return on Investments Calculator in Example 1.

Chapters 14 and 15

New to the book and previously appearing only online, these two chapters dealing with Voting and Apportionment (14) and Graph Theory (15) have been revised for inclusion in this edition.

KEY CONTINUING FEATURES

The text has been carefully rewritten in order to promote student success. Pedagogical themes such as *problem solving, motivation, connections,* and *assessment and review* are incorporated throughout the text. Important pedagogical features have been retained in this new edition in order to continue to promote student success.

The tenth edition continues to incorporate the "Standards of Introductory College Mathematics" set forth by AMATYC. Accordingly, deductive proof (Chapters 1 and 2), numeracy (Chapters 4 and 5), symbolism and algebra (Chapter 6), functions (Chapter 7), geometry and measurement (Chapter 8), and probability (Chapter 11) and statistics (Chapter 12) are among the topics covered in the book.

We also made many significant efforts to address the NCTM curriculum recommendations regarding **communication** (*In Other Words and Collaborative Learning*), **problem solving** (Chapter 1 and as a pedagogical theme throughout the book), **reasoning** (Chapter 3), **connections** (*Discovery* feature and mathematical systems), **algebra** (Chapters 6 and 7), **geometry** (Chapter 8), **mathematical structures** (Chapter 9), **probability** (Chapters 10 and 11), and **statistics** (Chapter 12).

GUIDED TOUR

Problem Solving

Problem solving is a pedagogical theme incorporated throughout the text to promote students success. Specific *Problem Solving* examples are formatted using the RSTUV method (Read, Select, Think, Use, and Verify) to guide the reader through the problem. The solution is carefully developed to the right of the problem-solving steps. Students are encouraged to cover the solution, write their own solutions, and check their work in order to build problem-solving skills. This feature also includes references to similar problems in the exercise sets.

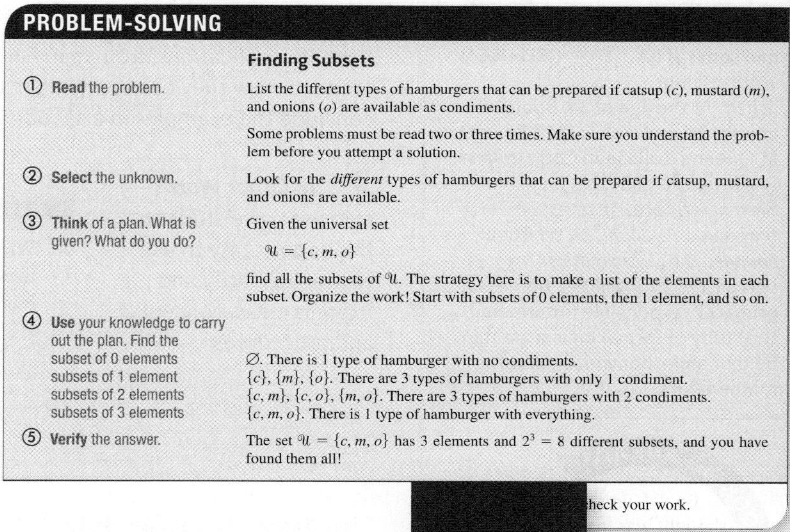

PROBLEM-SOLVING

Finding Subsets

① **Read** the problem.

List the different types of hamburgers that can be prepared if catsup (c), mustard (m), and onions (o) are available as condiments.

Some problems must be read two or three times. Make sure you understand the problem before you attempt a solution.

② **Select** the unknown.

Look for the *different* types of hamburgers that can be prepared if catsup, mustard, and onions are available.

③ **Think** of a plan. What is given? What do you do?

Given the universal set

$$\mathcal{U} = \{c, m, o\}$$

find all the subsets of $\mathcal{U}$. The strategy here is to make a list of the elements in each subset. Organize the work! Start with subsets of 0 elements, then 1 element, and so on.

④ **Use** your knowledge to carry out the plan. Find the
subset of 0 elements
subsets of 1 element
subsets of 2 elements
subsets of 3 elements

$\emptyset$. There is 1 type of hamburger with no condiments.
$\{c\}$, $\{m\}$, $\{o\}$. There are 3 types of hamburgers with only 1 condiment.
$\{c, m\}$, $\{c, o\}$, $\{m, o\}$. There are 3 types of hamburgers with 2 condiments.
$\{c, m, o\}$. There is 1 type of hamburger with everything.

⑤ **Verify** the answer.

The set $\mathcal{U} = \{c, m, o\}$ has 3 elements and $2^3 = 8$ different subsets, and you have found them all!

heck your work.

Motivation

Each chapter begins with a preview that details the material to be covered in the chapter and the ways in which the topics are related to each other.

Getting Started

Each section begins with a *Getting Started* vignette. The applications mentioned are drawn from a vast array of fields and offer a motivating introduction for the techniques and ideas covered in the section.

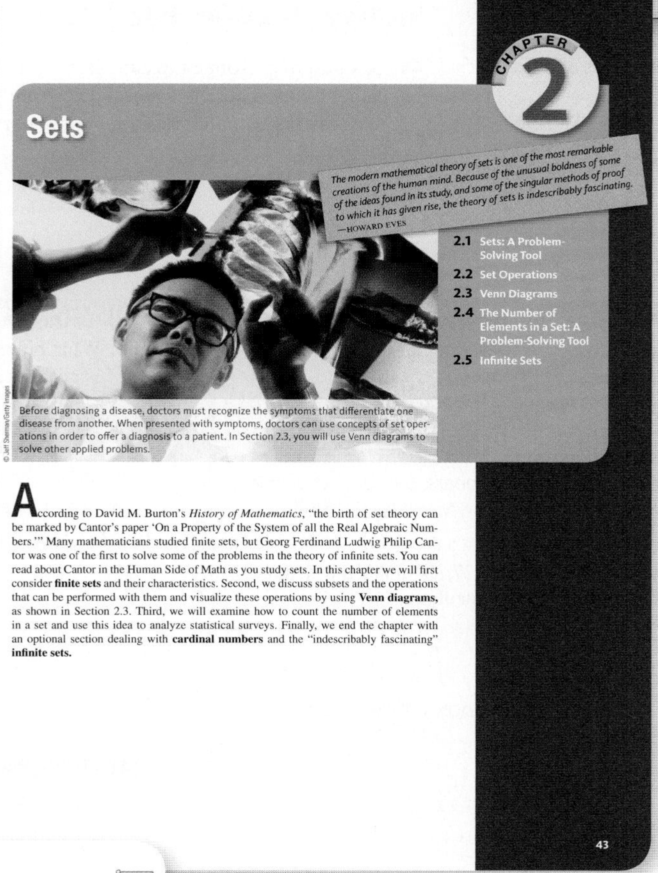

CHAPTER 2

Sets

The modern mathematical theory of sets is one of the most remarkable creations of the human mind. Because of the unusual boldness of some of the ideas found in its study, and some of the singular methods of proof to which it has given rise, the theory of sets is indescribably fascinating.
—HOWARD EVES

Before diagnosing a disease, doctors must recognize the symptoms that differentiate one disease from another. When presented with symptoms, doctors can use concepts of set operations in order to offer a diagnosis to a patient. In Section 2.3, you will use Venn diagrams to solve other applied problems.

© Jeff Sherman/Getty Images

According to David M. Burton's *History of Mathematics*, "the birth of set theory can be marked by Cantor's paper 'On a Property of the System of all the Real Algebraic Numbers.'" Many mathematicians studied finite sets, but Georg Ferdinand Ludwig Philip Cantor was one of the first to solve some of the problems in the theory of infinite sets. You can read about Cantor in the Human Side of Math as you study sets. In this chapter we will first consider **finite sets** and their characteristics. Second, we discuss subsets and the operations that can be performed with them and visualize these operations by using **Venn diagrams,** as shown in Section 2.3. Third, we will examine how to count the number of elements in a set and use this idea to analyze statistical surveys. Finally, we end the chapter with an optional section dealing with **cardinal numbers** and the "indescribably fascinating" **infinite sets.**

43

Objectives

A list of objectives corresponding to the objective heads in the exposition and the end-of-section exercises appear at the beginning of each section.

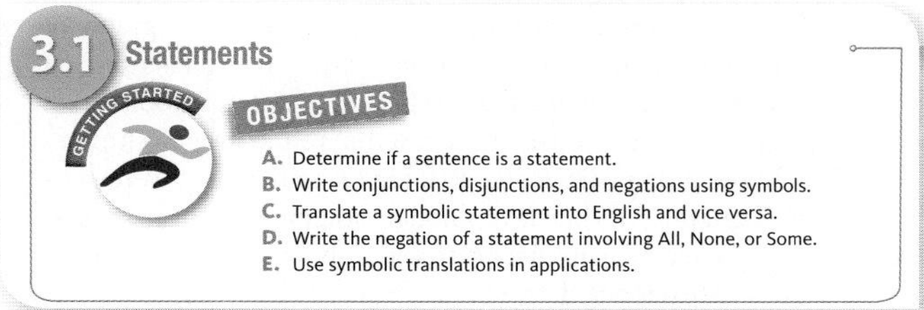

3.1 Statements

GETTING STARTED

OBJECTIVES

A. Determine if a sentence is a statement.
B. Write conjunctions, disjunctions, and negations using symbols.
C. Translate a symbolic statement into English and vice versa.
D. Write the negation of a statement involving All, None, or Some.
E. Use symbolic translations in applications.

Human Side of Math

George Boole was born in Lincoln, England, on November 2, 1815.

© Topham/The Image Works
(1815–1864)

Throughout the years, Boole had some of his writings published. At the age of 34, Boole was appointed professor of mathematics at Queen's College in Cork, Ireland.

At the age of 39, he published his masterpiece, *An Investigation of the Laws of Thought, on Which Are Founded the Mathematical Theories of Logic and Probabilities.* Boole was primarily responsible for bringing the study of formal logic from the field of philosophy into that of mathematics.

LOOKING AHEAD

Boole's work on logic and thought was instrumental in establishing modern symbolic logic, which is the focus of this chapter.

Human Side of Math
Each chapter presents the *Human Side of Math,* a margin feature, which is a brief biography of a person who devised or contributed to the development of the mathematical topics covered in the chapter. *Looking Ahead* links the biography to the upcoming material.

Connections

Real-life applications, from many disciplines, are included throughout the book to show students how they can apply the material covered in the text. These applications usually conclude the examples in a section and appear in the exercise sets.

In Other Words
exercises give students the opportunity to use writing to clarify and express ideas, concepts, and procedures.

IN OTHER WORDS

62. Write in your own words why the conditional statement "If p then q" is **false** only when p is true and q is false, and it is true otherwise.

USING YOUR KNOWLEDGE

44. A small drip from a tap can waste as much as 4 liters of water a day. There is a small drip from your tap, so you are wasting as much as 4 liters of water each day.

Using Your Knowledge
exercises help students to generalize concepts and apply them immediately to similar real-life situations.

CALCULATOR CORNER

You can use a calculator to find the distance between two points. For example, to find the distance between (2, −3) *and* (8, 5), *you must use equation* (3). *Here are the steps you need. Press*

[2nd] [$\sqrt{x}$] [(] [8] [−] [2] [)] [x^2] [+] [(] [5] [−] [(−)] [3] [)] [ENTER]

Note that in this case the answer appears as 10. *If you work Example 5 using a calculator, your answer will be* 9.219544457, *an approximation for* $\sqrt{85}$.

1. For problems 19, 21, 23, 25, and 27, estimate the distance between the two points with your calculator.

Calculator Corner
exercises provide essential background on how to solve problems using a calculator.

DISCOVERY

55. What binary numeral represents the lightest shade of gray that is not white?

Discovery
exercises are more challenging problems that help students to make connections between concepts and to develop better critical thinking and problem-solving skills.

COLLABORATIVE LEARNING

3. Select a local restaurant with both take-out and on-premise facilities. One team makes a graph of the number of persons purchasing take-out, and the other team makes a graph of the number of persons purchasing on-premise meals during a 3-hour period. Label your x axis 1, 2, and 3 and your y axis with the number of meals purchased. Are the graphs similar? Would the graphs differ if a different 3-hour period were chosen? Explain. (If you have enough students to form several teams, the teams can select different 3-hour periods and see if there is a difference between graphs.)

Collaborative Learning
exercises give students the opportunity to express their thoughts verbally and to become accustomed to working in groups. The type of work involved in these exercises including *problem solving, modeling, reasoning,* and *connecting* to other disciplines.

SKILL CHECKER

2. If $f(x) = (x - 1)^2 - 2$, find and graph $f(0), f(1), f(-1), f(2)$, and $f(-2)$.

Skill Checker exercises, included in relevant sections, help students check their mastery of the skills that they will need in order to proceed to the next section.

Graph It examples appear in the margin next to corresponding examples. The *Graph Its* illustrate an alternate method of solving a problem or checking a solution with the use of a graphing utility.

GRAPH IT

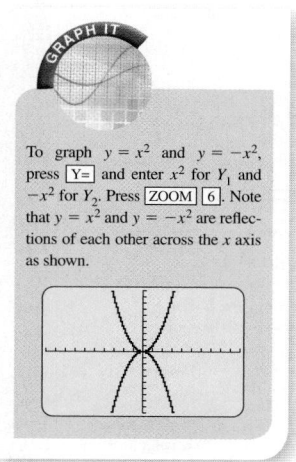

To graph $y = x^2$ and $y = -x^2$, press [Y=] and enter x^2 for Y_1 and $-x^2$ for Y_2. Press [ZOOM] [6]. Note that $y = x^2$ and $y = -x^2$ are reflections of each other across the x axis as shown.

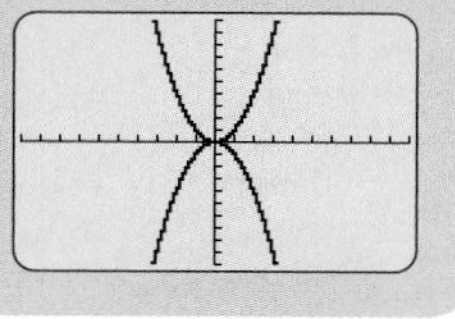

WEB IT EXERCISES

Team 2

1. The length of the lines in the Koch fractal get smaller with each iteration. What about the rate of growth of the total length of the perimeter?

The Web It feature directs students to annotated links on the text-specific Web site. The links correlate to material covered in the text and provide students with access to additional information on a topic, practice problems, tutorials, or downloadable software. In later chapters, selected exercise sets conclude with optional *Web It* exercises that require the use of the Internet.

Assessment and Review

The *Chapter Summary* provides brief definitions and examples for key topics within a given chapter. It also contains section references to encourage students to reread sections.

CHAPTER 3 Summary

SECTION	ITEM	MEANING	EXAMPLE
3.1A	p, q, r, etc.	Statements	p: Today is Monday. q: The sky is blue.
3.1B	$p \wedge q$	Conjunction (p **and** q)	Today is Monday **and** the sky is blue.
	$p \vee q$	Disjunction (p **or** q)	Today is Monday **or** the sky is blue.
	$\sim p$	Negation (**not** p)	Today is **not** Monday.
3.2A, B, C	p q | $p \wedge q$ $p \vee q$ $\sim p$ T T | T T F T F | F T F F T | F T T F F | F F T	Truth tables for the statements $p \wedge q$, $p \vee q$, and $\sim p$	
3.2E	$p \Leftrightarrow q$	The statements p and q are equivalent; that is, they have identical truth tables.	$\sim(p \vee q) \Leftrightarrow \sim p \wedge \sim q$
3.3A	$p \rightarrow q$	p conditional q	**If** today is Monday, **then** I will go to school.
3.3B	$p \leftrightarrow q$	p biconditional q	Today is Monday **if and only if I** go to school.
3.3A, B	p q | $p \rightarrow q$ $p \leftrightarrow q$ T T | T T T F | F F F T | T F F F | T T	Truth tables for the conditional and the biconditional	
3.4A	$q \rightarrow p$ $\sim p \rightarrow \sim q$ $\sim q \rightarrow \sim p$	Converse of $p \rightarrow q$ Inverse of $p \rightarrow q$ Contrapositive of $p \rightarrow q$	
3.4B	p is **sufficient** for q. q is **necessary** for p. p **only if** q q **if** p	Statements equivalent to "If p, then q"	
3.4C	A tautology	A statement that is always true	2 is even. $p \vee \sim p$
	A contradiction	A statement that is always false	2 is odd. $p \wedge \sim p$
3.4D	$p \Rightarrow q$	p implies q; used when the conditional $p \rightarrow q$ is a tautology.	The animal is a dog (d) implies that the animal is a mammal (m), since $d \rightarrow m$ is a tautology.
3.5A	$p \rightarrow q$ p $\therefore q$	An argument (a set of statements, the premises, and a claim that another statement, the conclusion, follows from the premises)	If it rains, then I get wet. It rains. $\therefore$ I get wet.

CHAPTER 1 Practice Test

1. What does RSTUV mean?
2. What is inductive reasoning?
3. Identify the pattern and find the next three terms.

   1, 2, 7, 19, 41, 76, ____, ____, ____

4. a. Follow this procedure: Select a number, multiply it by 4, add 6 to the product, divide the sum by 2, and subtract 3 from the quotient.
   b. Follow the same steps as in part (a) using the numbers 1, 10, and 100. What results do you get?
   c. Make a conjecture about the relationship between the original number and the final results.
5. Round 319.26 to
   a. the nearest tenth. b. the nearest hundred.
6. a. Read the meter for today.

   b. If the reading for yesterday was 6002 kilowatt-hours, how many kilowatt-hours have you consumed since yesterday?
   c. If a kilowatt-hour costs \$.10, how much was your 1-day bill?
   d. If you estimate the same consumption each day for a 30-day period (a month), what is your estimated monthly bill?
7. The relationship between the height H of a person and the length t of their tibia (the bone connecting the knee to the ankle) is

   Male: $H = 32.2 + 2.4t$ Female: $H = 28.6 + 2.5t$

   a. Estimate the height of a person (to the nearest inch) with a 15-in. tibia if the person is a female.
   b. Do the same as in part (a) if the person is a male.
8. The circle graphs show the budget requirements and resources for the city of St. Petersburg.

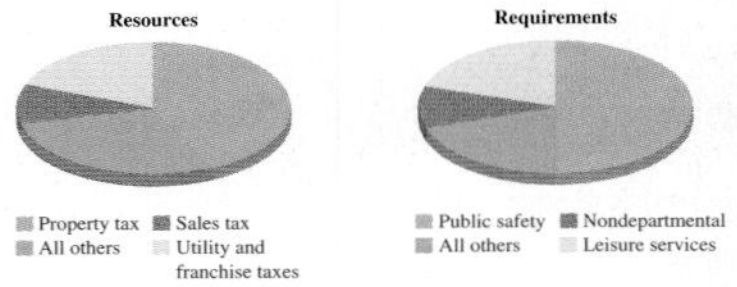

Source: http://www.stpete.org/budget/.

   a. What is the biggest category in the requirements chart?
   b. About what fraction of the requirements is for public safety?
   c. What is the smallest category in the resources chart?

continued

ANSWERS TO PRACTICE TEST

CHAPTER 1		What to Review *If You Missed It*		
QUESTION	**ANSWER**	**SECTION**	**EXAMPLE(S)**	**PAGE(S)**
1	Read the problem. Select the unknown. Think of a plan. Use the techniques you are studying to carry out the plan. Verify the answer.	1.1A	**Problem-Solving Box**	2–3
2	The process of arriving at a general conclusion on the basis of repeated observations of specific examples	1.1B	**Definition of Inductive Reasoning**	4
3	Look at the following differences: 1 2 7 19 41 76 → [127] [197] [289] ··· 1 5 12 22 35 → 51 70 92 ··· 4 7 10 13 → 16 19 22 ··· 3 3 3 3 3 3 ··· The third differences are constant, so the next numbers in each line can be constructed by addition. For example, $3 + 13 = 16$ $16 + 35 = 51$ $51 + 76 = 127$, or simply $3 + 13 + 35 + 76$ The next three terms are 127, 197, and 289.	1.1B	1–3	5–6
4	a. $n, 4n, 4n + 6, 2n + 3, 2n$ b. Using 1, the final result is 2. Using 10, the final result is 20. Using 100, the final result is 200. c. The conjecture is that the final result is twice the original number.	1.1B	4	7
5	a. $319.\underline{2}6 \rightarrow 319.3$ b. $\underline{3}19.26 \rightarrow 300$	1.2	1	14–15
6	a. 6064 kWh b. 62 kWh c. \$6.20 d. \$186.00	1.2	2	15–16
7	a. Female: $H = 28.6 + 2.5(15) \approx 66$ in. b. Male: $H = 32.2 + 2.4(15) \approx 68$ in.	1.2	4–6	17–19
8	a. Public safety b. $\frac{1}{2}$ c. Sales tax	1.3	1	24
9	a. About \$50 million b. About \$52 million c. About \$116 million d. About \$75 million e. About \$25 million	1.3	2–3	26–27
10	a. 6.91 b. 6.76 c. 0.15 d. They seem to be decreasing.	1.3	4–5	27–28

The Practice Test at the end of the chapter is followed by the *Answers to Practice Test*. The answers to each question are keyed to the specific section, example, and page that the students should reference if they miss a problem. This provides students with a means to diagnose skills and concepts that they have mastered and identifies those that require further work. This tool also assists students in taking responsibility for their own learning.

Answers to Practice Test

Courses for Which This Book is Intended

This textbook contains a large selection of topics and is suitable for use in various courses. The entire book can be covered easily in a full year's course, while many alternative choices can be made for a two-quarter or a one-semester course. Here are some of the courses for which the book is suggested:

- General education or Liberal arts mathematics [the text follows most of the CUPM (Committee on the Undergraduate Program in Mathematics) and AMATYC recommendations for liberal arts mathematics
- Topics in contemporary mathematics
- College mathematics or Survey of mathematics
- Introduction to mathematics or Applications of mathematics

A few more advanced topics may be included or omitted at the instructor's discretion. These choices will not affect the continuity of any chapter presentation or syllabus as a whole. The topics include the following sections: 2.5 Infinite Sets; 3.7 Switching Networks; 7.8 Linear Programming; 8.6 Networks, Non-Euclidean Geometry, and Topology; 8.7 Right Triangle trigonometry, 8.8 Chaos and Fractals; and 9.5 Game Theory.

SUPPLEMENTS

FOR THE STUDENT	FOR THE INSTRUCTOR
	Instructor's Edition **(ISBN: 978-1-285-08230-1)** The Instructor's Edition features an appendix containing the answers to all problems in the book, as well as an appendix denoting which problems can be found in Enhanced WebAssign.
Student Solutions Manual **(ISBN: 978-1-285-42074-5)** *Author:* Ann Ostberg The Student Solutions Manual contains study tips, worked-out solutions to all odd-numbered exercises, and all the solutions to the Chapter Practice Tests in the text.	***Complete Solutions Manual*** **(ISBN: 978-1-285-42079-0)** *Author:* Ann Ostberg The Complete Solutions Manual provides worked-out solutions to all of the problems in the text.
Enhanced WebAssign® **Printed Access Card: 978-0-538-73810-1** **Online Access Code: 978-1-285-18181-3** Exclusively from Cengage Learning, Enhanced WebAssign combines the exceptional mathematics content that you know and love with the most powerful online homework solution, WebAssign. Enhanced WebAssign engages students with immediate feedback, rich tutorial content, and interactive, fully customizable eBooks (YouBook), helping students to develop a deeper conceptual understanding of their subject matter. Online assignments can be built by selecting from thousands of text-specific problems or supplemented with problems from any Cengage Learning textbook.	***Enhanced WebAssign*** **Printed Access Card: 978-0-538-73810-1** **Online Access Code: 978-1-285-18181-3** Enhanced WebAssign (assigned by the instructor) provides you with instant feedback on homework assignments. This online homework system is easy to use and includes helpful links to textbook sections, video examples, and problem-specific tutorials
Enhanced WebAssign: Start Smart Guide for Students **(ISBN: 978-0-495-38479-3)** If your instructor has chosen to package Enhanced WebAssign with your text, this manual will help you get up and running quickly with the Enhanced WebAssign system so that you can study smarter and improve your performance in class.	***Enhanced WebAssign: Start Smart Guide for Students*** **(ISBN: 978-0-495-38479-3)** The Enhanced WebAssign: Start Smart Guide for Students helps students get up and running quickly with Enhanced WebAssign so that they can study smarter and improve their performance in class.
	PowerLecture with Diploma **(ISBN: 978-1-285-42082-0)** This DVD-ROM provides you with dynamic media tools for teaching. You can create, deliver, and customize tests (both print and online) in minutes with Diploma's Computerized Testing featuring algorithmic equations. The Solution Builder's online solutions manual easily builds solution sets for homework or exams. Lecture Powerpoints®, art and figures from the book, and an electronic test bank are also included on this instructor resource.
	Solution Builder This online instructor database offers complete worked solutions to all exercises in the text, allowing you to create customized, secure solutions printouts (in PDF format) matched exactly to the problems you assign in class. For more information, please visit www.cengage.com/solutionbuilder.
Author's Website www.onlinebello.com Containing videos and interactive presentations for the first 13 chapters, Research Questions, Tutorials, Practice Tests (with answers) for all chapters, Web Links and additional resources.	***Author's Website www.onlinebello.com*** Containing videos and interactive presentations for the first 13 chapters, Research Questions, Tutorials, Practice Tests (with answers) for all chapters, Web Links and additional resources.

ACKNOWLEDGEMENTS

For their help on earlier editions, we wish to express our appreciation to Dr. Heriberto Hernandez, Bill Albrecht, Barbara Burrows, Joe Clemente, Gary Etgen, Josephine Rinaldo, and Prakash Sach. We thank the following colleagues for all their helpful criticisms and suggestions: Diana Fernandez, James Gard, George Kosan, Chester Miles, Donald Clayton Rose, Donald Clayton Rose II, and, especially, Charles Osborne. Thanks also to the people involved in the preparation of ancillary materials for previous editions: Alex Ambrioso, Marcus McWaters, Mark Oglesby, Rose Reyes, Robert Schatzow, T. Tran, and William Wilder. We would also like to thank all of our new reviewers for their many valuable suggestions and constructive criticism: Corey Bruns, *University of Wisconsin-Whitewater;* Vincent Dimicelli, *Oral Roberts University;* Jon Prewitt, *University of Wyoming;* and Christina Vertullo, *Marist College.*

We would also like to thank Kathleen Deselle, Project Editor and Lauri Semarne, our final accuracy checker, Rose Kernan of Nesbit Graphics, Tanya Nigh the Content Coordinator, and Jeremy Glover, our Photo Researcher. Stefanie Beeck, our Developmental Editor, did a fantastic job in overseeing this project; we are especially grateful for her dedication and tireless efforts on our behalf. We also wish to express our appreciation to Marc Bove, our Editor, who guided and coordinated the whole project from beginning to end.

We also wish to thank those who contributed to the ninth edition: Professor Stephen Suen, of the University of South Florida, who shared the information on his Web site and offered valuable comments regarding Chapters 1, 2, 10, and 12; Professor Manoug Manougian, of the University of South Florida, pointed out ways to improve some of the material regarding sets, lines, and probability. Professor John Davis provided valuable suggestions for the probability chapter. Debbie Garrison checked answers in the *Instructor's Answer Key* and helped in the statistics chapter. Fran Hopf checked some of the *Student's Solutions Manual,* Louis Camara and Karol McIntosh checked the statistics chapter, and Jolene Rhodes reviewed the graph theory chapter. We also thank Mile Krajcesvki and Scott Rimbey of the University of South Florida.

We wish to express our sincere thanks to the many users—students and instructors alike—of the previous editions. We hope that this ninth edition will please them even more. We always welcome comments and suggestions from students, professors, and readers. You may send them to us at the following address: Ignacio Bello, Mathematics Department, University of South Florida (Phy 342), 4202 Fowler Avenue, Tampa, FL, 33620, or e-mail Ignacio Bello at cubanmath@aol.com.

Finally, we would like to acknowledge the passing of our colleague Jack R. Britton. His dedication to the study of mathematics provided a foundation for the current edition of this textbook.

—I.B.

—A.K.

CHAPTER 1

Problem Solving

It's not where you're from; it's where you're going. It's not what you drive; it's what drives you. It's not what's on you; it's what's in you. It's not what you think; it's what you know. —GATORADE COMMERCIAL

In leaner economic times, families are forced to adhere to more strict household budgets. Families must carefully allot the amount of money that they spend on necessity and luxury items in order to live within their means. Graphs are a useful tool for creating and analyzing a budget. In Section 1.3 you will learn how to interpret different types of graphs.

The question really is, Do you know how to solve problems? If you are not sure, we will help you right here, right now. As René Descartes said: "It is not enough to have a good mind. The main thing is to use it well." How? We start this chapter by giving you a procedure that you can use to solve any type of problem. Why?

> *Quite simply, students cannot solve word problems reliably because they are presented with inconsistent models of problem solving that contradict the logical processes they have learned in other courses and in everyday life.**

Together, we can fix that!

Our RSTUV procedure is based on a concept developed by George Polya, a Hungarian mathematician and professor featured in this chapter's Human Side of Math. Along with our procedure, we discuss an important concept in problem solving: inductive reasoning.

The rest of the chapter is devoted to problem-solving techniques that will help you solve any problem: patterns (Section 1.1), estimations (Section 1.2), or a picture in the form of a graph (Section 1.3). Along the way, we will try to have some fun and remember two important ideas:

> *The value of a problem is not so much in coming up with the answer as in the ideas and attempted ideas it forces on the would-be solver.*
>
> —ISRAEL NATHAN HERSTEIN

> *Math is fun, and you can do it!*
>
> —IGNACIO BELLO

*Source: www.hawaii.edu/suremath/why1.html.

1.1 Inductive and Deductive Reasoning

GETTING STARTED

OBJECTIVES

A. Understand the RSTUV problem-solving procedure.
B. Understand and use inductive and deductive reasoning.
C. Use the RSTUV procedure to solve problems.

Human Side of Math

(1887–1985)

George Polya was awarded a Ph.D. in mathematics with a minor in physics in 1912. His mathematical output was broad and included papers in number theory, combinatorics, and voting systems.

After a brief stay at Brown University in 1942. Polya moved to Stanford University in 1942. He published many articles and books; however, his book *How to Solve It* became a resounding success, selling more than 1 million copies. The book outlined his famous problem-solving strategy.

Polya also contributed greatly in the classroom. He regularly visited schools and inspired many students to pursue a career in mathematics. ■

LOOKING AHEAD

In this chapter we will look at the concepts developed by George Polya and use them to learn how to solve problems.

Knowledge of mathematics is power. As a student, mathematics gives you the power to pursue many careers. As a citizen, it gives you the power to reach informed decisions. As a nation, it gives us the power to compete in a technological world. Many students today are not prepared for the jobs of tomorrow or even for the jobs of today! In fact, three out of four Americans stop studying mathematics before completing career or job prerequisites. The mathematics you learn today may have an impact on the job you get tomorrow. Over 75% of all jobs require proficiency in simple algebra and geometry, either as a prerequisite to enter a training program or as part of an examination required to be licensed in a specific field. In addition, earning a college degree requires taking at least a minimal amount of mathematics courses. Unfortunately, many students are burdened by unpleasant experiences in mathematics. They convince themselves that they can't do mathematics, so they won't. They believe that they never liked mathematics, so they don't. Now it is time to change all that. This time try mathematics with an attitude—a positive one. The way to start is by learning how to solve problems, and we will give you a procedure to do just that!

A Problem-Solving Procedure

One of the first problem-solving models was developed by George Polya, a Hungarian-born mathematician and researcher. A problem-solving strategy is *your plan for action.* First, you must choose your problem-solving strategy. What strategies did Polya recommend? Here are a few.

Look for a pattern.	Make a table.
Draw a picture or diagram.	Use logical reasoning.
Make a model.	Work a simpler problem first.
Use a formula.	Make a list.

Polya's original procedure as it appeared in *How to Solve It* (Princeton, NJ: Princeton University Press, 1973) consisted of four parts.

1. Understand the problem.
2. Devise a plan.
3. Carry out the plan.
4. Look back.

We expand this procedure so that you can use it as a model to solve *any* problem. Here are the five steps we shall use.

RSTUV Problem-Solving Procedure

1. **R**ead the problem, not once or twice but until you understand it.
2. **S**elect the unknown; that is, find out what the problem asks for.
3. **T**hink of a plan to solve the problem.
4. **U**se the techniques you are studying to carry out the plan.
5. **V**erify your answer.

Look at the first letter in each sentence. To help you remember the steps, we call them the **RSTUV** procedure.

Problem solving will be presented in a two-column format. Cover the answers in the right column (a 3-by-5 index card will do), and write *your own answers* as you practice the problems. After you complete the problems, uncover the answers and check if your answers are correct. Sometimes, you will be given a similar example and its solution.

PROBLEM-SOLVING

Hints and Tips

Our problem-solving procedure (RSTUV) contains five steps. The steps are given in the left column, and hints and tips in the right.

① **Read** the problem.	Mathematics is a language, so it is important to learn how to read it. If you do not understand or even get through reading the problem the first time, read it again and pay attention to key words or instructions such as *compute, draw, write, construct, make, show, identify, state, simplify, solve,* and *graph.*
② **Select** the unknown.	How can you answer a question if you do not understand the question and cannot determine the unknown? One good way to look for the unknown is to look for the question mark "?" and carefully read the preceding material. Try to determine what information is given and what is missing from the problem.
③ **Think** of a plan.	Problem solving requires many skills and strategies. Some strategies are *look for a pattern; examine a related problem; make tables, pictures, and diagrams; write an equation; work backward;* and *make a guess.*
④ **Use** the techniques you are studying to carry out the plan.	If you are studying a mathematical technique, use your knowledge about the technique to solve the given problem. Look for procedures that can be used to solve each problem. Then carry out the plan and check each step.
⑤ **Verify** the answer.	Look back and check the result of the original problem. Is the answer reasonable? Can you find the answer some other way?

B Inductive and Deductive Reasoning

As we mentioned, one of the strategies used in problem solving is to find a pattern. Reasoning based on examining a variety of cases, discovering patterns, and forming conclusions is called **inductive reasoning.** For example, you want to make sure that you have a good instructor in your next mathematics course. You ask several of your friends about different instructors. They all say that Professor X is a good instructor. You conclude that Professor X is indeed a good instructor. This is an example of inductive reasoning, but it may be a hasty generalization. Now consider this example: Suppose you become a doctor and one of your patients comes to you and says,

> It hurts when I press here (pressing his side with his index finger).
> And when I press here (pressing his other side with the index finger).
> And here (pressing his leg with his index finger).
> And here, here, and here (pressing his other leg and both arms with the same index finger).

You examine the patient all over, trying to invoke your inductive powers. What can you conclude? (The answer is on page 9.)

Inductive Reasoning

Inductive reasoning is the process of arriving at a **general** conclusion **(a conjecture)** on the basis of repeated observations of specific examples. The **conjecture** may or may not be true.

Look at panels A, B, and C of Figure 1.1. Panel A consists of 1 square. Panel B consists of 1 large square and 4 smaller squares. Panel C consists of 1 large square, 4 medium squares, and 9 smaller squares. How many squares are there in panels D and E? Draw the next figure in the pattern and write an expression for the total number of squares.

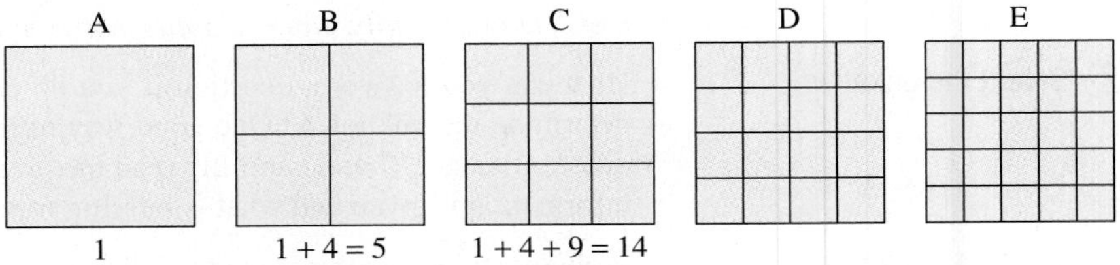

FIGURE 1.1

Panel D has $1 + 4 + 9 + 16 = 30$ squares and panel E has $1 + 4 + 9 + 16 + 25 = 55$ squares. The next square in the pattern (see Figure 1.2) consists of $1 + 4 + 9 + 16 + 25 + 36 = 91$ squares. An arrangement of numbers according to a pattern is called a **sequence,** and each number in the sequence is called a **term.** Thus, the sequence of the number of squares is 1, 5, 14, 30, 55, and 91. Here, the first term is 1, the second term is 5, and so on.

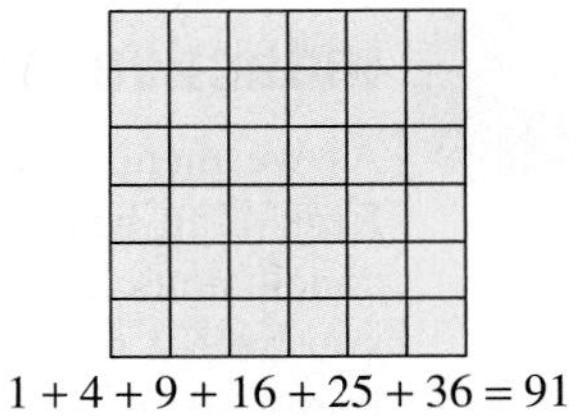

FIGURE 1.2

EXAMPLE 1 Identifying Patterns and Finding Terms

Identify the pattern in each sequence and find the next three terms.

(a) 1, 4, 7, 10, ____, ____, ____ **(b)** 1, 2, 4, 8, ____, ____, ____

Solution

The strategy is to examine the difference between successive terms to discover the pattern.

(a) The difference between adjacent numbers is 3. Thus, the pattern is *add 3*. The next three terms are $10 + 3 = 13$, $13 + 3 = 16$, and $16 + 3 = 19$.

(b) Each number after the first is *two times* the preceding number. The pattern is *multiply by 2,* and the next three terms are $2 \times 8 = 16$, $2 \times 16 = 32$, and $2 \times 32 = 64$.

EXAMPLE 2 Identifying Patterns and Finding Terms

Identify the pattern in each sequence and find the next term.

(a) 4, 9, 3, 8, 2, ____ **(b)** 1, 2, 8, 22, 47, ____

Solution

(a) Examine the differences between successive terms.

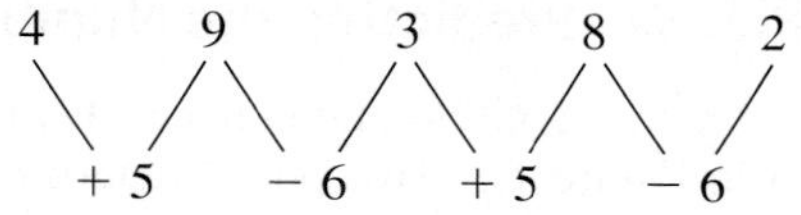

The pattern is *add 5, subtract 6.*

Add 5: $2 + 5 =$ (7)

Subtract 6: $7 - 6 =$ (1)

Thus, the term after 2 is $2 + 5 =$ (7) and the term after 7 is $7 - 6 =$ (1)

Another way of looking at this pattern is to concentrate on the alternate terms, 4, 3, 2, _?_ and 9, 8, _?_, as shown. The answer is the same!

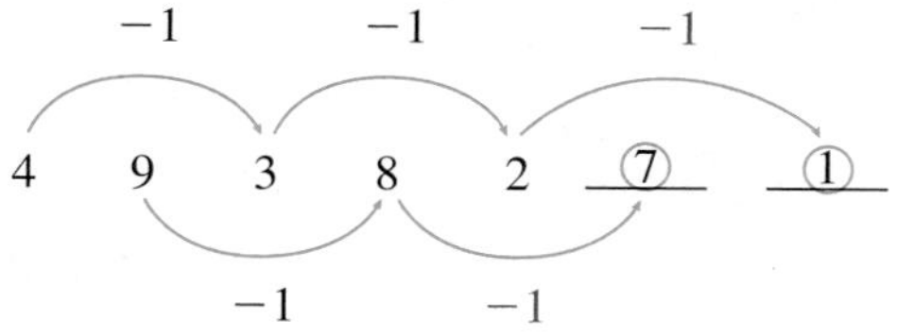

Moral: There may be more than one way to identify patterns!

(b) Examine the differences between successive terms.

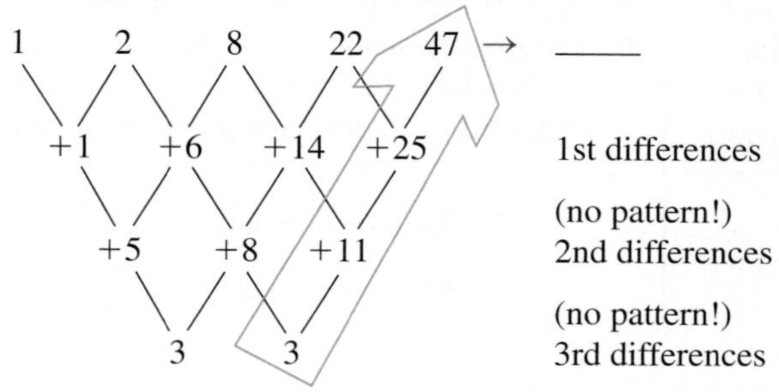

Now, add the numbers inside the blue arrow $3 + 11 + 25 + 47$ and you get the next term, 86. The technique here is to get the first differences, second differences, third differences, and so on, until you get a constant, and then add up the diagonal as shown.

A Word of Warning: Some sequences follow more than one pattern. Thus, the next three terms in the sequence

1   2   4
 +1   +2

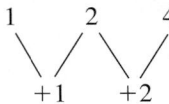

are 7, 11, and 16 if the pattern is *add 1, add 2, add 3,* and so on. On the other hand, if you view the sequence 1, 2, 4 as *doubling* the preceding number, the next three terms in the sequence are 8, 16, and 32! Sometimes it is necessary to examine a large number of cases before realizing that the conjectured pattern does not continue, as the next example shows. If there is just *one* case in which the conjecture does not work, you have a *counterexample* and the conjecture is false. Be reluctant to accept a conjecture as an absolute truth unless you can prove it using **deductive reasoning.**

Deductive Reasoning

The process of arriving at a **specific** conclusion on the basis of one or more general principles.

Note: You do not need a graphing calculator to use this book, but we occasionally show calculator screens from the TI-83 or TI-84 calculator to support our results.

EXAMPLE 3 Predicting the Number of Regions

Choose points on a circle and connect them to form distinct, nonoverlapping regions as shown in Figure 1.3. Two points determine $2 = 2^1$ regions, three points determine $4 = 2 \times 2 = 2^2$ regions, and four points determine a total of $8 = 2 \times 2 \times 2 = 2^3$ regions. These results are entered in the table. How many regions would you predict for

(a) five points? (b) six points?

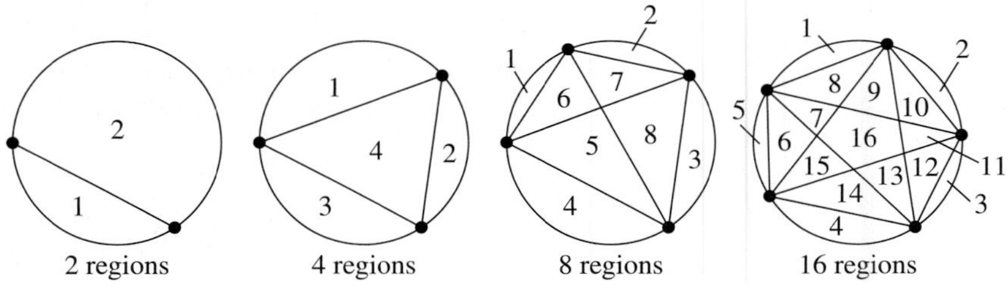

FIGURE 1.3

Solution

(a) $16 = 2 \times 2 \times 2 \times 2 = 2^4$ regions, as shown in Figure 1.3.

(b) The pattern predicts $2^5 = 32$. However, if you choose six unequally spaced points on the circle and count the regions correctly, you get only 31 regions. How many regions do you get if the points are equally spaced? Try it!

Number of Points	2	3	4	5	6
Number of Regions	$2 = 2^1$	$4 = 2^2$	$8 = 2^3$	$16 = 2^4$	?

What would happen for the seventh point? As it turns out, adding a seventh point would yield 57 regions. The pattern is

1, 2, 4, 8, 16, 31, 57

GRAPH IT

In order to find the number of regions using a grapher, let y_1 be the number of regions. Then go to [Y=] and enter the formula

$$y_1 = \frac{(x^4 - 6x^3 + 23x^2 - 18x + 24)}{24}$$

using x's instead of n's, pressing the [^] key to enter exponents, and inserting parentheses as shown. Now press [2nd] TABLE, and the values for the number of points and the corresponding number of regions appear as shown.

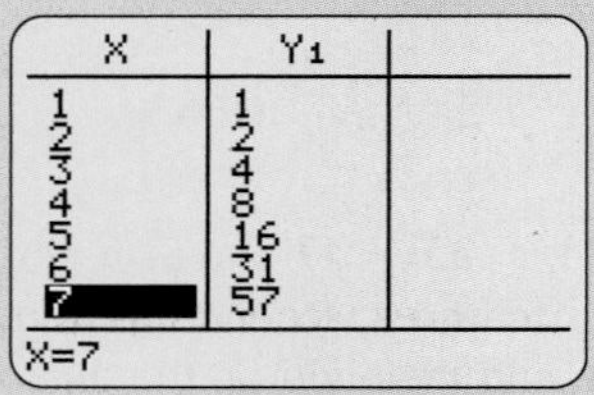

and the formula to find the number of regions is

$$\frac{n^4 - 6n^3 + 23n^2 - 18n + 24}{24}$$

How do we know that this is right? We can test it by substituting $n = 1, n = 2, n = 3$, obtaining 1, 2, 4, and so on. We can also use a grapher, as shown in the margin. However, we cannot be sure about a conjecture until a general formula or pattern is proved because just *one* counterexample can make the conjecture false. Unfortunately, we are not in a position to prove or disprove this formula because the result uses combinatorics, which will be discussed in Chapter 10. The next example illustrates the use of inductive as well as deductive reasoning, the process of proving a conclusion from one or more general statements.

EXAMPLE 4 Making and Proving Conjectures

Consider this procedure. Select a number. Multiply the number by 9. Add 6 to the product and divide the sum by 3. Subtract 2 from the quotient.

(a) Follow the procedure for four different numbers and make a conjecture about the relationship between the original number and the final result.

(b) Represent the original number by n and prove the conjecture in part (a).

Solution

Let us select four different numbers—say, 5, 10, 21, and 100—and apply the procedure given in the example.

(a)

Select a number.	5	10	21	100
Multiply the number by 9.	$9 \cdot 5 = 45$	$9 \cdot 10 = 90$	$9 \cdot 21 = 189$	$9 \cdot 100 = 900$
Add 6 to the product.	$45 + 6 = 51$	$90 + 6 = 96$	$189 + 6 = 195$	$900 + 6 = 906$
Divide the sum by 3.	$\frac{51}{3} = 17$	$\frac{96}{3} = 32$	$\frac{195}{3} = 65$	$\frac{906}{3} = 302$
Subtract 2 from the quotient.	$17 - 2 = 15$	$32 - 2 = 30$	$65 - 2 = 63$	$302 - 2 = 300$

Since we have to make a conjecture relating the original number and the final result, let us look at the original numbers and the final results.

5	10	21	100
15	30	63	300

Do you see the pattern? Using inductive reasoning, we make a conjecture that the final result is three times the original number. But can we prove it? Let us go to part (b) and repeat the process using ***n*** as the original number.

(b)

Select a number.	n
Multiply the number by 9.	$9 \cdot n$
Add 6 to the product.	$9n + 6$
Divide the sum by 3.	$\frac{9n + 6}{3} = 3n + 2$
Subtract 2 from the quotient.	$3n + 2 - 2 = 3n$

It gets a little tricky here. You have to divide $9n$ by 3 and get $3n$ and 6 by 3 and get 2.

The final result $3n$ is indeed three times the original number n; this proves our original conjecture.

Here is one that will amaze your friends. Try it with your own age and the amount of change in your pocket and make a conjecture about what the final result means. For example, if your final result is 2015, what does that mean?

1. Take your age. ____
2. Multiply it by 2. ____
3. Add 5. ____
4. Multiply this sum by 50. ____
5. Subtract 365. ____
6. Add the amount of loose change in your pocket. (Must be less than $1!) ____
7. Add 115. ____

C Problem Solving: Applications

Did you know that sequences, patterns, and induction were used to find some of the planets of our solar system (see Figure 1.4)? In 1772, the German astronomer Johann Bode discovered a pattern in the distances of the planets from the Sun. He started with the numbers 0, 3, 6, 12, and so on, then added 4 to each of the numbers as shown below.

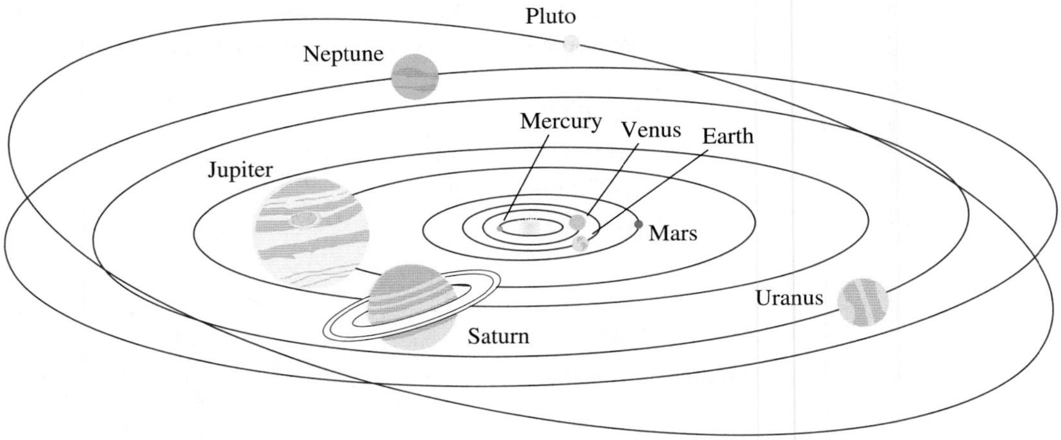

FIGURE 1.4

Note: Pluto has been "demoted" by the International Astronomical Union and is now officially classified as a "dwarf planet." http://www.space.com/2791-pluto-demoted-longer-planet-highly-controversial-definition.html.

EXAMPLE 5 The Number of a Planet

P1	P2	P3	P4	P5	P6	P7	P8
Mercury	Venus	Earth	Mars	____	Jupiter	Saturn	____
↓	↓	↓	↓	↓	↓	↓	↓
$0 + 4$	$3 + 4$	$6 + 4$	$12 + 4$	____	$48 + 4$	$96 + 4$	____

Use the RSTUV procedure to find which number corresponds to

(a) the fifth planet. **(b)** the eighth planet.

PROBLEM-SOLVING

Discovering Planets Using Inductive Reasoning

① **Read** the problem.

You are asked to find the numbers corresponding to the *fifth* and *eighth* missing planets.

② **Select** the unknown.

The unknowns are the missing numbers in the pattern.

③ **Think** of a plan. Is there a pattern? Can you find it?

If you can find a pattern, you can find the missing numbers. All the numbers are of the form ____ + 4. The numbers in front of the 4 for the first four planets are 0, 3, 6, and 12. The numbers in this sequence after the 3 are obtained by *doubling*, the first number (3, 6, 12) and adding 4.

$0 + 4$	$3 + 4$	$6 + 4$	$12 + 4$	$\underline{24 + 4}$	$48 + 4$	$96 + 4$	$\underline{192 + 4}$
	×2	×2	×2	×2	×2	×2	
↓	↓	↓	↓	↓	↓	↓	↓
		2×3+4	2×6+4	2×12+4	2×24+4	2×48+4	2×96+4
4	7	10	16	28	52	100	196

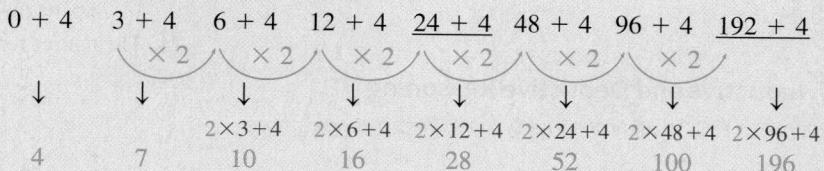

④ **Use** inductive reasoning to find the pattern.

(a) The number for the fifth planet should be $2 \times 12 + 4 = 28$. (This "planet" is really Ceres, a planetoid or asteroid.)

(b) The number for the eighth planet is $2 \times 96 + 4 = 196$. (This corresponds to Uranus, discovered by William Herschel in 1781.)

⑤ **Verify** the solution.

The differences between successive terms in the sequence follow the doubling pattern shown below.

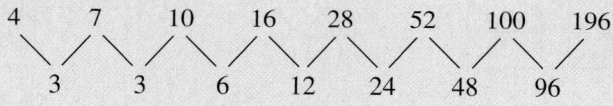

4 7 10 16 28 52 100 196

3 3 6 12 24 48 96

The numbers in this sequence—4, 7, 10, 16, and so on—are very important because they correspond to 10 times the distance of the planets from the Sun measured in astronomical units, where 1 astronomical unit is the average distance of Earth from the Sun.

What about the answer to the doctor question on page 4? There are many, but here is one: The patient had a broken index finger!

1.1 EXERCISES

A Problem-Solving Procedure

1. What are the four steps in Polya's problem-solving procedure?
2. What do the letters in the RSTUV procedure stand for?
3. When solving a problem, what is the first thing you should try to determine?

The first step in the RSTUV procedure is to Read the problem: Read the following information and do problems 4–10.

A recent poll found that 72% of U.S. adult cellphone users send and receive text messages. How much does text messaging cost? The table shows the prices for two different companies.

AT&T		Sprint	
Monthly Fee	**Messages**	**Monthly Fee**	**Messages**
\$ 5.00	200	\$ 5.00	300
\$15.00	1500	\$10.00	1000
\$20.00	Unlimited	\$20.00	Unlimited

4. Which of the two plans is the most economical?
5. Pedro pays \$15 a month for his plan. Which plan does he use?
6. If you send about 1400 text messages a month, which plan is the most economical?

7. If you send 900 text messages a month, which plan is the most economical? How much does it cost?
8. Children aged 9–12 send an average of 1146 text messages a month. Which plan is the most economical for this age group?
9. The average teenager sends 3339 text messages a month. Which plan is the most economical for teenagers?
10. Is there a difference between the number of messages sent by males and females? Yes! The average female teenager sends 4050 texts messages per month while the average male teenager sends 2539. How much does it cost a female teenager for sending those 4050 text messages? What is the cost for a male teenager? By the way, 86% of females aged 14–17 have unlimited texting.

B Inductive and Deductive Reasoning

In problems 11–20, identify the pattern and find the next three terms.

11. 1, 2, 4, 7, ____, ____, ____
12. 2, 5, 10, 17, ____, ____, ____
13. 1, 5, 1, 10, 1, 15, ____, ____, ____
14. $3, 3^2, 3^4, 3^8$, ____, ____, ____
15.

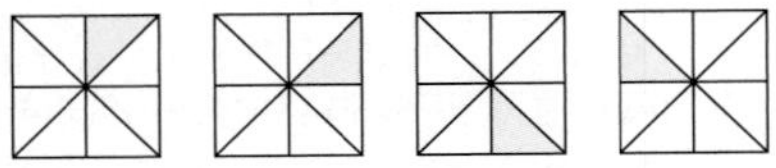

16.

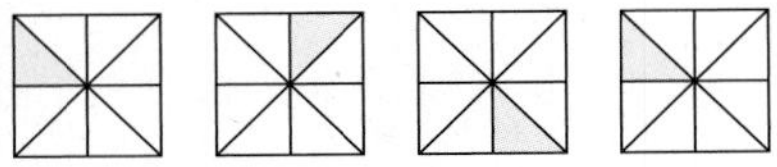

17. $1, \frac{1}{2}, \frac{1}{4}, \frac{1}{8}$, ____, ____, ____
18. $\frac{1}{14}, \frac{1}{9}, \frac{1}{12}, \frac{1}{7}, \frac{1}{10}$, ____, ____, ____
19. 1, 5, 2, 6, 3, ____, ____, ____
20. 6, 1, 9, 5, 12, 9, 15, ____, ____, ____
21. The figures represent the *triangular numbers*.

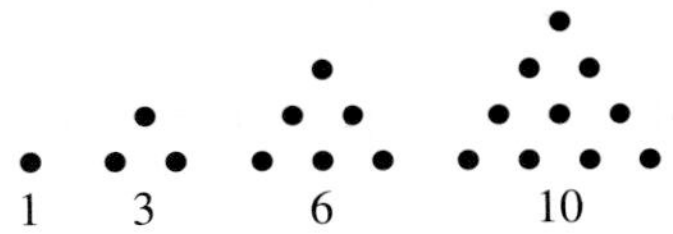

a. Draw the next triangular number.
b. Describe the pattern and list the next three triangular numbers.
c. What is the tenth triangular number?

22. The first 10 triangular numbers are

1 3 6 10 15 21 28 36 45 55

a. Find the difference between adjacent triangular numbers. For example, $3 - 1 = 2$ and $6 - 3 = 3$. What numbers do you get?
b. Find the sum between adjacent triangle numbers. For example, $1 + 3 = 4$. What numbers do you get?
c. Follow the pattern and find the sum of the ninth and tenth triangular numbers.
d. Find the sum of the fourteenth and fifteenth triangular numbers.

23. The fourth triangular number is 10 and the sum $1 + 2 + 3 + 4 = 10$.
a. What is the eighth triangular number?
b. What is $1 + 2 + 3 + 4 + 5 + 6 + 7 + 8$?
c. What is the twelfth triangular number?
d. What is $1 + 2 + 3 + \cdots + 12$?
e. Make a conjecture regarding the nth triangular number and the sum of the first n counting numbers.
f. Carl Friedrich Gauss, a German mathematician born in 1777, was confronted with a similar problem when he was 7 years old. His teacher wanted Gauss to find the sum

$$1 + 2 + 3 + \cdots + 99 + 100$$

Gauss noticed that $1 + 100 = 101$, $2 + 99 = 101$, $3 + 98 = 101, \ldots$; thus, you have 50 pairs of numbers, each pair summing to 101. What is the result? Use the idea in parts **(a)**–**(e)**.

24. The figures represent the *square numbers*.

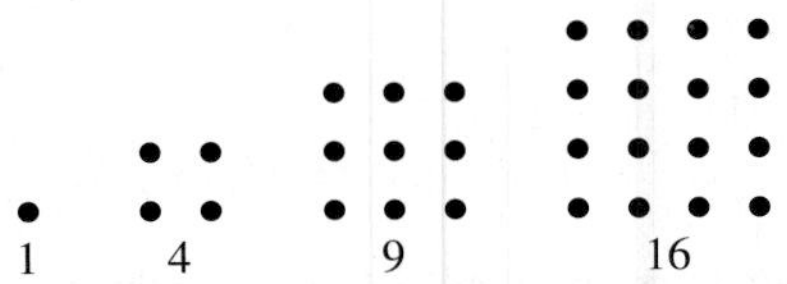

a. Draw the next square number.
b. Describe the pattern and list the next three square numbers.
c. What is the twelfth square number?

25. The numbers in problems 21 and 24 are examples of *figurate numbers*. Another type of figurate number is the *pentagonal number*, shown below.

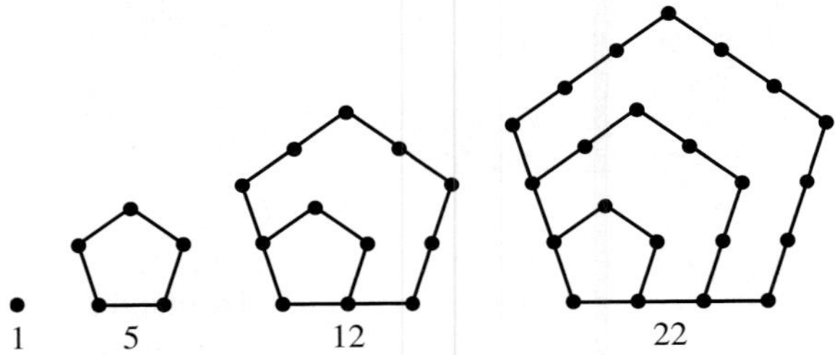

a. Draw the next pentagonal number.
b. Describe the pattern.
c. What is the sixth pentagonal number?

26. The figures below show the number of line segments that can be drawn between two points and between three, four, and five noncollinear points. How many line segments can be drawn between
a. six noncollinear points?
b. nine noncollinear points?

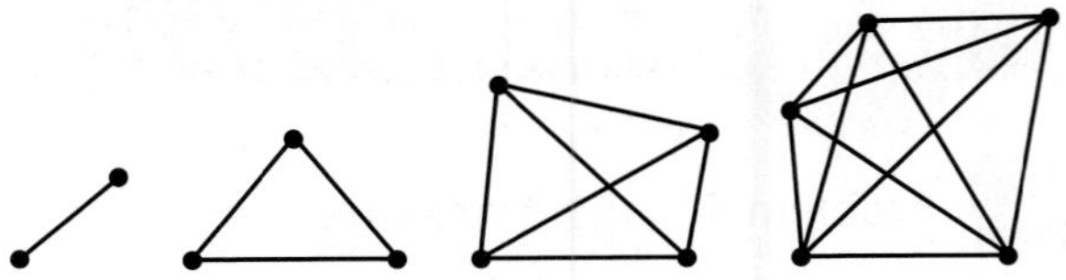

27. The figures below show all the diagonals that can be drawn from one vertex of a quadrilateral (four sides), pentagon (five sides), hexagon (six sides), and heptagon (seven sides). How many diagonals can be drawn from one vertex of a decagon (ten sides)?

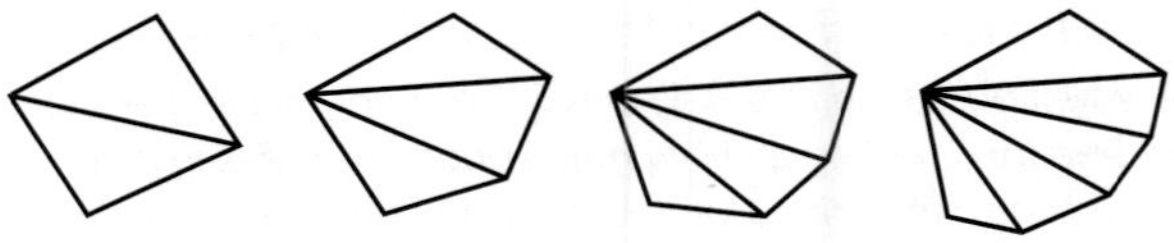

28. Follow this procedure.

Select a number.
Add 7 to it.
Multiply the sum by 3.
Subtract 6 from the product.
Divide by 3.
Subtract 5 from the quotient.

a. Follow the procedure above for four different numbers and make a conjecture about the relationship between the original number and the final result.

b. Represent the original number by n and prove the conjecture in part (**a**).

29. Follow this procedure.

Select a number.
Add 7 to it.
Multiply the sum by 3.
Subtract 6 from the product.
Divide by 3.
Subtract the original number from the quotient.

a. Follow the procedure above for four different numbers and make a conjecture about the relationship between the original number and the final result.

b. Represent the original number by n and prove the conjecture in part (**a**).

30. Follow this procedure.

Select a number.
Add 5 to it.
Multiply the sum by 4.
Divide the product by 2.
Subtract 10 from the quotient.

a. Follow the procedure above for four different numbers and make a conjecture about the relationship between the original number and the final result.

b. Represent the original number by n and prove the conjecture in part (**a**).

31. Follow this procedure.

Select a number.
Add 5 to it.
Multiply the sum by 4.
Divide the product by 2.
Subtract twice the original number from the quotient.

a. Follow the procedure above for four different numbers and make a conjecture about the relationship between the original number and the final result.

b. Represent the original number by n and prove the conjecture in part (**a**).

32. Pick a number and follow this pattern.

1. If the number is even, divide by 2.
2. If the number is odd, multiply by 3, then add 1.

Whatever answer you get, follow rules 1 and 2 again and proceed until you get a 1. For example, start with 13 for good luck. Here is the pattern.

$$13 \to 40 \to 20 \to 10 \to 5 \to 16 \to 8 \to 4 \to 2 \to 1$$

a. What is the pattern if you start with 22?

b. What is the pattern if you start with 15?

c. What do you notice about the last three numbers in each pattern?

d. Can you find any number so that the last three numbers in the pattern are different from the last three numbers you obtained in parts (**a**) and (**b**)?

33. Pick a number and write it in words; then do the following:

1. Write the number of letters in the words.
2. Write the number obtained in step 1 in words.
3. Repeat steps 1 and 2.

For example, if you pick the number 24, the pattern is

twenty-four, 10, ten, 3, three, 5, five, 4, four, 4

a. Pick a different number and follow the pattern. What is the last number in the pattern?

b. Can you explain why this works?

34. Consider the pattern

$$1 = 1^2$$
$$1 + 3 = 2^2$$
$$1 + 3 + 5 = 3^2$$
$$1 + 3 + 5 + 7 = 4^2$$

a. What are the next three lines in this pattern?

b. The pattern suggests that if you add the first two odd numbers, you get 2^2; if you add the first three odd numbers, you get 3^2; and so on. What would the answer be if you added the first 10 odd numbers?

35. Consider the pattern

$$1^2 = 1^3$$
$$(1 + 2)^2 = 1^3 + 2^3$$
$$(1 + 2 + 3)^2 = 1^3 + 2^3 + 3^3$$

a. What are the next three lines in this pattern?

b. What does this pattern suggest?

36. Consider the pattern

$$3^2 + 4^2 = 5^2$$
$$3^3 + 4^3 + 5^3 = 6^3$$

a. What do you think is the next line in this pattern?

b. Is the result you get in part (**a**) a true statement?

C Problem Solving: Applications

37. At the age of 19, Galileo Galilei, an Italian astronomer, mathematician, and physicist, made discoveries that led to the invention of the pendulum clock. The following table lists the lengths of a series of pendulums having different swing times. Find the pattern that relates the length of the pendulum to the time of the swing.

Time of Swing	Length of Pendulum
1 sec	1 unit
2 sec	4 units
3 sec	9 units
4 sec	16 units

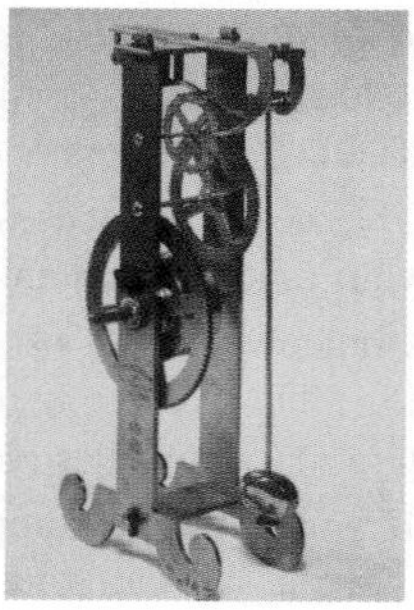

A model of Galileo's escapement and pendulum made in 1883.

38. There is a pattern relating length of foot and shoe size. For men, the pattern is

Foot Length	9 in.	10 in.	11 in.	12 in.	13 in.	14 in.
Shoe Size	5	8	11			

a. Fill in the table with the appropriate numbers.

b. Matthew McGrory has an 18-in.-long foot. (He is in the *Guinness Book of Records.*) Follow the pattern and find his shoe size.

39. The pattern relating foot length and shoe size for women is

Foot Length	8 in.	9 in.	10 in.	11 in.	12 in.	13 in.
Shoe Size	3	6	9			

a. Fill in the table with the appropriate numbers.

b. Suppose a woman wears size 8 shoes. What is the length of her foot?

40. According to the Health Insurance Association of America, the average daily room charge by U.S. hospitals is as shown in the following table:

Year	1980	1985	1990	1995	2000	2005	2010
Daily Cost	$127	$212	$297				

a. Fill in the table with the appropriate numbers.

b. What is the pattern?

c. Do you think the pattern will continue after 1995?

IN OTHER WORDS

41. Use a dictionary to find the definition of *deduction* and then explain in your own words the difference between inductive and deductive reasoning.

42. Explain in your own words the definition of the word *problem.*

43. Briefly describe an instance in which you used induction as a problem-solving strategy to solve a problem.

USING YOUR KNOWLEDGE

As we have learned, Inductive reasoning *goes from specific to general while* deductive reasoning *goes from general to specific.*

In problems 44–47, determine whether the reasoning used is an example of inductive *or* deductive *reasoning.*

44. A small drip from a tap can waste as much as 4 liters of water a day. There is a small drip from your tap, so you are wasting as much as 4 liters of water each day.

45. The average toilet uses 3 gallons per flush (gpf). You just flushed your toilet, so you have used 3 gallons of water.

46. Homeowners in Los Angeles get a 30% tax credit for installing a house solar system, so anybody who installs a solar system in California should get a 30% tax credit.

47. If you put your computer in "sleep mode" when you're not using it, you can save $178 per year. Your computer is in sleep mode, so you will save $178 per year.

COLLABORATIVE LEARNING

The Fibonacci numbers 1, 1, 2, 3, 5, and so on *are related to the number of petals in certain flowers, the leaf arrangements in certain plants, the number of spirals in pine cones, and the arrangement of seeds on flower heads.*

1. Have each student select one of the examples listed, examine it, and report to the rest of the class on his or her findings.

A bee colony consists of the queen ♀, worker bees *(females who produce no eggs), and* drone bees ♂ *(males who do no work). Male bees are produced by the queen's unfertilized eggs, so male bees have a mother but no father! All the females are produced when the queen mates with a male, so females have two parents. The family tree of a female bee and that of a male drone bee are shown in the figures.*

© JSseng/Shutterstock.com

Source: http://earthsky.org/biodiversity/can-a-bee-colony-replace-its-queen

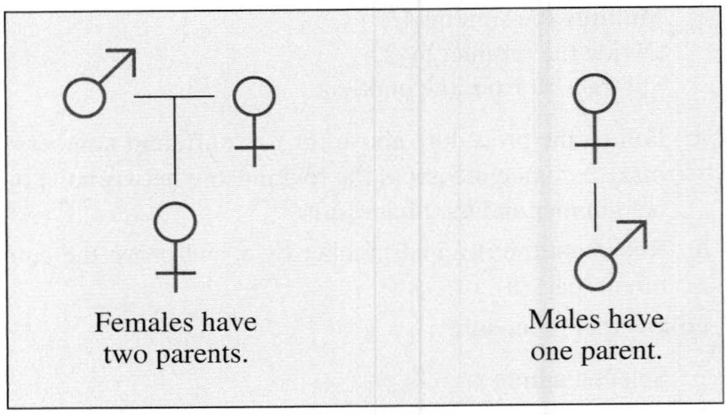
Females have two parents.
Males have one parent.

Family tree of a male (drone) bee.

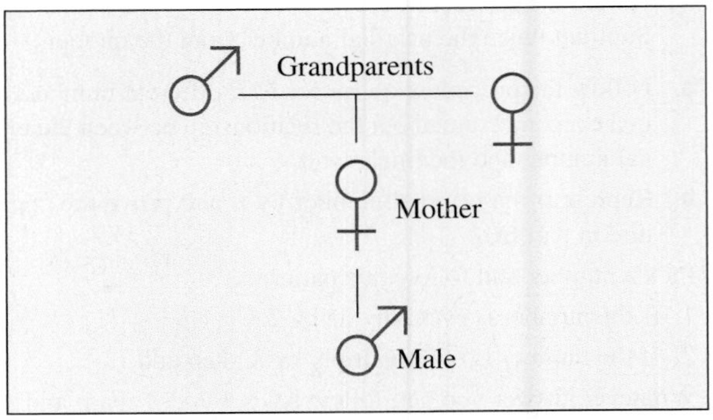
Grandparents
Mother
Male

2. Have one of the students in the class draw the next generation for a male bee, starting with the family tree of a male bee shown in the diagram. Then have another student draw the next generation, and so on.

3. Count the number of bees in the first generation (1), the second generation (1), the third generation (2), and so on. Compare the numbers you get with the Fibonacci numbers. What is your conclusion?

4. Here are the first 15 Fibonacci numbers.

1	1	2	3	5	8	13	21	34	55
89	144	233	377	610					

Note: Every *third* Fibonacci number

2, 8, 34, 144, 610

is a multiple of 2.

a. Have a member of the class examine all the multiples of 3 in the list. Is there a similar conclusion regarding multiples of 3?

b. Have another member of the class examine all the multiples of 5 in the list. What conclusion can be reached regarding multiples of 5?

c. Have another member of the class examine all the multiples of 8 in the list. What conclusion can be reached regarding multiples of 8?

On the basis of the observations made by the members of the class, what could be a general rule regarding the numbers in the Fibonacci sequence and their multiplicity?

1.2 Estimation: A Problem-Solving Tool

GETTING STARTED

OBJECTIVES

A. Use the rules for rounding numbers and estimation to solve problems.

B. Use the RSTUV procedure to solve applications.

Have you attended a football game or other sporting event lately? How does the event staff estimate attendance? Does it matter? Read on and see.

The Million Man March took place on Monday, October 16, 1995, along the Mall in Washington, D.C. The National Park Service announced that 400,000 people took part in the event. The Nation of Islam, organizers of the march, vehemently objected, called it a gross underestimate of what was counted on-site to be a crowd 1.5 to 2 million strong, and threatened to sue the National Park Service. (Source: http://tinyurl.com/2ca4akh.)

The crowd at the Million Man March and estimates of the number of persons in several different areas.

How was the controversy settled? Here are the problem-solving steps they used.

1. Ten color photographs of the crowd were collected.
2. The area of the mall in the photos was divided into square grids.
3. The crowd density was estimated on the basis of different degrees of packing in each square meter, ranging from six people per square meter to one person per 5 square meters.

4. The number of people per square meter was multiplied by the number of square meters (grids), and an estimate of 878,587 was reached, with an estimated error margin of 25% (about 219,647).
5. Therefore, the Million Man March had between 658,940 and 1,098,234 participants. Why?

Here are some more facts that would result in a better estimate. At what time were the photos taken (peak attendance was between 12 and 2 P.M.)? Some areas were more densely populated (six people per square meter) than others (one person per 5 square meters). What was the exact area of the mall? To see the answers to some of these questions and a revised crowd estimate, read the article cited in the photo credits at the end of this book.

A Rounding Numbers and Estimation

As you can see from Getting Started, an important step in solving problems is to be able to estimate to make sure the answer you arrive at makes sense. One way to estimate, or approximate, an answer is to use round numbers. For example, suppose you want to buy 2 soft drinks (at \$0.99 each) and 2 bags of popcorn at \$1.75 each. To estimate the cost of the items, you can round like this.

$0.99 → $1 So the drinks are about $2 \times \$1 = \$2$.
$1.75 → $2 So the popcorn is about $2 \times \$2 = \$4$.
Your total purchase is about \$6.

Some people prefer to write the procedure using the symbol $\approx$ to indicate an approximation. Thus, we can also write

$\$0.99 \approx \$1$ So the drinks are about \$2.
$\$1.75 \approx \$2$ So the popcorn is about \$4.
The total purchase is still about \$6.

Below is the procedure we use to round off numbers (left) with a worked-out example on the right.

Rule for Rounding Numbers

Rule	*Example:* Round 258.34 to the nearest hundred.
1. **Underline** the place to which you are rounding.	1. **Underline** the 2: $\underline{2}58.34$.
2. If the first number to the *right* of the underlined place is 5 *or more,* **add** one to the underlined number. Otherwise, *do not change* the underlined number.	2. The first number to the *right* of 2 is 5, so we **add** 1 to the underlined digit 2 to get 3.
3. *Change* all the numbers to the *right* of the underlined number to zeros.	3. *Change* all the digits to the right of 3 to zeros, obtaining 300.00 or 300. Note that if you count by hundreds (100, 200, and so on), 258.34 is closer to 300 than to 200. The procedure is written as $\underline{2}58.34 \rightarrow 300$

EXAMPLE 1 Estimating the Amount of a Purchase

A student bought perfume for \$7.99, nail enamel for \$2.29, candy for \$3.79, adhesive paper for \$1.89, a curling iron for \$8.69, and sunglasses for \$7.19. Find a reasonable estimate of the total amount spent.

GRAPH IT

Your grapher can round numbers for you; however, you have to know how to tell it what to do. Suppose you want to round the answer $31.84 of Example 1 to the nearest dollar. Tell the grapher you want to do math with a number by pressing MATH ▶ 2. Enter the 31.84 , and tell the grapher you want no decimals by entering a 0. Press ENTER. You get 32! (See below.)

```
7.99+2.29+3.79+1
.89+8.69+7.19
             31.84
round(31.84,0)
                32
```

Solution

If we round each of the amounts to the nearest dollar, we have

$7.99 \to 8$	$3.79 \to 4$	$8.69 \to 9$
$2.29 \to 2$	$1.89 \to 2$	$7.19 \to 7$

Since $8 + 2 + 4 + 2 + 9 + 7 = 32$, a reasonable estimate for the total amount spent is $32.

Note that in Example 1 we could have decided to round to the nearest dime, obtaining $8 + $2.30 + $3.80 + $1.90 + $8.70 + $7.20, or $31.90. This is a better estimate because the true cost is $31.84. However, *estimates are not supposed to give exact answers but rather tell us if the answers we are getting are reasonable.* Next, we look at a specialized type of rounding: electric meters.

How to Read Your Electric Meter

- Stand directly in front of your meter. Looking at dials from an angle can distort the reading.
- Read your meter dials from *right* to *left*.
- If the dial hand is between numbers, use the smaller of the two numbers.
- If the dial hand is positioned *exactly* on a number, look at the dial to the right to determine the correct reading. *Has the dial to the right passed zero?*
- If *no,* use the smaller number on the dial you're reading.
- If *yes,* use the number the hand is pointing to on the dial you're reading.

Source: Used with permission from WE Energies. www.we-energies.com.

FIGURE 1.5

Do you see why the reading on the first dial of B in Figure 1.5 is 9 and not 0? It is because the pointer is on the number 0, which means that you must look at the dial to the right of it. That dial is before 9 and has not passed 0, so we use the smaller number on the dial we are reading—in this case 9 (not 10 or 0).

EXAMPLE 2 Reading Your Light Meter

(a) Read the meter dials for today as shown in Figure 1.6.

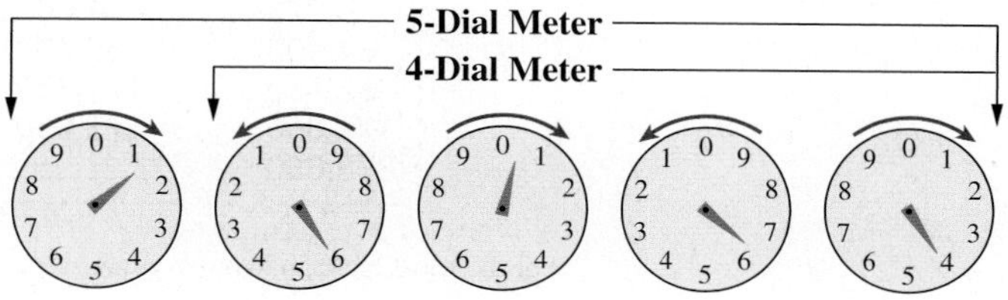

FIGURE 1.6

(b) If the reading yesterday was 16,003 kWh, how many kilowatt-hours have been consumed since yesterday?

(c) If a kilowatt-hour costs $.08, how much is your 1-day bill?

(d) If you estimate the same consumption each day for a 30-day period, what is your estimated monthly electricity bill?

Solution

(a) The reading is 1 6 0 6 4.

(b) The reading today is 1 6 0 6 4, and yesterday it was 1 6 0 0 3, so we have consumed 16,064 − 16,003 = 61 kWh.

(c) Your 1-day bill is $0.08 \times 61 = \$4.88$.

(d) For 30 days it would be $30 \times 4.88 = \$146.40$ because your 1-day bill is $4.88.

One of the most important estimations you can make is the estimation of your taxes. This estimation depends on your earnings and marital status. Let us use our problem-solving procedure to see how it works.

B Problem Solving Using Estimation

EXAMPLE 3 Estimating Taxable Income

Suppose you are single and estimate that the taxable income on line 5 of your tax return is $40,000. How much would you estimate your taxes to be?

Solution

We are going to use our problem-solving procedure to find the answer.

PROBLEM-SOLVING

Calculating Estimated Taxes

① **Read** the problem.

We are looking for your estimated taxes.

② **Select** the unknown.

The unknown is the estimated amount of taxes you have to pay.

③ **Think** of a plan.

We can use an estimated tax table from the Internal Revenue Service (IRS). The table is available on the Internet at http://www.irs.gov and it is called Form 1040 ES, Estimated Tax for Individuals. Select the table for singles.*

Single –Schedule X

Schedule X–Use if your **2010** filing status is **Single**

If line 5 is: Over–	But not over–	**The tax is:**	*of the amount over–*
$0	$8,375	---------- **10%**	**$0**
8,375	34,000	**$837.50 + 15%**	**8,375**
34,000	82,400	**4,681.25 + 25%**	**34,000**
82,400	171,850	**16,781.25 + 28%**	**82,400**
171,850	373,650	**41,827.25 + 33%**	**171,850**
373,650	---------	**108,421.25 + 35%**	**373,650**

*For the latest table go to http://www.irs.gov/pub/irs-pdf/f1040es.pdf.

④ **Use** the techniques you are studying to carry out the plan.

The problem says that line 5 is \$40,000, which is over \$34,000 but not over \$82,400 (third row). This means that the tax is \$4681.25 + 25% of the amount over \$34,000.

⑤ **Verify** the answer.

Since your taxable income is \$40,000, the amount over \$34,000 is \$40,000 − \$34,000 = \$6000.

Thus, your tax is \$4681.25 + 0.25(\$6000)
= \$4681.25 + \$1500
= \$6181.25

You can use an online calculator to verify this. Results may vary slightly because the \$40,000 already includes a deduction for singles.)

Try Example 4 Now Cover the solution, write your own solution, and then check your work.

Can you estimate the height of a person with only a bone as a clue? Anthropological detectives do! Suppose a detective finds a 17.9-in. femur bone (that is the one connecting the hip bone to the knee bone) from a male. To find the height H of its owner, use the formula $H = 1.88f + 32$, where f is the length of the femur bone. If the bone is 17.9 in. long, the owner's height H (to the nearest inch) must have been $H = 1.88(17.9) + 32 \approx 66$ in. ($\approx$ means "approximately equal to").

EXAMPLE 4 Estimating Height from Femur Length

A detective found a 17.9-in. femur bone. He is looking for a missing female 66 in. tall. The formula indicating the relationship between the femur of a female and her height is $H = 1.94f + 28$.

(a) Determine if the femur could belong to the missing female.

(b) Estimate a person's height (to the nearest inch) with a 17.9-in. femur bone.

(c) How much difference would there be in the height if you round off the measurements in the original formulas to the nearest whole number?

Solution

(a) Substituting 17.9 in $H = 1.94f + 28$, we obtain

$$H = 1.94(17.9) + 28$$
$$\approx 63 \text{ in.}$$

(b) The height of a person depends on whether the person is a male or a female.

If the person is a male, use $H = 1.88(17.9) + 32 \approx 66$ in.

If the person is a female, use $H = 1.94(17.9) + 28 \approx 63$ in.

(c) When rounded to the nearest whole numbers, the formulas would be:

Male: $H = 2f + 32 = 2(17.9) + 32 \approx 68$ in.

Female: $H = 2f + 28 = 2(17.9) + 28 \approx 64$ in.

Thus, the difference in the male's height with the new formula is 2 in. (68 instead of 66) and for the female is 1 in. (64 instead of 63).

Now that we know that there is a relationship between the length of your bones and your height, is there a relationship between the length of your bones and your weight? Of course there is! However, a better measurement for your healthy weight is your body mass index (BMI). According to the National Heart, Lung and Blood Institute, you can figure out your BMI using this formula.

$$\text{BMI} = \frac{705W}{H^2}$$

where W is your weight (in pounds) and H is your height (in inches). In order to interpret your BMI, you use the following table.

If Your BMI Is	You Are
18 or below	Underweight
19–24	Normal
25–29	Overweight
30 or more	Obese

EXAMPLE 5 Estimating Your Body Mass Index

Suppose you weigh 162 lb and are 69 in. tall.

(a) Find your BMI to two decimal places.

(b) Refer to the table and interpret the results.

(c) Round the height, weight, and answer to the nearest 10, and use the formula

$$\text{BMI} = \frac{700W}{H^2}$$

to estimate your BMI.

Solution

(a) $\text{BMI} = \dfrac{705W}{H^2}$, where $W = 162$ and $H = 69$.

$$= \frac{705 \cdot 162}{69^2} \approx 23.99$$

(b) According to the table, if your BMI is between 19 and 24, your weight is "normal" for your height.

(c) When the height and weight are rounded to the nearest 10, $162 \rightarrow 160$ and $69 \rightarrow 70$ and

$$\text{BMI} = \frac{700 \cdot 160}{70 \cdot 70} = \frac{10 \cdot 16}{7} \approx 22.9, \text{ or } 20 \text{ (to the nearest 10)}$$

which is still "normal" (see the table).

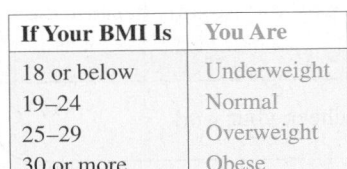

We have examined the weight of humans based on their BMI, but what is the "normal" weight for a horse? First, we have to figure out how to weigh a horse! According to Lon Lewis, author of *Feeding and Care of the Horse,*

> The importance of accurate equine weight estimates is unquestionable. Veterinarians, equine management facilities, stables, and individual horse owners rely on accurate weight information to determine proper medication dosage, feed and nutrition considerations, racing performance, and transportation requirements.

Here is the formula you use to estimate the weight of a horse.

$$W \text{ (in pounds)} = \frac{G^2 \cdot L}{330}$$

where G (inches) is the horse's girth, the circumference of the horse's body about 4 in. behind its front legs, and L (inches) is its length (see Figure 1.7).

To learn the basics of horse feeding, see http://www.equusite.com/articles/basics/basicsFeeding.shtml.

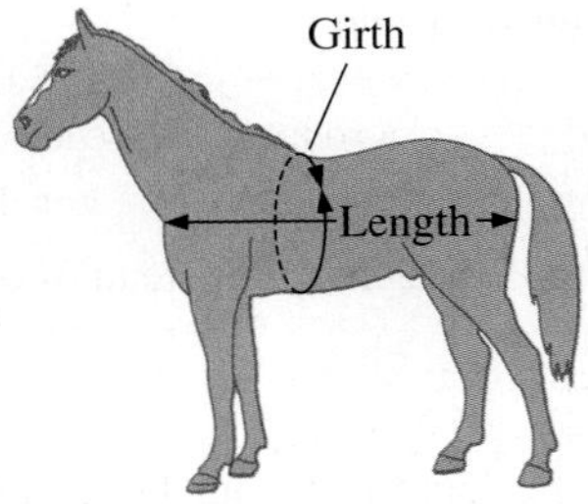

Source: http://www.equusite.com/articles/basics/basicsFeeding.shtml.

FIGURE 1.7

EXAMPLE 6 Estimating the Weight of a Horse

(a) Estimate the weight of a 65-in.-long horse with a 70-in. girth.

(b) A horse requires about 0.6 gal of water, 1 lb of hay, and $\frac{1}{2}$ lb of grain for each 100 lb of body weight daily. Estimate how much water, hay, and grain this horse needs.

Solution

(a) Substitute 70 for G and 65 for L in

$$W = \frac{G^2 \cdot L}{330}$$

obtaining

$$\frac{70 \cdot 70 \cdot 65}{330} \approx 965 \text{ lb}$$

Check this with a horse-weight calculator at http://www.gaitedhorses.net/Articles/horseweight.html.

(b) We have to estimate how many 100 lb of body weight the horse has. It is about $\frac{965}{100} = 9.65$. We can approximate the 9.65 to 10 to be safe. Thus, our horse needs 0.6 gal of water for every 100 lb of body weight; that is, $10 \times 0.6 = 6$ gal per day. The horse also needs 1 lb of hay for each 100 lb of body weight—that is, $10 \times 1 = 10$ lb of hay per day—and, finally, it needs $\frac{1}{2}$ lb of grain for each 100 lb of body weight—that is, $10 \times \frac{1}{2} = 5$ lb of grain per day.

1.2 EXERCISES

A Rounding Numbers and Estimation

1. An investor owns 416.38 shares of a mutual fund valued at \$30.28 per share. Find a reasonable estimate of the value of the investor's stock (to the nearest hundred dollars) by rounding 416.38 to the nearest 100 and \$30.28 to the nearest dollar.

2. Water is sold in thousand-gallon units. If a unit of water costs \$1.88 and 50.439 units were used, find a reasonable estimate of the bill to the nearest hundred dollars.

3. A student bought artichokes for \$7.80, cucumbers for \$2.29, lettuce for \$3.75, tomatoes for \$1.85, and broccoli for \$2.90. Find a reasonable estimate of the total amount the student spent on vegetables by rounding each price to the nearest dollar.

4. A student bought a towel for \$8.99, soap for \$2.39, toothpaste for \$3.79, shampoo for \$1.79, a pair of shorts for \$8.79, and a hat for \$9.99. Find a reasonable estimate of the total purchases by rounding each quantity to the nearest dollar.

5. A herbicide is to be applied at the rate of 5.75 gal per acre. Find, to the nearest hundred gallons, a reasonable estimate for the amount of herbicide needed for $154\frac{1}{2}$ acres.

6. A bag of bahia grass covers 1.75 acres. What is a reasonable estimate of the number of acres that could be covered with $158\frac{1}{2}$ bags of seed? Answer to the nearest hundred acres.

7. To find the batting average A of a player (to three decimal places), divide the number of hits H by the number of times the player has been at bat (AB). Pete Rose holds the record for most career hits with 4256 in 14,053 at bats.

a. What is Rose's career batting average?

b. Estimate his average by rounding 4256 and 14,053 to the nearest hundred.

8. The highest batting average for a season belongs to Hugh Duffy, who played for Boston. He had 236 hits in 539 at bats.

a. What was Duffy's batting average?

b. Estimate his batting average by rounding the hits and the at bats to the nearest ten.

9. The *Guinness Book of Records* reports that the lowest earned run average (ERA) for a season belongs to Ferdinand M. Schupp, who in 1916 pitched 140 innings (IP) for New York and only allowed 14 earned runs (ER). If

$$\text{ERA} = \frac{9 \times \text{ER}}{\text{IP}}$$

what was Schupp's ERA rounded to three decimal places?

10. In 1914, Hubert "Dutch" Leonard of the Boston Red Sox gave up 25 earned runs in $222\frac{2}{3}$ innings. Find Leonard's ERA rounded to three decimal places. Is it lower than Schupp's?

The following information, from cooking.com, will be used in problems 11–16. As a rough average, one medium-sized, medium-hungry person could consume what is listed below.

4 to 8 hors d'oeuvres	$\frac{1}{4}$ *lb vegetables*
1 cup soup	$\frac{1}{3}$ *lb rice, beans, etc.*
$\frac{1}{4}$ *head of lettuce*	$\frac{1}{4}$ *lb raw pasta*
$\frac{1}{3}$ *lb boneless meat or fish*	$\frac{1}{4}$ *cup gravy*

Suppose you are planning a banquet for 100 people.

11. Estimate how many hors d'oeuvres you will need for the banquet.

12. Estimate how many cups of soup you will need for the banquet. If 1 gal is 16 cups, how many gallons of soup do you need?

13. Estimate how many pounds (to the nearest pound) of boneless meat or fish you will need for the banquet.

14. Estimate how many pounds (to the nearest pound) of rice, beans, and so on you will need for the banquet.

15. Estimate how many pounds of raw pasta you will need for the banquet.

16. Estimate how many cups of gravy you will need for the banquet. How many gallons is that?

17. **a.** Read the meter for today.

b. If the reading yesterday was 5102, how many kilowatt-hours have been used?

c. If electricity costs 8 cents per kilowatt-hour, how much is your 1-day bill?

d. If you estimate the same consumption each day for a 30-day period, what is your estimated monthly electricity bill?

18. **a.** Read the meter for today.

b. If the reading yesterday was 5501, how many kilowatt-hours have been used?

c. If electricity costs 8 cents per kilowatt-hour, how much is your 1-day bill?

d. If you estimate the same consumption each day for a 30-day period, what is your estimated monthly electricity bill?

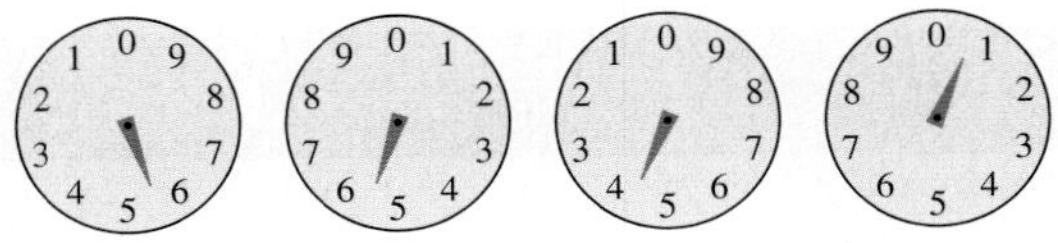

19. **a.** Read the meter for today.

b. If the reading yesterday was 6951, how many kilowatt-hours have been used?

c. If electricity costs 8 cents per kilowatt-hour, how much is your 1-day bill?

d. If you estimate the same consumption each day for a 30-day period, what is your estimated monthly electricity bill?

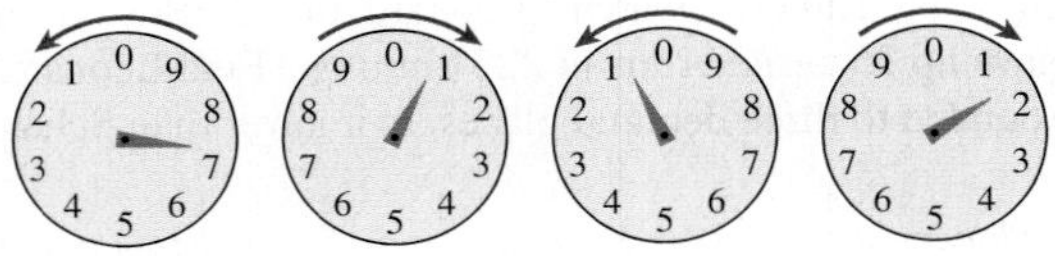

20. **a.** Read the meter for today.

b. If the reading yesterday was 6100, how many kilowatt-hours have been used?

c. If electricity costs 8 cents per kilowatt-hour, how much is your 1-day bill?

d. If you estimate the same consumption each day for a 30-day period, what is your estimated monthly electricity bill?

21. On the basis of the table in Example 3, what would your estimated tax be if your taxable income were \$60,000?

22. On the basis of the table in Example 3, what would your estimated tax be if your taxable income were \$50,000?

B Problem Solving Using Estimation

Use the following information in problems 23–24.

The relationship between the length h of a humerus bone (the one connecting your shoulder to your elbow) and the height H of a person is given by

Male: $H = 2.89h + 27.81$

Female: $H = 2.75h + 28.14$

23. A detective found a 15-in. humerus bone belonging to a male.

a. How tall was the male?

b. What would the difference in height be if you rounded the measurements in the original formula to the nearest whole number?

24. Suppose the 15-in. humerus bone belonged to a female.

a. How tall was she?

b. What would the difference in height be if you rounded the measurements in the original formula to the nearest whole number?

25. Use the information in Example 5 to find the BMI for a person 68 in. tall and weighing 150 lb. What can you conclude from your answer?

26. Repeat problem 25 if the person is 70 in. tall and weighs 170 lb.

27. Use the information in Example 6 to estimate the weight of a 66-in.-long horse with a 70-in. girth. How much hay, grain, and water should this horse consume daily?

28. Repeat problem 27 for a 70-in.-long horse with a 70-in. girth. How much hay, grain, and water should this horse consume daily? Answers to the nearest whole number.

29. The Ohio Turnpike estimates that the annual cost C of routine maintenance per lane-mile is $C = 596 + 0.0019V + 21.7A$, where C is the annual cost of routine maintenance per lane-mile (in 1967 dollars), V is the volume of traffic on the roadway (measured in equivalent standard axle loads, ESAL, so that a heavy truck is represented as equivalent to many automobiles), and A is the age of the pavement in years since the last resurfacing. Estimate C (to the nearest dollar) when $V = 500{,}300$ ESAL and $A = 5$ years.

30. Repeat problem 29 for $V = 500{,}000$ and $A = 10$ years.

31. Can you estimate the age of your dog? One way to do it is to assume that if your dog is 1 year old, it would be the equivalent of 15 years old in human years. If your dog is 2 years old, it would be the equivalent of 24 years old in human years. After the second year, you add 4 dog years for every actual year.

a. Estimate the equivalent human age of a 5-year-old dog.

b. Estimate the equivalent human age of a 10-year-old dog.

32. What about cats? According to the *Daily Cat,* here is the conversion:

Cat Years	Human Years
1	16–18
2	21–25
3	29

After the third year, add 4 cat years for every actual year.

a. Estimate the equivalent human age of a 5-year-old cat.

b. Estimate the equivalent human age of a 10-year-old cat.

You can estimate the distance between two points on a map by using a scale. In the accompanying map, each inch represents approximately 15 *mi. Thus, the distance from the beginning of Interstate* 90 *to its intersection with Route* 128 *(about* 1 *in. on the map) represents an actual distance of* 15 *mi.*

33. Estimate the distance between the intersection of 90 and 128 and the intersection of 90 and 495.

34. Estimate the distance between the intersection of 90 and 495 and the intersection of 90 and 290.

35. Estimate the distance between the intersection of 90 and 290 and the intersection of 90 and 86.

36. Estimate the distance between the intersection of 90 and 86 and the intersection of 90 and 32.

37. Estimate the distance between the intersection of 90 and 32 and the intersection of 90 and 91.

Use the following assumptions in problems 38–42. *Your car makes about* 20 *mi/gal, and gasoline costs about* $4.00*/gal.*

38. How much does it cost to travel the distance in problem 33?

39. How much does it cost to travel the distance in problem 34?

40. How much does it cost to travel the distance in problem 35?

41. How much does it cost to travel the distance in problem 36?

42. How much does it cost to travel the distance in problem 37?

43. A gray whale eats about 268,000 lb of amphipods (a marine crustacean) per month. In a month with 30 days, estimate how many pounds of amphipods a gray whale consumes in a day.

44. If the average weight of an amphipod is 0.004 oz, estimate how many amphipods a gray whale might eat in a day.

45. A 12,000-lb killer whale might eat as much as 14,000 lb of herring per month. In a month with 30 days, estimate to the nearest hundredth how many pounds of herring a killer whale would eat in a day.

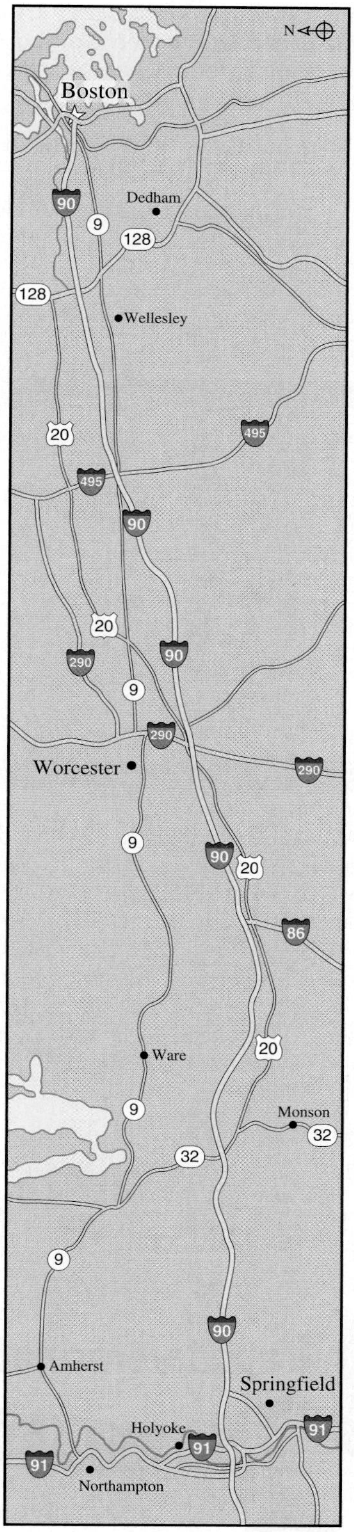

46. If the average weight of a herring is 3.2 oz, estimate how many herring a killer whale would eat in a day. (Source: Oregon Coast Aquarium: www.aquarium.org.)

Use the following information for problems 47–48. Your basal metabolic rate (BMR) is the amount of energy your body needs to maintain body temperature, breathe, and make your heart beat. To estimate the BMR, use the following formulas:

Male	Multiply the body weight by 10; add twice the body weight to this value.
Female	Multiply body weight by 10; add the body weight to this value.

47. What is the BMR for a 150-lb male?

48. What is the BMR for a 120-lb female?

IN OTHER WORDS

49. Write the procedure that you use to round the number 157 to the nearest hundred.

50. Explain, in your own words why the reading on the first dial is 9 and not 0.

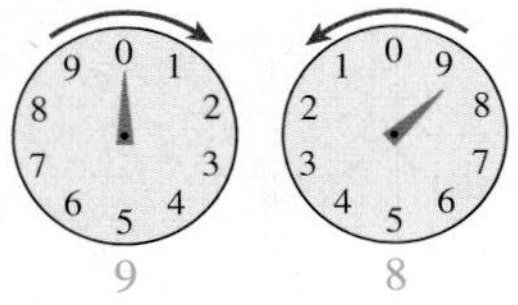

USING YOUR KNOWLEDGE

In Getting Started, we discussed how the number of participants in the Million Man March was estimated. How does the event staff estimate the number of people in the Tournament of Roses Parade? Below is the method Robert Gillette, a reporter for the Los Angeles Times, *uses to calculate the number of people in a specific area.*

He measures the depth of the standing-room area, which is 23 ft. Then he multiplies by the 5.5-mi parade route and doubles the amount because there are spectators on both sides of the street, obtaining 23 ft · 5.5 mi · 2. Unfortunately, the answer will be in feet · miles. 1 mi = 5280 ft.

51. Find 23 ft · 5.5 · 5280 ft · 2.

52. Assume that each spectator occupies 2 ft^2 of space (2 ft thick and 1 ft wide). How many spectators fit in the space you obtained in problem 51? That's the estimate Mr. Gillette provides!

COLLABORATIVE LEARNING

Don't Eat the Beans!

How many fish in the lake? How many deer in the forest? We cannot let you go fishing, capture every fish in the lake, and count them, let alone catch deer in the forest. In this Collaborative Learning, we will discuss an **estimation** method called **capture-recapture** and simulate the fishing and hunting. You need several bags of lima beans, one for each group (1-lb bags are ideal), and a nontoxic washable marker. In this investigation, the bag of beans represents the lake or the forest. The objective is to find out the total number of beans (fish or deer) in the bag. Here are the steps for each group:

Step 1 Reach into the lake, remove T fish, and tag them by marking them with the marker. Return the fish to the lake (meaning: put beans back in the bag!).

Step 2 Allow the fish to mingle (shake the bag!), remove a handful of fish H, and count them. Count the number of tagged (marked) fish M in the handful.

Step 3 Make a table like the one below.

Group	Number (T) of Tagged	Number (H) in Handful
1		
2		
.		
.		
.		

The method assumes that the ratio of the actual population P to the sample size T is the same as the ratio of the number of marked fish H to the number marked in the recapture sample M; hence, $PM = TH$. Thus, the formula for the population is

$$\text{Population} = \frac{TH}{\text{M}}$$

This method of estimation is called the *Lincoln Index.* If you marked the beans with a nontoxic marker, you may reuse them; otherwise, *don't eat the beans.*

You can calculate your percent of error by counting the beans in the bag (B), recording by how many beans your count is off (O), and calculating the percent O/B.

1.3 Graph Interpretation: A Problem-Solving Tool

GETTING STARTED

OBJECTIVES

A. Interpret the information on a circle graph.

B. Interpret the information on a bar graph.

C. Interpret the information on a line graph.

Do you have a budget? What are your main expenses? The **circle graph (pie chart)** on the next page (Figure 1.8) gives general guidelines to establish your budget. In a circle graph, a circle is divided into sectors (wedges) that are *proportional* to the size of the category. The information can also be presented using a **bar graph** (Figure 1.9), in which the size of the categories is proportional to the *length* of the bars.

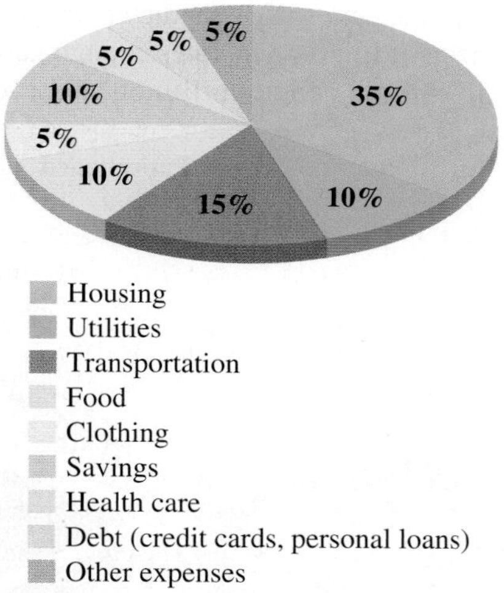

FIGURE 1.8 Circle Graph (pie chart) of budget.

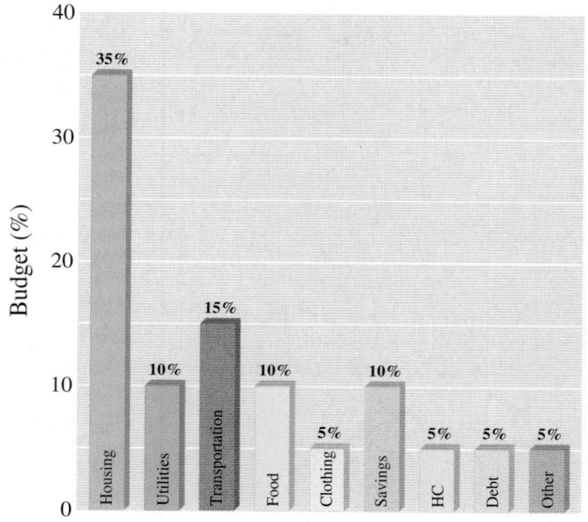

FIGURE 1.9 Bar Graph of budget.

You can learn more about budgeting at http://www.cnbc.com/id/26641187/ or at http://www.budgetmath.com/budgetcalculator.php. Enter your monthly take-home pay into the menu, and the budget pie calculator automatically determines your expense allocation.

Now, which category in the budget above is the main expense? From either the circle or the bar graph, you can see that the greatest percentage of the money will go toward housing. What about the category that receives the least percentage of the money? There are four of them. Can you name them?

In this section we will concentrate on solving problems that involve the interpretation of different graphs: circle (pie), bar, and line.

A Interpreting Circle Graphs (Pie Charts)

Can you predict the weather using a circle graph? The Bureau of Meteorology does this in Australia! The following charts (Figure 1.10) tell us how often Australia will have low (dry), normal, or high (wet) weather, depending on the type of year (El Niño, Normal, or La Niña). Now, if you know that you are having an El Niño year, what can you say about rainfall? The probability that it will be dry is about 50% (half the circle), wet 17%, and normal 33%. Can you predict what will happen if you know that you are having a La Niña year?

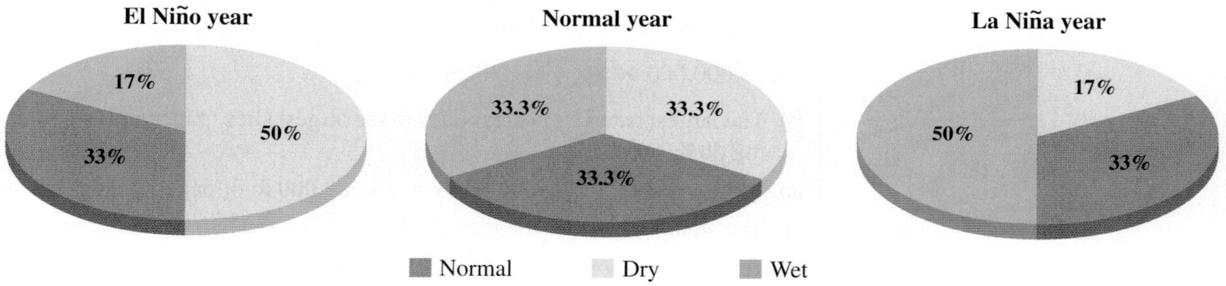

Source: www.bom.gov.au/lam/Students_Teachers/climprob/rainprbprim.shtml.

FIGURE 1.10

EXAMPLE 1 Interpreting Circle Graphs

The garbage pizza. A project by the Illinois Environmental Protection Agency and The Waste Management and Research Center created a pizza, but not the ones with the pepperoni, cheese, and jalapenos. No, no, they created the **garbage pizza,** illustrating the fact that each citizen of Illinois generates enough garbage each day to make a 5.5 lb pizza. If there are 13 million people in Illinois and each produces 5.5 lb of garbage daily:

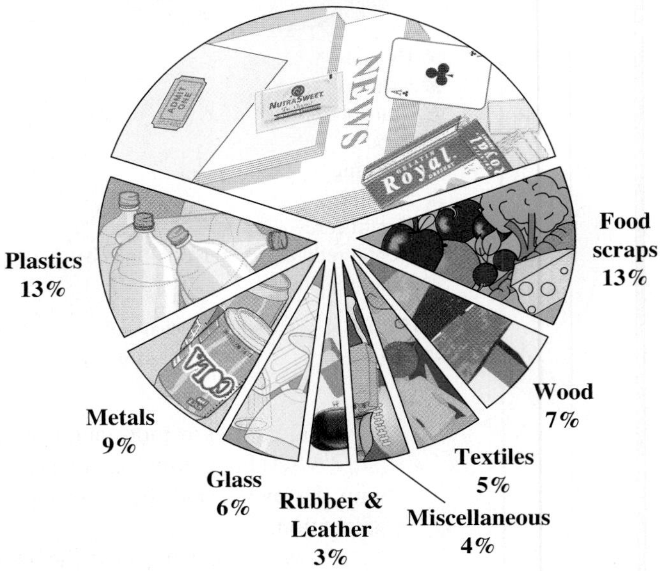

Source: Used with permission from Illinois Department of Commerce and Economic Opportunity. http://illinoisbiz.biz/NR/rdonlyres/6D266100-B8A5-4D3C-8728-AC68480C9450/0/GarbagePizza.pdf.

FIGURE 1.11

(a) Estimate how many pounds of garbage are produced each day in Illinois.

(b) According to the graph, which category of garbage is the largest and what percent is it?

(c) Use the answers from parts (a) and (b) to estimate the amount of paper and paperboard in the garbage.

(d) Which is the smallest slice of the pizza made of and what percent does it represent?

(e) How many pounds of textiles are in the garbage each day?

Solution

(a) Remember, you can follow the RSTUV procedure, so Read carefully, and Select the unknown, which is the estimate of how many pounds of garbage are produced each day in Illinois. Since there are 13 million people in Illinois, each producing 5.5 lb of garbage, the estimated number of pounds of garbage produced daily in Illinois is

$13{,}000{,}000 \times 5.5 = 71{,}500{,}000$ lb

(b) The largest category corresponds to the largest slice, paper and paperboard, comprising **40%** of the pizza.

(c) **40%** of the total **71,500,000** lb $=$ 28,600,000 lb of paper and paperboard.

(d) The smallest slice of the pizza is **3%** and corresponds to rubber and leather.

(e) Textiles correspond to 5% of 71,500,000 lb or $5\% \times 71{,}500{,}000 = 3{,}575{,}000$ million lb of textiles.

Source: http://tinyurl.com/6fu9vun.

B Interpreting Bar Graphs

Sometimes bar graphs show categories that you want to compare by drawing the bars side by side. Did your family save money for your college education? How much? Figure 1.12 shows three different household categories:

Saved less than \$5000 Saved \$5000 to \$19,999 Saved \$20,000 or more

Which is your household category? What is the percent difference between the households that saved less than \$5000 and those that saved \$20,000 or more?

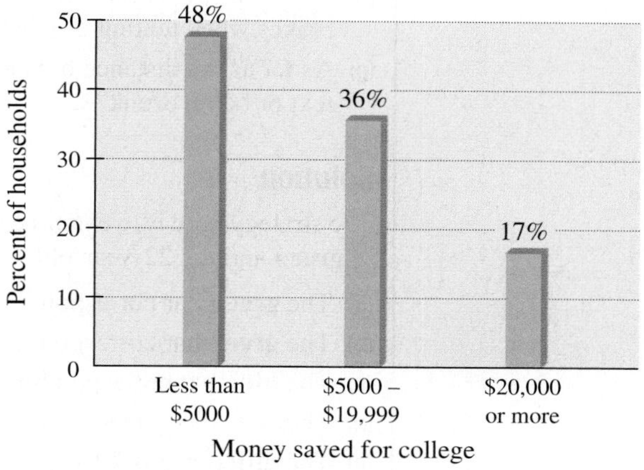

By Darryl Haralson and Jeff Dionise, *USA TODAY*. Source: State Farm.

FIGURE 1.12

What is the percent difference between the households that saved the most and those that saved the least, and how much money is involved?

Have you been texting and driving? An article in *Car and Driver* claims that the risks may be greater than drinking and driving! We can explain how by looking at the results of an experiment that used bar graphs to show the dangers involved when the driver is impaired or distracted. If you don't believe it, let us explain the experiment: A simulated red brake light lit up, and drivers were supposed to hit the brakes when traveling at 70 mph. The graph shows how far they traveled before hitting the brakes when drivers were either **(a) texting, (b) reading a text message,** or **(c)** their **blood alcohol level was 0.08** (impaired; legally intoxicated in most states). Examine the bar graphs and note that the results varied depending on many factors, such as speed at which you are driving, condition of your brakes, type of phone used and age of the driver, a seasoned 37-year-old (**green** bars) against a quick-responding 22-year-old (**blue** bars). We ask some questions about the experiment in Example 2.

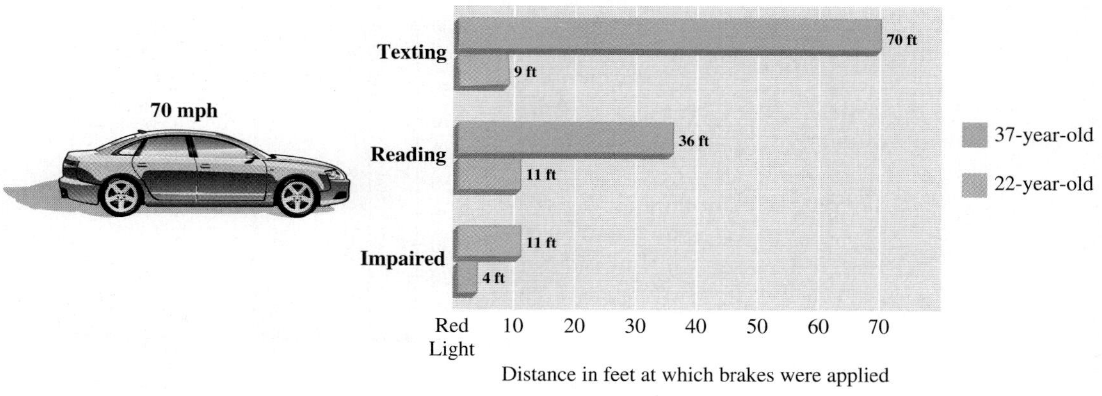

Graphic Source: Adapted from *Tampa Tribune,* June 29, 2009.

FIGURE 1.13

EXAMPLE 2 Texting and Driving Impaired

How far did the car travel before the driver hit the brakes when

(a) the 37-year-old was texting?

(b) the 37-year-old was drunk (blood alcohol level of 0.08)?

(c) the 22-year-old was texting?

(d) the 22-year-old was drunk (blood alcohol level of 0.08)?

(e) What was the difference in the distance traveled by the 37-year-old before hitting the brakes when texting or when drunk?

(f) What was the difference in the distance traveled by the 22-year-old before hitting the brakes when texting or when drunk?

(g) As far as the distance traveled before hitting the brakes, which was worse, reading a text or being drunk?

Solution

The strategy here is to examine the bar graph. Remember that the 37-year-old results are in **green** and the 22-year-old results are in **blue**.

(a) The **green** bar corresponding to texting is 70 ft long.

(b) The **green** bar corresponding to impaired is 4 ft long.

(c) The **blue** bar corresponding to texting is 9 ft long.

(d) The **blue** bar corresponding to impaired is 11 ft long.

(e) The difference is $70 - 4 = 66$ ft.

(f) $9 - 11 = -2$ ft. He traveled 2 ft more when impaired.

(g) For the 37-year-old *reading* was worse (he traveled further before applying the brakes), but the 22-year-old was able to apply the brakes much sooner than the 37-year-old in all cases *except* when driving impaired! Why do you think that is?

Can bar graphs save you money? Suppose you have a \$1000 credit card balance that charges 18% interest and you only make the minimum \$25 payment each month. It will take you forever (well, actually 5 years) to pay it off. If you decide to pay the balance off in 12 months, how much will your payments be? The bar graph (Figure 1.14) tells you, provided you know how to read it!

First, start at the 0 point and move right horizontally until you get to the category labeled 12 months (blue arrow), and then go up vertically to the end of the bar (red arrow). According to the vertical scale labeled Monthly payment, the arrow is 92 units long, which means that the monthly payment will be \$92 per month. How much money will you save? In 60 months, making the minimum \$25 payment, your total payments would be $60 \times \$25 = \$1500$. In 12 months, making \$92 payments, you will pay $12 \times 92 = \$1104$. Thus, the savings are $\$1500 - \$1104$, or \$396.

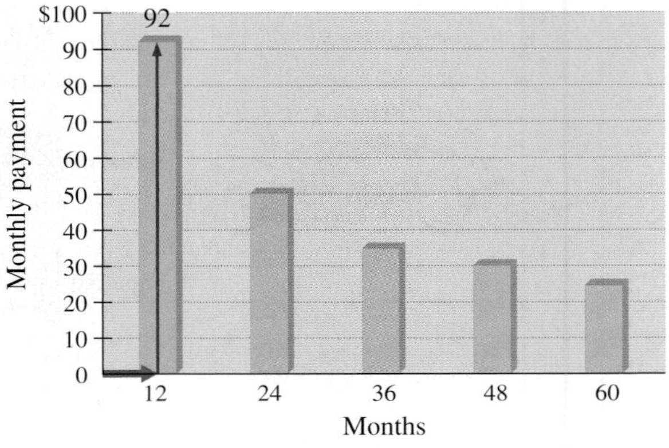

Source: Charts provided by KJE Computer Solutions, LLC. For more information please see http://www.dinkytown.net.

FIGURE 1.14

EXAMPLE 3 Estimating Savings on Your Credit Card

Find the savings if you decide to pay the balance in 24 months.

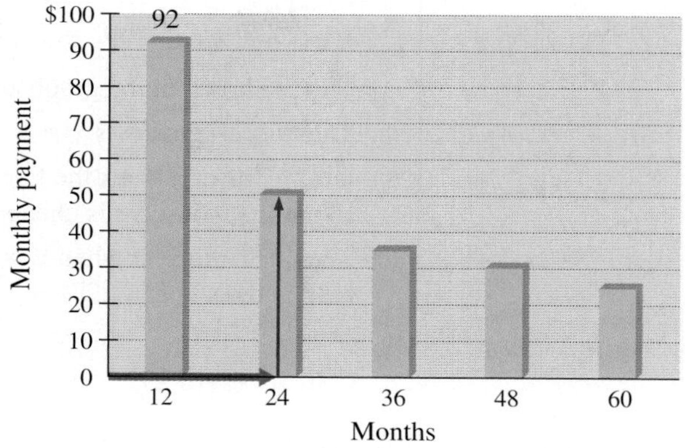

Source: Charts provided by KJE Computer Solutions, LLC. For more information please see http://www.dinkytown.net.

FIGURE 1.15

Solution

Review Figure 1.15 to find the savings! To find the payment corresponding to 24 months on the horizontal axis, move *right* to the category *labeled* 24 months and then *vertically* to the end of the bar. According to the vertical scale, the monthly payment will be \$50. If you pay \$50 for 24 months, you would pay $24 \times \$50 = \$1200$ and have savings of \$300 (\$1500 − \$1200). Remember, when paying off any debts, the faster you pay, the more interest you save!

C Interpreting Line Graphs

We can save money on your electric bill too! The cost of using a 60 watt incandescent bulb costing just one quarter (\$0.25) for 8 hours each day is about \$0.08 while an equivalent 14 watt fluorescent bulb costing \$1.50 is \$0.03 each day. We use line graphs to compare the cost of using each of the bulbs for 30 days.

EXAMPLE 4 Using Line Graphs to Save Money

The total cost y for using an incandescent bulb is $y = 0.25 + 0.08x$ (the \$0.25 cost of the bulb plus the cost for x days $0.08x$). The total cost y of using the fluorescent bulb for x days is $y = 1.50 + 0.03x$.

(a) How much does it cost to run the incandescent bulb for 30 days?

(b) How much does it cost to run the fluorescent bulb for 30 days?

(c) Which bulb is cheaper to run during the first week?

(d) When is the cost of operating each bulb the same?

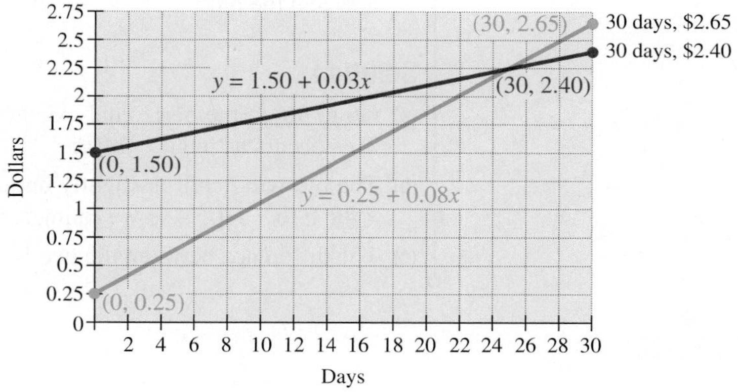

Source: Graph courtesy of blog.whitesites.com.

FIGURE 1.16

Solution

(a) The incandescent bulb costs $y = 0.25 + 0.08x$, where x is the number of days. For a month, $x = 30$ days so the cost is

$$y = 0.25 + 0.08(30) = 0.25 + 2.40 = \$2.65$$

This is shown in the graph as $(30, 2.65)$.

(b) The fluorescent costs $y = 1.50 + 0.03(30) = 1.50 + 0.90 = \$2.40$.

(c) During the first week the line I for the incandescent is *below* that of F the fluorescent, so the incandescent is cheaper the first week.

(d) The lines intersect when $x = 25$ days. Note that in 25 days the cost of operating each bulb is the same, \$2.25.

EXAMPLE 5 Chill Out!

Figure 1.17 shows the new wind-chill temperatures (top, yellow) and the old wind-chill temperatures (bottom, white) for different wind speeds.

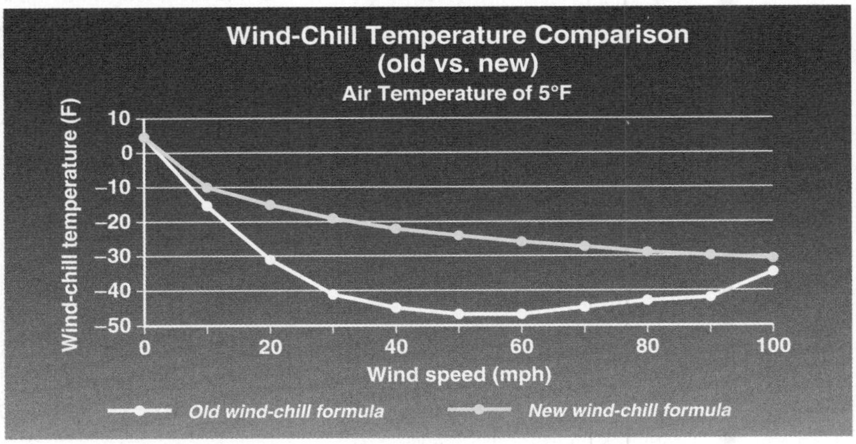

Source: www.erh.noaa.gov/er/iln/tables.htm.

FIGURE 1.17

(a) If the wind speed is 90 mph, what is the approximate new wind-chill factor?

(b) If the wind speed is 90 mph, what is the approximate old wind-chill factor?

(c) When the wind is 90 mph, what is the wind-chill temperature difference between the new and the old?

Solution

(a) Go to 90 on the horizontal axis and up vertically until you meet the yellow graph. This occurs at about −30°F.

(b) The old wind chill is slightly under −40°F (be careful here, the numbers go from −40°F to −50°F), so we estimate the answer as −42°F.

(c) The difference between the two is about 12°F (from −30°F to −42°F).

1.3 EXERCISES

A Interpreting Circle Graphs (Pie Charts)

In problems 1–10, answer the questions about the circle graph.

In Example 1 we had a garbage pizza from Illinois. Did you know that a lot of the stuff in the garbage ends up in the landfill? The city of Lubbock, Texas, modeled the pizza shown based on the materials sent to the landfill, which total 1000 tons each day.

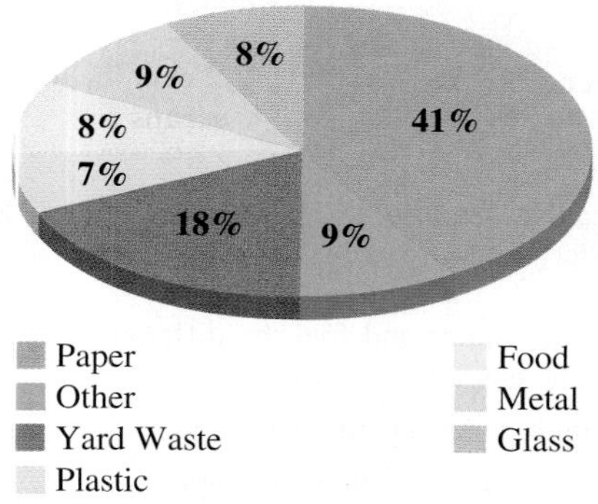

Source: Used with permissions from City of Lubbock Water Utilities Conservation Education Department. http://water.ci.lubbock.tx.us/pdf/EDU/garbagePizzaLP.pdf.

1. According to the graph:
   a. What is the largest category of materials sent to the landfill daily? What percent?
   b. What is the smallest category of materials sent to the landfill daily? What percent?
   c. How many tons of paper and how many tons of plastic are going to the landfill each day?
2. Referring to the graph:
   a. What percent of the material going to the landfill is glass?
   b. How many tons of glass go to the landfill daily?
   c. What is the difference (in tons) in the amount of paper and glass going to the landfill daily?
3. The circle graph that follows shows the percent of different types of cheese produced.

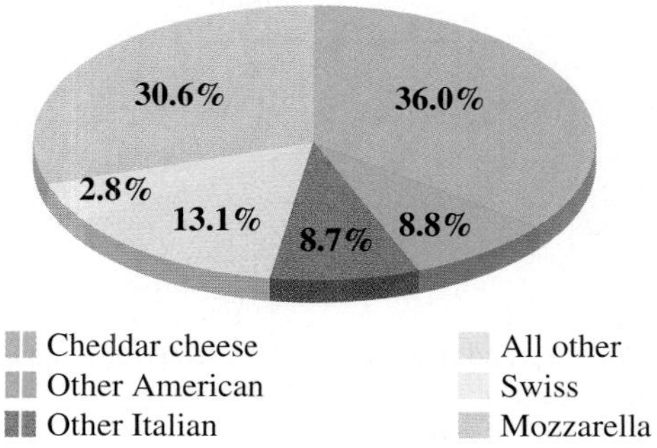

Source: U.S. Department of Agriculture.

   a. Which type of cheese was produced the most?
   b. Which type of cheese was produced the least?
   c. If you assume that the cheese that is produced the most is also the most popular, which is the second most popular cheese?
4. What does a Californian Sea Lion eat? The circle graph illustrates the answer. Suppose you are in charge of feeding the Californian Sea Lions in the zoo.

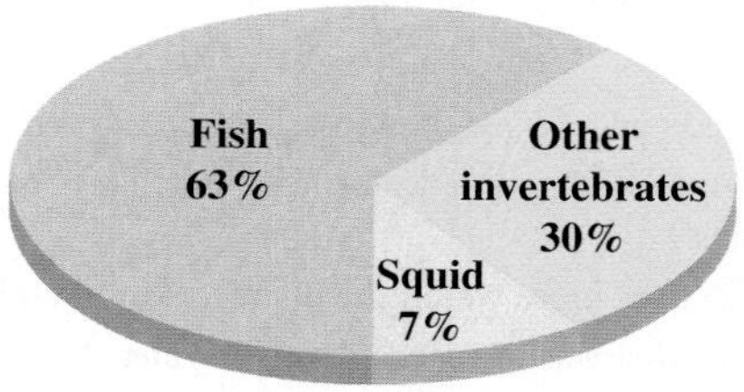

Source: http://tinyurl.com/88p3846.

   a. Which food would you stock the most?
   b. If you buy 100 lb of Californian Sea Lion feed, how many pounds should be squid?
   c. If you buy 200 lb of Californian Sea Lion feed, how many pounds should be squid?
   d. If octopuses, shrimp, and crabs, preferably in the same amounts, fall in the category of "other invertebrates" and you buy 300 lb of Californian Sea Lion feed, how many pounds of crab should it contain?
   e. A male Californian Sea Lion weighs about 660 lb and eats about 50 lb of food each day. How many pounds of fish does he eat?
   f. A female Californian Sea Lion, on the other hand, weighs about 220 lb and eats 15 lb of food each day. How many pounds of squid does she eat each day?
   g. How many pounds of shrimp does a female Californian Sea Lion eat every day?

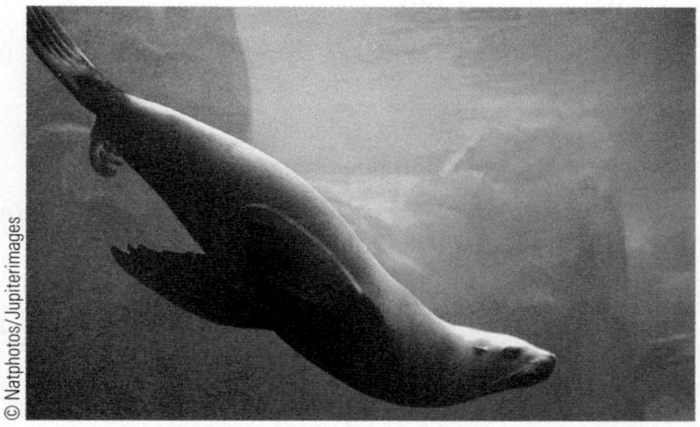

5. The graph shows the average indoor water use in the United States.

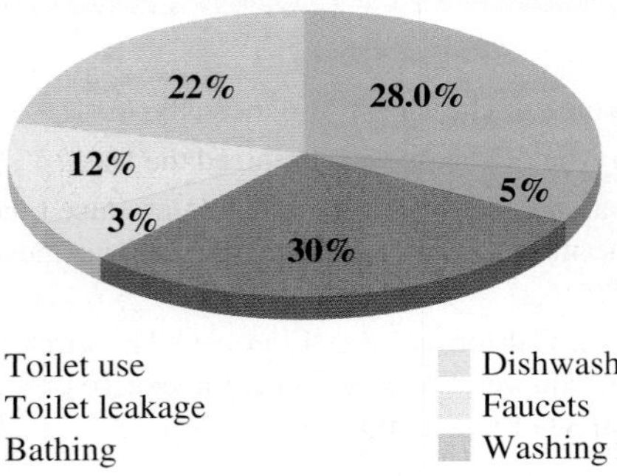

Source: U.S. Geological Survey.

a. Where is water used the most?
b. If you use 500 gal of water, how much would you use for bathing?
c. Which uses more water, the dishwasher or a toilet leak?
d. If your dishwasher used 5 gal of water, how much water would be used by the faucets?

6. The pie chart shows the fraction of each ingredient (by weight) used in making a sausage pizza.

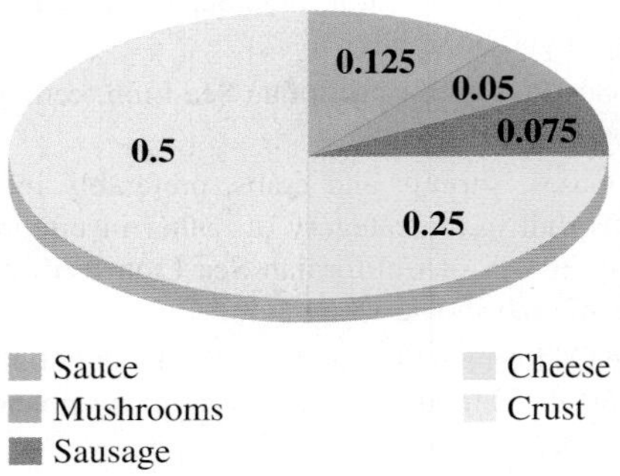

Source: Copyright Mathematics League, Inc. May not be reproduced in any form without permission from Mathematics League Inc.

a. What fraction of the pizza is crust?
b. What fraction of the pizza is cheese?
c. Which ingredient makes the smallest part of the pizza by weight?
d. If you estimated that a pizza weighs 4 lb, how many pounds would be crust and how many pounds cheese?
e. If you were to make 100 of these 4-lb pizzas, how many pounds of cheese would you need?

7. Have you looked in your trash lately? You have an average trash can if your trash divides into the same percents as those shown.
a. What is the most prevalent item in average trash?
b. Which is the second most prevalent item in average trash?
c. If you have an average trash load weighing 50 lb, how many pounds of paper would it contain? How many pounds of yard trimmings? Actually, you probably recycle and do not have as much paper!

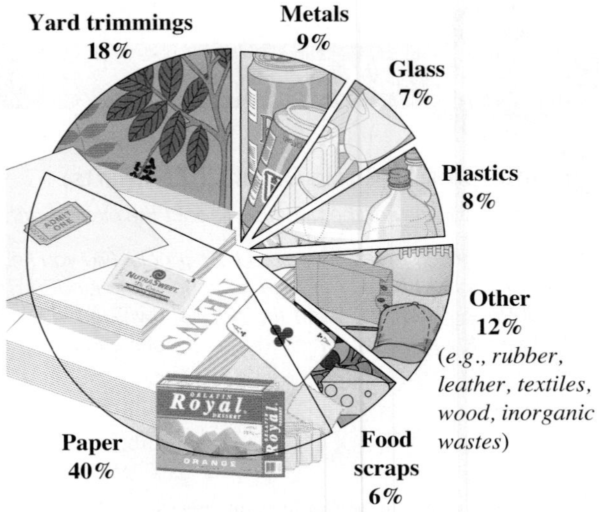

Source: http://www.epa.gov/osw/nonhaz/municipal/msw99.htm. Gives data for multiple years.

8. Refer to the graphs and find the difference between college students and employed persons in:
a. the number of sleeping hours.
b. the time spent in leisure and sports.
c. the time spent in eating and drinking.

Full-Time University/College Students

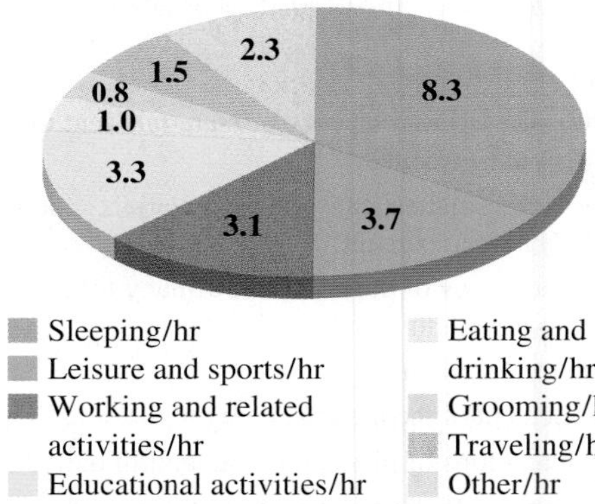

Total = 24.0 hr

Employed Persons 25–54 With Children

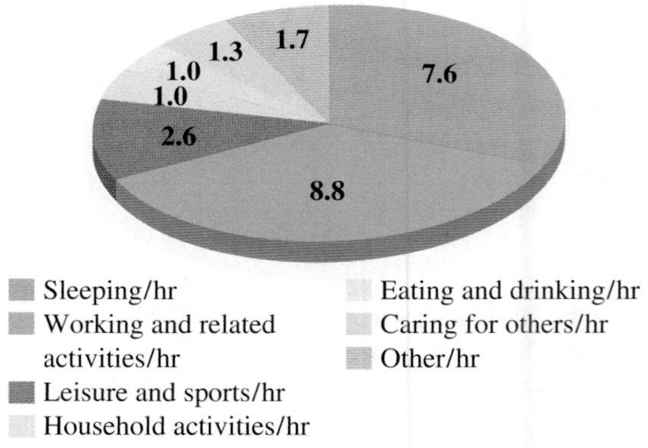

Total = 24.0 hr

Source: Bureau of Labor Statistics.

9. The circle graph shows the breakdown of how the world produces its energy.

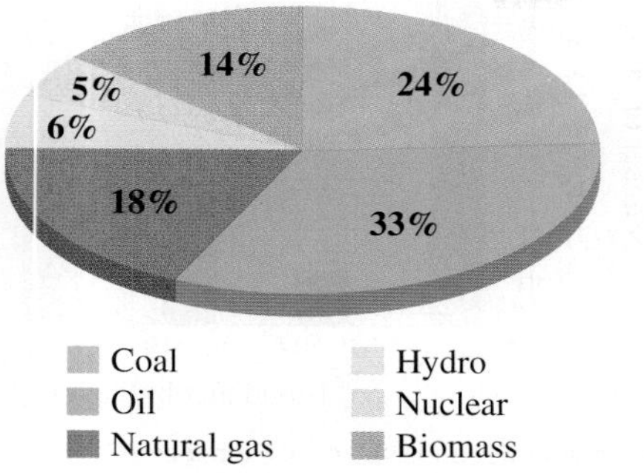

Source: http://pratclif.com/climatechange/Greenhouse%20Gases.htm.

a. Which energy source produces the most energy?

b. Which energy source produces the least energy?

c. Fossil fuels (coal, oil, and natural gas) emit greenhouse gases when burned. Which of the three fossil fuels produces the least energy?

10. Suppose you paid **$10,000** in federal income taxes. The chart shows where the money went!

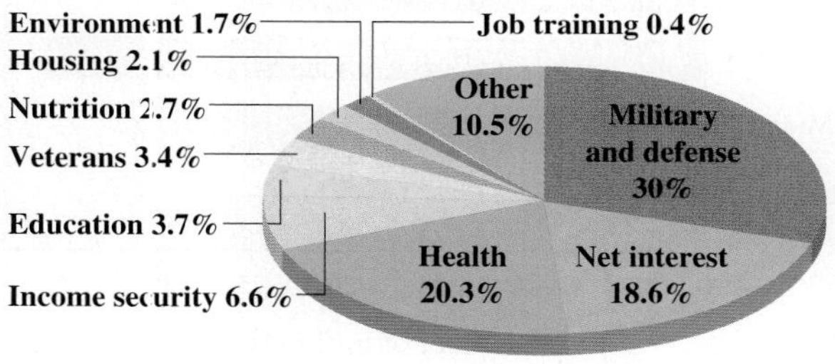

Source: www.nationalpriorities.org/en/budget-basics/federal-budget-101/spending/.

For a different view, see the pie chart at http://www.warresisters.org/pages/piechart.htm.

a. Where did the highest percentage of the money go?

b. What percent of the money went to health?

c. How much money went to health?

d. Which category received the least money?

e. How much money went to education?

f. What is the difference between the amount of money spent for military and defense and the amount of money spent for education?

g. What percent of the money is unaccounted for?

B Interpreting Bar Graphs

In problems 11–24, answer the questions about the bar graphs.

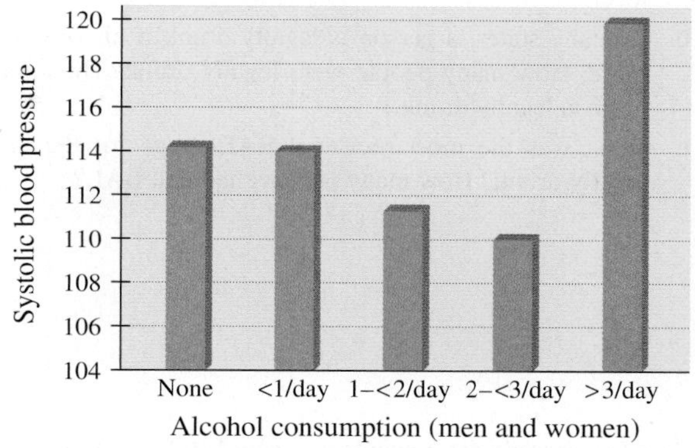

Source: Reprinted by permission of Dr. David J. Hanson from www2.potsdam.edu/alcoholinfo/Health/Health.html.

11. Can moderate alcohol consumption (yes, we said *moderate*) reduce blood pressure? Judge for yourself by examining the bar graph that illustrates the average systolic blood pressure among young adults. Find the average systolic blood pressure for young adults consuming

a. no drinks per day.

b. less than 1 drink per day ($<$1/day).

c. at least 1 but less than 2 drinks per day (1 – $<$2/day).

d. Which category has the lowest blood pressure? What is the measure of the blood pressure?

e. Which category has the highest blood pressure? What is the measure of the blood pressure?

12. People who abstain from drinking have double the risk of a stroke as drinkers. How can we deduce this from the bar graph? Look at the vertical scale (0 to 3.5).

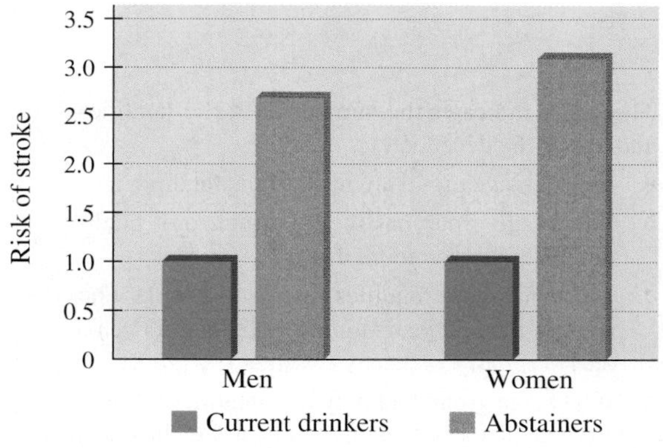

Source: Reprinted by permission of Dr. David J. Hanson from www2.potsdam.edu/alcoholinfo/Health/Health.html.

a. What is the risk of stroke for current drinking men?

b. What is the risk of stroke for men who abstain?

c. Estimate how many more times the risk of stroke is for abstaining men than for current drinking men?

d. What is the risk of stroke for current drinking women?

e. What is the risk of stroke for abstaining women?

f. Estimate how many more times is the risk of stroke for abstaining women than for current drinking women.

g. Which category has the highest risk of stroke?

13. The bar graph shows the number of traffic accident victims who died at the scene of the accident and the blood alcohol level (BAL) of the driver.
    a. What was the number of fatalities with a negative (no) blood alcohol level?
    b. In many states, a person is legally drunk if his or her BAL is 0.10 or more. How many people were legally drunk? (In some states, 0.08 or more is legally drunk.)
    c. What was the most prevalent BAL range for the people who were legally drunk? How many persons had that BAL?

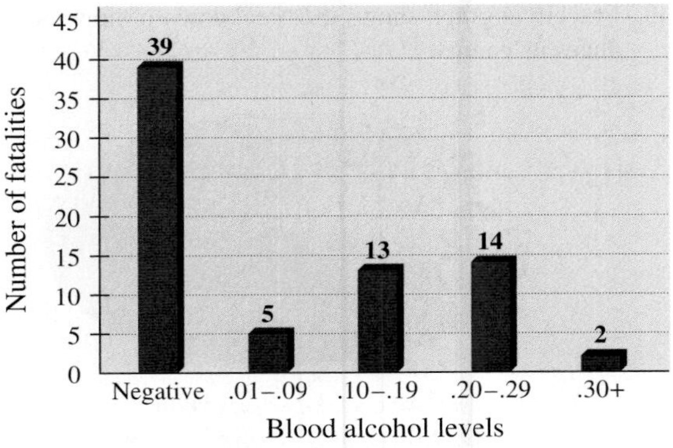

Source: King County Medical Examiner's Office.

14. At what time do fatal accidents occur? Refer to the graph.
    a. Find the number of fatalities between 12:01 and 3:00 A.M.
    b. Find the number of fatalities between 3:01 and 6:00 A.M.
    c. What is the most likely time period for a fatal traffic accident to occur?
    d. Aside from "unknown," what is the least likely time period for a fatal traffic accident to occur?

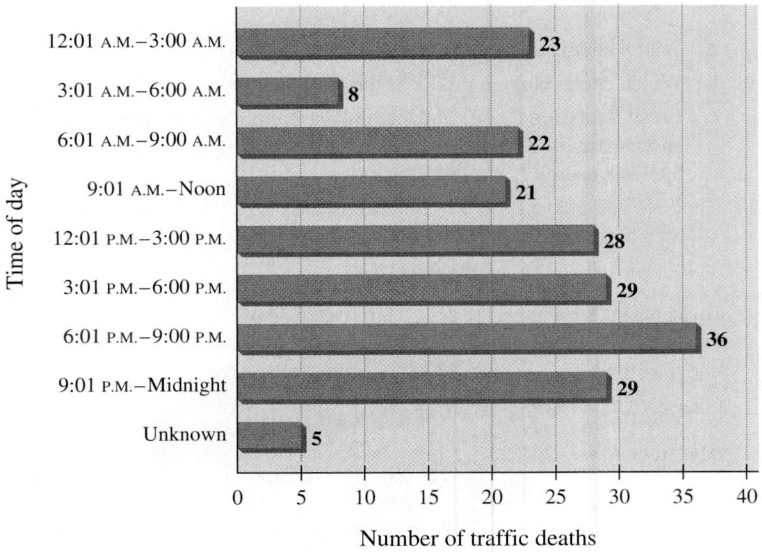

Source: King County Medical Examiner's Office.

15. The graph indicates the number of traffic fatalities and age of the decedent.
    a. In which age group are most of the fatalities?
    b. Which age group has the least (nonzero) fatalities? Why do you think that is?
    c. Are there more fatalities involving people who are less than 50 years old or more than 50 years old?
    d. Which age group had only two fatalities? Why?

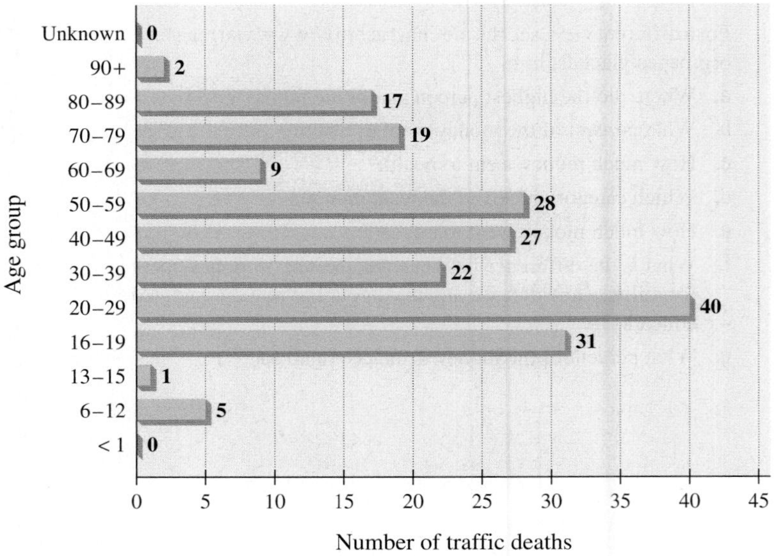

Source: King County Medical Examiner's Office.

16. In a survey of 3000 people by the Pew Research Center, the percent of Americans owning each device is as shown in the bar graph.

a. What device was owned the most?

b. What percent of the people owned an mp3 player?

c. What was the percent difference between people that owned a desktop and a laptop computer?

17. Referring to the survey of 3000 adults shown in the graph:

a. How many owned a cell phone?

b. How many owned a desktop computer?

c. How many owned a laptop computer?

d. What is the difference between the number of people that owned a laptop and those that owned a desktop computer?

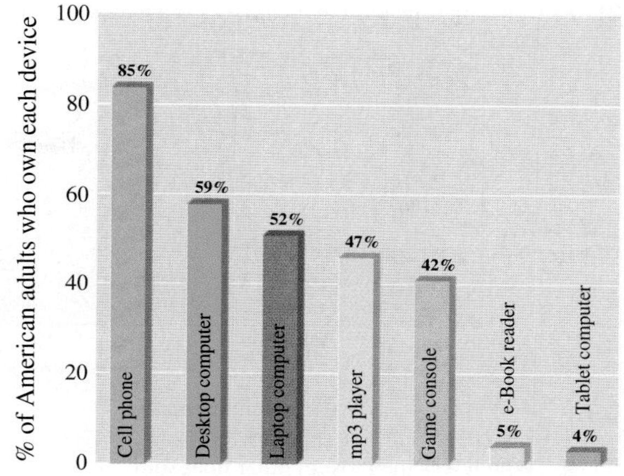

Source: Copyright © 2012 Pew Internet & American Life Project. http://pewinternet.org/Reports/2010/Gadgets.aspx.

18. Which has more calories, ice cream or yogurt? The graph shows the number of calories for $\frac{1}{2}$ cup of ice cream or yogurt.

a. How many calories are in the Cherry Garcia ice cream?

b. How many calories are in the Cherry Garcia yogurt?

c. How many calories are in the Chocolate Fudge ice cream?

d. How many calories are in the Chocolate Fudge yogurt?

e. Which is the product with the least calories?

f. Which is the product with the most calories?

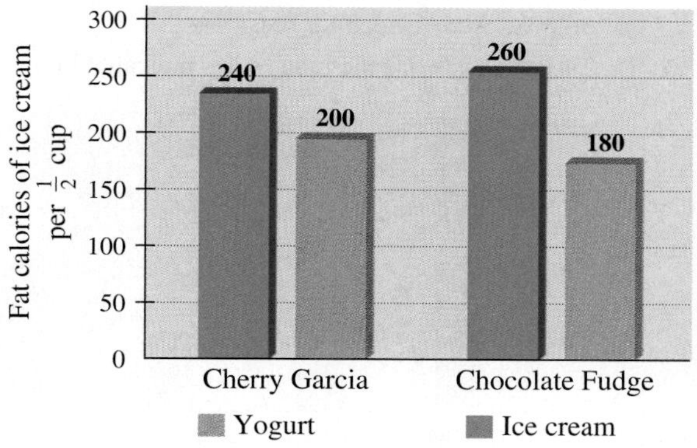

Source: http://www.fitsugar.com/Calories-Ben-Jerrys-Ice-Cream-326487.

19. Refer to the graph in problem 18.

a. How many calories would you save if you ate a whole cup of the product with the least calories instead of a cup of the product with the most calories?

b. How many extra calories would you consume when you have a pint of the product with the most calories in the graph instead of the product with the least calories? *Hint:* 2 cups = 1 pint.

20. What is the most popular spectator sport in Japan? A survey, shown in the bar graph, of 3000 Japanese aged 20 or older says that it is baseball!

a. What is the second most popular sport? What percent of the respondents said they preferred high school baseball?

b. What was the least popular spectator sport in the survey? What percent of the people preferred this sport?

c. Name the three sports that enjoyed about the same popularity in the survey.

d. How many more people preferred Japanese professional baseball than major league baseball?

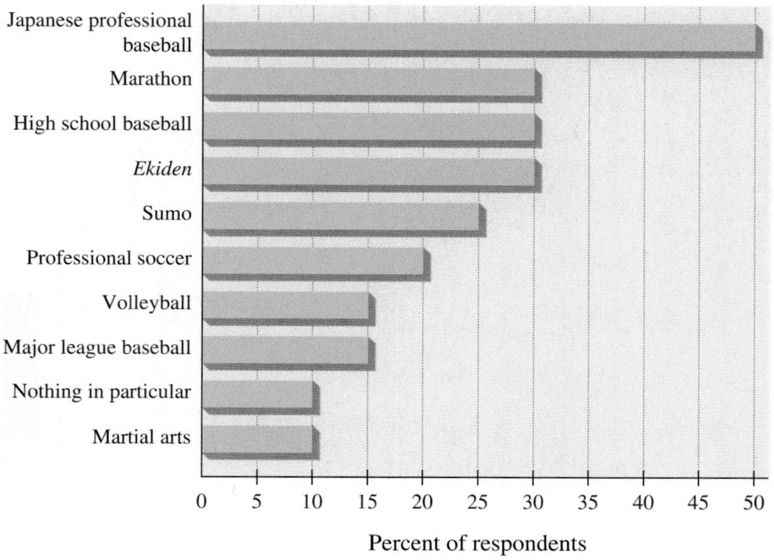

Source: http://griddle.baseballtoaster.com/archives/325056.html.

21. La Cubanita Cafe has the breakfast sales indicated in the graph.

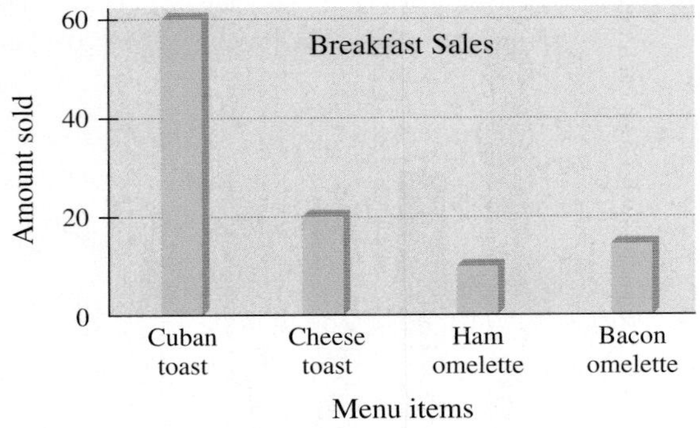

a. Which was the most popular item sold?

b. Which was the second most popular item?

c. Each of the items is served with $\frac{1}{4}$ loaf of Cuban bread. Estimate how many breakfasts were sold and how many loaves of bread were needed for breakfast.

22. La Cubanita Cafe has the lunch sales indicated in the graph.

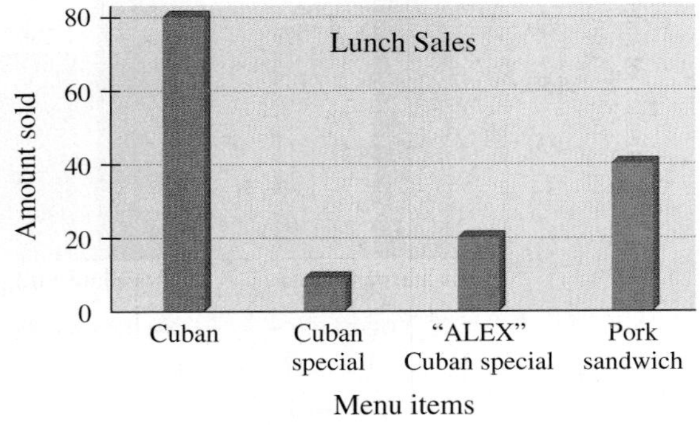

a. Which was the most popular sandwich sold?

b. Which was the least popular sandwich sold?

c. Each sandwich requires $\frac{1}{4}$ loaf of Cuban bread. Estimate how many sandwiches were sold and how many loaves of bread were needed to make those sandwiches.

23. Do you think the passwords you use in your computer are safe? Think again! The graph shows **188,279** passwords leaked online! Using the dotted lines, estimate:

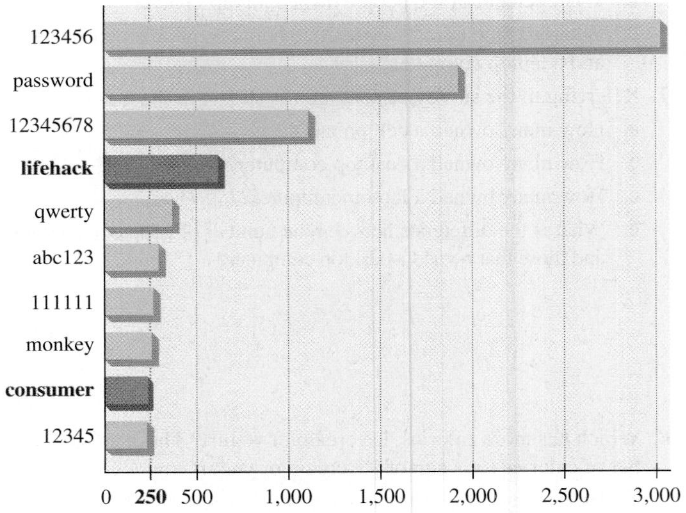

The most popular among 188,279 Gawker Media passwords that leaked online.

Source: http://blogs.wsj.com/digits/2010/12/13/the-top-50-gawker-media-passwords.

a. about how many persons used **123456** as their password.

b. about how many persons used the word **consumer** as their password?

c. about how many persons used **lifehack** as their password?

24. The graph shows the percent of users using the indicated password from each mail service.

a. To the nearest one-tenth percent shown in the graph, what percent of the people used **iloveyou** as their password in Yahoo?

b. How many people used **iloveyou** as their password in Yahoo?

c. To the nearest one-tenth percent shown in the graph, what percent of the people used **blahblah** as their password in Google?

d. How many people used **blahblah** as their password in Google?

What passwords did users have?

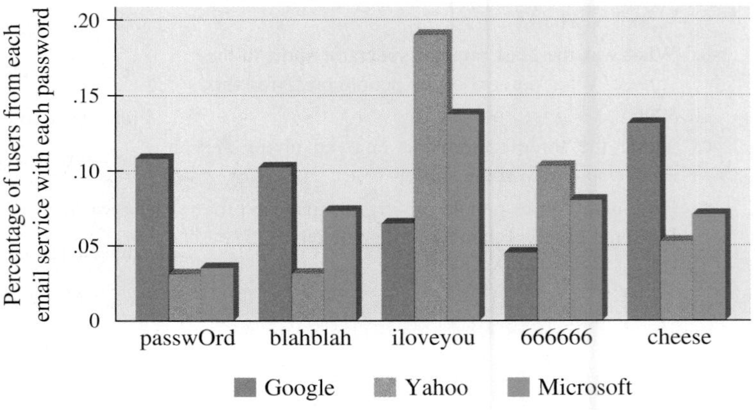

Source: Anonymized set of 188,279 leaked Gawker Media passwords.

C Interpreting Line Graphs

In problems 25–36, answer the questions about the line graph.

25. The graph shows the total and senior populations (in millions) in the United States from 1950 to 2050.

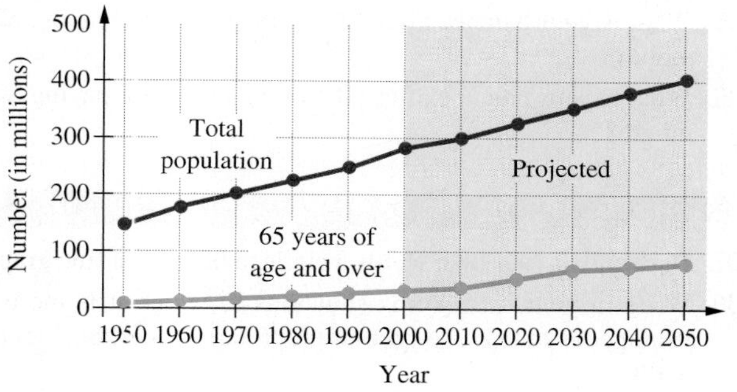

Source: http://tinyurl.com/6zd3mhy.

What was or will be the approximate total population:

a. in 1960? **b.** in 1970? **c.** in 1990?

d. in 2010? **e.** in 2020?

26. Refer to the graph in problem 25. What was or will be the approximate population of those 65 and older in:

a. 1960 **b.** 1980 **c.** 2020

d. 2040 **e.** 2050

27. According to some scientists the emission gases into the atmosphere causes the temperature to increase by about 0.025 degrees Celsius each year after 2000.

a. Referring to the graph, in what year will the temperature change reach 1°C (one degree Celsius)?

b. In what year will the temperature change reach 2.5°C?

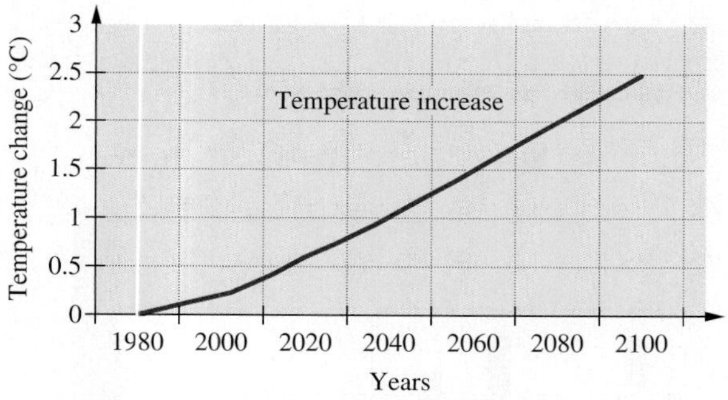

Source: http://www.lenntech.com/greenhouse-effect/greenhouse-effect-mechanism.htm

28. As we mentioned in problem 27, the emission of gases into the atmosphere causes the temperature to increase by about 0.025 degrees Celsius each year after 2000.

a. If the temperature is increasing by 0.025 degrees Celsius each year after 2000, what will the total temperature increase I be x years after 2000?

b. What will be the temperature increase I be **40** years after the year 2000 (in 2040)?

c. Does the result of part (b) agrees with the results in the graph?

29. How old is your dog? The graph gives the relationship between a dog's age in human years and a dog's age in dog years. Thus, if a dog is 1 year in human years, it is about 12 years in dog years.

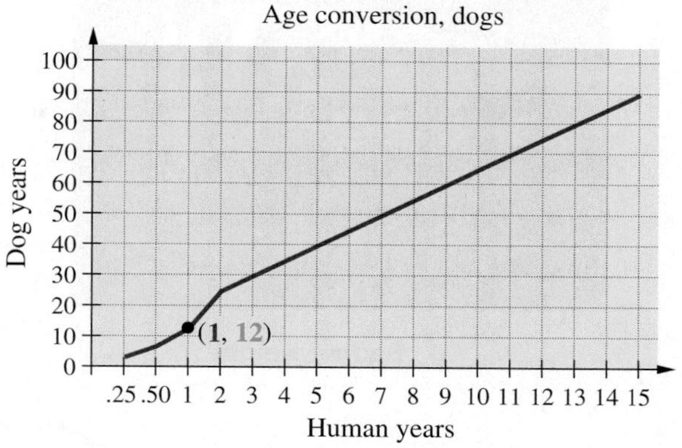

Data from http://tinyurl.com/6mawrwh

a. If a dog is 9 years old in human years, how old is it in dog years?

b. If retirement age is 65 for humans, what is the equivalent retirement age for dogs in human years? (Answer to the nearest whole number.)

c. If the drinking age for humans is 21, what is the equivalent drinking age for dogs in human years? (Answer to the nearest whole number.)

30. We need equal time for cats! The graph gives the relationship between a cat's age in human years and a cat's age in cat years.

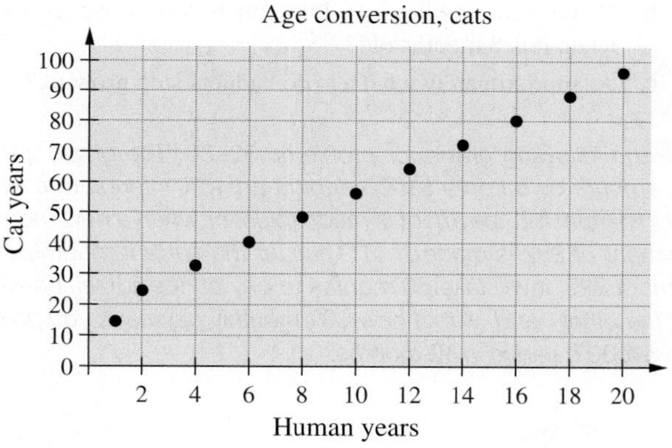

Source: http://cats.about.com/cs/healthissues/a/agechart.htm. www.cats.alpha.pl/catsage.htm.

a. If a cat is 6 years old in human years, how old is it in cat years?

b. If retirement age is 65 for humans, what is the equivalent retirement age for cats in human years? (Answer to the nearest whole number.)

c. If the drinking age for humans is 21, what is the equivalent drinking age for cats in human years? (Answer to the nearest whole number.)

d. Comparing your answers to problem 29, who would retire first in human years, a cat or a dog?

31. Do you know what a badger is? It is a small burrowing animal that looks like a weasel.

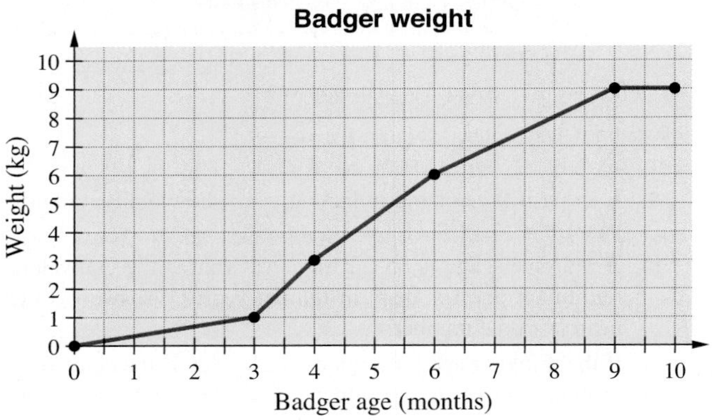

Source: http://www.wildlife-web.org.uk/badger/facts/breeding.html.

a. To the nearest kilogram, how much does a badger weigh when it is 4 months old? (1 kg ≈ 2.2 lb)

b. To the nearest kilogram, how much does a badger weigh when it is 8 months old?

c. At approximately what age do badgers stop growing?

Use the following graph for problems 32–36. The graph shows the amount owed on a $1000 *debt at an* 18% *interest rate when the minimum* $25 *payment is made (blue) or when a new monthly payment of* $92 *is made (red). Thus, at the current monthly payment of* $25, *it will take* 60 *months to pay off the* $1000 *balance. On the other hand, with a new* $92 *monthly payment, you pay off the* $1000 *balance in* 12 *months.*

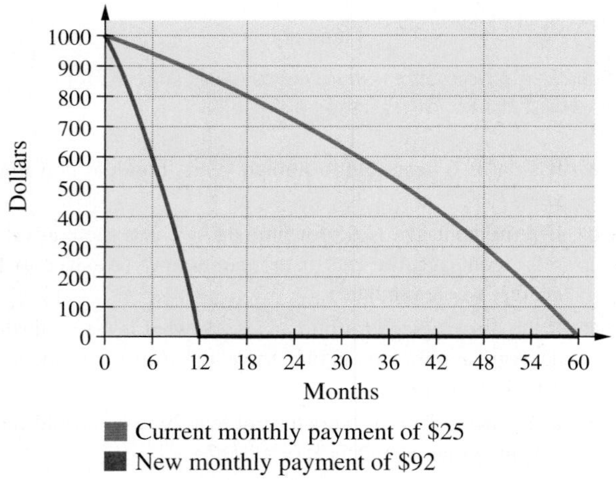

Source: Charts provided by KJE Computer Solutions, LLC. For more information please see http://www.dinkytown.net.

32. What is your balance after 6 months if you are paying $25 a month?

33. What is your balance after 6 months if you are paying $92 a month?

34. What is your balance after 18 months if you are paying $25 a month?

35. What is your balance after 48 months if you are paying $25 a month?

36. What is your balance after 60 months if you are paying $25 a month?

IN OTHER WORDS

37. Describe in your own words a circle, a bar, and a line graph.

38. Write in your own words situations in which it is more advantageous to use one type of graph (circle, bar, or line) than another.

39. What type of graph would you use if you had to show

a. a relationship between groups that do not affect each other?

b. continuing data?

c. how parts of a whole relate to each other?

d. In each case, discuss why you would use the type of graph you indicated.

USING YOUR KNOWLEDGE

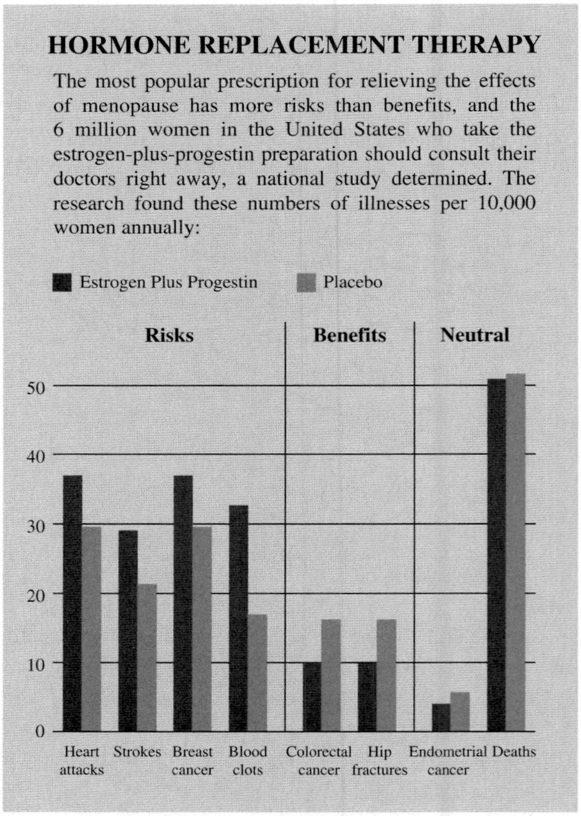

Sun Journal, April 17, 2002, page A7 http://tinyurl.com/6vbq6ug, *Journal of the American Medical Association.*

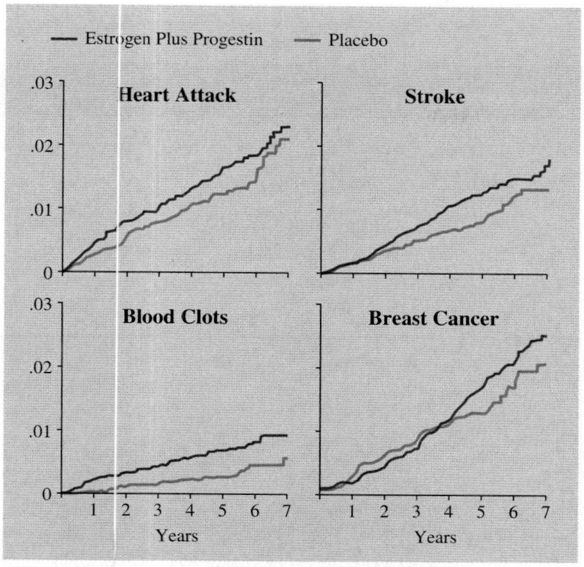

The *Tampa Tribune* graphic. Sources: Knight Ridder/Tribune, *Journal of the American Medical Association.*

40. A recent milestone study regarding hormone replacement therapy for relieving the effects of menopause showed that there were more risks than benefits in the treatment. How did they persuade doctors to stop the experiments? By studying the statistics using bar and line graphs. Look at the bar graphs on the left. The red bars show the number of women (per 10,000) suffering heart attacks, strokes, breast cancer, and blood clots when taking the estrogen plus progestin (medicine), while the blue bars show the comparable numbers for women taking a placebo (fake medicine).

a. Estimate the total number of women (per 10,000) who had heart attacks, strokes, breast cancer, and blood clots while taking the estrogen-plus-progestin medicine.

b. Estimate the total number of women (per 10,000) who had heart attacks, strokes, breast cancer, and blood clots while taking the placebo.

c. Estimate the numerical difference in the total number (per 10,000) of women taking the estrogen-plus-progestin medicine, having heart attacks, strokes, breast cancer, and blood clots as compared with the number (per thousand) taking the placebo.

d. There were some benefits associated with taking the medicine. What were those benefits and how could you measure them?

e. There were some areas that were neutral (not much difference between taking the medicine and taking the placebo). Which were those areas?

41. The four line graphs relate the *risk* of some illnesses (*vertical* scale, from 0 to 0.03) and the *length* of time the women have taken the medicine (*horizontal* scale, from 0 to 7 years). Study the graphs and determine in which years (to the nearest year) the placebo group (blue) had

a. fewer heart attacks than the medicine group (red).

b. fewer strokes than the medicine group.

c. fewer blood clots than the medicine group.

d. less breast cancer than the medicine group.

e. In what year and from what condition was the difference between taking medicine and taking a placebo greatest? What was the numerical difference in the risk?

f. Which was the only condition in which the patients taking the medicine fared better than the ones taking the placebo? In which years were the patients with this condition and taking the medicine better off than the ones taking the placebo?

CHAPTER 1 Summary

SECTION	ITEM	MEANING	EXAMPLE
1.1A	RSTUV	A five-step problem-solving procedure	Read the problem. Select the unknown. Think of a plan. Use a strategy to carry out the plan. Verify your answer.
1.1B	Inductive reasoning	The process of arriving at a general conclusion on the basis of repeated observations of specific examples	The pattern 1, 3, 6, 10, . . . is obtained by adding 2, adding 3, adding 4, and so on.
	Deductive Reasoning	The process of arriving at a specific conclusion on the basis of one or more general principles	All students text while driving and Jackie is a student, so Jackie texts while driving.
	Sequence	An arrangement of numbers according to a pattern	1, 3, 6, 10, . . . is a sequence.
	Term	Each number or item in a sequence	1, 3, 6, 10, and so on, are terms in the sequence 1, 3, 6, 10, ...

continued

CHAPTER 1 Summary – *continued*

SECTION	ITEM	MEANING	EXAMPLE
1.2A	Estimation	The process of arriving at an approximate answer to a question	
	Rounding	The process by which numbers are approximated to a certain level of precision	To round the number 46.27 to one decimal or the nearest unit, write 46.$\underline{2}$7 → 46.3 4$\underline{6}$.27 → 46
1.3A	Circle (pie) chart	A circle (pie) chart is a circle graph divided into sectors, each displaying the size of some related piece of information.	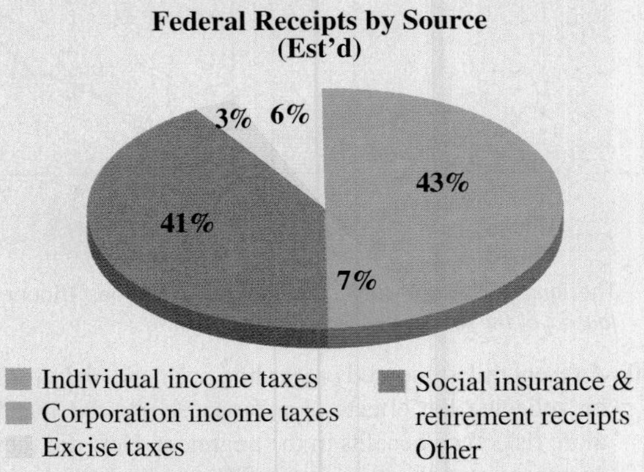 The circle graph shows the revenue sources of the federal government. Source: www.scienceblogs.com.
1.3B	Bar graph	Bar graphs consist of an axis with horizontal or vertical bars that represent different values for each bar. The set of numbers along a side of the bar graph is called the scale.	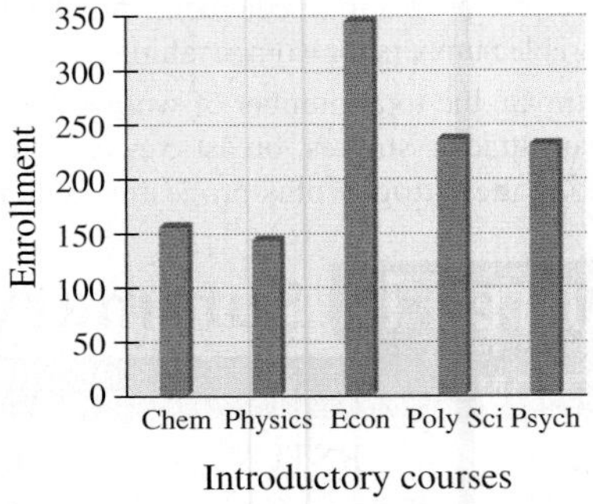 The bar graph represents the enrollment in different courses at a university. Source: "Introductory Courses," from Review of Tables, Bar Graphs and Circle Graphs, Center In Support of Teachers And Learning, Syracuse University, 1998. Used with permission. http://cstl.syr.edu/fipse/TabBar/RevBar/REVBAR.HTM.
1.3C	Line graph	A line graph is a tool used to represent information and summarize how the information is related and varies, depending on one another.	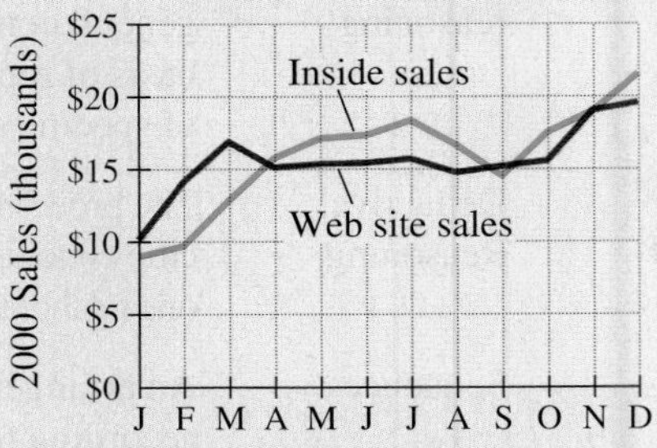 The graph shows how Web site sales and inside sales compare to each other. Source: Line graph built using NetCharts Server by Visual Mining, Inc. www.visualmining.com.

CHAPTER 1 Practice Test

1. What does RSTUV mean?

2. What is inductive reasoning?

3. Identify the pattern and find the next three terms.

   1, 2, 7, 19, 41, 76, _____, _____, _____

4. a. Follow this procedure: Select a number, multiply it by 4, add 6 to the product, divide the sum by 2, and subtract 3 from the quotient.
   b. Follow the same steps as in part (a) using the numbers 1, 10, and 100. What results do you get?
   c. Make a conjecture about the relationship between the original number and the final results.

5. Round 319.26 to
   a. the nearest tenth.
   b. the nearest hundred.

6. a. Read the meter for today.

   b. If the reading for yesterday was 6002 kilowatt-hours, how many kilowatt-hours have you consumed since yesterday?
   c. If a kilowatt-hour costs $.10, how much was your 1-day bill?
   d. If you estimate the same consumption each day for a 30-day period (a month), what is your estimated monthly bill?

7. The relationship between the height H of a person and the length t of their tibia (the bone connecting the knee to the ankle) is

   Male: $H = 32.2 + 2.4t$ Female: $H = 28.6 + 2.5t$

   a. Estimate the height of a person (to the nearest inch) with a 15-in. tibia if the person is a female.
   b. Do the same as in part (a) if the person is a male.

8. The circle graphs show the budget requirements and resources for the city of St. Petersburg.

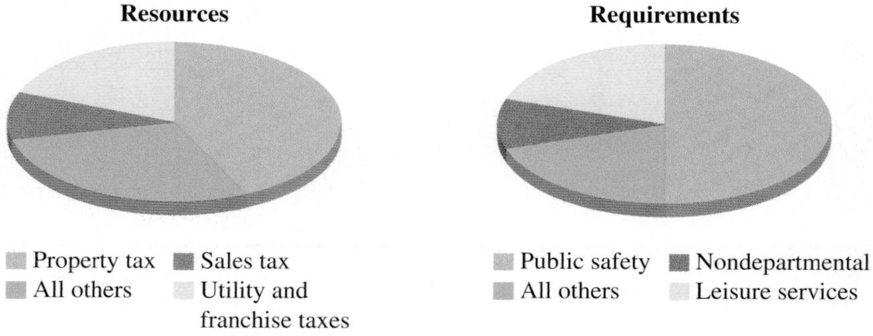

Source: http://www.stpete.org/budget/.

   a. What is the biggest category in the requirements chart?
   b. About what fraction of the requirements is for public safety?
   c. What is the smallest category in the resources chart?

continued

CHAPTER 1 Practice Test – *continued*

9. The bar graph shows the property tax (orange) versus police and fire expenses (green) for the city of St. Petersburg.

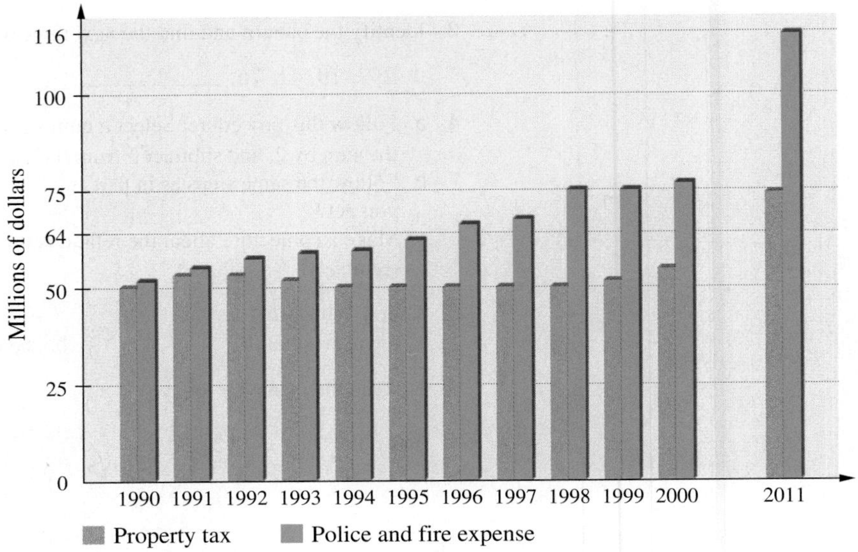

Source: http://www.stpete.org/budget/.

a. How much were the property taxes in 1990?
b. What were the police and fire expenses in 1990?
c. Estimate the police and fire expenses for 2011.
d. Estimate the property taxes for 2011.
e. What is the difference in property taxes in 1998 and in 2011?

10. The line graph shows the 30-year fixed mortgage rates on different dates.
a. What was the rate on 5/15?
b. What was the rate on 6/5?
c. What was the difference in rates between 5/15 and 6/5?
d. What seems to be the trend for 30-year fixed-rate mortgages?

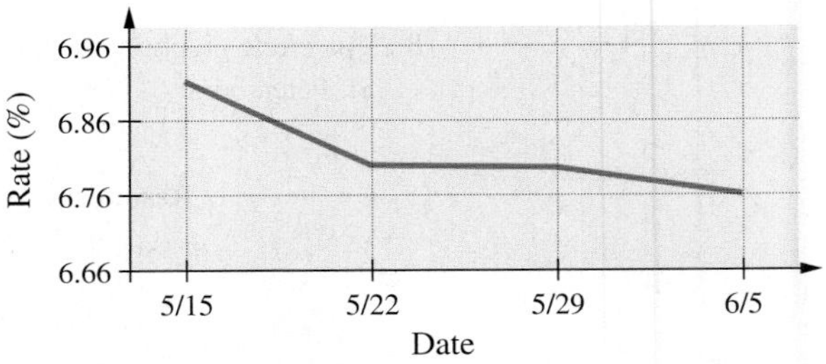

Source: Copyright © 2003 Bankrate.com. Used with permission. Chart, "Mortgage rate," from http://www.bankrate.com/kip/subhome/mtg_m1.asp.

ANSWERS TO PRACTICE TEST

CHAPTER 1		What to Review *If You Missed It*		
QUESTION	**ANSWER**	**SECTION**	**EXAMPLE(S)**	**PAGE(S)**
1	Read the problem. Select the unknown. Think of a plan. Use the techniques you are studying to carry out the plan. Verify the answer.	1.1A	Problem-Solving Box	2–3
2	The process of arriving at a general conclusion on the basis of repeated observations of specific examples	1.1B	Definition of Inductive Reasoning	4
3	Look at the following differences: 1 2 7 19 41 76 → $\boxed{127}$ $\boxed{197}$ $\boxed{289}$ · · · ↖ 1 5 12 22 35 → 51 70 92 · · · ↖ 4 7 10 13 → 16 19 22 · · · ↖ 3 3 3 3 3 3 · · · The third differences are constant, so the next numbers in each line can be constructed by addition. For example, $3 + 13 = 16$ $16 + 35 = 51$ $51 + 76 = 127$, or simply $3 + 13 + 35 + 76$ The next three terms are 127, 197, and 289.	1.1B	1–3	5–6
4	**a.** n, $4n$, $4n + 6$, $2n + 3$, $2n$ **b.** Using 1, the final result is 2. Using 10, the final result is 20. Using 100, the final result is 200. **c.** The conjecture is that the final result is twice the original number.	1.1B	4	7
5	**a.** $319.\underline{2}6 \to 319.3$ **b.** $\underline{3}19.26 \to 300$	1.2	1	14–15
6	**a.** 6064 kWh **b.** 62 kWh **c.** \$6.20 **d.** \$186.00	1.2	2	15–16
7	**a.** Female: $H = 28.6 + 2.5(15) \approx 66$ in. **b.** Male: $H = 32.2 + 2.4(15) \approx 68$ in.	1.2	4–6	17–19
8	**a.** Public safety **b.** $\frac{1}{2}$ **c.** Sales tax	1.3	1	24
9	**a.** About \$50 million **b.** About \$52 million **c.** About \$116 million **d.** About \$75 million **e.** About \$25 million	1.3	2–3	26–27
10	**a.** 6.91 **b.** 6.76 **c.** 0.15 **d.** They seem to be decreasing.	1.3	4–5	27–28

CHAPTER 2

Sets

The modern mathematical theory of sets is one of the most remarkable creations of the human mind. Because of the unusual boldness of some of the ideas found in its study, and some of the singular methods of proof to which it has given rise, the theory of sets is indescribably fascinating.
—HOWARD EVES

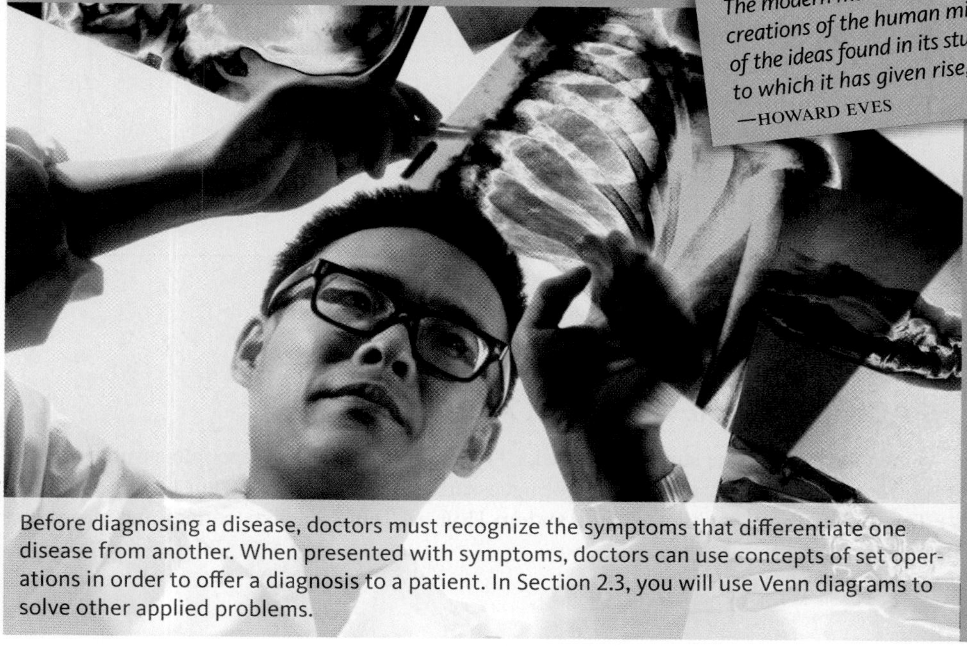

Before diagnosing a disease, doctors must recognize the symptoms that differentiate one disease from another. When presented with symptoms, doctors can use concepts of set operations in order to offer a diagnosis to a patient. In Section 2.3, you will use Venn diagrams to solve other applied problems.

According to David M. Burton's *History of Mathematics*, "the birth of set theory can be marked by Cantor's paper 'On a Property of the System of all the Real Algebraic Numbers.'" Many mathematicians studied finite sets, but Georg Ferdinand Ludwig Philip Cantor was one of the first to solve some of the problems in the theory of infinite sets. You can read about Cantor in the Human Side of Math as you study sets. In this chapter we will first consider **finite sets** and their characteristics. Second, we discuss subsets and the operations that can be performed with them and visualize these operations by using **Venn diagrams,** as shown in Section 2.3. Third, we will examine how to count the number of elements in a set and use this idea to analyze statistical surveys. Finally, we end the chapter with an optional section dealing with **cardinal numbers** and the "indescribably fascinating" **infinite sets.**

2.1 Sets: A Problem-Solving Tool

GETTING STARTED

OBJECTIVES

A. Determine if a set is well defined and identify its elements.
B. Describe a set in words, by listing its elements (roster method) and by using set builder notation.
C. Determine if two sets are equal.
D. Find the number of subsets of a set with n elements and list them.
E. Use the RSTUV procedure to solve problems involving the subsets of a set.

Human Side of Math

© D.E. Smith Collection, Rare Book and Manuscript Library, Columbia University

(1845–1919)

Georg Cantor made the first successful attempts to answer questions concerning infinite sets. His most important contributions appeared in papers published between 1874 and 1884. These papers attacked the basic questions of infinite sets.

Unfortunately, Cantor did not receive much recognition during this period and was rewarded by ridicule from many of his most famous contemporaries.

It was only later in his life that Cantor's ideas gained a measure of recognition from his colleagues. Today, we know that much of the foundation of set theory rests directly on Cantor's work. ■

LOOKING AHEAD

In this chapter we look at the ideas of sets and infinite sets, ideas that were the main focus of Cantor's research and writings.

PACKAGING, RECYCLING, AND SETS

When the clerk at the supermarket asks, "Paper or plastic?" most people assume that the correct answer is *paper*. That is not necessarily correct. (If you want to see why, read *The Green Pages,* published by Random House.) Table 2.1 lists some kitchen product packaging.

Table 2.1 Kitchen Product Packaging

Packaging	Recycled	Recyclable
Cellophane	No	No
Glass bottles	Yes	Yes
Plastic	No	Yes

Which set of products is recycled? Which set of products is recyclable? Which set of products is neither recycled nor recyclable? Can you think of a product that is recycled but not recyclable? Is the set of recycled products the same as the set of recyclable products? You will answer more questions like these later in this section in Exercises 2.1, problems 31 and 32.

The idea of a **set** is familiar in everyday life. Do you have a set of dishes, a set of tools, or a set of books? Each of these sets is regarded as a unit.

Sets, however, need not consist of physical objects; they can consist of abstract ideas. For instance, the Ten Commandments is a set of moral laws. The Constitution is the basic set of laws of the United States.

A Well-Defined Sets and Set Membership

We study sets in this book not only because much of elementary mathematics can be stated and developed by using this concept but also because many mathematical ideas can be stated most simply in the language of sets.

Sets

A **set** is a well-defined collection of objects, called **elements** or **members** of the set.

The main property of a set in mathematics is that it is **well defined.** This means that given any object, it must be clear whether that object is a member (element) of the set. Thus, if we consider the set of even whole numbers, we know that every even whole number, such as 0, 2, 4, 6, and so on, is an element of this set. Thus, the set of even whole numbers is well defined. On the other hand, the set of funny comic strips in the daily newspaper is *not* well defined, because what one person thinks is funny may not be the same as what another person thinks is funny.

EXAMPLE 1 Well-Defined Sets

Which of the following descriptions define sets?

(a) Interesting numbers **(b)** Multiples of 2

(c) Good writers **(d)** Current directors of General Motors

(e) Numbers that can be substituted for x so that $x + 4 = 5$

Solution

Descriptions (b), (d), and (e) are well defined and therefore define sets. Descriptions (a) and (c) are *not* well defined because people do not agree on what is "interesting" or what is "good." Descriptions (a) and (c) therefore do not define sets.

We use capital letters, such as A, B, C, X, Y, and Z, to denote sets and use lowercase letters, such as a, b, c, x, y, and z, to denote **elements** (members) of sets. It is customary, when practical, to list the elements of a set in braces and to separate these elements with commas. Thus, $A = \{1, 2, 3, 4\}$ means that "A is the set consisting of the elements 1, 2, 3, and 4." To indicate the fact that "4 is an element of the set A," or "4 is in A," we write $4 \in A$. To indicate that "6 is not an element of A," we write $6 \notin A$.

EXAMPLE 2 Set Membership

Let $X = \{\text{Eva, Mida, Jack, Janice}\}$. Which of the following are correct statements?

(a) Mida $\in X$ **(b)** Jack $\notin X$ **(c)** Janice $\in \{\text{Eva, Mida, Jack, Janice}\}$

(d) $E \in X$ **(e)** $X \in X$

Solution

Statements (a) and (c) are the only correct statements.

B Describing Sets in Three Ways

Sets can be described in three ways.

Three Methods to Describe Sets

1. By giving a **verbal or written description** of the set
2. By **listing the elements of the** set **within** braces **(roster method)**
3. By using **set-builder notation** (shown on the following page)

Below are some examples of sets described by giving a description in words or a list.

Description	*List*
The set of counting numbers less than 5	$\{1, 2, 3, 4\}$
The set of natural Earth satellites	{Moon}
The set of counting or natural numbers N	$\{1, 2, 3, \ldots\}$ The three dots, called an *ellipsis*, mean that the list goes on in the same pattern without end.
The set of names for the months of the year	{January, February, March, . . . December}
The set of odd counting numbers less than 15	$\{1, 3, 5, \ldots, 13\}$ The three dots mean the odd numbers after 5 and before 13 are in the set but are not listed.
The set of whole numbers less than or equal to 3	$\{0, 1, 2, 3\}$

In *set-builder notation,* we use a defining property to describe the set. A vertical bar (|) is used to mean "such that," and the words to the right of the bar describe the rule. Thus, the preceding sets can be written as follows:

Set-Builder Notation	*Read*
$\{x \mid x$ is a counting number less than $5\}$	The set of all elements x such that x is a counting number less than 5
$\{x \mid x$ is a natural Earth satellite$\}$	The set of all elements x such that x is a natural Earth satellite
$\{x \mid x$ is a counting number$\}$	The set of all elements x such that x is a counting (natural) number
$\{x \mid x$ is the name of one of the months of the year$\}$	The set of all elements x such that x is the name of one of the months of the year
$\{x \mid x$ is an odd counting number less than $15\}$	The set of all elements x such that x is an odd counting number less than 15
$\{x \mid x$ is a whole number less than or equal to $3\}$	The set of all elements x such that x is a whole number less than or equal to 3

EXAMPLE 3 Writing Descriptions of Sets

Write descriptions for the following sets:

(a) $\{a, b, c, \ldots, z\}$ **(b)** $\{1, 3, 5, \ldots\}$ **(c)** $\{3, 6, 9, \ldots, 27\}$

Solution

(a) The set of letters in the English alphabet

(b) The set of odd counting numbers

(c) The set of counting numbers that are multiples of 3 and less than or equal to 27

EXAMPLE 4 Using Roster and Set-Builder Notation

Describe the following sets using the listing (roster) method and using set-builder notation:

(a) The set of digits in the number 1896
(b) The set of odd counting numbers greater than 6
(c) The set of counting numbers greater than 0 and less than 1
(d) The set of counting numbers that are multiples of 4

Solution

List (Roster)	*Set-Builder Notation*
(a) $\{1, 8, 9, 6\}$	$\{x \mid x \text{ is a digit in the number } 1896\}$
(b) $\{7, 9, 11, \ldots\}$	$\{x \mid x \text{ is an odd counting number and } x > 6\}$ The symbol $>$ means "greater than."
(c) $\{\ \}$	$\{x \mid x \text{ is a counting number and } 0 < x < 1\}$ The symbol $<$ means "less than," and $0 < x < 1$ can be read as "x is between 0 and 1" or "x is greater than 0 and is less than 1."
(d) $\{4, 8, 12, \ldots\}$	$\{x \mid x \text{ is a counting number that is a multiple of } 4\}$
(e) $\{a, e, i, o, u\}$	$\{x \mid x \text{ is a vowel in the English alphabet}\}$

A set with *no* elements, as in part (c) of Example 4, can be denoted by the symbol $\{\ \}$ or $\emptyset$. *Note:* The notation $\emptyset$ is preferred.

Notation for the Empty Set

The symbol $\{\ \}$ or $\emptyset$ represents the **empty,** or **null,** set.

EXAMPLE 5 From Set-Builder to Roster Notation

Write the following sets using the listing (roster) method:

(a) $\{x \mid x$ is a counting number less than 10, and x is divisible by $4\}$.
(b) $\{x \mid x$ is a counting number between 8 and 13, and x is divisible by $7\}$.

Solution

(a) The counting numbers less than 10 that are divisible by 4 are 4 and 8. Hence, the required set is $\{4, 8\}$.

(b) None of the numbers between 8 and 13 is divisible by 7. Thus, the required set is empty, and the answer can be written as $\{\ \}$ or $\emptyset$. No roster!

Note: It would *not* be correct to write $\{\emptyset\}$ for the answer to part (b) because the set $\{\emptyset\}$ is not empty, it contains the element $\emptyset$.

We now have used three different types of notation to write sets: description, roster, and set builder. Why do we have three types of notation? Because some sets can only be written using one of the notations.

In order to illustrate this fact, we will write some of the sets of numbers that will be used later in the book. Do not worry if you do not know about these sets of numbers; we are only illustrating the fact that sets can be written different ways!

Written Description	Roster Notation	Set-Builder Notation
The set of natural (counting) numbers N	$\{1, 2, 3, \ldots\}$	$\{x \mid x$ is a natural number$\}$
The set of whole numbers W	$\{0, 1, 2, 3, \ldots\}$	$\{x \mid x$ is a whole number$\}$
The set of integers I	$\{\ldots, -2, -1, 0, 1, 2, \ldots\}$	$\{x \mid x$ is an integer$\}$
The set of positive integers I^+	$\{1, 2, 3, \ldots\}$	$\{x \mid x$ is a positive integer$\}$
The set of negative integers I^-	$\{\ldots, -3, -2, -1\}$	$\{x \mid x$ is a negative integer$\}$
The set of rational numbers, Q	*Impossible* to give roster. $\frac{5}{3}, -\frac{3}{7}$, 8, and 0 are rational. Any rational number may be written as a terminating decimal (0.8, −3.4) or a repeating decimal (0.333 . . . , −2.666 . . .).	$\{x \mid x = a/b$, a and b integers and $b \neq 0$.
The set of irrational numbers H	*Impossible* to give roster. Nonterminating, nonrepeating decimals (0.101001000 . . . , and numbers like $\sqrt{2}$, $-\sqrt{7}$) are irrationals.	$\{x \mid x$ is not rational$\}$ or $\{x \mid x$ cannot be written as a quotient of integers$\}$
The set of real numbers R	*Impossible* to give roster. Any rational or irrational number is a real number.	$\{x \mid x$ is a rational or an irrational number$\}$ or $\{x \mid x$ is a number that can be written as a decimal$\}$

C Equality of Sets

Note that the order in which the elements of a set are listed does not affect membership in the set. Thus, if we are asked to write the set of digits in the year in which Columbus discovered America, we may write the set as $\{1, 4, 9, 2\}$. Someone else may write the set as $\{1, 2, 4, 9\}$. Both are correct! Thus, we see that the sets $\{1, 4, 9, 2\}$ and $\{1, 2, 4, 9\}$ are **equal;** that is $\{1, 4, 9, 2\} = \{1, 2, 4, 9\}$. Similarly, $\{a, b, c, d, e\} = \{e, d, c, b, a\}$.

Definition of Equal Sets

In general, two sets A and B are **equal,** denoted by $A = B$, if they have the same elements (members) not necessarily listed in the same order.

EXAMPLE 6 Determining Whether Two Sets are Equal

Determine if the given sets are equal:

(a) $\{1, 3, 2\}$ and $\{1, 2, 3\}$

(b) The set of digits in the year in which the Declaration of Independence was adopted and the set $\{1, 7, 7, 6\}$

Solution

(a) The sets $\{1, 3, 2\}$ and $\{1, 2, 3\}$ contain the same elements, so $\{1, 3, 2\} = \{1, 2, 3\}$.

(b) The two sets also contain the same elements, so they are equal. Thus, the set of digits in the year in which the Declaration of Independence was adopted equals $\{1, 7, 7, 6\}$. By convention, we do not list the elements of a set more than once, and the order in which we write the elements is not important. Thus $\{1, 7, 7, 6\} = \{1, 7, 6\} = \{1, 6, 7\}$

Note that two sets may be equal even when their written descriptions are different. For example, the set of counting numbers and the set of natural numbers are equal because they consist of the same elements. 1, 2, 3, and so on.

D Subsets and the Number of Elements in a Set

Sometimes all the elements of a set A are also elements of another set B. For example, if A is the set of all students in your class, and B is the set of all students in your school, every element of A is also in B (because every student in your class is a student in your school). In such cases, we say that the set A is a **subset** of the set B. We denote this by writing $A \subseteq B$. Thus, if G is the set of all generations, the silent generation S is a subset of G, $S \subseteq G$.

Definition of Subset

The set A is a **subset** of B (denoted by $A \subseteq B$) if every element of A is also an element of B.

Thus, if $A = \{a, b\}$, $B = \{a, b, c\}$, and $C = \{b\}$, then $A \subseteq B$, $C \subseteq A$, and $C \subseteq B$.

It is a consequence of the definition of a subset that $A = B$ when both $A \subseteq B$ and $B \subseteq A$. Furthermore, for any set A, since every element of A is an element of A, according to the definition of a subset, $A \subseteq A$.

The definition of a subset may be restated in the following form:

Alternative Definition of a Subset

The set A is a **subset** of B if there is no element of A that is not an element of B.

From this definition it follows that $\varnothing \subseteq A$ because there is no element of $\varnothing$ that is not in A. This reasoning holds for every set, so *the empty set is a subset of every set.*

Is {STOP} a proper subset of {STOP, KEEP MOVING}?

Definition of Proper Subset

A set A is said to be a **proper subset** of B, denoted by $A \subset B$, if A is a subset of B but $A \neq B$ (A is not equal to B).

In other words, $A \subset B$ means that all elements of A are also in B, but B contains at least one element that is not in A. For example, if $B = \{1, 2\}$, the proper subsets of B are $\varnothing$, $\{1\}$, and $\{2\}$, but the set $\{1, 2\}$ itself is not a *proper* subset of B.

In everyday discussion, we are usually aware of the "universe of discourse," that is, the set of all things we are talking about. In dealing with sets, the universe of discourse is called the **universal set.**

Definition of a Universal Set

The **universal set** $\mathcal{U}$ is the set of all elements under discussion.

Thus, if we agree to discuss all the letters in the English alphabet, then the set $\mathcal{U} = \{a, b, c, \ldots, z\}$ is our universal set. On the other hand, if we are to discuss the counting numbers, our universal set is $\mathcal{U} = \{1, 2, 3, \ldots\}$ and if we are discussing Facebook users $\mathcal{U}$ will be the set of all Facebook users.

EXAMPLE 7 Finding Subsets of a Set

Find all the subsets of the set $\mathcal{U} = \{a, b, c\}$.

Solution

Form subsets of the set $\mathcal{U}$ by assigning some, none, or all of the elements of $\mathcal{U}$ to these subsets. Organize the work as follows:

Form all the subsets with no elements.	$\varnothing$
Form all the subsets with 1 element.	$\{a\}, \{b\}, \{c\}$
Form all the subsets with 2 elements.	$\{a, b\}, \{a, c\}, \{b, c\}$
Form all the subsets with 3 elements.	$\{a, b, c\}$

The set in this example has 3 elements and $2^3 = 2 \times 2 \times 2 = 8$ subsets. Similarly, a set such as $\{a, b\}$, containing 2 elements, has $2^2 = 2 \times 2 = 4$ subsets, namely, $\varnothing$, $\{a\}$, $\{b\}$, and $\{a, b\}$. The Discovery section of Exercises 2.4 shows another way of constructing all the subsets of a given set. It also illustrates the following:

The Number of Subsets of a Set

A set of n elements has 2^n subsets.

EXAMPLE 8 Counting the Subsets of a Set

If $A = \{a_1, a_2, a_3, \ldots, a_8\}$, how many subsets does A have?

Solution

Because the set A has 8 elements, A has $2^8 = 256$ subsets.

EXAMPLE 9 Listing Proper Subsets

List all the proper subsets of the set $\mathcal{U} = \{1, 2, 3\}$.

Solution

The proper subsets are $\varnothing$, $\{1\}$, $\{2\}$, $\{3\}$, $\{1, 2\}$, $\{1, 3\}$, and $\{2, 3\}$. By the definition of a proper subset, the set $\{1, 2, 3\}$ is *not* a proper subset of $\mathcal{U}$. Thus, a set with n elements has $2^n - 1$ proper subsets.

The ideas in the preceding examples can be applied to many practical problems. You have heard the slogans "Have it your way" and "I'm loving it." Now, suppose that you have a small hamburger place and you want to advertise that you have a great variety of burgers. If you have three condiments (catsup, mustard, and onions), how many different types of hamburgers can you prepare? (By the way, Wendy's did something similar some time ago. See problem 77 of Exercises 2.1.) To solve this problem, use the RSTUV procedure. The strategy here is to *make a list* of the subsets, as shown next.

PROBLEM-SOLVING

Finding Subsets

① **Read** the problem.

List the different types of hamburgers that can be prepared if catsup (c), mustard (m), and onions (o) are available as condiments.

Some problems must be read two or three times. Make sure you understand the problem before you attempt a solution.

② **Select** the unknown.

Look for the *different* types of hamburgers that can be prepared if catsup, mustard, and onions are available.

③ **Think** of a plan. What is given? What do you do?

Given the universal set

$$\mathcal{U} = \{c, m, o\}$$

find all the subsets of $\mathcal{U}$. The strategy here is to make a list of the elements in each subset. Organize the work! Start with subsets of 0 elements, then 1 element, and so on.

④ **Use** your knowledge to carry out the plan. Find the
subset of 0 elements
subsets of 1 element
subsets of 2 elements
subsets of 3 elements

$\varnothing$. There is 1 type of hamburger with no condiments.
$\{c\}, \{m\}, \{o\}$. There are 3 types of hamburgers with only 1 condiment.
$\{c, m\}, \{c, o\}, \{m, o\}$. There are 3 types of hamburgers with 2 condiments.
$\{c, m, o\}$. There is 1 type of hamburger with everything.

⑤ **Verify** the answer.

The set $\mathcal{U} = \{c, m, o\}$ has 3 elements and $2^3 = 8$ different subsets, and you have found them all!

Try Example 10 Now Cover the solution, write your own solution, and then check your work.

EXAMPLE 10 Denny's Menus

The restaurant ad has four items on the menu named \$2, \$4, \$6, \$8 according to their price.

(a) Write the set corresponding to all items on the menu.

(b) If you can order one, two, three, or four items for dinner, how many choices do you have? List them.

(c) If there are four items a, b, c, d costing \$2 each and four items e, f, g, h costing \$4 each, write all sets of orders costing \$4.

There's always something new and tasty on our
$2
$4
$6
$8
VALUE MENU
all day, every day…

Source: http://tinyurl.com/4gvbvrg.

Solution

(a) The set corresponding to the four items on the menu is $\{\$2, \$4, \$6, \$8\}$.

(b) There are 4 items in the set, so the number of choices is $2^4 - 1 = 16 - 1 = 15$. We are not listing the empty set (no dinner) as a choice!

One-item dinner: $\{\$2\}, \{\$4\}, \{\$6\}, \{\$8\}$
Two-item dinner: $\{\$2, \$4\}, \{\$2, \$6\}, \{\$2, \$8\}, \{\$4, \$6\}, \{\$4, \$8\}, \{\$6, \$8\}$
Three-item dinner: $\{\$2, \$4, \$6\}, \{\$2, \$4, \$8\}, \{\$2, \$6, \$8\}, \{\$4, \$6, \$8\}$
Four-item dinner: $\{\$2, \$4, \$6, \$8\}$

(c) $\{a, a\}, \{a, b\}, \{a, c\}, \{a, d\}, \{b, b\}, \{b, c\}, \{b, d\}, \{c, c\}, \{c, d\}, \{d, d\}, \{e\}, \{f\}, \{g\}, \{h\}$

2.1 EXERCISES

A Well-Defined Sets and Set Membership

In problems 1–8, which of the descriptions describe a set?

1. Grouchy people
2. Good tennis players in the United States
3. Retired baseball players with lifetime batting averages of .400 or better
4. Students taking mathematics courses at Yale University at the present moment
5. $\{x \mid x \text{ is an odd counting number}\}$
6. $\{x \mid x \text{ is an even counting number}\}$
7. $\{x \mid x \text{ is a good college course}\}$
8. $\{x \mid x \text{ is a bad instructor}\}$
9. Let $A = \{\text{Desi, Gidget, Jane, Dora}\}$. Which of the following are correct statements?

   a. $D \in A$ b. Desi $\in A$
   c. $A \in$ Jane d. $D \notin A$
   e. Jane $\notin A$

In problems 10–14, let $X = \{a, b, x, y\}$. Fill in the blank with $\in$ or $\notin$ to make each statement correct.

10. a ____ X 11. x ____ X
12. X ____ X 13. A ____ X
14. $\{bay\}$ ____ X

In problems 15–20, determine whether each statement is true or false.

15. $2 \in \{2, 4, 6, 8\}$ 16. $6 \in \{1, 3, 5, 11\}$
17. $0 \in \mathbf{N}$ (the set of counting numbers)
18. $0 \in \mathbf{W}$ (the set of whole numbers)
19. $5 \in \{x \mid x \in \mathbf{N} \text{ and } x \text{ is odd}\}$
20. $10 \in \{x \mid x \in \mathbf{N} \text{ and } x < 10\}$

B Describing Sets (with Verbal Descriptions)

In problems 21–30, write a verbal description of the set.

21. $\{a, z\}$ 22. $\{m, a, n\}$
23. {Adam, Eve} 24. {Christopher Columbus}
25. $\{7, 2, 6, 3, 5, 4, 1\}$ 26. $\{2, 6, 12, 20, 30\}$
27. $\{1, 3, 5, \ldots, 51\}$

How many hours do you sleep each day? Here are some sets that refer to the graph. Describe them.

28. $\{9.7\}$
29. $\{9.3\}$
30. $\{9.4\}$

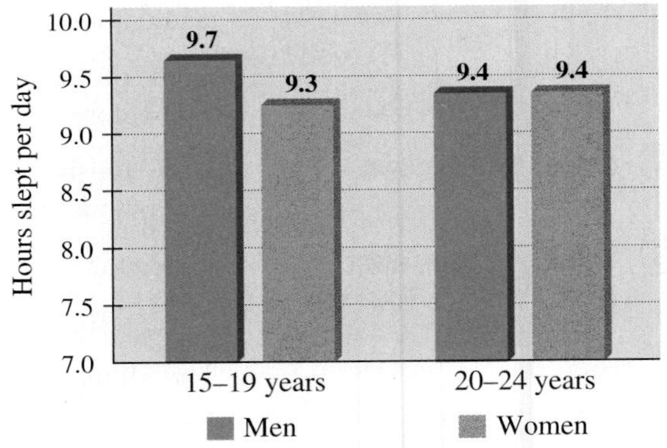

Source: Dept of Labor Time Use Survey.

The following table, which lists toxic substances found in the fat tissue of humans, was compiled by the National Adipose Tissue Survey of the Public Health Service and will be used in problems 31 and 32.

Compound	Possible Sources of Exposure	Frequency in Test Subjects
Chloroform	Drinking water	76%
Dioxin	Wood treatment, herbicides, auto exhaust	100%
Heptachlor	Termite control	67%
Toluene	Gasoline	91%
Xylene	Gasoline, paints	100%

31. Which set of compounds was found in everybody's tissue?
32. Which set of compounds was found in less than 90% of the people?

In problems 33–38, write the sets using the listing (roster) method.

33. $\{x \mid x \text{ is a counting number less than } 8\}$.
34. $\{x \mid x \text{ is a counting number less than } 2\}$.
35. $\{n \mid n \text{ is a whole number less than } 7\frac{1}{2}\}$.
36. $\{n \mid n \text{ is a whole number less than } 8\frac{1}{4}\}$.
37. $\{x \mid x \text{ is a counting number between 3 and } 8\}$.
38. $\{x \mid x \text{ is a counting number between 2 and } 7\}$.

In problems 39–42, refer to the graph on the next page and use roster notation to write the set of generations in which:

39. More than 50% go online wirelessly.
40. Less than 50% go online wirelessly.
41. The members are younger than 65.
42. The members are older than 64.

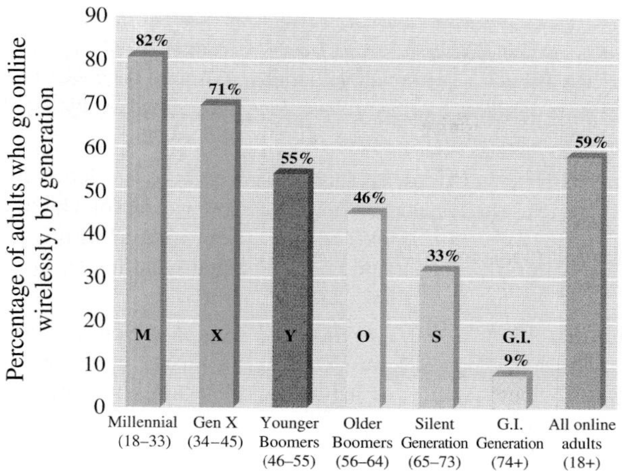

Source: Copyright © 2012 Pew Internet & American Life Project. http://pewinternet.org/~/media//Files/Reports/2010/PIP_Generations_and_Tech10.pdf.

After consulting the following list, you will have to make some choices: manufacturer, mileage, type of transmission, and so on. The set consisting of the ranking numbers of the cars made by Honda corresponds to {3, 5}. *Use the ranking numbers to find the set of cars:*

Rank	Make & Model	Fuel Economy City/HWY MPG	Fuel Economy 150 mile MPG
1	Toyota Prius IV Hybrid	32/55	53
2	Smart For Two Passion	30/44	46
3	Honda Insight EX	29/45	46
4	Volkswagen Golf (manual)	27/49	44
5	Honda Civic Hybrid	26/47	45
6	Volkswagen TDI (manual)	25/49	37
7	Toyota Camry Hybrid	28/41	37
8	Ford Fusion Hybrid	25/40	41
9	Scion xD Toyota (manual)	25/40	42
10	Mini Cooper (manual)	24/41	41

43. made by Volkswagen
44. with automatic transmissions
45. with manual transmissions
46. that seat at most two passengers
47. that has the highest 150 mile MPG
48. that has the lowest 150 mile MPG
49. that make more than 50 highway MPG

C Equality of Sets

In problems 50–56, state whether the sets A and B are equal.

50. $A = \{2n + 1 \mid n \text{ is a counting number}\}$
$B = \{2n - 1 \mid n \text{ is a counting number}\}$

51. $A = \{4n \mid n \text{ is a counting number}\}$
$B = \{2n \mid n \text{ is a counting number}\}$

52. $A = \{1, 1, 2, 2, 3\}$, $B = \{1, 2, 3\}$

53. $A = \{x \mid x \text{ is a cow that has jumped over the moon}\}$
$B = \{x \mid x \text{ is an astronaut who has landed on Pluto}\}$

54. Let $A = \{5\}$, $B = \{f, i, v, e\}$, $C = \{e, f, v, i\}$, and D be the set of letters in the word *repeat*. Find the following:
a. The set containing five elements
b. The set equal to B
c. The set of letters in the word *five*

55. Let $A = \{1, 2, 3, 4\}$, $B = \{4, 3, 2, 1\}$, and $C = \{4, 3, 2, 1, 0\}$. Fill in the blanks with $=$ or $\neq$ to make true statements.
a. A ____ B **b.** A ____ C
c. B ____ C

56. Let $A = \{x \mid x \text{ is a counting number between 4 and 5}\}$, $B = \varnothing$, and $C = \{\varnothing\}$. Fill in the blanks with $=$ or $\neq$ to make true statements.
a. A ____ B **b.** A ____ C
c. B ____ C

D Subsets and Problem Solving

In problems 57–62, list all the subsets and indicate which are proper subsets of the given set.

57. $\mathcal{U} = \{a, b\}$ **58.** $\mathcal{U} = \{1, 2, 3\}$
59. $\mathcal{U} = \{1, 2, 3, 4\}$ **60.** $\mathcal{U} = \{\varnothing\}$
61. $\{1, 2\}$ **62.** $\{x, y, z\}$

63. How many subsets does the set $A = \{a, b, c, d\}$ have?
64. How many proper subsets does the set $\{1, 2, 3, 4\}$ have?
65. If $A = \{\frac{1}{1}, \frac{1}{2}, \frac{1}{3}, \ldots, \frac{1}{10}\}$, how many subsets does A have?
66. How many proper subsets does set A of problem 65 have?
67. A set has 32 subsets. How many elements are there in the set?
68. A set has 31 proper subsets. How many elements are there in the set?
69. A set has 64 subsets. How many elements are there in the set?
70. A set has 63 proper subsets. How many elements are there in the set?
71. Is $\varnothing$ a subset of $\varnothing$? Explain.
72. Is $\varnothing$ a proper subset of $\varnothing$? Explain.
73. If A is the set of numbers that are divisible by 2 and B is the set of numbers that are divisible by 4, is $A \subseteq B$? Is $B \subseteq A$?
74. Give an example of a set P and a set Q such that $P \in Q$ and $P \subseteq Q$.
75. Gino's Pizza offers the following set of toppings: $\{C, M, O, P, S\}$, where C, M, O, P, and S mean cheese, mushrooms, onions, pepperoni, and sausage. How many types of pizza can you order with
a. one topping?
b. two toppings?
c. three toppings?
76. Referring to problem 75, how many different kinds of pizza with at least one topping can you order?

77. Some time ago, Wendy's Hamburger claimed that it could prepare your hamburger 256 ways. How many condiments do you need in order to be able to prepare 256 different hamburgers?

78. If Gino's Pizza decides to top Wendy's claim and advertises that it has 500 different types of pizza, what is the minimum number of toppings it must carry?

IN OTHER WORDS

79. Find the definition of the word *set* in a dictionary. Does the definition contain the word *collection* or the word *thing*? Now, find the definitions of the words *collection* and *thing*. Why do you think it is almost impossible to give a formal definition of the word *set*?

80. Is the set of all good students in your class well defined? Why or why not? If it is not well defined, can you make it well defined? How?

81. Explain why

   a. $\varnothing \notin \varnothing$.
   b. $\varnothing \in \{\varnothing\}$.
   c. $\varnothing \neq \{0\}$.
   d. $\varnothing = \{\ \}$.

82. Explain why for any nonempty set A and universal set $\mathcal{U}$,

   a. $A \subseteq A$.
   b. $A \not\subset A$.
   c. $\varnothing \subset A$.
   d. $\varnothing \subseteq A$.
   e. $A \subseteq \mathcal{U}$.

USING YOUR KNOWLEDGE

Gepetto Scissore, a barber in the small town of Sevilla, who was naturally called the Barber of Sevilla, decided that as a public service he would shave all those men and only those men of the village who did not shave themselves. Let $S = \{x \mid x$ *is a man of the village who shaves himself*$\}$ *and* $D = \{x \mid x$ *is a man of the village who does not shave himself*$\}$.

83. If g represents Gepetto,

   a. is $g \in S$?
   b. is $g \in D$?

The preceding problem is a popularization of the Russell paradox, named after its discoverer, Bertrand Russell. In studying sets, it seems that one can classify sets as those that are members of themselves and those that are not members of themselves. Suppose that we consider the two sets of sets

$$M = \{X \mid X \in X, X \text{ is a set}\}$$

and

$$N = \{X \mid X \notin X, X \text{ is a set}\}$$

84. a. Is $N \in M$?
   b. Is $N \in N$?

   Think about the consequences of your answers!

DISCOVERY

You should find the following paradox amusing, puzzling, and perhaps even thought provoking. Define a self-descriptive word *to be a word that makes good sense when put into both blanks of the sentence "_____ is a(n) _____ word." Two simple examples of self-descriptive words are "English" and "short." Just try them out!*

Now define a non-self-descriptive word *to be a word that is not self-descriptive. Most words will fit into this category. Try it out again. Now consider the following question.*

85. Let S be the set of self-descriptive words, and let S' be the set of non-self-descriptive words. How would you classify the word *non-self-descriptive*? Is it an element of S? Or is it an element of S'? You should get into difficulty no matter how you answer these questions. Think about it!

86. *Russell's Paradox on the Web.* Suppose you construct a Web page (Paradox.html) that has a link to every Web page that does not link to itself. Does Paradox.html have a link to itself?

COLLABORATIVE LEARNING

This group activity is designed to determine the number of subsets of a set of n elements that have to be selected before we find a pair with the property that one *is a subset of the other. Form three groups. One group will work with the set* $\{1, 2\}$, *the second group with the set* $\{+, -\}$, *and the third group with the set* $\{a, b\}$. *Each of the groups will do the following.*

1. Find all subsets of the set you are working with.

The object is to find a pair of subsets so that *one is a subset of the other.*

2. How many subsets does your group have to select before you find two of the selected subsets are such that *one is a subset of the other?*
3. Answer the same question when the given sets for each of the groups are $\{1, 2, 3\}$, $\{+, -, \times\}$, and $\{a, b, c\}$.
4. Answer the same question when the given sets for each of the groups are $\{1, 2, 3, 4\}$, $\{+, -, \times, /\}$, and $\{a, b, c, d\}$.
5. Each of the groups fills in a table like the one below.

Try to answer this question: How many subsets of a set of n elements have to be selected so that two of the selected subsets have the property that one is a subset of the other. *Compare answers and report to the rest of the class.*

Number of Elements in the Set	Number of Subsets	Number of Subsets That Have to Be Selected Before Finding Two of the Selected Subsets So That One is a Subset of the Other
1		
2		
3		
4		

To see a proof of the result obtained, go to www.cut-the-knot.org/pigeonhole/subsets.shtml.

2.2 Set Operations

GETTING STARTED

OBJECTIVES

A. Find the intersection and the union of two or more sets.
B. Find the complement of a set.
C. Find the difference of two sets.
D. Solve applications involving sets, unions, and intersections.

DIAGNOSIS AND SET OPERATIONS

When diagnosing diseases, doctors have to know the symptoms that distinguish one disease from another, *the differential diagnosis*. Some symptoms for hypoglycemia (too little sugar in the blood) and hyperglycemia (too much sugar in the blood or diabetes) are identical. Do you need a blood test to make the diagnosis? Not so fast! Doctors know a **universal** set of symptoms $\mathcal{U}$ that may indicate the presence of hypoglycemia or hyperglycemia. (See Table 2.2.) To distinguish between hyper and hypo, they discard the symptoms that are **common**—nausea and headaches—and concentrate on the rest of the symptoms to make the diagnosis. We can also represent the set of symptoms by using a picture called a **Venn diagram.** To diagram the symptoms for Too Much Sugar in the Blood, call them D for diabetes, let the universal set $\mathcal{U}$ be a rectangle and D a circle inside the rectangle with the symptoms h, s, n, r as the elements of the set D listed inside. We will study similar questions in problems 40–50 and in the Using Your Knowledge, problems 81–87, but you can see some of the actual symptoms of diabetes by visiting http://www.diabetes.org.

© I. Bello

Dr. Margaret Colleran looks for some of these symptoms to diagnose diabetes.

Table 2.2

Too Little Sugar in the Blood	Too Much Sugar in the Blood
Nausea (n)	Headache (h)
Visual disturbances (v)	Stomach cramps (s)
Trembling (t)	Nausea (n)
Headache (h)	Rapid breathing (r)

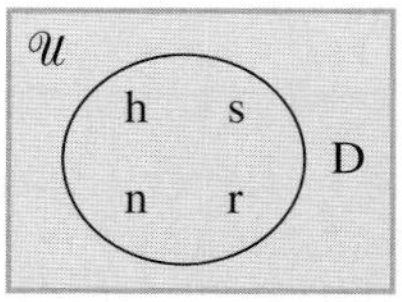

A Intersections and Unions

We can clearly see that the set of symptoms *common* to both sets listed in Table 2.2 is $\{n, h\}$. The set $\{n, h\}$ is called the **intersection** of the two given sets.

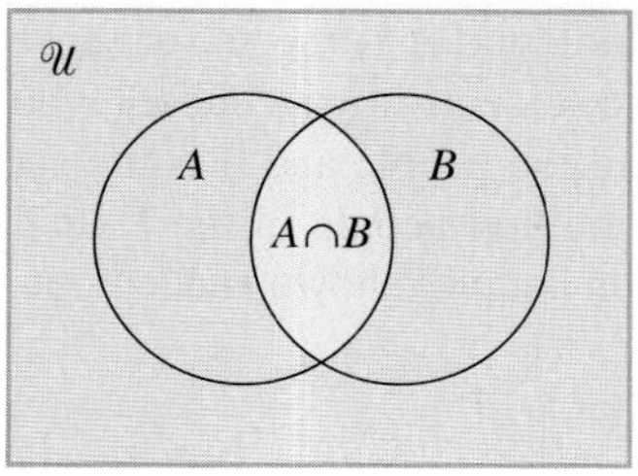

FIGURE 2.1 If A and B are represented by circles and the universal set $\mathcal{U}$ by a rectangle, $A \cap B$ is the shaded area common to both sets.

Definition of the Intersection of Sets

If A and B are sets, the **intersection** of A and B, denoted by $A \cap B$ (read "A intersection B"), is the set of all elements that are common to both A and B. That is,

$$A \cap B = \{x \mid x \in A \textbf{ and } x \in B\}$$

Thus, if $A = \{a, b, c, d\}$ and $B = \{b, d, e\}$, then $A \cap B = \{b, d\}$. See Figure 2.1.

If we list all the symptoms mentioned in Table 2.2, we obtain the set $\{n, v, t, h, s, r\}$. This set is called the **union** of the two given sets.

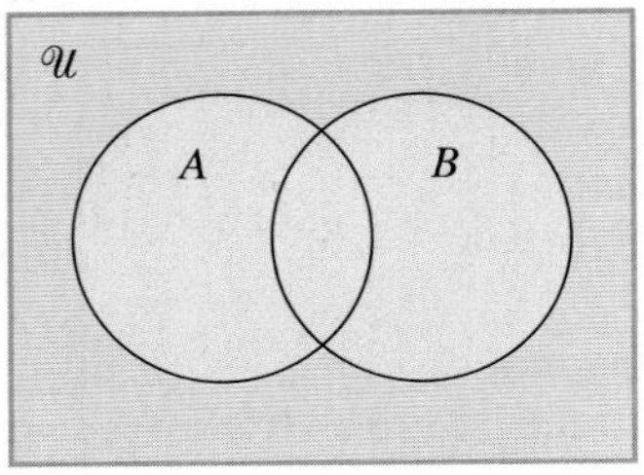

FIGURE 2.2 If *A* and *B* are represented by circles and the universal set 𝒰 by a rectangle, $A \cup B$ is the shaded area.

Definition of the Union of Sets

If *A* and *B* are sets, the **union** of *A* and *B*, denoted by $A \cup B$ (read "*A* union *B*"), is the set of all elements that are either in *A* or in *B* or in both *A* and *B*. That is,

$$A \cup B = \{x \mid x \in A \textbf{ or } x \in B\}$$

Note that we use the *inclusive or;* that is, $x \in A$, $x \in B$, or *x* is in both *A* and *B*. Hence, if $A = \{1, 3, 4, 6\}$ and $B = \{3, 6, 7\}$, then $A \cup B = \{1, 3, 4, 6, 7\}$. See Figure 2.2.

EXAMPLE 1 Finding Unions and Intersections

Let $A = \{a, b, c, d, e\}$ and $B = \{a, c, e, f\}$. Find the following:

(a) $A \cap B$ (b) $A \cup B$

Solution

(a) $A \cap B$ is the set of all elements common to both *A* and *B*. That is, $A \cap B = \{a, c, e\}$.
(b) $A \cup B$ is the set of all elements in *A* or *B* or both. That is, $A \cup B = \{a, b, c, d, e, f\}$. Note that *a*, *c*, and *e* occur in both sets, yet we list each of these elements only once.

Two sets with no elements in common are said to be **disjoint.** If sets *A* and *B* are disjoint, then $A \cap B = \varnothing$. For example, the set $A = \{1, 2, 3\}$ and the set $B = \{4, 5\}$ are disjoint; they have no elements in common, or $A \cap B = \varnothing$. Similarly, if *D* represents the set of people diagnosed with diabetes and *U* the set of those that are undiagnosed, *D* and *U* are **disjoint.**

B Complement of a Set

We are often interested in the set of elements in the universal set 𝒰 under discussion that are *not* in some specified subset *A* of 𝒰.

Definition of the Complement of a Set

Let 𝒰 be the universal set, and let *A* be a subset of 𝒰. **The complement** of *A*, denoted by A' (read "*A* prime" or "*A* complement"), is the set of elements in 𝒰 that are not in *A*. That is, $A' = \{x \mid x \in \mathcal{U} \text{ and } x \notin A\}$. This set is also symbolized by $\mathcal{U} - A$.

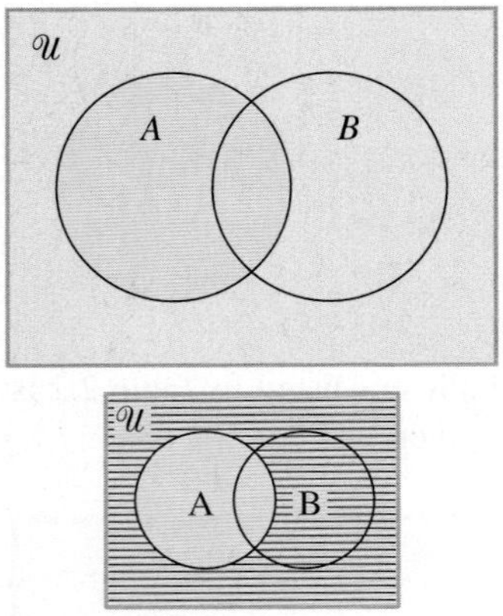

FIGURE 2.3 The set $A' = \mathcal{U} - A$ consists of all the elements in 𝒰 but not in *A*. You can also show the complement of a set by shading the region *outside* of the circle *A* as shown.

For example, if 𝒰 is the set of students in your school, and *A* is the set of those students who have taken algebra, then A' is the set of those students in your school who have not taken algebra. Similarly, if 𝒰 is a set of 25.8 million people and *A* is the set of people that have been diagnosed with diabetes (18.8 million people in the United States), then A' is the set of undiagnosed people (7 million people) shown shaded outside of *A* and represented by $A' = \mathcal{U} - A$ (see Figure 2.3).

EXAMPLE 2 Finding Complements

Let $\mathcal{U} = \{1, 2, 3, 4, 5, 6\}$, $A = \{1, 3, 5\}$, and $B = \{2, 4\}$. Find the following:

(a) A' (b) B' (c) $A' \cap B'$ (d) $A \cap B$

Solution

(a) $A' = \{2, 4, 6\}$ **(b)** $B' = \{1, 3, 5, 6\}$ **(c)** $A' \cap B' = \{6\}$

(d) $A \cap B = \emptyset$, because there are no elements common to these two sets.

Note that, because $\emptyset \subseteq \mathcal{U}$, and no element of $\mathcal{U}$ is an element of $\emptyset$, it follows that $\emptyset' = \mathcal{U}$ and $\mathcal{U}' = \emptyset$.

EXAMPLE 3 Finding Complements of Unions and Intersections

If A, B, and $\mathcal{U}$ are the same as in Example 2, find the following:

(a) $(A \cup B)'$ **(b)** $(A \cap B)'$ **(c)** $A' \cup B'$ **(d)** $A \cup (A \cup B)'$

Solution

(a) $A \cup B = \{1, 3, 5\} \cup \{2, 4\} = \{1, 2, 3, 4, 5\}$
Hence, $(A \cup B)' = \{6\}$.
[Note that in order to find $(A \cup B)'$, you must first find $A \cup B$ and then take its complement. Always do the operations inside parentheses *first.*]

(b) $A \cap B = \{1, 3, 5\} \cap \{2, 4\} = \emptyset$
Hence, $(A \cap B)' = \emptyset' = \{1, 2, 3, 4, 5, 6\} = \mathcal{U}$.

(c)
$$\begin{aligned} A' \cup B' &= \{1, 3, 5\}' \cup \{2, 4\}' \\ &= \{2, 4, 6\} \cup \{1, 3, 5, 6\} \\ &= \{1, 2, 3, 4, 5, 6\} = \mathcal{U} \end{aligned}$$

(d) Since $(A \cup B)' = \{6\}$ [see part (a)],
$A \cup (A \cup B)' = \{1, 3, 5\} \cup \{6\} = \{1, 3, 5, 6\}$

Notice that the answers to parts (b) and (c) are identical; that is, $(A \cap B)' = A' \cup B'$. Also notice that the answers to Example 2(c) and Example 3(a) are identical; that is, $(A \cup B)' = A' \cap B'$. In general, we have

De Morgan's Law

For any sets A and B, $(A \cap B)' = A' \cup B'$ and $(A \cup B)' = A' \cap B'$.

[See Exercises 2.3, problem 34(a) and (b).]

It is also possible to form intersections, unions, and complements using more than two sets, as in the next example.

EXAMPLE 4 Unions, Intersections, and Complements

Let $\mathcal{U} = \{a, b, c, d, e, f\}$, $A = \{a, c, e\}$, $B = \{b, e\}$, and $C = \{a, b, d\}$. Find $(A \cup B) \cap C'$.

Solution

Since $A \cup B$ is in parentheses, find $A \cup B$ first.

$$A \cup B = \{a, c, e\} \cup \{b, e\} = \{a, b, c, e\}$$

Then

$$C' = \{c, e, f\}$$

Hence

$$\begin{aligned} (A \cup B) \cap C' &= \{a, b, c, e\} \cap \{c, e, f\} \\ &= \{c, e\} \end{aligned}$$

C Difference of Two Sets

In some cases, we may be interested in only part of a given set. For example, we may want to consider the set of all nonpoisonous snakes. If we let S be the set of all snakes and P the set of all poisonous snakes, we are interested in the set of all snakes except (excluding) the poisonous ones. This set will be denoted by $S - P$.

Definition of the Difference of Sets

If A and B are two sets, the **difference** of A and B, denoted by $A - B$ (read "A minus B"), is the set of all elements that are in A and not in B. That is, $A - B = \{x \mid x \in A \text{ and } x \notin B\}$.

Notice that

1. the definition of A' is a special case of the preceding definition because $\mathcal{U} - A = A'$ (see the definition of the complement of set A).
2. $A \cap B' = A - B$ because $A \cap B'$ is the set of all elements in A and not in B, and this is precisely the definition of $A - B$.

EXAMPLE 5 Finding Differences of Sets

Let $\mathcal{U} = \{1, 2, 3, 4, 5, 6\}$, $A = \{1, 2, 3, 4\}$, and $B = \{1, 2, 5\}$. Find

(a) $\mathcal{U} - A$. (b) A'. (c) $A - B$. (d) $B - A$.

Solution

(a) $\mathcal{U} - A$ is the set of all elements in $\mathcal{U}$ and not in A, that is, $\{5, 6\}$.

(b) A' is the set of all elements in $\mathcal{U}$ and not in A, that is, $\{5, 6\}$.

(c) $A - B$ is the set of all elements in A and not in B, that is, $\{3, 4\}$.

(d) $B - A$ is the set of all elements in B and not in A, that is, $\{5\}$.

D Applications

Unions, intersections, and complements can be used to visualize and clarify certain situations. For example, according to the American Diabetes Association, there are three types of diabetes: Type 1 (juvenile), Type 2 (the most common), and Gestational G (during pregnancy).

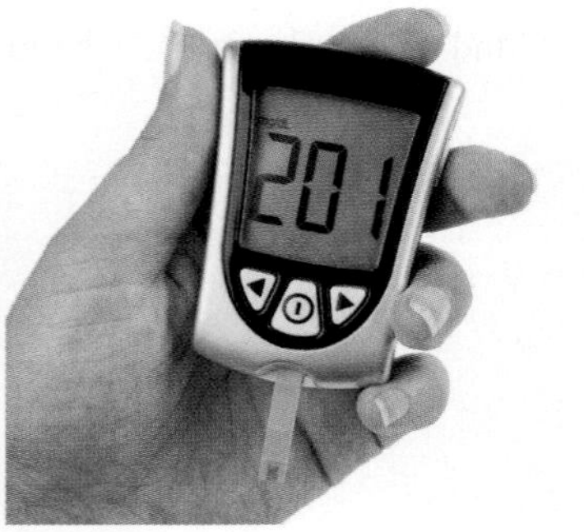

EXAMPLE 6 Diabetes Basics

A study of 1001 diabetes patients classified them as T_1, T_2, or G as shown in the diagram. Use set notation to identify the patients and find the number that:

(a) do not have gestational diabetes.

(b) have both T_1 and T_2 diabetes.

(c) have either T_1 or T_2 diabetes.

(d) are not included in part (c).

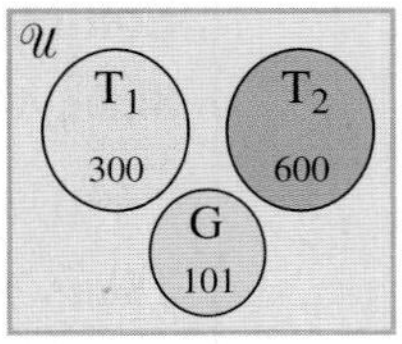

Solution

(a) The patients who do not have gestational diabetes are in set G', the complement of G. There are 900 of those.

(b) There are no patients who have both T_1 and T_2 diabetes, T_1 and T_2 are disjoint; that is, $T_1 \cap T_2 = \varnothing$. There are 0 elements in $T_1 \cap T_2$.

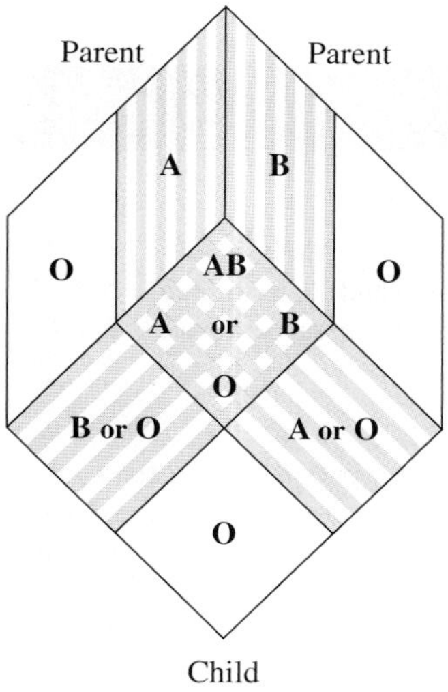

FIGURE 2.4

(c) The patients who have either T_1 or T_2 diabetes are in the set $T_1 \cup T_2$. There are 900 of those.

(d) The patients not included in part (c) must be in the complement of $T_1 \cup T_2$, that is, in $(T_1 \cup T_2)'$. There are 101 of those.

EXAMPLE 7 Parents' and Children's Blood Types

In 1900, Karl Landsteiner identified four blood groups as A, B, AB, and O (which is neither A nor B). Figure 2.4 shows how blood types are passed from parents to a child.

(a) If one parent has A blood and the other O blood, which blood type could their child have?

(b) Blood types can be used to settle paternity cases. Suppose a child has B blood. What are the possible blood types for the parents?

(c) What blood type in a child would be the most difficult to use to identify paternity?

Solution

(a) Select blood type A at the top left (blue lines) and O at the top right (white). Follow the columns to their intersection. The child could have A or O blood.

(b) Look at the bottom part of the cube. The B appears twice: where O and B intersect and where A and B intersect. Thus, one parent can be O and the other B or one parent can be A and the other B. Note that two parents with type B blood will have a child with type B blood.

(c) Again, look at the bottom of the cube and note that type O appears four times; this means that there are four different sets of parental combinations. Type O blood in a child is the most difficult to use to identify paternity.

EXAMPLE 8 Movies, Directors, and Intersections

What is your favorite movie? The lists give the 10 best movies of all time according to the critics (set C) and according to readers of a movie magazine (set R). (Source: www.filmsite.org/mrshowbz.html.)

Critics' Picks (set C)

1. *Casablanca* (1942), director Michael Curtiz
2. *The Godfather Part II* (1974), director Francis Ford Coppola
3. *North by Northwest* (1959), director Alfred Hitchcock
4. *Citizen Kane* (1941), director Orson Welles
5. *Lawrence of Arabia* (1962), director David Lean
6. *Manhattan* (1979), director Woody Allen
7. *Gone With the Wind* (1939), director Victor Fleming
8. *Chinatown* (1974), director Roman Polanski
9. *The Man Who Shot Liberty Valance* (1962), director John Ford
10. *City Lights* (1931), director Charles Chaplin

Readers' Picks (set R)

1. *Star Wars* (1977), director George Lucas
2. *The Godfather* (1972), director Francis Ford Coppola
3. *Pulp Fiction* (1994), director Quentin Tarantino
4. *Casablanca* (1942), director Michael Curtiz
5. *Gone With the Wind* (1939), director Victor Fleming
6. *Raiders of the Lost Ark* (1981), director Steven Spielberg
7. *Schindler's List* (1993), director Steven Spielberg
8. *Citizen Kane* (1941), director Orson Welles
9. *The Empire Strikes Back* (1980), director Irvin Kershner
10. *It's a Wonderful Life* (1946), director Frank Capra

(a) Find $C \cap R$. (b) How many movies are in both lists?

(c) Find the set of directors in the intersection of both lists.

Solution

(a) $C \cap R$ is the set of all elements common to C and R, that is,

{*Casablanca, Citizen Kane, Gone With the Wind*}

(b) There are three movies that are in both lists.

(c) The set of directors in the intersection of both lists is

{Michael Curtiz, Francis Ford Coppola, Orson Welles, Victor Fleming}

2.2 EXERCISES

A Intersections and Unions

In problems 1–8, let set $A = \{1, 2, 3, 4, 5\}$, $B = \{1, 3, 4, 6\}$, and $C = \{1, 6, 7\}$. Find the following:

1. a. $A \cap B$ b. $A \cap C$ c. $B \cap C$
2. a. $A \cup B$ b. $A \cup C$ c. $B \cup C$
3. a. $A \cap (B \cup C)$ b. $A \cup (B \cap C)$
4. a. $(A \cap B) \cup C$ b. $(A \cap B) \cup (A \cap C)$
5. $A \cup (B \cup C)$
6. $(A \cup B) \cap (A \cup C)$
7. $A \cap (B \cap C)$
8. $(A \cup B) \cap C$

In problems 9 and 10, let $A = \{\{a, b\}, c\}$, $B = \{a, b, c\}$, and $C = \{a, b\}$. Find the following:

9. a. $A \cap B$ b. $A \cap C$
10. a. $A \cup B$ b. $A \cup C$

In problems 11–14, let $A = \{\{a, b\}, \{a, b, c\}, a, b\}$ and $B = \{\{a, b\}, a, b, c, \{b, c\}\}$. Which of the given statements are correct?

11. a. $\{b\} \subseteq \{A \cap B\}$ b. $\{b\} \in (A \cap B)$
12. a. $\{a, b\} \subseteq (A \cap B)$ b. $\{a, b\} \in (A \cap B)$
13. a. $\{a, b, c\} \subseteq (A \cup B)$ b. $\{a, b, c\} \in (A \cup B)$
14. a. $c \subseteq (A \cap B)$ b. $c \in (A \cap B)$

B Complement of a Set

The sets $\mathcal{U} = \{a, b, c, d, e, f\}$, $A = \{a, c, e\}$, $B = \{b, d, e, f\}$, and $C = \{a, b, d, f\}$ will be used in problems 15–26. Find each specified set.

15. a. A' b. B'
16. a. $A' \cap B'$ b. $(A \cap B)'$
17. a. $(A \cup B)'$ b. $A' \cup B'$
18. a. $(A \cup B) \cap C'$ b. $(A \cup B)' \cap C$
19. a. $(A \cap B) \cup C'$ b. $C \cup (A \cap B)'$
20. a. $A' \cup B$ b. $A \cup B'$
21. a. $A' \cap B$ b. $A \cap B'$
22. a. $A' \cap (A \cup B')$ b. $A \cup (A \cap B')$
23. a. $C' \cup (A \cap B)'$ b. $C' \cup (A \cup B)'$
24. a. $(C \cup B)' \cap A$ b. $(C \cup B) \cap A'$
25. a. $\mathcal{U} - A$ b. $\mathcal{U} - B$
26. a. $A - B$ b. $B - A$

C Difference of Two Sets

In problems 27 and 28, let $\mathcal{U} = \{1, 2, 3, 4, 5\}$, $A = \{2, 3, 4\}$, and $B = \{1, 4, 5\}$. Find each specified set.

27. a. B' b. $\mathcal{U} - B$
28. a. $A - B$ b. $B - A$

In problems 29–38, $\mathcal{U}$ is some universal set of which A is a subset. In each case find the indicated set in terms of A, $\mathcal{U}$, or $\varnothing$ alone.

29. $\varnothing'$
30. $\mathcal{U}'$
31. $A \cap \varnothing$
32. $A \cap A$
33. $A \cap \mathcal{U}$
34. $A \cup \varnothing$
35. $A \cap A'$
36. $A \cup A'$
37. $(A')'$
38. $A \cup A$
39. If $A = \{1, 2, 3\}$, $B = \{2, 3, 4\}$, and $C = \{1, 3, 5\}$, find the smallest set that will serve as a universal set for A, B, and C.

D Applications

Problems 40–45 refer to the following data, the results of an attempt to analyze factors in popularity between members of the same sex and between members of opposite sexes. A psychologist asked 676 college men and women to consider a few persons whom they liked and to tell why they liked those persons.

Traits Men Liked in Women (M_w)	Traits Women Liked in Men (W_m)
Beauty	Intelligence
Intelligence	Consideration
Cheerfulness	Kindliness
Congeniality	Cheerfulness

Traits Men Liked in Men (M_m)	Traits Women Liked in Women (W_w)
Intelligence	Intelligence
Cheerfulness	Cheerfulness
Friendliness	Helpfulness
Congeniality	Loyalty

40. Find the smallest set that will serve as a universal set for M_w, W_m, M_m, *and* W_w.
41. Find the set of traits that are mentioned only once.
42. Find $M_w \cap W_w$.
43. Find $M_w \cap M_m$.
44. What set of traits is common to M_m and M_w?
45. Name the traits that are common to all four of the sets; that is, find $M_w \cap M_m \cap W_w \cap W_m$.

In an article in the Harvard Business Review, 606 participants reported on 17 specific changes in their bosses' behaviors from one year to the next. Here are some of the traits that were most frequently mentioned in each of these years:

First Year	Second Year
Encourages suggestions.	Is self-aware.
Sets goals with me.	Listens carefully.
Gets me to have high goals.	Follows up on action.
Listens carefully.	Gets me to have high goals.
Is aware of others.	Encourages suggestions.
Is self-aware.	Sets goals with me.

Let S_1 be the set of traits mentioned in the first year; let S_2 be the set of traits mentioned in the second year.

46. Find $S_1 \cap S_2$, the set of traits mentioned in both years.
47. What traits were mentioned only once?
48. Find the smallest set that will serve as a universal set for S_1 and S_2.

49. Find S_1' relative to the universal set found in problem 48.

50. Find S_2' relative to the universal set found in problem 48.

Problems 51–62 refer to this diagram.

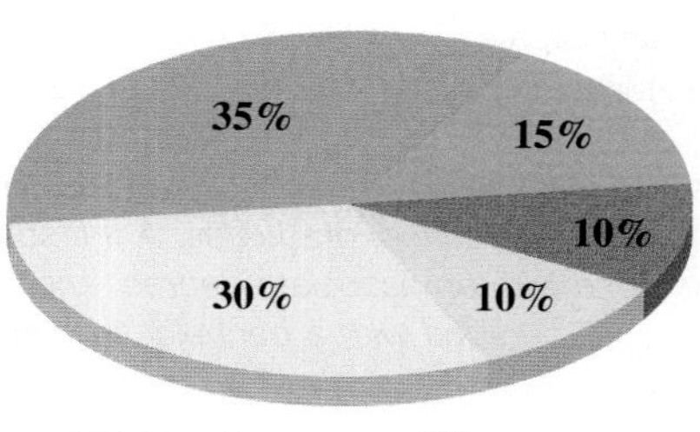

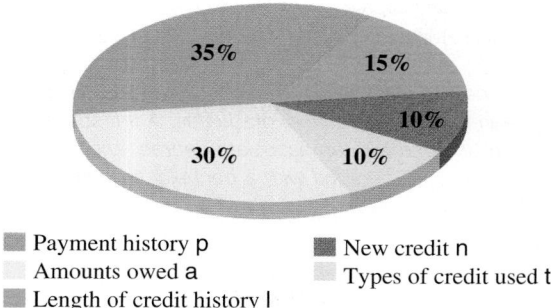

Payment history p
Amounts owed a
Length of credit history l
New credit n
Types of credit used t

FICO® Credit Scores are calculated from the set of five categories of credit data in your credit report.

Source: http://www.myfico.com.

51. Write the set of all five categories in your credit report.

52. Write the set of categories C that actually use the word "credit" in the description.

53. What is C'?

54. Write the set of categories M that account for more than 30% of your score.

55. Write the set of categories H that account for the highest portion of your score.

56. What is the set of categories that account for less than 15% of your score?

57. What is H'.

58. What is $H \cup C$?

59. What is $(H \cup C)'$?

60. What is $H \cap C$?

61. What is $(H \cap C)'$?

62. What is $H' \cup C'$?

*Which Web sites do you visit? Are they the most **popular** or the most **visited**? The two lists show both the 10 most **popular** Web sites and the 10 most **visited** Web sites and will be used in problems 63–66.*

1. Google.com	1. Facebook.com
2. Facebook.com	2. Google.com
3. Youtube.com	3. Twitter
4. Yahoo.com	4. Live.com
5. Live.com	5. MSN.com
6. Blogspot.com	6. MySpace.com
7. Baidu.com	7. Blogger.com
8. Wikipedia.org	8. Wikipedia.org
9. Twitter.com	9. Yahoo.com
10. Qq.com	10. YouTube.com

Source: http://mostpopularwebsites.net/, (left column) and www.lovetoknow.com/top10/most-visited-websites.html (right column).

63. Find the set of all names that appear only once.

64. Find the set of all names that have the same ranking on both lists.

65. If the universal set consists of the names on both lists and M is the set of names on the first list, what is M'?

66. If the universal set consists of the names on both lists and L is the set of names on the second list, what is L'?

In problems 67–76, refer to the chart. Use the name of the manufacturer BMW, Ford, and so on, to identify the set using the given description. For example, if you want a car with an annual fuel cost of $1345, the corresponding set is {Nissan, Toyota (Camry)}.

	Eng Size/ Cylinders	MPG/ City/Hwy	Annual Fuel Cost
	MIDSIZE CARS		
BMW			
ActiveHybrid 7L	4.4/8	17/24	$2,408
FORD			
Fusion Hybrid FWD	2.5/4	41/36	$1,137
LEXUS			
LS 600h L	5.0/8	19/23	$2,408
LINCOLN			
MKZ Hybrid FWD	2.5/4	41/36	$1,137
MERCURY			
Milan Hybrid FWD	2.5/4	41/36	$1,137
NISSAN			
Altima Hybrid	2.5/4	33/33	$1,345
TOYOTA			
Camry Hybrid	2.4/4	31/35	$1,345
Prius	1.8/4	51/48	$888

Source: http://www.fueleconomy.gov/feg/FEG2011.pdf.

Find the set of cars with the following specifications:

67. A 2.4-liter engine size (second column)

68. A 41-mpg fuel economy in the city

69. The highest fuel economy in the city

70. The lowest fuel economy in the city

71. The best fuel economy on the highway

72. The largest engine (second column)

73. The smallest engine

74. The lowest annual fuel cost

75. The highest annual fuel cost

76. The 2.5 engine with the lowest annual fuel cost

IN OTHER WORDS

In problems 77–80, diagrams are given showing certain relationships between sets A and B represented by the circular areas. State these relationships in your own words, and find sets A and B that satisfy the conditions shown in the diagrams. Hint: In problem 77, A may be a set of cats and B a set of dogs.

77.
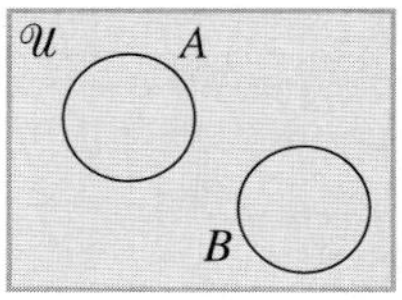

78.
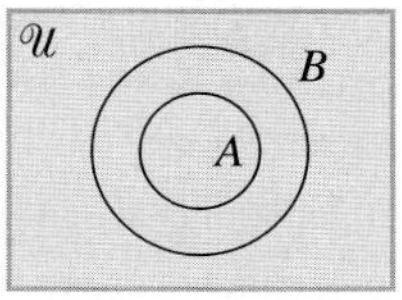

79.
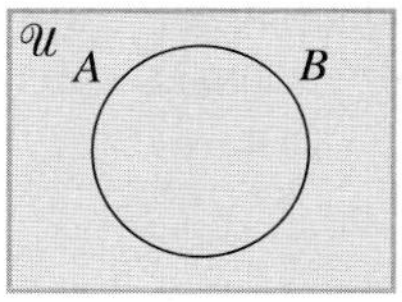

80.
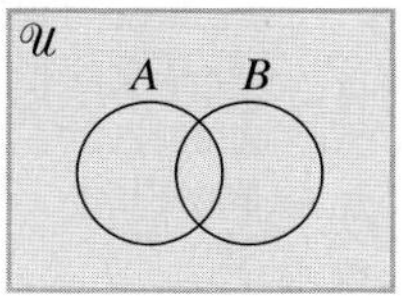

USING YOUR KNOWLEDGE

The ideas of sets, subsets, unions, intersections, and complements are used in zoology and in other branches of science. Here are some typical applications.

81. A zoology book lists the following characteristics of giraffes and okapis:

Giraffes	Okapis
Tall	Short
Long neck	Short neck
Long tongue	Long tongue
Skin-covered horns	Skin-covered horns
Native to Africa	Native to Africa

Let G be the set of characteristics of giraffes, and let O be the set of characteristics of okapis.

a. Find $G \cap O$.

b. What set of characteristics is common to both okapis and giraffes?

c. Find the smallest set $\mathcal{U}$ that will serve as a universal set for G and O.

d. Find G'. e. Find O'.

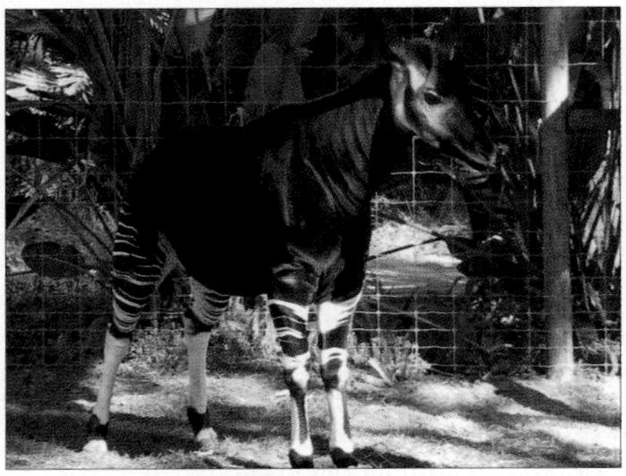

© Photo by Alyssa Norton

Giraffes and Okapis have many common characteristics.

Problems 82–87 refer to the following table. The table shows the number of heavy alcohol users (five or more drinks per occasion on five or more days in the past month) by age group.

Age	Male	Female
12–17	224,000	51,000
18–25	2,192,000	921,000
26–34	2,174,000	603,000
35 and older	3,293,000	685,000

Source: U.S. Department of Health and Human Services.

Let M be the set of males, F be the set of females, A be the set of persons 12–17 years old, B be the set of persons 18–25 years old, C be the set of persons 26–34 years old, and D be the set of persons 35 and older.

82. How many elements are in the set $M \cap D$?

83. How many elements are in the set $F \cap D$?

84. How many elements are in the set $(F \cup M) \cap D$?

85. Which category has the fewest members? Which set corresponds to that category?

86. Describe the set $M \cup F$.

87. Describe the set $M \cap F$.

Is it worth it to go to college? The following table shows the average annual earnings by degree (high school, associate, bachelor's).

Education	Male (M)	Female (F)
High school	$43,493	$31,666
Associate degree	$54,830	$39,935
Bachelor's degree	$94,206	$60,293

Let M be the set of males, F the set of females, H the set of average earnings of high school graduates, A the set of average earnings of persons with an associate degree, and B the set of average earnings of persons with a bachelor's degree. In problems 88–94, find the average earnings for the persons in the following sets:

88. $M \cap B$

89. $F \cap B$

90. $A \cap M$

91. $A \cap F$

92. Which set has the lowest earnings?

93. Describe the set $H \cap M$.

94. Describe the set $M \cup F$.

Source: Statistical Abstract of the United States.

COLLABORATIVE LEARNING

Form three groups of students: the Asteroids, the Comets, and the Intergalactics. Now examine the table below very carefully. Cut out each of the properties (labels) from the table. The Asteroids are to select the properties that pertain to asteroids only, the Comets select the properties that pertain to comets only, and the Intergalactics select the properties that pertain to both comets and asteroids.

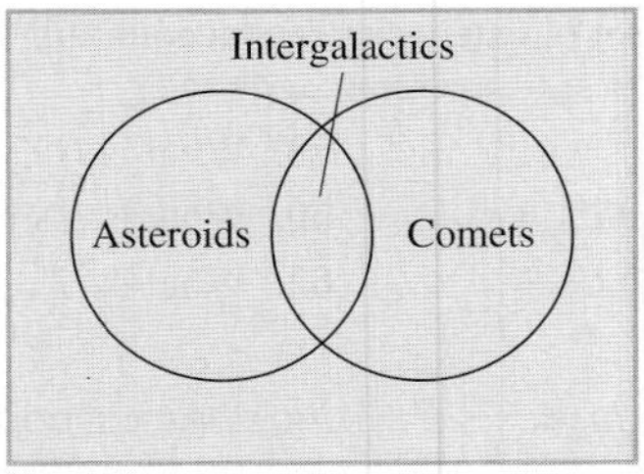

To get some information about the topics in the table, consult an online encyclopedia (MSN Encarta) or try http://tinyurl.com/dt9jg.

Take a large piece of paper and draw a diagram like the one above. The Asteroids should paste (glue) the properties pertaining to asteroids only in the proper region, the Comets should paste the properties pertaining to comets only in the proper region, and the Intergalactics should paste the properties common to both in the proper region.

Want to see the answer? Go to www.enchantedlearning.com/subjects/astronomy/activities/venn/cometasteroid/answers.shtml.

Made of frozen ice, gas, and dust	Have a long gas tail	Also known as planetoids
Made of rock and/or metal	Have a long dust tail	Surrounded by hydrogen cloud
Orbit the Sun	Have a long ion tail	Have no atmosphere
Ceres is the biggest	Have no tail	Part of our solar system
Halley is one	Highly elliptical orbit	Sungrazers are ones that crash into the Sun
Some come close to the Earth	Most orbit between Mars and Jupiter	Some have hit the Earth

2.3 Venn Diagrams

GETTING STARTED

OBJECTIVES

A. Use Venn diagrams to visualize relationships between sets.
B. Use Venn diagrams to verify the equality of sets.
C. Solve problems using Venn diagrams.

BLOOD TYPES AND VENN DIAGRAMS

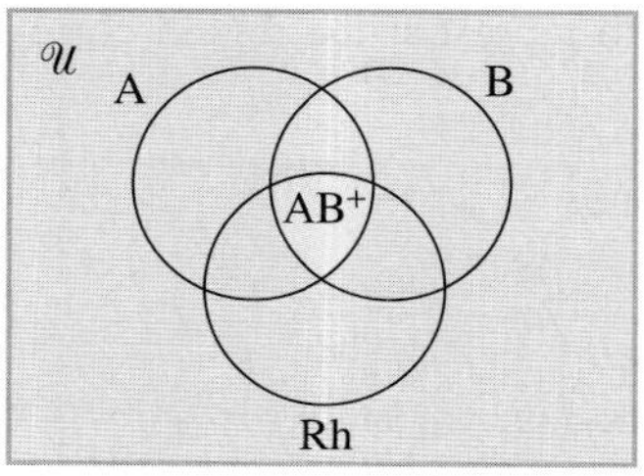

FIGURE 2.5

Did you know that there are many different types and groups of human blood? Blood is classified by indicating which of three particular antigens A, B, and Rh are present. If we represent the set of persons carrying antigens A, B, and Rh by circles enclosed in a rectangle representing the set $\mathcal{U}$ of all persons, the result shown is called a **Venn diagram, Euler circle,** or **Euler diagram.** A person can be A or B or AB depending on which antigens the person has; a type O person has neither A nor B antigen. A person is Rh positive if the person has the Rh antigen and Rh negative otherwise. Plus and minus signs are used to indicate positive and negative blood types. Thus, AB^+ means that a person has all three antigens, as shown in Figure 2.5. You can learn more about the distribution of blood types in the Using Your Knowledge section.

What else can we do with Venn diagrams? We can show that the *commutative, associative,* and *distributive laws,* familiar from arithmetic, apply to sets by using Venn diagrams to verify that:

$$\left.\begin{aligned} A \cup B &= B \cup A \\ A \cap B &= B \cap A \end{aligned}\right\}$$

Commutative laws (You can take the union or intersection of two sets in a different ***order*** and get the same answer.)

$$\left.\begin{aligned} A \cup (B \cup C) &= (A \cup B) \cup C \\ A \cap (B \cap C) &= (A \cap B) \cap C \end{aligned}\right\}$$

Associative laws (You can ***group*** sets differently when taking unions or intersections and get the same answer.)

$$\left.\begin{aligned} A \cup (B \cap C) &= (A \cup B) \cap (A \cup C) \\ A \cap (B \cup C) &= (A \cap B) \cup (A \cap C) \end{aligned}\right\}$$

Distributive laws

We verify these laws in problems 30–32 of Exercises 2.3.

The ideas of sets, subsets, and the operations used to combine sets can be illustrated graphically by the use of diagrams called *Venn diagrams,* after John Venn (1834–1923), the English mathematician and logician who invented them. In these diagrams, we represent the universal set $\mathcal{U}$ by a rectangle, and we use regions enclosed by simple curves (usually circles) drawn inside the rectangle to represent the sets being considered. For example, if A is a subset of a universal set $\mathcal{U}$, we can represent this universal set by the set of points in the interior of the rectangle shown in Figure 2.6. The interior of the circle represents the set of points in A, whereas the set of points inside the rectangle and outside the circle represents the set A'. Obviously, closed figures other than circles can be used to represent the points of the set A. Figure 2.7 shows a Venn diagram in which A is represented by the points inside a triangle.

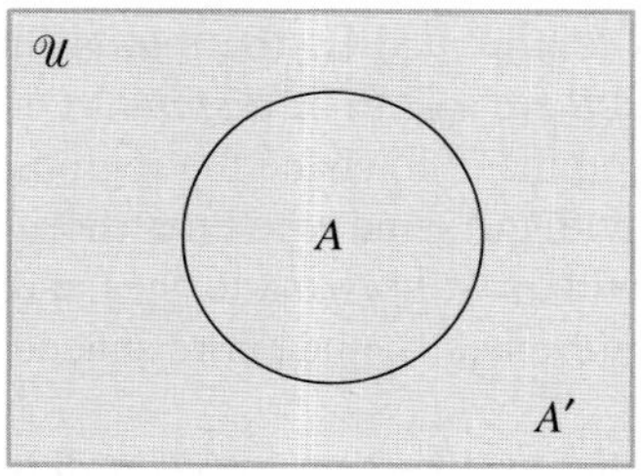

FIGURE 2.6

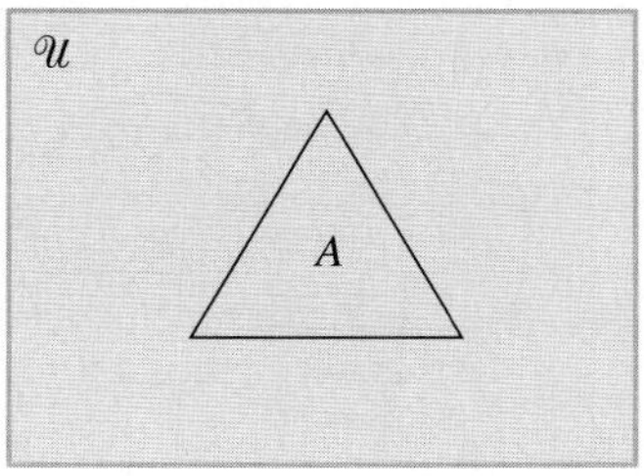

FIGURE 2.7

A Drawing Venn Diagrams

Venn diagrams are illustrated in the following examples:

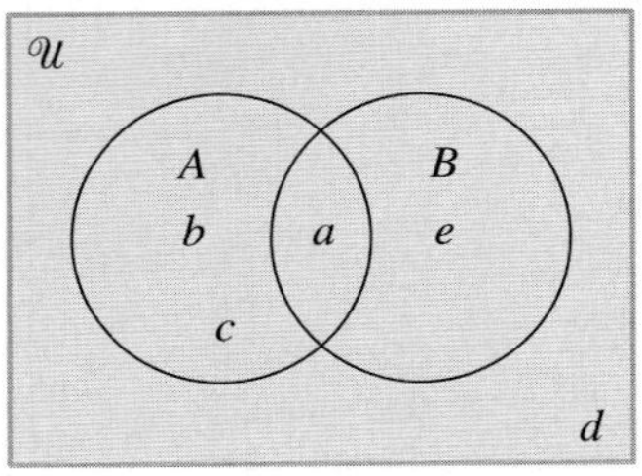

FIGURE 2.8

EXAMPLE 1 Drawing Venn Diagrams

Let $\mathcal{U} = \{a, b, c, d, e\}$, $A = \{a, b, c\}$, and $B = \{a, e\}$. Draw a Venn diagram to illustrate this situation.

Solution

Draw a rectangle whose interior points represent the set $\mathcal{U}$ and two circles whose interior points represent the points in A and B. The completed diagram appears in Figure 2.8 at the left. Note that a is in both A and B because $A \cap B = \{a\}$. Also, d is the only element that is in $\mathcal{U}$, but not in A or in B, so $(A \cup B)' = \{d\}$.

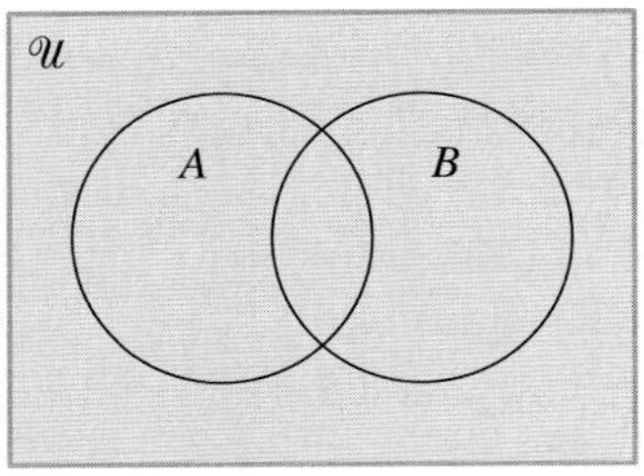

FIGURE 2.9

Intersections and unions of sets can be represented by Venn diagrams. For example, given two sets A and B, you can draw a Venn diagram to represent the region corresponding to $A \cap B$. Proceed as follows:

1. As usual, the points inside the rectangle represent $\mathcal{U}$, and the points inside the two circles represent A and B (Figure 2.9). Note that A and B overlap to allow for the possibility that A and B have points in common.
2. Shade the set A using vertical lines (Figure 2.10).
3. Shade the set B using horizontal lines (Figure 2.11). The region in which the lines *intersect* (cross-hatched in diagram) corresponds to $A \cap B$.

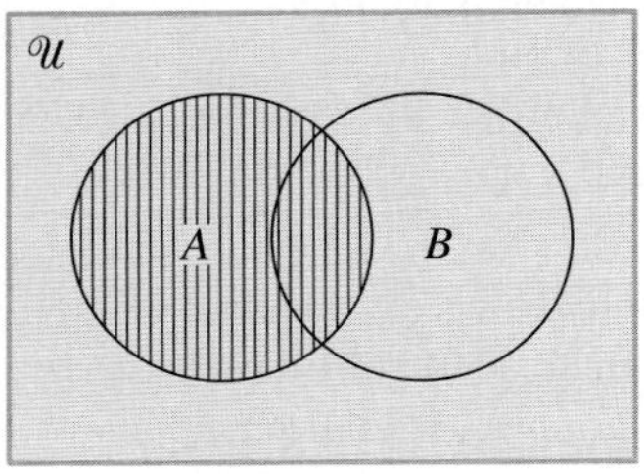

FIGURE 2.10

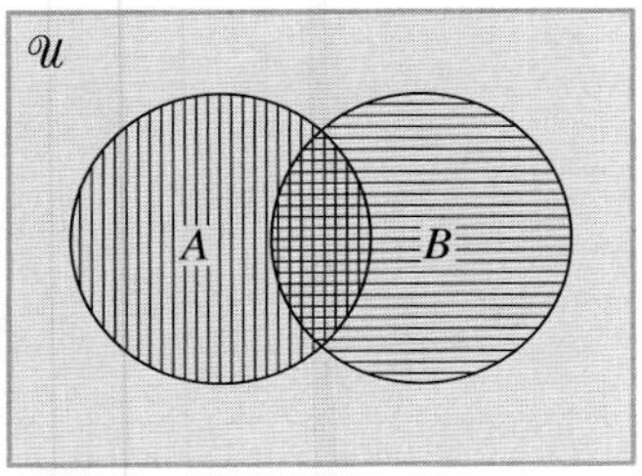

FIGURE 2.11

EXAMPLE 2 Venn Diagrams for Complements and Intersections

Draw a Venn diagram to represent the set $A' \cap B$.

Solution

Proceed as in Example 1.

1. Draw a rectangle and two circles as in Figure 2.12.
2. Shade the points of A' (the points in $\mathcal{U}$ and outside A) with vertical lines.
3. Shade the points of B with horizontal lines. Then $A' \cap B$ is represented by the cross-hatched region in Figure 2.12.

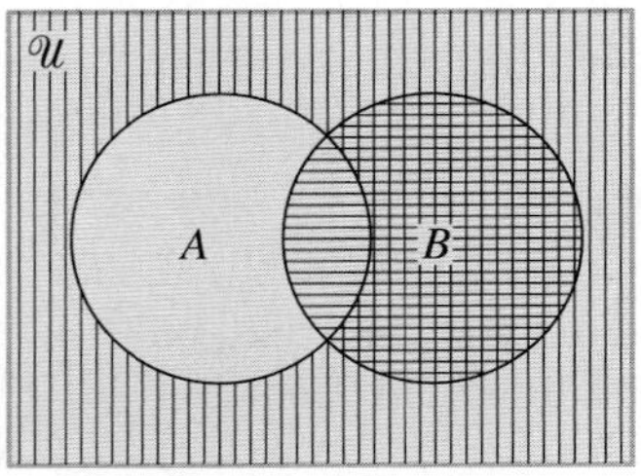

FIGURE 2.12 $A' \cap B$

We may associate with the formation of $A \cap B$ a command to shade the region representing the set to the left of the symbol $\cap$ one way and the region representing the set to the right of the symbol another way. For example, in finding $A \cap B$, because A is to the left of $\cap$, we shade region A vertically, and because B is to the right of the symbol $\cap$, we shade region B horizontally. As before, $A \cap B$ is represented by the region in which the lines intersect. (Recall that if $A \cap B = \varnothing$, A and B are said to be *disjoint.*) On the other hand, the operation $\cup$ may be thought of as a command to shade the regions representing the sets to the left and right of the symbol $\cup$ with the same type lines (horizontal or vertical). Thus, in finding $A \cup B$, we shade A with, say, horizontal lines and shade B in the same way. The union of A and B will be represented by the entire shaded region (see Figure 2.13).

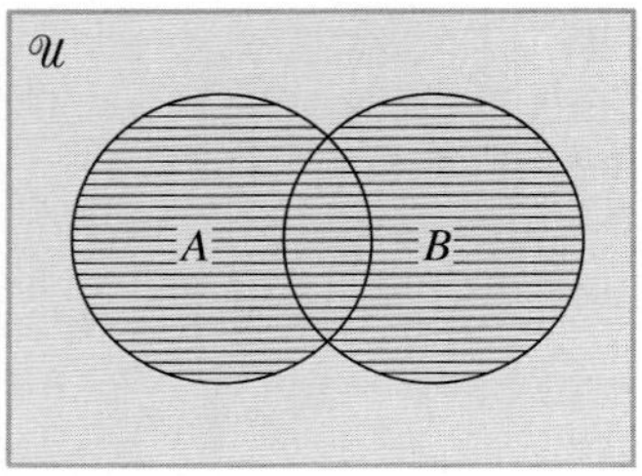

FIGURE 2.13 $A \cup B$

A somewhat simpler procedure can be adopted in the construction of Venn diagrams. As before, we start with a rectangle and two circles representing the sets $\mathcal{U}$, A,

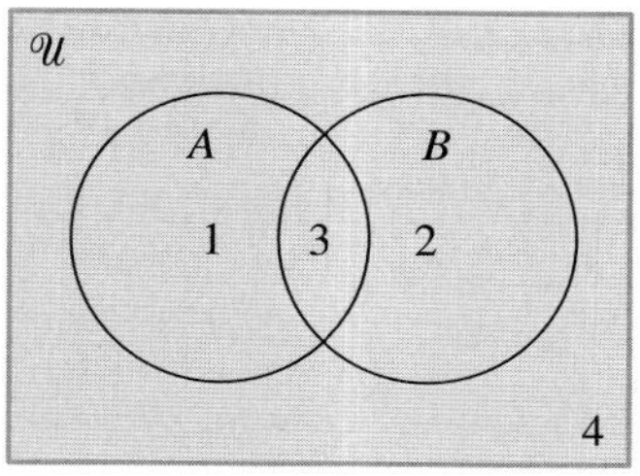

FIGURE 2.14

and B, respectively. We then number the four regions into which the universal set is divided (see Figure 2.14). *Note:* The numbering of the regions is completely arbitrary. By referring to the figure, we can identify the various sets as follows:

$A \cap B$ is the set of elements common to A and B—represented by region 3.
$A' \cap B$ is the set of elements not in A and in B—represented by region 2.
$A \cap B'$ is the set of elements in A and not in B—represented by region 1.
$A \cup B$ is the set of elements in A or in B or in both A and B—represented by regions 1, 2, and 3.
A' is the set of elements that are not in A—represented by regions 2 and 4.
B' is the set of elements that are not in B—represented by regions 1 and 4.

B Verifying Equality

Venn diagrams are convenient for analyzing problems involving sets as long as there are not too many subsets of $\mathcal{U}$ to be considered. For example, referring to Figure 2.14, we note that $A \cap B$ is the set of points in A and in B (region 3), but $B \cap A$ is the set of points in B and in A (region 3). Hence, these two sets refer to the same region, and we can verify that $A \cap B = B \cap A$.

We now use this technique to verify one of De Morgan's laws:

$$(A \cap B)' = A' \cup B'$$

PROBLEMSOLVING

Verifying One of De Morgan's Laws

① **Read** the problem.

Verify that $(A \cap B)' = A' \cup B'$.

② **Select** the unknown.

We actually have two unknowns: $(A \cap B)'$ and $A' \cup B'$.

③ **Think** of a plan.

The technique used to verify equality consists of showing that the regions corresponding to the sets $(A \cap B)'$ and $A' \cup B'$, respectively, are the same. To do this, we start with a diagram similar to the one in Figure 2.14.

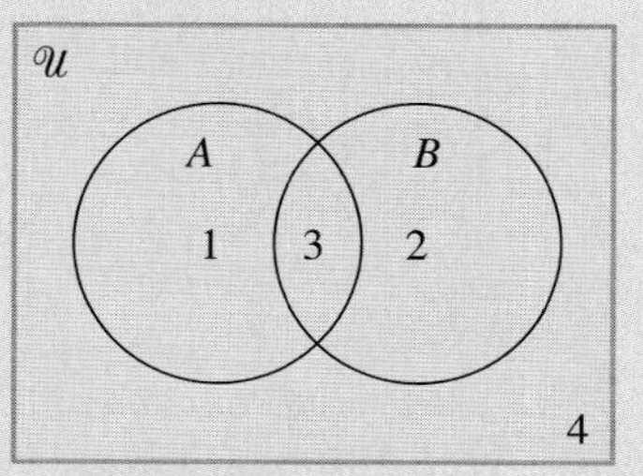

④ **Use** the techniques you are studying to carry out the plan.

The region corresponding to $A \cap B$ is region 3. Thus, the regions corresponding to $(A \cap B)'$, the complement of $(A \cap B)$, are all the regions that *are not* region 3, that is, regions 1, 2, and 4. Thus, $(A \cap B)'$ is represented by regions 1, 2, and 4.

Now, let us find the regions for $A' \cup B'$.

A' consists of the regions outside of A, that is, 2 and 4.
B' consists of the regions outside of B, that is, 1 and 4.
The union of regions 2, 4 and 1, 4, is $A' \cup B'$ and consists of regions 1, 2, and 4. Since $(A \cap B)'$ and $A' \cup B'$ both consist of regions 1, 2, and 4, we have $(A \cap B)' = A' \cup B'$

⑤ **Verify** the answer.

You can try some examples to verify that the result is true.

Try Example 3 Now

Cover the solution, write your own solution, and then check your work.

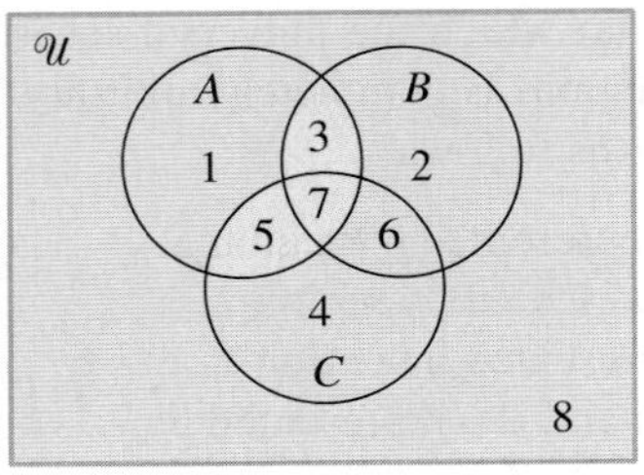

FIGURE 2.15

Venn diagrams can be used to illustrate three or more sets where the diagrams are drawn so the three sets overlap, creating eight different regions, as shown in Figure 2.15. Here are some sets and their corresponding regions in Figure 2.15.

$A \cap B \cap C$	Region 7	$A \cap B$	Regions 3 and 7
$A \cap C$	Regions 5 and 7	$B \cap C$	Regions 6 and 7
$A \cup B$	Regions 1, 2, 3, 5, 6, and 7	$A \cup C$	Regions 1, 3, 4, 5, 6, and 7
$B \cup C$	Regions 2, 3, 4, 5, 6, and 7		

EXAMPLE 3 Using Venn Diagrams to Verify Equality

If A, B, and C are subsets of $\mathcal{U}$, use the preceding method to verify the **distributive law,** $A \cap (B \cup C) = (A \cap B) \cup (A \cap C)$.

Solution

We have drawn the rectangle and the circles representing the sets $\mathcal{U}$, A, B, and C and numbered regions 1, 2, 3, 4, 5, 6, 7, and 8 in Figure 2.15. Note that when you had 2 sets, you used $2^2 = 4$ regions. In this example, you have 3 sets; hence, you need $2^3 = 8$ regions.

First consider $A \cap (B \cup C)$.

(a) A is represented by regions 1, 3, 5, and 7.

(b) $B \cup C$ is represented by regions 2, 3, 4, 5, 6, and 7.

(c) $A \cap (B \cup C)$ is therefore represented by the regions common to the two sets in parts (a) and (b), that is, by regions 3, 5, and 7.

Next consider $(A \cap B) \cup (A \cap C)$.

(d) $A \cap B$ is represented by the regions common to the circles representing A and B, that is, by regions 3 and 7.

(e) $A \cap C$ is represented by the regions common to the circles representing A and C, that is, by regions 5 and 7.

(f) $(A \cap B) \cup (A \cap C)$ is therefore represented by all the regions found in parts (d) and (e), that is, by regions 3, 5, and 7.

Because $A \cap (B \cup C)$ and $(A \cap B) \cup (A \cap C)$ are both represented by regions 3, 5, and 7, you see that

$$A \cap (B \cup C) = (A \cap B) \cup (A \cap C)$$

In problems 30, 31, and 34, you will verify the *commutative,* the *associative,* and *De Morgan's laws.*

C Applications

As we saw in Getting Started, human blood is grouped according to the presence of three antigens, A, B, and Rh. Suppose that we want to use a Venn diagram to visualize all the different blood groups. We begin with three circles representing the sets of persons having antigens A, B, and Rh, respectively (Figure 2.16). As we can see, there are eight different regions, so there are eight different blood groups. Blood groups inside the set Rh will carry a plus sign (+), and those outside Rh will carry a minus sign (−). Blood with neither the A nor the B antigen will be labeled type O.

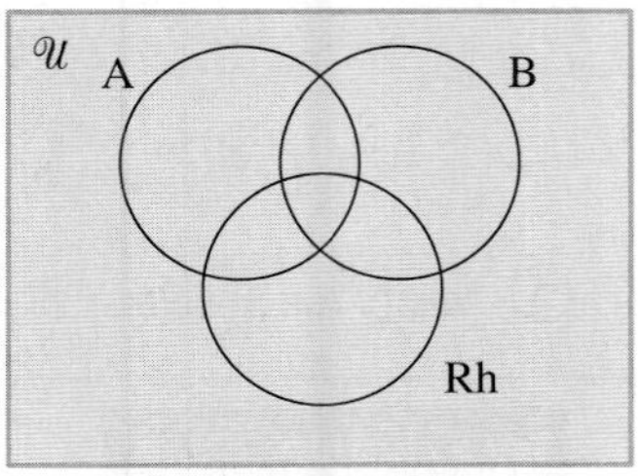

FIGURE 2.16

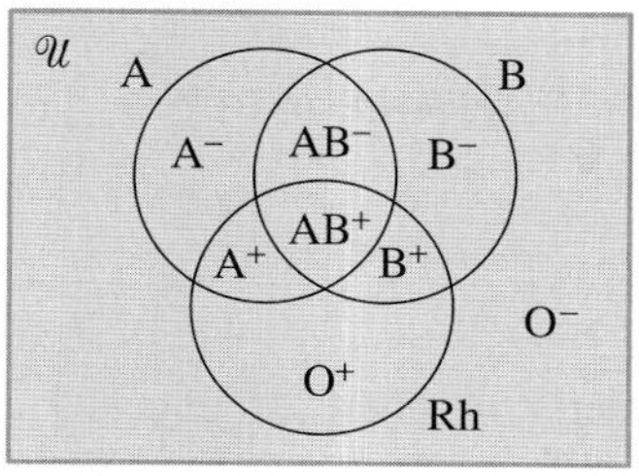

FIGURE 2.17 Human blood types

EXAMPLE 4 Identifying Blood Groups

Draw a Venn diagram to identify all possible blood groups.

Solution

The eight possible groupings of blood are A^-, A^+, B^-, B^+, AB^-, AB^+, O^-, and O^+, where A^+ means that the person has both A and Rh antigens, A^- means that the person has antigen A but not Rh, and similarly for the remaining groupings. Note in Figure 2.17 that the circle labeled A represents the set of persons having the A antigen and A^+, A^-, AB^+, or AB^- blood, and likewise for the other two circles. Read more about blood types in the Using Your Knowledge section.

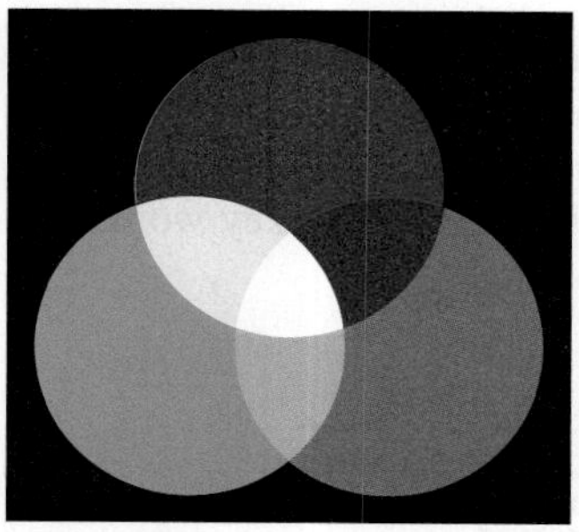

FIGURE 2.18

EXAMPLE 5 Colors and Venn Diagrams

Do you have an RGB monitor or television set? What does RGB mean, anyway? It means "Red, Green, and Blue," the additive primary colors. Suppose that you make a Venn diagram consisting of three circles, one red, one green, and one blue, as shown in Figure 2.18.

(a) Which color is the intersection of the three circles?

(b) The secondary colors are found by blending two of the primary colors. Name the secondary colors of light and their primary components.

Solution

(a) The intersection of the three circles is white.

(b) The secondary colors are yellow (red and green), magenta (red and blue), and cyan (green and blue).

EXAMPLE 6 Health Care Expenses

Annual health care expenses for one-half of the U.S. population totaled less than \$800 per individual, but expenses were far higher among the elderly, (age 65+ (E)), the obese (O), and people who identified themselves as unhealthy (H′), groups that together represented 33% of the population but accounted for 60% of health care spending. How much was spent on those groups? About \$2300 per individual! Figure 2.19 shows the percent of people in different categories.

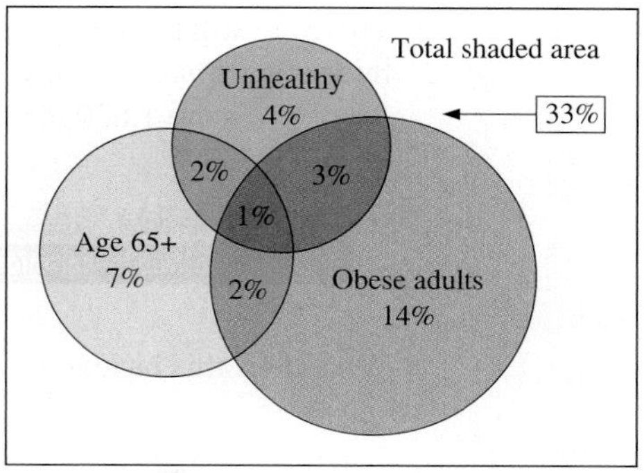

Source: Department of Health and Human Services, Medical Expenditure Panel Survey http://prescriptions.blogs.nytimes.com/tag/graphic.

FIGURE 2.19

(a) Using the sets E, O, and H′, what set is represented by the total shaded area?

(b) What percent of the people are in the shaded area?

(c) What percent of the people are unhealthy?

(d) What percent of the people are in the set $O \cap E \cap H'$ (elderly and obese and unhealthy)?

Solution

(a) The shaded area represents the people who are elderly or obese or unhealthy, $E \cup O \cup H'$.

(b) The total shaded area represents **33%** of the people (check it out by adding the percents).

(c) The sum of all the percents inside set H' is 4% + 2% + 1% + 3% = **10%**.

(d) The intersection of O, E, and H' has 1% of the people.

Have you done an Internet search lately? The computer uses concepts of set operations in order to complete the search. For example, suppose you want to buy a car. First, you must go to the Web and select a *search engine* (a *program* that searches documents for specified *key words* and returns a list of the documents that contain the key words). In this illustration, we use Google. We write the word *car* as shown.

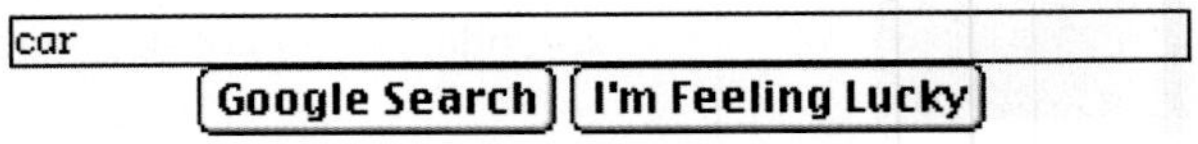

© Google

Press Google Search.

The bar shows how many results (hits) you have—1,320,000,000. Too many! In order to decrease the number of results, we can state the size of the car that you want to purchase. We indicate *midsize* by typing the word *midsize* next to the word *car* and then pressing the Return key. The results have decreased to 2,490,000.

There are still too many results, so we add the category *American*. We indicate *American* by writing *American* next to *car* and *midsize* and pressing the Return key. Now we are down to a mere 1,830,000 Web pages or documents that mention *car midsize American*.

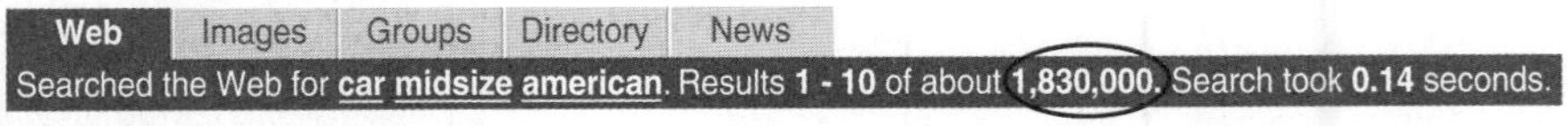

What does this have to do with Venn diagrams? This is what is happening.

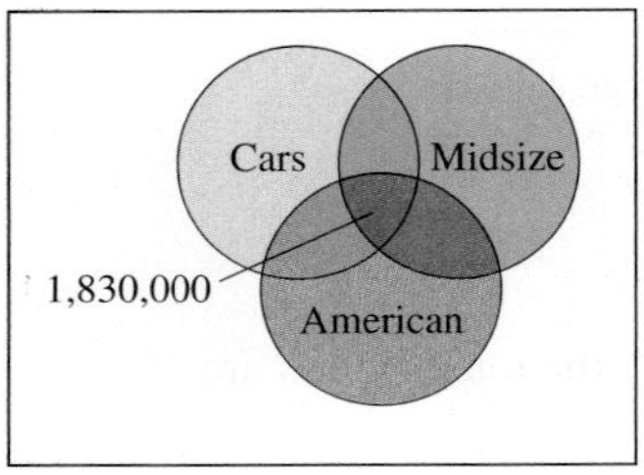

EXAMPLE 7 Venn Diagrams and the Web

Make a Venn diagram of the sets we obtained at each of the steps in the process we just described. The first set contains the Web pages that mention *cars,* as shown in yellow. The second set contains the Web pages that mention *midsize* cars (blue). Finally, the third category is *American* (purple) and the *intersection* of the three regions has 1,830,000 Web pages that mention *car midsize American.*

2.3 EXERCISES

A Drawing Venn Diagrams

1. Draw a Venn diagram to illustrate the relationships among the sets $\mathcal{U} = \{1, 2, 3, 4, 5\}$, $A = \{1, 2\}$, and $B = \{1, 3, 5\}$.
2. Do the same as in problem 1 for the sets $\mathcal{U} = \{a, b, c, d, e, f\}$, $A = \{a, b, c\}$, and $B = \{d, e, f\}$.

In problems 3–8, draw a Venn diagram (see Figure 2.14) and shade the region representing each specified set.

3. $A \cap B'$
4. $A' \cup B'$
5. $(A \cup B) - (A \cap B)$
6. $A \cup B'$
7. $A' \cap B'$
8. $(A \cup B) - A$

In problems 9–17, use the numbered regions of the diagram below to identify each specified set.

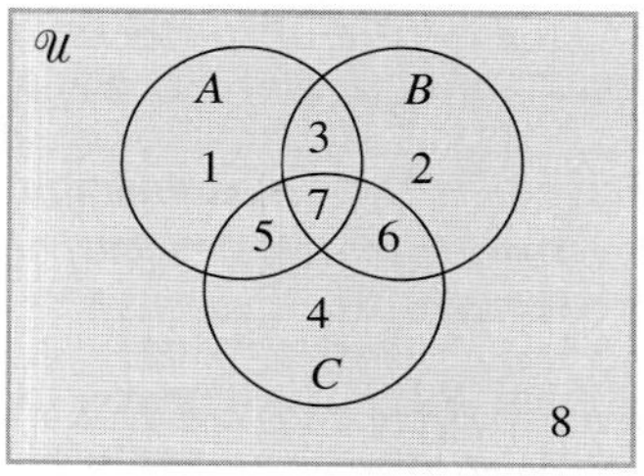

9. $A - (B \cup C)$
10. $C \cap (A \cup B)$
11. $(A \cap B \cap C) - (A \cap B)$
12. $(A \cap B') \cup (A \cap C')$
13. $(A \cup B') \cap C$
14. $(A \cup B) - C$
15. $(A \cap B') \cup C$
16. $B \cap C' \cap A$
17. $(A \cup B \cup C)'$

In problems 18–25, draw a Venn diagram to illustrate each specified set.

18. $\{x \mid x \in A \text{ or } x \in B\}$
19. $\{x \mid x \notin A \text{ or } x \notin B\}$
20. $\{x \mid x \in A \text{ and } x \notin B\}$
21. $\{x \mid x \in A \text{ and } (x \in B \text{ and } x \notin C)\}$
22. $\{x \mid x \in A \textit{ and } x \in B\}$
23. $\{x \mid x \notin A \textit{ and } x \in B\}$
24. $\{x \mid x \in A \textit{ or } (x \in B \text{ or } x \in C)\}$
25. $\{x \mid x \notin A \textit{ and } (x \in B \text{ and } x \in C)\}$

B Verifying Equality

In problems 26–29, draw a Venn diagram that satisfies each equation.

26. $A \cap B = \varnothing$
27. $A \cap B = B$
28. $(A \cup B) \cap C = \varnothing$
29. $A \cap (A \cap B) = A$

In problems 30–34, use the numbered regions in the diagram for problems 9–17 to verify each equality.

30. a. $A \cup B = B \cup A$
    b. $A \cap B = B \cap A$
    (These two equations are called the **commutative laws** for set operations.)
31. a. $A \cup (B \cup C) = (A \cup B) \cup C$
    b. $A \cap (B \cap C) = (A \cap B) \cap C$
    (These two equations are called the **associative laws** for set operations.)
32. $A \cup (B \cap C) = (A \cup B) \cap (A \cup C)$
    [This equation and the equation $A \cap (B \cup C) = (A \cap B) \cup (A \cap C)$, which was verified in Example 3, are known as the **distributive laws** for set operations.]
33. a. $A \cup A' = \mathcal{U}$
    b. $A \cap A' = \varnothing$
    c. $A - B = A \cap B'$
34. a. $(A \cup B)' = A' \cap B'$
    b. $(A \cap B)' = A' \cup B'$
    (These two equations are known as **De Morgan's laws.**)
35. Referring to the diagram for problems 9–17, the set of regions $\{3, 7\}$ represents which of the following?
    a. $A \cap B$ b. $A \cap B \cap C$
    c. $(A \cup B) \cap C$ d. $(A \cap B) \cup C$
    e. None of these
36. Referring to the diagram for problems 9–17, the set of regions $\{1, 2, 3\}$ represents which of the following?
    a. $(A \cup B) \cap C$ b. $(A \cup B) \cap C'$
    c. $(A \cap B) \cup C$ d. $(A \cap B) \cup C'$
    e. None of these
37. Given $A \cap B = \{a, b\}$, $A \cap B' = \{c, e\}$, $A' \cap B = \{g, h\}$, and $(A \cup B)' = \{d, f\}$, use a Venn diagram to find the following:
    a. A, B, and $\mathcal{U}$ b. $A \cup B$ c. $(A \cap B)'$
38. Given $A \cap B = \{b, d\}$, $A \cup B = \{b, c, d, e\}$, $A \cap C = \{b, c\}$, and $A \cup C = \{a, b, c, d\}$, use a Venn diagram to find the following:
    a. A, B, and C b. $A \cap B \cap C$ c. $A \cup B \cup C$
39. Draw a Venn diagram representing the most general situation for four sets A, B, C, and D. (*Hint:* There should be $2^4 = 16$ regions, but *do not* use circles!)

Exercises 40–43 refer to the diagram in Example 6. Find the percent of people that are:

40. a. unhealthy, but not obese
    b. unhealthy, not obese, and over 65
41. a. obese but not unhealthy
    b. obese, not unhealthy, and under 65
42. a. not in the shaded area
    b. in one shaded set only
43. a. in two shaded sets only
    b. in all shaded sets

C Applications

44. Referring to Example 6, use set notation to write the set corresponding to the shaded area
45. Referring to Example 6, use set notation to write the set corresponding to the area that is **not** shaded.

The following information will be used in problems 46–48.

Do you frequent social network Web sites? Here are the the 10 most popular ones according to EBizMBA rankings (set E) or by the reviews they got (set R).

E = {1Facebook, 2Twitter, 3MySpace, 4Linkedin, 5Ning, 6Tagged, 7Classmater, 8hi5, 9Myyearbook, 10Meetup} http://www.ebizmba.com/articles/social-networking-websites

R = 1Facebook, 2MySpace, 3Bebo, 4Friendster, 5hi5, 6Orkut, 7PerfSpot, 8Zorpia, 9Netlog, 10Habbo} http://social-networking-websites-review.toptenreviews.com

46. Write the set E ∩ R, the set of Web sites listed on E and R.

47. What is the number one Web site in set E and the number one Web site in R?

48. If you are looking for a place to advertise, which Web site would you select? Why?

Are you ready for a Web game? You need a computer for this one! Following the procedure of Example 7, go to Google.com. When we entered the word *car* (a query), we got 1,320,000,000 responses. There is a game called "Googlewhack" whose rules are at (where else?) www.googlewhack.com. The goal: Enter two words; get one response. For example, as of this printing, if you enter the words

Traumatizing monkiness

in advanced search you should get one response. (To make the game more interesting, you can now make a question whose answer is the two words you entered!) Here is our mathematical variation of the game: Mathegoogle.

49. Can you enter two words and get two results?

50. Can you enter three words and get three results?

51. Can you enter four words and get four results?

52. The generalization: Enter n words and get n results. (Do as many as you want.)

IN OTHER WORDS

In problems 53–56, write in words the set represented by the shaded region of each Venn diagram.

53.

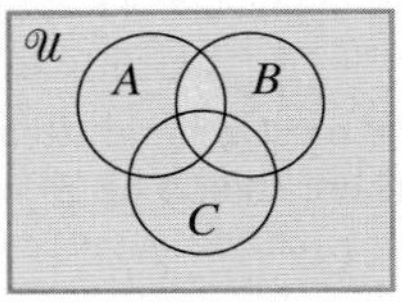

54.

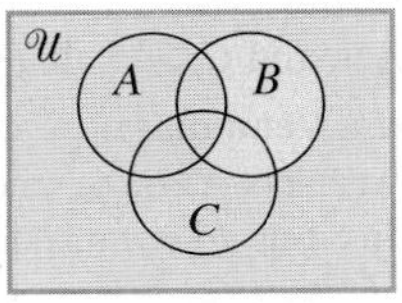

55.

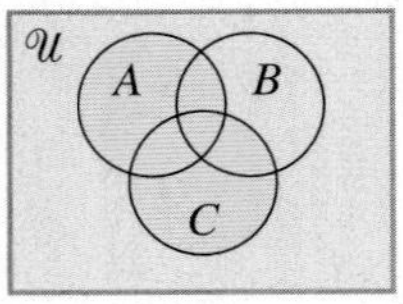

56.

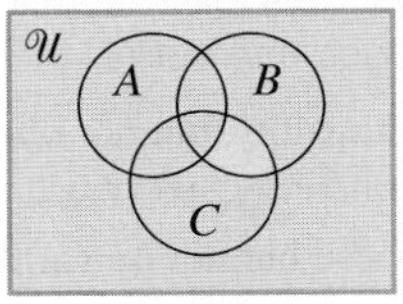

Does spending more on health care guarantee a better life expectancy? Not according to the table! The country with the highest total annual health expenditure per capita, the United States, does not have the best life expectancy for its citizens. The corresponding female and male life expectancies are as in columns 3 and 4.

57. Let A be the set of countries with female life expectancy greater than 83 and let B be the set of countries with male life expectancy greater than 78. Write the sets A and B and draw the corresponding Venn diagram.

58. If A and B are as in problem 57, what is the annual per capita health expenditure for citizens of $A \cap B$?

	Annual per capita health expenditures	Life expectancy at birth (female)	Life expectancy at birth (male)
USA	7285	81	76
Luxembourg	5734	83	77
Norway	4763	83	78
Switzerland	4417	84	80
Malta	4053	82	78
Canada	3900	83	79
Austria	3763	83	78
France	3709	85	78

Source: WHO, World Health Statistics 2010 {expenditures in Int. $, life expectancy in years) http://www.who.int/whosis/whostat/2010/en/index.html.

59. Let A be the set of countries with female life expectancy less than 83 and let B be the set of countries with male life expectancy less than 78. Write the sets A and B and draw the corresponding Venn diagram.

60. If A and B are as in problem 59, what is the annual per capita health expenditure for citizens of $A \cap B$?

USING YOUR KNOWLEDGE

In Example 4 of this section, blood was classified into eight different types. In blood transfusions, the recipient (the person receiving the blood) must have all or more of the antigens present in the donor's blood. For instance, an A^+ person cannot donate blood to an A^- person, because the recipient does not have the Rh antigen, but an A^- person can donate to an A^+ person. Refer to Figure 2.17.

61. Identify the blood type of universal recipients.

62. Identify the blood type of universal donors.

63. Can an AB^- person give blood to a B^- person?

64. Can a B^- person give blood to an AB^- person?

65. Can an O^+ person give blood to an O^- person?

66. Can an O^- person give blood to an O^+ person?

The approximate distribution of blood types in the U.S. population is as follows. (Distribution may be different for specific racial and ethnic groups.)

O Rh-positive	38%	**B Rh-positive**	9%
O Rh-negative	7%	**B Rh-negative**	2%
A Rh-positive	34%	**AB Rh-positive**	3%
A Rh-negative	6%	**AB Rh-negative**	1%

Source: http://www.aabb.org/resources/bct/Pages/bloodfaq.aspx. You can read all about blood on this site!

Can you use your knowledge to find what percent of the people have antigen

67. A?

68. B?

69. O? *Hint:* See Figure 2.17 to see which people have O blood.

70. Based on your answers to 67–69, which blood types (A, B, or O) are the most and least common?

DISCOVERY

John Venn invented the diagrams introduced in this section to illustrate his work, Symbolic Logic. *The Swiss mathematician Leonhard Euler* (1707–1783) *used similar diagrams to illustrate his work. For this reason, Venn diagrams are sometimes called* Euler circles *or* Euler diagrams.

We have seen in the preceding examples that if we have one set, the corresponding Venn diagram divides the universe into two regions. Two sets divide the universe into four regions, and three sets divide it into eight regions.

71. What is the maximum number of regions into which four sets will divide the universe?

72. The diagram for a division of the universal set into the 16 regions corresponding to four given sets may look like the figure that follows. Can you guess the maximum number of regions into which n sets will divide the universe?

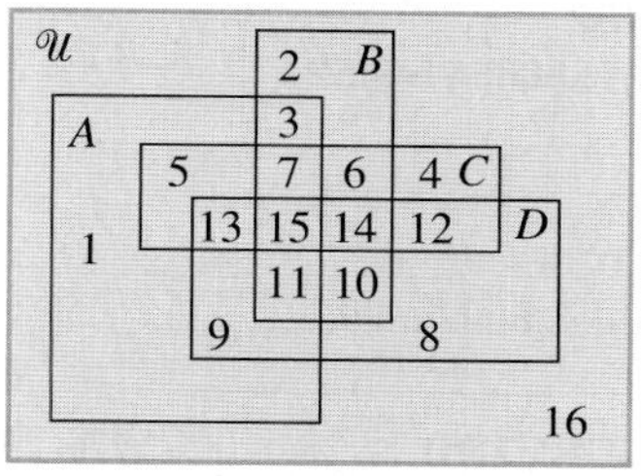

73. Referring to the diagram for problem 72, find the regions corresponding to the following:

a. $A \cap B \cap C' \cap D$ **b.** $(A \cup B \cup C)'$

COLLABORATIVE LEARNING

This group activity is designed to determine how to mix the additive *primary colors,* red, green, *and* blue, *to obtain* white *and how to mix the* subtractive *primary colors,* yellow, cyan *(light blue), and* magenta *(purple), to obtain* black.

Form two groups of students. One group should have a piece of black paper and three different-colored markers or cans of paint (red, green, and blue) or three plastic disks similar to those in Example 5. (You can use plastic report cover protectors to make the disks.) The other group should have a piece of white paper and three different-colored markers or cans of paint—cyan (light blue), magenta (purple), and yellow—or three plastic disks.

Each of the groups should make a Venn diagram similar to the one in Example 5 consisting of three circles of different colors.

1. Which color is the intersection of the three additive primary colors?

2. Which color is the intersection of the three subtractive secondary colors?

3. Which other intersection of three colors (if any) would produce white?

4. Which other intersection of three colors (if any) would produce black?

Additive secondary colors are composed of two of the primary colors.

5. Which color do you get if you mix red and green?

6. Which color do you get if you mix red and blue?

7. Which color do you get if you mix green and blue?

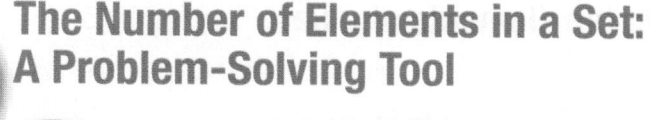

2.4 The Number of Elements in a Set: A Problem-Solving Tool

GETTING STARTED

OBJECTIVES

A. Use Venn diagrams to find the number of elements in a set.

B. Use Venn diagrams to solve applications involving surveys.

TEST REGISTRATION AND COUNTING

When registering for the Test of English as a Foreign Language (TOEFL) or the Test of Spoken English (TSE), students must indicate which test they plan to take by checking one of the boxes on the envelope (see Figure 2.20 on the following page). Suppose that a total of 800 students are registered for the TOEFL exam and 500 students are registered for the TSE; 200 of these students indicate that they will take both tests. How many students are participating; that is, how many students are registered? To answer this question, we have to develop a notation indicating how many elements we have in each set. If F is the set of students registered for TOEFL and S is the set of students registered for TSE, we are asked to find the total number of registered students. (They can be taking TOEFL only, TSE only, or both.) We answer this question and more in Example 1. Similar questions are presented in Exercises 2.4, problems 7–8.

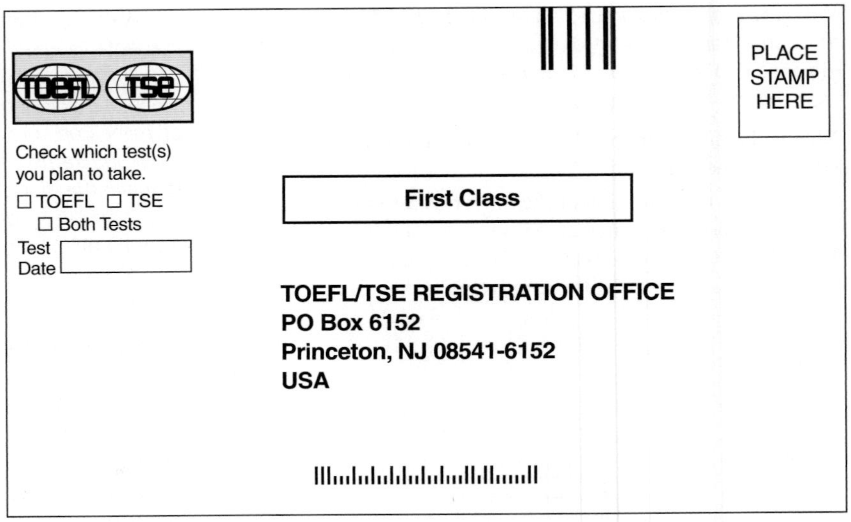

FIGURE 2.20

One of the simplest counting techniques involves the counting of elements in a given set. If A is any set, the number of elements in A is denoted by $n(A)$. The number $n(A)$ is frequently called the **cardinal number** of A. If $n(A)$ is a whole number, the set A is a **finite** set. For example, if $A = \{g, i, r, l\}$, then $n(A) = 4$. Likewise, if $B = \{@, \#, \$\}$, then $n(B) = 3$, and of course, A and B are finite sets. We shall be interested here in counting the number of elements in sets formed by the operations of union, intersection, and taking complements.

A Counting the Elements of a Set

EXAMPLE 1 TOEFL and TSE Survey

In a particular school, 800 students are registered for TOEFL, 500 are registered for TSE, and 200 are registered for both tests.

(a) What is the total number of registered students?

(b) How many students are taking TOEFL only?

(c) How many students are taking TSE only?

Solution

Let F be the set of students registered for TOEFL and S be the set of students registered for TSE. First draw a Venn diagram with overlapping regions to show the information (Figure 2.21).

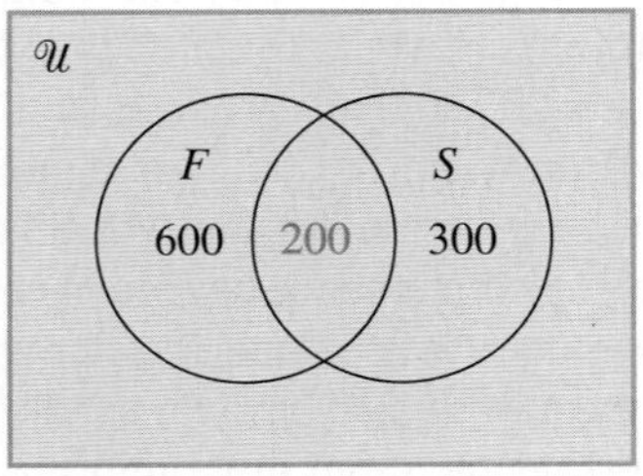

FIGURE 2.21

1. $S \cap F$ has 200 students. Write 200 in the region corresponding to $S \cap F$.
2. Since $n(F) = 800$ and 200 students are in the intersection of F and S, the number of students taking TOEFL only is $800 - 200 = 600$, as shown in Figure 2.21.
3. The number of students taking TSE only is $500 - 200 = 300$.

   (a) The number of registered students is

   $$n(F \cup S) = 600 + 200 + 300 = 1100$$

   (b) The number of students taking TOEFL only is 600.

   (c) The number of students taking TSE only is 300.

Note that $n(F) = 600 + 200 = 800$ and $n(S) = 200 + 300 = 500$. Thus,

$$n(F \cup S) = n(F) + n(S) - n(S \cap F)$$

that is, $\downarrow \quad \downarrow \quad \downarrow \quad \downarrow$

$$1100 = 800 + 500 - 200$$

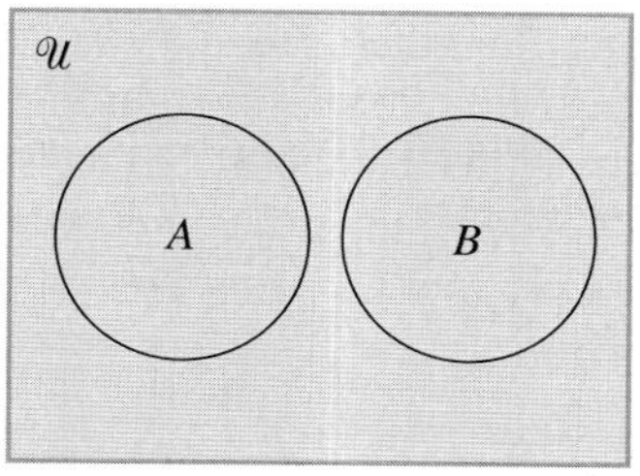

FIGURE 2.22 $A \cap B = \varnothing$

We now examine the problem of finding the number of elements in the union of two sets in a more general way. Let us assume that A and B are any two given sets. We must consider two possibilities.

1. $A \cap B = \varnothing$ (see Figure 2.22): In this case, $n(A \cup B) = n(A) + n(B)$.
2. $A \cap B \neq \varnothing$ (see Figure 2.23): In this case, $A \cup B$ includes all the elements in A and all the elements in B, but each element is counted only once. It is thus clear that $n(A) + n(B)$ counts the elements in $A \cap B$ twice and so exceeds $n(A \cup B)$ by $n(A \cap B)$. Therefore,

   $n(A \cup B) = [n(A) + n(B)] - n(A \cap B)$

   or

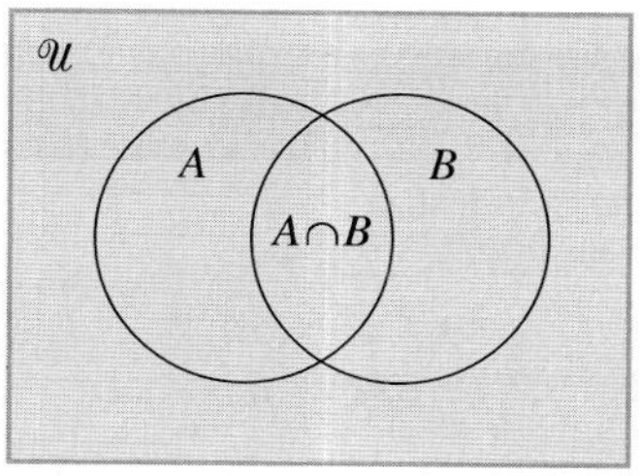

FIGURE 2.23 $A \cap B \neq \varnothing$

Number of Elements in $A \cup B$

$$n(A \cup B) = n(A) + n(B) - n(A \cap B) \qquad (1)$$

Notice that equation (1) is correct even if $A \cap B = \varnothing$ because in that case $n(A \cap B) = 0$.

EXAMPLE 2 Finding $n(A \cup B)$

If $n(A) = 20$, $n(B) = 30$, and $n(A \cap B) = 10$, find $n(A \cup B)$.

Solution

Using equation (1), we have

$$n(A \cup B) = n(A) + n(B) - n(A \cap B) = 20 + 30 - 10 = 40$$

It is possible to develop a formula similar to equation (1) for the case in which three or more sets are considered. However, we will rely on the use of Venn diagrams to solve such problems. For example, suppose we want to buy a pair of running shoes on the Internet using a search engine like Google. How many Web pages include information about running shoes? Go to Google.com, type the word *shoes*, and press Google Search (or Enter). The blue bar tells us that there are about 603,000,000 Web pages with information about shoes. How many pages do we have to choose from if we want *running shoes?* Type the word *running* after shoes and press Enter. Now, you have 44,900,000 pages with information about running shoes.*

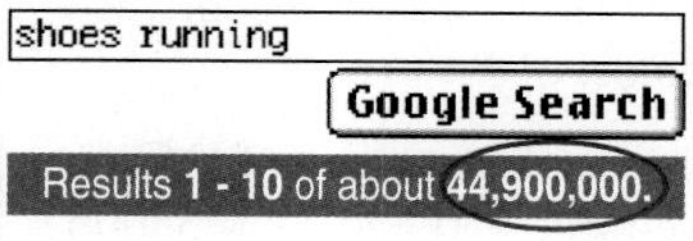

EXAMPLE 3 Buying Shoes and Venn Diagrams

If S is the set of pages dealing with shoes and R is the set of pages dealing with running,

(a) what is $n(S)$? **(b)** what is $n(S \cap R)$?

(c) Draw a Venn diagram and find the number of pages that deal with nonrunning shoes.

Solution

(a) Since there are about 603,000,000 pages dealing with shoes, $n(S) = 603{,}000{,}000$.

(b) Since there are 44,900,000 pages dealing with shoes that are running shoes, $n(S \cap R) = 44{,}900{,}000$.

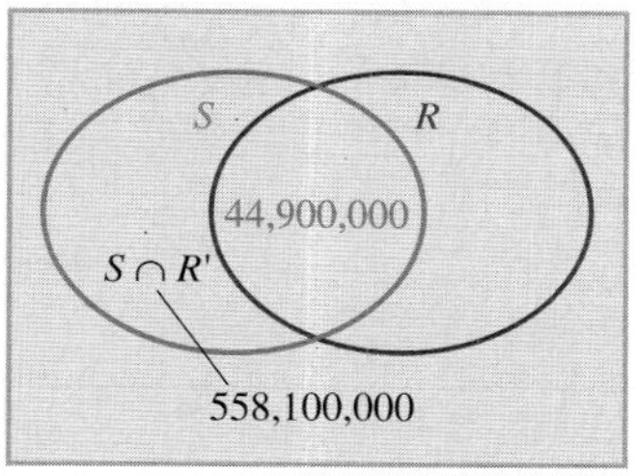

FIGURE 2.24

*These numbers change daily, so your numbers may be different.

(c) Draw two overlapping circles labeled S and R. We know that there are 44,900,000 elements in the intersection of S and R, so we enter 44,900,000 as shown in Figure 2.24. The elements that represent nonrunning shoes are in S and not in R, that is, in $S \cap R'$. Since we have 603,000,000 in S and 44,900,000 in $S \cap R$, the number of elements in $S \cap R'$ is $603{,}000{,}000 - 44{,}900{,}000 = 558{,}100{,}000$.

B Applications: Surveys

Venn diagrams can also be used to study surveys, as shown next. The strategy used to solve these problems is to make a diagram and assign to each region the correct number of elements.

PROBLEM-SOLVING

Surveys

① **Read** the problem.

To estimate the number of persons interested in recycling aluminum cans, glass, and newspapers, a company conducts a survey of 1000 people and finds that

200 recycle glass (G)
450 recycle cans (C)
15 recycle paper and glass
10 recycle all three
300 recycle paper (P)
50 recycle cans and glass
60 recycle cans and paper

(a) How many people do not recycle at all?

(b) How many people recycle cans only?

② **Select** the unknown.

We want to find the number of people who do not recycle at all and the number of people who recycle cans only.

③ **Think** of a plan. The strategy is to draw a Venn diagram.

We draw a Venn diagram with three overlapping circles labeled C, G, and P (Figure 2.25).

④ **Use** the information to carry out the plan.

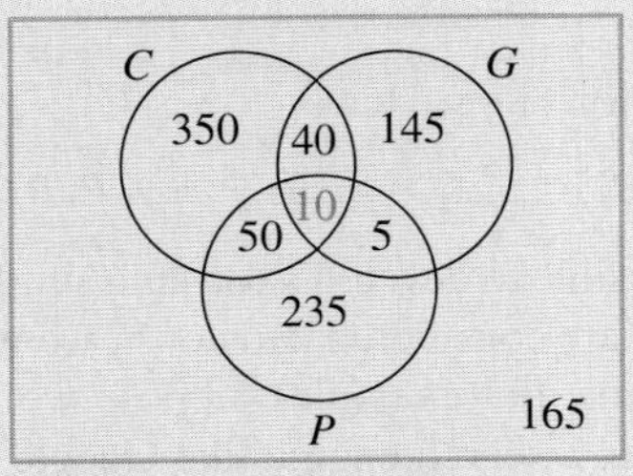

FIGURE 2.25

Do we know how to distribute the 200 people who recycle glass inside the circle G?

We have to start with the 10 persons who recycle all three and place them in $C \cap G \cap P$. Since 15 recycle paper and glass, the intersection of P and G must have 15 people. We already have 10 in $C \cap G \cap P$, so we add 5 in the remainder of $P \cap G$.

Similarly, we place 50 more in the remainder of $C \cap P$ and 40 in the remainder of $C \cap G$. We now have $10 + 50 + 40 = 100$ persons in C, so we place $450 - 100 = 350$ in the region corresponding to C only. Similarly, we place $200 - 55 = 145$ in the region corresponding to G only and $300 - 65 = 235$ in the region corresponding to P only.

We have $350 + 40 + 145 + 50 + 10 + 5 + 235 = 835$ people inside the circles.

(a) Since 1000 persons were surveyed, $1000 - 835 = 165$ persons are outside the three circles and do not recycle at all.

(b) 350 recycle cans only.

⑤ **Verify** the answer.

The sum of all the numbers in the diagram is 1000.

Try Example 4 Now

Cover the solution, write your own solution, and then check your work.

According to a survey by the Book Industry Study Group (BISG). "College Students Want Their Textbooks the Old-Fashioned Way: In Print." Here are the survey figures: 12% say they prefer e-books (E), 65% prefer the bookstore (B), and 20% buy at Amazon.com (A).

We make three other assumptions:

1. No student prefers all three categories (E, B, and A) at once.
2. No students prefer Amazon (A) and the bookstore (B) at once.
3. 2% of the e-book buyers prefer the bookstore, and 6% prefer Amazon.com.

Source: http://tinyurl.com/39cmcmf.

EXAMPLE 4 Bookstore Preference Survey

What is the future for e-books, bookstores, and Amazon? Let us first look at the information from the survey to a draw a Venn diagram and find the percent of students that:

(a) prefer e-books *only*.

(b) prefer the bookstore *only*.

(c) prefer Amazon.com *only*.

After you finish, you should be able to make a more informed decision.

Solution

Use the RSTUV procedure. After you read the problem, you will see that the unknowns are the three preferences, so we will translate the information and place it in a Venn diagram by steps, as follows:

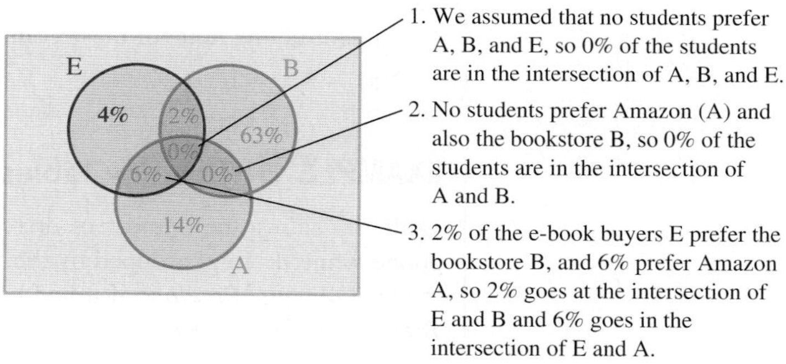
E
B
4%
2%
63%
0%
6%
0%
14%
A
1. We assumed that no students prefer A, B, and E, so 0% of the students are in the intersection of A, B, and E.
2. No students prefer Amazon (A) and also the bookstore B, so 0% of the students are in the intersection of A and B.
3. 2% of the e-book buyers E prefer the bookstore B, and 6% prefer Amazon A, so 2% goes at the intersection of E and B and 6% goes in the intersection of E and A.

FIGURE 2.26

According to the survey, 12% of the students must be in circle **E**, and so far we have 6% + 2% = 8%, so in the region corresponding to E *only* we place 4% of the students.

Similarly, circle **B** must have 65% of the students, and so far it has **2%**, so an additional **63%** of the students must be in the region corresponding to **B** *only*. Finally, the set A (Amazon.com) must have 20% of the students, and so far we only have 6%, so we write 14% in the region for A *only*. Thus,

(a) **4%** of the students prefer e-books *only*.

(b) 63% prefer the bookstore *only*.

(c) 14% prefer Amazon.com *only*.

Thus, based on this data, you may conclude that you should invest in a bookstore or an online Web site where books are sold.

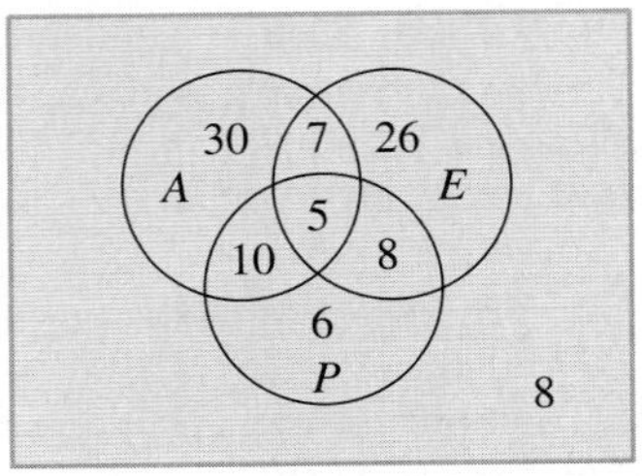

FIGURE 2.27

EXAMPLE 5 Surveying Courses

In a survey of 100 students, the numbers taking algebra (A), English (E), and philosophy (P) are shown in Figure 2.27.

(a) How many students are taking algebra or English but not both?

(b) How many students are taking algebra or English but not philosophy?

(c) How many students are taking one or two of these courses but not all three?

(d) How many students are taking at least two of these courses?

(e) How many students are taking at least one of these courses?

Solution

(a) Here, we want all the elements in A or E but not in both. We read the numbers from the Venn diagram to get

$$30 + 10 + 26 + 8 = 74$$

Note that we have taken all the numbers in $A \cup E$ except those in $A \cap E$.

(b) Here, we need all the numbers in A or E that are not in P. From the diagram, we find

$$30 + 7 + 26 = 63$$

(c) The required number here is the number in the entire universal set, 100, minus the number taking all three courses, 5, or none of these courses, 8. Thus, the result is

$$100 - 5 - 8 = 87$$

(d) The required number here is the number in

$$(A \cap E) \cup (A \cap P) \cup (E \cap P)$$

which is

$$7 + 5 + 10 + 8 = 30$$

(e) We can get the required number by taking the number in the universal set minus the number taking none of these courses. We find the result to be

$$100 - 8 = 92$$

EXAMPLE 6 Reading Tables

Table 2.3 shows the number of drivers who have *talked, texted,* or *e-mailed* on a cell phone while driving, grouped by their driver status: ***Current*** if they have driven within the last 30 days. ***Previous*** if it had been more than 30 days since they have driven and ***Total,*** the sum of ***Previous*** and ***Current*** drivers.

Table 2.3

While Driving	Previous	Current	Total
Talked	21	1234	1255
Texted	4	532	536
E-Mailed	0	112	112

Source: http://tinyurl.com/4ub3knp.

Find the number of:

(a) ***total*** drivers who talked while driving.

(b) ***current*** drivers who talked or texted while driving.

(c) ***previous*** drivers who talked, texted and e-mailed while driving.

(d) Which is the most prevalent distracting behavior: ***talking, texting,*** or ***driving?***

(e) Which is the most prevalent distracting behavior among ***Previous*** drivers?

(f) Which is the least prevalent distracting behavior among ***Current*** drivers?

Solution

(a) To find the total number of drivers who talked while driving, go to the intersection of the first row (**Talked**) and fourth column (**Total**) to get the answer **1255**.

(b) **Current** drivers who talked or texted are in the third column, rows 1 or 2. There are 1234 + 532 = **1766** of them.

(c) **Previous** drivers who talked, texted, or e-mailed are in the second column, rows 1, 2, or 3. There are 21 + 4 + 0 = **25** of them.

(d) The most prevalent distracting behavior in general is talking while driving: **1255** instances.

(e) The most prevalent distracting behavior among **Previous** drivers (column 2) is talking while driving: **21** instances.

(f) Among **Current** drivers (column 3) the least prevalent distracting behavior is e-mailing: **112** instances.

Results of polls are often shown using a table. Here are the basic relationships between each of the three habits being considered (smoking, drinking, overweight) in this analysis and self-reported "excellent" health.

	Excellent Physical Health	**Excellent Mental Health**
0 Habits	42%	47%
1 Habit	31%	45%
2 Habits	27%	40%
3 Habits	17%	42%

Source: The Gallup Organization: Three Deadly Habits.

EXAMPLE 7 Interpreting a Gallup Poll

Referring to the table,

(a) what percent of the people have 0 habits and claim to be in excellent physical health?

(b) what percent of the people have 3 habits and claim to be in excellent physical health?

(c) is there a relationship between the number of habits and excellent physical health?

(d) what percent of the people who are not overweight and do not drink or smoke report excellent physical health?

(e) what percent of the people who are not overweight and do not drink or smoke report excellent mental health?

Solution

Note that the number of habits refers to the row and that the health (physical or mental) refers to the **column**. Column 2 for physical and column **3** for mental.

(a) 0 habits (row 1) and excellent physical health (column 2) lists 42%. Thus, **42%** of the people have 0 habits and claim to be in excellent physical health.

(b) The percent of people with 3 habits (row 4) in excellent physical health (column **2**) is **17%.**

(c) The table suggests that as the number of habits increases, physical health decreases.

(d) If you are not overweight and do not drink or smoke, then you have 0 habits (row **1**). If you are in excellent physical health, you are in column **2**. The number in row **1,** column **2**, is 42%. Thus, the percent of people who are not overweight, do not drink or smoke, and claim to be in excellent physical health is **42%.**

(e) The percent of people who are not overweight, do not drink or smoke, and claim to be in excellent mental health is **47%** (row 1, column **3**).

2.4 EXERCISES

A Counting the Elements of a Set

1. Suppose that $n(A) = 15$, $n(B) = 20$, and $n(A \cap B) = 5$. Find $n(A \cup B)$.
2. Suppose that $n(A) = 12$, $n(B) = 6$, and $n(A \cup B) = 14$. Find $n(A \cap B)$.
3. Suppose that $n(A) = 15$, $n(A \cap B) = 5$, and $n(A \cup B) = 30$. Find $n(B)$.
4. There are 50 students in an algebra (A) class and 30 students in a chemistry (C) class. Find
   a. $n(A)$.
   b. $n(C)$.
   c. the total number of students taking either algebra or chemistry if it is known that none of the students are taking both courses.
   d. the number of students taking algebra and/or chemistry if it is known that 10 students are taking both courses.
5. On checking with 100 families, it was found that 75 families subscribe to *Time*, 55 to *Newsweek*, and 10 to neither magazine. How many subscribe to both?
6. If, on checking with 100 families, it was found that 83 subscribe to *Time*, 40 to *Newsweek*, and 30 to both magazines, how many subscribe to neither?

B Applications: Surveys

7. In a survey of 100 students, the numbers taking various courses were found to be English, 60; mathematics, 40; chemistry, 50; English and mathematics, 30; English and chemistry, 35; mathematics and chemistry, 35; and courses in all three areas, 25.
   a. How many students were taking mathematics, but neither English nor chemistry?
   b. How many were taking mathematics and chemistry, but not English?
   c. How many were taking English and chemistry, but not mathematics?
8. Mr. N. Roll, the registrar at a university, has observed that, of the students,

   45% have a 9 A.M. class.
   45% have a 10 A.M. class.
   40% have an 11 A.M. class.
   20% have a 9 and a 10 A.M. class.
   10% have a 9 and an 11 A.M. class.
   15% have a 10 and an 11 A.M. class.
   5% have a 9, a 10, and an 11 A.M. class.

   a. What percent of the students have only a 9 A.M. class?
   b. What percent of the students have no classes at these times?

How much will you have to pay for your college education? It depends on what college you select! Here is a chart that shows the different costs for different types of colleges.

Expenses	Tuition Fees	Rooms Board	Books Supplies	Transporation	Others
Public 2-yr.	$2713	$7259	$1133	$1491	$2041
Public 4-yr. (In-state)	$7605	$8535	$1137	$1073	$1989
Public 4-yr (Out-State)	$19,595	$8535	$1137	$1073	$1989

9. Refer to the chart and find the highest expense, its cost, and the total annual cost at a:
   a. public 2-year college
   b. public 4-year college (in-state)
   c. public 4-year college (out of state)
10. Refer to the chart and find the difference in annual cost between attending a:
    a. public 2-year college and a public 4-year in-state college.
    b. public 2-year college and a public 4-year out-of-state college.
    c. public 4-year in-state college and a public 4-year out-of-state college.

The information on the table for problems 9 and 10 can be visualized by using a graph, as follows.

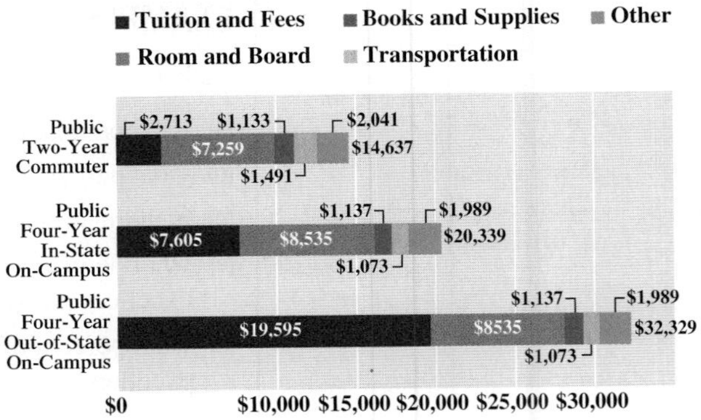

Source: The College Board, Annual Survey of Colleges.

11. Refer to the graph and find the lowest expense and its cost at a:
    a. public 2-year college
    b. public 4-year college (in-state)
    c. public 4-year college (out of state)
12. Refer to the graph and find the difference in annual price between tuition and fees at a:
    a. public 2-year college and a public 4-year in-state college.
    b. public 2-year college and a public 4-year out-of-state college.
    c. public 4-year in-state college and a public 4-year out-of-state college.

The table shows the percent of American adults in each generation who owns each device.

	Millennials Set M (Ages 18–34)	Gen X Set X (35–46)	Younger Boomers Set Y (47–56)
Cell phone (C)	95	92	86
Desktop computer (D)	57	69	65
Laptop computer (L)	70	61	49
iPod/MP3 player (I)	74	56	42
Game console (G)	63	63	38

Source: Pew Research Center's Internet and American Life Project.

13. Find the percent of people in:

a. $C \cap M$ b. $D \cap X$ c. $L \cap Y$

d. $X \cap I$ e. $Y \cap G$

14. Here are some facts regarding the information in the table:

a. **Desktop computers (D)** are most popular with adults, with 69% of **Gen X** owning them. Referring to the table, to what set does this correspond?

b. 65% of Younger Boomers **(Y)** own **desktop computers.** To what set in the table set does this correspond?

c. While almost half of all adults own an mp3 player like an iPod (**I**), this device is by far the most popular with Millennials (**M**), the youngest generation—74% of adults ages 18–34 own an mp3 player. To what set does this correspond in the table?

d. 56% of the next oldest generation, Gen X (ages 35–46), own an mp3 player like an iPod (I). To what set does this correspond in the table?

15. In a survey of 100 customers at the Royal Hassle Restaurant, it was found that

40 had onions on their hamburgers.
35 had mustard on their hamburgers.
50 had catsup on their hamburgers.
15 had onions and mustard on their hamburgers.
20 had mustard and catsup on their hamburgers.
25 had onions and catsup on their hamburgers.
5 had onions, mustard, and catsup on their hamburgers.

a. How many customers had hamburgers with onions only?

b. How many customers had plain hamburgers (no condiments)?

c. How many customers had only one condiment on their hamburgers?

16. A survey of 900 workers in a plant indicated that 500 owned houses, 600 owned cars, 345 owned boats, 300 owned cars and houses, 250 owned houses and boats, 270 owned cars and boats, and 200 owned all three.

a. How many of the workers did not own any of the three items?

b. How many of the workers owned only two of the items?

17. A coffee company was willing to pay \$1 to each person interviewed about his or her likes and dislikes on types of coffee. Of the persons interviewed, 200 liked ground coffee, 270 liked instant coffee, 70 liked both, and 50 did not like coffee at all. What was the total amount of money the company had to pay?

18. In a recent survey, a statistician reported the following data:

15 persons liked brand A.
18 persons liked brand B.
12 persons liked brand C.
8 persons liked brands A and B.
6 persons liked brands A and C.
7 persons liked brands B and C.
2 persons liked all three brands.
2 persons liked none of the three brands.

When the statistician claimed to have interviewed 30 persons, he was fired. Can you explain why?

19. In problem 18, a truthful statistician was asked to find out how many people were interviewed. What was this statistician's answer?

20. In an experiment, it was found that a certain substance could be of type x or type y (not both). In addition, it could have one, both, or neither of the characteristics m and n. The following table gives the results of testing several samples of the substance. Let M and N be the sets with characteristics m and n, respectively, and let X and Y be the sets of type x and y, respectively. How many samples are in each of the following sets?

a. $M \cap X$ b. $(X \cup Y) \cap (M \cup N)$

c. $(Y \cap M) - (Y \cap N')$ d. $(X \cup Y) \cap (M \cup N')$

	m Only	n Only	m and n	Neither m nor n
x	6	9	10	20
y	7	11	15	9

21. The number of students taking algebra (A) or chemistry (C) is shown in the diagram on the right. Find the following:

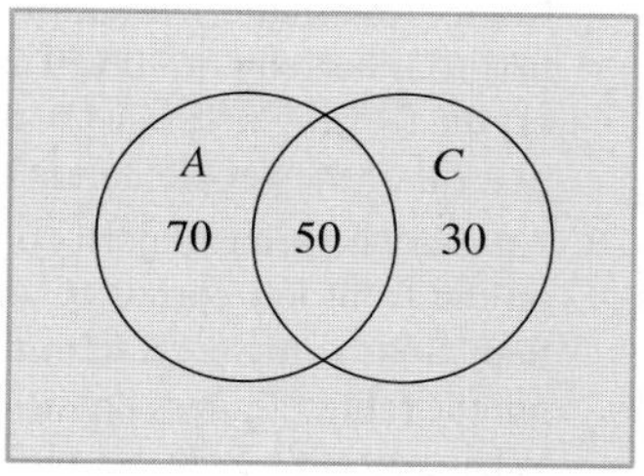

a. $n(A)$

b. $n(C)$

c. $n(A \cap C)$

22. Referring to the diagram for problem 21, find $n(A \cup C)$.

23. If the total number of students surveyed to obtain the data for problem 21 is 200, find

a. $n(A')$. b. $n(C')$. c. $n(A' \cap C')$.

24. With the total number of students as in problem 23, find

a. $n(A' \cup C)$. b. $n(A \cup C')$

25. On checking with 100 investors to see who owned electric company stock (E), transportation stock (T), or municipal bonds (M), the numbers shown in the diagram below were found.

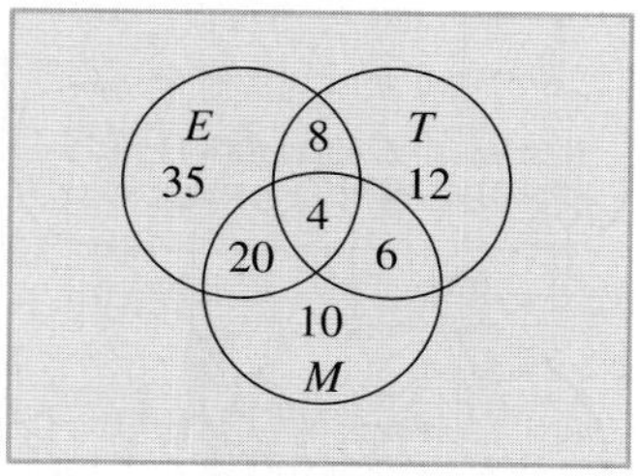

a. How many investors owned electric company or transportation stock but not both?

b. How many owned electric company or transportation stock but not municipal bonds?

c. How many had one or two of these types of investments but not all three?

d. How many had at least two of these types of investments?

e. How many had none of these types of investments?

26. A number of people were interviewed to find out who buys products A, B, and C regularly. The results are shown in the diagram below.

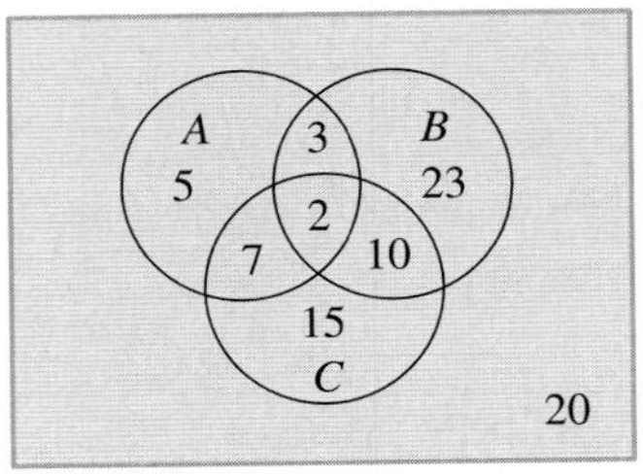

a. How many buy product A?

b. How many buy product A but not B?

c. How many buy product B or C, but not A?

d. How many do not buy product C?

e. How many people were interviewed?

A book titled *Are You Normal?* by Bernice Kanner offers many amusing but important pieces of information gleaned from actual surveys.

Solve problems 27–29 using a Venn diagram.

27. *What do you eat first, the frosting or the cake?* Astonishingly, only about 3% of us eat them together. Most people (69%) take Marie Antoinette's infamous words literally: They eat cake first (C). Just shy of 30%—more with younger people—pluck off the frosting first (F). On the basis of this information, what percent of the people do not eat cake first?

28. An overwhelming majority of us (91%) write our return address on the front left corner of an envelope (L), avoiding the back flap (B) as if it were a uranium mine. Just 7% of letter writers put the return address on the back flap, and 2% do it either way. What percent of the people do not write a return address on their envelopes?

29. *Is the glass half-full or half-empty?* Some 46% of men and 52% of women describe themselves as optimists (O), whereas 8% of men and 11% of women see themselves as pessimists (P). The rest say they are neither. What percent of the men are neither? *Hint:* Draw a diagram for men *only*.

30. On the basis of the information in problem 29, what percent of the women are neither?

IN OTHER WORDS

Classify the following statements as true or false. If true, explain why. If false, give a counter example.

31. If $n(A) = n(B)$, then $A = B$.

32. If $A = B$, then $n(A) = n(B)$.

33. If $A - B = \varnothing$, then $n(A) = n(B)$.

34. If $n(A) = n(B)$, then $A - B = \varnothing$.

USING YOUR KNOWLEDGE

The cartoon below seems to indicate that it is impossible to have the following morale statistics:

58% want out (WO).
14% hate his guts (HG).
56% plan to desert (PD).
8% are undecided (UD) (do not plan to do any of the above).

However, a new statistician is hired and finds that in addition to the original information, the following statements are also true:

12% want to do only one thing—hate his guts.
36% want to do exactly two things. Of these,
34% want out and plan to desert, and
2% hate his guts and want out.

Of course, nobody in his right mind would do all three things.

35. On the basis of all the information, both old and new, draw a Venn diagram and show that it is possible to have the statistics quoted in the cartoon.

DISCOVERY

In Section 2.1 we discussed the subsets of a given set. It is interesting to diagram the formation of such subsets. We imagine that the elements of the given set are listed, and we look at each element in turn and decide whether to include it in the subset. For example, suppose that the given set is {a, b}. Then our diagram has two steps, as shown in the following diagram.

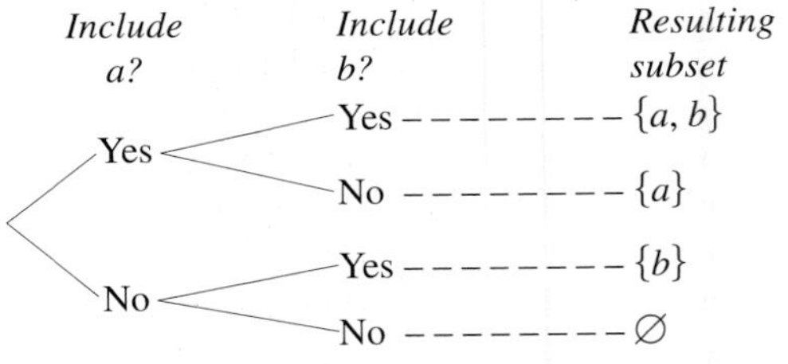

This diagram makes it clear that there are 2 × 2, or 4, subsets in all.

The following diagram is for the three-element set {a, b, c}.

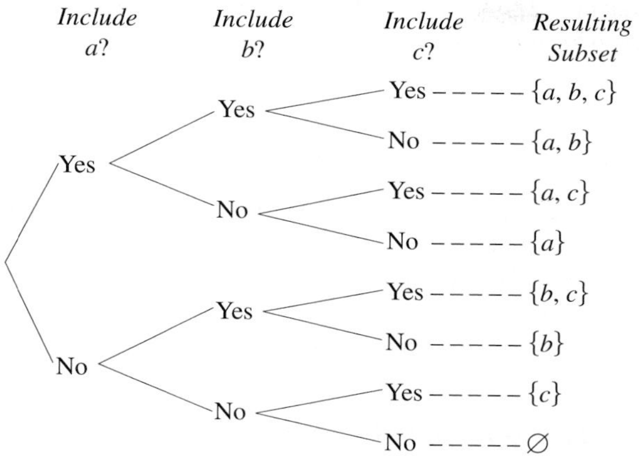

Diagrams like these are called ***tree diagrams,*** *and we shall discuss them in more detail in Chapter 10. The second tree diagram shows that a three-element set has 2 × 2 × 2, or 8, subsets. Can you discover an easy way to explain this?*

36. Can you discover the tree diagram for a four-element set and its subsets?

37. Can you discover how to count the number of subsets of a four-element set?

38. Can you now discover how to explain why an n-element set has

$$\underbrace{2 \times 2 \times 2 \times \cdots \times 2}_{n \text{ twos}}$$

or 2^n, subsets?

2.5 Infinite Sets

GETTING STARTED

OBJECTIVES

A. Determine the cardinal number of a set and decide whether two sets have the same cardinal number.

B. Determine if two sets are equivalent.

C. Determine if a set is finite or infinite.

INFINITE SETS AND ONE-TO-ONE CORRESPONDENCES

Is the number of stars infinite? Mathematically speaking, if S is the set of all stars, what is $n(S)$? We do know that if $A = \{1, 2, 3\}$, then $n(A) = 3$. Now, suppose that $N = \{1, 2, 3, \ldots\}$; what is $n(N)$? To find $n(N)$ is to determine how many natural (counting) numbers there are! Georg Cantor studied this problem and assigned the **transfinite cardinal** $\aleph_0$ (read "aleph null"; $\aleph$ is the first letter of the Hebrew alphabet) to $n(N)$. Thus, $n(N) = \aleph_0$. Now, which set has more elements, $N = \{1, 2, 3, \ldots\}$ or $E = \{2, 4, 6, \ldots\}$?

At first, it seems that there should be twice as many natural numbers as there are even numbers. But consider the **one-to-one correspondence**

$$\begin{array}{l} N = \{1, 2, 3, \ldots, n, \ldots\} \\ \quad\;\;\; \updownarrow\;\; \updownarrow\;\; \updownarrow \qquad\;\; \updownarrow \\ E = \{2, 4, 6, \ldots, 2n, \ldots\} \end{array}$$

where every natural number n in N is paired with the even number $2n$ in E. Can you see that there are as many even numbers as there are natural numbers? The two sets are said to be **equivalent.** Moreover, there are as many natural numbers as there are fractions, as you will discover later in the book. For now, you will learn how to use one-to-one correspondences to determine whether sets are equivalent (see problems 11–15 in Exercises 2.5). In problems 16–20, you will even determine whether a set is infinite!

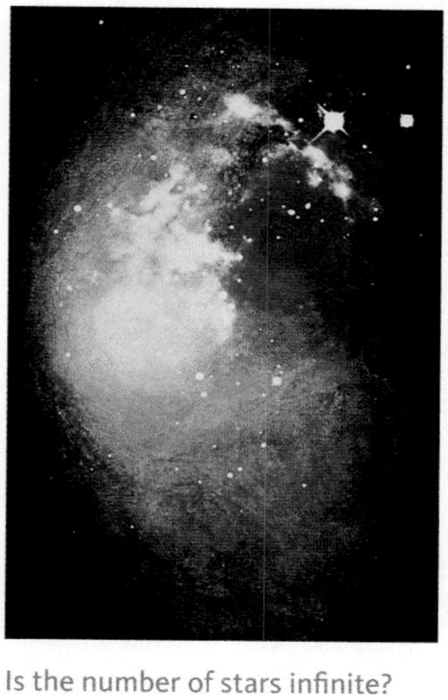

Is the number of stars infinite? The infrared map of the Orion nebula shown above unveils a new star formation.

What is an infinite set? In the years 1871–1884, Georg Cantor created a completely new mathematical discipline, **set theory.** Cantor asked himself: "What do we mean when we say of two finite sets that they consist of equally many things, that they have the same number, that they are equivalent?" The tools he used to answer this question were *cardinal numbers* and *one-to-one correspondences.*

A Cardinal Numbers

In Section 2.4 we noted that the cardinal number of a set A is the number of elements in A, denoted by $n(A)$ as before. Thus, if $A = \{a, b, c\}$, the cardinal number of A is $n(A) = 3$. To ascertain whether two sets have the same cardinal number, we determine whether each element of A can be matched with a unique element of B and vice versa. That is, we check whether there is a one-to-one correspondence between A and B.

EXAMPLE 1 Showing that *A* and *B* Have the Same Cardinality

Show that the sets $A = \{\#, \$, \&, \bigstar\}$ and $B = \{@, c, 2, ¢\}$ have the same cardinal number.

Solution

You have to show that there is a one-to-one correspondence between the elements of A and those of B. One such correspondence is given in Figure 2.28. If, as before, $n(A)$ represents the number of elements in A, $n(A) = n(B) = 4$. Can you find a different correspondence?

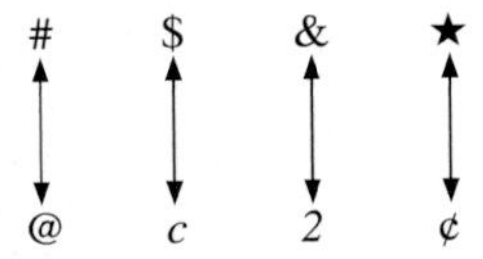

FIGURE 2.28

B Equivalent Sets

Definition of Equivalent Sets

If two sets A and B can be placed into a one-to-one correspondence with each other, the two sets are said to be **equivalent,** denoted by $A \sim B$.

Note that when sets A and B are **equivalent,** $n(A) = n(B)$; that is, A and B have the same number of elements.

Thus, the set of vowels V in the English alphabet is equivalent to the set of the first five counting numbers F, as can be seen by the correspondence

$$\begin{array}{ccccc} a & e & i & o & u \\ \updownarrow & \updownarrow & \updownarrow & \updownarrow & \updownarrow \\ 1 & 2 & 3 & 4 & 5 \end{array}$$

We then say that $V \sim F$. Recall that this also means that $n(V) = n(F)$.

EXAMPLE 2 Showing that *N* and *E* Are Equivalent

Show that the set N of counting numbers and the set E of even counting numbers are equivalent.

Solution

Set up the correspondence

$$\begin{array}{cccccccc} 1 & 2 & 3 & 4 & \cdots & n & n+1 & \cdots \\ \updownarrow & \updownarrow & \updownarrow & \updownarrow & & \updownarrow & \updownarrow & \\ 2 & 4 & 6 & 8 & \cdots & 2n & 2(n+1) & \cdots \end{array}$$

Since the elements of the two sets can be placed into a one-to-one correspondence, $N \sim E$. In mathematics, when a set S is equivalent to the set N of counting numbers, S is said to be **denumerable.**

C Infinite Sets

At first sight, it may seem strange that the set of counting numbers and a proper subset of itself (the set of even counting numbers) can be put into a one-to-one correspondence. This apparent paradox puzzled mathematicians for years until Georg Cantor resolved it. Cantor defined an infinite set as follows:

Definition of an Infinite Set

A set is **infinite** if it is equivalent to one of its proper subsets.

In his theory, he assigned the cardinal number $\aleph_0$ to the set of counting numbers; that is, if $N = \{1, 2, 3, \ldots\}$, then $n(N) = \aleph_0$.

With this convention it is possible to find the cardinal number of certain infinite sets. For example, because the set E of even counting numbers is equivalent to N, we must have $n(N) = n(E) = \aleph_0$.

To show that N is infinite, we note that N has the proper subset E that can be put into a one-to-one correspondence with N. Thus, we conclude that N is an infinite set. In contrast to the cardinal number of a finite set, that of an infinite set is usually called a **transfinite cardinal number.**

EXAMPLE 3 Showing Equivalency and Cardinality

Consider the set $S = \{1^2 = 1, 2^2 = 4, 3^2 = 9, \ldots, n^2, \ldots\}$.

(a) Show that S is equivalent to N.

(b) Find the cardinality of S.

(c) Show that S is infinite.

Solution

(a) To show that S and N are equivalent, set up a one-to-one correspondence between S and N as follows:

$$\begin{array}{cccccc} 1 & 4 & 9 & \cdots & n^2 & \cdots \\ \updownarrow & \updownarrow & \updownarrow & & \updownarrow & \\ 1 & 2 & 3 & \cdots & n & \cdots \end{array}$$

Thus, S and N are equivalent; that is, $S \sim N$.

(b) Since S and N are equivalent and $n(N) = \aleph_0$, $n(N) = n(S) = \aleph_0$.

(c) To show that S is infinite, you must place S into a one-to-one correspondence with one of its proper subsets. Here is such a correspondence.

$$\begin{array}{ccccccc} 1 & 4 & 9 & 16 & \cdots & n^2 & \cdots \\ \updownarrow & \updownarrow & \updownarrow & \updownarrow & & \updownarrow & \\ 4 & 9 & 16 & 25 & \cdots & (n+1)^2 & \cdots \end{array}$$

Note that

$$\{4, 9, 16, 25, \ldots, (n + 1)^2, \ldots\} \subseteq \{1, 4, 9, 16, \ldots, n^2, \ldots\}$$

2.5 EXERCISES

A Cardinal Numbers

In problems 1–5, find the cardinality of each set.

1. $A = \{a, b, c, \ldots, z\}$
2. $B = \{x \mid x$ is one of the Ten Commandments$\}$
3. $C = \{x \mid x$ is a star on the American flag$\}$
4. $D = \{\frac{1}{2}, \frac{1}{4}, \frac{1}{6}, \ldots\}$
5. $E = \{\frac{1}{1}, \frac{1}{4}, \frac{1}{9}, \ldots\}$

B Equivalent Sets

In problems 6–10, show that the two sets are equivalent.

6. $A = \{1, 2, 3, 4, 5\}$ and $B = \{a, b, c, d, e\}$
7. $P = \{2, 4, 8, 12\}$ and $Q = \{6, 12, 24, 36\}$
8. $W = \{0, 1, 2, 3, \ldots\}$ and $N = \{1, 2, 3, \ldots\}$
9. $I^- = \{-1, -2, -3, \ldots\}$ and $N = \{1, 2, 3, \ldots\}$
10. $N = \{1, 2, 3, \ldots\}$ and $F = \{\frac{1}{1}, \frac{1}{2}, \frac{1}{3}, \ldots\}$

Problems 11–15 show that the sets are equivalent by setting up a one-to-one correspondence between the two given sets.

11. The set N of counting numbers and the set O of odd counting numbers
12. The set N of counting numbers and the set F of positive multiples of 5
13. The set E of even counting numbers and the set G of even counting numbers greater than 100
14. The set O of odd counting numbers and the set E of even counting numbers
15. The set G of even counting numbers greater than 200 and the set T of even counting numbers greater than 300

C Infinite Sets

In problems 16–20, determine whether each set is finite or infinite.

16. $\{1, 2, 3, \ldots, 999{,}999\}$
17. $\{100, 200, 300, \ldots\}$
18. $\{5, 10, 15, \ldots\}$
19. $\{\frac{1}{3}, \frac{2}{3}, \frac{3}{3}, \ldots\}$
20. $\{2^{64}, 2^{32}, 2^{16}, \ldots, 2\}$

Use the sets $A = \{1, 2, 3, 4, 5, 6\}$, $B = \{a, b, c, d\}$, $C = \{w, x, y, z\}$, *and* $D = \{d, c, b, a\}$ *to answer problems 21–23.*

21. Which set(s) are equal and equivalent?
22. Which set(s) are equivalent but not equal?
23. Which set(s) are not equivalent and not equal?

IN OTHER WORDS

As you recall, $n(\mathbf{N}) = \aleph_0$ *and* $\aleph_0$ *is called a* transfinite cardinal. *Can you perform arithmetic operations with these cardinals? Fill in the blanks and justify your answers.*

24. $\aleph_0 + 1 =$ ____
25. $\aleph_0 + \aleph_0 =$ ____
26. $2 \times \aleph_0 =$ ____
27. $\aleph_0 \times \aleph_0 =$ ____
28. Let $A = \{1, 3, 5, \ldots\}$ and $B = \{2, 4, 6, \ldots\}$. As you recall, $n(A \cup B) = n(A) + n(B)$ if A and B are disjoint. Substitute A and B in the equation and state your result.
29. Consider the line segment shown. It is 1 unit long.

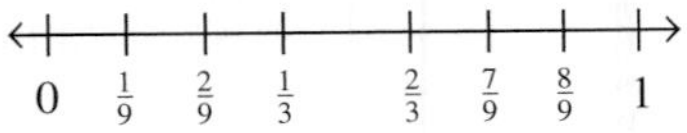

Draw an identical segment on a sheet of paper. Cut off the middle piece, the piece between $\frac{1}{3}$ and $\frac{2}{3}$, and paste it on a second sheet of paper. Then divide the piece between 0 and $\frac{1}{3}$ into three equal parts, each of length $\frac{1}{9}$. Cut off the middle piece, the piece between $\frac{1}{9}$ and $\frac{2}{9}$, and paste it next to the first piece you pasted on the paper. Repeat the process with the piece between $\frac{2}{3}$ and 1. The middle piece you will cut off is the piece between $\frac{7}{9}$ and $\frac{8}{9}$. Paste this next to the second piece on the paper. Imagine that this process is continued.

   a. The points $\frac{1}{3}, \frac{2}{3}, \frac{1}{9}$, and $\frac{2}{9}$ are the first four points of the Cantor set. What are the next two points?

   b. If you continue the pasting process, what do you think will be the total length of the pieces you pasted?

30. Do you think the Cantor set and the set of all points on the line segment in problem 29 are equivalent? Explain.

USING YOUR KNOWLEDGE

Have you ever heard of the Infinity Hotel? It is a peculiar establishment indeed. The only prerequisite for employment is a thorough knowledge of infinite sets. In fact, the *Employment Handbook* consists entirely of the section you have just read. Georg was hired as manager, and his first day on the job was a cinch.

The hotel soon filled all of its rooms, $1, 2, 3, \ldots, n, n + 1$, and so on. Trouble started on the second day with the arrival of a new guest. Where would Georg put this new guest? He thought about it for a split second, and then up went a neatly handwritten sign.

> If you are presently in room n, please move next door to room $n + 1$.

Where would the nice family in room 222 go? And what about the newcomer?

The third day things got more involved, for a group of eager customers arrived, in a brand-new Infiniti no less. Tensions were high at the hotel. Could Georg accommodate them all? No time was wasted. Without hesitation, the next sign went up.

> If you are presently in room n, please move to room $2n$.

What an odd arrangement of rooms that would leave!

Use your knowledge to answer the following questions:

31. On the second day, where would the family in room 222 go?
32. On the second day, in which room would the newcomer go?
33. Which rooms were vacated for the people in the Infiniti?
34. Where would the guest of problem 32 go on the third day?
35. On the third day, where would the family in room 333 go?

Do you know the difference between equivalent and equal sets?

Use your knowledge and the graph to solve problem 36.

The Most Populated Twitter Cities

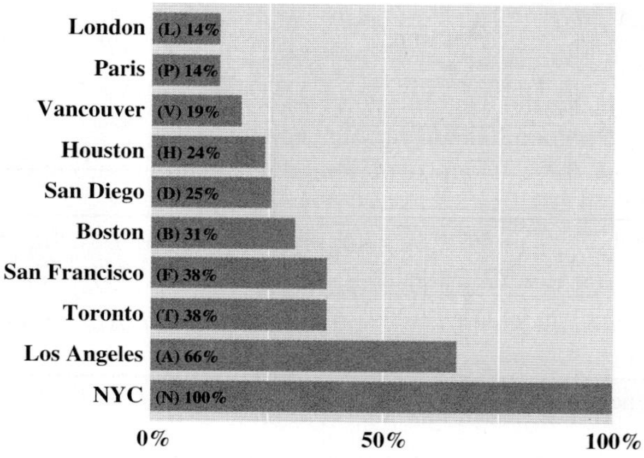

Description: The bar chart shows the number of Twitter users from the top 10 cities relative to the number of users in New York City. The chart shows that the number of users in New York City is four times that in San Diego.

36. Let A be the set of all cities with a 14% score and B the set of cities with a 38% score.

a. Write the sets A and B using roster notation.

b. Are sets A and B equivalent?

c. Are sets A and B equal?

d. Are sets A and B finite or infinite?

DISCOVERY

Here is one of the most striking results obtained by Cantor while studying the theory of *nondenumerable* sets (sets that cannot be put into a one-to-one correspondence with the set of counting numbers). This result may appear incredible to you, but if you have mastered the idea of a one-to-one correspondence, you should be able to prove it!

Two unequal line segments contain the same number of points!

Cantor reasoned in the following manner: Two sets contain the same number of elements if and only if the elements can be paired off one to one. Then he diagrammed the two unequal line segments. (Call the line segments $\overline{AB}$ and $\overline{CD}$ as in the diagram below.) Notice that line segment $\overline{OQ}$ cuts $\overline{CD}$ at P, and $\overline{AB}$ at Q. You may regard P and Q as corresponding points.

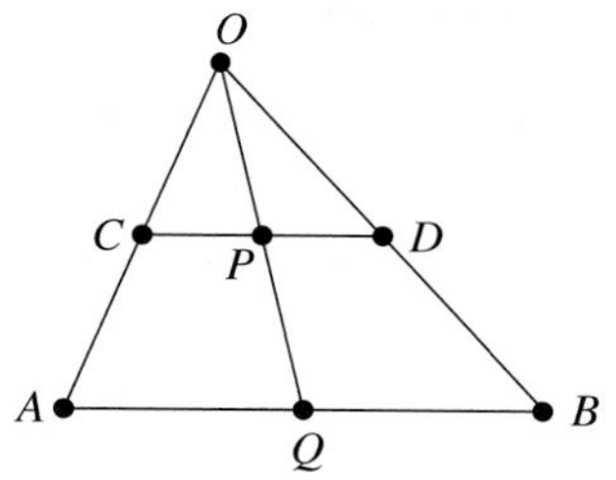

37. Can you discover the proof that there are as many points in $\overline{AB}$ as in $\overline{CD}$?

CHAPTER 2 Summary

SECTION	ITEM	MEANING	EXAMPLE
2.1A	$\{\ \}$	Set braces	$\{1, 2, 3\}$ is a set.
	$\in$	Is an element of	$2 \in \{1, 2, 3\}$
	$\notin$	Is not an element of	$4 \notin \{1, 2, 3\}$
2.1B	$\{1, 2\}$	List (roster) notation	
	$\{x \mid x \text{ has property } P\}$	Set-builder notation	$A = \{x \mid x \text{ is a counting number}\}$
	$\{\ \}$ or $\varnothing$	The empty, or null, set	The set of words that rhyme with *orange* is an empty set
2.1C	$=$	Equals	$\{1, 2\} = \{2, 1\}$
2.1D	$\subseteq$	Is a subset of	$\{1, 2\} \subseteq \{1, 2, 3\}$
	$\subset$	Is a proper subset of	$\{a\} \subset \{a, b\}$
	$\mathcal{U}$	The universal set	$\mathcal{U}$ is the set of all elements under discussion.
2.2A	$\cap$	Intersection	$\{1, 2, 3\} \cap \{2, 3, 4\} = \{2, 3\}$
	$\cup$	Union	$\{1, 2, 3, 4\} \cup \{2, 3, 4\} = \{1, 2, 3, 4\}$
2.2B	A'	Complement of set A	If $\mathcal{U} = \{1, 2, 3, 4, 5\}$ and $A = \{1, 2\}$, then $A' = \{3, 4, 5\}$.

continued

CHAPTER 2 Summary – *continued*

SECTION	ITEM	MEANING	EXAMPLE
2.2B	De Morgan's Laws	$(A \cap B)' = A' \cup B'$ $(A \cup B)' = A' \cap B'$	If $\mathcal{U} = \{1, 2, 3, 4, 5\}$, $A = \{1, 2, 3, 4, 5\}$, and $B = \{1, 2\}$, then $A \cap B = \{1, 2\}$, and $(A \cap B)' = \{3, 4, 5\}$, $A' = \varnothing$, $B' = \{3, 4, 5\}$, and $A' \cup B' = \{3, 4, 5\}$.
2.2C	$A - B$	Set difference	$A - B = \{3, 4, 5\}$
2.4	$n(A)$	Cardinal number of set A	If $A = \{a, b, c\}$ and $B = \{d, e\}$, then $n(A) = 3$ and $n(B) = 2$.
	Finite set A	A set A for which $n(A)$ is a whole number	If $A = \{1, 5, 17\}$, $n(A) = 3$ and A is finite.
2.5B	$A \sim B$	Set equivalence	If $A = \{a, b\}$ and $B = \{1, 2\}$, A and B are equivalent.
2.5C	Infinite set	A set that can be placed into a one-to-one correspondence with one of its proper subsets	N is infinite since it can be placed into a one-to-one correspondence with its proper subset E, the even numbers.
	$\aleph_0$	The cardinal number for the set N of counting numbers	$n(N) = \aleph_0$

CHAPTER 2 Practice Test

1. Which of the following descriptions define a set?
   a. Brilliant students
   b. Students with math SAT scores over 400
   c. Natural numbers greater than 5
   d. Natural numbers less than 1

2. List the elements of the set

   $\{x \mid x \text{ is a counting number between 2 and 10}\}$

3. Describe the following sets verbally and in set-builder notation:
   a. $\{a, e, i, o, u\}$
   b. $\{2, 4, 6, 8\}$

4. List all the proper subsets of the set {\$, ¢, %}.

5. Complete the following definitions by filling in the blanks with the symbol $\in$ or $\notin$.
   a. $A \cup B = \{x \mid x$ _____ A or x _____ $B\}$
   b. $A \cap B' = \{x \mid x$ _____ A and x _____ $B\}$
   c. $A' = \{x \mid x$ _____ $\mathcal{U}$ and x _____ $A\}$
   d. $A - B = \{x \mid x$ _____ A and x _____ $B'\}$

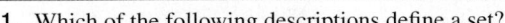

6. Let $\mathcal{U}$ = {Ace, King, Queen, Jack}, A = {Ace, Queen, Jack}, and B = {King, Queen}. Find the following:
   a. A'
   b. $(A \cup B)'$
   c. $A \cap B$
   d. $\mathcal{U} - (A \cap B)'$

7. If, in addition to the sets in problem 6, C = {Ace, Jack}, find the following:
   a. $(A \cap B) \cup C$
   b. $(A' \cup C) \cap B$

8. Draw a pair of Venn diagrams to show that $A - B = A \cap B'$.

9. Draw a Venn diagram to illustrate the set $A \cap B \cap C'$.

CHAPTER 2 Practice Test

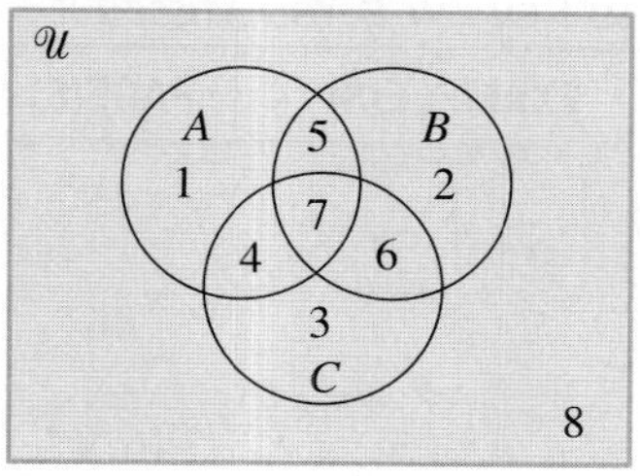

10. Find the sets of numbered regions in the diagram at the left that represent the following sets:
    a. $(A \cup B) \cap C'$
    b. $A' \cup (B' \cap C)$

11. Use the numbered regions in the diagram of problem 10 to verify that $(A \cap B) \cup C = (A \cup C) \cap (B \cup C)$.

12. Use the numbered regions in the diagram of problem 10 to verify that $(A \cap B)' = A' \cup B'$.

13. Refer to the diagram of problem 10 and determine which of the following sets (if any) is represented by regions 5, 6, and 7.
    a. $B - (A \cup C)$
    b. $(A \cup C) \cap B$
    c. $(A \cap B \cap C) - (A \cap C)$
    d. $(A \cup C') \cap B$

14. Refer to the diagram of problem 10 and determine which of the following sets (if any) is represented by regions 6 and 7.
    a. $A \cap B \cap C$
    b. $(A \cup C) \cap B$
    c. $A \cap C$
    d. $(A \cap C) \cup B$

15. Let $\mathcal{U} = \{1, 2, 3, 4, 5, 6, 7, 8\}$, $A = \{1, 3, 5, 7\}$, $B = \{2, 4, 6, 8\}$, and $C = \{1, 4, 5, 8\}$. Fill in the blanks with $=$ or $\neq$ to make correct statements.
    a. $n(A \cup C)$ ______ 6
    b. $n(B \cap C)$ ______ 3

16. Let $n(A) = 25$ and $n(B) = 35$. Find $n(A \cup B)$ if
    a. $A \cap B = \emptyset$.
    b. $n(A \cap B) = 5$.

17. Let $n(A) = 15$, $n(B) = 25$, and $n(A \cup B) = 35$. Find the following:
    a. $n(A \cap B)$
    b. $n(\mathcal{U})$ if $n(A' \cap B') = 8$

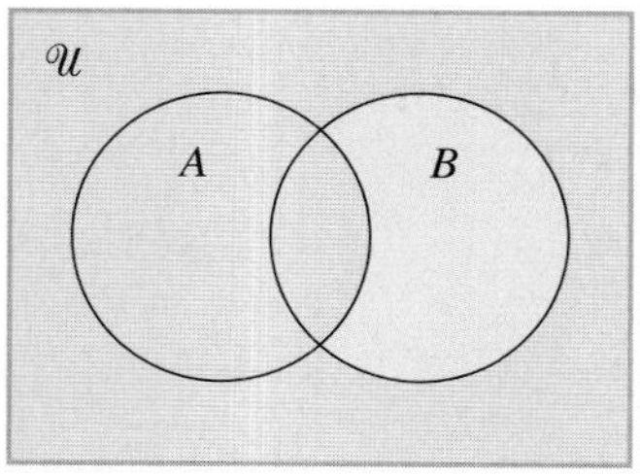

18. In the diagram at the left the rectangular region represents the universal set $\mathcal{U}$, and the circular regions represent the subsets A and B of $\mathcal{U}$. Find an expression for the shaded region in the diagram.

19. On checking 200 students, it is found that 70 are taking French, 40 are taking German, 75 are taking Spanish, 10 are taking French and German, 30 are taking French and Spanish, 15 are taking German and Spanish, and 70 are taking no language. If it is known that no students are taking all three languages, draw a Venn diagram to determine the answers to the following questions.
    a. How many are taking two languages?
    b. How many are taking Spanish and no other language?
    c. How many are taking Spanish and not French?

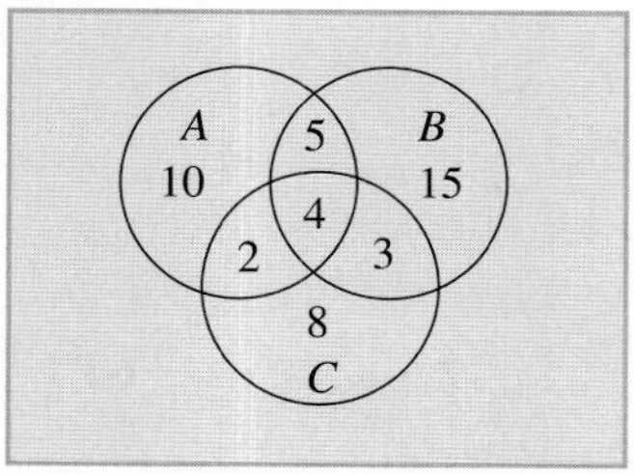

20. A survey of people to determine who regularly buys products A, B, and C gave the numbers shown in the diagram at the left.
    a. How many people were surveyed?
    b. How many buy product A but not B?
    c. How many buy product B or C but not A?
    d. How many buy both products B and C but not A?
    e. How many do not buy either product B or product C?

21. Show that the sets $\{1, 3, \ldots, 2n - 1, \ldots\}$ and $\{2, 4, \ldots, 2n, \ldots\}$ have the same cardinal number.

22. Show that the sets $\{1, 2, \ldots, n, \ldots\}$ and $\{4, 16, \ldots, (2n)^2, \ldots\}$ are equivalent.

23. Find the cardinality of the set $\{1, 4, \ldots, n^2, \ldots, 144\}$.

24. Find the cardinality of the set $\{1, 4, \ldots, n^2, \ldots\}$.

25. Show that the set of all proper fractions with numerator 1 is infinite.

ANSWERS TO PRACTICE TEST

CHAPTER 2		What to Review *If You Missed It*		
QUESTION	**ANSWER**	**SECTION**	**EXAMPLE(S)**	**PAGE(S)**
1	b, c, and d	2.1	1	45
2	$\{3, 4, 5, 6, 7, 8, 9\}$	2.1	3	46
3	**a.** The set of vowels in the English alphabet: $\{x \mid x \text{ is a vowel in the English alphabet}\}$ **b.** The set of even counting numbers less than 10: $\{x \mid x \text{ is an even counting number less than } 10\}$	2.1	3, 4, 5	46, 47
4	The proper subsets are $\varnothing$, {\$}, {¢}, {%}, {\$, ¢}, {\$, %}, and {¢, %}.	2.1	7, 8, 9	50
5	**a.** Both blanks take the symbol $\in$. **b.** First blank takes $\in$; second blank takes $\notin$. **c.** First blank takes $\in$; second blank takes $\notin$. **d.** Both blanks take the symbol $\in$.	2.1	2	45
6	**a.** {King} **b.** $\varnothing$ **c.** {Queen} **d.** {Queen}	2.2	1–3	56, 57
7	**a.** {Ace, Queen, Jack} **b.** {King}	2.2	4, 5	57, 58
8	The shaded region in the diagram on the left corresponds to $A - B$. The darkest region in the diagram on the right corresponds to $A \cap B'$. This shows that $A - B = A \cap B'$. 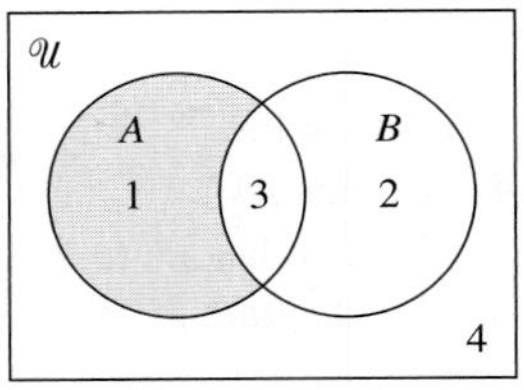 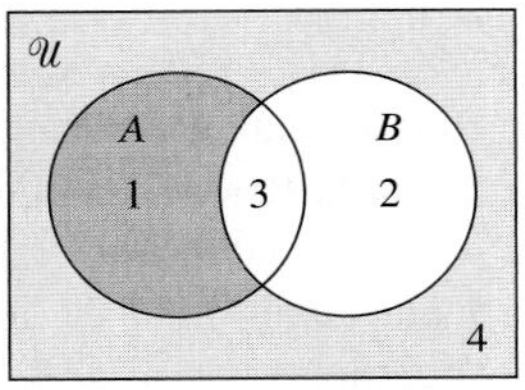	2.3	1, 2	64
9	The darkest region in the diagram corresponds to the set $A \cap B \cap C'$. 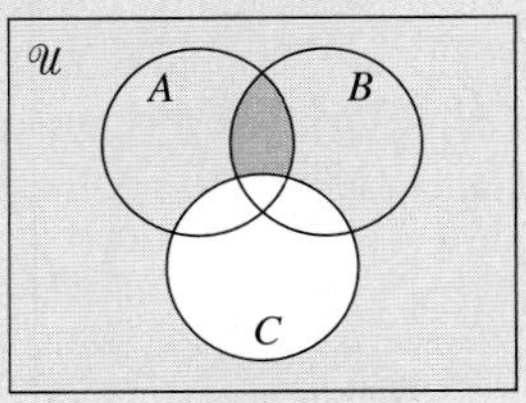	2.3	2	64
10	**a.** Regions 1, 2, and 5 **b.** Regions 2, 3, 4, 6, and 8	2.3	2	64
11	$(A \cap B) \cup C$ corresponds to regions 3, 4, 5, 6, and 7, and $(A \cup C) \cap (B \cup C)$ corresponds to the same regions. This verifies the equation $(A \cap B) \cup C = (A \cup C) \cap (B \cup C)$.	2.3	3	66
12	$(A \cap B)'$ and $A' \cup B'$ both correspond to regions 1, 2, 3, 4, 6, and 8. This verifies the equation $(A \cap B)' = A' \cup B'$.	2.3	3	66
13	Part (**b**) is correct.	2.3	5, 6	67, 68
14	None of these	2.3	5, 6	67, 68

ANSWERS TO PRACTICE TEST

CHAPTER 2		What to Review *If You Missed It*		
QUESTION	**ANSWER**	**SECTION**	**EXAMPLE(S)**	**PAGE(S)**
15	a. $=$ b. $\neq$	2.4	1, 2	72, 73
16	a. 60 b. 55	2.4	2	73
17	a. 5 b. 43	2.4	2, 3	73, 74
18	$B - A$ or $B \cap A'$ or $A' \cap B$	2.4	4	75
19	a. 55 b. 30 c. 45	2.4	4, 5	75, 76
20	a. 47 b. 12 c. 26 d. 3 e. 10	2.4	4, 5	75, 76
21	The following correspondence shows that the two sets have the same cardinal number: $1 \quad 3 \quad \cdots \quad 2n-1 \quad \cdots$ $\updownarrow \quad \updownarrow \quad \quad \updownarrow$ $2 \quad 4 \quad \cdots \quad 2n \quad \cdots$	2.5	1	82
22	The following correspondence shows that the two sets are equivalent: $1 \quad 2 \quad \cdots \quad n \quad \cdots$ $\updownarrow \quad \updownarrow \quad \quad \updownarrow$ $4 \quad 16 \quad \cdots \quad (2n)^2 \quad \cdots$	2.5	2	82
23	12	2.5	3	83
24	$\aleph_0$	2.5	3	83
25	A one-to-one correspondence can be set up between the given set $\{\frac{1}{2}, \frac{1}{3}, \frac{1}{4}, \ldots, \frac{1}{n}, \ldots\}$ and a subset of itself $\{\frac{1}{3}, \frac{1}{4}, \frac{1}{5}, \ldots, \frac{1}{n+1}, \ldots\}$, so the given set is infinite.	2.5	3	83

CHAPTER 3

Logic

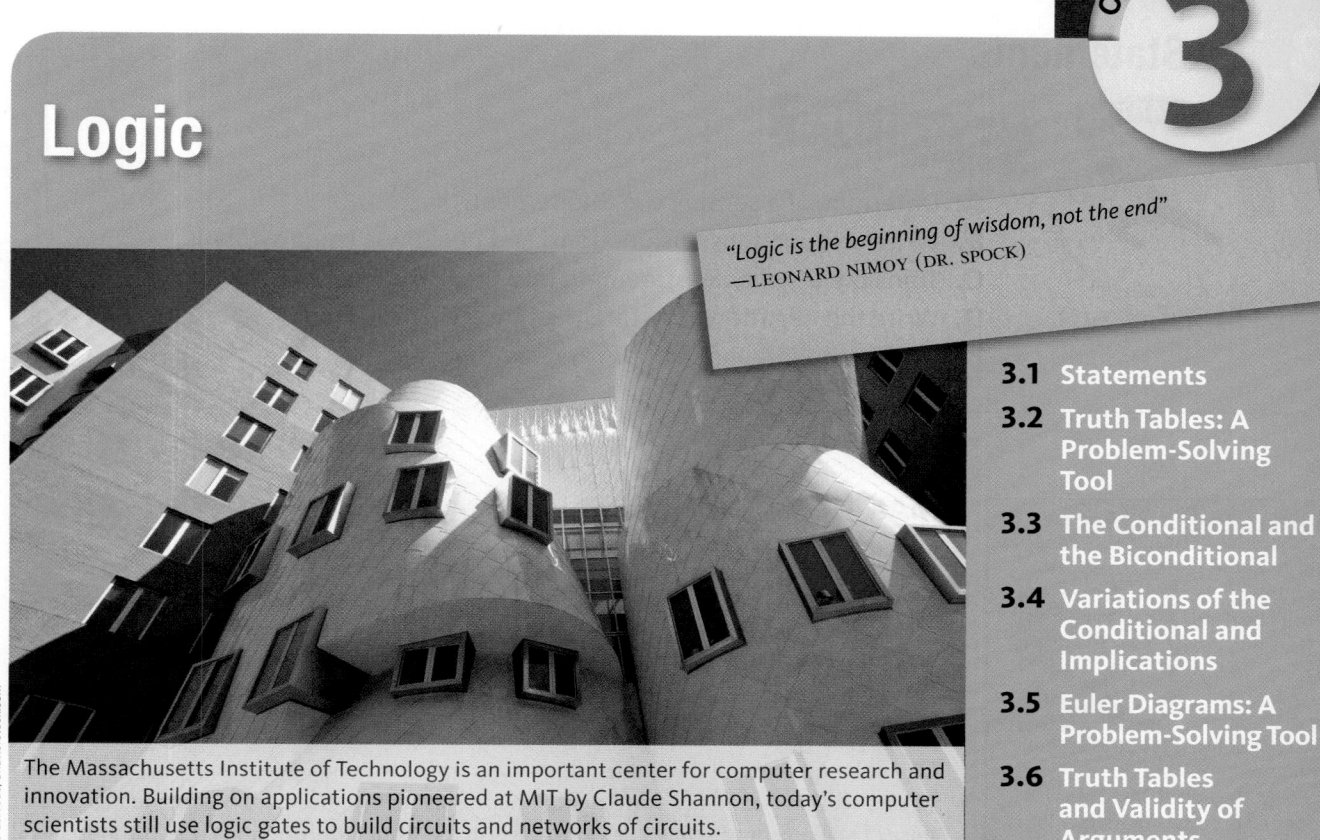

"Logic is the beginning of wisdom, not the end"
—LEONARD NIMOY (DR. SPOCK)

The Massachusetts Institute of Technology is an important center for computer research and innovation. Building on applications pioneered at MIT by Claude Shannon, today's computer scientists still use logic gates to build circuits and networks of circuits.

One of our most precious possessions is our ability to think and reason. Logic, the methods and principles used in distinguishing correct from incorrect thinking, logical thinking, and correct reasoning, is used in many fields—law, insurance, science, and mathematics, to name a few. The study of logic dates back to the Greek philosopher Aristotle (ca. 384–322 B.C.), who systematized the principles of reasoning and laws of logic in his *Organon.*

We start this chapter with a basic concept in logic, *statements.* We learn how to write statements and how to determine the conditions under which they are true or false. This technique dates back to the German mathematician and logician Gottlob Frege (1848–1925), who first tried to rewrite the established body of mathematics in logical symbolism.

In order to determine the truth or falsity of more complex statements, we develop a problem-solving tool called a **truth table** (Section 3.2) and then turn our attention to conditional and biconditional statements and their variations, as well as the related idea of implication. How do we determine whether an argument is **valid** (Section 3.6)? We do this by using **Euler diagrams** in Section 3.5 and **truth tables** in Section 3.6.

3.1 Statements

GETTING STARTED

OBJECTIVES

A. Determine if a sentence is a statement.
B. Write conjunctions, disjunctions, and negations using symbols.
C. Translate a symbolic statement into English and vice versa.
D. Write the negation of a statement involving All, None, or Some.
E. Use symbolic translations in applications.

Human Side of Math

© Topham/The Image Works
(1815–1864)

George Boole was born in Lincoln, England, on November 2, 1815.

Throughout the years, Boole had some of his writings published. At the age of 34, Boole was appointed professor of mathematics at Queen's College in Cork, Ireland.

At the age of 39, he published his masterpiece, *An Investigation of the Laws of Thought, on Which Are Founded the Mathematical Theories of Logic and Probabilities.* Boole was primarily responsible for bringing the study of formal logic from the field of philosophy into that of mathematics.

LOOKING AHEAD

Boole's work on logic and thought was instrumental in establishing modern symbolic logic, which is the focus of this chapter.

MAKING A STATEMENT

Consider the following directions:

> Lessee shall not paint, paper, or otherwise redecorate or make alterations to the premises without the prior written consent of Lessor.
> Checking "Yes" will not change your tax or reduce your refund.
> Make sure your application is signed on page 3 and in the appropriate place on page 4.

Can you guess where these directions come from? Do you understand what they mean? In this section you study **statements,** that is, sentences that can be classified as true or false. The preceding sentences were constructed using **conjunctions, disjunctions,** and **negations.** You will study these types of sentences and practice how to write them in symbols in Exercises 3.1, problems 9–16.

Now look at an excerpt from a menu, given below.

6. Country Fried Steak Breakfast
Includes 2 Eggs (any style), Country Fried Steak and Gravy, Grits or Breakfast Potatoes, Toast or Biscuits, and Fruit Jelly $6.99

Can you get Eggs, Country Fried Steak and Gravy, Grits and Breakfast Potatoes, and Toast and Biscuit and Jelly? Not unless you pay extra! When translating statements containing commas into symbolic form, the commas indicate which simple statements are grouped together. Thus, using the symbols $\wedge$ for *and,* and $\vee$ for *or,* your breakfast menu can be translated as

$$e \wedge (s \wedge a) \wedge (g \vee p) \wedge (t \vee b) \wedge j$$

You will learn how to translate sentences into symbols and vice versa in Exercises 3.1, problems 9–25.

The word *logic* is derived from the Greek word *logos,* which can be interpreted as "reason" or "discourse." The principles discovered by the Greeks were first systematized by Aristotle, and Aristotle's type of reasoning constitutes the traditional logic that has been studied and taught from his era to the present day. A simple illustration of Aristotelian logic goes as follows:

All men are mortal.		All students have cell phones.
Socrates was a man.	or	Desi is a student.
Therefore, Socrates was mortal.		Therefore, Desi has a cell phone.

This is a typical argument that is known as a **syllogism,** a type of deductive reasoning in which a ***conclusion*** is derived from the ***premises.***

Whether we are trying to solve a problem, taking part in a debate, or working a crossword puzzle, we are engaging in a mental activity called ***logical reasoning.*** This reasoning is usually expressed in declarative sentences. We now turn our attention to the study of these sentences.

A Recognizing Statements

In this and the following sections we will examine a certain type of declarative sentence called a ***statement*** and the manner in which we can combine such sentences and arrive at valid conclusions.

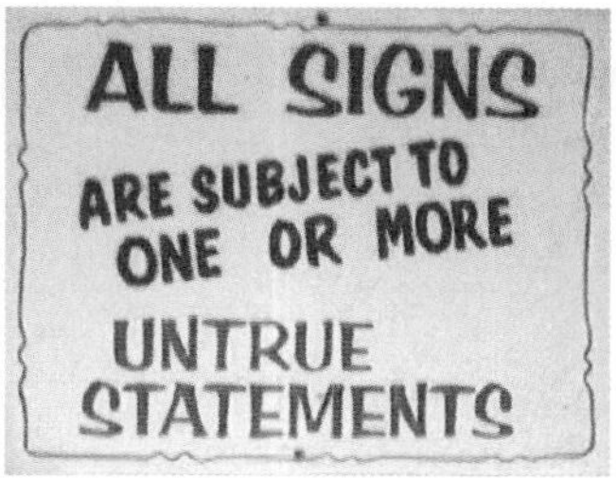

© I. Bello

Is this a statement? Is it true or false?

© Frontpage/Shutterstock.com

© I. Bello

Are these statements or commands?

Definition of Statement

A **statement** is a declarative sentence that can be classified as true or false but not both simultaneously.

This capability of being classified as true or false makes statements different from questions, commands, or exclamations. Questions can be asked, commands given, and exclamations shouted, but only statements can be classified as true or false. The sentences in Example 1 are illustrations of statements.

EXAMPLE 1 Sentences That Are Statements

(a) Boston is the capital of Massachusetts.

(b) The number 2 is even and less than 20.

(c) There are 5 trillion grains of sand in Florida.

(d) Either you study daily or you will get an F in this course.

(e) If you build it, they will come.

Note that the truth or falsity of the first statement in Example 1 can be determined by a direct check. The third statement is also true or false, even though there are no immediate or practical methods to determine its truth or falsity.

In contrast to the statements in Example 1, the following are illustrations of **nonstatements.**

EXAMPLE 2 Sentences That Are Not Statements

(a) What time is it?

(b) Elvis for president!

(c) Good grief, Charlie Brown!

(d) Close the door.

(e) This statement is false.

The sentences in Example 2 are not statements. Notice that if we assume that sentence (e) is true, then it is false, and if we assume that it is false, then it is true. Hence, the sentence cannot be classified as either true or false, so it is not a statement. A self-contradictory sentence of this type is called a **paradox.**

B Conjunction, Disjunction, and Negation

Having explained what is meant by a statement, we now turn our attention to various combinations of statements. In Example 1, for instance, statements (a) and (c) have only one component each (that is, each says only one thing), whereas statement (b) is a combination of two components, namely, "2 is even" and "2 is less than 20." Statements (a) and (c) are **simple;** statements (b), (d), and (e) are **compound.**

As a further example, "John has a cell phone" is a simple statement. On the other hand, "John has a cell phone *and* he has a credit card" is a compound statement because it is a combination of the two simple statements "John has a cell phone" and "he has a credit card."

There are many ways in which simple statements can be combined to form compound statements. Different combinations are formed by using words called **connectives** to join the statements. Two of the most common connectives are the words *and* and *or.* Suppose we use the letters p and q to represent the statements.

p: It is 100° today.
q: The air conditioner in this room is broken.

Then we can form the following compound sentences:

p **and** q: It is 100° today *and* the air conditioner in this room is broken.
p **or** q: It is 100° today *or* the air conditioner in this room is broken.

In the study of logic, the word *and* is symbolized by $\wedge$ and the word *or* by $\vee$ as mentioned earlier. Thus,

p **and** q	is written	$p \wedge q$
p **or** q	is written	$p \vee q$

Using these ideas, we make the following definitions:

Definition of Conjunction ($p \wedge q$)

If two statements are combined by the word **and** (or an equivalent word such as **but**), the resulting statement is called a **conjunction.** If the two statements are symbolized by p and q, respectively, then the conjunction is symbolized by $p \wedge q$.

Definition of Disjunction ($p \vee q$)

If two statements are combined by the word **or** (or an equivalent word such as **otherwise**), the result is called a **disjunction.** If the two statements are symbolized by p and q, respectively, then the disjunction is symbolized by $p \vee q$.

EXAMPLE 3 Writing Conjunctions in Symbols

Symbolize the following conjunctions:

(a) Tom is buying a laptop and Mary is buying an iPhone.
(b) Ann is passing math but she is failing English.

Solution

(a) Let t stand for "Tom is buying a laptop" and m stand for "Mary is buying an iPhone." Then the conjunction "Tom is buying a laptop and Mary is buying an iPhone" can be symbolized by $t \wedge m$.

(b) Let p stand for "Ann is passing math" and f stand for "she is failing English." The given conjunction can then be symbolized by $p \wedge f$. Here, the word *but* is used in place of *and.*

EXAMPLE 4 Writing Disjunctions in Symbols

Symbolize the disjunction "We create jobs or we increase taxes."

Solution

Letting c stand for "We create jobs" and i stand for "we increase taxes," we can symbolize the disjunction by $c \vee i$.

Another important construction in logic is negating a given statement.

> **Definition of Negation ($\sim p$)**
>
> The **negation** of a given statement is a statement that is ***false*** whenever the given statement is ***true*** and *true* whenever the given statement is *false*. If the given statement is denoted by p, its negation is denoted by $\sim p$. (The symbol $\sim$ is called a *tilde*.)

The negation of a statement can always be written by prefixing it with a phrase such as "It is not the case that." Sometimes the negation can be obtained simply by inserting the word *not* in the given statement. For example, the negation of the statement "Today is Friday" can be written as

"*It is not the case that* today is Friday."

or as

"Today is *not* Friday."

Similarly, if p stands for "It is hot today," then $\sim p$ (read "not p") can be written either as "It is not the case that it is hot today" or as "It is not hot today."

In the preceding illustrations, we have negated simple statements. We often have to consider the negation of compound statements, as in the next example.

C Translate a Symbolic Statement into English and Vice Versa

EXAMPLE 5 Translating Symbolic Statements into English

Let p be "the sky is blue," and let q be "it is raining." Translate the following statements into English:

(a) $\sim(p \wedge q)$ (b) $\sim p \wedge \sim q$ (c) $\sim q \wedge p$

Solution

(a) It is not the case that the sky is blue and it is raining. Another form of the negation is "The sky is not blue or it is not raining."

(b) The sky is not blue and it is not raining. You can also translate this statement as "The sky is neither blue nor is it raining."

(c) It is not raining and the sky is blue.

The two forms of the solution to part (a) of Example 5 illustrate the fact that the negation of $p \wedge q$ can be written either as $\sim(p \wedge q)$ or as $\sim p \vee \sim q$.

Negation of the Conjunction *p* and *q*

$\sim(p \wedge q)$ means $\sim p \vee \sim q$

Similarly,

Negation of the Disjunction *p* or *q*

$\sim(p \vee q)$ means $\sim p \wedge \sim q$

Thus, the statement "p or q" is false when and only when p and q are *both* false. These two facts are known as **De Morgan's laws.**

De Morgan's Laws

For any statement p and q,

$\sim(p \wedge q)$ means $\sim p \vee \sim q$

and

$\sim(p \vee q)$ means $\sim p \wedge \sim q$

You will be asked to verify De Morgan's laws in Exercises 3.2, problems 45 and 46. Compare the preceding two laws with De Morgan's laws for sets, $(A \cap B)' = A' \cup B'$ and $(A \cup B)' = A' \cap B'$.

EXAMPLE 6 Translating from English into Symbols

Consider the two statements

p: Sherlock Holmes is alive.
q: Sherlock Holmes lives in London.

Write the following statements in symbolic form:

(a) Sherlock Holmes is alive and he lives in London.
(b) Either Sherlock Holmes is alive or he lives in London.
(c) Sherlock Holmes is neither alive nor does he live in London.
(d) It is not the case that Sherlock Holmes is alive and he lives in London.

Solution

(a) $p \wedge q$ (b) $p \vee q$ (c) $\sim p \wedge \sim q$ (d) $\sim(p \wedge q)$

Note the use of parentheses in symbolic statements to indicate which items are to be taken as a unit. Thus, in part (a) of Example 5 and in part (d) of Example 6, $\sim(p \wedge q)$ means the negation of the entire statement $p \wedge q$. It is important to distinguish $\sim(p \wedge q)$ from $\sim p \wedge q$. The latter means that only statement p is negated. For example, if p is "John likes Mary" and q is "Mary likes John," then $\sim(p \wedge q)$ is "It is not true that John and Mary like each other." But $\sim p \wedge q$ is "John does not like Mary, but Mary likes John."

We use commas to indicate which simple statements are grouped together when the statements are written in words, as in the next example. Be very careful when translating a verbal statement containing commas into symbolic form!

EXAMPLE 7 Writing Statements in Symbols

Write the following in symbolic form:

(a) "You are a full-time student (f) or over 21 (o), and a resident of the state (r)."

(b) "You are a full-time student, or over 21 and a resident of the state."

Solution

(a) $(f \vee o) \wedge r$ (b) $f \vee (o \wedge r)$

Statements (a) and (b) do not have the same meaning!

EXAMPLE 8 Writing Negations, Disjunctions, and Conjunctions

Let p be the statement "Adam likes Eve," and let q be the statement "Eve likes Adam." Symbolize and write in words:

(a) The negation of the conjunction of p and q

(b) The disjunction of the negations of p and q

(c) The conjunction of the negations of p and q

(d) What can you conclude about the statements in (a), (b), and (c) according to De Morgan's laws?

© I. Bello

What is the negation of this statement?

Solution

(a) The conjunction of p and q is $p \wedge q$. Thus, the negation of the conjunction of p and q is $\sim(p \wedge q)$. In words: it is not the case that Adam likes Eve and Eve likes Adam. That is, it is not the case that Adam and Eve like each other.

(b) The negations of p and q are $\sim p$ and $\sim q$, respectively. Thus, the disjunction of the negations of p and q is $\sim p \vee \sim q$. In words: either Adam does not like Eve or Eve does not like Adam.

(c) $\sim p \wedge \sim q$. In words: Adam does not like Eve and Eve does not like Adam. That is, Adam and Eve do not like each other.

(d) By De Morgan's laws, the statements $\sim(p \wedge q)$ and $\sim p \vee \sim q$ in parts (a) and (b), respectively, have the same meaning.

D Write the Negation of a Statement Involving *All*, *None*, or *Some*

Statements involving the **universal quantifiers**—*all, no,* and *every*—or the **existential quantifiers**—*some* and *there exists at least one*—are more complicated to negate. Table 3.1 may help you.

Table 3.1

Statement	Negation
All a's are b's.	**Some** a's **are not** b's.
No a's are b's.	**Some** a's are b's.

Thus, the following statements p and $\sim p$ are negations of each other, as are q and $\sim q$:

p: **All** homeowners participate in recycling.
$\sim p$: **Some** homeowners **do not** participate in recycling, or "**Not** all homeowners participate in recycling."
q: **Some** of us will graduate.
$\sim q$: **None** of us will graduate.

Keep in mind that the definition of a negation requires that the negation of a statement must be ***false*** whenever the statement is ***true*** and ***true*** whenever the statement is ***false***. You can check this by looking at statements q and $\sim q$ above.

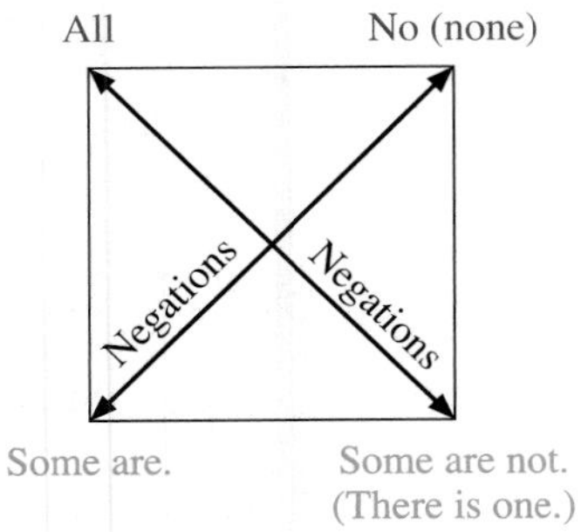

To help you remember how to negate statements, use this diagram.

EXAMPLE 9 Writing Negations Involving All, None, and Some

Write the negation of each of the following:

(a) All of us like pistachio nuts.

(b) Nobody likes freezing weather.

(c) Some students work part-time.

Solution

(a) Some of us do not like pistachio nuts. An alternative form is "Not all of us like pistachio nuts."

(b) Somebody likes freezing weather.

(c) No student works part-time.

Note: Remember that the negation of *all* is *some do not* and the negation of *some* is *none*.

E Applications

EXAMPLE 10 Translating English into Symbols

Write the indicated statements in symbols.

(a) Do you know what happens when you sign an application for a credit card? Here is the fine print:

> I request that a Visa account be opened (o) and cards be issued as indicated (i), and I authorize the bank to receive (r) and exchange (e) information and investigate (n) the references and data (d) collected pertinent to my creditworthiness.

(b) Here is a tip from a software manual.

> Some of the things you can use the Control Panel for are changing your screen colors, installing or changing settings for hardware and software, and setting up or changing settings for a network.

Write a statement that will indicate how you can use the Control Panel.

Solution

(a) $(o \wedge i) \wedge (r \wedge e) \wedge (n \wedge d)$

(b) First, we have to determine how many statements are present. This can be done by assigning a letter to each of the statements.

Changing your screen colors is p.
Installing settings for hardware is q.
Installing settings for software is r.
Changing settings for hardware is s.
Changing settings for software is t.
Setting up settings for a network is u.
Changing settings for a network is v.

The translation is $p \wedge (q \vee s) \wedge (r \vee t) \wedge (u \vee v)$.

In Section 1.3 we learned how to interpret bar graphs. Now we are ready to use that knowledge to determine if statements about those graphs are true or false.

EXAMPLE 11 Credit Card Surveys and Statements

The bar graph shows the results of a survey regarding the number of credit cards people own (None, 1, 2, 3, 4, or 5 or more). Determine if the given statements are true or false.

(a) The most common number of credit cards owned was **none (0).**

(b) The least number of credit cards owned was **1.**

(c) There were fewer people owning **4** cards than people owning **5 or more.**

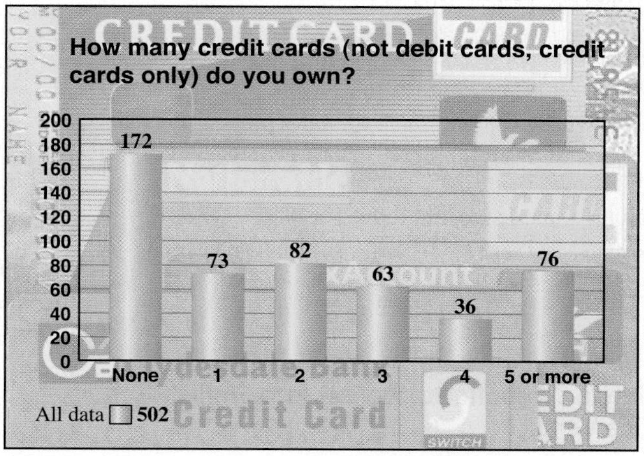

Source: Data from www.insightexpress.com, modified from original content.

Solution

To determine the truth or falsity of the statements, look at the length of the bars (bars are labeled at the top with the number of people answering).

(a) **True** (the longest bar is the one labeled **None: 172 people**)

(b) **False** (the shortest bar is the one labeled **4: 36 people**)

(c) **True** (the number of people owning 4 cards was **36**, which is less than the number of people owning 5 or more cards: **76**)

3.1 EXERCISES

A Recognizing Statements

In problems 1–8, determine whether each sentence is a statement. Classify each sentence that is a statement as simple or compound. If it is compound, give its components.

1. Circles are dreamy.
2. Lemons and oranges are citrus fruits.
3. Jane is taking an English course, and she has four themes to write.
4. Apples are citrus fruits.
5. Do you like mathematics?
6. Walk a mile.
7. Students at Ohio State University are required to take either a course in history or a course in economics.
8. Today is Sunday, and tomorrow is Monday.

B Conjunction, Disjunction, and Negation

In problems 9–16, write each statement in symbolic form using the indicated letters to represent the corresponding components.

9. This is April (a), and income tax returns must be filed (f).
10. Logic is a required subject for lawyers (r) but not for most engineers ($\sim e$).
11. Sherlock Holmes is a detective (d) or a fictitious character in four novels (f).
12. Snoopy is not an aviator ($\sim a$), or the Sopwith Camel is an airplane (p).
13. Violets are blue (b), but roses are pink (p).
14. The stock market goes up (u); nevertheless, my stocks stay down (d).
15. I will take art (a) or music (m) next term.
16. I will not drive to New York ($\sim d$); however, I shall go by train (t) or by plane (p).

C Translate a Symbolic Statement into English and Vice Versa

In problems 17–20, let p be "David has a Facebook page" and let q be "David has a Twitter account." Write each statement in symbolic form.

17. David has both a Facebook page and a Twitter account.
18. David has a Twitter account but not a Facebook page.
19. David does not have a Twitter account or a Facebook page.
20. It is not the case that David has a Twitter account and a Facebook page.

In problems 21–25, let p be "Ricky loves Lucy" and let q be "Lucy loves Ricky." Give a verbal translation of each statement.

21. $p \vee \sim q$
22. $\sim(p \vee q)$
23. $p \wedge \sim q$
24. $\sim p \wedge \sim q$
25. $\sim(p \wedge q)$

D Write the Negation of a Statement

In problems 26–31, write the negation of each sentence.

26. It is a long time before the end of the term.
27. Bill's store is making a good profit.
28. The number 10 is a round number.
29. My dog is a spaniel.
30. Your cat is not a Siamese.
31. I do not like to work overtime.

In problems 32–34, determine whether the statements p and q are negations of each other.

32. p: Sally is a very tall girl.
    q: Sally is a very short girl.
33. p: All squares are rectangles.
    q: Some squares are not rectangles.
34. p: All whole numbers are even.
    q: At least one whole number is not even.

In problems 35–49, give the negation of each statement.

35. All men are mortal.
36. Some women are engineers.
37. Some basketball players are not 6 ft tall.
38. Some things are not what they appear to be.

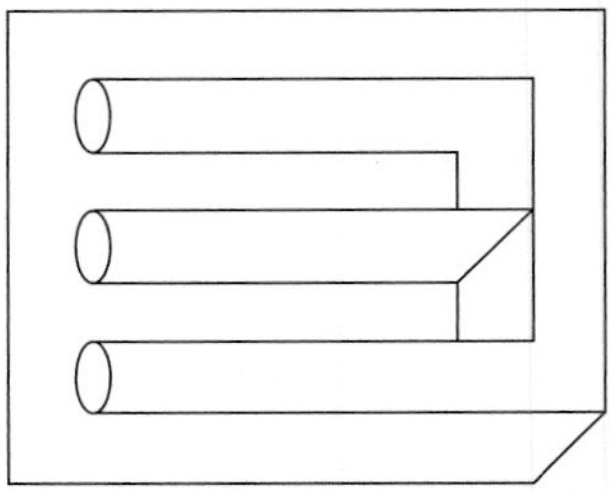

Some things are not what they appear to be.

39. Either he is bald or he has a 10-in. forehead.
40. Nobody does not like Sara Lee.
41. Some circles are round.
42. Some men earn less than \$8 per hour, and some men earn more than \$50 per hour.
43. Somebody up there loves me.
44. Nothing is certain but death and taxes.
45. Everybody likes to go on a trip.
46. No one can sue us under this coverage.
47. All persons occupying your covered auto are insured.
48. None of your contributions are deductible.
49. Some expenses are not subject to the 2% limit.
50. The statement "Not all people are awkward" is directly transformed into the statement "Some people are not awkward" by which one of the following logical equivalences?
    a. "If p, then q" means the same as "If not q, then not p."
    b. "All are not p" means the same as "None are p."
    c. "Not all are p" means the same as "Some are not p."
    d. "Not (not p)" means the same as "p."

E Applications

51. The chairperson of the city council told the members that if they declared a holiday, at least one of the 10 banks in the city would remain open. The chairperson was mistaken. Which of the following statements (if any) is consistent with this situation?
    a. The council did not declare a holiday, and all the banks remained closed.
    b. The council did not declare a holiday, and all the banks remained open.
    c. The council declared a holiday, and none of the banks remained closed.
    d. The council declared a holiday, and none of the banks remained open.

Write the statements in problems 52–55 in symbolic form.

52. You are legally married (m) or divorced (d), and currently enrolled (e).
53. I am a dependent person (d) and my parents are residents (p), or I have maintained legal residence in the state (r).
54. "You must be a U.S. citizen (c) or an eligible noncitizen (n), and be enrolled as a degree-seeking student (e)."—*Excerpt from a Pell Grant brochure*
55. "You must be a resident (r) and be ranked in the top 10% of your graduating class (t) or GED scores (g)."—*Excerpt from the Paul Douglas Teacher Scholarship*

IN OTHER WORDS

56. Let p be "Today is Friday." Let q be "Tomorrow is Saturday." Write the negation of each of the following in words:
    a. $p \wedge q$ b. $p \wedge \sim q$ c. $p \vee q$
57. Let p be "The diagram is a square." Let q be "The diagram is a rectangle." Write the negation of each of the following in words:
    a. $p \vee q$ b. $\sim p \wedge q$ c. $\sim p \vee \sim q$
58. In Example 2 we discussed the paradoxical statement "This sentence is false." Now, take a 3-by-5 card. On one side of the card write

    The sentence on the other side of this card is true.

    On the other side of the card write

    The sentence on the other side of this card is false.

    Is the first sentence true or false? Explain.
59. On another 3-by-5 card write these three sentences:
    (1) This sentence contains five words.
    (2) This sentence contains eight words.
    (3) Exactly one sentence on this card is true.
    Which statement(s) are true, and which false?
60. Consider the sentence "This sentence is true." Is this sentence a statement? Explain.

USING YOUR KNOWLEDGE

In Section 1.3 we learned how to interpret circle graphs. Use your knowledge to determine some facts regarding average costs at public and private universities. In problems 61–65, refer to the following diagram to determine if the statements are true or false.

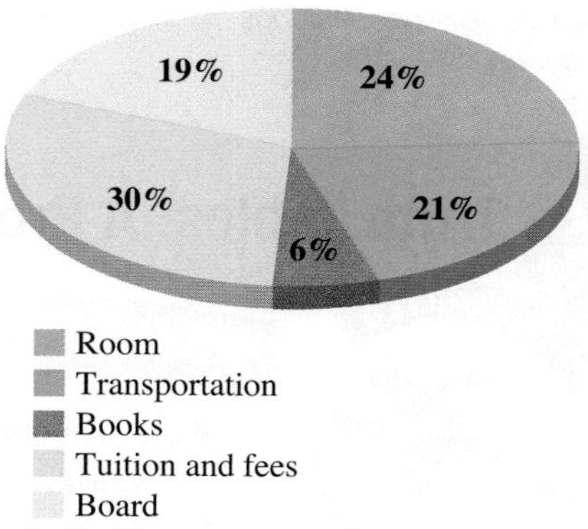

Average annual costs at public universities.
Source: http://www.westwood.edu/resources/student-budget.

61. The biggest expense is transportation.
62. The smallest expense is board.
63. The expenses for transportation and room are greater than the expenses for tuition and fees and board.
64. The biggest expense is not tuition and fees.
65. The cost of room and books is the same as that of tuition and fees.

How much more money can you make based on your gender, education, and ethnicity? See the graph! In problems 66–68 refer to the graph and decide if the given statement is true or false.

Median Earnings of Full-Time Year-Round Workers Ages 25–34, by Race/Ethnicity, Gender, and Education Level, 2008

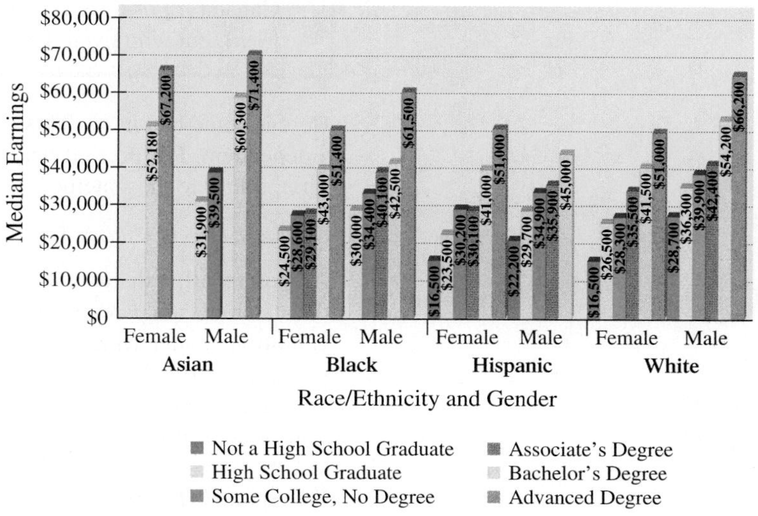

Sources: U.S. Census Bureau, 2009; Education Pays 2010.

66. Among females with an advanced degree, Asians have the highest median income.

67. Among male high school graduates, blacks have the highest median income.

68. Asian females with an advanced degree earn more than white females with an advanced degree.

The individual earnings in the graph can be defined by using ***conjunctions, disjunctions, and negations.*** *For example, the* ***highest*** *median earnings belongs to Asians and males and advanced degrees ($71,400).*

In problems 69–70 use conjunctions, disjunctions, and negations to define:

69. a. The category with the **lowest** earnings in the graph
    b. The category with the second lowest earnings in the graph

70. a. The category with the second **highest** earnings in the graph
    b. The ethnicity of the group with the highest earnings for both genders

3.2 Truth Tables: A Problem-Solving Tool

GETTING STARTED

OBJECTIVES

- **A.** Form the conjunction of two statements and determine its truth value.
- **B.** Form the disjunction of two statements and determine its true value.
- **C.** Find the negation of a statement and determine its truth value.
- **D.** Construct the truth table for a given statement.
- **E.** Determine if two statements are equivalent by using a truth table.

TAX FORMS AND TRUTH VALUES

Have you ever *really* read the instructions for your 1040 tax form? For example, suppose you are interested in knowing whether a person qualifies as your dependent. You turn to the appropriate page of the instruction booklet, and it says that for someone to qualify as your dependent, he or she must pass five qualifying tests, including the following:

> **Test 3—Citizen or Resident**
>
> The person must have been a U.S. citizen [u] or resident alien [r], a resident of Canada [c] or Mexico [m], or your adopted child [a] who is not a U.S. citizen [$\sim u$], but who lived with you all year in a foreign country [l].

Here is some bad news. This is only *one* of the *five* tests required to qualify a person as a dependent. For present purposes, let us consider if a person qualifies under this test. First, translate the statement to symbolic form as follows:

$$(u \vee r) \vee (c \vee m) \vee (a \wedge \sim u \wedge l)$$

As you recall, a disjunction is true when any of its components is true; thus, if any of the statements in parentheses is true, the test is satisfied. Can you think of three different conditions under which the test is satisfied? How can you make the third statement in parentheses true? In this section you will learn to identify circumstances under which compound statements are true or false. Then you will practice doing this in problems 17–25 of Exercises 3.2.

We regard T (for true) and F (for false) as the possible **truth values** of a statement. Thus, the statement "George Washington was the first president of the United States" has the truth value T, and the statement "The moon is made of green cheese" has the truth value F.

One of the objectives of logic is to determine the truth value of a compound statement when the truth values of its components are known. In order to attack this problem, we must first assign appropriate truth values to such statements as $p \wedge q$, $p \vee q$, and $\sim p$.

Although the symbols $\wedge$, $\vee$, and $\sim$ were introduced in Section 3.1, they were not completely defined. We shall complete their definitions by assigning appropriate truth values to statements involving these symbols.

A The Conjunction $\wedge$ (and)

Suppose you are offered a position in a firm requiring that

p: An applicant must be at least 18 years of age.

and

q: An applicant must be a college graduate.

To be eligible for this position, you must meet *both* requirements; that is, both p and q must be true. Thus, it seems desirable to say that for a conjunction to be true, both components must be true. Otherwise, the conjunction is false.

If we have a conjunction with two components, p and q, we have four possible pairs of truth values for these statements, namely,

1. p true, q true
2. p true, q false
3. p false, q true
4. p false, q false

Table 3.2 Conjunction ($\wedge$)

1	2	3
p	q	$p \wedge q$
T	*T*	*T*
T	*F*	*F*
F	*T*	*F*
F	*F*	*F*

As in the preceding example, it seems reasonable to assign the value T to the statement $p \wedge q$ only when both components are true. The assignment of these truth values can be summarized by means of a table called a **truth table,** as shown in Table 3.2. This truth table is to be regarded as the definition of the symbol $\wedge$ and it expresses the following fact:

Truth Value of the Conjunction p and q ($p \wedge q$)

The conjunction $p \wedge q$ is true when p and q are both true; otherwise, the conjunction is false.

Thus, the conjunction of the statements f: Nat has a Facebook page and t: Nat has a Twitter account is true when Nat has both a Facebook page and a Twitter account.

Note that other English words such as *but, nevertheless, still, however,* and so on are sometimes used in place of the connective *and.* Thus, the statement "Mary is a teenager but not under 15" is a conjunction of the two statements "Mary is a teenager" and "Mary is not under 15." On the other hand, the statement "Mary and Sue are sisters" is not a conjunction (unless they are sisters in a sorority or convent).

B The Disjunction $\vee$ (or)

As we shall see, there are two types of disjunctions, and we shall illustrate these by examples.

EXAMPLE 1 Forming Disjunctions and Analyzing Their Truth

Let p be "I will pass this course."
Let q be "I will flunk this course."

Form the disjunction of p and q, and discuss its truth values.

Solution

The statement "I will pass this course or I will flunk it" is the desired disjunction. This statement will be true only when *exactly* one of the components is true; it will be false otherwise.

EXAMPLE 2 More Disjunctions and Truth Values

Consider the two statements:

m: I will study Monday.
s: I will study Saturday.

Form the disjunction of *m* and *s*, and discuss its truth values.

Solution

The statement "I will study Monday or I will study Saturday" is the required disjunction. It will be false only when both components are false; it will be true otherwise.

If we compare the disjunctions in Examples 1 and 2, it is clear that in the statement contained in Example 1, only one of the two possibilities can occur: I will either pass the course or I will *not* pass the course. However, in Example 2, I have the possibility of studying Monday or Saturday or both. The meaning of the second usage is clarified by replacing the word *or* by *and/or.* Instead of arguing which usage should be called the disjunction of the two statements, we shall refer to the *or* used in Example 1 as the **exclusive or** or the **exclusive disjunction.** The *or* used in Example 2 will be called the **inclusive or** or the **inclusive disjunction** and will be denoted by $\vee$. The truth table defining the symbol $\vee$ appears in Table 3.3 and expresses the following important fact:

Table 3.3 Disjunction ($\vee$)

1	2	3
p	q	$p \vee q$
T	*T*	*T*
T	*F*	*T*
F	*T*	*T*
F	*F*	*F*

Truth Value of the Disjunction *p* or *q* ($p \vee q$)

The **inclusive disjunction** $p \vee q$ (read "*p* or *q*") is false only when *p* and *q* are both false; otherwise, it is true.

In the remainder of this chapter it will not be necessary to use the exclusive disjunction.

C The Negation ~ (not)

Finally, we consider the **negation** of a statement. In the English language, a negation is usually formed by inserting a *not* into the original statement. Of course, this is not the only way to negate a statement. A column by Bill Gold, which appeared in the *Washington Post,* tells the story of a woman who offered a bus driver a $5 bill and asked for tokens. His reply? "I am sorry, lady, but there ain't no bus driver got no change or no tokens, no time, nowhere, no more."

EXAMPLE 3 Negating Statements

Let *p* be the statement "I will go to college." Express the statement $\sim p$ in words, and discuss its truth values.

Solution

Either of the statements "I will not go to college" or "It is not the case that I will go to college" is the negation of the statement *p* and can be symbolized by $\sim p$. Because every statement is either true or false (and not both), we see that $\sim p$ must be false whenever *p* is true, and $\sim p$ must be true whenever *p* is false.

Table 3.4 Negation ($\sim$)

1	2
p	$\sim p$
T	F
F	T

Table 3.4 defines the negation symbol $\sim$. This table expresses the definition:

> **Truth Value of the Negation, $\sim p$**
>
> $\sim p$ is false whenever p is true, and $\sim p$ is true whenever p is false.

EXAMPLE 4 Driver's License Renewals

Your driver's license will be renewed under the following conditions: You are a safe driver, have no physical disability, and are not addicted to drugs or intoxicants. Let s be the statement "You are a safe driver," p be the statement "You have a physical disability," and q be the statement "You are addicted to drugs or intoxicants." Write a statement in symbolic form whose truth will guarantee that your driver's license will be renewed.

Solution

$s \wedge \sim p \wedge \sim q$

In many cases it is convenient to construct truth tables to determine the truth values of certain compound statements involving the symbols $\wedge$ (and), $\vee$ (or), and $\sim$ (not). It is important to keep the following in mind:

1. A conjunction $p \wedge q$ is true when p and q are both true and is false otherwise.
2. A disjunction $p \vee q$ is false when p and q are both false and is true otherwise.
3. If p and $\sim p$ are negations of each other, then $\sim p$ is false whenever p is true, and $\sim p$ is true whenever p is false.

EXAMPLE 5 Singles and Taxes

When filing your Form 1040A, you will be classified as *single* if any *one* of the following is true:

You were not married ($\sim m$).
You were legally separated under a decree of divorce (d) or of separate maintenance (s).
You were widowed before January 1 (w) and did not remarry ($\sim r$).

(a) Write in symbols the conditions under which you will be classified as *single.*

(b) Write the conditions under which you will be classified as *not single.*

Solution

(a) We take the disjunction of the three given statements.

$\sim m \vee (d \vee s) \vee (w \wedge \sim r)$

(b) We have to make the disjunction $\sim m \vee (d \vee s) \vee (w \wedge \sim r)$ false; this means that each of the components must be false.

For $\sim m$ to be false, m must be true.
For $d \vee s$ to be false, both d must be false and s must be false.
For $(w \wedge \sim r)$ to be false, either w has to be false or $\sim r$ must be false; that is, r must be true.

Thus, for you to be classified as *not single,* you must be *all* of the following:

Married (m)
Not legally separated under a decree of divorce ($\sim d$) *and* not legally separated under a decree of separate maintenance ($\sim s$)
Either a widower (w) *or* remarried (r)

Note that the statement $m \wedge \sim d \wedge \sim s \wedge (\sim w \vee r)$ is the negation of $\sim m \vee (d \vee s) \vee (w \wedge \sim r)$; that is, *not single* is the negation of *single.*

D Making Truth Tables

We have already constructed truth tables for the basic statements, conjunctions, disjunctions, and negations. We now give you a procedure that can be used to help you construct any truth table containing compound statements.

Procedure for Constructing Truth Tables

1. Examine the statement and determine if the final result is a negation, conjunction, or disjunction. For example, $\sim p \vee q$ is a disjunction (you are connecting the negation $\sim p$ and the statement q with the disjunction $\vee$); the statement $\sim(p \wedge \sim q)$ is a negation (you are negating $p \wedge \sim q$); the statement $p \wedge (q \vee r) \Leftrightarrow (p \wedge q) \vee (p \wedge r)$ is called an *equivalency* (you have to show that the statements $p \wedge (q \vee r)$ and $(p \wedge q) \vee (p \wedge r)$ have identical truth tables).
2. Complete the columns under the simple statements p, q, and r.
3. Complete the columns under the connectives with parentheses.
4. Complete the column under any remaining statements and their negations.
5. Complete the column under any remaining connectives, keeping in mind that the answer will appear under the final column determined in step 1. It is a good idea to highlight or circle the column containing the final answer and number the columns in the order they were completed.

Table 3.5

1	2	3	4	
p	q	$\sim p$	$\vee$	q
T	*T*	*F*	*T*	
T	*F*	*F*	*F*	
F	*T*	*T*	*T*	
F	*F*	*T*	*T*	

Note: You do *not* have to write the truth values for q in the far-right column; simply refer to column 2.

Some students prefer to write the columns like this.

1	2	3		4	
p	q	$\sim p$	$\sim p$	$\vee$	q
T	*T*	*F*		*T*	
T	*F*	*F*		*F*	
F	*T*	*T*		*T*	
F	*F*	*T*		*T*	

EXAMPLE 6 Truth Tables with Negations and Disjunctions

Construct the truth table for the statement $\sim p \vee q$.

Solution

1. We write the four possible pairs of truth values for p and q in columns 1 and 2 of Table 3.5.
2. Using column 1 as a reference, we negate statement p to get the entries in column 3. (We simply write *F* in the rows where we wrote *T* for p and *T* in the rows where we wrote *F* for p.)
3. To finish Table 3.5, we look at column 3 ($\sim p$) and column 2 (q). We combine columns 3 ($\sim p$) and 2 (q) using the disjunction *or,* denoted by $\vee$, to get the truth value for $\sim p \vee q$ and write the result in column 4. We recall (see Table 3.3) that a disjunction is false only when both its components are false; it is true otherwise. Thus, we write *F* in the second row of column 4 where both components, $\sim p$ and q, are false, and we write *T* in the other rows. This completes Table 3.5.

EXAMPLE 7 Finding When a Disjunction Is False

Let p be "I lie," and let q be "I would tell you." When will the statement "I do not lie or I would tell you" be false?

Solution

The statement under consideration can be symbolized as $\sim p \vee q$. From Table 3.5, we see that $\sim p \vee q$ is false when p is true and q is false. Hence, the given statement is false when "I lie" and "I would not tell you."

EXAMPLE 8 Truth Tables Involving Negating Conjunctions

Construct the truth table for the statement $\sim(p \wedge \sim q)$.

Solution

As in Example 6, the plan is first to break down the given statement into its primitive components. The statement $\sim(p \wedge \sim q)$ is the negation of $p \wedge \sim q$, which is the conjunction of the components p and $\sim q$. We can write the truth values of $\sim q$ from those of q, and p is a primitive component. Thus, we use p, q, and $\sim(p \wedge \sim q)$ as headings for the truth table.

To find the truth values of $\sim(p \wedge \sim q)$, we must have the truth values of p, q, $\sim q$, and $p \wedge \sim q$, so we number the columns in that order. Table 3.6 is filled out in the following steps:

Table 3.6

1	2	5	4	3
p	q	$\sim(p$	$\wedge$	$\sim q)$
T	T	T	F	F
T	F	F	T	T
F	T	T	F	F
F	F	T	F	T

Remember, you can also write the columns like this.

1	2	3	4	5
p	q	$\sim q$	$p \wedge \sim q$	$\sim(p \wedge \sim q)$
T	T	F	F	T
T	F	F	F	F
F	T	T	F	T
F	F	T	F	T

1. We write the four possible pairs of truth values for p and q in columns 1 and 2.
2. Using column 2 (q) as our reference, we negate q to get $\sim q$ (column 3).
3. To get column 4 ($p \wedge \sim q$), we combine columns 1 (p) and 3 ($\sim q$), using the conjunction *and,* denoted by $\wedge$. We recall (see Table 3.2) that a conjunction is true only when both its components are true and is false otherwise. Thus, we write T in the second row of column 4, where p and $\sim q$ are both true, and we write F in the other rows.
4. We negate the truth values in column 4 to get those of $\sim(p \wedge \sim q)$ in column 5. The statement $\sim(p \wedge \sim q)$ has the truth values shown in column 5 of the table.

E Equivalent Statements

Notice that the statements given in Examples 6 and 8 have exactly the same truth values, *TFTT*; hence, the two statements must have the same meaning.

Definition of Equivalent ($\Leftrightarrow$)

Two statements p and q that have **identical** truth values are said to be **equivalent** (denoted by $p \Leftrightarrow q$).

Accordingly, from Examples 6 and 8, we can write an equivalent statement in symbolic form.

An Example of Equivalence

$\sim p \lor q \Leftrightarrow \sim(p \land \sim q)$

PROBLEM-SOLVING

Equivalent Statements

Show that $p \land (q \lor r) \Leftrightarrow (p \land q) \lor (p \land r)$.

① **Read** the problem and select the unknown. Show that two statements are equivalent. What does this mean?

To show that two statements are equivalent, you have to show that $p \land (q \lor r)$ and $(p \land q) \lor (p \land r)$ have identical truth tables.

② **Think** of a plan. Make a truth table for each of the statements. How many lines will each truth table have?

Because there are three statements, p, q, and r, each of which has two possible truth values, there are $2 \times 2 \times 2 = 8$ possible cases. Thus, the truth table must have 8 lines.

③ **Use** truth tables to carry out the plan. Break the statement $p \land (q \lor r)$ into components and label the columns accordingly. Then proceed as in the previous examples to make the truth table.

The components of $p \land (q \lor r)$ are p and $(q \lor r)$. Thus, the truth table (Table 3.7) must have columns for p, q, r, $q \lor r$, and $p \land (q \lor r)$. Table 3.7 is filled out in the same manner as the tables for the previous examples—by steps.

1. In the first three columns, write the possible truth values for p, q, and r. In column 1, enter four T's and four F's; in column 2, enter two T's, two F's, two T's, and two F's; in column 3, enter alternately one T and one F. This gives all the possible combinations of T's and F's for the three statements.
2. To obtain the truth values of $q \lor r$, combine columns 2 and 3 with a disjunction $\lor$, as shown in column 4. Because $q \lor r$ is false only when both q and r (rows 4 and 8) are false, enter F's in rows 4 and 8 and T's in the remaining rows.
3. To obtain the truth values of $p \land (q \lor r)$, combine columns 1 (p) and 4 ($q \lor r$) with a conjunction $\land$. Since a conjunction is true only when both components are true, complete column 5 by writing T's in the first three rows and F's in the other rows. The given statement has the truth values shown in column 5 of Table 3.7.

Table 3.7

1	2	3	5	4
p	q	r	$p \land$	$(q \lor r)$
T	T	T	T	T
T	T	F	T	T
T	F	T	T	T
T	F	F	F	F
F	T	T	F	T
F	T	F	F	T
F	F	T	F	T
F	F	F	F	F

You can also write the columns in order like this:

1	2	3	4	5
p	q	r	$(q \lor r)$	$p \land (q \lor r)$
T	T	T	T	T
T	T	F	T	T
T	F	T	T	T
T	F	F	F	F
F	T	T	T	F
F	T	F	T	F
F	F	T	T	F
F	F	F	F	F

Break the statement $(p \wedge q) \vee (p \wedge r)$ into components.

The components of $(p \wedge q) \vee (p \wedge r)$ are $(p \wedge q)$ and $(p \wedge r)$, and these two components have components p, q, and r. The truth table (Table 3.8) is filled out in the same manner as Table 3.7; that is, do columns 4, 5, and then 6.

Table 3.8

1	2	3	4	6	5
p	q	r	$(p \wedge q)$	$\vee$	$(p \wedge r)$
T	T	T	T	T	T
T	T	F	T	T	F
T	F	T	F	T	T
T	F	F	F	F	F
F	T	T	F	F	F
F	T	F	F	F	F
F	F	T	F	F	F
F	F	F	F	F	F

You can also write the columns in order like this:

1	2	3	4	5	6
p	q	r	$(p \wedge q)$	$(p \wedge r)$	$(p \wedge q) \vee (p \wedge r)$
T	T	T	T	T	T
T	T	F	T	F	T
T	F	T	F	T	T
T	F	F	F	F	F
F	T	T	F	F	F
F	T	F	F	F	F
F	F	T	F	F	F
F	F	F	F	F	F

④ **Verify** the answer. Are the results of the two tables identical?

Since the truth values in the final columns of the two tables (column 6) are identical, the two statements are equivalent.

Try Example 9 Now

Cover the solution, write your own solution, and then check your work.

EXAMPLE 9 Showing Equivalency

(a) Show that $(\sim p \vee q) \wedge r \Leftrightarrow (\sim p \wedge r) \vee (q \wedge r)$.

(b) Let p be the statement "You recycle paper," let q be the statement "You recycle glass," and let r be the statement "You are an environmentalist." If we know that you recycle paper, under what condition(s) will the statement $(\sim p \vee q) \wedge r$ be true?

Solution

(a) To show that $(\sim p \vee q) \wedge r \Leftrightarrow (\sim p \wedge r) \vee (q \wedge r)$, we have to show that the truth tables for both statements are identical. We first construct the table for $(\sim p \vee q) \wedge r$ (Table 3.9). The components for this statement are p, q, r, $\sim p$, and $(\sim p \vee q)$, as shown in Table 3.9. The statement $\sim p \vee q$ is false only when $\sim p$ and q are both false. Thus, in column 5 we enter F's in rows 3 and 4 and T's in the rest of the rows. Finally, $(\sim p \vee q) \wedge r$ is true only when both $(\sim p \vee q)$ in column 5 and r in column 6 are true. Thus, in column 7 we enter T's in rows 1, 5, and 7 and F's in the rest of the rows. The final truth values appear in column 7.

The components for $(\sim p \wedge r) \vee (q \wedge r)$ are p, q, r, $\sim p$, $(\sim p \wedge r)$, and $(q \wedge r)$, as shown in Table 3.10. Thus, $(\sim p \wedge r)$ (column 5) is true only when $\sim p$ and r are both

Table 3.9

1	2	3	4	5	7	6
p	q	r	$\sim p$	$(\sim p \vee q)$	$\wedge$	r
T	T	T	F	T	T	T
T	T	F	F	T	F	F
T	F	T	F	F	F	T
T	F	F	F	F	F	F
F	T	T	T	T	T	T
F	T	F	T	T	F	F
F	F	T	T	T	T	T
F	F	F	T	T	F	F

Table 3.10

1	2	3	4	5	7	6
p	q	r	$\sim p$	$(\sim p \wedge r)$	$\vee$	$(q \wedge r)$
T	T	T	F	F	T	T
T	T	F	F	F	F	F
T	F	T	F	F	F	F
T	F	F	F	F	F	F
F	T	T	T	T	T	T
F	T	F	T	F	F	F
F	F	T	T	T	T	F
F	F	F	T	F	F	F

true (rows 5 and 7 in column 5), and $(q \wedge r)$ (column 6) is true only when both q and r are true (rows 1 and 5 in column 6). Finally, $(\sim p \wedge r) \vee (q \wedge r)$ in column 7 is false only when both $(\sim p \wedge r)$ and $(q \wedge r)$ are false (rows 2, 3, 4, 6, and 8 in column 7). The final truth values are in column 7. Since columns 7 in Tables 3.9 and 3.10 are identical, the statements are equivalent.

(b) Since p has truth value T (first four rows), $(\sim p \vee q) \wedge r$ is true only when q and r are both true (row 1), that is, when the components q "You recycle glass" and r "You are an environmentalist" are both true.

3.2 EXERCISES

A The Conjunction ∧ (and)

B The Disjunction ∨ (or)

C The Negation ~ (not)

In problems 1–4, let p be "Today is Friday" and let q be "Today is Monday."

1. Write in words the disjunction of the two statements.
2. Write in words the conjunction of the two statements.
3. Write in words the negation of statement p.
4. Which of the statements in problems 1–3 always has the truth value F?

In problems 5–7, let g be "He is a gentleman" and let s be "He is a scholar." Write the following in words:

5. The disjunction of the two statements
6. The negation of the statement g
7. The conjunction of the two statements

In problems 8–10, use statements g and s of problems 5–7 and write each statement in symbolic form.

8. He is not either a gentleman or a scholar.
9. He is a gentleman and a scholar.
10. He is neither a gentleman nor a scholar.
11. Consider the statements p and q.

    p: It is raining.
    q: I will go to the beach.

    Write the statements in parts (**a**) and (**b**) in symbolic form.

    a. It is raining but I will go to the beach.
    b. It is raining or I will go to the beach.
    c. Assume that p is true and q is false. Find the truth values of the statements given in parts (**a**) and (**b**).

In problems 12–16, let p be "Mida is cooperative" and let q be "Desi is uncooperative." Write each statement in symbolic form.

12. Mida and Desi are both cooperative.
13. Neither Desi nor Mida is uncooperative.
14. It is not the case that Mida and Desi are both uncooperative.
15. Either Mida is cooperative or Desi is uncooperative.
16. Assume that Mida is cooperative and Desi is uncooperative. Which of the statements in problems 12–15 are true?

In problems 17–21, suppose that p is true and q is false. Write each statement in symbolic form, and find its truth value.

17. Either p or q
18. Either p or not q
19. Neither p nor q
20. p or q, but not both
21. Not q and not p

In problems 22–26, consider the following statements:

g: I go to college.
j: I join the army.

Suppose that g is false and j is true. Write each statement in symbolic form, and find its truth value.

22. Either I go to college or I join the army.
23. I go to college or I do not join the army.
24. I neither go to college nor join the army.
25. I go to college or I join the army, but not both.
26. I do not go to college and I do not join the army.

D Making Truth Tables

In problems 27–40, construct a truth table for each statement.

27. $p \vee \sim q$
28. $\sim(p \vee q)$
29. $\sim p \wedge q$
30. $\sim p \vee \sim q$
31. $\sim(p \vee \sim q)$
32. $\sim(\sim p \vee \sim q)$
33. $\sim(\sim p \wedge \sim q)$
34. $(p \vee q) \wedge \sim(p \wedge q)$
35. $(p \wedge q) \vee (\sim p \wedge q)$
36. $(p \wedge \sim q) \wedge (\sim p \wedge q)$
37. $p \wedge (q \vee r)$
38. $p \vee (q \wedge r)$
39. $(p \vee q) \vee (r \wedge \sim q)$
40. $[(p \wedge q) \vee (q \wedge \sim r)] \vee (r \wedge \sim s)$

What is one of the three worst things to say when asking for a personal loan? I have a job (j) but I hate it (h)

Source: http://tinyurl.com/6568dnv

41. a. Under which conditions is the statement "I have a job but I hate it" true?

b. Under which conditions is the statement "I have a job but I hate it" false?

c. Under which conditions is the statement "I have a job or I hate it" true?

d. Under which conditions is the statement "I have a job or I hate it" false?

42. Let u be "I am upside down on my mortgage" and p be "I plan to walk away from my house"

a. What does the statement u and p mean in plain English? See http://tinyurl.com/4duhnbq for more information!

b. When is the statement "I am neither upside down on my mortgage nor do I plan to walk away from my house" true?

c. When is the statement "I am either upside down on my mortgage or I plan to walk away from my house" true?

d. Under which conditions is the statement "Either I am upside down on my mortgage or I plan to walk away from my house" false?

In problems 43-46 use truth tables to show that the two statements are equivalent.

43. $p \vee (q \wedge r)$ and $(p \vee q) \wedge (p \vee r)$

44. $p \wedge (q \vee r)$ and $(p \wedge q) \vee (p \wedge r)$

45. $\sim(p \vee q)$ and $\sim p \wedge \sim q$

46. $\sim(p \wedge q)$ and $\sim p \vee \sim q$

In problems 47 and 48, use truth tables to show the equivalence.

47. $(p \wedge q) \vee \sim p \Leftrightarrow q \vee \sim p$

48. $(p \vee q) \wedge (\sim p \vee \sim q) \Leftrightarrow (p \wedge \sim q) \vee (\sim p \wedge q)$

49. a. Verify the entries in the following table:

p	q	$p \wedge q$	$p \wedge \sim q$	$\sim p \wedge q$	$\sim p \wedge \sim q$
T	T	T	F	F	F
T	F	F	T	F	F
F	T	F	F	T	F
F	F	F	F	F	T

b. Look at the last four columns of this table. Each of these columns has one T and three F's, and there is exactly one T on each line. This T occurs on the line where both components of the corresponding column heading are true. The headings of these last four columns are called **basic conjunctions.** By using theseconjunctions, you can write statements hav-ing any given four-entry truth table. For in-stance, a statement with the truth table $TFFT$ is $(p \wedge q) \vee (\sim p \wedge \sim q)$. Explain this.

c. By forming disjunctions of the basic conjunctions, you can write statements with given truth tables as noted in part (**b**). Write a statement having truth table $FTTF$. Do the same for $FTTT$. Can you write a simpler statement for the truth table $FTTT$?

50. The ideas in problem 49 can be generalized to include statements with any given number of components. Thus, the statement $p \wedge \sim q \wedge \sim r$ would have a truth table with a T on the line corresponding to p true, q false, and r false and F's on the other seven lines. What would be the truth table for $(p \wedge \sim q \wedge r) \vee (\sim p \wedge \sim q \wedge \sim r)$?

51. To be eligible for a position in a banking firm, an applicant must be at least 25 years old (t), have a college degree in business administration (d), and be married (m). Assume that t, d, and m are true statements. Which of the following three applicants (if any) is eligible for the above position?

Joe is married, has a college degree in fine arts, and is 26 years old.
Mary is married, has a degree in business administration, and is 22 years old.
Ellen has a degree in business administration, is 25 years old, and is single.

52. To qualify for a \$40,000 loan, an applicant must have a gross income of \$30,000 if single (\$50,000 combined income if married) and assets of at least \$10,000. Which of the following three applicants (if any) would qualify for the loan?

Mr. Perez is married, has two children, and makes \$35,000 at his job. His wife does not work.
Ms. Jefferson and her husband have assets of \$50,000. One makes \$22,000; the other makes \$19,000.
Tran Quang is a bachelor and works at two jobs. He makes \$28,000 at one job and \$5000 at the other; his only asset is a \$7000 Toyota.

IN OTHER WORDS

Mathematics has a specialized vocabulary. For example, the negation of "9 is less than 3" is "9 is not less than 3," but it can also be "9 is greater than or equal to 3."

In problems 53–57, negate each statement without using the word not.

53. 7 is less than 5.

54. 8 is more than 9.

55. 0 is greater than 3.

56. $\frac{1}{3}$ is greater than or equal to 1.

57. $\frac{1}{2}$ is less than or equal to $\frac{1}{8}$.

58. Let f be "I will go fishing." Let g be "The sun is shining." Write the following in words:

a. The conjunction of f and g

b. The negation of g

c. The disjunction of f and g

59. For the statements given in problem 58, write in words the negation of the conjunction of f and g. State under what circumstances this negation would be true.

USING YOUR KNOWLEDGE

The Higher Education Act states that any student is eligible to apply for a loan, provided the student fulfills the following requirements:

1. Enrolled (e) and in good standing (g), or accepted for enrollment (a) at an eligible school
2. Registered for at least one-half the normal full-time work load as determined by the school (h)
3. A citizen (c) or national (n) of the United States, or in the United States for other than a temporary purpose ($\sim t$)

60. Translate requirements 1, 2, and 3 into symbolic form.

61. What is the general symbolic compound statement whose truth implies that the student can apply for a loan?

62. A three-component statement whose truth implies that the student can apply for a loan is $a \wedge b \wedge c$. What are two others?

DISCOVERY

Four men, Mr. Baker, Mr. Carpenter, Mr. Draper, and Mr. Smith, live in Logictown. One is a baker, one a carpenter, one a draper, and one a smith, but none follows the vocation corresponding to his name. A logician tries to find out who is who and obtains the following partially correct information:

Mr. Baker is the smith.
Mr. Carpenter is the baker.
Mr. Draper is not the smith.
Mr. Smith is not the draper.

63. If it is known that three of the four statements are false, who is the carpenter? (*Hint:* Consider the four possible sets of truth values given for the statements in the table below.)

Statement	I	II	III	IV
1	*T*	*F*	*F*	*F*
2	*F*	*T*	*F*	*F*
3	*F*	*F*	*T*	*F*
4	*F*	*F*	*F*	*T*

3.3 The Conditional and the Biconditional

GETTING STARTED

OBJECTIVES

A. Write a conditional in symbolic form and determine its truth value.
B. Write a biconditional in symbolic form and determine its truth value.
C. Recognize statements equivalent to conditionals and find their negations.

ON WHAT CONDITION?

Have you read your insurance policy or your income tax instructions lately? They contain many of the connectives we have studied and more. Here is an excerpt from an automobile insurance policy.

> If the final recomputed premium exceeds the premium stated on the declarations page, you must pay the excess to Allstate.

(If you do not understand this, it may cost you money.) Here is another statement.

> If an injured person unreasonably refuses to take the examination, we are not required to pay any subsequent personal injury protection benefits.

(Failure to understand this one may cost you your benefits!)

What about income taxes? Here is an excerpt from an income tax form.

> If you checked NO to any of the above questions, you may not take the earned income credit.

(Here you may make a mistake on your return, resulting in an audit.)

Or what about this one?

> If your return is more than 60 days late, the minimum penalty will be $100 or the amount of any tax you owe, whichever is smaller.

Do you know what the penalty will be?

© Comstock/Jupiterimages

The field of law requires the ability to apply logic to reasoning and argument.

Finally, look at a hypothetical application of conditional statements in the field of law. A man was being tried for participation in a robbery. Here is a partial transcript of the proceedings.

Prosecutor:	"If the defendant is guilty, then he had an accomplice."
Defense attorney:	"That is not true!"
Judge:	"In that case, I declare a mistrial. The defendant needs a new attorney."

Why? The attorney said that the statement "If the defendant is guilty (g), then he had an accomplice (a)," or symbolically $g \to a$, was not true; that is, $g \to a$ was false. Now, look at the second row of Table 3.11. When is a conditional false? When the antecedent (g in this case) is true and the consequent (a in this case) is false. What does that mean in terms of the defendant?

Table 3.11

p	q	$p \to q$
T	T	T
T	F	F
F	T	T
F	F	T

It is sometimes necessary to specify the conditions under which a given event will be true. For example, one might say, "If the weather is nice, then I will go to the beach." If we let p stand for "the weather is nice" and q stand for "I will go to the beach," then the preceding compound statement is of the form "If p, then q." Statements of this kind are called **conditional statements** and are symbolized by $p \to q$. (Read "if p, then q" or "p arrow q" or "p conditional q.") In $p \to q$, statement p is called the **antecedent** and q the **consequent.**

A The Conditional

To understand the truth table for the conditional, consider the sign in the margin. It promises "If you stop here, your pain will too." Under which circumstances is this promise broken? Only if you *do* stop here and your pain *does not* stop. Thus, we should write F for $p \to q$ if p is true and q is false; otherwise, we should write T.

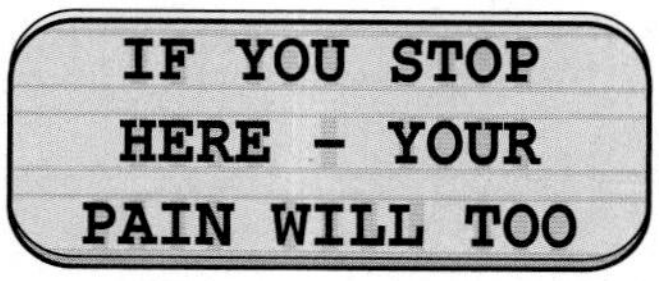

A chiropractor's sign makes use of a conditional statement.

Table 3.11 expresses these facts. It shows that if p and q are both true, then $p \to q$ is true, and if p is true and q is false, then $p \to q$ is false. In the last two lines of Table 3.11, p is false, so it would be incorrect to say that $p \to q$ is false. Since we want a complete truth table, we have assigned the value T to $p \to q$ in these two lines. See problem 52, Exercises 3.3.

Note that "All p's are q's" is translated as "If it is a p, then it is a q." This idea will be used in Exercises 3.3, problems 35–39.

Truth Value of the Conditional Statement $p \to q$

The **conditional statement** $p \to q$ ("if p, then q") is false only when p is true and q is false; otherwise, it is true.

EXAMPLE 1 Diesel Logic

(a) Write the statement in the photograph in symbolic form using

v: the pump runs very slowly	r: release nozzle trigger
c: count to 20	t: try again

(b) When is the statement false?

A gas pump sign also uses a conditional statement.

Solution

(a) The statement is written as the conditional $v \to (r \land c \land t)$.

(b) A conditional is false when the antecedent v is true and the consequent $(r \land c \land t)$ is *false*, that is, when the pump is running very slowly and you did not release the trigger or count to 20 or try again.

B The Biconditional

In certain statements the conditional is used twice; in the second conditional, the antecedent and the consequent of the first conditional are reversed. For example, the statement "If money is plentiful, then interest rates are low, and if interest rates are low, then money is plentiful" uses the conditional twice in this manner. It is for this reason that such statements, which can be written in the form $(p \to q) \wedge (q \to p)$, are called **biconditionals.** The biconditional is usually symbolized by the shorter form $p \leftrightarrow q$ (read as p if and only if q or p biconditonal q).

Definition of the Biconditional Statement $p \leftrightarrow q$

$$p \leftrightarrow q \Leftrightarrow (p \to q) \wedge (q \to p)$$

Table 3.12 is the truth table for the statement $(p \to q) \wedge (q \to p)$. It is filled out in the usual way.

1. In columns 1 and 2, we write the four possible pairs of truth values for p and q.

Table 3.12

1	2	3	5	4
p	q	$(p \to q)$	$\wedge$	$(q \to p)$
T	T	T	T	T
T	F	F	F	T
F	T	T	F	F
F	F	T	T	T

You can also write the columns in order like this:

1	2	3	4	5
p	q	$(p \to q)$	$(q \to p)$	$(p \to q) \wedge (q \to p)$
T	T	T	T	T
T	F	F	T	F
F	T	T	F	F
F	F	T	T	T

2. We combine columns 1 (p) and 2 (q) with the conditional ($\to$) to form column 3 $(p \to q)$. Since $p \to q$ is false only when p is true and q is false, we write F in the second row and T in the other rows.
3. We combine columns 2 (q) and 1 (p)—*in that order*—with the conditional ($\to$) to form column 4 $(q \to p)$. Because $q \to p$ is false only when q is true and p is false, we write F in the third row and T in the other rows.
4. We combine columns 3 $(p \to q)$ and 4 $(q \to p)$ with the conjunction $\wedge$ to form column 5 $[(p \to q) \wedge (q \to p)]$. Since the conjunction is true only when both components are true, we write T in the first and fourth rows and F in the other two rows. This completes Table 3.12, which is to be regarded as the definition of the symbol $\leftrightarrow$ and it expresses the following fact:

Truth Value of the Biconditional Statement $p \leftrightarrow q$

The **biconditional** $p \leftrightarrow q$ is true when and only when p and q have the same truth values; it is false otherwise.

EXAMPLE 2 Finding the Truth Value of Conditionals

Give the truth value of each of the following, assuming that the week starts on Sunday.

(a) If Tuesday is the last day of the week, then the next day is Sunday.

(b) If Tuesday is the third day of the week, then the next day is Sunday.

(c) If Tuesday is the third day of the week, then Wednesday is the fourth day of the week.

(d) If Tuesday is the last day of the week, then the next day is Wednesday.

Solution

All these statements are of the form $p \rightarrow q$, where p is the antecedent and q is the consequent. (Recall that the antecedent is the "if" part, and the consequent is the "then" part.)

(a) Because p is false, the statement $p \rightarrow q$ is true.

(b) Because p is true and q is false, the statement $p \rightarrow q$ is false.

(c) Because p and q are both true, the statement $p \rightarrow q$ is true.

(d) Because p is false, the statement $p \rightarrow q$ is true.

Note the results in (a) and (d). The moral is that if you start off with a false assumption, then you can prove anything!

EXAMPLE 3 Finding the Truth Value of Biconditionals

Is the statement $(3 + 5 = 35) \leftrightarrow (2 + 7 = 10)$ true or false?

Solution

This statement is of the form $p \leftrightarrow q$, where p is "$3 + 5 = 35$" and q is "$2 + 7 = 10$." Since the biconditional $p \leftrightarrow q$ is true when p and q have the same truth value, and p and q in this example are both false, the given biconditional statement is true.

EXAMPLE 4 Finding When Conditionals Are False

Let p be "x is a fruit," and let q be "x is ripe." Under what conditions is the statement $p \rightarrow q$ false?

Solution

The statement $p \rightarrow q$ is a conditional statement and thus is false only when p is true and q is false; hence, the given statement is false if x is a fruit that is not ripe.

C Equivalency and Negation of Conditionals

EXAMPLE 5 Showing the Equivalency of $p \rightarrow q$ and $\sim p \vee q$

Show that the statements $p \rightarrow q$ and $\sim p \vee q$ are equivalent; that is, show that $(p \rightarrow q) \Leftrightarrow (\sim p \vee q)$. Use the equivalence to write the statement "If you are under 18, then you must register" as a disjunction.

Solution

To show that two statements are equivalent, we must show that they have identical truth tables. The statement $p \rightarrow q$ is false only when p is true and q is false (see Table 3.13).

To make a truth table for $\sim p \vee q$ (see Table 3.14), we write the components p, q, $\sim p$, and $\sim p \vee q$, as shown. We negate statement p by writing truth values in column 3 opposite to those shown in column 1.

The statement $\sim p \vee q$, shown in column 4, is false only when both components, $\sim p$ and q, are false (row 2); otherwise it is true. Since the final results *TFTT* are identical, the statements are equivalent; that is, $(p \rightarrow q) \Leftrightarrow (\sim p \vee q)$.

Now, let p be the statement "You are under 18" and q be the statement "You must register." Since $(p \rightarrow q) \Leftrightarrow (\sim p \vee q)$, the statement "If you are under 18, then you must register" can be written as the disjunction "You are not under 18 or you must register."

Table 3.13

1	2	3
p	q	$p \rightarrow q$
T	*T*	*T*
T	*F*	*F*
F	*T*	*T*
F	*F*	*T*

Table 3.14

1	2	3	4
p	q	$\sim p$	$\sim p \vee q$
T	*T*	*F*	*T*
T	*F*	*F*	*F*
F	*T*	*T*	*T*
F	*F*	*T*	*T*

The equivalence in Example 5 $(p \to q) \Leftrightarrow (\sim p \vee q)$, is of great importance because it allows us to handle a conditional statement in terms of the logical symbols for negation and disjunction, making it convenient to find the negation of a conditional. This equivalence will be used in several of the problems in Exercises 3.3 and later in this chapter.

Conditional Equivalence

$$(p \to q) \Leftrightarrow (\sim p \vee q)$$

Note that since $(p \to q) \Leftrightarrow (\sim p \vee q)$, the negation of $p \to q$ is equivalent to the negation of $\sim p \vee q$; that is, the negation of a conditional statement can be written as follows:

Negation of a Conditional Statement

$$\sim(p \to q) \Leftrightarrow \sim(\sim p \vee q)$$

See problem 40 in Exercises 3.3 for the simplification of the right-hand side of this equivalence.

Sometimes, conditional statements are implicit, as shown in the excerpt of a brochure dealing with stress given in Example 6.

EXAMPLE 6 Writing Statements in Symbolic Form

Frustration mounts (f) when equipment (e) or materials (m) necessary to do an assigned task are insufficient, work schedules are overly demanding (o), the workload is too great (w), or work demands regularly spill over into time reserved for personal life (s).

Use the indicated letters to represent the corresponding components and write the statement in symbolic form.

Solution

Note that in this case, the conclusion reached is (f). We translate the statement as $[(e \vee m) \vee o \vee w \vee s] \to f$. (We hope that frustration did not mount when doing this problem!)

3.3 EXERCISES

A The Conditional

1. Show that the statement $\sim q \to \sim p$ is equivalent to $p \to q$.

In problems 2 and 3, use truth tables to show the equivalences.

2. $p \to \sim q \Leftrightarrow \sim(p \wedge q)$
3. $\sim p \to q \Leftrightarrow p \vee q$

In problems 4–7, find the truth value of each statement.

4. If $2 + 2 = 22$, then $22 = 4$.
5. If $2 + 2 = 4$, then $8 = 5$.
6. If $2 + 2 = 22$, then $8 = 4 + 4$.
7. If $2 + 2 = 22$, then $4 = 26$.

In problems 8–11, find all the number replacements for x that make each sentence true.

8. If $2 + 2 = 4$, then $x - 2 = 5$.
9. If $2 + 2 = 22$, then $x - 2 = 5$.
10. If $x + 2 = 6$, then $3 + 2 = 5$.
11. If $x + 2 = 6$, then $2 + 2 = 32$.

"IF YOU ARE NOT ONLINE, you will not be noticed, or it will be assumed you are behind the times."

Source: http://tinyurl.com/4hmsrus, p. 63, *AARP* magazine, *Brand Me*, by Andrew Reiner.

Let o: you are online, n: you will be noticed, b: you are behind the times

12. a. When is the statement $p \rightarrow q$ false?
b. When is the statement $\sim o \rightarrow (\sim n \vee b)$ false?
13. Referring to Problem 12:
a. When is $\sim o$ true?
b. When is $(\sim n \vee b)$ false?
c. What are the truth values of o, n and b when $\sim o \rightarrow (\sim n \vee b)$ is false?

In problems 14–16, construct a truth table for each statement. Note the importance of the parentheses and the brackets to indicate the order in which items are grouped.

14. $[(p \rightarrow q) \rightarrow p] \rightarrow q$
15. $(p \rightarrow q) \leftrightarrow (p \vee r)$
16. $(p \rightarrow q) \leftrightarrow (p \rightarrow \sim q)$

B The Biconditional

In problems 17 and 18, construct a truth table for each statement.

17. $p \rightarrow (q \wedge r)$
18. $(p \rightarrow q) \wedge (p \rightarrow r)$
19. Are the statements in problems 17 and 18 equivalent?

In problems 20–25, let p be "I will adopt it" and let q be "It is a poodle." Translate each statement into symbolic form.

20. If it is a poodle, then I will adopt it.
21. If I will adopt it, then it is a poodle.
22. It is a poodle if and only if I will adopt it.
23. If it is not a poodle, then I will not adopt it.
24. If I will not adopt it, then it is not a poodle.
25. If it is a poodle, then I will not adopt it.

In problems 26–28, let ~s be "You are out of Schlitz" and let ~b be "You are out of beer." Translate each statement into symbolic form.

26. If you are out of Schlitz, you are out of beer.
27. If you are out of beer, you are out of Schlitz.
28. Having beer is equivalent to having Schlitz.

C Equivalency and Negation of Conditionals

In problems 29–31, write each statement in symbolic form using ~ and ∨. Also write the corresponding statements in words. (Hint: $p \rightarrow q$ is equivalent to $\sim p \vee q$.)

29. If the temperature is above 80° (a), then I will go to the beach (b).
30. If Mida is home by 5 (h), then dinner will be ready by 6 (r).
31. If Eva has a day off (a), then she will go to the beach (g).

In Example 5 it was shown that $p \rightarrow q$ is equivalent to $\sim p \vee q$. In problems 32–34, use this equivalence to write each statement as a disjunction.

32. If you work, you have to pay taxes.
33. If you've got the time, we've got the beer.
34. If you find a better one, then you buy it.

The statement "All even numbers are divisible by 2" can be translated as "If it is an even number, then it is divisible by 2." In general, the statement "All ______ are ______" can be translated as "If it is a ______, then it is a ______." In problems 35–39, use this idea to write each statement in the if–then form.

35. All dogs are mammals.
36. All cats are felines.
37. All men are created equal.
38. All prime numbers greater than 2 are odd numbers.
39. All rectangles whose diagonals are perpendicular to each other are squares.
40. Because $p \rightarrow q$ is equivalent to $\sim p \vee q$ (see Example 5), the negation of $p \rightarrow q$ should be equivalent to the negation of $\sim p \vee q$. Show that the negation of $\sim p \vee q$ is $p \wedge \sim q$; that is, show that $\sim(\sim p \vee q)$ is equivalent to $p \wedge \sim q$.
41. From problem 40 it is clear that the negation of $p \rightarrow q$ is equivalent to $p \wedge \sim q$. Verify this by means of a truth table.

Problem 41 verified that the negation of $p \rightarrow q$ is $p \wedge \sim q$. This means that to negate an "if ______, then ______" statement, we simply assert the if clause and deny the then clause. For instance, the negation of the statement "If you are out of Schlitz, you are out of beer" is the statement "You are out of Schlitz, but you are not out of beer." In problems 42–47, write in words the negation of each statement.

42. If you earn a lot of money, then you pay heavy taxes.
43. If Johnny does not play quarterback, then his team loses.
44. If Alice passes the test, then she gets the job.
45. If I kiss you once, I kiss you again.
46. If Saturday is a hot day, I will go to the beach.
47. Evel Knievel will lose his life if he is careless.
48. From problem 41 you can see that $p \wedge \sim q$ has truth values *FTFF*. If you know that $p \wedge \sim q$ is the negation of $p \rightarrow q$, how can you define the truth table for $p \rightarrow q$?

In problems 49–51, write each statement in the if-then form.

49. Johnny does not play quarterback or his team wins.
50. Alice fails the test or she gets the job.
51. Joe had an accident or he would be able to get car insurance.
52. In defining $p \rightarrow q$, it is easy to agree that if p is true and q is true, then $p \rightarrow q$ is true; also, if p is true and q is false, then $p \rightarrow q$ is false. Assuming that the entries in the first two rows

in the following table are *TF*, respectively, we have four possible definitions for $p \to q$, as listed in the table.

		Definition of $p \to q$			
p	q	1	2	3	4
T	*T*	*T*	*T*	*T*	*T*
T	*F*	*F*	*F*	*F*	*F*
F	*T*	*F*	*F*	*T*	*T*
F	*F*	*F*	*T*	*F*	*T*

a. Show that if we use definition 1, then $p \to q$ and $p \wedge q$ have the same truth table.

b. Show that if we use definition 2, then $p \to q$ and $p \leftrightarrow q$ have the same truth table.

c. Show that if we use definition 3, then $p \to q$ and q have the same truth table.

Thus, the table shows that if we wish $p \to q$ to be different from $p \wedge q$, $p \leftrightarrow q$, and q, then we must use definition 4.

53. A mother promises her child "If you eat the spinach and the liver, then you may go out to play." The child eats only the spinach, but the mother lets him go out to play. Has she broken her original promise?

54. Now suppose the mother in problem 53 says "If you do not eat the spinach and liver, then you may not go out to play." If the child then eats only the spinach and the mother lets him go out to play, has she broken her promise?

55. Which of the following statements is logically equivalent to "If Mary is in Tampa, then she is in Florida"?
   a. Mary is in Florida, or she is in Tampa.
   b. If Mary is not in Tampa, then she is not in Florida.
   c. If Mary is in Florida, then she is in Tampa.
   d. If Mary is not in Florida, then she is not in Tampa.

56. Which of the following statements is logically equivalent to "If you want to buy organic food, you have to let your grocer know"?
   a. You want to buy organic food, or you let your grocer know.
   b. If you do not let your grocer know, then you do not want to buy organic food.
   c. If you let your grocer know, then you want to buy organic food.
   d. If you do not want to buy organic food, then you do not let your grocer know.

57. Which statement is the logical negation of "If you studied hard, you passed the course"?
   a. If you didn't study hard, you didn't pass the course.
   b. If you didn't pass the course, you didn't study hard.
   c. You didn't study hard, but you passed the course.
   d. You studied hard, and you did not pass the course.

58. Which statement is the logical negation of "If it rains, we will not go to the beach"?
   a. If it doesn't rain, then we will go to the beach.
   b. It is raining, and we do not go to the beach.
   c. If we go to the beach, then it will not rain.
   d. It is raining, and we will go to the beach.

IN OTHER WORDS

59. Assume that the chiropractor's advertisement "If you stop here, your pain will too," found on page 113, is a true statement. Does it follow logically that if you do not stop, your pain will not stop either? Explain.

60. Here is an excerpt from an automobile insurance policy. "If the loss is \$50 or less, we will not make any payment." A policyholder suffers a \$75 loss. What are the insurance company's options? Explain.

61. A sophomore college student reads the following statement: "If you are entering college for the first time, you are required to take the placement examination." Does the student have to take the placement examination? Explain.

62. Write in your own words why the conditional statement "If p then q" is **false** only when p is true and q is false, and it is true otherwise.

63. Write in your own words the conditions under which the statement $p \leftrightarrow q$ must be true and the conditions under which it must be false.

64. What does it mean to you when we say that two statements are **equivalent?**

65. What is the difference between $\leftrightarrow$ and $\Leftrightarrow$?

USING YOUR KNOWLEDGE

A certain credit union issues the following memorandum with its monthly statement of account: "Please carefully examine the enclosed memorandum. Report all differences to the Auditing Division. If no differences are reported in 10 days, we shall understand that the balance is correct as shown."

Let d be "A difference is found."
Let r be "A report is made in 10 days."
Let a be "The credit union makes the adjustment."

66. Write in symbols "If a difference is found, then a report is made in 10 days."

67. Write in symbols "If a report is made in 10 days, the credit union makes the adjustment."

68. Write in symbols "If a difference is found, then a report is made in 10 days and the credit union makes the adjustment."

69. Does the statement in problem 68 indicate that the credit union will make no adjustment if a late report of differences is made?

DISCOVERY

A logician is captured by a tribe of savages, whose chief makes the following offer: "One of these two roads leads to certain death and the other to freedom. You may select either road after asking any one question of one of these two warriors. I must warn you, however, that one of them is always truthful and the other always lies."

Let p be "The first road leads to freedom."
Let q be "You are telling the truth."

70. What should the question be? (*Hint:* Construct a question so that if p is true, the answer is "Yes" and, if p is false, the answer is "No." Complete the following table, and then refer to problem 49, Exercises 3.2, to find the desired question.)

p	q	Answer	Truth Table of Question to Be Asked
T	*T*	Yes	
T	*F*	Yes	
F	*T*	No	
F	*F*	No	

71. Three logicians, *A*, *B*, and *C*, are wearing hats, which they know are either black or white, but not all three are white. *A* can see the hats of *B* and *C*, *B* can see the hats of *A* and *C*, and

C is blind. They are asked in turn if they know the color of their own hat. The answers are *A*, no; *B*, no; and *C*, yes. What color is *C*'s hat, and how does she know?

72. Two women stand at a fork in the road. One fork leads to Someplaceorother; the other fork leads to Nowheresville. One of these people always answers the truth to any yes/no question that is asked of her. The other always lies when asked any yes/no question. By asking one yes/no question, can you determine the road to Someplaceorother?

73. While three logicians were sleeping under a tree, a malicious child painted their heads red. On waking, each logician spies the child's handiwork as it applied to the heads of the other two. Naturally they start laughing. Suddenly one falls silent. Why?

COLLABORATIVE LEARNING

Go to your library, Post Office, IRS office, or http://www.irs.ustreas.gov/formspubs/index.html and get Form 1040EZ. Here is a statement appearing in this form:

> *Use this form (u) if you had only wages (w), salaries (s), tips (t), taxable scholarships (ts) or fellowship grants (g), unemployment compensations (c), or Alaska Permanent Fund dividends (d), and your taxable interest income was not over $400 ($\sim o$).*

1. Write this statement in symbols.
2. Ask the members of the group if they qualify to use Form 1040EZ, and discuss why or why not.
3. If your taxable interest income was $400, can you use Form 1040EZ? Discuss why or why not.
4. Suppose that a person in the group received a Form 1099 indicating that the person earned some miscellaneous income. Can that person use Form 1040EZ? Discuss why or why not.
5. The form has the following warning:

   Remember, you must report all wages, salaries, and tips even if you do not get a W-2 form from your employer.

   Let r be the statement "You must report all wages, salaries, and tips," and let w be "You get a W-2 form from your employer." If a **tautology** is defined as *a statement that is always true* and a **contradiction** as *a statement that is always false,* according to the warning, which statement does the IRS want you to believe is a tautology and which statement a contradiction? Give reasons for your decision.

SKILL CHECKER

The Skill Checker exercises sometimes appear at the end of exercise sets and help you to maintain previously studied skills that you may need in the next section.

For example, the Using Your Knowledge feature in Section 3.4 shows a relationship between logic and sets. To understand this relationship better, complete the following truth table now.

p	q	$\sim p$	$p \vee q$	$p \wedge q$
T	*T*			
T	*F*			
F	*T*			
F	*F*			

3.4 Variations of the Conditional and Implications

GETTING STARTED

OBJECTIVES

A. Write the converse, the inverse, and the contrapositive of a conditional statement.

B. Translate statements involving sufficient and necessary conditions into symbolic form.

C. Use truth tables to show that a statement is a tautology or a contradiction.

D. Use truth tables to show that a statement implies another statement.

CONDITIONAL STATEMENTS IN ADVERTISING

Can lawyers advertise in your state? Suppose that you are a lawyer and you want to subtly convey the message that you are a contingency lawyer; that is, you get paid a certain percentage of the money awarded in the cases you win. How would you word your message? You could say either of the following:

1. I win if you pay.
2. Pay only if I win.

© I. Bello

This lawyer's sign wisely emphasizes winning, not paying.

Do the messages give you the impression that if you have enough money, you can buy the wins? Here are two other wordings.

3. Paying is sufficient for winning.
4. Winning is a necessary condition for paying.

These two statements still place a lot of importance on paying. Probably the best message is the one in the photo.

5. If I do not win, you do not pay.

Here the emphasis is on winning rather than paying. Do you realize that the five statements are equivalent? You will see why in this section when the different forms in which a conditional statement can be expressed are discussed.

In the preceding section we observed that equivalent statements have identical truth tables and can be considered different forms of the same statement. In this section we shall be concerned with some of the different forms in which the conditional statement $p \to q$ can be expressed.

A Converse, Inverse, and Contrapositive

The conditional differs from conjunctions, disjunctions, and biconditionals in that the two components may *not* be interchanged to give an equivalent statement. Thus, $p \vee q \Leftrightarrow q \vee p$ and $p \wedge q \Leftrightarrow q \wedge p$, but $p \to q$ is *not* equivalent to $q \to p$.* If we attempt to discover a statement that is equivalent to $p \to q$ (that is, that has an identical truth table) and involves p and q and the conditional or $\sim p$ and $\sim q$ and the conditional, we find the following possibilities:

© I. Bello

Write the converse, the inverse, and the contrapositive of the statement. Which one is equivalent to "If you think you had reservations you're in the wrong place"?

Statements Related to the Conditional Statement

$q \to p$	**Converse** of $p \to q$
$\sim p \to \sim q$	**Inverse** of $p \to q$
$\sim q \to \sim p$	**Contrapositive** of $p \to q$

Table 3.15 shows the truth tables for these statements. Notice that $p \to q$ is equivalent to its contrapositive, $\sim q \to \sim p$ (because they have identical truth tables).

Equivalent (Conditional and Contrapositive)

Equivalent (Converse and Inverse)

Table 3.15

p	q	Conditional $p \to q$	Converse $q \to p$	Inverse $\sim p \to \sim q$	Contrapositive $\sim q \to \sim p$
T	T	T	T	T	T
T	F	F	T	T	F
F	T	T	F	F	T
F	F	T	T	T	T

The contrapositive of a statement is used in proving theorems for which a direct proof is difficult but the proof of the contrapositive is easy. Thus, to prove that "If n^2 is odd, then n is odd," we can prove the contrapositive "If n is not odd, then n^2 is not odd." That is, "If n is even, then n^2 is even."

*Recall that p and q are equivalent (denoted by $p \Leftrightarrow q$) if p and q have identical truth tables.

EXAMPLE 1 Writing the Contrapositive of a Statement

Write in words the contrapositive of the statement "If n is an even integer, then n^2 is an even integer."

Solution

The given statement is of the form $p \rightarrow q$, where p is "n is an even integer" and q is "n^2 is an even integer." The contrapositive is $\sim q \rightarrow \sim p$, which translates into "If n^2 is not an even integer, then n is not an even integer."

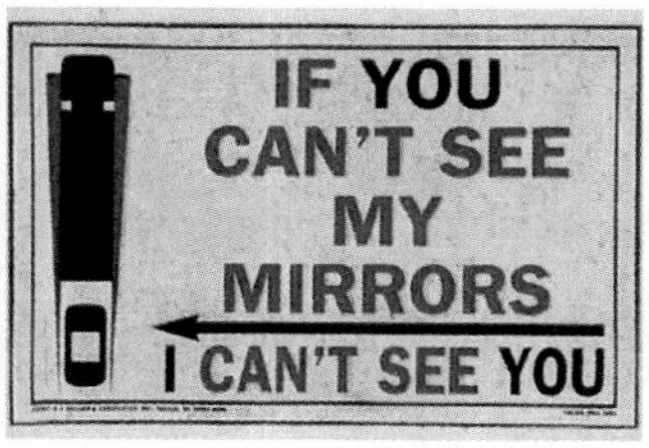

© I. Bello

The contrapositive is also helpful in giving a different perspective to statements containing negatives. For example, the contrapositive of the statement "If you were not at the party, then you were not invited" is "If you were invited, then you were at the party." The contrapositive says that everyone who was invited was at the party. This may not be clear from the original statement.

Have you seen this sign in the back of trucks on the highway? Is there another way of telling you that for the driver to see you, you have to see his mirrors? There is: the contrapositive!

EXAMPLE 2 Writing Contrapositives

Write the contrapositive of "If *you* can't see my mirrors ($\sim m$), *I* can't see *you* ($\sim y$)."

Solution

The statement is of the form $\sim m \rightarrow \sim y$. The contrapositive of $p \rightarrow q$ is $\sim q \rightarrow \sim p$. Thus, the contrapositive of $\sim m \rightarrow \sim y$ is $\sim(\sim y) \rightarrow \sim(\sim m)$ or, in simple terms, $y \rightarrow m$. This means that "If I can see you, then you can see my mirrors."

© I. Bello

EXAMPLE 3 Writing Conditionals, Converses, Inverses, and Contrapositives

Let t be "I will tip" and let s be "Service is good." Write in symbols and in words:

(a) The conditional "If s, then t" **(b)** The converse of $s \rightarrow t$

(c) The inverse of $s \rightarrow t$ **(d)** The contrapositive of $s \rightarrow t$

Solution

(a) The conditional "If s, then t" is symbolized by $s \rightarrow t$. In words, "If service is good, then I will tip."

(b) The converse of $s \rightarrow t$ is $t \rightarrow s$. In words, "If I will tip, then service is good."

(c) The inverse of $s \rightarrow t$ is $\sim s \rightarrow \sim t$. In words, "If service is not good, then I will not tip."

(d) The contrapositive of $s \rightarrow t$ is $\sim t \rightarrow \sim s$. In words, "If I do not tip, service is not good."

B Conditional Equivalents

Frequently in mathematics the words **necessary** and **sufficient** are used in conditional statements. To say that p is sufficient for q means that when p happens (is true), q will also happen (will also be true). Hence, "p is sufficient for q" is equivalent to "If p, then q."

Similarly, the sentence "q is necessary for p" means that if q does not happen, neither will p. That is, $\sim q \rightarrow \sim p$. The statement $\sim q \rightarrow \sim p$ is equivalent to $p \rightarrow q$, so the sentence "q is necessary for p" is equivalent to "If p, then q."

Table 3.16

Statement	Equivalent Forms
If p, then q	p is sufficient for q; q is necessary for p; p only if q; q if p

Finally, "p only if q" also means that if q does not happen, neither will p; that is, $\sim q \rightarrow \sim p$. The statement $\sim q \rightarrow \sim p$ is equivalent to $p \rightarrow q$, so the sentence "p only if q" is equivalent to $p \rightarrow q$. The equivalences discussed, together with the variation "q if p," are summarized in Table 3.16. To aid you in understanding this table, notice that in the statement $p \rightarrow q$, p is the sufficient condition (the antecedent) and q is the necessary condition (the consequent).

From Table 3.16, you can see that the statements

p is necessary and sufficient for q
q is necessary and sufficient for p
q if and only if p

are all equivalent to the statement "p if and only if q" and can be symbolized by $p \leftrightarrow q$.

EXAMPLE 4 Writing Variations of the Conditional

Let s be "You study regularly" and let p be "You pass this course." Translate the following statements into symbolic form.

(a) You pass this course only if you study regularly.

(b) Studying regularly is a sufficient condition for passing this course.

(c) To pass this course, it is necessary that you study regularly.

(d) Studying regularly is a necessary and sufficient condition for passing this course.

(e) You do not pass this course unless you study regularly. (*Hint:* a unless b means $\sim b \rightarrow a$.)

Solution

(a) $p \rightarrow s$

(b) Because s, studying regularly, is the sufficient condition, write $s \rightarrow p$.

(c) Since s is the necessary condition, write $p \rightarrow s$.

(d) $p \leftrightarrow s$ or $s \leftrightarrow p$.

(e) "You do not pass this course unless you study regularly" can be written as $\sim p$ unless s, which means $\sim s \rightarrow \sim p$.

Two statements p and q were defined to be equivalent (symbolized by $p \Leftrightarrow q$) if they had identical truth tables. An alternative definition states that p is equivalent to $q (p \Leftrightarrow q)$ if the biconditional $p \leftrightarrow q$ is always true. (Can you see why these definitions are the same?)

C Tautologies and Contradictions

Tautology and Contradiction

A statement that is always true is called a **tautology.** A statement that is always false is called a **contradiction.**

Is the statement "Objects in mirror are closer than they appear" a tautology?

EXAMPLE 5 Using Truth Tables to Show Tautologies

Show the following by means of a truth table:

(a) The statement $p \vee \sim p$ is a tautology.

(b) The statement $p \wedge \sim p$ is a contradiction.

Table 3.17

p	$\sim p$	$p \vee \sim q$
T	F	T
F	T	T

Table 3.18

p	$\sim p$	$p \wedge \sim p$
T	F	F
F	T	F

Solution

(a) Table 3.17 gives the truth table for $p \vee \sim p$. Note that in every possible case, $p \vee \sim p$ is true; therefore, the statement $p \vee \sim p$ is a tautology.

(b) Table 3.18 gives the truth table for $p \wedge \sim p$. Note that in every possible case, $p \wedge \sim p$ is false; therefore, $p \wedge \sim p$ is a contradiction (always false).

It is easy to restate the definition of equivalence in terms of a tautology.

> **Definition of Equivalent**
>
> The statement p is **equivalent** to the statement q ($p \Leftrightarrow q$) if and only if the **biconditional** $p \leftrightarrow q$ is a **tautology.**

EXAMPLE 6 Using Truth Tables to Show Tautologies

Show that the biconditional $\sim(p \wedge q) \leftrightarrow (\sim p \vee \sim q)$ is a tautology.

Solution

To show that the biconditional $\sim(p \wedge q) \leftrightarrow (\sim p \vee \sim q)$ is a tautology, we use the definition of equivalent and show that $\sim(p \wedge q)$ and $\sim p \vee \sim q$ are equivalent (have the same truth table). First, do the truth table for $\sim(p \wedge q)$. The statement $(p \wedge q)$ is true when both p and q are true (row 1, Table 3.19) and false otherwise. Thus, in column 1 the first row is true; all other rows are false. To negate $(p \wedge q)$, write the opposite values of those shown in column 1 in column 2, the truth table of $\sim(p \wedge q)$. To get the truth table for $\sim p \vee \sim q$, start by negating p and then negate q, as shown in columns 3 and 4, respectively. Then use the results of columns 3 and 4 as guides to complete column 5. Remember that $\sim p \vee \sim q$ is false only when both components $\sim p$ and $\sim q$ are false. This occurs in row 1 only, so in column 5 enter F for the first row and T's for the rest of the rows. Since columns 2 and 5 are identical and the biconditional is true when both statements have the same truth values, $\sim(p \wedge q) \leftrightarrow (\sim p \vee \sim q)$ is a tautology.

Table 3.19

		2	1	3	5	4
p	q	$\sim$	$(p \wedge q)$	$\sim p$	$\vee$	$\sim q$
T	T	F	T	F	F	F
T	F	T	F	F	T	T
F	T	T	F	T	T	F
F	F	T	F	T	T	T

Same truth values: Equivalent

You can also write the columns in order like this:

		1	2	3	4	5
p	q	$(p \wedge q)$	$\sim(p \wedge q)$	$\sim p$	$\sim q$	$\sim p \vee \sim q$
T	T	T	F	F	F	F
T	F	F	T	F	T	T
F	T	F	T	T	F	T
F	F	F	T	T	T	T

Same truth values: Equivalent

D Implications

Another relationship between statements that is used a great deal by logicians and mathematicians is that of **implication.**

> Note that an **implication** is a *relationship* between the statements p and q, while a **conditional** is simply a *connective.*

> **Definition of Implication**
>
> The statement p is said to **imply** the statement q (symbolized by $p \Rightarrow q$) if and only if the conditional $p \rightarrow q$ is a tautology.

EXAMPLE 7 Showing Implications

Show that $[(p \rightarrow q) \wedge p] \Rightarrow q$.

Solution

First method By the definition of *implication* we must show that $[(p \rightarrow q) \wedge p] \rightarrow q$ is a tautology. A conditional is true whenever the antecedent is false, so we need to check only the cases in which the antecedent is true. Thus, if $(p \rightarrow q) \wedge p$ is true, then $p \rightarrow q$ is true and p is true. But if p is true, then q is also true (why?), so both sides of the conditional are true. This shows that the conditional is a tautology, and thus, $(p \rightarrow q) \wedge p$ implies q.

Second method A different procedure, which some people prefer, uses truth tables to show an implication. In order to show that $a \Rightarrow b$, we need to show that $a \rightarrow b$ is a tautology. In our case, we have to show that $[(p \rightarrow q) \wedge p] \rightarrow q$ is a tautology. We do this by constructing a truth table where column 1 is $p \rightarrow q$, which is false only when p is true and q if false (row 2). Column 2 corresponds to the conjunction $(p \rightarrow q) \wedge p$, which is true only when both $p \rightarrow q$ and p are true (row 1). In column 3, we simply copy the truth values of q and finally, in column 4, we look at the conditional $[(p \rightarrow q) \wedge p] \rightarrow q$. Recall that a conditional is false only when the antecedent, in this case $[(p \rightarrow q) \wedge p]$ is true and the consequent, in this case q, is false. But there is no row in which $[(p \rightarrow q) \wedge p]$ is ***true*** and q is ***false,*** so we enter T's for all truth values in column 4. Thus, the statement $[(p \rightarrow q) \wedge p] \rightarrow q$ is a tautology, which means that $[(p \rightarrow q) \wedge p] \Rightarrow q$.

Table 3.20

		1	2	3	4
p	q	$p \rightarrow q$	$(p \rightarrow q) \wedge p$	q	$[(p \rightarrow q) \wedge p] \rightarrow q$
T	T	T	T	T	T
T	F	F	F	F	T
F	T	T	F	T	T
F	F	T	F	F	T

We can convince ourselves of this fact by making a truth table for the statement $[(p \rightarrow q) \wedge p] \rightarrow q$. The result is a tautology (all true).

3.4 EXERCISES

A Converse, Inverse, and Contrapositive

1. Write in words the contrapositive of the statement "If n is not an even number, then n is not divisible by 2."
2. Let p be "You brush your teeth with Clean," and let q be "You have no cavities." Write the converse, contrapositive, and inverse of the statement $p \rightarrow q$, "If you brush your teeth with Clean, then you have no cavities."

B Conditional Equivalents

In problems 3–5, let p and q be defined as in problem 2. Translate each statement into symbolic form.

3. You have no cavities only if you brush your teeth with Clean.
4. Having no cavities is a sufficient condition for brushing your teeth with Clean.
5. To have no cavities, it is necessary that you brush your teeth with Clean.

In problems 6–14, write each statement in if–then form.

6. If I kissed you once, I will kiss you again.
7. To be a mathematics major, it is necessary to take calculus.
8. A good argument is necessary to convince Eva.
9. A two-thirds vote is sufficient for a measure to carry.
10. To have rain, it is necessary to have clouds.
11. A necessary condition for a stable economy is that we have low unemployment.
12. A sufficient condition for joining a women's club is being a woman.

13. Birds of a feather flock together.
14. All dogs are canines.
15. Use a truth table to show that, in general, the converse and the inverse of the statement $p \to q$ are equivalent (have identical truth tables).

In problems 16–23, let h be "honk" and u be "you ♥ Ultimate." Write the following in symbolic form: You can write "love" instead of using the symbol ♥

© I. Bello

16. Honk if you ♥ Ultimate.
17. If you ♥ Ultimate, honk.
18. Honk only if you ♥ Ultimate.
19. A necessary condition for loving Ultimate is to honk.
20. A sufficient condition for loving Ultimate is to honk.
21. To honk is a necessary condition for loving Ultimate.
22. To ♥ Ultimate is a sufficient condition for honking.
23. To ♥ Ultimate, it is sufficient and necessary that you honk.
24. Write in symbols the converse, inverse, and contrapositive of "Honk if you ♥ Ultimate."
25. Write in symbols the converse, inverse, and contrapositive of "Honk only if you ♥ Ultimate."

In problems 26–28, let p be "I will pass this course" and let s be "I will study daily." Write each statement in symbolic form.

26. Studying daily is necessary for my passing this course.
27. A necessary and sufficient condition for my passing this course is studying daily.
28. I will pass this course if and only if I study daily.
29. Write the converse, inverse, and contrapositive of each of the following statements:
    a. If you do not eat your spinach, you will not be strong.
    b. If you eat your spinach, you will be strong.
    c. You will be strong only if you eat your spinach.
30. Which statements in problem 29 are equivalent?

In problems 31–35, write the converse of each statement. State whether each converse is always true.

31. If an integer is even, then its square is divisible by 4.
32. If it is raining, then there are clouds in the sky.
33. In order to get a date, I must be neat and well dressed.
34. If M is elected to office, then all our problems are over.
35. In order to pass this course, it is sufficient to get passing grades on all the tests.

In problems 36–40, write the contrapositive of each statement.

36. In an equilateral triangle, the three angles are equal.
37. If the research is adequately funded, we can find a cure for cancer.
38. Black is beautiful.
39. All radicals want to improve the world.
40. Everyone wants to buy a smart phone.
41. The statement "If n is even, then $3n$ is even" is directly transformed into the statement "If $3n$ is not even, then n is not even" by which one of the following logical equivalences?
    a. "Not (p and q)" is equivalent to "not p or not q."
    b. "If p, then q" is equivalent to "(not p) or q."
    c. "If p, then q" is equivalent to "if not q, then not p."
42. The statement "If it can be recycled, place it in this container" is directly transformed into the statement "If it is not placed in this container, then it cannot be recycled" by which one of the following logical equivalences?
    a. "If p, then q" is equivalent to "(not p) or q."
    b. "If p, then q" is equivalent to "if not q, then not p."
    c. "Not (p and q)" is equivalent to "not p or not q."
43. Which of the following statements is *not* logically equivalent to "If the day is cool, I will go fishing"?
    a. I will go fishing or the day is not cool.
    b. If I go fishing, the day is cool.
    c. If I do not go fishing, then the day is not cool.
    d. The day is not cool or I go fishing.
44. Select the statement that is *not* logically equivalent to "If the class is canceled, Mary will go to the library."
    a. Mary will go to the library or the class is not canceled.
    b. It is not true that Mary will not go to the library and the class is canceled.
    c. If Mary does not go to the library, the class is canceled.
    d. If Mary does not go to the library, the class will not be canceled.

C Tautologies and Contradictions

45. Show by means of a truth table that the statement $(p \wedge q) \to p$ is a tautology. This demonstrates that $(p \wedge q) \Rightarrow p$.
46. Show by means of a truth table that the statement $[(p \to q) \wedge (q \to r)] \to (p \to r)$ is a tautology. This demonstrates that $[(p \to q) \wedge (q \to r)] \Rightarrow (p \to r)$.
47. Show by means of a truth table that the statement $p \leftrightarrow \sim p$ is a contradiction.

D Implications

In problems 48–54, two statements are given. Determine whether they are equivalent, one implies the other, or neither is the case.

48. $\sim(p \vee q); \sim p \wedge \sim q$
49. $\sim p \wedge q; p \to q$
50. $\sim p \to \sim q; \sim p \to q$
51. $p \vee (p \wedge q); p$
52. $p \wedge (p \vee q); p$
53. $\sim p \vee \sim q; p \wedge \sim q$
54. $(p \wedge q) \to r; \sim p \vee \sim q \vee r$

IN OTHER WORDS

55. Explain the difference between the words *necessary* and *sufficient*.
56. Write in words two statements of the form "If p, then q," using the word *sufficient*.

57. Write in words two statements of the form "If p, then q," using the word *necessary*.

58. Write in words two statements of the form "If p, then q," using the words *only if.*

59. Explain the difference between $p \to q$ and $p \Rightarrow q$.

60. Explain why a true statement is implied by any statement.

61. Explain why a false statement implies any statement.

USING YOUR KNOWLEDGE

In describing sets using set-builder notation, the close connection between a set and the statement used to define that set is apparent. If we are given a universal set $\mathcal{U}$, there is often a simple way in which to select a subset of $\mathcal{U}$ corresponding to a statement about the elements of $\mathcal{U}$. For example, if $\mathcal{U} = \{1, 2, 3, 4, 5, 6\}$ and p is the statement "The number is even," the set corresponding to this statement is $P = \{2, 4, 6\}$; that is, P is the subset of $\mathcal{U}$ for which the statement p is true. The set P is called the ***truth*** *set of p. Similarly, P′ is the truth set of $\sim p$.*

Let $\mathcal{U} = \{a, b, c, d, e\}$. Then, let p be the statement "The letter is a vowel," let q be the statement "The letter is a consonant," and let r be the statement "The letter is the first letter in the English alphabet."

P, the truth set of p, is {a, e}.
Q, the truth set of q, is {b, c, d}.

Find the following:

R, the truth set of r
R′, the truth set of $\sim r$

Because p and q are statements, $p \vee q$ and $p \wedge q$ are also statements; hence, they must have truth sets. To find the truth set of $p \vee q$, select all the elements of $\mathcal{U}$ for which $p \vee q$ is true (that is, the elements that are vowels or consonants). Thus, the truth set of $p \vee q$ is $P \cup Q = \{a, b, c, d, e\} = \mathcal{U}$. Similarly, the truth set of $p \wedge q$ is the set of all elements of $\mathcal{U}$ that are vowels and consonants; that is, the truth set of $p \wedge q$ is $P \cap Q = \emptyset$.

62. With this information, complete the following table:

Statement Language	Set Language
p	P
q	Q
$\sim p$	P'
$\sim q$	
$p \vee q$	
$p \wedge q$	
$p \Rightarrow q$	
$p \Leftrightarrow q$	
t, a tautology	
c, a contradiction	

63. If P, Q, and R are the truth sets of p, q, and r, respectively, find the truth sets of the following statements:

a. $q \wedge \sim r$ b. $(p \wedge q) \wedge \sim r$

64. As in problem 63, find the truth sets of the following statements:

a. $p \wedge \sim(q \vee r)$ b. $(p \vee q) \wedge \sim(q \vee r)$

DISCOVERY

The following properties are used by mathematicians and logicians. In problems 65–69, express each statement in symbols and explain why it is true.

65. The contrapositive of the statement $\sim q \to \sim p$ is equivalent to $p \to q$.

66. The inverse of the inverse of $p \to q$ is equivalent to $p \to q$.

67. The contrapositive of the inverse of $p \to q$ is equivalent to $q \to p$.

68. The statement $r \vee s \vee \sim p \vee \sim q$ is equivalent to the contrapositive of $(p \wedge q) \to (r \vee s)$.

69. The statement $(\sim r \wedge \sim s) \vee (p \vee q)$ is equivalent to the converse of $(p \vee q) \to (r \vee s)$.

Some of the properties in problems 65–69 are summarized in the following table, where d stands for direct statement, c for converse, p for contrapositive, and i for inverse.

	d	***c***	***p***	***i***
d	*d*	*c*	*p*	*i*
c	*c*	*d*	*i*	*p*
p	*p*	*i*	*d*	*c*
i	*i*	*p*	*c*	*d*

Using the table, find the following:

70. The contrapositive of the contrapositive

71. The inverse of the inverse

72. The converse of the contrapositive

73. The inverse of the converse

74. The inverse of the contrapositive

COLLABORATIVE LEARNING

1. Assign several members in your group to find a logical implication in a newspaper or magazine or on the Internet. Copy the article and reference its location by giving the name and date of the publication. Provide each member of the group with a copy and let each member identify the antecedent and the consequent in the implication. State the inverse, converse, and contrapositive of the conditional associated with the implication. Does the contrapositive sound more convincing than the original implication? Why or why not?

2. As you recall, the statement $p \to q$ is *true* if p is *false*. Can your group find an example in a newspaper or magazine of such an occurrence?

3. The idea mentioned in item 2 has been used to create many logic puzzles. Here is one called Curry's paradox.

   If this sentence is true, then Santa Claus exists.

   Can you explain why this proves (implies) that Santa Claus does exist? See a proof at http://xorshammer.com/2008/08/13/loebs-theorem/.

4. As we have mentioned, many statements can be restated in the if–then form. Have the members of your group rewrite the following sentences symbolically in the if–then form.

   a. Time is the best medicine.
   b. The ideal doctor is patient.
   c. The mark of a true doctor is usually illegible.
   d. Wealth is the product of man's ability to think.
   e. Rich people are just poor people with money.

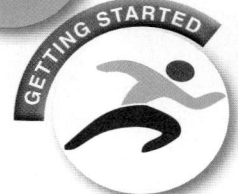

3.5 Euler Diagrams: A Problem-Solving Tool

GETTING STARTED

OBJECTIVES

A. Identify the premises and conclusion of an argument and draw its Euler diagram.
B. Use Euler diagrams to test the validity of an argument.
C. Supply the conclusion for an argument when the premises are given.

INSURANCE POLICIES AND EULER DIAGRAMS

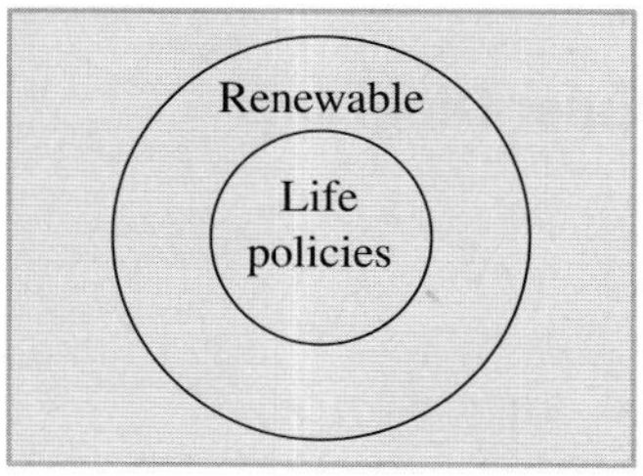

FIGURE 3.1 If it is a life policy, it is renewable. The set of life policies is a subset of the set of renewable policies.

Sometimes statements in logic involve relationships between sets. Thus, a renewal provision of a life insurance policy states "All life policies are renewable for additional term periods." This statement is equivalent to the following two statements:

1. If it is a life policy, then it is renewable for additional term periods.
2. The set of life policies is a subset of the set of all policies renewable for additional term periods.

Statements 1 and 2 can be visually represented by an Euler diagram (another name for a type of Venn diagram), as shown in Figure 3.1.

In this section you will learn the techniques used to diagram statements and then use these diagrams to determine whether given arguments are valid.

A Drawing Euler Diagrams: Premises and Conclusions

We shall now study the analysis of arguments by using Euler diagrams, a method that is most useful for arguments containing the words *all, some,* or *none.* In order to proceed, we must define what is meant by an **argument.**

> **Definition of an Argument**
>
> An **argument** is a set of statements, the **premises,** and a claim that another statement, the **conclusion,** follows from the premises.

We can represent four basic types of statements in Euler diagrams; these are illustrated in Figures 3.2–3.5.

All *P*'s are *Q*'s

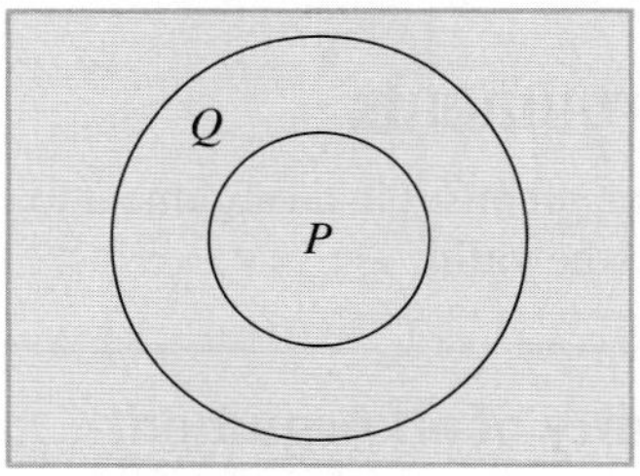

FIGURE 3.2 All *P*'s are *Q*'s. The set *P* is inside the set *Q*.

No *P*'s are *Q*'s

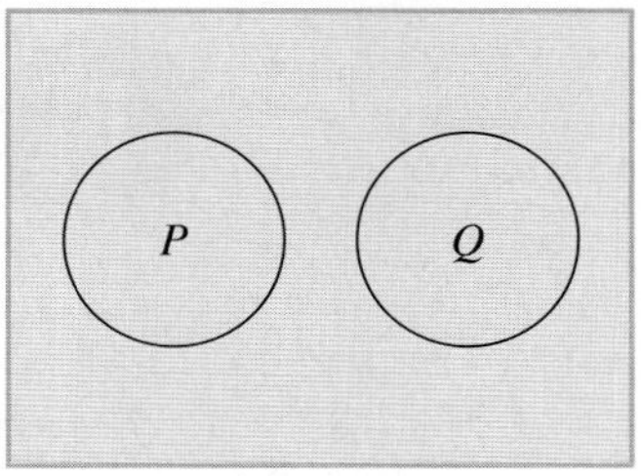

FIGURE 3.3 No *P*'s are *Q*'s. The set *P* and the set *Q* have no common elements.

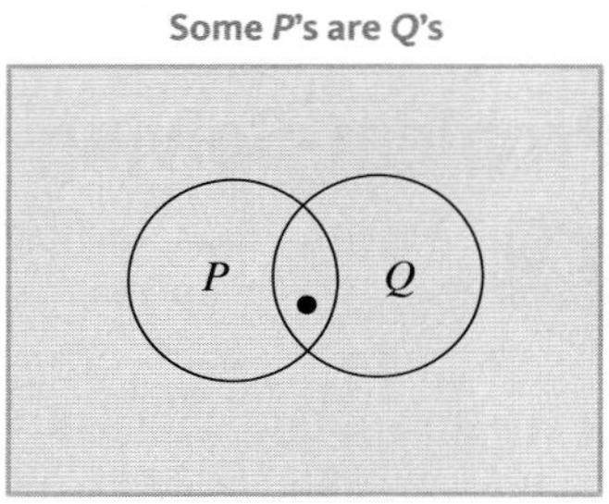

FIGURE 3.4 Some *P*'s are *Q*'s. There is an element (represented by the dot) that is in *P* and also in *Q*.

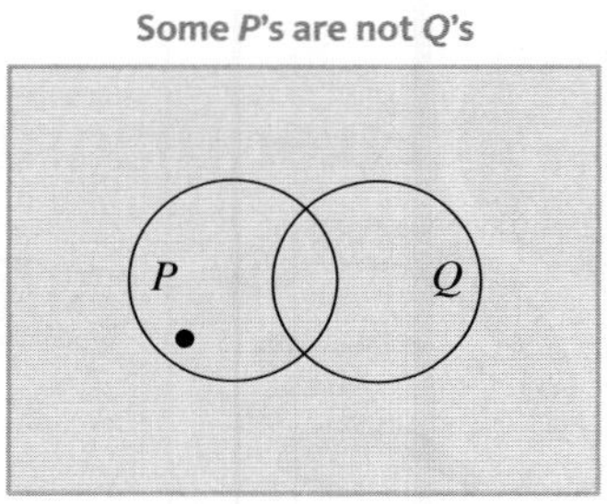

FIGURE 3.5 Some *P*'s are not *Q*'s. There is an element (represented by the dot) that is in *P* but not in *Q*.

The following examples discuss some simple arguments. Note that the premises are written on individual lines above a horizontal line; the conclusion is written below this line. This conclusion is preceded by the symbol $\therefore$, which is read "therefore."

EXAMPLE 1 Premises, Conclusions, and Euler Diagrams

Consider the following argument:

All men are mortal.
Socrates is a man.
$\therefore$ Socrates is mortal.

(a) Identify the premises and the conclusion.

(b) Make an Euler diagram for the premises.

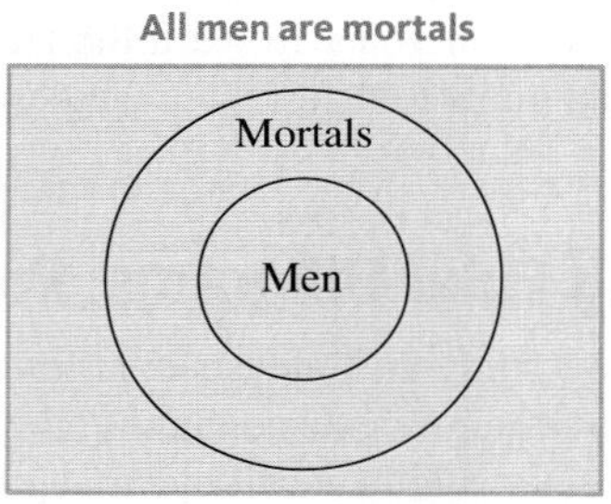

FIGURE 3.6

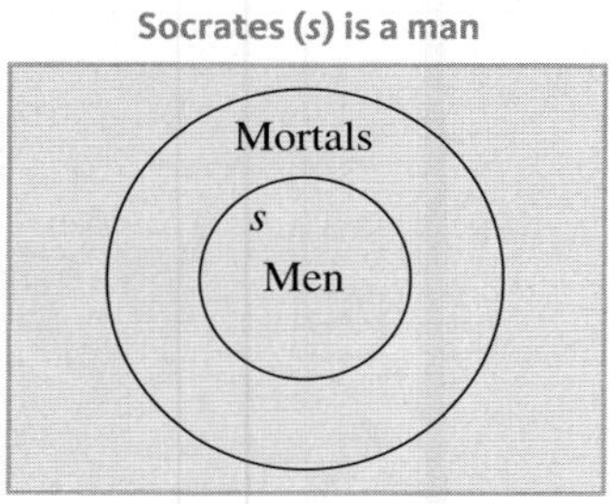

FIGURE 3.7

Solution

(a) The premises, which appear above the horizontal line, are "All men are mortal" and "Socrates is a man." The conclusion is "Socrates is mortal."

(b) To diagram the first premise, we begin by drawing a region to represent "mortals." Since all men are mortal, the region for "men" appears inside the region for mortals, as shown in Figure 3.6. The second premise, "Socrates is a man," indicates that "Socrates" goes inside the region representing "men." If *s* represents "Socrates," the diagram showing both premises appears in Figure 3.7.

B Valid Arguments

If we use the premises in an argument to reach a conclusion, we would like the resulting argument to be **valid.**

Validity of an Argument

An argument is **valid** if the conclusion is true whenever the premises are assumed to be true. If an argument is not valid, it is said to be **invalid.**

Thus, the argument shown in Figure 3.7 is valid because if Socrates is in the set of all men and the set of all men is inside the set of mortals, it must follow that Socrates is mortal.

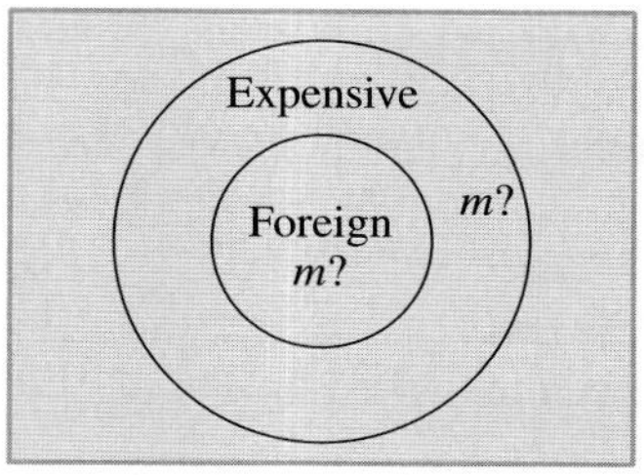

FIGURE 3.8 All foreign cars are expensive. My car *(m)* is expensive.

EXAMPLE 2 Using Euler Diagrams to Test Validity

Use an Euler diagram to test the validity of the following argument:

All foreign cars are expensive.
My car is expensive.
∴ My car is a foreign car.

Solution

The first premise means that the set of all foreign cars is a subset of the set of expensive cars; the second premise places "my car" (represented by *m*) within the set of expensive cars without specifying exactly where, as shown in Figure 3.8.

Since the information given is not enough to determine which alternative is correct—that is, *m* can be foreign or not—we say the argument is invalid.

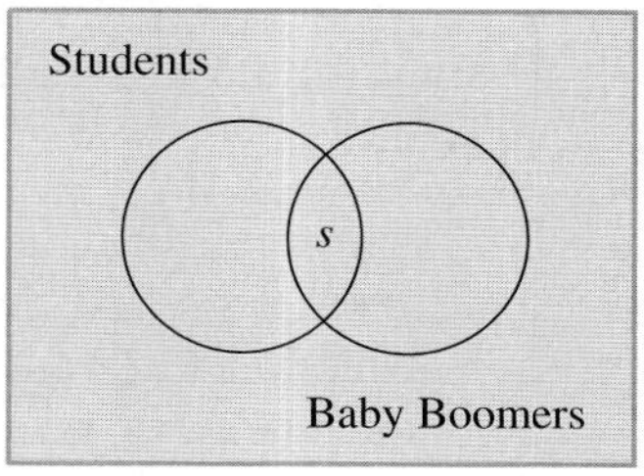

FIGURE 3.9 Some students are Baby Boomers.

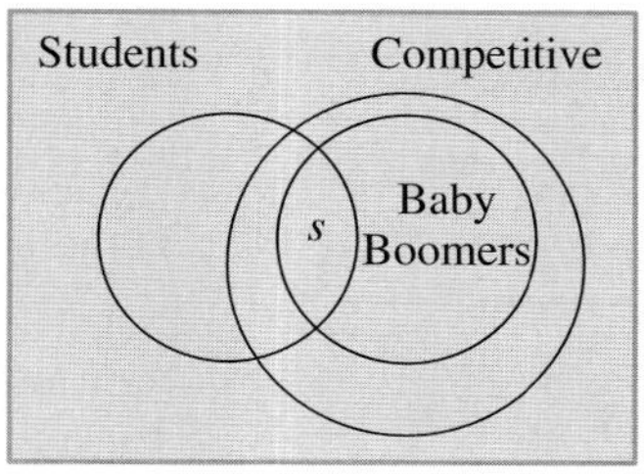

FIGURE 3.10 All Baby Boomers are competitive.

EXAMPLE 3 Using Euler Diagrams to Test Validity

Use an Euler diagram to test the validity of the following argument:

Some students are Baby Boomers.
All Baby Boomers are competitive.
∴ Some students are not competitive.

Solution

The diagram in Figure 3.9 shows the premise "Some students are "Baby Boomers" by two intersecting circles, the Students and the Baby Boomers, that includes at least one student (represented by *s*), in both circles. The second premise, "All Baby Boomers are competitive," can be shown by enclosing the set of Baby Boomers inside the set of competitive people, as in Figure 3.10 or as in Figure 3.11. Since we do not know which of these two drawings is correct, we cannot conclude that "some students are not competitive." Thus, the argument is invalid.

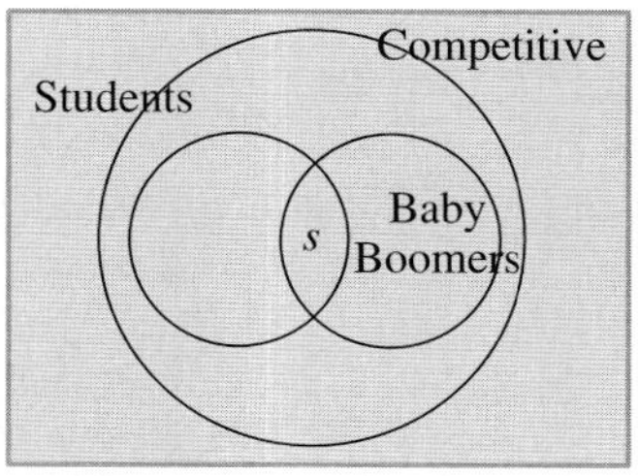

FIGURE 3.11 All Baby Boomers are competitive.

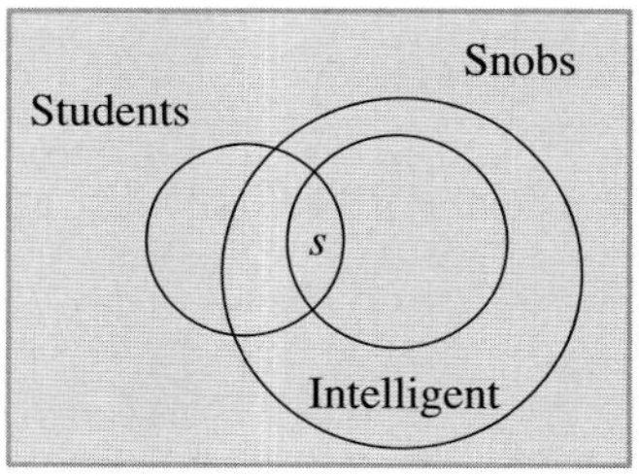

FIGURE 3.12 Some students (*s*) are intelligent. All intelligent people are snobs.

EXAMPLE 4 Using Euler Diagrams to Test Validity

Use an Euler diagram to test the validity of the following argument:

Some students are intelligent.
All intelligent people are snobs.
∴ Some students are snobs.

Solution

The first premise indicates that the set of students and the set of intelligent people have at least one element in common, represented by *s* (see Figure 3.12). Since all intelligent people are snobs, the set of intelligent people appears inside the circle of snobs. In this case, we can conclude that some students are snobs (that is, there is at least one student *s* who is also a snob). The argument is valid.

EXAMPLE 5 Using Euler Diagrams to Test Validity

Use an Euler diagram to determine the validity of the following argument:

All persons taking the test outside the United States should not register.
All persons not registered should write to the company.

∴ Persons taking the test outside the United States should write to the company.

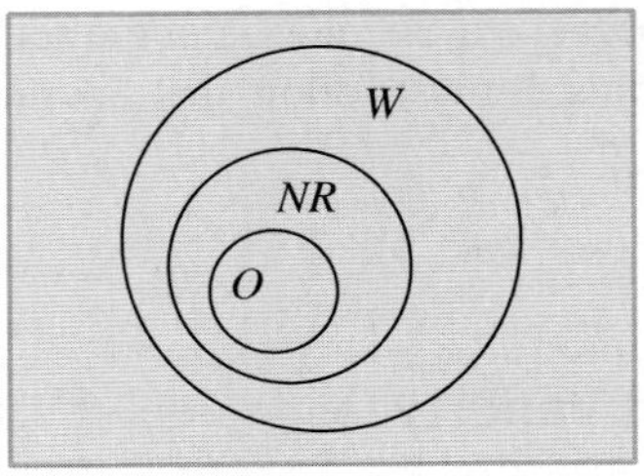

FIGURE 3.13 All persons taking the test outside the United States (*O*) should not register (*NR*). All persons not registered (*NR*) *should write to the company* (*W*).

Solution

Let *O* be the set of all persons taking the test outside the United States, let *NR* be the set of all persons not registered for the test, and let *W* be the set of all persons who should write to the company. The first premise is diagrammed by placing *O* inside *NR*; the second premise indicates that *NR* is inside the set *W* (see Figure 3.13). It follows from the diagram that the set *O* is inside the set *W*. Thus, the argument is valid.

Do you know who Lewis Carroll (Charles Lutwidge Dodgson) is? He is the author of *Alice in Wonderland, Through the Looking Glass,* and many other mathematical works, stories, and poems. Sometimes, Carroll presents several premises and asks about valid conclusions that could be derived from these premises. But he did not use Euler diagrams! He used what he called "Triliteral diagrams." Can we reach valid conclusions using our familiar Euler diagrams? Let us try one of Carroll's problems where two premises are given, and we need to find a valid conclusion. Here are the premises.

1. No son of mine is dishonest.
2. People always treat an honest man with respect.

To find a valid conclusion, Carroll translated the first statement as

1′. All sons of mine are honest.

and the second statement as

2′. All honest men are treated with respect.

Now, can we do an Euler diagram and find a valid conclusion using premises (1′) and (2′)? We will proceed as before.

1′. All sons of mine are honest.

This means that the set S (all sons of mine) is inside the set H (honest men) as shown in Figure 3.14.

2′. All honest men are treated with respect.

This means that the set H must be inside the set R (respect) (Figure 3.15). Now what can we conclude? Since the set S is completely inside the set R, one possible valid conclusion is

All sons of mine are treated with respect (see Figure 3.15).

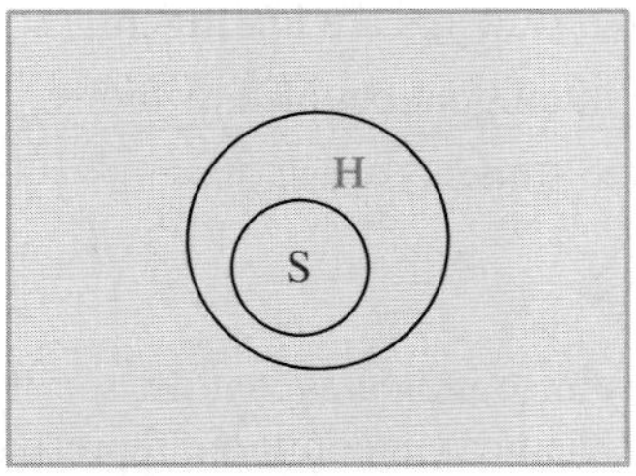

FIGURE 3.14 All sons of mine (S) are honest (H).

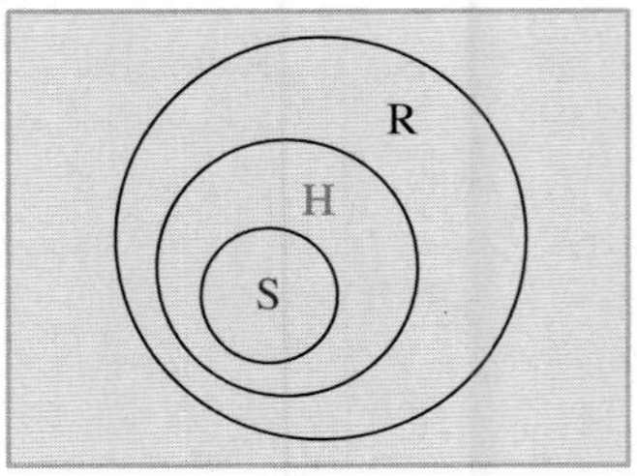

FIGURE 3.15 All sons of mine (S) are honest (H). All sons of mine (S) are treated with respect (R).

Note: Carroll translated this conclusion as the equivalent

No son of mine ever fails to be treated with respect.

C Supplying Valid Conclusions

Many practical situations require a valid conclusion based on available information. You do know that iPhones are smart phones and that some iPhones have free apps. What can you conclude?

© Courtesy of Apple

EXAMPLE 6 Supplying Valid Conclusions

Use Euler diagrams to supply a valid conclusion based on the following premises:

1. All iPhones are smart phones.
2. Some iPhones have free apps.

Can you get free apps for your smart phone? See the conclusion!

Solution

We translate each premise using an Euler diagram (see Figure 3.16).

1. All iPhones are smart phones.

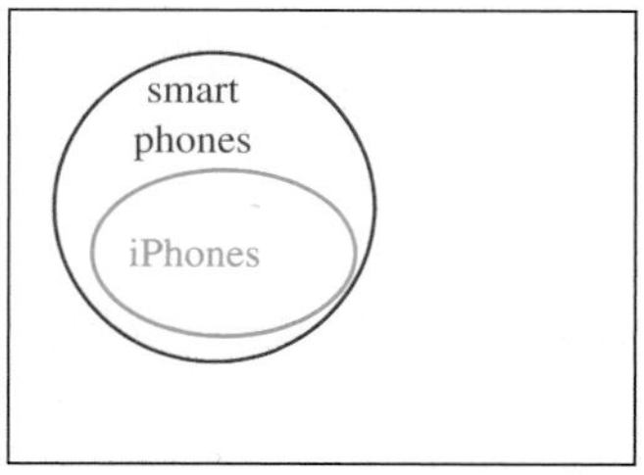

FIGURE 3.16

This means that the set of iPhones (blue circle) is a subset of the set of smart phones (red circle) as shown in Figure 3.16.

2. Some iPhones have free apps.

This means that there is an element (call it a) which is inside both the iPhones circle and the phones with free apps circle, as shown in Figure 3.17.

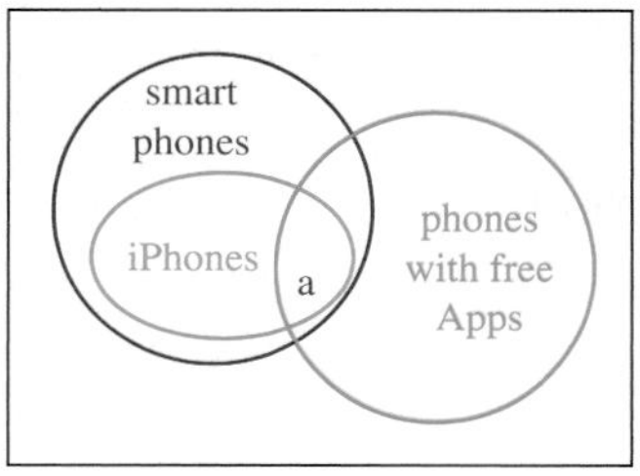

FIGURE 3.17

What can we conclude? Since the element a is inside the set of smart phones we can conclude that *"Some smart phones have free apps."*

3.5 EXERCISES

A Drawing Euler Diagrams: Premises and Conclusions

In problems 1–6, state the premises and the conclusion for each argument.

1. No misers are generous.
   Some old persons are not generous.
   ∴ Some old persons are misers.
2. No thieves are honest.
   Some dishonest people are convicted.
   ∴ Some thieves are convicted.
3. All diligent students get A's.
   All lazy students are not successful.
   ∴ All diligent students are lazy.
4. All students like logic.
   Robin likes logic.
   ∴ Robin is a student.
5. No kitten that loves fish is unteachable.
   No kitten without a tail will play with a gorilla.
   ∴ No unteachable kitten will play with a gorilla.
6. No birds are proud of their tails.
   Some birds cannot sing.
   ∴ Peacocks cannot sing.

B Valid Arguments

In problems 7–20, use Euler diagrams to determine the validity of each argument.

7. All professors are wise.
   Ms. Brown is a professor.
   ∴ Ms. Brown is wise.
8. All students are studious.
   Mr. Smith is studious.
   ∴ Mr. Smith is a student.
9. No drinkers are healthy.
   No joggers drink.
   ∴ No joggers are healthy.
10. All students are dedicated.
    All wealthy people are students.
    ∴ All wealthy people are dedicated.
11. All men are funny.
    Joey is a man.
    ∴ Joey is funny.
12. All football players are muscular.
    Jack is muscular.
    ∴ Jack is a football player.
13. All felines are mammals.
    No dog is a feline.
    ∴ No dogs are mammals.
14. Some students drink beer.
    All beer drinkers are dangerous.
    ∴ All students are dangerous.
15. No mathematics teacher is wealthy.
    No panthers teach mathematics.
    ∴ No panthers are wealthy.
16. All yuppies have short hair.
    Some athletes are yuppies.
    ∴ Some athletes have short hair.
17. All mathematics teachers have publications.
    Some Ph.D.'s have publications.
    ∴ Some Ph.D.'s are mathematics teachers.
18. All beer lovers like Schlitz.
    All people who like Schlitz get drunk.
    ∴ All beer lovers get drunk.
19. All heavy cars are comfortable to ride in.
    No car that is comfortable to ride in is poorly built.
    ∴ No heavy car is poorly built.
20. Some Prius owners save money.
    Some fast drivers save money.
    ∴ Some fast drivers are Prius owners.

In problems 21–26, use Euler diagrams to determine which (if any) of the given arguments are valid.

21. All bulldogs are ugly. This dog is ugly. So it must be a bulldog.
22. All peacocks are proud birds. This bird is not proud. Therefore, it is not a peacock.
23. All students who get A's in mathematics are smart. This student got a B in mathematics. Hence, this student is not smart.
24. No Southerners like freezing weather. Joe likes freezing weather. Therefore, Joe is not a Southerner.
25. Some people who fish are lucky. Fred is unlucky. Therefore, Fred is not a person who fishes.
26. Some students do well in history. Bobby failed history. Therefore, Bobby is not a student.

C Supplying Valid Conclusions

In problems 27–36, use an Euler diagram to determine which conclusion (a, b, or neither) can be logically deduced.

27. (1) All math teachers are salseros.
    (2) Some math teachers do not sing hip-hop.
    a. Some hip-hop singers are not salseros.
    b. Some salseros do not sing hip-hop.
28. (1) All math teachers can teach calculus.
    (2) Some students cannot teach calculus.
    a. Some students are not math teachers.
    b. Some math teachers are not students.
29. (1) No doctors are enthusiastic.
    (2) You are enthusiastic.
    a. You are not a doctor.
    b. You are a doctor.

30. (1) No Frenchmen like plum pudding.
(2) All Englishmen like plum pudding.

a. Some Frenchmen do not like plum pudding.
b. Englishmen are not Frenchmen.

31. (1) No old misers are cheerful.
(2) Some old misers are thin.

a. Some thin people are cheerful.
b. Some thin people are not cheerful.

32. (1) No professor can be crossed in love.
(2) A student may be crossed in love.

a. Some students are not professors.
b. Some professors are not students.

33. (1) No wasps are unfriendly.
(2) No puppies are unfriendly.

a. No puppies are wasps.
b. All wasps are not puppies.

34. (1) All pigs are fat.
(2) Nothing that is vegetarian is fat.

a. Pigs are not vegetarian.
b. Some pigs are vegetarian.

35. (1) Some math problems are difficult.
(2) All difficult problems need attention.

a. Some math problems need attention.
b. Some math problems are not difficult.

36. (1) No professors are salseros.
(2) Some professors are rappers.

a. Some rappers are not salseros.
b. Some professors are not rappers.

37. Given the following:

All highway patrol officers direct traffic.
Persons who direct traffic must be obeyed.

Use an Euler diagram to determine which conclusion(s) can be logically deduced.

a. Persons who direct traffic are highway patrol officers.
b. All highway patrol officers must be obeyed.
c. Some persons who direct traffic are not highway patrol officers.
d. None of the above.

38. All four of the following arguments have true conclusions, but one of the arguments is *not* valid. Use Euler diagrams to determine which argument is *not* valid.

a. All fish have gills and all trout are fish. Therefore, all trout have gills.
b. All trout have gills and all fish have gills. Therefore, all trout are fish.
c. All fish have tails and all trout are fish. Therefore, all trout have tails.
d. Every bird has a beak and the robin is a bird. Therefore, the robin has a beak.

IN OTHER WORDS

39. Can a valid argument reach

a. a true conclusion from true premises? Explain.
b. a false conclusion from true premises? Explain.

40. Can an invalid argument reach

a. a true conclusion from true premises? Explain.
b. a false conclusion from true premises? Explain.

41. If an argument is invalid, does it have to have false premises? Explain and give examples.

42. Suppose an argument has a false conclusion. Which of the following statements should be true? Give reasons.

a. All premises are false.
b. Some premises are false.
c. The argument must be invalid.

43. Suppose all premises in an argument are true. If the argument is valid, what can you say about the conclusion?

44. Suppose all premises in an argument are false. If the argument is valid, what can you say about the conclusion?

USING YOUR KNOWLEDGE

At the beginning of this chapter we mentioned a type of argument called a syllogism. *The validity of this type of argument can be tested by using the information about Venn diagrams presented in Chapter 2. We shall first diagram the four types of statements involved in these syllogisms.*

Recall that when we make a Venn diagram for two sets that are subsets of some universal set, we divide the region representing the universal set into four different regions, as shown in diagrams A–D.

Diagram A represents the statement "All P's are Q's." Note that region 1 must be empty, because all P's are Q's.

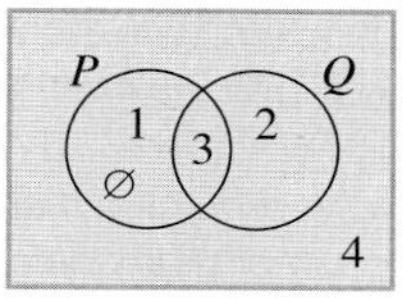

A

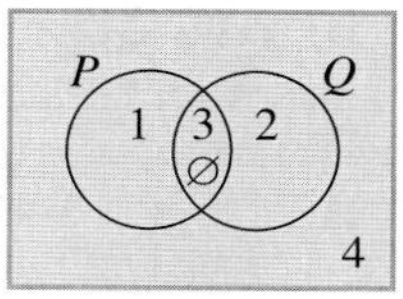

B

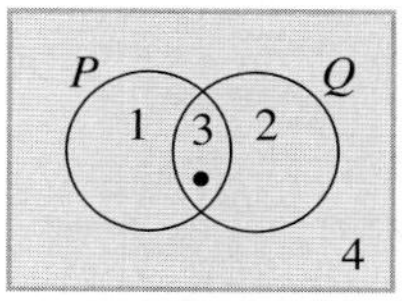

C

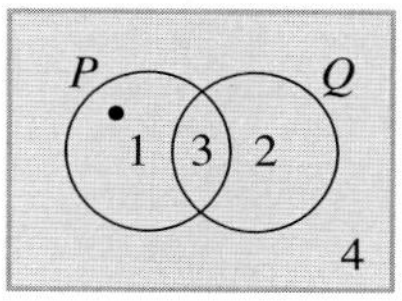

D

A. All *P*'s are *Q*'s. Since all the *P*'s are in *Q*, there are no elements in region 1.
B. No *P*'s are *Q*'s. Since no *P*'s are *Q*'s, there are no elements in region 3.
C. Some *P*'s are *Q*'s. Since some *P*'s are *Q*'s, there must be at least one element in *P* and *Q* (region 3).
D. Some *P*'s are not *Q*'s. Since some *P*'s are not *Q*'s, there must be at least one element in *P* and not in *Q* (region 1).

Diagram B represents the statement "No P's are Q's." Note that region 3 must be empty because no P's are Q's.

Diagram C represents the statement "Some P's are Q's." The dot in region 3 indicates that there is at least one P that is a Q.

Diagram D represents the statement "Some P's are not Q's." The dot in region 1 indicates that there is at least one P that is not a Q.

Similar considerations govern diagrams involving three sets, as shown when diagramming the following syllogism:

All kangaroos are marsupials.
All marsupials are mammals.
Therefore, all kangaroos are mammals.

In order to diagram this argument, we draw a rectangle and three circles and label the circles K (kangaroos), M (marsupials), and Ma (mammals). As before, these circles divide the rectangle (the universal set) into eight regions. The statement "All kangaroos are marsupials" makes regions 1 and 5 empty (see the following diagram); the statement "All marsupials are mammals" makes regions 2 and 3 empty (again, see the diagram). In order for the argument to be valid, regions 1 and 3 must be empty because we wish to conclude that all kangaroos are mammals. Since the diagram shows that this is the case, the conclusion follows and the argument is valid.

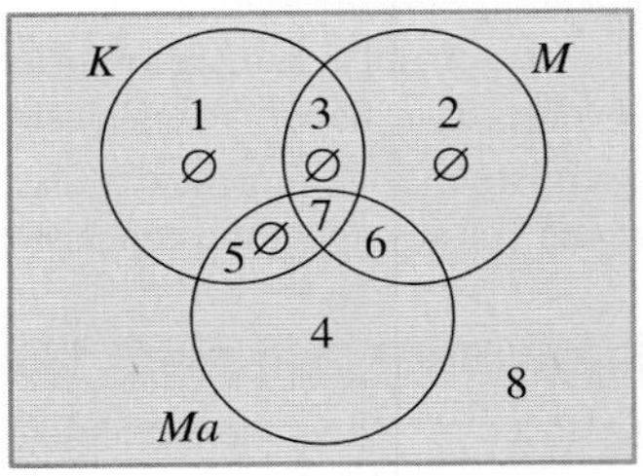

Using a similar technique and the diagram below, we can show that the following argument is invalid:

Some intelligent people are attractive.
All models are attractive.
Therefore, some intelligent people are models.

In order to diagram the statement "Some intelligent people are attractive," we put dots in both regions 3 and 7 and join them with a curved arrow symbol. This indicates that a dot may be in region 3 or in region 7 or dots may be in both regions, but we do not know which is the case. The second premise makes regions 4 and 5 empty. There is no statement in the argument that prevents region 7 from being empty. Thus, the conclusion could be false, so the argument is invalid.

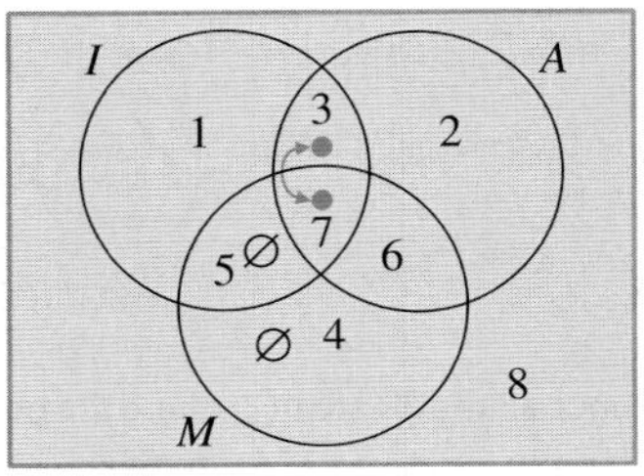

45–54. Use the ideas just discussed to examine the validity of the arguments in problems 11–20 of Exercises 3.5. Use the same ideas to solve problems 55 and 56.

55. Given the following premises:

No student who does not study will get an A in this course.
Some students in this course do not study.

Which of the following conclusions (if any) are valid?

a. Some students in this course will not get A's.
b. No students in this course will get A's.
c. All students in this course who do study will get A's.

56. Given the following premises:

Unless it rains, the grass will not grow.
If the grass grows, I will cut it.
It rains.

Which of the following conclusions (if any) are valid?

a. I will cut the grass.
b. The grass grows.
c. If the grass does not grow, I will not cut it.

57. Draw an Euler diagram to represent the two premises

All x's are y's.
All x's are z's.

Can you conclude that "Some y's are z's"? Explain why or why not.

58. Draw an Euler diagram to represent the two premises

All x's are y's.
No z is a y.

What can you conclude from the diagram? Explain.

59. Draw an Euler diagram to represent the two premises

All x's are y's.
Some z's are x's.

What can you conclude from the diagram? Explain.

60. On the basis of the knowledge you gained in solving problems 57–59, can you derive a valid conclusion involving an *existential* quantifier (some) from two premises involving *universal* quantifiers (all, no)? Explain.

SKILL CHECKER

In the next section we are going to use truth tables to determine if the conclusion of an argument is true whenever the premises are true. To help you succeed, construct and complete the following truth table:

1.

p	q	$\sim p$	$\sim q$	$p \to \sim q$	$p \vee \sim q$	$\sim p \wedge q$
T	T					
T	F					
F	T					
F	F					

2. You also have to remember how to form the contrapositive of a statement. As practice now, find the contrapositive of

a. $p \to q$.
b. $\sim q \to p$.
c. $\sim q \to \sim p$.
d. $p \to \sim q$.

3.6 Truth Tables and Validity of Arguments

GETTING STARTED

OBJECTIVES

A. Write an argument in symbolic form.
B. Use truth tables to determine the validity of an argument.
C. Supply a valid conclusion to a given argument using all premises.

FROM PREMISES TO VALID CONCLUSIONS

Here is an excerpt from the IRS instructions for Form 1040.

> If you do not file your return by the due date, the penalty is usually 5% of the amount due for each month or part of a month your return is late, unless you have a reasonable explanation.

Now suppose you filed your return 1 month late. Will there always be a penalty involved? Will it be 5% of the amount due? The answer is no in both cases. Do you see why?

In this section we shall study how to determine whether an argument is valid by writing the argument in symbolic form and then using truth tables to determine its validity (Exercises 3.6, problems 1–16). Moreover, we shall discuss how to reach valid conclusions from given premises. Of course, we must be careful about the conclusions we reach. A sixth-century B.C. paradox involving arguments claims that Epimenides, the poet and prophet of Crete, made the statement

> All Cretans are liars.

What is paradoxical about this statement? First, rewrite the situation as:

1. If it is a statement made by a Cretan, then it is not true.
2. The statement was made by a Cretan (Epimenides).
3. Thus statement 1 is not true.

But statement 3 makes statement 1 true! Do you see the problem? We shall stay away from such paradoxical arguments!

A Writing Arguments in Symbolic Form

In the preceding section an argument was defined as **valid** if the conclusion is true whenever all the premises are assumed to be true. If an argument is not valid, it is said to be **invalid.** This definition suggests that a truth table can be used to check the validity of an argument. In order to construct such a truth table efficiently, the argument must be in symbolic form. The following examples illustrate converting arguments into symbolic form.

EXAMPLE 1 Writing Arguments in Symbolic Form

Write the following argument in symbolic form:

If today is Sunday, then I will go to church.
Today is Sunday.
____
∴ I will go to church.

Solution

Let s be "Today is Sunday," and let c be "I will go to church." Then the argument is symbolized as

$$\begin{array}{l} s \to c \\ \underline{s \quad} \\ \therefore c \end{array}$$

EXAMPLE 2 Symbolizing an Argument

Symbolize the following argument:

A whole number is even or odd.
This whole number is not even.
∴ This whole number is odd.

Solution

Let e be "A whole number is even" and let o be "A whole number is odd." Then the argument is symbolized as

$$\begin{array}{l} e \vee o \\ \underline{\sim e \quad} \\ \therefore o \end{array}$$

B Using Truth Tables to Determine Validity

To determine whether an argument is valid, we use the following procedure:

IF YOU THINK YOU HAD RESERVATIONS
YOU'RE IN THE WRONG PLACE
© I. Bello

Determining Validity

1. Write each premise on a separate line.
2. Write the conclusion after the premises and separate it by a horizontal line.
3. Make a truth table using a column for each premise and a column for the conclusion.
4. Check *only* the rows in which *all* the premises are *true*. For the argument to be *valid*, the conclusion must also be *true*.

Let us see how this works in a practical situation.

PROBLEM-SOLVING

Determining Validity

① **Read** the problem and select the unknown. Determine whether the given argument is valid.

② **Think** of a plan.

Suppose you arrive at the restaurant shown in the photo and "you think you had reservations" (t). According to the sign then, "you're in the wrong (not right, $\sim r$) place." After you reconsider, "you don't think you had reservations." Can you conclude that you are in the right place after all?

③ **Use** the four-step procedure.

1. Write each premise on a separate line.
2. Draw a horizontal line after the last premise. Write the conclusion after the premises.
3. Make a truth table (Table 3.21).

Let us look at the argument and consider its validity.

$t \to \sim r$	First premise	If you think you had reservations, then you are in the wrong (not right) place.
$\sim t$	Second premise	You don't think you had reservations.
$\therefore r$	Conclusion	You are in the right place.

Table 3.21

			Premise	Premise	Conclusion
t	r	$\sim r$	$t \to \sim r$	$\sim t$	r
T	T	F	F	F	T
T	F	T	T	F	F
F	T	F	T	T	T
F	F	T	T	T	F ← True premises False conclusion

④ **Check** the rows in which the premises $t \to \sim r$ and $\sim t$ are true.

Check rows 3 and 4. In the fourth row, both premises are true, but the conclusion r is false, so the argument is *invalid*. You cannot conclude that you are in the right place.

Try Example 3 Now

Cover the solution, write your own solution, and then check your work.

EXAMPLE 3 Using Truth Tables to Determine Validity

Use a truth table to determine the validity of the argument in Example 2.

Solution

The argument is symbolized as

$$\begin{array}{l} e \lor o \\ \underline{\sim e} \\ \therefore o \end{array}$$

Make a truth table (Table 3.22) for this argument with a column for each premise and a column for the conclusion.

According to the definition of a valid argument, you need to examine only those rows of Table 3.22 where all the premises are true. Consequently, you need to check only the third row. (In rows 1, 2, and 4, at least one of the premises is false, and so these rows are crossed out.) For the argument to be valid, the remaining items in the conclusion column must all be T's. There is only one item, and it is T. Thus, Table 3.22 shows that the argument is valid.

TABLE 3.22

		Premise	Premise	Conclusion
e	o	$e \lor o$	$\sim e$	o
~~T~~	~~T~~	~~F~~	~~ⓕ~~	~~T~~
~~T~~	~~F~~	~~T~~	~~ⓕ~~	~~F~~
F	T	T	T	T
~~F~~	~~F~~	~~ⓕ~~	~~T~~	~~F~~ ← True premises False conclusion

EXAMPLE 4 Using Truth Tables to Determine Validity

Use a truth table to determine the validity of the following argument:

Either the puppy is cute or I will not adopt it.
The puppy is cute.
∴ I will adopt it.

Solution

By writing p for "The puppy is cute" and b for "I will adopt it," we can symbolize the argument in the form

$$p \vee \sim a$$
$$\underline{p\quad}$$
$$\therefore\ a$$

Now, we construct Table 3.23 for this argument.

Table 3.23

			Premise	Premise	Conclusion
p	b	$\sim b$	$p \vee \sim a$	p	a
T	T	F	T	T	T
T	F	T	T	T	F ← True premises False conclusion
~~F~~	~~T~~	~~F~~	~~F~~	~~F~~	~~T~~
~~F~~	~~T~~	~~T~~	~~T~~	~~F~~	~~F~~

Next, we cross out all the rows where an F occurs in a premise column (rows 3 and 4 in Table 3.23). In the remaining rows, the premises are all true, so the remaining items in the conclusion column must all be T's if the argument is valid. Since there is an F in the second row of this column, the argument is invalid.

EXAMPLE 5 Arguments and Overtime Pay

Use a truth table to determine the validity of the following argument: You will not get overtime pay unless you work more than 40 hr per week. You work more than 40 hr per week. So you will get overtime pay.

Solution

To symbolize the argument, let p be "You get overtime pay" and let m be "You work more than 40 hr per week." Then, the argument is as follows:

$$p \rightarrow m$$ *Note:* $\sim a$ unless b means $a \rightarrow b$. Why?
$$\underline{m\quad}$$
$$\therefore\ p$$

Table 3.24

		Premise	Premise	Conclusion
p	m	$p \rightarrow m$	m	p
T	T	T	T	T
~~T~~	~~F~~	~~F~~	~~F~~	~~T~~
F	T	T	T	F ← True premises False conclusion
~~F~~	~~F~~	~~T~~	~~F~~	~~F~~

Notice that "You will not get overtime pay unless you work more than 40 hours per week" means that "If you get overtime pay, then you work more than 40 hours per week." Table 3.24 is the truth table for this argument.

In the first and third rows of Table 3.24, both premises are true, but in the third row, the conclusion is false. Hence, the argument is invalid.

EXAMPLE 6 Using Truth Tables to Determine Validity

Use a truth table to determine the validity of the following argument:

All dictionaries are useful books.
All useful books are valuable.
∴ All dictionaries are valuable.

Solution

We first write the argument in symbolic form. The statement "All dictionaries are useful books" is translated as "If the book is a dictionary (d), then it is a useful book (u)." "All useful books are valuable" means "If the book is a useful book (u), then it is valuable (v)." "All dictionaries are valuable" is translated as "If the book is a dictionary (d), then it is valuable (v)." Thus, the argument is symbolized as

$$d \rightarrow u$$
$$u \rightarrow v$$
$$\therefore\ d \rightarrow v$$

From Table 3.25 we see that whenever all the premises are true (rows 1, 5, 7, and 8), the conclusion is also true. Hence, the argument is valid.

Table 3.25

			Premise	Premise	Conclusion
d	u	v	$d \rightarrow u$	$u \rightarrow v$	$d \rightarrow v$
T	T	T	T	T	T
~~T~~	~~T~~	~~F~~	~~T~~	~~F~~	~~F~~
~~T~~	~~F~~	~~T~~	~~F~~	~~T~~	~~T~~
~~T~~	~~F~~	~~F~~	~~F~~	~~T~~	~~F~~
F	T	T	T	T	T
~~F~~	~~T~~	~~F~~	~~T~~	~~F~~	~~T~~
F	F	T	T	T	T
F	F	F	T	T	T

True premises
True conclusion

The results of this problem can also be determined by using an Euler diagram. Try it and compare the results.

EXAMPLE 7 Translating Cartoons and Checking Validity

Translate the argument in the cartoon into symbolic form and check its validity.

Solution

Let r be "You do not know how to read."
Let w be "You cannot read *War and Peace*."
Let h be "Leo Tolstoy will hate you."

Then the argument can be translated as follows:

$$\begin{array}{l} r \to w \\ \underline{w \to h} \\ \therefore\ r \to h \end{array}$$

Since the form of this argument is identical to that in Example 6, this argument is also valid.

Examples 6 and 7 are illustrations of the fact that an argument of the form

$$\begin{array}{l} p \to q \\ \underline{q \to r} \\ \therefore\ p \to r \end{array}$$

is always valid.

In using a truth table to check the validity of an argument, we need to examine only those rows where the premises are all true. This points out a basic logical principle: **If there is no case in which the premises are all true, then the argument is valid regardless of the conclusion.**

This principle is used in the next example.

EXAMPLE 8 Determining the Validity of an Argument

Determine the validity of the following argument:

It is raining now.
<u>It is not raining now.</u>
∴ It is raining now.

Table 3.26

p	$\sim p$	$p \land \sim p$
T	F	F
F	F	F

Solution

We let p be "It is raining now" and symbolize the argument, getting

$$\begin{array}{l} p \\ \underline{\sim p} \\ \therefore\ p \end{array}$$

From Table 3.26 we see that there is no case in which the conjunction of the premises, $p \land \sim p$, is true. Thus, the argument is valid.

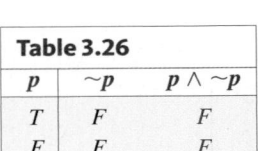

In many cases we are confronted with arguments of the following form:

1. $p \to q$
2. $q \to r$
3. $\underline{r \to s}$
4. $\therefore\ p \to s$

Four statements are involved in this argument, so the truth table to determine its validity will have $2^4 = 16$ rows. To construct such a table would be a tedious task, indeed. For this reason, we develop an alternative method for establishing the validity of such arguments. We first consider the premises $p \rightarrow q$ and $q \rightarrow r$. From these we can conclude (see Example 6) that $p \rightarrow r$. Hence, substituting our conclusion in the given argument, we have the following:

2′. $p \rightarrow r$
3. $\underline{r \rightarrow s}$
4. $\therefore p \rightarrow s$

But this new argument again has the form of the one in Example 6, so we know it is valid.

C Supply a Valid Conclusion to an Argument

In many cases, instead of determining the validity of an argument, we have to supply a valid conclusion for a given set of premises. Using the idea in Example 6, we can see that if the premises are $(p \rightarrow q), (q \rightarrow r), \ldots, (x \rightarrow y), (y \rightarrow z)$, a valid conclusion is $p \rightarrow z$. We illustrate this idea in Examples 9–11.

EXAMPLE 9 Supplying Conclusions Using All Premises

Supply a valid conclusion using all the following premises:

1. $p \rightarrow q$
2. $q \rightarrow r$
3. $\sim s \rightarrow \sim r$

Solution

The third premise can be rewritten as $r \rightarrow s$ because a statement and its contrapositive are equivalent. Hence, the entire argument can be written as follows:

1. $p \rightarrow q$
2. $q \rightarrow r$
3′. $r \rightarrow s$

Thus, a valid conclusion using all the premises is $p \rightarrow s$.

EXAMPLE 10 Showing Conclusions Involving TV Watching

Suppose you know the following to be true:

1. If Alice watches TV, then Ben watches TV.
2. Carol watches TV if and only if Ben watches.
3. Don never watches TV if Carol is watching.
4. Don always watches TV if Ed is watching.

Show that Alice never watches TV if Ed is watching.

Solution

Let a be "Alice watches TV."
Let b be "Ben watches TV."
Let c be "Carol watches TV."
Let d be "Don watches TV."
Let e be "Ed watches TV."

The preceding argument can be symbolized as follows:

1. $a \to b$
2. $c \leftrightarrow b$, or equivalently, 2′. $b \leftrightarrow c$
3. $c \to \sim d$
4. $e \to d$, or equivalently, 4′. $\sim d \to \sim e$

If these premises are arranged in the order 1, 2′, 3, and 4′, we obtain the following:

1. $a \to b$
2′. $b \leftrightarrow c$
3. $c \to \sim d$
4′. $\sim d \to \sim e$

Consequently, we can conclude that $a \to \sim e$; that is, "If Alice watches TV, then Ed does not watch TV," or equivalently, "Alice never watches TV if Ed is watching."

© I. Bello

In the preceding examples we have supplied a valid conclusion using all the given premises. Sometimes it may be necessary to supply an additional (hidden) premise to reach a valid conclusion. Here is one such instance. Look at the statement on the shampoo bottle. It says

If seal is broken (b), do not use ($\sim u$).

In symbols,

$b \to \sim u$

Can you ever use the shampoo? How would you use it without breaking the seal? Here is the hidden premise. If you use the shampoo, you have to break the seal. In symbols,

$u \to b$

EXAMPLE 11 Finding a Valid Conclusion

Supply a valid conclusion using the premises

1. $b \to \sim u$
2. $u \to b$ (hidden premise)

Solution

We arrange the premises so that the consequent of one statement corresponds to the antecedent of the next; that is, we write

$u \to b$ and then $b \to \sim u$

or simply

$u \to b \to \sim u$

Thus, the conclusion is

If you use the shampoo, then do not use it.

This means that we will not use the shampoo! For a dissenting opinion, see the photo on the left!

© I. Bello

You do *not* have to break the seal to use the shampoo.

In our day-to-day reasoning, we do not make truth tables or check our arguments in any formal fashion. Instead, we (perhaps unconsciously) learn a few argument forms, which we use as we need them. The most commonly used of these argument forms are as follows:

Modus Ponens (Law of Detachment)	*Modus Tollens (Law of Contraposition)*	*Hypothetical Syllogism*	*Disjunctive Syllogism*
$p \to q$	$p \to q$	$p \to q$	$p \vee q$
$\underline{p}$	$\underline{\sim q}$	$\underline{q \to r}$	$\underline{\sim p}$
$\therefore q$	$\therefore \sim p$	$\therefore p \to r$	$\therefore q$

The names of the first two of these are derived from the Latin and mean, respectively, "a manner of affirming" and "a manner of denying" (the parts of a conditional). The *modus ponens* and the two types of syllogisms have already been discussed in this section; see Examples 1 and 2, the problem-solving example, and Example 6. It is left for you to show the validity of the *modus tollens* in problem 20 of Exercises 3.6.

Let us discuss a more immediate problem. Have you been attending all your math class sessions, or do you have excessive absences? If you have been absent a number of times, here is an argument you and/or your instructor may consider.

1 absence does not constitute excessive absences.

If 1 absence does not constitute excessive absences, then 2 absences do not.

If 2 absences do not constitute excessive absences, then 3 absences do not.

.
.
.

<u>If 99 absences do not constitute excessive absences, then 100 absences do not.</u>

$\therefore$ 100 absences do not constitute excessive absences.

This type of argument form is called a *sorite* from the word *soros,* meaning "heap." (Can you find out why?) Does the argument seem valid to you? See the Collaborative Learning feature for more information.

3.6 EXERCISES

A Writing Arguments in Symbolic Form

In problems 1–16, symbolize each argument using the suggested abbreviations. In each case, determine the validity of the given argument.

1. If you eat your spinach (e), you can go out and play (p).
   You did not eat your spinach.
   Therefore, you cannot go out and play.
2. If you eat your spinach (e), you can go out and play (p).
   You cannot go out and play.
   Therefore, you did not eat your spinach.
3. If you study logic (s), mathematics is easy (e).
   Mathematics is not easy.
   Therefore, you did not study logic.
4. I will learn this mathematics (m), or I will eat my hat (e).
   I will not eat my hat.
   Therefore, I will learn this mathematics.
5. The Good Taste Restaurant has good food (g).
   Hence, the Good Taste Restaurant has good food, and I will recommend it to everyone (r).
6. If prices go up (u), management will scream (s).
   If management screams, then supervisors will get tough (t).
   Hence, if prices go up, supervisors will get tough.
7. If I work (w), then I have money (m).
   If I don't work, I have a good time (g).
   Therefore, I have money or a good time.
8. Babies (b) are illogical (i).
   Nobody is despised (d) who can manage a crocodile (m).
   Illogical persons are despised.
   Hence, babies cannot manage crocodiles.
9. If you have the time (t), we've got the beer (b).
   You have the time.
   So we've got the beer.
10. Bill did not go to class this morning ($\sim g$) because he wore a red shirt (r), and he never wears a red shirt to class.
11. Where there is smoke (s) there is fire (f).
    There is smoke.
    Hence, there is fire.

12. If you are enrolled (e) or have been accepted half-time at a college (h), you can apply for a loan (a).
You have not been accepted half-time at a college.
Hence, you cannot apply for a loan.

13. You will be eligible for a grant (e) if you meet all the criteria (m).
You do not meet all the criteria.
So you are not eligible for a grant.

14. We will pay for collision loss (p) only if collision coverage is afforded (a).
Collision coverage is not afforded.
Hence, we will not pay for collision loss.

15. If spouse is also filing (f), give spouse's Social Security number (s).
Spouse is not filing.
Hence, do not give spouse's Social Security number.

16. Additional sheets of paper are not attached ($\sim a$) unless more space is needed (m).
More space is needed.
Hence, additional sheets of paper are attached.

B Using Truth Tables to Determine Validity

Determine whether each argument in problems 17–21 is valid.

17. $p \vee q$
$\underline{\sim p}$
$\therefore q$

18. $p \to q$
$\underline{p}$
$\therefore q$

19. $p \to q$
$\underline{\sim p}$
$\therefore q$

20. $p \to q$
$\underline{\sim q}$
$\therefore \sim p$

21. $p \to q$
$\underline{q \to r}$
$\therefore \sim r \to \sim p$

C Supply a Valid Conclusion to an Argument

In problems 22–27, find valid conclusions using all the premises.

22. $p \to q$
$q \to r$
$\underline{r \to \sim s}$

23. $p \to q$
$\underline{\sim q \vee r}$
[*Hint:* $(\sim q \vee r) \Leftrightarrow (q \to r)$]

24. $p \to q$
$s \to \sim r$
$t \to r$
$q \to u$
$\underline{\sim u \vee t}$

25. $p \to q$
$q \to r$
$\sim s \to \sim r$
$\underline{p}$

26. $p \to \sim q$
$r \to q$
$\underline{r}$

27. $\sim p \to q$
$\sim p \vee r$
$\underline{\sim r}$

In problems 28–35, find valid conclusions using all the premises.

28. No people who assign work are lovable.
All supervisors assign work.

29. All politicians run for office.
No people who run for office are reliable.

30. No employee who doesn't arrive for work on time will be promoted.
Some employees don't arrive for work on time.

31. Some students are intelligent.
All intelligent people are snobs.

32. If it rains, then the grass will grow.
A sufficient condition for cutting the grass is that it will grow.
The grass is cut only if it is higher than 8 in.

33. The only books in this library that I do not recommend are unhealthy.
All bound books are well written.
All romances are healthy in tone.
I do not recommend any unbound books.

34. All ducks can fly.
No land bird eats shrimp.
Only flightless birds do not eat shrimp.

35. If you are not patriotic, then you do not vote.
Aardvarks have no emotions.
You cannot be patriotic if you have no emotions.

36. Given that
No music student who doesn't practice will learn to play well.
Some music students don't practice.
Which conclusion can be logically deduced?
a. Some music students won't learn to play well.
b. No music student will learn to play well.
c. All music students who practice will learn to play well.
d. None of these answers.

37. Given that
No college student who doesn't go to class will pass the course.
Some college students don't go to class.
Which conclusion can be logically deduced?
a. No college student will pass the course.
b. All college students who go to class will pass the course.
c. Some college students will not pass the course.
d. None of these answers.

38. Given that
No student who works late can be a party animal.
All supervisors work late.
Which conclusion can be logically deduced?
a. All supervisors are party animals.
b. Some supervisors are party animals.
c. No supervisors are party animals.
d. None of these answers.

39. Given that
No people who teach classes are dumb.
All teachers teach classes.
Which conclusion can be logically deduced?
a. All teachers are dumb.
b. No teacher is dumb.
c. Some teachers are dumb.
d. None of these answers.

40. Classify the arguments in problems 2, 4, 6, and 11 as *modus ponens, modus tollens*, hypothetical syllogism, or disjunctive syllogism.

In problems 41–44, two premises are given in each problem. Select the conclusion that will make each entire argument valid.

41. If I drive to work, then I will not be late.
<u>If I am not late, then I do not lose any pay.</u>
a. If I am not late, then I drive to work.
b. If I do not lose any pay, then I drive to work.
c. If I drive to work, then I do not lose any pay.
d. If I do not drive to work, then I lose some pay.

42. If the Bears win the final game, then they will play in the NFL playoffs.

If they play in the NFL playoffs, their owners will make a good profit.

a. If their owners made a good profit, then the Bears played in the NFL playoffs.

b. If their owners made a good profit, then the Bears won the final game.

c. If the Bears do not win the final game, then their owners will not make a good profit.

d. If the Bears win the final game, then their owners will make a good profit.

43. If all persons pay their bills on time, then no collection agencies are needed.

Unfortunately, some collection agencies are needed.

a. Some people pay their bills on time.

b. Some people do not pay their bills on time.

c. If there are no collection agencies, then all persons pay their bills on time.

d. All people pay their bills on time.

44. If all students learn from their books alone, then no teachers are needed.

However, some teachers are needed.

a. No students learn from their books alone.

b. Some students learn from their books alone.

c. If no teachers are needed, then all students learn from their books alone.

d. Some students do not learn from their books alone.

45. If Bill studies economics, he will make good money. If he studies business procedures, he will make good money. Bill studies economics but not business procedures. Which of the following (if any) is a logical conclusion?

a. Bill does not make good money.

b. Bill makes good money.

c. Bill does not get a college degree.

46. All college graduates are educated. All educated people dress neatly. Jackie dresses neatly. Which of the following (if any) is a logical conclusion?

a. Jackie is a college graduate.

b. Jackie is not a college graduate.

c. Jackie is educated.

IN OTHER WORDS

The job of advertisers is to convince people to buy their products. In problems 47 and 48, write the conclusions you think the advertisers want you to reach.

47. If you read X magazine, then you will not make bad financial decisions. You certainly do not want to make bad financial decisions, so _____.

48. If you do not join our club, you will not be popular. You did join, so _____.

49. The name of the fallacy in problem 47 is "affirming the consequent." Explain what this means.

50. The name of the fallacy in problem 48 is "denying the antecedent." Explain what this means.

DISCOVERY

Consider the following premises taken from Symbolic Logic, *a book written by Lewis Carroll (logician, mathematician, and author of* Alice's Adventures in Wonderland*):*

No kitten that loves fish is unteachable.
No kitten without a tail will play with a gorilla.
Kittens with whiskers always love fish.
No teachable kitten has green eyes.
Kittens that have no whiskers have no tails.

51. Find a valid conclusion using all the premises. (*Hint:* "No _____ is _____" is translated as "If it is a _____, then it is not a _____.")

COLLABORATIVE LEARNING

Form three groups called Library, Internet, *and* Other. *Let each of the groups find the answers to the following questions, compare the groups' answers, and write a report using information from all of the three groups:*

1. Who has been attributed with the discovery of the sorites?

2. How many sorites were there originally?

3. There is another variation of this argument form that uses subtraction (taking just 1 away is not going to make a difference!) rather than addition to reach its conclusion. It goes like this:

A person with **10,000** hairs on his or her head is not bald,
If a person with **10,000** hairs on his or her head is not bald, then a person with **9999** hairs on his or her head is not bald.
And so on.

Can you prove from these premises that a person with 1 hair on his or her head is not bald?

4. If you assume that your test can be postponed just 1 day, can you construct a sorite arguing that your test can be postponed forever?

5. Sometimes students argue that their lowest test score should be dropped. Can you construct a sorite showing that all your test grades (or at least the undesirable ones) should be dropped?

CHAPTER 3 Summary

<table>
<tr><th>SECTION</th><th>ITEM</th><th>MEANING</th><th>EXAMPLE</th></tr>
<tr><td>3.1A</td><td>p, q, r, etc.</td><td>Statements</td><td>p: Today is Monday.
q: The sky is blue.</td></tr>
<tr><td>3.1B</td><td>$p \wedge q$</td><td>Conjunction (p and q)</td><td>Today is Monday and the sky is blue.</td></tr>
<tr><td></td><td>$p \vee q$</td><td>Disjunction (p or q)</td><td>Today is Monday or the sky is blue.</td></tr>
<tr><td></td><td>$\sim p$</td><td>Negation (not p)</td><td>Today is not Monday.</td></tr>
<tr><td>3.2A, B, C</td><td><table>
<tr><th>p</th><th>q</th><th>$p \wedge q$</th><th>$p \vee q$</th><th>$\sim p$</th></tr>
<tr><td>T</td><td>T</td><td>T</td><td>T</td><td>F</td></tr>
<tr><td>T</td><td>F</td><td>F</td><td>T</td><td>F</td></tr>
<tr><td>F</td><td>T</td><td>F</td><td>T</td><td>T</td></tr>
<tr><td>F</td><td>F</td><td>F</td><td>F</td><td>T</td></tr>
</table></td><td>Truth tables for the statements $p \wedge q$, $p \vee q$, and $\sim p$</td><td></td></tr>
<tr><td>3.2E</td><td>$p \Leftrightarrow q$</td><td>The statements p and q are equivalent; that is, they have identical truth tables.</td><td>$\sim(p \vee q) \Leftrightarrow \sim p \wedge \sim q$</td></tr>
<tr><td>3.3A</td><td>$p \rightarrow q$</td><td>p conditional q</td><td>If today is Monday, then I will go to school.</td></tr>
<tr><td>3.3B</td><td>$p \leftrightarrow q$</td><td>p biconditional q</td><td>Today is Monday if and only if I go to school.</td></tr>
<tr><td>3.3A, B</td><td><table>
<tr><th>p</th><th>q</th><th>$p \rightarrow q$</th><th>$p \leftrightarrow q$</th></tr>
<tr><td>T</td><td>T</td><td>T</td><td>T</td></tr>
<tr><td>T</td><td>F</td><td>F</td><td>F</td></tr>
<tr><td>F</td><td>T</td><td>T</td><td>F</td></tr>
<tr><td>F</td><td>F</td><td>T</td><td>T</td></tr>
</table></td><td>Truth tables for the conditional and the biconditional</td><td></td></tr>
<tr><td>3.4A</td><td>$q \rightarrow p$
$\sim p \rightarrow \sim q$
$\sim q \rightarrow \sim p$</td><td>Converse of $p \rightarrow q$
Inverse of $p \rightarrow q$
Contrapositive of $p \rightarrow q$</td><td></td></tr>
<tr><td>3.4B</td><td>p is sufficient for q.
q is necessary for p.
p only if q
q if p</td><td>Statements equivalent to "If p, then q"</td><td></td></tr>
<tr><td>3.4C</td><td>A tautology</td><td>A statement that is always true</td><td>2 is even.
$p \vee \sim p$</td></tr>
<tr><td></td><td>A contradiction</td><td>A statement that is always false</td><td>2 is odd.
$p \wedge \sim p$</td></tr>
<tr><td>3.4D</td><td>$p \Rightarrow q$</td><td>p implies q; used when the conditional $p \rightarrow q$ is a tautology.</td><td>The animal is a dog (d) implies that the animal is a mammal (m), since $d \rightarrow m$ is a tautology.</td></tr>
<tr><td>3.5A</td><td>$p \rightarrow q$
p
$\therefore q$</td><td>An argument (a set of statements, the premises, and a claim that another statement, the conclusion, follows from the premises)</td><td>If it rains, then I get wet.
It rains.
∴ I get wet.</td></tr>
</table>

CHAPTER 3 Summary

SECTION	ITEM	MEANING	EXAMPLE
3.5B	Valid argument	An argument is valid if, whenever all the premises are true, the conclusion is also true.	All men are mortal. Socrates is a man. ∴ Socrates is mortal.
3.6C	Modus ponens	$p \rightarrow q$ p $\therefore q$	
	Modus tollens	$p \rightarrow q$ $\sim q$ $\therefore \sim p$	
	Hypothetical syllogism	$p \rightarrow q$ $q \rightarrow r$ $\therefore p \rightarrow r$	
	Disjunctive syllogism	$p \vee q$ $\sim p$ $\therefore q$	

CHAPTER 3 Practice Test

1. Which of the following are statements?
   a. Green apples taste good.
   b. 1991 was a leap year.
   c. No fish can live without water.
   d. Some birds cannot fly.
   e. If it rains today, my lawn will get wet.
   f. Can anyone answer this question?

2. Identify the components and the logical connective or modifier in each of the following statements. Write each statement in symbolic form using the suggested abbreviations.
   a. If the number of a year is divisible by 4 (d), then the year is a presidential election year (p).
   b. I love Bill (b), but Bill does not love me ($\sim m$).
   c. A candidate is elected president of the United States (e) if and only if he or she receives a majority of the electoral college votes (m).
   d. Janet can make sense out of symbolic logic (s) or fail this course (f).
   e. Janet cannot make sense out of symbolic logic ($\sim s$).

3. Let g be "He is a gentleman" and let s be "He is a scholar." Write the following in words:
   a. $\sim(g \wedge s)$
   b. $\sim g \wedge s$

4. Write the negation of each of the following statements:
   a. I will go to the beach or to the movies.
   b. I will stay in my room and do my homework.
   c. Pluto is not a planet.

5. Write the negation of each of the following statements:
   a. All cats are felines.
   b. Some dogs are well trained.
   c. No dog is afraid of a mouse.

continued

CHAPTER 3 Practice Test – *continued*

6. Write the negation of each of the following statements:
   a. If Joey does not study, he will fail this course.
   b. If Sally studies hard, she will make an A in this course.

7. In the following table, which of the truth tables under (*a*), (*b*), (*c*), (*d*), and (*e*) matches each of the following statements: $\sim p$, $p \to q$, $p \wedge q$, $p \vee q$, and $p \leftrightarrow q$?

p	q	(*a*)	(*b*)	(*c*)	(*d*)	(*e*)
T	T	T	T	F	T	T
T	F	F	F	F	F	T
F	T	F	F	T	T	T
F	F	T	F	T	T	F

8. Construct a truth table for the statement $(p \vee q) \wedge (\sim p \vee \sim q)$.

9. Construct a truth table for the statement $(p \vee q) \to \sim p$.

10. Which of the following statements is equivalent to $\sim p \vee q$?
    a. $\sim p \wedge \sim q$ b. $\sim(p \wedge \sim q)$

11. Under what condition is the following statement true? "Sally is naturally beautiful, or she knows how to use makeup."

12. Is the following statement true or false? If $2 + 2 = 5$, then $2 \times 3 = 6$.

13. Construct the truth table for the statement $(p \to q) \leftrightarrow (q \vee \sim p)$.

14. Write the following for the statement "If you make a golf score of 62 once, you will make it again":
    a. The converse   b. The inverse   c. The contrapositive

15. Let p be "You get overtime pay" and let m be "You work more than 40 hr per week." Symbolize the following statements.
    a. If you work more than 40 hr per week, then you get overtime pay.
    b. You get overtime pay only if you work more than 40 hr per week.
    c. You get overtime pay if and only if you work more than 40 hr per week.

16. Let b be "You get a bank loan" and let c be "You have a good credit record." Symbolize the following statements:
    a. For you to get a bank loan, it is necessary that you have a good credit record.
    b. Your having a good credit record is sufficient for you to get a bank loan.
    c. A necessary and sufficient condition for you to get a bank loan is that you have a good credit record.

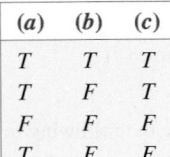

(*a*)	(*b*)	(*c*)
T	T	T
T	F	T
F	F	F
T	F	F

17. The table at the left gives the truth values for three statements a, b, and c. Find all the implications among these statements.

18. Which of the following statements are tautologies?
    a. $p \wedge \sim p$ b. $p \vee \sim p$ c. $(p \to q) \leftrightarrow (\sim q \vee p)$

19. Use an Euler diagram to check the validity of the following argument:

    All students study hard.
    John is not a student.
    ∴ John does not study hard.

20. Use an Euler diagram to check the validity of the following argument:

    No loafers work hard.
    Sally does not work hard.
    ∴ Sally is a loafer.

CHAPTER 3 Practice Test

21. Use a truth table to check the validity of the argument in problem 19.

22. Use a truth table to check the validity of the argument in problem 20.

23. Use a truth table to check the validity of the following argument:

    If you win the race, you are a good runner.
    You win the race.
    ∴ You are a good runner.

24. Supply a valid conclusion using all three premises: (1) $p \to q$, (2) $\sim p \to \sim r$, and (3) $s \to \sim q$.

ANSWERS TO PRACTICE TEST

CHAPTER 3		What to Review *If You Missed It*		
QUESTION	**ANSWER**	**SECTION**	**EXAMPLE(S)**	**PAGE(S)**
1	Parts (**b**), (**c**), (**d**), and (**e**) are statements. Each is either true or false. Part (**a**) is not a statement, because people do not agree on what is good. Part (**f**) is a question, so is neither true nor false.	3.1	1, 2	93
2	a. d: The number of years is divisible by 4. p: The year is a presidential election year. The logical connective is *if-then.* $d \to p$ b. b: I love Bill. $\sim m$: Bill does not love me. The logical connective is *and.* $b \wedge \sim m$ c. e: A candidate is elected president of the United States. m: He or she receives a majority of the electoral college votes. The logical connective is *if and only if.* $e \leftrightarrow m$ d. s: Janet can make sense out of symbolic logic. f: She fails this course. The logical connective is *or.* $s \vee f$ e. s: Janet can make sense out of symbolic logic. The logical modifier is *not.* $\sim s$	3.1	3, 4	94–95
3	a. It is not the case that he is a gentleman and a scholar. b. He is not a gentleman, but he is a scholar.	3.1	5	95
4	a. I will go neither to the beach nor to the movies. b. I will either not stay in my room or not do my homework. c. Pluto is a planet.	3.1	6d, 8a	96, 97
5	a. Some cats are not felines. b. No dog is well trained. c. Some dogs are afraid of a mouse.	3.1	9	98
6	a. Joey does not study, but he will not fail this course. b. Sally studies hard, but she does not get an A in this course.	3.2	3	104

continued

ANSWERS TO PRACTICE TEST – *continued*

<table>
<tr><th colspan="2">CHAPTER 3</th><th colspan="3">What to Review If You Missed It</th></tr>
<tr><th>QUESTION</th><th>ANSWER</th><th>SECTION</th><th>EXAMPLE(S)</th><th>PAGE(S)</th></tr>
<tr><td>7</td><td>(a) $p \leftrightarrow q$ (b) $p \wedge q$ (c) $\sim p$
(d) $p \rightarrow q$ (e) $p \vee q$</td><td>3.1–3.3</td><td>Tables 3.2, 3.3, 3.4, 3.11, and 3.12</td><td>103, 104, 105, 113 and 114</td></tr>
<tr><td>8</td><td><table>
<tr><td>1</td><td>2</td><td>3</td><td>7</td><td>4</td><td>6</td><td>5</td></tr>
<tr><td>p</td><td>q</td><td>$(p \vee q)$</td><td>$\wedge$</td><td>$(\sim p$</td><td>$\vee$</td><td>$\sim q)$</td></tr>
<tr><td>T</td><td>T</td><td>T</td><td>F</td><td>F</td><td>F</td><td>F</td></tr>
<tr><td>T</td><td>F</td><td>T</td><td>T</td><td>F</td><td>T</td><td>T</td></tr>
<tr><td>F</td><td>T</td><td>T</td><td>T</td><td>T</td><td>T</td><td>F</td></tr>
<tr><td>F</td><td>F</td><td>F</td><td>F</td><td>T</td><td>T</td><td>T</td></tr>
</table></td><td>3.2</td><td>6–9</td><td>106–107 and 109–110</td></tr>
<tr><td>9</td><td><table>
<tr><td>1</td><td>2</td><td>3</td><td>5</td><td>4</td></tr>
<tr><td>p</td><td>q</td><td>$(p \vee q)$</td><td>$\rightarrow$</td><td>$\sim p$</td></tr>
<tr><td>T</td><td>T</td><td>T</td><td>F</td><td>F</td></tr>
<tr><td>T</td><td>F</td><td>T</td><td>F</td><td>F</td></tr>
<tr><td>F</td><td>T</td><td>T</td><td>T</td><td>T</td></tr>
<tr><td>F</td><td>F</td><td>F</td><td>T</td><td>T</td></tr>
</table></td><td>3.2</td><td>6, 8</td><td>106, 107</td></tr>
<tr><td>10</td><td>Statement (b)</td><td>3.2</td><td>9</td><td>109–110</td></tr>
<tr><td>11</td><td>When at least one of the statements “Sally is naturally beautiful” and “Sally knows how to use makeup” is true.</td><td>3.3</td><td>2</td><td>114–115</td></tr>
<tr><td>12</td><td>The premise “2 + 2 = 5” is false, so the statement (a conditional) is true.</td><td>3.3</td><td>3</td><td>115</td></tr>
<tr><td>13</td><td><table>
<tr><td>1</td><td>2</td><td>3</td><td>6</td><td>5</td><td>4</td></tr>
<tr><td>p</td><td>q</td><td>$(p \rightarrow q)$</td><td>$\leftrightarrow$</td><td>$(q \vee$</td><td>$\sim p)$</td></tr>
<tr><td>T</td><td>T</td><td>T</td><td>T</td><td>T</td><td>F</td></tr>
<tr><td>T</td><td>F</td><td>F</td><td>T</td><td>F</td><td>F</td></tr>
<tr><td>F</td><td>T</td><td>T</td><td>T</td><td>T</td><td>T</td></tr>
<tr><td>F</td><td>F</td><td>T</td><td>T</td><td>T</td><td>T</td></tr>
</table></td><td>3.3</td><td>5</td><td>115</td></tr>
<tr><td>14</td><td>a. If you make a golf score of 62 again, then you made it once.
b. If you do not make a golf score of 62 once, then you will not make it again.
c. If you do not make a golf score of 62 again, then you did not make it once.</td><td>3.4</td><td>1–3</td><td>121</td></tr>
<tr><td>15</td><td>a. $m \rightarrow p$ b. $p \rightarrow m$ c. $p \leftrightarrow m$</td><td>3.4</td><td>4</td><td>122</td></tr>
<tr><td>16</td><td>a. $b \rightarrow c$ b. $c \rightarrow b$ c. $b \leftrightarrow c$</td><td>3.4</td><td>4</td><td>122</td></tr>
<tr><td>17</td><td>Statement (b) implies (a); (b) implies (c); (c) implies (a).</td><td>3.4</td><td>7</td><td>124</td></tr>
<tr><td>18</td><td>Only statement (b).</td><td>3.4</td><td>5, 6</td><td>122, 123</td></tr>
</table>

ANSWERS TO PRACTICE TEST

CHAPTER 3

What to Review *If You Missed It*

QUESTION	ANSWER	SECTION	EXAMPLE(S)	PAGE(S)
19	Nothing in the premises tells whether the J (for John) is inside or outside of the circle H. Thus, the argument is invalid. (See diagram below.)	3.5	1–4	128–129
20	Nothing in the premises tells whether S (for Sally) goes inside the circle L or not. Thus, the argument is invalid. (See diagram below.)	3.5	1–5	128–130
21	With s for "He is a student" and h for "He studies hard," the argument can be symbolized and a truth table constructed as follows (see below).	3.6	3–5	137–139
22	With f for "She is a loafer" and h for "She works hard," the argument can be symbolized and a truth table constructed as follows (see below).	3.6	3–5	137–139

19 Nothing in the premises tells whether the J (for John) is inside or outside of the circle H. Thus, the argument is invalid.

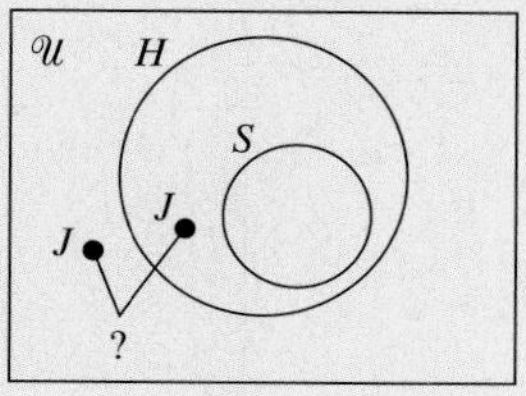

20 Nothing in the premises tells whether S (for Sally) goes inside the circle L or not. Thus, the argument is invalid.

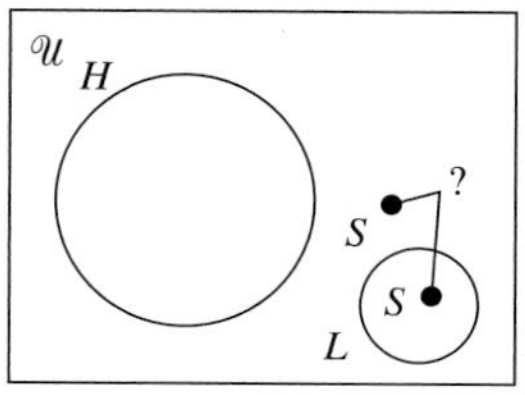

21 With s for "He is a student" and h for "He studies hard," the argument can be symbolized and a truth table constructed as follows:

$$\begin{array}{l} s \to h \\ \underline{\sim s} \\ \therefore \sim h \end{array}$$

		Prem.	Prem.	Concl.
s	h	$s \to h$	$\sim s$	$\sim h$
~~T~~	~~T~~	~~T~~	~~F~~	~~F~~
~~T~~	~~F~~	~~F~~	~~F~~	~~T~~
F	T	T	T	F
F	F	T	T	T

In the third row of the table, both premises are true and the conclusion is false, so the argument is invalid.

22 With f for "She is a loafer" and h for "She works hard," the argument can be symbolized and a truth table constructed as follows:

$$\begin{array}{l} f \to \sim h \\ \underline{\sim h} \\ \therefore f \end{array}$$

		Prem.	Prem.	Concl.
f	h	$f \to h$	$\sim h$	f
~~T~~	~~T~~	~~F~~	~~F~~	~~T~~
T	F	T	T	T
~~F~~	~~T~~	~~T~~	~~F~~	~~F~~
F	F	T	T	F

In the fourth row of the truth table, the premises are both true and the conclusion is false, so the argument is invalid.

continued

ANSWERS TO PRACTICE TEST — *continued*

<table>
<tr><th colspan="2">CHAPTER 3</th><th colspan="3">What to Review If You Missed It</th></tr>
<tr><th>QUESTION</th><th>ANSWER</th><th>SECTION</th><th>EXAMPLE(S)</th><th>PAGE(S)</th></tr>
<tr><td>23</td><td>With w for “You win the race” and r for “You are a good runner,” the argument can be symbolized and a truth table constructed as follows:

$w \rightarrow r$
w
$\therefore r$

<table>
<tr><th></th><th></th><th>Prem.</th><th>Prem.</th><th>Concl.</th></tr>
<tr><th>r</th><th>w</th><th>$w \rightarrow r$</th><th>w</th><th>r</th></tr>
<tr><td>T</td><td>T</td><td>T</td><td>T</td><td>T</td></tr>
<tr><td>T</td><td>F</td><td>T</td><td>F</td><td>T</td></tr>
<tr><td>F</td><td>T</td><td>F</td><td>T</td><td>F</td></tr>
<tr><td>F</td><td>F</td><td>T</td><td>F</td><td>F</td></tr>
</table>

The first row of the table is the only row where the premises are both true. In this row the conclusion is also true, so the argument is valid.</td><td>3.6</td><td>6–8</td><td>139–140</td></tr>
<tr><td>24</td><td>$\sim s$.

$p \rightarrow q$
$\sim p \rightarrow \sim r$
$s \rightarrow \sim q$

is equivalent to

$p \rightarrow q$
$r \rightarrow p$
$q \rightarrow \sim s$

which is equivalent to

$r \rightarrow \sim s$</td><td>3.6</td><td>9, 11</td><td>141, 142</td></tr>
</table>

Numeration Systems

The natural philosophers are mostly gone. We modern scientists are adding too many decimals.
—MARTIN H. FISCHER

The laws of exponents are useful when calculating with large numbers. In Section 4.2, you will use the laws of exponents to help calculate large quantities such as the daily consumption of vegetables by an average American.

Imagine yourself in Egypt 5500 years ago, at a time when Egyptians used their fingers as standard counting units. To keep a record of counted objects, the Egyptians used short, straight strokes called **tally marks.** Representing the numbers from 1 to 9 by the proper number of tally marks and using the symbol ∩ to represent the numeral 10. The result was an ***additive*** system where the position of the numeral has no significance; ∩ | and | ∩ both represent 11. Number values are simply added. (See the margin.)

In Babylon, you would find the oldest system known in which the value of a numeral depends on its placement. Using 60 as the base, ▼▼ means $1 + 1 = 2$, but ▼ ▼ means $60 + 1 = 61$.

The Roman numeral system uses base 10, as the Egyptians did, and constructs numerals by means of simple addition and subtraction. XI means $10 + 1 = 11$, but IX is $10 - 1 = 9$.

Then you will study our present decimal system, also called the *Hindu-Arabic system*. Exponents play a major role in this system when we write numbers in expanded form. You will notice that the base commonly used is 10, but you will look at number systems using bases other than 10 as well.

You will be surprised to know that **binary** systems, using 2 as a base, were among the earliest systems invented. Even today, some South Sea Islanders have a binary system in which counting by 2 means repeating the words for 1 and 2. For these islanders, *urapun* is 1, *okosa* is 2, *okosa urapun* 3, *okosa okosa* 4, and so on. How does the computer count? Well, for a computer, 1_2 (one base two) is 1, 10_2 (one zero base two) is 2, 11_2 (one one base two) is 3, and so on. Do you see the similarity?

From antiquity to the present, the ideas are the same!

Source: easycalculation.com/funny/numerals/egyptian.php

4.1 Egyptian, Babylonian, and Roman Numeration Systems

GETTING STARTED

OBJECTIVES

Convert numerals to decimals and perform operations in:

A. the Egyptian numeral system.
B. the Babylonian numeral system.
C. the Roman numeral system.

FROM EGYPTIANS TO TOLSTOY

The Egyptian system of numeration is additive; that is, the numeral || represents $1 + 1 = 2$ and ||| ∩ represents $1 + 1 + 1 + 10 = 13$. An additive system found in Leo Tolstoy's novel *War and Peace* gives each letter of the French alphabet the number shown in Table 4.1. (Note there is no j.) Thus, the number associated with the name Sue is $90 + 110 + 5 = 205$. Similarly, the number associated with the name Pierre, a character in the novel, is $60 + 9 + 5 + 80 + 80 + 5 = 239$. This character, Pierre Bezukhof, wondered what the number corresponding to the Emperor would be. So he wrote

Le empereur Napoleon

Table 4.1

a	b	c	d	e	f	g	h	i	k	l	m	n
1	2	3	4	5	6	7	8	9	10	20	30	40
o	p	q	r	s	t	u	v	w	x	y	z	
50	60	70	80	90	100	110	120	130	140	150	160	

and added the numbers for these letters, 20 for l, 5 for e, 30 for m, and so on. Can you find his answer? It was 666, the number of the beast prophesied in the Bible. Thus, Pierre reasoned that Napoleon must die. But who would vanquish the feared beast? He had some ideas.

l'empereur Alexandre? La nation russe?

One was too low, the other too high. Can you find which is which? In desperation, Pierre wrote

Comte Pierre Bezukhov

Now the number was far away from what he wanted. He changed the spelling and added his nationality to get

Le russe Besuhof

See whether you can find his number. He knew that he was now near the coveted answer, and he finally wrote

l'russe Besuhof

This gave him the desired answer: He himself would take care of Napoleon! Can you find the final number that Pierre obtained and determine its relationship to Napoleon's number?

In this section we will examine some relationships among the Egyptian, Babylonian, and Roman numeral systems and our own decimal system.

Human Side of Math

© Neveshkin Nikolay / Shutterstock.com

(ca. 780–850)

One of the most influential mathematicians of the early Arab empire was Mohammed ibn Musa al-Khwarizmi. He wrote two books, one on algebra and one on the Hindu numeral system.

Our present-day symbols for the digits 1–9 originated with the Hindus. These numerals were designed for a decimal (base 10) system of counting.

It was not until about the year 500 that the Hindus devised a positional notation for the decimal system. They discarded the separate symbols for numbers greater than 9 and standardized the symbols for the digits from 1 through 9. The symbol for zero came into use much later.

LOOKING AHEAD

In this chapter, we will look at ancient numeration systems and then at our familiar Hindu-Arabic system that al-Khwarizmi championed over 1000 years ago, centuries before it became widely used.

Napoleon Bonaparte, French military leader and emperor of France from 1804 to 1815.

Table 4.2 Ancient Numerals

	Egyptian	Sumerian	Mayan
1	|	|	•
2	||	||	••
3	|||	|||	•••
4	||||	||| / |	••••
5	||| / ||	||| / ||	—
6	||| / |||	||| / |||	• / —
7	|||| / |||	||| / ||| / |	•• / —
8	|||| / ||||	||| / ||| / ||	••• / —
9	||| / ||| / |||	||| / ||| / |||	•••• / —

During the period of recorded history (beginning about 4000 B.C.), people began to think about numbers as abstract concepts. That is, they recognized that two fruits and two arrows have something in common—a quantity called *two*—which is independent of the objects. The perception of this quantity was probably aided by the process of tallying. Different tallying methods have been found in different civilizations. For example, the Incas of Peru used knots in a string or rope to take the census, the Chinese used pebbles or sticks for computations, and the English used tally sticks as tax receipts. As a result of human efforts to keep records of numbers, the first numerals, reflecting the process of tallying, were developed. (A **numeral** is a symbol that represents a number. For example, the numeral 2 represents the number two.) Table 4.2 shows three ancient sets of numerals. The property shared by these three numeration systems is that they are **additive;** that is, the values of the written symbols are added to obtain the number represented.

A The Egyptian System

Let us look at the Egyptian system in greater detail. The Egyptians used hieroglyphics (sacred picture writing) for their numerals. The first line shown in Table 4.3 shows these symbols and their probable numerical values. Convenient names for the hieroglyphics are given below the symbols in Table 4.3.

As we can see from Table 4.3, the Egyptians used a **base of 10.** That is, when the tallies were added and they reached 10, the 10 tallies were replaced by the symbol ∩. The Egyptians generally wrote their numbers from right to left, although they sometimes wrote from left to right or even from top to bottom! Thus, the number 12 could have been represented by || ∩ or by ∩ ||. For this reason, we say that the Egyptian system is *not* a positional system but an ***additive*** one. In contrast, our own **decimal system** (called *decimal* because we use a base of 10) is a **positional system.** In our system, the numerals 12 and 21 represent different numbers.

To represent a number such as 1324 in the Egyptian system, write 1324 as a sum, then match each quantity in the sum with its corresponding Egyptian symbol (see Table 4.3). Thus, 1324 = 1000 + 300 + 20 + 4

𓆼 𓍢𓍢𓍢 ∩∩ ||||

You can save time by translating directly from Table 4.3 like this:

1 3 2 4

𓆼 𓍢𓍢𓍢 ∩∩ ||||

Table 4.3 Numerals

Egyptian, about 3000 B.C.						
𓏺	𓎆	𓍢	𓆼	𓂭	𓆐	𓁨
1 Stroke	10 Heel Bone	100 Coil of Rope	1000 Lotus Flower	10,000 Pointing Finger	100,000 Tadpole	1,000,000 Astonished Man
Babylonian, about 2000 B.C.						
𒁹	𒌋	𒌋𒐖	𒌋𒌋	𒁹	𒁹𒌋	𒑊
1	10	12	20	60	600	0
Early Greek, about 400 B.C.						
I	𐅃	Δ	𐅄	H	𐅅	𐅆
1	5	10	50	100	500	5000
Mayan, about 300 B.C.						
𝋡	𝋥	𝋧	𝋪	𝋬	𝋯	𝋡𝋠
1	5	7	10	12	15	20
Tamil, Early Christian Era						
௧	௨	௩	௫	௬	௰	௲
1	2	3	5	6	10	1000
Hindu-Arabic, Contemporary						
0	1	2	3	4	5	6

EXAMPLE 1 Write 21,340 as an Egyptian Numeral

Solution

The symbols for 10,000, 1000, 100, and 10 are 𓂭 𓆼 𓍢 𓎆

Write 2 1 3 4 0

and translate 𓂭𓂭 𓆼 𓍢𓍢𓍢 𓎆𓎆𓎆𓎆

What about the 0? We ***do not need it*** because we have 4 𓎆's, which make 40. There is no 0 in the Egyptian system!

To change from an Egyptian number to a decimal one, we reverse the process. Thus,

𓍢𓍢 𓎆𓎆𓎆 𓏺𓏺

corresponds to 200 + 30 + 2 or 232

EXAMPLE 2 Write 𓆼𓆼𓆼 𓍢𓍢 𓎆 𓏺𓏺𓏺𓏺 in Decimal Notation

Solution

Refer to Table 4.3, translate and add 𓆼𓆼𓆼 𓍢𓍢 𓎆 𓏺𓏺𓏺𓏺

3000 + 200 + 10 + 4 = 3214

The Egyptian system was not well suited for arithmetical operations, and ancient records show very little about the calculations they may have performed. As we have mentioned, computation in the Egyptian system was based on the **additive principle.** For example, to add 24 to 48, the Egyptians proceeded as follows:

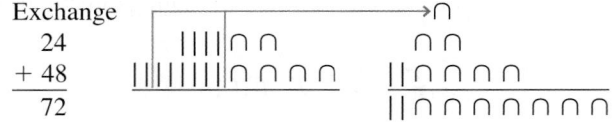

Exchange	𓏺𓏺𓏺𓏺𓏺𓏺𓏺𓏺𓏺𓏺 →	𓎆
24	𓏺𓏺𓏺𓏺 𓎆𓎆	𓎆𓎆
+ 48	𓏺𓏺𓏺𓏺𓏺𓏺𓏺𓏺 𓎆𓎆𓎆𓎆	𓏺𓏺 𓎆𓎆𓎆𓎆
72		𓏺𓏺 𓎆𓎆𓎆𓎆𓎆𓎆𓎆

As you can see, before the computation was done, 10 of the strokes were replaced by a heel bone (see the names of the Egyptian symbols in Table 4.3).

The Egyptians performed subtraction in a similar manner. Thus, to subtract 13 from 22, they proceeded as follows:

		Exchange →
22	||∩∩	||||||||||||∩
−13	|||∩	||| ∩
9		|||||||||

The procedure for Egyptian multiplication is explained in the Rhind papyrus (an ancient document found at Thebes and bought in Egypt by A. Henry Rhind and named in his honor). The operation was performed by **successive duplications.** Multiplying 19 by 7, for example, the Egyptians would take 19, double it, and then double the result. Then they would add each of the two columns; thus

7 ×	19
\ 1	19
\ 2	38
\ 4	76
1 + 2 + 4 = 7	19 + 38 + 76 = 133

The slanted bar \ is used to indicate which numbers from the second row should be added.

Procedure for Multiplying by Successive Duplications

1. Make two columns headed by 1 and the second number you are multiplying by.
2. Double the numbers in each of the columns and write the results under the originals.
3. Use a slanted bar \ to select the numbers that add to the first number being multiplied.
4. Add the numbers in the second column of the rows marked with the slanted bar \.
5. The sum is the result of the multiplication.

In the Rhind papyrus, the problem 22 times 27 looks like this:

	22 ×	27
	1	27
	\ 2	54
	\ 4	108
	8	216
	\16	432
Total	22	594 ← Answer
	2 + 4 + 16 = 22	54 + 108 + 432 = 594

Note that the numbers to be added are in the second column of the lines starting with the slanted bar \ (54 + 108 + 432 = 594).

EXAMPLE 3 Successive Duplications and the Rhind Papyrus

Problem 79 of the Rhind papyrus states, "Sum the geometrical progression of five terms, of which the first term is 7 and the multiplier 7." It can be shown that the solution of the problem is obtained by multiplying 2801 by 7. Use the method of successive duplications to find the answer.

Solution

	7 ×	2801
	\ 1	2,801
	\ 2	5,602
	\ 4	11,204
Total	7	19,607
	1 + 2 + 4 = 7	2801 + 5602 + 11,204 = 19,607

It is said that in later years the Egyptians adopted another multiplication technique generally known as **mediation and duplation.** This system consists of halving the first factor and doubling the second. For example, to find the product 19 × 7, we successively halve 19, discarding remainders at each step, and successively double 7. The process is completed when a 1 appears in the left-hand column.

	Half	*Double*	
19 is odd. →	19	(7)	$\frac{19}{2} \approx 9$ and $\frac{9}{2} \approx 4$
9 is odd. →	9	(14)	
	4	28	
	2	56	
1 is odd. →	1	(112)	

Notice that half of 19 is regarded as 9 because all the remainders are discarded. Opposite each number in the left-hand column there is a corresponding number in the column of numbers being doubled. The product 19 × 7 is found by adding the circled numbers—those opposite the odd numbers in the column of halves. (Can you see why this works?) Thus, 19 × 7 = 7 + 14 + 112 = 133.

EXAMPLE 4 Multiplication by Mediation and Duplation

Use the method of mediation and duplation to find the product 18 × 43.

Solution

	Half	*Double*	
	18	43	
9 is odd. →	9	(86)	
	4	172	18 × 43 = 86 + 688 = 774
	2	344	
1 is odd. →	1	(688)	

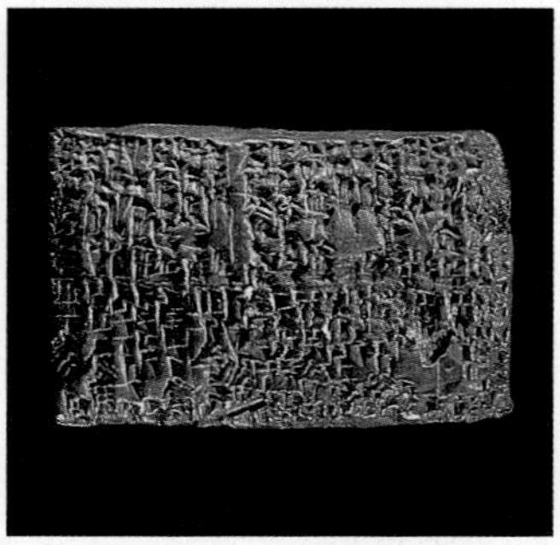
© Lee Boltin Picture Library/Bridgeman

Sumerian clay tablets and inscriptions contain numbers dating back as far as 4000 B.C.

Additive numeral systems were devised to keep records of large numbers. As these numbers became larger and larger, it became evident that tallying them was difficult and awkward. Thus, numbers began to be arranged in groups and exchanged for larger units, as in the Egyptian system in which 10 tallies were exchanged for a heel bone (∩). The scale used to determine the size of the group to be exchanged (10 in the case of the Egyptians) was the **base** for the system. These additive systems were advantageous for record-keeping operations, but computation in these systems was extremely complicated. As problems became even more complex, a new concept evolved to help with computations, that of a **positional numeral system.** In such a system, a numeral is selected as the base; then symbols ranging from 1 to the numeral that is 1 less than the base are also selected. Numbers are represented by placing the symbols in a specified order. For example, the Babylonians used a sexagesimal (base 60) system. In their system, a vertical wedge ▼ was used to represent 1, and the symbol ◀ represented 10. [These symbols first appeared on the clay tablets of the Sumerians (see the photograph) and Chaldeans but were later adopted by the Babylonians.]

B The Babylonian System

The Babylonian numerals, which may look odd to you, were simply wedge marks in clay. Figure 4.1 shows a few numerals. Notice that the same symbols are used for the numerals 1 and 60. To distinguish between them, a wider space was left between the characters. Thus, ▼▼▼ represents the numeral 3, whereas ▼ ▼▼ is 62.

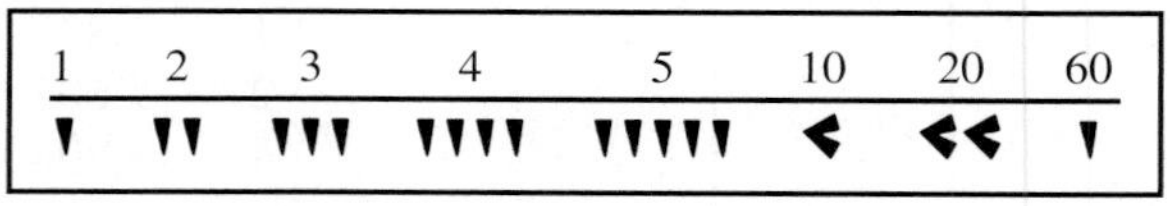

FIGURE 4.1 Babylonian numerals (1900 B.C.–1800 B.C.)

What does 231 mean in base 10 notation? It means 2 hundreds, 3 tens, and 1 unit; that is,

10^2 = 100s	10s	Units
2	3	1

Since the Babylonians used base 60, the number 231 would be written as

▼▼▼	◀◀◀◀◀▼
60s	Units

which means 3 sixties (▼▼▼ or 180) and 51 (◀◀◀◀◀▼) units. Note that

$180 + 51 = 231$

EXAMPLE 5 Writing Decimal Numerals in Babylonian Notation

Write the numbers 82, 733, and 4443 in Babylonian notation.

Solution

82 = 1 × 60 + 22 = ▼ ◀◀▼▼

733 = 12 × 60 + 13 = ◀▼▼ ◀▼▼▼

4443 = 1 × 3600 + 14 × 60 + 3 = ▼ ◀▼▼▼▼ ▼▼▼

EXAMPLE 6 Writing Babylonian Numerals in Decimal Notation

Write the given Babylonian numerals in decimal notation.

(a) ▼▼ ◀▼▼▼ (b) ◀ ▼▼▼▼▼ (c) ◀▼▼▼▼▼ (d) ▼▼ ◀▼ ◀▼▼

Solution

(a) ▼▼ ◀▼▼▼ = 2 × 60 + 13 = 133

(b) ◀ ▼▼▼▼▼ = 10 × 60 + 5 = 605

(c) ◀▼▼▼▼▼ = 10 + 5 = 15

(d) ▼▼ ◀▼ ◀▼▼ = 2 × 3600 + 11 × 60 + 12 = 7872

Note that the symbols in (b) and (c) are the same, but the spacing is different. The lack of a symbol for zero in the Babylonian system was a significant shortcoming that made it difficult to distinguish between numbers such as 12 = ◀▼▼ = 10 + 2 and 602 = ◀ ▼▼ = 600 + 2.

In the decimal system we use zero to distinguish between 10 (one ten, no units) and 1 (one unit). So the Babylonians introduced a zero (𒑱) which they sometimes used in the middle of a number by writing 602 as ◀𒑱▼▼.

Our degree-minute-second system of measuring angles undoubtedly stems from the Babylonian division of a circle into 360 equal parts. Addition of angles in this system is essentially Babylonian-style addition.

The next example illustrates the method used by the Babylonians to add numbers.

EXAMPLE 7 Adding Numbers in Babylonian Notation

Write in Babylonian notation and add 64 + 127.

Solution

64	▼	▼▼▼▼	→ ◀
127	▼▼	▼▼▼▼▼▼ ▼	
191	▼▼▼	◀▼	191 = 3(60) + 11

C The Roman System

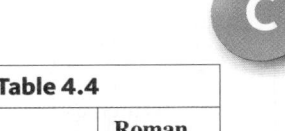

Table 4.4	
Number	Roman Numeral
1	(I)
5	V
10	(X)
50	L
100	(C)
500	D
1000	M

The circled numbers are the ones allowed to be *subtracted* from larger numbers For example,
IV = 5 − 1 = 4
IX = 10 − 1 = 9
CD = 500 − 100 = 400

The Roman numeral system developed between 500 B.C. and A.D. 100 is still used today—for example, on the faces of clocks, for chapter numbers in books, on cornerstones of buildings, and for copyright dates on films and television shows. How does the Roman system work? The Roman symbol for the number 1 is I, which is repeated for 2 and 3. Thus, II is 2, and III is 3. Though similar to the Egyptian system, the Romans introduced a special symbol for the number 5. They then used another special symbol for 10 and repeated this symbol for 20 and again for 30. Other special symbols are used for 50, 100, 500, and 1000, as shown in Table 4.4. Why did the Romans use the letters I, C, and M? Find out at http://en.wikipedia.org/wiki/Roman_numerals.

Although both the Roman and Egyptian systems used the addition principle, the Romans went one step further and used the **subtraction principle** as well. For instance, instead of writing IIII for the number 4, the Romans wrote IV with the understanding that the I (1) was to be *subtracted* from the V (5). In the Roman system, the value of a numeral is found by starting at the left and adding the values of the succeeding symbols to the right, unless the value of a symbol is less than that of the symbol to its right. In that case, the smaller value is *subtracted* from the larger one. Thus, XI = 10 + 1 = 11, but IX = 10 − 1 = 9. Only the numbers 1, 10, and 100 are allowed to be subtracted, and these only from numbers not more than two steps larger. For example, I can be subtracted from V to give IV = 4 or from X to give IX = 9 but cannot be subtracted from C or L. Thus, 99 is written as LXLIX *not* IC. Here are some other examples.

Addition Principle	*Subtraction Principle*
LX = 50 + 10 = 60	XL = 50 − 10 = 40
CX = 100 + 10 = 110	XC = 100 − 10 = 90
MC = 1000 + 100 = 1100	CM = 1000 − 100 = 900

EXAMPLE 8 Writing Roman Numerals in Decimal Notation

Write the following Roman numerals in decimal notation:

(a) DCXII (b) MCMXLIX

Solution

(a) Since the value of each symbol is larger than that of the one to its right, we simply add these values.

DCXII = 500 + 100 + 10 + 1 + 1 = 612

(b) In this case the values of some symbols are less than the values of the symbols to their right, so we use the subtraction principle and write

$$\begin{aligned}\text{M(CM)(XL)(IX)} &= 1000 + (1000 - 100) + (50 - 10) + (10 - 1)\\ &= 1000 + 900 + 40 + 9\\ &= 1949\end{aligned}$$

The largest number that can be written using Roman numerals without using either the bar or the subtraction principle is

MMMDCCCLXXXVIII

What is this number in decimal notation?

Another way in which the Roman system goes further than the Egyptian system is the use of a **multiplication principle** for writing larger numbers. A multiplication by 1000 is indicated by placing a bar over the entire numeral. Thus,

$$\begin{aligned}\overline{\text{X}} &= 10 \times 1000 = 10{,}000\\ \overline{\text{LI}} &= 51 \times 1000 = 51{,}000\\ \overline{\text{DC}} &= 600 \times 1000 = 600{,}000\\ \overline{\text{M}} &= 1000 \times 1000 = 1{,}000{,}000\end{aligned}$$

EXAMPLE 9 Writing Decimal Numerals as Roman Numerals

Write the following in Roman numerals:

(a) 33,008 **(b)** 42,120

Solution

(a) 33 is written as XXXIII in Roman numerals, so $33{,}000 = \overline{\text{XXXIII}}$. To write 33,008, 8 must be added. Thus

$$33{,}008 = 33{,}000 + 8 = \overline{\text{XXXIII}}\text{VIII}$$

(b) $42 = \text{XLII}$, so $42{,}000 = \overline{\text{XLII}}$. Since $120 = \text{CXX}$,

$$42{,}120 = \overline{\text{XLII}}\text{CXX}$$

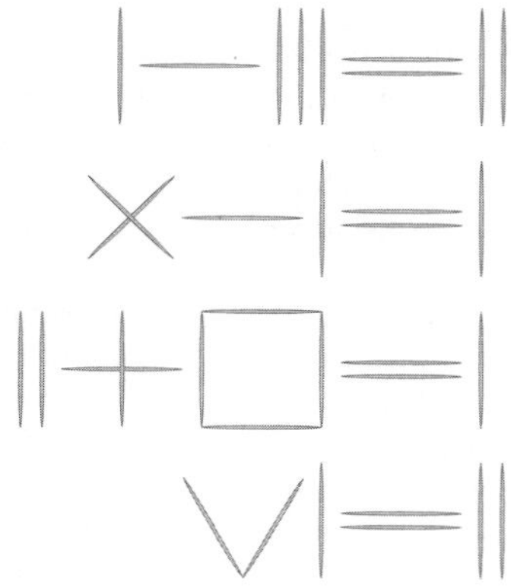

FIGURE 4.2

EXAMPLE 10 From False to True in One Move

Now that you know about Roman numerals, we can have some fun with them. Get some toothpicks and construct the four false equations shown in Figure 4.2. Can you make them true by moving only one stick? *Note:* You can use the symbol for any mathematical operation or notation to make the equation true. The square represents 0.

Solution

We do not want to spoil all your fun, so we will only give you hints. On the first one, you have to move the equal sign; on the second one, you need a multiplication sign; the third one takes the ± sign; and the last one involves the $\sqrt{\ }$ sign. Now can you do it?

4.1 EXERCISES

A The Egyptian System

In problems 1–6, use the symbols given in Tables 4.2 and 4.3 to write each number in Egyptian notation.

1. 24 **2.** 54 **3.** 142
4. 1247 **5.** 835 **6.** 11,209

In problems 7–12, translate each Egyptian numeral into decimal notation.

7. 𓍢𓎆𓏺𓏺𓏺

8. 𓆼𓍢𓍢𓍢𓍢𓍢𓍢𓍢𓍢𓍢𓏺𓏺𓏺𓏺

9. 𓍢𓍢𓍢𓎆𓎆𓏺𓏺 **10.** 𓎆𓎆𓎆𓎆𓏺𓏺𓏺𓏺𓏺

11. 𓂭𓆼𓍢𓍢𓎆𓎆𓎆𓏺𓏺 **12.** 𓍢𓍢𓍢𓎆𓎆𓎆𓏺𓏺𓏺
𓍢𓍢𓍢𓎆𓎆 𓏺𓏺

In problems 13–16, write each number in Egyptian notation and perform the indicated operation.

13. $\begin{array}{r} 34 \\ +\ 23 \\ \hline \end{array}$ **14.** $\begin{array}{r} 148 \\ +\ 45 \\ \hline \end{array}$

15. $\begin{array}{r} 432 \\ -\ 143 \\ \hline \end{array}$ **16.** $\begin{array}{r} 1203 \\ -\ 502 \\ \hline \end{array}$

In problems 17–20, use the Egyptian method of successive duplications to find each product.

17. 15×40 **18.** 25×15
19. 22×51 **20.** 21×63

In problems 21–24, use the Egyptian method of mediation and duplation to find each product.

21. 18×32 **22.** 15×32
23. 12×51 **24.** 40×61

B The Babylonian System

In problems 25–34, write each number in Babylonian notation.

25. 6 **26.** 24
27. 32 **28.** 64
29. 123 **30.** 144
31. 258 **32.** 192
33. 3733 **34.** 3883

In problems 35–40, write each Babylonian number in decimal notation.

35. 𒁹 𒌋𒌋𒌋𒁹𒁹 **36.** 𒌋𒁹𒁹𒁹 𒌋𒁹𒁹 **37.** 𒁹𒁹𒁹 𒌋𒁹𒁹
38. 𒌋𒁹𒁹𒁹𒁹𒁹 𒁹𒁹𒁹 **39.** 𒁹 𒌋𒁹𒁹 𒁹𒁹 **40.** 𒁹𒁹 𒌋𒁹 𒁹𒁹𒁹𒁹

In problems 41–44, write each number in Babylonian notation and perform the addition using the Babylonian system.

41. $\begin{array}{r} 32 \\ +\ 43 \\ \hline \end{array}$ **42.** $\begin{array}{r} 63 \\ +\ 81 \\ \hline \end{array}$

43. $\begin{array}{r} 133 \\ +\ 68 \\ \hline \end{array}$ **44.** $\begin{array}{r} 242 \\ +\ 181 \\ \hline \end{array}$

C The Roman System

In problems 45–50, write each number in decimal notation.

45. CXXVI **46.** DCXVII
47. $\overline{\text{XLII}}$ **48.** $\overline{\text{XXX}}\text{DCI}$
49. $\overline{\text{XC}}\text{CDV}$ **50.** $\overline{\text{LD}}\text{DC}$

In problems 51–56, write each number in Roman numerals.

51. 72 **52.** 631
53. 145 **54.** 1709
55. 32,503 **56.** 49,231

Numerology, like astrology, is a pseudoscience concerning itself with birth dates, names, and other personal characteristics. A popular scheme used by numerologist Juno Jordan gives each letter the value of the number above it as shown. Thus, A is 1, M is 4, and Z is 8.

1	2	3	4	5	6	7	8	9
A	B	C	D	E	F	G	H	I
J	K	L	M	N	O	P	Q	R
S	T	U	V	W	X	Y	Z	

The number associated with James is

$$1 + 1 + 4 + 5 + 1 = 12 = 1 + 2 = \mathbf{3}$$

For the surname Brown, we have

$$2 + 9 + 6 + 5 + 5 = 27 = 2 + 7 = \mathbf{9}$$

Thus, the final number associated with James Brown is $\mathbf{3} + \mathbf{9} = 12 = 1 + 2 = \mathbf{3}$. What does this mean? It means that he has the characteristics corresponding to the number 3 in the following list:

1. Creative, inventive, positive
2. Gentle, imaginative, romantic
3. Ambitious, proud, independent
4. Rebels, unconventional
5. Mercurial, high-strung, risk-taker
6. Magnetic, romantic, artistic
7. Independent, individualistic
8. Lonely, misunderstood
9. Fighter, determined, leader

Thus, James Brown should be ambitious, proud, and independent! Do problems 57–60 just for fun. Do not take the results seriously!

57. Find the number for John Fitzgerald Kennedy.
58. Find the number for Sonya Kovalevski.
59. Find the number for Ringo Starr.
60. Find your own number.

IN OTHER WORDS

61. Can you write 99 as IC in Roman numerals? Explain.
62. What are the differences between the Egyptian and our decimal systems of numeration?
63. What are the differences between the Babylonian numeration system and our decimal system of numeration?
64. What are the differences between the Roman numeration system and our decimal system of numeration?
65. What are the differences between the Egyptian and the Babylonian systems of numeration?
66. Explain why it is difficult to distinguish between 605 and 15 in the Babylonian system.

USING YOUR KNOWLEDGE

The Rhind papyrus is a document that was found in the ruins of a small ancient building in Thebes. The papyrus was bought in 1858 by a Scottish antiquarian, A. Henry Rhind, and most of it is preserved in the British Museum, where it was named in Rhind's honor.

The scroll was a handbook of Egyptian mathematics containing mathematical exercises and practical examples. Many of the problems were solved by the **method of false position.**

For example, one of the simple problems states "A number and its one-fourth added together become 15. Find the number." The solution by false position goes like this: Assume that the number is 4. A number (4) and its one-fourth ($\frac{1}{4}$ of 4) added become 15; that is,

$$4 + \tfrac{1}{4}(4) \text{ must equal } 15$$

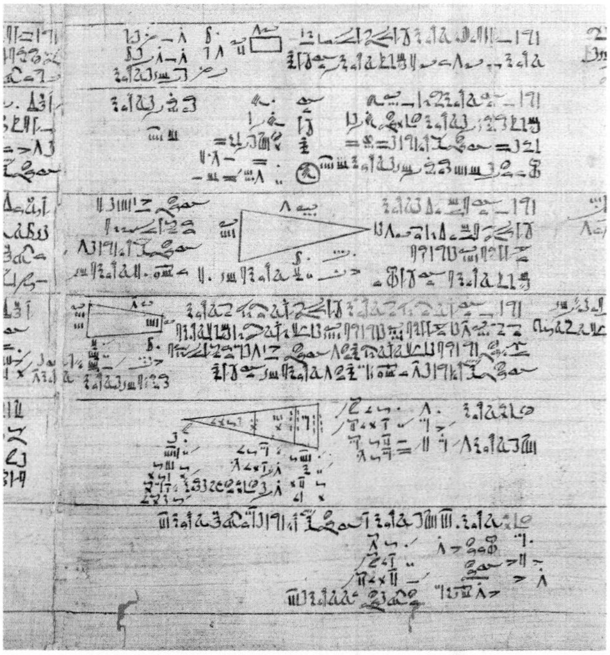

A portion of the Rhind papyrus dating back to ca. 1650 B.C. It is the most extensive mathematical document from ancient Egypt.

But

$$4 + \tfrac{1}{4}(4) = 5$$

and we need 15, which is 3 times the 5 we obtained. Therefore, the correct answer must be 3 times the assumed answer, that is, 3×4, or 12.

See if you can use the method of false position to solve the following problems:

67. A number and its one-sixth added together become 21. What is the number?

68. A number, its one-half, and its one-quarter add up to 28. Find the number.

69. If a number and its two-thirds are added and from the sum one-third of the sum is subtracted, then 10 remains. What is the number?

DISCOVERY

A Babylonian tablet giving the values of $n^3 + n^2$ for $n = 1$ to 30 was discovered a few years ago. The decimal equivalents of the first few entries in the table can be found as follows:

For $n = 1$, we have $1^3 + 1^2 = 2$.
For $n = 2$, we have $2^3 + 2^2 = 12$.
(Recall that $2^3 = 2 \times 2 \times 2 = 8$ and $2^2 = 2 \times 2 = 4$.)
For $n = 3$, we have $3^3 + 3^2 = 36$.

Complete the following:

$4^3 + 4^2 =$ ______ $\qquad 5^3 + 5^2 =$ ______
$6^3 + 6^2 =$ ______ $\qquad 7^3 + 7^2 =$ ______
$8^3 + 8^2 =$ ______ $\qquad 9^3 + 9^2 =$ ______
$10^3 + 10^2 =$ ______

Using the preceding information, find the solution of the following.

70. $n^3 + n^2 - 810 = 0$

71. $n^3 + n^2 - 576 = 0$

72. There are many equations for which this method does not seem to work. For example, $n^3 + 2n^2 - 3136 = 0$. However, a simple transformation will reduce the sum of the first two terms to the familiar form $(\ )^3 + (\ )^2$. For example, let $n = 2x$. Now try to solve the following equation:

$$n^3 + 2n^2 - 3136 = 0$$

4.2 The Hindu-Arabic (Decimal) System

GETTING STARTED

OBJECTIVES

A. Write numbers in decimal and in expanded form.
B. Add and subtract numbers in decimal and in expanded form.
C. Use the laws of exponents to multiply, divide, and raise numbers to a power.
D. Multiply and divide numbers in decimal and in expanded form.
E. Solve applications involving exponents.

PACKAGING, GARBAGE, AND EXPONENTS

Do you know that in just one day Americans throw out 1.5×10^5 tons of packaging material? How many pounds is that? Since 1 ton $= 2 \times 10^3$ lb, the amount of packaging material thrown out is

$$\underbrace{(1.5 \times 10^5)}_{\text{tons}} \times \underbrace{(2 \times 10^3)}_{\text{lb/ton}} \text{ lb}$$

Source: http://tinyurl.com/3d27uj8.

How do you find this number? First, $1.5 \times 2 = 3$, so you need to find

$$3 \times 10^5 \times 10^3 \text{ lb}$$

In this section you will learn the laws of exponents for multiplication. These laws state that $a^m \times a^n = a^{m+n}$ and $a^m \div a^n = a^{m-n}$. Using the law for multiplication, you get

$$3 \times 10^5 \times 10^3 = 3 \times 10^{5+3} = 3 \times 10^8 = 300{,}000{,}000 \text{ lb}$$

Thus, 300 million lb of packaging material is thrown out daily.

Now suppose a tractor trailer can carry a 15-ton load. How many tractor trailers do you need to carry out the packaging material? The answer is

$$\frac{\text{Total weight of material}}{\text{Weight per load}} = \frac{3 \times 10^8 \text{ lb}}{15 \text{ tons/load}}$$

The environmental stress created by landfills, such as this one, necessitates a greater awareness of waste management and recycling.

Since 1 ton = 2000 lb, 15 tons = 30,000 lb = 3×10^4 lb. The answer is

$$\frac{3 \times 10^8 \text{ lb}}{3 \times 10^4 \text{ lb/load}} = \frac{10^8}{10^4} \text{ loads}$$

To find this answer, you need to divide 10^8 by 10^4. Using the law of exponents for division,

$$\frac{10^8}{10^4} = 10^{8-4} = 10^4$$

Thus, the number of tractor trailers needed is $1 \times 10^4 = 10{,}000$!

In this section you will work with exponents and write standard numbers in expanded form containing exponents and vice versa.

A few more consumption problems will be addressed in Exercises 4.2, problems 50–55.

Our familiar **decimal system** is also called the **Hindu-Arabic system.** This numeration system is a positional system with 10 as its base, and it uses the symbols (called **digits**) 0, 1, 2, 3, 4, 5, 6, 7, 8, and 9. Furthermore, each symbol in this system has a **place value;** that is, the value represented by a digit depends on the position of that digit in the numeral. For instance, the digit 2 in the numeral 312 represents 2 ones, but in the numeral 321 the digit 2 represents 2 tens.

A Expanded and Decimal Forms

To illustrate the idea of place value further, we can write both numbers in **expanded form.**

$$\begin{aligned} 312 &= 3 \text{ hundreds} + 1 \text{ ten} + 2 \text{ ones} \\ &= (3 \times 100) + (1 \times 10) + (2 \times 1) \\ 321 &= 3 \text{ hundreds} + 2 \text{ tens} + 1 \text{ one} \\ &= (3 \times 100) + (2 \times 10) + (1 \times 1) \end{aligned}$$

These numbers can also be written using exponential form, a notation introduced by the French mathematician René Descartes. As the name indicates, **exponential form** uses the idea of exponents.

Exponents

An **exponent** is a number that indicates how many times another number, called the **base,** is a factor in a product.

Thus, in 5^3 (read "5 cubed" or "5 to the third power"), the exponent is 3, the base is 5, and $5^3 = 5 \times 5 \times 5 = 125$. Similarly, in 2^4, 4 is the exponent, 2 is the base, and $2^4 = 2 \times 2 \times 2 \times 2 = 16$. On the basis of this discussion, we state the following definition:

Definition of a^n

If a is any number and n is any counting number, then a^n (read "a to the nth power") is the product obtained by using a as a factor n times; that is,

$$a^n = \underbrace{a \times a \times \cdots \times a}_{n\ a\text{'s}}$$

For any nonzero number a, we define $a^0 = 1$.

Using this definition, we can write $1 = 10^0$, $10 = 10^1$, $100 = 10^2$, $1000 = 10^3$, $10{,}000 = 10^4$, and so on. Thus, in expanded form,

$$\begin{aligned}312 &= (3 \times 100) + (1 \times 10) + (2 \times 1)\\ &= (3 \times 10^2) + (1 \times 10^1) + (2 \times 10^0)\end{aligned}$$

Exponents

The exponent 1 usually is not written; we understand that $10^1 = 10$ and, in general, $a^1 = a$. Also, we used $10^0 = 1$ in the last term of the equation above. With these conventions, we can write any number in expanded form.

EXAMPLE 1 Writing Decimal Numerals in Expanded Form

Write 3406 in expanded form.

Solution

$$3406 = (3 \times 10^3) + (4 \times 10^2) + (0 \times 10^1) + (6 \times 10^0)$$

Notice that we could have omitted the term (0×10^1), because $0 \times 10 = 0$. Using the same ideas, we can convert any number from expanded form into our familiar decimal form.

EXAMPLE 2 Converting from Expanded to Decimal Form

Write $(5 \times 10^3) + (2 \times 10^1) + (3 \times 10^0)$ in ordinary decimal form.

Solution

$$\begin{aligned}(5 \times 10^3) + (2 \times 10^1) + (3 \times 10^0) &= (5 \times 1000) + (2 \times 10) + 3\\ &= 5023\end{aligned}$$

B Addition and Subtraction in Expanded and Decimal Form

The ideas of expanded form and place value can greatly simplify computations involving addition, subtraction, multiplication, and division. In the following examples, on the left we present the usual way in which these operations are performed, and on the right we present the expanded form depending on place value.

EXAMPLE 3 Adding Using Decimal Numerals and Using Expanded Form

Add 38 and 61 in the usual way and using expanded form.

Solution

$$\begin{array}{rl} 38 & (3 \times 10^1) + (8 \times 10^0)\\ +\ 61 & (6 \times 10^1) + (1 \times 10^0)\\ \hline 99 & (9 \times 10^1) + (9 \times 10^0)\end{array}$$

EXAMPLE 4 Subtracting Using Decimal Numerals and Using Expanded Form

Subtract 32 from 48 in the usual way and using expanded form.

Solution

$$\begin{array}{rr} 48 & (4 \times 10^1) + (8 \times 10^0) \\ -\ 32 & -\ (3 \times 10^1) + (2 \times 10^0) \\ \hline 16 & (1 \times 10^1) + (6 \times 10^0) \end{array}$$

C The Laws of Exponents

Before illustrating multiplication and division, we need to determine how to multiply and divide numbers involving exponents. For example, $2^2 \times 2^3 = (2 \times 2) \times (2 \times 2 \times 2) = 2^5$, and in general,

$$a^m \times a^n = \underbrace{(a \times a \times a \times \cdots \times a)}_{m\ a\text{'s}} \times \underbrace{(a \times a \times a \times \cdots \times a)}_{n\ a\text{'s}}$$
$$= a^{m+n}$$

In order to divide 2^5 by 2^2, we proceed as follows:

$$\frac{2^5}{2^2} = \frac{\cancel{2} \times \cancel{2} \times 2 \times 2 \times 2}{\cancel{2} \times \cancel{2}} = 2 \times 2 \times 2 = 2^3$$

In general, if $m > n$,

$$a^m \div a^n = \frac{a^m}{a^n} = a^{m-n}$$

Product and Quotient Laws for Exponents

$$a^m \times a^n = a^{m+n} \quad \text{and} \quad a^m \div a^n = \frac{a^m}{a^n} = a^{m-n}, \quad m > n$$

EXAMPLE 5 Using the Law of Exponents

Perform the following indicated operations, and leave the answers in exponential form.

(a) $4^5 \times 4^7$ **(b)** $3^{10} \div 3^4$

Solution

(a) $4^5 \times 4^7 = 4^{5+7} = 4^{12}$ **(b)** $3^{10} \div 3^4 = 3^{10-4} = 3^6$

Note that by the definition of a^n, we have, for example,

$$(2^3)^2 = 2^3 \times 2^3 = 2^{3+3} = 2^{3\times 2} = 2^6$$

and

$$(5^2)^4 = 5^2 \times 5^2 \times 5^2 \times 5^2 = 5^{2+2+2+2} = 5^{2\times 4} = 5^8$$

In general,

Power Law for Exponents

$$(a^m)^n = a^{m\times n}$$

EXAMPLE 6 Show Me the Result

Show that $32^2 = 2^{10}$.

Solution

Direct computation shows that $32 = 2^5$. Thus

$$32^2 = (2^5)^2 = 2^{5\times 2} = 2^{10}$$

D Multiplication and Division in Expanded and Decimal Form

EXAMPLE 7 Multiplying Using Decimal Numbers and Using Expanded Form

Multiply 32 and 21 in the usual way and using expanded form.

Solution

$$\begin{array}{r} 32 \\ \times\ 21 \\ \hline 32 \\ 64 \\ \hline 672 \end{array} \qquad \begin{array}{r} (3\times 10) + (2\times 10^0) \\ \times\ (2\times 10) + (1\times 10^0) \\ \hline (3\times 10) + (2\times 10^0) \\ (6\times 10^2) + (4\times 10) \\ \hline (6\times 10^2) + (7\times 10) + (2\times 10^0) \end{array}$$

EXAMPLE 8 Dividing Using Decimal Numbers and Using Expanded Form

Divide 63 by 3 in the usual way and using expanded form.

Solution

$$\begin{array}{r} 21 \\ 3\overline{)63} \end{array} \qquad \begin{array}{r} (2\times 10) + (1\times 10^0) \\ 3\overline{)(6\times 10) + (3\times 10^0)} \end{array}$$

E Applications

A computer uses a collection of ones (1s) and zeros (0s) to store information. The smallest piece of information is defined as a **bit.** As information gets more complex, larger units are needed, as shown in the accompanying table. As you can see,

$$1 \text{ byte} = 8 = 2^3 \text{ bits}$$

and

$$1 \text{ kilobyte (kB)} = 1024 = 2^{10} \text{ bytes}$$

UNIT	DEFINITION
1 bit	The smallest piece of information two possible values: "0" or "1"
1 byte	8 bits
1 kB (Kilobyte)	1,024 bytes
1 MB (Megabyte)	1,048,576 bytes
1 GB (Gigabyte)	1,073,741,824 bytes
1 TB (Terabyte)	1,099,511,627,776 bytes
1 PB (Petabyte)	1,125,899,906,842,624 bytes

EXAMPLE 9 Using Your Powers

Write 1 MB and 1 GB as powers of 2.

Solution

Since 1 kB $= 2^{10}$ bytes, we may suspect that 1 MB is 1000 times as big. Since 1000 is about $2^{10} = 1024$,

$$1 \text{ MB} = 2^{10} \cdot 2^{10} = 2^{20} \text{ bytes}$$

and

$$1 \text{ GB} = 2^{10} \cdot 2^{10} \cdot 2^{10} = 2^{30} \text{ bytes}$$

Check this out with a calculator!

4.2 EXERCISES

A Expanded and Decimal Forms

In problems 1–6, write each number in expanded form.

1. 432 **2.** 549 **3.** 2307
4. 3047 **5.** 12,349 **6.** 10,950

In problems 7–15, write each number in decimal form.

7. 5^0
8. $(3 \times 10) + (4 \times 10^0)$
9. $(4 \times 10) + (5 \times 10^0)$
10. $(4 \times 10^2) + (3 \times 10) + (2 \times 10^0)$
11. $(9 \times 10^3) + (7 \times 10) + (1 \times 10^0)$
12. $(7 \times 10^4) + (2 \times 10^0)$
13. $(7 \times 10^5) + (4 \times 10^4) + (8 \times 10^3) + (3 \times 10^2) + (8 \times 10^0)$
14. $(8 \times 10^9) + (3 \times 10^5) + (2 \times 10^2) + (4 \times 10^0)$
15. $(4 \times 10^6) + (3 \times 10) + (1 \times 10^0)$

B Addition and Subtraction in Expanded and Decimal Form

In problems 16–19, add in the usual way and using expanded form.

16. 32 + 15 **17.** 23 + 13
18. 21 + 34 **19.** 71 + 23

In problems 20–23, subtract using decimal numerals and using expanded form.

20. 34 − 21 **21.** 76 − 54
22. 45 − 22 **23.** 84 − 31

C The Laws of Exponents

In problems 24–35, perform the indicated operation, and leave each answer in exponential form.

24. $3^5 \times 3^9$ **25.** $7^8 \times 7^3$ **26.** $4^5 \times 4^2$
27. $6^{19} \times 6^{21}$ **28.** $5^8 \div 5^3$ **29.** $6^{10} \div 6^3$
30. $7^{15} \div 7^3$ **31.** $6^{12} \div 6^0$ **32.** $(3^2)^4$
33. $(5^4)^3$ **34.** $(7^3)^5$ **35.** $(10^3)^{10}$

D Multiplication and Division in Expanded and Decimal Form

In problems 36–39, multiply in the usual way and using expanded form.

36. 41 × 23 **37.** 25 × 51
38. 91 × 24 **39.** 62 × 25

In problems 40–43, divide in the usual way and using expanded form.

40. 48 ÷ 4 **41.** 64 ÷ 8
42. 93 ÷ 3 **43.** 72 ÷ 6

In problems 44 and 45, write each answer in exponential form.

44. Each American produces about 5 lb of garbage every day. If the U.S. population is assumed to be 3×10^8, how many pounds of garbage per day are produced nationwide?

45. If the *New York Times* printed one Sunday edition on recycled paper instead of new paper, 75,000 trees would be saved. How many trees would be saved if the *New York Times* used recycled paper for one month (4 Sundays)?

E Applications

In problems 46–56, write the answer in scientific notation.

46. How many pet reptiles are there in the United States? According to the American Pet Products Manufacturers Association, there are 4.4×10^6 pet households, each owning 2.5 reptiles on average. How many pet reptiles is that?

Source: www.infoplease.com/ipa/A0931712.html.

47. What about pet dogs? There are 45.5×10^6 pet households, each owning 1.7 dogs on average. How many dogs is that?

48. According to Nielsen Net, about 7.2×10^7 unique searches were made using Google in a given month (30 days). How many unique searches per day is that? Source: www.infoplease.com/ipa/A0902390.html.

49. About 4.8×10^7 unique searches were made using Yahoo in a given month (30 days). How many unique searches per day is that?

50. A typical American consumes almost 400 lb of vegetables per year. If there are 320 million Americans, how many pounds of vegetables a year is that?

51. Of the 400 lb of vegetables consumed per person per year, 200 lb are fresh. If there are 320 million Americans, what is the total fresh vegetable consumption in the United States? (Source: http://www.census.gov.)

52. Americans consume 20.2 lb of ice cream per person per year. If there are 320 million Americans, how many pounds of ice cream are consumed each year? (Source: http://www.hoards.com/blog_dairyconsumption.)

53. Americans eat 58.8 lb of chicken per person per year. If there are 320 million Americans, how many pounds of chicken are consumed each year? (Source: http://www.census.gov.)

54. Turkey consumption is down to 13.9 lb per person per year. If there are 320 million Americans, how many pounds of turkey are consumed each year? (Source: http://www.census.gov.)

55. The average American drinks 24 gal of coffee each year. If there are 320 million Americans, how many gallons of coffee is that? (Source: U.S. Dept. of Agriculture, Economic Research Service.)

56. Americans drink 50 gal of carbonated soft drinks each year. If there are 320 million Americans, how many gallons of soft drinks are consumed each year? (Source: *Statistical Abstract of the United States.*)

57. The United States produces about 270 million tons of garbage each year. Since a ton is 2000 lb and there are about 360 days in a year, the number of pounds of garbage produced each day of the year for each man, woman, and child in the United States is

$$\frac{(2.7 \times 10^8) \times (2 \times 10^3)}{(3 \times 10^8) \times (3.6 \times 10^2)}$$

How many pounds is that? Answer to the nearest pound.

Garbage Champions. Quick, which three nations produce the most garbage per capita? Look at the graph! Ireland and Norway each produce about 800 kg per person each year, which is equivalent to 1.8×10^3 lb per person.

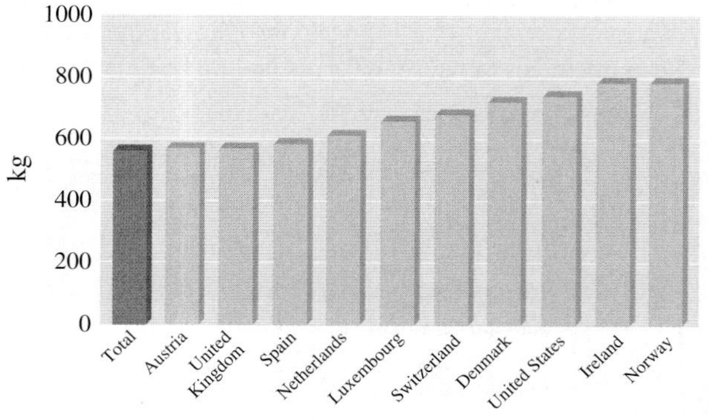

Source: OECD Factbook 2009.

58. If the population of Norway is 4.7×10^6, how many pounds of garbage are produced in Norway every year?

59. If the population of Ireland is 4.2×10^6, how many pounds of garbage are produced in Ireland every year?

60. Scientists have estimated that the total energy received from the Sun each minute is 1.02×10^{19} cal. Since the area of the Earth is 5.1×10^8 km^2, and 1 km^2 is 10^{10} cm^2, the amount of energy received per square centimeter of earth surface per minute (the solar constant) is

$$\frac{1.02 \times 10^{19}}{(5.1 \times 10^8) \times 10^{10}} \text{ cal}$$

Write the answer as a whole number.

IN OTHER WORDS

61. Explain what you must do to multiply a^m by a^n.

62. Explain what you must do to divide a^m by a^n.

63. Explain what you must do to raise a^m to the nth power.

64. By the laws of exponents,

$$\frac{a^m}{a^n} = a^{m-n}, \quad m > n$$

What does

$$\frac{a^m}{a^n} = \frac{a^m}{a^m}, \quad m = n$$

equal in exponential form and as a number? Explain. On the basis of your answer, how would you define a^0?

DISCOVERY

The Rhind papyrus contains a problem that deals with exponents. Problem 79 is very difficult to translate, but historian Moritz Cantor formulates it as follows:

> An estate consisted of seven houses; each house had seven cats; each cat ate seven mice; each mouse ate seven heads of wheat; and each head of wheat was capable of yielding seven hekat measures of grain: Houses, cats, mice, heads of wheat, and hekat measures of grain, how many of these in all were in the estate?

Here is the solution.

Houses	$7 = 7^1$
Cats	$49 = 7^2$
Mice	$343 = 7^3$
Heads of wheat	$2{,}401 = 7^4$
Hekat measures	$16{,}807 = 7^5$
Total	19,607

Because the items in the problem correspond to the first five powers of 7, it was at first thought that the writer was introducing the terminology houses, cats, mice, and so on, for first power, second power, third power, and so on!

65. A similar problem can be found in *Liber Abaci,* by Leonardo Fibonacci (A.D. 1170–1250). Can you find the answer?

There are seven old women on the road to Rome. Each woman has seven mules; each mule carries seven sacks; each sack contains seven loaves; with each loaf are seven knives; and each knife is in seven sheaths. Women, mules, sacks, loaves, knives, and sheaths, how many are there in all on the road to Rome?

66. A later version of the same problem reads as follows:

As I was going to St. Ives
I met a man with seven wives;
Every wife had seven sacks;
Every sack had seven cats;
Every cat had seven kits.
Kits, cats, sacks, and wives,
How many were going to St. Ives?

Hint: The answer is not 2801. If you think it is, then you did not read the first line carefully.

4.3 Number Systems with Bases Other Than 10

GETTING STARTED

OBJECTIVES

A. Convert numbers in other bases to base 10 using grouping.
B. Convert numbers in other bases to base 10 using expanded notation.
C. Convert numbers in base 10 to other bases using division.
D. Solve applications involving bar codes and zip codes.

BINARY CARD MAGIC

Have you heard of binary cards? The five-card set shown below has a series of numbers on each card, the largest of which is 31. Say you have a smaller set of three cards A, B, and C that have numbers on them as follows:

A	5	3	1	7
B	6	3	2	7
C	6	7	4	5

Now, pick a number, any number, from 1 to 7—say, 3.

Is it on card A? Yes. Note that the lowest number on A is 1.
Is it on card B? Yes. Note that the lowest number on B is 2.
Is it on card C? No.

The answer (that is, the number you picked) is 1 + 2, the sum of the lowest numbers on the cards containing the number you picked. How does this work and why? It will be much easier to understand the trick if you know a little bit more about **binary** numbers, which you examine in this section. As a matter of fact, the Using Your Knowledge section in Exercises 4.3 explains how you can make your own set of cards and make the trick work.

A set of five binary cards.

As you learned in Section 4.1, in a positional number system a number is selected as the base, and objects are grouped and counted using that base. In the decimal system, the base chosen was 10, probably because the fingers are a convenient aid in counting.

A Other Number Bases

As we saw earlier, it is possible to use other numbers as bases for numeration systems. For example, if we decide to use 5 as our base (that is, count in groups of five), then we can count the 17 asterisks that follow in this way:

(*****) (*****) (*****) **

3 fives + 2 ones

We write 32_{five}, where the subscript "five" indicates that we are grouping by fives.

If we select 8 as our base, the asterisks are grouped this way:

(********) (********) *

2 eights + 1 one

We write 21_{eight}. Thus, if we use subscripts to indicate the manner in which we are grouping the objects, we can write the number 17 as

$$17_{\text{ten}} = 32_{\text{five}} = 21_{\text{eight}}$$

Using groups of seven, we can indicate the same number of asterisks by

$$23_{\text{seven}} = 2 \text{ sevens} + 3 \text{ ones}$$

Note: In the following material, when no subscript is used, it will be understood that the number is expressed in base 10.

EXAMPLE 1 Writing Decimals in Bases 8, 5, and 7

Arrange 13 asterisks in groups of eight, five, and seven, and write the number 13 in the following:

(a) Base 8 **(b)** Base 5 **(c)** Base 7

Solution

(a) (********) ***** $= 15_{\text{eight}}$

1 eight + 5 ones

(b) (*****) (*****) *** $= 23_{\text{five}}$

2 fives + 3 ones

(c) (*******) ****** $= 16_{\text{seven}}$

1 seven + 6 ones

B Changing to Base 10

Recall that $a^0 = 1$ for $a \neq 0$. So, $10^0 = 1$ and $2 \times 10^0 = 2$.

Now consider the problem of "translating" numbers written in bases other than 10 into our decimal system. For example, what number in our decimal system corresponds to 43_{five}? First, recall that in the decimal system, numbers can be written in expanded form. For example, $342 = (3 \times 10^2) + (4 \times 10) + (2 \times 10^0)$. As you can see, when written in expanded form, each digit in 342 is multiplied by the proper power of 10 (the base being used). Similarly, when written in expanded form, each digit in the numeral 43_{five} must be multiplied by the proper power of 5 (the base being used). Thus

$$43_{\text{five}} = (4 \times 5^1) + (3 \times 5^0) = 23$$

EXAMPLE 2 Converting from Bases 5 and 8 to Decimal

Write the following numbers in decimal notation:

(a) 432_{five} (b) 312_{eight}

Solution

(a) $432_{\text{five}} = (4 \times 5^2) + (3 \times 5^1) + (2 \times 5^0) = 117$

(b) $312_{\text{eight}} = (3 \times 8^2) + (1 \times 8^1) + (2 \times 8^0) = 202$

In the seventeenth century, the German mathematician Gottfried Wilhelm Leibniz advocated use of the **binary system** (base 2). This system uses only the digits 0 and 1, and the grouping is by twos. The advantage of the binary system is that each position in a numeral contains one of just two values (0 or 1). Thus, electric switches, which have only two possible states, *off* or *on,* can be used to designate the value of each position. Computers using the binary system have revolutionized technology and the sciences by speedily performing calculations that would take humans years to complete. Handheld calculators operate internally on the binary system.

Now consider the problem of converting a number from base 2 to decimal notation. It will help you to keep in mind that in the binary system, numbers are built up by using blocks that are powers of the base 2.

$$2^0 = 1, \quad 2^1 = 2, \quad 2^2 = 4, \quad 2^3 = 8, \quad 2^4 = 16, \quad \ldots$$

When you write 1101 in the binary system, you are saying in the yes/no language of the computer, "a block of 8, yes; a block of 4, yes; a block of 2, no; a block of 1, yes." Thus,

$$\begin{aligned} 1101_{\text{two}} &= (1 \times 2^3) + (1 \times 2^2) + (0 \times 2^1) + (1 \times 2^0) \\ &= 8 + 4 + 0 + 1 \\ &= 13 \end{aligned}$$

EXAMPLE 3 Converting from Binary to Decimal

Write the number 10101_{two} in decimal notation.

Solution

We write

$$\begin{aligned} 10101_{\text{two}} &= (1 \times 2^4) + (0 \times 2^3) + (1 \times 2^2) + (0 \times 2^1) + (1 \times 2^0) \\ &= 16 + 4 + 1 \\ &= 21 \end{aligned}$$

So far we have used only bases less than 10, of which the most important ones are base 2 (**binary**) and base 8 (**octal**), because they are used by computers. Bases greater than 10 are also possible, but then new symbols are needed for the digits greater than 9. For example, base 16 (**hexadecimal**) is also used by computers, with the "digits" A, B, C, D, E, and F used to correspond to the decimal numbers 10, 11, 12, 13, 14, and 15, respectively. We can change numbers from hexadecimal to decimal notation in the same way that we did for bases less than 10.

Some scientific calculators convert between decimal, binary, and octal. For example, enter 625.

EXAMPLE 4 Converting from Hexadecimal to Decimal

Write the number $5AC_{\text{sixteen}}$ in decimal notation.

Solution

$$\begin{aligned} 5AC_{\text{sixteen}} &= (5 \times 16^2) + (10 \times 16^1) + (12 \times 16^0) \\ &= (5 \times 256) + (160) + 12 \\ &= 1280 + 160 + 12 \\ &= 1452 \end{aligned}$$

C Changing from Base 10

Up to this point we have changed numbers from bases other than 10 to base 10. Now we shall change numbers from base 10 to other bases. A good method for doing this depends on successive divisions. For example, to change 625 to base 8, we start by dividing 625 by 8 and obtain 78 with a remainder of 1. We then divide 78 by 8 and get 9 with 6 remaining. Next, we divide 9 by 8 and obtain a quotient of 1 and a remainder of 1. We diagram these divisions as follows:

8	625		
8	78	1	Remainder
8	9	6	Remainder
	1	1	Remainder

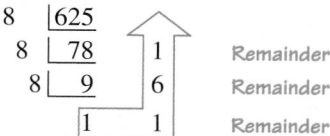

The answer is read upward as 1161_{eight} (see the arrow).

Why does this method work? Suppose we wish to find how many eights there are in 625. To find out, we divide 625 by 8. The quotient 78 tells us that there are 78 eights in 625, and the remainder tells us that there is 1 left over. Dividing the 78 by 8 (which is the same as dividing the 625 by $8 \times 8 = 64$) tells us that there are 9 sixty-fours in 625, and the remainder tells us that there are 6 eights left over. Finally, dividing the quotient 9 by 8 gives a new quotient of 1 and a remainder of 1. This tells us that there is 1 five hundred twelve $(8 \times 8 \times 8)$ contained in 625 with 1 sixty-four left over. Thus, we see that

$$625 = (1 \times 8^3) + (1 \times 8^2) + (6 \times 8) + (1 \times 8^0) = 1161_{\text{eight}}$$

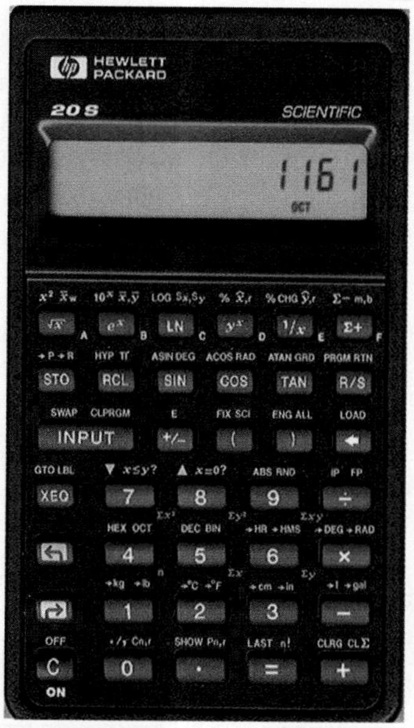

© I. Bello

Press [➡] HEX OCT. You get the answer 1161_{eight}.

EXAMPLE 5 Changing Decimals to Bases 2 and 5

Change the number 33 to the following:

(a) Base 2 (b) Base 5

Solution

(a)

2	33	
2	16	1
2	8	0
2	4	0
2	2	0
	1	0

Thus, $33 = 100001_{\text{two}}$.

(b)

5	33	
5	6	3
	1	1

Thus, $33 = 113_{\text{five}}$.

EXAMPLE 6 Changing Decimal Numerals to Bases 8 and 6

Change the number 4923 to the following:

(a) Octal notation (b) Hexadecimal notation

Solution

(a)

8	4923	
8	615	3
8	76	7
8	9	4
	1	1

Thus, $4923 = 11473_{\text{eight}}$.

(b)

16	4923	
16	307	11
16	19	3
	1	3

Thus, $4923 = 133\text{B}_{\text{sixteen}}$.

D Applications

How does your computer work? A computer uses a collection of ones (1s) and zeros (0s), known as binary digits or bits, to store or read information. In particular, all color information (monitor and color printer) is stored numerically. One bit uses a 0 or a 1 to represent each pixel on a screen. A color depth of 1 bit can only be a black-and-white picture.

EXAMPLE 7 Following Patterns

Complete the following table:

1 bit allows	$2^1 = 2$	colors, black and white.
4 bits allow	______	different color combinations.
8 bits allow	______	different color combinations.
16 bits allow	______	color combinations.
24 bits allow	______	color combinations.

24 bits 8 bits 6 bits 4 bits 1 bit

Solution

The pattern here is $2^1 = 2$, $2^4 = 16$, $2^8 = 256$, $2^{16} = 65{,}536$, and $2^{24} = 16{,}777{,}216$. Thus, a monitor that supports 24 bits can show more than 16 million color combinations!

Have you seen an envelope with symbols like the ones at the bottom of the address in Figure 4.3? What are these symbols, and what do they mean? Because the symbols are composed of bars, they are called **bar codes.** One of the simplest bar codes is the **Postnet code** used by the U.S. Postal Service to represent the ZIP code + 4 for addresses. In this case, the bars represent the numbers **33675-5096.** The tenth digit is a *checking* digit (see Exercises 4.3, problems 41 and 42).

I. Bello
Ibello Hcc Usf
Ybor Campus POB 5096
Tampa FL 33675-5096

FIGURE 4.3

The code is made up of 52 bars starting with a long bar, followed by 10 groups of five bars, each containing two long and three short bars and ending with a long bar. The long bars represent 1s, and the short bars 0s. The relationships between decimal digits, bar codes, and Postnet binary codes are shown in Table 4.5.

Table 4.5

Decimal	Bar Code	Binary Code
1	ıııll	00011
2	ıılıl	00101
3	ıı llı	00110
4	ılııl	01001
5	ılılı	01010
6	ıllıı	01100
7	lıııl	10001
8	lıılı	10010
9	lılıı	10100
0	llııı	11000

Do you see the relationship between the binary codes for the numbers 1–6 in Postnet code and in regular binary? Try omitting the last digit! Now, look at the binary codes for 7–10. All the numbers start with 1. Do you see how to form the codes for these numbers?

EXAMPLE 8 Zipping to Postnet

Write the ZIP code 33657 using Postnet binary code.

Solution

Start and end with a long bar, and copy the binary code for the digits 33657 like this:

Start with a long bar.	3	3	6	5	7	End with a long bar.
l	ııllı	ııllı	ıllıı	ılılı	lıııl	l

4.3 EXERCISES

A Other Number Bases

In problems 1–4, write numerals in the bases indicated by the manners of grouping.

1. (***) (***) **

2. (*****) (*****) (*****) ***

3. (****) (****) (****) *

4. (***********) (***********) (***********) ******

In problems 5–8, draw diagrams as shown in problems 1–4, and then write each decimal number in the given base.

5. 15 in base 8
6. 15 in base 5
7. 15 in base 7
8. 15 in base 12

B Changing to Base 10

In problems 9–16, write each number in decimal notation.

9. 42_{five}
10. 31_{five}
11. 213_{eight}
12. 563_{eight}
13. 11011_{two}
14. 101001_{two}
15. 123_{sixteen}
16. $\text{ACE}_{\text{sixteen}}$

C Changing from Base 10

In problems 17–32, use the method of successive divisions.

17. Write the number 15 in base 5 notation.
18. Write the number 27 in base 5 notation.
19. Write the number 28 in binary notation.
20. Write the number 43 in binary notation.
21. Write the number 25 in hexadecimal notation.
22. Write the number 121 in hexadecimal notation.
23. Write the number 25 in base 6 notation.
24. Write the number 38 in base 6 notation.
25. Write the number 64 in base 7 notation.
26. Write the number 123 in base 7 notation.
27. Write the number 38 in octal notation.
28. Write the number 135 in octal notation.
29. Write the number 1467 in hexadecimal notation.
30. Write the number 145,263 in hexadecimal notation.
31. Write the number 73 in binary and in octal notation.
32. Write the number 87 in octal and in hexadecimal notation.

D Applications

In problems 33–36, write each ZIP code in binary code and as a decimal.

33.
34.
35.
36.

In problems 37–40, write each ZIP code in bar code.

37. 02218
38. 70605
39. 95472
40. 15744

IN OTHER WORDS

41. The ZIP code + 4 shown at the beginning of this section contains 52 bars and starts and ends with a long bar. If each digit in a ZIP code + 4 number consists of 5 bars, is this consistent with the fact that the complete ZIP code + 4 number has 52 bars? Explain.
42. As it turns out, there is an extra digit in the ZIP code + 4 shown at the beginning of this section. The digit represented by the five bars *before* the last long bar is called the *checking digit*.
    a. What is this checking digit?
    b. The first part of the procedure used to find the checking digit for 33675-5096 consists of adding the digits in 33675. Write the rest of the procedure.

You may need a dictionary to answer questions 43–46.

43. What does *binary* mean? What does the prefix *bi*-indicate?
44. What does *octal* mean? What does the prefix *oct*-indicate?
45. What does *hexadecimal* mean? What does the prefix *hexa*-indicate?
46. The binary system uses the numbers 0 and 1; the octal uses 0, 1, 2, 3, 4, 5, 6, and 7; and the hexadecimal uses 0, 1, 2, 3, 4, 5, 6, 7, 8, 9, A, B, C, D, E, and F. Why are the A, B, C, D, E, and F needed?

USING YOUR KNOWLEDGE

Here is a trick that you can use to amaze your friends. Write the numbers from 1 to 7 in binary notation. They look like this:

Decimal	Binary
1	1
2	10
3	11
4	100
5	101
6	110
7	111

Now label three columns *A*, *B*, and *C*. In column *A*, write the numbers that have a 1 in the units place when written in binary notation; in column *B*, write the numbers that have a 1 in the second position from the right when written in binary notation; and then in column *C*, write the numbers with a 1 in the third position from the right when written in binary notation.

A	*B*	*C*
1	2	4
3	3	5
5	6	6
7	7	7

Ask someone to think of a number between 1 and 7 and tell you in which columns the number appears. Say that the number is 6 (which appears in columns *B* and *C*). You find the sum of the numbers at the top of columns *B* and *C*. This sum is 2 + 4 = 6, and you have the desired number!

47. Can you explain why this works?
48. If you extend this trick to cover the first 15 numbers, how many columns do you need?
49. Can you discover how to do the trick with 31 numbers?

CALCULATOR CORNER

Converting from Base b to Base 10 For convenience and to save space, we write the base *b* as an ordinary decimal rather than spelling it out. Thus, for example, 47_8 means exactly the same thing as 47_{eight}. Suppose that 4735_8 is to be converted to base 10. We know that

$$4735_8 = (4 \times 8^3) + (7 \times 8^2) + (3 \times 8) + 5$$

Since the three quantities in parentheses are all divisible by 8, we can rewrite the expression to get

$$4735_8 = 8 \times [(4 \times 8^2) + (7 \times 8) + 3] + 5$$

Next, we see that the two quantities in parentheses inside the square brackets are divisible by 8, so we can rewrite again to get

$$4735_8 = 8 \times \{8 \times [(4 \times 8) + 7] + 3\} + 5$$

Now we can evaluate the last expression by a simple step-by-step procedure. Start with the innermost parentheses, multiply 4 by the base 8, and add 7 to the result. Then multiply the last result by 8 and add 3 to the product. Finally, multiply the preceding result by 8 and add 5 to the product. The final sum is the required answer.

The arithmetic can be done on a calculator by keying in the following:

[4] [×] [8] [+] [7] [=] [×] [8] [+] [3] [=]
[×] [8] [+] [5] [=]

The calculator will show the result 2525.

Notice that we multiplied the first octal digit, 4, by the base, 8, and added the next octal digit, 7. Then we multiplied the result by the base and added the next octal digit, 3. Finally, we multiplied by the base again and added the last octal digit, 5.

This procedure holds for any base. Thus, to convert from any base b to base 10, do the following:

a. Multiply the first digit of the number by b, and add the second digit to the result.

b. Multiply the preceding result by b, and add the third digit of the given numeral.

c. Continue the same procedure until you have added the last digit of the given numeral.

The calculator will show the final answer. Be sure that you work from left to right when using the digits of the given numeral.

As another example, let us convert the hexadecimal numeral $BF3_{16}$ to base 10. Recall that the hexadecimal digits B and F are the numbers 11 and 15, respectively, in decimal notation, so we key in the following:

[1] [1] [×] [1] [6] [+] [1] [5] [=] [×] [1] [6] [+]
[3] [=]

Our calculator will show the result 3059.

Convert each of the following numerals to decimal notation:

1. 1101_2 **2.** 231_4 **3.** 423_5

4. 752_8 **5.** 3572_8 **6.** 873_9

COLLABORATIVE LEARNING

We already know that we can change a number from a given base to decimal notation by writing the number in expanded notation as we did in Example 4. Now, we are going a step further; we are going to translate words from a given base (16 in this case) to numbers. Take the word $FACE_{16}$. As you recall (see Example 4), $F = 15$, $A = 10$, $C = 12$, and $E = 14$. Thus, $\text{FACE}_{16} = 15 \cdot 16^3 + 10 \cdot 16^2 + 12 \cdot 16^1 + 14$. Now your base converter or a simple calculator will tell you that $\text{FACE}_{16} = 64{,}206$.

1. When the base of a number system is greater than 10, the missing digits come from the alphabet. Thus, when using base 12, 11 = A and 12 = B. Using this idea, discuss letters we use as numbers in different bases (such as 13, 16, and so on). If we follow this scheme, what is the highest base we can use?

2. $\text{ADD}_{36} = (10 \cdot 36^2 + 13 \cdot 36^1 + 13) = 13{,}441$. The number 13,441 is prime (it is only divisible by itself and 1).

We will call the word ADD_{36} a prime word. Can you find other prime words in base 36?

3. Assign group members to find prime words in base 36. Can you find a prime three-letter word starting with B? What about with Z?

4. Collect all prime words from the members in your group. Write prime sentences using the words. An example: TWIN TOBOGGANIST TOURED TANZANIAN TOWN (discovered by David Gogomolov). What is the longest sentence your group can create?

4.4 Binary, Octal, and Hexadecimal Arithmetic

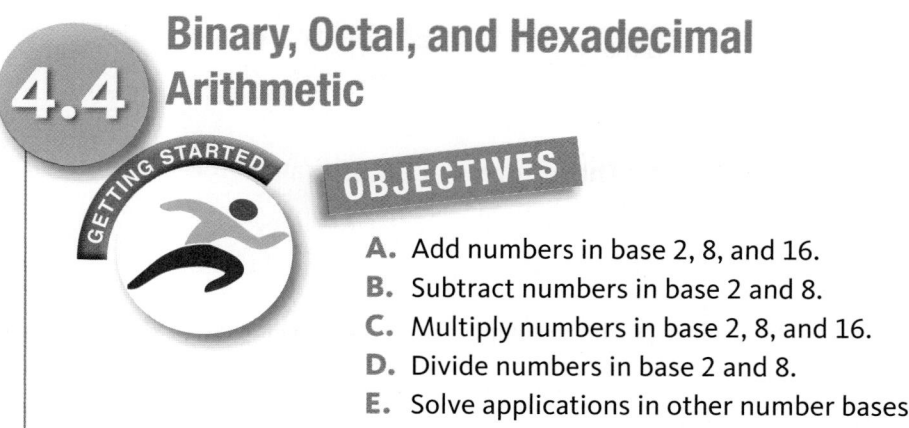

GETTING STARTED

OBJECTIVES

A. Add numbers in base 2, 8, and 16.

B. Subtract numbers in base 2 and 8.

C. Multiply numbers in base 2, 8, and 16.

D. Divide numbers in base 2 and 8.

E. Solve applications in other number bases.

MODEMS AND ASCII CODE

Do you know what a modem is? It is a device that transmits data to or from a computer. How does one work? Suppose you are writing a message starting with the letter A on your computer. A stream of digital bits with 0 volts for binary 0 and a constant voltage for binary 1 flows from the computer into the modem carrying the American Standard Code for Information Interchange (ASCII) code for the letter A: 01000001. At the receiving end, the signal is demodulated—that is, changed back—and resumes its original form, a series of pulses representing 0s and 1s resulting in 01000001, the letter A. You can learn how these letters are encoded in different bases by working problems in Exercises 4.4.

Table 4.6 Binary Addition

+	0	1
0	0	1
1	1	10

Now that we know how to represent numbers in the binary system, we look at how computations are done in that system. First, we construct an addition table like the ones for base 10 arithmetic. See Table 4.6.

The only entry that looks peculiar is the 10 in the addition table, but recall that 10_2 means 2_{10}, which is exactly the result of adding 1 + 1. (Be sure to read 10 as "one zero," not as "ten.")

A Addition

Binary addition is done in the same manner as addition in base 10. We line up the corresponding digits and add column by column.

EXAMPLE 1 Adding Two Terms in Binary

Add 1010_2 and 1111_2.

Solution

$$\begin{array}{r} {\scriptstyle 1\,1} \\ 1\,0\,1\,0_2 \\ \underline{1\,1\,1\,1_2} \\ 1\,1\,0\,0\,1_2 \end{array}$$

$0 + 1 = 1$

$1 + 1 = 10_2$ Write 0 and carry 1 to the next column.

$1 + 0 + 1 = 10_2$ Write 0 and carry 1 to the next column.

$(1 + 1) + 1 = 10_2 + 1 = 11_2$

Thus, $1010_2 + 1111_2 = 11001_2$.

EXAMPLE 2 Adding Three Terms in Binary

Perform the addition $1101_2 + 110_2 + 11_2$.

Solution

We shall omit the subscript 2 in the computation, but keep in mind that all numerals are binary.

$$\begin{array}{r} {\scriptstyle 1\,1\,1} \\ 1\,1\,0\,1 \\ 1\,1\,0 \\ \underline{1\,1} \\ 1\,0\,1\,1\,0 \end{array}$$

$1 + 0 + 1 = 10$ Write 0 and carry 1 to the next column.

$(1 + 1) + 0 + 1 = 10 + 1 = 11$ Write 1 and carry 1 to the next column.

$(1 + 1) + 1 = 10 + 1 = 11$ Write 1 and carry 1 to the next column.

$1 + 1 = 10$

Thus, $1101_2 + 110_2 + 11_2 = 10110_2$.

Yuki woman in mourning.

When counting in the decimal system, you can use 10 fingers. In the binary system you can use 2 fingers. What could you use in an octal system? The answer is not at your fingertips but *between* your fingers! The Yuki Indians of California use the spaces between their fingers for counting. Thus, some of their counting is in base 4, and some is in base 8 (octal or octonary).

Arithmetic in base 8 and base 16 systems can be done using Tables 4.7 and 4.8 in much the same way as in the base 10 system.

Table 4.7 Octal Addition Table

+	0	1	2	3	4	5	6	7
0	0	1	2	3	4	5	6	7
1	1	2	3	4	5	6	7	10
2	2	3	4	5	6	7	10	11
3	3	4	5	6	7	10	11	12
4	4	5	6	7	10	11	12	13
5	5	6	7	10	11	12	13	14
6	6	7	10	11	12	13	14	15
7	7	10	11	12	13	14	15	16

Table 4.8 Hexadecimal Addition Table (base 16)

+	0	1	2	3	4	5	6	7	8	9	A	B	C	D	E	F
0	0	1	2	3	4	5	6	7	8	9	A	B	C	D	E	F
1	1	2	3	4	5	6	7	8	9	A	B	C	D	E	F	10
2	2	3	4	5	6	7	8	9	A	B	C	D	E	F	10	11
3	3	4	5	6	7	8	9	A	B	C	D	E	F	10	11	12
4	4	5	6	7	8	9	A	B	C	D	E	F	10	11	12	13
5	5	6	7	8	9	A	B	C	D	E	F	10	11	12	13	14
6	6	7	8	9	A	B	C	D	E	F	10	11	12	13	14	15
7	7	8	9	A	B	C	D	E	F	10	11	12	13	14	15	16
8	8	9	A	B	C	D	E	F	10	11	12	13	14	15	16	17
9	9	A	B	C	D	E	F	10	11	12	13	14	15	16	17	18
A	A	B	C	D	E	F	10	11	12	13	14	15	16	17	18	19
B	B	C	D	E	F	10	11	12	13	14	15	16	17	18	19	1A
C	C	D	E	F	10	11	12	13	14	15	16	17	18	19	1A	1B
D	D	E	F	10	11	12	13	14	15	16	17	18	19	1A	1B	1C
E	E	F	10	11	12	13	14	15	16	17	18	19	1A	1B	1C	1D
F	F	10	11	12	13	14	15	16	17	18	19	1A	1B	1C	1D	1E

EXAMPLE 3 Octal Addition

Add $705_8 + 374_8$.

Solution

```
  1 1
  7 0 5
+ 3 7 4
1 3 0 1 ←—— 5 + 4 = 11 (Table 4.7)              Write 1 and carry 1.
              1 + 0 + 7 = 10 (Table 4.7)        Write 0 and carry 1.
              1 + (7 + 3) = 1 + 12 = 13 (Table 4.7)
```

The required sum is 1301_8.

As in base 10, you can consult Table 4.8 to do the next Example.

EXAMPLE 4 Hexadecimal Addition

Add $1AB2_{16} + 2CD3_{16}$.

Solution

```
  1 1
  1 A B 2
+ 2 C D 3
  4 7 8 5
```

- $2 + 3 = 5$
- $B + D = 18$ (Table 4.8) Write 8 and carry 1.
- $(A + C) + 1 = 16 + 1 = 17$ (Table 4.8) Write 7 and carry 1.
- $1 + 1 + 2 = 4$

The answer is 4785_{16}. (You can check this by converting to base 10.)

B Subtraction

To subtract in the binary system, we line up corresponding digits and subtract column by column, "borrowing" as necessary.

EXAMPLE 5 Subtraction in Binary

Subtract 101_2 from 1010_2.

Solution

```
  0 10 0 10
  1 0 1 0
−   1 0 1
    1 0 1
```

- $0 - 1$ requires borrowing; then, $10 - 1 = 1$.
- $0 - 0 = 0$
- $0 - 1$ requires borrowing; then, $10 - 1 = 1$.

The result is $1010_2 - 101_2 = 101_2$. You can check this answer by adding $101_2 + 101_2$ to get 1010_2.

Subtraction in the octal system is done in a similar manner.

EXAMPLE 6 Octal Subtraction

Subtract $643_8 - 45_8$.

Solution

```
  5 13
    3 13
  6 4 3
−   4 5
  5 7 6
```

- $3 - 5$ requires borrowing. Change the 4 to 3 and add 10 to the first 3 to give 13. Then subtract $13 - 5 = 6$ (Table 4.7).
- $3 - 4$ requires borrowing. Change the 6 to 5 and add 10 to the 3 to give 13. Then subtract $13 - 4 = 7$ (Table 4.7).
- Bring down the 5.

The result shows that $643_8 - 45_8 = 576_8$. This can be checked by addition as in Example 3.

C Multiplication

Multiplying in base 2 is similar to multiplying in base 10; just remember the multiplication facts in Table 4.9.

Table 4.9 Binary Multiplication

×	0	1
0	0	0
1	0	1

EXAMPLE 7 Multiplication in Binary

Multiply 1110_2 by 110_2.

Solution

```
     1110
   ×  110
    11100     ← Multiply by 0, and write one 0. Then multiply by 1, using the
                same line.
   1110       ← Indent two places and multiply by 1.
  1010100     ← Add the partial products.
```

The computation shows that $110_2 \times 1110_2 = 1010100_2$.

What about octal multiplication? First, study Table 4.10 for the multiplication facts you need, then proceed in the same manner as in base 10.

Table 4.10 Octal Multiplication Table

×	0	1	2	3	4	5	6	7
0	0	0	0	0	0	0	0	0
1	0	1	2	3	4	5	6	7
2	0	2	4	6	10	12	14	16
3	0	3	6	11	14	17	22	25
4	0	4	10	14	20	24	30	34
5	0	5	12	17	24	31	36	43
6	0	6	14	22	30	36	44	52
7	0	7	16	25	34	43	52	61

EXAMPLE 8 Octal Multiplication

Multiply 237_8 by 14_8.

Solution

```
   237
 ×  14
  1174 ←  4 × 7 = 34 (Table 4.10)                     Write 4 and carry 3.
  237  ←  4 × 3 = 14 (Table 4.10); 14 + 3 = 17        Write 7 and carry 1.
  3564    4 × 2 = 10 (Table 4.10); 10 + 1 = 11
          1 × 237 = 237
```

Addition of the partial products gives the final answer, 3564_8. The check is left to you.

Now, we promise, here is the last table you need: the table for hexadecimal multiplication. Study it before you try the next example!

Table 4.11 Hexadecimal Multiplication Table (base 16)

×	0	1	2	3	4	5	6	7	8	9	A	B	C	D	E	F
0	0	0	0	0	0	0	0	0	0	0	0	0	0	0	0	0
1	0	1	2	3	4	5	6	7	8	9	A	B	C	D	E	F
2	0	2	4	6	8	A	C	E	10	12	14	16	18	1A	1C	1E
3	0	3	6	9	C	F	12	15	18	1B	1E	21	24	27	2A	2D
4	0	4	8	C	10	14	18	1C	20	24	28	2C	30	34	38	3C
5	0	5	A	F	14	19	1E	23	28	2D	32	37	3C	41	46	4B
6	0	6	C	12	18	1E	24	2A	30	36	3C	42	48	4E	54	5A
7	0	7	E	15	1C	23	2A	31	38	3F	46	4D	54	5B	62	69
8	0	8	10	18	20	28	30	38	40	48	50	58	60	68	70	78
9	0	9	12	1B	24	2D	36	3F	48	51	5A	63	6C	75	7E	87
A	0	A	14	1E	28	32	3C	46	50	5A	64	6E	78	82	8C	96
B	0	B	16	21	2C	37	42	4D	58	63	6E	79	84	8F	9A	A5
C	0	C	18	24	30	3C	48	54	60	6C	78	84	90	9C	A8	B4
D	0	D	1A	27	34	41	4E	5B	68	75	82	8F	9C	A9	B6	C3
E	0	E	1C	2A	38	46	54	62	70	7E	8C	9A	A8	B6	C4	D2
F	0	F	1E	2D	3C	4B	5A	69	78	87	96	A5	B4	C3	D2	E1

EXAMPLE 9 Hexadecimal Multiplication

Multiply $2B4_{16}$ by $B1_{16}$.

Solution

```
    2 B 4
  ×   B 1
  -------
    2 B 4   ←  1 × 2B4 = 2B4
  1 D B C   ←  B × 4 = 2C (Table 4.11); write C and carry the 2. Then, B × B = 79 (Table 4.11);
  -------      B × B = 79 (Table 4.11); 79 + 2 = 7B (Table 4.8); write B and carry the 7.
  1 D E 7 4    Then B × 2 = 16 (Table 4.11); 16 + 7 = 1D (Table 4.8).
      ↑ ↑
      | └───── B + C = 17 (Table 4.8); write 7 and carry the 1.
      └─────── (2 + B) + 1 = D + 1 = E (Table 4.8)
```

The answer is $1DE74_{16}$.

D Division

The procedure used for division in the base 10 system can also be used in the binary system. This is illustrated next.

EXAMPLE 10 Division in Binary

Divide 110111_2 by 101_2.

Solution

```
                        1 0 1 1
                 1 0 1) 1 1 0 1 1 1
Step 1 ─────────→  − 1 0 1
                   ---------
Step 2 ─────────→      1 1 1
Step 3 ─────────→    − 1 0 1
                     -------
Step 4 ─────────→        1 0 1
Step 5 ─────────→      − 1 0 1
                       -------
                             0 ← Remainder
```

Step 1 $1 \times 101 = 101$. Write 1 in the quotient above the 110 and then subtract.

Step 2 Bring down the next digit. 101 does not go into 11, so write 0 in the quotient and bring down the next digit.

Step 3 $1 \times 101 = 101$. Write 1 in the quotient and then subtract.

Step 4 Bring down the final digit.

Step 5 $1 \times 101 = 101$. Write 1 in the quotient and then subtract to get the remainder.

The division here is exact; the quotient is 1011_2, and the remainder is 0.
You can check the answer by multiplying the quotient 1011_2 by the divisor 101_2. Thus

$$\begin{array}{r} 1011 \\ \times \quad 101 \\ \hline 1011 \\ 10110 \\ \hline 110111 \end{array}$$

Therefore, the answer is correct.

EXAMPLE 11 Octal Division

Divide 4357_8 by 21_8.

Solution

$$\begin{array}{r} 206 \\ 21\overline{)4357} \\ 42 \\ \hline 157 \\ 146 \\ \hline 11 \end{array}$$

- $2 \times 21 = 42$. Write 2 in the quotient above the 43.
- Subtract and bring down the 5. The 21 does not go into 15, so write 0 in the quotient and bring down the 7.
- $6 \times 21 = 146$ (Table 4.10). Write 6 in the quotient.
- Subtract to get the remainder.

The computation shows that the quotient is 206_8 and the remainder is 11_8.

As before, the answer can be checked by multiplying the quotient by the divisor and adding the remainder. Thus,

$$\begin{array}{r} 206 \\ \times \quad 21 \\ \hline 206 \\ 414 \\ \hline 4346 \\ + \quad 11 \\ \hline 4357 \end{array}$$

which shows the answer is correct.

E Applications

Binary numbers can be used to transmit, print, and encode pictures or images. (More about this later in the Discovery section.) How would you "translate," or code, a picture to binary numbers? Look at the next example (Figure 4.4 on the following page).

EXAMPLE 12 Say Hi in Binary

Translate, or code, a white square with a 0 and a black square with a 1.

On the first line, all squares are white, so the first line corresponds to

0000000000000000

The second line is

0000000001100110

What are the third, fourth, and last lines?

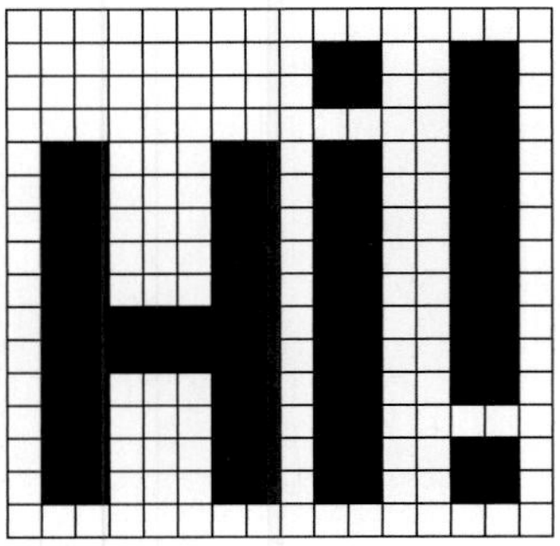

FIGURE 4.4

Solution

The third line is

0000000001100110

The fourth line is

0000000000000110

The last line is

0000000000000000

You have encoded the information into a 16-bit binary code!

Can you answer these questions? Which line(s) has(have) the most 1s? Which line(s) has(have) the same number of 1s? What about the least number of 1s?

4.4 EXERCISES

A Addition

In problems 1–6, perform the indicated additions (base 2).

1. $\begin{array}{r} 111_2 \\ +\ 10_2 \\ \hline \end{array}$
2. $\begin{array}{r} 111_2 \\ +\ 101_2 \\ \hline \end{array}$
3. $\begin{array}{r} 1101_2 \\ +\ 110_2 \\ \hline \end{array}$
4. $\begin{array}{r} 1111_2 \\ +\ 1101_2 \\ \hline \end{array}$
5. $\begin{array}{r} 110_2 \\ 101_2 \\ +\ 111_2 \\ \hline \end{array}$
6. $\begin{array}{r} 1101_2 \\ 1110_2 \\ +\ 101_2 \\ \hline \end{array}$

In problems 7–10, perform the indicated additions (base 8).

7. $531_8 + 47_8$
8. $425_8 + 364_8$
9. $7256_8 + 634_8$
10. $5732_8 + 747_8$

In problems 11–14, perform the indicated additions (base 16).

11. $3CB_{16} + 4C_{16}$
12. $4FE_{16} + 35_{16}$
13. $98D_{16} + 2B_{16}$
14. $CBD_{16} + AF_{16}$

B Subtraction

In problems 15–20, perform the indicated subtractions (base 2).

15. $\begin{array}{r} 111_2 \\ -\ 10_2 \\ \hline \end{array}$
16. $\begin{array}{r} 110_2 \\ -\ 11_2 \\ \hline \end{array}$
17. $\begin{array}{r} 1000_2 \\ -\ 111_2 \\ \hline \end{array}$
18. $\begin{array}{r} 1101_2 \\ -\ 111_2 \\ \hline \end{array}$
19. $\begin{array}{r} 1111_2 \\ -\ 101_2 \\ \hline \end{array}$
20. $\begin{array}{r} 1010_2 \\ -\ 101_2 \\ \hline \end{array}$

In problems 21–24, perform the indicated subtractions (base 8).

21. $534_8 - 25_8$
22. $617_8 - 47_8$
23. $3264_8 - 756_8$
24. $4763_8 - 654_8$

C Multiplication

In problems 25–30, multiply as indicated (base 2).

25. $\begin{array}{r} 110_2 \\ \times\ 11_2 \\ \hline \end{array}$
26. $\begin{array}{r} 101_2 \\ \times\ 10_2 \\ \hline \end{array}$
27. $\begin{array}{r} 1111_2 \\ \times\ 11_2 \\ \hline \end{array}$
28. $\begin{array}{r} 1110_2 \\ \times\ 111_2 \\ \hline \end{array}$
29. $\begin{array}{r} 1011_2 \\ \times\ 101_2 \\ \hline \end{array}$
30. $\begin{array}{r} 1011_2 \\ \times\ 111_2 \\ \hline \end{array}$

In problems 31–34, perform the indicated multiplications (base 8).

31. $57_8 \times 6_8$
32. $45_8 \times 7_8$
33. $216_8 \times 32_8$
34. $312_8 \times 65_8$

C Hexadecimal Multiplication

In problems 35–38, perform the indicated multiplications (base 16).

35. $2C5_{16} \times 3B_{16}$
36. $4DE_{16} \times 12_{16}$
37. $6F3_{16} \times AB_{16}$
38. $29A_{16} \times E0F_{16}$

D Division

In problems 39–44, divide as indicated (base 2).

39. $10_2\overline{)1101_2}$

40. $11_2\overline{)1101_2}$

41. $11_2\overline{)1110_2}$

42. $11_2\overline{)11011_2}$

43. $101_2\overline{)111011_2}$

44. $111_2\overline{)1110111_2}$

In problems 45–48, perform the indicated divisions (base 8).

45. $317_8 \div 7_8$

46. $4355_8 \div 5_8$

47. $4215_8 \div 15_8$

48. $7342_8 \div 31_8$

IN OTHER WORDS

49. Explain why it is easier to add and multiply in the binary system (base 2) than in the hexadecimal system (base 16).

50. Why is it easier to write a number in expanded form in the decimal system than in the binary (base 2) or hexadecimal (base 16) system?

USING YOUR KNOWLEDGE

51. Numerology converts letters to numbers with A = 1, B = 2, C = 3, . . . , as shown below.

1	2	3	4	5	6	7	8	9
A	B	C	D	E	F	G	H	I
J	K	L	M	N	O	P	Q	R
S	T	U	V	W	X	Y	Z	

a. In numerology, the number 4 corresponds to the word HE (H = 8, E = 5 because 8 + 5 = 13 and 1 + 3 = 4). It also corresponds to AL (1 + 3 = 4). Can you find some two-letter words corresponding to 7? to 11? to 18?

b. What about some three-letter words corresponding to 7, 11, and 18?

52. Here are some questions that pertain to one and only one of the numbers (7, 11, or 18). Which one?

a. Number of orifices (holes) in the human head

b. Atomic number of sodium

c. One, Allah, Brahma (numerology)

d. Number of dwarfs in Snow White tale

e. It, my, no, jar (numerology)

f. Number of stars in the Big Dipper

g. Atomic number of argon

h. Fox, hen, red (numerology)

i. Atomic number of nitrogen

j. James Polk, Andrew Jackson, Ulysses S. Grant

DISCOVERY

Did you know that the first images of Mars were rendered using crayons? If you don't believe it read on!

A camera installed on the spacecraft *Mariner IV* took the first images of the planet Mars and sent them back to Earth by radio signals on July 14, 1965. On Earth, a computer received the pictures in the form of binary numerals consisting of 6 bits. (A **bit** is a binary digit.) The shade of each dot in the final picture was determined by these 6 bits.

The numeral 000000_2 (0 in base 10) indicated a white dot, and the numeral 111111_2 (63 in base 10) indicated a black dot. The 62 numerals between represented various shades of gray between white and black. To make a complete picture, 40,000 dots, each described by 6 bits, were needed!

53. If one of the numerals received was 110111_2, what was the corresponding decimal numeral?

54. Does the dot corresponding to the numeral received in problem 53 represent a shade of gray closer to white or to black?

55. What binary numeral represents the lightest shade of gray that is not white?

56. What binary numeral represents the darkest shade of gray that is not black?

The image was actually acquired by a television camera and then *rendered* using crayons. Do you want to see how? Go to http://directedplay.com/first_tv_image_of_mars.html.

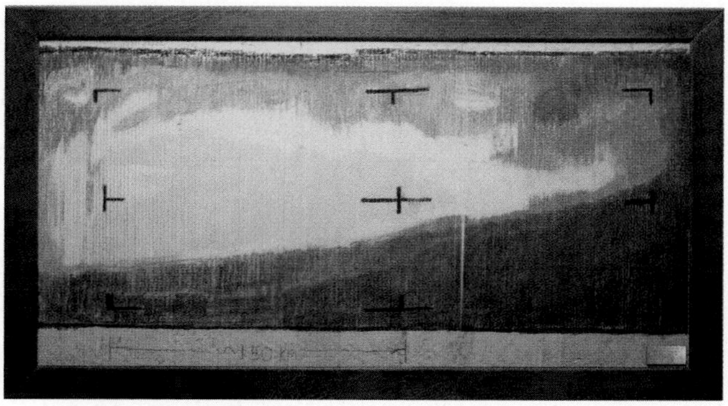

© NASA/JPL/Dan Goods

http://photojournal.jpl.nasa.gov/catalog/PIA14032.

COLLABORATIVE LEARNING

Form two (or more) groups of students and provide each group with a 16-bit binary code chart like the ones shown below. Each group should construct a diagram similar to the one shown in Example 12 but using the word *LO*! Write the 16 lines of code on a 3-by-5 card.

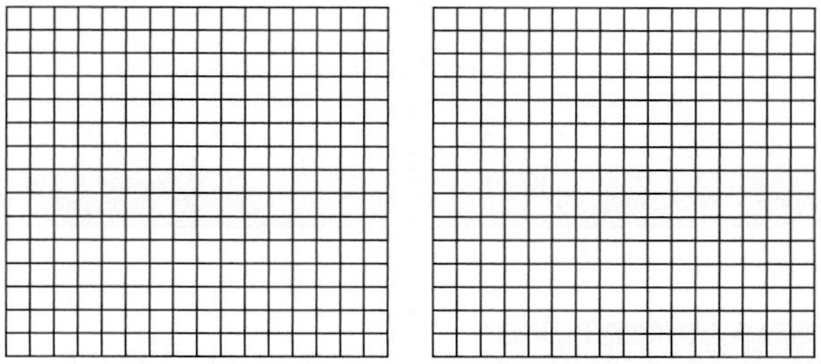

1. Are the numbers on the first and last lines of code identical? If so, does that mean that the rest of the numbers will be identical? Discuss this.

2. The number of bits (the simplest pieces of information, a 0 or a 1) to write each line can be shortened. For example, the fourth line in Example 12 can be written as

   13 0   2 1   1 0

   Is there a problem with this notation? What is the problem? Can you fix this problem?

3. To encode a character, say, the letter A, takes 8 bits = 1 byte. How many bits would it take to write *supercalifragilisticexpialidocious?* Each of the groups can find the number of bits it would take to write what they consider the longest word in the English language. Is the answer the same for both groups?

CHAPTER 4 Summary

SECTION	ITEM			MEANING	EXAMPLE
	Egyptian	*Babylonian*	*Roman*		
4.1	|	▼	I	1	
	|||||	▼▼▼▼▼	V	5	
	∩	◀	X	10	
	∩∩∩∩∩	◀◀◀◀◀	L	50	
	𓍢		C	100	
	𓍢𓍢𓍢𓍢𓍢		D	500	
	𓆼		M	1000	
	𓂭		$\overline{X}$	10,000	
	𓆐		$\overline{C}$	100,000	
	𓁨		$\overline{M}$	1 million	
4.2 A	a^n			$\underbrace{a \times a \times \cdots \times a}_{n\ a\text{'s}}$	$10^3 = 10 \times 10 \times 10$
	$(2 \times 10^2) + (4 \times 10^1) + (5 \times 10^0)$			Expanded form of 245	
4.2 B	$a^m \times a^n = a^{m+n}$			Law of exponents	$5^3 \times 5^6 = 5^9$
	$a^m \div a^n = a^{m-n}$			Law of exponents	$4^7 \div 4^2 = 4^5$
4.3 A	43_{five}			$(4 \times 5^1) + (3 \times 5^0)$	
4.3 B	10001_{two}			$(1 \times 2^4) + (1 \times 2^0)$	
	$A_{16}, B_{16}, C_{16}, D_{16}, E_{16}, F_{16}$			10, 11, 12, 13, 14, 15	
	17_{eight}			$(1 \times 8^1) + (7 \times 8^0)$	

CHAPTER 4 Practice Test

1. Write the following in Egyptian numerals:
   a. 63 b. 735
2. Write the following in decimal notation:
   a. ∩∩||| b. 𓍢∩∩|
3. Write the following in Babylonian numerals:
   a. 63 b. 735
4. Write the following in decimal notation:
   a. ▼ ◀◀▼▼ b. ▼▼ ◀▼
5. Do the multiplication 23×21 using the following:
   a. The Egyptian method of successive duplication
   b. The Egyptian method of mediation and duplation

CHAPTER 4 Practice Test

6. Write the following in decimal notation:
   a. LXVII b. $\overline{\text{XLVIII}}$

7. Write the following in Roman numerals:
   a. 53 b. 42 c. 22,000

8. Write the following in expanded form:
   a. 2507 b. 189

9. Write the following in decimal notation:
   a. $(3 \times 10^3) + (7 \times 10^2) + (2 \times 10^0)$ b. $(5 \times 10^4) + (9 \times 10^3) + (4 \times 10)$

10. Do the following computations in the usual way and in expanded form:
    a. $75 + 32$ b. $56 - 24$

11. Perform the indicated operations, leaving the answers in exponential form:
    a. $3^4 \times 3^8$ b. $2^9 \div 2^3$

12. Do the following computations in the usual way and in expanded form:
    a. 83×21 b. $54 \div 7$

13. Change the following to decimal notation:
    a. 203_4 b. 143_5 c. 1101_2

14. Change the following to decimal notation:
    a. 152_8 b. $A2C_{16}$

15. Convert the number 33 to the following:
    a. Base 5 b. Base 6

16. Convert the following to binary notation:
    a. 39 b. 527

17. Convert the number 47 to the following:
    a. Base 8 b. Base 16

18. Perform the indicated computations in the binary system.
    a. $\begin{array}{r} 1101_2 \\ +\ 101_2 \\ \hline \end{array}$ b. $\begin{array}{r} 1101_2 \\ -\ 111_2 \\ \hline \end{array}$

19. Perform the indicated computations in the binary system.
    a. $1101_2 \times 11_2$ b. $10110_2 \times 101_2$

20. Do the indicated computations in the binary system.
    a. $10110_2 \div 11_2$ b. $110111_2 \div 110_2$

21. Add $632_8 + 46_8$ in the octal system.

22. Multiply 37_8 by 5_8 in the octal system.

23. Subtract 46_8 from 632_8 in the octal system.

24. Divide 572_8 by 6_8 in the octal system.

25. Do the indicated computations in the hexadecimal system:
    a. $2BC_{16} + 5D_{16}$ b. $3C4_{16} \times 2B_{16}$

ANSWERS TO PRACTICE TEST

CHAPTER 4		What to Review *If You Missed It*		
QUESTION	**ANSWER**	**SECTION**	**EXAMPLE(S)**	**PAGE(S)**
1	a. ∩∩∩||| ∩∩∩ b. 𓍢𓍢𓍢𓍢∩∩||| 𓍢𓍢𓍢∩||	4.1	1	156
2	a. 23 b. 121	4.1	2	156
3	a. ▼ ▼▼▼ b. ◀▼▼ ◀▼▼▼▼▼	4.1	5	159
4	a. 82 b. 131	4.1	6	159
5	a. \1 21 \2 42 \4 84 8 168 \16 336 483 b. 23 (21) 11 (42) 5 (84) 2 168 1 (336) 483	4.1	3, 4	157, 158
6	a. 67 b. 48,000	4.1	8	160
7	a. LIII b. XLII c. $\overline{\text{XLII}}$	4.1	9	161
8	a. $(2 \times 10^3) + (5 \times 10^2) + (0 \times 10) + (7 \times 10^0)$ b. $(1 \times 10^2) + (8 \times 10) + (9 \times 10^0)$	4.2	1	165
9	a. 3702 b. 59,040	4.2	2	165
10	a. 75 + 32 = 107 $(7 \times 10) + 5$ $+(3 \times 10) + 2$ $(10 \times 10) + 7$ $= (1 \times 10^2) + 7$ $= 107$ b. 56 − 24 = 32 $(5 \times 10) + 6$ $(-)(2 \times 10) + 4$ $(3 \times 10) + 2$ $= 32$	4.2	3, 4	165, 166
11	a. $3^4 \times 3^8 = 3^{4+8} = 3^{12}$ b. $2^9 \div 2^3 = 2^{9-3} = 2^6$	4.2	5	166
12	a. 83 × 21: 83, 166, 1743 $(8 \times 10) + 3$ $\times (2 \times 10) + 1$ $(8 \times 10) + 3$ $(16 \times 10^2) + (6 \times 10)$ $(16 \times 10^2) + (14 \times 10) + 3$ $= (1 \times 10^3) + (6 \times 10^2)$ $+ (1 \times 10^2) + (4 \times 10) + 3$ $= (1 \times 10^3) + (7 \times 10^2)$ $+ (4 \times 10) + 3 = 1743$	4.2	7, 8	167

ANSWERS TO PRACTICE TEST

CHAPTER 4		What to Review *If You Missed It*		
QUESTION	**ANSWER**	**SECTION**	**EXAMPLE(S)**	**PAGE(S)**
12	**b.** $7\overline{)54}$ = 7R5; -49; 5 $7 \times 10^0\overline{)(5 \times 10) + (4 \times 10^0)}$ = (7×10^0) R (5×10^0); $-[(4 \times 10) + (9 \times 10^0)]$; (5×10^0)	4.2	7, 8	167
13	**a.** 35 **b.** 48 **c.** 13	4.3	2, 3	172
14	**a.** 106 **b.** 2604	4.3	4	173
15	**a.** 113_5 **b.** 53_6	4.3	5	173
16	**a.** 100111_2 **b.** 1000001111_2	4.3	5	173
17	**a.** 57_8 **b.** $2F_{16}$	4.3	6	174
18	**a.** 10010_2 **b.** 110_2	4.4	1, 2, 5	178, 180
19	**a.** 100111_2 **b.** 1101110_2	4.4	7	181
20	**a.** 111_2 R 1_2 **b.** 1001_2 R 1_2	4.4	10	182–183
21	700_8	4.4	3	179
22	233_8	4.4	8	181
23	564_8	4.4	6	180
24	77_8	4.4	11	183
25	**a.** 319_{16} **b.** $A1EC_{16}$	4.4	4, 9	180, 182

CHAPTER 5

Number Theory and the Real Numbers

God created the integers, all else is the work of man.
— LEOPOLD KRONECKER

Throughout its history, there have been several changes made to the game of basketball to increase its pace. After an extensive study and the use of ratios, the 24-second clock was added to the game. In Section 5.3, you will study ratios and their many uses as a problem-solving tool.

In Chapter 4 we took a journey through time and the numbers of antiquity. Now we shall explore more recent developments in the history of mathematics by studying the **natural** or **counting** numbers, their properties, and their uses. We will also look closely at some special natural numbers: the **primes.** Since ancient times, mathematicians have been fascinated by the divisors of numbers and on that basis classified the numbers as abundant, perfect, or deficient. Prime numbers have only two divisors, themselves and 1. The search for prime numbers continues today using supercomputers, and the results are used in such sophisticated areas as cryptography, the art or science dealing with making information unintelligible and for restoring the encrypted information to intelligible form.

As useful as they are, the natural numbers are not enough for the needs of everyday life. We need numbers to measure such things as subzero temperatures, yardage losses in a football game, and the extent of the national debt. In other words, we need **negative** numbers, which we shall consider when we study the **integers.**

Division of one integer by another yields a new number, a **rational** number. Rational numbers can also be written as decimals. We might imagine that the rationals would be the end of this numerical journey. However, the Pythagoreans, a secret society of scholars in ancient Greece (ca. 540–500 B.C.), made a stunning discovery. The **irrational** numbers defied their knowledge of number properties, because they could not write them as the ratio of two whole numbers.

The union of the rationals and the irrationals yields the **real** numbers. One of the most interesting real numbers is π, and we shall trace different attempts to find its value. We shall then learn how to operate with irrational numbers written using radical notation. Finally, we shall see how to find the sums of certain sequences of numbers. In Chapter 6 we shall find out how all these numbers are used in a new world: algebra.

5.1 Number Theory: Primes and Composites

GETTING STARTED

OBJECTIVES

A. Classify natural numbers as cardinals, ordinals, or for identification.
B. Determine if a natural number is prime or composite.
C. Find the prime factorization of a composite number.
D. Determine if a number is divisible by 2, 3, or 5.
E. Find the GCF, LCD, and LCM of two numbers.
F. Solve applications using GCF's and LCD's.

Human Side of Math

© D.E. Smith Collection, Rare Book and Manuscript Library, Columbia University

(1823–1891)

Leopold Kronecker was born on December 7, 1823, in Liegnitz, Prussia. Throughout his schooling, Kronecker's performance was diverse and brilliant; however, his greatest talent was in mathematics.

He finished an outstanding memoir on the theory of equations, which was published in 1853. Throughout his mathematical work, much of it on number theory and the theory of equations, he tried to make concise and expressive formulas tell the whole story. Most of Kronecker's papers have a strong arithmetic flavor; he wanted to explain everything in terms of the whole numbers and in a finite number of steps, a style that has had a great influence on modern mathematics.

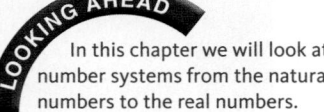

LOOKING AHEAD

In this chapter we will look at number systems from the natural numbers to the real numbers.

EMIRPS AND PRIMES

Do you know what an *emirp* is? It is a prime number that turns into another prime number when its digits are reversed; 13 and 31, 37 and 73 are emirps. A **prime number** is a number that has exactly two distinct factors, itself and 1. Prime numbers are used in cryptography, the encoding of secret messages. The lowest prime is 2 and the largest known prime at this time is $2^{43,112,609}$, discovered by Edson Smith at the University of California and the Great Internet Research Prime Search (GIMPS) on August 23, 2008. Here you will learn about prime and composite (not prime) numbers, factors, and divisors and their uses.

© UCLA Department of Mathematics

On August 23, 2008 Dr. Edson Smith (wearing cap) at the University of California, Los Angeles (UCLA) Mathematics Department, discovered the largest prime known at this time $2^{43,112,609} - 1$. The number has 12,978,189 digits. Source: http://tinyurl.com/3mp55o2.

The proper divisors of a number have fascinated mathematicians as far back as the Pythagoreans, who classified numbers according to the sum of their proper divisors (all the divisors, except the number itself) as follows:

Sum of Number's Proper Divisors	*Classification of Number*
More than the number	*Abundant* (12 and 20)
Equal to the number	*Perfect* (6 and 28)
Less than the number	*Deficient* (14 and 15)

You will learn more about prime, perfect, abundant, and deficient numbers in the Discovery section of Exercises 5.1. Can all numbers be written as a sum of primes: $10 = 5 + 5$, $18 = 11 + 7$, and $21 = 19 + 2$? (See problem 71, Exercises 5.1.) Here is another problem. 17 is prime and 19 is prime; their difference is 2. Also, 43 is prime and 41 is prime; their difference is 2. These pairs of numbers are called **twin primes.** Are there infinitely many twin primes? Nobody knows!

How can you find whether the number of primes is infinite? (See problem 15, Exercises 5.1.) One way is to find a formula that generates primes. Here is one such formula: $n^2 - n + 17$. When $n = 1, 1 - 1 + 17 = 17$, a prime number. When $n = 2, 2^2 - 2 + 17 = 4 - 2 + 17 = 19$, a prime number. Will this formula generate primes all the time? Can you find another formula?

The largest prime known as of this writing, $2^{43,112,609} - 1$, has 12,978,189 digits and was discovered by Edson Smith at UCLA and GIMPS. There is even a prime number page with the list of the largest 20 prime numbers at http://primes.utm.edu.

Look at the numbers on the keys of your calculator. They can be used to form a special set of numbers, called the set N of **natural** or **counting numbers** $\{1, 2, 3, \ldots\}$. In this section you will see some uses and properties of the set of natural numbers and one of its important subsets: the set of prime numbers.

A Classifying Natural Numbers

The natural numbers can be used in three different ways: as cardinals (for counting or showing how many), as ordinals (for indicating order in a series), or for identification. Thus, the number of elements in $A = \{a, b, c, d\}$ is 4. We then say that the **cardinal number of** A is 4 and write $n(A) = 4$. Read as "n of A is 4." Here, the number 4 is used as a **cardinal number.**

Numbers can also be used to assign an *order,* or position, to the elements of a set, that is, to indicate which element is *first, second, third,* and so on. We then refer to these numbers as **ordinal numbers.** Finally, numbers can be used for **identification.** Our Social Security numbers, passport numbers, and savings account numbers are used for identification purposes.

EXAMPLE 1 Classifying Numbers

Determine whether the underlined word is used as a cardinal or an ordinal number or for identification.

(a) If she kissed you once, would she kiss you two times?

(b) My account number is 123456.

(c) This is my first and last warning.

Solution

(a) Cardinal (b) Identification (c) Ordinal

Now consider some relationships among natural numbers and the terminology used to express these relationships. Suppose there are 40 students in your class and you wish to divide them into 5 equal groups. Each group will have 8 students, and no student will be left out. Thus, 40 divided by 5 is exactly 8 with no remainder. In other words, 5 is an **exact divisor** of 40, or more briefly, 5 is a **divisor** or **factor** of 40. Similarly, 63 divided by 7 is exactly 9, so 7 is a divisor, or factor, of 63. However, 7 is not a divisor, or factor, of 60 because 60 is not exactly divisible by 7.

B Prime and Composite Numbers

If 40 is written as a product of factors, the product—for example, 5×8—is called a **factorization** of 40. The 5 and 8 are factors (divisors) of 40, and the number 40 is a **multiple** of each of these factors. Note that 8 itself has divisors other than 8 and 1 (2 and 4), but the only divisors of 5 are itself and 1, so 5 is a prime number.

Definition of Prime and Composite Numbers

A natural number with exactly two distinct divisors (1 and itself) is called a **prime number** or is said to be **prime.**

Any number with more than two distinct divisors is called a **composite number** or is said to be **composite.**

The number 1 is by definition neither prime nor composite, because it has only one divisor (itself).

According to the definition, 5 is a prime number, and 40 and 8 are composite.

In the third century B.C., the Greek mathematician Eratosthenes devised the following procedure to find prime numbers: He listed all the numbers from 2 up to a given number (say, from 2 through 50, as in Figure 5.1). He concluded that 2 is prime, but every multiple of 2 (4, 6, 8, and so on) is composite because it is divisible by 2. He then circled 2 as a prime and crossed out all multiples of 2. Next, because 3 is prime, he circled it and crossed out all following multiples of 3. Similarly, he circled 5 (the next prime) and crossed out its multiples. He continued this process until he reached 11, the first prime whose square exceeds 50. We note that all the multiples of 11 $(11 \cdot 2, 11 \cdot 3, \text{and } 11 \cdot 4)$ were eliminated earlier when the multiples of 2 and 3 were crossed out. In the same way, the multiples of any prime larger than 11 were also eliminated. Hence, all the numbers left in the table were primes. Eratosthenes then circled those numbers. If the table had gone as far as 200, he would have had to continue his stepwise exclusion of composite numbers until he came to 17, the first prime whose square exceeds 200. (Can you explain why?) Because it sifts out prime numbers, the preceding method is called the **Sieve of Eratosthenes.**

	2	3	~~4~~	5	~~6~~	7	~~8~~	~~9~~	~~10~~
11	~~12~~	13	~~14~~	~~15~~	~~16~~	17	~~18~~	19	~~20~~
~~21~~	~~22~~	23	~~24~~	~~25~~	~~26~~	~~27~~	~~28~~	29	~~30~~
31	~~32~~	~~33~~	~~34~~	~~35~~	~~36~~	37	~~38~~	~~39~~	~~40~~
41	~~42~~	43	~~44~~	~~45~~	~~46~~	47	~~48~~	~~49~~	~~50~~

FIGURE 5.1

There is a page where you can test if a number is prime by simply entering the number. Go to http://mste.illinois.edu/dildine/js/prime.html and check it out!

EXAMPLE 2 Prime or Composite?

Is the number 197 prime or composite?

Solution

To answer this question, we must determine whether 197 has factors other than 1 and itself. Thus, we try dividing by the consecutive prime numbers 2, 3, 5, 7, 11, 13, ... Since 197 is not even, it is not divisible by 2. It is also not divisible by 3 or 5 or 7 or 11 or 13, as we can find by trial. Where do we stop? In trying to divide 197 by 3, 5, 7, 11, and 13, we notice that the quotient (answer) is ***greater*** than the prime trial divisor each time (for example, dividing 197 by 13 gives a quotient of 15 with a remainder, with the trial divisor 15 ***greater*** than 13). The Sieve of Eratosthenes (Figure 5.1) gives the next prime as 17. If we try to divide 197 by 17, we get a quotient (11) and a remainder, but this time the quotient 11 is ***less*** than the prime trial divisor 17 with a remainder, showing that 17 is not a factor of 197. Consequently, we need go no further (can you see why?), and we have shown that 197 is prime.

C Factorization

The following theorem shows the importance of prime numbers.

> **Theorem 5.1 Fundamental Theorem of Arithmetic**
>
> Every composite number can be expressed as a unique product of primes (disregarding the order of the factors).

Thus,

$$180 = 2 \cdot 2 \cdot 3 \cdot 3 \cdot 5 = 2^2 \cdot 3^2 \cdot 5$$

and

$$92 = 2 \cdot 2 \cdot 23 = 2^2 \cdot 23$$

The prime factorization of a composite number can be found by "dividing out" the prime factors of the number, starting with the smallest factor. Thus,

$$40 = 2 \cdot 20 = 2 \cdot 2 \cdot 10 = 2 \cdot 2 \cdot 2 \cdot 5 = 2^3 \cdot 5$$

and

$$63 = 3 \cdot 21 = 3 \cdot 3 \cdot 7 = 3^2 \cdot 7$$

Some students prefer to keep track of the factors by using a factor tree. Thus, to find the prime factorization of 40 and 63, we make two trees as shown.

Divide 40 by the smallest prime, 2.	$40 = 2 \times 20$	
Divide 20 by 2 to find the factors of 20.	$20 = 2 \times 10$	
Divide 10 by 2 to find the prime factors of 10.	$10 = 2 \times 5$	

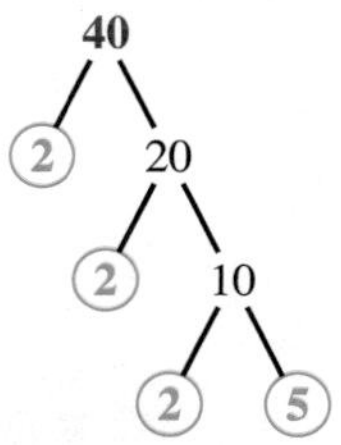

Thus,

$$40 = \textcircled{2} \times \textcircled{2} \times \textcircled{2} \times \textcircled{5} = 2^3 \times 5$$

Similarly,

Divide 63 by the smallest prime that divides 63, that is, by 3.	$63 = 3 \times 21$	
Now, divide 21 by 3 to find the prime factors of 21.	$21 = 3 \times 7$	

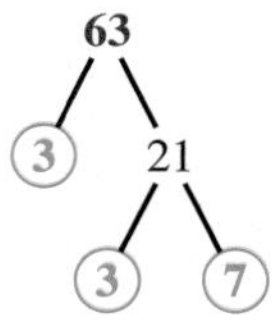

Thus,

$$63 = \textcircled{3} \times \textcircled{3} \times \textcircled{7} = 3^2 \times 7$$

To save time and space, we can write these computations using repeated divisions as follows:

Divide by 2 →	2	40	Divide by 3 →	3	63
Divide by 2 →	2	20	Divide by 3 →	3	21
Divide by 2 →	2	10	Divide by 7 →	7	7
Divide by 5 →	5	5			1
		1			

Reading downward, as indicated by the arrows, we get

$$40 = 2 \cdot 2 \cdot 2 \cdot 5 = 2^3 \cdot 5 \qquad \text{and} \qquad 63 = 3 \cdot 3 \cdot 7 = 3^2 \cdot 7$$

as before.

EXAMPLE 3 Writing a Number as a Product of Primes

Write 1440 as a product of primes.

Solution

2	1440
2	720
2	360
2	180
2	90
3	45
3	15
5	5
	1

Hence, $1440 = 2 \cdot 2 \cdot 2 \cdot 2 \cdot 2 \cdot 3 \cdot 3 \cdot 5 = 2^5 \cdot 3^2 \cdot 5$.

D Divisibility Rules

Finding the prime factorization of a number or determining whether the number is prime or composite can require a number of trial divisions. Some of these divisions can be avoided if we know the **divisibility rules** demonstrated in Table 5.1.

Table 5.1

Divisible by	Test	Example
2	The number ends in 0, 2, 4, 6, or 8.	345,678 ends in 8, so it is divisible by 2.
3	The sum of the number's digits is divisible by 3.	258 is divisible by 3, since $2 + 5 + 8 = 15$, which is divisible by 3.
5	The number ends in 0 or 5.	365 ends in 5, so it is divisible by 5.

There are other rules for divisibility by larger primes such as 7 and 11, but most people feel that these rules are too complicated to bother with; it is easier to check by direct division. To see other divisibility rules (for 4, 6, 8, 9, 10, and 12), see the table in the Using Your Knowledge section of Exercises 5.1.

EXAMPLE 4 Determining Divisibility by 2, 3, or 5

Which of the following numbers is divisible by 2, 3, or 5?

(a) 8925

(b) 39,120

(c) 2553

Solution

(a) 8925 is not divisible by 2. The sum of the digits $8 + 9 + 2 + 5 = 24$ is divisible by 3; hence, 8925 is divisible by 3. Since 8925 ends in 5, it is divisible by 5.

(b) 39,120 is divisible by 2, 3, and 5. Note that $3 + 9 + 1 + 2 = 15$ is divisible by 3, so 39,120 is divisible by 3. Since 39,120 ends in a 0, the number 39,120 is divisible by 5.

(c) 2553 is not divisible by 2 or 5, but is divisible by 3 because the sum of its digits, $2 + 5 + 5 + 3 = 15$, is divisible by 3.

E Using Prime Factorization: GCF and LCM

The number 8 is the **greatest common factor** of 16 and 24. We abbreviate greatest common factor by **GCF** and write GCF(16, 24) = 8. A fraction a/b is said to be in **simplest form** if GCF$(a, b) = 1$. In this case we say that a and b are **relatively prime.** If GCF$(a, b) \neq 1$, the fraction is reduced to lowest terms by dividing a and b by their GCF. The most commonly used way of finding the GCF of a set of numbers is as follows:

How to Find the GCF

1. Write the prime factorization of each number.
2. Select *all* the primes that are common to *all* the factorizations and apply to each such prime the smallest exponent to which it occurs.
3. The product of the factors selected in step 2 is the GCF of all the numbers.

The GCF is easier to find if you write the same primes in a column, as in the next example.

EXAMPLE 5 Finding GCFs to Reduce Fractions

Find the GCF (216, 234), and then reduce $\frac{216}{234}$ to lowest terms.

Solution

Step 1 We write the prime factorization of each number.

Pick the one with the smallest exponent in each column.

$$216 = 2^3 \cdot 3^3$$
$$234 = 2 \cdot 3^2 \cdot 13$$

Step 2 We select the *common* prime factors with their *smallest* exponents; these factors are 2 and 3^2.

Step 3 GCF(216, 234) $= 2 \cdot 3^2 = 18$.

To reduce the fraction $\frac{216}{234}$ to lowest terms, we divide out the GCF(216, 234), which we found to be 18. Thus, we write

$$\frac{216}{234} = \frac{18 \cdot 12}{18 \cdot 13} = \frac{12}{13}$$

Notice that we can obtain the 12 and the 13 from the respective prime factorizations. We just use all the factors except those in the GCF.

A second use of prime factorization occurs in the addition of fractions, where we need to find a common denominator. For example, to add $\frac{3}{8}$ and $\frac{5}{12}$, we must first select a common denominator for the two fractions. Such a denominator is any natural number that is exactly divisible by both 8 and 12. Thus, we could use $8 \cdot 12 = 96$. However, it is usually most efficient to use the **least** (smallest) **common denominator (LCD).** In our case, we note that

$$8 = 2^3 \qquad \text{and} \qquad 12 = 2^2 \cdot 3$$

To have a common multiple of 8 and 12, we must include 2^3 and 3 (remember we are looking for a multiple of *both* numbers), at the very least. Thus, we see that the **least common multiple (LCM)** of 8 and 12 is $2^3 \cdot 3 = 24$ (see margin), so the LCD of $\frac{3}{8}$ and $\frac{5}{12}$ is 24.

The procedure that we used to find the LCM (8, 12) in the Graph It can be generalized to find the LCM of any two or more natural numbers.

GRAPH IT

The numerical calculations in this section can be done with a grapher (graphing calculator), but be aware that calculator procedures vary. (When in doubt, read the manual!) Start at the home screen by pressing [ON] [2ND] [MODE]. To find the LCM of 8 and 12, tell the grapher you want a calculation by pressing [MATH] [▶]. Specify which type by pressing [8], which calculates LCMs; press 8 [,] 12 [)] [ENTER] to get the answer 24 as shown in the window. To get the Greatest Common Divisor GCD (or gcd) follow the same steps but press [9] instead of [8]. Can you find the LCM of three numbers with your grapher? Moral: You have to know your math, even with a great grapher!

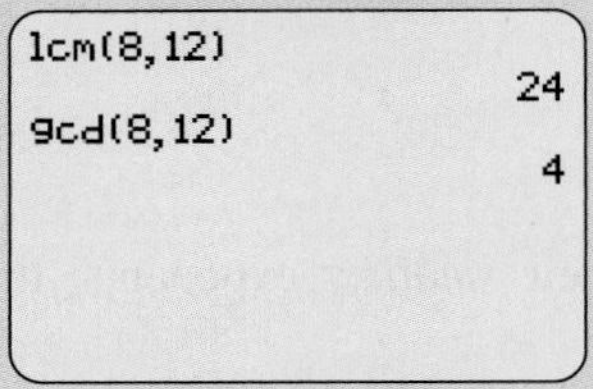

How to Find the LCM

1. Write the prime factorization of each number.
2. Select every prime that occurs, raised to the *highest* power to which it occurs, in these factorizations.
3. The product of the factors selected in step 2 is the LCM.

EXAMPLE 6 Finding LCMs to Add Fractions

Find the (18, 21, 28), and use it to add $\frac{1}{18} + \frac{1}{21} + \frac{1}{28}$.

Solution

Step 1

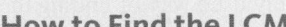

Pick the one with the greatest exponent in each column.

$$18 = 2 \cdot 3^2$$
$$21 = \quad 3 \cdot 7$$
$$28 = 2^2 \quad \cdot 7$$

Step 2 We select every prime factor (not just the common factors) with the greatest exponent to which it occurs and obtain 2^2, 3^2, and 7.

Step 3 $\text{LCM}(18, 21, 28) = 2^2 \cdot 3^2 \cdot 7 = 252$

We now use the LCM 252 to replace the given fractions by equivalent fractions with 252 as their common denominator. To obtain these equivalents, we refer to the factored forms of the denominators and the LCM. Since the LCM is

$$252 = 2^2 \cdot 3^2 \cdot 7 \qquad \text{and} \qquad 18 = 2 \cdot 3^2$$

we have to multiply 18 by $2 \cdot 7 = 14$ to get 252. Hence, we multiply the fraction $\frac{1}{18}$ by 1 in the form $\frac{14}{14}$ to get

$$\frac{1 \times 14}{18 \times 14} = \frac{14}{252}$$

Note: $\frac{1}{18}$ is *not* changed; it is written as the equivalent fraction $\frac{14}{252}$.

Note that the LCM is sometimes called the LCD, or Lowest Common Denominator, of two or more denominators.

The same procedure can be used for the other two fractions.

$$\frac{1}{21} = \frac{1 \times 12}{21 \times 12} = \frac{12}{252} \qquad \frac{1}{28} = \frac{1 \times 9}{28 \times 9} = \frac{9}{252}$$

Then we add.

$$\frac{1}{18} + \frac{1}{21} + \frac{1}{28} = \frac{14}{252} + \frac{12}{252} + \frac{9}{252} = \frac{14 + 12 + 9}{252} = \frac{35}{252}$$

Same denominators

Since $35 = 5 \times 7$ and $252 = 36 \times 7$, we can reduce the last fraction by dividing out the 7. This gives a final answer of $\frac{5}{36}$.

GRAPH IT

To do Example 7, enter 7 [÷] 24 [−] 5 [÷] 84 [ENTER]. You get a decimal! Don't panic; enter [MATH] [1] [ENTER] to convert the decimal to the fraction $\frac{13}{56}$. Caution: Subtraction is done using the blue key [−]. What does the gray key [(−)] do?

EXAMPLE 7 Subtraction of Fractions

Do the subtraction $\frac{7}{24} - \frac{5}{84}$.

Solution

To do this subtraction, we have to change the fractions to equivalent fractions with a common denominator. We factor the denominators to get

$$24 = 2^3 \cdot 3 \qquad \text{and} \qquad 84 = 2^2 \cdot 3 \cdot 7$$

Thus, the LCM of 24 and 84 is $2^3 \cdot 3 \cdot 7 = 168$. Consequently, we multiply the first fraction by $\frac{7}{7}$ and the second by $\frac{2}{2}$ to write each fraction with 168 as a denominator. Thus,

$$\frac{7}{24} - \frac{5}{84} = \frac{7 \cdot 7}{24 \cdot 7} - \frac{5 \cdot 2}{84 \cdot 2}$$

$$= \frac{49 - 10}{168} = \frac{39}{168} = \frac{3 \cdot 13}{3 \cdot 56} = \frac{13}{56}$$

PROBLEM-SOLVING

Hot Dogs and Buns

① **Read** the problem.

Can you ever apply these ideas to anything besides adding and subtracting fractions? You bet your buns! Have you noticed that hot dogs come in packages of 10, but buns come in packages of 8 (or 12)? What is the smallest number of packages of hot dogs (10 to a package) and buns (8 to a package) you must buy so that you have as many hot dogs as you have buns?

② **Select** the unknown.

We want to find the smallest number of packages of hot dogs and the smallest number of packages of buns you have to buy so that you have the same number of hot dogs and buns.

continued

③ **Think** of a plan.	What we need is the same number of hot dogs and buns; that is, we need the smallest multiple (LCM) of 10 and 8.
④ **Use** the LCM procedure.	$10 = 2 \times 5$ and $8 = 2^3$ Thus, the LCM is $2^3 \times 5 = 40$. But 40 *is not* the answer. We were asked how many packages of hot dogs (10 to a package) and buns (8 to a package) we needed. Since we need 40 hot dogs and 40 buns, we need *4* packages of hot dogs and *5* packages of buns.
⑤ **Verify** the solution.	4 packages of hot dogs contain 40 hot dogs. 5 packages of buns contain 40 buns.
Try Example 8 Now	Cover the solution, write your own solution, and then check your work.

© I. Bello

George wonders why there are buns left!

EXAMPLE 8 Hot Dogs and Buns

What is the smallest number of packages of hot dogs (10 to a package) and buns (12 to a package) you must buy so that you have as many hot dogs as you have buns?

Solution

As before, we write 10 and 12 in factored form.

$$10 = 2 \times 5 \qquad \text{and} \qquad 12 = 2^2 \times 3$$

The LCM is $2^2 \times 3 \times 5 = 60$. Thus, we need $\frac{60}{10} = 6$ packages of hot dogs and $\frac{60}{12} = 5$ packages of buns.

EXAMPLE 9 Reduced Distances

A motorist on a 2500-mi trip drove 500 mi the first day, 600 mi the second day, and 750 mi the third day. What (reduced) fraction of the total distance did he drive each of these days?

Solution

First day $\quad \dfrac{500}{2500} = \dfrac{1 \times 500}{5 \times 500} = \dfrac{1}{5}$

Second day $\quad \dfrac{600}{2500} = \dfrac{6 \times 100}{25 \times 100} = \dfrac{6}{25}$

Third day $\quad \dfrac{750}{2500} = \dfrac{3 \times 250}{10 \times 250} = \dfrac{3}{10}$

The procedures used to find the GCF and LCM of two or more numbers are very similar. If you are asked to find the GCF *and* LCM of two numbers, you can follow the procedure used below to find the GCF and LCM of 42, 28, and 210.

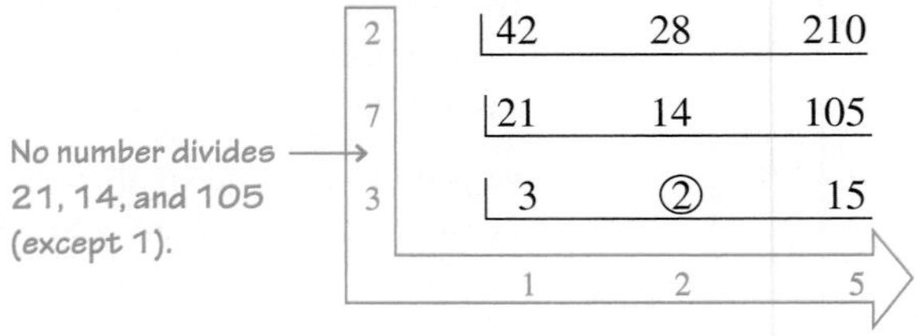

The LCM is $2 \times 7 \times 3 \times 1 \times 2 \times 5 = 420$.

> **Finding the GCF and LCM**
>
> 1. Write the numbers over a horizontal line and divide them by a prime divisor that is common to them all.
> 2. Repeat the procedure with the quotients until there is no longer any common divisor.
> 3. The product of all the divisors in steps 1 and 2 is the GCF (in the example, $2 \times 7 = 14$).
> 4. Divide by a prime factor common to two or more numbers. If any of the numbers is not divisible by this prime, circle the number and carry it down to the next line.
> 5. The LCM is the product of all the divisors in steps 1, 2, and 4 and the numbers in the final row.

5.1 EXERCISES

A Classifying Natural Numbers

In problems 1–5, identify the underlined items as cardinal numbers, as ordinal numbers, or for identification only.

1. My telephone number is 123-7643.
2. This is the second problem in this exercise.
3. It takes two to tango.
4. One, two, three, go!
5. First National Bank is number one.

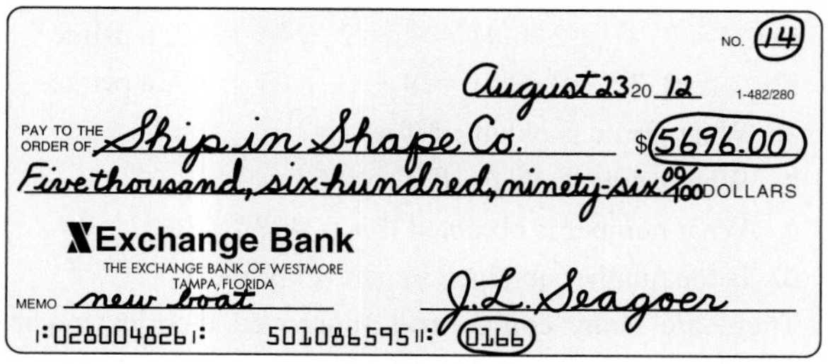

6. Three numbers (14, 5696, and 0166) are circled on the check. Identify each of these numbers as a cardinal number, an ordinal number, or for identification only.

B Prime and Composite Numbers

7. Continue the Sieve of Eratosthenes (Figure 5.1 on page 194), and find all the primes between 50 and 100.

In problems 8–11, use Figure 5.1 and the results of problem 7 to find how many primes there are between the given numbers.

8. 1 and 25
9. 25 and 50
10. 50 and 75
11. 75 and 100
12. Refer to Figure 5.1, and find
    a. the smallest prime.
    b. an even prime.
13. Refer to Figure 5.1.
    a. Find a pair of primes that are consecutive counting numbers.
    b. Can there be a second pair of primes that are consecutive counting numbers? Why?
14. Primes that differ by 2 are called **twin primes.** The smallest twin primes are 3 and 5. Refer to Figure 5.1 and find two other pairs of twin primes.
15. To show that there is no largest prime, Euclid (in about 300 B.C.) gave the following *proof by contradiction:* Assume that there is a largest prime; call it P. Now form a number—say, m—by taking the product of all the primes from 2 through P and adding 1 to the result. This gives $m = (2 \cdot 3 \cdot 5 \cdot 7 \cdot \cdots \cdot P) + 1$.
    a. m is not divisible by 2. Why?
    b. m is not divisible by 3. Why?
    c. m is not divisible by 5. Why?
    d. m is not divisible by any of the primes from 2 through P. Why?
    e. m is greater than P, so it cannot be a prime. Why?
    f. m cannot be a composite number. Why?

    Now we have a contradiction! Since m is a natural number greater than 1, it must be either prime or composite. But if our assumption that P is the largest prime is correct, then m cannot be either prime or composite. Therefore, the assumption is invalid, and there is no largest prime.

C Factorization

In problems 16–21, find all the factors (divisors) of each number.

16. 28
17. 50
18. 119
19. 128
20. 1365
21. 1001

In problems 22–27, find the prime factorization of each number or state if the number is prime.

22. 24 **23.** 41 **24.** 82
25. 91 **26.** 191 **27.** 148

In problems 28–31, find the natural number whose prime factorization is given.

28. $2 \cdot 3^2 \cdot 5^2$ **29.** $2 \cdot 5 \cdot 7^2$
30. $2 \cdot 3 \cdot 5 \cdot 11$ **31.** $24 \cdot 3 \cdot 5^2$

D Divisibility Rules

In problems 32 and 33, determine whether each number is divisible by 2, 3, or 5.

32. a. 468 **b.** 580 **c.** 795 **d.** 3942
33. a. 6345 **b.** 8280 **c.** 11,469,390

34. Find the smallest whole number multiple of 4 that leaves a remainder of 1 when divided by either 5 or 7.

35. How many whole numbers leave a remainder of 1 when divided into either 23 or 45?

E Using Prime Factorization: GCF and LCM

In problems 36–45, find the GCF of the given numbers or state that the numbers are relatively prime.

36. 14 and 210 **37.** 135 and 351
38. 315 and 350 **39.** 147 and 260
40. 368 and 80 **41.** 282 and 329
42. 12, 18, and 30 **43.** 12, 15, and 20
44. 285, 315, and 588 **45.** 100, 200, and 320

In problems 46–52, reduce each fraction to lowest terms.

46. $\frac{80}{92}$ **47.** $\frac{62}{88}$ **48.** $\frac{140}{280}$ **49.** $\frac{156}{728}$
50. $\frac{315}{420}$ **51.** $\frac{96}{384}$ **52.** $\frac{716}{4235}$

In problems 53–63, find the LCM of the given numbers and use it to add the fractions.

53. 15 and 55; $\frac{1}{15} + \frac{1}{55}$
54. 17 and 136; $\frac{1}{17} + \frac{1}{136}$
55. 32 and 124; $\frac{3}{32} + \frac{1}{124}$
56. 124 and 155; $\frac{3}{124} + \frac{1}{155}$
57. 180 and 240; $\frac{1}{180} + \frac{1}{240}$
58. 284 and 568; $\frac{3}{284} + \frac{1}{568}$
59. 12, 18, and 30; $\frac{1}{12} + \frac{1}{18} + \frac{1}{30}$
60. 12, 15, and 20; $\frac{1}{12} + \frac{1}{15} + \frac{1}{20}$
61. 285, 315, and 588; $\frac{1}{285} + \frac{1}{315} + \frac{1}{588}$
62. 100, 200, and 320; $\frac{1}{100} + \frac{1}{200} + \frac{1}{320}$
63. 200, 300, and 420; $\frac{1}{200} + \frac{1}{300} + \frac{1}{420}$

F Applications

64. *Common cold.* There is no cure for it, but here are some things you can do. Grandma was right—chicken soup actually is good for a cold!
One serving every 6 hours.
Zinc lozenges could help you get better sooner. One lozenge every 2 hours.
Aspirin, acetaminophen, and ibuprofen to relieve some symptoms: Two tablets every 4 hours.
You start your three medications (soup, lozenges, and aspirin) at 12 P.M. In how many hours will you have to take all three medications again?

65. *Common cold.* If in addition to the soup (every 6 hours), the lozenges (every 2 hours), and the aspirin (every 4 hours) you take a 12-hour nasal spray and you start your medications at 12 P.M., in how many hours will you have to take all four medicines again?

66. *Tamales and pastries.* The meat used for filling in the tamales and pastries is delivered every 2 days. If all items were fresh today, in how many days will they have fresh tamales (made fresh every 5 days), fresh pastries (made fresh every 4 days) filled with fresh meat (delivered fresh every 2 days)?

67. *Tamales and pastries.* La Cubanita Restaurant prepares fresh tamales every 5 days. Pastries are freshly made every 4 days. Andreas had fresh tamales and pastries today. In how many days will the tamales and pastries be made fresh again?

68. Do you know what is in your trash? $\frac{1}{5}$ is yard waste; $\frac{1}{10}$ is food waste; $\frac{1}{4}$ is metal, glass, and plastics; $\frac{1}{8}$ is wood, rubber, and miscellaneous. The rest is paper and cardboard, which can be recycled. What fraction of the garbage is paper and cardboard?

69. How do you use your water indoors? On the average, $\frac{3}{10}$ is used for showering and bathing, $\frac{1}{5}$ is used for laundry, $\frac{1}{20}$ is lost to leaky toilets, $\frac{3}{20}$ is used for dish washing and faucets. Where does the rest go? Toilet flushing! What fraction of the water is used for toilet flushing?

70. Mathematicians dream of finding a formula that will yield an infinite number of primes only when natural numbers are substituted into the formula. No such formula has ever been found, but there are formulas that give a large number of primes. One such formula is $n^2 - n + 41$. This formula gives primes for all natural numbers n less than 41. The following are examples:

For $n = 1$, $1^2 - 1 + 41 = 41$, a prime.
For $n = 2$, $2^2 - 2 + 41 = 4 - 2 + 41 = 43$, a prime.
For $n = 3$, $3^2 - 3 + 41 = 9 - 3 + 41 = 47$, a prime.

a. What prime is obtained if $n = 4$?
b. What prime is obtained if $n = 5$?
c. What number is obtained if $n = 41$?
d. Is the number obtained in part (**c**) prime?

71. There are many **conjectures** (unproved theories) regarding primes. One of these was transmitted to Leonhard Euler in 1742 by C. Goldbach. Goldbach conjectured that every even natural number except 2 could be written as the sum of two primes. For example, $4 = 2 + 2$, $6 = 3 + 3$, $8 = 3 + 5$, $10 = 5 + 5$, and so on.

a. Write 100 as the sum of two primes.
b. Write 200 as the sum of two primes. (*Hint:* Look at the given examples.)

72. In 1931, the Russian mathematician Lev Schnirelmann proved that every natural number can be written as the sum of not more than 300,000 primes. Another mathematician, I. M. Vinogradoff, has proved that every sufficiently large natural number can be expressed as the sum of at most four primes!

a. Try to write 20 as the sum of three primes.
b. Try to write 43 as the sum of four primes.

IN OTHER WORDS

73. Look at the definition of prime and composite and explain why the number 1 cannot be classified either as a prime number or as a composite number.

74. In view of your explanation in problem 73, how would you classify the number 1?

75. To determine that 211 is prime, start by trying to divide it by 2, 3, 5, and 7. What is the highest prime you will have to try in order to determine that 211 is prime? Explain.

76. Explain why Euclid's proof that there is no largest prime (problem 15) also shows that the number of primes is infinite.

USING YOUR KNOWLEDGE

The validity of the divisibility by 3 rule can be shown by using some of the properties of the natural numbers. For example, consider the number 2853. Since $10 = 9 + 1$, $100 = 99 + 1$, *and* $1000 = 999 + 1$, *you can write*

$$2853 = 2(999 + 1) + 8(99 + 1) + 5(9 + 1) + 3$$
$$= 2 \cdot 999 + 2 + 8 \cdot 99 + 8 + 5 \cdot 9 + 5 + 3$$
$$= 2 \cdot 999 + 8 \cdot 99 + 5 \cdot 9 + (2 + 8 + 5 + 3)$$

Now, as you can see, the first three terms of the last expression are all divisible by 3 because 999, 99, and 9 are all divisible by 3. Thus, the number is divisible by 3 if and only if the sum of the numbers in parentheses is divisible by 3. But the numbers in parentheses are exactly the digits 2, 8, 5, and 3 of the number 2853. Since the sum of these digits is 18, which is exactly divisible by 3, the number 2853 is also divisible by 3.

The reasoning used for 2853 applies to any natural number. Hence, the divisibility by 3 rule is valid.

77. If some of the digits of a number are 3s, 6s, or 9s, you can omit them in figuring the sum of the digits to check for divisibility by 3. For example, 2,963,396,607 is divisible by 3, because $2 + 7 = 9$ is divisible by 3. Explain this.

78. Is 5,376,906,391 divisible by 3?

79. The way in which we wrote

$$2853 = 2(999 + 1) + 8(99 + 1) + 5(9 + 1) + 3$$

shows that 2853 is divisible by 9 if and only if the sum of its digits is divisible by 9. Explain this.

The following table shows some other simple divisibility rules for the natural numbers:

Divisible by	If and Only If
4	The last two digits of the number form a number divisible by 4.
6	The number is divisible by both 2 and 3.
8	The last three digits of the number form a number divisible by 8.
9	The sum of the digits of the number is divisible by 9.
10	The number ends in 0.
12	The number is divisible by both 3 and 4.

The rule for divisibility by 8 can be obtained as follows: Consider the number 2,573,649,336. This can be written in the form $2{,}573{,}649 \times 1000 + 336$. *Since 1000 is divisible by 8, the entire number is divisible by 8 if and only if 336 is. Since 336 is divisible by 8, the given number is also divisible by 8. This reasoning applies to the natural numbers in general. Therefore, the rule is valid.*

80. Which of the following numbers are divisible by 9? by 6?

a. 405 **b.** 676
c. 7488 **d.** 309,907,452

81. Which of the following numbers are divisible by 4? by 8?

a. 1436 **b.** 21,408
c. 347,712 **d.** 40,924

82. Which of the following numbers are divisible by 10? by 12?

a. 4920 **b.** 943
c. 52,341,120 **d.** 60,210

DISCOVERY

A natural number is said to be ***perfect*** *if the number is the sum of its proper divisors. (**The proper divisors** of a number include all its divisors except the number itself.) For example, 6 is a perfect number because the proper divisors of the number 6 are 1, 2, and 3 and* $1 + 2 + 3 = 6$.

Some historians believe that the Pythagoreans were the first to define perfect numbers. In any event, it is certain that the Pythagoreans knew about these numbers and endowed them with mystical properties. In ancient Greek numerology, 6 was regarded as the most beautiful of all numbers; it is not only a perfect number (equal to the sum of its proper divisors), but it is also the product of all its proper divisors: $6 = 1 \times 2 \times 3$.

83. Can you discover why 6 is the smallest perfect number? This fact may be what led St. Augustine in about the year A.D. 400 to assert, "God created all things in 6 days because 6 is a perfect number."

84. The next perfect number after 6 is a number between 25 and 30. Can you discover what number this is?

85. The third perfect number is 496. Find its proper divisors and so prove that 496 is a perfect number.

86. In about the year A.D. 800, Alcuin remarked that the whole human race descended from the 8 souls of Noah's Ark, and he regarded this as imperfect. Can you discover why?

When the sum of the proper divisors of a number is less than the number, the number is called ***deficient.*** *For example, 4 is a deficient number because its proper divisors are 1 and 2, and* $1 + 2 = 3$, *which is less than 4. Similarly, 7 is a deficient number, because it has only 1 as a proper divisor.*

87. If n is any prime number, can you discover whether n is a deficient number?

88. It is known that there are infinitely many prime numbers. Can you use this fact to prove that there are infinitely many deficient numbers?

89. In problems 83–85, we found the perfect numbers 6, 28, and 496. The next perfect number is 8128. Aside from the fact that they are perfect numbers, what do you notice about these four numbers?

90. Look at the first four perfect numbers in binary that follow:

110
11100
111110000
1111111000000

If you continue this pattern, what do you think the next perfect number is? Can it be odd?

COLLABORATIVE LEARNING

How do you discover prime numbers? For small primes, the Sieve of Eratosthenes is acceptable, or you can go to a table of primes.

For a list of the first 1000 primes go to http://primes.utm.edu/lists/small/1000.txt.

To discover larger primes you need a new method. For many years mathematicians felt that numbers of the form $2^n - 1$ were always prime. Form two or more study groups and determine whether the following numbers are prime:

1. **a.** $2^{11} - 1$ **b.** $2^{17} - 1$ **c.** $2^{19} - 1$

2. In 1603; Pietro Cataldi conjectured that $2^n - 1$ was prime when $n = 23$, 29, 31, and 37. Let some members of the group check the result for 23 and 29 and other members check it for 31 and 37. Discuss your finding with the rest of the group.

3. In 1644, Marin Mersenne finally showed that $2^n - 1$ was prime for certain values of n. Find what values do make $2^n - 1$ prime.

4. Divide into several groups and prepare reports about the following topics:

a. Abundant numbers **b.** Frugal numbers
c. Equidigital numbers **d.** Extravagant numbers
e. Economical numbers

5.2 Whole Numbers, Integers, and Order of Operations

GETTING STARTED

OBJECTIVES

A. Find the additive inverse and the absolute value of integers.
B. Perform the four fundamental operations with integers.
C. Use the order of operations to evaluate expressions.
D. Solve applications involving integers.

THOSE ABSURD NUMBERS!

Look at the thermometer in the photo. It uses *zero, positive* numbers and *negative* numbers to measure temperature. The set $\{\ldots, -2, -1, 0, 1, 2, \ldots\}$ is called the set of *integers* and will be studied in this section.

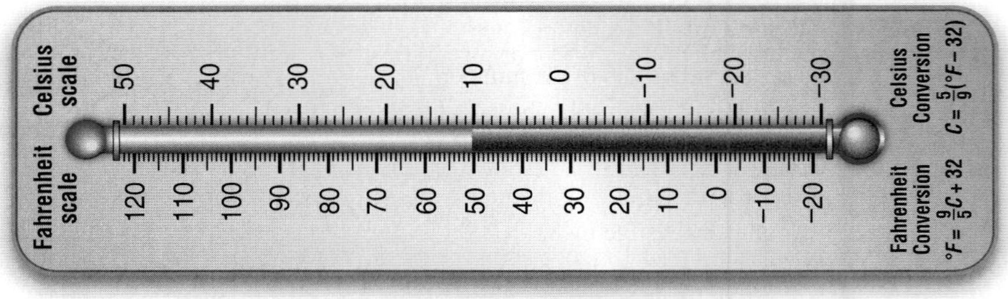

A Properties of Whole Numbers and Integers

The number 1 has the unique property that multiplication of any natural number a by 1 gives the number a again. Because the *identity* of the number a is preserved under multiplication by 1, the number 1 is called the **multiplicative identity,** and this property is called the **identity property for multiplication.**

Identity Property for Multiplication

If a is any natural number, then

$$a \cdot 1 = 1 \cdot a = a$$

It can be shown that 1 is the only element with this property.

Is there an **additive identity?** That is, is there an element z such that $a + z = a$ for every a in N? There is no such element in N but don't worry: the number zero (0) provides us with an **identity for addition.** Therefore, we enlarge the set N by adjoining this new element to it. The set consisting of all the natural numbers and the number 0—that is, the set $\{0, 1, 2, 3, \ldots\}$—is called the set of **whole numbers** and is denoted by the letter W. It is an important basic assumption that the set W obeys the same fundamental laws of arithmetic as the natural numbers do. Moreover, adding 0 to a whole number does not change the identity of the whole number. Thus, we have the following:

Identity Property for Addition

If a is any whole number, then

$$0 + a = a + 0 = a$$

As with the number 1, the number 0 is unique. It also can be shown that if a is any natural number, then

Properties of 0

$$a - 0 = a, \quad 0 \cdot a = 0, \quad \text{and} \quad 0 \div a = \frac{0}{a} = 0$$

Note that division by 0 is **not possible,** that is, $a \div 0 = \frac{a}{0}$ is **not defined.**

The set W is extremely useful when the idea of "How many?" is involved. However, the whole numbers are inadequate even for some simple everyday problems. For instance, the below-zero temperature on a winter's day cannot be described by a whole number, and the simple equation $x + 3 = 0$ has no solution in W. Because similar problems occur repeatedly in the applications of mathematics, the set of whole numbers is extended to include the **negative numbers,** $-1, -2, -3, \ldots$. This new set, called the set of **integers,** is denoted by the letter I, so $I = \{\ldots, -3, -2, -1, 0, 1, 2, 3, \ldots\}$. The set I consists of the following three subsets:

1. The **positive integers:** $1, 2, 3, \cdots$
2. The number **0**
3. The **negative integers:** $-1, -2, -3, \cdots$

For every positive integer n, there is a negative integer $-n$. To see this, we represent the integers using a **number line.** Draw a horizontal straight line, choose any point on the line, and label it 0. Then measure successive equal intervals to the *right* of 0, and mark the endpoints with the *positive* integers 1, 2, 3, and so on. Mark the endpoints to the *left* of 0 with the *negative* integers. The result is a number line, as shown in Figure 5.2. We graph the integers 3 and -3 by adding dots to the number line. Note that 3 and -3 are the *same distance* from 0 on the number line but in *opposite directions.* This is why 3 and -3 are **opposites.** The following are some other numbers and their opposites:

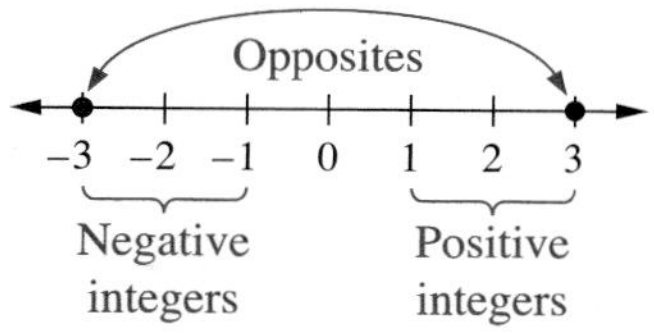

FIGURE 5.2

Number	*Opposite (Additive Inverse)*
5	-5
-8	$-(-8) = 8$
2	-2

EXAMPLE 1 Find the Additive Inverse of

(a) 9 (b) 7

Solution

(a) The additive inverse of 9 is -9.

(b) The additive inverse of -7 is $-(-7) = 7$.

GRAPH IT

Remember the gray key [(−)]? It calculates the additive inverse of a number. Thus, the additive inverse of 5 is -5 and the additive inverse of -12 is 12. Press [(−)] [(−)] 12 [ENTER] to verify this as shown.

```
-5
            -5
--12
            12
```

We can always verify that two numbers are opposites by addition. Thus, 5 and -5 and -12 and 12 are opposites because $5 + (-5) = 0$ and $(-12) + 12 = 0$. Because of this, 5 and -5, and -12 and 12 are also known as **additive inverses.** This discussion can be summarized as follows:

Additive Inverse Property

If n is any integer, then there exists a unique integer $-n$ such that

$$n + (-n) = (-n) + n = 0$$

The *numbers n* and $-n$ are said to be **additive inverses (opposites)** of each other.

Moreover, since 5 and -5 are the same distance from 0, we say that their *absolute values* are the same. The **absolute value** of a number a is **defined** as the distance between the number a and 0 on the number line and is denoted by $|a|$ (read "the absolute value of a"). The definition summarizes the discussion.

Absolute Value

The absolute value of a number n is its distance from 0 and is denoted by $|n|$. In general,

$$|a| = \begin{cases} n, & \text{if } n > 0 \\ 0, & \text{if } n = 0 \\ -n, & \text{if } n < 0 \end{cases}$$

Using the definition of absolute value, $|5| = 5$ and $|-5| = 5$, and $|-8| = 8$ and $|8| = 8$. Since $|a|$ represents a distance, $|a|$ is *never* negative. Also, since 0 is 0 units from 0, $|0| = 0$.

EXAMPLE 2 Find the Absolute Value of

(a) $|-6|$ (b) $|7|$ (c) $|0|$

Solution

(a) $|-6| = 6$ *−6 is 6 units from 0.*

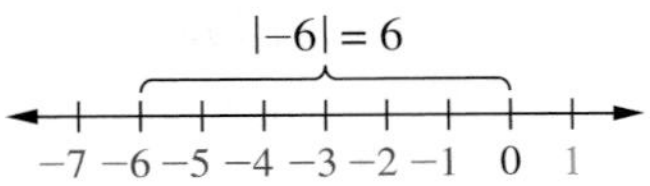

(b) $|-7| = 7$ *7 is 7 units from 0.*

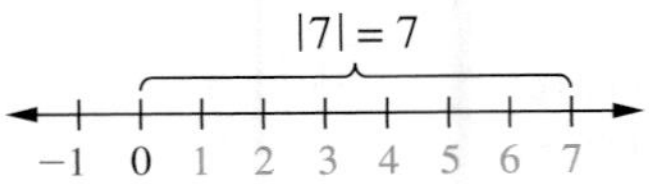

(c) $|0| = 0$ *0 is 0 units from 0.*

$|0| = 0$

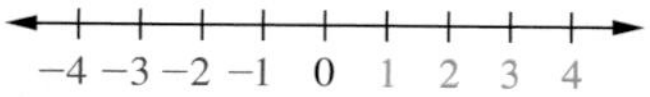

B Operations with Integers

The idea of **absolute value** can be used to define the addition of integers. Here is the procedure:

> **To Add Integers**
>
> 1. If both numbers have the *same* sign, add their absolute values and give the sum the common sign.
> 2. If the numbers have *opposite* signs, subtract their absolute values and give the difference the sign of the number with the greater absolute value.

Thus, $3 + 7 = 10$, $4 + 9 = 13$, $-3 + (-7) = -10$, and $-4 + (-9) = -13$. To add $-8 + 5$ we first notice that the numbers have *opposite* signs. So we subtract their absolute values and give the difference the sign of the number with the greater absolute value. Thus,

$$-8 + 5 = -(8 - 5) = -3$$

Use the sign of the larger integer. *Subtract the smaller integer from the larger one.*

(You can think about this problem in another way. You are adding a negative to a positive, but you have more negatives, so the answer is negative. How many more negatives do you have? 3, so the answer is -3.) Similarly,

$$+8 + (-5) = +(8 - 5) = 3$$

Use the sign of the larger integer. *Subtract the smaller integer from the larger one.*

EXAMPLE 3 Adding Integers

Add:

(a) $-8 + (-6)$ (b) $-10 + 6$
(c) $10 + (-6)$ (d) $10 + (-3) + 8 + (-2)$

Solution

(a) $-8 + (-6) = -(8 + 6) = -14$ *−8 and −6 have the same sign. Add their absolute value and give the sum the − sign.*

(b) $-10 + 6 = -(10 - 6) = -4$ *−10 and 6 have different signs. Subtract their absolute value and give the sum the + sign.*

(c) $10 + (-6) = 10 - 6 = +4 = 4$ *10 and −6 have different signs. Subtract their absolute value and give the sum the + sign.*

(d) We add the positives 10 and 8 and the negatives (-3) and (-2); then we add the results like this

$$10 + (-3) + 8 + (-2)$$

$$18 + (-5) = 13$$

Now that you know how to add integers, we can view the operation of subtraction as the *opposite* of addition, and any subtraction problem can be transformed into an addition problem as follows:

Subtraction Problem	*Equivalent Addition Problem*
$3 - 1$	$3 + (-1) = 2$
$10 - 7$	$10 + (-7) = 3$
$-3 - 5$	$-3 + (-5) = -8$
$2 - (-3)$	$2 + 3 = 5$

This motivates the following definition:

Definition of Subtraction

If a and b are any integers, the **subtraction** of b from a is defined as

$$a - b = a + (-b)$$

This means that subtracting b from a is the same as adding the inverse (opposite) of b to a.

EXAMPLE 4 Subtracting Integers

Subtract:

(a) $15 - 6$ (b) $-20 - 3$

(c) $-10 - (-8)$ (d) $8 - 13$

(e) $4 - (-5) - 3 + 7$

Solution

(a) $15 - 6 = 15 + (-6) = +(15 - 6) = 9$

(b) $-20 - 3 = -20 + (-3) = -(20 + 3) = -23$

(c) $-10 - (-8) = -10 + 8 = -(10 - 8) = -2$

(d) $8 - 13 = 8 + (-13) = -(13 - 8) = -5$

(e) Use the definition of subtraction to write as an addition problem, then add the positives together and the negatives together:

$$\begin{aligned} & 4 - (-5) - 3 + 7 \\ &= 4 + 5 + (-3) + 7 \\ &= 16 + (-3) \\ &= 13 \end{aligned}$$

We have learned how to *add* and *subtract* integers. We are now ready to **multiply** and **divide** integers. The result of *multiplying* two or more integers is called the **product** of the integers. Here is the notation we need:

Writing the Product of Two Integers

The **product** of the integers a and b can be written in four ways:

Using the multiplication sign: $a \times b$

Using the raised dot: $a \cdot b$

Using parentheses: $(a)(b)$ or $a(b)$ or $(a)b$

Using juxtaposition (writing a and b next to each other): ab

In each of these cases the integers being multiplied, a and b, are called **factors.**

Now, suppose you are on a 4-week diet and each week you *lose* 3 pounds (written as -3) Your weight loss for the 4 weeks is

$$4 \cdot (-3) \quad \text{or} \quad 4(-3)$$

Since you lost 3 pounds each of the 4 weeks, you have 4 losses of 3 pounds each. Thus, $4 \cdot (-3) = \underbrace{(-3) + (-3) + (-3) + (-3)}_{\text{four } (-3)\text{'s}} = -12$

Also note that $(-3) \cdot 4 = -12$. As you can see, the product of a *negative* and a *positive* Integer is *negative*. What about the product of two *negative* integers, say $-4 \cdot (-3)$? Look for the pattern in the following table!

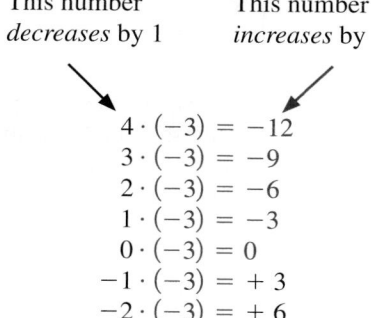

This number *decreases* by 1 (↘ first factor) This number *increases* by 3 (↙ product)

$$\begin{aligned} 4 \cdot (-3) &= -12 \\ 3 \cdot (-3) &= -9 \\ 2 \cdot (-3) &= -6 \\ 1 \cdot (-3) &= -3 \\ 0 \cdot (-3) &= 0 \\ -1 \cdot (-3) &= +3 \\ -2 \cdot (-3) &= +6 \\ -3 \cdot (-3) &= +9 \\ -4 \cdot (-3) &= +12 \end{aligned}$$

As you can see, $-4 \cdot (-3) = +12$.

Table 5.2 summarizes these results. Note that the product of integers with the same (*like*) signs is *positive* and the product of integers with different (*unlike*) signs is *negative*.

Table 5.2

Rules of Signs in Multiplication	Examples
1. Positive × positive = positive	$4 \times 3 = 12$
2. Positive × negative = negative	$4 \times (-3) = -12$
3. Negative × negative = positive	$(-4) \times (-3) = 12$

EXAMPLE 5 Multiplying Integers

Multiply:

(a) $9 \cdot 8$

(b) $-5 \cdot 3$

(c) $-5 \cdot (-4)$

(d) $7 \cdot (-6)$

Solution

(a) $9 \cdot 8 = 72$

(b) $\underbrace{-5 \cdot 3}_{\text{Unlike signs}} = -15$ Negative answer.

(c) $\underbrace{-5 \cdot (-4)}_{\text{Like signs}} = 20$ Positive answer.

(d) $\underbrace{7 \cdot (-6)}_{\text{Unlike signs}} = -42$ Negative answer.

As you recall from Section 4.2, and **exponent** is a number that indicates how many times another number, called the **base,** is a factor in a **product** so the rules of sign still apply. Thus, $(-2)^2 = \underbrace{(-2)(-2)}_{\text{Like signs}} = +4$ Positive answer. and $(-7)^3 = (-7)(-7)(-7) = (49)(-7) = -343$

$$49 \cdot (-7) = -343$$

Note that -2^2 is *negative,* so $-2^2 = -2 \cdot 2 = -4$

EXAMPLE 6 Integers Raised to a Power

Evaluate:

(a) $(-3)^2$ (b) -3^2 (c) $(-2)^3$ (d) -2^3

Solution

(a) $(-3)^2 = (-3) \cdot (-3) = 9$

(b) $-3^2 = -\underbrace{(3 \cdot 3)} = -9$

(c) $(-2)^3 = (-2) \cdot (-2) \cdot (-2) = 4 \cdot (-2) = -8$

(d) $-2^3 = -(2 \cdot 2 \cdot 2) = -8$

We are now ready to do division. Fortunately, the *sign rules* for division are similar to those of multiplication, since $a \div c$ means that $a = b \times c$, so we can summarize all the sign rules for $\times$ and $\div$ concisely.

Sign Rules for × and ÷	
When Multiplying or Dividing Numbers with	**The Answer Is**
Same (like) signs	+
Opposite (unlike) signs	−

EXAMPLE 7 Dividing Integers

Divide (if possible):

(a) $35 \div 7$ (b) $\frac{-12}{4}$ (c) $24 \div (-12)$

(d) $\frac{-10}{-5}$ (e) $\frac{0}{10}$ (f) $\frac{10}{0}$

Solution

(a) $35 \div 7 = 5$ (b) $\frac{-12}{4} = -3$ (c) $24 \div (-12) = -2$

(d) $\frac{-10}{-5} = 2$ (e) $\frac{0}{10} = 0$ (f) $\frac{10}{0}$ is not defined

C Order of Operations

Suppose we wish to evaluate the expression $8 - 3 \times 5$. Which evaluation is correct?

$$8 - 3 \times 5 = 5 \times 5 = 25 \quad \text{or} \quad 8 - 3 \times 5 = 8 - 15 = -7$$

In this example, -7 is the correct evaluation. To avoid this sort of ambiguity, there is an agreed and established order in which operations are to be performed. In such calculations, we always use the following order of operations:

Order of Operations (PEMDAS)

1. Evaluate all quantities inside parentheses. (P)
2. Do all exponentiations. (E)
3. Do all multiplications and divisions as they occur from left to right. (MD)
4. Do all additions and subtractions as they occur from left to right. (AS)

You can remember the order of operations if you remember
Please
Excuse
My Dear
Aunt Sally

Note: $8 \div 4 \times 2 = 2 \times 2 = 4$ Division done first (It *occurs* first.)

$8 \times 4 \div 2 = 32 \div 2 = 16$ Multiplication done first (It *occurs* first.)

Note: Sometimes we use the centered dot symbol "·" to indicate multiplication.

EXAMPLE 8 Simplifying Expressions

Simplify $8 \div 2^2 \cdot 2 + 3(5 - 2) - 3 \cdot 2$.

Given

$8 \div 2^2 \cdot 2 + 3(5 - 2) - 3 \cdot 2$

$= 8 \div 2^2 \cdot 2 + 3(3) - 3 \cdot 2$

$= 8 \div 4 \cdot 2 + 3(3) - 3 \cdot 2$

$= 2 \cdot 2 + 3(3) - 3 \cdot 2$

$= 4 + 3(3) - 3 \cdot 2$

$= 4 + 9 - 3 \cdot 2$

$= 4 + 9 - 6$

$= 13 - 6$

$= 7$

Solution

1. Evaluate quantities inside parentheses. $(5 - 2) = 3$
2. Do exponentiations. $2^2 = 4$
3. Do multiplications and divisions as they occur.
   Divide: $8 \div 4 = 2$.
   Multiply: $2 \times 2 = 4$.
   Multiply: $3 \times 3 = 9$.
   Multiply: $3 \times 2 = 6$.
4. Do additions and subtractions as they occur.
   Add: $4 + 9 = 13$.
   Subtract: $13 - 6 = 7$.

We may use more than one type of grouping, symbols, such as brackets [ ] and braces { }. When grouping symbols occur within other grouping symbols, computations in the innermost symbols are done *first*. Thus, to simplify

$$[2 \cdot (14 + 88)] + 12$$

we *first* add 14 and 88 (the computation inside the innermost grouping symbol), then multiply the result 102 by 2, and finally add 12. The procedure looks like this:

$[2 \cdot (14 + 88)] + 12 = [2 \cdot (102)] + 12$ Add inside parentheses: $14 + 88 = 102$.

$= 204 + 12$ Multiply inside brackets: $2 \cdot 102 = 204$.

$= 216$ Add $204 + 12 = 216$.

EXAMPLE 9 Simplifying Expressions

Simplify $20 \div 4 + \{2 \cdot 3^2 - [3 + (6 - 2)]\}$.

$20 \div 4 + \{2 \cdot 3^2 - [3 + (6 - 2)]\}$

$= 20 \div 4 + \{2 \cdot 3^2 - [3 + 4]\}$ Subtract inside parentheses $(6 - 2 = 4)$.

$= 20 \div 4 + \{2 \cdot 3^2 - 7\}$ Add inside brackets $[3 + 4 = 7]$.

$= 20 \div 4 + \{2 \cdot 9 - 7\}$ Do exponents $(3^2 = 9)$.

$= 20 \div 4 + \{18 - 7\}$ Multiply first inside braces $(2 \cdot 9 = 18)$.

$= 20 \div 4 + 11$ Then subtract inside braces $(18 - 7 = 11)$.

$= 5 + 11$ Next, divide 20 by 4 $(20 \div 4 = 5)$.

$= 16$ Finally, add $5 + 11 = 16$.

D Applications Involving Integers

The integers can be used to indicate points *above* (+) or below (−) average as shown in the graph on the following page.

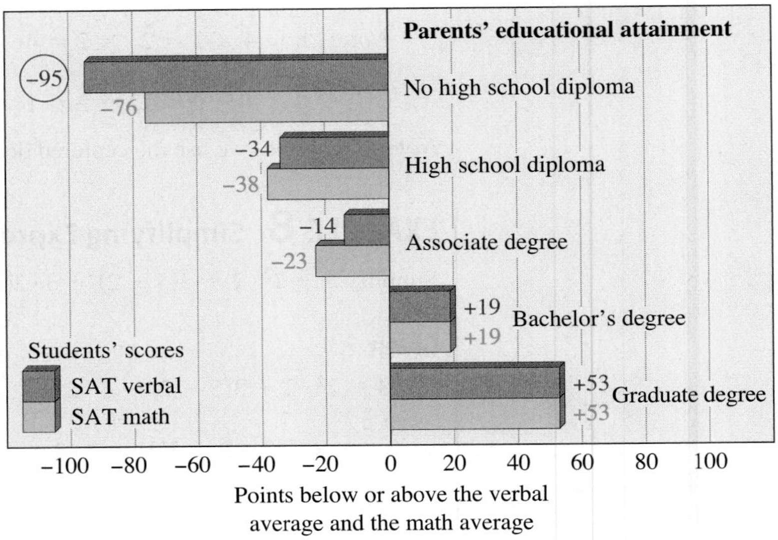

Source: The College Board.

FIGURE 5.3

EXAMPLE 10 Interpreting Graphs Using Integers

Is there a relationship between how much education your parents received (educational attainment) and your scores on the SAT? Figure 5.3 shows that the verbal scores for test takers with parents who had no high school diploma is −95 that is, 95 points *below* average. (By the way, the average score in math was 514 and in verbal 506.)

(a) What integer corresponds to the verbal scores of test takers whose parents had a high school diploma? What does the integer mean?

(b) What integer corresponds to the math scores of test takers whose parents had a graduate degree? What does the integer mean?

Solution

(a) The verbal scores for test takers whose parents had a high school diploma appear in red to the left of the row labeled "High school diploma." The score is -34. It means that the verbal score of the test taker was 34 points *below* the verbal average (506). Thus, the verbal score for the test taker was $506 - 34 = 472$.

(b) The math scores for test takers whose parents had a graduate degree appear in blue to the right of the row labeled "Graduate degree." The score is $+53$.

For your convenience, we summarize the properties of the integers under addition and multiplication.

Properties of Addition

1. The set of integers is closed with respect to addition. The sum of any two integers a and b is always an integer; that is, $a + b$ is an integer.
2. The set of integers has the commutative property of addition. For any two integers a and b, $a + b = b + a$.
3. The set of integers has the associative property of addition. For any three integers a, b, and c, $a + (b + c) = (a + b) + c$.
4. The set of integers has a unique identity (the number 0) for addition. $a + 0 = a$ and $0 + a = a$.
5. Each integer a has a unique additive inverse $(-a)$ in the set of integers. $a + (-a) = 0$.

Properties of Multiplication

1. The set of integers is closed with respect to multiplication. The product of two integers a and b is always an integer.
2. The set of integers has the commutative property of multiplication. For any two integers a and b, $a \cdot b = b \cdot a$.
3. The set of integers has the associative property of multiplication. For any three integers a, b, and c, $a \cdot (b \cdot c) = (a \cdot b) \cdot c$.
4. The set of integers has a unique identity (number 1) for multiplication. $a \cdot 1 = a$ and $1 \cdot a = a$.
5. Not all the integers have multiplicative inverses in the set of integers. For example, the multiplicative inverse for 3 would be a number b such that $3 \cdot b = 1$. But b is not an integer.

Besides these properties, the set of integers has the distributive property of multiplication over addition.

Distributive Property

$a(b + c) = ab + ac$ and $(a + b)c = ac + bc$

5.2 EXERCISES

A Properties of Whole Numbers and Integers

In problems 1–5, find the additive inverse of:

1. 9 **2.** 11 **3.** -10 **4.** -17 **5.** 0

In problems 6–10, find the absolute value of:

6. $|14|$ **7.** $|27|$ **8.** $|-24|$
9. $|-16|$ **10.** $|-19|$

B Operations with Integers

In problems 11–20, find the sum.

11. $-3 + 5$ **12.** $-18 + 21$
13. $8 + (-1)$ **14.** $19 + (-6)$
15. $-8 + 13$ **16.** $-9 + 11$
17. $-17 + 4$ **18.** $-18 + 9$
19. $-4 + 8 + 6 + (-2)$ **20.** $-17 + 5 + (-6) + 7$

In problems 21–30, write each problem as an equivalent addition problem and find the answer.

21. $3 - 8$ **22.** $8 - 3$
23. $3 - 4$ **24.** $-3 - 4$
25. $-5 - 2$ **26.** $-3 - 5$
27. $5 - (-6)$ **28.** $6 - (-3)$
29. $-3 - (-4)$ **30.** $-5 - (-6)$

In problems 31–60, multiply or divide.

31. $16 \cdot 2$ **32.** $9 \cdot 4$
33. $-7 \cdot 8$ **34.** $-10 \cdot 4$
35. $2 \cdot (-5)$ **36.** $9 \cdot (-9)$
37. $-4 \cdot (-5)$ **38.** $-6 \cdot (-3)$
39. $-7 \cdot (-10)$ **40.** $-9 \cdot (-2)$
41. $10 \div 2$ **42.** $\frac{14}{2}$
43. $\frac{-20}{5}$ **44.** $-50 \div 10$
45. $-40 \div 8$ **46.** $\frac{-30}{10}$
47. $150 \div (-15)$ **48.** $96 \div (-6)$
49. $\frac{140}{-7}$ **50.** $\frac{91}{-13}$
51. $-98 \div (-14)$ **52.** $-120 \div (-30)$
53. $\frac{-98}{-7}$ **54.** $\frac{-92}{-4}$
55. $\frac{-3}{0}$ **56.** $\frac{0}{-9}$
57. $\frac{0}{-33}$ **58.** $-10 \div 0$
59. $-19 \div 0$ **60.** $0 \div (-11)$

In problems 61–70, find the value.

61. $(-8)^2$
62. -8^2
63. -6^2
64. $(-6)^2$
65. -6^3
66. $(-6)^3$
67. $(-3)^4$
68. -3^4
69. $(-4)^3$
70. -4^3

C Order of Operations

In each of problems 71–84, use the order of operations to simplify the expression.

71. a. $-3(4 + 5)$ b. $-4(4 - 5)$
72. a. $-2(-3 + 1)$ b. $-5(-4 + 2)$
73. a. $-5 + (-5 + 1)$ b. $-8 + (-2 + 5)$
74. a. $-2(4 - 8) - 9$ b. $-3(5 - 7) - 11$
75. $(-2 - 4)(-3) - 8(5 - 4)$
76. $(-3 - 5)(-2) + 8(3 + 4 - 5)$
77. $6 \times 2 \div 3 + 6 \div 2 \times (-3)$
78. $8 \div 2 \times 4 - 8 \times 2 \div 4$
79. $4 \cdot 9 \div 3 \cdot 10^3 - 2 \cdot 10^2$
80. $5 \cdot (-2) \cdot 3^2 + 6 \div 3 \cdot 5 \cdot 3^2$
81. $20 \div 5 + \{3 \cdot 4 - [4 + (5 - 3)]\}$
82. $30 \div 6 + \{4 \div 2 \cdot 3 - [3 + (5 - 4)]\}$
83. $(20 - 15) \cdot [20 \div 2 - (2 \cdot 2 + 2)]$
84. $(30 - 10) \cdot [52 \div 4 - (3 \cdot 3 + 3)]$

D Applications Involving Integers

In problems 85–90, refer to the chart in Example 10.

85. What integer corresponds to the verbal score of test takers whose parents earned an associate degree? What was their score?
86. What integer corresponds to the math score of test takers whose parents earned an associate degree? What was their score?
87. What integer corresponds to the verbal score of test takers whose parents earned a bachelor's degree? What was their score?
88. What integer corresponds to the math score of test takers whose parents earned a bachelor's degree? What was their score?
89. What integer corresponds to the verbal score of test takers whose parents earned a graduate degree? What was their score?
90. Find the different between the integers corresponding to the verbal (−95) and math (−76) scores for a test taker whose parents did not earn a high school diploma.

The Environmental Lapse The *Environmental Lapse* is the rate of decrease of temperature with altitude (elevation): the higher you are, the lower the temperature. As a matter of fact, the temperature drops about 4°F(−4°F) for each 1000 ft of altitude. Source: www.answers.com.

Fill in the blanks in the chart:

	Altitude in (1000 ft)	Altitude × Rate of Change	Temperature Change
	1	1(−4)	−4°F
	2	2(−4)	−8°F
91.	5	____	____
92.	10	____	____
93.	15	____	____

The Metric Environmental Lapse In the metric system, the environmental lapse is about −7°C (negative 7 degrees Celsius) for each kilometer of altitude.

Fill in the blanks in the chart:

	Altitude in Kilometers	Altitude × Rate of Change	Temperature Change
	1	1(−7)	−7°C
	2	2(−7)	−14°C
94.	3	____	____
95.	5	____	____
96.	6	____	____

97. *Pikes Peak* You are at the base of Pikes Peak and the temperature is about 70°F. You climb to the top of the peak, about 14,000 ft. Give an expression that would tell you the temperature at the top. (*Hint*: Use the facts given for problems 91–93). What is that temperature in degrees Fahrenheit?
98. *Mount McKinley* Mount McKinley is about 20,000 ft high. If the temperature at the base is 70°F, what is the temperature at the top in degrees Fahrenheit?
99. *Mount McKinley* Mount McKinley is about 6000 m high, and the temperature at the base is 20°C. What is the temperature at the top in degrees Celsius? (*Hint:* Use the facts given for problems 94–96.)
100. *Mount Everest* You are at the base of Mount Everest, and the temperature is about 20°C. If you could climb to the top of Mount Everest, an elevation of more than 8000 m, what expression would tell you the temperature at the top? What is that temperature in degrees Celsius?

IN OTHER WORDS

101. Write in your own words the following rule of signs:

    Positive × positive = positive

102. Write in your own words the following rule of signs:

    Positive × negative = negative

103. Write in your own words the following rule of signs:

    Negative × negative = positive

    Two numbers having the *same* sign are said to have *like* signs. If two numbers have *different* signs, they are said to have *unlike* signs. Use the words *like* and *unlike* to summarize the rules of signs given in Table 5.2.

USING YOUR KNOWLEDGE

The oxidation number (or valence) of a molecule is found by using the oxidation numbers of the atoms present in the molecule. For example, the oxidation number of hydrogen (H) is +1, that of sulfur (S) is +6, and that of oxygen (O) is −2. Thus, we can get the oxidation number of sulfuric acid (H_2SO_4) as follows:

$$H_2SO_4$$

$$2(+1) + (+6) + 4(-2) = 2 + 6 - 8 = 0$$

Use this idea to find the oxidation number of

104. Phosphate, PO_4, if the oxidation number of phosphorus (P) is +5 and that of oxygen (O) is −2.

105. Sodium dichromate, $Na_2Cr_2O_7$, if the oxidation number of sodium (Na) is +1, that of chromium (Cr) is +6, and that of oxygen (O) is −2.

106. Baking soda, $NaHCO_3$, if the oxidation number of sodium (Na) is +1, that of hydrogen (H) is +1, that of carbon (C) is +4, and that of oxygen (O) is −2.

COLLABORATIVE LEARNING

Form two or more groups.

1. Let each group select three integers from 0 to 9, and subtract its *reversal* (the *reversal* of 856 is 658). Then, if the difference is *positive*, add its reversal. If the difference is *negative*, subtract its reversal. Here are three possibilities for three numbers.

856	159	872
− 658	− 951	− 278
198	− 792	594
+ 891	− 297	+ 495

What answer did your group get? Did all groups get the same answer? Why do you think this works?

5.3 Operations with Rational Numbers, Expanded and Scientific Notation

GETTING STARTED

OBJECTIVES

A. Use the Fundamental Property of Rational Numbers to reduce and write fractions with a specified denominator.

B. Add, subtract, multiply, divide, and simplify fractions using the order of operations.

C. Write decimals in expanded form.

D. Convert and perform addition, subtraction, multiplication and division of decimals in scientific notation.

E. Perform operations using decimals.

BASKETBALL AND RATIOS

During the 1953–1954 basketball season, the NBA had a problem with the game: It was boring! Fans wanted plenty of action, shooting, and scoring, but if a team had an early lead, their best ball handler would dribble in the backcourt until he was fouled. How could the game be speeded up? Danny Biasone, the owner of the Syracuse Nationals, an obscure team from upstate New York, thought that more shots could be encouraged by limiting the time a team could have the ball. But how many seconds should be allowed between shots? He figured out that in a fast-paced game, a team would take about 60 shots during the 48 minutes the game lasted (4 quarters of 12 minutes each). He then looked at the ratio

$$\frac{\text{Seconds}}{\text{Shots}}$$

Now, the number of shots for both teams combined would be 2×60, and the number of seconds in each game is 48×60. Thus, the ratio becomes

$$\frac{\text{Seconds}}{\text{Shots}} = \frac{48 \times 60}{2 \times 60} = \frac{24}{1}$$

and now you know how the 24-second shot clock was born!

In this section you will study the rational numbers, which are numbers that can be written in the form *a*/*b*, where *a* and *b* are integers, and the operations that can be performed using these numbers.

In Section 5.2 we extended the set of natural numbers and obtained the set of integers. As we saw in studying the multiplication of integers, not all the integers have multiplicative inverses; for instance, there is no integer b such that $3 \cdot b = 1$. Just as the lack of additive inverses impairs the usefulness of the set of natural numbers, so does the lack of multiplicative inverses impair the usefulness of the set of integers.

A Rational Numbers as Fractions

The difficulty lies in the fact that the set of integers is not closed under division; division of two integers can produce fractions such as $\frac{3}{4}, \frac{5}{7}, \frac{8}{3}$, and so on. Thus, we extend the system of integers to include such fractions and call the resulting system the set of **rational numbers.** The set of rational numbers is symbolized by the letter Q. (Note that a common fraction is often called a *ratio;* hence the name rational numbers.)

Definition of a Rational Number

A **rational number** is a number that can be put in the form

$$\frac{a}{b}, \quad \text{where } a \text{ and } b \text{ are integers and } b \neq 0$$

Cartoon by Paul Kicklighter.

The following are some important facts about rational numbers:

1. Every integer is a rational number because the integers can be written in the form $\cdots, -\frac{2}{1}, -\frac{1}{1}, \frac{0}{1}, \frac{1}{1}, \frac{2}{1}, \ldots$.
2. The integer a in the definition of a rational number is called the **numerator,** and the integer b is called the **denominator.**
3. The restriction $b \neq 0$ is necessary. By the definition of division, if $a/b = c$, then $a = bc$. So, if $b = 0$, this means that $a = 0$. Thus, if $a \neq 0$, then the attempted division by 0 leads to a contradiction. If $a = 0$, then the equation $0 = 0 \cdot c$ is true for every number c; that is, the quotient c is not uniquely defined. The only way to avoid this dilemma is to **forbid division by 0.**
4. The definition of a rational number includes the words "a number that *can* [emphasis here] be put in the form a/b, where a and b are integers and $b \neq 0$." Why could it not say "a number of the form a/b, where a and b are integers and $b \neq 0$"? To answer this question, consider the number $0.333 \cdots$. This number is *not* in the form a/b, but because $0.333 \cdots = \frac{1}{3}$, it *can* be put in the form a/b, where $a = 1$ and $b = 3$. Similarly, $1\frac{3}{4}$ is not in the form a/b. But because $1\frac{3}{4} = \frac{7}{4}$, the number *can* be put in the form a/b, where $a = 7$ and $b = 4$. From this discussion we conclude that $0.333 \cdots$ and $1\frac{3}{4}$ are rational numbers.

How do we recognize the fact that $\frac{1}{3}$ and $\frac{3}{9}$ represent the same rational number? To do this, we need to define the equality of rational numbers.

Definition of the Equality of Rational Numbers

$$\frac{a}{b} = \frac{c}{d} \quad \text{if and only if} \quad ad = bc$$

Thus, $\frac{1}{3} = \frac{3}{9}$ because $1 \cdot 9 = 3 \cdot 3$, and $\frac{1}{8} = \frac{4}{32}$ because $1 \cdot 32 = 8 \cdot 4$. Using the definition of the equality of rational numbers, we can obtain the following useful result:

Theorem 5.2 Fundamental Property of Rational Numbers

If a, b, and k are integers, where $b \neq 0$ and $k \neq 0$, then

$$\frac{a}{b} = \frac{ak}{bk}$$

Theorem 5.2 enables us to reduce $\frac{4}{6}$ by writing

$$\frac{4}{6} = \frac{2 \cdot 2}{3 \cdot 2}$$

and "canceling" the 2s to obtain $\frac{4}{6} = \frac{2}{3}$. The theorem also assures us that if we multiply the numerator and denominator of a fraction by the same nonzero number k, the fraction is unchanged in value. Thus,

$$\frac{1}{2} = \frac{1 \cdot 2}{2 \cdot 2} = \frac{2}{4} \quad \text{and} \quad \frac{1}{8} = \frac{1 \cdot 3}{8 \cdot 3} = \frac{3}{24}$$

EXAMPLE 1 Reducing Fractions

Using Theorem 5.2 to reduce $\frac{10}{30}$.

Solution

$$\frac{10}{30} = \frac{1 \cdot 10}{3 \cdot 10} = \frac{1}{3}$$

EXAMPLE 2 Fractions with Specified Denominators

Using Theorem 5.2, find a rational number with a denominator of 12 and equal to $\frac{5}{6}$.

Solution

$$\frac{5}{6} = \frac{5 \cdot 2}{6 \cdot 2} = \frac{10}{12}$$

B Operations with Rational Numbers

We now define the operations of addition, subtraction, multiplication, and division of rational numbers.

Definition of the Product of Two Rational Numbers

The **product** of two rational numbers a/b and c/d is defined by

$$\frac{a}{b} \cdot \frac{c}{d} = \frac{ac}{bd}$$

Thus,

$$\frac{2}{7} \cdot \frac{3}{5} = \frac{2 \cdot 3}{7 \cdot 5} = \frac{6}{35}$$

Definition of the Sum of Two Rational Numbers

The **sum** of two rational numbers a/b and c/d is defined as

$$\frac{a}{b} + \frac{c}{d} = \frac{ad + bc}{bd}$$

For example,

$$\frac{2}{7} + \frac{3}{5} = \frac{(2 \cdot 5) + (7 \cdot 3)}{7 \cdot 5} = \frac{10 + 21}{35} = \frac{31}{35}$$

Note: If $d = b$, it is easy to show that the definition of the sum of two rational numbers gives

$$\frac{a}{b} + \frac{c}{b} = \frac{a + c}{b}$$

as we should expect.

This means that to add two fractions with the **same** denominator ***b*,** you simply add the numerators a and c and keep the denominator ***b*.**

Definition of the Difference of Two Rational Numbers

The **difference** of two rational numbers a/b and c/d is defined as

$$\frac{a}{b} - \frac{c}{d} = \frac{a}{b} + \frac{-c}{d} = \frac{ad - bc}{bd}$$

Thus,

$$\frac{1}{3} - \frac{1}{4} = \frac{1}{3} + \frac{-1}{4} = \frac{(1 \cdot 4) - (3 \cdot 1)}{3 \cdot 4} = \frac{4 - 3}{12} = \frac{1}{12}$$

Now suppose that we want to do the addition $\frac{3}{4} + \frac{1}{16}$. Using the definition of the sum of two rational numbers, we proceed as follows:

$$\frac{3}{4} + \frac{1}{16} = \frac{(3 \cdot 16) + (4 \cdot 1)}{4 \cdot 16} = \frac{48 + 4}{64} = \frac{52}{64} = \frac{13}{16}$$

However, it is easier to use the LCD of 4 and 16 (instead of 64).

$$\frac{3}{4} = \frac{3 \cdot 4}{4 \cdot 4} = \frac{12}{16}$$

and thus,

$$\frac{3}{4} + \frac{1}{16} = \frac{12}{16} + \frac{1}{16} = \frac{13}{16}$$

The number 16 is the *least common denominator* (LCD) of $\frac{3}{4}$ and $\frac{1}{16}$. Recall from Section 5.1 that this number is the LCM (least common multiple) of the given denominators, so it can be obtained by following the procedure discussed in Section 5.1. The next example illustrates the use of this idea.

EXAMPLE 3 Adding Fractions

Perform the addition $\frac{3}{8} + \frac{7}{36}$.

Solution

First find the LCM of 8 and 36 by using the procedure given in Section 5.1,

$$\begin{aligned} 8 &= 2^3 \\ 36 &= 2^2 \cdot 3^2 \\ \hline \text{LCM} &= 2^3 \cdot 3^2 = 72 \end{aligned}$$

or you can try the multiples of 36 until you obtain the first one that can be divided by 8. Since the first two multiples of 36 are 36 and then 72 and the 72 is divisible by 8, the LCM is 72. In either case LCM(8, 36) = 72. Thus,

$$\frac{3}{8} = \frac{3 \cdot 9}{8 \cdot 9} = \frac{27}{72} \quad \text{and} \quad \frac{7}{36} = \frac{7 \cdot 2}{36 \cdot 2} = \frac{14}{72}$$

so that

$$\frac{3}{8} + \frac{7}{36} = \frac{27}{72} + \frac{14}{72} = \frac{41}{72}$$

using 72 as the LCD.

Definition of the Reciprocal of a Rational Number

The **reciprocal** of a rational number

$$\frac{a}{b} \quad \text{is} \quad \frac{b}{a}, \qquad a \neq 0 \text{ and } b \neq 0$$

Note that

$$\frac{a}{b} \cdot \frac{b}{a} = 1$$

Thus, the product of any nonzero rational number and its reciprocal is 1. For this reason, the reciprocal of a rational number is its **multiplicative inverse.**

GRAPH IT

The reciprocal of $-\frac{3}{4}$ is obtained by entering ([(−)] [3] [÷] 4) [x^{-1}] [MATH] [1] [ENTER].

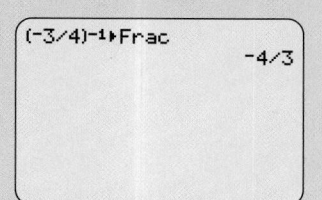

```
(-3/4)-1▸Frac
                -4/3
```

How would you find the reciprocal of $1\frac{5}{8}$?

EXAMPLE 4 Finding Reciprocals

Find the reciprocals of the following:

(a) $\frac{1}{3}$ **(b)** $-\frac{3}{4}$ **(c)** $1\frac{3}{8}$

Solution

(a) The reciprocal of $\frac{1}{3}$ is $\frac{3}{1} = 3$.

(b) The reciprocal of $-\frac{3}{4}$ is $-\frac{4}{3}$. Note that $\left(-\frac{3}{4}\right)\left(-\frac{4}{3}\right) = (-1)(-1)\left(\frac{3}{4}\right)\left(\frac{4}{3}\right) = 1$.

(c) We first write $1\frac{3}{8}$ in the form *a*/*b*. Because $1\frac{3}{8} = \frac{11}{8}$, the reciprocal of $1\frac{3}{8}$ is $\frac{8}{11}$.

Note: The reciprocal of any negative rational number is always negative, as shown in part (b) of Example 4.

Definition of the Quotient of Two Rational Numbers

The quotient of two rational numbers a/b and c/d is defined as

$$\frac{a}{b} \div \frac{c}{d} = \frac{a}{b} \cdot \frac{d}{c}, \qquad c \neq 0$$

Briefly, we say "to *divide* by a number, *multiply* by its reciprocal."

$$\frac{1}{3} \div \frac{2}{7} = \frac{1}{3} \cdot \frac{7}{2} = \frac{7}{6} \quad \text{and} \quad \frac{4}{5} \div \frac{3}{5} = \frac{4}{5} \cdot \frac{5}{3} = \frac{4 \cdot 5}{3 \cdot 5} = \frac{4}{3}$$

Reciprocal (arrows point to $\frac{2}{7}$ and $\frac{7}{2}$) — Reciprocal (arrows point to $\frac{3}{5}$ and $\frac{5}{3}$)

As a consequence of these definitions of the basic operations, the set of rational numbers under addition and multiplication is closed and has the associative, commutative, and distributive properties. It also has additive identity (0) and additive inverses. With respect to multiplication, the set of rational numbers has a multiplicative identity (1), and every rational number except 0 has a multiplicative inverse (its reciprocal).

It can be shown that the definitions we have given are the only possible ones if we require that the rational numbers obey the same basic laws of arithmetic as the integers do. (Just imagine how unpleasant it would be if $\frac{1}{2} + \frac{1}{4} \neq \frac{1}{4} + \frac{1}{2}$.)

If you think of a and b as positive numbers, you can see that the rules of signs in division are exactly the same as those in multiplication: The quotient of two numbers with like signs is positive and of two numbers with unlike signs is negative. For example,

$$\frac{9}{3} = \frac{-9}{-3} = 3 \quad \text{and} \quad \frac{-9}{3} = \frac{9}{-3} = -3$$

If the operations under discussion involve **mixed numbers,** first write the mixed numbers as fractions. Thus, to add $2\frac{3}{4} + \frac{5}{6}$, note that $2\frac{3}{4} = 2 + \frac{3}{4} = \frac{8}{4} + \frac{3}{4} = \frac{11}{4}$. A simpler way to do this (in just one step) is

$$2\frac{3}{4} = \frac{2 \cdot 4 + 3}{4} = \frac{11}{4}$$

Same denominator (arrows point to the 4 in $2\frac{3}{4}$ and the denominator 4)

Thus,

$$2\frac{3}{4} + \frac{5}{6} = \frac{11}{4} + \frac{5}{6} = \frac{33}{12} + \frac{10}{12} = \frac{43}{12} = 3\frac{7}{12}$$

or, separating the whole and fractional parts,

$$2\frac{3}{4} + \frac{5}{6} = 2 + \frac{3}{4} + \frac{5}{6} = 2 + \frac{9}{12} + \frac{10}{12} = 2 + \frac{19}{12} = \frac{24}{12} + \frac{19}{12} = \frac{43}{12} = 3\frac{7}{12}$$

Note that to convert the fraction $\frac{43}{12}$ to a mixed number, we divide 43 by 12 (the answer is 3) and write the remainder 7 as the numerator of the remaining fraction, with the denominator unchanged.

EXAMPLE 5 Operations with Fractions

Perform the following indicated operations:

(a) $3\frac{1}{4} + 4\frac{1}{6}$ (b) $5 - 2\frac{1}{7}$

(c) $3\frac{1}{4} \times (-8)$ (d) $21 \div \left(-4\frac{1}{5}\right)$

GRAPH IT

To verify part (d), enter 21 [÷] ([(−)] 4 [−] 1 [÷] 5) [ENTER] to get −5 as shown in the window.

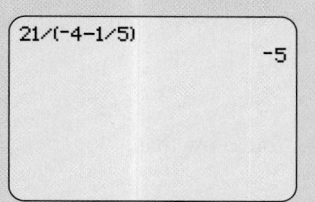

```
21/(-4-1/5)
                -5
```

Did you notice that $-4\frac{1}{5}$ was entered as $\left(-4 - \frac{1}{5}\right)$?

Solution

(a) We first change the mixed numbers to fractions.

$$3\frac{1}{4} = \frac{3 \times 4 + 1}{4} = \frac{13}{4} \quad \text{and} \quad 4\frac{1}{6} = \frac{4 \times 6 + 1}{6} = \frac{25}{6}$$

We then obtain the LCD, which is 12, and change the fractions to equivalent ones with 12 as a denominator.

$$3\frac{1}{4} + 4\frac{1}{6} = \frac{13}{4} + \frac{25}{6} = \frac{39}{12} + \frac{50}{12} = \frac{89}{12} = 7\frac{5}{12}$$

or, separating the whole and fractional parts,

$$3\frac{1}{4} + 4\frac{1}{6} = (3 + 4) + \frac{1}{4} + \frac{1}{6}$$

$$= 7 + \frac{3}{12} + \frac{2}{12} = 7 + \frac{5}{12} = 7\frac{5}{12}$$

(c) Write $3\frac{1}{4}$ as $\frac{13}{4}$, and recall that the product of two numbers with unlike signs is negative.

$$3\frac{1}{4} \times (-8) = \frac{13}{\cancel{4}_{1}} \times (-\cancel{8}^{-2}) = -26$$

(d) Change the $-4\frac{1}{5}$ to $-\frac{21}{5}$, invert, and then multiply to get

$$21 \times \left(-\frac{5}{21}\right) = -5$$

Note that the answer is negative.

If there are several operations involved, we follow the order of operations given on page 210.

EXAMPLE 6 Simplifying Several Operations

Simplify $\left(\frac{1}{2}\right)^3 \div \frac{1}{4} \cdot \frac{1}{2} + \frac{1}{3}\left(\frac{5}{2} - \frac{1}{2}\right) - \frac{1}{3} \cdot \frac{1}{2}$.

$$\left(\frac{1}{2}\right)^3 \div \frac{1}{4} \cdot \frac{1}{2} + \frac{1}{3}\left(\frac{5}{2} - \frac{1}{2}\right) - \frac{1}{3} \cdot \frac{1}{2}$$

$$= \left(\frac{1}{2}\right)^3 \div \frac{1}{4} \cdot \frac{1}{2} + \frac{1}{3}(2) - \frac{1}{3} \cdot \frac{1}{2}$$ Do operations inside parentheses: $\left(\frac{5}{2} - \frac{1}{2}\right) = \left(\frac{4}{2}\right) = (2)$

$$= \frac{1}{8} \div \frac{1}{4} \cdot \frac{1}{2} + \frac{1}{3}(2) - \frac{1}{3} \cdot \frac{1}{2}$$ Do exponents: $\left(\frac{1}{2}\right)^3 = \frac{1}{8}$

$$= \frac{1}{2} \cdot \frac{1}{2} + \frac{1}{3}(2) - \frac{1}{3} \cdot \frac{1}{2}$$ Do division: $\frac{1}{8} \div \frac{1}{4} = \frac{1}{8} \cdot \frac{4}{1} = \frac{1}{2}$

$$= \frac{1}{4} + \frac{2}{3} - \frac{1}{6}$$ Do multiplication: $\frac{1}{2} \cdot \frac{1}{2} = \frac{1}{4}; \frac{1}{3}(2) = \frac{2}{3}; \frac{1}{3} \cdot \frac{1}{2} = \frac{1}{6}$

$$= \frac{11}{12} - \frac{1}{6}$$ Do addition: $\frac{1}{4} + \frac{2}{3} = \frac{3}{12} + \frac{8}{12} = \frac{11}{12}$

$$= \frac{9}{12}$$ Do subtraction: $\frac{11}{12} - \frac{1}{6} = \frac{11}{12} - \frac{2}{12} = \frac{9}{12}$

$$= \frac{3}{4}$$ Reduce: $\frac{9}{12}$ to $\frac{3}{4}$

As you probably know, the number $\frac{1}{2}$ can be written in decimal form, that is, as 0.5. Because all rational numbers can be written in the form *a*/*b*, it is always possible to change a rational number *a*/*b* to its decimal form simply by dividing *a* by *b*. For example, $\frac{1}{2} = 0.5$, $\frac{1}{8} = 0.125$, and $\frac{1}{4} = 0.25$. Of course, if the denominator of a fraction is already a power of 10 (10, 100, 1000, and so on), then the fraction can easily be written as a decimal. Thus,

$$\frac{7}{10} = 0.7, \qquad \frac{19}{100} = 0.19, \qquad \text{and} \qquad \frac{17}{1000} = 0.017$$

You should keep in mind that the successive places to the right of the decimal point have the place values

$$\frac{1}{10^1}, \quad \frac{1}{10^2}, \quad \frac{1}{10^3}, \quad \frac{1}{10^4}, \ldots$$

This idea will be used when writing decimals in *expanded form.*

C Decimals in Expanded Form

You learned in Section 4.2 that a positive integer can always be written in expanded form as, for instance,

$$361 = (3 \times 10^2) + (6 \times 10^1) + (1 \times 10^0)$$

Can you do something like this for a decimal, say, 3.52? You know that

$$0.5 = \frac{5}{10} \qquad \text{and} \qquad 0.02 = \frac{2}{100}$$

so

$$3.52 = (3 \times 10^0) + \left(5 \times \frac{1}{10^1}\right) + \left(2 \times \frac{1}{10^2}\right)$$

To make the notation more convenient and consistent, we define **negative exponents** as follows:

$$10^{-1} = \frac{1}{10^1} = \frac{1}{10}, \quad 10^{-2} = \frac{1}{10^2} = \frac{1}{100}, \quad 10^{-3} = \frac{1}{10^3} = \frac{1}{1000}, \ldots$$

Definition of Negative Exponents

If n is a positive integer and $a \neq 0$,

$$a^{-n} = \frac{1}{a^n}$$

It can be shown that **negative exponents obey exactly the same laws as positive exponents.**

Using these negative exponents, you can write decimals in expanded form. For example,

$$3.52 = (3 \times 10^0) + (5 \times 10^{-1}) + (2 \times 10^{-2})$$

and

$$362.754 = (3 \times 10^2) + (6 \times 10^1) + (2 \times 10^0) + (7 \times 10^{-1}) + (5 \times 10^{-2}) + (4 \times 10^{-3})$$

These look like very natural generalizations of the expanded form that you used for positive exponents.

The definition of negative exponents yields a good pattern.

$10^3 = 1000$
$10^2 = 100$
$10^1 = 10$
$10^0 = 1$
$10^{-1} = \frac{1}{10}$
$10^{-2} = \frac{1}{100}$
$10^{-3} = \frac{1}{1000}$

And so on

EXAMPLE 7 Writing Decimals in Expanded Form

(a) Write 25.603 in expanded form.

(b) Write $(7 \times 10^2) + (2 \times 10^0) + (6 \times 10^{-1}) + (9 \times 10^{-4})$ in standard decimal form.

Solution

(a) $$\begin{aligned}25.603 &= (2 \times 10^1) + (5 \times 10^0) + (6 \times 10^{-1}) + (0 \times 10^{-2}) + (3 \times 10^{-3})\\ &= (2 \times 10^1) + (5 \times 10^0) + (6 \times 10^{-1}) + (3 \times 10^{-3})\end{aligned}$$

(b) Notice that the exponent in 10^{-n} tells you that the first nonzero digit comes in the nth decimal place. With this in mind,

$$(7 \times 10^2) + (2 \times 10^0) + (6 \times 10^{-1}) + (9 \times 10^{-4}) = 702.6009$$

D Rationals Written in Scientific Notation

In science, very large or very small numbers frequently occur. For example, a red cell of human blood contains 270,000,000 hemoglobin molecules, and the mass of a single carbon atom is 0.000 000 000 000 000 000 000 019 9 g. Numbers in this form are difficult to write and to work with, so they are written in *scientific notation.*

Definition of Scientific Notation

A number is said to be in **scientific notation** if it is written in the form

$$m \times 10^n$$

where m is a number greater than or equal to 1 and less than 10, and n is an integer.

For any given number, the m is obtained by placing the decimal point so that there is exactly one nonzero digit to its left. The n is then the number of places that the decimal point must be moved from its position in m to its original position; it is positive if the point must be moved to the right and negative if the point must be moved to the left. The following are examples:

$5.3 = 5.3 \times 10^0$	Decimal point in 5.3 must be moved **0** places.
$87 = 8.7 \times 10^1 = 8.7 \times 10$	Decimal point in 8.7 must be moved **1** place to the right to get 87.
$68{,}000 = 6.8 \times 10^4$	Decimal point in 6.8 must be moved **4** places to the right to get 68,000.
$0.49 = 4.9 \times 10^{-1}$	Decimal point in 4.9 must be moved **1** place to the **left** to get 0.49.
$0.072 = 7.2 \times 10^{-2}$	Decimal point in 7.2 must be moved **2** places to the **left** to get 0.072.
$0.0003875 = 3.875 \times 10^{-4}$	Decimal point in 3.875 must be moved **4** places to the **left** to get 0.0003875.

GRAPH IT

Your grapher has to be in the mode to do scientific notation! Press MODE ➤ ENTER and then 2ND MODE to go to the home screen. For Example 8(a), enter 270,000,000 ENTER to obtain 2.7E8, which means 2.7×10^8 as shown in the window.

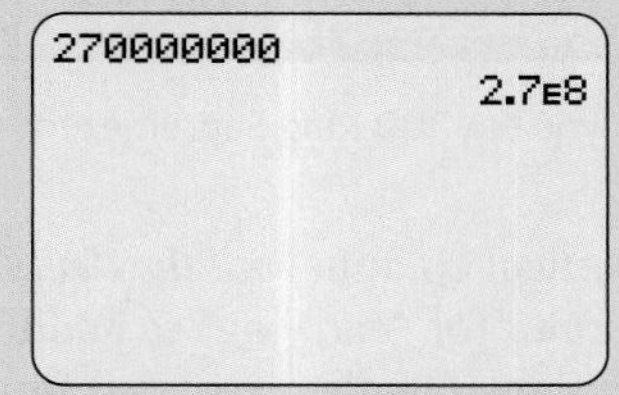

Go ahead and try Example 8(b)!

EXAMPLE 8 Writing Numbers in Scientific Notation

Write the following in scientific notation:

(a) 270,000,000

(b) 0.000 000 000 000 000 000 000 019 9

Solution

(a) $270{,}000{,}000 = 2.7 \times 10^8$

(b) $0.000\ 000\ 000\ 000\ 000\ 000\ 000\ 019\ 9 = 1.99 \times 10^{-23}$

EXAMPLE 9 From Scientific Notation to Decimals

Write the following in standard decimal notation:

(a) 2.5×10^{10} (b) 7.4×10^{-6}

Solution

(a) $2.5 \times 10^{10} = 25{,}000{,}000{,}000$

(b) $7.4 \times 10^{-6} = 0.0000074$

We noted earlier in this section that negative exponents obey the same laws as positive exponents. We can verify this quite easily in simple cases. For example,

$$10^4 \times 10^{-2} = 10{,}000 \times \frac{1}{100} = 100 = 10^2 = 10^{4+(-2)}$$

$$10^{-2} \times 10^{-3} = 0.01 \times 0.001 = 0.00001 = 10^{-5} = 10^{-2+(-3)}$$

We use the laws of exponents to do the calculations in the next example.

EXAMPLE 10 Calculations in Scientific Notation

Do the following calculation, and write the answer in scientific notation:

$$(5 \times 10^4) \times (9 \times 10^{-7})$$

Solution

$$\begin{aligned}(5 \times 10^4) \times (9 \times 10^{-7}) &= (5 \times 9) \times (10^4 \times 10^{-7}) \\ &= 45 \times 10^{4-7} \\ &= 45 \times 10^{-3} \\ &= (4.5 \times 10^1) \times 10^{-3} \\ &= 4.5 \times 10^{1-3} \\ &= 4.5 \times 10^{-2}\end{aligned}$$

E Operations with Decimals

We have already studied the operations of addition, subtraction, multiplication, and division with whole numbers, integers, and fractions. We now consider the same operations with decimals. To add or subtract decimals, we proceed as with whole numbers, making sure that the numbers to be added have the same number of decimal places. Thus, to add 5.1 and 2.81, we attach a 0 to 5.1 so that it has two decimal places and then add. To see why this works, we write the numbers in expanded form and add as follows:

$$\begin{aligned}5.10 &= 5 + \tfrac{1}{10} + \tfrac{0}{100} \\ \underline{2.81} &= \underline{2 + \tfrac{8}{10} + \tfrac{1}{100}} \\ 7.91 &= 7 + \tfrac{9}{10} + \tfrac{1}{100}\end{aligned}$$

© I. Bello

Can you buy 100 King Supremes for under $1?

In practice, we place the numbers to be added in a vertical column *with the decimal points aligned,* and then add or subtract as required. The rules for "carrying" in addition and "borrowing" in subtraction are justified here also, as shown by the expanded forms in the next examples.

EXAMPLE 11 Adding and Subtracting Decimals

(a) Add 4.81 and 3.7. (b) Subtract 6.53 from 8.71.

Solution

(a) We attach a 0 to the 3.7, align the decimal points, and add.

Short Form

$$\begin{array}{r} 4.81 \\ +\ 3.70 \\ \hline 8.51 \end{array} \leftarrow \text{Attach a 0.}$$

Expanded Form

$$\begin{array}{l} \quad 4 + \frac{8}{10} + \frac{1}{100} \\ + 3 + \frac{7}{10} + \frac{0}{100} \\ \hline \quad 7 + \frac{15}{10} + \frac{1}{100} \\ = 7 + \frac{10}{10} + \frac{5}{10} + \frac{1}{100} \\ = 8 + \frac{5}{10} + \frac{1}{100} \\ = 8.51 \end{array}$$

(b) *Short Form*

$$\begin{array}{r} 8.71 \\ -\ 6.53 \\ \hline 2.18 \end{array}$$

Expanded Form

$$\begin{array}{l} \quad 8 + \frac{7}{10} + \frac{1}{100} = 8 + \frac{6}{10} + \frac{11}{100} \\ -6 + \frac{5}{10} + \frac{3}{100} = 6 + \frac{5}{10} + \frac{3}{100} \\ \hline \qquad\qquad\qquad\quad 2 + \frac{1}{10} + \frac{8}{100} = 2.18 \end{array}$$

Note: In the first line of the expanded form, we wrote

$$\frac{7}{10} = \frac{6}{10} + \frac{1}{10} = \frac{6}{10} + \frac{10}{100}$$

and then combined the hundredths.

To understand the rule for multiplying decimals, look at the following example, in which the decimals are first replaced by equivalent fractions:

EXAMPLE 12 Multiplying Decimals

Multiply 0.37×7.2.

Solution

$$0.37 \times 7.2 = \frac{37}{100} \times \frac{72}{10} = \frac{37 \times 72}{1000}$$

The numerator 37×72 tells us that the 37 and the 72 are to be multiplied as usual for whole numbers. The 1000 in the denominator tells us that the final answer will have three decimal places, the sum of the number of decimal places in the two factors. Thus, we can multiply the 0.37 and the 7.2 just as if they were whole numbers and then place the decimal point so that there are three decimal places in the product. The short form of the multiplication follows:

$$\begin{array}{r} 0.37 \\ \times\quad 7.2 \\ \hline 74 \\ 259\ \ \\ \hline 2.664 \end{array} \quad \begin{array}{l} \leftarrow \text{2 decimal places} \\ \leftarrow \text{1 decimal place} \\ \\ \\ \leftarrow 2 + 1 = \text{3 decimal places} \end{array}$$

A division involving decimals is easier to understand if the divisor is a whole number. If the divisor is not a whole number, we can make it so by moving the decimal point to the right the same number of places in both the divisor and the dividend. This procedure can be justified as in the next example.

EXAMPLE 13 Division: Unit Cost

A $6\frac{1}{2}$-oz can of tuna fish is on sale for 55¢. What is the cost per ounce to the nearest tenth of a cent?

Solution

The cost per ounce can be obtained by dividing the 55¢ cost by the 6.5 ounces. Thus, we have to find $55 \div 6.5$, and we can make the divisor a whole number by writing the division in fractional form.

$$\frac{55}{6.5} = \frac{550}{65} \qquad \text{Multiply numerator and denominator by 10.}$$

This is equivalent to moving the decimal point one place to the right in both the divisor and the dividend. Then we divide in the usual way.

$$\begin{array}{r} 8.46 \\ 65\overline{)550.00} \\ \underline{520} \\ 30\,0 \\ \underline{26\,0} \\ 4\,00 \\ \underline{3\,90} \\ 10 \end{array}$$

To two decimal places, the cost per ounce is 8.46¢. Therefore, to the nearest tenth of a cent, the answer is 8.5¢. (See Section 1.2 A to review the rounding rules.)

5.3 EXERCISES

A Rational Numbers as Fractions

In problems 1–4, identify the numerator and denominator of each rational number.

1. $\frac{3}{4}$
2. $\frac{4}{5}$
3. $\frac{3}{-5}$
4. $\frac{-4}{5}$

In problems 5–7, identify the rational numbers that are equal by using the definition of equality.

5. $\frac{17}{41}, \frac{289}{697}, \frac{714}{1682}$
6. $\frac{438}{529}, \frac{19}{23}, \frac{323}{391}$
7. $\frac{11}{91}, \frac{111}{911}, \frac{253}{2093}$

In problems 8–16, reduce each rational number.

8. $\frac{14}{21}$
9. $\frac{95}{38}$
10. $\frac{42}{86}$
11. $\frac{21}{48}$
12. $\frac{15}{12}$
13. $\frac{30}{28}$
14. $\frac{22}{33}$
15. $\frac{52}{78}$
16. $\frac{224}{84}$

It is possible to add and subtract rational numbers by converting them to equivalent rational numbers with the same denominator. In problems 17–19, express each sum as a sum of rational numbers with a denominator of 18.

17. $\frac{2}{9} + \frac{1}{6} + \frac{7}{18}$
18. $\frac{7}{3} + \frac{7}{9} + \frac{5}{6}$
19. $\frac{1}{3} + \frac{1}{6} + \frac{1}{9}$

B Operations with Rational Numbers

In problems 20–90, perform the indicated operations and reduce each answer (if possible).

20. $\frac{1}{7} + \frac{1}{3}$
21. $\frac{1}{7} + \frac{1}{9}$
22. $\frac{2}{7} + \frac{3}{11}$
23. $\frac{3}{4} + \frac{5}{6}$
24. $\frac{1}{12} + \frac{7}{18}$
25. $\frac{3}{17} + \frac{7}{19}$
26. $\frac{1}{3} - \frac{1}{7}$
27. $\frac{1}{7} - \frac{1}{9}$
28. $\frac{2}{7} - \frac{3}{11}$
29. $\frac{3}{4} - \frac{5}{6}$
30. $\frac{7}{18} - \frac{1}{12}$
31. $\frac{7}{19} - \frac{3}{17}$
32. $\frac{3}{4} \times \frac{2}{7}$
33. $\frac{2}{5} \times \frac{5}{3}$
34. $\frac{7}{9} \times \frac{3}{8}$
35. $\frac{3}{4} \div \frac{2}{7}$
36. $\frac{2}{5} \div \frac{5}{3}$
37. $\frac{7}{9} \div \frac{3}{8}$
38. $\left(\frac{-2}{5}\right) \times \frac{4}{9}$
39. $\left(-\frac{6}{7}\right) \times \left(-\frac{3}{11}\right)$
40. $\frac{4}{5} \div \left(\frac{-7}{9}\right)$
41. $\left(-\frac{3}{4}\right) \div \left(-\frac{7}{6}\right)$
42. $\frac{3}{4} \div \left(-\frac{1}{5}\right)$
43. $\frac{1}{8} \div \left(-\frac{3}{4}\right)$
44. $\left(-\frac{1}{4}\right) + \left(-\frac{1}{7}\right)$
45. $\left(-\frac{1}{8}\right) + \left(\frac{1}{4}\right))$
46. $\left(\frac{1}{3} + \frac{1}{4}\right) + \frac{7}{8}$
47. $\frac{3}{8} - \left(\frac{1}{4} - \frac{1}{8}\right)$
48. $\left(\frac{1}{5} \times \frac{1}{4}\right) \times \frac{3}{7}$
49. $\frac{1}{2} \times \left(\frac{7}{8} \times \frac{7}{5}\right)$
50. $\frac{1}{2} \div \left(\frac{1}{8} \div \frac{1}{4}\right)$
51. $\left(\frac{1}{2} \div \frac{1}{8}\right) \div \frac{1}{4}$
52. $\frac{3}{4} + \frac{1}{2}\left(\frac{3}{2} + \frac{1}{4}\right)$
53. $\frac{2}{3}\left(\frac{1}{2} + \frac{3}{4}\right) + \frac{2}{3}$
54. $\frac{1}{2}\left(\frac{3}{4} - \frac{1}{2}\right) - \frac{1}{12}$
55. $\frac{1}{3}\left(\frac{3}{2} - \frac{1}{5}\right) - \frac{1}{30}$

56. $\frac{1}{2}(\frac{5}{2} - \frac{1}{3}) - \frac{5}{12}$

57. $1\frac{1}{2} + \frac{1}{7}$

58. $5 - 1\frac{1}{3}$

59. $\frac{1}{4} \times 1\frac{1}{7}$

60. $5 \div (-2\frac{1}{2})$

61. $3\frac{1}{4} + \frac{1}{6}$

62. $4 - 2\frac{1}{4}$

63. $\frac{1}{5} \times 2\frac{1}{7}$

64. $6 \div (-1\frac{1}{5})$

65. $-3 + 2\frac{1}{4}$

66. $-\frac{2}{3} - (-2)$

67. $(-8) \times 2\frac{1}{4}$

68. $7 \div (-2\frac{1}{3})$

69. $-2 + 1\frac{1}{5}$

70. $-\frac{3}{4} - (-3)$

71. $(-9) \times 3\frac{1}{3}$

72. $(-\frac{1}{6}) \div (-\frac{5}{7})$

73. $7\frac{1}{4} + (-\frac{1}{8})$

74. $-3\frac{1}{8} - (-2)$

75. $(-1\frac{1}{4}) \times (-2\frac{1}{10})$

76. $(-1\frac{1}{8}) \div (-2\frac{1}{4})$

77. $\frac{1}{2} \times \frac{1}{6} - \frac{1}{3} + \frac{1}{4}$

78. $\frac{3}{8} - 6(\frac{1}{4} - \frac{1}{8})$

79. $\frac{1}{3} - \frac{1}{3} \times \frac{2}{3} \div \frac{2}{5}$

80. $\frac{1}{2} \div \frac{1}{4} - \frac{3}{4}$

81. $(2\frac{1}{2}) \times (-3\frac{1}{4}) - (-7\frac{1}{8}) \div 3$

82. $(-6\frac{2}{5}) \div (-4) + (2\frac{1}{10}) \times (-2)$

83. $12 \div 6 - (\frac{1}{3} + \frac{1}{2})$

84. $18 \div 9 - (\frac{1}{4} + \frac{1}{6})$

85. $\frac{1}{3} \cdot \frac{1}{4} \div \frac{1}{2} + (\frac{5}{6} - \frac{1}{2})$

86. $\frac{1}{3} \cdot \frac{1}{6} \div \frac{1}{2} + (\frac{4}{5} - \frac{1}{2})$

87. $\frac{1}{6} \div \frac{1}{3} \cdot \frac{1}{3} \cdot \frac{1}{3} + (\frac{1}{4} - \frac{1}{9})$

88. $\frac{1}{10} \div \frac{1}{2} \cdot \frac{1}{2} \cdot \frac{1}{2} + (\frac{2}{3} - \frac{1}{2})$

89. $8 \div \frac{1}{2} \cdot \frac{1}{2} \cdot \frac{1}{2} - (\frac{1}{3} + \frac{1}{5})$

90. $6 \div \frac{1}{3} \cdot \frac{1}{3} \cdot \frac{1}{3} - (\frac{1}{3} + \frac{1}{5})$

C Decimals in Expanded Form

In problems 91–94, write each number in expanded notation.

91. 692.087

92. 30.2959

93. 0.00107

94. 4.30008

In problems 95–98, write each number in standard decimal notation.

95. $(5 \times 10^3) + (2 \times 10^1) + (3 \times 10^{-1}) + (9 \times 10^{-2})$

96. $(4 \times 10^2) + (5 \times 10^0) + (6 \times 10^{-2}) + (9 \times 10^{-4})$

97. $(4 \times 10^{-3}) + (7 \times 10^{-4}) + (2 \times 10^{-6})$

98. $(2 \times 10^{-1}) + (5 \times 10^{-2}) + (4 \times 10^{-4})$

D Rationals Written in Scientific Notation

In problems 99–102, write each number in scientific notation.

99. 935

100. 0.372

101. 0.0012

102. 3,453,000

In problems 103–106, write each number in standard notation.

103. 8.64×10^4

104. 9.01×10^7

105. 6.71×10^{-3}

106. 4.02×10^{-7}

In problems 107–112, simplify and write each answer in scientific notation.

107. $0.0346 \div 1{,}730{,}000$

108. $0.00741 \times 225{,}000$

109. $(3.1 \times 10^5) \times (2.2 \times 10^{-6})$

110. $(4.9 \times 10^{-2}) \times (3.5 \times 10^{-1})$

111. $\dfrac{(2 \times 10^6)(6 \times 10^{-5})}{4 \times 10^3}$

112. $\dfrac{(8 \times 10^2)(3 \times 10^{-2})}{24 \times 10^{-3}}$

E Operations with Decimals

In problems 113–120, perform the indicated operations.

113. a. $3.81 + 0.93$ b. $-3.81 + (-0.93)$

114. a. $18.64 - 0.983$ b. $-18.64 - 0.983$

115. a. $2.08 - 6.238$ b. $3.07 - 8.934$

116. a. 2.48×2.7 b. $(-2.48) \times (-2.7)$

117. a. $(-0.03) \times (-1.5)$ b. $(-3.2) \times (-0.04)$

118. a. $10.25 \div 0.05$ b. $2.16 \div 0.06$

119. a. $(-0.07) \div 1.4$ b. $(-0.09) \div (-4.5)$

120. a. $(-1.8) \div (0.09)$ b. $3.6 \div (-0.012)$

F Applications

Reducing Fractions *The circle graph has 12 "slices" and will be used in problems 121–123.*

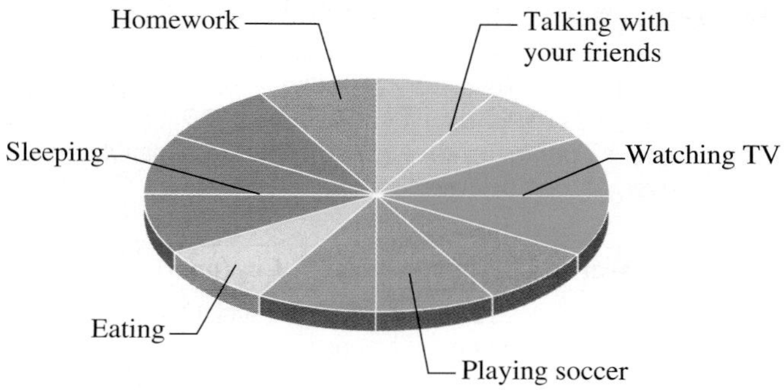

Source: Images Courtesy of Learn Things, Ltd.

The circle graph is divided into 12 equal parts (slices).

121. What reduced fraction of the time was spent eating?

122. What reduced fraction of the time was spent watching TV?

123. What fraction of the time was spent doing homework?

SCIENTIFIC NOTATION APPLICATIONS

124. *Norwegian garbage* The average Norwegian produces 4.8 lb of garbage each day. Since there are about 4.6 million Norwegians and 365 days in a year, the annual number of pounds of garbage produced in Norway is $4.8 \times (4.6 \times 10^6) \times (3.65 \times 10^2)$.
   a. Write this number in scientific notation.
   b. Write this number in standard notation.

125. *Irish garbage* The average Irish person also produces 4.8 lb of garbage each day. Since there are about 5.6 million Irish people and 365 days in a year, the annual number of pounds of garbage produced in Ireland is $4.8 \times (5.6 \times 10^6) \times (3.65 \times 10^2)$.
   a. Write this number in scientific notation.
   b. Write this number in standard notation.

APPLICATIONS INVOLVING THE ORDER OF OPERATIONS

126. *Gasoline actane rating* Have you noticed the octane rating of gasoline at the gas pump? This octane rating is given by the equation

$$\frac{R + M}{2}$$

Where R is a number measuring the performance of gasoline using the Research Method and M is a number measuring the performance of gasoline using the Motor Method. If a certain gasoline has $R = 92$ and $M = 82$, what is its octane rating?

127. *Exercise pulse rate* If A is your age, the minimum pulse rate you should maintain during aerobic activities is $0.72(220 - A)$. What is the minimum pulse rate you should maintain if you are the specified age?

a. 20 years old. b. 45 years old

128. *Cell phone rates* At the present time, the Verizon America Choice 900 plan costs \$59.99 per month and gives you 900 anytime minutes with unlimited night and weekend minutes. After 900 minutes, you pay \$0.40 per minute. The monthly cost C is $C = \$59.99 + 0.40(m - 900)$, where m is minutes used.

a. Find the monthly cost for a talker that used 1000 minutes.

b. Find the monthly cost for a talker that used 945 minutes.

APPLICATIONS INVOLVING DECIMALS

Some scientists claim a relationship between global warming and CO_2 (carbon dioxide concentration in the atmosphere). The world's most current data for atmospheric CO_2 (in parts per million, ppm) is from measurements at the Mauna Loa Observatory in Hawaii, started by David Keeling in 1958.

Year	Co_2 (ppm)	Year	Co_2 (ppm)
1967	322.16	2007	384.42
1968	323.04	2008	385.96
1969	324.62	2009	388.79

Source: http://co2now.org.

In problems 129–132, refer to the table to find:

129. The difference in CO_2 concentration between 2007 and 1967.

130. The difference in CO_2 concentration between 2008 and 1968.

131. The difference in CO_2 concentration between 2009 and 1969.

132. Was the CO_2 concentration increasing in the 1960s? 2000s?

IN OTHER WORDS

133. Explain in your own words some of the advantages of decimals over ordinary fractions.

134. Explain why, when multiplying two decimals, the number of decimal places in the answer is equal to the sum of the number of decimal places in the two factors.

USING YOUR KNOWLEDGE

Many products (such as cereal, milk, etc.) list their nutrition information per serving. For example, Product 19 contains 3 g of protein. If the recommended daily allowance (RDA) of protein is 70 g, Product 19 provides $\frac{3}{70}$ of your daily protein needs. In the following problems, find the fraction of the protein RDA (70 g) provided by the given product, then write your answer as a decimal, to two digits.

135. Special K, 4 g per serving

136. Spinach (1 cup), 5 g

137. 1 egg, 7 g

COLLABORATIVE LEARNING

Do you know what unit pricing is? You should if you want to save money. We are ready for the supermarket scavenger hunt. Form two or more groups. The purpose is to determine whether when buying groceries, bigger is better and/or generic is cheaper. Many supermarket items carry a label stating the unit price *of the item The* unit price *is the price of the item divided by the number of units (ounces, grams, etc.). Your first task is to determine whether the unit price given by the supermarket is correct. To find the* best buy, *find the unit price for each item and select the best unit price.*

1. Make a list of 10 different items you usually buy at the supermarket. Have one group select brand-name items, and another group generic items, each containing the same amount of units. Record the results. Are brand-name items always more expensive than generic?
2. For the same 10 items, have a group select one size, and another group a different size. Compare unit prices. Is the bigger size always cheaper? *Hint:* We found two items for which this was not always the case: Sun Maid Raisins and Goya Sardines.

5.4 Rationals and Irrationals as Decimals: Percents

GETTING STARTED

OBJECTIVES

A. Write a fraction as a decimal.

B. Write a repeating decimal as a fraction.

C. Write a percent as a decimal or a fraction and vice versa.

D. Classify a square root as rational or irrational.

E. Classify a decimal as rational or irrational.

F. Given two numbers, determine their relationship as $=$, $>$ or $<$.

G. Find a rational or irrational number between two decimals or between a decimal and a fraction.

The New York Stock Exchange (NYSE), the world's largest, converted to decimals. Price increases are now reported in dollars and cents instead of fractions. Announcements will now say that a particular stock, for example, is "up \$1.75" above its previous value instead of "up 1 and $\frac{3}{4}$."

STOCK PRICES AND FRACTIONS

Before April 9, 2001, stock prices were quoted using fractions. Thus, a stock costing $16\frac{31}{32}$ would **be listed as** \$16.97. Is there a difference in the price? Absolutely not, but the fractional part $\frac{31}{32}$ will now be written as .97. The pricing of stocks using fractions goes back hundreds of years.

The tradition of pricing stocks in fractions with 16 as the denominator takes its roots from the fact that Spanish traders some 400 years ago quoted prices in fractions of Spanish gold doubloons. A doubloon could be cut into 2, 4, or even 16 pieces. Presumably, it was too difficult to split those $\frac{1}{16}$ wedges any further. Source: http://www.invest-faq.com/articles/triv-sixteenths.html). Quotes were even priced in 32nds! Can you imagine the problems that would arise if prices were in $\frac{3}{7}$s or $\frac{7}{11}$s? (Try dividing 3 by 7, or 7 by 11.)

What do you think the denominators of all the fractions that are easy to convert to decimals (10, 2, 4, and 8) have in common? The answer is in Theorem 5.3 of this section. As a matter of fact, after you read and understand Theorem 5.3, you will be able to tell whether a fraction has a terminating or a nonterminating decimal representation (problems 25–30, Exercises 5.4). You will also learn to write this representation and even change a terminating or nonterminating repeating decimal to a fraction (problems 43–58, Exercises 5.4). You finish this section by studying a special type of decimal: *percents.*

As we mentioned in Section 5.3, a rational number can always be written in decimal form. If the number is a fraction, we divide the numerator by the denominator and obtain either a terminating or a nonterminating decimal.

A Terminating and Nonterminating Decimals

Numbers such as $\frac{1}{2}$, $\frac{1}{8}$, and $\frac{1}{5}$ are said to have **terminating decimal representations** because division of the numerator by the denominator terminates (ends). However, some rational numbers—for example, $\frac{1}{3}$—have **infinite repeating decimal representations.** Such a representation is obtained by dividing the numerator of the fraction by its denominator. In the case of $\frac{1}{3}$, we obtain.

```
   0.333 ···
3)1.0
   9
   10
    9
    10
     9
     1 ···
```

For convenience, we shall write $0.333\cdots$ as $0.\overline{3}$. The bar over the 3 indicates that the 3 repeats indefinitely. Similarly,

$$\frac{1}{7} = 0.142857142857\cdots = 0.\overline{142857}$$

GRAPH IT

Can you verify that $\frac{1}{3} = 0.\overline{3}$ and $\frac{1}{7} = 0.\overline{142857}$? Enter 1 [÷] 3; you get a terminating (not an infinite) decimal approximation as shown. For $\frac{1}{7}$, the approximation is 0.1428571429 (not infinite either). Again, the moral is: You have to know your math!

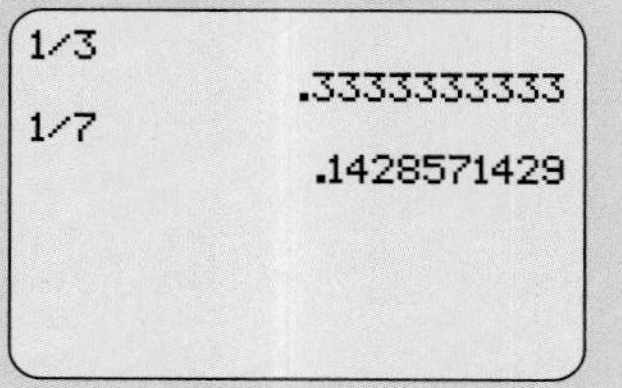

EXAMPLE 1 Fractions to Decimals

Write the following as decimals, and state the value in the second decimal place.

(a) $\frac{3}{4}$ (b) $\frac{2}{3}$

Solution

(a) Dividing 3 by 4, we obtain

```
   0.75
4)3.0
   28
    20
    20
     0
```

Thus, $\frac{3}{4} = 0.75$, and the value in the second decimal place is $\frac{5}{100}$.

(b) Dividing 2 by 3, we obtain

$$
\begin{array}{r}
0.666\cdots \\
3\overline{)2.0} \\
\underline{1\,8} \\
20 \\
\underline{18} \\
20 \\
\underline{18} \\
2\cdots
\end{array}
$$

Thus, $\frac{2}{3} = 0.666\cdots = 0.\overline{6}$, and the value in the second decimal place is $\frac{6}{100}$.

You should be able to convince yourself of the truth of Theorem 5.3, which indicates which rational numbers have terminating decimal representations.

Theorem 5.3 Criterion for Terminating Decimals

A rational number a/b (in lowest terms) has a terminating decimal expansion if and only if b has no prime factors other than 2 and 5.

Notice that the denominator b does not have to have **2** ***and*** **5** as factors; it can only have **one** of them as a factor, or perhaps **neither.** For example,

$\frac{1}{25} = 0.04$ has a terminating decimal expansion and $25 = 5 \times 5$ has only **5** as a factor.

$\frac{1}{4} = 0.25$ has a terminating decimal expansion and $4 = 2 \times 2$ has only **2** as a factor.

$\frac{8}{1} = 8$ has a terminating decimal expansion and 1 has neither **2** nor **5** as a factor.

It is easy to see that every rational number has an infinite repeating decimal representation. In the case of a terminating decimal, you can simply adjoin an infinite string of 0s. For example, $\frac{3}{4} = 0.75\overline{0}$, $\frac{1}{20} = 0.05\overline{0}$, and so on. If the rational number a/b has no terminating decimal representation, then it must have a repeating decimal representation, as you can see by carrying out the division of a by b. The only possible remainders are 1, 2, 3, . . . , and $b - 1$. Therefore, after at most $(b - 1)$ steps of the division, a remainder must occur for the second time. Thereafter, the digits of the quotient must repeat. The following division illustrates the idea:

$$
\begin{array}{r}
1.692307 \\
13\overline{)22} \\
\underline{13} \\
90 \\
\underline{78} \\
120 \\
\underline{117} \\
30 \\
\underline{26} \\
40 \\
\underline{39} \\
100 \\
\underline{91} \\
9
\end{array}
$$

Notice that the remainder 9 occurs just before the digit 6 appears in the quotient and again just after the digit 7 appears in the quotient. Thus, the repeating part of the decimal must be 692307, and $\frac{22}{13} = 1.\overline{692307}$.

Of the first 20 counting numbers, only 7, 17, and 19 have reciprocals with the maximum possible number of digits in the repeating part of their decimal representations:

$\frac{1}{7} = 0.\overline{142857}$

$\frac{1}{17} = 0.\overline{0588235294117647}$

$\frac{1}{19} = 0.\overline{052631578947368421}$

B Changing Infinite Repeating Decimals to Fractions

The preceding discussion shows that **every rational number can be written as an infinite repeating decimal.** Is the converse of this statement true? That is, does every infinite repeating decimal represent a rational number? If the repeating part is simply a string of 0s so that the decimal is actually terminating, it can be written as a rational number with a power of 10 as the denominator. For example, $0.73 = \frac{73}{100}$, $0.7 = \frac{7}{10}$, and $0.013 = \frac{13}{1000}$. If the decimal is repeating but not terminating, then we can proceed as in the next example.

GRAPH IT

To change $0.\overline{23}$ to a fraction, enter 0.232323232323 [ENTER] [MATH] [1] [ENTER] and obtain $\frac{23}{99}$ as shown.

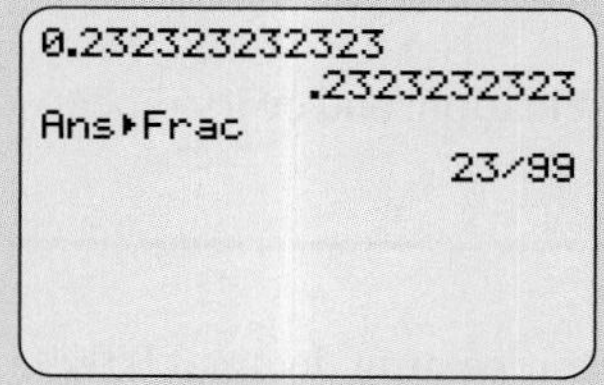

EXAMPLE 2 Repeating Decimals to Fractions

Write $0.\overline{23}$ as a quotient of integers.

Solution

If $x = 0.232323\cdots$, then $100x = 23.232323\cdots$. Now we can remove the repeating part by subtraction as follows:

$$\begin{array}{rl} 100x &= 23.232323\cdots \\ (-) \quad x &= 0.232323\cdots \\ \hline 99x &= 23 \end{array}$$

Then, dividing by 99, we get

$$x = \frac{23}{99}$$

As you can see, every infinite repeating decimal represents a rational number. Here is the procedure for obtaining this representation.

Changing an Infinite Repeating Decimal to a Fraction

1. Let $x =$ the given decimal.
2. Multiply by a power of 10 to move the decimal point to the right of the first sequence of digits that repeats.
3. If the decimal point is not at the left of the first repeating sequence of digits, multiply by a power of 10 to place it there.
4. Subtract the result of step 3 from that of step 2.
5. Divide by the multiplier of x in the result of step 4 to get the desired fraction.

The idea in steps 2 and 3 is to line up the repeating parts so that they drop out in the subtraction in step 4.

EXAMPLE 3 More Repeating Decimals to Fractions

Write $3.5212121\cdots$ as a quotient of two integers.

Solution

1. Let $x = 3.5212121\cdots$. We want the decimal point here so that the "21" repeats.
2. Since we want the decimal point to the right of the first 21, we multiply by 1000.

   $1000x = 3521.212121\cdots$

GRAPH IT

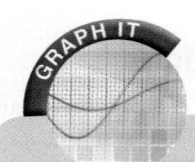

To write 3.5212121 . . . as a fraction takes several steps. Since $3.5212121\cdots =$ $3.5 + 0.0212121\cdots$, let us make the 0.021212121 . . . a fraction by entering 0.0212121212121 [ENTER] [MATH] [1] [ENTER]; we get $\frac{7}{330}$. Add $\frac{7}{330}$ to 3.5 and convert to a fraction by pressing [+] 3.5 [ENTER] [MATH] [1] [ENTER], getting $\frac{581}{165}$ as shown.

```
              .0212121212
Ans▸Frac
                    7/330
Ans+3.5
              3.521212121
Ans▸Frac
                  581/165
```

3. In this step, we want the decimal point to the left of the first 21 in

   $3.5212121\cdots$ Here.

   so we multiply x by 10.

   $10x = 35.212121\cdots$

4. $$\begin{aligned} 1000x &= 3521.212121\cdots \\ (-)\quad 10x &= 35.212121\cdots \\ \hline 990x &= 3486 \end{aligned}$$ The decimal parts drop out.

5. We divide by 990 to get

   $$x = \frac{3486}{990} = \frac{581 \cdot 6}{165 \cdot 6} = \frac{581}{165}$$

This discussion can be summarized as follows:

Rational Numbers as Decimals

Every rational number has a repeating decimal representation, and every repeating decimal represents a rational number.

If you use the procedure of Examples 2 and 3 for the repeating decimal $0.999\cdots$, you come out with the result $0.999\cdots = 1$.

If you are bothered by this result, the following examples may convince you of its truth:

1. $\frac{1}{3} = 0.333\cdots$
   $\frac{2}{3} = 0.666\cdots$
   What is the result when you add these two equations?
2. $\frac{4}{9} = 0.444\cdots$
   $\frac{5}{9} = 0.555\cdots$
   What is the result when you add these two equations?
3. $\frac{1}{9} = 0.111\cdots$

   What do you get by multiplying both sides of this equation by 9? (You can try it on your calculator! Begin by entering 1; then press [÷] [9] [×] [9] [=] and watch the display.)

C Percent

In many of the daily applications of decimals, information is given in terms of **percents.** The interest rate on a mortgage may be **5%** (read "**5** percent"), the Dow-Jones stock average may increase by 2%, your savings account may earn interest at 1%, and so on. The word *percent* comes from the Latin words *per* and *centum* and means "by the hundred." Thus, 2% is the same as $\frac{2}{100}$ or the decimal 0.2.

Changing a Percent to a Decimal

Move the decimal point in the number two places to the left and omit the % symbol.

EXAMPLE 4 Percents to Decimals

Write the following as decimals:

(a) 18% (b) 11.5% (c) 0.5%

Solution

(a) 18% = 0.18 (b) 11.5% = 0.115 (c) 0.5% = 0.005

To change a decimal to a percent, just reverse the procedure.

Changing a Decimal to a Percent

Move the decimal point two places to the right and affix the percent sign.

EXAMPLE 5 Decimals to Percents

Change the following to percents:

(a) 0.25 (b) 1.989

Solution

(a) 0.25 = 25% (b) 1.989 = 198.9%

Changing a Fraction to a Percent

Divide the numerator by the denominator, and then convert the resulting decimal to a percent.

EXAMPLE 6 Fractions to Percents

Write the following as percents. (Give the answers to one decimal place.)

(a) $\frac{2}{5}$ (b) $\frac{3}{7}$

Solution

(a) $\frac{2}{5} = 0.40 = 40\%$

(b) $\frac{3}{7} \approx 0.42857$ By ordinary division

≈ 0.429 Rounded to three decimal places

$= 42.9\%$

D Rationals, Irrationals, and Square Roots

All the numbers we have studied can be written in the form $\frac{a}{b}$, that is, as rational numbers. The Pythagoreans, a Brotherhood of Mathematicians living in the fifth century B.C., stated but could not prove, that every number was indeed rational. They were so certain that the entire universe was made up of whole numbers that they classified them into categories such as "perfect" and "amicable." In the midst of these charming fantasies, Hippasus, a member of the brotherhood, discovered that $\sqrt{2}$, the square root of 2, could **not** be obtained by dividing any whole number by another; that is, $\sqrt{2}$ is **not** rational, that is, it is **irrational.**

Definition of an Irrational Number

Numbers that are not rational are called **irrational.**

The method used to prove that $\sqrt{2}$ is irrational is called *reductio ad absurdum,* meaning "reduction to the absurd," and can be generalized to prove that the square roots of all numbers that are **not** perfect squares are ***irrational.*** Thus, $\sqrt{2}$, $\sqrt{3}$, $\sqrt{5}$, $\sqrt{6}$, and so on are irrational. The symbol $\sqrt{}$ is called the *radical* sign, and the number under the radical, the 2, is called the *radicand.*

You probably noticed that $\sqrt{4}$ is not on the list of irrationals; this is because 4 is a **perfect** square. That is, $\sqrt{4} = 2$. Here are the next few perfect squares: $\sqrt{9} = 3$, $\sqrt{16} = 4$ and $\sqrt{25} = 5$. Note that 1 is a perfect square because $\sqrt{1} = 1$.

EXAMPLE 7 Classifying Square Roots

Classify the following as rational or irrational:

(a) $\sqrt{36}$ (b) $\sqrt{44}$ (c) $\sqrt{81}$

Solution

(a) $\sqrt{36} = 6$ is rational. (b) $\sqrt{44}$ is irrational. (c) $\sqrt{81} = 9$ is rational.

E Irrational and Decimal Numbers

Irrational numbers such as $\sqrt{2}$ can be approximated to any finite number of decimal places. But these decimal numbers can never repeat (as in $\frac{1}{7}$) or terminate (as in $\frac{1}{2}$) because if they did, they would be rational numbers. For example,

$$\sqrt{2} = 1.4142\cdots \quad \text{or} \quad \sqrt{2} = 1.414213\cdots$$

We use this idea to define irrational numbers.

Representation of an Irrational Number

An **irrational number** is a number that has a **nonterminating, nonrepeating** decimal representation.

For example, $0.909009000\cdots$ (the successive sets of digits are 90, 900, 9000, and so on) is nonterminating and nonrepeating and thus is irrational. Another irrational number is the decimal $1.23456789101112\cdots$, where we continue writing the digits of the successive counting numbers. Here again, although there is a definite pattern, the decimal is nonrepeating and nonterminating. The set consisting of all decimals is called the set R of **real numbers.** This set includes all the numbers we have studied: the natural numbers, the whole numbers, the integers, the rational numbers, and the irrational numbers. (Keep in mind that rational numbers can be written as quotients of two integers and irrationals cannot.) The rationals and the irrationals completely cover the number line: To each point on the line, there corresponds a unique real number, and to each real number, there corresponds a unique point on the line.

EXAMPLE 8 Classifying Decimals

Classify the following numbers as rational or irrational:

(a) $0.35626262\cdots$ (b) $0.305300530005\cdots$ (c) 0.12345678
(d) $-\frac{1}{3}$ (e) $\sqrt{65}$ (f) $\sqrt{144}$

Solution

(a) A repeating decimal, therefore rational
(b) A nonrepeating, nonterminating decimal, therefore irrational
(c) A terminating decimal, therefore rational
(d) A fraction, therefore rational
(e) Irrational
(f) $\sqrt{144} = 12$, therefore rational

F Greater Than, Less Than, and the Trichotomy Law

Looking at the decimal approximations of $\sqrt{2}$ given earlier, we can see that 1.4 is less than $\sqrt{2}$ but 1.5 is greater; that is, $\sqrt{2}$ is between 1.4 and 1.5. Can we always find an irrational number between any two rational numbers? In order to answer this question, we must first make the ideas of **less than** ($<$) and **greater than** ($>$) more precise.

Definition of "Less Than" and "Greater Than"

If a and b are real numbers, then

$a < b$ if and only if there is a positive number c such that $a + c = b$
$b > a$ if and only if $a < b$

Thus, $3 < 5$ because $3 + 2 = 5$, $-4 < -1$ because $-4 + 3 = -1$, $5 > 3$ because $3 < 5$, and $\frac{1}{3} = 0.333\cdots < \frac{1}{2} = 0.5$ because $\frac{1}{3} + \frac{1}{6} = \frac{1}{2}$.

A basic property of the real numbers is given by the following statement:

The Trichotomy Law

If a and b are any real numbers, then exactly one of the following relations must occur:

$$a = b \tag{1}$$
$$a < b \tag{2}$$
$$a > b \tag{3}$$

Thus, if $a \ngtr b$ (a is not greater than b), then $a \le b$ (a is less than or equal to b). If $a \nless b$ (a is not less than b), then $a \ge b$ (a is greater than or equal to b).

It is not difficult to compare two rational numbers, but what about comparing an irrational number such as $\sqrt{48}$ and a rational number such as 6.9? We know that the numbers are close because $\sqrt{49} = 7$, which is close to 6.9, but can we fill in the blank with $<$ or $>$ to obtain a correct statement in the following expression?

$\sqrt{48}$ ______ 6.9

By squaring both sides, we get the equivalent comparison

$48 \_\_\_\_ (6.9)^2 = 47.61$

which shows that the $>$ symbol is the correct choice. Thus,

$\sqrt{48} > 6.9$

GRAPH IT

To test that $\sqrt{30} < 5.5$, enter [2nd] [√] 30 [)]. Now, for the test, enter [2nd] [TEST] [5] and 5.5. Press [ENTER] and you get a 1 as shown. This means that the statement is true. (A 0 value denotes a false statement.)

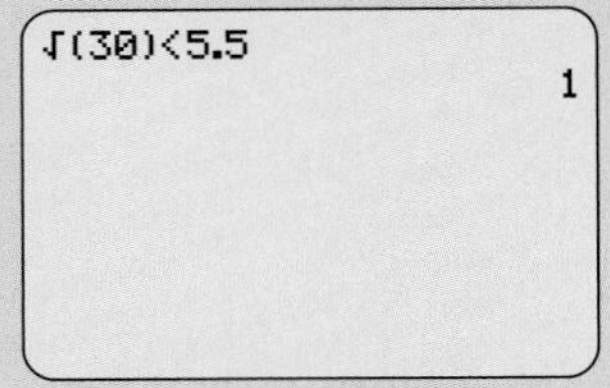

EXAMPLE 9 Using the Trichotomy Law

Insert $<$, $>$, or $=$ in the following to make correct statements:

(a) $\sqrt{60} \_\_\_\_ 7.7$ **(b)** $\sqrt{30} \_\_\_\_ 5.5$

Solution

(a) As before, we write $\sqrt{60} \_\_\_\_ 7.7$

Squaring both sides, $60 \_\_\_\_ (7.7)^2 = 59.29$

Since $60 > 59.29$, we have $\sqrt{60} > 7.7$

(b) Squaring both sides, we get $30 \_\_\_\_ (5.5)^2 = 30.25$

Since $30 < (5.5)^2 = 30.25$, $\sqrt{30} < 5.5$

G Density of the Rational Numbers

We now return to the question "Can we always find an irrational number between any two rational numbers?" The answer is affirmative. For example, to find an irrational number between $\frac{1}{3}$ and $\frac{1}{2}$, we first write $\frac{1}{3}$ and $\frac{1}{2}$ as decimals.

$\frac{1}{2} = 0.5$

$\frac{1}{3} = 0.333 \cdots$

Obviously, the number 0.4 is between 0.5 and $0.333 \cdots$; however, this number is not irrational. We now add a nonrepeating, nonterminating part to this number as shown.

$\frac{1}{2} = 0.5$

$0.4101001000 \cdots$ Nonterminating, nonrepeating

$\frac{1}{3} = 0.333 \cdots$

The number $0.4101001000 \cdots$ is bigger than $0.333 \cdots$, smaller than 0.5, and irrational. We could have found infinitely many other numbers using a similar technique. Can you find two more?

EXAMPLE 10 Finding Numbers Between Decimals

Find the following:

(a) A rational number between 0.121 and 0.122

(b) An irrational number between 0.121 and 0.122

Solution

(a) The rational number 0.1215 is between 0.121 and 0.122 as shown.

0.121

0.1215

0.122

(b) The irrational number $0.121567891011 \cdots$ is between 0.121 and 0.122 as shown.

0.121

$0.121567891011 \cdots$ Nonterminating, nonrepeating

0.122

In the preceding discussion we saw that we are able to find an irrational number between any two given rational numbers. We can also show that it is possible to find a rational number between any two given rational numbers. For example, given the rational numbers $\frac{4}{7}$ and $\frac{5}{7}$, we write

$$\frac{4}{7} = \frac{4 \cdot 2}{7 \cdot 2} = \frac{8}{14} \quad \text{and} \quad \frac{5}{7} = \frac{5 \cdot 2}{7 \cdot 2} = \frac{10}{14}$$

We can now see by inspection that one rational number between $\frac{4}{7}$ and $\frac{5}{7}$ is $\frac{9}{14}$. If the two given rationals do not have the same denominator, then we can proceed as in the next example.

EXAMPLE 11 Finding Numbers Between Decimals and Fractions

Find a rational number between $0.\overline{4}$, and $\frac{6}{13}$.

Solution

Since $0.\overline{4} = \frac{4}{9}$, the problem is equivalent to that of finding a rational number between $\frac{4}{9}$ and $\frac{6}{13}$. We can do this easily by changing to fractions with common denominators. Thus,

$$\frac{4}{9} = \frac{4 \cdot 13}{9 \cdot 13} = \frac{52}{117} \quad \text{and} \quad \frac{6}{13} = \frac{6 \cdot 9}{13 \cdot 9} = \frac{54}{117}$$

Therefore, an obvious choice for the number we seek is $\frac{53}{117}$.

We have been able to find a rational number between two given ones; that is: ***between any two rational numbers there is another rational number.*** Mathematicians express this idea with the following property:

> **Density of the Rational Numbers**
>
> The set of rational numbers is dense.

5.4 EXERCISES

A Terminating and Nonterminating Decimals

In problems 1–24, write each number in decimal form.

1. $\frac{9}{10}$
2. $\frac{3}{10}$
3. $\frac{11}{10}$
4. $\frac{27}{10}$
5. $\frac{17}{100}$
6. $\frac{38}{100}$
7. $\frac{121}{100}$
8. $\frac{3520}{100}$
9. $\frac{3}{1000}$
10. $\frac{143}{1000}$
11. $\frac{1243}{1000}$
12. $\frac{25,360}{1000}$
13. $\frac{3}{5}$
14. $\frac{7}{8}$
15. $\frac{9}{16}$
16. $\frac{15}{32}$
17. $\frac{5}{8}$
18. $\frac{5}{4}$
19. $\frac{5}{7}$
20. $\frac{7}{6}$
21. $\frac{4}{15}$
22. $6\frac{1}{4}$
23. $7\frac{1}{7}$
24. $3\frac{2}{3}$

In problems 25–30, determine whether each number has a terminating decimal expansion. If it does, give the expansion.

25. $\frac{3}{16}$
26. $\frac{3}{14}$
27. $\frac{1}{64}$
28. $\frac{4}{28}$
29. $\frac{31}{3125}$
30. $\frac{9}{250}$

In problems 31–42, rewrite each repeating decimal, using a bar and as few digits as possible.

31. $0.555555\cdots$
32. $0.777777\cdots$
33. $0.646464\cdots$
34. $0.737373\cdots$
35. $0.235235\cdots$
36. $0.930930\cdots$
37. $0.215555\cdots$
38. $0.7132222\cdots$
39. $0.079353535\cdots$
40. $0.23515151\cdots$
41. $5.070707\cdots$
42. $9.23373737\cdots$

B Changing Infinite Repeating Decimals to Fractions

In problems 43–58, write each number as a fraction (a quotient of two integers). Reduce if possible.

43. $0.\overline{8}$
44. $0.\overline{6}$
45. $0.\overline{31}$
46. $0.\overline{21}$
47. $0.\overline{114}$
48. $0.\overline{102}$
49. $2.\overline{31}$
50. $5.\overline{672}$
51. $1.\overline{234}$

52. $0.\overline{017}$
53. $1.\overline{27}$
54. $2.4\overline{8}$
55. $0.45\overline{75}$
56. $0.23\overline{15}$
57. $0.\overline{2016}$
58. $0.201\overline{6}$

C Percent

In problems 59–67, write each percent as a decimal.

59. 29%
60. 23.4%
61. 0.9%
62. 56.9%
63. 45.69%
64. 0.008%
65. 34.15%
66. 93.56%
67. 0.0234%

In problems 68–76, write each decimal as a percent.

68. 0.38
69. 3.45
70. 9.998
71. 0.567
72. 0.00452
73. 9.003
74. 0.0004
75. 0.0045
76. 0.0008

In problems 77–80, write each fraction as a percent.

77. $\frac{3}{5}$
78. $\frac{4}{7}$ (to one decimal place)
79. $\frac{5}{6}$ (to one decimal place)
80. $\frac{7}{8}$

D Rationals, Irrationals, and Square Roots

In problems 81–90, classify each number as rational or irrational.

81. $\sqrt{120}$
82. $\sqrt{121}$
83. $\sqrt{125}$
84. $\sqrt{169}$
85. $\sqrt{\frac{9}{16}}$
86. $\sqrt{\frac{9}{15}}$
87. $\frac{3}{5}$
88. $-\frac{22}{7}$
89. $-\frac{5}{3}$
90. -0

E Irrational and Decimal Numbers

In problems 91–101, classify each number as rational or irrational.

91. $0.232323\cdots$
92. $0.023002300023\cdots$
93. $0.121231234\cdots$
94. 0.121231234
95. $6\frac{1}{4}$
96. $\sqrt{6\frac{1}{4}}$
97. $\sqrt{3\frac{1}{4}}$
98. $0.24681012\cdots$
99. 0.1122334455
100. 3.1415
101. π

F Greater Than, Less Than, and the Trichotomy Law

In problems 102–115, insert <, >, or =, as appropriate.

102. 3 ____ 4
103. 17 ____ 11
104. $\frac{1}{5}$ ____ $\frac{1}{4}$
105. $\frac{12}{19}$ ____ $\frac{11}{17}$
106. $\frac{5}{7}$ ____ $\frac{10}{14}$
107. $1\frac{2}{3}$ ____ $\frac{8}{6}$
108. $\sqrt{20}$ ____ 4.5
109. $3.777\cdots$ ____ $\sqrt{15}$
110. $0.333\cdots$ ____ $0.333444\cdots$
111. 0.101001000 ____ $0.1101001000\cdots$
112. $0.999\cdots$ ____ 1
113. $0.333\cdots + 0.666\cdots$ ____ 1
114. $3(0.333\cdots)$ ____ 1
115. 0.112233 ____ $0.111222333\cdots$

G Density of the Rational Numbers

116. Find a rational number between 0.31 and 0.32.
117. Find a rational number between 0.28 and 0.285.
118. Find an irrational number between 0.31 and 0.32.
119. Find an irrational number between 0.28 and 0.285.
120. Find a rational number between $0.101001000\cdots$ and $0.102002000\cdots$.
121. Find a rational number between $0.303003000\cdots$ and $0.304004000\cdots$.
122. Find an irrational number between $0.101001000\cdots$ and $0.102002000\cdots$.
123. Find an irrational number between $0.303003000\cdots$ and $0.304004000\cdots$.
124. Find a rational number between $\frac{3}{11}$ and $\frac{4}{11}$.
125. Find a rational number between $\frac{7}{9}$ and $\frac{9}{11}$.
126. Find an irrational number between $\frac{4}{9}$ and $\frac{5}{9}$.
127. Find an irrational number between $\frac{2}{11}$ and $\frac{3}{11}$.
128. Find a rational number between $0.\overline{5}$ and $\frac{2}{3}$.
129. Find a rational number between 0.1 and $0.\overline{1}$.

IN OTHER WORDS

130. Answer true (T) or false (F) for each of the following statements and give reasons to support each answer:
    a. Some repeating decimals are not rational numbers.
    b. All counting numbers are rational numbers.
    c. Some integers are not rational numbers.
    d. $0.20200200020000\cdots$ is a repeating decimal.
    e. All terminating decimals are rational numbers.

USING YOUR KNOWLEDGE

*Have you met anybody nice today or did you have an unpleasant experience? Perhaps the person you met was very nice or your experience was very unpleasant. Psychologists and linguists have a numerical way to indicate the difference between nice and very nice or between unpleasant and very unpleasant. Suppose you assign a positive number (**+ 2**, for example) to the adjective* nice, *a negative number (say,* **− 2***) to* unpleasant, *and a positive number greater than 1 (say* **+ 1.75***) to* very. *Then,* very nice *means*

Very ↓ nice ↓

$$(1.75)\cdot(2) = 3.50$$

and very unpleasant *means*

Very ↓ unpleasant ↓

$$(1.75)\cdot(-2) = -3.50$$

Here are some adverbs and adjectives and their average numerical values, as rated by a panel of college students. (Values differ from one panel to another.)

131. Slightly wicked
132. Decidedly average
133. Rather lovable
134. Very good

Adverbs		Adjectives	
Slightly	0.54	Wicked	−2.5
Rather	0.84	Disgusting	−2.1
Decidedly	1.16	Average	−0.8
Very	1.25	Good	3.1
Extremely	1.45	Lovable	2.4

DISCOVERY

In this section we developed a procedure for expressing an infinite repeating decimal as a quotient of two integers. For example,

$$0.\overline{3} = 0.333\cdots = \tfrac{3}{9}$$
$$0.\overline{6} = 0.666\cdots = \tfrac{6}{9}$$
$$0.\overline{21} = 0.212121\cdots = \tfrac{21}{99}$$
$$0.\overline{314} = 0.314314314\cdots = \tfrac{314}{999}$$

135. From these examples, can you discover how to express $0.\overline{4} = 0.444\cdots$ as a quotient of integers?

136. Can you express $0.\overline{4321}$ as a quotient of integers?

5.5 Radicals and Real Numbers

GETTING STARTED

OBJECTIVES

A. Simplify radicals and rationalize denominators.
B. Multiply and divide expressions involving radicals.
C. Add and subtract expressions involving radicals.
D. Solve applications involving radicals.
E. Classify numbers as natural, integers, rationals, or irrationals.

A plane can break the sound barrier.

THE "RADICAL" NOTION OF SUPERSONIC SPEED

How fast can this plane travel? The answer is classified information, but it exceeds twice the speed of sound (747 mph). It is then said that the plane's speed is more than Mach 2. The formula for calculating the Mach number is

$$M = \sqrt{\frac{2}{\gamma}}\sqrt{\frac{P_2 - P_1}{P_1}}$$

where P_1 and P_2 are air pressures. This expression can be simplified by multiplying both radical expressions and *rationalizing* the denominator.

In this section you will add, subtract, multiply, and divide radical expressions, that is, expressions containing radicals.

In the preceding section we studied irrational numbers of the form $\sqrt{n}$, where n is a positive number but not a perfect square. We did this with the help of the Pythagoreans, who solved the equation $x^2 = 2$. Irrational numbers of the form $\sqrt{n}$ are called **radicals.** In general, $\sqrt[n]{m}$ is a **radical expression** with index n and radicand m. The index 2 is usually omitted, so we write $\sqrt{n}$ instead of $\sqrt[2]{n}$. We study next some simple operations on radicals.

A Simplifying Radicals

The velocity v (in feet per second) of an object in free fall depends on the distance d that it has fallen. The formula is

$$v = \sqrt{32d}$$

Thus, after an object has fallen 1 ft $(d = 1)$, its velocity is $\sqrt{32}$ ft/sec, and after 2 ft $(d = 2)$, it is $\sqrt{64}$ ft/sec. The number $\sqrt{32}$ is an irrational number, because 32 is not a perfect square, but 64 is a perfect square $(8^2 = 64)$, so $\sqrt{64} = 8$ is a rational number. Note that $\sqrt{32}$ is positive. We interpret $\sqrt{n}$ to mean the positive square root of n. Can we simplify $\sqrt{32}$? We say that $\sqrt{n}$ is in **simplest form** if n has no factor (other than 1) that is a perfect square. Using this definition, we can see that $\sqrt{32}$ is not in simplest form because the perfect square 16 is a factor of 32. The simplification can be done using the following property:

Multiplication of Radicals

If a and b are nonnegative real numbers, then

$$\sqrt{a \cdot b} = \sqrt{a} \cdot \sqrt{b}$$

Thus,

$$\sqrt{32} = \sqrt{16 \cdot 2} = \sqrt{16} \cdot \sqrt{2} = 4\sqrt{2}$$

In general, the simplest form of a number involving the radical sign $\sqrt{\ }$ is obtained by using the perfect squares 1, 4, 9, 16, 25, 36, 49, 64, 81, 100, and so on, as factors under the radical and then using the multiplication property, as in the next example.

EXAMPLE 1 Simplifying Radicals

Simplify the following if possible:

(a) $\sqrt{75}$ (b) $\sqrt{70}$

Solution

(a) The largest perfect square dividing 75 is 25. Thus, we write

$$\sqrt{75} = \sqrt{25 \cdot 3} = \sqrt{25} \cdot \sqrt{3} = 5\sqrt{3}$$

(b) There is no perfect square (except 1) that divides 70. (Try dividing by 4, 9, 16, 25, and 36.) Thus, $\sqrt{70}$ cannot be simplified any further.

The property $\sqrt{a \cdot b} = \sqrt{a} \cdot \sqrt{b}$ can be used to **rationalize** the denominator of certain expressions, that is, to free the denominator of radicals. Thus, if we wish to rationalize the denominator in the expression $6/\sqrt{3}$, we use the fundamental principle of fractions and multiply the numerator and the denominator of the fraction by $\sqrt{3}$ (because we know that $\sqrt{3} \cdot \sqrt{3} = 3$), as follows:

$$\frac{6}{\sqrt{3}} = \frac{6 \cdot \sqrt{3}}{\sqrt{3} \cdot \sqrt{3}} = \frac{6 \cdot \sqrt{3}}{\sqrt{9}} = \frac{6 \cdot \sqrt{3}}{3} = 2\sqrt{3}$$

EXAMPLE 2 Rationalizing the Denominator

Rationalize the denominator in the expression $5/\sqrt{10}$.

Solution

We multiply the numerator and the denominator by $\sqrt{10}$ and then simplify.

$$\frac{5}{\sqrt{10}} = \frac{5 \cdot \sqrt{10}}{\sqrt{10} \cdot \sqrt{10}} = \frac{5 \cdot \sqrt{10}}{\sqrt{100}} = \frac{5 \cdot \sqrt{10}}{10} = \frac{\sqrt{10}}{2}$$

B Multiplication and Division of Radicals

Can we simplify $\sqrt{\frac{3}{4}}$? (This is one of the two answers you will get if you solve the equation $x^2 = \frac{3}{4}$.) This time, the perfect square 4 appears in the denominator, so to simplify the expression, we use the following property:

Division of Radicals

If a and b are positive numbers, then

$$\sqrt{\frac{a}{b}} = \frac{\sqrt{a}}{\sqrt{b}}$$

Thus,

$$\sqrt{\frac{3}{4}} = \frac{\sqrt{3}}{\sqrt{4}} = \frac{\sqrt{3}}{2}$$

EXAMPLE 3 Simplifying Radicals Involving Quotients

Simplify the following:

(a) $\sqrt{\frac{32}{25}}$ (b) $\sqrt{\frac{36}{7}}$

Solution

(a) $\sqrt{\frac{32}{25}} = \frac{\sqrt{32}}{\sqrt{25}} = \frac{\sqrt{32}}{5}$

$$= \frac{\sqrt{16 \cdot 2}}{5}$$

$$= \frac{4 \cdot \sqrt{2}}{5}$$

(b) $\sqrt{\frac{36}{7}} = \frac{\sqrt{36}}{\sqrt{7}} = \frac{6}{\sqrt{7}}$

But now we must rationalize the denominator by multiplying the numerator and the denominator of the fraction $6/\sqrt{7}$ by $\sqrt{7}$ to obtain

$$\frac{6 \cdot \sqrt{7}}{7}$$

as our final answer. An easier way to get this result would be to multiply the numerator and the denominator of the original fraction $\frac{36}{7}$ by 7 first to obtain

$$\sqrt{\frac{36}{7}} = \sqrt{\frac{36 \cdot 7}{7 \cdot 7}} = \frac{\sqrt{36 \cdot 7}}{\sqrt{7 \cdot 7}} = \frac{6\sqrt{7}}{7}$$

Keep this in mind when doing the exercises!

The two properties we have presented are used to do multiplication and division of radicals. Thus,

$$\sqrt{6} \cdot \sqrt{2} = \sqrt{12} \quad \text{Using multiplication of radicals}$$

$$= \sqrt{4 \cdot 3} = 2\sqrt{3} \quad \text{Using multiplication of radicals}$$

Similarly,

$$\frac{\sqrt{32}}{\sqrt{2}} = \sqrt{\frac{32}{2}} = \sqrt{16} = 4 \quad \text{Using division of radicals}$$

EXAMPLE 4 Multiplication and Division of Radicals

Perform the indicated operations and simplify.

(a) $\sqrt{6} \cdot \sqrt{3}$ (b) $\sqrt{40}/\sqrt{5}$

Solution

(a) $\sqrt{6} \cdot \sqrt{3} = \sqrt{18} = \sqrt{9 \cdot 2} = 3\sqrt{2}$ (b) $\dfrac{\sqrt{40}}{\sqrt{5}} = \sqrt{\dfrac{40}{5}} = \sqrt{8} = \sqrt{4 \cdot 2} = 2\sqrt{2}$

C Addition and Subtraction of Radicals

The addition and subtraction of radicals can be accomplished using the distributive property. Note that radicals can be combined only when their radicands (the quantities under the radical signs) and indexes are the same. Thus, to add $5\sqrt{2} + 3\sqrt{2}$ or subtract $5\sqrt{2} - 3\sqrt{2}$, we write

$$5\sqrt{2} + 3\sqrt{2} = (5 + 3)\sqrt{2} = 8\sqrt{2}$$

or

$$5\sqrt{2} - 3\sqrt{2} = (5 - 3)\sqrt{2} = 2\sqrt{2}$$

Sometimes we may have to use the multiplication and division of radicals mentioned earlier before the additions or subtractions can be accomplished. Thus, to add $\sqrt{48} + \sqrt{27}$, we use the first property to write $\sqrt{48} = \sqrt{16 \cdot 3} = 4\sqrt{3}$ and $\sqrt{27} = \sqrt{9 \cdot 3} = 3\sqrt{3}$. We then have

$$\sqrt{48} + \sqrt{27} = 4\sqrt{3} + 3\sqrt{3} = 7\sqrt{3}$$

EXAMPLE 5 Addition and Subtraction of Radicals

Perform the indicated operations.

(a) $\sqrt{50} - \sqrt{8}$ (b) $\sqrt{75} + \sqrt{48} - \sqrt{147}$

Solution

(a) $\sqrt{50} - \sqrt{8} = \sqrt{25 \cdot 2} - \sqrt{4 \cdot 2}$
$= 5\sqrt{2} - 2\sqrt{2}$
$= 3\sqrt{2}$

(b) $\sqrt{75} + \sqrt{48} - \sqrt{147} = \sqrt{25 \cdot 3} + \sqrt{16 \cdot 3} - \sqrt{49 \cdot 3}$
$= 5\sqrt{3} + 4\sqrt{3} - 7\sqrt{3}$
$= 2\sqrt{3}$

D Applications

EXAMPLE 6 Applications Involving Radicals

The greatest speed s (in miles per hour) at which a bicyclist can safely turn a corner of radius r ft is $s = 4\sqrt{r}$. Find the greatest speed at which a bicyclist can safely turn a corner with a 20-ft radius, and write the answer in simplest form.

Solution

$$s = 4\sqrt{r} = 4\sqrt{20} = 4\sqrt{4 \cdot 5} = 4 \cdot 2\sqrt{5} = 8\sqrt{5} \text{ mph}$$

This is slightly less than 18 mph.

E Classifying Real Numbers

In the preceding sections we have mentioned the natural numbers (**N**), the whole numbers (**W**), the integers (**I**), the rational numbers (**Q**), and the real numbers (**R**). Do you know the relationship between all these sets of numbers? Recall from Chapter 2 that the notation $N \subset W$ means that N is a proper subset of W; that is, every element of N is also an element of W, so we can concisely state the relationship between these numbers as

$$N \subset W \subset I \subset Q \subset R$$

as shown in Figure 5.4.

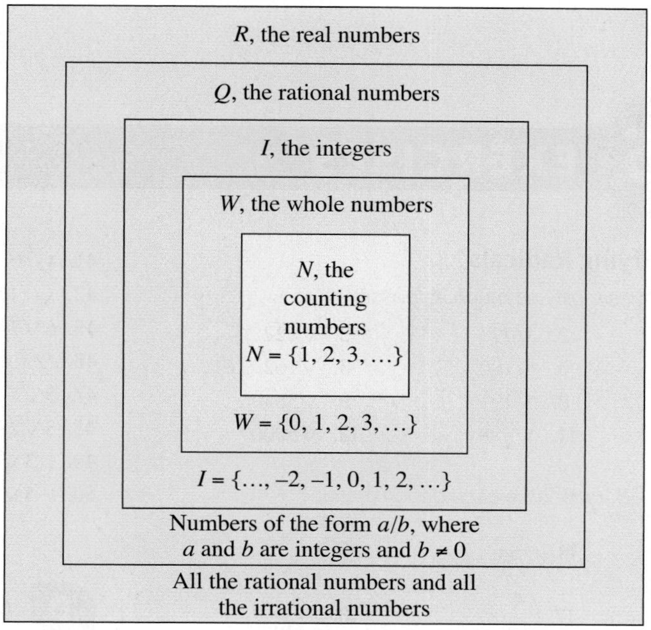

FIGURE 5.4

EXAMPLE 7 Classifying Real Numbers

Classify the following numbers by making a check mark in the appropriate row:

Set	$\sqrt{4}$	$0.\overline{3}$	$\sqrt{2}$	$-\frac{5}{7}$	0
Natural numbers					
Whole numbers					
Integers					
Rational numbers					
Irrational numbers					
Real numbers					

Solution

The correct check marks are shown below.

Set	$\sqrt{4}$	$0.\bar{3}$	$\sqrt{2}$	$-\frac{5}{7}$	0
Natural numbers	✔				
Whole numbers	✔				✔
Integers	✔				✔
Rational numbers	✔	✔		✔	✔
Irrational numbers			✔		
Real numbers	✔	✔	✔	✔	✔

5.5 EXERCISES

A Simplifying Radicals

In problems 1–12, simplify as much as possible.

1. $\sqrt{90}$
2. $\sqrt{72}$
3. $\sqrt{122}$
4. $\sqrt{175}$
5. $\sqrt{180}$
6. $\sqrt{162}$
7. $\sqrt{200}$
8. $\sqrt{191}$
9. $\sqrt{384}$
10. $\sqrt{486}$
11. $\sqrt{588}$
12. $\sqrt{5000}$

In problems 13–18, rationalize each denominator.

13. $\dfrac{3}{\sqrt{7}}$
14. $\dfrac{6}{\sqrt{5}}$
15. $-\dfrac{\sqrt{2}}{\sqrt{5}}$
16. $-\dfrac{\sqrt{3}}{\sqrt{7}}$
17. $\dfrac{4}{\sqrt{8}}$
18. $\dfrac{3}{\sqrt{27}}$

B Multiplication and Division of Radicals

In problems 19–27, simplify each expression.

19. $\sqrt{\frac{3}{49}}$
20. $\sqrt{\frac{7}{16}}$
21. $\sqrt{\frac{4}{3}}$
22. $\sqrt{\frac{25}{11}}$
23. $\sqrt{\frac{8}{49}}$
24. $\sqrt{\frac{18}{25}}$
25. $\sqrt{\frac{18}{50}}$
26. $\sqrt{\frac{24}{75}}$
27. $\sqrt{\frac{32}{125}}$

In problems 28–36, perform the indicated operations and simplify.

28. $\sqrt{7}\cdot\sqrt{8}$
29. $\sqrt{5}\cdot\sqrt{50}$
30. $\sqrt{10}\cdot\sqrt{5}$
31. $\dfrac{\sqrt{28}}{\sqrt{2}}$
32. $\dfrac{\sqrt{22}}{\sqrt{2}}$
33. $\dfrac{\sqrt{10}}{\sqrt{250}}$
34. $\dfrac{\sqrt{10}}{\sqrt{490}}$
35. $\dfrac{\sqrt{33}}{\sqrt{22}}$
36. $\dfrac{\sqrt{18}}{\sqrt{12}}$

C Addition and Subtraction of Radicals

In problems 37–50, perform the indicated operations and simplify.

37. $\sqrt{3}+\sqrt{12}$
38. $\sqrt{32}-\sqrt{8}$
39. $\sqrt{125}+\sqrt{80}$
40. $\sqrt{24}-\sqrt{150}$
41. $\sqrt{3^2+4^2}$
42. $\sqrt{5^2+(12)^2}$
43. $\sqrt{(13)^2-(12)^2}$
44. $\sqrt{(25)^2-(24)^2}$
45. $6\sqrt{7}+\sqrt{7}-2\sqrt{7}$
46. $\sqrt{3}+11\sqrt{3}-3\sqrt{3}$
47. $5\sqrt{7}-3\sqrt{28}-2\sqrt{63}$
48. $3\sqrt{28}-6\sqrt{7}-2\sqrt{175}$
49. $-3\sqrt{45}+\sqrt{20}-\sqrt{5}$
50. $-5\sqrt{27}+\sqrt{12}-5\sqrt{48}$

D Applications

51. The formula that approximates the time t (in hours) a storm will last based on the diameter d (in miles) of the storm is given by $t=\sqrt{\left(\frac{d}{6}\right)^3}$.
    a. How long will a storm 6 mi in diameter last?
    b. How long will a storm 10 mi in diameter last? Give the answer with a rationalized denominator and as an approximation.
52. *Meteorology* A storm 3 mi in diameter is threatening a baseball game, which must be resumed within an hour or the game will have to be postponed.

a. How long will the storm last? (Give the answer with a rationalized denominator).

b. Will the game be resumed or postponed?

53. The speed S (in meters per second, m/sec) of a tsunami is given by the equation $S = \sqrt{g} \cdot \sqrt{d}$, where $g \approx 10$ m/sec^2 is the acceleration due to gravity and d is the average depth of the water in meters.

a. Find the speed S of a tsunami when the average depth d of the water is 40 m.

b. On March 11, 2011, an earthquake of magnitude 9.0 occurred off the coast of Japan, triggering a massive tsunami. If the average depth of the Pacific Ocean is 4267 m, about how fast was the tsunami moving?

54. *Tsunami speed* An earthquake of magnitude 4.2 occurred on February 14, 2010, near San Diego, California. If the depth of the water is 30 m, how fast was the resulting tsunami traveling?

55. The compound interest rate r that is paid when you borrow \$$P$ and pay \$$A$ at the end of 2 years is

$$r = \sqrt{\frac{A}{P}} - 1$$

Find the rate when \$100 is borrowed and the amount paid at the end of the 2 years is \$144.

56. When you are at an altitude of a ft above Earth, your view V_m (in miles) extends as far as a circle called the *horizon* and is given by

$$V_m = \sqrt{\tfrac{3}{2}a}$$

The greatest altitude reached in a manned balloon is 123,800 ft and was attained by Nicholas Piantanida.

a. In simplified form, what was the view in miles from this balloon?

b. If $\sqrt{1857} \approx 43$, what was the view in miles?

If air resistance is neglected, the terminal velocity v of a falling body in meters per second is given by

$$v = \sqrt{20h + v_0}$$

57. Find v if $h = 10$ and $v_0 = 25$ m/sec.

58. Find v if a body is dropped ($v_0 = 0$) from a height of 45 m.

59. If the velocity as measured in feet per second is

$$v = \sqrt{64h + v_0}$$

$h = 12$ ft, and $v_0 = 16$ ft/sec, find v.

60. Find v if a body is dropped ($v_0 = 0$) from a height of 25 ft.

In problems 61–66, evaluate $\sqrt{b^2 - 4ac}$.

61. $a = 1, b = 5, c = 4$

62. $a = 1, b = 3, c = 2$

63. $a = 2, b = -3, c = -20$

64. $a = \frac{1}{2}, b = -\frac{1}{12}, c = -1$

65. $a = \frac{1}{12}, b = \frac{1}{3}, c = -1$

66. $a = \frac{1}{12}, b = \frac{1}{2}, c = \frac{2}{3}$

E Classifying Real Numbers

In problems 67–76, classify each number by making a check mark in the appropriate row.

	67.	68.	69.	70.	71.	72.	73.	74.	75.	76.
Set	**4.2**	$-\frac{3}{8}$	**0**	$\sqrt{3}$	$\sqrt{9}$	**5**	$0.\overline{66}$	$1\frac{5}{8}$	$\sqrt{20}$	π
Natural numbers										
Whole numbers										
Integers										
Rational numbers										
Irrational numbers										
Real numbers										

IN OTHER WORDS

77. Explain why we cannot use the definition $\sqrt{a} \cdot \sqrt{b} = \sqrt{ab}$ when a and b are negative numbers.

78. Explain why every integer is a rational number.

USING YOUR KNOWLEDGE

At the beginning of the next section we shall see that after the man in the picture had fallen 1 ft, his velocity was $\sqrt{32} = 4\sqrt{2}$ ft/sec. Can you estimate $\sqrt{32}$?

Mathematicians use a method called interpolation to approximate this answer. Since we know that $\sqrt{25} = 5$ and $\sqrt{36} = 6$, $\sqrt{32}$ should be between 5 and 6. If we place $\sqrt{25}$, $\sqrt{32}$, and $\sqrt{36}$ in a column, the interpolation is done as shown in the diagram.

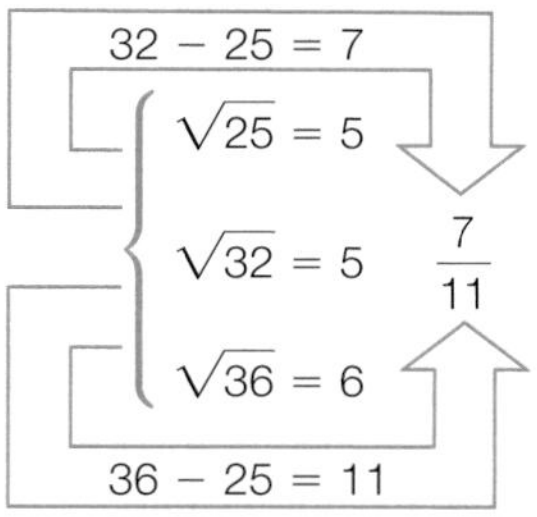

Thus, $\sqrt{32}$ is approximately $5\frac{7}{11}$. If we wish, we can write this answer as a decimal by dividing 7 by 11, obtaining $0.\overline{63}$ and writing the approximation as $5.\overline{63}$. (If you use a calculator to find the square root of 32, the answer is 5.6569.)

Use this knowledge to approximate the following square roots. Give each answer as a mixed number and then as a decimal to two places.

79. $\sqrt{40}$

80. $\sqrt{68}$

81. $\sqrt{85}$

82. $\sqrt{108}$

COLLABORATIVE LEARNING

It is said that the Babylonians used an averaging method to find the square root of a number. Here is how the method worked. Suppose you want to find the square root of 4, that is, $\sqrt{4}$. Start with the first guess. Say the guess is 1. Now take the average of 4 and 1, which is 2.5. Now the second guess is the average of 2.5 and $\frac{4}{2.5}$, which is 2.05. Your next guess will be the average of 2.05 and $\frac{4}{2.05}$, that is, 2.0006098. If you keep this procedure going, you will reach the conclusion that $\sqrt{4}$ is 2.

Now form two or more groups, and each group must find $\sqrt{10}$, $\sqrt{867}$, and $\sqrt{900}$.

Now use the Babylonian method to approximate the numbers approximated in problems 79–82. Which is the better approximation? Which method do you prefer?

5.6 Number Sequences

GETTING STARTED

OBJECTIVES

A. Find terms and the common difference of an arithmetic sequence.
B. Find the sum of a finite arithmetic sequence.
C. Find the terms of a finite geometric sequence.
D. Find the sum of a finite geometric sequence.
E. Use the sum of an infinite geometric sequence to write a repeating decimal as a fraction.
F. Use the RSTUV procedure to solve problems involving sequences.

"THE TWELVE DAYS OF CHRISTMAS" AND PROGRESSIONS

Do you know the song "The Twelve Days of Christmas"? How many gifts do you get each day? What is the total number of gifts you receive? If you sing along, you will recall that the song goes like this:

Day 1	A partridge in a pear tree	1 gift
Day 2	A partridge in a pear tree and two turtle doves	$1 + 2$ gifts
Day 3	A partridge in a pear tree, two turtle doves, and three French hens	$1 + 2 + 3$ gifts
⋮	⋮	⋮

On the twelfth day, you get $1 + 2 + 3 + \cdots + 11 + 12$ gifts. This sum is an **arithmetic progression.** Can you add it quickly?

According to a story told by E. T. Bell, in late-eighteenth-century Germany, a precocious boy of 10 was admitted to the class in arithmetic in which none of the children were expected to know about progressions. It was easy for the heroic Buttner (the teacher) to give out a long problem in addition whose answer he could find by a formula in a few seconds. The problem was to add

$$1 + 2 + 3 + 4 + \cdots + 98 + 99 + 100$$

The student who first got the answer was to lay his slate on the table, the next student to lay his slate on top of the first's, and so on. Buttner had barely finished stating the problem when a boy flung his slate on the table. "*Ligget se* [There it lies]," he said in his peasant dialect. The rest of the hour, while the class worked on the problem, the boy sat with his hands folded, favored now and then by a sarcastic glance from Buttner, who imagined the boy to be just another blockhead. At the end of the period, Buttner looked over the answers. On the boy's slate there appeared but a single number. Do you know what that number was?

In later years, the boy confessed to having recognized the pattern

$$1 + 2 + 3 + 4 + \cdots + 97 + 98 + 99 + 100$$

101

in which the sum of each pair of numbers is 101. Since there are 50 pairs of numbers, the total sum would be $50 \times 101 = 5050$, the number on the boy's slate.

In this section you will see the magic formula so you too can add arithmetic progressions! By the way, you will get 6×13 gifts on the twelfth day of Christmas (if you have been good). What about the boy? Carl Friedrich Gauss became one of the most renowned European mathematicians of his time.

How far will the skydiver fall in the first 5 sec?

The photograph shows a skydiver plunging toward the ground. Do you know how far he will fall in the first 5 sec? A free-falling body travels about 16 ft in the first second, 48 ft in the next second, 80 ft in the third second, and so on. The number of feet traveled in each successive second is

16, 48, 80, 112, 144, . . .

This list of numbers is an example of a **number sequence.** In general, a list of numbers having a first number, a second number, a third number, and so on is called a **sequence;** the numbers in the sequence are called the **terms.** The following are examples of sequences:

1. The odd positive integers — 1, 3, 5, 7, . . .
2. The positive multiples of 3 — 3, 6, 9, 12, . . .
3. The powers of 10 — $10^1, 10^2, 10^3, \ldots$
4. The interest on the first three payments on a \$10,000 car being paid over 3 years at 12% annual interest — \$8.33, \$8.11, \$7.89, . . .

A Arithmetic Sequences

The sequences (1), (2), and (4) on the preceding page are *arithmetic sequences.* An **arithmetic sequence,** or **arithmetic progression,** is a sequence in which each term after the first is obtained by *adding* a quantity called the **common difference** to the preceding term. Thus,

16, 48, 80, 112, 144, . . .

is an arithmetic sequence in which each term is obtained by adding the common difference 32 to the preceding term. This means that the common difference for an arithmetic sequence is just the difference between any two consecutive terms.

EXAMPLE 1 Finding Common Differences

Find the common difference in each sequence.

(a) 7, 37, 67, 97, . . . **(b)** 10, 5, 0, −5, . . .

Solution

(a) The common difference is $37 - 7 = 30$ (or $67 - 37$, or $97 - 67$).

(b) The common difference is $5 - 10 = -5$ (or $0 - 5$, or $-5 - 0$).

It is customary to denote the first term of an arithmetic sequence by a_1 (read "a sub 1"), the common difference by d, and the nth term by a_n. Thus, in the sequence 16, 48, 80, 112, 144, . . . , we have $a_1 = 16$ and $d = 32$. The second term of the sequence, a_2, is

$$a_2 = a_1 + 32 = 16 + 32 = 48$$

Since each term is obtained from the preceding one by adding 32,

$$a_3 = a_2 + 32 = (a_1 + 1 \cdot 32) + 32 = a_1 + 2 \cdot 32 = 80$$
$$a_4 = a_3 + 32 = (a_1 + 2 \cdot 32) + 32 = a_1 + 3 \cdot 32 = 112$$
$$a_5 = a_4 + 32 = (a_1 + 3 \cdot 32) + 32 = a_1 + 4 \cdot 32 = 144$$

By following this pattern, we find the **general term** a_n to be

General Term a_n of a Sequence

$$a_n = a_1 + (n - 1) \cdot d$$

EXAMPLE 2 Finding Terms and Differences

Consider the sequence 7, 10, 13, 16, ... Find the following:

(a) a_1, the first term
(b) d, the common difference
(c) a_{11}, the eleventh term
(d) a_n, the nth term

Solution

(a) The first term a_1 is 7.
(b) The common difference d is $10 - 7 = 3$.
(c) The eleventh term is $a_{11} = 7 + (11 - 1) \cdot 3 = 7 + 10 \cdot 3 = 37$.
(d) $a_n = a_1 + (n - 1) \cdot d = 7 + (n - 1) \cdot 3 = 4 + 3n$

B Sum of an Arithmetic Sequence

Let us go back to our original problem of finding how far the skydiver falls in 5 sec. The first five terms of the sequence are 16, 48, 80, 112, and 144; thus, we need to find the sum

$$16 + 48 + 80 + 112 + 144$$

Since successive terms of an arithmetic sequence are obtained by adding the common difference d, the sum S_n of the first n terms is

$$S_n = a_1 + (a_1 + d) + (a_1 + 2d) + (a_1 + 3d) + \cdots + a_n \quad (1)$$

We can also start with a_n and obtain successive terms by subtracting the common difference d. Thus, with the terms written in reverse order,

$$S_n = a_n + (a_n - d) + (a_n - 2d) + \cdots + a_1 \quad (2)$$

Adding equations (1) and (2), we find that the d's drop out, and we obtain

$$\begin{aligned} 2S_n &= (a_1 + a_n) + (a_1 + a_n) + \cdots + (a_1 + a_n) \\ &= n(a_1 + a_n) \end{aligned}$$

Thus,

Theorem 5.4 Sum of a Finite Arithmetic Sequence

The sum of a finite arithmetic sequence with n terms is

$$S_n = \frac{n(a_1 + a_n)}{2}$$

We are now able to determine the sum S_5, the distance the skydiver dropped in 5 sec. The answer is

$$S_5 = \frac{5(16 + 144)}{2} = 400 \text{ ft}$$

C Geometric Sequences

The sequence 10, 100, 1000, and so on is *not* an arithmetic sequence because there is no common difference. This sequence is obtained by *multiplying* each term by 10 to get the next term. Such sequences are called *geometric sequences.* A **geometric sequence,** or **geometric progression,** is a sequence in which each term after the first is obtained by multiplying the preceding term by a number r, called the **common ratio.** Thus, the common ratio r can be found by taking the ratio of two successive terms. For example, in the sequence 8, 16, 32, . . . , the first term a_1 is 8, and the common ratio is $\frac{16}{8} = 2$ $\left(\text{or } \frac{32}{16}\right)$. Thus, the first n terms in a geometric sequence are

$$a_1, \quad a_1r, \quad a_1r^2, \quad a_1r^3, \quad \ldots, \quad a_1r^{n-1}$$

EXAMPLE 3 More Terms and Ratios

Consider the sequence $1, \frac{1}{10}, \frac{1}{100}, \frac{1}{1000}, \ldots$. Find the following:

(a) a_1 (b) r (c) a_n

Solution

(a) a_1 is the first term, 1.

(b) r is the common ratio of any two successive terms. Thus,

$$r = \frac{\frac{1}{10}}{1} = \frac{1}{10}$$

(c) $a_n = a_1r^{n-1} = 1 \cdot \left(\frac{1}{10}\right)^{n-1} = \frac{1}{10^{n-1}}$

D Sum of a Geometric Sequence

Can we find the sum S_n of the first n terms in a geometric sequence?

By definition	$S_n = a_1 + a_1r + a_1r^2 + \cdots + a_1r^{n-1}$
Multiplying by r	$rS_n = a_1r + a_1r^2 + a_1r^3 + \cdots + a_1r^n$
Subtracting	$S_n - rS_n = a_1 - a_1r^n = a_1(1 - r^n)$
By the distributive property	$S_n(1 - r) = a_1(1 - r^n)$
Dividing by $1 - r$	$S_n = \dfrac{a_1(1 - r^n)}{1 - r}$

Theorem 5.5 Sum of a Finite Geometric Sequence

The sum of a geometric sequence $a_1, a_1r, a_1r^2, a_1r^3, \cdots, a_1r^{n-1}$ with a common ratio $r \neq 1$ is

$$S_n = \frac{a_1(1 - r^n)}{1 - r}$$

GRAPH IT

To find the *sum* of a *sequence*, tell your grapher you are doing some math involving sums (press [2nd] [LIST] [➤] [➤] [5]) of sequences (press [2nd] [LIST] [➤] [5]). To do Example 4(b), you have to enter the expression for the sequence, the name of the variable, and where you want to begin and end the sum, so we enter (.2 × .5 ^ (N − 1), N, 1, 5). Note that to enter the variable N, you have to press [ALPHA] N. Now press [ENTER] and make the answer a fraction by pressing [MATH] [1] [ENTER] obtaining $\frac{31}{80}$ as before.

```
sum(seq(.2*.5^(N-1),N,1,
5)
                   .3875
Ans▸Frac
                   31/80
```

Thus, the sum of the first three powers of 10—that is, $10 + 10^2 + 10^3$—can be found by noting that $a_1 = 10$, $r = 10^2/10 = 10$, and

$$S_3 = \frac{10(1 - 10^3)}{1 - 10} = \frac{(10)(-999)}{-9} = 1110$$

as expected.

EXAMPLE 4 Finding Terms and Sums

The first term of a geometric sequence is $\frac{1}{5}$, and $r = \frac{1}{2}$. Find the following:

(a) a_5, the fifth term **(b)** S_5, the sum of the first five terms

Solution

(a) The nth term in a geometric sequence is $a_1 r^{n-1}$; thus,

$$a_5 = \left(\frac{1}{5}\right)\left(\frac{1}{2}\right)^{5-1} = \left(\frac{1}{5}\right)\left(\frac{1}{2}\right)^4 = \left(\frac{1}{5}\right)\left(\frac{1}{16}\right) = \frac{1}{80}$$

(b) The sum of the first n terms of a geometric sequence is

$$S_n = \frac{a_1(1 - r^n)}{(1 - r)}$$

so

$$S_5 = \frac{\frac{1}{5}\left[1 - \left(\frac{1}{2}\right)^5\right]}{1 - \frac{1}{2}} = \frac{\frac{1}{5}\left(\frac{31}{32}\right)}{\frac{1}{2}} = \frac{62}{160} = \frac{31}{80}$$

E Infinite Geometric Sequences

Let us now return to the repeating decimals we discussed in Section 5.5. These decimals can be written using an **infinite geometric sequence.** Thus, the decimal $0.333\cdots$ can be written as

$$0.333\cdots = \frac{3}{10} + \frac{3}{100} + \frac{3}{1000} + \cdots$$

where the common ratio is $\frac{1}{10}$. The sum of the first n terms of this sequence is

$$S_n = \frac{a_1(1 - r^n)}{1 - r} = \frac{a_1}{1 - r} \cdot (1 - r^n)$$

where $a_1 = \frac{3}{10}$ and $r = \frac{1}{10}$.

If we want to find the sum of *all* the terms, we note that as n increases, $\left(\frac{1}{10}\right)^n$ becomes smaller and smaller. Thus, S_n approaches (becomes closer and closer to)

$$\frac{a_1}{1 - r} = \frac{\frac{3}{10}}{1 - \frac{1}{10}} = \frac{\frac{3}{10}}{\frac{9}{10}} = \frac{1}{3}$$

that is, $0.333\cdots = \frac{1}{3}$. Figure 5.5 gives a good graphic representation of the sum of an infinite geometric progression approaching a limit. We can generalize this discussion to obtain the following result:

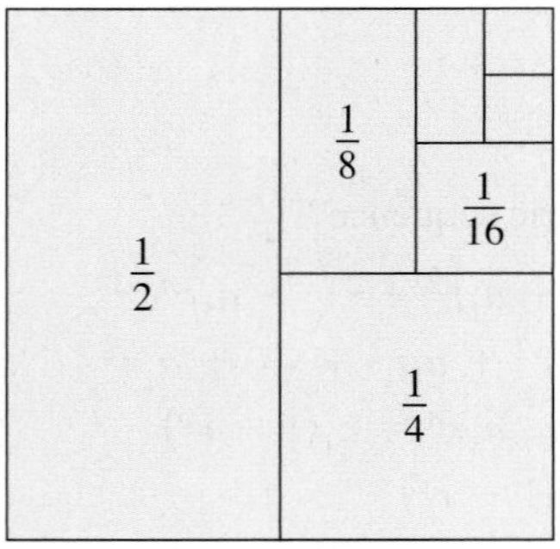

FIGURE 5.5 What do you think is the sum of the sequence $\frac{1}{2} + \frac{1}{4} + \frac{1}{8} + \cdots$?

Theorem 5.6 Sum of an Infinite Geometric Sequence

If r is a number between -1 and 1, the sum of the infinite geometric sequence $a_1, a_1 r, a_1 r^2, \ldots$ is

$$S = \frac{a_1}{1 - r}$$

EXAMPLE 5 Writing Decimals as Sequences

Use the sum of an infinite geometric sequence to write the following repeating decimals as fractions:

(a) $0.666\cdots$ (b) $0.121212\cdots$ (c) $3.222\cdots$

Solution

(a) $0.666\cdots = \frac{6}{10} + \frac{6}{100} + \frac{6}{1000} + \cdots$. This is a geometric sequence with first term $a_1 = \frac{6}{10}$ and ratio $r = \frac{1}{10}$. The sum of this sequence is

$$\frac{a_1}{1-r} = \frac{\frac{6}{10}}{1-\frac{1}{10}} = \frac{\frac{6}{10}}{\frac{9}{10}} = \frac{6}{9} = \frac{2}{3}$$

Thus, $0.666\cdots = \frac{2}{3}$.

(b) $0.121212\cdots = \frac{12}{100} + \frac{12}{10{,}000} + \cdots$. This is a geometric sequence with $a_1 = \frac{12}{100}$, $r = \frac{1}{100}$, and sum

$$\frac{a_1}{1-r} = \frac{\frac{12}{100}}{1-\frac{1}{100}} = \frac{\frac{12}{100}}{\frac{99}{100}} = \frac{12}{99} = \frac{4}{33}$$

Thus, $0.121212\cdots = \frac{4}{33}$.

(c) $3.222\cdots = 3 + \frac{2}{10} + \frac{2}{100} + \frac{2}{1000} + \cdots$. The repeating part, $0.222\cdots$, is a geometric sequence with $a_1 = \frac{2}{10}$, $r = \frac{1}{10}$, and sum

$$\frac{a_1}{1-r} = \frac{\frac{2}{10}}{1-\frac{1}{10}} = \frac{\frac{2}{10}}{\frac{9}{10}} = \frac{2}{9}$$

Thus, $3.222\cdots = 3\frac{2}{9} = \frac{29}{9}$.

F Applications

PROBLEM-SOLVING

Number Sequences

Suppose you have two job offers for a 2-week (14-day) trial period. Job A starts at \$50 per day with a \$50 raise each day. Job B starts at \$.50 per day and your salary is doubled every day. Find the total amount paid by each of the jobs at the end of the 14 days.

① **Read** the problem.

② **Select** the unknown.

You need to find the total amount each job pays.

③ **Think** of a plan.
Find the amount job A pays at the end of 14 days. Then find the amount job B pays at the end of 14 days.

The pay for job A starts at \$50 ($a_1 = 50$) and increases by \$50 each day ($d = 50$). The salary for the fourteenth day is $a_{14} = 50 + 13 \cdot 50 = 700$. The pay for job B starts at \$.50 ($a_1 = 0.50$) and doubles every day ($r = 2$).

④ **Use** the formulas for the sum of an arithmetic progression and for the sum of a geometric progression to find the amount each job pays for 14 days.

For job A, the sum of the arithmetic progression for 14 days is

$$S_{14} = \frac{n(a_1 + a_n)}{2} = \frac{14 \cdot 750}{2} = \$5250$$

continued

For job B, the sum of the geometric progression for 14 days is

$$S_{14} = \frac{a_1(1 - r^n)}{1 - r} = \frac{0.50(1 - 2^{14})}{1 - 2}$$

$$= \frac{0.50(1 - 2^{14})}{-1}$$

⑤ **Use** a calculator to find 2^{14}.

$$= 0.50(2^{14} - 1)$$
$$= 0.50\ (16{,}383)$$
$$= \$8191.50$$

Job B pays much more!

⑥ **Verify** your answer. The verification is left for you.

Try Example 6 Now Cover the solution, write your own solution, and then check your work.

EXAMPLE 6 Chess and Sequences

The game of chess is said to have originated in Persia. Legend has it that the shah (or king) was so happy that he offered the inventor of the game anything he wanted. The inventor asked that one grain of wheat be placed on the first square of the chessboard, two grains on the second, four on the third, and so on. There are 64 squares on a chessboard.

(a) How many grains were to be placed on the 64th square?

(b) What is the total number of grains the inventor would receive?

Solution

(a) List the number of grains in each square.

Square 1	Square 2	Square 3	Square 4	. . .	Square 64
1	2	$4 = 2^{3-1}$	$8 = 2^{4-1}$	. . .	$2^{63} = 2^{64-1}$

(b) The sum of the geometric progression 1, 2, 4, . . . , 2^{63}, where $a_1 = 1$ and $r = 2$ (because the number of grains is doubled for each successive square), is

$$S_{64} = \frac{1(1 - 2^{64})}{1 - 2} = \frac{1 - 2^{64}}{-1}$$

$$= 2^{64} - 1$$

By the way, since 2^{10} is about 1000, $2^{60} = (2^{10})^6$ is about $(1000)^6$, or 1,000,000,000,000,000,000 (1 quintillion).

5.6 EXERCISES

A Arithmetic Sequences

In problems 1–10, find the following:

a. The first term

b. The common difference d

c. The tenth term

d. The nth term

1. 7, 13, 19, 25, . . .
2. 3, 6, 9, 12, . . .
3. 43, 34, 25, 16, . . .
4. 3, −1, −5, −9, . . .
5. 2, −3, −8, −13, . . .
6. $\frac{2}{3}, \frac{5}{6}, 1, \frac{7}{6}, \ldots$
7. $\frac{-5}{6}, \frac{-1}{3}, \frac{1}{6}, \frac{2}{3}, \ldots$
8. $\frac{-1}{4}, \frac{1}{4}, \frac{3}{4}, \frac{5}{4}, \ldots$
9. 0.6, 0.2, −0.2, −0.6, . . .
10. 0.7, 0.2, −0.3, −0.8, . . .

B Sum of an Arithmetic Sequence

In problems 11–20, find S_{10} and S_n for the sequences given in problems 1–10.

C Geometric Sequences

In problems 21–26, find the following:

a. The first term

b. The common ratio r

c. The tenth term

d. The nth term

21. $3, 6, 12, 24, \ldots$

22. $5, 15, 45, 135, \ldots$

23. $\frac{1}{3}, 1, 3, 9, \ldots$

24. $\frac{1}{5}, 1, 5, 25, \ldots$

25. $16, -4, 1, -\frac{1}{4}, \ldots$

26. $3, -1, \frac{1}{3}, -\frac{1}{9}, \ldots$

D Sum of a Geometric Sequence

In problems 27–32, find S_{10} and S_n for the sequences given in problems 21–26. Give answers in simplified exponential form.

E Infinite Geometric Sequences

In problems 33–36, find the sum of each infinite geometric sequence.

33. $6, 3, \frac{3}{2}, \frac{3}{4}, \ldots$

34. $12, 4, \frac{4}{3}, \frac{4}{9}, \ldots$

35. $-8, -4, -2, -1, \ldots$

36. $9, -3, 1, -\frac{1}{3}, \ldots$

In problems 37–40, use sequences to write each repeating decimal as a fraction.

37. $0.777 \cdots$

38. $1.555 \cdots$

39. $2.101010 \cdots$

40. $1.272727 \cdots$

F Applications

41. A property valued at \$30,000 will depreciate (decline in value) \$1380 the first year, \$1340 the second year, \$1300 the third year, and so on.

a. What will be the depreciation the tenth year?

b. What will be the value of the property at the end of the tenth year?

42. Strikers at a plant were ordered to return to work and were told they would be fined \$100 the first day they failed to do so, \$150 the second day, \$200 the third day, and so on. If the strikers stayed out for 10 days, what was their total fine?

43. A well driller charges \$50 for the first foot; for each succeeding foot, the charge is \$5 more than that for the preceding foot. Find the following:

a. The charge for the tenth foot

b. The total charge for a 50-ft well

44. When dropped on a hard surface, a Super Ball takes a series of bounces, each one about $\frac{9}{10}$ as high as the preceding one. If a Super Ball is dropped from a height of 10 ft, find the following:

a. How high it will bounce on the tenth bounce

b. The approximate distance the ball travels before coming to rest (*Hint:* Draw a picture.)

45. If \$100 is deposited at the end of each year in a savings account paying 10% compounded annually, at the end of 5 years the compound amount of each deposit is

$$100, \quad 100(1.10), \quad 100(1.10)^2, \quad 100(1.10)^3, \quad \text{and} \quad 100(1.10)^4$$

How much money is in the account right after the last deposit? [*Hint:* $(1.10)^5 = 1.61051$.]

46. The dosage for Prednisone, a medicine used to treat rheumatic, blood, and respiratory disorders, is 6 tablets the first day (day 1), 5 tablets day 2, 4 tablets day 3, and so on. If a_n is the number of tablets taken on day n:

a. What is a_3?

b. What is a_6?

c. What is a_n?

d. Use Theorem 5.4 to find the total number of tablets you take?

e. If each tablet is 60 mg, how many mg do you take on the fourth day?

f. How many mg do you take the *n*th day?

47. In the Getting Started section for this part we discussed the pattern

$$1 + 2 + 3 + 4 + \cdots + 97 + 98 + 99 + 100$$

101

where the sum of each pair is 101 and there are $\frac{100}{2} = 50$ pairs. Thus, the total sum is 50×101. Generalize this idea to find the sum of the following sequence:

$$1 + 2 + 3 + \cdots + (n - 1) + n$$

48. a. Use the ideas of problem 47 to find the sum of the following sequence:

$$2 + 4 + 6 + \cdots + (2n - 2) + 2n$$

b. You can check the answer to part (**a**) by doubling the answer you get for problem 47. Why? Did you get the same answer?

IN OTHER WORDS

49. What is the difference between an arithmetic sequence and a geometric sequence?

50. Explain why the Fibonacci sequence 1, 1, 2, 3, 5, . . . is neither an arithmetic sequence nor a geometric sequence.

USING YOUR KNOWLEDGE

The graph on the next page shows the forecast share of U.S. personal computer sales for different types of computers. The forecast for Tablet computers in 2008 was virtually unknown (0!), but that changed dramatically. On average, the share of Tablet computers increased 4.5% each year until 2012. Use this information in problems 51–52.

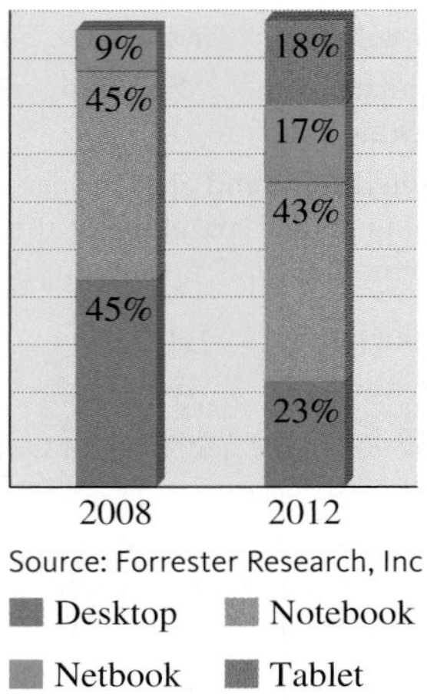

Source: Forrester Research, Inc

51. Write a formula for the nth term of an arithmetic sequence that models the percentage of sales of Tablet computers n years after 2007.

52. Use the formula from problem 51 to project the forecast share of Tablet computers in 2016.

On average, the forecast shares of Notebook computers ***decreased*** *0.5 each year until 2012.*

53. Write a formula for the nth term of an arithmetic sequence that models the percentage of sales of Notebook computers n years after 2007.

54. Use the formula from problem 53 to project the forecast share of Notebook computers in 2016.

CHAPTER 5 Summary

SECTION	ITEM	MEANING	EXAMPLE
5.1	$N = \{1, 2, 3, \ldots\}$	The natural numbers	All counting numbers such as 10, 27, 38, and so on
5.1A	$n(A)$	The cardinal number of A	If $A = \{a, b\}$, then $n(A) = 2$.
	1st, 2nd, 3rd, . . .	Ordinal numbers	This is the *first* one.
	123-45-6789	Number used for identification	A Social Security number
5.1B	Prime number	A number with exactly two divisors, 1 and itself	2, 3, 5, 7, 11, . . .
	Composite number	A number with more than two divisors	4, 33, 50, . . .
5.1C	$12 = 2^2 \cdot 3$	Prime factorization of 12	
5.1E	GCF	Greatest common factor	18 is the GCF of 216 and 234.
	LCM	Least common multiple	252 is the LCM of 18, 21, and 28.
5.2A	$a \cdot 1 = 1 \cdot a = a$	Identity property for multiplication	$1 \cdot 97 = 97$ and $83 \cdot 1 = 83$
	$W = \{0, 1, 2, \ldots\}$	The set of whole numbers	
	$0 + a = a + 0 = a$	Identity property for addition	$0 + 13 = 13$ and $84 + 0 = 84$
	$a - 0 = a, 0 \cdot a = 0, 0 \div a = 0$	Properties of 0	$3 - 0 = 3, 0 \cdot 3 = 0, 0 \div 3 = 0$
	$I = \{\ldots, -1, 0, 1, \ldots\}$	The set of integers	

CHAPTER 5 Summary

SECTION	ITEM	MEANING	EXAMPLE
5.2A	(number line) −2 −1 0 1 2	The number line	
	$n + (-n) = 0$	Additive inverse property	$3 + (-3) = 0$
	$\|n\|$	Absolute value of n	$\|5\| = 5$, $\|-5\| = 5$
5.2B	$a - b = a + (-b)$	Definition of subtraction	$3 - 7 = 3 + (-7)$
	$a \cdot b$ or $a \times b$	The product of a and b	$4 \cdot 6 = 24$
	The product or quotient of two numbers with the same (**like**) signs is positive, with different (unlike) signs, it is negative.	Rules of signs for multiplication and division of signed numbers	$8 \times 2 = +16$ $8/2 = +4$ $8 \times (-2) = -16$ $8/(-2) = -4$ $-8 \times 2 = -16$ $-8/2 = -4$ $-8 \times (-2) = 16$ $-8/(-2) = +4$
5.2D	Closed set	A set with an operation defined on it such that when the operation is performed on elements of the set, the result is also an element of the set	The natural numbers are closed under multiplication. The integers are closed under subtraction, but the natural numbers are *not*. ($3 - 5 = -2$ is *not* a natural number.)
	$a + b = b + a$	Commutative property of addition	$3 + 5 = 5 + 3$
	$a \cdot b = b \cdot a$	Commutative property of multiplication	$6 \cdot 7 = 7 \cdot 6$
	$a + (b + c) = (a + b) + c$	Associative property of addition	$-4 + (2 + 5) = (-4 + 2) + 5$
	$a \cdot (b \cdot c) = (a \cdot b) \cdot c$	Associative property of multiplication	$-2 \cdot (4 \cdot 7) = (-2 \cdot 4) \cdot 7$
	$a \cdot (b + c) = a \cdot b + a \cdot c$	Distributive property	$3 \cdot (4 + 7) = 3 \cdot 4 + 3 \cdot 7$
5.3A	$Q = \left\{ r \,\middle\|\, r = \frac{a}{b}, a, b \in I, b \neq 0 \right\}$	The set of rational numbers	$\frac{3}{5}$, $-\frac{7}{3}$, and $3\frac{1}{2}$ are rational numbers.
	If a, b, and k are integers, where $b \neq 0$ and $k \neq 0$, then $\frac{a}{b} = \frac{ak}{bk}$	Fundamental property of rational numbers	$\frac{5}{7} = \frac{5 \times 3}{7 \times 3} = \frac{15}{21}$
5.3B	$\frac{b}{a}$, $a \neq 0$	The reciprocal, or multiplicative inverse, of a/b	$\frac{3}{4}$ and $\frac{4}{3}$ are reciprocals.
	$\frac{a}{b} \div \frac{c}{d} = \frac{a}{b} \cdot \frac{d}{c}$, $c \neq 0$	Quotient of two rational numbers	$\frac{4}{5} \div \frac{3}{5} = \frac{4}{5} \cdot \frac{5}{3} = \frac{4 \cdot 5}{3 \cdot 5} = \frac{4}{3}$
5.3C	$a^{-n} = \frac{1}{a^n}$, $a \neq 0$	Definition of negative exponents	$4^{-2} = \frac{1}{4^2}$
5.3D	$m \times 10^n$, where m is greater than or equal to 1 and less than 10, and n is an integer	Scientific notation	7.4×10^{-6}

continued

CHAPTER 5 Summary – *continued*

SECTION	ITEM	MEANING	EXAMPLE
5.4A	$0.\overline{142857}$	A nonterminating, repeating decimal	$0.\overline{142857} = 0.142857142857\cdots$
5.4C	%	Percent sign	3%
5.4D	Irrational number	A number that is not rational	$\sqrt{2}, 3\sqrt{5}, \pi$
5.4E	Irrational number	A number that has a nonterminating, nonrepeating decimal representation	$0.101001000\cdots$
5.5A	$<, >, =$	Symbols for less than, greater than and equal	$8 > 5, 5 < 8$ and $0.999\cdots = 1$
	$\sqrt{\ }$	Radical sign	$\sqrt{2}$
5.5B	$\sqrt{a \cdot b} = \sqrt{a} \cdot \sqrt{b}$	Multiplication of radicals	$\sqrt{32} = \sqrt{16 \cdot 2} = \sqrt{16} \cdot \sqrt{2} = 4\sqrt{2}$
	$\sqrt{\frac{a}{b}} = \frac{\sqrt{a}}{\sqrt{b}}$	Division of radicals	$\sqrt{\frac{2}{7}} = \frac{\sqrt{2}}{\sqrt{7}}$
5.6A	d	The common difference of an arithmetic sequence	In the sequence, 4, 9, 14, . . . , $d = 5$.
	$a_n = a_1 + (n - 1) \cdot d$	The nth term of an arithmetic sequence	In the above sequence, $a_n = 4 + (n - 1) \cdot 5 = 5n - 1$
5.6B	R	The set of real numbers	$3, -8, 0, \frac{1}{5}, 0.5$ and $\sqrt{2}$ are real numbers.
	$S_n = \frac{n(a_1 + a_n)}{2}$	The sum of the first n terms of an arithmetic sequence	In the above sequence, $S_5 = \frac{5(4 + 24)}{2} = 70$
5.6C	r	The common ratio of a geometric sequence	The common ratio of 5, 10, 20, . . . is $r = 2$.
	$a_n = a_1 r^{n-1}$	The nth term of a geometric sequence	In the sequence 5, 10, 20, . . . , $a_n = 5 \cdot 2^{n-1}$.
5.6D	$S_n = \frac{a_1(1 - r^n)}{1 - r}$	The sum of the first n terms of a geometric sequence	For the sequence 5, 10, 20, . . . , $S_4 = \frac{5(1 - 2^4)}{1 - 2} = 75$.
5.8E	$S = \frac{a_1}{1 - r}$	The sum of the infinite geometric sequence $a_1, a_1 r, a_1 r^2, \ldots,$ where r is between -1 and 1	The sum of the sequence 2, 1, $\frac{1}{2}, \frac{1}{4}, \ldots$ is $S = \frac{2}{1 - \frac{1}{2}} = 4$.

CHAPTER 5 Practice Test

1. Tell whether the underlined item is used as a cardinal number, an ordinal number, or for identification.
   a. Sally came in third in the 100-yd dash.
   b. Bill's lottery ticket won two dollars.
   c. Jane's auto license number was 270–891.

2. a. A prime number is ______.
   b. A composite number is ______.

3. Write 1220 as a product of primes.

4. Write the prime numbers between 50 and 70.

5. Is 143 prime or composite?

6. Of the numbers 2345, 436, 387, and 1530, identify those divisible by
   a. 2. b. 3. c. 5.

7. Find the GCF of 216 and 254 and reduce the fraction $\frac{216}{254}$ to lowest terms.

8. Find the LCM of 18, 54, and 60 and evaluate $\frac{1}{18} + \frac{1}{54} - \frac{1}{60}$.

9. A father left $\frac{1}{4}$ of his estate to his daughter, $\frac{1}{2}$ to his wife, and $\frac{1}{8}$ to his son. If the rest went for taxes, what fraction of the estate was that?

10. Find:
    a. the additive inverse of 27
    b. $|41|$

11. Change the following to equivalent addition problems and give the results:
    a. $8 - 19$ b. $8 - (-19)$ c. $-8 - 19$ d. $-8 - (-19)$

12. Multiply:
    a. $6 \cdot 7$ b. $-8 \cdot 9$
    c. $-3 \cdot (-7)$ d. $5 \cdot (-8)$

13. Evaluate:
    a. $(-7)^2$ b. -7^2
    c. $(-4)^3$ d. -4^3

14. a. $81 \div 9$ b. $\frac{-15}{5}$
    c. $12 \div (-2)$ d. $\frac{-20}{-10}$
    e. $\frac{0}{15}$ f. $\frac{15}{0}$

15. Evaluate a. $4 \times 12 \div 3 \times 10^3 - 2(-6 + 4) \times 10^4$.
    b. $\left(\frac{1}{2}\right)^3 \div \frac{1}{4} \cdot \frac{1}{2} + \frac{1}{3}\left(\frac{7}{2} - \frac{3}{2}\right) - \frac{1}{2} \cdot \frac{1}{3}$.

16. Find a rational number with a denominator of 16 and equal to $\frac{3}{4}$.

17. Find the reciprocals of the following:
    a. $\frac{2}{3}$ b. $-\frac{4}{7}$ c. $2\frac{5}{8}$ d. -8

18. Perform the indicated operations.
    a. $\frac{7}{8} \times \left(-\frac{5}{16}\right)$ b. $-\frac{7}{8} \div \left(-\frac{5}{16}\right)$

19. a. Write 23.508 in expanded form.
    b. Write $(8 \times 10^2) + (3 \times 10^0) + (4 \times 10^{-2})$ in decimal form.

20. Calculate $(6 \times 10^4) \times (8 \times 10^{-6})$ and write the answer in scientific notation.

continued

CHAPTER 5 Practice Test – *continued*

21. Perform the indicated operations.
a. $6.73 + 2.8$ b. $9.34 - 4.71$ c. 0.29×6.7 d. $17.36 \div 3.1$

22. Write the following as decimals:
a. $\frac{3}{4}$ b. $\frac{1}{15}$

23. Write the following as quotients of two integers:
a. $0.\overline{12}$ b. $2.6555 \cdots$

24. Write the following as decimals:
a. 21% b. 9.35% c. 0.26%

25. Write the following as percents:
a. 0.52 b. 2.765 c. $\frac{3}{5}$ d. $\frac{2}{11}$ (to one decimal place)

26. Classify the following as rational or irrational:
a. $\sqrt{49}$ b. $\sqrt{45}$ c. $\sqrt{121}$
d. $0.41252525 \cdots$ e. $0.212112111 \cdots$ f. $0.246810 \cdots$

27. Insert $<$, $>$ or $=$ to make the statement correct.
a. $\sqrt{59}$ ____ 7.7 b. $\sqrt{31}$ ____ 5.5

28. Find a rational number between $0.\overline{2}$ and 0.25

29. Find an irrational number between $0.\overline{2}$ and 0.25

30. Simplify the following if possible:
a. $\sqrt{96}$ b. $\sqrt{58}$

31. Simplify the following:
a. $\frac{4}{\sqrt{20}}$ b. $\sqrt{\frac{48}{49}}$

32. Perform the indicated operations and simplify.
a. $\sqrt{8} \cdot \sqrt{6}$ b. $\frac{\sqrt{56}}{\sqrt{7}}$

33. Perform the indicated operations.
a. $\sqrt{90} - \sqrt{40}$ b. $\sqrt{32} + \sqrt{18} - \sqrt{50}$

34. The length c of the hypotenuse of a right triangle is given by $c = \sqrt{a^2 + b^2}$, where a and b are the lengths of the other two sides. If a right triangle has sides measuring 4 in. and 6 in., respectively, what is the length of the hypotenuse? Simplify the answer.

35. Classify the given numbers by making check marks in the appropriate rows.

	a.	b.	c.	d.	e.
Set	$\sqrt{16}$	$-\frac{5}{4}$	$\sqrt{5}$	$0.\overline{8}$	$-2\frac{3}{4}$
Natural numbers					
Whole numbers					
Integers					
Rational numbers					
Irrational numbers					
Real numbers					

36. Classify the following as arithmetic or geometric sequences:
a. 2, 4, 8, 16, . . . b. 5, 8, 11, 14, . . .

37. Find the sum of the first 10 terms of 9, 13, 17, 21, ...

38. Find the sum of the first five terms of the sequence $1, \frac{1}{2}, \frac{1}{4}, \frac{1}{8}, \ldots$.

CHAPTER 5 Practice Test

39. The first term of a geometric sequence is $\frac{1}{3}$ and $r = \frac{1}{2}$. Find the following:
    a. a_5, the fifth term b. S_5, the sum of the first five terms

40. Use the sum of an infinite geometric sequence to write the following repeating decimals as fractions:
    a. $0.444 \cdots$ b. $0.212121 \cdots$ c. $2.555 \cdots$

ANSWERS TO PRACTICE TEST

CHAPTER 5		What to Review *If You Missed It*		
QUESTION	**ANSWER**	**SECTION**	**EXAMPLE(S)**	**PAGE(S)**
1	a. Ordinal number b. Cardinal number c. Identification	5.1	1	193
2	a. A natural number with exactly two distinct divisors b. A natural number with more than two distinct divisors	5.1	Def. of prime and composite numbers	194
3	$2^2 \times 5 \times 61$	5.1	3	196
4	53, 59, 61, and 67	5.1	2	194
5	Composite ($143 = 11 \times 13$)	5.1	2	194
6	a. 436 and 1530 are divisible by 2. b. 387 and 1530 are divisible by 3. c. 2345 and 1530 are divisible by 5.	5.1	4	197
7	$\text{GCF}(216, 254) = 2; \frac{216}{254} = \frac{108}{127}$	5.1	6	198–199
8	$\text{LCM}(18, 54, 60) = 540; \frac{1}{18} + \frac{1}{54} - \frac{1}{60} = \frac{31}{540}$	5.1	7	199
9	$\frac{1}{8}$	5.1	8	200
10	a. -27 b. 41	5.2	1, 2	206, 207
11	a. $8 - 19 = 8 + (-19) = -11$ b. $8 - (-19) = 8 + (+19) = 27$ c. $-8 - 19 = -8 + (-19) = -27$ d. $-8 - (-19) = -8 + (+19) = 11$	5.2	3, 4	207, 208
12	a. 42 b. -72 c. 21 d. -40	5.2	5	209
13	a. 49 b. -49 c. -64 d. -64	5.2	6	210
14	a. 9 b. -3 c. -6 d. 2 e. 0 f. Not defined	5.2	7	210
15	a. 56,000 b. $\frac{3}{4}$	5.2	8, 9	211
16	$\frac{12}{16}$	5.3	2	217
17	a. $\frac{3}{2}$ b. $-\frac{7}{4}$ c. $\frac{8}{21}$ d. $-\frac{1}{8}$	5.3	4	219

continued

ANSWERS TO PRACTICE TEST — *continued*

CHAPTER 5		What to Review *If You Missed It*		
QUESTION	**ANSWER**	**SECTION**	**EXAMPLE(S)**	**PAGE(S)**
18	a. $-\frac{35}{128}$ b. $\frac{14}{5}$	5.3	5	220–221
19	a. $2 \times 10 + 3 + 5 \times 10^{-1} + 8 \times 10^{-3}$ b. 803.04	5.3	7a, 7b	223
20	4.8×10^{-1}	5.3	8, 9, 10	223, 224
21	a. 9.53 b. 4.63 c. 1.943 d. 5.6	5.3	11, 12, 13	225, 226
22	a. 0.75 b. $0.0666\cdots$	5.4	1	229–230
23	a. $\frac{4}{33}$ b. $\frac{239}{90}$	5.4	2, 3	231, 232
24	a. 0.21 b. 0.0935 c. 0.0026	5.4	4	233
25	a. 52% b. 276.5% c. 60% d. 18.2%	5.4	5, 6	233
26	a. Rational b. Irrational c. Rational d. Rational e. Irrational f. Irrational	5.4	7, 8	234, 235
27	a. $<$ b. $>$	5.4	9	236
28	0.24 (Other answers are possible.)	5.4	10, 11	236, 237
29	$0.23456\cdots$ (Other answers are possible.)	5.4	10, 11	236, 237
30	a. $4\sqrt{6}$ b. $\sqrt{58}$ is in simplest form.	5.5	1	240
31	a. $\frac{2\sqrt{5}}{5}$ b. $\frac{4\sqrt{3}}{7}$	5.5	2, 3	240, 241
32	a. $4\sqrt{3}$ b. $2\sqrt{2}$	5.5	4	242
33	a. $\sqrt{10}$ b. $2\sqrt{2}$	5.5	5	242
34	$2\sqrt{13}$	5.5	6	242–243
35	a. Check natural numbers, whole numbers, integers, rational numbers, and real numbers. b. Check rational numbers and real numbers. c. Check irrational numbers and real numbers. d. Check rational numbers and real numbers. e. Check rational numbers and real numbers.	5.5	7	243–244
36	a. A geometric sequence b. An arithmetic sequence	5.6	Def., part (C)	249
37	270	5.6	Theorem 5.4	248
38	$\frac{31}{16}$	5.6	4	250
39	a. $\frac{1}{48}$ b. $\frac{31}{48}$	5.6	4	250
40	a. $\frac{4}{9}$ b. $\frac{7}{33}$ c. $\frac{23}{9}$	5.6	5	251

CHAPTER 6

Equations, Inequalities, and Problem Solving

God does Arithmetic.
—CARL FRIEDRICH GAUSS

Maintaining a nutritional diet is a key element of a healthy lifestyle. In Section 6.6, you will use ratios to find the nutritional value of certain foods.

We are now ready to begin the study of algebra. The word *algebra* is the European derivation of *al-jabr,* part of the title of al-Khwarizmi's treatise *Hisab al-jabr w'al muqabalah,* "The Science of Reunion and Reduction." The study of algebra starts with its foundations: open sentences, statements, equations, and inequalities.

We will consider how to solve first-degree (linear) equations and inequalities (Section 6.1) and how to graph the solutions of inequalities (Sections 6.2 and 6.3). Next, we study quadratic equations and their methods of solution, factoring and the quadratic formula, and then use this information to solve different types of word problems. We end the chapter by examining ratio, proportion, and variation, emphasizing applications to consumer problems such as unit pricing.

Now, remember that precocious boy of 10 who amazed his teacher by adding $1 + 2 + 3 + \cdots + 100$ with lightning speed? In his doctoral dissertation he provided the first proof of the fundamental theorem of algebra. You can read more about Carl Friedrich Gauss in the Human Side of Math.

6.1 Solutions of First-Degree (Linear) Sentences

GETTING STARTED

OBJECTIVES

A. Find the solution set of an equation or inequality.
B. Solve equations using the elementary operations and the procedure given in the text.
C. Solve a formula for a specified variable.
D. Solve first-degree (linear) inequalities.
E. Solve applications involving equations and inequalities.

Human Side of Math

© Bettmann/CORBIS
(1777–1855)

Carl Friedrich Gauss, who has been called the Prince of Mathematicians, was born in Brunswick, Germany, in 1777. Gauss entered Caroline College in Brunswick at the age of 15 and in a short time began his research into higher arithmetic. When he left the college in 1795, he had already invented the method of least squares. His doctoral thesis gave the first proof of the fundamental theorem of algebra, that every algebraic equation has at least one root among the complex numbers.

His *Disquisitiones Arithmeticae (Arithmetical Researches),* published in 1801, is regarded as the basic work in the theory of numbers. He also made great contributions to astronomy, geodesy (the measurement of the Earth), geometry, theoretical physics, complex numbers, and functions, as well as the invention of the electric telegraph in the early 1830s.

LOOKING AHEAD

Much of Gauss's work in pure mathematics dealt with number theory, the concept of complex numbers, and the solutions to algebraic equations, which is the focus of this chapter.

CRICKETS, ANTS, AND TEMPERATURES

Does temperature affect animal behavior? You must know about bears hibernating in the winter and the languid nature of students in the spring. But what about the behavior of crickets and ants? Can you tell whether crickets will stop chirping before ants stop crawling? In the Discovery section, you will find that the number N of chirps a cricket makes per minute *satisfies* the *equation* $N = 4(F - 40)$, where F is the temperature in degrees Fahrenheit. What happens as the temperature increases? In problem 113, Exercises 6.1, you will find that the speed S (in cm/sec) for certain types of ants is $S = \frac{1}{6}(C - 4)$, where C is the temperature in degrees Celsius (see photo on next page). What happens as the temperature decreases? The relationship between Fahrenheit and Celsius temperature is given by $F = \frac{9}{5}C + 32$. Armed with this information, can you tell whether crickets stop chirping before ants stop crawling?

Elementary algebra was first treated in a systematic fashion by the Arabs during the period before the Renaissance, when Europe was almost at a standstill intellectually. By the early 1600s, algebra had become a fairly well-developed branch of mathematics, and mathematicians were beginning to discover that a marriage of algebra and geometry could be highly beneficial to both subjects.

It has been said that algebra is arithmetic made simple, and it is true that a small amount of elementary algebra enables us to solve many problems that would be quite difficult by purely arithmetic means. In this chapter we shall consider some of the simpler algebraic techniques that are used in problem solving.

We have already made frequent use of various symbols, usually letters of the alphabet, as placeholders for the elements of a set of numbers. For example, we wrote

$$a + b = b + a, \qquad a, b \text{ real numbers}$$

as a symbolic way of stating the commutative property of addition. Of course, we mean that a and b can each be replaced by any real number. In this case the set of real numbers is the **replacement set** for a and b. A symbol that can be replaced by any one of a set of numbers is called a **variable.**

Letters of the alphabet as well as symbols such as $\square$ are often used to indicate variables in arithmetic. The study of sentences and expressions involving variables is, however, a part of algebra.

In algebra, as in arithmetic, the commonly used **verb phrases** are

$=$	is equal to	$\neq$	is not equal to
$>$	is greater than	$\geq$	is greater than or equal to
$<$	is less than	$\leq$	is less than or equal to

By using these verb phrases along with specific numbers and variables joined by the usual operations of arithmetic, we can form many types of sentences. Some examples of simple algebraic sentences are

$$x - 1 = 3, \quad 3x - 2 \neq 4, \quad x - 1 \geq 3, \quad \text{and} \quad x + 7 < -9x$$

The parts that are added or subtracted in these algebraic sentences are called **terms.** Thus, the terms in $3x - 2$ are $3x$ and -2. The numerical part of the term $3x$, 3, is its **numerical coefficient,** or simply its **coefficient.** Terms that differ only in their numerical coefficients are called **like terms.** For example, $-7x$ and $3x$ are like terms; $2y^2$ and $-5y^2$ are like terms, but $2y^2$ and $2y$ are not.

A Equations and Inequalities

In the four preceding sentences, x is a variable, that is, a placeholder for the numbers by which it can be replaced. Until x is replaced by a number, none of these sentences is a statement because it is neither true nor false. For this reason, we call such sentences **open sentences.** Because only one variable is involved, we refer to the sentences as **open sentences in one variable.** Sentences in which the verb phrase is "=" are called **equations;** if the verb phrase is any of the others we have listed, then the sentence is called an **inequality.**

In order to study an open sentence in one variable, we obviously must know what the replacement set for that variable is. We are interested in knowing for which of the possible replacements the sentence is a true statement. To **solve** an open sentence is to find its solution set.

© Dmitry Kosterev/Shutterstock.com

For some types of ants, the speed at which they move varies directly with changes in temperature.

Definition of Solution Set

The set of elements of the replacement set that make the open sentence a true statement is called the **solution set** for the given replacement set.

EXAMPLE 1 Finding Solution Sets

Suppose the replacement set for x is $\{2, 4, 6\}$. For each of the following open sentences, find the solution set:

(a) $x - 1 = 3$ (b) $3x - 2 \neq 4$

(c) $x - 1 \geq 3$ (d) $x + 7 < -9x$

Solution

(a) We substitute the elements of the replacement set into the open sentence $x - 1 = 3$.

For $x = 2$, we get $2 - 1 = 1$, not 3.
For $x = 4$, we get $4 - 1 = 3$, which makes the sentence a true statement.
For $x = 6$, we get $6 - 1 = 5$, not 3.

Thus, $x = 4$ is the only replacement that makes the sentence $x - 1 = 3$ a true statement, so the solution set is $\{4\}$.

(b) We make the permissible replacements into the open sentence $3x - 2 \neq 4$.

For $x = 2$, we get $3(2) - 2 = 4$, which *is* equal to 4, so the sentence is a false statement.
For $x = 4$, we get $3(4) - 2 = 10$, which is not equal to 4, so the sentence is a true statement.
For $x = 6$, we get $3(6) - 2 = 16$, which also satisfies the "$\neq 4$," so the sentence is a true statement.

Thus, the solution set is $\{4, 6\}$.

(c) We make the permissible replacements into $x - 1 \geq 3$.

For $x = 2$, we get $2 - 1 = 1$, which is less than 3, not greater than or equal to 3. Hence, the sentence is a false statement.
For $x = 4$, we get $4 - 1 = 3$, which satisfies the "≥ 3," so the sentence is a true statement.
For $x = 6$, we get $6 - 1 = 5$, which satisfies the "≥ 3," so the sentence is a true statement.

The solution set is thus $\{4, 6\}$.

(d) We make the permissible replacements into $x + 7 < -9x$.

For $x = 2$, we get $2 + 7 = 9$, which is not less than $-9(2) = -18$, so the sentence is a false statement.
For $x = 4$, we get $4 + 7 = 11$, which is not less than $-9(4) = -36$, so the sentence is a false statement.
For $x = 6$, we get $6 + 7 = 13$, which is not less than $-9(6) = -54$, so the sentence is a false statement.

Since none of the replacements makes the sentence $x + 7 < -9x$ a true statement, the solution set is $\varnothing$.

Now that we have examined how to determine whether a certain number satisfies an equation or inequality, we consider how to find these numbers, that is, how to *solve* equations or inequalities by finding equivalent equations or inequalities whose solutions are obvious.

B Solving Equations

First, we consider which operations can be performed on a sentence to obtain an **equivalent** sentence, that is, one with exactly the same solution set as the original sentence. Such operations are called **elementary operations.**

Elementary Operations

For the equation

$$a = b$$

the following elementary operations yield equations **equivalent** to the original equation:

1. **Addition** $\quad a + c = b + c$
2. **Subtraction** $\quad a - c = b - c$
3. **Multiplication** $\quad a \times c = b \times c, \quad c \neq 0$
4. **Division** $\quad a \div c = b \div c, \quad c \neq 0$

Briefly stated, we can add or subtract the same number on both sides, or multiply or divide both sides by the same nonzero number. To solve an equation, we use the elementary operations as needed to obtain an equivalent equation of the form

$$x = n \quad \text{or} \quad n = x$$

where the number n is the desired solution.

For example, to solve the equation

$$55 = 0.20m + 25$$

we must *isolate* m, that is, get m all by itself on one side of the equation. Hence, we proceed as follows:

Subtract 25.	$55 - 25 = 0.20m + 25 - 25$
Simplify.	$30 = 0.20m$
Divide by 0.20.	$\dfrac{30}{0.20} = \dfrac{0.20m}{0.20}$
or	$150 = m$

Thus, the solution set of $55 = 0.20m + 25$ is $\{150\}$.

EXAMPLE 2 Solving Equations

Solve the equation $x + 2 = 5$.

Solution

To solve the equation, we first want to get the variable x by itself on one side. Therefore, we subtract 2 from both sides to eliminate the $+2$ on the left-hand side.

$$x + 2 - 2 = 5 - 2$$

This simplifies to

$$x = 3$$

The solution set is $\{3\}$. We used elementary operation 2.

EXAMPLE 3 Solving More Equations

Solve the equation $2x - 8 = 5x - 6$.

Solution

To have a positive number of x's on the right, we subtract $2x$ on both sides and get

$$2x - 8 - 2x = 5x - 6 - 2x \quad \text{or} \quad -8 = 3x - 6$$

To eliminate the -6 on the right side, we add 6 to both sides and obtain

$$-8 + 6 = 3x - 6 + 6 \quad \text{or} \quad -2 = 3x$$

Since the 3 on the right multiplies the x, we divide both sides by 3.

$$\frac{-2}{3} = \frac{3x}{3}$$

That is,

$$-\frac{2}{3} = x \quad \text{or} \quad x = -\frac{2}{3}$$

The solution set is $\left\{-\frac{2}{3}\right\}$, and we used elementary operations 1, 2, and 4.

The equations in Examples 2 and 3 are called **linear** or **first-degree** equations in one variable because the highest exponent of the variable is 1. In general, we have the following:

> **Definition of a First-Degree Expression**
>
> An expression of the form $ax + b$, where a and b are real numbers and $a \neq 0$, is called a **first-degree (or linear) expression in x,** and an equation of the form
>
> $$ax + b = 0 \qquad a \neq 0$$
>
> is called a **first-degree** (or **linear**) **equation in x.**

GRAPH IT

Your grapher can solve equations by using the EQUATION SOLVER. Press [MATH] [0]. If there is nothing entered, the display will show

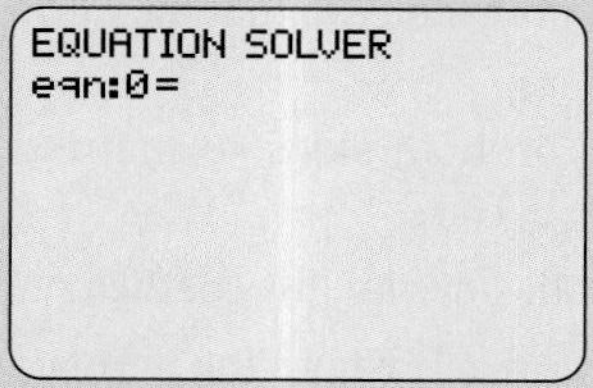

If an equation has been entered, press [▲] [CLEAR]. There are many optional steps, but we will only cover the basics. To solve $x + 2 = 5$, subtract 5 from both sides and enter $x - 3$ [ENTER] [ALPHA] [ENTER] to obtain the answer 3 as shown.

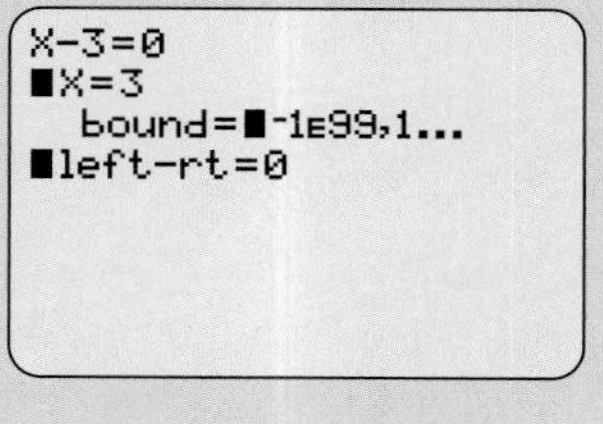

GRAPH IT

To do Example 3, subtract $(5x - 6)$ from both sides of the equation to obtain $-3x - 2 = 0$. Press [MATH] [0] [▲] [CLEAR]. Enter $-3x - 2$ to the right of the 0. (Recall that the $-$ in $-3x$ is entered as [(−)].) To obtain the answer, press [ENTER] [ALPHA] [ENTER] and get $-0.666\cdots$, or $-\frac{2}{3}$.

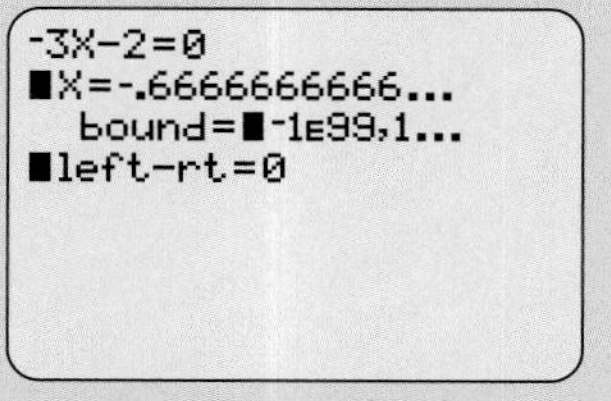

GRAPH IT

Is there an easier way to solve $2x - 8 = 5x - 6$? Yes, graphically. To solve $2x - 8 = 5x - 6$, call the left side Y_1 and the right side Y_2. We want to find the values for which $Y_1 = Y_2$. Press [Y=] and enter $2x - 8$ for Y_1 and $5x - 6$ for Y_2. Press [ZOOM] [6]. The two lines shown represent all the possible values for x in $Y_1 = 2x - 8$ and $Y_2 = 5x - 6$. What we need is the x value that makes $Y_1 = Y_2$. This happens when the lines intersect. Ask the grapher for that x by pressing [2nd] [CALC] [5]. The grapher asks three questions, but just go ahead and press [ENTER] three times. The intersection occurs when x is $-0.666\cdots$, or $-\frac{2}{3}$.

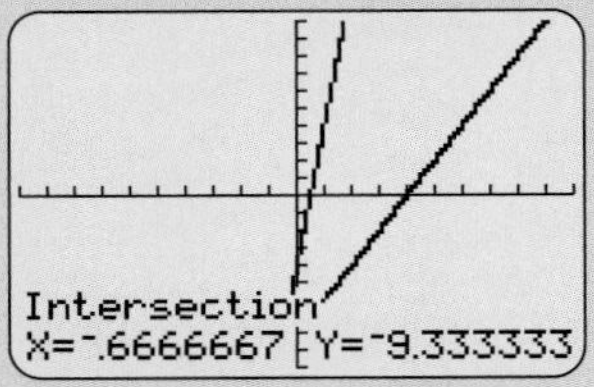

Do you really know how to solve equations by graphing? Let us see. To do Example 4, what will you let Y_1 be? What about Y_2? Be careful with the parentheses! If you get the graph shown using a standard window, you are on the right track. Press [2nd] [CALC] [5] and [ENTER] three times as before. Did you get -2?

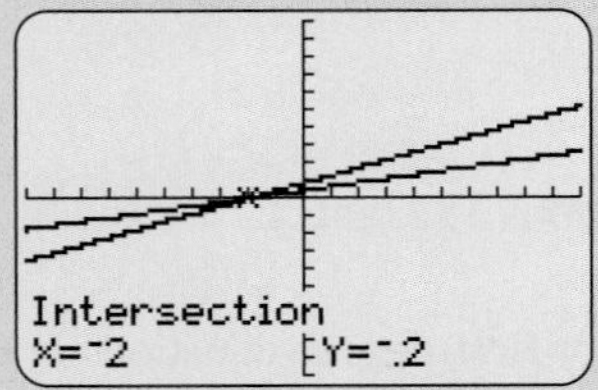

To help in solving linear equations, we suggest the following procedure:

Procedure to Solve Linear Equations

1. If there are fractions, multiply each term on both sides of the equation by the lowest common denominator (LCD) of the fractions.
2. Simplify both sides of the equation if necessary (remove parentheses and combine like terms).
3. Add or subtract the same expression (terms) on both sides so that the variable is isolated on one side.
4. Add or subtract the same numbers (constants) on both sides so that the variable is isolated on one side.
5. If the coefficient of the variable is not 1, divide both sides by this coefficient.
6. The resulting equation is in the form $x = a$ (or $a = x$), where the number a is the solution of the equation.
7. Check the answer by substituting it into the original equation. Both sides must simplify to the same number.

EXAMPLE 4 Solving Equations Involving Fractions

Solve the equation

$$\frac{(x+1)}{5} = \frac{(x-2)}{2} + \frac{9}{5}$$

Solution

We use the suggested procedure for the given equation.

1. Multiply each term by the LCD 10. (You obtain an equivalent equation.)

$$10\frac{(x+1)}{5} = 10\frac{(x-2)}{2} + 10 \cdot \frac{9}{5}$$

2. Simplify by removing parentheses and combining like terms.

$$2(x+1) = 5(x-2) + 18$$
$$2x + 2 = 5x - 10 + 18 \qquad \text{or} \qquad 2x + 2 = 5x + 8$$

3. Since the coefficient of x is greater on the right side than on the left, we subtract $2x$ on both sides and get

$$2x + 2 - 2x = 5x + 8 - 2x \qquad \text{or} \qquad 2 = 3x + 8$$

4. To eliminate the 8 on the right side, we subtract 8 on both sides.

$$2 - 8 = 3x + 8 - 8 \qquad \text{or} \qquad -6 = 3x$$

5. To make the coefficient of x equal 1, we divide both sides by 3.

$$\frac{-6}{3} = \frac{3x}{3}$$

6. We get

$$-2 = x$$

Thus, the solution is $x = -2$.

7. *Check in the original equation:* For $x = -2$, the left side of the given equation becomes

$$\frac{-2+1}{5} = \frac{-1}{5} = -\frac{1}{5}$$

and the right side becomes

$$\frac{-2-2}{2} + \frac{9}{5} = -2 + \frac{9}{5}$$

$$= -\frac{10}{5} + \frac{9}{5} = -\frac{1}{5}$$

Since the two sides agree, the solution is correct.

EXAMPLE 5 Solving for a Variable

Solve for p.

$$1 + 3 \times 2p = 7 + \frac{3(2p)^2}{3p}$$

Solution

First, we simplify the given equation by using the correct order of operations in doing the indicated multiplications and divisions.

$$1 + 3 \times 2p = 7 + \frac{3(2p)^2}{3p} \quad \text{Given.}$$

$$1 + 6p = 7 + \frac{4p^2}{p} \quad \text{Simplify, since } \frac{\cancel{3}(2p)^2}{\cancel{3}p} = \frac{4p^2}{p}.$$

$$1 + 6p = 7 + 4p$$

$$1 + 2p = 7 \quad \text{Subtract } 4p \text{ from both sides.}$$

$$2p = 6 \quad \text{Subtract 1 from both sides.}$$

$$p = 3 \quad \text{Divide both sides by 2.}$$

Check: For $p = 3$, the left side becomes

$$1 + 3 \times 6 = 19$$

and the right side becomes

$$7 + \frac{3(6^2)}{9} = 7 + \frac{36}{3} = 7 + 12 = 19$$

Since the two sides agree, the answer $p = 3$ is correct.

C Solving Formulas for a Variable

As you can see from Example 5, sometimes we are asked to solve for a variable in a *literal equation* containing several variables. To solve the literal equation $H = 2.89h + 70.64$ relating a man's height H and the length of his humerus bone h, for h, we use a procedure similar to the one used for solving linear equations (page 266). Here are some suggestions to follow when solving for a *specified variable:*

Procedure to Solve for a Specified Variable

1. Add or subtract the same expression on both sides of the equation so that the terms containing the *specified variable* (the one for which you are solving) are isolated on one side. The terms that *do not* contain the specified variable are thus on the other side.
2. If necessary, use the distributive property to write the side containing the specified variable as a product of the variable and a sum (or difference) of terms.
3. Then use the rules for solving linear equations.

EXAMPLE 6 Solving Formulas for a Variable

Anthropologists know how to estimate the height of a man (in centimeters) using only a bone. They use the formula

$$\underbrace{H}_{\text{Height of the man}} = 2.89\underbrace{h}_{\text{Length of the humerus}} + 70.64$$

(a) Solve for h. (b) A man is 157.34 cm tall. How long is his humerus?

Solution

(a) We have to solve for $\textcircled{h}$, so we isolate h on one side of the equation. Given

$$H = 2.89h + 70.64$$

$$H - 70.64 = 2.89\textcircled{h} + 70.64 - 70.64 \quad \text{Subtract 70.64.}$$

$$H - 70.64 = 2.89\textcircled{h} \quad \text{Simplify.}$$

$$\frac{H - 70.64}{2.89} = \textcircled{h} \quad \text{Divide by 2.89.}$$

Now we can find h for any given value of H.

(b) Substitute 157.34 for H to get

$$h = \frac{157.34 - 70.64}{2.89} = \frac{86.7}{2.89} = 30$$

The man's humerus is 30 cm long.

D Solving Inequalities

Definition of First-Degree Inequality

An **inequality of the first degree in x** is an inequality of the form

$$ax + b < 0 \qquad a \neq 0$$

or of the form $ax + b > 0$.

Note: If $<$ is replaced by $\leq$ and $>$ is replaced by $\geq$, the results are still inequalities of the first degree in x.

We can solve such inequalities by means of elementary operations that produce equivalent inequalities whose solution sets are obvious, such as $x = 3$ or $x = -5$, or, in general, $x = \square$ or $\square = x$. These operations are as follows:

Elementary Operations for Inequalities

For the inequality

$$a < b$$

the following elementary operations yield inequalities **equivalent** to the original inequality:

1. **Addition** $a + c < b + c$
2. **Subtraction** $a - c < b - c$
3. **Multiplication** $ac < bc$ for $c > 0$
   $ac > bc$ for $c < 0$
4. **Division** $\frac{a}{c} < \frac{b}{c}$ for $c > 0$
   $\frac{a}{c} > \frac{b}{c}$ for $c < 0$

Briefly stated, we can add or subtract the same number on both sides. The sense (direction) of the inequality is **unchanged** if both sides are multiplied or divided by the same *positive* number. The sense (direction) of the inequality is **reversed** if both sides are multiplied or divided by the same *negative* number. For instance, if both sides of $-2 < 1$ are multiplied by -3, we get $6 > -3$. Similarly, if both sides of $-9 < -6$ are divided by -3, the result is $3 > 2$.

The preceding operations have been stated for the inequality $a < b$, but the same operations are valid for $a > b$. You can convince yourself of the validity of these operations by noting that the geometric equivalent of $a < b$ is ***a* precedes *b* on the number line.** (Figure 6.1 clarifies this idea.) *Note:* Since $a \le b$ means $a < b$ **or** $a = b$, the elementary operations listed above may also be used for inequalities of the type $a \le b$ and $a \ge b$.

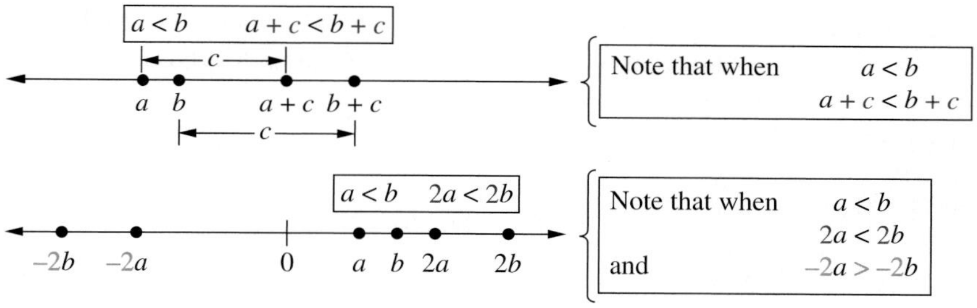

FIGURE 6.1

Linear (first-degree) inequalities can be solved by a procedure similar to that used for equations. This is illustrated in the next examples, where x represents a real number.

EXAMPLE 7 Solving Inequalities Involving >

Solve the inequality $3x + 2 > x + 6$.

Solution

1. The two sides are already in simplified form.
2. Subtract x from both sides.

$$3x + 2 - x > x + 6 - x$$
$$2x + 2 > 6$$

3. Subtract 2 from both sides.

$$2x + 2 - 2 > 6 - 2$$
$$2x > 4$$

4. Divide both sides by 2.

$$\frac{2x}{2} > \frac{4}{2}$$
$$x > 2$$

5. The solution set is $\{x|x > 2\}$.
6. A partial check can be made by substituting a number from the proposed solution set into the original inequality. For instance, 3 is in the set $\{x|x > 2\}$. For $x = 3$, the left side becomes

$$3(3) + 2 = 11$$

and the right side becomes

$$3 + 6 = 9$$

Since $11 > 9$, $x = 3$ does satisfy the inequality. Because the solution set contains infinitely many numbers, we cannot check by substituting one number at a time. However, if the number selected did *not* check, then something would be wrong, and we could check the work to find the error.

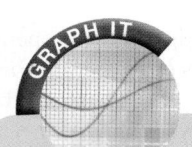

GRAPH IT

To solve $2x - 3 < 5x + 7$, let $Y_1 = 2x - 3$ and $Y_2 = 5x + 7$. Press ZOOM 6. Y_1 is **below** Y_2 to the right of the point at which the lines intersect. This intersection is found by pressing 2nd CALC 5 and ENTER three times. Thus, $Y_1 < Y_2$ to the right of $-3.333\cdots$, that is, when $x > -3\frac{1}{3} = -\frac{10}{3}$.

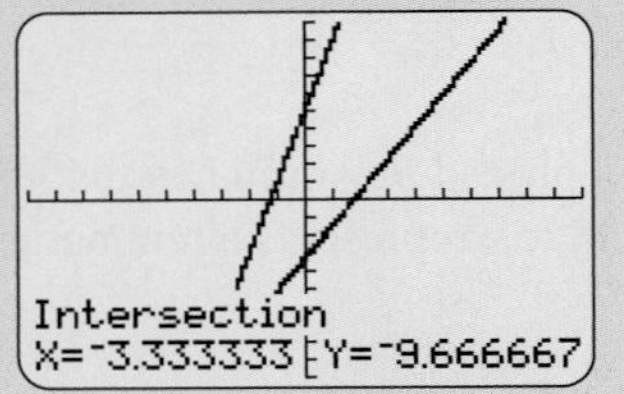

EXAMPLE 8 Solving Inequalities Involving <

Solve the inequality $2x - 3 < 5x + 7$.

Solution

1. The two sides are already in simplified form.
2. Subtract $5x$ from both sides.

$$2x - 3 - 5x < 5x + 7 - 5x$$
$$-3x - 3 < 7$$

3. Add 3 to both sides.

$$-3x - 3 + 3 < 7 + 3$$
$$-3x < 10$$

4. Divide both sides by -3.

$$x > -\frac{10}{3}$$ Do not forget to change < to >.

5. The solution set is $\left\{x|x > -\frac{10}{3}\right\}$. Be sure to notice that **division by −3 reversed the sense (direction) of the inequality.**
6. The check is left for you to do. An easy number to use is 0.

If, in step 2, you were to subtract $2x$ from both sides of the inequality, you would avoid dividing by a negative number later. However, in this case, the answer would be $-\frac{10}{3} < x$. If you are asked what x is, then you must write the equivalent answer $x > -\frac{10}{3}$. Which way should you do it? Whichever way you understand best!

EXAMPLE 9 Solving Inequalities Involving Fractions

Solve the inequality $-\frac{1}{2}x < \frac{1}{2} + x$.

Solution

This time we want to eliminate the fractions and the negative sign on the left. This is done by multiplying both sides by -2. Since this multiplier is negative, the inequality sign is reversed. Here are the steps.

Reverse the inequality sign!

$$(-2)(-\tfrac{1}{2})x > (-2)(\tfrac{1}{2} + x)$$

or

$$x > -1 - 2x$$

Now we add $2x$ to both sides to get

$$3x > -1$$

Then we divide both sides by 3 (do not reverse the inequality because 3 is positive) and obtain the answer

$$x > -\tfrac{1}{3}$$

The solution set is $\{x \mid x \text{ is a real number and } x > -\frac{1}{3}\}$.

E Applications

One of the most important ideas in elementary mathematics is the use of **percent.** Basically, there are three types of problems involving percent. These may be illustrated as follows:

Statement	*Translation*
1. 40% of 60 is what number?	$0.40 \times 60 = n$
2. What percent of 50 is 10?	$r \times 50 = 10$
3. 20 is 40% of what number?	$20 = 0.40 \times n$

All these problems (which, incidentally, can be stated in different ways) can be solved easily by using what we have studied in this section. The basic idea is that "r% of n is p" translates into the equation

$$0.01rn = p \quad \text{Recall that } r\% = \frac{r}{100} = 0.01r. \tag{1}$$

Each type of percent problem can be solved by substituting the known data into equation (1) or by **translating** the problem into an equation and then solving for the unknown.

Saving Lives
Community hospitals without on-site cardiac units can save more lives with angioplasty than with drug treatment, a new study of 451 heart attack victims shows.

Clot-breaking drug
Angioplasty

Number of patients with the following outcome, six months after treatment:

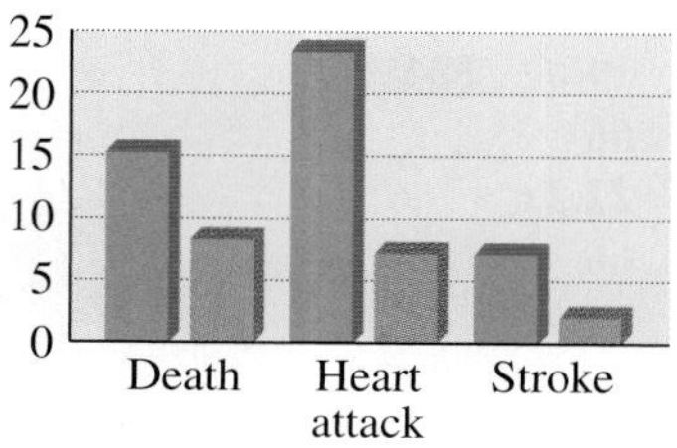

Note: The study was conducted at 11 community hospitals without on-site cardiac surgery units.

Source: From "Study: Angioplasty can be done at many more hospitals," by Lindsay Tanner (Sun Journal, April 17, 2002) Reprinted by permission of The Associated Press.

EXAMPLE 10 Saving Lives with Angioplasty

The study cited in the margin claims that you can save more lives with angioplasty (a procedure in which a balloon-tipped instrument is inserted in your arteries, the balloon is inflated, and the artery is unclogged!) than with a blood-clot-breaking drug called TPA. Of the 451 patients studied, 226 were randomly assigned for TPA and 225 for angioplasty. After 6 months:

(a) 7.1% of the drug therapy patients died. To the nearest whole number, how many patients is that?

(b) What percent of the 451 patients received an angioplasty?

(c) The 225 patients receiving an angioplasty should correspond to about half (50%) of the total number n of patients in the study. What should n be?

Solution

(a) Here, we need 7.1% of 226, which is $0.071 \cdot 226 = 16.046$, or 16 when rounded to the nearest whole number.

(b) We need to find what percent r of 451 is 225, which means $451r = 225$

Dividing both sides by 451, we obtain $r = 225/451$, which is about 50% (to the nearest percent). Thus, about 50% of the patients received an angioplasty.

(c) This time we need to solve $225 = 50\%n$, which means $225 = 0.50n$

Dividing both sides by 0.50, we find that $n = 225/0.50 = 450$, which does correspond to about 50% of the 451 patients actually in the study.

EXAMPLE 11 Beverages or Insurance?

According to the Bureau of Labor Statistics, the amount of money I (in billions) spent annually on vehicle insurance by persons under 25 years of age is as shown in the graph in **blue** and can be approximated by

$$I = 22.2x + 390 \text{ (billion)}$$

where x is the year number (1, 2, 3, 4 or 5). The amount A spent annually on alcoholic beverages is in **red** and can be approximated by

$$A = 28.2x + 324 \text{ (billion)}$$

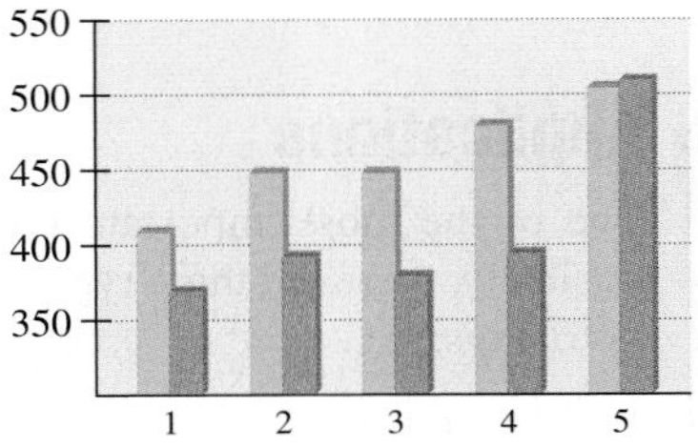

	Ins	Alc Bev
1	408	369
2	449	392
3	449	379
4	479	394
5	504	509

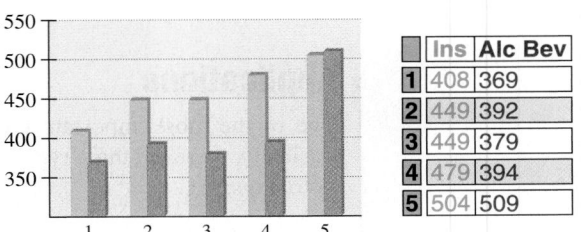

Source: Bureau of Labor Statistics.

In how many years will the amount A of money spent on alcoholic beverages equal the amount I spent on insurance?

Solution

For the amount of money spent on alcoholic beverages to be equal to the amount spent on insurance, A must equal I; that is,

$$28.2x + 324 = 22.2x + 390$$

To find out when this occurs, we must solve for the year number x.

$$\begin{array}{lrcl}
\text{Given:} & 28.2x + 324 & = & 22.2x + 390 \\
\text{Subtract } \mathbf{324} & 28.2x + 324 - 324 & = & 22.2x + 390 - 324 \\
 & 28.2x & = & 22.2x + 66 \\
\text{Subtract } \mathbf{22.2x} & 28.2x - 22.2x & = & 22.2x - 22.2x + 66 \\
 & 6x & = & 66 \\
\text{Divide by } \mathbf{6} & x & = & 11
\end{array}$$

Thus, $I = A$ when $x = \mathbf{11}$, that is, in **11** years.

Algebra is used in many ways in our daily lives. For example, do you know the exact relationship between your shoe size S and the length L of your foot? Here are the formulas used in the United States.

$S = 3L - 22$ for men $\qquad$ $S = 3L - 21$ for women

We use these ideas next.

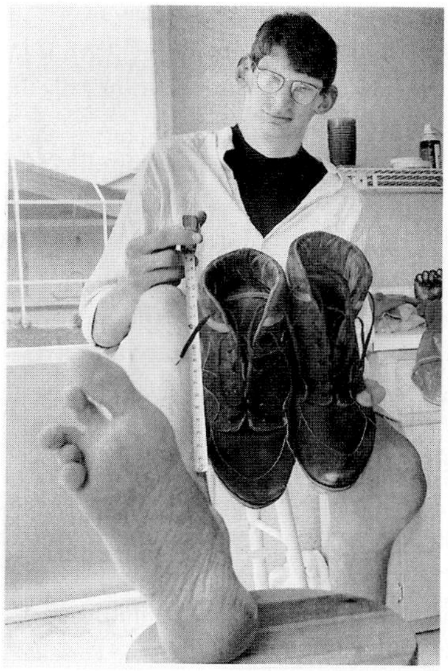
© The Tampa Tribune

Fred Bellett, Tampa Tribune
FBellet@tampatrib.com

EXAMPLE 12 Big Foot and Equations

(a) If a man wears a size 12 shoe, what is the length L of his foot?

(b) If you know that a woman's shoe size is not bigger than a size 6, what can you say about the length of her foot?

Solution

(a) The formula for the length of a man's foot is $S = 3L - 22$

Since the man wears a size 12, $12 = 3L - 22$
We would like to solve for L.

Add 22. $22 + 12 = 3L - 22 + 22$

Simplify. $34 = 3L$

Divide both sides by 3. $\frac{34}{3} = L$

Thus, the man's foot is $\frac{34}{3} = 11\frac{1}{3}$ in. long. By the way, the man in the photo has an 18-in.-long foot.

(b) If the woman's shoe size S is not bigger than 6, then

$$S = 3L - 21 \le 6$$

Add 21. $3L - 21 + 21 \le 6 + 21$

Simplify. $3L \le 27$

Divide both sides by 3. $L \le 9$

Thus, the woman's foot is less than 9 in. long.

6.1 EXERCISES

A Equations and Inequalities

In problems 1–4, determine which of the given numbers are solutions of the given inequality.

1. $2 + x \le 2 - x$
   a. 2 b. −2 c. 0 d. 5
2. $3x + 1 < 2x + 4$
   a. $\frac{1}{3}$ b. 4 c. 0 d. 3
3. $3x - 2 \ge 2x - 1$
   a. 0 b. 3 c. −2 d. 1
4. $x > 3 - 2x$
   a. 1 b. 2 c. 0 d. −2
5. Determine which of the following are solutions of $2x - 1 = 3$.
   a. −1 b. 1 c. 2 d. 0
6. Determine which of the following are solutions of $\frac{1}{5}(3x - 2) = 2$.
   a. −1 b. 0 c. 2 d. 4

B Solving Equations

In problems 7–32, solve each equation.

7. $x + 10 = 15$
8. $x - 5 = 8$
9. $2x - 1 = 5$
10. $3x + 1 = 4$
11. $2x + 2 = x + 4$
12. $3x + 1 = x - 3$
13. $3x + 1 = 4x - 8$
14. $2x + 3 = 3x - 1$
15. $7 = 3x + 4$
16. $22 = 4x + 2$
17. $4 = 3x - 2$
18. $1 = 5x - 8$
19. $7n + 10 - 2n = 4n - 2 + 3n$
20. $13a - 6 + a = 5a + 3 + 3a$
21. $2(x + 5) = 13$
22. $6(x + 2) = 17$
23. $\frac{1}{2}(x - 2) = 5$
24. $\frac{2}{3}(5x - 4) = 1$
25. $3(x + 1) - x = 2(9 - x)$
26. $14y - 14 - 3y = 10y - 6(1 - y)$
27. $8(x - 1) = x + 2$
28. $x + 6 = 6(x - 1)$
29. $\frac{1}{4}(x - 2) = \frac{1}{3}(x - 4)$
30. $\frac{1}{2}(3x - 1) = \frac{2}{5}(3x + 1)$
31. $3 \times 2p + 5 = 37 - \frac{4p^2}{2p}$
32. $15 + \frac{12t^2}{3t} = 3 \times 3t - 5$

C Solving Formulas for a Variable

In problems 33–38, solve the given formula for the indicated letter.

33. $V = \pi r^2 h$ for h
34. $V = \frac{1}{3}\pi r^2 h$ for h
35. $V = LWH$ for W
36. $V = LWH$ for H
37. $P = s_1 + s_2 + b$ for b
38. $P = s_1 + s_2 + b$ for s_2

39. The distance D traveled in time T by an object moving at rate R is given by $D = RT$.
   a. Solve for T.
   b. The distance between two cities A and B is 220 mi. How long would it take a driver traveling at 55 mph to go from A to B?
40. The ideal height H (in inches) of a man is related to his weight W (in pounds) by the formula $W = 5H - 190$.
   a. Solve for H.
   b. If a man weighs 160 lb, what is his height?
41. The number of hours H a growing child should sleep is $H = 17 - \frac{A}{2}$, where A is the age of the child in years.
   a. Solve for A.
   b. At what age would you expect a child to sleep 8 hours?
42. The area A of a trapezoid is given by $A = \frac{1}{2}h(a + b)$.
   a. Solve for b.
   b. If the area of a trapezoid is 60 square units, its height h is 10 units, and side a is 7 units, what is the length of side b?

D Solving Inequalities

Find the solution set for each of the following if the replacement set is the set of real numbers.

43. $x - 3 < 1$
44. $x - 2 < 2$
45. $x - 4 > -1$
46. $x + 3 > -2$
47. $2x - 1 > x + 2$
48. $3x - 3 > 2x + 1$
49. $2x + 3 \le 9 + 5x$
50. $x + 8 \ge 2x - 1$
51. $x + 1 > \frac{1}{2}x - 1$
52. $x - 1 < \frac{1}{2}x + 2$
53. $x \ge 4 + 3x$
54. $x - 1 \le 5 + 3x$
55. $\frac{1}{3}x - 2 \ge \frac{2}{3}x + 1$
56. $\frac{1}{4}x + 1 \le \frac{3}{4}x - 1$
57. $2x - 2 > x + 1$
58. $3x - 2 > 2x + 2$
59. $x + 3 > \frac{1}{2}x + 1$
60. $x + 1 < \frac{1}{2}x + 4$
61. $x \ge 2 + 4x$
62. $x - 2 \le 6 + 3x$
63. $2x + 1 < 2x$
64. $5x \le 5x + 4$
65. $8x + 2 \le 3(x + 4)$
66. $9x + 3 \le 4(x + 2)$
67. $3(x + 4) > -5x - 4$
68. $5(x + 2) < -3x + 2$
69. $-2(x + 1) \ge 3x - 4$
70. $-3(2 - x) \ge 5x - 7$
71. $a(x - 1) \le a(2x + 3)$, with $a < 0$
72. $b(1 - 2x) > 5b - 4bx$, with $b < 0$

E Applications

73. 40% of 80 is what number?
74. Find 15% of 60.
75. 315 is what percent of 3150?
76. 8 is what percent of 4?
77. What percent of 40 is 5?
78. 20 is what percent of 30?
79. 30% of what number is 60?
80. 10 is 40% of what number?
81. If you "drive sensibly," you can **improve** your mileage by 10%! Assume your car gets 20 mpg and uses 600 gallons of gas a year:
   a. What will your new mileage be if you drive sensibly?
   b. How many gallons a year will you use if you drive sensibly?
82. An extra 100 lb in the trunk **cuts** your gas mileage by **2%.** Assume your car gets 20 mpg and uses 600 gallons of gas a year:
   a. How many gallons a year will you save if you ditch the 100 lb of junk in the trunk?
   b. How many gallons of gas will you use when you ditch the 100 lb of junk in the trunk?
83. On a 60-item test, a student got 40 items correct. What percent is that? (Round to the nearest percent.)
84. The price of an article on sale was 90% of the regular price. If the sale price was \$18, what was the regular price?
85. Two stores sell an item that they normally price at \$140. Store A advertises a sale price of 25% off the regular price, and store B advertises a sale price of \$100. Which is the lower price?
86. ABC Savings & Loan loans the Adams family \$40,000 toward the purchase of a \$48,000 house. What percent of the purchase price is the loan?
87. The table shows the amount of money spent annually over a 5-year period on books and maps,

$$B = 1.73x + 30 \text{ (in billions)}$$

and the amount spent on magazines, newspapers, and sheet music,

$$M = 0.53x + 33 \text{ (billion)}$$

where x is the year number (1, 2, 3, 4, or 5). In how many years will the amount B spent on books and maps be the same as the amount M spent on magazines, newspapers, and sheet music?

	Books, Maps	Mag, News
1	28.8	32.1
2	31.6	33.5
3	33.7	35.0
4	34.6	34.5
5	35.8	34.2

Source: U.S. Bureau of Economic Analysis, *Survey of Current Business*, January 2004, www.census.gov/prod/2004pubs/04statab/arts.pdf.

88. According to the Bureau of Labor Statistics, the amount of money I spent annually on vehicle insurance by persons between 25 years and 34 years of age is as shown in the table and can be approximated by

$$I = 50.8x + 664.2 \text{ (billion)}$$

where x is the year number (1, 2, 3, 4, or 5). The annual amount A spent on alcoholic beverages can be approximated by

$$A = 12.6x + 368.2 \text{ (billion)}$$

   a. Find the value of x so that $I = A$.
   b. Based on your answer to part (a), can the amount of money spent on alcoholic beverages ever equal the amount spent on insurance?

	Ins	Alc Bev
1	705	365
2	774	431
3	822	393
4	872	395
5	910	446

Source: Bureau of Labor Statistics

89. The graph shows the total enrollment of 18–24-year-old students in degree-granting institutions and can be approximated by

$$E = 0.15N + 7.77 \text{ (millions)}$$

where N represents the number of years after 1989. Use the equation to find the projected number E of students enrolled in

a. **2002.** How close is your answer to the value 9.9 given in the graph?

b. **2014.** How close is your answer to the value 11.5 given in the graph?

c. The graph does not show a projected value for the year 2010. Use the equation to predict the enrollment for the year 2010.

Enrollment, by age of student

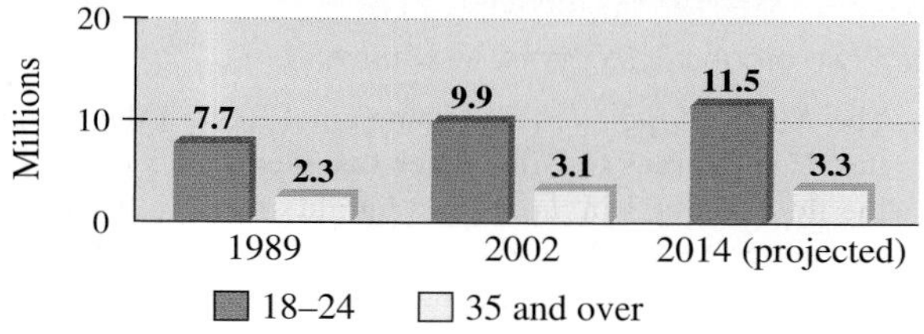

Source: U.S. Dept. of Education, NCES: Integrated Post-secondary Education Data System (IPEDS), "Fall Enrollment Survey." http://nces.ed.gov/pubs2005/2005074_1.pdf.

90. The graph shows the total student enrollment in degree-granting institutions and can be approximated by

$$E = 0.24N + 13.5$$

where N represents the number of years after 1989. Use the equation to find the projected number E of students enrolled in

a. **2002.** How close is your answer to the value 16.7 given in the graph?

b. **2014.** How close is your answer to the value 19.5 given in the graph?

c. The graph does not project a value for the year 2019. Use the equation to predict the enrollment for 2019.

Enrollment in millions

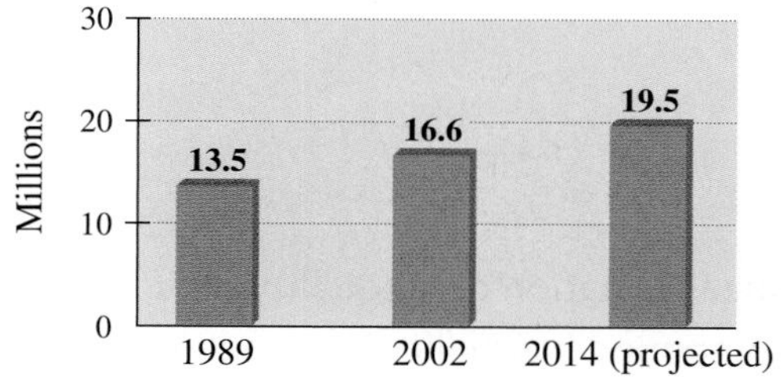

Source: http://nces.ed.gov/pubs2005/2005074_1.pdf.

As you recall from Example 12, the relationship between your shoe size S and the length of your foot L (in inches) is given by

$S = 3L - 22$ for men

$S = 3L - 21$ for women

91. If Tyrone wears a size 11 shoe, what is the length L of his foot?

92. If Maria wears a size 7 shoe, what is the length L of her foot?

93. Sam's size 7 tennis shoes fit Sue perfectly! What size women's tennis shoe does Sue wear?

94. The largest shoes ever sold was a pair of size 42 shoes made for the giant Harley Davidson of Avon Park, Florida. How long is Mr. Davidson's foot?

95. How long a foot requires a size 14 shoe, the largest standard shoe size for men?

96. How long is your foot when your shoe size is the same as the length of your foot and you are

a. a man? b. a woman?

97. In 1951, Eric Shipton photographed a 23-in. footprint believed to be that of the Abominable Snowman.

a. What size shoe would the Abominable Snowman need?

b. If the Abominable Snowman turned out to be the Abominable Snowwoman, what size shoe would she need?

98. When the variable cost per unit is \$12 and the fixed cost is \$160,000, the total cost for a certain product is $C = 12n + 160{,}000$ (n is the number of units sold). If the unit price is \$20, the revenue R is $20n$. What is the minimum number of units that must be sold to make a profit? (You need $R > C$ to make a profit.)

99. The cost of first-class mail is \$0.44 for the first ounce and \$0.20 for each additional ounce. A delivery company will charge \$5 for delivering a package weighing up to 2 lb (32 oz). When would the U.S. Post Office price, represented by $P = 0.44 + 0.20(x - 1)$ (where x is the weight of the package in ounces), be cheaper than the delivery company's price?

100. The parking cost at a citywide garage is $C = 1 + 0.75(h - 1)$, where h is the number of hours you park and C is the cost in dollars. When is the cost C less than \$10?

101. Do you follow major league baseball? When do you think the average number of runs per game was highest? It was in 1996. The average number of runs scored per game for the National League can be approximated by $N = 0.165x + 4.68$. For the American League the approximation is $A = -0.185x + 5.38$, where x is the number of years after 1996. When will $N > A$—that is, when will the National League run production exceed that of the American League?

IN OTHER WORDS

102. In your own words define the *replacement set* for an equation.

103. In your own words define the *solution set* for an equation.

104. If a real number a is in the replacement set of an equation, will it always be in the solution set? Explain.

105. If a particular number s is in the solution set of an equation, will it always be in the replacement set? Explain.

106. Can you think of an equation in which the replacement set and the solution set are the same?

USING YOUR KNOWLEDGE

The source for problems 107–108 *is* The Completely Revised and Updated Fast-Food Guide *or* http://chowbaby.com. *You can use your knowledge and the facts you have learned in this section to solve problems like this one. Of the calories in a McDonald's biscuit with sausage and eggs,* 60% *are fat calories (calories derived from the fat in the food). If there are* 351 *fat calories in this product, what is the total number of calories in a McDonald's biscuit with sausage and eggs? Let this number be c. Since* 60% *of c is* 351, *we have*

$$60\% \cdot c = 351$$

$$0.60c = 351$$

$$60c = 35{,}100 \quad \text{Multiplying both sides by 100}$$

$$c = \frac{35{,}100}{60} = 585 \quad \text{Dividing by 60}$$

Thus, there are 585 *total calories in a McDonald's biscuit with sausage and eggs. (See the* Fast-Food Guide *for a wealth of nutritional information on fast foods.)*

107. Of the total calories in a McDonald's apple pie, about 50% are fat calories. If there are 125 fat calories in a McDonald's apple pie, how many total calories are there in the apple pie?

108. Of the total calories in a Big Mac, 55% are fat calories. If 270 of the calories in a Big Mac are fat calories, how many total calories are there in a Big Mac? (Source: http://nutrition.mcdonalds.com/nutritionexchange/nutritionfacts.pdf.)

109. The Burger King Whopper also contains 50% fat calories. If 355 of the calories in a Whopper are fat calories, how many total calories are there in a Whopper? (Source: http://www.fastfoodnutrition.org/r-nutrition-facts/Burger%20King-item.html.)

DISCOVERY

110. The number of chirps N that a cricket makes per minute satisfies the equation

$$N = 4(F - 40)$$

where F is the temperature in degrees Fahrenheit. A farmer claimed that a cricket chirped 150 times a minute when the temperature was 80°F. Is this possible?

111. Referring to problem 110, if the temperature were 77.5°F, how many chirps per minute would the cricket make?

112. At what temperature will the cricket of problem 110 stop chirping?

113. The speed S (in centimeters per second) at which a certain type of ant crawls is $S = \frac{1}{6}(C - 4)$, where C is the temperature in degrees Celsius. Find the ant's speed when the temperature is 10°C.

114. At what temperature will the ant in problem 113 stop crawling? Now, does the cricket stop chirping before the ant stops crawling?

COLLABORATIVE LEARNING

Form two groups of students: the Ants and the Crickets.

1. The Ants group has to find some ants! Record the temperature C in degrees Celsius. Place two meter sticks parallel on the floor about 3 in. apart and let ants walk in between the two meter sticks. Record the distance a single ant travels (in centimeters) and the time it takes it to travel that distance (in seconds). Do this several times as temperatures vary (maybe morning and noon).

   Do your results satisfy the equation $S = \frac{1}{6}(C - 4)$, where S is the speed of the ant in centimeters per second and C is the Celsius temperature? How close are your results to the ones in the formula? Explain why results may differ.

2. The Cricket group has to find some crickets! Record the temperature F in degrees Fahrenheit. Time the number of chirps c a cricket makes in 1 min. (You have to try to isolate the chirps of a single cricket!) Do this several times at different temperatures (early after sunset and later in the evening). Do your results satisfy the equation $c = 4(F - 40)$, where F is the temperature in degrees Fahrenheit? How close are your results to the ones in the formula? Explain why results may differ.

6.2 Graphs of Algebraic Sentences

GETTING STARTED

OBJECTIVES

A. Graph the solution set of a linear equation or inequality.
B. Graph the solution set of a compound inequality that uses "and."
C. Graph the solution set of a compound inequality that uses "or."
D. Solve applications involving equations or inequalities.

IN KING SOLOMON'S GARDEN

It is said that in ancient times King Solomon was the wisest of men. There is a legend that goes like this: One day when he was resting in his palace garden, Solomon, who was so wise that he could even understand the language of all animals and plants, heard gentle voices close to him. On further inspection he discovered two snails in a solemn meeting.

> The first snail said, "Brother, see'st thou yon straight pole that riseth upright from the ground 30 cubits high?" And the second snail answered, "Yea, even so do I."
>
> "It is my desire," said the first snail, "to climb to the very top of it. How long thinketh thou it will take me?"
>
> "That certainly shall depend on the speed with which thou climbest."
>
> "It is not as simple as that," said the would-be climber. "I can ascend but 3 cubits during the day, but in the evening I fall asleep and slip back 2 cubits so that, in effect, I move up but 1 cubit every 24 hours."
>
> "Tis plain then," said the second snail, "that thou will take 30 days to reach the top of the pole. Why dost thou plague me with such a simple problem? Prithee be silent and allow me to sleep."
>
> King Solomon smiled. He alone knew whether the second snail was right.

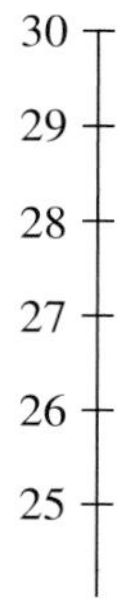

FIGURE 6.2

What do you think? (*Hint:* It will obviously take the snail 25 days to reach 25 cubits of height. From then on, draw a graph on the number line in Figure 6.2 and find the number of days it took the snail to get to the top.)

In this section you learn how to graph algebraic sentences (equations and inequalities) on the number line.

A Graphs of Algebraic Sentences

The solution set of an open sentence in one variable can always be represented by a set of points on the number line. This set of points is often called the **graph** of the equation or the inequality, as the case may be. We illustrate various types of graphs in the following examples:

EXAMPLE 1 Graphing Equations with the Integers as Replacements

Graph the solution set of the equation $x + 1 = 0$, where the replacement set is the set of integers.

Solution

Subtracting 1 from both sides, we see that the solution set is the singleton set $\{-1\}$. The graph consists of the single point -1 on the number line. We draw a solid dot to indicate this graph (see Figure 6.3).

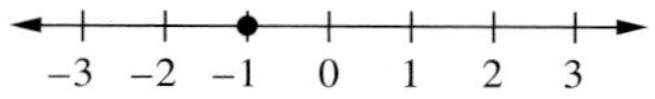

FIGURE 6.3 The singleton set $\{-1\}$.

EXAMPLE 2 More Equations with the Integers as Replacements

Graph the solution set of the inequality $x + 1 \le 0$, where the replacement set is the set of integers.

Solution

Subtracting 1 from both sides yields the equivalent inequality $x \le -1$. Thus, the solution set is the set of all integers that are less than or equal to -1—that is, the set $\{\ldots, -3, -2, -1\}$. To show this graph, we draw dots at the corresponding points on the number line (see Figure 6.4). Start at -1 and, as suggested by the notation $x \le -1$, draw solid dots at -1, -2, -3, and so on.

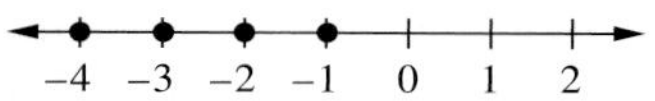

FIGURE 6.4 $\{\ldots, -3, -2, -1\}$.

EXAMPLE 3 Graphing Inequalities Involving ≤

Graph the solution set of the inequality $x + 1 \le 0$, where x is a real number.

Solution

Proceeding as in Example 2, we see that the solution set is the set of all real numbers less than or equal to -1—that is, $\{x | x \le -1, x \text{ real}\}$. We display this set by drawing a heavy line starting at -1 on the number line and going to the left. The point at -1 is marked with a solid dot to show that it is included in the set (see Figure 6.5).

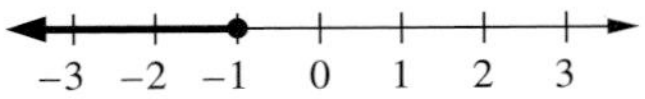

FIGURE 6.5 The set $\{x | x \le -1\}$.

EXAMPLE 4 Graphing Inequalities Involving ≠

Graph the solution set of the inequality $x + 2 \ne 5$, where x is a real number.

Solution

The number 3 is the only replacement for x such that $x + 2 = 5$, so the solution set is all real numbers except 3—that is, $\{x | x \ne 3, x \text{ real}\}$. The graph consists of the entire number line except for the point 3. In Figure 6.6, the graph is shown as a heavy line, and the point 3 is marked with an open circle to indicate its exclusion from the solution set.

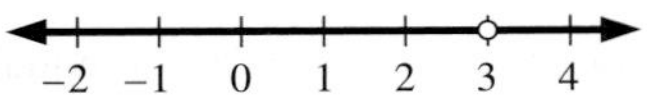

FIGURE 6.6 The set $\{x | x \ne 3\}$.

EXAMPLE 5 More Inequalities with Real Numbers

Graph the solution set of the inequality $-2 \le x < 1$, where the replacement set is the set of real numbers.

Solution

The solution set consists of all the real numbers between -2 and 1, with the -2 included and the 1 excluded. The graph is shown in Figure 6.7.

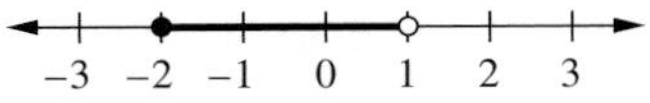

FIGURE 6.7 The set $\{x | -2 \le x < 1\}$.

A piece of the number line such as that in Figure 6.7 is called a **finite interval** (or a **line segment**). The endpoints in Figure 6.7 are -2 and 1. We call the interval **closed** if both endpoints are included, **open** if both endpoints are excluded, and **half-open** if only one of the endpoints is included. The interval in Figure 6.7 is half-open.

If a and b are real numbers with $a < b$, the various types of finite intervals and how they are written in interval notation are as shown in Figure 6.8. The notation for **infinite** intervals is discussed in the Using Your Knowledge section of Exercises 6.2.

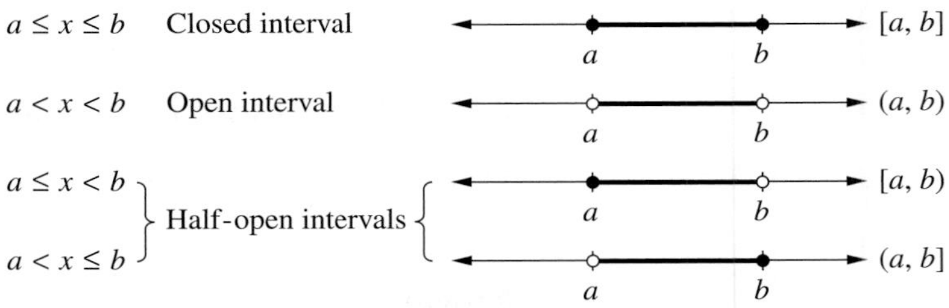

FIGURE 6.8 Finite intervals.

In this section we consider compound algebraic sentences consisting of two or more simple sentences of the type that occurred in the preceding sections. We are concerned with the connectives *and* and *or* used in exactly the same sense as in Chapter 3 and with how to graph the compound algebraic sentences.

B Sentences with *and*

As we work with finding the solution sets of compound sentences, note that if no replacement set is specified, we assume that the replacement set consists of all real numbers for which the members of the inequalities are defined.

EXAMPLE 6 Graphing Inequalities with *and*

Consider the sentence $x + 1 < 3$ and $x - 1 > -1$. Find its solution set.

Solution

The sentence given here is a compound sentence of type $p \wedge q$ (p and q), where p is $x + 1 < 3$ and q is $x - 1 > -1$. Such a sentence as $p \wedge q$ is true only when both p and q are true. Consequently, the solution set of the compound sentence is the **intersection** of the solution sets of the two components.

We have

$$\begin{aligned} x + 1 &< 3 &\quad \text{and} \quad& x - 1 > -1 \\ x + 1 - 1 &< 3 - 1 &\quad \text{and} \quad& x - 1 + 1 > -1 + 1 \\ x &< 2 &\quad \text{and} \quad& x > 0 \end{aligned}$$

Rewriting the second inequality, we see that x must satisfy the conditions

$$0 < x \quad \text{and} \quad x < 2$$

Thus, the solution set can be written in set notation as

$$\{x \mid 0 < x\} \cap \{x \mid x < 2\}$$

or, more efficiently, $\{x \mid 0 < x < 2\}$.

This result is most easily seen in Figure 6.9.

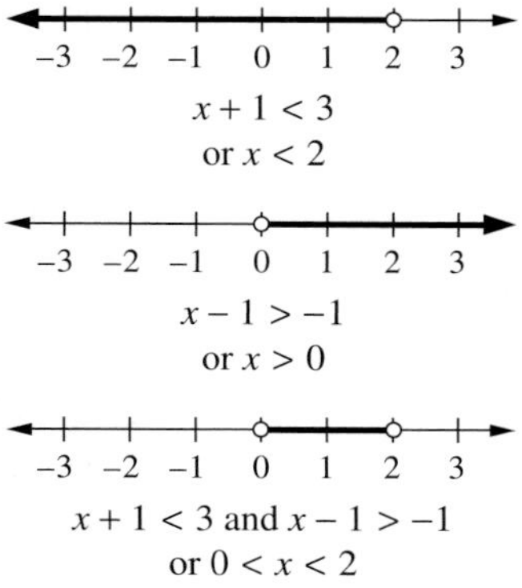

FIGURE 6.9 To graph $0 < x < 2$, place an open circle at 0, an open circle at 2, and draw the line segment *between* 0 and 2.

We can also obtain this result by first graphing $x + 1 < 3$, or equivalently, $x < 2$ (see Figure 6.9), and then graphing $x - 1 > -1$, or equivalently, $x > 0$. The intersection of these two graphs consists of all numbers between 0 and 2, as shown in Figure 6.9.

EXAMPLE 7 More Inequalities with *and*

Find the solution set of $x - 1 > 4$ and $x + 2 < 5$.

Solution

We have

$$\begin{aligned} x - 1 &> 4 &\quad \text{and} \quad& x + 2 < 5 \\ x - 1 + 1 &> 4 + 1 &\quad \text{and} \quad& x + 2 - 2 < 5 - 2 \\ x &> 5 &\quad \text{and} \quad& x < 3 \end{aligned}$$

Since there are no numbers satisfying both of these conditions (see Figure 6.10), there are no solutions; the solution set is empty.

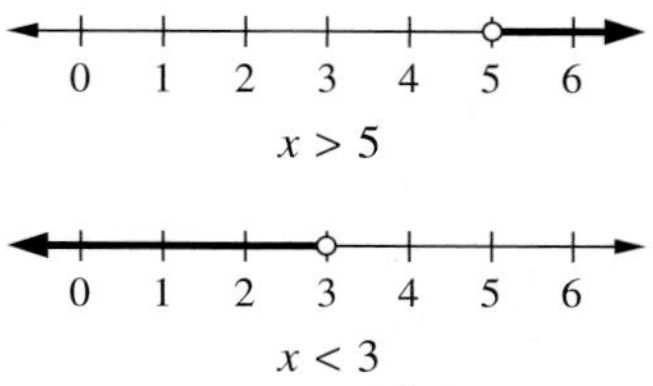

FIGURE 6.10

EXAMPLE 8 Inequalities with *and* Where *x* Is an Integer

Find the solution set of the sentence $x \le 5$ and $x + 1 \ge 0$ if x is an integer.

Solution

If x is an integer, then the solution set of $x \le 5$ is the set of all integers less than or equal to 5. Similarly, the solution set of $x + 1 \ge 0$ is the set of all integers greater than or equal to -1. The intersection of these two sets is the set $\{-1, 0, 1, 2, 3, 4, 5\}$, which is the desired solution set (see Figure 6.11).

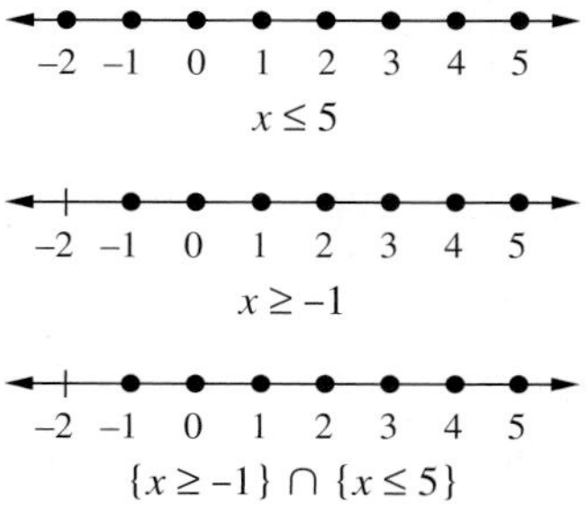

FIGURE 6.11

C Sentences with *or*

EXAMPLE 9 Inequalities with *or*

Find the solution set of the sentence $x + 1 < 5$ or $x - 1 > 6$.

Solution

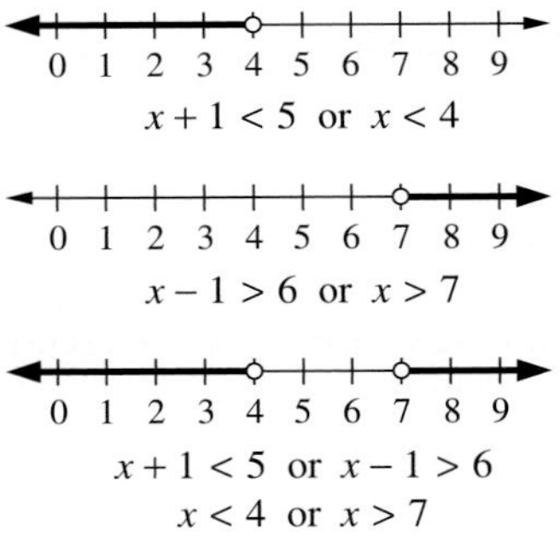

FIGURE 6.12

The replacement set is the set of all real numbers. (Why?) Because this is a sentence of the type $p \vee q$ $(p \text{ or } q)$, we know that the solution set is the **union** of the solution sets of the two components. We have

$$\begin{aligned} x + 1 &< 5 \quad \text{or} \quad & x - 1 &> 6 \\ x &< 4 \quad \text{or} \quad & x &> 7 \end{aligned}$$

Thus, the required solution set is

$$\{x \mid x < 4\} \cup \{x \mid x > 7\}$$

or stated in another way,

$$\{x \mid x < 4 \text{ or } x > 7\}$$

The graph in Figure 6.12 illustrates the solution.

D Applications

EXAMPLE 10 Solving Inequalities Involving Laptops and Desktops

Do you own a laptop or a desktop computer? The percent of American adults owning laptop computers L has *grown* from about 30% in 2006 to 50% in 2010 and can be approximated by $L = 5t + 30$, where t is the number of years ***after*** 2006. In the same period, the percent of American adults owning desktop computers D has *fallen* from about 70% to 58% and can be approximated by $D = -3t + 70$.

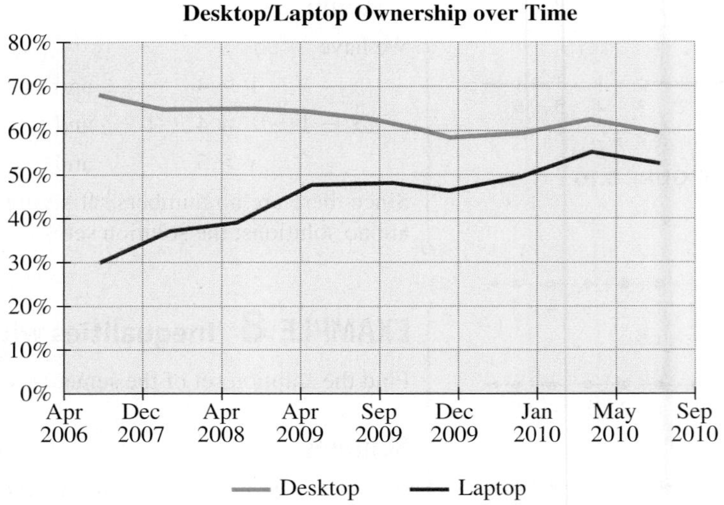

Source: Copyright © 2012 Pew Internet & American Life Project. http://pewinternet.org/Reports/2010/Gadgets.aspx.

(a) Write an inequality predicting when the percent of Americans owning laptop computers L will be above 60%.

(b) Write an inequality predicting when the percent of Americans owning desktop computers D will be above 40%.

(c) Write and solve a compound inequality describing the years in which the conditions in (a) and (b) are met.

Solution

(a) Since we want to predict when $L = 5t + 30$ will be *above* 60%, the inequality will be

$$5t + 30 > 60$$

(b) Here we want $D = -3t + 70$ to be *above* 40%. The inequality will be

$$-3t + 70 > 40$$

(c) Since both inequalities must be satisfied, we have to solve

$$\begin{array}{llcll}
5t + 30 & > 60 & \text{and} & -3t + 70 & > 40 \\
5t + 30 - 30 & > 60 - 30 & \text{and} & -3t + 70 - 70 & < 40 - 70 \\
5t & > 30 & \text{and} & -3t & > -30 \\
t & > 6 & \text{and} & t & < 10 \\
6 & < t & \text{and} & t & < 10
\end{array}$$

$$6 < t < 10$$

This means that between 6 and 10 years after 2006 (between 2012 and 2016) the percent of Americans owning laptop computers will be ***above*** 60% and the percent of Americans owning desktop computers will be *above* 40%. If you are the manufacturer or seller of computers, what implications does this result have? Will you manufacture more or fewer laptops? What about desktops?

6.2 EXERCISES

A Graphs of Algebraic Sentences

In problems 1–8, take x to be an integer and graph the solution set of each sentence.

1. $x + 2 = 4$
2. $x - 1 = 3$
3. $x + 1 \geq 2$
4. $x + 2 < 5$
5. $x - 3 \neq 1$
6. $-3 < x \leq 2$
7. $-2 \leq x \leq 4$
8. $-2 < x < 4$

In problems 9–26, take x to be a real number and graph the solution set of each sentence.

9. $x < 4$
10. $x \geq 2$
11. $x - 2 \leq 0$
12. $x - 2 \geq 4$
13. $-2 \leq x \leq 4$
14. $x - 3 \neq 1$
15. $x + 2 > 5$
16. $x - 2 = 1$
17. $-1 < x < 2$
18. $x \geq 3$
19. $x + 4 < 5$
20. $x + 5 < 4$
21. $x + 1 < x$
22. $x + 1 > x$
23. $2x + 3 < x + 1$
24. $-x + 5 \leq 2x + 2$
25. $3x - 7 \geq -7$
26. $2x + 5 < 5$

B Sentences with *and*

C Sentences with *or*

In problems 27–34, let each replacement set be the set of integers. Give the solution set by listing its elements.

27. $x \leq 4$ and $x - 1 \geq -2$
28. $x > 0$ and $x \leq 5$
29. $x + 1 \leq 7$ and $x > 2$
30. $x > -5$ and $x - 1 < 0$
31. $2x - 1 > 1$ and $x + 1 < 4$
32. $x - 1 < 1$ or $3x - 1 > 11$
33. $x < -5$ or $x > 5$
34. $x \geq 0$ or $x < -2$

In problems 35–52, let each replacement set be the set of real numbers. Graph the solution set unless it is the empty set.

35. $x + 1 \geq 2$ and $x \leq 4$
36. $x \leq 5$ and $x > -1$
37. $x > 2$ and $x < -2$

38. $x + 2 \le 4$ or $x + 2 \ge 6$
39. $x - 1 > 0$ and $x + 1 < 5$
40. $x \le 0$ or $x > 3$
41. $x \le x + 1$ and $x \ge 2$
42. $x + 2 \ge -2$ or $x < 0$
43. $x - 2 \ge 2$ and $x < 0$
44. $x + 3 \le 0$ or $x - 1 > 0$
45. $x \ge 0$ and $x - 1 \ge 2$
46. $x \ge 0$ and $x - 1 \le 2$
47. $x < 0$ or $x - 1 < 2$
48. $x < 0$ and $x - 1 > 2$
49. $x + 1 > 2$ and $x - 2 < 3$
50. $x - 1 > 3$ and $x + 1 > 2$
51. $x - 1 > 0$ or $x + 2 < 4$
52. $x + 1 > 2$ or $x - 1 < 2$

D Applications

53. The average annual cost C of owning a midsized car is \$4953 plus \$0.12 per mile. (Source: www.vtpi.org/tdm/tdm82.htm.)
 a. Write an expression that models the average annual cost of operating a midsized car for m mi.
 b. A company budgets between \$6000 and \$6500 for each car in the company pool. Write an inequality to describe the number of miles m that a midsized car in the company pool can be driven.
 c. Solve the inequality in part (**b**) and interpret the solution.
54. The average annual cost C of operating a full-size car is \$6689 plus \$0.15 per mile. (Source: www.vtpi.org/tdm/tdm82.htm.)
 a. Write an expression that models the average annual cost of operating a full-size car for m mi.
 b. A company budgets between \$7000 and \$7500 for each car in the company pool. Write an inequality to describe the number of miles m that a full-size car in the company pool can be driven.
 c. Solve the inequality in part (**b**) and interpret the solution.
55. The **C**orporate **A**verage **F**uel **E**conomy (**CAFE**) regulations in the United States are federal regulations intended to improve the average fuel economy of cars and light trucks (trucks, vans, and sport utility vehicles) sold in the United States. The combined car and light truck miles per gallon (mpg) can be approximated by $E = 1.5N + 27$, where N is the number of years after 2010. In what year will E be greater than 36?
56. Use the information in problem 55 and determine in how many years you would expect the combined car and light truck miles per gallon E to be greater than 42 mpg.

IN OTHER WORDS

57. Use the word *between* to indicate which numbers are represented in the following graphs:
 a. 

 b. 

 c. 

 d. 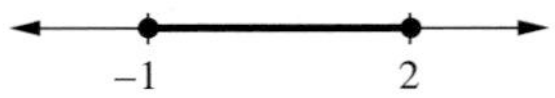

58. Write in words the sets of numbers represented in the following graphs:
 a. 

 b. 

 c. 

 d. 

59. Write in words the sets of numbers represented in the following graphs:
 a. 

 b. 

 c. 

 d. 

USING YOUR KNOWLEDGE

The graph of the inequality $x \le -1$ in Example 3 is an ***infinite interval*** *on the number line and can be written as $(-\infty, -1]$ using interval notation. The symbol $-\infty$ (read "negative infinity") does not represent a number; it simply means that the interval includes all numbers less than or equal to -1. The square bracket on the right indicates that -1 is part of the interval. The interval $(-\infty, -1]$ is called a* half-open interval. *If -1 were not included, we would write the* open interval *as follows: $(-\infty, -1)$. Note that the interval notation for $\{x|x > -2\}$ is $(-2, \infty)$, where the ∞ (read "infinity") symbol indicates that the interval includes all numbers greater than -2 (-2 itself is not included in the interval). The interval is an open interval. The following are some types of infinite intervals, their notation, and their graphs:*

Set Notation	*Interval Notation*	*Graph*
$\{x\|x > a\}$	(a, ∞)	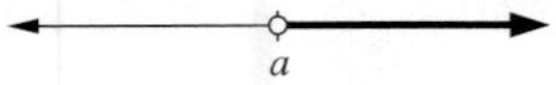
$\{x\|x < b\}$	$(-\infty, b)$	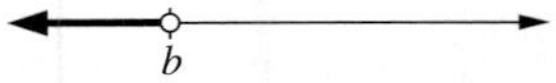
$\{x\|x \ge a\}$	$[a, \infty)$	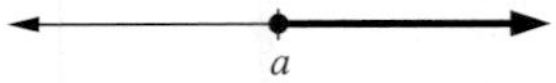
$\{x\|x \le b\}$	$(-\infty, b]$	

Use interval notation to write the following:

60. $\{x|x \ge -4\}$
61. $\{x|x < 5\}$
62. $\{x|x \le -6\}$
63. $\{x|x > 9\}$
64. $\{x|3 < x < 7\}$
65. $\{x|-4 \le x < -1\}$
66. $\{x|0 < x \le 8\}$
67. $\{x|-1 \le x \le 10\}$

DISCOVERY

Let J be Joe's height.
Let B be Bill's height.
Let F be Frank's height.
Let S be Sam's height.

What can you conclude from the information in the cartoon? To find the answer, you have to know how to translate the given information into symbols.

68. The second panel says that Bill is taller than Frank *and* Frank is taller than Joe. Write a compound inequality indicating these relationships.

Now translate each of the following statements into an equation or an inequality.

69. Joe is 5 ft (60 in.) tall.
70. Bill is taller than Frank.
71. Frank is 3 in. shorter than Sam.
72. Frank is taller than Joe.
73. Sam is 6 ft 5 in. (77 in.) tall.
74. According to the statement in problem 70, Bill is taller than Frank, and according to the statement in problem 72, Frank is taller than Joe. Write these two statements as an inequality of the form $a > b > c$.
75. On the basis of the answer to problem 74 and the fact that you can obtain Frank's height by using the results of problems 70, 71, and 73, what can you say about Bill's height?

6.3 Sentences Involving Absolute Values

GETTING STARTED

OBJECTIVES

A. Understand and evaluate expressions involving absolute values.

B. Solve and graph equations and inequalities involving absolute values.

C. Solve applications involving absolute values.

BUDGET VARIANCE AND ABSOLUTE VALUE

Budgeting expenses is an important family activity.

Have you ever been on a budget? Businesses and individuals usually try to predict how much money will be spent on certain items over a given period of time, but it is almost impossible to know exactly the final expenditures in different categories. For example, suppose you budget \$120 for a month's utilities. Any heat wave or cold snap could make your actual expenses jump to \$150. The \$30 difference, representing a 25% increase $\left(\frac{30}{120} = 25\%\right)$, might be an acceptable *variance.* To keep your budget "on target," you can make several variance checks during the year, possibly at the end of each month. Now, suppose b represents the budgeted amount for a certain item, a represents the actual expense, and you want to be within \$10 of your estimate. The item will **pass** the variance test if the actual expenses a are within \$10 of the budgeted amount b, that is, if

$$-10 \le b - a \le 10$$

Is there a way to write this information using a single inequality? You can if you use *absolute values.* The **absolute value** of a number x, denoted by $|x|$ (read "the absolute value of x"), is its numerical value with the sign disregarded. For example, $|-3| = 3$ and $|+7| = 7$. Thus, $-10 \le b - a \le 10$ is equivalent to $|b - a| \le 10$. Do you see why?

In general, if a and b are as before, a certain item will pass the variance test if $|b - a| \le c$, where c is the variance. The quantity c can be a definite amount or a percent of the budget. Now suppose you budget \$50 for gas and you want to be within 10% of your budget. How much gas money can you spend and still be within your variance? Intuitively, you can see that if you spend between \$45 and \$55, you will be within your 10% variance.

The amount of variance is given by

$$0.10 \cdot 50 = 5$$

and $|b - a| \le c$ becomes $|50 - a| \le 5$, or

$$-5 \le 50 - a \le 5$$

Subtracting 50 from each member,

$$-55 \le -a \le -45$$

Multiplying each term by -1,

$$55 \ge a \ge 45$$

or

$$45 \le a \le 55$$

The answer that you expected!

In problems 37–39 of Exercises 6.3, you will solve some more problems dealing with variance.

A Absolute Value

Sometimes we need to solve equations or inequalities that involve absolute values. The **absolute value** of a number x is defined to be the distance on the number line from 0 (the origin) to x and is denoted by $|x|$ (read "absolute value of x"). For example, the number 2 is 2 units away from 0, so $|2| = 2$. The number -2 is also 2 units away from 0, so $|-2| = 2$ (see Figure 6.13). Similarly, we see that $|8| = 8$, $|\frac{1}{2}| = \frac{1}{2}$, $|-5| = 5$, and $|-\frac{1}{4}| = \frac{1}{4}$. In general, if x is any real nonnegative number $(x \ge 0)$, then $|x|$ is simply x itself. But if x is a negative number $(x < 0)$, then $|x|$ is the corresponding positive number obtained by reversing the sign of x.

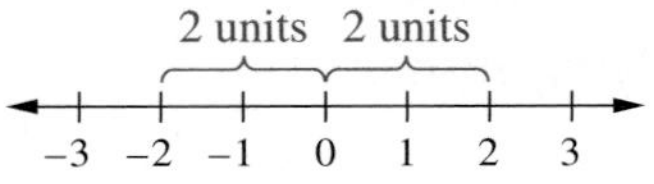

FIGURE 6.13

Definition of Absolute Value

The **absolute value** of x is given by

$$|x| = \begin{cases} x & \text{if } x \ge 0 \\ -x & \text{if } x < 0 \end{cases}$$

B Equations and Inequalities with Absolute Values

EXAMPLE 1 Solving Equations of the Form $|x| = a$

Find and graph the solution set of $|x| = 2$.

Solution

We look for all numbers that are 2 units away from the origin (the 0 point). Since 2 and -2 are the only two numbers that satisfy this condition, the solution set of the equation $|x| = 2$ is $\{2, -2\}$. The graph of this set is shown in Figure 6.14. Note that this solution set can be described by the compound sentence $x = 2$ or $x = -2$.

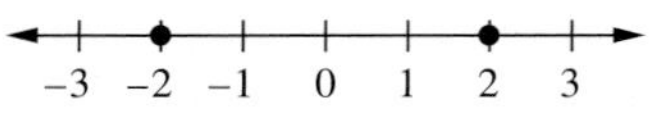

FIGURE 6.14

EXAMPLE 2 Solving Inequalities of the Form $|x| < a$

Find and graph the solution set of the inequality $|x| < 2$.

Solution

Here we look for all real numbers x that are less than 2 units away from 0. Since 2 and -2 are each exactly 2 units away from 0, we need all points between -2 and 2, that is, all numbers that satisfy the inequality

$$-2 < x < 2$$

The solution set is thus $\{x \mid -2 < x < 2\}$. The graph appears in Figure 6.15.

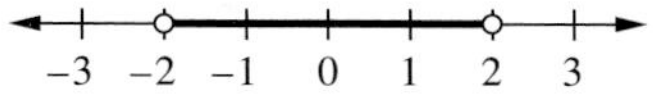

FIGURE 6.15

Equivalency for $|x| < a$

In general, if a is any positive number, then

$$|x| < a \qquad \text{is equivalent to} \qquad -a < x < a$$

EXAMPLE 3 Graphing Inequalities of the Form $|x| \le a$

Graph the solution set of $|x| \le 4$.

Solution

Since $|x| \le 4$ is equivalent to $-4 \le x \le 4$, the graph of the solution set is as shown in Figure 6.16.

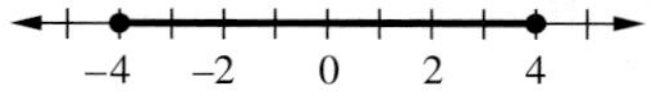

FIGURE 6.16

EXAMPLE 4 Graphing Inequalities of the Form $|x| < a$

Find the solution set of the inequality $|x - 1| < 4$.

Solution

Since $|x| < a$ is equivalent to $-a < x < a$,

$$|x - 1| < 4 \qquad \text{is equivalent to} \qquad -4 < x - 1 < 4$$

As in the case of equations, we still want to isolate x, so in the middle member of the inequality we need to add 1. Of course, we must do the same to all the members. Thus, we get

$$-4 + 1 < x - 1 + 1 < 4 + 1$$

or

$$-3 < x < 5$$

Thus, the solution set is $\{x \mid -3 < x < 5\}$, or $(-3, 5)$ in interval notation. (See Using Your Knowledge in Section 6.2 for more information about interval notation.)

GRAPH IT

To graph $|x - 1| < 4$, let Y_1 be the absolute value of $x - 1$ by pressing [Y=] [MATH] [▶] [1] and $x - 1$. Let Y_2 be 4 by pressing [▼] and 4. Press [ZOOM] [6]. When is $|x - 4|$, the V-shaped curve, below 4? Between -3 and 5!

EXAMPLE 5 Graphing Inequalities of the Form $|x| \ge a$

Find and graph the solution set of $|x| \ge 3$.

Solution

The solution set of $|x| = 3$ consists of all points that are exactly 3 units away from 0. Hence, the solution set of $|x| \ge 3$ consists of all points that are 3 or more units away

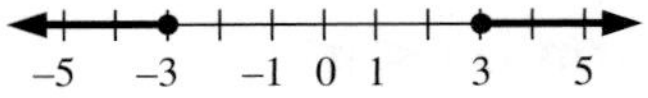

FIGURE 6.17

from 0. As you can see from Figure 6.17, these points can be described by the compound sentence

$$x \geq 3 \quad \text{or} \quad x \leq -3$$

We can therefore write the solution set of $|x| \geq 3$ in the form

$$\{x \mid x \geq 3\} \cup \{x \mid x \leq -3\}$$

Note that the answer can also be written in the form $\{x \mid x \geq 3 \text{ or } x \leq -3\}$ or in interval notation $(-\infty, -3] \cup [3, \infty)$.

To get a graph similar to the one in Example 5 using your grapher, enter [Y=] [MATH] [➤] [1] to get the absolute value; then enter x [)]. Now press [2nd] [MATH] [4] 3 to enter $\geq$ 3, and finally press [ZOOM] [6]. Same graph!

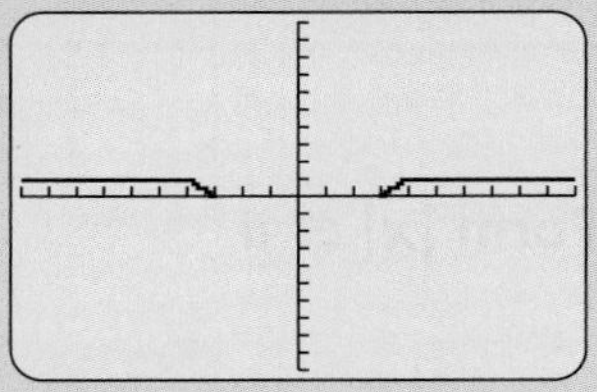

The idea in Example 5 can be generalized as follows:

Equivalency for $|x| > a$

If $a \geq 0$, then $|x| > a$ is equivalent to the compound sentence

$$x > a \quad \text{or} \quad x < -a$$

Note: Be sure to remember to reverse the inequality sign for $-a$, as in the next examples.

EXAMPLE 6 Graphing Inequalities of the Form $|x| > a$

Graph the solution set of $|x| > 2$.

Solution

$|x| > 2$ is equivalent to the compound sentence $x > 2$ or $x < -2$. The graph of the solution set appears in Figure 6.18.

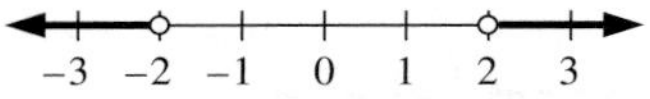

FIGURE 6.18

EXAMPLE 7 Graphing Inequalities of the Form $|x + a| \geq b$

Graph the solution set of $|x + 1| \geq 2$.

Solution

$|x| \geq a$ is equivalent to $x \geq a$ or $x \leq -a$. Therefore, $|x + 1| \geq 2$ is equivalent to $x + 1 \geq 2$ or $x + 1 \leq -2$; that is, $x \geq 1$ or $x \leq -3$. The graph of the solution set is shown in Figure 6.19.

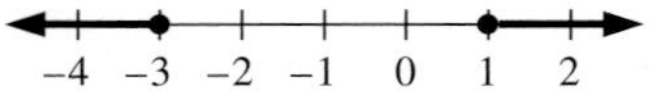

FIGURE 6.19 The dots at −3 and 1 indicate that −3 and 1 are part of the solution set.

C Applications

Absolute value inequalities are used when the difference between two quantities is less or greater than a fixed amount. For example, an average male 5 ft 10 in. tall should weigh between 144 and 154 lb, inclusive. Ideally, 149 lb is the desired weight for a small-framed person 25–59 years of age. (Source: Metropolitan Life Insurance Co.) This means a person in this category should be within 5 lb (above or below) of 149 lb; that is, $|w - 149| \leq 5$, where w is the weight of the person. Do you see why?

$$|w - 149| \leq 5 \quad \text{is equivalent to} \quad -5 \leq w - 149 \leq 5$$

$$\text{Adding 149,} \quad 149 - 5 \leq w \leq 5 + 149$$

$$144 \leq w \leq 154$$

This still means that the person should weigh between 144 and 154 lb, inclusive.

EXAMPLE 8 Inequalities and Margin of Error

When surveys or polls are taken, the margin of error is usually stated. For example, a Roper Starch worldwide poll indicated that 62% of Americans picked out a "letdown in moral values" as one of the "major causes of our problems today." The margin of error e was given as ± 4 points.

(a) Write an absolute value inequality that represents the percentage p of people who believe the statement.

(b) Write an inequality giving a range for the percentage p of people who believe the statement.

Solution

(a) Since the margin of error is 4 points, $|p - 62| \le 4$.

(b) The inequality in (a) is equivalent to

$$-4 \le p - 62 \le 4$$

Adding 62,

$$58 \le p \le 66$$

This means that between 58 and 66% of the people, inclusive, believe the statement.

Remember that in any variance problem, $|b - a| \le c$ where b is the budgeted amount, a is the actual expense, and c is the acceptable variance.

6.3 EXERCISES

A Absolute Value

In problems 1–10, evaluate each expression.

1. $|-10|$ **2.** $|15|$ **3.** $|-\frac{1}{8}|$

4. $|\frac{3}{4}|$ **5.** $|5 - 8|$ **6.** $|8 - 5|$

7. $|0| + |-2|$ **8.** $|-2| - |-3|$ **9.** $-|8|$

10. $-|3| + |-4|$

11. Determine which of the following are solutions of $|1 - 3x| > 3$.

a. 2 **b.** $-\frac{1}{2}$ **c.** $\frac{5}{3}$ **d.** 0

12. Determine which of the following are solutions of $|x - 2| < 2$.

a. 0 **b.** 1 **c.** -1 **d.** -2

B Equations and Inequalities with Absolute Values

In problems 13–18, find the set of integers for which each sentence is true.

13. $|x| < 1$ **14.** $|x| > -2$ **15.** $|x| = 5$

16. $|x| \le 3$ **17.** $|x| \ge 1$ **18.** $|x| < 4$

In problems 19–36, graph the solution set of each sentence and write the solution set (if possible) in interval notation.

19. $|x| = 1$ **20.** $|x| = 2.5$ **21.** $|x| \le 4$

22. $|x| > 1$ **23.** $|x + 1| < 3$ **24.** $|x - 2| < 1$

25. $|x| \ge 1$ **26.** $|x| > -1$ **27.** $|x - 1| > 2$

28. $|x - 3| \ge 1$ **29.** $|2x| < 4$ **30.** $|3x| \le 9$

31. $|3x| \ge 6$ **32.** $|2x| > 5$ **33.** $|2x - 3| \le 3$

34. $|3x + 1| \le 8$ **35.** $|2x - 3| > 3$ **36.** $|3x + 1| > 8$

C Applications

In problems 37–39, use $|b - a| \le c$, where b is the budgeted amount, a is the actual expense, and c is the variance.

37. A company budgets \$500 for office supplies. How much money can it spend if its variance is \$50?

38. A company budgets \$800 for maintenance. How much money can it spend if an acceptable variance is 5% of its budgeted amount?

39. George budgets \$300 for miscellaneous monthly expenses. His actual expenses for 1 month amounted to \$290. Was he within a 5% budget variance?

40. Write the absolute value inequalities that correspond to the following graphs:

a.

b.

c.

d.

41. An average female, medium frame, 5 ft 6 in. tall, should weigh between 130 and 144 lb, inclusive. Using w for the weight,

a. write an absolute value inequality representing this situation.

b. simplify the inequality.

42. An average male, large frame, 5 ft 8 in. tall, should weigh between 152 and 172 lb, inclusive. Using w for the weight,

a. write an absolute value inequality representing this situation.

b. simplify the inequality.

43. A plumber wants to cut a 12-ft length of pipe with no more than a 2% error. If L is the length of the actual cut,

a. write an absolute value inequality representing the situation.

b. simplify the inequality.

44. A machinist has to build a 1-in.-long bushing with no more than a 1% error in the length L.

a. Write an absolute value inequality representing the situation.

b. Simplify the inequality.

45. In a recent year, the score s on the verbal portion of the SAT for males was 505. If the margin of error on this test is ± 4 points,

a. write an absolute value inequality representing the average score for males on the SAT.

b. simplify the inequality.

46. In a recent year, the average cholesterol level c for 20- to 34-year-olds was 186. According to Mosby's *Diagnostic and Laboratory Test Reference* (© 2004), this value can vary by as much as 15%.

a. Write an absolute value inequality representing the situation.

b. Simplify the inequality.

In problems 47–50 use $|b - a| \le c$ where b is the budgeted amount, a is the actual expense, and c is the acceptable variance.

47. A company budgets \$500 for office supplies. If its acceptable variance is \$50, write an inequality giving the amounts between which the actual expense a must fall.

48. A company budgets \$800 for maintenance. If its acceptable variance is 5% of its budgeted amount, write an inequality giving the amounts between which the actual expense a must fall.

49. George budgets \$300 for miscellaneous monthly expenses. His actual expenses for 1 month amounted to \$290. Was he within a 5% budget variance?

50. If George from problem 49 spent \$310, was he within a 5% budget variance?

IN OTHER WORDS

51. Write in words: $|x| < a$ is equivalent to $-a < x < a$.

52. Write in words: $|x| > a$ is equivalent to $x > a$ or $x < -a$.

53. What is the solution of $|x - 2| > -5$? Explain. Can you generalize these results?

54. What is the solution of $|x - 1| < 0$? Explain. Can you generalize these results?

SKILL CHECKER

Next section: Quadratic equations! To solve them using the quadratic formula, you need to review Sections 5.2 (Order of Operations) and 5.5 (Simplifying Radicals). Do that first and then try these practice problems.

1. $\sqrt{(-2)^2 - 4(1)(-1)}$

2. $\sqrt{1^2 - 4(3)(-5)}$

3. $\sqrt{(-2)^2 - 4(2)(-1)}$

4. $\sqrt{(-3)^2 - 4(1)(-2)}$

5. $\sqrt{3^2 - 4(2)(-5)}$

6. $\sqrt{5^2 - 4(2)(-7)}$

7. $\sqrt{(-6)^2 - 4(9)(-2)}$

8. $\sqrt{(-8^2) - 4(2)(5)}$

9. $\sqrt{8^2 - 4(4)(-5)}$

10. $\sqrt{2^2 - 4(2)(-5)}$

6.4 Quadratic Equations

GETTING STARTED

OBJECTIVES

A. Factor quadratic expressions.

B. Solve quadratic equations by factoring.

C. Solve quadratic equations by using the quadratic formula.

D. Solve quadratic equations involving the Pythagorean Theorem.

E. Solve applications involving quadratic equations.

FIREFIGHTING AND FACTORING QUADRATICS

How much water is a fire engine pumping if the friction loss is 36 lb/in.^{2}? You can find out by solving the equation

$$2g^2 + g - 36 = 0 \qquad (g \text{ in hundreds of gallons per minute})$$

Firefighters use high-pressure hoses to bring a fire under control.

This equation is a *quadratic equation in standard form,* which can be solved by *factoring.* We do this by undoing the multiplication that yielded $2g^2 + g - 36$, writing $(2g + 9)(g - 4) = 0$, and then reasoning that if the product of $(2g + 9)$ and $(g - 4)$ is 0, at least one of the factors must be 0; that is, $2g + 9 = 0$ or $g - 4 = 0$. The first equation gives $g = -\frac{9}{2}$, an impossible answer because g represents hundreds of gallons per minute. The second equation gives $g = 4$ (hundred gallons per minute), an acceptable answer. But wouldn't it be nice if you had a formula that you could use to give you the answer? Fortunately, there is such a formula. It is called the *quadratic formula,* and you will use it in this section to solve quadratic equations.

In the preceding sections we considered the solution of first-degree (linear) sentences. We now turn our attention to a certain type of *second-degree* sentence that is called a *quadratic equation.*

Definition of a Quadratic Equation

A **quadratic equation** is a second-degree sentence with standard form

$$ax^2 + bx + c = 0$$

where a, b, and c are real numbers and $a \neq 0$.

We first consider quadratic equations where the second-degree expression $ax^2 + bx + c$ can be written as a product of two first-degree (binomial) expressions. Suppose that we have the product $(x + p)(x + q)$. Then, by the distributive property $a(b + c) = ab + ac$, with $a = x + p$ and $b + c = x + q$, we get

$$\begin{aligned}(x + p)(x + q) &= (x + p)x + (x + p)q \\ &= x^2 + px + qx + pq \\ &= x^2 + (p + q)x + pq\end{aligned}$$

A good way to remember how to multiply two binomials is to remember the **FOIL** method. To multiply $(x - 1)(x + 2)$, we write the following:

1. Multiply First terms. $\quad (x - 1)(x + 2) = x^2 \cdots \quad$ ($x \cdot x$)
2. Multiply Outside terms. $\quad (x - 1)(x + 2) = x^2 + 2x \cdots \quad$ ($x \cdot 2$)
3. Multiply Inside terms. $\quad (x - 1)(x + 2) = x^2 + 2x - x \cdots \quad$ ($-1 \cdot x$)
4. Multiply Last terms. $\quad (x - 1)(x + 2) = x^2 + 2x - x - 2 \quad$ ($-1 \cdot 2$)
5. Combine like terms. $\quad (x - 1)(x + 2) = x^2 + x - 2$

The result $x^2 + x - 2$ has three terms, and it is called a trinomial.

A Factoring Quadratic Expressions

These ideas can sometimes be "reversed" to write a quadratic expression in the product (factored) form. For example, in order to write $x^2 + 5x + 6$ in factored form, we try to find two integers p and q such that $pq = 6$ and $p + q = 5$. By inspection (looking in the table at left), we see that $p = 2$ and $q = 3$ will work. Therefore,

Possible Factors	Sum 5
$\pm1, \pm6$	
$\pm2, \pm3$	$+2, +3$

$$x^2 + 5x + 6 = (x + 2)(x + 3)$$

To **factor** an expression means to write it as a product of lower-degree expressions using integers as coefficients, as in the above illustration. We will use the fact that $x^2 + 5x + 6 = (x + 2)(x + 3)$ in Example 3. Note that $x^2 - 2$ is *not* factorable using integers since we cannot find integers a and b such that $x^2 - 2 = (x + a)(x + b)$. However, $x^2 - 2 = (x + \sqrt{2})(x - \sqrt{2})$!

EXAMPLE 1 Factoring Quadratic Expressions

Factor the following:

(a) $x^2 + x - 2$ (b) $x^2 - 2x - 8$ (c) $2x^2 - 5x - 3$

Solution

Possible Factors	Sum 1
$\pm 1, \pm 2$	$+2, -1$

(a) We must find two numbers whose product is -2 and whose sum is 1. By inspection or from the table, we see that these numbers are 2 and -1. Thus,

$$x^2 + x - 2 = (x + 2)(x - 1)$$

Possible Factors	Sum -2
$\pm 1, \pm 8$ $\pm 2, \pm 4$	$-4, +2$

(b) Here we need two numbers whose product is -8 and whose sum is -2. By inspection or from the table, we see that these numbers are -4 and 2. Thus,

$$x^2 - 2x - 8 = (x - 4)(x + 2)$$

(c) To factor $2x^2 - 5x - 3$, we need to find integers a, b, c, and d such that

$$2x^2 - 5x - 3 = (ax + b)(cx + d)$$

$ac = 2$

$bd = -3$

Using **FOIL** to multiply the right side, ac must be 2 (the coefficient of the first term) and bd must be -3 (the last term in $2x^2 - 5x - 3$). The positive factors of $ac = 2$ are 2 and 1. The possible factors of $bd = -3$ are $-1, 3$ or $3, -1$, or $-3, 1$ or $1, -3$. We try different arrangements of these factors until we obtain the correct middle term, $-5x$, as follows:

	$(ax + b)(cx + d)$	
$b = -1, d = 3$	$(2x - 1)(x + 3) = 2x^2 + 6x - 1x - 3$	Incorrect
$b = 3, d = -1$	$(2x + 3)(x - 1) = 2x^2 - 2x + 3x - 3$	Incorrect
$b = -3, d = 1$	$(2x - 3)(x + 1) = 2x^2 + 2x - 3x - 3$	Incorrect
$b = 1, d = -3$	$(2x + 1)(x - 3) = 2x^2 \underbrace{- 6x + 1x}_{-5x} - 3$	Correct!

Thus, $2x^2 - 5x - 3 = (2x + 1)(x - 3)$.

EXAMPLE 2 Factoring More Quadratic Expressions

Factor $6x^2 - 7x - 3$.

Solution

We need to find integers a, b, c, and d such that

$$6x^2 - 7x - 3 = (ax + b)(cx + d)$$

The positive factors of $ac = 6$ are 6, 1 or 3, 2. The factors of $bd = -3$ are $-3, 1$ or $1, -3$. After trying different possibilities, $a = 3$, $c = 2$, $b = 1$, and $d = -3$ will yield $6x^2 - 7x - 3 = (3x + 1)(2x - 3)$.

What if the expression is not factorable? We use the *ac* rule to determine whether an expression factors.

> **Factorable Quadratic Expression**
>
> $ax^2 + bx + c$ is factorable if there are two integers whose product is ac and whose sum is b. If $ax^2 + bx + c$ is *not* factorable, it is prime.

Using this idea, $6x^2 - 7x - 1$ and $3x^2 + 2x - 4$ are prime (not factorable). Do you see why?

B Solving Quadratic Equations by Factoring

The next examples show how factoring can sometimes be used to solve quadratic equations.

EXAMPLE 3 Solving Quadratics by Factoring

Solve the following equations:

(a) $x^2 + 5x + 6 = 0$ (b) $5x^2 - 14x = 3$

GRAPH IT

To solve $x^2 + 5x + 6 = 0$, enter $Y_1 = x^2 + 5x + 6$ and ZOOM 6. Where is $Y_1 = 0$? Press 2nd CALC 2. When the grapher asks for the left bound, use ◀ to move the cursor to the left side of the curve. Press ENTER. Use ▶ to move below the curve to find the right bound. Press ENTER twice. One of the roots is -3 as shown.

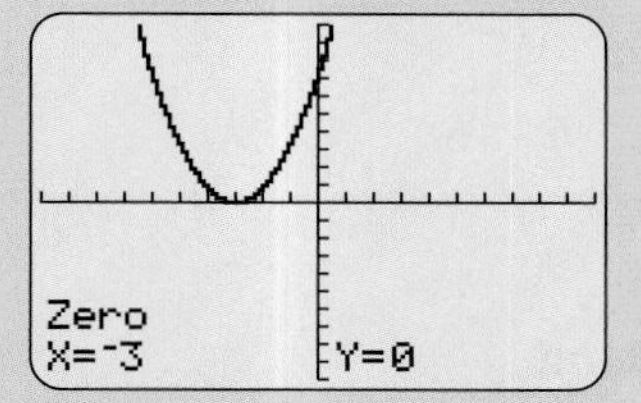

Solution

(a) We have already shown that $x^2 + 5x + 6 = (x + 2)(x + 3)$. Thus,

$$(x + 2)(x + 3) = 0$$

With 0 on one side of the equation, we can make use of the property of the real number system that says that **a product of two real numbers is 0 if and only if at least one of them is 0.** Thus, the preceding equation is true if and only if

$$x + 2 = 0 \quad \text{or} \quad x + 3 = 0$$

$$x = -2 \quad \text{or} \quad x = -3$$

The solution set of the given equation is $\{-3, -2\}$.

Check: By substitution in the left side of the given equation, we find for $x = -3$, $x^2 + 5x + 6 = (-3)^2 + 5(-3) + 6 = 9 - 15 + 6 = 0$. This checks the solution $x = -3$. For $x = -2$, we get $x^2 + 5x + 6 = (-2)^2 + 5(-2) + 6 = 4 - 10 + 6 = 0$, which checks the solution $x = -2$.

(b) Subtract 3 from both sides of the equation to obtain

$$5x^2 - 14x - 3 = 0$$

The positive factors of 5 are 5 and 1, whereas the factors of -3 are -3, 1 or 1, -3. Thus,

$$5x^2 - 14x - 3 = (5x + 1)(x - 3) = 0$$

Hence,

$$5x + 1 = 0 \quad \text{or} \quad x - 3 = 0$$

That is,

$$x = -\tfrac{1}{5} \quad \text{or} \quad x = 3$$

Therefore, the solution set of $5x^2 - 14x = 3$ is $\{3, -\frac{1}{5}\}$. Make sure that you check that the solution is correct!

EXAMPLE 4 Solving Quadratics That Are Differences of Squares

Solve the equation $x^2 - 9 = 0$.

Solution

The equation $x^2 - 9 = 0$ can be solved by factoring because the difference of two squares, $x^2 - p^2$, can always be written as the product $(x - p)(x + p)$. Checking this multiplication, we get

$$(x - p)(x + p) = x^2 \underbrace{- px + px}_{0} - p^2 = x^2 - p^2$$

Thus, $x^2 - 9 = 0$ becomes

$$(x - 3)(x + 3) = 0$$

which gives the solution set $\{-3, 3\}$.

We could have avoided factoring by adding 9 to both sides to obtain

$$x^2 = 9$$

Taking the square roots of both sides, we have

$$x = \pm 3$$

so the solution set is $\{-3, 3\}$, as before.

EXAMPLE 5 Solving Quadratics by Root Extraction

Solve the equation $3x^2 + 2 = 50$.

Solution

We first subtract 2 from both sides to obtain

$$3x^2 = 48$$

We then divide both sides by 3 to get

$$x^2 = 16$$

As in Example 4, we find the solution set by taking square roots of both sides. This gives the solution set $\{-4, 4\}$.

C The Quadratic Formula

Quadratic Formula

The solutions of a quadratic equation in standard form

$$ax^2 + bx + c = 0 \qquad a \neq 0$$

are given by the **quadratic formula,**

$$x = \frac{-b \pm \sqrt{b^2 - 4ac}}{2a}$$

We use this formula when expressions are *not* factorable. For example, $5x^2 - 7x - 3 = 0$ and $3x^2 + 2x - 4 = 0$ involve the expressions $5x^2 - 7x - 3$ and $3x^2 + 2x - 4$, which are not factorable. To solve these equations we would use the quadratic formula.

The derivation of this formula is given in Exercises 6.4, problem 55. The symbol $\pm$ in the formula means that there are two solutions, one with the plus sign and the other with the minus sign. If the quantity under the radical sign, $b^2 - 4ac$ (called the *discriminant*), is positive, there are two real number solutions. If $b^2 - 4ac$ is 0, the two solutions are the same, so there is actually just one solution, $-b/2a$. If the quantity $b^2 - 4ac$ is negative, there are no real number solutions.

PROBLEM-SOLVING

Quadratic Equations

① **Read** the problem.

Solve the equation $x^2 - 2x = 1$.

② **Select** the unknown.

Find the values of the variable x such that $x^2 - 2x = 1$.

③ **Think** of a plan.
Is the equation a quadratic equation? If it is, write it in standard form. Can you factor it? If not, use the quadratic formula to solve it.

The equation $x^2 - 2x = 1$ is a quadratic equation. To write it in standard form, subtract 1 from both sides to obtain $x^2 - 2x - 1 = 0$. Since you cannot factor this equation, you write $1x^2 - 2x - 1 = 0$ and compare it with $ax^2 + bx + c = 0$. Thus, $a = 1$, $b = -2$, and $c = -1$.

④ **Use** the quadratic formula to carry out the plan.
Find a, b, and c and substitute their values in

$$x = \frac{-b \pm \sqrt{b^2 - 4ac}}{2a}$$

How many solutions should you get?

Substituting these values in

$$\frac{-b \pm \sqrt{b^2 - 4ac}}{2a}$$

you obtain

$$x = \frac{-(-2) \pm \sqrt{(-2)^2 - 4(1)(-1)}}{2(1)}$$

$$= \frac{2 \pm \sqrt{4 + 4}}{2} = \frac{2 \pm \sqrt{8}}{2} = \frac{2 \pm \sqrt{4 \cdot 2}}{2} = \frac{2 \pm 2\sqrt{2}}{2}$$

Make sure the final answer is simplified.

This answer is *not* simplified. Divide each number in the numerator and denominator by 2 to obtain $1 \pm \sqrt{2}$. Thus,

$$x = 1 + \sqrt{2} \quad \text{or} \quad x = 1 - \sqrt{2}$$

⑤ **Verify** the answer.

The verification is left to you. Note that $(1 \pm \sqrt{2})^2 = 1 \pm 2\sqrt{2} + 2$.

Try Example 6 Now

Cover the solution, write your own solution, and then check your work.

EXAMPLE 6 Solving Quadratics by Using the Quadratic Formula

Use the quadratic formula to solve $x^2 - 4x - 12 = 0$.

Solution

To obtain the correct values of a, b, and c, we rewrite the equation in standard quadratic form as

$$1x^2 + (-4)x + (-12) = 0$$

which we compare with

$$\begin{matrix} \uparrow & & \uparrow & & \uparrow & \\ ax^2 & + & bx & + & c & = 0 \end{matrix}$$

Now we see that $a = 1$, $b = -4$, and $c = -12$. Thus,

$$x = \frac{-(-4) \pm \sqrt{(-4)^2 - (4)(1)(-12)}}{(2)(1)}$$

$$= \frac{4 \pm \sqrt{16 + 48}}{2} = \frac{4 \pm \sqrt{64}}{2} = \frac{4 \pm 8}{2}$$

so that

$$x = \frac{4 + 8}{2} = \frac{12}{2} = 6$$

or

$$x = \frac{4 - 8}{2} = \frac{-4}{2} = -2$$

Hence, the solution set is $\{-2, 6\}$.

Note: The instructions in the preceding problem required the use of the quadratic formula. In general, however, try to *factor* the equation *first.*

EXAMPLE 7 Solving Nonfactorable Equations

Solve the equation $3x^2 + x - 5 = 0$.

Solution

This equation is *not* factorable because we are unable to find two integers whose product is $3(-5) = -15$ and whose sum is 1, so we use the quadratic formula. We compare

$$ax^2 + bx + c = 0 \quad \text{and} \quad 3x^2 + 1x - 5 = 0$$

and see that $a = 3$, $b = 1$, and $c = -5$. Hence,

$$x = \frac{-1 \pm \sqrt{1^2 - 4(3)(-5)}}{2(3)} = \frac{-1 \pm \sqrt{61}}{6}$$

The solution set is

$$\left\{\frac{-1 - \sqrt{61}}{6}, \frac{-1 + \sqrt{61}}{6}\right\}$$

These numbers cannot be expressed exactly in any simpler form. By using the table of square roots in the back of the book (or a calculator), we find that $\sqrt{61} \approx 7.81$. This gives the approximate solutions

$$\frac{-1 - 7.81}{6} \approx -1.47 \quad \text{and} \quad \frac{-1 + 7.81}{6} \approx 1.14$$

EXAMPLE 8 Solving Using the Quadratic Formula

Solve the equation $2x^2 - 2x = 1$.

Solution

In order to use the quadratic formula, we must first write the equation in standard quadratic form. We can do this by subtracting 1 from both sides of the given equation to obtain $2x^2 - 2x - 1 = 0$. This equation is *not* factorable because there are no two integers whose product is $2(-1) = -2$ and whose sum is -2, so we use the quadratic formula. To find a, b, and c, we write

$$2x^2 - 2x - 1 = 0$$

which we compare with

$$ax^2 + bx + c = 0$$

Thus, $a = 2$, $b = -2$, and $c = -1$. Now, we can substitute into the quadratic formula to find

$$x = \frac{-(-2) \pm \sqrt{(-2)^2 - 4(2)(-1)}}{2(2)} = \frac{2 \pm \sqrt{4 + 8}}{4} = \frac{2 \pm \sqrt{12}}{4}$$

$$= \frac{2 \pm 2\sqrt{3}}{4} = \frac{1 \pm \sqrt{3}}{2}$$

so the solutions are

$$x = \frac{1 \pm \sqrt{3}}{2}$$

The solution set is

$$\left\{\frac{1 + \sqrt{3}}{2}, \frac{1 - \sqrt{3}}{2}\right\}$$

or, using decimal approximations, $\{1.37, -0.37\}$

Examples 6–8 display the tremendous advantage of the quadratic formula over other methods of solving quadratic equations. It is not necessary to attempt to write the left side as a product of first-degree expressions. You need only recognize the values of a, b, and c and make direct substitutions into the quadratic formula. Note that if the equation is easily factorable, it is easier and faster to solve it by factoring.

D The Pythagorean Theorem

Quadratic equations can be used to find the lengths of the sides of right triangles using the *Pythagorean theorem.*

Theorem 6.1 Pythagorean Theorem

In any right triangle (a triangle with one 90° angle, as shown in Figure 6.20), the square of the longest side (the hypotenuse) is equal to the sum of the squares of the other two sides (the legs). In symbols,

$$c^2 = a^2 + b^2$$

It is interesting to note that there are infinitely many triples of whole numbers (a, b, c) that satisfy the equation $c^2 = a^2 + b^2$. Such triples are called **Pythagorean triples.**

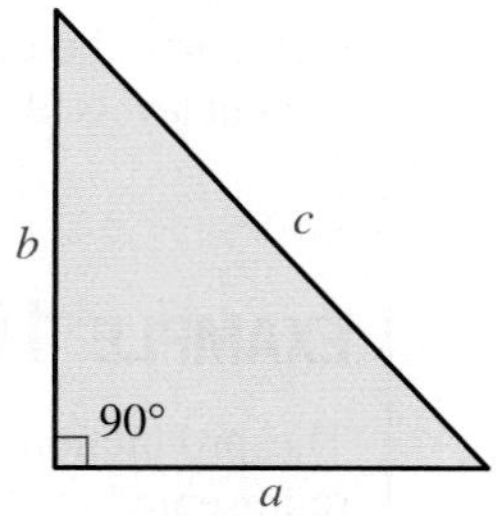

FIGURE 6.20

EXAMPLE 9 Using the Pythagorean Theorem to Find Lengths

The lengths of the three sides of a right triangle are consecutive integers. What are these lengths?

Solution

Let the length of the shortest side be x. Since the lengths of the sides are consecutive integers, we have the following:

Length of the shortest side	x
Length of the next side	$x + 1$
Length of the hypotenuse	$x + 2$

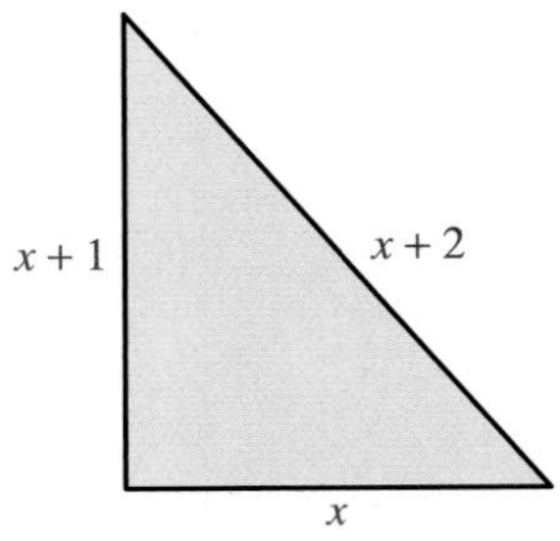

FIGURE 6.21

See Figure 6.21. By the Pythagorean theorem,

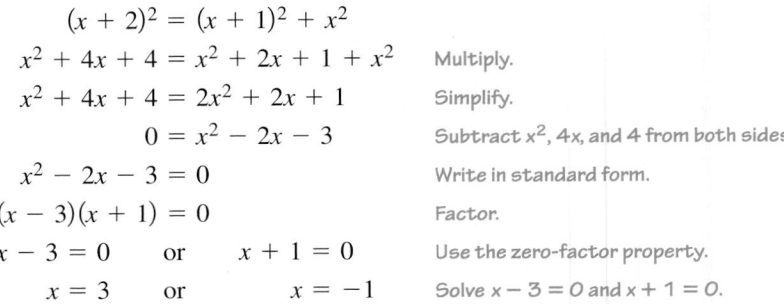

$$(x + 2)^2 = (x + 1)^2 + x^2$$

$$x^2 + 4x + 4 = x^2 + 2x + 1 + x^2 \quad \text{Multiply.}$$

$$x^2 + 4x + 4 = 2x^2 + 2x + 1 \quad \text{Simplify.}$$

$$0 = x^2 - 2x - 3 \quad \text{Subtract } x^2, 4x, \text{ and 4 from both sides.}$$

$$x^2 - 2x - 3 = 0 \quad \text{Write in standard form.}$$

$$(x - 3)(x + 1) = 0 \quad \text{Factor.}$$

$$x - 3 = 0 \quad \text{or} \quad x + 1 = 0 \quad \text{Use the zero-factor property.}$$

$$x = 3 \quad \text{or} \quad x = -1 \quad \text{Solve } x - 3 = 0 \text{ and } x + 1 = 0.$$

Since the lengths of the sides must be positive, we discard the negative answer, -1. Thus, the shortest side is 3 units, so the other two sides are 4 and 5 units.

Note that if we have one Pythagorean triple of the form $(a, a + 1, c)$, we can find another by substituting the a and c of the original triple into

$$(3a + 2c + 1, 3a + 2c + 2, 4a + 3c + 2)$$

This is so because using $c^2 = a^2 + (a + 1)^2$, we can show that

$$(3a + 2c + 1)^2 + (3a + 2c + 2)^2 = (4a + 3c + 2)^2$$

This proves that there are infinitely many Pythagorean triples of the form $(a, a + 1, c)$. For instance, if we let $a = 3$, $b = 4$, and $c = 5$, we find

$$(3 \cdot 3 + 2 \cdot 5 + 1, 3 \cdot 3 + 2 \cdot 5 + 2, 4 \cdot 3 + 3 \cdot 5 + 2) = (20, 21, 29)$$

as another such triple. If we now let $a = 20$, $b = 21$, and $c = 29$, we get the next such triple: $(119, 120, 169)$, and so on.

E Applications

Many problems can be studied by using quadratic equations. For example, do you use hair spray containing chlorofluorocarbons (CFCs) for propellants? A U.N.-sponsored conference negotiated an agreement to stop producing CFCs by the year 2000 because they harm the ozone layer. Can we check to see whether the goal has been reached if current levels of production continue? We shall see in Example 10. (Source: www.ejil.org)

EXAMPLE 10 Applications with CFCs and Quadratics

The production of CFCs for use as aerosol propellants (in thousands of tons) can be represented by $P(t) = -0.4t^2 + 22t + 120$, where t is the number of years after 1960. When will production be stopped?

Solution

Production will be stopped when $P(t) = 0$. We need to solve the equation

$$P(t) = -0.4t^2 + 22t + 120 = 0$$

$$-4t^2 + 220t + 1200 = 0 \quad \text{Multiply by 10 (to clear decimals).}$$

$$t^2 - 55t - 300 = 0 \quad \text{Divide by } -4 \text{ (to obtain } t^2\text{).}$$

$$(t - 60)(t + 5) = 0 \quad \text{We need two numbers whose product is } -300 \text{ and whose sum is } -55\ (-60 \text{ and } 5).$$

$$t - 60 = 0 \quad \text{or} \quad t + 5 = 0 \quad \text{By the zero-factor property}$$

$$t = 60 \quad \text{or} \quad t = -5 \quad \text{Solve each equation.}$$

Since t represents the number of years *after* 1960, production will be zero (stopped) 60 years after 1960, or in 2020 (not in the year 2000 as promised!). The answer $t = -5$ has to be discarded because it represents 5 years *before* 1960, but the equation applies only to years *after* 1960.

Before you attempt the exercises, we remind you of the steps used to solve quadratic equations by factoring:

Procedure to Solve Quadratics by Factoring

1. Perform the necessary operations on both sides of the equation so that the right-hand side is 0.
2. Use the factoring strategy we have learned to factor the left side of the equation, if necessary.
3. Use the zero product property and make each of the factors on the left equal 0.
4. Solve each of the resulting equations.
5. Check the results by substituting the solutions obtained in step 4 in the original equation.

The U.S. government is committed to enacting health insurance reform that provides health care stability and security for all Americans, but you can use your knowledge to explore national health expenditures and make your own predictions based on the historical per capita cost at http://tinyurl.com/mp32zx. We shall do that in the next example.

EXAMPLE 11 National Health Insurance and Quadratics

The annual per capita national health expenditures can be approximated by $H(t) = -3t^2 + 300t + 6300$, where t is the number of years after 2003.

In what year will annual expenditures reach **\$9000?**

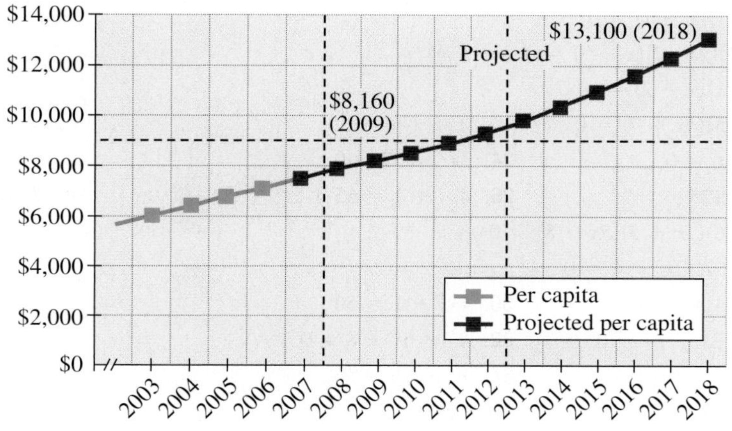

Source: http//tinyurl.com/mp32zx.

Solution

We need the expenditures $H(t) = -3t^2 + 300t + 6300$ to be **\$9000.** Thus, we have to solve the equation

$$
\begin{aligned}
H(t) &= -3t^2 + 300t + 6300 = \mathbf{\$9000} \\
&-3t^2 + 300t + 6300 - 9000 = \mathbf{\$9000} - 9000 && \text{Subtract 9000} \\
&-3t^2 + 300t - 2700 = 0 && \text{Simplify} \\
&t^2 - 100t + 900 = 0 && \text{Divide by } -3 \\
&(t - 10)(t - 90) = 0 && \text{Factor} \\
&t - 10 = 0 \text{ or } t - 90 = 0 && \text{Zero factors} \\
&t = 10 \text{ or } t = 90 && \text{Solve}
\end{aligned}
$$

Thus in $t = 10$ yrs, that is, in $2003 + 10 = 2013$ or in $2003 + 90 = 2093$ the annual expenditures will reach **\$9000.** How close is that projection to the results in the graph? Do problems 69 and 70 and see!

6.4 EXERCISES

A Factoring Quadratic Expressions

In problems 1–14, factor each expression.

1. $x^2 + 6x + 8$
2. $x^2 + 7x + 10$
3. $x^2 - x - 12$
4. $x^2 - 3x - 10$
5. $x^2 + 7x - 18$
6. $x^2 - 12x + 11$
7. $x^2 - 10x + 25$
8. $x^2 - 8x + 16$
9. $x^2 + 10x + 25$
10. $x^2 + 16x + 64$
11. $2x^2 + x - 3$
12. $3x^2 + 10x + 3$
13. $6x^2 - 5x + 1$
14. $6x^2 - 11x + 3$

B Solving Quadratic Equations by Factoring

In problems 15–38, solve each equation.

15. $(x - 2)(x - 4) = 0$
16. $(x + 2)(x + 3) = 0$
17. $(x + 2)(x - 3) = 0$
18. $(x + 5)(x - 6) = 0$
19. $x(x - 1)(x + 1) = 0$
20. $(x + 1)(x + 2)(x - 3) = 0$
21. $(2x - 1)(x + 2) = 0$
22. $(3x + 5)(4x + 7) = 0$
23. $x^2 - 16 = 0$
24. $3x^2 - 27 = 0$
25. $5x^2 = 125$
26. $4x^2 + 1 = 65$
27. $(3x - 6)(2x + 3)(5x - 8) = 0$
28. $2x(x + 7)(2x - 3) = 0$
29. $6x^2 - 1 = 215$
30. $4x^2 + 1 = 50$
31. $x^2 - 12x + 27 = 0$
32. $x^2 - 6x + 8 = 0$
33. $x^2 - 8x = 20$
34. $x^2 - 9x = 36$
35. $10x^2 + 7x + 1 = 0$
36. $6x^2 + 17x + 5 = 0$
37. $3x^2 + 2x = 5$
38. $2x^2 - x = 6$

C The Quadratic Formula

In problems 39–54, solve each equation by using the quadratic formula.

39. $2x^2 + 3x - 5 = 0$
40. $3x^2 - 7x + 2 = 0$
41. $2x^2 + 5x - 7 = 0$
42. $4x^2 - 7x - 15 = 0$
43. $x^2 + 5x + 3 = 0$
44. $2x^2 + 7x - 4 = 0$
45. $5x^2 - 8x + 2 = 0$
46. $3x^2 + 5x + 1 = 0$
47. $7x^2 - 6x = -1$
48. $7x^2 - 12x = -5$
49. $9x^2 - 6x - 2 = 0$
50. $2x^2 - 8x + 5 = 0$
51. $2x^2 + 2x = 1$
52. $2x^2 - 6x = 5$
53. $4x^2 = -8x + 5$
54. $2x^2 = 2x + 5$
55. The following procedure can be used to obtain the quadratic formula. Suppose that the quadratic equation is given in standard form.

$$ax^2 + bx + c = 0, \qquad a \neq 0$$

Then

$$ax^2 + bx = -c \qquad \text{Why?}$$

Now we multiply both sides by $4a$ to get

$$4a^2x^2 + 4abx = -4ac$$

By adding b^2 to both sides, we get

$$4a^2x^2 + 4abx + b^2 = b^2 - 4ac$$

The left side of this equation is the square of $(2ax + b)$. (Verify this!) Thus, we have

$$(2ax + b)^2 = b^2 - 4ac$$

Next, we take the square roots of both sides to get

$$2ax + b = \pm\sqrt{b^2 - 4ac}$$

From this equation, we get

$$2ax = -b \pm \sqrt{b^2 - 4ac} \qquad \text{Explain.}$$

and

$$x = \frac{-b \pm \sqrt{b^2 - 4ac}}{2a} \qquad \text{Explain.}$$

(These solutions can be checked in the original equation.)

D The Pythagorean Theorem

Solve problems 56–60, using the Pythagorean theorem.

56. The sides of a right triangle are consecutive even integers. Find their lengths.

57. The hypotenuse of a right triangle is 4 cm longer than the shortest side and 2 cm longer than the remaining side. Find the dimensions of this triangle.

58. The hypotenuse of a right triangle is 16 in. longer than the shortest side and 2 in. longer than the remaining side. Find the dimensions of this triangle.

59. The hypotenuse of a right triangle is 8 in. longer than the shortest side and 1 in. longer than the remaining side. Find the dimensions of this triangle.

60. People have been interested in right triangles for thousands of years. The right triangle relationship $a^2 + b^2 = c^2$ seems to have been known to the Babylonians and the ancient Egyptians. Among the interesting problems about right triangles is this one: Find the right triangles with integer sides such that the hypotenuse is 1 unit longer than one of the legs. You can solve this problem by letting the legs be x and y units long, so the hypotenuse is $y + 1$ units long. Then, you have

$$x^2 + y^2 = (y + 1)^2$$

a. Solve this equation for x^2. You should find $x^2 = 2y + 1$. Since x and y are to be positive integers, $2y + 1$ is an odd integer. This means that x^2 is an odd integer, so x also must be an odd integer. You can see that $x \neq 1$ because this would make $y = 0$ (no triangle!). However, if x is any odd integer greater than 1, there is a right triangle with the desired relationship between the sides. If you choose $x = 3$ and solve $x^2 = 2y + 1$ for y, you find $y = 4$. This gives you the well-known 3-4-5 right triangle.

b. Make a table of the next four triangles of this type.

E Applications

In problems 61–64, use

$$h = 5t^2 + V_0 t$$

where h is the distance (in meters) traveled in t sec by an object thrown downward with an initial velocity V_0 (in meters per second).

61. An object is thrown downward with an initial velocity of 5 m/sec from a height of 10 m. How long does it take the object to hit the ground?

62. An object is thrown downward from a height of 28 m with an initial velocity of 4 m/sec. How long does it take the object to reach the ground?

63. An object is thrown downward from a building 15 m high with an initial velocity of 10 m/sec. How long does it take the object to hit the ground?

64. How long will it take a package thrown downward from a plane with an initial velocity of 10 m/sec to hit the ground 175 m below?

65. The number of endangered U.S. plants and animals species can be approximated by

$E(t) = t^2 + 26t + 169$, where t is the number of years after 1980.

a. Factor $t^2 + 26t + 169$

b. How many endangered species are predicted for 2020?

66. The total number of threatened *and* endangered species can be approximated by

$T(t) = t^2 + 28t + 196$, where t is the number of years after 1980.

a. Factor $t^2 + 28t + 196$

b. How many threatened and endangered species are predicted for 2020?

Source: http://ecos.fws.gov/tess_public/TESSBoxscore.

67. *Hybrid Car Depreciation.* There are many reasons to buy a hybrid car (better gas mileage, less emissions), but one that is often overlooked is that they may depreciate less than other cars. If the depreciation rate is r% and the amount you paid for a car is P, after two years the value of the car will be $P - 2Pr + Pr^2$.

a. Factor $P - 2Pr + Pr^2$ completely.

b. If a Prius hybrid costs $25,000 now, how much will it be worth in two years assuming the depreciation rate r is 15%?

68. *Regular Car Depreciation.* The two-year depreciation for a $25,000 Toyota Camry is $25{,}000r^2 - 50{,}000r + 25{,}000$.

a. Factor this expression completely.

b. If the depreciation rate of the Camry is 20%, how much will the car be worth in two years?

69. *Another View.* The Kaiser Family Foundation has the projected per capita approximation shown in the graph of **Example 11**. According to the example the expenditures for 2013 were $9000.

a. How does the $9000 result compare with the expenditures for 2013 projected in the graph?

b. How do the results using $H(t) = -3t^2 + 300t + 6300$ for the year 2018 $(t = 15)$ and the $13,100 approximation predicted in the graph compare?

Source: http://tinyurl.com/cp5xmq.

70. An apartment owner wants to increase the monthly rent from the current $250 in n increases of $10.

a. What is the expression for the new price after the n increases of $10?

b. If the number of apartments rented is $70 - 2n$ and the revenue is the number of apartments rented times the rent, what is the expression for the revenue?

c. If the owner wants to receive $17,980 per month, how many $10 increases can the owner make?

d. What will be the monthly rent?

IN OTHER WORDS

71. Write in your own words the procedure you would use to multiply two binomials using the **FOIL** method.

72. Write the steps you would use to factor $x^2 + 8x + 7$.

73. Write the steps you would use to solve a quadratic equation by factoring.

74. Write the steps you would use to solve a quadratic equation with the quadratic formula.

The solutions of the quadratic equation $ax^2 + bx + c = 0$ $(a \neq 0)$ are

$$x = \frac{-b \pm \sqrt{b^2 - 4ac}}{2a}$$

75. Which type of solution do you get if $b^2 - 4ac = 0$?

76. Which type of solution do you get if $b^2 - 4ac > 0$?

77. Which type of solution do you get if $b^2 - 4ac < 0$?

USING YOUR KNOWLEDGE

Have you been to a baseball game lately? Did anybody hit a home run? The trajectory of a baseball is usually very complicated, but we can get help from The Physics of Baseball, *by Robert Adair. According to Mr. Adair, after t sec, starting 1 sec after the ball leaves the bat, the height of a ball hit at a 35° angle, rotating with an initial backspin of 2000 revolutions per minute (rpm), and hit at about 110 mph, is given by*

$$H(t) = -80t^2 + 340t - 260 \text{ (in feet)}$$

78. How many seconds will pass before the ball hits the ground?

The distance traveled by the ball is given by

$$D(t) = -5t^2 + 115t - 110 \text{ (in feet)}$$

79. How far will the ball travel before it hits the ground?

80. Using $D(t)$, how far will a ball travel in 6 sec, the time it takes a high fly ball to hit the ground?

DISCOVERY

Charlie Brown received a chain letter. Several days later, after receiving more letters, he found that the number he had received was a perfect square. (The numbers 1^2, 2^2, 3^2, and so on are perfect squares.) Charlie decided to throw away some of the letters, and being very superstitious, he threw away 13^2 of them. To his surprise, he found that the number he had left was still a perfect square.

81. What is the maximum number of letters Charlie could have received before throwing any away? (*Hint:* Let x^2 be the initial number of letters, and let y^2 be the number he had left. Then $x^2 = y^2 + 13^2$. Remember that x and y are integers, and you will want to make y as large as possible relative to x because you want x to be as large as possible.)

CALCULATOR CORNER

Your calculator can be extremely helpful in finding the roots of a quadratic equation by using the quadratic formula. Of course, the roots you obtain are being approximated by decimals. It is most convenient to start with the radical part in the solution of the quadratic equation and then store this value so that you can evaluate both roots without having to backtrack or copy down any intermediate steps. Look at the following equation:

$$2x^2 + 7x - 4 = 0$$

Using the quadratic formula, the solution is obtained by following these key strokes using a scientific calculator.

[7] [x^2] [−] [4] [×] [2] [×] [4] [+/−] [=]
[$\sqrt{x}$] [STO] [7] [+/−] [+] [RCL] [=] [÷] [2] [÷] [2] [=]

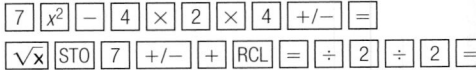

The display will show 0.5. To obtain the other root, key in

[7] [+/−] [−] [RCL] [=] [÷] [2] [÷] [2] [=]

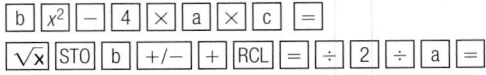

which yields −4. In general, to solve the equation $ax^2 + bx + c = 0$ using your calculator, key in the following:

[b] [x^2] [−] [4] [×] [a] [×] [c] [=]
[$\sqrt{x}$] [STO] [b] [+/−] [+] [RCL] [=] [÷] [2] [÷] [a] [=]

and

[b] [+/−] [−] [RCL] [=] [÷] [2] [÷] [a] [=]

1. If your instructor allows it, do problems 39–54 using a calculator.

COLLABORATIVE LEARNING

Wouldn't it be nice if we looked at a factorable quadratic equation of the form $x^2 + bx + c = 0$ and we knew what the solution was? We are going to see how to do just that!

1. Form three groups. The first group does the first three problems, the second group the next three, and the third group the last three.

	Factors	*Solutions*
1. $x^2 + 3x + 2 = 0$	_____	_____
2. $x^2 + 5x + 6 = 0$	_____	_____
3. $x^2 + 7x + 12 = 0$	_____	_____
4. $x^2 - 3x + 2 = 0$	_____	_____
5. $x^2 - 5x + 6 = 0$	_____	_____
6. $x^2 - 7x + 12 = 0$	_____	_____
7. $x^2 - x - 2 = 0$	_____	_____
8. $x^2 - x - 6 = 0$	_____	_____
9. $x^2 - x - 12 = 0$	_____	_____

Each group should determine the relationship between the factors and the solutions and then make a conjecture regarding the solution of factorable quadratics of the form

$$x^2 + bx + c = 0$$

Do all groups reach the same conjecture?

2. What about $ax^2 + bx + c = 0$? Here is a hint. Look at the ac rule. Find the two integers whose product is ac and whose sum is b. In Example 3(b), $5x^2 - 14x - 3 = 0$, $ac = 5(-3) = -15$, and the two integers whose product is -15 and whose sum is -14 are 1 and -15. The solutions for the equation [as shown in Example 3(b)] are $-\frac{1}{5}$ and 3. Do you see any pattern linking 1 and -15 to $-\frac{1}{5}$ and 3? If you do not, look at problems 35–38. Do you see any pattern now?

6.5 Modeling and Problem Solving

GETTING STARTED

OBJECTIVES

A. Use the RSTUV procedure to solve problems.
B. Use mathematical models to solve problems.

PUTTING ON THE BRAKES

Do you remember the **RSTUV** procedure that you studied in Chapter 1? You are certainly going to need it in this section, but with a small modification. The most difficult task in solving word problems is *translating* the problem into the language of algebra so that you obtain an accurate mathematical model representing all the conditions of the problem. Because of this, the third step of the procedure will emphasize this idea of translation. What types of problems will you be working? There are many of them, including some that may save your life! For example, do you know what the stopping distance d is for a car traveling v mph if the driver has a reaction time of t sec? Now suppose you are driving a car at 20 mph and you are 42 ft away from an intersection. If your reaction time is 0.6 sec, can you stop the car in time? See Example 3 and problems 27–34 in Exercises 6.5, and you will be able to tell!

© NASA/Troy Cryder

The space shuttle *Atlantis* slowly rolls to its final mission in July 2011.

Source: NASA. With the Shuttle Program ending, many people think that it's the end of NASA's manned spaceflight program. The space shuttle is simply being replaced by safer and more efficient means. So what's next? There will be plenty of options after the space shuttle. The era of manned spaceflight is not ending; instead it's taking a new course.

A Problem Solving

In the preceding sections we considered how to solve certain kinds of equations. Now we are ready to apply this knowledge to solve problems. These problems will be stated in words and are consequently called **word** or **story problems.** Word problems frighten many students, but you should not panic. We have the **RSTUV** procedure, a surefire method for tackling such problems.

Let us start with a problem that you might have heard about. It has to do with space exploration.

PROBLEM-SOLVING

Word Problems

When fully loaded, a space shuttle and its payload (cargo) weigh about 215,000 lb. The shuttle itself weighs 85,000 lb more than the payload. What is the weight of each?

① **Read** the problem carefully and decide what it asks for.

The problem asks for the weight of each, that is, the weight of the shuttle and the weight of the payload.

② **Select** a variable to represent the unknown.

Let p represent the weight of the payload in pounds. Since the shuttle weighs 85,000 lb more than the payload, the shuttle weighs $p + 85{,}000$ lb.

③ **Think** of a plan. Can you translate the information into an equation or inequality?

Translate the first sentence in the problem into an algebraic statement.

The shuttle and its payload weigh 215,000 lb. ← *This is a verbal model for the problem.*

④ **Use** algebra to solve for the unknown.

$$(p + 85{,}000) + p = 215{,}000$$ ← *This is an algebraic model for the problem.*

$$p + 85{,}000 + p = 215{,}000$$

$$2p + 85{,}000 - 85{,}000 = 215{,}000 - 85{,}000$$

$$2p = 130{,}000$$

$$p = 65{,}000$$

Thus, the payload weighs 65,000 lb, and the shuttle weighs $65{,}000 + 85{,}000 = 150{,}000$ lb.

⑤ **Verify** the answer.

To verify the answer, note that the combined weight of the shuttle and its payload is $150{,}000 + 65{,}000 = 215{,}000$ lb, as stated in the problem.

Try Example 1 Now Cover the solution, write your own solution, and then check your work.

EXAMPLE 1 Modeling and Interest

Angie bought a 6-month, \$10,000 certificate of deposit. At the end of the 6 months, she received \$650 simple interest. What rate of interest did the certificate pay?

Solution

1. Read the problem. It asks for the rate of simple interest.
2. Select the variable r to represent this rate.
3. Translate the problem. Here, we need to know that the formula for simple interest is

   $I = Prt$ ← *This is an algebraic model for the problem.*

   where I is the amount of interest, P is the principal, r is the interest rate, and t is the time in years. For our problem, $I = \$650$, $P = \$10{,}000$, r is unknown, and $t = \frac{1}{2}$ year. Thus, we have

   $650 = (10{,}000)(r)\left(\frac{1}{2}\right)$ or $650 = 5000r$

4. Use algebra to solve the equation

   $$650 = 5000r$$

   Divide by 5000. $$\frac{650}{5000} = r$$

   Express decimally. $$r = 0.13$$

   Hence, the certificate paid 13% simple interest.

5. Verify the answer. Is the interest earned on a \$10,000, six-month certificate at a 13% rate \$650? Evaluating Prt, we have

$$(10{,}000)(0.13)\left(\tfrac{1}{2}\right) = 650$$

Since the answer is yes, 13% is correct.

The next problem may help you to save some money. When you rent a car, you may be able to choose either a mileage rate or a flat rate. For example, if you wish to rent an intermediate sedan for 1 day, you can pay \$25 plus \$.20 for each mile traveled or a \$50 flat rate. Which is the better deal? That depends on how far you plan to drive. To be more specific, how many miles could you travel for \$50 if you used the mileage rate? You will find the answer in the next example, but be aware that car rental rates vary widely. You can compare rates at http://www.kayak.com or http://www.priceline.com.

EXAMPLE 2 Renting Cars and Solving Equations

Jim Smith rented a car at \$25 per day plus \$.20 per mile. How many miles can Jim travel for \$50?

Solution

Again, we proceed by steps as follows:

1. Read the problem carefully. We are looking for the number of miles Jim can travel for \$50.
2. Select m to represent this number of miles.
3. Translate the problem into an equation; that is, make a model that represents the conditions of the problem. To do this, we must realize that Jim is paying \$.20 for each mile plus \$25 for the day. Thus, we have the following information for Jim's travels:

1 mi	The cost is $0.20(1) + 25$.
2 mi	The cost is $0.20(2) + 25$.
	.
	.
	.
m mi	The cost is $0.20m + 25$. ← Algebraic model

Because we want to know how many miles Jim can drive for \$50, we must put the cost for m miles equal to \$50; this gives the equation

$$0.20m + 25 = 50$$

4. Use algebra to solve the equation

$$0.20m + 25 = 50$$

Subtract 25. $\quad 0.20m = 25$

Multiply by 100. $\quad 20m = 2500 \quad$ This gets rid of the decimal.

Divide by 20. $\quad m = \dfrac{2500}{20} = 125$

Thus, Jim can travel 125 mi for \$50.

5. Verify that $(0.20)(125) + 25 = 50$. (This is left for you to do.)

From this information, you can deduce that if you want to rent an intermediate sedan for 1 day and plan to drive over 125 mi, then the flat rate is the better of the two options.

Talking about distances, the next example could even save some lives. Have you seen the Highway Patrol booklet that indicates the **braking distance** b (in feet) that it takes to stop a car after the brakes are applied? This information is usually given in a chart, but there is a formula that gives close estimates under normal driving conditions. The braking distance formula is

$$b = 0.06v^2 \quad \leftarrow \text{Algebraic model}$$

where v is the speed of the car (in miles per hour) when the brakes are applied. Thus, if you are traveling 20 mph, you will travel

$$b = 0.06(20^2) = 0.06(400) = 24 \text{ ft}$$

after you apply the brakes.

EXAMPLE 3 Putting on the Brakes with Quadratics

A car traveled 150 ft *after* the brakes were applied. (It might have left a skid mark that long.) How fast was the car going when the brakes were applied?

Solution

1. Read the problem carefully.
2. Select the variable v to represent the velocity.
3. Translate: The braking distance $b = 150$, and the braking distance formula reads $b = 0.06v^2$. Thus, we have the equation

   $$0.06v^2 = 150 \quad \leftarrow \text{Algebraic model}$$

4. Use algebra to solve the last equation

   Multiply by 100. $\quad 6v^2 = 15{,}000 \quad$ This gets rid of the decimal.

   Divide by 6. $\quad v^2 = \dfrac{15{,}000}{6} = 2500$

   Take square roots. $\quad v = 50 \quad \text{or} \quad -50$

   Since the -50 makes no sense in this problem, we discard it. Thus, the car was going 50 mph when the brakes were applied.

5. Verify the answer by substituting 50 for v in the braking distance formula.

The formula in Example 3 gives the *braking distance* for a car traveling at v miles per hour. But there are other factors involved, notably, the *reaction time* of the driver and the *coefficient of friction* of the road (dry road: 0.8; 0.7 or 0.6 for an average vehicle with worn tires and 0.4 or 0.5 with poor road condition and worn tires). When some of these factors are taken into account, the stopping distance for a car may be as shown in the diagram in Example 4.

EXAMPLE 4 Applications: Auto Stopping Distance

At speed m (in miles per hour), the stopping distance $D(m)$, in feet, for a car is

$$D(m) = 0.05\,m^2 + 2.2\,m + 0.75$$

If you are one car length (13 ft) behind a stopped car, how fast can you be traveling and still be able to stop before hitting the car?

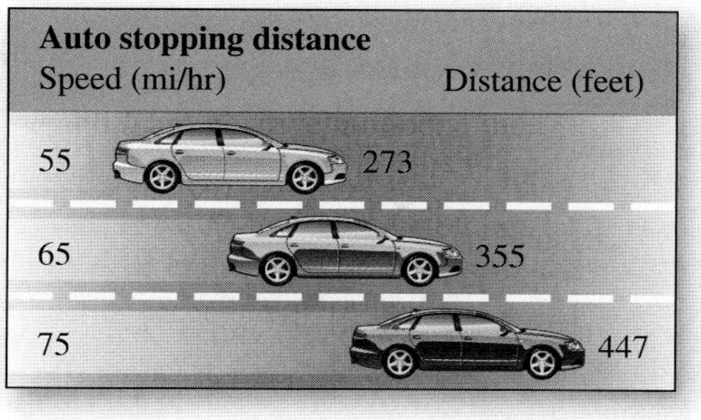

Here is a stop-distance calculator you can use to calculate stopping distances under different conditions. http://www.csgnetwork.com/stopdistcalc.html

Solution

In this case, the actual distance is 13 ft, so we have to solve

$$
\begin{aligned}
D(m) = 0.05m^2 + 2.2m + 0.75 &= 13 \\
5m^2 + 220m + 75 &= 1300 && \text{Multiply by 100 (clear the decimals).} \\
5m^2 + 220m - 1225 &= 0 && \text{Subtract 1300 (write in standard form).} \\
m^2 + 44m - 245 &= 0 && \text{Divide by 5.} \\
(m - 5)(m + 49) &= && \text{Factor.} \\
m = 5 \text{ or } m &= -49 && \text{Use the zero-factor property and solve.}
\end{aligned}
$$

So, you can be going 5 mi per hour and stop in 13 ft. If your speed is over 5 mi per hour, you will hit the car!

You have probably noticed the frequent occurrence of certain words in the statements of word problems. Because these words are used frequently, Table 6.1 presents a brief mathematics dictionary to help you translate them properly.

The next example shows how some of these words are used in a word problem.

Table 6.1 Mathematics Dictionary

Words	Translation	Example	Translation
Add to More than Sum of Increased by Added to	+	Add n to 7. 7 more than n The sum of n and 7 n increased by 7 7 added to n	$n + 7$
Subtract from Less than Minus Difference of Decreased by Subtracted from	−	Subtract 9 from x. 9 less than x x minus 9 Difference of x and 9 x decreased by 9 9 subtracted from x	$x - 9$
Of The product of Times Multiply by	×	$\frac{1}{2}$ of a number x The product of $\frac{1}{2}$ and x $\frac{1}{2}$ times a number x Multiply $\frac{1}{2}$ by x.	$\frac{1}{2}x$
Divide by Divided by The quotient of	÷	Divide 10 by x. 10 divided by x The quotient of 10 and x	$\frac{10}{x}$
The same, yields, gives, is, equals	=	x equals 12. x is 12. x yields 12.	$x = 12$

Do you remember the set of integers we have studied? Here is some extra information about integers that will help you with the next example.

Terminology	Notation	Examples
Two consecutive integers	$n, n + 1$	3, 4; −6, −5
Three consecutive integers	$n, n + 1, n + 2$	7, 8, 9; −4, −3, −2
Two consecutive even integers	$n, n + 2$	8, 10; −6, −4
Two consecutive odd integers	$n, n + 2$	13, 15; −21, −19

EXAMPLE 5 A Consecutive Integer Problem

The product of two consecutive even integers is 10 more than 7 times the larger of the two integers. Find the integers.

Solution

1. **Read the problem.** We are asked to find two consecutive ***even*** integers.
2. **Select the unknown.** Let n and $n + 2$ be the integers ($n + 2$ being the larger).
3. **Think of a plan.** We first translate the problem.

The product of two consecutive integers	is	10	more than	7 times the larger
$n(n + 2)$	$=$	10	$+$	$7(n + 2)$

4. **Use algebra to solve the equation.**

$$n^2 + 2n = 10 + 7n + 14 \quad \text{Use the distributive property.}$$
$$n^2 + 2n = 24 + 7n \quad \text{Simplify.}$$
$$n^2 + 2n - 24 - 7n = 0 \quad \text{Subtract } 24 + 7n$$
$$n^2 - 5n - 24 = 0 \quad \text{Simplify.}$$
$$(n - 8)(n + 3) = 0 \quad \text{Factor } (-8 \cdot 3 = -24, -8 + 3 = -5)$$
$$n - 8 = 0 \quad \text{or} \quad n + 3 = 0 \quad \text{Use the zero-factor property.}$$
$$n = 8 \quad \text{or} \quad n = -3 \quad \text{Solve each equation.}$$

If $n = 8$ is the first integer, the second is $n + 2 = 8 + 2 = 10$. The solution $n = -3$ is not acceptable because -3 is *not* even. Thus, only one pair of even integers satisfies the problem: 8 and 10.

5. **Verify the solution.**

The product of two consecutive integers	is	10	more than	7 times the larger	
$8 \cdot 10$	$=$	10	$+$	$7 \cdot 10$	
80	$=$	10	$+$	70	is true!

EXAMPLE 6 Checking for the Best Deal

The Better Business Bank has two types of checking accounts, A and B. Type A has a monthly service charge of \$3 plus \$.25 for each check written. Type B has a monthly service charge of \$5 plus \$.10 for each check written. What is the greatest number of checks that can be written before type A becomes the more expensive of the two?

Solution

Let x be the number of checks written. The cost of each account is as follows:

Type A	$3 + 0.25x$ dollars
Type B	$5 + 0.10x$ dollars

Hence, we need to find the greatest value of x such that

$$\underbrace{3 + 0.25x}_{\text{Type A}} \le \underbrace{5 + 0.10x}_{\text{Type B}} \quad \leftarrow \text{Algebraic model}$$

This inequality can be solved as follows:

Given.	$3 + 0.25x \le 5 + 0.10x$
Subtract 3 from both sides.	$0.25x \le 2 + 0.10x$
Subtract 0.10*x* from both sides.	$0.15x \le 2$
Divide both sides by 0.15.	$x \le \dfrac{2}{0.15}$
	$x \le 13\frac{1}{3}$

Since x must be a whole number, it follows that 13 is the required answer. Note that if you write more than 13 checks, a type A account will be more expensive.

B Mathematical Modeling

In the preceding problems we have translated verbal sentences into algebraic equations that include all the conditions of the problem. This procedure is called **mathematical modeling.** Intuitively, we say that a model is a replica or copy of the situation at hand. Thus, a **mathematical model** is a structure that displays the features of the problem being solved. Some structures that lend themselves to modeling are equations or formulas, inequalities, and graphs. Now we shall explore a situation that leads to a more sophisticated mathematical model than those studied previously.

EXAMPLE 7 Distance Learning and Modeling

One of the most radical changes in the way educational material is presented involves what is called *distance learning.* One of the models for distance learning uses television broadcasts (cable or regular channels) of lessons that students can view at home. From the point of view of an educational institution, is this a cost-effective method of presenting (teaching) a 3-credit-hour course? The following information is needed to solve this problem:

The primary *costs* to the institution are

- S Salary of the instructor, \$500 for each credit hour
- L Licensing fee for using copyrighted materials on TV, \$500
- F Fee per student paid to the copyright holder, \$15
- N Number of students

The *revenues* to the institution are

- T Tuition, \$40 per credit hour
- C Contribution by state [In Florida, the state provides about \$2800 per FTE (1 full-time equivalent = 40 credit hours) at the community-college level and more at the university level.]

Solution

To solve this problem, we use the **RSTUV** procedure. This time, however, there is no formula or "back of the book" to tell us when we are correct.

1. ***R**ead the problem.* Notice that we are referring to only one type of distance learning: television instruction.
2. ***S**elect the unknown.* The question is: From the institution's standpoint, is this a cost-effective method of presenting a mathematics course? A first step might be to define what is meant by *cost-effective.* We can start by looking at the *break-even point,* the point at which the revenue to the school equals the expense for the course.

3. *Think of a plan.* Find the cost and the revenue for the institution based on N students taking the course. Equate the two expressions and solve for N. This will tell us the number of students needed to break even.
4. *Use the model to carry out the plan.* Let us figure out the costs. How much is the instructor's salary? \$500 per credit hour. For a 3-credit-hour course, we have

Instructor's salary (S)	$3 \cdot 500 = \$1500$
Licensing fee (L)	\$ 500
Copyright holder fee (F) for N students	$15 \cdot N = 15N$
Cost to the institution	$1500 + 500 + 15N = 2000 + 15N$

The revenues to the institution are

Tuition (T) for N students	$40 \cdot N = 40N$
State contribution (C) for N students taking a 3-credit-hour course (Multiply the number of students N by 3 and divide by 40 to find the number of FTEs. Then, multiply the result by \$2800.)	$\left(\frac{3 \cdot N}{40}\right) \cdot 2800 = 210N$
Revenue to the institution	$40N + 210N = 250N$

The break-even equation
$$\textit{Cost} = \textit{revenue}$$
$$2000 + 15N = 250N$$
Solving for N,
$$2000 = 235N$$
$$\frac{2000}{235} = N$$
$$8.51064 = N$$
To the nearest whole number,
$$9 \approx N$$

Note that 9 is the smallest number of students for which the institution will incur no loss. Thus, *using this model,* if 9 students register for the course, the institution makes a small amount of money. Try this problem using the pertinent information (S, L, F, T, C, and FTE) for your state!

How would the break-even point be affected if there were more expenses (for example, utilities, building construction, maintenance, equipment) than the ones detailed here?

5. *Verify the answer.* Try the problem for 9 students and see whether the institution does make a small amount of money above the break-even point.

A similar mathematical model can be used to determine the cost effectiveness of teaching courses using e-learning. What is the difference between e-learning and distance learning? Go to http://tinyurl.com/7abfr7d or http://tinyurl.com/6f49xn8 and find out!

6.5 EXERCISES

A Problem Solving

1. Write an equation that is equivalent to this description: The product of 4 and a number m is the number increased by 18.
2. Given three consecutive, positive, even integers, write an inequality that is equivalent to the statement: The product of the smallest integer—say, $2n$—and the largest integer is always less than the square of the middle integer.
3. Write an equation that represents this statement: The product of two consecutive even integers is 20 less than 10 times the larger of the two integers.
4. The square of a number x, decreased by twice the number itself, is 10 more than the number. Write an equation that represents this statement.

In problems 5–14, write each statement as an equation, and then solve it.

5. If 4 times a number is increased by 5, the result is 29. Find the number.

6. Eleven more than twice a number is 19. Find the number.

7. The sum of 3 times a number and 8 is 29. Find the number.

8. If 6 is added to 7 times a number, the result is 69. Find the number.

9. If the product of 3 and a number is decreased by 2, the result is 16. Find the number.

10. Five times a certain number is 9 less than twice the number. What is the number?

11. Two times the square of a certain number is the same as twice the number increased by 12. What is the number?

12. If 5 is subtracted from half the square of a number, the result is 1 less than the number itself. Find the number.

13. One-third the square of a number decreased by 2 yields 10. Find the number.

14. One-fifth the square of a certain number, plus 2 times the number, is 15. What is the number?

In problems 15–37, use the ***RSTUV*** *method to obtain the solution.*

15. The space shuttle consists of the orbiter, the external tank, two solid-fuel boosters, and fuel. At the time of liftoff, the weight of all these components was 4.16 million lb. The tank and the boosters weighed 1.26 million lb less than the orbiter and fuel. What was the weight of the orbiter and fuel?

16. The external tank and the boosters of the space shuttle weighed 2.9 million lb, and the boosters weighed 0.34 million lb more than the external tank. Find the weight of the tank and of the boosters.

17. Pedro is twice as old as Maria. The sum of their ages is 30 less than 5 times Maria's. How old are Pedro and Maria?

18. Mary is 12 years old and her brother Joey is 2 years old. In how many years will Mary be just twice as old as Joey?

19. The cost of renting a car is \$18 per day plus \$0.20 per mile traveled. Margie rented a car and paid \$44 at the end of the day. How many miles did Margie travel?

20. In baseball, the slugging average of a player is obtained by dividing his or her total bases (1 for a single, 2 for a double, 3 for a triple, and 4 for a home run) by his or her official number of times at bat. José Cataña has 2 home runs, 1 triple, 2 doubles, and 9 singles. His slugging average is 1.2. How many times has he been at bat?

21. Peter buys a \$10,000, 3-month certificate of deposit. At the end of the 3 months, he receives interest of \$50. What was the rate of interest on the certificate?

22. A loan company charges \$84 for a 2-year loan of \$1400. What simple interest rate is the loan company charging?

23. The cost of renting a sedan for 1 day is $(0.25m + 20)$ dollars, where m is the number of miles traveled.

a. How many miles could you drive for \$71?

b. If you plan to make a 60-mi round trip, should you use a \$40 flat rate or the mileage rate?

24. The Greens need to rent a station wagon to move some furniture. If the round trip distance is 50 mi, should the Greens use a \$50 flat rate or a rate of \$40 per day plus \$0.22 per mile?

25. If P dollars are invested at r percent compounded annually, then at the end of 2 years, the amount will have grown to

$$A = P(1 + r)^2$$

At what rate of interest will \$1000 grow to \$1040.40 in 2 years?

26. Use the formula in problem 25 to find at which rate of interest \$1000 will grow to \$1060.90 in 2 years.

27. As given in the text, the braking distance b (in feet) for a car traveling v mph is

$$b = 0.06v^2$$

After the driver applied the brakes, a car traveled 54 ft. How fast was the car going when the brakes were applied?

28. The **reaction distance** r (in feet) is the distance a car travels while the driver is moving his or her foot (reacting) to apply the brakes. The formula for this distance is

$$r = 1.5tv$$

where t is the driver's reaction time (in seconds) and v is the speed of the car (in miles per hour). A car going 30 mph travels 22.5 ft while the driver is reacting to apply the brakes. What is the driver's reaction time?

Use the following information in problems 29–34. The stopping distance d (in feet) for a car traveling v mph when the driver has a reaction time of t is given by

$$d = 1.5tv + 0.06v^2$$

29. A car is traveling 30 mph. If the driver's reaction time is 0.5 sec, what is the stopping distance?

30. The reaction time of a driver is 0.5 sec. If the stopping distance is 187.5 ft, how fast is the car going?

31. An automobile going 20 mph is 42 ft away from an intersection when the traffic light turns red. If the automobile stops right at the intersection, what is the driver's reaction time?

32. You may have heard about the reflecting collars that can save the life of a dog or a cat. If your car's headlights will illuminate objects up to 200 ft away and you are driving 50 mph when you see a dog on the road at the edge of the illuminated distance, what must be your reaction time if you can stop just short of hitting the dog?

33. Loren, who has a reaction time of $\frac{2}{3}$ sec, was taking a driving test. When the examiner signaled for a stop, she stopped her car in 44 ft. How fast was she going at the instant of the stop signal?

34. Pedro reacts very quickly. In fact, his reaction time is 0.4 sec. When driving on a highway, Pedro saw a danger signal ahead and tried to stop. If his car traveled 120 ft before stopping, how fast was he going when he saw the signal?

35. Two consecutive integers are such that 6 times the smaller is less than 5 times the larger. Find the largest integers for which this is true.

36. A wallet contains 20 bills, all \$1 and \$5 bills. If the total value is less than \$80, what is the greatest possible number of \$5 bills in the wallet? What is the largest total value of money in the wallet?

37. Americans use about 100 billion aluminum cans each year. Approximately two-thirds as many of these cans are either thrown away or left to litter the landscape as are recycled. About how many billion aluminum cans will not be recycled this year?

B Mathematical Modeling

In problems 38–48, make models to solve the problems.

38. Referring to Example 7, the office of Institutional Research claims that the break-even point for a 3-credit-hour course is 15 students. This means that other costs O, perhaps utilities, maintenance, and so on, have been added to the costs to the institution.

a. Find O.

b. Repeat Example 7 using the costs for your college or university. Assume that the licensing fee and the fee paid to the copyright holder are still \$500 and \$15 per student, respectively.

c. Find the amount of other expenses O that your institution must pay.

39. Another and more expensive type of distance learning involves transmitting the contents of a lesson to other sites via satellite. The primary costs to the institution in this case are

s Studio time, \$100 per hour
U Uplink satellite service, \$150 per hour
G GTE connection fee and satellite rental time, \$1000 per hour
S Salary of instructors, \$1000 per credit hour

The revenues for the institution are

T Tuition (cost per credit hour × number of credit hours × number of students)
C Contribution of state, \$2800 per FTE (1 FTE = 40 credit hours)

If the class carries 3 credit hours, meets 40 hours during the term, and projected enrollment is N students, do or answer the following:

a. Write an expression for the revenue to the institution.

b. What is the cost to the institution?

c. Write the break-even equation for this model.

d. Solve for N in terms of T.

e. If the tuition per credit hour is \$40, what is the least number of students needed to incur no loss?

40. Should you consider fuel efficiency, measured in miles per gallon, when buying a new car? Suppose that car A costs \$20,000 and gets 20 mi/gal, whereas car B costs \$25,000 but gets 25 mi/gal. Further, assume that the price of gasoline is \$4/gal and that you plan to drive the car for m mi. Taking into account price and fuel efficiency *only,*

a. write an expression C_A for the cost of car A.

b. write an expression C_B for the cost of car B.

c. how many total miles m would you have to drive so that the cost is the same for both cars?

d. on the basis of this information, how would you make your decision on which car to buy?

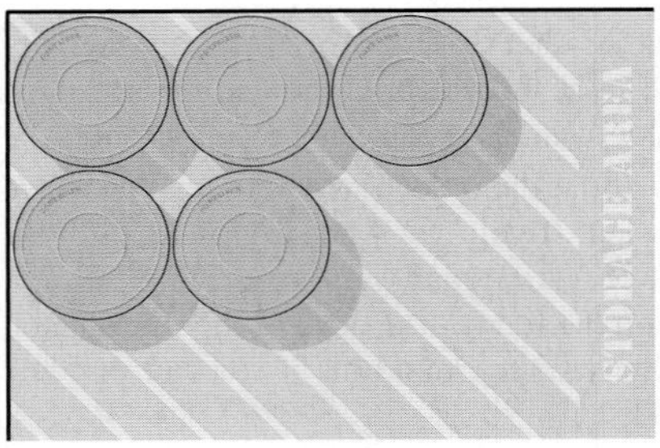

Storage area: Identical row alignment.

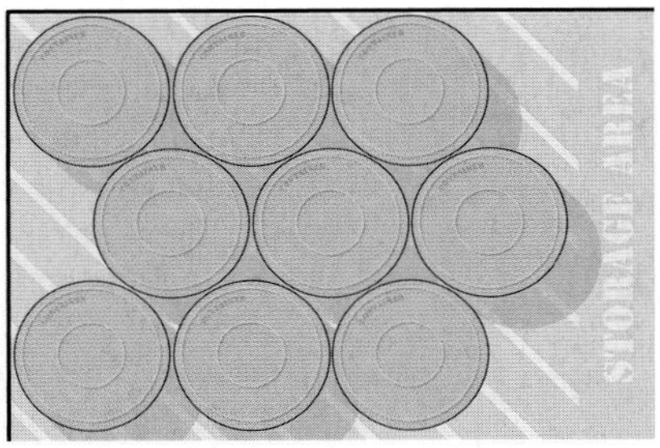

Storage area: Staggered row alignment.

Identical Row Alignment

Unit Size	Cost per Month	Number per Row	Rows	Layers	Total	Units Needed	Cost for 2 Months
A							
B							
C							

Staggered Row Alignment

Unit Size	Cost per Month	Number per Row	Rows	Layers	Total	Units Needed	Cost for 2 Months
A							
B							
C							

41. A paint contractor needs to find short-term (2-month) storage for 5-gal containers of Evermore Stucco Paint at minimum expense. Each container is a right circular cylinder with a diameter of 1 ft and a height of 15 in. All 350 containers must be stored in an upright position. It is not advisable to have more than five containers in each layer (stack). Storage units are available in three sizes as follows:

Size A: 5 × 5 × 4 ft high for \$25 a month
Size B: 5 × 10 × 8 ft high for \$90 a month
Size C: 10 × 10 × 8 ft high for \$128 a month

a. How many containers will fit into each storage area? [*Hint:* How many containers can you put in each row; how many rows and how many layers can you have? Note that you can store the containers in identical rows as shown in the diagram above on the left, or staggered as shown in the diagram above on the right. To answer (**a**), complete the tables on the left.]

b. What is the least expensive way to store the containers?

c. What is the next-thriftiest choice?

d. If the containers could be layered (stacked) as high as you wished, what would be the least expensive way to store the containers?

42. Is there a relationship between the amount of time you study and your grade-point average (GPA)? Of course there is! This problem will show you how to maximize GPA on the basis of study time.

Suppose that you are taking mathematics, science, and English. Each of the classes is worth 3 credit hours. At the present time you have C's in all classes, but you know the following:

Your mathematics grade can be improved by one letter for each additional 3 hours per week of studying mathematics.
Your science grade can be improved by one letter for each additional 2 hours per week of studying science.
Your English grade can be improved by one letter for each additional 1 hour per week of studying English.

If you decide to spend 10 extra hours per week studying mathematics, science, and English, how many hours should you spend studying each of the three subjects to maximize your GPA? [*Hint:* Organize the possibilities using a table like the following; then find the resulting GPA for each strategy. The GPA for each course is calculated by multiplying the number of points for each grade $(A = 4, B = 3, C = 2, D = 1, F = 0)$ times the number of credits the course carries. For example, a C in a 3-credit course is worth 6 grade points $(2 \cdot 3 = 6)$, whereas a B in a 4-credit course is worth 12 grade points $(3 \cdot 4 = 12)$. The GPA is then found by adding the total grade-point values for all courses and dividing by the total number of credit hours.]

Hours Spent and Grade Earned			
Mathematics	**Science**	**English**	**GPA**
6(A)	4(A)	0(C)	$\frac{30}{9} = 3.33$

43. Referring to problem 42, suppose you have D's in all your classes, but your mathematics and science courses are 4-credit-hour courses. If you decide to spend 12 extra hours per week studying mathematics, science, and English, how many hours should you spend studying each of the three subjects to maximize your GPA?

44. How often do you rent movies? How much is the charge for returning them late? Rock-Busters charges $3 to rent a movie as long as you return it by 2 P.M. the second day after you check it out. If you return it late, however, you are charged an additional $2.50 per overdue day for new releases and $1.50 per overdue day for other movies. Video Renters charges $2.50 per movie as long as the movie is returned by 3 P.M. of the second day after you check it out. If you return it late, you are charged $2 for each day the movie is overdue, regardless of whether the movie is a new release.

a. Make a table for new and old movies overdue 1, 2, and 3 days at each store.

b. Write an algebraic model representing the total cost of having both a new release and an old movie overdue for n days at Rock-Busters; then do the same for Video Renters.

c. How much are the total charges when you return a new release and an old movie 5 days overdue?

45. At Blockbuster in Tampa, it costs $3 to rent a movie. New releases are due the next day at midnight, but you can keep old movies for 2 days without incurring additional charges. Overdue charges are $2 per movie per day. At Red Rabbit, new releases are $3 per day and they must be returned by 7 P.M. the next day. Overdue charges are $3 per movie per additional day. Old movies are $1.60 for 2 days, and overdue charges are $1.50 per movie per day.

a. Make a table for new and old movies returned after 2, 3, and 4 days at each store.

b. Construct an algebraic model representing the total cost of having a new movie and an old movie returned after n days at Blockbuster; then do the same for Red Rabbit.

c. At each of these stores, what are the total charges when you have a new movie and an old movie returned after 5 days?

46. On Saturdays, the cost of parking at Park and Shop is $5 for the first hour and $0.50 for each additional hour. Safe Park charges $4.75 for the first hour and $0.60 for each additional hour.

a. Make a table to compare the costs for 1, 2, 3, 4, and 5 hours of parking at each location.

b. Write an algebraic expression representing the cost of parking n hours at each location.

47. When traffic lights are installed, planning must include the duration of the green and the yellow lights. How can we determine the duration of the yellow light assuming that the intersection is 80 ft wide and the speed limit is 45 mph?

a. The stopping distance d (in feet) for a car traveling v mph when the driver has a reaction time of t sec is

$$d = 1.5tv + 0.06v^2$$

Reaction times vary from 0.3 to 1 sec, but the average is about 0.6 sec. With this additional information, what is d?

b. On the basis of the answer to part (**a**), what is the nearest a car traveling 45 mph can be to the intersection and still stop safely?

c. The total maximum distance a car must travel through the intersection is the width of the intersection plus the distance from the intersection. What is this distance?

d. On the basis of the previous information, what should the minimum duration for the yellow light be? Answer to the nearest hundredth of a second. (*Hint:* $d = rt$, where r is rate, but watch your units!)

48. If the reaction time of the driver is 1 sec, what should the minimum duration for the yellow light be?

IN OTHER WORDS

49. When reading a word problem, what is the first thing you should try to determine?

50. How can you verify a word-problem answer?

USING YOUR KNOWLEDGE

Have you ever heard of Chamberlain's formula, *which claims to be a model that tells you how many years you should drive your present car before you buy a new one? If y is this number of years, then Chamberlain's formula reads*

$$y = \frac{GMC}{(G - M)DP}$$

where G is the new car's gas mileage, M is your present car's gas mileage, C is the cost in dollars of the new car, D is the number of miles you drive in a year, and P is the dollar price of gasoline per gallon.

For instance, suppose that the new car's gas mileage is 24 mi/gal, the old car's mileage is 12 mi/gal, the price of the new car is \$25,600, you drive 24,000 mi per year, and the cost of gasoline is \$4.00/gal. This means that $G = 24$, $M = 12$, $C = 25{,}600$, $D = 24{,}000$, and $P = \$4.00$, so

$$y = \frac{(24)(12)(25{,}600)}{(12)(24{,}000)(4)} = \frac{32}{5} \approx 6.4$$

Thus, according to the formula, your old car should have been driven about 6.4 years before the purchase is justified.

Now try these problems.

51. Suppose the new car's gas mileage is 32 mi/gal, the old car's gas mileage is 12 mi/gal, the price of the new car is \$28,000, you drive 30,000 mi/year, and the cost of gasoline is \$4.00/gal. How many years should your old car have been driven to justify buying the new one?

52. Suppose that G, M, D, and P have the same values as in problem 51 and you have driven your present car for 5 years. What price C would you be justified in paying for the new car?

53. Disregarding such factors as depreciation, the decrease in value of the car over time; maintenance; replacement cost; and so on, under which conditions does Chamberlain's formula yield unrealistic values for y?

6.6 Ratio, Proportion, and Variation

GETTING STARTED

OBJECTIVES

A. Find the ratio of two numbers.

B. Understand and solve proportions.

C. Understand and solve problems involving direct and inverse variation.

D. Solve applications involving ratios, proportions, and variation.

JUNK FOOD AND RATIOS

You have probably heard the term *junk food,* but do you know what foods fall into this category? The U.S. Department of Agriculture suggests looking at the *ratio* of nutrients to calories and multiplying the result by 100. The procedure adds the RDAs (recommended daily allowances) for the first eight nutrients listed on the label, divides by the number of calories in one serving, and multiplies by 100. After that, they give you a recommendation.

For instance, the sum of the first eight nutrients for the cereal label shown in Figure 6.22 is 139, and the number of calories in one serving is 100. Thus, the ratio of nutrients to calories is

$$\frac{139}{100} \times 100 = 139$$ Now, what do you do with this number?

If the answer is less than 32, the nutritional value of the food is questionable.

In this section you will study many kinds of ratios and their uses. For example, you will study unit pricing (see Example 2) to make you more aware as a consumer. Then you will learn how to compare ratios by studying proportions, and you will end the section by looking at different types of variation.

A Ratios

Many quantities can be compared by using ratios. You probably have heard of the student-teacher ratio or the gear ratio in your automobile. The definition of a ratio is on the next page.

Definition of a Ratio

A **ratio** is a quotient of two numbers. The ratio of a number a to another number b can be written as

$$a \text{ to } b \qquad \textbf{or} \qquad a{:}b \qquad \textbf{or} \qquad \frac{a}{b}$$

The last form is used most often, but is frequently written as a/b.

What is the ratio of paper towels to ice cream pints you can buy with the same amount of money?

NUTRITION INFORMATION

SERVING SIZE: 1 OZ (28.4 g, ABOUT 4 BISCUITS)
SERVINGS PER PACKAGE: 20

	CEREAL	WITH $\frac{1}{2}$ CUP VITAMINS A & D SKIM MILK
CALORIES	**100**	140*
PROTEIN	3 g	7 g
CARBOHYDRATE	24 g	30 g
FAT	0 g	0 g*
CHOLESTEROL	0 mg	0 mg*
SODIUM	5 mg	65 mg
POTASSIUM	80 mg	280 mg

*WHOLE MILK SUPPLIES AN ADDITIONAL 30 CALORIES, 4 g FAT, AND 15 mg CHOLESTEROL.

PERCENTAGE OF U.S. RECOMMENDED DAILY ALLOWANCES (U.S. RDA)

PROTEIN	**4**	15
VITAMIN A	**25**	30
VITAMIN C	**25**	25
THIAMIN	**25**	30
RIBOFLAVIN	**25**	35
NIACIN	**25**	25
CALCIUM	**	15
IRON	**10**	10
VITAMIN D	**10**	25
VITAMIN B_6	**25**	25
FOLIC ACID	**25**	25
PHOSPHORUS	**8**	20
MAGNESIUM	**8**	10
ZINC	**10**	15
COPPER	**4**	6

**CONTAINS LESS THAN 2% OF THE U.S. RDA OF THIS NUTRIENT.

FIGURE 6.22

EXAMPLE 1 Ratios of Nutrients

Write the ratio of nutrients (139) to calories (100) in three different ways.

Solution

$$139 \text{ to } 100 \qquad 139{:}100 \qquad \frac{139}{100}$$

Unit pricing allows shoppers to quickly compare relative costs of the same or similar products when they are sold in different weights or volumes.

Of course, if the ratio in Example 1 had been 140 to 100, you could write it in reduced form as

$$7 \text{ to } 5 \qquad \text{or} \qquad 7{:}5 \qquad \text{or} \qquad \frac{7}{5}$$

You encounter many ratios in your everyday life. For example, the expression *miles per gallon* is a ratio, the ratio of the number of miles traveled to the number of gallons of gas used. Thus, if your car travels 294 mi on 12 gal of gas, your miles per gallon ratio is $\frac{294}{12} = \frac{49}{2} = 24.5$.

Ratios can also be used to compare prices. For example, most people have the misconception that the more you buy of an item, the cheaper it is. Is this always true? Not necessarily. The photo shows two cans of Hunt's tomato sauce bought in the same store. The 15-oz can costs 68¢, whereas the 8-oz can costs 32¢. Which can is the better buy? To compare these prices, we need to find the price of 1 oz of tomato sauce;

that is, we need the **unit price** (the price per ounce). This unit price is given by the ratio

$$\frac{\text{Price}}{\text{Number of ounces}}$$

For the 15-oz can $\quad$ For the 8-oz can

$\frac{68}{15} = 4.5\overline{3}$ $\quad$ $\frac{32}{8} = 4$

Thus, the 15-oz can is more expensive. (Note that you could buy 16 oz, two 8-oz cans, for only 64¢, instead of the 15-oz can for 68¢!)

EXAMPLE 2 Unit Costs and Ratios

A 4-oz can of mushrooms costs \$0.74, whereas an 8-oz can of the same brand costs \$1.44. Find the cost per ounce for

(a) the 4-oz can. **(b)** the 8-oz can.

(Round answers to the nearest tenth of a cent.)

Solution

(a) For the 4-oz can, the cost per ounce is

$$\frac{74}{4} = 18.5¢$$

(b) For the 8-oz can, the cost per ounce is

$$\frac{144}{8} = 18¢$$

Note that if we wish to find which of the two cans in Example 2 is the better buy, we do not have to look at the unit prices. Two 4-oz cans would cost us \$1.48 for 8 oz, whereas the 8-oz can costs only \$1.44.

B Proportions

Let us return to the problem of the car that traveled 294 mi on 12 gal of gas. How many miles would this car travel on 10 gal of gas? The ratio of miles per gallon for the car is $\frac{294}{12}$, or $\frac{49}{2}$. If we let m be the number of miles the car would travel on 10 gal of gas, the ratio of miles per gallon would be $m/10$. Since the two ratios must be equal,

$$\frac{49}{2} = \frac{m}{10}$$

This equation is an equality between two ratios; it is called a **proportion.**

> **Definition of Proportion**
>
> A **proportion** is an equality between two ratios that can be written as
>
> $$\frac{a}{b} = \frac{c}{d}$$

To solve the proportion

$$\frac{49}{2} = \frac{m}{10}$$

which is simply an equation involving fractions, we proceed as before.

1. Multiply both sides by 10 so that the m is by itself on the right.

$$\frac{49}{2} \cdot 10 = \frac{m}{10} \cdot 10$$

2. Simplify: $245 = m$
3. Thus, the car can go 245 mi on 10 gal of gas.

Proportions often can be solved by a shortcut method that depends on the following definition of equality of fractions:

Equality of Fractions

If $\frac{a}{b} = \frac{c}{d}$, then $ad = bc$

Thus, to solve the proportion

$$\frac{3}{4} = \frac{15}{x}$$

we use the cross-products and write

$$3 \cdot x = 15 \cdot 4$$
$$3x = 60$$
$$x = 20$$

EXAMPLE 3 Proportions and Foot Lengths

The ratio of your foot length to your height (in inches) is 1 to 6.7. In 1951, Eric Shipton published photographs of what he thought were the Abominable Snowman's footprints. Each footprint was 23 in. long. How tall is the Abominable Snowman?

Solution

We use the five-step procedure outlined in Section 6.5 as follows:

1. Read the problem carefully.
2. Select a variable to represent the unknown. Here, we let h be the height of the Abominable Snowman.
3. Translate the problem. Since the original ratio is 1/6.7, the ratio for the Snowman is $23/h$. But these ratios must be equal, so

$$\frac{1}{6.7} = \frac{23}{h}$$

4. Use cross-products to solve the equation.

$$1 \cdot h = 6.7 \cdot 23$$
$$h = 154.1 \text{ in.} = 12 \text{ ft } 10.1 \text{ in.}$$

5. Verify your answer. If we substitute $h = 154.1$ in the original proportion, we obtain

$$\frac{1}{6.7} = \frac{23}{154.1}$$

which is a true statement because $1 \cdot 154.1 = 6.7 \cdot 23$.

C Variation

Sometimes we say that a variable is **proportional to** or **varies directly as** another variable x. For example, the number m of miles you drive a car is proportional to, or varies directly as, the number g of gallons of gas used. This means that the ratio m/g is a constant, the miles per gallon the car attains. In general, we have the following definition:

> **Direct Variation**
>
> y **varies directly as** x if there is a constant k such that $y = kx$. The constant k is the constant of variation or proportionality.

In real life, we can find k by experimenting. Suppose you are dieting and want to eat McDonald's fries, but only 100 calories' worth. The fries come in small, medium, or large sizes, with 210, 450, or 540 calories, respectively. (Source: www.shapefit.com/mcdonalds.html.) You can use *estimation* (Chapter 1) and eat approximately 1/2 of a small order ($210/2 \approx 105$ calories), but you can estimate better! The number of fries in the small, medium, and large sizes are 45, 97, and 121—thus, the calories per fry are

$$\frac{210}{45} \approx 4.7 \text{ (small)}, \qquad \frac{450}{97} \approx 4.6 \text{ (medium)}, \qquad \frac{540}{121} \approx 4.5 \text{ (large)}$$

EXAMPLE 4 You Want Fries with That?

The calories C in a bag of McDonald's French fries vary directly as the number n of fries in the bag. Suppose you buy a large bag of fries (121 fries, 540 calories). (Source: www.shapefit.com/mcdonalds.html.)

(a) Write an equation of variation between C and n.

(b) Find k.

(c) If you want to eat 100 calories' worth, how many fries would you eat?

Solution

(a) If C varies directly as n, $C = kn$.

(b) A large bag of fries has $C = 540$ calories and $n = 121$ fries, thus

$C = kn$ becomes $540 = k(121)$

or

$$k = \frac{540}{121} \approx 4.5$$

(c) If you want to eat $C = 100$ calories' worth, then

$C = kn = 4.5n$ becomes $100 = 4.5n$

Solving for n by dividing both sides by 4.5, $n = \frac{100}{4.5} \approx 22$.

So, if you eat about 22 fries, you will have eaten about 100 calories. Note that this is indeed about one half of a small bag!

Now that we have eaten some calories, let us see how we can spend (burn) some calories.

EXAMPLE 5 Variation and Bicycling

If you weigh about 160 lb and you jog (5 mph) or ride a bicycle (12 mph), you use C calories, which are proportional to the time t (in minutes) that you jog or ride.

(a) Find an equation of variation between C and t.
(b) If jogging for 15 min burns 150 calories, find k.
(c) How many calories would you burn if you jogged for 20 min?
(d) To lose 1 lb, you have to burn about 3500 calories. How many minutes do you have to bicycle in order to lose 1 lb?

Solution

(a) Since the calories used C are proportional to the time t (in minutes), an equation of variation is $C = kt$.
(b) If jogging for 15 min ($t = 15$) uses $C = 150$ calories,

$C = kt$ becomes	$150 = k(15)$.
Dividing both sides by 15,	$10 = k$
Note that now $C = kt$ becomes	$C = 10t$

(c) We want to know how many calories C you would use if you jogged for $t = 20$. Substitute 20 for t in $C = 10t$, obtaining

$$C = 10(20) = 200$$

Thus, you will use 200 calories if you jog for 20 min.
(d) To lose 1 lb, you need to use $C = 3500$ calories.

$C = 10t$ becomes	$3500 = 10t$
Dividing both sides by 10,	$350 = t$

Thus, you need 350 min of bicycling to lose 1 lb! By the way, if you bicycle for 350 min at 12 mph, you will be 70 mi away!

Sometimes, as a quantity increases, a related quantity decreases proportionately. For example, the more time we spend practicing a task, the less time it will take us to do the task. In this case, we say that the quantities **vary inversely as** each other.

Inverse Variation

y **varies inversely as** x if there is a constant k such that

$$y = \frac{k}{x}$$

EXAMPLE 6 Applications with Speed and Distance

The rate of speed r at which a car travels is inversely proportional to the time t it takes to travel a given distance.

(a) Write an equation of variation.
(b) If a car travels at 60 mph for 3 hr, what is k, and what does k represent?

Solution

(a) The equation is

$$r = \frac{k}{t}$$

(b) We know that $r = 60$ when $t = 3$. Thus,

$$60 = \frac{k}{3}$$

$$k = 180$$

In this case, k represents the distance traveled, and the new equation of variation is

$$r = \frac{180}{t}.$$

EXAMPLE 7 Boom Boxes and Variation

Have you ever heard one of those loud "boom" boxes or a car sound system that makes your stomach tremble? The loudness L of sound is inversely proportional to the square of the distance d that you are from the source.

(a) Write an equation of variation.

(b) The loudness of rap music coming from a boom box 5 ft away is 100 dB (decibels). Find k.

(c) If you move 10 ft away from the boom box, how loud is the sound?

Solution

(a) The equation is

$$L = \frac{k}{d^2}$$

(b) We know that $L = 100$ for $d = 5$, so

$$100 = \frac{k}{5^2} = \frac{k}{25}$$

Multiplying both sides by 25, we find that $k = 2500$, and the new equation of variation is

$$L = \frac{2500}{d^2}$$

(c) Since $k = 2500$,

$$L = \frac{2500}{d^2}$$

When $d = 10$,

$$L = \frac{2500}{10^2} = 25 \text{ dB}$$

D Application

EXAMPLE 8 Melting Snow

Figure 6.23 shows the number of gallons of water g (in millions) produced by an inch of snow in different cities. Note that the larger the area of the city, the more gallons of water are produced, so g is directly proportional to A, the area of the city (in square miles).

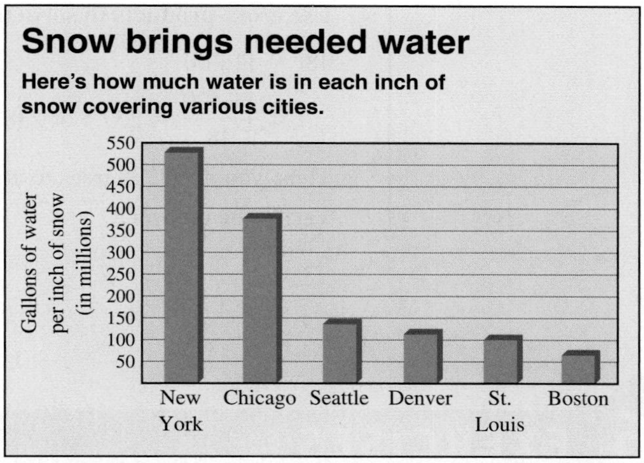

FIGURE 6.23

Source: Figure, "Snow Brings Needed Water," from USA TODAY. Copyright © 1993. Reprinted with permission.

(a) Write an equation of variation.

(b) If the area of St. Louis is about 62 mi^2, what is k?

(c) Find the amount of water produced by 1 in. of snow falling in Anchorage, Alaska, with an area of 1700 mi^2.

Solution

(a) Since g is directly proportional to A, $g = kA$.

(b) From Figure 6.23, we can see that $g = 100$ (million) is the number of gallons of water produced by 1 in. of snow in St. Louis. Since it is given that $A = 62$, $g = kA$ becomes

$$100 = k \cdot 62 \qquad \text{or} \qquad k = \frac{100}{62} = \frac{50}{31}$$

(c) For Anchorage, $A = 1700$; thus $g = \frac{50}{31} \cdot 1700 \approx 2742$ million gal of water.

How much air pollution does your car create? A car that gets 20 mi per gal driven 12,000 mi a year will use 600 gal of gas and will produce about 11,400 (19×600) lb of CO_2. (Each gallon of gas produces about 19 lb of CO_2.) Did you know that by planting trees, you can help save the environment? We find out how many trees are needed to absorb this CO_2 next.

EXAMPLE 9 Using Trees to Absorb CO_2

A tree absorbs 48 lb of CO_2 per year. At that rate, how many trees are needed to absorb 11,400 lb of CO_2?

Solution

We use the RSTUV procedure.

1. **Read the problem.** We want to find how many trees are needed to absorb 11,400 lb of CO_2.
2. **Select the unknown.** Let t be the number of trees needed to absorb the 11,400 lb of CO_2.
3. **Think of a plan.**

   1 tree absorbs 48 lb. The rate of absorption is $\frac{1}{48}$.

   t trees need to absorb 11,400 lb at a $\frac{t}{11{,}400}$ rate.

   To maintain the rate, we must have the proportion: $\frac{t}{11{,}400} = \frac{1}{48}$.

4. **Use cross-products to solve the problem.**

$48t = 11{,}400$ Cross multiply

$t = \frac{11{,}400}{48} = 237.5$ or 238 Divide by 48

Thus, you need 238 trees to absorb the CO_2 produced by a single car!

5. **Verify the answer!**

6.6 EXERCISES

A Ratios

1. *Voyager* was the first plane to fly nonstop around the world without refueling. At the beginning of the trip, the fuel in the 2000-lb plane weighed 7000 lb. Write the ratio of fuel to plane weight in three different ways.
2. During the last six years of his life, Vincent Van Gogh produced 700 drawings and 800 oil paintings. Write the ratio of drawings to oil paintings in three different ways.
3. The first suspension bridge built in England has a 70-ft span. The world's longest suspension bridge, from 1964 until 1981, the Verrazano Narrows Bridge in New York, is 4260 ft long. Write the ratio of the span of the first suspension bridge to that of the Verrazano Narrows Bridge in three different ways.
4. A woman has a 28-in. waist and 34-in. hips. Write the waist-to-hip ratio in three different ways. (If the waist-to-hip ratio is over 1.0 for men or over 0.8 for women, the risk of heart attack or stroke is five to ten times greater than for persons with a lower ratio.)
5. The reduced transmission ratio in an automobile is the ratio of engine speed to drive-shaft speed. Find the reduced transmission ratio for an engine running at 2000 rev/min when the drive-shaft speed is 600 rev/min.
6. Most job seekers can expect about 6 job leads and/or interviews for every 100 resumes they mail out. What is the ratio of job leads and/or interviews to resumes?
7. The average U.S. car is driven 12,000 mi per year and burns 700 gal of gas. How many miles per gallon does the average U.S. car get? (Give the answer to the nearest whole number.)
8. Are generic products always cheaper than name brands? Not necessarily! It depends on where you buy the products. When comparing two cans of mushrooms, the name brand 8-oz can costs \$1.09 and the generic 4-oz can costs \$0.53.
   a. To the nearest tenth of a cent, what is the cost per ounce of the name brand 8-oz can?
   b. To the nearest tenth of a cent, what is the cost per ounce of the generic 4-oz can?
   c. Which can is the better buy?
   d. In Example 2, the 4-oz can cost 18.5¢ per ounce. Which is the better buy, the generic can here or the 4-oz can of Example 2?
9. As a consumer, you probably believe that cheaper is always better, but be careful. Here is a situation that should give you food for thought!
   a. Dermassage dishwashing liquid costs \$1.31 for 22 oz. To the nearest cent, what is the cost per ounce?
   b. White Magic dishwashing liquid costs \$1.75 for 32 oz. To the nearest cent, what is the cost per ounce?
   c. On the basis of price alone, which is the better buy, Dermassage or White Magic?

   But how much do you use per wash? *Consumer Reports* estimated that it costs 10¢ for 10 washes with Dermassage and 18¢ for the same number of washes with White Magic. Thus, Dermassage is more economical.
10. Is cheaper still better? Here is another problem. A&P Wool Washing Liquid costs \$0.79 for 16 oz. Ivory Liquid is \$1.25 for 22 oz.
    a. To the nearest cent, what is the price per ounce of the A&P Wool Washing Liquid?
    b. To the nearest cent, what is the price per ounce of the Ivory Liquid?
    c. On the basis of price alone, which is the better buy?

    But wait. How much do you have to use? According to *Consumer Reports,* it costs 17¢ for 10 washes with the A&P Wool Washing Liquid, but Ivory Liquid is only 12¢ for 10 washes!

B Proportions

In problems 11–16, solve each proportion.

11. $\frac{x}{9} = \frac{4}{3}$
12. $\frac{x}{6} = \frac{5}{12}$
13. $\frac{8}{x} = \frac{4}{3}$
14. $\frac{6}{x} = \frac{18}{7}$
15. $\frac{3}{8} = \frac{9}{x}$
16. $\frac{3}{5} = \frac{9}{x}$
17. A machine manufactures 9 toys every 2 hr. Let n be the number of toys it produces in 40 hr. Write a proportion using this information and the ratio of n to 40.
18. A woman has several rectangular flower beds that she wants to be of equal area. If L ft is the length of a bed that is 3 ft wide, and the length is 10 ft when the width is 2 ft, write a proportion using the ratio of L to 10.

19. When flying a hot-air balloon, you get $\frac{1}{2}$ hr of flight time for each 20-lb tank of propane gas. How many tanks of gas do you need for a 3-hr flight?

20. When serving shrimp, you need $\frac{1}{2}$ lb of cooked shrimp without the shell to make 3 servings. How many pounds of cooked shrimp do you need for 90 servings?

21. The official ratio of width to length for the U.S. flag is 10 to 19. If a flag is 35 in. wide, how long should it be?

22. Do you like tortillas? Tom Nall does. As a matter of fact, he ate 74 tortillas in 30 min! How many could he eat in 45 min at that rate?

23. If your car gets 30 mi per gal, you need only 400 gal of gas a year and you will then produce 19×400 or 7600 lb of CO_2. If a tree absorbs 48 lb of CO_2, write the proportion you need to maintain the 1-tree rate of absorption and the number of trees needed to absorb the 7600 lb of carbon.

24. Do you know what a xerus is? It is a small rodent that looks like a cross between a squirrel and a chipmunk. The ratio of tail to body length in one of these animals is 4 to 5. If the body of a xerus is 10 in. long, how long is its tail?

25. A zoologist tagged and released 250 fish into a lake. A few days later, 53 fish were taken at random locations from the lake and 5 of them were found to be tagged. Approximately how many fish are there in the lake?

C Variation

26. The amount of annual interest I received on a savings account is directly proportional to the amount of money m you have in the account.
   a. Write an equation of variation.
   b. If \$480 produced \$26.40 in interest, what is k?
   c. How much annual interest would you receive if the account had \$750?

27. Have you burned a CD or DVD lately? At a speed of **1***X* a CD or CD-RW recorder writes 150 KB (kilobytes) of data per second! If the recording speed S (in bytes) is proportional to ***n*** in an ***n****X* disc:
   a. write an equation of variation
   b. if the recording speed of a **2***X* CD is 307,200 bytes, what is k?
   c. what is the recording speed of a **20***X* CD?

   By the way, *a byte* (abbreviation for binary term) is a unit of digital information capable of holding a single character. What does the writing speed mean to you? At an **8***X* speed, it takes 9 min to write a typical disk, but at **16***X* it will only take you 5 min!

   Source: http://www.osta.org/technology/cdqa5.htm.

28. The distance d an automobile travels after the brakes have been applied varies directly as the square of its speed s.
   a. Write an equation of variation.
   b. If the stopping distance for a car going 30 mph is 54 ft, what is k?
   c. What is the stopping distance for a car going 60 mph?

29. The weight of a person varies directly as the cube of the person's height h (in inches). The **threshold weight** T (in pounds) for a person is defined as the "crucial weight, above which the mortality risk for the patient rises astronomically."

   Source: Journal of the American Medical Association (JAMA).
   a. Write an equation of variation relating T and h.
   b. If $T = 196$ when $h = 70$, find k.
   c. To the nearest pound, what is the threshold weight for a person 75 in. tall?

30. To remain popular, the number S of new songs a rock band needs to produce each year is inversely proportional to the number y of years the band has been in the business.
   a. Write an equation of variation.
   b. If, after 3 years in the business, the band needs 50 new songs, how many songs will it need after 5 years?

31. When a camera lens is focused at infinity, the f-stop on the lens varies inversely with the diameter d of the aperture (opening).
   a. Write an equation of variation.
   b. If the f-stop on a camera is 8 when the aperture is $\frac{1}{2}$ in., what is k?
   c. Find the f-stop when the aperture is $\frac{1}{4}$ in.

32. Boyle's law states that if the temperature is held constant, then the pressure P of an enclosed gas varies inversely as the volume V. If the pressure of the gas is 24 lb/in.^{2} when the volume is 18 in.^{3}, what is the pressure if the gas is compressed to 12 in.^{3}?

33. For the gas of problem 32, if the pressure is 24 lb/in.^{2} when the volume is 18 in.^{3}, what is the volume if the pressure is increased to 40 lb/in.^{2}?

34. The weight W of an object varies inversely as the square of its distance d from the center of the Earth.
   a. Write an equation of variation.
   b. An astronaut weighs 121 lb on the surface of the Earth. If the radius of the Earth is 3960 mi, find the value of k for this astronaut. (Do not multiply out your answer.)
   c. What will this astronaut weigh when she is 880 mi above the surface of the Earth?

35. One of the manuscript pages of this book had about 600 words and was typed using a 12-point font. If the average number of words w that can be printed on a manuscript page is inversely proportional to the font size s,
   a. write an equation of variation.
   b. what is k?
   c. how many words could be typed on the page if a 10-point font were used?

36. The price P of oil varies inversely with the supply S (in million barrels per day). In the year 2011 the price of one barrel of oil was \$100, and OPEC production was 25 million barrels per day.
   a. Write an equation of variation.
   b. What is k?
   c. In OPEC plans to increase production to 26 million barrels per day, what would the price of one barrel be? Answer to the nearest cent.

37. According to the National Center for Health Statistics, the number of births b (per 1000 women) is inversely proportional to the age a of the woman. The number b of births (per 1000 women) for 27-year-olds is 110.
   a. Write an equation of variation.
   b. What is k?
   c. What would you expect the number b of births (per 1000 women) to be for 33-year-old women?

38. The number of miles m you can drive in your car is directly proportional to the amount of fuel g in your gas tank.

a. Write an equation of variation.

b. The greatest distance yet driven without refueling on a single fill in a standard vehicle is 1691.6 mi. If the twin tanks used to do this carried a total of 38.2 gal of fuel, what is k?

c. How many miles per gallon is this?

39. The distance d (in miles) traveled by a car is directly proportional to the average speed s (in miles per hour) of the car, even when driving in reverse!

a. Write an equation of variation.

b. The highest average speed attained in any nonstop reverse drive of more than 500 mi is 28.41 mph. If the distance traveled was 501 mi, find k.

c. What does k represent?

40. Have you called in on a radio contest lately? According to Don Burley, a radio talk-show host in Kansas City, the listener response to a radio call-in contest is directly proportional to the size of the prize.

a. If 40 listeners call when the prize is $100, write an equation of variation using N for the number of listeners and P for the prize in dollars.

b. How many calls would you expect for a $5000 prize?

41. You would think that your blood alcohol content (BAC) would be directly proportional to how many beers you drink in an hour. Strangely enough, for both males and females of a specific weight, the BAC is directly proportional to the number $(N - 1)$ of beers they drank during the last hour.

a. Write an equation of variation between BAC and the number of beers he drank during the last hour.

b. For a 150-lb average man, his BAC after 3 beers is 0.052. Find k.

c. What is his BAC after 5 beers?

d. How many beers can the man drink before going over the 0.08 BAC limit?

42. For a 130-lb average female, her BAC is still directly proportional to the number $(N - 1)$ of beers she had during the last hour.

a. Write an equation of variation between BAC and the number of beers she drank during the last hour.

b. For a 130-lb average female, her BAC after 3 beers is 0.06. Find k.

c. What is her BAC after 5 beers?

d. How many beers can the woman drink before going over the 0.08 BAC limit?

43. The number of chirps C a cricket makes each minute is directly proportional to 37 less than the temperature F in degrees Fahrenheit.

a. If a cricket chirps 80 times when the temperature is 57°F, what is the equation of variation?

b. How many chirps per minute would the cricket make when the temperature is 90°F?

44. According to George Flick, the ship's surgeon of the SS *Constitution,* the number of hours H your life is shortened by smoking cigarettes varies jointly as N and $t + 10$, where N is the number of cigarettes you smoke and t is the time in minutes it takes you to smoke each cigarette. If it takes 5 min to smoke a cigarette and smoking 100 of them shortens your life span by 25 hr, how long would smoking 2 packs a day for a year (360 days) shorten your life span? (*Note:* There are 20 cigarettes in a pack.)

45. Have you made copies of a CD or DVD lately? How long did it take you? It depends on the disc. A **2***X* disk is twice as fast as a **1***X* disk, and an ***nX*** disk is ***n*** times as fast as a **1***X* disk. The time T (in minutes) it takes to write or read data to a CD or DVD is inversely proportional to the ***n*** speed of the disk.

a. Write an equation of variation for the time T it takes to write or read data to a CD or DVD.

b. It takes 35 minutes for a 2*X* CD to be read completely. Find k.

c. How long will it take for a 48*X* CD to be read completely?

Source: http://tinyurl.com/42ymkgg.

46. At depths of more than 1000 m (a kilometer), water temperature T (in degrees Celsius) in the Pacific Ocean varies inversely as the water depth d (in meters). If the water temperature at 4000 m is 1°C, what would it be at 8000 m?

47. Anthropologists use the cephalic index C in the study of human races and groupings. This index is directly proportional to the width w and inversely proportional to the length L of the head. The width of the head in a skull found in 1921 and named Rhodesian man was 15 cm, and its length was 21 cm. If the cephalic index of Rhodesian man was 98, what would the cephalic index of Cro-Magnon man be, whose head was 20 cm long and 15 cm wide?

48. BAC is inversely proportional to weight W. For a 130-lb male, his BAC after drinking 3 beers in the last hour is 0.06.

a. Write an equation of variation between BAC and the weight of the person drinking 3 beers in the last hour.

b. What is the BAC of a 260-lb male after drinking 3 beers in the last hour?

c. In most states, you are legally drunk if your BAC is 0.08. What is the weight of a male whose BAC is exactly 0.08 after drinking 3 beers in the last hour?

d. What would your BAC be if you weighed more than the male in part (**c**)?

49. BAC is inversely proportional to weight W. For a 130-lb female, her BAC after drinking 3 beers in the last hour is 0.066.

a. Write an equation of variation between BAC and the weight of a person drinking 3 beers in the last hour.

b. What is the BAC of a 260-lb female after drinking 3 beers in the last hour?

c. In most states, you are legally drunk if your BAC is 0.08. What is the weight of a female whose BAC is exactly 0.08 after drinking 3 beers in the last hour?

d. What would your BAC be if you weighed more than the female in part (**c**)?

IN OTHER WORDS

50. Explain the difference between a ratio and a proportion.

51. Explain the difference between direct variation and inverse variation.

52. Write the steps you use to solve a proportion.

53. What does it mean when we say that the proportion $a/b = c/d$ can be solved using cross-products?

54. Can you solve $x/2 + x/4 = 3$ using cross-products? Explain.

55. What does it mean when we say that "the number of miles you drive a car is proportional to the number of gallons of gas the car uses"?

56. What does it mean when we say that "the number of gallons of gas your car uses is proportional to the speed at which you drive the car"? Is it directly proportional or inversely proportional?

USING YOUR KNOWLEDGE

57. Do you know what your Sun Protection Factor (SPF) is? The SPF of a sunscreen indicates the time period you can stay in the sun without burning, based on your complexion. The time T you are in the sun is directly proportional to your SPF (S).

© iStockphoto.com/o-che

Source: http://www.fitsugar.com/What-Does-SPF-Mean-Which-Sunscreen-Right-Your-Skin-3173539.

For example, suppose you can stay in the sun for 15 min without burning. Then, $T = 15S$ and we assume that your S is **1.** If you want to stay in the sun for 30 minutes, $T = 30 = 15S$, and now you need a sunscreen with an SPF of **2,** written as SPF**2**. Thus, you can stay out twice as much time in the sun $(\mathbf{2} \times 15 = 30)$ without burning.

a. Write an equation of variation relating the time T and the SPF S.

b. What SPF do you need if you want to stay out for an hour without burning?

COLLABORATIVE LEARNING

Health professionals use many ratios to detect abnormalities. Form three different groups: Library, Internet, and Other. What is the leading cause of death in the United States? Heart disease! Let each of the groups find the answers to the following questions:

1. How many deaths a year are attributed to heart disease? What is the total number of annual deaths? What is the ratio of deaths attributed to heart disease to the total number of deaths? Do the answers of the groups agree? Why or why not?

There are several ratios associated with heart disease. Let us look at some of them.

2. Let each of the groups find out what the HDL/cholesterol ratio measures. What is the recommended value of this ratio?
3. There is another noninvasive way to measure your cardiac health (see problem 4 of Exercises 6.6). This time, divide the groups into males and females. Complete the following table:

	Waist (w)	Hips (h)	Ratio w/h
Women			
Men			

As you recall, for women, the risk of heart disease increases when w/h > 0.8, for men, when w/h > 1.

CHAPTER 6 Summary

SECTION	ITEM	MEANING	EXAMPLE
6.1	Variable	A symbol that may be replaced by any one of a set of numbers	x, y, z
	Terms	The parts to be added or subtracted	The terms in $4x - 5$ are $\mathbf{4x}$ and $\mathbf{-5}$.
	Coefficient	The numerical part of the term	The coefficient of $7y$ is **7.**
	Like terms	Terms that differ only in their numerical coefficient.	$-8x$ and $3x$ are like terms.
6.1A	Open sentence	A sentence in which the variable can be replaced by a number	$x + 3 = 5; x - 1 < 7$
	Equation	A sentence in which the verb is $=$	$x + 7 = 9$
	Inequality	A sentence in which the verb is $>$, $<$, $\neq$, $\geq$, or $\leq$	$x + 7 < 9; x > 8; x \neq 9$
	Solution set	The set of elements of the replacement set that make the open sentence a true statement	$\{3\}$ is the solution set of $x + 2 = 5$ when the replacement set is the set of whole numbers.
6.1B	First-degree equation	An equation that can be written in the form $ax + b = 0$; $a \neq 0$. The unknown quantity x (or m) has an exponent of 1 only.	$x + 7 = 8 - 2x; 20 = 3m$

continued

CHAPTER 6 Summary – *continued*

SECTION	ITEM	MEANING	EXAMPLE
6.1B	Elementary operations	Operations that can be performed on a sentence to obtain an equivalent sentence	**Addition:** If $a = b$, then $a + c = b + c$ Subtraction: If $a = b$, then $a - c = b - c$ Multiplication: If $a = b$, then $a \times c = b \times c$, $c \neq 0$ **Division:** If $a = b$, then $a/c = b/c$, $c \neq 0$
6.1C	First-degree inequality	An inequality that can be written in the form $ax + b < 0$ or $ax + b > 0$ ($>$ can be replaced by $\geq$ and $<$ by $\leq$ and we still have a first-degree inequality.)	$3x + 5 < 8$; $5x - 2 \geq 3x + 1$
6.2A	Finite intervals: Closed interval	$a \leq x \leq b$	 $[a, b]$
	Open interval	$a < x < b$	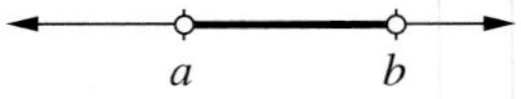 (a, b)
	Half-open intervals	$\begin{cases} a \leq x < b \\ a < x \leq b \end{cases}$	 $[a, b)$  $(a, b]$
6.3A	Absolute value	The distance on the number line from 0 to the number	$\lvert 3 \rvert = 3$; $\lvert -7 \rvert = 7$; $\lvert \frac{-2}{3} \rvert = \frac{2}{3}$
	If a is a positive number,	$\lvert x \rvert < a$ is equivalent to $-a < x < a$.	$\lvert x \rvert < 5$ is equivalent to $-5 < x < 5$.
	If a is a positive number,	$\lvert x \rvert > a$ is equivalent to $x > a$ or $x < -a$.	$\lvert x \rvert > 5$ is equivalent to $x > 5$ or $x < -5$.
6.4	Quadratic equation	A second-degree sentence that can be written in the form $ax^2 + bx + c = 0$, $a \neq 0$	$x^2 - 7x = 6$; $8x^2 - 3x - 4 = 0$
6.4C	Quadratic formula	For the equation $ax^2 + bx + c = 0$, $x = \dfrac{-b \pm \sqrt{b^2 - 4ac}}{2a}$	For the equation $x^2 - x - 1 = 0$, $x = \dfrac{1 \pm \sqrt{1 - 4(1)(-1)}}{2} = \dfrac{1 \pm \sqrt{5}}{2}$
6.4D	Pythagorean theorem	In any right triangle, the square of the hypotenuse c is equal to the sum of the squares of the other two sides.	If a and b are the sides of a right triangle and c is the hypotenuse, $a^2 + b^2 = c^2$.
6.5			

Procedure for Solving Word Problems

1. Read the problem carefully, and decide what it asks for (the unknown).
2. Select a variable to represent this unknown.
3. Think of a plan.
4. Use the rules of algebra to solve for the unknown.
5. Verify the solution.

CHAPTER 6 Summary

SECTION	ITEM	MEANING	EXAMPLE
6.6A	Ratio	A quotient of two numbers	The ratio of 5 to 7 is 5/7, the ratio of *a* to *b* is *a*/*b*
6.6B	Proportion	An equality between two ratios	$\frac{a}{b} = \frac{c}{d}$ is a proportion
6.6C	Varies directly	y varies directly as x if $y = kx$.	The number of calories *C* consumed is directly proportional to the number of hours *t* you exercise.
	Varies inversely	y varies inversely as x if $y = k/x$.	Your blood alcohol level BAC is inversely proportional to your weight *W*.

CHAPTER 6 Practice Test

1. If the replacement set is the set of integers, solve the following equations:
   a. $x + 7 = 2$ **b.** $x - 4 = 9$

2. If the replacement set is the set of integers, find the solution set for each of the following inequalities:
   a. $x + 5 > 4$ **b.** $2 + x \geq -x - 1$

3. Solve
   a. $2x + 2 = 3x - 2.$ **b.** $\dfrac{x+3}{5} = \dfrac{x-1}{3} + \dfrac{6}{5}.$

4. For women, the relationship between shoe size S and length of foot L is $S = 3L - 21$.
   a. Solve for L.
   b. If a woman wears a size 6 shoe, what is the length of her foot?

5. Solve

$$\frac{x}{2} + 2 \geq \frac{-(x+1)}{4}.$$

6. Graph the solution set of
   a. $x - 3 \leq 0.$ **b.** $-2x + 4 > x + 1.$

7. Graph the solution set (if it is not empty) of
   a. $x + 2 \geq 3$ and $x \leq 4.$ **b.** $x - 3 \geq 1$ and $x \leq 0.$

8. Graph the solution set of
   a. $x < 0$ or $x - 2 < 1.$ **b.** $x + 2 < 3$ or $x - 1 > 2.$

9. Solve the equation $|x| = 3.$

10. Graph the solution set of $|x| < 2.$

11. Graph the solution set of $|x - 2| < 2.$

12. Graph the solution set of $|x| > 2.$

13. Graph the solution set of $|x - 2| > 3.$

14. Factor
   a. $x^2 + 3x + 2.$ **b.** $x^2 - 3x - 4.$

15. Solve
   a. $(x - 1)(x + 2) = 0.$ **b.** $x(x - 1) = 0.$

16. Solve, by factoring, $x^2 + 7x + 10 = 0.$

continued

CHAPTER 6 Practice Test – *continued*

17. Solve, by factoring, $x^2 - 3x = 10$.

18. Solve
a. $9x^2 - 16 = 0$. b. $25x^2 - 4 = 0$.

19. Use the quadratic formula to solve $2x^2 + 3x - 5 = 0$.

20. Use the quadratic formula to solve $x^2 - 2x = 2$.

21. The hypotenuse of a right triangle is 9 cm longer than one of the legs and 2 cm longer than the other leg. Find the dimensions of the triangle.

22. Suppose that you rent a car for 1 day at the rate of \$21 per day plus \$0.21 per mile. How many miles could you drive in 1 day for a rental charge of \$63?

23. Three times the sum of two consecutive integers is 45. What are the integers?

24. A pair of consecutive integers is such that 12 times the smaller is more than 9 times the larger. What is the least pair of integers for which this is true?

25. The product of two odd consecutive integers is 7 less than 10 times the smaller of the two integers. Find the integers.

26. On a certain day, the New York Stock Exchange reported that 688 stocks went up, 801 went down, and 501 were unchanged.
a. Write the ratio of losers to gainers in three different ways.
b. What is the ratio of losers to the total number of stocks?

27. A supermarket is selling a certain kind of cracker for 50¢ for an 8-oz box and 76¢ for a 12-oz box.
a. Find the unit price for each box.
b. Which is the better buy?

28. We know that corresponding sides of similar rectangles are proportional. One rectangle is 5 by 8 ft, and the short side of a similar rectangle is 9 ft long.
a. Write a proportion for the length x of the long side of the second rectangle.
b. Find the missing length.

29. The cost C of fuel per hour for running an airplane is directly proportional to the square of the speed x.
a. Write an equation of variation.
b. If the cost is \$100 per hour for a speed of 150 mph, find the value of k.
c. Find the cost per hour for a speed of 180 mph.

30. The time t of exposure to photograph an object at a fixed distance from the camera is inversely proportional to the intensity I of the illumination.
a. Write an equation of variation.
b. If the correct exposure is $\frac{1}{30}$ sec when I is 300 units, find the value of k.
c. If I is increased to 600 units, what is the correct exposure time?

ANSWERS TO PRACTICE TEST

CHAPTER 6		What to Review *If You Missed It*		
QUESTION	**ANSWER**	**SECTION**	**EXAMPLE(S)**	**PAGE(S)**
1	**a.** $x = -5$ **b.** $x = 13$	6.1	1	263–264
2	**a.** $\{0, 1, 2, 3, \ldots\}$ **b.** $\{-1, 0, 1, 2, 3, \ldots\}$	6.1	1	263–264
3	**a.** $x = 4$ **b.** $x = -2$	6.1	2–4	265–267
4	**a.** $\frac{S + 21}{3}$ **b.** 9 in.	6.1	6	268
5	$\{x \mid x \geq -3\}$	6.1	7–9	269–271
6	**a.** 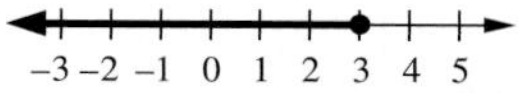 **b.** 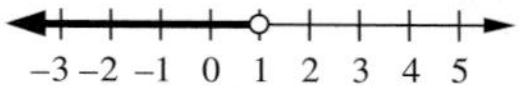	6.2	1–5	277–278
7	**a.** 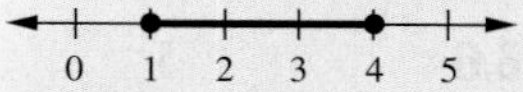 **b.** The solution set is empty.	6.2	6–8	279
8	**a.** 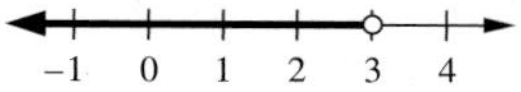 **b.** 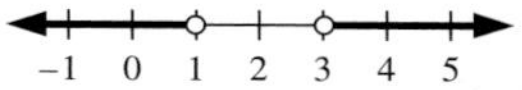	6.2	9	280
9	$x = \pm 3$	6.3	1	284
10	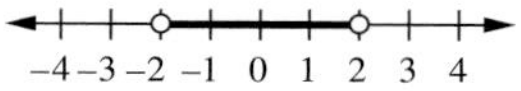	6.3	2, 3	285
11	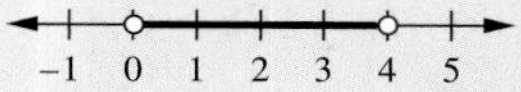	6.3	4	285
12	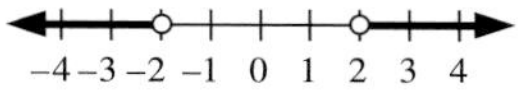	6.3	5, 6	285, 286
13		6.3	7	286
14	**a.** $(x + 1)(x + 2)$ **b.** $(x + 1)(x - 4)$	6.4	1, 2	290
15	**a.** $x = -2$ or $x = 1$ **b.** $x = 0$ or $x = 1$	6.4	3	291
16	$x = -5$ or $x = -2$	6.4	3	291
17	$x = -2$ or $x = 5$	6.4	3	291
18	**a.** $x = \pm\frac{4}{3}$ **b.** $x = \pm\frac{2}{5}$	6.4	4, 5	292
19	$x = -\frac{5}{2}$ or $x = 1$	6.4	6, 7	293–294
20	$x = 1 + \sqrt{3}$ or $x = 1 - \sqrt{3}$	6.4	8	294–295

continued

ANSWERS TO PRACTICE TEST — *continued*

CHAPTER 6		What to Review *If You Missed It*		
QUESTION	**ANSWER**	**SECTION**	**EXAMPLE(S)**	**PAGE(S)**
21	8 cm, 15 cm, 17 cm	6.4	9	296
22	200 mi	6.5	2	303
23	7 and 8	6.5	5	306
24	4 and 5	6.5	5	306
25	7 and 9	6.5	5	306
26	**a.** 801 to 688; 801:688; $\frac{801}{688}$ **b.** $\frac{801}{1990}$	6.6	1	313
27	**a.** $6\frac{1}{4}$¢ per oz for the 8-oz box; $6\frac{1}{3}$¢ per oz for the 12-oz box **b.** The 8-oz box	6.6	2	314
28	**a.** $\frac{x}{8} = \frac{9}{5}$ **b.** 14.4 ft	6.6	3	315
29	**a.** $C = kx^2$ **b.** $k = \frac{1}{225}$ **c.** \$144 per hour	6.6	4–8	316–319
30	**a.** $t = k/I$ **b.** $k = 10$ **c.** $\frac{1}{60}$ sec	6.6	4–8	316–319

CHAPTER 7

Functions and Graphs

It is not enough to have a good mind; the main thing is to use it well. —RENÉ DESCARTES

To maximize efficiency in activities such as running and cycling and to achieve the greatest health benefits, individuals need to identify the target pulse rate for their age group. In Section 7.2, you will utilize linear functions to explore target pulse rates and relations to represent real-life data such as maximum target pulse rates.

In Chapter 6 we studied first- and second-degree equations with *one* variable. In this chapter we shall study similar equations with *two* variables. The main feature here, however, is an introduction to some simple ideas that belong to the area that is called **analytic geometry,** a blend of algebra and geometry in which algebra is used to study geometry and geometry is used to study algebra. The key to this combination is a workable system of associating **points in the plane** with **ordered pairs of numbers.**

We start the chapter by studying sets of ordered pairs called **relations,** concentrating on a special type of relation called a **function.** We examine function notation and how to represent relations and functions by means of **graphs.** We also study the formula giving the distance between any two points in the Cartesian plane and the slope (inclination) of a line passing through these two points. We explore the ways to write the equations of a line depending on the information that is given and the ways to solve systems of linear equations with two unknowns by using algebraic or graphical methods.

7.1 Graphing Relations and Functions

GETTING STARTED

OBJECTIVES

- **A.** Find the domain and range of relations and functions and evaluate functions.
- **B.** Solve applications involving functions.
- **C.** Graph relations and functions.
- **D.** Solve applications involving graphs.

Human Side of Math

(1596–1650)

René Descartes was born on March 31, 1596, near Tours, France. At the age of 32, Descartes was persuaded to prepare his research for publication. At 38, he compiled what was to be one grand treatise on the world, but fear of ecclesiastic displeasure with his conclusions caused him to refrain from having it printed.

In 1637, at age 41, his friends persuaded him to print his masterpiece known as *The Method.* It included an essay on geometry. His *Analytic Geometry* (a combination of algebra and geometry) revolutionized the realm of geometry and made much of modern mathematics possible.

LOOKING AHEAD

The Cartesian coordinate system, a legacy of the work of René Descartes, is introduced in Section 7.1 and used throughout this chapter in studying functions and graphs.

FUNCTIONS FOR FASHIONS

Did you know that women's clothing sizes are getting smaller? According to a J. C. Penney catalog, "Simply put, you will wear one size smaller than before." Is there a relationship between the new sizes and waist size? Look at Table 7.1. It gives a $1\frac{1}{2}$-in. leeway for waist sizes. In Table 7.1, consider the first numbers in the waist sizes corresponding to different dress sizes, that is, 30, 32, 34, and 36. For dress sizes 14 to 22, the waist size is 16 in. more than the dress size. To formalize this relationship, you can write

$$w(s) = s + 16 \quad \text{(read "}w\text{ of }s\text{ equals }s\text{ plus 16")}$$

What would the waist size of a woman who wears size 14 be? It would be

$$w(14) = 14 + 16 = 30$$

For size 16,

$$w(16) = 16 + 16 = 32$$

and so on. It works! Can you do the same for hip sizes? If you get

$$h(s) = s + 26.5$$

you are on the right track. Examples 5 and 6 and problems 28 and 29 in Exercises 7.1 will give you more practice with relationships between number pairs.

The word *relation* might remind you of members of your family—parents, brothers, sisters, cousins, and so on. You have already studied mathematical relations such as "is a subset of," "is less than," and "is equivalent to." Relations can be expressed by using ordered pairs. In this section you first examine relations in general and then concentrate on a very important type of relation called a **function** and its applications. To help understand these concepts, you end the section by learning how to make pictures, or graphs, of these relations and functions.

A Relations and Functions

Definition of a Relation

A **relation** is a set of ordered pairs of the form (x, y). The set of all possible x values is the **domain** of the relation, and the set of all possible y values is the **range** of the relation.

Table 7.1 Women's Sizes

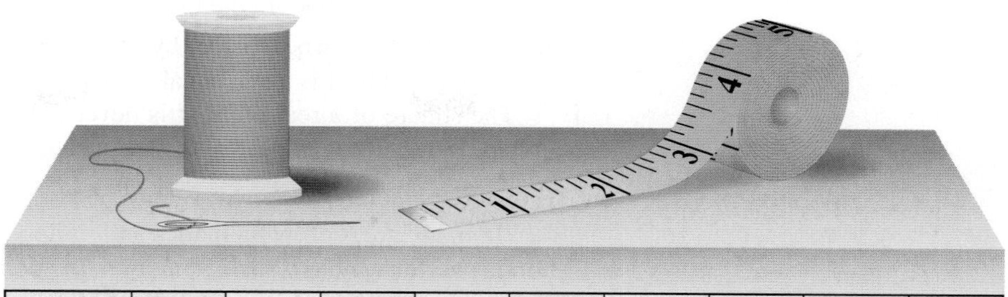

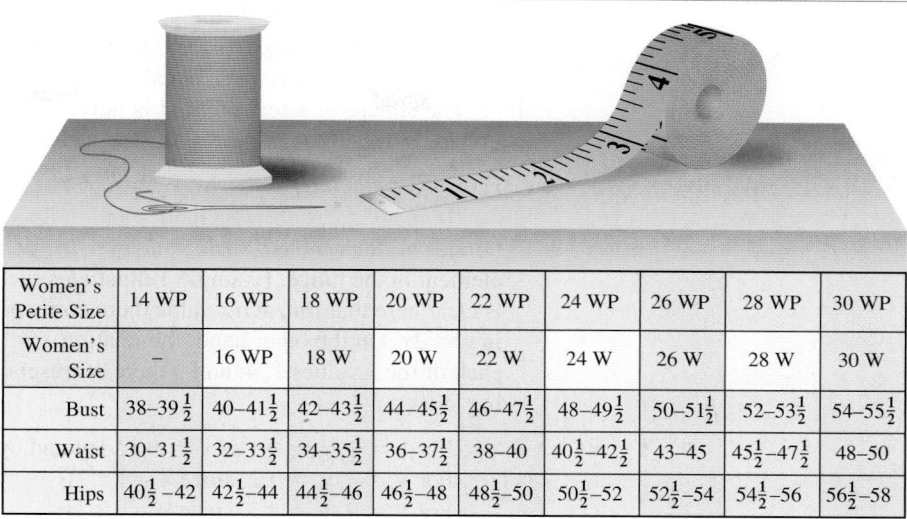

Women's Petite Size	14 WP	16 WP	18 WP	20 WP	22 WP	24 WP	26 WP	28 WP	30 WP
Women's Size	–	16 WP	18 W	20 W	22 W	24 W	26 W	28 W	30 W
Bust	38–39$\frac{1}{2}$	40–41$\frac{1}{2}$	42–43$\frac{1}{2}$	44–45$\frac{1}{2}$	46–47$\frac{1}{2}$	48–49$\frac{1}{2}$	50–51$\frac{1}{2}$	52–53$\frac{1}{2}$	54–55$\frac{1}{2}$
Waist	30–31$\frac{1}{2}$	32–33$\frac{1}{2}$	34–35$\frac{1}{2}$	36–37$\frac{1}{2}$	38–40	40$\frac{1}{2}$–42$\frac{1}{2}$	43–45	45$\frac{1}{2}$–47$\frac{1}{2}$	48–50
Hips	40$\frac{1}{2}$–42	42$\frac{1}{2}$–44	44$\frac{1}{2}$–46	46$\frac{1}{2}$–48	48$\frac{1}{2}$–50	50$\frac{1}{2}$–52	52$\frac{1}{2}$–54	54$\frac{1}{2}$–56	56$\frac{1}{2}$–58

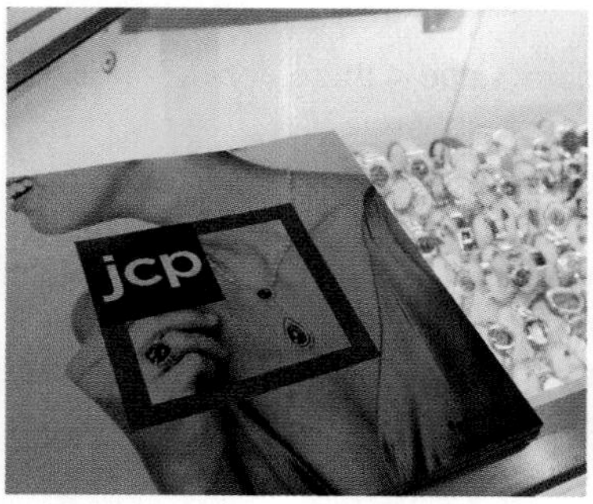

The first J. C. Penney store opened in 1902 in Kemmerer, Wyoming.

For instance, the set $R = \{(4, -3), (2, -5), (-3, 4)\}$ is a relation in which all the pairs have been specifically listed. Notice that the set of first members, the **domain,** is $\{-3, 2, 4\}$, and the set of second members, the **range,** is $\{-5, -3, 4\}$. The listing in the relation R shows how the elements of the first set are associated with the elements of the second set to form the ordered pairs of the given relation. Different ways of associating the elements of the two sets will, of course, result in different relations. Thus,

$$S = \{(-3, -5), (2, -3), (4, 4)\}$$

is an example of a relation different from R but formed from the same two sets of first and second numbers.

Rule for Finding Domain and Range

Unless otherwise specified, the **domain** of a relation is taken to be the largest set of real numbers that can be substituted for x and that result in real numbers for y. The **range** is then determined by the rule of the relation.

For example, if

$$Q = \{(x, y) \mid y = \sqrt{x}\}$$

which means that Q is the set consisting of all ordered pairs (x, y) such that $y = \sqrt{x}$, then we may substitute any *nonnegative* real number for x and obtain a real number for y. But x cannot be replaced by a negative number. (Why?) Thus, the domain is the set of all nonnegative real numbers, and the range, in this case, is the same set. Why?

EXAMPLE 1 Finding Domain and Range

Find the domain and the range of

(a) $R = \{(x, y) \mid y = 2x\}$. (b) $S = \{(x, y) \mid y = x^2 + 1\}$.

Solution

(a) The variable x can be replaced by any real value because 2 times any real number is a real number. Hence, the domain is $\{x \mid x \text{ a real number}\}$. The range is also the set of real numbers because every real number is 2 times another real number. Thus, the range is $\{y \mid y \text{ a real number}\}$.

(b) The variable x can be replaced by any real value because the result of squaring a real number and adding 1 is again a real number. Thus, the domain of S is $\{x \mid x \text{ a real number}\}$. The square of a real number is never negative, $x^2 \geq 0$, so $x^2 + 1 \geq 1$. Hence, the rule $y = x^2 + 1$ implies $y \geq 1$. Consequently, the range of S is $\{y \mid y \geq 1\}$.

In many areas of mathematics and its applications, the most important kind of relation is one for which to each element in the domain there corresponds one and only one element in the range. Example 1 illustrates such a relation with $R = \{(x, y) \mid y = 2x\}$. It is clear here that for each x value there corresponds exactly one y value because the rule is $y = 2x$. On the other hand, the relation $x = y^2$ is not this type of relation, because to each of the x values 1, 4, and 9 there corresponds more than one y value, as the following shows:

For $x = 1$, $y = +1$ or $y = -1$, denoted by $y = \pm 1$, since $1 = (\pm 1)^2$
For $x = 4$, $y = \pm 2$, since $4 = (\pm 2)^2$
For $x = 9$, $y = \pm 3$, since $9 = (\pm 3)^2$

Definition of a Function

A **function** is a relation for which to each domain value x there corresponds exactly one range value y; that is, for every x there is only one y.

You bump into functions every day: the correspondence between the weight of a letter and the amount of postage you pay, the correspondence between the cost of a piece of meat and the number of pounds it weighs, and the correspondence between the number of miles per gallon that you get and the speed at which you drive. These are all simple examples of functions. You can undoubtedly think of many more.

GRAPH IT

Your grapher evaluates functions! First, enter [Y=] $2x + 3$ [ZOOM] [6] and then press [2nd] [CALC] [1]. Next, enter the desired x value, say, 1, and [ENTER]. The y value 5 is shown.

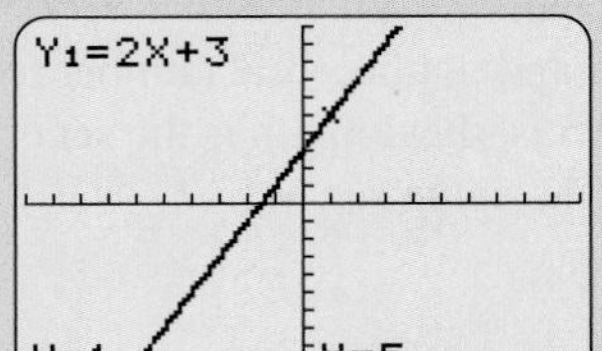

If you press [TRACE] [◀], you can evaluate at other points. If your points (x's) are integers, press [ZOOM] [8] [ENTER] [TRACE] and [◀] or [▶] to evaluate the function when x is an integer. Try when x is 0, −6, or 4.

EXAMPLE 2 Determining If a Relation Is a Function

(a) Is the relation $\{(x, y) \mid y = 2x + 3, x \text{ a real number}\}$ a function? Explain.

(b) Is the relation $\{(x, y) \mid x = y^2 + 1\}$ a function? Explain.

Solution

(a) If x is a real number, then y is the unique real number $2x + 3$. For instance, if $x = 2$, then $y = 2(2) + 3 = 7$; if $x = -\frac{1}{2}$, then $y = 2(-\frac{1}{2}) + 3 = 2$. Clearly, for each real x value, the expression $2x + 3$ gives one and only one y value. Thus, the given relation has exactly one range value corresponding to each domain value and is therefore a function.

(b) For this relation the domain is $\{x \mid x \geq 1\}$. Why? If $x = 5$, then the rule $x = y^2 + 1$ gives $5 = y^2 + 1$, or $y^2 = 4$. Thus, $y = 2$ or -2 because $2^2 = (-2)^2 = 4$. So the pairs $(5, 2)$ and $(5, -2)$ are both elements of this relation. The fact that there are two range values, 2 and -2, for the domain value 5 shows that the given relation is not a function.

How do we denote functions? We often use letters such as f, F, g, G, h, and H to do this. Thus, for the relation in Example 2(a), we use set notation to write

$$f = \{(x, y) \mid y = 2x + 3\}$$

because we know this relation to be a function. Another very commonly used notation to denote the range value that corresponds to a given domain value x is $y = f(x)$. (This is usually read "f of x.")

The $f(x)$ notation, called **function notation,** is quite convenient because it denotes the value of the function for the given value of x. For example, if

$$f(x) = 2x + 3$$

then

$$\begin{aligned} f(1) &= 2(1) + 3 = 5 \\ f(0) &= 2(0) + 3 = 3 \\ f(-6) &= 2(-6) + 3 = -9 \\ f(4) &= 2(4) + 3 = 11 \\ f(a) &= 2(a) + 3 = 2a + 3 \\ f(w + 2) &= 2(w + 2) + 3 = 2w + 7 \end{aligned}$$

and so on. Whatever appears between the parentheses in $f(\,)$ is to be substituted for x in the rule that defines $f(x)$. The result is y; that is, $f(x) = y$.

Instead of describing a function in set notation, we frequently say "the function defined by $f(x) = \cdots$," where the three dots are to be replaced by the expression for the value of the function. For instance, "the function defined by $f(x) = 2x + 3$" has the same meaning as "the function $f = \{(x, y) \mid y = 2x + 3\}$."

GRAPH IT

To do Example 3, enter [Y=] and $3x + 5$. Since we want to evaluate at integral values, enter [ZOOM] [8] [ENTER] [TRACE]. Now use the [▶] or [◀] to see different values for x and y. Find $f(4)$ and $f(2)$.

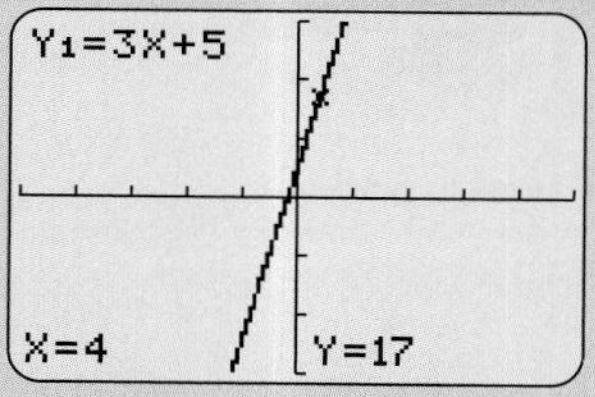

EXAMPLE 3 Evaluating a Function

Let $f(x) = 3x + 5$. Find

(a) $f(4)$. (b) $f(2)$. (c) $f(2) + f(4)$. (d) $f(x + 1)$.

Solution

(a) Since $f(x) = 3x + 5$,

$f(4) = 3 \cdot 4 + 5 = 12 + 5 = 17$

(b) $f(2) = 3 \cdot 2 + 5 = 6 + 5 = 11$

(c) Since $f(2) = 11$ and $f(4) = 17$,

$f(2) + f(4) = 11 + 17 = 28$

(d) $f(x + 1) = 3(x + 1) + 5 = 3x + 8$

EXAMPLE 4 Evaluating More Functions

A function g is defined by $g(x) = x^3 - 2x^2 + 3x - 4$. Find

(a) $g(2)$. (b) $g(-3)$. (c) $g(2) - g(-3)$.

Solution

(a) $g(2) = 2^3 - 2(2^2) + 3(2) - 4 = 8 - 8 + 6 - 4 = 2$

(b) $g(-3) = (-3)^3 - 2(-3)^2 + 3(-3) - 4$

$= -27 - 18 - 9 - 4 = -58$

(c) $g(2) - g(-3) = 2 - (-58) = 60$

In the preceding problems we evaluated a specified function. Sometimes, as was the case in Getting Started, we must *find* the function, as shown next.

EXAMPLE 5 Finding Functional Relationships from Ordered Pairs

Consider the ordered pairs (2, 6), (3, 9), (1.2, 3.6), and $\left(\frac{2}{5}, \frac{6}{5}\right)$. There is a linear functional relationship $y = f(x)$ between the numbers in each pair. Find $f(x)$ and use it to fill in the missing numbers in the pairs (_____, 12), (_____, 3.3), and (5, _____).

Solution

The given pairs are of the form (x, y). A close examination reveals that each of the y's in the pairs is 3 times the corresponding x; that is, $y = 3x$, or $f(x) = 3x$. Now, in each of the ordered pairs (____, 12), (____, 3.3), and (5, ____), the y value must be 3 times the x value. Thus,

$$(\underline{\quad\quad}, 12) = (4, 12)$$
$$(\underline{\quad\quad}, 3.3) = (1.1, 3.3)$$
$$(5, \underline{\quad\quad}) = (5, 15)$$

B Applications of Functions

In recent years, aerobic exercises such as jogging, swimming, bicycling, and roller blading have been taken up by millions of Americans. To see if you are exercising too hard (or not hard enough), you should stop from time to time and take your pulse to determine your heart rate. The idea is to keep your rate within a range known as the **target zone,** which is determined by your age. The next example explains how to find the **lower limit** of your target zone by using a function.

© Alexey Fursov/Shutterstock.com

In-line skaters benefit from a low-impact, highly aerobic workout.

EXAMPLE 6 Finding Heartbeats per Minute

The lower limit L (heartbeats per minute) of your target zone is a *function* of your age a (in years) and is given by

$$L(a) = -\tfrac{2}{3}a + 150$$

Find the value of L for people who are

(a) 30 years old. **(b)** 45 years old.

(c) What age a corresponds to a lower limit $L(a)$ of 112?

Solution

(a) We need to find $L(30)$, and because

$$\begin{aligned} L(a) &= -\tfrac{2}{3}a + 150 \\ L(30) &= -\tfrac{2}{3}(30) + 150 \\ &= -20 + 150 = 130 \end{aligned}$$

This result means that a 30-year-old person should try to attain at least 130 heartbeats per minute while exercising.

(b) Here, we want to find $L(45)$. Proceeding as before, we obtain

$$\begin{aligned} L(45) &= -\tfrac{2}{3}(45) + 150 \\ &= -30 + 150 = 120 \end{aligned}$$

(c) If $L(a) = 112$, we have

$$\begin{aligned} -\tfrac{2}{3}a + 150 &= 112 \\ -2a + 450 &= 336 && \text{Multiply by 3.} \\ -2a &= -114 && \text{Subtract 450.} \\ a &= 57 && \text{Divide by } -2. \end{aligned}$$

Thus, if you are 57 years old, your lower limit is 112.

(Find the value of L for your own age.)

C Graphing Relations and Functions

We shall now study a method for drawing pictures of relations and functions. Figure 7.1 shows two number lines drawn perpendicular to each other. The horizontal line is labeled x and is called the ***x* axis.** The vertical line is labeled y and is called the ***y* axis.** The intersection of the two axes is the **origin.** We mark a number scale with the 0 point at the origin on each of the axes. The four regions into which the plane is divided by these axes are called **quadrants** and are numbered I, II, III, and IV, as shown in Figure 7.1. This diagram forms a **Cartesian coordinate system** (named after René Descartes). We can make pictures of relations on such a coordinate system.

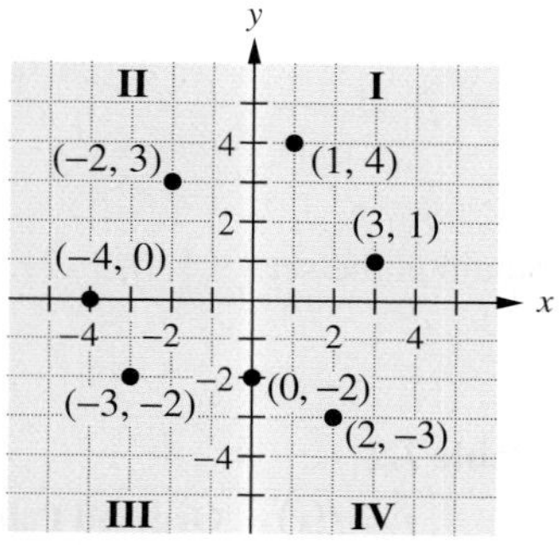

FIGURE 7.1 Cartesian coordinate system.

Figure 7.1 shows the usual way in which the positive directions along the axes are chosen. On the x axis, to the right of the origin is positive and to the left is negative. On the y axis, up from the origin is positive and down is negative. In order to locate a point (x, y), we move x units horizontally along the x axis and then y units vertically. For instance, to locate $(-2, 3)$, we move 2 units horizontally in the negative direction (left) along the x axis and then 3 units up, parallel to the y axis. Several points are plotted in Figure 7.1.

The Cartesian coordinate system furnishes us with a one-to-one correspondence between the points in the plane and the set of all ordered pairs of numbers; that is, corresponding to a given ordered pair there is exactly one point, and corresponding to a given point there is exactly one ordered pair. The **graph** of a relation is the set of points corresponding to the ordered pairs of the relation.

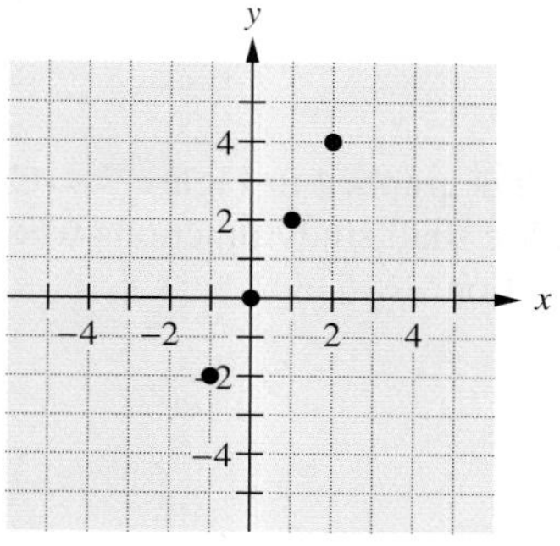

FIGURE 7.2

EXAMPLE 7 Graphing Relations

Graph the following relations:

(a) $R = \{(x, y) \mid y = 2x, x \text{ an integer between } -1 \text{ and } 2\text{, inclusive}\}$

(b) $T = \{(x, y) \mid y^2 = x, y \text{ an integer between } -3 \text{ and } 3\text{, inclusive}\}$

Solution

(a) The domain of R is $\{-1, 0, 1, 2\}$. By using the rule of R, $y = 2x$, we can find the ordered pairs $(-1, -2)$, $(0, 0)$, $(1, 2)$, and $(2, 4)$ that belong to R. Note that since $y = 2x$, the y coordinate is always *twice* the x coordinate. The graph of the relation is shown in Figure 7.2.

(b) We are given the range $\{y \mid y \text{ an integer between } -3 \text{ and } 3\text{, inclusive}\}$, and by squaring each of these integers, we find the domain, $\{0, 1, 4, 9\}$. The set of pairs $\{(0, 0), (1, 1), (1, -1), (4, 2), (4, -2), (9, 3), (9, -3)\}$ is thus the relation T. The graph of the relation consists of the seven dots shown in Figure 7.3. If the domain of this relation had been all nonnegative real numbers $(x \geq 0)$, the graph would have been a curve called a **parabola** (shown dashed in Figure 7.3).

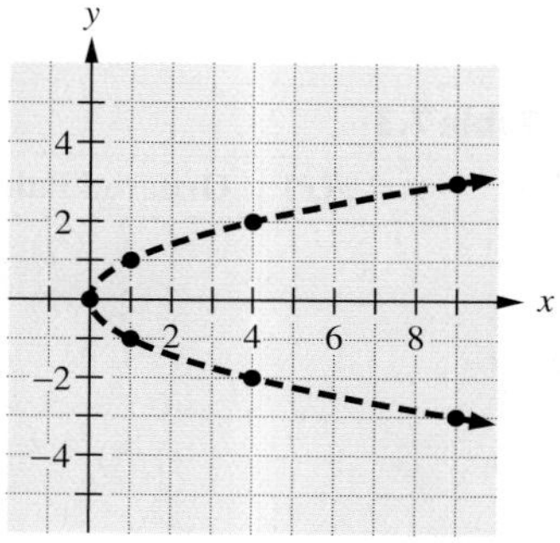

FIGURE 7.3

Since a function is simply a special kind of relation, a function can also be graphed on a Cartesian coordinate system. It is customary to represent the x values along the horizontal axis and the $f(x)$, or y, values along the vertical axis and graph the resulting ordered pairs (x, y).

Because a function has just one value for each value of x in the domain, the graph of the function cannot be cut in more than one point by any vertical line. Thus, we have a simple **vertical line test** for a function.

Vertical Line Test

If a vertical line can be drawn so that it intersects the graph of a relation at more than one point, then the relation is *not* a function.

If the graph of a relation is known, we can tell by inspection whether the relation is a function. For example, the parabola in Figure 7.3 is the graph of a relation, but that relation is *not* a function because any vertical line to the right of the y axis cuts the graph in two points. On the other hand, if we had defined the range of the relation so that its graph were only the lower (or only the upper) portion of the parabola, then the relation would be a function.

EXAMPLE 8 Graphing Functions

Graph the function f defined by $f(x) = 2 - 3x$ if the domain is the set $\{-1, 0, 1, 2\}$.

Solution

We calculate the values of the function using the rule $f(x) = 2 - 3x$ to obtain the values in Table 7.2. Figure 7.4 shows the graph.

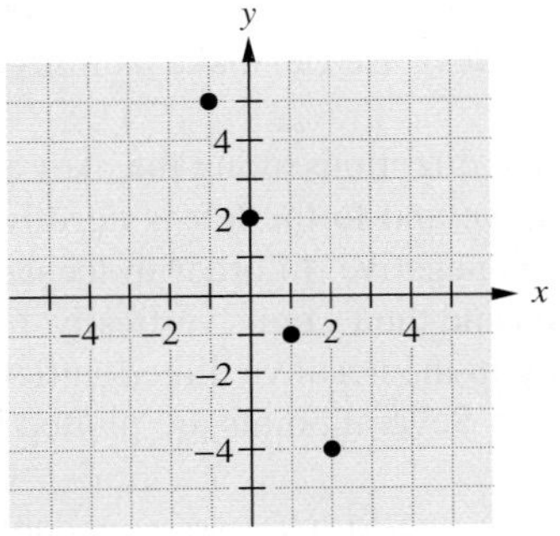

FIGURE 7.4

Table 7.2

x	$y = f(x)$	Ordered Pair
-1	5	$(-1, 5)$
0	2	$(0, 2)$
1	-1	$(1, -1)$
2	-4	$(2, -4)$

There is something remarkable about the set of points graphed in Figure 7.4. Can you see what it is? The points all lie on a straight line! We shall study functions whose graphs are straight lines (linear functions) in the next section.

EXAMPLE 9 Graphing Functions

Graph the function g defined by $g(x) = 2 - x^2$ if the domain is the set of real numbers.

Solution

The rule $g(x) = 2 - x^2$ tells us that to find the range value corresponding to an x value, we must square the x value and subtract the result from 2. Using this procedure for integral values of x between -3 and 3, inclusive, we obtain the values in Table 7.3. We then graph the ordered pairs and join them with a smooth curve, as shown in Figure 7.5. Notice that the graph is a parabola, as in Example 7.

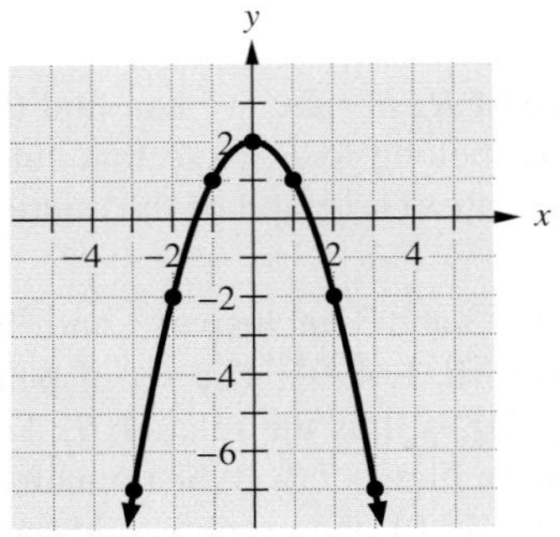

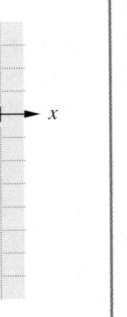

FIGURE 7.5

Table 7.3

x	$y = g(x)$	Ordered Pair
-3	-7	$(-3, -7)$
-2	-2	$(-2, -2)$
-1	1	$(-1, 1)$
0	2	$(0, 2)$
1	1	$(1, 1)$
2	-2	$(2, -2)$
3	-7	$(3, -7)$

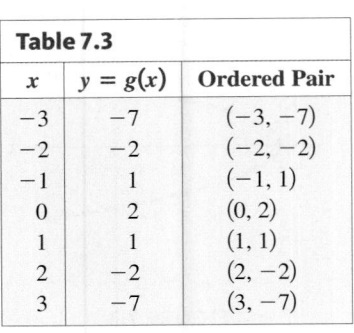

D Applications of Graphs

Table 7.4

Letters	
Weight Not Over ≤	**Price**
1 ounce	\$0.45
2 ounces	\$0.65
3 ounces	\$0.85
3.5 ounces	\$1.05

EXAMPLE 10 Graphing First-class Postage

First-class postage for postcards and letters weighing up to 3.5 ounces are as shown in Table 7.4. Find the cost of mailing a letter weighing:

(a) Less than or equal to 1 ounce. **(b)** Less than or equal to 2 ounces.

(c) Less than or equal to 3 ounces. **(d)** Less than or equal to 3.5 ounces.

(e) Draw a graph showing the prices in parts (a), (b), (c) and (d).

Solution

Make a table of values (Table 7.5), as in Examples 8 and 9. Table 7.5 gives the answers for parts (a), (b), (c), and (d).

(e) The graph is shown in Figure 7.6. The open circles in the line segments indicate that the left-hand endpoints of the line segments are not included in the graph.

The solid dots mean that the right-hand endpoints are included. We used the Postage Price Calculator at http://postcalc.usps.gov to verify these values.

Table 7.5

	Weight w	Cost
(a)	$0 < w \le 1$	\$0.45
(b)	$1 < w \le 2$	\$0.65
(c)	$2 < w \le 3$	\$0.85
(d)	$3 < w \le 3.5$	\$1.05

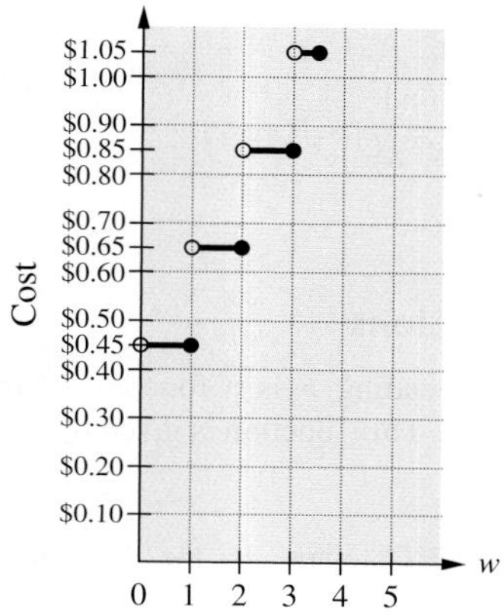

FIGURE 7.6

EXAMPLE 11 Finding Domain and Range for Social Networking Sites

Who is more likely to use social networking sites, males or females? As you can see in the graph, it actually depends on what year you are referring to. During 2008 and after more females used social networking sites. Do you see why?

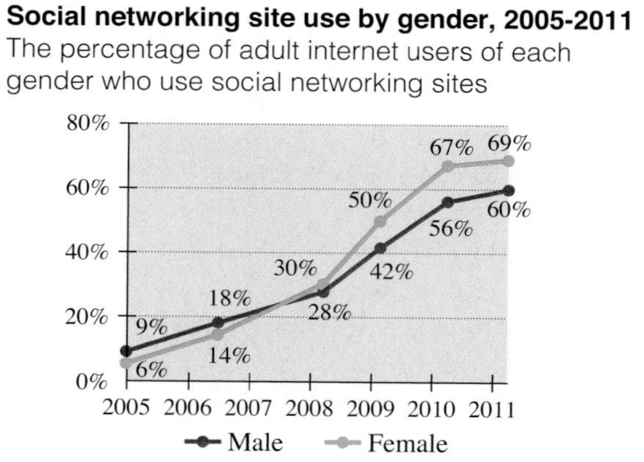

Source: Copyright © 2012 Pew Internet & American Life Project. http://www.pewinternet.org/~/media/Files/Reports/2011/PIP-SNS-Update-2011.pdf

FIGURE 7.7 Social Networking site use by gender.

Referring to Figure 7.7,

(a) what is the domain for both graphs?

(b) what is the range for the percentage of female users?

(c) what is the *exact* year in which the percentage of female users equaled the percentage of male users?

Solution

(a) The domain is the set of all possible x values for the years {2005, 2006, 2007, 2008, 2009, 2010, 2011}

(b) The range for the percentage of female users is consists of the set of all possible y values for the green line, that is, {6%, 14%, 28%, 50%, 67%, 69%}

(c) In 2008, the year in which the lines intersect.

7.1 EXERCISES

A Relations and Functions

In problems 1–14, find the domain and the range of each relation. (Hint: Remember that you cannot divide by 0 or take the square root of a negative number.)

1. $\{(1, 2), (2, 3), (3, 4)\}$
2. $\{(3, 1), (2, 1), (1, 1)\}$
3. $\{(1, 1), (2, 2), (3, 3)\}$
4. $\{(4, 1), (5, 2), (6, 1)\}$
5. $\{(x, y) \mid y = 3x\}$
6. $\{(x, y) \mid y = 2x + 1\}$
7. $\{(x, y) \mid y = x + 1\}$
8. $\{(x, y) \mid y = 1 - 2x\}$
9. $\{(x, y) \mid y = x^2\}$
10. $\{(x, y) \mid y = 2 + x^2\}$
11. $\{(x, y) \mid y^2 = x\}$
12. $\{(x, y) \mid x = 1 + y^2\}$
13. $\left\{(x, y) \mid y = \dfrac{1}{x}\right\}$
14. $\left\{(x, y) \mid y = \dfrac{1}{x - 2}\right\}$

In problems 15–22, decide whether each relation is a function. State the reason for your answer in each case.

15. $\{(x, y) \mid y = 5x + 6\}$
16. $\{(x, y) \mid y = 3 - 2x\}$
17. $\{(x, y) \mid x = y^2\}$
18. $\{(x, y) \mid x + 1 = y^2\}$
19. $\{(x, y) \mid y = \sqrt{x}, x \geq 0\}$
20. $\{(x, y) \mid x = \sqrt{y}, y \geq 0\}$
21. $\{(x, y) \mid x = y^3\}$
22. $\{(x, y) \mid y = x^3\}$
23. A function f is defined by $f(x) = 3x + 1$. Find
 a. $f(0)$. b. $f(2)$. c. $f(-2)$.
24. A function g is defined by $g(x) = -2x + 1$. Find
 a. $g(0)$. b. $g(1)$. c. $g(-1)$.
25. A function F is defined by $F(x) = \sqrt{x - 1}$. Find
 a. $F(1)$. b. $F(5)$. c. $F(26)$.
26. A function G is defined by $G(x) = x^2 + 2x - 1$. Find
 a. $G(0)$. b. $G(2)$. c. $G(-2)$.
27. A function f is defined by $f(x) = 3x + 1$. Find
 a. $f(x + h)$. b. $f(x + h) - f(x)$.
 c. $\dfrac{f(x + h) - f(x)}{h}$, $h \neq 0$.
28. Given are the ordered pairs $(2, 1)$, $(6, 3)$, $(9, 4.5)$, and $(1.6, 0.8)$. There is a simple functional relationship, $y = f(x)$, between the numbers in each pair. What is $f(x)$? Use this to fill in the missing numbers in the pairs (____, 7.5), (____, 2.4), and (____, $\frac{1}{7}$).
29. Given are the ordered pairs $(\frac{1}{2}, \frac{1}{4})$, $(1.2, 1.44)$, $(5, 25)$, and $(7, 49)$. There is a simple functional relationship, $y = g(x)$, between the numbers in each pair. What is $g(x)$? Use this to fill in the missing numbers in the pairs ($\frac{1}{4}$, ____), (2.1, ____), and (____, 64).
30. Given that $f(x) = x^3 - x^2 + 2x$, find
 a. $f(-1)$. b. $f(-3)$. c. $f(2)$.
31. If $g(x) = 2x^3 + x^2 - 3x + 1$, find
 a. $g(0)$. b. $g(-2)$. c. $g(2)$.

B Applications of Functions

32. The Fahrenheit temperature reading F is a function of the Celsius temperature reading C. This function is given by

$$F(C) = \tfrac{9}{5}C + 32$$

 a. If the temperature is 15°C, what is the Fahrenheit temperature?
 b. Water boils at 100°C. What is the corresponding Fahrenheit temperature?
 c. The freezing point of water is 0°C or 32°F. How many Fahrenheit degrees below freezing is a temperature of −10°C?
 d. The lowest temperature attainable is −273°C; this is the zero point on the absolute temperature scale. What is the corresponding Fahrenheit temperature?
33. Refer to Example 6. The *upper limit* U of your target zone when exercising is also a function of your age a (in years) and is given by

$$U(a) = -a + 190$$

 Find the highest and safest heart rate for people who are
 a. 50 years old. b. 60 years old.
34. Refer to Example 6 and problem 33. The target zone for a person a years old consists of all the heart rates between $L(a)$ and $U(a)$, inclusive. Thus, if a person's heart rate is R, that person's target zone is described by $L(a) \leq R \leq U(a)$. Find the target zone for people who are
 a. 30 years old. b. 45 years old.
35. The ideal weight w (in pounds) of a man is a function of his height h (in inches). This function is defined by

$$w(h) = 5h - 190$$

 a. What should the weight be for a man 70 in. tall?
 b. What should the height be for a man who weighs 200 lb?
36. The cost C in dollars of renting a car for 1 day is a function of the number m of miles traveled. For a car renting for \$20 per day and \$.20 per mile, this function is given by

$$C(m) = 0.20m + 20$$

a. Find the cost of renting a car for 1 day and driving 290 mi.

b. If an executive paid \$60.60 after renting a car for 1 day, how many miles did she drive?

37. The pressure P (in pounds per square foot) at a depth d ft below the surface of the ocean is a function of the depth. This function is given by

$$P(d) = 63.9d$$

Find the pressure on a submarine at a depth of

a. 10 ft. b. 100 ft.

38. If a ball is dropped from a point above the surface of the Earth, the distance s (in meters) that the ball falls in t sec is a function of t. This function is given by

$$s(t) = 4.9t^2$$

Find the distance that the ball falls in

a. 2 sec. b. 5 sec.

39. The function $S(t) = \frac{1}{2}gt^2$ gives the distance that an object falls from rest in t sec. If S is measured in feet, then the gravitational constant g is approximately 32 ft/sec^2. Find the distance that the object falls in

a. 3 sec. b. 5 sec.

40. An experiment, carefully carried out, showed that a ball dropped from rest fell 64.4 ft in 2 sec. What is a more accurate value of g than that given in problem 39?

C Graphing Relations and Functions

In problems 41–50, graph each relation.

41. $\{(x, y) \mid y = x, x$ an integer between -1 and 4, inclusive$\}$
42. $\{(x, y) \mid y = -x, x$ an integer between -1 and 4, inclusive$\}$
43. $\{(x, y) \mid y = 2x + 1, x$ an integer between 0 and 5, inclusive$\}$
44. $\{(x, y) \mid x + 2y = 3, x$ an odd integer between 0 and 10$\}$
45. $\{(x, y) \mid 2x - y = 4, x$ an integer between -2 and 2, inclusive$\}$
46. $\{(x, y) \mid y = x^2, x$ an integer between -3 and 3, inclusive$\}$
47. $\{(x, y) \mid y = \sqrt{x}, x = 0, 1, 4, 9, 16, 25,$ or $36\}$
48. $\{(x, y) \mid x = \sqrt{y}, x$ an integer between 0 and 3, inclusive$\}$
49. $\{(x, y) \mid x + y < 5, x, y$ nonnegative integers$\}$
50. $\{(x, y) \mid y > x, x$ and y positive integers less than 4$\}$

In problems 51–54, graph the given function for each domain (replacement set for x).

51. $f(x) = x + 1, x$ an integer between -3 and 3, inclusive
52. $f(x) = 3x - 1, x$ an integer between -1 and 3, inclusive
53. $g(x) = x^2 + 1, x$ an integer between -3 and 3, inclusive
54. $h(x) = -x^2, x$ an integer between -3 and 3, inclusive

D Applications of Graphs

55. Anthropologists can determine a person's height in life by using the person's skeletal remains as a clue. For example, the height (in centimeters) of a man with a humerus bone of length x cm can be obtained by multiplying 2.89 by x and adding 70.64 to the result.

a. Find a function $h(x)$ that gives the height of a man whose humerus bone is x cm long.

b. Use your function h from part (**a**) to predict the height of a man whose humerus bone is 34 cm long.

56. A plumber charges \$25 per hour plus \$30 for the service call. If $c(h)$ is the function representing the total charges, and h is the number of hours worked, find the following:

a. $c(h)$

b. The total charges when the plumber works for 2, 3, or 4 hours

c. Graph the points obtained in part (b).

57. What type of data plan do you use with your smartphone? Verizon has announced a pay per use data plan with the data allowances and monthly access fees shown.

Monthly Data Allowance	Monthly Access Fee
Pay per Use	\$0
75 MB-0.1 GB	\$10
2 GB	\$30
5 GB	\$50
10 GB	\$80

a. Make a graph of the monthly fees based in the given allowance. Is the graph a step function?

b. What is the access fee if you use 5 GB?

c. Can you determine the monthly access fee from the table if you use 8 GB?

d. If you pay \$10 for GB or fraction thereof after your monthly allowance, what is the access fee for 8 GB? What about for 8.6 GB?

The worst ecological disaster in U.S. history began on April 20, 2010, and was caused by an explosion in the oil rig Deepwater Horizon, *which resulted in the deaths of 11 people and triggered a massive oil spill into the Gulf of Mexico. Estimates of the exact amount of the oil spilled vary based on the source, but it is clearly a* **function** *of the number of days n it lasted and the leak rate of the oil, estimated by the United States Geological Service (USGS) to be 504,000 gallons each day! The function u that estimates the amount of oil spilled in n days can be defined as $u(n) = 504{,}000n$ gallons/day.*

Source: http://www.flickr.com/photos/roughneckcity/4583551442.

To find out how much oil spilled the first month (30 days), let $n = 30$:

$$u(30) = 504{,}000(30) = 15{,}120{,}000 \text{ gallons}$$

58. a. Using the function $u(n) = 504{,}000n$ estimate how many gallons were spilled during the first 100 days.

b. Outside estimates indicate that the leak may have been 1.05 million gallons each day! Define a function o that will estimate the amount of oil spilled in n days using the 1.05 million gallons a day estimate.

c. Use the function in part (b) to estimate how many gallons of oil were spilled in 60 days.

59. a. A British Petroleum (BP) worst-case scenario uses the function $b(n) = 2.520n$ million gallons a day to estimate the leak. Using this estimate, how many gallons were spilled the first 100 days?

b. Define a function e that will estimate the amount of oil spilled in n days using the expert's worst case of 4.2 million gallons a day estimate.

c. Using the function in part (b) estimate how many gallons of oil were spilled in 60 days.

60. ***Oil recovery*** A containment cap installed by BP recovered about 441,000 gallons of oil and gas per day and transported them to the *Discoverer Enterprise* drill ship on the surface.

a. Define a function r that will estimate the amount of oil that can be recovered in n days using the 441,000 gallons a day estimate.

b. Use the function in part (a) to estimate how many gallons of oil were recovered in 60 days.

61. ***More oil recovery*** According to BP's worst-case scenario, the amount of oil *spilled in n* days can be estimated by the function $b(n) = 2.520n$ million gallons, while the function $r(n) = 441{,}000n$ gallons represents the amount of oil that can be *recovered* in n days.

a. The function $a(n) = b(n) - r(n)$ represents the *actual* amount of oil that spilled into the Gulf daily. Find $a(n)$.

b. How many gallons were actually spilled into the Gulf over a 60-day period?

IN OTHER WORDS

62. Consider the function $f(x) = \dfrac{1}{x^2 - 1}$. What numbers are excluded from the domain and why?

63. Consider the function $g(x) = \sqrt{x - 1}$. What numbers are excluded from the domain and why?

64. Consider the function $h(x) = \dfrac{x}{\sqrt{x + 1}}$. What numbers are excluded from the domain and why?

65. What is the graph of a function?

66. Is every relation a function? Explain why or why not.

67. Is every function a relation? Explain why or why not.

68. Why does the vertical line test work?

USING YOUR KNOWLEDGE

69. Many interesting functions can be defined using the ideas of this section. Let's return to the cricket from Getting Started 6.1 whose chirping frequency is a function of the temperature. The following table shows the number of chirps per minute and the temperature in degrees Fahrenheit. Find a function that relates the number c of chirps per minute and the temperature x.

Temperature (°F)	Chirps per Minute
40	0
41	4
42	8
43	12
44	16

70. The function relating the number of chirps per minute of the cricket and the temperature is given by $f(x) = 4(x - 40)$. If the temperature is 80°F, how many chirps per minute will you hear from your friendly house cricket?

71. An interesting function in physics was discovered by the Italian scientist Galileo Galilei. This function relates the distance an object (dropped from a given height) travels and the time elapsed. The following table shows the time (in seconds) and the distance (in feet) traveled by a rock dropped from a tall building. Find the relationship between the number t of seconds elapsed and the distance $f(t)$ traveled.

Time Elapsed (sec)	Distance (ft)
1	$16 = 16 \times 1$
2	$64 = 16 \times 4$
3	$144 = 16 \times 9$
4	$256 = 16 \times 16$
5	$400 = 16 \times 25$
6	$576 = 16 \times 36$

72. Assume that a rock took 10 sec to reach the ground when dropped from a helicopter. Using the results of problem 71, find the height of the helicopter.

DISCOVERY

Have you ever seen a pendulum clock? Galileo Galilei also made various discoveries about swinging weights, and these discoveries led to the invention of the pendulum clock. Galileo discovered that there was a relationship between the time of the swing of a pendulum and its length. The following table shows corresponding values of these two quantities. (The unit length is about 25 cm.)

Time of Swing $f(x)$	Length of Pendulum (x)
1 sec	1 unit
2 sec	4 units
3 sec	9 units
4 sec	16 units
5 sec	25 units

73. Judging from the table, what is the rule connecting the time $f(x)$ of the swing and the length x of the pendulum?

74. From the pattern given in the table, find the length of a pendulum that takes 6 sec for a swing.

75. Find the length of a pendulum that takes 100 sec for a swing.

76. The University of South Florida has a Foucault pendulum in its physics building. This pendulum takes 7 sec for a swing. Find the length of the pendulum.

This Foucault pendulum is on display in the visitors' entrance lobby of the United Nations General Assembly building in New York.

COLLABORATIVE LEARNING

Many decisions in business and other areas are made on the basis of information provided in the form of a graph. For example, suppose you have a restaurant and make a graph of the on-premise and off-premise meals purchased at the restaurant for a given week or get a graph from the Web detailing the number of on-premise and off-premise meals sold at a restaurant. Form two teams and answer the following questions within your team, and then discuss them with the entire group.

1. On the basis of the graph, would you expand dining facilities or kitchen facilities?
2. How can you predict the number of annual on-premise and off-premise meals per person in the year 2013? Can you use the same technique to predict the number for any year?
3. Select a local restaurant with both take-out and on-premise facilities. One team makes a graph of the number of persons purchasing take-out, and the other team makes a graph of the number of persons purchasing on-premise meals during a 3-hour period. Label your x axis 1, 2, and 3 and your y axis with the number of meals purchased. Are the graphs similar? Would the graphs differ if a different 3-hour period were chosen? Explain. (If you have enough students to form several teams, the teams can select different 3-hour periods and see if there is a difference between graphs.)
4. On the basis of your graphs, can you predict how many take-out and how many on-premise meals are sold annually at this particular restaurant? What about the number of take-out and on-premise meals per person? If you have a prediction, is it close to the one given in your original graph? Why or why not?

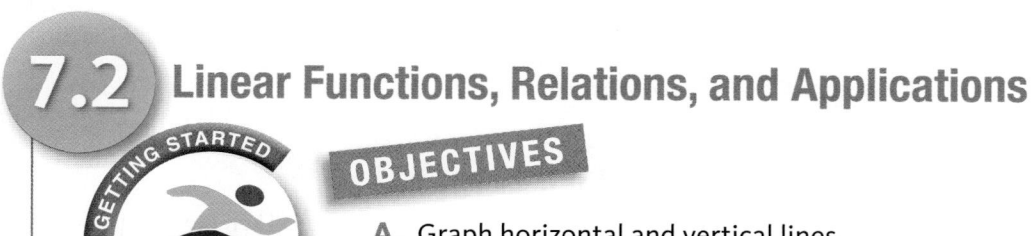

7.2 Linear Functions, Relations, and Applications

GETTING STARTED

OBJECTIVES

A. Graph horizontal and vertical lines.
B. Graph linear functions using intercepts.
C. Use the distance formula to find the distance between two points.
D. Solve applications involving graphs.

Source: www.lyon.edu.

FITNESS AND GRAPHING FUNCTIONS

Have you been to a fitness center lately? Some of them display a graph showing your desirable heart rate **target zone** based on your age. The idea is to elevate your heart rate so that it is within a prescribed range. If your heart races during exercise, the consequences may be fatal. Thus, it is recommended that your heart rate (pulse) not exceed 190 beats per minute regardless of age. For a 70 year old, the recommended upper limit is 120 beats per minute. This information is shown in Table 7.6.

Table 7.6

Age	Pulse
0	190
70	120

Now, suppose $U(a)$ is the upper limit in heartbeats per minute for a person whose age is a; can you find $U(a)$? Assume that $U(a)$ is linear; it must be defined by an equation of the form $U(a) = ma + b$. Now find m and b. According to Table 7.6, when $a = 0$, $U(a) = 190$. Thus,

$$U(0) = m \cdot 0 + b = 190$$

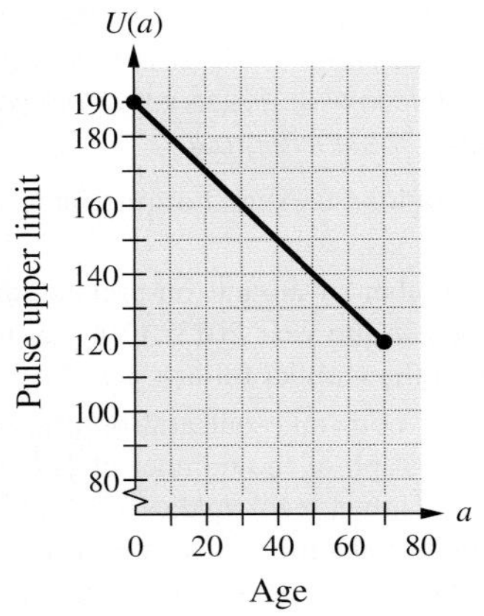

FIGURE 7.8

and

$$b = 190$$

Also from Table 7.6,

$$U(70) = 120$$

Thus, $U(70) = m \cdot 70 + 190 = 120$

Subtracting 190, $70m = -70$

Solving for m, $m = -1$

Since $m = -1$ and $b = 190$, $U(a) = -1a + 190$; that is, $U(a) = -a + 190$. To graph $U(a)$ between 10 and 70, let $a = 10$; then $U(10) = -10 + 190 = 180$. Graph (10, 180). The point (70, 120) is in Figure 7.8, so plot it and draw a straight line through (70, 120) and (10, 180). The result is the graph for $U(a)$. Note that all points on the graph are solutions of (satisfy) $U(a) = -a + 190$. Why do you think the domain is between 10 and 70?

In Section 7.7C, Example 6, you will also graph $L(a)$, the lower limit in heartbeats per minute. The region between the two graphs is the **target zone** for the heart rate while exercising. You will explore more problems like this one in problems 29–31 of Exercises 7.2.

A relation of the form

$$\{(x, y) \mid y = ax + b\}$$

where a and b are real numbers, always defines the function $f(x) = ax + b$. (Why?) A function of this special form is called a **linear function** because its graph is a straight line. All the points (x, y) on the graph of $y = ax + b$ are solutions of the equation $y = ax + b$. In this section you will learn how to draw the graph of a linear function.

A Vertical and Horizontal Lines

Let us look first at the case in which $a = 0$ in $y = ax + b$. Then the rule of the function is $y = b$ for *all real values of* x. Note that x is unrestricted (any real number) but for any value of x, $y = b$. This means that the graph consists of all points such as $(0, b)$, $(-1, b)$, $(\sqrt{2}, b)$, $(10.26, b)$, and so on. Thus, the graph is a straight line parallel to the x axis and b units from this axis. If $b > 0$, the line will be above the x axis, and if $b < 0$, the line will be below the x axis. (What if $b = 0$?) Figure 7.9 shows the graphs of $\{(x, y) \mid y = b\}$ for $b = -3$ and for $b = 2$.

A relation such as $\{(x, y) \mid x = c\}$, where c is a real number, is not a function because y can have any real value. For instance, if $R = \{(x, y) \mid x = 2\}$, then $(2, -1)$, $(2, 0)$, $(2, 1.75)$, and so on are all ordered pairs belonging to R. Because x has the fixed value 2, all these points are on the line parallel to and 2 units to the right of the y axis. In general, the equation $x = c$ (or the relation $\{(x, y) \mid x = c\}$) has for its graph a vertical line, that is, a line parallel to and c units from the y axis.

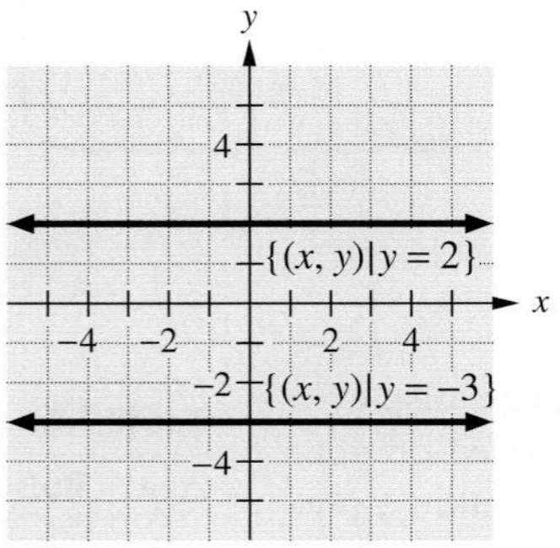

FIGURE 7.9

Horizontal and Vertical Lines

The graph of the function $\{(x, y) \mid y = b\}$ or, equivalently, of the equation $y = b$ is a **horizontal** line parallel to the x axis and b units from it.

The graph of the relation $\{(x, y) \mid x = c\}$ or, equivalently, of the equation $x = c$ is a **vertical** line parallel to the y axis and c units from it.

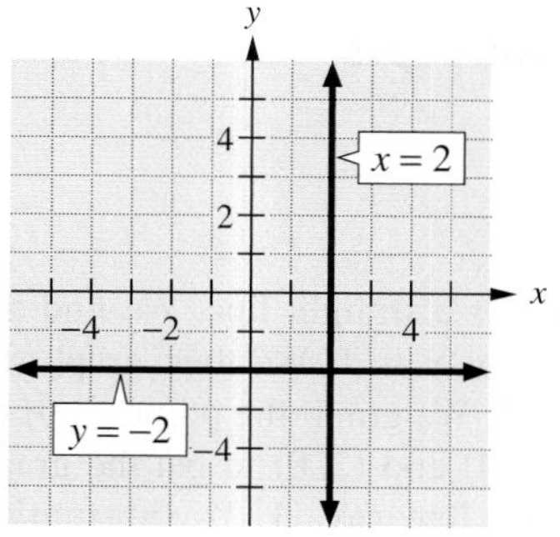

FIGURE 7.10

EXAMPLE 1 Graphing Horizontal and Vertical Lines

Graph

(a) $y = -2$. (b) $x = 2$.

Solution

(a) The graph of $y = -2$ is a horizontal line parallel to the x axis and two units below it. Note that for any x you choose, y is always -2. The graph is shown in Figure 7.10.

(b) The graph of $x = 2$ is a vertical line parallel to the y axis as shown in Figure 7.10.

B Graphs of Linear Functions and Equations

We will now examine the general procedure that can be used to draw the graph of a linear function in the form $f = \{(x, y) \mid y = ax + b\}$ or, equivalently, $f(x) = ax + b$.

PROBLEM-SOLVING

Graphing Linear Functions

① **Read** the problem.

Graph the function defined by $f(x) = 3x - 6$.

② **Select** the unknown. What are we looking for?

We want to draw the graph of $f(x) = 3x - 6$. To do this, we need to find ordered pairs (x, y) that satisfy the relation $f = \{(x, y) \mid y = 3x - 6\}$.

③ **Think** of a plan. Is the graph a straight line? If it is, we know that two points will determine the line.

The function is of the form $y = ax + b$, so its graph, consisting of the ordered pairs (x, y) satisfying the equation $y = ax + b$, is a straight line. To graph this function, we find two points on the line and draw the line through them. The result will be the graph of the function.

④ **Use** the preceding idea to carry out the plan. Find two points and then join them with a line. (Try to use points that are easy to graph.)

For ease of computation, we let $x = 0$, to obtain $y = 3 \cdot 0 - 6$, or $y = -6$. Thus, $(0, -6)$ is one of the points. For $y = 0$, we have $0 = 3x - 6$, or $6 = 3x$; that is, $x = 2$. This makes $(2, 0)$ another point on the line. Now we graph $(0, -6)$ and $(2, 0)$ as in Figure 7.11 and draw a line through them. The result is the graph of $f(x) = 3x - 6$.

⑤ **Verify** the answer. How can we do this?

Select a point on the line, say $(3, 3)$, and verify that it satisfies the equation $y = 3x - 6$. If $x = 3$ and $y = 3$, $3 = 3 \cdot 3 - 6$ is a true statement.

The x coordinate of the point where the line crosses the x axis is called the **x intercept** of the line. Similarly, the y coordinate of the point where the line crosses the y axis is called the **y intercept.** For $f(x) = 3x - 6$, the x intercept is 2 and the y intercept is -6. Note that, in general, we may say either "graph the function f, where $f(x) = ax + b$," or "graph the equation $y = ax + b$."

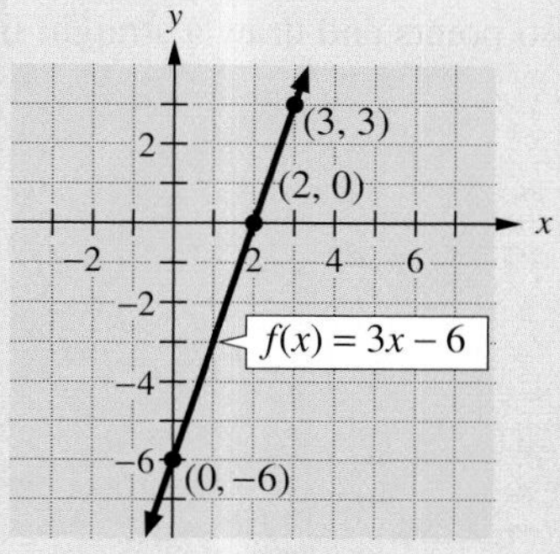

FIGURE 7.11

Try Example 2 Now

Cover the solution, write your own solution, and then check your work.

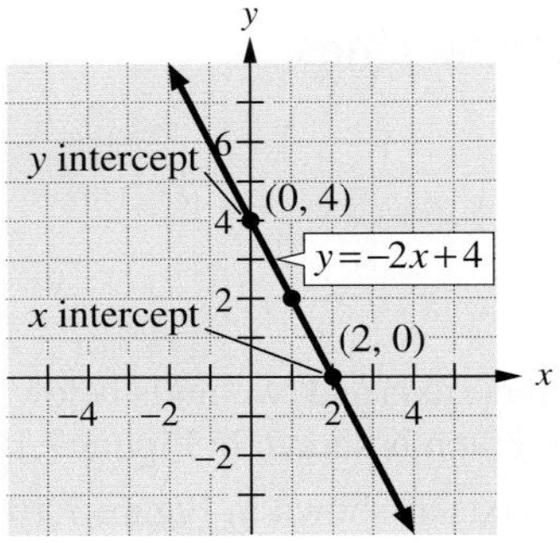

FIGURE 7.12

EXAMPLE 2 Graphing Equations Using Intercepts

Graph the equation $y = -2x + 4$ using the intercepts.

Solution

Since the equation is of the form $y = ax + b$, its graph is a straight line. We find the y intercept by letting $x = 0$ to obtain $y = -2 \cdot 0 + 4$, or $y = 4$. We then graph the point $(0, 4)$. For $y = 0$, we have $0 = -2x + 4$, or $x = 2$. We graph the point $(2, 0)$ as in Figure 7.12. We then draw a straight line through $(0, 4)$ and $(2, 0)$ to get the graph of $y = -2x + 4$. For verification, we select a point on the line, say, $(1, 2)$. Substituting $x = 1$ and $y = 2$ into $y = -2x + 4$, we have $2 = -2(1) + 4$, a true statement.

Now that we have graphed some particular straight lines, we will examine other relations whose graphs are straight lines. We can show that the relation described by $\{(x, y) \mid ax + by = c\}$, where a and b are not both 0, is always a linear relation. If $b \neq 0$, we can solve the equation $ax + by = c$ for y and obtain

$$by = -ax + c$$

$$y = -\frac{a}{b}x + \frac{c}{b}$$

Because a, b, and c are all real numbers, this equation is the rule for a linear function. If $b = 0$ in $ax + by = c$, then

$$ax = c \qquad \text{so that} \qquad x = +\frac{c}{a}$$

which is the rule for a linear relation (not a function) corresponding to a vertical line c/a units from the y axis. Because of these facts, the equation $ax + by = c$, with a and b not both 0, is called a **linear equation;** its graph is always a straight line, which can be drawn using our familiar intercept procedure, as shown next.

EXAMPLE 3 Graphing More Equations Using Intercepts

Graph the equation $2x + 3y = 6$.

Solution

Because the equation $2x + 3y = 6$ is a linear equation, we know that its graph is a straight line. Thus, any two points on the line will determine the line. For $x = 0$, we have $3y = 6$, or $y = 2$, so the point $(0, 2)$ is on the line. For $y = 0$, we get $x = 3$, so $(3, 0)$ is a second point on the line. We graph these two points and draw a straight line through them to get the graph shown in Figure 7.13.

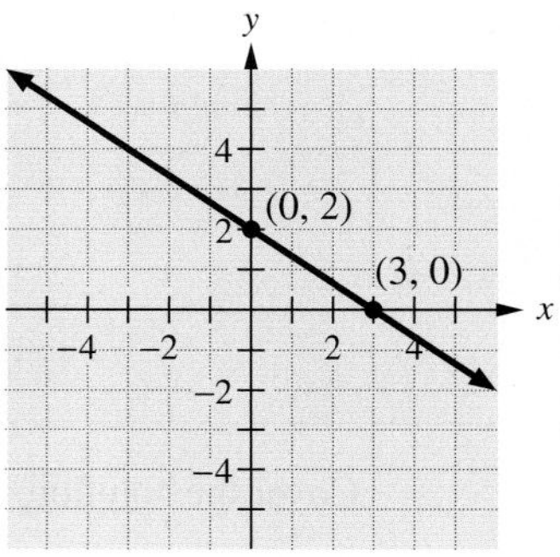

FIGURE 7.13

C Distance Between Two Points

In this section we have noted that the line $y = b$ is a line parallel to the x axis and b units from it (see Figure 7.9). Similarly, the line $x = a$ is a line parallel to the y axis and a units from it (see Example 1). It is not difficult to find the distance between two points on a horizontal or on a vertical straight line, that is, on a line $y = b$ or on a line $x = a$.

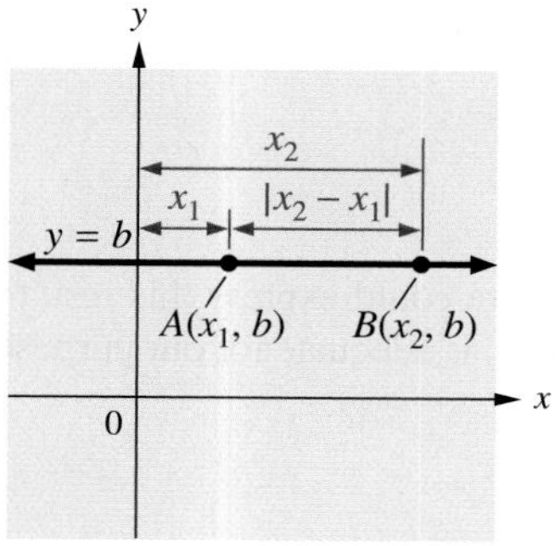

FIGURE 7.14

Suppose that we have two points—say, A and B—on the same horizontal line, the line $y = b$ in Figure 7.14. Then their coordinates are (x_1, b) and (x_2, b), as in Figure 7.14. Because x_1 and x_2 are the **directed distances** of the respective points from the y axis, the length of AB is $|x_2 - x_1|$. Denoting this length by $|AB|$, we have the formula

$$|AB| = |x_2 - x_1| \tag{1}$$

Similarly, if the two points C and D are on the same vertical line, their coordinates are (a, y_1) and (a, y_2), and the length of CD is

$$|CD| = |y_2 - y_1| \tag{2}$$

To obtain a formula for the distance between *any* two points, we use the *Pythagorean theorem.*

The Pythagorean Theorem

If a triangle is a right triangle (has one 90° angle), then the square of the hypotenuse c equals the sum of the squares of the other two sides a and b; that is,

$$a^2 + b^2 = c^2$$

(See Figure 7.15.)

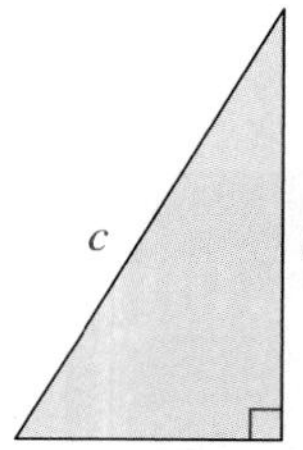

$a^2 + b^2 = c^2$

FIGURE 7.15

The Pythagorean theorem will be discussed in greater detail in Section 8.4.

In Figure 7.16, $A(x_1, y_1)$ and $B(x_2, y_2)$ represent two general points. The line BC is drawn parallel to the y axis and the line AC is drawn parallel to the x axis, so ABC is a right triangle with right angle at C. Because A and C are on the same horizontal line, they must have the same y coordinates. Likewise, B and C are on the same vertical line, so they have the same x coordinates. Thus, the coordinates of C must be (x_2, y_1). By the Pythagorean theorem, the length of AB is given by $|AB| = \sqrt{|AC|^2 + |BC|^2}$. By equations (1) and (2), $|AC| = |x_2 - x_1|$ and $|BC| = |y_2 - y_1|$. Thus, we have the following:

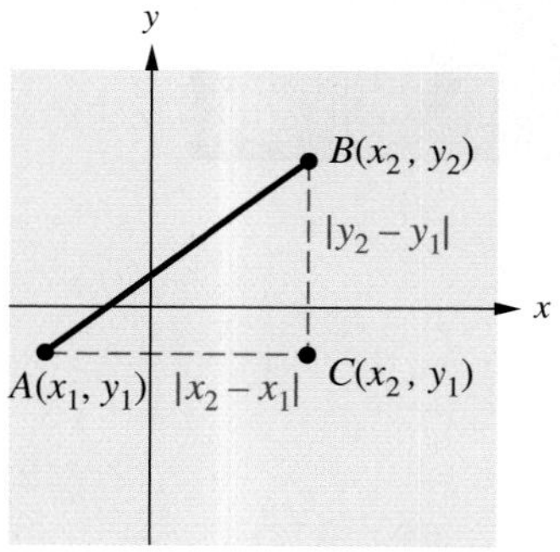

$|AB| = \sqrt{(x_2 - x_1)^2 + (y_2 - y_1)^2}$

FIGURE 7.16

The Distance Between Two Points

The distance between two points $A\ (x_1, y_1)$ and $B\ (x_2, y_2)$ is given by

$$|AB| = \sqrt{(x_2 - x_1)^2 + (y_2 - y_1)^2} \tag{3}$$

EXAMPLE 4 Finding the Distance Between Two Points

Find the distance between the points $A(2, -3)$ and $B(8, 5)$.

Solution

By equation (3),

$$|AB| = \sqrt{(8 - 2)^2 + [5 - (-3)]^2}$$
$$= \sqrt{6^2 + 8^2} = \sqrt{36 + 64} = \sqrt{100} = 10$$

The distance between A and B is 10 units.

EXAMPLE 5 Finding More Distances

Find the distance between the points $A(-1, -4)$ and $B(-3, 5)$.

Solution

As in the preceding example, we find

$$\begin{aligned}|AB| &= \sqrt{[-3-(-1)]^2 + [5-(-4)]^2}\\ &= \sqrt{(-2)^2 + 9^2} = \sqrt{4+81} = \sqrt{85}\end{aligned}$$

With the aid of a table of square roots (or a calculator), we could express this result in decimal form. However, the indicated root form, $\sqrt{85}$ units, is adequate for our purposes.

EXAMPLE 6 Distances and Hurricanes

One of the most destructive forces in nature is a hurricane. In the following grid, each unit represents 100 mi. At 3 P.M. the center of the hurricane was at $(2, -1)$. Hurricane-force winds extend 15 mi out from the center, and it is predicted that the center will be at $(1, -1)$ in 5 hours. Computer models indicate that after that, the hurricane will move directly NW toward Tampa at the same speed.

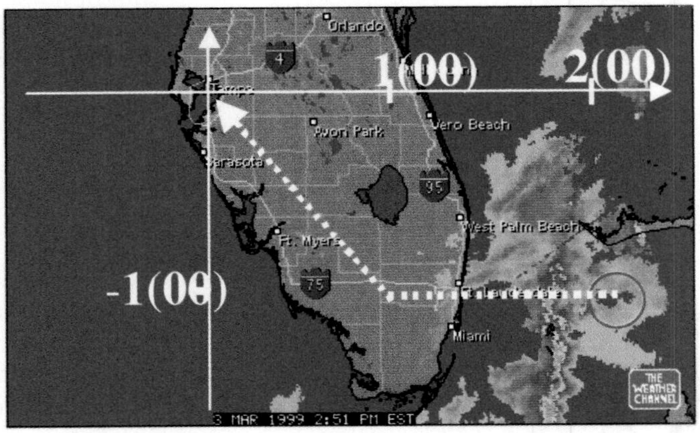

(a) How fast is the hurricane moving?

(b) How far is the hurricane from Tampa at 8 P.M.?

(c) Will Tampa feel hurricane force winds at 8 P.M.?

Solution

(a) The hurricane moved from $(2, -1)$ to $(1, -1)$, a distance of 100 mi (see the grid in the figure) in 5 hours. Thus, the hurricane is moving at 20 mph.

(b) At 8 P.M. the center of the hurricane is at $(1, -1)$, so we have to find the distance from $(1, -1)$ to $(0, 0)$. Let $(x_2, y_2) = (0, 0)$ and $(x_1, y_1) = (1, -1)$. Substituting in the distance formula, $d = \sqrt{(0-1)^2 + [0-(-1)]^2} = \sqrt{2}$. Since each unit represents 100 mi, the actual distance from Tampa is $100\sqrt{2} \approx 141$ mi.

(c) Yes. Theoretically at least, hurricane-force winds extend 150 mi from the center, and the hurricane center is approximately 141 mi from Tampa.

D Applications

In order to make sensible decisions in problem solving and in certain consumer problems, it is helpful to be able to make a quick sketch of a linear function. Such a situation is illustrated in the next example.

EXAMPLE 7 Comparing Cellular Costs

Suppose the cost of cellular telephone service from company A is \$200 for the telephone plus \$.25 per minute of air time (the time spent talking on the telephone). If m is the number of minutes of air time and $C_1(m)$ is the corresponding cost in dollars, then

$$C_1(m) = 200 + 0.25m$$

For company B the cost is \$100 for the telephone plus \$.50 per minute of air time. If $C_2(m)$ is the corresponding cost, then

$$C_2(m) = 100 + 0.50m$$

(a) Graph C_1 and C_2 on the same set of axes.

(b) When will the cost be the same for these two companies?

(c) If cost were the only consideration, from which company would you get the service if you are planning to have more than 400 minutes of air time per month?

Solution

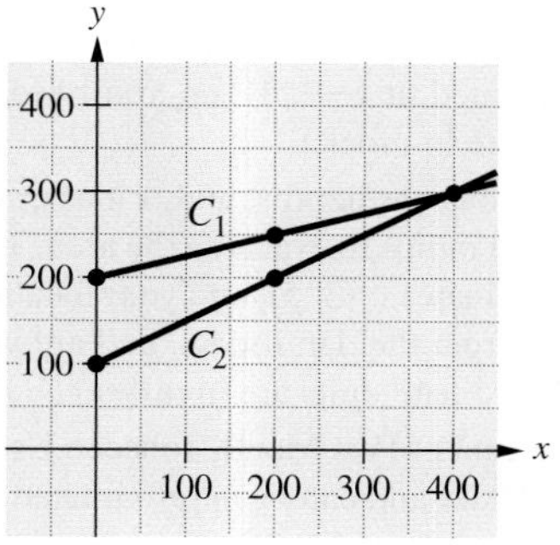

FIGURE 7.17

(a) Since C_1 and C_2 are both linear functions of m, their graphs are straight lines. For $m = 0$, $C_1(0) = 200$, so $(0, 200)$ is on the graph of C_1. For $m = 100$, $C_1(200) = 200 + 0.25(200) = 250$, so $(200, 250)$ is also on this graph. We draw a line through these two points as shown in Figure 7.17. Similarly, for $m = 0$, $C_2(0) = 100$, and for $m = 200$, $C_2(200) = 200$. Thus, the two points $(0, 100)$ and $(200, 200)$ are on the graph of C_2. Again, we draw a line through these two points as shown in Figure 7.17.

(b) Since both lines pass through the point $(400, 300)$, it is clear that the cost is the same for both companies when 400 minutes of air time are used.

(c) You can see from the graph that company A will cost less if you are planning to use more than 400 minutes of air time per month.

Note: Most companies give you a set number of free minutes before they charge for additional minutes. There are many plans available; check them and select the best one for your situation.

7.2 EXERCISES

A Vertical and Horizontal Lines

B Graphs of Linear Functions and Equations

1. In the table, the entries in the two columns have a common, simple linear relationship, $y = ax$. Find the missing entry.

x	3	2	$\frac{1}{2}$	
y	$2\frac{1}{4}$	$1\frac{1}{2}$	$\frac{3}{8}$	3

2. In the table, the entries in the two columns have a common, simple quadratic relationship, $y = ax^2$. Find the missing entry.

x	$\frac{1}{2}$	1	2	
y	$\frac{1}{2}$	2	8	50

In problems 3–18, graph each linear function or equation.

3. $f(x) = 3x + 6$
4. $f(x) = 2x + 5$
5. $f(x) = 3$
6. $f(x) = -2$
7. $x = -1$
8. $x = 4$
9. $f(x) = -x + 2$
10. $f(x) = -2x - 4$
11. $g(x) = -3x - 6$
12. $g(x) = -2x + 6$
13. $3x + 2y = 6$
14. $4x + 3y = 12$
15. $-2x + 3y = 6$
16. $-3x + 2y = 12$
17. $4x - 3y = 12$
18. $3x - 5y = 15$

C Distance Between Two Points

In problems 19–28, find the distance between the given points.

19. $(2, 4)$ and $(-1, 0)$
20. $(3, -2)$ and $(8, 10)$
21. $(-4, -5)$ and $(-1, 3)$
22. $(5, 7)$ and $(-2, 3)$
23. $(4, -8)$ and $(1, -1)$
24. $(-2, -2)$ and $(6, -4)$

25. (3, 0) and (3, −2)
26. (4, −1) and (6, −1)
27. (−2, 3) and (−2, 7)
28. (1, −5) and (8, −5)

D Applications

29. Elite Catering charges \$500 to plan a banquet plus \$25 per plate. Society Catering's charges are \$1000 for the planning and \$20 per plate. Let $E(x)$ and $S(x)$ represent the cost of a banquet for x persons catered by Elite and Society, respectively.
   a. Find $E(x)$ and $S(x)$.
   b. Graph $E(x)$ and $S(x)$ on the same set of axes.
   c. Find the number of persons for which the cost is the same with either company.

30. The costs (in dollars) of a repair call taking x hours or fraction thereof from companies A and B are, respectively,

$$C_1(x) = 20x + 30 \quad \text{and} \quad C_2(x) = 10x + 50$$

   a. Graph C_1 and C_2 on the same set of axes.
   b. For how many hours is the cost the same for either company?

31.

Monthly Data Allowance	Monthly Access Fee	Rate after Allowance
2 GB	\$30	
5 GB	\$50	\$10/1 GB

A Verizon subscriber opts for the 2GB data plan. If d is the data used (in GB's) and $m(d)$ is the Monthly Access Fee for using d GB's:
   a. Find $m(2)$ and $m(5)$.
   b. Find the cost $m(d)$ for $2 < d \leq 3$.
   c. Find the cost $m(d)$ for $3 < d \leq 4$.
   d. Find the cost $m(d)$ for $4 < d < 5$.
   e. Draw a graph of $m(d)$ for $2 < d < 5$.

There are companies that offer unlimited data usage; check your data use and get the most economic plan for your needs!

32.

Monthly Data Allowance	Monthly Access Fee	Rate after Allowance
2 GB	\$30	
5 GB	\$50	
10 GB	\$80	\$10/1 GB

Use the extended data plan chart to answer these questions:
   a. Find $m(10)$:
   b. Find the cost $m(d)$ for $5 < d \leq 6$.
   c. Find the cost $m(d)$ for $6 < d \leq 7$.
   d. Find the cost $m(d)$ for $7 < d \leq 8$.
   e. Find the cost $m(d)$ for $8 < d \leq 9$.
   f. Find the cost $m(d)$ for $9 < d < 10$.
   g. Draw a graph of $m(d)$ for $5 < d < 10$.

33. Does your area have an evacuation map? In the case of floods, for example, persons in low-lying areas are ordered to evacuate. Suppose an evacuation order is issued for all people living within a radius of 10 mi from an area with coordinates (2, −3). If your house is located at (−2, 3), do you need to evacuate? (Coordinate units are in miles.)

34. When a train carrying poisonous gas derails, authorities order all people living within a 5-mi radius to evacuate the area. The derailment location has coordinates (−3, 5), and your location is at (2, 7). How far are you from the derailment, and are you in the evacuation zone? (Coordinate units are in miles.)

35. The red graph shows the percent of Past Month Tobacco Users among Persons Aged 12 or Older and can be approximated by $P(t) = -0.3t + 30$, where t is the number of years after 2002. Find the percent of users:
   a. in 2002 and 2009 by using the graph.
   b. in 2002 and 2009 by using $P(t) = -0.3t + 30$.
   c. Use $P(t) = -0.3t + 30$ to predict the percent of Past Month Tobacco users aged 12 or older in 2012.
   d. Use $P(t) = -0.3t + 30$ to predict the year in which the percent of Past Month Tobacco Users among persons 12 or older will reach 24%.

Past month tobacco use among persons aged 12 or older: 2002-2009

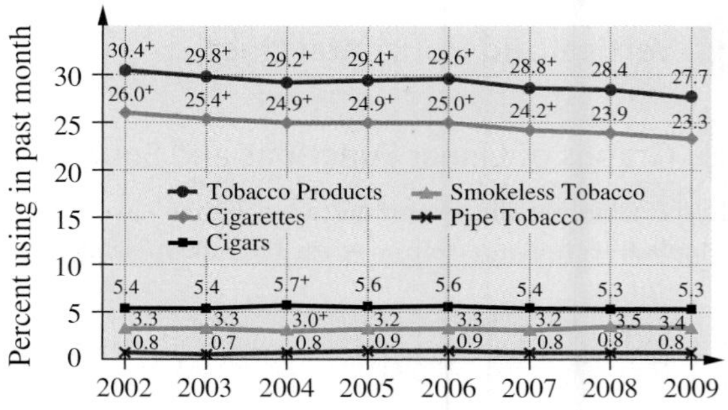

Source: http://oas.samhsa.gov/NSDUH/2k9NSDUH/2k9Results.htm#Ch4.

36. Do you send text messages with your cell phone? The graph shows that the percent of teens sending text messages increases with age. We can approximate the percent $P(a)$ by $P(a) = 7a - 63$, where a is the age of the person. Assuming that the trend continues,

a. use $P(a)$ to estimate the percentage of 18-year-olds who use text messaging.

b. use $P(a)$ to estimate the percentage of 19-year-olds who use text messaging.

c. According to this model, by what percent does the amount of text messages sent increase every year?

d. Based on the graph, what was the percent *increase* in text messages sent between 12- and 13-year-olds? Does your answer fit the pattern given by $P(a)$?

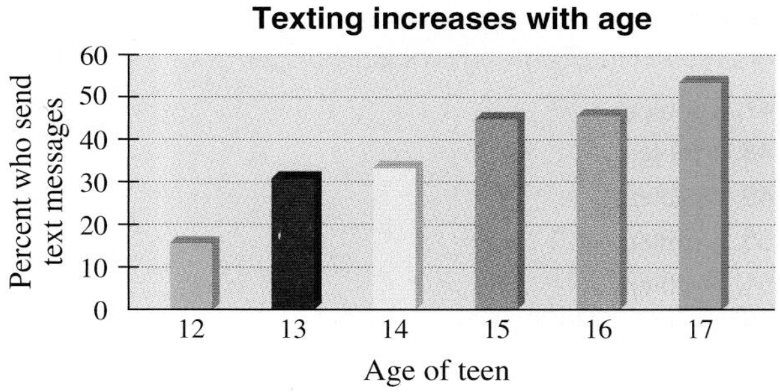

Source: Copyright © 2012 Pew Internet & American Life Project. http://www.pewinternet.org/~/media/Files/Reports/2005/PIP_Teens_Tech_July2005web.pdf.pdf.

37. The table shows the mean verbal and math SAT scores from 2006 to 2010.

Year	Verbal	Math
2006	497	518
2007	494	515
2008	494	515
2009	493	515
2010	492	516

Source: http://nces.ed.gov/programs/digest/d10/tables/dt10_151.asp.

a. Graph the points representing the data for both the verbal and the math portions.

b. Calculate the average verbal score V and the average math score M for 2006 to 2010.

c. Graph $y = V$ and $y = M$ in the same coordinate system. How well do $y = V$ and $y = M$ model the data you graphed?

d. Are $y = V$ and $y = M$ functions? How do you know?

38. The table shows the mean English and math ACT scores from 2006 to 2010.

Year	English	Math
2006	20.6	20.8
2007	20.7	21.0
2008	20.6	21.0
2009	20.6	21.0
2010	20.5	21.0

Source: www.act.org.

a. Graph the points representing the data for both the English and the math portions.

b. Calculate the average English score E and the average math score M for 2006 to 2010.

c. Graph $y = E$ and $y = M$ in the same coordinate system. How well do $y = E$ and $y = M$ model the data you graphed?

d. Are $y = E$ and $y = M$ functions? How do you know?

IN OTHER WORDS

39. Suppose the three vertices of a triangle are $A(a_1, a_2)$, $B(b_1, b_2)$, and $C(c_1, c_2)$. Explain in detail how you can determine whether the triangle is a right triangle.

40. Explain in detail how you can use the Problem Solving procedure given in this section to graph $y = b$.

41. Explain in detail how you can use the Problem Solving procedure given in this section to graph $x = c$.

42. Explain in detail the steps you would use in graphing $f(x) = ax + b$; then look at the Discovery problem and see if your steps are similar.

USING YOUR KNOWLEDGE

There are many applications that require the knowledge you have obtained to save you some money! The graph shows the amount owed on a \$1000 debt at an 18% interest rate when the minimum \$25 payment is made (blue) or when a new monthly payment of \$92 is made. Thus, at the current monthly payment of \$25, it will take 60 months to pay the \$1000 balance (you got to \$0!). With a new \$92 monthly payment you pay off the \$1000 balance in 12 months. To know the balance, you have to know how to read the graph!

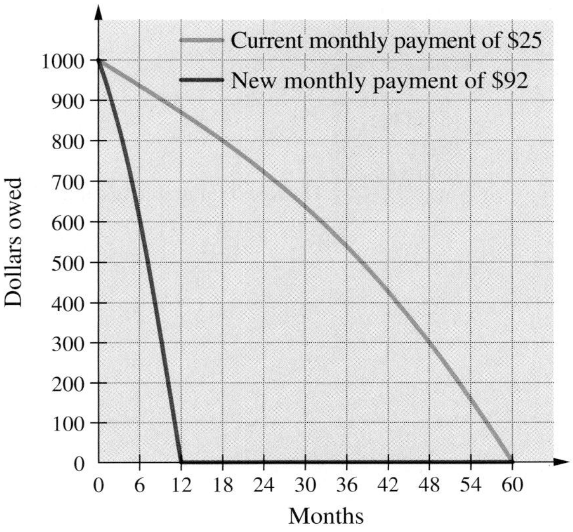

Source: http://www.dinkytown.net/java/PayoffCC2.html.

43. What is your balance after 6 months if you are paying \$25 a month?

44. What is your balance after 6 months if you are paying \$92 per month?

45. What is your balance after 18 months if you are paying \$25 a month?

46. What is your balance after 48 months if you are paying \$25 a month?

DISCOVERY

The ideas developed in this section for graphing lines can be summarized by means of a flowchart. A ***flowchart*** *is a pictorial representation showing the logical steps that have to be taken in order to perform a task.*

The basic component of a flowchart is a box that contains a command. For example, $\boxed{x \to 0}$ *says to take x, a previously given quantity, and let it be equal to 0. In mathematics, this instruction is given as*

Let $x = 0$.

The figure shows a flowchart that can be used to find the graph of any line not passing through the origin.

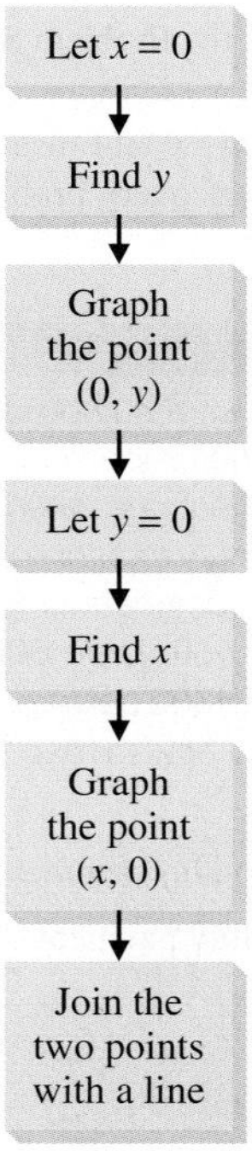

For $y = 2x + 6$

$y = 2 \cdot 0 + 6 = 6$

$y = 6$

$0 = 2x + 6$

$x = -3$

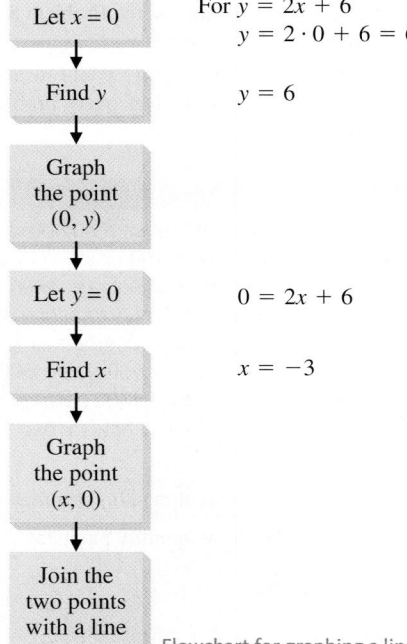

Flowchart for graphing a line.

An example of how it works for the line $y = 2x + 6$ *follows:*

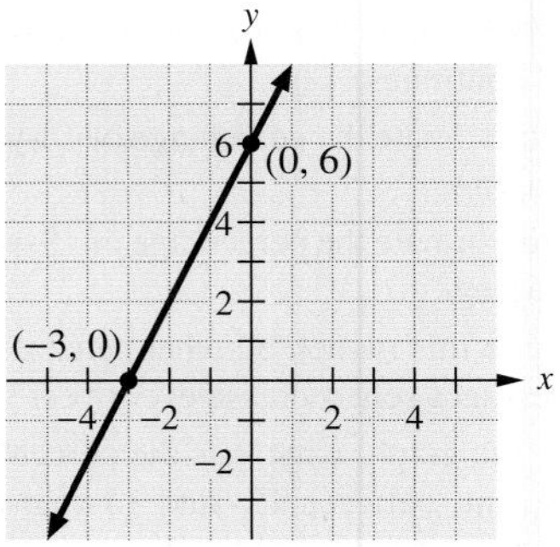

Use the flowchart technique to graph the linear relations you graphed in the following problems of Exercises 7.2.

47. Problem 3

48. Problem 4

49. Problem 9

50. Problem 10

51. Problem 11

52. Problem 12

53. Problem 13

54. Problem 14

55. Problem 15

56. Problem 16

57. Problem 17

58. Problem 18

CALCULATOR CORNER

You can use a calculator to find the distance between two points. For example, to find the distance between $(2, -3)$ *and* $(8, 5)$, *you must use equation (3). Here are the steps you need. Press*

[2nd] [$\sqrt{x}$] [(] [8] [−] [2] [)] [x^2] [+] [(] [5] [−] [(−)] [3] [)] [ENTER]

Note that in this case the answer appears as 10. If you work Example 5 using a calculator, your answer will be 9.219544457, an approximation for $\sqrt{85}$.

1. For problems 19, 21, 23, 25, and 27, estimate the distance between the two points with your calculator.

7.3 Slopes and Equations of a Line

GETTING STARTED

OBJECTIVES

- **A.** Given two points, find the slope of a line.
- **B.** Given the slope and either a point or the y-intercept, find the equation of a line.
- **C.** Find the equation of a line parallel to a given line.
- **D.** Solve applications involving finding equations.

A GRAPHIC LOOK AT ENGINE DEPOSITS

Study the advertisement in Figure 7.18. It shows that engine deposits increase if you do *not* use Texaco gasoline and decrease if you do. How fast do the deposits increase or decrease? To find out, you can look at the ratio of deposit weight (in milligrams) to tanks of gas. Without Texaco gas, the deposits increased from 250 to 400 mg after using approximately one tank of gas. Thus,

$$\frac{\text{Mg of deposit}}{\text{Tanks of gas}} = \frac{400 - 250}{1} = 150\,\frac{\text{mg}}{\text{tank}}$$

How fast did the deposits decrease? They decreased from 400 to 300 mg after using about 12 tanks of Texaco. The ratio of decrease is given by

$$\frac{\text{Mg of deposit}}{\text{Tanks of gas}} = \frac{300 - 400}{13 - 1} = -\frac{100}{12} = -8\frac{1}{3}\,\frac{\text{mg}}{\text{tank}}$$

The ratio of milligrams of deposit to tanks of gas, or in general, the ratio of rise (difference in y values) to run (difference in x values) for a line, is called the **slope** of the line. The slope of the increasing line is 150 mg per tank, whereas the slope of the decreasing line is $-8\frac{1}{3}$ mg per tank. Note that the slope of an *increasing* line (rising from left to right) is *positive* and the slope of a *decreasing* line (falling from left to right) is *negative.* Also, the two lines look almost perpendicular to each other, so if one has slope m, the other one must have slope $-1/m$ (see problem 54 in Exercises 7.3). Is this the case? If not, what is wrong? Think of how you can redraw the graph more accurately to reflect the actual situation.

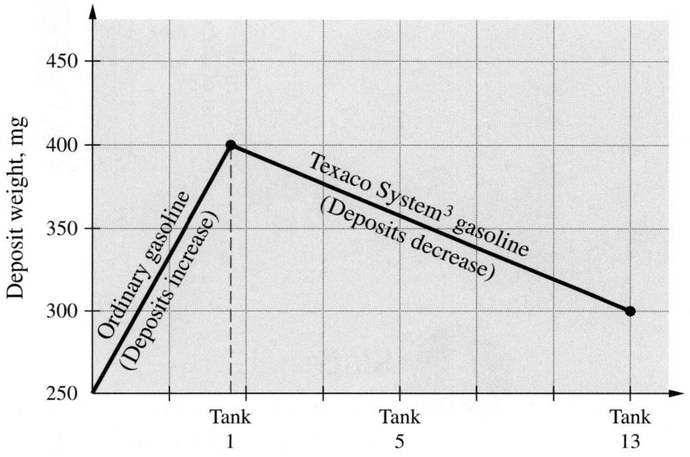

FIGURE 7.18 In the BMW test, Texaco's new System gasoline removed performance-robbing deposits left by ordinary gasoline.

Let us look at a more relevant problem: **Tuition and Fees** in Four-Year Public Institutions. As you can see from the graph, they keep increasing! Can you tell what the average increase has been from 2000 to 2010? The average for the 10 years is the ***difference*** in cost between 2010 (**$7605**) and 2001 (**$3766**) ***divided*** by the 10 years between 2010 and 2000:

$$\frac{7605 - 3766}{2010 - 2000} = \frac{3839}{10} = \$383.90/\text{year}$$

This means that the ***rate*** of change in Tuition and Fees in Four-Year Public Institutions over 10 years is about $383.90 per year. In general, when you look at a line graph and speak of its "***rate of change***," you are referring to the slope of the line.

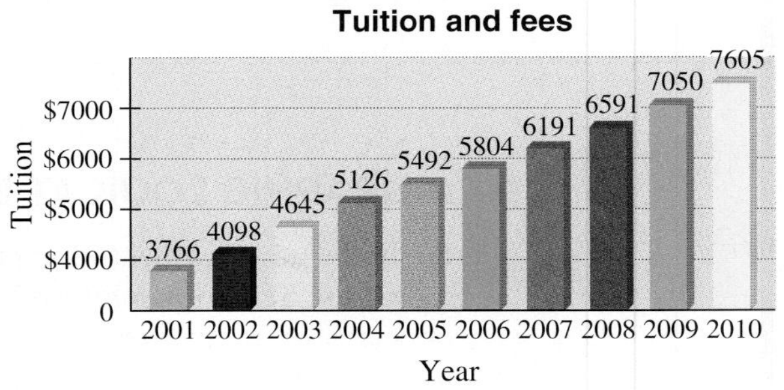

How are you going to pay for increasing **Tuition** and **Fees**? A lot of students get a **Pell Grant**. However, the graph in Figure 7.19 indicates that the ***maximum*** Pell Grant you can get, based on a percent of the average cost of attendance, is ***decreasing***. To find the ***rate of change*** of the maximum Pell Grant proceed as before: Get the *difference* in the percents between 2010 (**29%**) and 2001 (**42%**) and *divide* by the 10 years between 2010 and 2000.

$$\frac{29 - 42}{2010 - 2000} = \frac{-13\%}{10} = -1.3\%/\text{year}$$

Thus, the rate of change of the maximum Pell Grant you can get is *decreasing* by 1.3% each year.

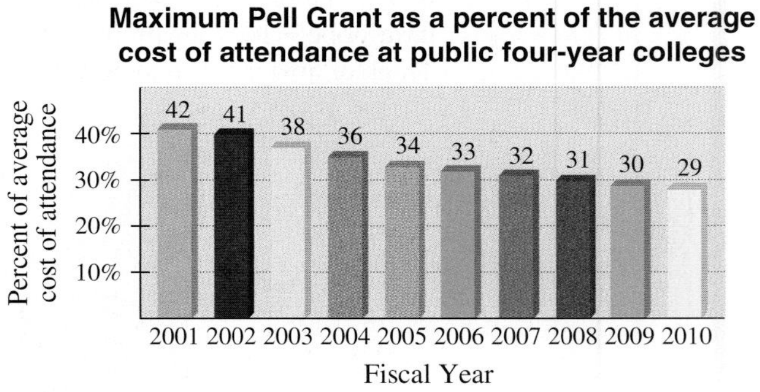

FIGURE 7.19

A Slope

In mathematics, an important feature of a straight line is its *steepness.* We can measure the steepness of a nonvertical line by means of the ratio of the **vertical rise** (or **fall**) to the corresponding **horizontal run.** We call this ratio the **slope.** For example, a staircase that rises 3 ft in a horizontal distance of 4 ft is said to have a slope of $\frac{3}{4}$ (see Figure 7.20).

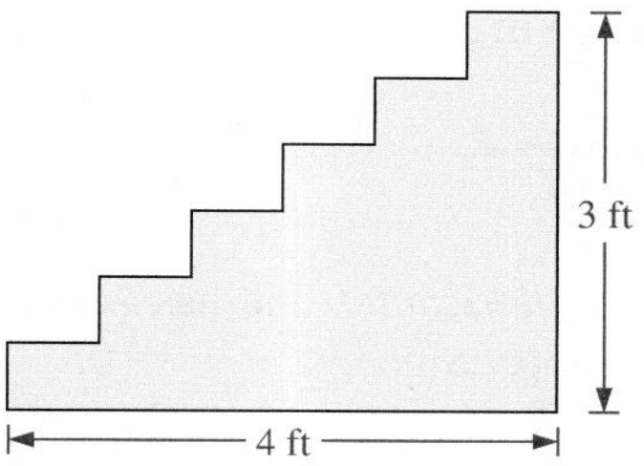

FIGURE 7.20 Slope $= \frac{3}{4}$.

By the way, most building codes specify that the maximum safe slope for stairs is 0.83. Is this staircase safe?

In general, we use the following definition:

Definition of Slope

A line going through two points (x_1, y_1) and (x_2, y_2), where $x_1 \neq x_2$, has **slope** m, where

$$m = \frac{y_2 - y_1}{x_2 - x_1} = \frac{\text{rise}}{\text{run}} = \frac{\text{change in } y}{\text{change in } x}$$

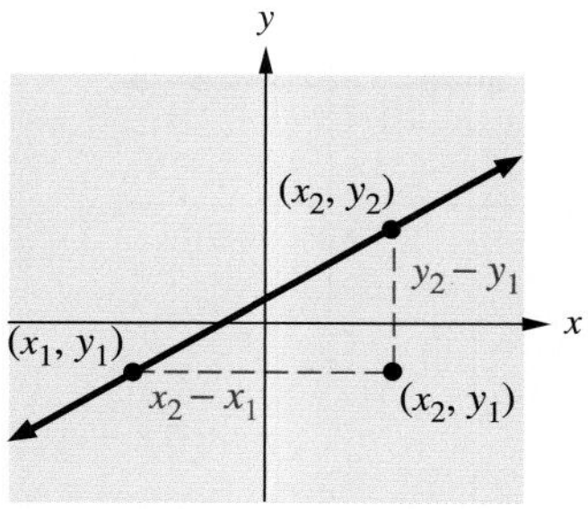

FIGURE 7.21 The slope of a line: $m = \frac{y_2 - y_1}{x_2 - x_1}$, $x_1 \neq x_2$.

Figure 7.21 shows the horizontal run $x_2 - x_1$ and the vertical rise $y_2 - y_1$ used in calculating the slope. We do not define slope for a vertical line because $x_2 - x_1 = 0$, and division by 0 is not defined. The slope of a horizontal line is obviously 0 because all points on such a line have the same y values. (See an illustrated summary of these ideas at the end of this section, page 354.)

EXAMPLE 1 Finding Slopes Given Two Points

Find the slope of the line that passes through the points $(0, -6)$ and $(3, 3)$.

Solution

The two given points are shown in Figure 7.22. Suppose that you choose $(x_1, y_1) = (0, -6)$ and $(x_2, y_2) = (3, 3)$. Then you get

$$m = \frac{3 - (-6)}{3 - 0} = \frac{9}{3} = 3$$

If you choose $(x_1, y_1) = (3, 3)$ and $(x_2, y_2) = (0, -6)$, then

$$m = \frac{-6 - 3}{0 - 3} = \frac{-9}{-3} = 3$$

As you can see, it makes no difference which point is labeled (x_1, y_1) and which is labeled (x_2, y_2). Since an interchange of the two points simply changes the sign of both the numerator and the denominator in the slope formula, the result is the same in both cases.

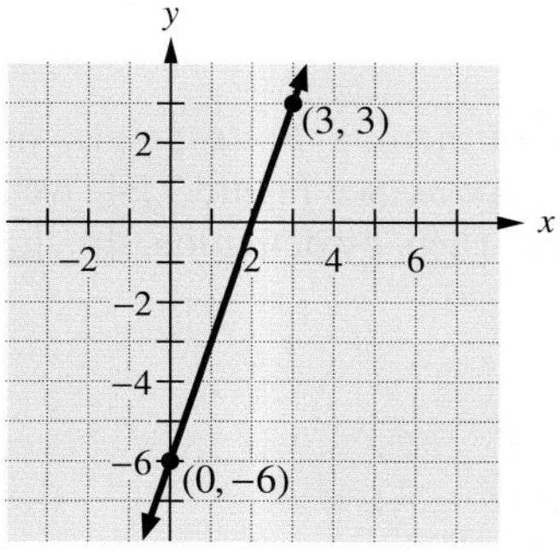

FIGURE 7.22 Line with positive slope.

EXAMPLE 2 Finding More Slopes Given Two Points

Find the slope of the line that passes through the two points $(3, -4)$ and $(-2, 3)$. See Figure 7.23.

Solution

We take $(x_1, y_1) = (-2, 3)$, so that $(x_2, y_2) = (3, -4)$. Then

$$m = \frac{-4 - 3}{3 - (-2)} = -\frac{7}{5}$$

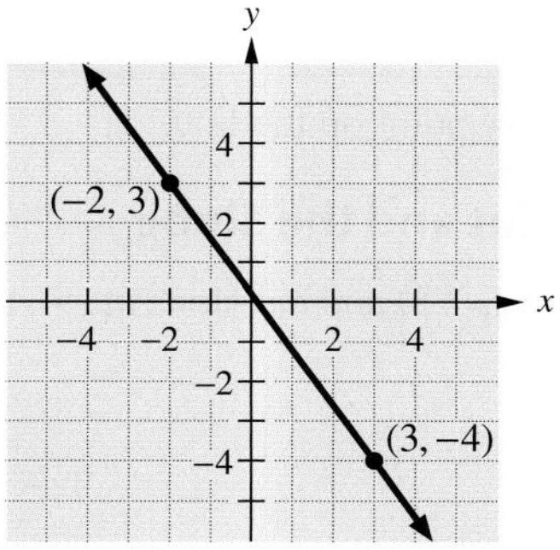

FIGURE 7.23 Line with negative slope.

Examples 1 and 2 are illustrations of the fact that a line that rises from left to right has a **positive slope** and one that falls from left to right has a **negative slope.** Note that the slope of a line gives **the change in *y* per unit change in *x*.** A summary for slopes follows:

Slope Summary

A line that *falls* from left to right has a *negative* slope.

The slope of a *vertical* line is *undefined.* Since $x_2 - x_1 = 0$,

$$m = \frac{y_2 - y_1}{x_2 - x_1} = \frac{y_2 - y_1}{0}$$

so *m* is *undefined.*

A line that *rises* from left to right has a *positive* slope.

A *horizontal* line has zero slope. Since $y_2 - y_1 = 0$,

$$m = \frac{y_2 - y_1}{x_2 - x_1} = \frac{0}{x_2 - x_1}$$

so $m = 0$.

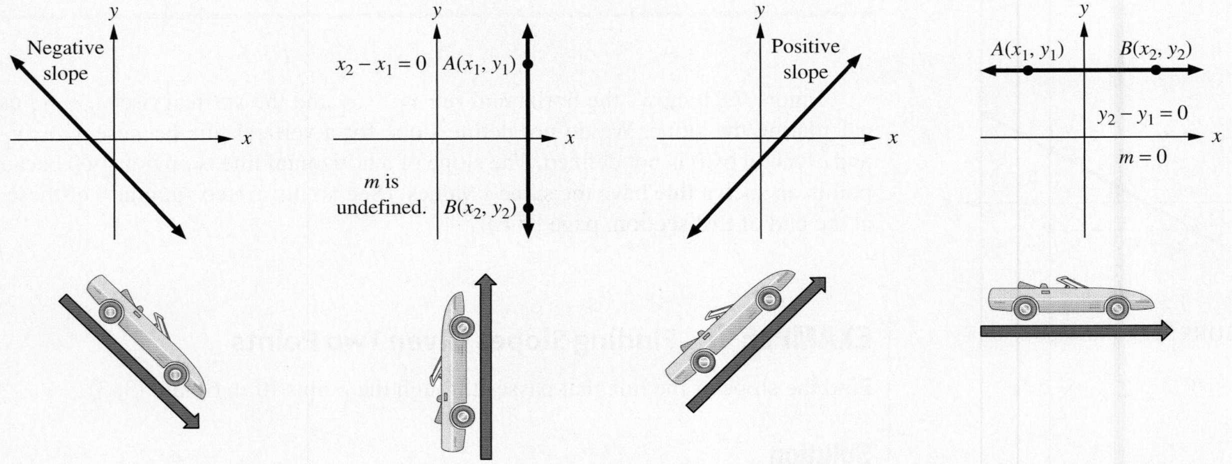

B Equations of Lines

The slope of a line can be used to obtain an equation of the line. For example, suppose the line passes through a point $P_1(x_1, y_1)$ and has slope *m*. See Figure 7.24. We let $P(x, y)$ be any second point (distinct from P_1) on the line. Then, by definition, the slope of the line in terms of these two points is

$$\frac{y - y_1}{x - x_1} = m$$

Multiplying both sides by $(x - x_1)$, we get $y - y_1 = m\,(x - x_1)$.

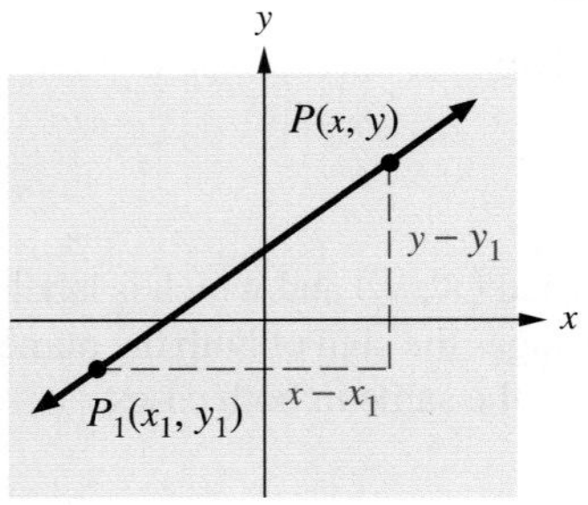

FIGURE 7.24

Point-Slope Equation of a Line

The **point-slope form** of the equation of a line with slope *m* and passing through the point (x_1, y_1) is

$$y - y_1 = m\,(x - x_1) \qquad (1)$$

This equation must be satisfied by the coordinates of every point on the line.

EXAMPLE 3 Finding Equations Given a Point and the Slope

Find an equation of the line that passes through the point $(2, -3)$ and has slope $m = -4$.

Solution

Using the point-slope equation (1), we get

$$\begin{aligned} y - (-3) &= -4(x - 2) \\ y + 3 &= -4x + 8 \\ y &= -4x + 5 \end{aligned}$$

EXAMPLE 4 Finding an Equation Given a Point and the Slope

Taxi fares in Key West are \$2.25 for the first $\frac{1}{5}$ mi and then \$2.50 for each additional mile. If a 10-mi ride costs \$26.75, find an equation for the total cost C of an m-mi ride. What will the price be for a 30-mi ride? (Source: www.keywesttaxi.com/Rates.htm.)

Solution

Since we know that a 10-mi ride costs \$26.75, and each additional mile costs \$2.50, we are given the point (10, 26.75) and the slope 2.5. Using the point-slope form, we have

$$C - 26.75 = 2.5(m - 10)$$

Or $$C = 2.5m - 25 + 26.75$$

That is, $$C = 2.5m + 1.75$$

For a 30-mi ride, $m = 30$ and $C = 2.5(30) + 1.75 = \$76.75$.

An important special case of equation (1) is that in which the given point is the point where the line intersects the y axis. Let this point be denoted by $(0, b)$; b is the y intercept of the line. Using equation (1), we obtain

$$y - b = m(x - 0)$$

and by adding b to both sides, we get $y = mx + b$.

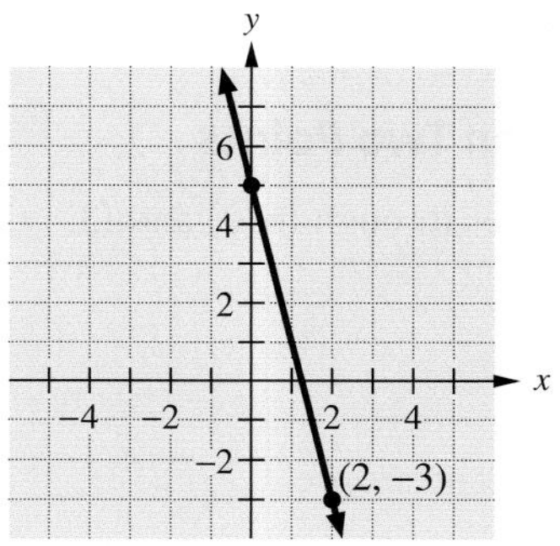

FIGURE 7.25 $y = -4x + 5$.

Slope-Intercept Form of a Line

The **slope-intercept form** of the equation of a line with slope m and y intercept b is

$$y = mx + b \qquad (2)$$

Notice that the answer to Example 3 was given in the slope-intercept form. This form is convenient for reading off the slope and the y intercept of the line. Thus, the answer to Example 3 immediately tells us that the slope of the line is -4 and the y intercept is 5 (see Figure 7.25).

GRAPH IT

To find the x or y intercept of a line, solve for y, press [Y=], and enter $y = (5 - 6x)/3$. To get integral values, press [ZOOM] [8] [ENTER] [TRACE]. Use the [▶] or [◀] buttons to find the y intercept 1.6666667 as shown.

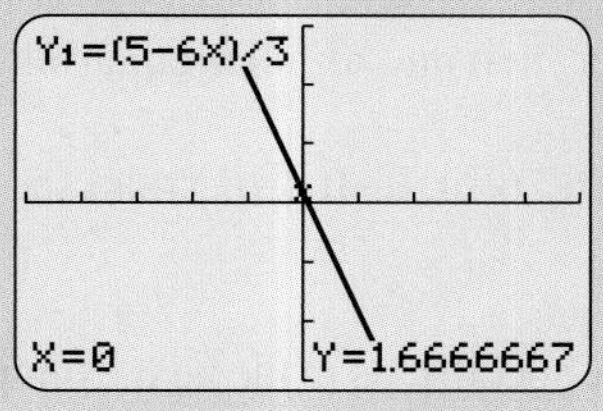

EXAMPLE 5 Finding the Slope and the y Intercept Given an Equation

Find the slope and the y intercept of the line with equation $6x + 3y = 5$.

Solution

By equation (2), the slope-intercept form of the equation of a line is $y = mx + b$, where m is the slope and b is the y intercept. We can solve the given equation for y by subtracting $6x$ from both sides and then dividing by 3, obtaining

$$y = -2x + \frac{5}{3}$$

an equation in the slope-intercept form, $y = mx + b$, with $m = -2$ and $b = \frac{5}{3}$. Thus, the slope m of the given line is -2, and the y intercept b is $\frac{5}{3}$.

The procedure of Example 5 can be followed for any equation of the form $Ax + By = C$, where $B \neq 0$, to obtain an equation in the slope-intercept form. If $B = 0$, then we can divide by A to get $x = C/A$, an equation of a line parallel to the y axis.

Standard Equation of a Straight Line

Every equation of the form

$$Ax + By = C$$

where A, B, and C are real numbers and A and B are not both 0, is an equation of a straight line.

On the other hand, we can show that every straight line has an equation of the form $Ax + By = C$. Any line that is not parallel to the y axis has a slope-intercept equation $y = mx + b$, which can be written in the form $mx - y = -b$ by subtracting b and y from both sides. This last equation is of the form $Ax + By = C$, with $A = m$, $B = -1$, and $C = -b$. For example, the equation $y = 2x + 5$ can be written in the form $2x - y = -5$ by subtracting 5 and y from both sides. This equation is the special case of $Ax + By = C$, with $A = 2$, $B = -1$, and $C = -5$. A line parallel to the y axis has an equation $x = a$, which is already of the form $Ax + By = C$, with $A = 1$, $B = 0$, and $C = a$.

General Equation of a Line

The **general form** of the equation of a straight line is

$$Ax + By = C \qquad (3)$$

Every straight line can be described by the equation $Ax + By = C$.

EXAMPLE 6 Finding the General Form Given Two Points

Find the general form of the equation of the line that passes through (6, 2) and (3, −2).

Solution

We first find the slope of the line.

$$m = \frac{-2 - 2}{3 - 6} = \frac{-4}{-3} = \frac{4}{3}$$

Then, using the point-slope form, with $P(6, 2)$ and $m = \frac{4}{3}$, we find the equation

$$y - 2 = \tfrac{4}{3}(x - 6)$$
$$3y - 6 = 4x - 24$$
$$4x - 3y = 18$$

We can check this answer by verifying that (6, 2) and (3, −2) are both solutions of the equation.

The ideas of Example 6 can often be used to obtain a simple formula that summarizes a group of data in a convenient form. For example, Table 7.7 shows the desirable weight range corresponding to a given height for men and for women.

Can we find an equation that illustrates the relationship between height and weight? First, we must realize the following two things:

1. Men are heavier, so there will be one equation for men and another equation for women.
2. The table gives only weight *ranges*. For instance, a 76-in. (6-ft 4-in.) man should weigh between 164 and 204 lb.

Hence, to write an equation requires ideally that we be more specific, as in the next example.

Table 7.7

Height (in.)	Men's Weight (lb)	Women's Weight (lb)	Height (in.)	Men's Weight (lb)	Women's Weight (lb)
62	108–134	98–123	70	140–174	130–163
63	112–139	102–128	71	144–179	134–168
64	116–144	106–133	72	148–184	138–173
65	120–149	110–138	73	152–189	
66	124–154	114–143	74	156–194	
67	128–159	118–148	75	160–199	
68	132–164	122–153	76	164–204	
69	136–169	126–158			

EXAMPLE 7 Relationship Between Height and Weight

Find an equation that gives the relationship between a man's height h (in inches) and his weight w (in pounds) using the lower weights in Table 7.7 as the desirable weights.

Solution

If we examine the heights and the corresponding weights in Table 7.7, we see that the heights increase by 1 in. from one entry to the next and the corresponding weights increase by 4 lb. This means that all the points (62, 108), (63, 112), . . . , (76, 164) lie on one straight line because the slope of a line connecting any consecutive pair of these points is the same as the slope of the line connecting any other consecutive pair. Thus, we want to find the equation of this line. The slope of the line is easily obtained by using the first pair of points (62, 108) and (63, 112).

$$m = \frac{112 - 108}{63 - 62} = 4$$

Then we can use the point-slope form of the equation to obtain

$$\begin{aligned} w - 108 &= 4(h - 62) \\ w - 108 &= 4h - 248 \\ w &= 4h - 140 \end{aligned}$$

We can check this against entries in Table 7.7. For example, for a 72-in. (6-ft) man, the equation gives

$$\begin{aligned} w &= 4(72) - 140 \\ &= 288 - 140 = 148 \end{aligned}$$

which agrees with the table entry.

C Parallel Lines

Since the slope of a line determines its direction, you can see that **two lines with the same slope and different y intercepts are parallel lines.** The next example makes use of this idea.

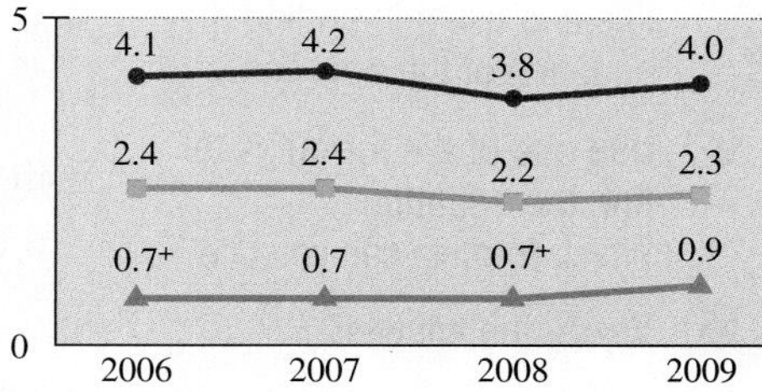

The lines showing the percent of people using Cigars, Smokeless Tobacco and Pipe Tobacco are *horizontal* lines that are almost *parallel*.

Source: Ch. 4, Fig 4.2 in http://www.oas.samhsa.gov/nsduh/2k9nsduh/2k9results.htm.

EXAMPLE 8 Finding Equations of Lines Parallel to a Given Line

Show that $3y = x + 2$ and $2x - 6y = 7$ describe parallel lines.

Solution

Solve each equation for y and obtain

$$y = \frac{1}{3}x + \frac{2}{3} \qquad \text{and} \qquad y = \frac{1}{3}x - \frac{7}{6}$$

These equations show that both lines have slope $\frac{1}{3}$. The y intercepts are different, so the lines are parallel.

Table 7.8

To Find the Equation of a Line, Given the Following:	Use
Two points (x_1, y_1) and (x_2, y_2), $x_1 \neq x_2$	Two-point form: $y - y_1 = m(x - x_1)$, where $m = (y_2 - y_1)/(x_2 - x_1)$
A point (x_1, y_1) and the slope m	Point-slope form: $y - y_1 = m(x - x_1)$
The slope m and the y intercept b	Slope-intercept form: $y = mx + b$

You have learned how to identify and work with many of the properties of lines. At this point, many students ask, "Which formula should we use in the problems?" Table 7.8 tells you which formula to use, depending on what information is given. Study Table 7.8 before you attempt the problems in Exercises 7.3. The resulting equation can always be written in the general form $Ax + By = C$.

PROBLEM-SOLVING

Finding the Equation of a Line

① **Read** the problem.

Find the equation of the line parallel to $2y = 6x + 5$ and passing through $(1, 2)$.

② **Select** the unknown.

You are asked to find the line parallel to $2y = 6x + 5$ and passing through $(1, 2)$.

③ **Think** of a plan.
Find the slope of the given line and use it in finding the equation of the new line.

If the new line is to be parallel to $2y = 6x + 5$ or, equivalently, $y = 3x + \frac{5}{2}$, the new line must have slope $m = 3$. Since the line passes through the point $(1, 2)$ and has slope $m = 3$, use the point-slope formula

$$y - y_1 = m(x - x_1)$$

④ **Use** one of the formulas to find the equation.
Which formula can you use?

with $m = 3$ and $(x_1, y_1) = (1, 2)$ to obtain

$$y - 2 = 3(x - 1)$$

⑤ **Verify** the answer.

To verify your answer, solve for y in $y - 2 = 3(x - 1)$ to obtain $y = 3x - 1$. This equation has slope 3, thus is parallel to the given line, and passes through $(1, 2)$ because $2 - 2 = 3(1 - 1)$.

Try Example 9 Now

Cover the solution, write your own solution, and then check your work.

EXAMPLE 9 Finding the Equation of a Line Parallel to Another

Find the equation of a line parallel to $3y = -6x + 8$ and with y intercept -3.

Solution

The line $3y = -6x + 8$ has slope -2. (Why?) Since we want to find a line parallel to $3y = -6x + 8$, the new line also must have slope $m = -2$. We now have the slope and y intercept of the line we want. Using the slope-intercept form $y = mx + b$, with $m = -2$ and $b = -3$, we obtain *the desired equation* $y = -2x - 3$.

D Applications

In problem 35 in Exercises 7.2 we approximated the percent of past month tobacco users among persons aged 12 or older by $P(t) = -0.3t + 30$. Now we are ready to show you how we did it so that you can do it too!

EXAMPLE 10 Finding the Equation of a Line

(a) Find the equation of the line shown in Figure 7.26. using the points (0, 30) and (7, 28) as approximations for the coordinates of the first and last points in the red graph.

(b) How can you interpret the slope of the line?

Solution

(a) We can find the equation of a line if we know the slope m and the y intercept b. The slope m of the line in the graph is

$$m = \frac{\text{rise}}{\text{run}} = \frac{28 - 30}{7} = \frac{-2}{7} \approx -0.3$$

and the y intercept $b = 30$ (see Figure 7.26). Thus, the equation of the line is $y = -0.3t + 30$ or, in function notation, $P(t) = -0.3t + 30$ where t is the number of years after 2002.

(b) The slope of the line indicates that the percent of past month tobacco users among persons aged 12 or older is *decreasing* at an annual rate of -0.3%.

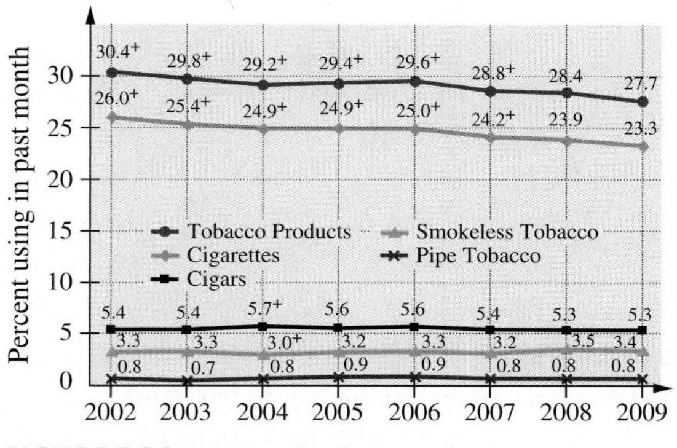

FIGURE 7.26 Past Month Tobacco Use among Persons Aged 12 or Older: 2002–2009.

GRAPH IT

We can use a grapher to find the equation of a line given two points. To do Example 1, press STAT 1 and enter 0 and 3 under L1 and -6 and 3 under L2; then press STAT ▶ 4 ENTER to get the equation $y = ax + b$, with $a = 3$ and $b = -6$, that is, the line $y = 3x - 6$. Graph this line. Now graph the two points we entered in the table by using 2ND STAT PLOT ENTER ENTER GRAPH. Does the line pass through the two points? (See Window 1.)

In Example 3 we are given the point $(2, -3)$. Since the slope is $-4 = \frac{-4}{1}$, move 1 unit right and 4 units down to reach the point $(3, -7)$. We now have two points. So we use the same procedure and find the equation of the line $y = ax + b$, with $a = -4$ and $b = 5$, that is, the line $y = -4x + 5$. (See Window 2.) In the Problem Solving section we are given the point $(1, 2)$, and we want a line parallel to $2y = 6x + 5$, that is, $y = \frac{6x + 5}{2}$, which has slope $3 = \frac{3}{1}$. This means that the change in x is 1 and the change in y is 3. Starting at the point $(1, 2)$, we go 1 unit right and 3 units up, ending at $(2, 5)$. We now have two points, $(1, 2)$ and $(2, 5)$, so we can follow our previous steps to make two lists and get an equation of the form $y = ax + b$. For $(1, 2)$ and $(2, 5)$, $a = 3$ and $b = -1$; that is, $y = 3x - 1$ as before. Now check Example 9.

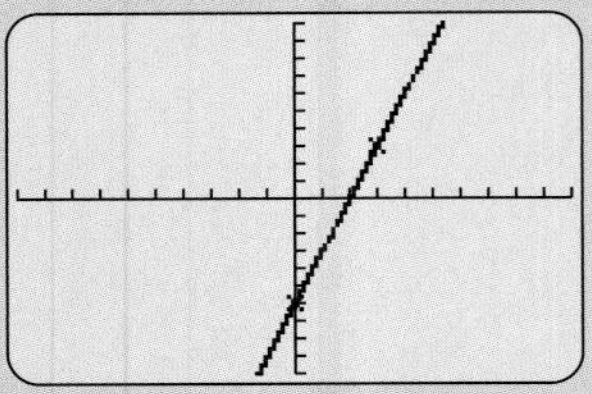

Window 1

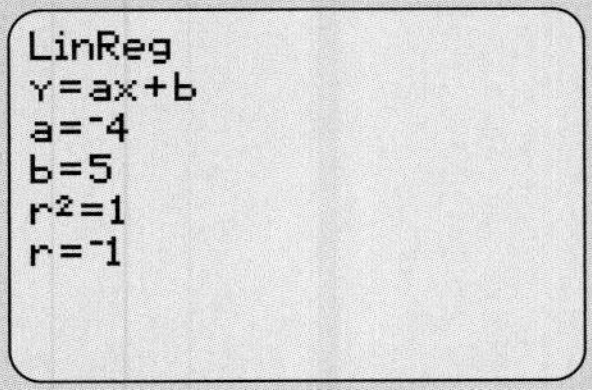

Window 2
$y = -4x + 5$

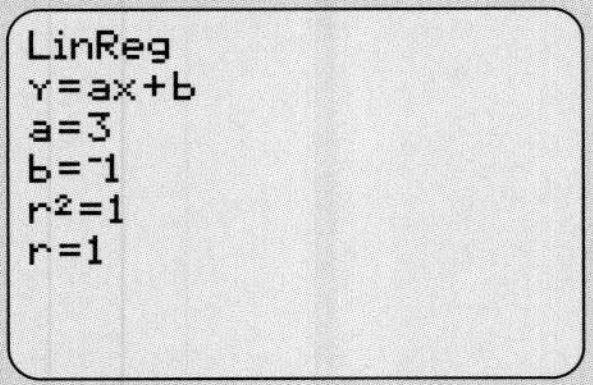

Window 3
$y = 3x - 1$

7.3 EXERCISES

A Slope

In problems 1–10, find the slope m of the line that passes through the two given points.

1. $(1, 2)$ and $(3, 4)$
2. $(1, -2)$ and $(-3, -4)$
3. $(0, 5)$ and $(5, 0)$
4. $(3, -6)$ and $(5, -6)$
5. $(-1, -3)$ and $(7, -4)$
6. $(-2, -5)$ and $(-1, -6)$
7. $(0, 0)$ and $(12, 3)$
8. $(-1, -1)$ and $(-10, -10)$
9. $(3, 5)$ and $(-2, 5)$
10. $(4, -3)$ and $(2, -3)$

B Equations of Lines

In problems 11–16, find the slope-intercept form (if possible) of the equation of the line that has the given properties (m is the slope).

11. Passes through $(1, 2)$; $m = \frac{1}{2}$
12. Passes through $(-1, -2)$; $m = -2$
13. Passes through $(2, 4)$; $m = -1$
14. Passes through $(-3, 1)$; $m = \frac{3}{2}$
15. Passes through $(4, 5)$; $m = 0$
16. Passes through $(3, 2)$; slope is not defined (does not exist)

In problems 17–26, find **(a)** *the slope and* **(b)** *the y intercept for the graph of the given equation.*

17. $y = x + 2$
18. $2x + y = 3$
19. $3y = 4x$
20. $2y = x + 4$
21. $x + y = 14$
22. $y - 4x = 8$
23. $y = 6$
24. $2y = 16$
25. $x = 3$
26. $3x = -6y + 9$

In problems 27–32, find the general form of the equation of the line that passes through the two given points.

27. $(1, -1)$ and $(2, 2)$
28. $(-3, -4)$ and $(-2, 0)$
29. $(3, 2)$ and $(2, 3)$
30. $(3, 0)$ and $(0, 5)$
31. $(0, 0)$ and $(1, 10)$
32. $(-4, -1)$ and $(-4, 3)$

33. Use Table 7.7 to find a formula relating the height h of a man and his ideal weight w given by the *second* number in the weight column. See Example 7.

34. Use Table 7.7 to find a formula relating the height h of a woman and her weight w as given by the *first* number in the weight column. See Example 7.

35. Repeat problem 34 using the *second* number in the weight column.

36. On the basis of your answer to problem 35, if a woman weighs 183 lb, how tall should she be? (This is not given in Table 7.7.)

37. Taxi fares in San Francisco are \$2 for the first mile and \$1.70 for each additional mile. If a 10-mi ride costs \$17.30, find an equation for the total cost C of an m-mi ride. What would the price be for a 30-mi ride?

38. A different taxicab company in San Francisco charges \$3 for the first mile and \$1.50 for each additional mile. If a 20-mi ride costs \$31.50, find an equation for the total cost C of an m-mi ride. What would the price of a 10-mi ride be? If you are taking a 50-mi ride, which company is cheaper, this one or the company in problem 37?

39. Pedro took a cab in San Francisco and paid the fare quoted in problem 37. Tyrone paid the fare quoted in problem 38. Amazingly, they paid the same amount! How far did they ride?

40. In New York, a 20-mi cab ride is \$32 and consists of an initial charge and \$1.50 per mile thereafter. Find an equation for the total cost C of an m-mi ride. How much would you have to pay for a 30-mi ride?

41. The cost C for San Francisco fares (problem 37) is \$2 for the first mile and \$1.70 for each mile thereafter. We can find C by following these steps.
   a. What is the cost of the first mile?
   b. If the whole trip is m mi, how many miles do you travel after the first mile?
   c. How much do you pay per mile after the first mile?
   d. What is the cost of each mile after the first mile?
   e. The total cost C is the sum of the cost of the first mile and the cost of the miles after the first. What is that cost? Is your answer the same as your answer to problem 37?

42. New York fares are easier to compute. They are simply \$2 for the initial fare and \$1.50 for each mile thereafter. Find the total cost C for an m-mi trip. Do you get the same answer as you did in problem 40?

43. Did you know that you could rent cell phones for your overseas travel? If you are in Paris, the cost for a 1-week rental, including 60 min of long-distance calls to New York, the rental fee, and \$2 for each airtime minute, was \$175.
   a. Find a formula for the total cost C of a rental phone that includes m min of long-distance calls to New York.
   b. What is the weekly rental fee for the phone?

44. Long-distance calls from the Hilton Hotel in Paris, France, to New York cost \$7.80 per minute.
   a. Find a formula for the cost C of m min of long-distance calls to New York.
   b. How many minutes can you use so that the charges are identical to those you would pay when renting the telephone of problem 43? Answer to the nearest minute.

C Parallel Lines

In problems 45–50, determine whether the given lines are parallel.

45. $y = 2x + 5$; $4x - 2y = 7$
46. $y = 4 - 5x$; $15x + 3y = 3$
47. $2x + 5y = 8$; $5x - 2y = -9$
48. $3x + 4y = 4$; $2x - 6y = 7$
49. $x + 7y = 7$; $2x + 14y = 21$
50. $y = 5x - 12$; $y = 3x - 8$

51. Find an equation of the line that passes through the point $(1, -2)$ and is parallel to the line $4x - y = 7$.

52. Find an equation of the line that passes through the point $(2, 0)$ and is parallel to the line $3x + 2y = 5$.

53. It is shown in analytic geometry that two lines $a_1x + b_1y = c_1$ and $a_2x + b_2y = c_2$ are perpendicular if and only if

$$a_1a_2 + b_1b_2 = 0$$

that is, **two lines are perpendicular if and only if the sum of the products of the corresponding coefficients of x and y in the general form of the equations is 0.** This leads to a very easy way of writing an equation of a line that is perpendicular to a given line. For instance, if the given line is $3x + 5y = 8$, then for each real number c, $5x - 3y = c$ is a line perpendicular to the given line. This is obvious because $(3)(5) + (5)(-3) = 0$. Notice that all we need to do to form the left side of the second equation is interchange the coefficients of x and y in the first equation and change the sign of one of these coefficients. If we wish to have the second line pass through a specified point, we select the value of c so that this happens. Thus, if the second line is to pass through $(3, 2)$, then c has to be selected so that $(3, 2)$ is in the solution set of the equation. Hence,

$$5(3) - 3(2) = c \quad \text{or} \quad c = 9$$

The line $5x - 3y = 9$ passes through $(3, 2)$ and is perpendicular to the line $3x + 5y = 8$. In each of the following problems, find an equation of the line that is perpendicular to the given line and passes through the given point:
   a. $2x + 5y = 7$; $(2, 0)$
   b. $y = 2x - 3$; $(1, 1)$
   c. $x - 2y = 3$; $(2, -2)$
   d. $4x + 5y = 9$; $(1, 1)$

54. If the lines $y = m_1x + b_1$, $m_1 \neq 0$, and $y = m_2x + b_2$ are perpendicular, then $m_2 = -1/m_1$. Show this by referring to problem 53. This leads to the simple statement that **the slopes of perpendicular lines are negative reciprocals of each other.** Why do we need the condition $m_1 \neq 0$?

55. A line passes through the two points $(0, 0)$ and $(100, 200)$. A second line passes through the two points $(0, 10)$ and $(790, -405)$. Can you see how to determine whether these are perpendicular lines? (*Hint:* Look at problem 54.)

D Applications

56. Do you keep a "regular" wireline telephone at home? The graph on the next page shows the number of Canadian wireless subscriptions (in millions) from 2000 to 2009. Assume that the number of wireless subscriptions (green line) is a straight line.
   a. The slope of the line is rise/run. Find the slope from 2000 to 2009, if t is the number of years after 2000 and y is the number of subscribers starting with 9 million in 2000 and ending with 24 million in 2009.
   b. What is the slope-intercept equation of the line?

c. If $P(t)$ represents a function indicating the number of millions of wireless subscribers, where t is the number of years after 2000, what is $P(t)$?

d. The slope of the line is simply a ratio. What does the ratio represent?

e. How many millions of wireless subscribers would you predict for the year 2020?

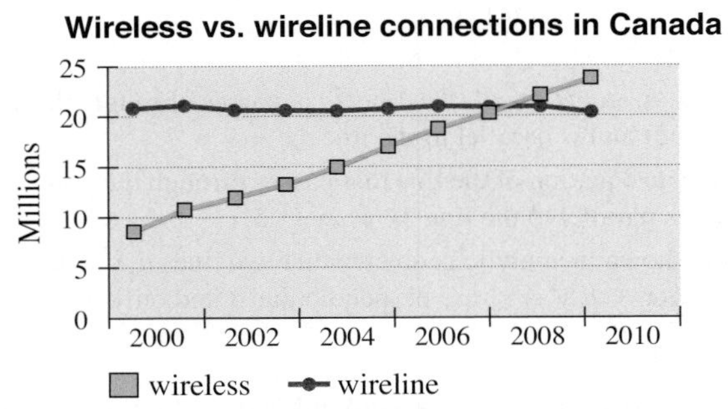

Source: Copyright © Giganomics Consulting, Inc. Reprinted by permission.

57. Do you use Twitter? How many followers do you have? The person with the most followers in 2011 was Lady Gaga, with about 12 million followers. There is a correlation between the number of followers f and the number of friends F in Twitter and you can find what it is if you find the equation of the line!

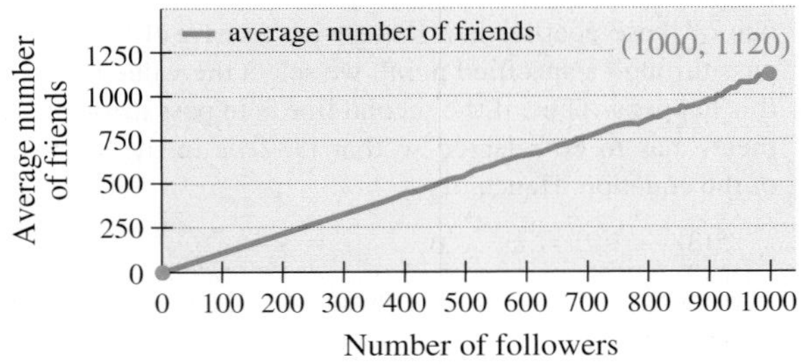

Source: Used with permission from http//www.sysomos.com/insidetwitter/appendix.

a. What is the slope of the line, and what does it represent?

b. What is the y intercept?

c. If $F(f)$ is the equation of the line correlating the number of followers f to the number of friends F, what is $F(f)$?

d. What are the projected number of friends F for Lady Gaga if she has 12 million followers?

58. *Daily fat consumption.* According to the U.S. Department of Agriculture, the daily fat consumption F per person can be approximated by

$$F = 190 + 0.8t \text{ (grams)}$$

where t is the number of years after 2000.

a. What is the slope of the line?

b. What does the slope represent?

59. *Daily seafood consumption.* According to the U.S. Department of Agriculture, the daily consumption T of tuna can be approximated by

$$T = 3.87 - 0.13t \text{ (pounds)}$$

and the daily consumption F of fish and shellfish can be approximated by

$F = -0.29t + 15.46$ (pounds), where t is the number of years after 2000.

a. Is the consumption of tuna increasing or decreasing?

b. Is the consumption of fish and shellfish increasing or decreasing?

c. Which consumption (tuna or fish and shellfish) is decreasing faster?

60. *Life expectancy of women.* The average life span (life expectancy) y of an American woman is given by $y = 0.16t + 79$, where t is the number of years after 2000. (Source: U.S. National Center for Health Statistics, *Statistical Abstract of the United States.*)

a. What is the slope of this line?

b. Is the life span of American women increasing or decreasing?

c. What does the slope represent?

61. *Life expectancy of men.* The average life span y of an American man is given by $y = 0.19t + 74$, where t is the number of years after 2000. (Source: U.S. National Center for Health Statistics, *Statistical Abstract of the United States.*)

a. What is the slope of this line?

b. Is the life span of American women increasing or decreasing?

c. What does the slope represent?

62. *Velocity of a thrown ball.* The speed v of a ball thrown up with an initial velocity of 15 m/sec is given by $v = 15 - 5t$, where v is the velocity (in meters per second) and t is the number of seconds after the ball is thrown.

a. What is the slope of this line?

b. Is the velocity of the ball increasing or decreasing?

c. What does the slope represent?

63. *Daily fat consumption.* The number of fat grams f consumed daily by the average American can be approximated by $f = 165 + 0.4t$, where t is the number of years after 2000. (Source: U.S. Department of Agriculture, *Statistical Abstract of the United States.*)

a. What is the slope of this line?

b. Is the consumption of fat increasing or decreasing?

c. What does the slope represent?

64. *Milk products consumption.* The number of gallons of milk products g consumed annually by the average American can be approximated by $g = 24 - 0.2t$, where t is the number of years after 2000.

a. What is the slope of this line?

b. Is the consumption of milk products increasing or decreasing?

c. What does the slope represent?

65. *Daily fat intake.* According to the U.S. Department of Agriculture, the total daily fat available for consumption per person can be approximated by $g = 140 + 0.94t$, where t is the number of years after 1970.

a. What was the daily fat available for consumption in 2000? Note that this is the fat *available* for consumption; you don't have to eat it all!

b. What was the daily fat available for consumption in 2010?

c. What was the daily fat available for consumption in 1970?

d. Is the total daily fat available for consumption increasing or decreasing? Watch your fat! A hamburger and fries have from 35–65 total fat grams!

66. *Death rates.* According to the U.S. Health and Human Services, the number D of deaths from heart disease per 100,000 population can be approximated by $D = -9.8t + 260$, where t is the number of years after 1998.

a. How many deaths per 100,000 population were there in 2008?

b. How many deaths per 100,000 population would you expect in 2018?

c. What is the slope of the line D, and what does it represent?

67. Nearly half of the U.S. population lives in coastal areas susceptible to coastal hazards, and the number of persons per square mile in these areas is increasing! How much? The number C of persons per square mile living in coastal areas can be approximated by $C = 2.5N + 175$, where N is the number of years after 1960.

a. What is the slope of $C = 2.5N + 175$?

b. What does the slope represent?

c. How many persons per square mile does the equation $C = 2.5N + 175$ predict for the year 2015 (55 years after 1960)?

d. Is the result you get in part (c) close to the one shown in the graph?

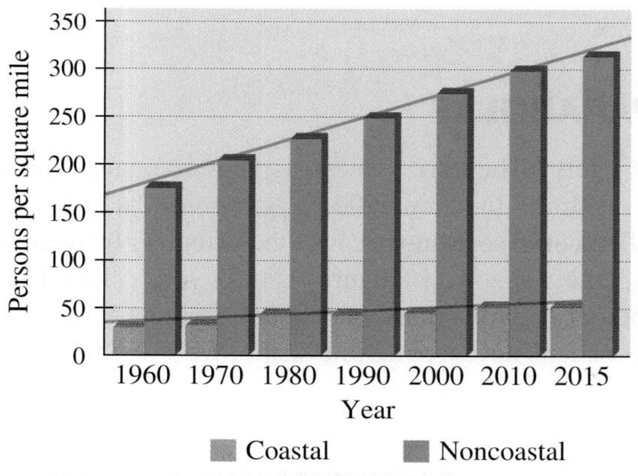

Source: http://tinyurl.com/7fdofbn, Figure 2.

IN OTHER WORDS

68. Explain why it is impossible to find the slope of a vertical line.

69. Explain why the slope of any horizontal line is 0.

70. Refer to problem 54. If $m_1 = 0$, then the first equation becomes $y = b_1$. What lines are perpendicular to this line? Explain. What are the equations of these perpendicular lines?

USING YOUR KNOWLEDGE

The accompanying table will be used in problems 71–75.

Building Codes Standards for Slope and Safety

Standards	Maximum Slope
Ramps—wheelchair	0.125
Ramps—walking	0.3
Driveway or street parking	0.22

71. The steepest street in the world is Baldwin Street in Dunedin, New Zealand, with a rise of 1 m for every 1.266 m.

a. What is the slope of this street? (Answer to two decimal places.)

b. Is it safe to park on this street?

72. Filbert Street, in San Francisco, has a rise of 10 ft for every 31.7 ft.

a. What is the slope of this street? (Answer to two decimal places.)

b. Is it safe to park on this street?

73. A walking ramp to the library has a run of 1.6 ft and a rise of 0.4 ft.

a. What is the slope of this ramp?

b. According to the standards, is this a safe ramp?

74. A wheelchair ramp connecting the street to the ticket office at the Sun Dome ends 8 ft above street level. What is the shortest run this ramp can have and still meet safety standards?

75. An architect is designing a driveway. When a grid is placed over the plans, the top of the driveway has coordinates (124, 20), and the bottom of the driveway has coordinates (108, 16). Will this driveway meet safety specifications? If the bottom of the driveway has coordinates (x, 16), what should x be so that the slope is the maximum allowable? (Answer to the nearest foot)

DISCOVERY

We've mentioned that graphs could be used to make an algebraic model when solving problems. Make a model to solve problems 76–78.

76. The Home Show at the Fairgrounds charged a flat parking fee and an additional amount for admission to the show. Study the chart and discover the parking fee and the admission price.

Total Paid	\$25	\$13	\$22
Number of Persons	7	3	6

77. Garcia's Plumbing charges a fixed fee for making a service call plus an hourly rate for each hour the plumber spends making the call. Study the table and discover the fixed fee and the hourly rate for each service call.

Total Paid	\$110	\$60	\$160
Number of Hours	3	1	5

78. A cellular calling plan charges a monthly fee plus an additional amount for each minute of air time (the time spent talking on the phone). Study the table and discover the monthly fee and the charge per minute of air time.

Total Paid	Air Time (minutes)
\$ 87.50	230
\$ 52.50	90
\$133.75	415

SKILL CHECKER

Do you remember how to graph relations and functions? We will need this concept in the next section! Try these practice problems.

1. If $f(x) = x^2$, find and graph $f(0)$, $f(1)$, $f(-1)$, $f(2)$, and $f(-2)$.
2. If $f(x) = (x - 1)^2 - 2$, find and graph $f(0), f(1), f(-1), f(2)$, and $f(-2)$.

If you need further practice, go to Section 7.1.

COLLABORATIVE LEARNING

Divide the class into teams of males and females. Place a ruler on the floor, take off your shoes, step on the ruler, and measure the size L of your foot (in inches). Now measure your height H (in inches).

1. Record the results as ordered pairs of the form (L, H).
2. Graph the ordered pairs in a coordinate system. Each unit should be 1 for L and 10 for H.
3. Average all the L's and all the H's in each group and form the ratio

$$\frac{\text{Average of H's}}{\text{Average of L's}} = \frac{\text{rise}}{\text{run}} = m$$

4. Graph the equation $y = mx$ on the same coordinate system you used in problem 2. Is it a close fit?
5. What would be the formula for finding the height of a male or a female based on foot size?
6. How would you state your result in terms of variation?
7. What would the constant of variation be for males?
8. What would the constant of variation be for females?

7.4 Quadratic Functions and Their Graphs

GETTING STARTED

OBJECTIVES

A. Graph a parabola of the form $y = f(x) = ax^2 + k$.
B. Graph a parabola of the form $y = f(x) = a(x - h)^2 + k$.
C. Graph a parabola of the form $y = f(x) = ax^2 + bx + c$.
D. Solve applications involving parabolas.

THE FOUNTAIN OF PARABOLAS

Have you seen any parabolas lately? They are as near as your fountain: The streams of water follow the path of a quadratic function called a *parabola.* Parabolas, ellipses, circles, and hyperbolas are called **conic sections** because they can be obtained by intersecting (slicing) a cone with a plane, as shown in Figure 7.27. As you will see later, these conic sections occur in many practical applications. For example, your satellite dish, your flashlight lens, and your telescope lens have a parabolic shape. We study parabolas next.

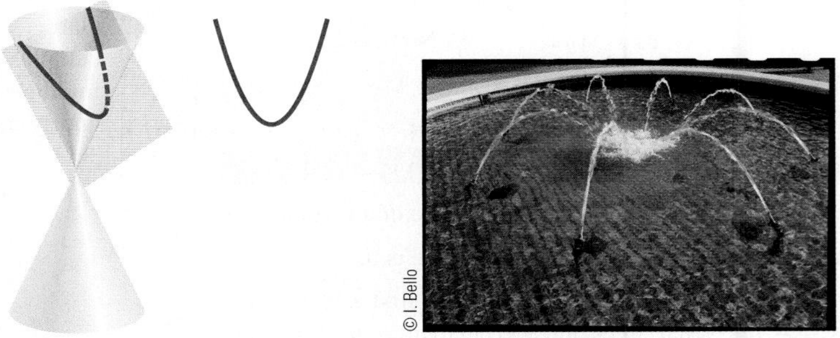

FIGURE 7.27 Parabola.

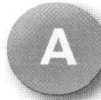

A Graphing the Parabola $y = f(x) = ax^2 + k$

In Section 7.2 we studied *linear functions* such as $f(x) = 2x + 5$ and $g(x) = -3x - 4$ whose graphs were straight lines. In this section we shall study equations (functions) defined by a quadratic (second-degree) function of the form

$$f(x) = ax^2 + bx + c$$

These functions are called **quadratic functions,** and their graphs are called **parabolas.**

Just as the simplest *line* to graph is $y = f(x) = x$, the simplest *parabola* to graph is $y = f(x) = x^2$. To draw this graph, we select values for x and find the corresponding values of y.

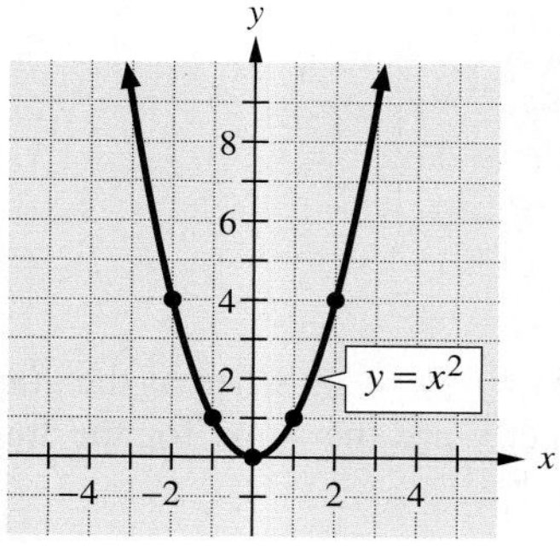

FIGURE 7.28

x Value	$f(x) = y$ Value
$x = -2$	$f(-2) = (-2)^2 = 4$
$x = -1$	$f(-1) = (-1)^2 = 1$
$x = 0$	$f(0) = (0)^2 = 0$
$x = 1$	$f(1) = (1)^2 = 1$
$x = 2$	$f(2) = (2)^2 = 4$

x	y	(x, y)
-2	4	$(-2, 4)$
-1	1	$(-1, 1)$
0	0	$(0, 0)$
1	1	$(1, 1)$
2	4	$(2, 4)$

Then we make a table of ordered pairs, plot the ordered pairs on a coordinate system, and draw a smooth curve through the plotted points as in Figure 7.28.

A very important feature of this parabola is its **symmetry** to the y axis. This means that if you folded the graph of $y = x^2$ along the y axis, the two halves of the graph would coincide because the same value of y is obtained for any value of x and its opposite $-x$. For instance, $x = 2$ and $x = -2$ both give $y = 4$ (see the preceding tables). Because of this symmetry, the y axis is called the **axis of symmetry** or, simply, the **axis** of the parabola. The point $(0, 0)$, where the parabola crosses its axis, is called the **vertex** of the curve. Note that the arrows on the curve in Figure 7.28 mean that the parabola goes on without end.

EXAMPLE 1 Graphing Parabolas Opening Downward

Graph $y = -x^2$.

Solution

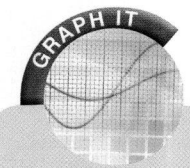

We could make a table of x and y values as before. However, note that for any x value, the y value will be the *negative* of the y value on the parabola $y = x^2$. (If you don't believe this, go ahead and make the table and check it, but it's easier to copy the table for $y = x^2$ with the negatives of the y values entered as shown.) Thus, the parabola $y = -x^2$ has the same shape as $y = x^2$, but it is turned in the *opposite* direction (opens *downward*). The graph of $y = -x^2$ is shown in Figure 7.29.

x	y	(x, y)
-2	-4	$(-2, -4)$
-1	-1	$(-1, -1)$
0	0	$(0, 0)$
1	-1	$(1, -1)$
2	-4	$(2, -4)$

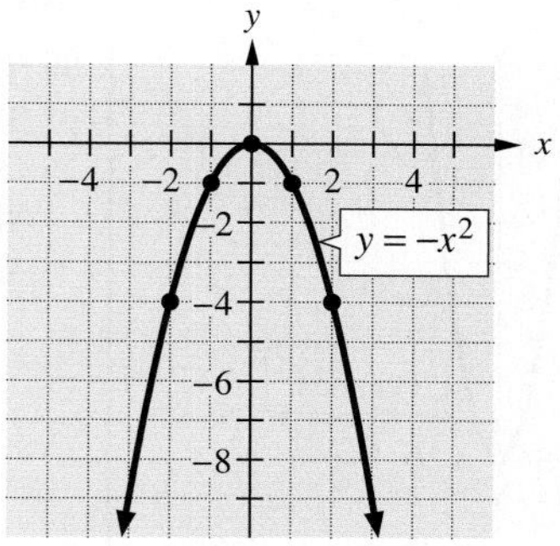

FIGURE 7.29

GRAPH IT

To graph $y = x^2$ and $y = -x^2$, press [Y=] and enter x^2 for Y_1 and $-x^2$ for Y_2. Press [ZOOM] [6]. Note that $y = x^2$ and $y = -x^2$ are reflections of each other across the x axis as shown.

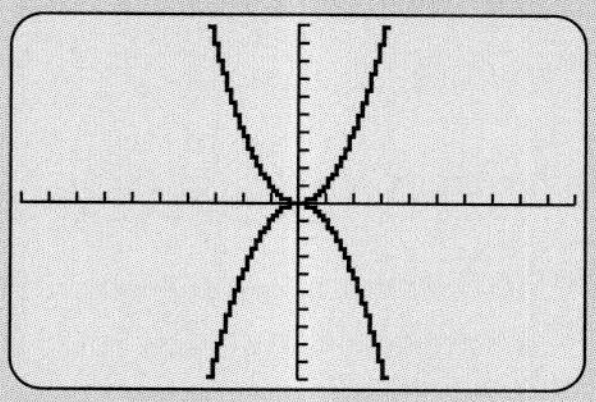

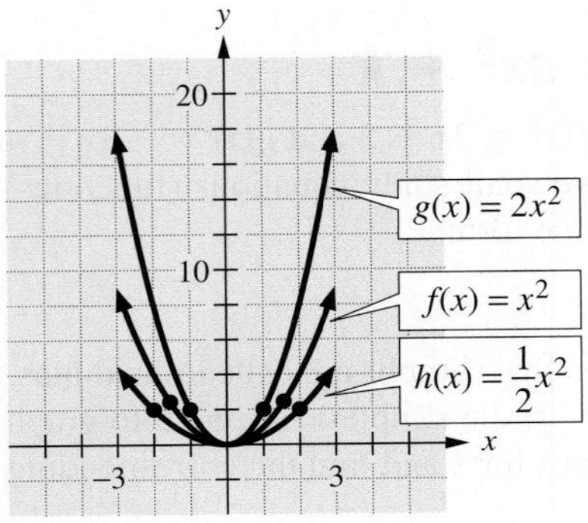

FIGURE 7.30

As you can see from the two preceding examples, when the coefficient of x^2 is positive (as in $y = x^2 = 1x^2$), the parabola opens upward (is **concave up**), but when the coefficient of x^2 is negative (as in $y = -x^2 = -1x^2$), the parabola opens downward (is **concave down**). In either case, the vertex is at $(0, 0)$. To determine the effect of a in $f(x) = ax^2$ in general, let's plot some points and see how the graphs of $g(x) = 2x^2$ and $h(x) = \frac{1}{2}x^2$ compare to the graph of $f(x) = x^2$. All three graphs are shown in Figure 7.30.

x	$g(x) = 2x^2$	x	$h(x) = \frac{1}{2}x^2$
−2	$2(-2)^2 = 8$	−2	$\frac{1}{2}(-2)^2 = 2$
−1	$2(-1)^2 = 2$	−1	$\frac{1}{2}(-1)^2 = \frac{1}{2}$
0	$2(0)^2 = 0$	0	$\frac{1}{2}(0)^2 = 0$
1	$2(1)^2 = 2$	1	$\frac{1}{2}(1)^2 = \frac{1}{2}$
2	$2(2)^2 = 8$	2	$\frac{1}{2}(-2)^2 = 2$

Note that the graph of $g(x) = 2x^2$ is narrower than that of $f(x) = x^2$, whereas the graph of $h(x) = \frac{1}{2}x^2$ is wider. The vertex and line of symmetry are the same for the three curves. In general, we have the following:

Properties of the Parabola $g(x) = ax^2$

The graph of $g(x) = ax^2$ is a parabola with the vertex at the origin and the y axis as its line of symmetry.

If a is *positive,* the parabola opens *upward;* if a is *negative,* the parabola opens *downward.*

If $|a|$ is greater than 1 ($|a| > 1$), the parabola is narrower than the parabola $f(x) = x^2$.

If $|a|$ is between 0 and 1 ($0 < |a| < 1$), the parabola is wider than the parabola $f(x) = x^2$.

Using this information, you can draw the graph of any parabola of the form $g(x) = ax^2$, as we illustrate in Example 2.

EXAMPLE 2 Graphing More Parabolas

Graph

(a) $f(x) = 3x^2$. **(b)** $g(x) = -3x^2$. **(c)** $h(x) = \frac{1}{3}x^2$.

Solution

(a) By looking at the properties of the parabola $y = ax^2$, we know that the vertex of the parabola $f(x) = 3x^2$ is at the origin and that the y axis is its line of symmetry. Since $3 > 0$, we also know that the parabola $f(x) = 3x^2$ opens upward and is narrower than the parabola $y = x^2$. We pick three easy points to complete our graph, which is shown in Figure 7.31.

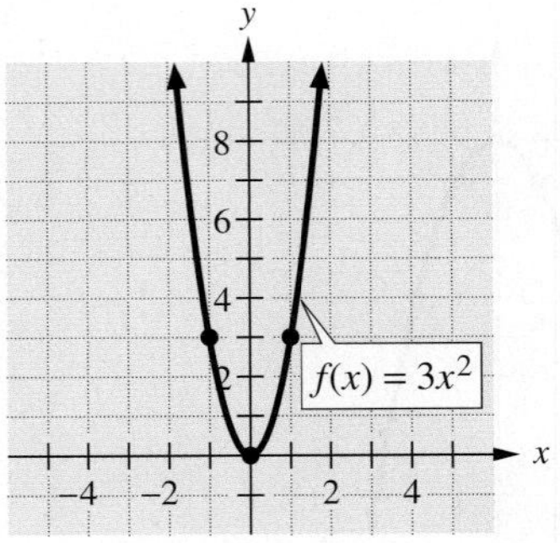

FIGURE 7.31

x	$y = 3x^2$
−1	$y = 3(-1)^2 = 3$
0	$y = 3(0)^2 = 0$
1	$y = 3(1)^2 = 3$

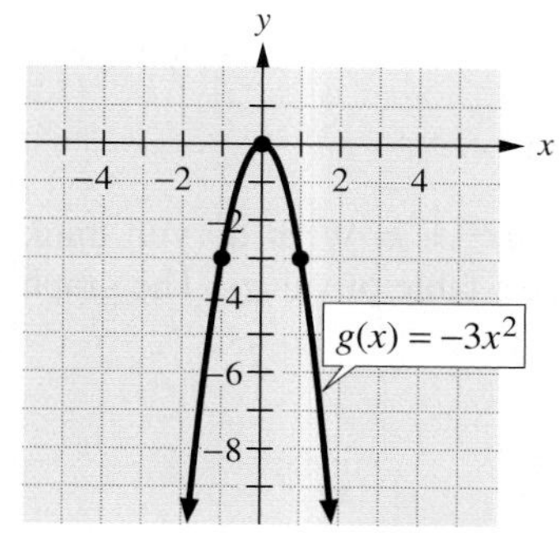

FIGURE 7.32

(b) The parabola $g(x) = -3x^2$ opens downward but is still narrower than the parabola $y = x^2$. As a matter of fact, the parabola $g(x) = -3x^2$ is the reflection of the parabola $f(x) = 3x^2$ across the x axis. Again, we pick three points to complete the graph, which is shown in Figure 7.32.

x	$y = -3x^2$
-1	$y = -3(-1)^2 = -3$
0	$y = -3(0)^2 = 0$
1	$y = -3(1)^2 = -3$

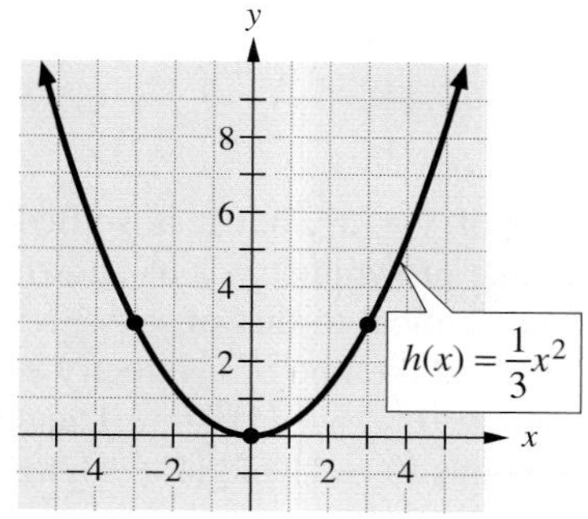

FIGURE 7.33

(c) The parabola $h(x) = \frac{1}{3}x^2$ opens upward because $\frac{1}{3} > 0$ but is wider than the parabola $y = x^2$. This time, instead of selecting $x = -1$, 0, and 1, we select $x = -3$, 0, and 3 for ease of computation. The completed graph is shown in Figure 7.33.

x	$y = \frac{1}{3}x^2$
-3	$y = \frac{1}{3}(-3)^2 = 3$
0	$y = \frac{1}{3}(0)^2 = 0$
3	$y = \frac{1}{3}(3)^2 = 3$

What do you think will happen if we graph the parabola $y = x^2 + 2$? Two things: First, the parabola opens upward because the coefficient of x^2 is understood to be $+1$. Second, all the points will be 2 units higher than those for the same value of x on the parabola $y = x^2$. Thus we can make the graph of $y = x^2 + 2$ by following the pattern of $y = x^2$. The graphs of $y = x^2 + 2$, $y = x^2 + 4$, $y = x^2 - 2$, and $y = x^2 - 4$ are shown in Figure 7.34. The points used to make the graphs are listed in the following table:

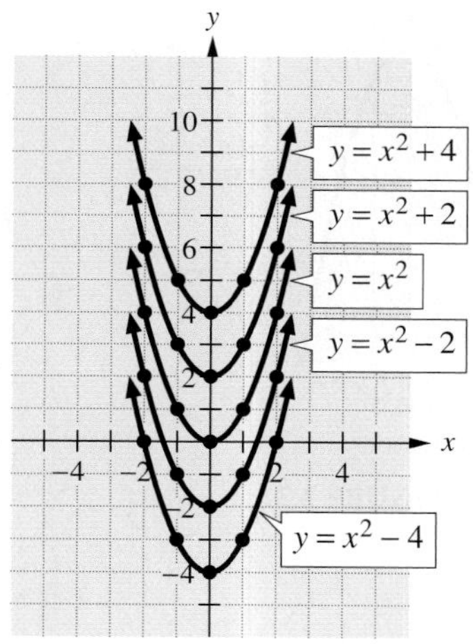

FIGURE 7.34

	For $y = x^2 + 2$		For $y = x^2 + 4$		For $y = x^2 - 2$		For $y = x^2 - 4$	
	x	y	x	y	x	y	x	y
Vertex →	0	2	0	4	0	-2	0	-4
	±1	3	±1	5	±1	-1	±1	-3
	±2	6	±2	8	±2	2	±2	0

Note that adding or subtracting a positive number k on the right-hand side of equation $y = x^2$ raises or lowers the graph (and the vertex) by k units.

EXAMPLE 3 Graphing Parabolas Opening Downward

Graph $y = -x^2 - 2$.

Solution

Since the coefficient of x^2 (which is understood to be -1) is negative, the parabola opens downward. It is also 2 units lower than the graph of $y = -x^2$. Thus the graph of $y = -x^2 - 2$ is a parabola opening downward with its vertex at $(0, -2)$. Letting $x = 1$, we get $y = -3$, and for $x = 2$, $y = -6$. Graph the two points $(1, -3)$ and $(2, -6)$ and, by symmetry, the points $(-1, -3)$ and $(-2, -6)$. The parabola passing through all these points is shown in Figure 7.35.

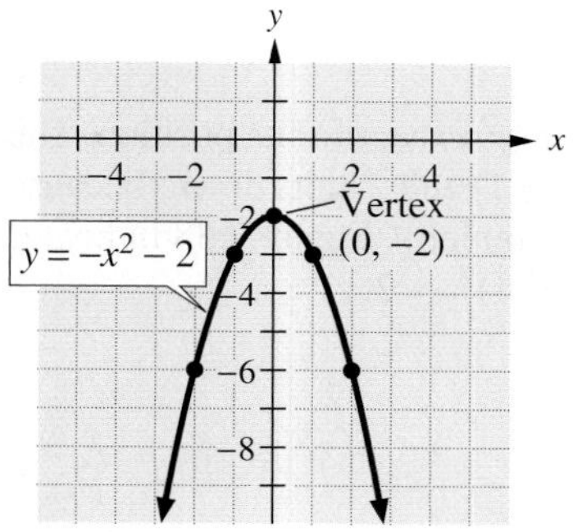

FIGURE 7.35

B Graphing a Parabola of the Form $y = f(x) = a(x - h)^2 + k$

So far we have graphed only parabolas of the form $y = ax^2 + k$. What do you think the graph of $y = (x - 1)^2$ looks like? As before, we make a table of values. The graph appears in Figure 7.36.

x	$y = (x - 1)^2$	
$x = -1$	$y = (-1 - 1)^2 = (-2)^2 = 4$	
$x = 0$	$y = (0 - 1)^2 = (-1)^2 = 1$	← y intercept
$x = 1$	$y = (1 - 1)^2 = (0)^2 = 0$	← Vertex
$x = 2$	$y = (2 - 1)^2 = 1^2 = 1$	
$x = 3$	$y = (3 - 1)^2 = 2^2 = 4$	

or

x	y
−1	4
0	1
1	0
2	1
3	4

Note that the shape of the graph is identical to that of $y = x^2$, but it is shifted 1 unit to the *right*. Thus, the vertex is at $(1, 0)$, and the line of symmetry is as shown in Figure 7.36. Similarly, the graph of $y = -(x + 1)^2$ is identical to that of $y = -x^2$ but shifted 1 unit to the *left*. Thus the vertex is at $(-1, 0)$, and the line of symmetry is as shown in Figure 7.37. Some easy points to plot are $x = 0, y = -(1)^2 = -1$ and $x = 1, y = -(1 + 1)^2 = -2^2 = -4$. When we plot the points $(0, -1)$ and $(1, -4)$, by symmetry, the points $(-2, -1)$ and $(-3, -4)$ are also on the graph.

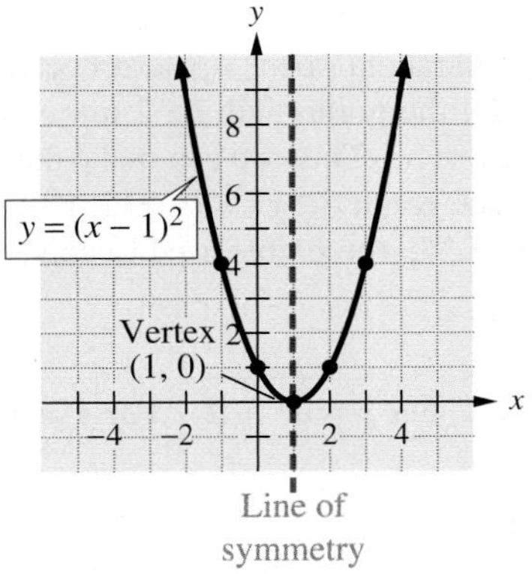

FIGURE 7.36

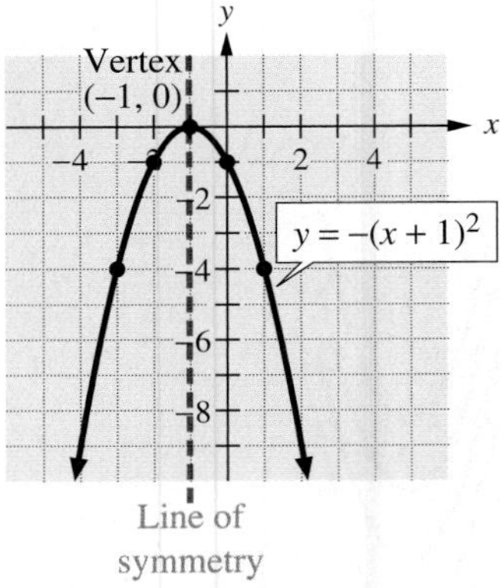

FIGURE 7.37

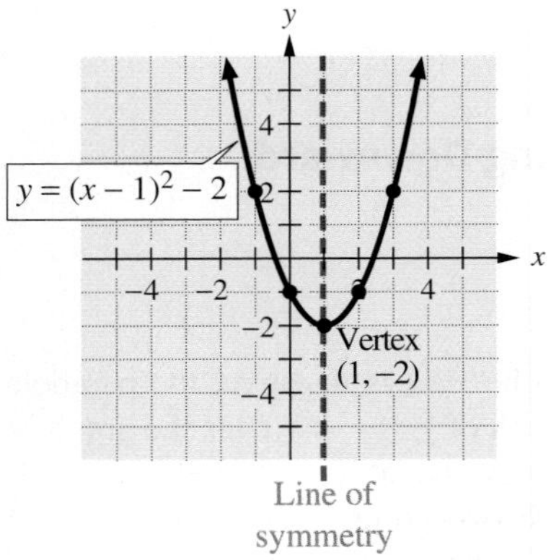

FIGURE 7.38

EXAMPLE 4 Graphing Parabolas Using Shifts

Graph $y = (x - 1)^2 - 2$.

Solution

The graph of this equation is identical to the graph of $y = x^2$ except for its position. The new parabola is shifted 1 unit to the right (because of the -1) and 2 units down (because of the -2). Thus the vertex is $(1, -2)$. Note the line of symmetry. Figure 7.38 indicates these two facts and shows the finished graph of $y = (x - 1)^2 - 2$.

$$y = (x - 1)^2 - 2$$

Opens upward (positive) — Shifted 1 unit right — Shifted 2 units down

Vertex $(1, -2)$

From these examples we can see that

1. The graph of $y = -x^2 - 2$ (Example 3) is exactly the same as the graph of $y = -x^2$ (Example 1) but moved 2 units *down.* In general, the graph of $y = ax^2 + k$ is the same as the graph of $y = ax^2$ but moved vertically k units. The vertex is at $(0, k)$.
2. The graph of $y = (x - 1)^2$ is the same as that of $y = x^2$ but moved 1 unit *right.* The vertex is at $(1, 0)$.
3. The graph of $y = (x - 1)^2 - 2$ (Example 4) is exactly the same as the graph of $y = (x - 1)^2$ but moved 2 units *down.* The vertex is at $(1, -2)$.

Here is the summary of this discussion.

> **Properties of the Parabola $y = a(x - h)^2 + k$**
>
> The graph of the parabola $y = a(x - h)^2 + k$ is the same as that of $y = ax^2$ but moved h units **horizontally** and k units **vertically.** The *vertex* is at the point (h, k), and the line of symmetry is $x = h$.

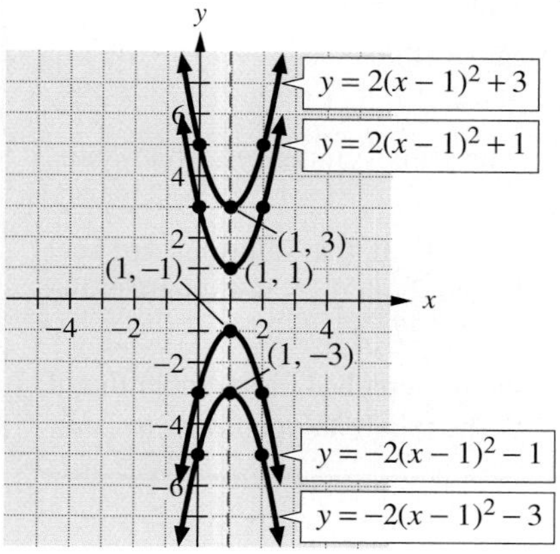

FIGURE 7.39

In conclusion, follow the given directions to graph an equation of the form

$$y = a(x - h)^2 + k \qquad \text{Vertex } (h, k)$$

- a: Opens upward for $a > 0$, downward for $a < 0$.
- h: Shifts the graph right or left.
- k: Moves the graph up or down.

The graphs of $y = 2(x - 1)^2 + 1$, $y = 2(x - 1)^2 + 3$, $y = -2(x - 1)^2 - 1$, and $y = -2(x - 1)^2 - 3$ are shown in Figure 7.39.

C Graphing the Parabola $y = f(x) = ax^2 + bx + c$

How can we graph $f(x) = ax^2 + bx + c$? If we learn to write $f(x) = ax^2 + bx + c$ as $f(x) = a(x - h)^2 + k$, we can do it by using the techniques we just learned. We do this by completing the square. Here's how.

$$f(x) = ax^2 + bx + c \qquad \text{Given.}$$

$$= (ax^2 + bx) + c \qquad \text{Group.}$$

$$= a\left(x^2 + \frac{b}{a}x + \quad\right) + c \qquad \text{Factor } a.$$

$$= a\left[x^2 + \frac{b}{a}x + \left(\frac{b}{2a}\right)^2 - \left(\frac{b}{2a}\right)^2\right] + c \qquad \text{To complete the square, add and subtract } \left(\frac{1}{2}\cdot\frac{b}{a}\right)^2 = \left(\frac{b}{2a}\right)^2 \text{ inside the brackets.}$$

$$= a\left(x + \frac{b}{2a}\right)^2 - a\left(\frac{b}{2a}\right)^2 + c \qquad \text{Use the distributive property and factor inside the brackets.}$$

$$= a\left(x + \frac{b}{2a}\right)^2 - a\cdot\frac{b^2}{4a^2} + c \qquad \text{Square } \frac{b}{2a}.$$

$$= a\left(x + \frac{b}{2a}\right)^2 - \frac{b^2}{4a} + c \qquad \text{Multiply } -a\cdot\frac{b^2}{4a^2} = -\frac{b^2}{4a}.$$

$$= a\left(x + \frac{b}{2a}\right)^2 + \frac{4ac - b^2}{4a} \qquad \text{Find the LCD of } -b^2/4a \text{ and } c.$$

Thus to write

$$f(x) = a\underbrace{\left(x + \frac{b}{2a}\right)^2}_{} + \underbrace{\frac{4ac - b^2}{4a}}_{}$$

as

$$f(x) = a(x - h)^2 + k$$

we must have

$$h = -\frac{b}{2a} \quad \text{and} \quad k = \frac{4ac - b^2}{4a}$$

the coordinates of the vertex. Note that you *do not* have to memorize the y coordinate of the vertex. After you find the x coordinate, substitute in the equation and find y.

Here is a summary of our discussion.

Graphing the Parabola $y = f(x) = ax^2 + bx + c$

1. To find the vertex, use one of the following methods:

   Method 1 Let $x = -b/2a$ in the equation and solve for y.

   Method 2 Complete the square and compare with $y = a(x - h)^2 + k$.
2. Let $x = 0$. The result c is the y intercept.
3. Since the parabola is symmetric to its axis, use this symmetry to find additional points.
4. Let $y = 0$. Find x by solving $ax^2 + bx + c = 0$. If the solutions are real numbers, they are the x intercepts. If not, the parabola does not intersect the x axis.
5. Draw a smooth curve through the points found in steps 1–4. Remember that if $a > 0$, the parabola opens *upward;* if $a < 0$, the parabola opens *downward.*

We demonstrate this procedure in Example 5.

EXAMPLE 5 Graphing Parabolas Using Two Methods

Graph $y = x^2 + 3x + 2$.

Solution

1. We first find the vertex using either of the two methods.

Method 1

Use the vertex formula for the x coordinate. Since $a = 1$, $b = 3$, and $c = 2$,

$$x = -\frac{b}{2a} = -\frac{3}{2}$$

Substituting for x in the equation gives

$$\begin{aligned} y &= x^2 + 3x + 2 \\ &= \left(-\frac{3}{2}\right)^2 + 3\left(-\frac{3}{2}\right) + 2 \\ &= \frac{9}{4} - \frac{9}{2} + 2 \\ &= \frac{9}{4} - \frac{18}{4} + \frac{8}{4} = -\frac{1}{4} \end{aligned}$$

The vertex is at $\left(-\frac{3}{2}, -\frac{1}{4}\right)$.

Method 2

Complete the square.

$$\begin{aligned} y &= (x^2 + 3x + \quad) + 2 \\ &= \left[x^2 + 3x + \left(\frac{3}{2}\right)^2\right] + 2 - \left(\frac{3}{2}\right)^2 \\ &= \left(x + \frac{3}{2}\right)^2 + 2 - \frac{9}{4} \\ &= \left(x + \frac{3}{2}\right)^2 - \frac{1}{4} \end{aligned}$$

The vertex is at $\left(-\frac{3}{2}, -\frac{1}{4}\right)$.

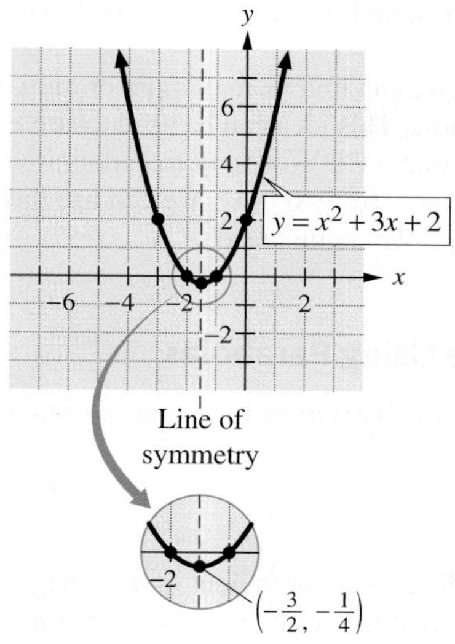

FIGURE 7.40

2. Let $x = 0$; then $y = x^2 + 3x + 2$ becomes $y = 2$. The y intercept is 2.
3. By symmetry, the point $(-3, 2)$ is also on the graph.
4. Let $y = 0$; $y = x^2 + 3x + 2$ becomes

$$\begin{aligned} 0 &= x^2 + 3x + 2 \\ &= (x + 2)(x + 1) \end{aligned}$$

Thus $x = -2$ or $x = -1$. The graph intersects the x axis at $(-2, 0)$ and $(-1, 0)$.

5. Since the coefficient of x^2 is 1, $a > 0$, and the parabola opens upward.

We draw a smooth curve through these points to obtain the graph of the parabola, as shown in Figure 7.40.

EXAMPLE 6 Parabolas Opening Down

Graph $y = -2x^2 + 4x - 3$.

Solution

1. To find the vertex, we can use either of these methods.

Method 1

Use the vertex formula.

Here $a = -2$ and $b = 4$, so

$$\begin{aligned} x &= -\frac{b}{2a} \\ &= \frac{-4}{2(-2)} \\ &= 1 \end{aligned}$$

Method 2

Complete the square.

$$\begin{aligned} y &= -2x^2 + 4x - 3 \\ &= -2(x^2 - 2x + \quad) - 3 \\ &= -2(x^2 - 2x + 1) - 3 + 2 \\ &= -2(x - 1)^2 - 1 \end{aligned}$$

The vertex is at $(1, -1)$.

If we substitute $x = 1$ in $y = -2x^2 + 4x - 3$,

$$\begin{aligned} y &= -2(1)^2 + 4(1) - 3 \\ &= -2 + 4 - 3 \\ &= -1 \end{aligned}$$

Thus the vertex is at $(1, -1)$.

2. If $x = 0$, $y = -2x^2 + 4x - 3 = -3$, the y intercept.
3. We graph the vertex $(1, -1)$ and the y intercept -3. To make a more accurate graph, we need some more points. Since the parabola is symmetric, we can find a point across from the y intercept by letting $x = 2$. Then

$$\begin{aligned} y &= -2(2)^2 + 4(2) - 3 \\ &= -8 + 8 - 3 = -3 \end{aligned}$$

as expected.

4. For $y = 0$, $0 = -2x^2 + 4x - 3$. However, the right-hand side is not factorable, and the vertex $(1, -1)$ is below the x axis. This means that this equation has no solution, and there are no x intercepts; the graph does not cross the x axis.
5. Since $a = -2 < 0$, the parabola opens downward. The completed graph is shown in Figure 7.41.

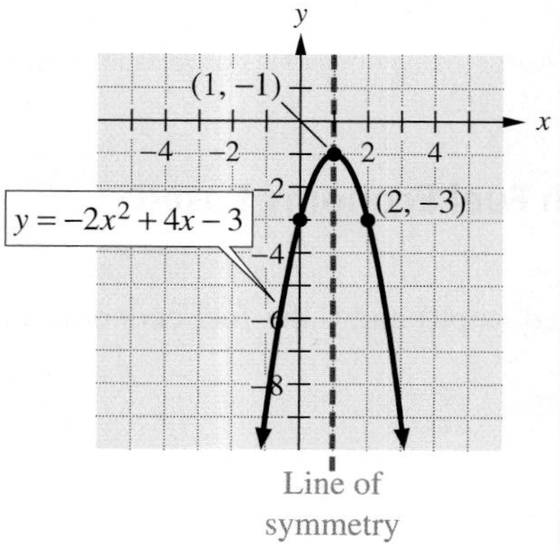

FIGURE 7.41

D Solving Applications Involving Parabolas

Every parabola of the form $y = ax^2 + bx + c$ that we have graphed has its vertex at either its maximum (highest) or minimum (lowest) point on the graph. If the graph

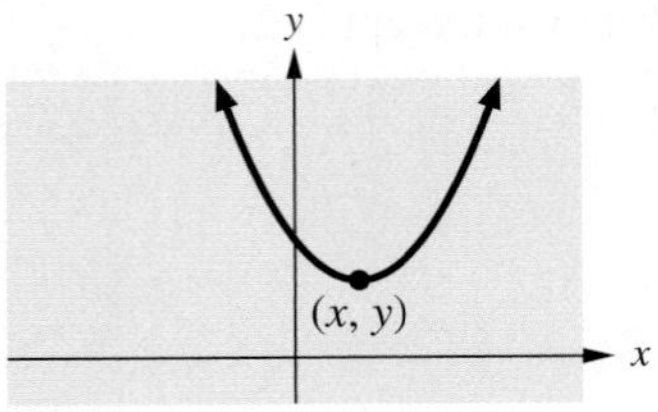

FIGURE 7.42 $f(x)$ has a minimum at the vertex (x, y).

opens upward, the vertex is the minimum (Figure 7.42), and if the graph opens downward, the vertex is the maximum (Figure 7.43).

Thus, if we are dealing with a quadratic function, we can find its maximum or minimum by finding the vertex of the corresponding parabola. This idea can be used to solve many real-world applications. For example, suppose that a CD company manufactures and sells x CDs per week. If the revenue is given by $R = 10x - 0.01x^2$, we can use the techniques we've just studied to maximize the revenue. We do this next.

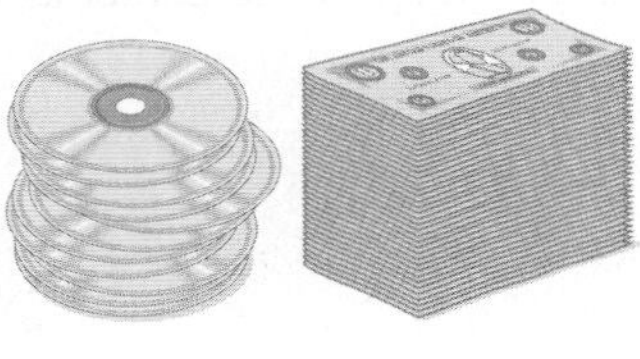

EXAMPLE 7 Finding Maximum Revenue Using Parabolas

If $R = 10x - 0.01x^2$, how many CDs does the company have to sell in order to obtain maximum revenue?

Solution

We first write the equation as $R = -0.01x^2 + 10x$. Since the coefficient of x^2 is negative, the parabola opens downward (is concave down), and the vertex is its highest point. Letting

$$x = -\frac{b}{2a} = -\frac{10}{-0.02} = 500$$

$R = 10(500) - 0.01(500)^2 = 5000 - 2500 = 2500$. Thus, when the company sells $x = 500$ CDs a week, the revenue is a maximum: \$2500.

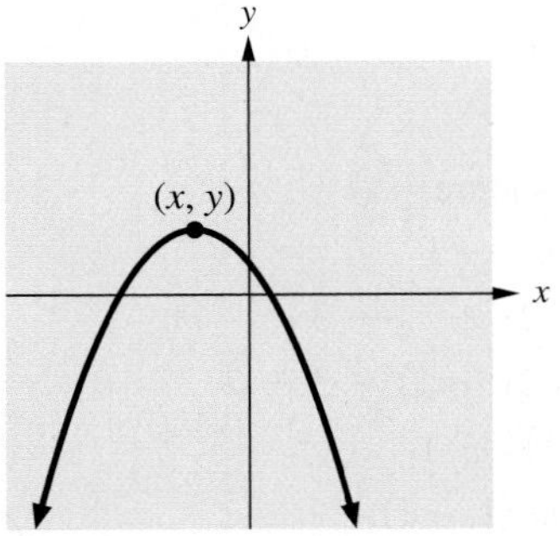

FIGURE 7.43 $f(x)$ has a maximum at the vertex (x, y).

The graph on the right shows the gas mileage y of a car based on its speed x in mph. How was that graph constructed? A fairly accurate approximation for fuel economy is $y = -0.01x^2 + x + 5$, where x is the speed in miles per hour with the graph starting at $x = 5$. You should recognize the general shape of the graph as that of a parabola. Let us create our own graph and see how close we come to the original!

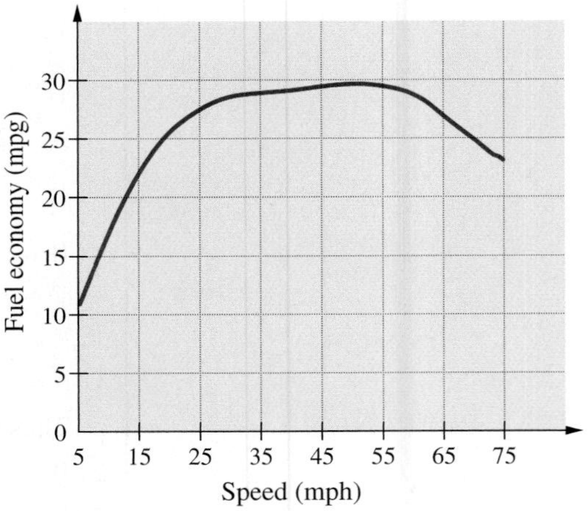

Source: http://www.fueleconomy.gov/FEG/driveHabits.shtml.

EXAMPLE 8 Using Parabolas to Graph Fuel Economy Based on Speed

Graph $y = -0.01x^2 + x + 5$, where x is the speed (mph) and y the fuel economy in miles per gallon (mpg).

Solution

Let us look at some facts about $y = -0.01x^2 + x + 5$.

1. $y = -0.01x^2 + x + 5$ is of the form $y = ax^2 + bx + c$, with $a = -0.01$, $b = 1$, and $c = 5$.

$$y = -0.01\,x^2 + 1x + 5$$
$$a = -0.01 \quad b = 1 \quad c = 5$$

so its graph is a *parabola*.

2. Since the coefficient of $x^2(-0.01)$ is negative, the *parabola* opens downward.
3. The x coordinate of the vertex is $x = \frac{-b}{2a} = \frac{-1}{2(-0.01)} = \frac{1}{0.02} = \frac{1}{2/100} = 50$ and $y = -0.01(50)^2 + 50 + 5 = -0.01(2500) + 50 + 5 = -25 + 50 + 5 = 30.$

   This means that the vertex is at $(50, 30)$.
4. When $x = 5$, $y = -0.01(5)^2 + 5 + 5$
   $= -0.01(25) + 5 + 5$
   $= -0.25 + 10 = 9.75.$
5. When $x = 70$, $y = -0.01(70)^2 + 70 + 5$
   $= -0.01(4900) + 70 + 5$
   $= -49 + 70 + 5 = 26.$

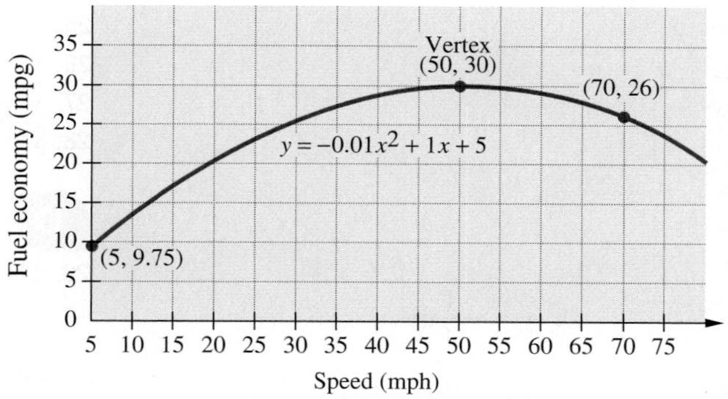

Graph the three points we have obtained: $(5, 9.75)$, the vertex $(50, 30)$, and $(70, 26)$. Join them with a smooth parabola opening downward as shown. As you can see, the result is very similar to the original graph.

We close this section by presenting a summary of the material we have studied in Table 7.9.

Table 7.9 Summary of Parabolas

Description	Graph When $a > 0$	Graph When $a < 0$
$f(x) = ax^2 + k$ A parabola with vertex at $(0, k)$ When $\lvert a\rvert > 1$, the graph is narrower than the graph of $y = x^2$. When $0 < \lvert a\rvert < 1$, it is wider.	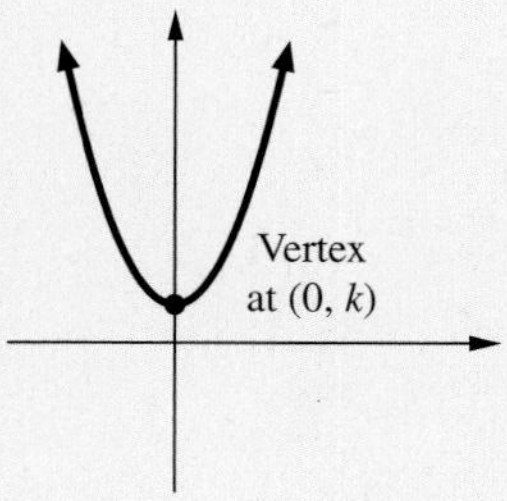 For $a > 0$, the parabola opens upward.	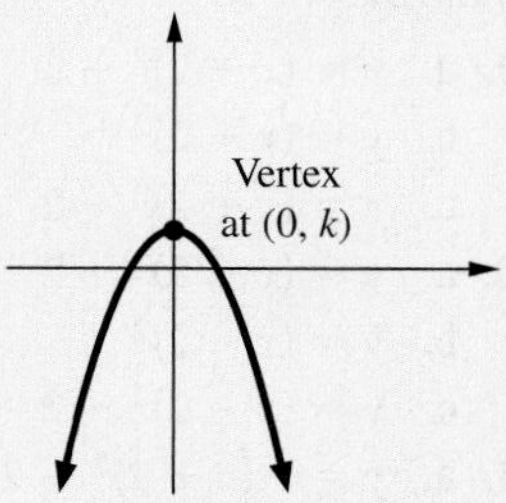 For $a < 0$, the parabola opens downward.
$f(x) = a(x - h)^2 + k$ A parabola with vertex at (h, k) When $\lvert a\rvert > 1$, the graph is narrower than the graph of $y = x^2$. When $0 < \lvert a\rvert < 1$, it is wider.	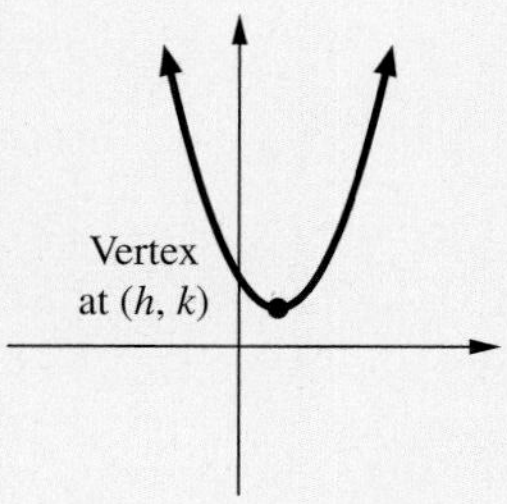 For $a > 0$, the parabola opens upward.	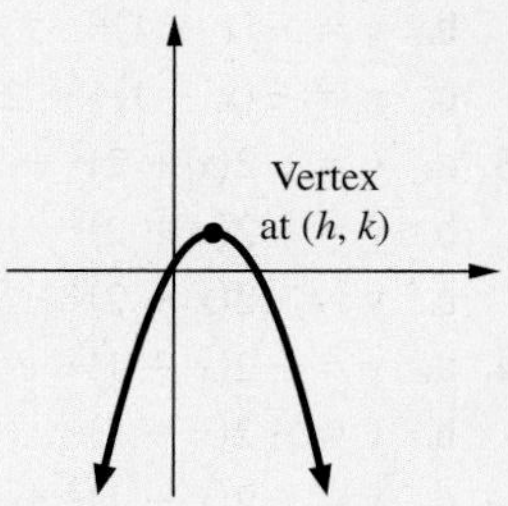 For $a < 0$, the parabola opens downward.

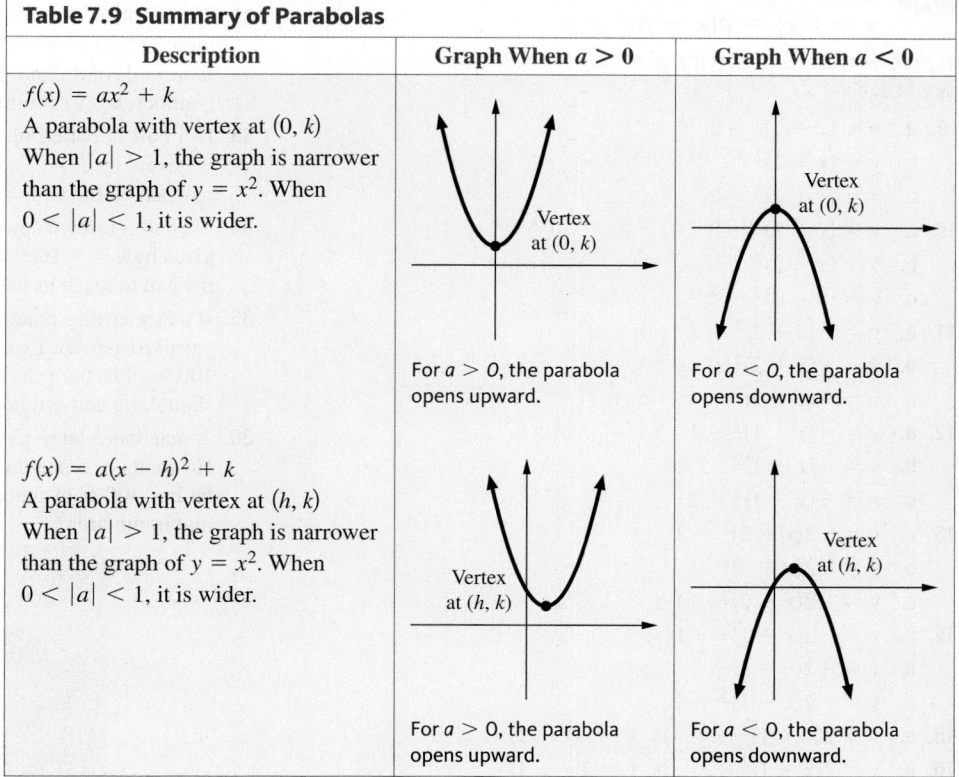

7.4 EXERCISES

A Graphing the Parabola $y = f(x) = ax^2 = k$

In problems 1–8, graph the given equations on the same coordinate axes.

1. a. $y = 2x^2$
   b. $y = 2x^2 + 2$
   c. $y = 2x^2 - 2$
2. a. $y = 3x^2 + 1$
   b. $y = 3x^2 + 3$
   c. $y = 3x^2 - 2$
3. a. $y = -2x^2$
   b. $y = -2x^2 + 1$
   c. $y = -2x^2 - 1$
4. a. $y = -4x^2$
   b. $y = -4x^2 + 1$
   c. $y = -4x^2 - 1$
5. a. $y = \frac{1}{4}x^2$ b. $y = -\frac{1}{4}x^2$
6. a. $y = \frac{1}{5}x^2$ b. $y = -\frac{1}{5}x^2$
7. a. $y = \frac{1}{3}x^2 + 1$ b. $y = -\frac{1}{3}x^2 + 1$
8. a. $y = \frac{1}{4}x^2 + 1$ b. $y = -\frac{1}{4}x^2 + 1$

B Graphing a Parabola of the Form $y = f(x) = a(x - h)^2 = k$

In problems 9–16, graph the given equations on the same coordinate axes.

9. a. $y = (x + 2)^2 + 3$
   b. $y = (x + 2)^2$
   c. $y = (x + 2)^2 - 2$
10. a. $y = (x - 2)^2 + 2$
    b. $y = (x - 2)^2$
    c. $y = (x - 2)^2 - 2$
11. a. $y = -(x + 2)^2 - 2$
    b. $y = -(x + 2)^2$
    c. $y = -(x + 2)^2 - 4$
12. a. $y = -(x - 1)^2 + 1$
    b. $y = -(x - 1)^2$
    c. $y = -(x - 1)^2 + 2$
13. a. $y = -2(x + 2)^2 - 2$
    b. $y = -2(x + 2)^2$
    c. $y = -2(x + 2)^2 - 4$
14. a. $y = -2(x - 1)^2 + 1$
    b. $y = -2(x - 1)^2$
    c. $y = -2(x - 1)^2 + 2$
15. a. $y = 2(x + 1)^2 + \frac{1}{2}$ b. $y = 2(x + 1)^2$
16. a. $y = 2(x + 1)^2 - \frac{1}{2}$ b. $y = 2(x + 1)^2$

C Graphing the Parabola $y = f(x) = ax^2 + bx + c$

In problems 17–28, use the five-step procedure in the text to sketch the graph. Label the vertex and the intercepts.

17. $y = x^2 + 2x + 1$
18. $y = x^2 + 4x + 4$
19. $y = -x^2 + 2x + 1$
20. $y = -x^2 + 4x - 2$
21. $y = -x^2 + 4x - 5$
22. $y = -x^2 + 4x - 3$
23. $y = 3 - 5x + 2x^2$
24. $y = 3 + 5x + 2x^2$
25. $y = 5 - 4x - 2x^2$ (*Hint:* $\sqrt{56} \simeq 7.5$)
26. $y = 3 - 4x - 2x^2$ (*Hint:* $\sqrt{40} \simeq 6.3$)
27. $y = -3x^2 + 3x + 2$ (*Hint:* $\sqrt{33} \simeq 5.7$)
28. $y = -3x^2 + 3x + 1$ (*Hint:* $\sqrt{21} \simeq 4.6$)

D Solving Applications Involving Parabolas

29. The profit P (in dollars) for a company is given by $P = -5000 + 8x - 0.001x^2$, where x is the number of items produced each month. How many items does the company have to produce in order to obtain maximum profit? What is this profit?
30. The revenue R for Shady Glasses is given by $R = 1500p - 75p^2$, where p is the price of each pair of sunglasses (R and p in dollars). What should the price be to maximize revenue?
31. After spending x thousand dollars in an advertising campaign, the number N of units sold is given by $N = 50x - x^2$. How much should be spent in the campaign to obtain maximum sales?
32. The number N of units of a product sold after a television commercial blitz is $N = 40x - x^2$, where x is the amount spent in thousands of dollars. How much should be spent on television commercials to obtain maximum sales?
33. If a ball is batted up at 160 ft/sec, its height h ft after t sec is given by $h = -16t^2 + 160t$. Find the maximum height reached by the ball.
34. If a ball is thrown upward at 20 ft/sec, its height h ft after t sec is given by $h = -16t^2 + 20t$. How many seconds does it take for the ball to reach its maximum height, and what is this height?
35. If a farmer digs potatoes today, she will have 600 bu (bushels) worth \$1 per bu. Every week she waits, the crop increases by 100 bu, but the price decreases \$.10 a bushel. Show that she should dig and sell her potatoes at the end of 2 weeks.
36. A man has a large piece of property along Washington Street. He wants to fence the sides and back of a rectangular plot. If he has 400 ft of fencing, what dimensions will give him the maximum area?

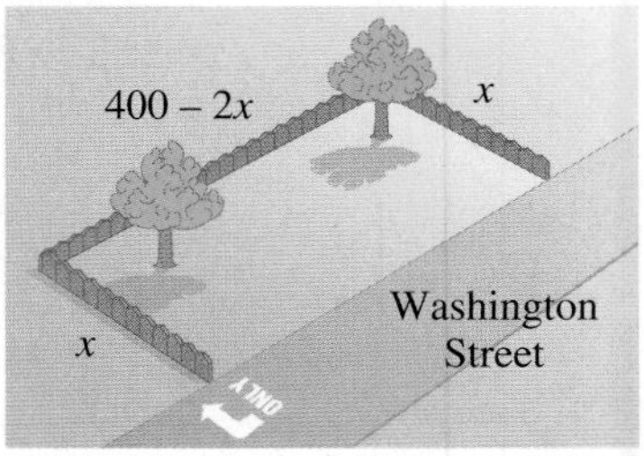

37. Have you read the story "The Celebrated Jumping Frog of Calaveras County"? According to the *Guinness Book of Records*, the second greatest distance covered by a frog in a triple jump is 21 ft $5\frac{3}{4}$ in. at the annual Calaveras Jumping Jubilee; this occurred on May 18, 1986.

   a. If Rosie the Ribiter's (the winner) path in her first jump is approximated by $R = -\frac{1}{98}x^2 + \frac{6}{7}x$ (where x is the horizontal distance covered in inches), what are the coordinates of the vertex of Rosie's path?

   b. Find the maximum height attained by Rosie in her first jump.

   c. Use symmetry to find the horizontal length of Rosie's first jump.

   d. Make a sketch for R showing the initial position (0, 0), the vertex, and Rosie's ending position after her first jump.

38. Amazingly, Rosie's jump is not the best triple jump on record. That distinction belongs to Santjie, a South African frog that jumped 33 ft $5\frac{1}{2}$ in. on May 21, 1977.

   a. If Santjie's path in his first jump is approximated by $S = -\frac{1}{200}x^2 + \frac{7}{10}x$ (where x is the distance covered in inches), what are the coordinates of the vertex of Santjie's path?

   b. Find Santjie's maximum height in his first jump.

   c. Use symmetry to find the horizontal length of Santjie's first jump.

   d. Make a sketch for S showing the initial position (0, 0), the vertex, and Santjie's ending position after his first jump.

39. A baseball hit at an angle of 35° has a velocity of 130 mph. Its trajectory can be approximated by the equation $d = -\frac{1}{400}x^2 + x$, where x is the distance the ball travels in feet.

   a. What are the coordinates of the vertex of the trajectory?

   b. Find the maximum height attained by the ball.

   c. Use symmetry to find how far the ball travels horizontally.

   d. Make a sketch for d showing the initial position (0, 0), the vertex, and the ending position of the baseball.

40. Is there a relationship between mothers who smoke and the percent of low-birth-weight babies? Do Problems 40 and 41 to see!

   a. What is the (approximate) lowest percent of low-birth-weight babies for mothers who smoke? At what (approximate) age does it occur?

   b. What is the (approximate) highest percent of low-birth-weight babies for mothers who smoke? At what (approximate) age does it occur?

   c. If the function representing the graph is of the form $f(x) = ax^2 + bx + c$, what can you say about a?

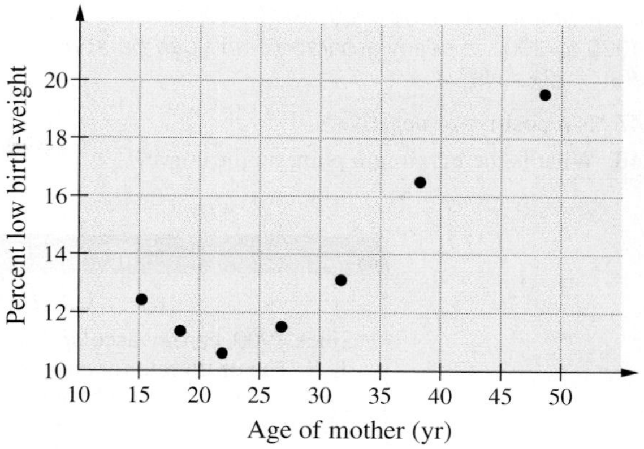

Source: www.uvm.edu/~dhowell/gradstat/psych340/Lectures/CorrelReg/correl1.html.

Mothers who smoke.

41. The relationship between the percent of low birth weight and age for mothers who *do not* smoke is shown below.

   a. What is the (approximate) lowest percent of low-birth-weight babies for mothers who do not smoke? At what (approximate) age does it occur?

   b. What is the (approximate) highest percent of low-birth-weight babies for mothers who do not smoke?

   c. At what (approximate) age do mothers who smoke have the lowest percent of low-birth-weight babies?

   d. At what (approximate) age do mothers who *do not* smoke have the highest percent of low-birth-weight babies?

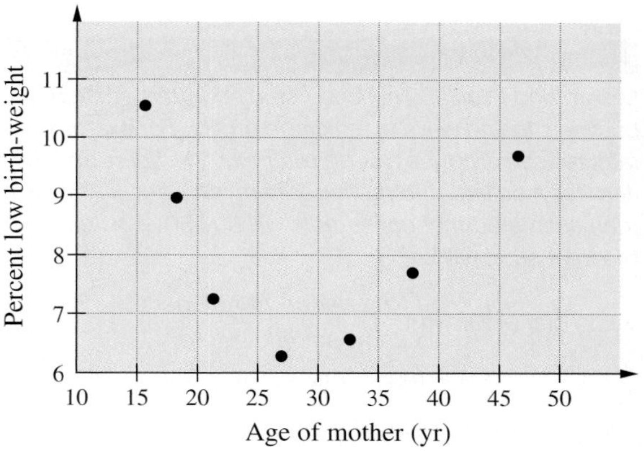

Source: www.uvm.edu/~dhowell/gradstat/psych340/Lectures/CorrelReg/correl1.html.

Mothers who do not smoke.

IN OTHER WORDS

42. Explain how you determine whether the graph of a quadratic function opens up or down.

43. What causes the graph of the function $f(x) = ax^2$ to be wider or narrower than the graph of $f(x) = x^2$?

44. What is the effect of the constant k on the graph of the function $f(x) = ax^2 + k$?

45. How does a parabola that has two x intercepts and vertex at (1, 1) open; that is, does it open up or down? Why?

46. Why does the graph of a function never have two y intercepts?

In the graph below, the death rate for cardiovascular disease from 1920 to 2001 is nearly a parabola and can be approximated by $f(x) = a(x - h)^2 + k$.

47. Is a positive or negative?

48. What is the maximum point on the curve?

49. What are the approximate coordinates for the vertex of the curve?

50. On the basis of the graph, what would you predict the number of deaths (per 100,000 population) due to cardiovascular disease to be in the year 2010?

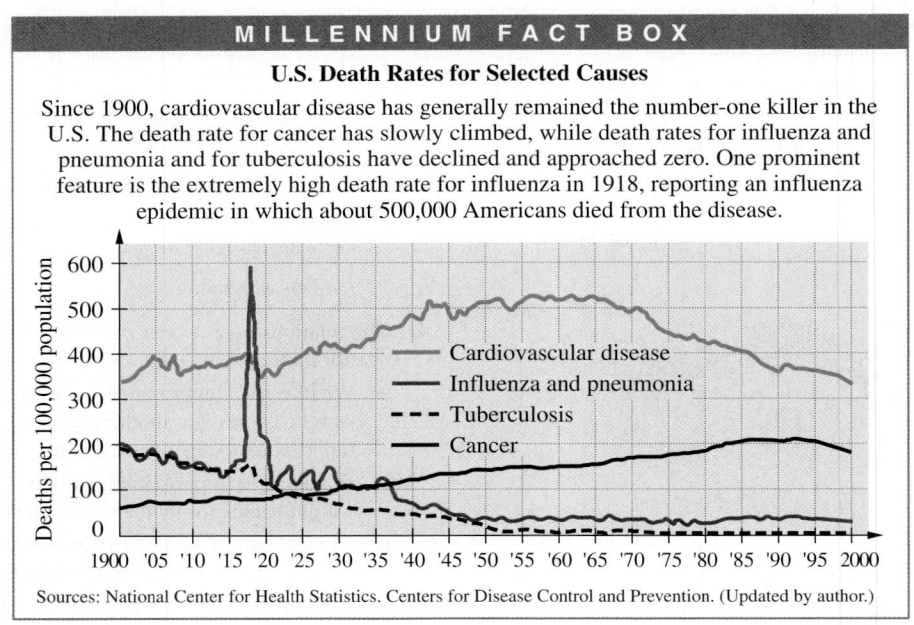

MILLENNIUM FACT BOX

U.S. Death Rates for Selected Causes

Since 1900, cardiovascular disease has generally remained the number-one killer in the U.S. The death rate for cancer has slowly climbed, while death rates for influenza and pneumonia and for tuberculosis have declined and approached zero. One prominent feature is the extremely high death rate for influenza in 1918, reporting an influenza epidemic in which about 500,000 Americans died from the disease.

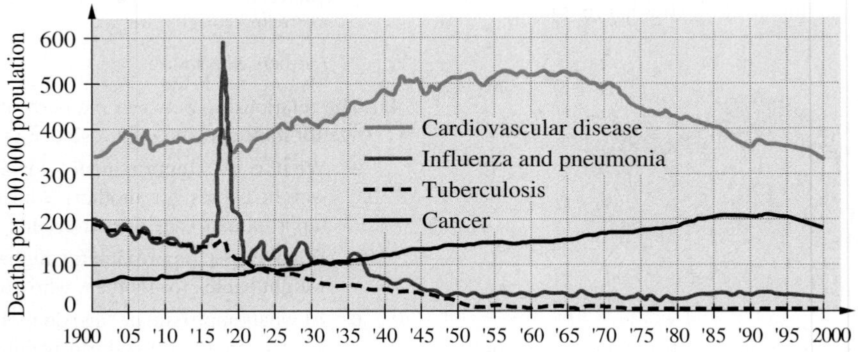

Sources: National Center for Health Statistics. Centers for Disease Control and Prevention. (Updated by author.)

USING YOUR KNOWLEDGE

Maximizing Profits. The ideas studied in this section are used in business to find ways to maximize profits. For example, if a manufacturer can produce a certain item for \$10 each, and then sell the item for x dollars, the profit per item will be $x - 10$ *dollars. If it is then estimated that consumers will buy* $60 - x$ *items per month, the total profit will be*

$$\text{Total profit} = \begin{pmatrix}\text{Number of}\\ \text{items sold}\end{pmatrix}\begin{pmatrix}\text{Profit per}\\ \text{item}\end{pmatrix}$$
$$= (60 - x)(x - 10)$$

The graph for the total profit is this parabola:

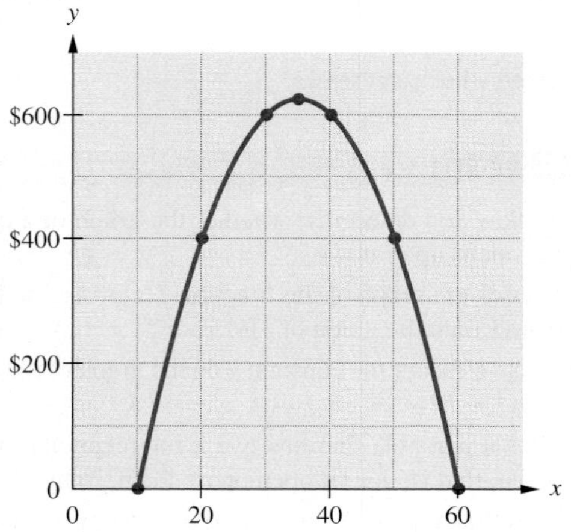

When will the profits be at a maximum? When the manufacturer produces 35 items. Note that 35 is exactly halfway between

$$10 \quad \text{and} \quad 60 \quad \left(\frac{10 + 60}{2} = 35\right)$$

At this price, the total profits will be.

$$\begin{aligned} P_T &= (60 - 35)(35 - 10) \\ &= (25)(25) \\ &= \$625 \end{aligned}$$

Use your knowledge to answer the following questions.

51. What price would maximize the profits of a certain item costing \$20 each if $60 - x$ items are sold each month (where x is the selling price of each item)?

52. Sketch the graph of the resulting parabola.

53. What will the maximum profits be?

7.5 Exponential and Logarithmic Functions

GETTING STARTED

OBJECTIVES

A. Graph exponential functions.
B. Solve applications involving exponential functions.
C. Graph logarithmic functions.
D. Solve applications involving exponential or logarithmic functions.

DON'T DRINK AND DRIVE!

Is there a relationship between blood alcohol level (BAC) and the probability of having an accident? Absolutely! As the chart shows, the probability $P(b)$ of having an accident, written as a percent, is a function of your blood alcohol level b. The formula is given by the equation

$$P(b) = e^{lb} \tag{1}$$

As you can see from the chart, this probability is 25% when the BAC is 0.15%. Can we find k using this information? To do this, let $P(b) = 25$ and $b = 0.15$ in equation (1). We then have

$$25 = e^{0.15k} \tag{2}$$

Equation (2) is an example of an *exponential* equation, because the variable k occurs in the exponent. We shall solve this equation in Example 9. We will even be able to predict what BAC theoretically leads to certain disaster—the alcohol level b that corresponds to a 100% probability of an accident.

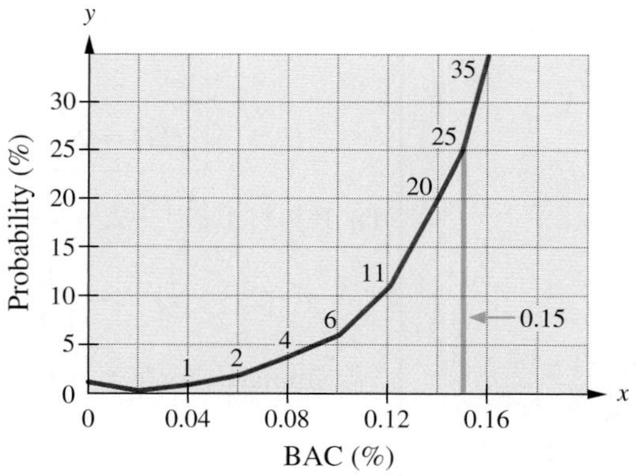

Source: Adapted from http://www.saaq.gouv.qc.ca/t2002/actes/pdf/(06a).pdf, Figure 1.

In this section we shall graph exponential functions and see how such functions can be used to solve real-world problems.

A Graphing Exponential Functions

Exponential functions take many forms. For example, the following functions are exponential functions because the variable (or unknown) is an exponent:

$$f(x) = 3^x \qquad F(y) = \left(\frac{1}{2}\right)^y \qquad H(z) = (1.02)^{z/2}$$

In general, we have the following definition:

Definition of an Exponential Function

An **exponential function** is a function defined for all real values of x by

$$f(x) = b^x, \quad b > 0, b \neq 1$$

The variable b in the definition of an exponential function *must not* equal 1 because $f(x) = 1^x = 1$ is a constant function, *not* an exponential function.

In this definition, b is a constant called the **base,** and the **exponent** x is the variable.

The exponential function defined by $f(t) = 2^{t/10}$ can be graphed and used to predict the number of bacteria present after a period of time t. To make this graph, we first construct a table giving the value of the function for certain convenient times.

t	0	10	20	30
$f(t) = 2^{t/10}$	1	2^1	2^2	2^3

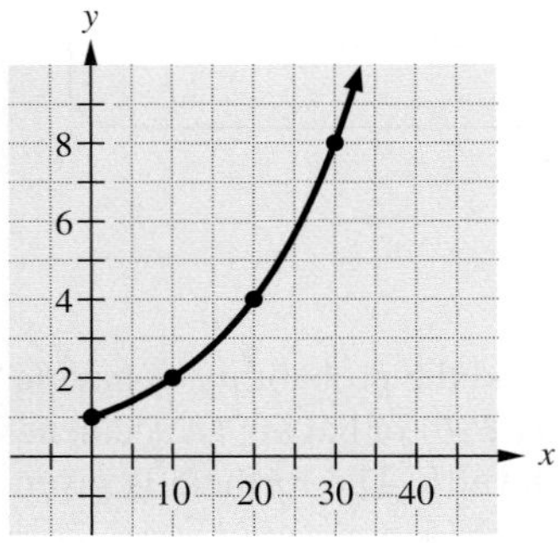

FIGURE 7.44

The corresponding points can then be graphed and joined with a smooth curve, as shown in Figure 7.44. In general, we graph an exponential function by plotting several points calculated from the function and then drawing a smooth curve through these points.

EXAMPLE 1 Graphing Exponential Functions

Graph on the same coordinate system

(a) $f(x) = 2^x$. (b) $g(x) = \left(\frac{1}{2}\right)^x$.

Solution

(a) We first make a table with convenient values for x and find the corresponding values for $f(x)$. We then graph the points and connect them with the smooth curve $y = 2^x$, as shown in Figure 7.45.

x	−2	−1	0	1	2
$f(x) = 2^x$	$2^{-2} = \frac{1}{4}$	$2^{-1} = \frac{1}{2}$	$2^0 = 1$	$2^1 = 2$	$2^2 = 4$

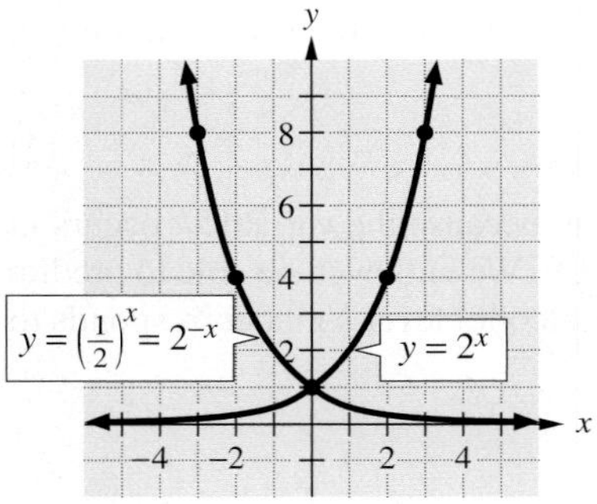

FIGURE 7.45

(b) If we let $x = -2$,

$$g(-2) = \left(\tfrac{1}{2}\right)^{-2} = \frac{1}{\left(\frac{1}{2}\right)^2} = 4$$

Similarly, for $x = -1$,

$$g(-1) = \left(\tfrac{1}{2}\right)^{-1} = \frac{1}{\left(\frac{1}{2}\right)^1} = 2$$

For $x = 0$, 1, and 2, the function values are $\left(\frac{1}{2}\right)^0 = 1$, $\left(\frac{1}{2}\right)^1 = \frac{1}{2}$, and $\left(\frac{1}{2}\right)^2 = \frac{1}{4}$, as shown in the table.

x	−2	−1	0	1	2
$g(x) = \left(\frac{1}{2}\right)^x$	4	2	1	$\frac{1}{2}$	$\frac{1}{4}$

We can save time if we realize that $\left(\frac{1}{2}\right)^x = (2^{-1})^x$, whose values are shown in the table for $f(x)$ in part (a). The graph of $g(x) = \left(\frac{1}{2}\right)^x = 2^{-x}$ is shown in Figure 7.45. Note that the graphs approach the x axis but do not intersect it. In these examples, the x axis is called the *horizontal asymptote* of the graphs.

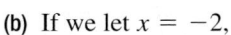

To do Example 1, enter $Y_1 = 2^x$. Enter $Y_2 = \left(\frac{1}{2}\right)^x$ by pressing [(] 1 [÷] 2 [)] [^] [X, T, θ, n] and press [ZOOM] [6]. The result is shown in the window.

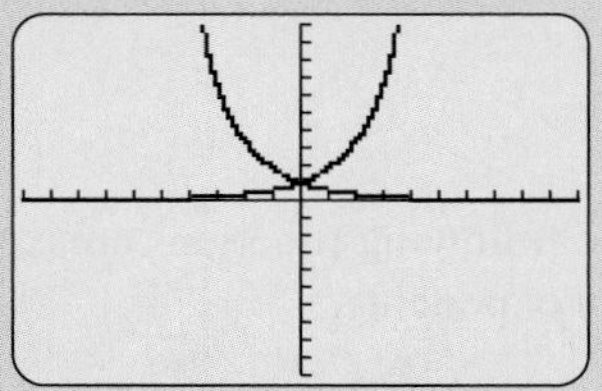

GRAPH IT

The Graph It at the end of this section shows how to do this numerical work with a grapher.

Also, the two graphs in Figure 7.45 are symmetric to each other with respect to the y axis. In general, we have the following fact:

Symmetric Graphs

The graphs of $y = b^x$ and $y = b^{-x}$ are **symmetric** with respect to the y axis.

In our definition of the function $y = b^x$, it was required only that $b > 0$ and $b \neq 1$. For many practical applications, however, there is a particularly important base, the irrational number e. The value of e is approximately 2.7182818. The reasons for using this base are made clear in more advanced mathematics courses, but for our purposes, we need only note that e is defined as the value that the quantity $(1 + 1/n)^n$ approaches as n increases indefinitely. In symbols,

$$\left(1 + \frac{1}{n}\right)^n \to e \approx 2.7182819 \quad \text{as} \quad n \to \infty$$

To show this, we use increasing values of n (1000, 10,000, 100,000, 1,000,000) and evaluate the expression $(1 + 1/n)^n$ using a calculator with a $\boxed{x^y}$ key.

$$\begin{aligned} &\text{For } n = 1000, (1 + 1/n)^n &&= (1.001)^{1000} &&= 2.7169239 \\ &\text{For } n = 10{,}000, (1 + 1/n)^n &&= (1.0001)^{10{,}000} &&= 2.7181459 \\ &\text{For } n = 100{,}000, (1 + 1/n)^n &&= (1.00001)^{100{,}000} &&= 2.7182682 \\ &\text{For } n = 1{,}000{,}000, (1 + 1/n)^n &&= (1.000001)^{1{,}000{,}000} &&= 2.7182805 \end{aligned}$$

Enter 1.001 $\boxed{x^y}$ 1000 $\boxed{=}$

As you can see, the value of $(1 + 1/n)^n$ is indeed getting closer to $e \approx 2.7182819$.

To graph the functions $f(x) = e^x$ and $g(x) = e^{-x}$, we make a table giving x different values (say, $-2, -1, 0, 1, 2$) and find the corresponding $y = e^x$ and $y = e^{-x}$ values. This can be done with a calculator with an $\boxed{e^x}$ key. On such calculators, you usually have to enter $\boxed{\text{INV}}$ or $\boxed{\text{2nd}}$ to find the value of e^x. [Enter 1 $\boxed{\text{2nd}}$ (or $\boxed{\text{INV}}$) $\boxed{e^x}$, and the calculator will give the value 2.7182818.] We use these ideas next.

EXAMPLE 2 Graphing e^x and e^{-x}

Use the values in the table to graph $f(x) = e^x$ and $g(x) = e^{-x}$. (Use the same coordinate system.)

x	-2	-1	0	1	2
e^x	0.1353	0.3679	1	2.7183	7.3891

x	-2	-1	0	1	2
e^{-x}	7.3891	2.7183	1	0.3679	0.1353

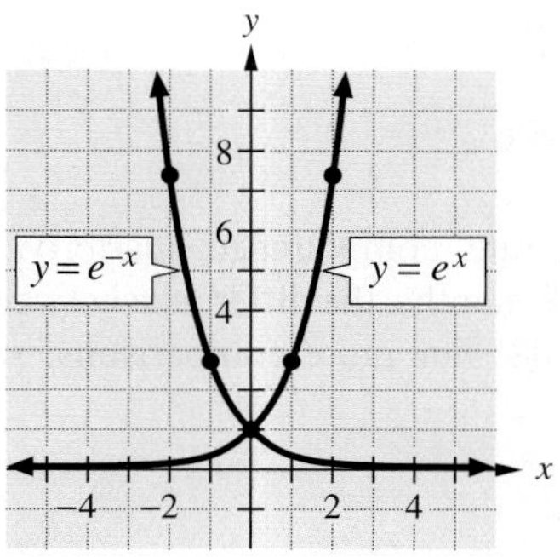

FIGURE 7.46

Solution

Plotting the given values, we obtain the graphs of $f(x) = e^x$ and $g(x) = e^{-x}$ shown in Figure 7.46. Note that e^x and e^{-x} are symmetric with respect to the y axis.

B Applications Involving Exponential Functions

Do you have some money invested? Is it earning interest compounded annually, quarterly, monthly, or daily? Does the frequency of compounding make a difference? Some banks have instituted what is called *continuous interest compounding*.

We can compare continuous compounding and n compoundings per year by examining their formulas.

Continuous compounding $A = Pe^{rt}$
n compoundings per year $A = P(1 + r/n)^{nt}$

where A = compound amount
P = principal
r = interest rate
t = time in years
n = periods per year (second formula only)

Note that as the number of times the interest is compounded increases, n increases, and it can be shown that

$$\left(1 + \frac{r}{n}\right)^{nt}$$

gets closer to e^{rt}. Let's see the difference between the two formulas.

EXAMPLE 3 Finding the Compound Amount

Find the compound amount

(a) for \$100 compounded continuously for 18 months at 6%.

(b) for \$100 compounded quarterly for 18 months at 6%.

Solution

(a) Here, $P = 100$, $r = 0.06$, and $t = 1.5$, so

$$A = 100e^{(0.06)(1.5)}$$
$$= 100e^{0.09}$$

A calculator gives the value

$$e^{0.09} \approx 1.0942$$

Thus

$$A = (100)(1.0942) \approx 109.42$$

and the compound amount is \$109.42.

(b) As before, $P = 100$, $r = 0.06$, $t = 1.5$, and $n = 4$, so

$$1 + \frac{r}{n} = 1 + \frac{0.06}{4} = 1.015 \quad \text{and} \quad nt = 4 \cdot 1.5 = 6$$

Thus the compound amount for \$100 at the same rate, compounded quarterly, is given by $A = 100(1.015)^6 \approx 109.34$. Note that at 18 months, the difference between continuous and quarterly compounding is only \$.08! For more comparisons, see Using Your Knowledge in Exercises 7.5.

EXAMPLE 4 Finding the Amount

A radioactive substance decays so that G, the number of grams present, is given by

$$G = 1000e^{-1.2t}$$

where t is the time in years. Find, to the nearest gram, the amount of the substance present

(a) at the start. **(b)** in 2 years.

GRAPH IT

In Example 4, let $Y_1 = 1000e^{-1.2t}$. To use a $[-1, 10]$ by $[-100, 1000]$ window and Yscl = 100, press WINDOW and enter −1 for Xmin, 10 for Xmax, −100 for Ymin, and 1000 for Ymax, with Yscl = 100. Do you now see that the substance is *decaying*? Now let's calculate the value of the function when $x = 2$ as required in the example. Press 2nd CALC 1. Answer the grapher question by entering $X = 2$ and press ENTER. The result is $Y = 90.717953$ as shown in the window. Rounding the answer to the nearest gram, the answer is 91, as before.

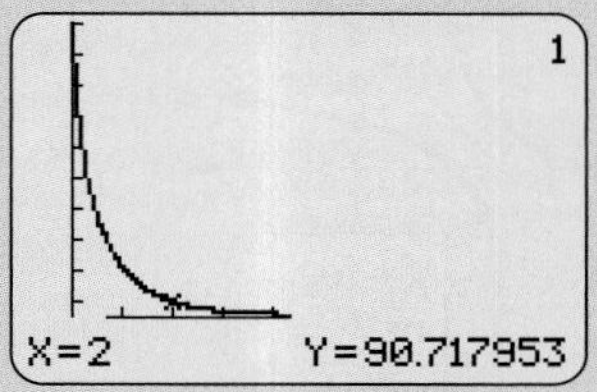

Solution

(a) Here, $t = 0$, so $G = 1000e^0 = 1000(1) = 1000$; that is, 1000 g of the substance are present at the start.

(b) Since $t = 2$, $G = 1000e^{-2.4}$. To evaluate G, we use a calculator and obtain

$$e^{-2.4} \approx 0.090718$$

so that

$$G \approx (1000)(0.090718)$$
$$= 90.718$$

There are about 91 g present in 2 years.

EXAMPLE 5 Finding Population

Thomas Robert Malthus invented a model for predicting population based on the idea that when the birth rate (B) and the death rate (D) are constant and no other factors are considered, the population P is given by

$$P = P_0 e^{kt}$$

where P = population at any time t
P_0 = initial population
k = annual growth rate $(B - D)$
t = time in years after 1980

According to the *Statistical Abstract of the United States,* the population in 2000 was 281,421,906, the birth rate was 0.0147, and the death rate was 0.0087. Use this information to project the number of people in the United States in the year 2010.

Solution

The initial population is $P_0 = 281{,}421{,}906$, $k = 0.0147 - 0.0087 = 0.006$, and the number of years from 2000 to 2010 is $t = 10$.

$$P = 281{,}421{,}906e^{0.006\times 10}$$
$$= 281{,}421{,}906e^{0.06}$$
$$\approx 298{,}824{,}065$$

Thus, the projected population is 298,824,065. The *Statistical Abstract* predicts 298,710,000. Both projections are wrong; we passed 300 million in October 2006! To see the actual Census Projections from 2010 to 2050, go to http://www.census.gov/population/www/projections/summarytables.html.

C Logarithmic Functions

Most of the functions and equations we have discussed in this section did not have variables used as *exponents.* The equation

$$3^x = 9$$

is an *exponential* equation with solution 2 because $3^2 = 9$. The 2 is the exponent (power) to which the base 3 must be raised to obtain 9. The exponent 2 is called the **logarithm** to the base 3 of 9, and we write

$$2 = \log_3 9 \qquad \text{(read "2 equals the log base 3 of 9")}$$

Please note that the logarithm is simply an exponent, the exponent to which the base must be raised to get a certain number. In general,

> **Definition of a Logarithm**
>
> $y = log_b x$ is equivalent to $b^y = x \quad b > 0, b \neq 1$

Remember that this definition simply means that the logarithm of a number is an exponent. For example,

$4 = \log_2 16$	is equivalent to	$2^4 = 16$	The logarithm is the exponent.
$2 = \log_5 25$	is equivalent to	$5^2 = 25$	The logarithm is the exponent.
$-3 = \log_{10} 0.001$	is equivalent to	$10^{-3} = 0.001$	The logarithm is the exponent.

The graph of the function $f(x) = \log_b x$ is found by interchanging the roles of x and y in the function $y = g(x) = b^x$ and graphing $x = b^y$. Geometrically, this is done by reflecting the graph of $g(x) = b^x$ about the line $y = x$, as shown in Figures 7.47 and 7.48.

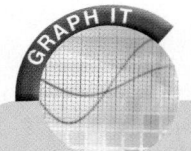

GRAPH IT

Note that you cannot graph $f(x) = \log_2 x$ automatically using a grapher. The button LOG on your grapher means $\log_{10}$, that is, the log to the base 10.

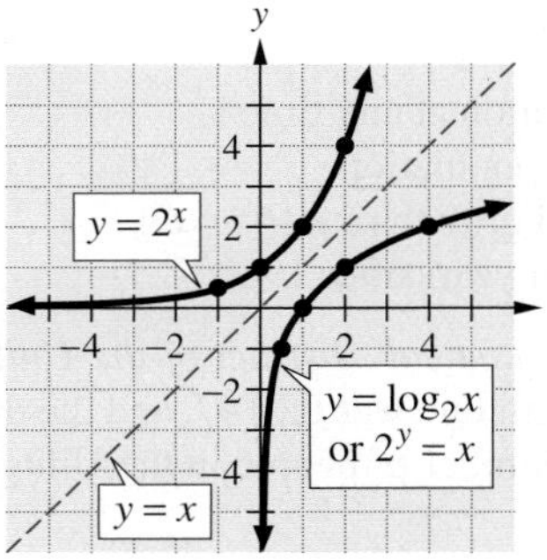

FIGURE 7.47 The graph of $y = f(x) = \log_2 x$ is obtained by reflecting the graph of $y = 2^x$ along the line $y = x$. Thus the points $(-1, \frac{1}{2})$, $(0, 1)$, $(1, 2)$, and $(2, 4)$ become $(\frac{1}{2}, -1)$, $(1, 0)$, $(2, 1)$, and $(4, 2)$.

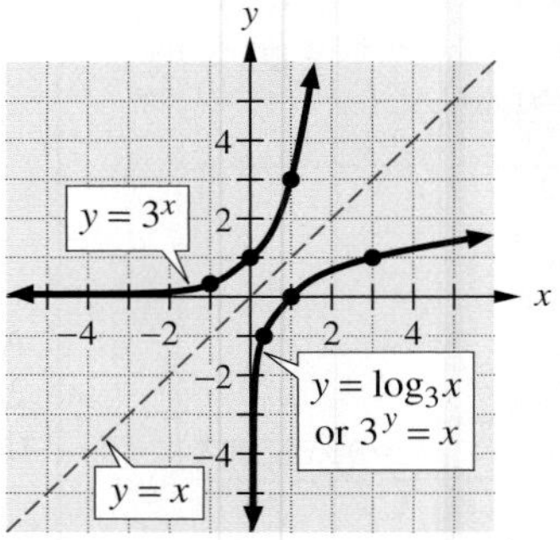

FIGURE 7.48 The graph of $y = f(x) = \log_3 x$ is obtained by reflecting the graph of $y = 3^x$ along the line $y = x$. Thus the points $(-1, \frac{1}{3})$, $(0, 1)$, and $(1, 3)$ become $(\frac{1}{3}, -1)$, $(1, 0)$, and $(3, 1)$.

EXAMPLE 6 Graphing Logarithmic Functions

Graph $y = f(x) = \log_4 x$.

Solution

By the definition of logarithm, $y = \log_4 x$ is equivalent to $4^y = x$. We can graph $4^y = x$ by first assigning values to y and calculating the corresponding x values.

y	$x = 4y$	Ordered Pair
0	$x = 4^0 = 1$	$(1, 0)$
1	$x = 4^1 = 4$	$(4, 1)$
2	$x = 4^2 = 16$	$(16, 2)$
-1	$x = 4^{-1} = \frac{1}{4}$	$(\frac{1}{4}, -1)$
-2	$x = 4^{-2} = \frac{1}{16}$	$(\frac{1}{16}, -2)$

We then graph the ordered pairs and connect them with a smooth curve, the graph of $y = \log_4 x$. To confirm that our graph is correct, graph $y = 4^x$ on the same coordinate axes (see Figure 7.49). As expected, the graphs are reflections of each other across the line $y = x$.

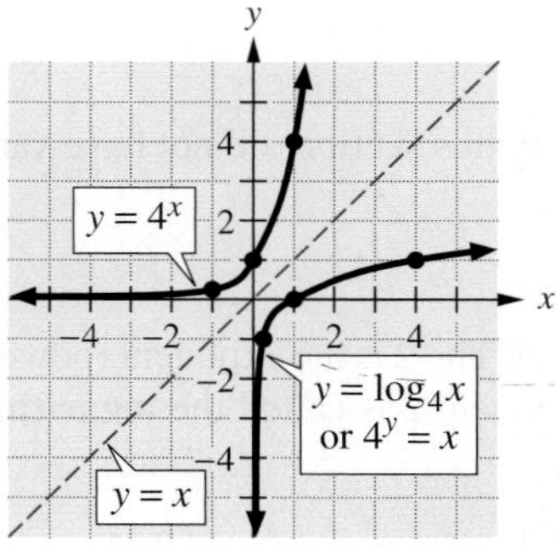

FIGURE 7.49

Here are some properties of the graphs of $y = f(x) = \log_b x$.

Properties of Logarithmic Graphs

1. The point (1, 0) is always on the graph because $\log_b 1 = 0$, since $b^0 = 1$.
2. For $b > 1$, the graph will rise from left to right (increase).
3. For $0 < b < 1$, the graph will fall from left to right (decrease).
4. The y axis is the vertical asymptote for $f(x)$.
5. The domain of $f(x) = \log_b x$ is $(0, \infty)$ and the range is $(-\infty, \infty)$.

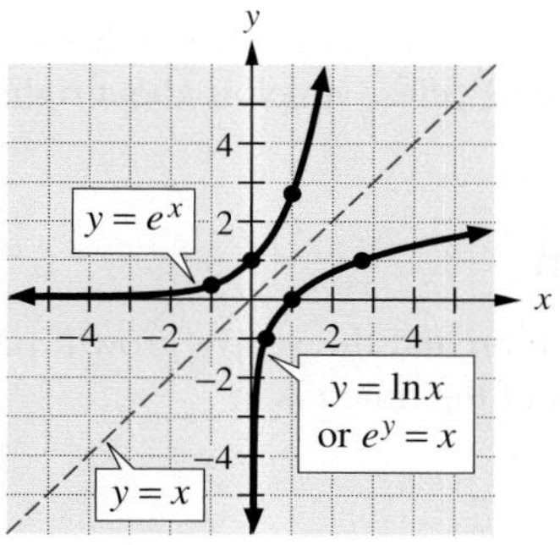

FIGURE 7.50

We have mentioned that e is an important base used in applications of exponential functions. The corresponding logarithmic function $y = \log_e x$ is so important that there is a special symbol for $\log_e x$; it is **ln** x (read "el-en of x"). Thus

$$\ln x = \log_e x$$

As before, to graph $y = \ln x$, we interchange the roles of x and y in $y = e^x$ and graph $x = e^y$ (see Example 2) as shown in Figure 7.50. The graph of $y = \ln x$ is a reflection $y = e^x$ along the line $y = x$. We interchanged the ordered pairs $(-1, 0.3679)$, $(0, 1)$, and $(1, e)$ and graphed $(0.3679, -1)$, $(1, 0)$, and $(e, 1)$.

Since a logarithm is simply an exponent, the expression $\ln e^k$ is the exponent to which the base e must be raised in order to obtain e^k. There is only one number that will do this, and it is k itself. Here is the idea.

Inverse Property of Logarithms

For all real numbers k, $\ln e^k = k$.

We use this idea in the following examples.

D Applications Involving Exponential or Logarithmic Equations

Exponential and logarithmic equations have many applications in such areas as business, engineering, social science, psychology, and science. The following examples will give you an idea of the variety and range of their use.

EXAMPLE 7 Finding the Time It Takes Money to Double

With continuous compounding, a principal of P dollars accumulates to an amount A given by the equation

$$A = Pe^{rt}$$

where r is the interest rate and t is the time in years. If the interest rate is 6%, how long would it take for the money in your bank account to double?

Solution

With $A = 2P$ and $r = 0.06$, the equation becomes

$$2P = Pe^{0.06t}$$

or

$$2 = e^{0.06t} \quad \text{Divide by } P.$$

We want to solve this equation for t, so we take natural logarithms of both sides.

$$\ln 2 = \ln e^{0.06t} = 0.06t \ln e = 0.06t \qquad \text{Recall that } \ln e^k = k.$$

Thus, $\ln 2 = 0.06t$ and

$$t = \frac{\ln 2}{0.06}$$

Using a calculator, we find $\ln 2 \approx 0.69315$ so that

$$t \approx \frac{0.69315}{0.06} \approx 11.6$$

This means that it would take about 11.6 years for your money to double. The verification is left to you. By the way, there is a rule, called ***the rule of 72,*** that estimates how long it takes money invested at $r\%$ to double: just divide 72 by r! In Example 7, $r = 6$, so we can estimate that the money will double in about 72/6 or 12 years, which is about right!

EXAMPLE 8 Estimating World Population

In 1984, the population of the world was about 4.8 billion and the yearly growth rate was 2%. The equation giving the population P in terms of the time t is

$$P = 4.8e^{0.02t}$$

Estimate the world population P in the year 2050.

Solution

We are looking for the population P in the year 2050. Since $P = 4.8$ for $t = 0$, the equation shows that t is measured from the year 1984. To estimate the population in 2050, we use $t = 66$ in the equation.

$$P = 4.8e^{(0.02)(66)} = 4.8e^{1.32}$$

The value $e^{1.32} \approx 3.7434$ can be found with a calculator. Hence

$$P \approx (4.8)(3.7434) \approx 17.97$$

Thus, our estimate for the population in 2050 is about 18 billion. What would your population estimate be for today? The computation is left to you.

EXAMPLE 9 Correlating BAC and Certainty of an Accident

(a) Solve (round to the nearest tenth): $25 = e^{0.15k}$, the equation in the Getting Started.

(b) Substitute the value of k obtained in part(a) and find the blood alcohol level b at which the probability of having an accident is 100%. Round to the nearest hundredth.

Solution

(a)

$$25 = e^{0.15k} \qquad \text{Given}$$

$$\ln 25 = \ln e^{0.15k} \qquad \text{Take the natural logarithm of both sides.}$$

$$\ln 25 = 0.15k \qquad \text{Since } \log_a b^x = x,\ \ln e^{0.15k} = 0.15k \text{ (Power property of logarithms).}$$

$$\frac{\ln 25}{0.15} = k \qquad \text{Divide both sides by } 0.15.$$

Thus,

$$k = \frac{\ln 25}{0.15} = \frac{3.2189}{0.15} \approx 21.5 \quad \text{(to the nearest tenth)}$$

Now, let us use the RSTUV procedure to do part (**b**).

1. **Read the problem.**
2. **Select the unknown.** We are asked to find b so that $P(b) = 100$. To do this we must solve the equation

$$100 = e^{21.5b}$$

3. **Think a plan.** First, we take natural logarithms of both sides of the equation, then solve for b.
4. **Use algebra to solve the problem.**

$$\ln 100 = \ln e^{21.5b} \quad \text{Take the natural logarithm of both sides.}$$

$$\ln 100 = 21.5b \quad \text{Power property of logarithms } (\log_b b^x = x).$$

$$\frac{\ln 100}{21.5} = b \quad \text{Divide by 21.5.}$$

or $$b = \frac{\ln 100}{21.5}$$

This is the exact value. Using a calculator to approximate b to the nearest hundredth, $b \approx 0.21\%$.

5. **Verify the answer.** The verification that $100 = e^{21.5(0.214)}$ is left to you (use your calculator). When the blood alcohol level is about 0.21%, the probability of an accident is 100%. If your blood alcohol level is 0.21%, you are probably too drunk to even get in your car.

EXAMPLE 10 Finding the Half-Life of an Element

The element cesium-137 decays at the rate of 2.3% per year. Find the half-life of this element.

Solution

The half-life of a substance is found by using the equation

$$A(t) = A_0 e^{-kt}$$

where $A(t)$ is the amount present at time t (years), k is the decay rate, and A_0 is the initial amount of the substance present. In this problem,

$$k = 2.3\% = 0.023 \quad \text{and} \quad A(t) = \tfrac{1}{2}A_0$$

and we want to find t.

With this information, the basic equation becomes

$$\tfrac{1}{2}A_0 = A_0 e^{-0.023t}$$

$$\tfrac{1}{2} = e^{-0.023t} \quad \text{Divide by } A_0.$$

Now take natural logarithms of both sides.

$$\ln \tfrac{1}{2} = \ln e^{-0.023t}$$

$$\ln 1 - \ln 2 = -0.023t$$

$$t = \frac{\ln 2}{0.023} \quad \text{Since } \ln 1 = 0$$

$$\approx \frac{0.69315}{0.023} \approx 30.14$$

Thus, the half-life of cesium-137 is about 30.14 years. The verification is left to you.

GRAPH IT

The numerical work preceding Example 2 can be done with a grapher. To find $(1.001)^{1000}$, press [2nd] [QUIT] [CLEAR] (to clear your home screen) and then 1 [·] 0 0 1 [^] 1 0 0 0 [ENTER]. For a more dramatic approximation for $e = 2.718281828$, tell the grapher to graph the sequence of numbers $(1 + 1/n)^n$ as n increases. Press [MODE], move the cursor three lines down to the line starting with "FUNC," and select "SEQ." Go down to the next line and select "DOT"; then press [ENTER]. (You have told the grapher you are about to graph a sequence.) Now press [Y=]. The symbols $u(n)$ and $v(n)$ are on your screen. Let's define the sequence $u(n)$ by entering $(1 + 1/n)^n$. (The n is entered by pressing [X, T, θ, n]). To adjust the window, press [WINDOW] and select Xmin = −1, Xmax = 10, Xscl = 1, Ymin = −1, Ymax = 3, and Yscl = 1. Now press [GRAPH]. The result is shown in Window 1.

To show that the sequence of dots is getting closer to e, use the draw feature to graph $y = e$. [Since you have entered a sequence, you can't enter the function $f(x) = e$.] Press [2nd] [DRAW] [6] and then enter [2ND] [e^x] 1 [ENTER]. The result is shown in Window 2. Do you now see how the sequence of dots representing $(1 + 1/n)^n$ approaches e?

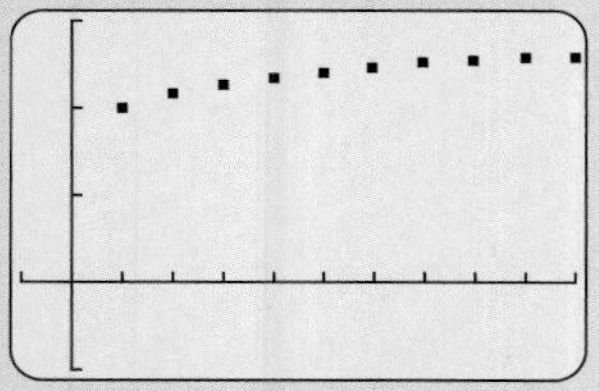

Window 1

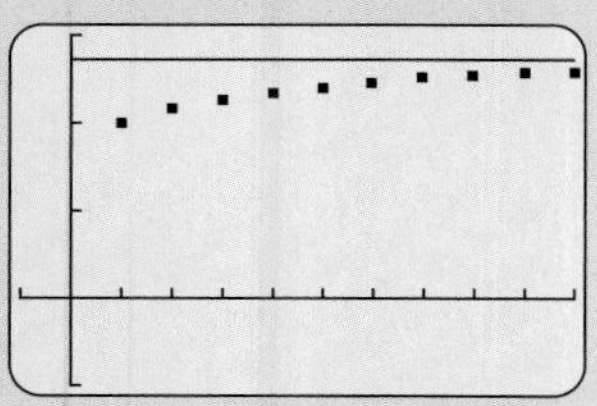

Window 2

7.5 EXERCISES

A Graphing Exponential Functions

In problems 1–6, find the value of the given exponential for the indicated values of the variable.

1. 5^x
   a. $x = -1$
   b. $x = 0$
   c. $x = 1$
2. 5^{-x}
   a. $x = -1$
   b. $x = 0$
   c. $x = 1$
3. 3^t
   a. $t = -2$
   b. $t = 0$
   c. $t = 2$
4. 3^{-t}
   a. $t = -2$
   b. $t = 0$
   c. $t = 2$
5. $10^{t/2}$
   a. $t = -2$
   b. $t = 0$
   c. $t = 2$
6. $10^{-t/2}$
   a. $t = -2$
   b. $t = 0$
   c. $t = 2$

*In problems 7–10, graph the functions given in parts (**a**) and (**b**) on the same coordinate system.*

7. a. $f(x) = 5^x$
   b. $g(x) = 5^{-x}$
8. a. $f(t) = 3^t$
   b. $g(t) = 3^{-t}$
9. a. $f(x) = 10^x$
   b. $g(x) = 10^{-x}$
10. a. $f(t) = 10^{t/2}$
    b. $g(t) = 10^{-t/2}$

B Applications Involving Exponential Functions

*In problems 11–14, find the compound amount if the compounding is (**a**) continuous or (**b**) quarterly.*

11. \$1000 at 9% for 10 years
12. \$1000 at 9% for 20 years
13. \$1000 at 6% for 10 years
14. \$1000 at 6% for 20 years
15. The population of a town is given by the equation $P = 2000(2^{0.2t})$, where t is the time in years from 2000. Find the population in
    a. 2005. b. 2010. c. 2015.
16. A colony of bacteria grows so that its number B is given by the equation $B = 1200(2^t)$, where t is in days. Find the number of bacteria.
    a. at the start ($t = 0$). b. in 5 days. c. in 10 days.
17. A radioactive substance decays so that G, the number of grams present, is given by $G = 2000e^{-1.05t}$, where t is the time in years. Find the amount of the substance present.
    a. at the start. b. in 1 year. c. in 2 years.

18. Solve problem 17 when the equation for the number of grams present in a decaying radioactive substance is $G = 2000e^{-1.1t}$.

In problems 19–26, you may use a calculator with $\boxed{e^x}$ *and* $\boxed{x^y}$ *keys, or you can use your grapher.*

19. In 2010, the number of persons of Hispanic origin living in the United States was 50.5 million. If their birth rate is 0.0234 and their death rate is 0.003, predict the number of persons of Hispanic origin living in the United States for the year 2020. (Use a calculator.) (*Hint:* See Example 5.) (Source: U.S. Census 2010.)

20. In 2010, the number of African Americans living in the United States was 39.6 million. If their birth rate is 0.017 and their death rate is 0.0072, predict the number of African Americans living in the United States in the year 2020. (*Hint:* See Example 5.) (Source: U.S. Census 2010.)

21. Do you have a credit card? According to the Federal Reserve, the total credit C carried by U.S. consumers is as shown in the red graph and can be approximated by

$$C = 941e^{0.0053t} \text{ (billion dollars)}$$

where t is the number of months after December 2007.

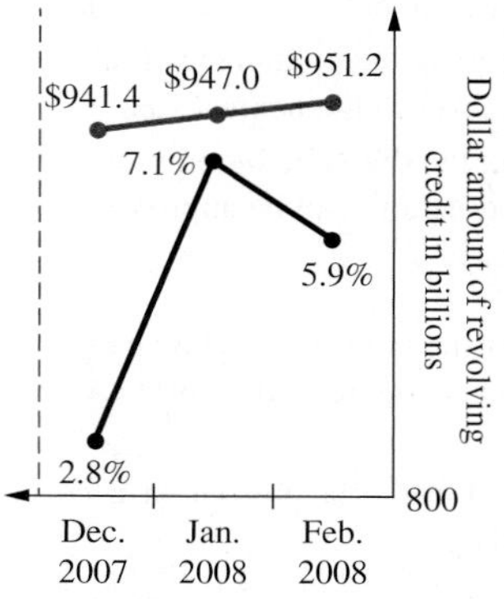

Source: Federal Reserve.

a. When did the total credit reach one trillion dollars (1000 billion)?

b. The total credit in December 2007 was 941 billion dollars. When will the total credit be twice this amount?

22. The number of Smartphone sales $S(t) = 190e^{0.11t}$ (in millions), where t is the number of years after 2004, is predicted to exceed the PC sales of about 360 million in the year 2011 ($t = 7$).

Smartphone sales to beat PC sales by 2011

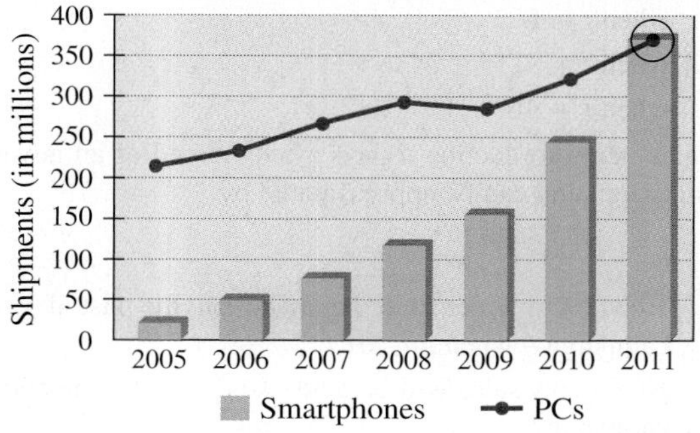

Source: http://tinyurl.com/8986wcf.

a. Find $S(t)$ for $t = 7$ and in the year 2015 ($t = 15$).

b. By how many million does Smartphone sales beat PC sales in 2011?

23. According to the *Statistical Abstract of the United States,* about $\frac{2}{3}$ of all aluminum cans distributed are recycled. If a company distributes 500,000 cans, the number still in use after t years is given by the exponential function $N(t) = 500{,}000(\frac{2}{3})^t$. How many cans are still in use after

a. 1 year? **b.** 2 years? **c.** 10 years?

24. If the value of an item each year is about 60% of its value the year before, after t years the salvage value of an item costing C dollars is given by $S(t) = C(0.6)^t$. Find the salvage value of a computer costing $10,000

a. 1 year after it was purchased.

b. 10 years after it was purchased.

25. The atmospheric pressure A (in pounds per square inch) can be approximated by the exponential function $A(a) = 14.7(10)^{-0.000018a}$, where a is the altitude in feet.

a. The highest mountain in the world, Mount Everest, is about 29,000 ft high. Find the atmospheric pressure at the top of Mount Everest.

b. In the United States, the highest mountain is Mount McKinley in Alaska, whose highest point is about 20,000 ft. Find the atmospheric pressure at the top of Mount McKinley.

26. The atmospheric pressure A (in pounds per square inch) can also be approximated by $A(a) = 14.7e^{-0.21a}$, where a is the altitude in miles.

a. If we assume that the altitude of Mount Everest is about 6 mi, what is the atmospheric pressure at the top of Mount Everest?

b. If we assume that the altitude of Mount McKinley is about 4 mi, what is the atmospheric pressure at the top of Mount McKinley?

C Logarithmic Functions

In problems 27 and 28 graph the function.

27. $f(x) = \log_5 x$ **28.** $f(x) = \log_6 x$

D Applications Involving Exponential or Logarithmic Equations

In problems 29–32, assume continuous compounding and follow the procedure in Example 7 to find how long it takes a given amount to double at the given interest rate.

29. $r = 5\%$ **30.** $r = 7\%$

31. $r = 6.5\%$ **32.** $r = 7.5\%$

33. Suppose that the population of the world grows at the rate of 1.2% and that the population in 2000 was about 6.1 billion. Follow the procedure of Example 8 to estimate the population in the year 2010. (Source: www.un.org/esa/population/publications/wpp2000/highlights.pdf.)

34. Repeat problem 33 for a growth rate of 1.75%.

In problems 35–38, assume that the number of bacteria present in a culture after t min is given by $B = 1000e^{0.04t}$. *Find the time it takes for the number of bacteria present to be*

35. 2000. **36.** 5000.

37. 25,000. **38.** 50,000.

39. When a bacteria-killing solution is introduced into a certain culture, the number of live bacteria is given by the equation $B = 100{,}000e^{-0.2t}$, where t is the time in hours. Find the number of live bacteria present at the following times:

a. $t = 0$ b. $t = 2$

c. $t = 10$ d. $t = 20$

40. The number of honey bees in a hive is growing according to the equation $N = N_0e^{0.015t}$, where t is the time in days. If the bees swarm when their number is tripled, find how many days until this hive swarms.

In problems 41–44, follow the procedure of Example 10 to find the half-life of the substance.

41. Plutonium, whose decay rate is 0.003% per year

42. Krypton, whose decay rate is 6.3% per year

43. A radioactive substance whose decay rate is 5.2% per year

44. A radioactive substance whose decay rate is 0.2% per year

45. The atmospheric pressure P in pounds per square inch at an altitude of h feet above the Earth is given by the equation $P = 14.7e^{-0.00005h}$. Find the pressure at an altitude of

a. 0 ft. b. 5000 ft. c. 10,000 ft.

46. If the atmospheric pressure in problem 45 is measured in inches of mercury, then $P = 30e^{-0.207h}$, where h is the altitude in miles. Find the pressure

a. at sea level. b. at 5 mi above sea level.

47. Has free agency affected salaries? According to the National Football League Players Association (NFLPA), average NFL salaries (in millions of dollars) are as shown in the graph below and can be approximated by

$$S = 0.94e^{0.09t}$$

where t is the number of years after 2000.

In 2011, owners locked players out of training camps and the NFL Commissioner insisted that player salaries were increasing at a rate faster than the league's revenues.

a. Use $S = 0.94e^{0.09t}$ to find out in how many years players' average salaries will reach \$3 million. (Answer to the nearest year.) Source: *USA Today*.

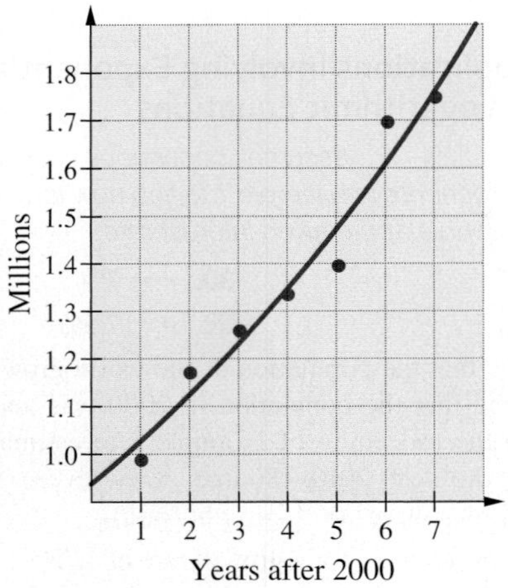

What about the claim that players' salaries are increasing at a rate faster than league revenues?

b. Use the graph to find the player salaries (to the nearest tenth of a million) in year 1 and in year 6 and find the percent increase.

c. Owner revenues increased from 6.49 billion in 2005 to 8.88 billion in 2009. What was the percent increase?

d. Which increase was higher, the players or the owners?

48. According to the *Statistical Abstract of the United States*, about $\frac{2}{3}$ of all aluminum cans distributed are recycled. If a company distributes 500,000 cans, the number in use after t years is

$$N(t) = 500{,}000\left(\frac{2}{3}\right)^t$$

How many years will it take for the number of cans to reach 100,000? (Answer to the nearest year.)

49. Do you have a fear of flying? The U.S. Department of Transportation has good news for nervous fliers: The number of general aviation accidents A has gone down significantly in the last 40 years! It can be approximated by

$$A = 5000e^{-0.04t}$$

where t is the number of years after 1970.

a. How many accidents were there in 1970?

b. How many accidents were there in 1990?

c. In what year do you predict the number of accidents reached 1000? (Answer to the nearest year.)

50. After exercise, the diastolic blood pressure of normal adults is a function of time and can be approximated by

$$P = 90e^{-0.5t}$$

where t is the time in minutes. How long would it be before the diastolic pressure decreased to 80? (Answer to two decimal places.)

51. The number of bacteria present in a certain culture can be approximated by

$$B = 50{,}000e^{0.2t}$$

where t is measured in hours and $t = 0$ corresponds to 12 noon. Find the number of bacteria present at

a. noon. b. 2 P.M. c. 6 P.M.

52. If a bactericide (a bacteria killer) is introduced into a bacteria culture, the number of bacteria can be approximated by

$$B = 50{,}000e^{-0.1t}$$

where t is measured in hours. Find the number of bacteria present

a. when $t = 0$.

b. when $t = 1$.

c. when $t = 10$.

53. Sales begin to decline d days after the end of an advertising campaign and can be approximated by

$$S = 1000e^{-0.1d}$$

a. How many sales will be made on the last day of the campaign—when $d = 0$?

b. How many sales will be made 10 days after the end of the campaign?

54. The demand function for a certain commodity is approximated by

$$p = 100e^{-q/2}$$

where q is the number of units demanded at a price of p dollars per unit.

a. If there is a 100-unit demand for the product, what will its price be?

b. If there is no demand for the product, what will its price be?

55. The concentration C of a drug in the bloodstream at time t (in hours) can be approximated by

$$C = 100\,(1 - e^{-0.5t})$$

a. What will the concentration be when $t = 0$?

b. What will the concentration be after 1 hour? (Round to 1 decimal place.)

56. The number of people $N(t)$ reached by a particular rumor at time t is approximated by

$$N(t) = \frac{5050}{1 + 100e^{-0.06t}}$$

a. Find $N(0)$.

b. Find $N(0)$.

57. The stellar magnitude M of a star is defined by

$$M = -2.5 \log\left(\frac{B}{B_0}\right)$$

where B is the brightness of the star and B_0 the minimum of brightness.

a. Find the stellar magnitude of the North Star, 2.1 times as bright as B_0. (Round to 4 decimal places.)

b. Find the stellar magnitude of Venus, 36.2 times as bright as B_0. (Round to 4 decimal places.)

58. The percent P of adult height a male has reached at age $A(13 \le A \le 18)$ is

$$P = 16.7 \log (A - 12) + 87$$

a. What percent of adult height has a 13-year-old male reached?

b. What percent of adult height has an 18-year-old male reached? (Round to the nearest thousandth of a percent.)

USING YOUR KNOWLEDGE

In this section you learned that for continuous compounding, the compound amount is given by $A = Pe^{rt}$. For ordinary compound interest, the compound amount is given by $A = P(1 + r/n)^{nt}$, where r is the annual interest rate and n is the number of periods per year. Suppose you have \$1000 to put into an account where the interest rate is 6%. How much more would you have at the end of 2 years for continuous compounding than for monthly compounding?

For continuous compounding, the amount is given by

$$\begin{aligned} A &= 1000e^{(0.06)(2)} = 1000e^{0.12} \\ &= (1000)(1.1275) \quad \text{Use a calculator.} \\ &= 1127.50 \end{aligned}$$

Thus the amount is \$1127.50. For monthly compounding,

$$\frac{r}{n} = \frac{0.06}{12} = 0.005 \quad \text{and} \quad nt = 24$$

Thus the amount is given by $A = 1000(1 + 0.005)^{24} = 1000(1.005)^{24}$. Compound interest tables or your calculator gives the value

$$(1.005)^{24} = 1.1271598$$

so that $A = 1127.16$ (to the nearest hundredth). Thus the amount is \$1127.16. Continuous compounding earns you only \$0.34 more! But, see what happens when the period t is extended in problems 59 and 60!

59. Make the same comparison where the time is 10 years.

60. Make the same comparison where the time is 20 years.

IN OTHER WORDS

61. The definition of the exponential function $f(x) = b^x$ does not allow $b = 1$.

a. What type of graph will $f(x)$ have when $b = 1$?

b. Is $f(x) = b^x$ a function when $b = 1$? Explain.

62. List some reasons to justify the condition $b > 0$ in the definition of the exponential function $f(x) = b^x$.

63. Discuss the relationship between the graphs of $f(x) = b^x$ and $g(x) = b^{-x}$.

64. In Example 5, we predicted the U.S. population for the year 2010 to be 298,824,065. The U.S. Census Bureau predicted 299,862,000. Can you give some reasons for this discrepancy? To check the latest projections, try www.census.gov.

SKILL CHECKER

In the next section you will solve a system of simultaneous equations by graphing. To graph equations simultaneously, you had better practice graphing just one equation at a time. Here are some practice problems for you. Graph them!

1. $x + y = 4$

2. $2x - y = 4$

3. $2x - y = 5$

4. $x - 2y = 4$

If you are unsure of how to graph these problems, review Sections 7.1 and 7.2.

7.6 Two Linear Equations in Two Variables

GETTING STARTED

OBJECTIVES

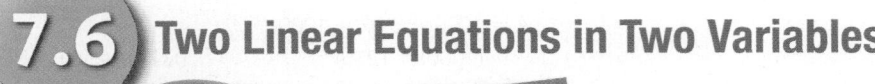

A. Solve a system of two equations by graphing.
B. Solve a system of two equations by algebraic methods (elimination).
C. Solve applications involving systems of two equations by graphing.
D. Solve applications involving systems of two equations by substitution.

WOMEN AND MEN IN THE WORK FORCE

Figure 7.51 shows the percentage of women (W) and men (M) in the work force since 1955. Can you tell from the graph in which year the percentage will be the same? It will happen after 2005! If t is the number of years after 1955, W the percentage of women in the work force, and M the percentage of men, the graphs will *intersect* at a point (a, b). The coordinates of the point of intersection (if there is one) are the common solution of both equations. If the percents W and M are approximated by

$$W = 0.055t + 34.4 \text{ (percent)}$$
$$M = -0.20t + 83.9 \text{ (percent)}$$

you can find the year after 1955 when the same percentage of women and men were in the work force by graphing M and W and locating the point of intersection. We will do that later!

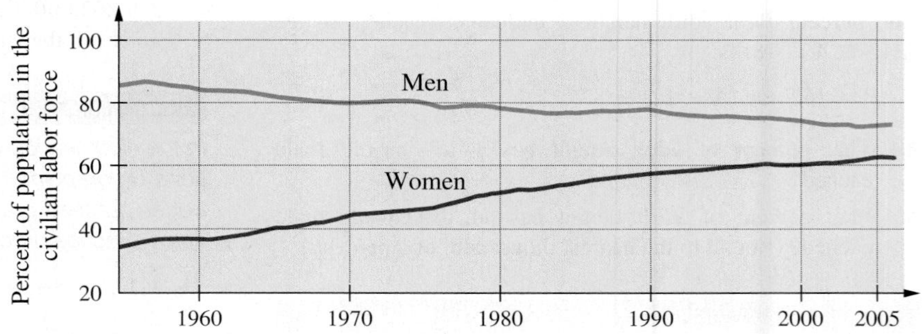

Source: U.S. Bureau of Labor Statistics.

FIGURE 7.51 Women and men in the work force.
For an excellent report dealing with Women and the Economy with updates to this data go to http://tinyurl.com/345qm7x.

There are many applications of algebra that require the solution of a **system of linear equations.** We shall consider only the simple case of two equations in two variables.

As we have seen, a linear equation $Ax + By = C$ has a straight line for its graph. Hence, two such equations will graph into two straight lines in the plane. Two distinct lines in the plane can either *intersect* at a point or else be *parallel* (have no intersection). If the lines intersect, then the coordinates of the point of intersection are called the **solution of the system of equations.** If the lines are parallel, then, of course, the system has no solution.

A Solution by Graphing

One way to solve a system of two equations in two variables is to graph the two lines and read the coordinates of the point of intersection from the graph. The next two examples illustrate this graphical method.

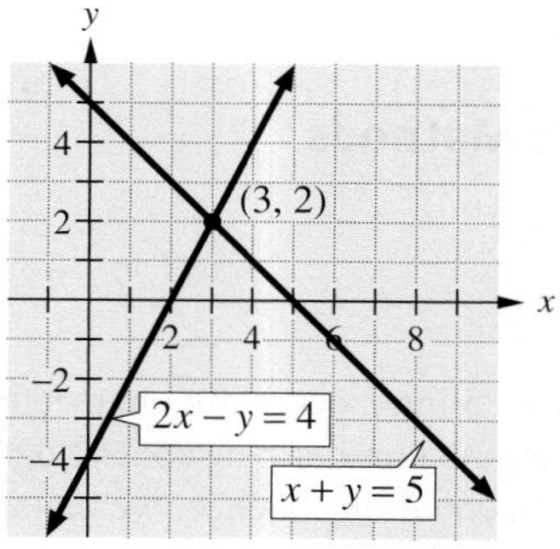

FIGURE 7.52

EXAMPLE 1 Solving Systems by the Graphical Method

Use the graphical method to find the solution of the system

$$2x - y = 4$$
$$x + y = 5$$

Solution

We graph the two equations as shown in Figure 7.52. The point of intersection of the two lines appears to be (3, 2). We check this set of coordinates in the given system. For $x = 3$ and $y = 2$,

$$2x - y = 2 \cdot 3 - 2 = 4$$
$$x + y = 3 + 2 = 5$$

Thus, the two equations are both satisfied, and the desired solution is $x = 3$, $y = 2$, or (3, 2).

GRAPH IT

To do Example 1, make sure you are in the function mode. Solve each equation for y and enter them as $Y_1 = 2x - 4$ and $Y_2 = 5 - x$. Press [ZOOM] [6]. To find the intersection, press [2nd] [CALC] [5] and [ENTER] three times. The intersection is $x = 3$ and $y = 2$ as shown.

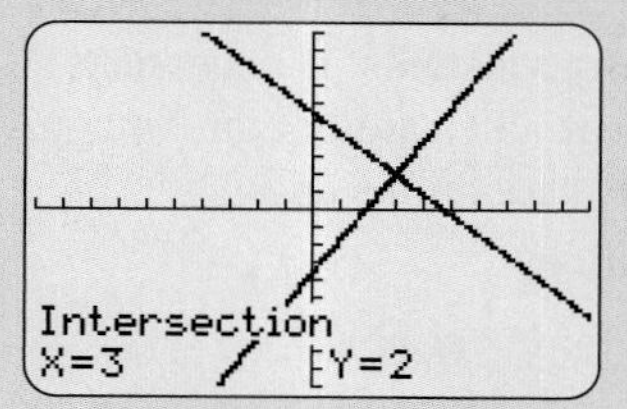

EXAMPLE 2 Using Systems of Equations to Analyze Costs

If you are about to build a house, you might consider the following two types of heating:

1. Solar heating, which requires a \$10,000 initial investment and a \$200 annual cost
2. Oil heating, with a \$2000 initial investment and an annual cost of \$1000

(a) Write an equation giving the total cost y (in dollars) of solar heating over x years.

(b) Repeat part (a) for oil heating.

(c) Graph the equations obtained in parts (a) and (b) for a period of 12 years.

(d) When will the total costs for the two systems be equal?

Solution

(a) The cost y of solar heating is given by $y = 10{,}000 + 200x$.

(b) The cost y of oil heating is given by $y = 2000 + 1000x$.

(c) Note that the x coordinate represents the number of years and the y coordinate represents the number of dollars in the corresponding total cost. For the solar heating equation, we find the two points (0, 10,000) and (5, 11,000). These two points and the line through them are shown in Figure 7.53. For the oil heating equation, we find the two points (0, 2000) and (5, 7000). These two points and the line through them are also shown in Figure 7.53.

(d) As you can see from Figure 7.53, the lines intersect at the point where $x = 10$ and $y = 12{,}000$. Thus, the total costs are equal at the end of 10 years.(After 10 years, the total cost for solar heating is much less than that for oil heating.)

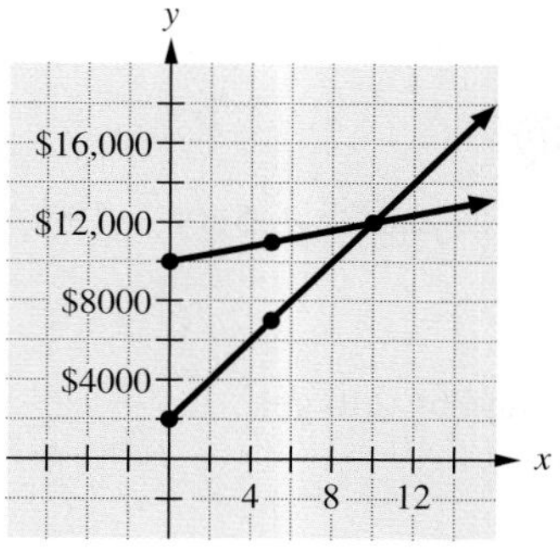

FIGURE 7.53

One word of warning: You should always check apparent solutions by substituting the respective values of x and y back into the original equations. **Picture (graph) solutions often give only approximations of actual solutions.** Remember what happened in Getting Started?

B Solution by Algebraic Methods

If the solution of the system is a pair of simple numbers that can be read exactly from the graph, then the graphical method is quite satisfactory. Naturally, you should always check a proposed solution in the given equations. Unfortunately, most systems have solutions that are not easy to read exactly from graphs, and for such systems an algebraic method of solving is needed. There is a quite simple method that is best explained by means of examples, as follows:

EXAMPLE 3 Solving Systems by Algebraic Methods

Solve the system of Example 1 by algebraic means.

Solution

The point (x, y) where the lines $2x - y = 4$ and $x + y = 5$ intersect is the intersection of the solution sets of the two equations. This means that the number pair consisting of the x value and the y value of this point must satisfy both equations. Hence, we can use the following procedure: Since the y terms in the two equations are the same except for sign, we add the two equations term by term to eliminate the y terms and get an equation in one variable.

$$\begin{array}{r} 2x - y = 4 \\ \underline{x + y = 5} \\ 3x \qquad = 9 \end{array}$$

Thus, $x = 3$. By substituting this x value into the second equation, we get

$$3 + y = 5 \quad \text{or} \quad y = 2$$

We have now found the same solution as before, (3, 2).

If both variables occur in both equations, we can proceed as follows:

Solving a System by Elimination

1. Eliminate one of the variables by
   a. multiplying one or both equations by nonzero constants, if necessary, so that the resulting coefficients for one of the variables are of equal magnitude and opposite in sign in the two respective equations and
   b. adding corresponding terms of the two equations.
2. Solve the resulting linear equation for the remaining variable.
3. Substitute the solution back into one of the original equations to find the value of the second variable.

This procedure is illustrated in the next example.

EXAMPLE 4 Solving Systems Algebraically

Find the point of intersection of the two lines $3x - 2y = 19$ and $2x + 5y = -19$.

Solution

Step 1a We multiply the first equation by 5 and the second by 2 to get

$$\begin{array}{r} 15x - 10y = 95 \\ 4x + 10y = -38 \end{array}$$

Opposites

Step 1b We then add the two equations to get

$$19x = 57$$

Step 2 Solving for x gives $x = 3$.

Step 3 We substitute $x = 3$ into the first of the given equations to obtain

$$\begin{aligned} 3 \cdot 3 - 2y &= 19 \\ 9 - 2y &= 19 \\ -2y &= 10 \\ y &= -5 \end{aligned}$$

The point of intersection is thus $(3, -5)$.

EXAMPLE 5 Systems with No Solution

Solve the following system (if possible):

$$\begin{aligned} 2x - y &= 5 \\ 4x - 2y &= 7 \end{aligned}$$

Solution

Step 1a We multiply the first equation by -2 to obtain the system

$$\begin{aligned} -4x + 2y &= -10 \\ 4x - 2y &= 7 \end{aligned}$$

Step 1b Adding these two equations, we get the *impossible* result

$$0 = -3$$

Thus, the system has no solution. The lines represented by the two equations are parallel, and there is no point of intersection.

Notice that the method of addition of the equations (used in Examples 4 and 5) will detect parallel lines as in Example 5 by arriving at an *impossible* result: $0 = a$ nonzero number. The next example shows that different equations can represent the same line.

EXAMPLE 6 Solving Systems with Many Solutions

Solve the following system (if possible):

$$\begin{aligned} 2x - y &= 5 \\ 4x - 2y &= 10 \end{aligned}$$

Solution

Step 1a We multiply the first equation by 2 to get

$$4x - 2y = 10$$

which is exactly the second equation. Thus, we see that the two equations represent the same line, and every solution of one of these equations satisfies the other. If we put $x = a$ in the first equation, and then solve for y to get $y = 2a - 5$, we can write the general solution of the system as $(a, 2a - 5)$, where a is any real number. For example, $(0, -5)$, $(3, 1)$, and $(-1, -7)$ are solutions of the system. The system has infinitely many solutions.

C Applications of Graphing

SAVE on avg. $110/year on INK

Most of the problems that we have discussed use x and y values ranging from -10 to 10. This is not the case when working with real-life applications! For example, the prices for two printers and their ink cartridges will be discussed in Example 7, but we will have to use a different type of coordinate system (grid) to compare costs. Have you bought ink cartridges lately? Kodak claims you can save \$110/year on ink (see their comparison calculator at http://tinyurl.com/yamj4za), but Hewlett-Packard (HP) denies it. (See their counterclaims at http://tinyurl.com/yh8s2so.) Let us compare these claims, taking into account the printer used.

Printer	Price	Ink Cost for Year	Total Cost for x Years
Kodak ESP7	\$150	\$ 70	$150 + 70x$ (dollars)
PhotoSmart	\$100	\$180	$100 + 180x$ (dollars)

EXAMPLE 7 Comparing Printing Costs

(a) Graph the annual costs y for the Kodak (K) and the PhotoSmart (P).

K: $y = 150 + 70x$

P: $y = 100 + 180x$

(b) Which has a less expensive start-up?

(c) What is the 1-year cost for the Kodak and the PhotoSmart?

(d) How much are your savings the first year?

Solution

(a) We first graph the equation $y = 150 + 70x$ using the table. The x axis will go from 0 to 1 and the y axis from 0 to 280. Graph the points $(0, 150)$ and $(1, 220)$ and join them with a green line, the graph of the Kodak, $y = 150 + 70x$.

x	y
0	150
1	220

To graph $y = 100 + 180x$, graph the points $(0,100)$ and $(1,280)$ and join them with a red line, the graph of the PhotoSmart, $y = 100 + 180x$. See Figure 7.54.

x	y
0	100
1	280

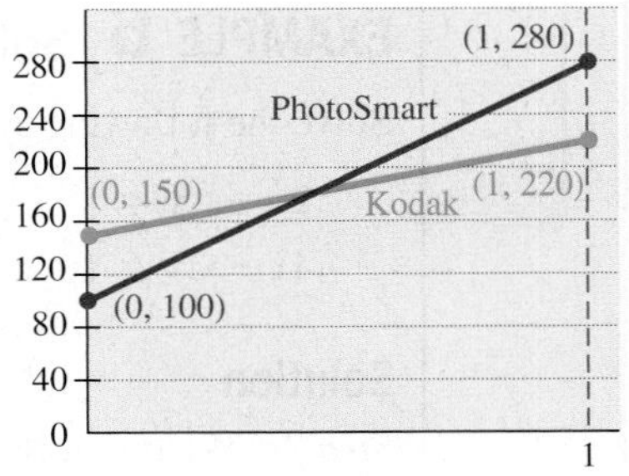

FIGURE 7.54

(b) When $x = 0$, the Kodak cost is \$150 and the PhotoSmart cost is \$100, so the PhotoSmart has the less expensive start-up.

(c) When $x = 1$, the Kodak costs \$220, as indicated by the point $(1, 220)$, and the PhotoSmart costs \$280, so the Kodak is cheaper after 1 year.

(d) By using the Kodak you save \$280 − \$220 = \$60 a year.

D Solving by Substitution

In Example 7 the graphs intersect at a point (x, y), where the cost is the same for both printers. Can we find the precise coordinates of the point (x, y)? To avoid graphing and to obtain a more precise answer, we can use the substitution method shown in the next example.

EXAMPLE 8 Finding When Printing Costs Are the Same

Find the point (x, y) at which the cost $y = 100 + 180x$ for the PhotoSmart printer and the cost $y = 150 + 70x$ for the Kodak printer are the same.

Solution

To find when the cost y is the same for both printers, we substitute $100 + 180x$ for y in

$$y = 150 + 70x \text{ obtaining}$$

$$100 + 180x = 150 + 70x$$

$$180x = 50 + 70x \quad \text{Subtract 100}$$

$$110x = 50 \quad \text{Subtract } 70x$$

$$x = \frac{50}{110} \quad \text{Divide by 110}$$

$$x = \frac{5}{11} \quad \text{Simplify}$$

Thus, when $x = \frac{5}{11}$, the cost $y = 100 + 180\left(\frac{5}{11}\right) = \frac{2000}{11} = \$181.82$ is the same for both printers. The point at which this occurs is at $x = \frac{5}{11}$ and $y = 181.82$ that is, $\left(\frac{5}{11}, 181.82\right)$.

Before you try the exercises, here is a summary that will help you decide what method to use.

Solving Systems of Equations: A Summary

Method	Suggested Use	Disadvantages
Graphical	When the coefficients of the variables and the solutions are integers. You get a picture of the situation.	If the solutions are not integers, they are hard to read on the graph.
Substitution	When one of the variables is isolated (alone) on one side of the equation	If fractions are involved, you may have much computation.
Elimination	When fractions, decimals, or variables with coefficients that are the same or additive inverses of each other ($2x$ and $-2x$, for example) are present	You may have lots of computations involving signed numbers.

7.6 EXERCISES

A Solution by Graphing

In problems 1–6, find the solution of the given system by the graphical method.

1. $x + y = 3; 2x - y = 0$
2. $x + y = 5; x - 4y = 0$
3. $2x - y = 10; 3x + 2y = 1$
4. $2x - 3y = 1; x + 2y = 4$
5. $3x + 4y = 4; 2x - 6y = 7$
6. $y = 5x - 12; y = 3x - 8$

B Solution by Algebraic Methods

In problems 7–30, find the solution of the given system by the method of addition that was used in Examples 4 and 5. If there is no solution or infinitely many solutions, state so.

7. $x + y = 3; 2x - y = 0$
8. $x + y = 5; x - 4y = 0$
9. $x + y = 6; 3x - 2y = 8$
10. $2x - y = 5; 5x + 3y = 18$
11. $2x - y = 10; 3x + 2y = 1$
12. $2x - 3y = 1; x + 2y = 4$
13. $5x + y = 4; 15x + 3y = 8$
14. $2x - y = -5; 4x - 2y = -10$
15. $2x + 5y = 12; 5x - 3y = -1$
16. $2x + 3y = 9; 11x + 7y = 2$
17. $3x + 4y = 4; 2x - 6y = 7$
18. $y = 5x - 12; y = 3x - 8$
19. $11x + 3 = -3y; 5x + 2y = 5$
20. $10x + 6y = 1; 5x = 9 - 3y$
21. $x = 2y - 3; x = -2y - 1$
22. $y = 4x - 2; 4x = 2y + 3$
23. $2x + 3y + 11 = 0; 5x + 6y + 20 = 0$
24. $3x + y = 4; 2x = 4y - 9$
25. $3x - 12y = -8; 2x + 2y = 3$
26. $4x + 8y = 7; 3x + 4y = 6$
27. $r - 4s = -10; 2r - 8s = 13$
28. $3r + 4s = 15; 4r - s = 20$
29. $6u - 2v = -27; 4u + 3v = 8$
30. $8w - 13z = 3z + 4; 12w - 3 = 18z$

C Applications of Graphing

31. Company A will cater a banquet for x guests at a cost of y dollars, where

$$y = 8x + 1000$$

For company B the cost is

$$y = 10x + 800$$

a. Use the method of addition to find the number of guests for which the two costs are equal.

b. Graph the two equations on the same set of axes from $x = 0$ to $x = 200$.

c. For which company is the cost less if there are more than the number of guests you found in part (**a**)?

32. A solar hot-water heating system has an initial investment of \$5400 and an annual cost of \$50. An electric hot-water heating system has an initial investment of \$1000 and an annual cost of \$600. Let y dollars be the total cost at the end of x years.

a. Write an equation giving the total cost of the solar heating system.

b. Write an equation giving the total cost of the electric heating system.

c. Graph the two equations you found in parts (**a**) and (**b**) on the same set of axes from $x = 0$ to $x = 10$.

d. Use the method of addition to solve the system of equations.

e. How long will it take for the total cost of the solar heat to become less than the total cost of the electric heat?

33. *Saturated fats.* According to *Restaurant Confidential* by Jacobson and Hurley, "all burgers are not created equal. You can't rely on calorie-counting guides that don't make the distinction among burgers served at fast-food establishments, family restaurants, and dinner houses." What's the problem?

© Josh Resnick/Shutterstock.com

The saturated fats! If x is the saturated fat content (in grams) in a McDonald's Quarter Pounder and y is the amount of saturated fat in a family-style restaurant, when you eat two Quarter Pounders ($2x$ saturated fat grams) and only one of the family-style burgers (y saturated fat grams), the amount of saturated fat is **30 grams,** 8 over the recommended daily allowance for a female between the ages of 19 and 50. If you add the saturated fats in the McDonald's (x grams) and the family-style restaurant (y grams) the result $x + y$ is exactly **22 grams,** the recommended amount of saturated fat you should have the whole day, even if you ate nothing else!

a. Write an equation for the amount of saturated fats when you eat one McDonald's and one family-style restaurant burger.

b. Write an equation for the amount of saturated fats P_Q contained in two Quarter Pounders.

c. Write an equation for the amount of saturated fats P_F contained in one family-style restaurant burger.

d. The total grams you eat when consuming two Quarter Pounders and one family-style restaurant burger is $2x + y$, or **30** grams. Write an equation for the total grams of fat in the meal.

e. We have not said how many grams of saturated fats there are in each burger, but we can find out! Graph $x + y = 22$ and $2x + y = 30$ on the same coordinate axis and find x (saturated fat grams in the McDonald's) and y (saturated fat grams in the family-style restaurant).

34. *Comparing McDonald's and Burger King.* If x is the saturated fat content (in grams) in a McDonald's Quarter Pounder and y is the amount of saturated fat in a Burger King Whopper Jr, when you eat two Quarter Pounders ($2x$ saturated fat grams) and only one Whopper Jr. burger (y saturated fat grams), the amount of saturated fat is **24 grams.** If you add the saturated fats in the McDonald's (x grams) and the Whopper Jr. (y grams) the result $x + y$ is only **16 grams,** under the recommended amount of saturated fats you should have the whole day.

a. Write an equation for the amount of saturated fats when you eat one McDonald's and one Whopper Jr. burger.

b. Write an equation for the amount of saturated fats P_Q contained in two Quarter Pounders.

c. Write an equation for the amount of saturated fats P_W contained in one Whopper Jr. burger.

d. The total grams you eat when consuming two Quarter Pounders and one Whopper Jr. burger is $2x + y$, or 24 grams. Write an equation for the total grams of fat in the meal.

e. We have not said how many grams of saturated fats are in each burger. Graph $x + y = 16$ and $2x + y = 24$ on the same coordinate axis and find x (saturated fat grams in the McDonald's) and y (saturated fat grams in the Whopper Jr.) and find out!

35. *Comparing McDonald's and Wendy's.* Are there any burgers with less saturated fat than McDonald's? Let's try Wendy's Jr. Bacon Cheeseburger. If x is the saturated fat content (in grams) in a McDonald's Quarter Pounder and y is the amount of saturated fat in Wendy's Jr. Bacon Cheeseburger, when you eat two Quarter Pounders ($2x$ saturated fat grams) and only one Wendy's burger (y saturated fat grams), the amount of saturated fat is **23 grams.** If you add the saturated fats in the McDonald's (x grams) and the Wendy's burger (y grams), the result $x + y$ is only **15 grams,** under the recommended amount of saturated fats you should have in a day.

a. Write an equation for the amount of saturated fats when you eat one McDonald's and one Wendy's Jr. Bacon Cheeseburger.

b. Write an equation for the amount of saturated fats P_Q containded in two Quarter Pounders.

c. Write an equation for the amount of saturated fats P_B contained in one Bacon Cheeseburger.

d. The total grams you eat when consuming two Quarter Pounders and one Bacon Cheeseburger is $2x + y$, or 23 grams. Write an equation for the total grams of fat in the meal.

e. We have not said how many grams of saturated fats are in each burger. Graph $x + y = 15$ and $2x + y = 23$ on the same coordinate axis and find x (saturated fat grams in the McDonald's) and y (saturated fat grams in the Bacon Cheeseburger) and find out!

36. The cost y of using an incandescent bulb costing just one quarter ($0.25) is $y = 0.25 + 0.08x$, where x is the number of days the bulb is used. The cost y of using a fluorescent bulb costing $ 1.50 is $y = 1.50 + 0.03x$.

a. Graph both costs in the same coordinate system.

b. Which has a less expensive start-up?

c. In how many days will the cost be the same?

In problems 37–41, use the following information: You want to watch 10 movies at home each month. You have two options.

Option 1: Get cable service. The cost is $20 for the installation fee and $35 per month.

Option 2: Buy a DVD Player and spend $25 each month renting movies. The cost is $200 for a DVD Player and $25 a month for movie rental fees.

37. a. If C is the cost of installing cable service plus the monthly fee for m months, write an equation for C in terms of m.

b. Complete the following table where C is the cost of cable service for m months:

m	6	12	18
C			

c. Graph the information obtained in parts (**a**) and (**b**). (*Hint:* Let m run from 1 to 24 and C run from 0 to 1000 in increments of 100.)

38. a. If C is the total cost of buying the DVD Player plus renting the movies for m months, write an equation for C in terms of m.

b. Complete the following table, where C is the cost of buying a DVD Player and renting movies for m months:

m	6	12	18
C			

c. Graph the information obtained in parts (**a**) and (**b**).

39. Make a graph of the information obtained in problems 37 and 38 on the same coordinate axes.

40. On the basis of the graph for problem 39, when is the cable service cheaper?

41. On the basis of the graph for problem 39, when is the DVD Player and rental option cheaper?

42. At Grady's restaurant, servers earn \$80 a week plus tips, which amount to \$5 per table.

a. Write an equation for the weekly wages W based on serving t tables.

b. Complete the following table, where W is the wages and t is the number of tables served:

t	5	10	15	20
W				

c. Graph the information obtained in parts (**a**) and (**b**).

43. At El Centro restaurant, servers earn \$100 a week, but the average tip per table is only \$3.

a. Write an equation for the weekly wages W based on serving t tables.

b. Complete the following table, where W is the wages and t is the number of tables served:

t	5	10	15	20
W				

c. Graph the information obtained in parts (**a**) and (**b**).

D Solving by Substitution

Use the information in the table and the substitution method for finding the point (x, y) at which the printing costs are equal for the two printers specified in problems 44–46.

	Cost	Cartridge	Yearly Cost
Canon MP560	\$100	\$ 80	$100 + 80x$ (dollars)
Epson Artisan	\$150	\$ 70	$150 + 70x$ (dollars)
Brother MFC 490	\$130	\$ 70	$130 + 70x$ (dollars)
Lexmark X4650	\$ 60	\$150	$60 + 150x$ (dollars)

44. Lexmark and Canon

45. Canon and Brother

46. Lexmark and Epson

USING YOUR KNOWLEDGE

Comparing Printing Costs. *We already compared printing costs in Example 7. Let us use our knowledge and the table below to compare the cost of several printers and their ink cartridges. Note that in some cases (Lexmark) the price of the printer is low but the price of the ink is high.*

Printer	Price	Ink Cost per Year	Total Cost per x Years
Canon MP560	\$100	\$ 80	$100 + 80x$ (dollars)
Epson Artisan	\$150	\$ 70	$150 + 70x$ (dollars)
Brother MFC 490	\$130	\$ 70	$130 + 70x$ (dollars)
Lexmark X4650	\$ 60	\$150	$60 + 150x$ (dollars)

47. Graph the total cost $y = 100 + 80x$ for the Canon.

48. Graph the total cost $y = 150 + 70x$ for the Epson.

49. Refer to the graphs for problems 47 and 48.

a. Which has a less expensive start-up, Canon or Epson?

b. What is the 1-year cost for Canon and for Epson?

c. How much are your savings the first year?

50. Graph the total cost $y = 130 + 70x$ for the Brother.

51. Graph the total cost $y = 60 + 150x$ for the Lexmark.

52. Refer to the graphs for problems 51 and 52.

a. Which has a less expensive start-up, Brother or Lexmark?

b. What is the 1-year cost for Brother and for Lexmark?

c. How much are your savings the first year?

53. Look at the graphs for problem 47–52. Which of the printers has the highest total cost, and what is the cost for one year?

IN OTHER WORDS

54. What does the solution of a system of linear equations represent?

55. How can you tell graphically whether a system has *no* solution?

56. How can you tell graphically whether a system has one solution?

Suppose you have a system of equations and you solve both equations for y and obtain

$$y = m_1x + b_1$$
$$y = m_2x + b_2$$

What can you say about the graph of the system when

57. $m_1 = m_2$ and $b_1 \neq b_2$? How many solutions do you have? Explain.

58. $m_1 = m_2$ and $b_1 = b_2$? How many solutions do you have? Explain.

59. $m_1 \neq m_2$? How many solutions do you have? Explain.

COLLABORATIVE LEARNING

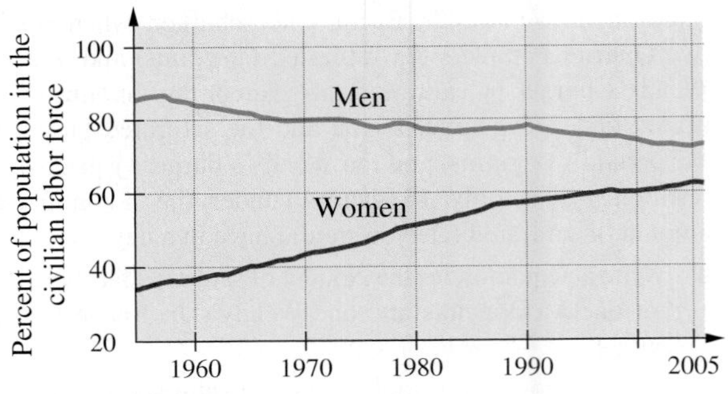

Source: U.S. Bureau of Labor Statistics.

Women and men in the work force.

For an excellent report dealing with Women and the Economy with updates to this data, go to http://tinyurl.com/345qm7x.

We promised in Getting Started that we would get back to this problem: finding the year in which the percent of men and women in the work force are equal. Divide your group into three teams. Here are the options.

Team 1 Extend the lines for the percent of men (M), the percent of women (W), and the horizontal axis.

1. In what year do the lines seem to intersect?
2. What would be the percent of men and women in the labor force in that year?

Team 2 Get some graph paper with a 20-by-20 grid, each grid representing 1 unit. Graph the lines

$$M = -0.20t + 83.9 \text{ (percent)}$$
$$W = 0.55t + 34.4 \text{ (percent)}$$

where t is the number of years after 1955.

1. Where do the lines intersect?
2. What does the point of intersection represent?

Team 3 The point at which the lines intersect will satisfy both equations; consequently at that point $M = W$. Substitute $-0.20t + 83.9$ for M and $0.55t + 34.4$ for W and solve for t.

1. What value did you get?
2. What is the point of intersection for the two lines and what does it represent?

Compare the results of teams 1, 2, and 3. Do they agree? Why or why not? Which is the most accurate method for obtaining an answer for this problem?

7.7 Linear Inequalities

GETTING STARTED

OBJECTIVES

A. Graph linear inequalities.
B. Solve systems of linear inequalities by graphing.
C. Solve applications involving systems of linear inequalities.

RHYME AND REASON

Do you like poetry? Perhaps you will understand the graphing of inequalities if we do it in verse.

*How to Graph a Linear Inequality, by Julie Ashmore**

Look here, my children, and you shall see
How to graph an inequality.
Here's a simple inequality to try:
x plus 2 is less than y. — $x + 2 < y$
First, make the "less than" "equal to";
So now y equals x plus 2. — $y = x + 2$
Then pick a point for x: say, 10;
Now plug that single constant in.
Add 10 plus 2 and you'll get y; — $x = 10, y = 10 + 2$
See if this pair will satisfy!
x: 10, y: 12; you'll find it's right, — (10, 12)
So graph this point to expedite.
Now find a second ordered pair — See Figure 7.55.
That fits in your equation there.
x: 3, y: 5 will do quite well. — (3, 5)
And it's correct, as you can tell.
Plot this point, and then you've got
To draw a line from dot to dot. — See Figure 7.55.
Make it neat and make it straight;
A ruler's edge I'd advocate.
The next step's hard! You've got to choose
Which side of this line you must use.
Change "equal to" back to "less than," — $x + 2 < y$
Just as it was when you began.
Pick a point on one side! I
Use 3 for x and 1 for y. — (3, 1)
Is 1 greater than 3 plus 2?
No! This side will never do! — $3 + 2 < 1$
On the other side, let's try
1 for x and 4 for y. — (1, 4)
1 plus 2 (which equals 3)
Is less than 4, as you can see. — $1 + 2 = 3 < 4$
Shade in the side that dot is on;
We've one more step to come upon. — See Figure 7.55.
Do the points upon your line

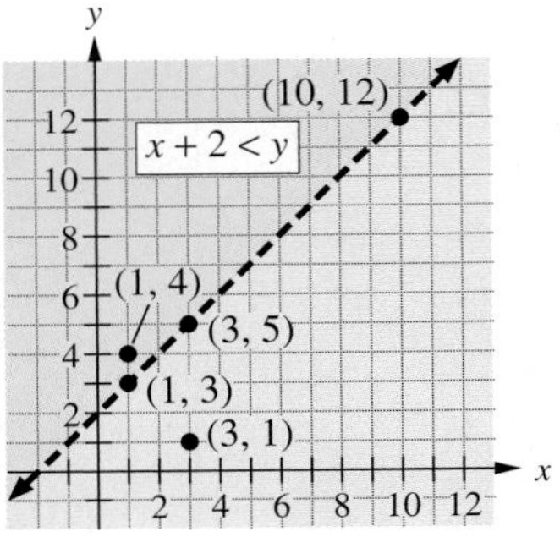

FIGURE 7.55

*Julie Ashmore was a young student in the John Burroughs School in St. Louis, Missouri, when she wrote this verse. How to Graph an Inequality, The Mathematics Teacher, Dec. 1977 Issue. Washington, DC: NCTM (This poem later appeared in two algebra textbooks.)

Fit the equation I assigned?
Use 1 and 3 for this last test; (1, 3)
They're "equal to," but they're not "less."
Make your line dotted to show this is true. $1 + 2 = 3$
And that is *all* you have to do! See Figure 7.55.

In this section we will see how to graph a relation in which the rule is a linear inequality, that is, an inequality of the type $ax + by + c \geq 0$. Let us use these ideas in a more practical way.

A Graphing Linear Inequalities

Suppose that you want to rent a car for a few days. Here are some prices for an intermediate car rented in Florida in a recent year:

Rental A	\$36 per day, \$.15 per mile
Rental B	\$49 per day, \$.33 per mile

The total cost C for the rental A car is

$$C = \underbrace{36d}_{\text{Cost for } d \text{ days}} + \underbrace{0.15m}_{\text{Cost for } m \text{ miles}}$$

Now suppose that you want the cost C to be \$180. Then $180 = 36d + 0.15m$. Graph this equation by finding the intercepts. When $d = 0$, $180 = 0.15m$, or

$$m = \frac{180}{0.15} = 1200$$

When $m = 0$, $180 = 36d$, or

$$d = \frac{180}{36} = 5$$

Join $(0, 1200)$ and $(5, 0)$ with a line, and then graph the discrete points corresponding to 1, 2, 3, or 4 days.

But what if you want the cost to be less than \$180? Then you have

$$36d + 0.15m < 180$$

You have graphed the points on the line $36d + 0.15m = 180$. Where are the points for which $36d + 0.15m < 180$? As the graph in Figure 7.56 shows, the line $36d + 0.15m = 180$ divides the plane into three parts.

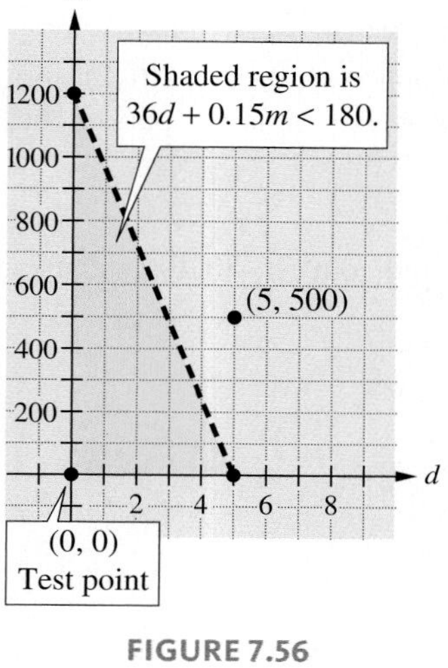

FIGURE 7.56

1. The points (half-plane) **below** the line
2. The points **on** the line
3. The points (half-plane) **above** the line

It can be shown that if any point on one side of the line $Ax + By = C$ satisfies the inequality $Ax + By < C$, then all points on that side satisfy the inequality and no point on the other side of the line does. Let's select $(0, 0)$ as a test point. Since

$$36 \cdot 0 + 0.15 \cdot 0 < 180$$
$$0 < 180$$

is true, all points below the line (shown shaded in Figure 7.56) satisfy the inequality. [As a check, note that $(5, 500)$, which is above the line, does not satisfy the inequality because $36 \cdot 5 + 0.15 \cdot 500 < 180$ is a false statement.] The line $36d + 0.15m = 180$ is *not* part of the graph and is shown dashed. To apply this result to our rental car problem, note that d must be an integer. The solution to our problem consists of the points on the heavy line segments at $d = 1, 2, 3$, and 4. The graph shows, for instance, that you can rent a car for 2 days and go about 700 mi at a cost less than $180. What we have just set up is called a *linear inequality*. Here are the definitions we need in order to proceed.

Definition of a Linear Inequality

A **linear inequality** is a statement that can be written in the form

$$Ax + By \leq C \quad \text{or} \quad Ax + By \geq C$$

where A and B are not both zero.

Note: If $<$ and $>$ are substituted for $\leq$ and $\geq$, we still have a linear inequality. Here is a summary of the procedure we used to graph the linear inequality above.

Graphing a Linear Inequality

1. Graph the line associated with the inequality. If the inequality involves $\leq$ or $\geq$, draw a solid line; this means the line is included in the solution. If the inequality involves $<$ or $>$, draw the line dashed, which means the line is not part of the solution.
2. Choose a test point [(0, 0) if possible] not on the line.
3. If the test point satisfies the inequality, shade the region containing the test point; otherwise, shade the region on the other side of the line.

PROBLEM-SOLVING

Graphing Linear Inequalities

① **Read** the problem.

Graph the linear inequality $2x < 3y - 6$.

② **Select** the unknown.

Find the solution set for the linear inequality $2x < 3y - 6$; that is, find its graph.

③ **Think** of a plan.
(a) First, graph
$2x = 3y - 6$.
(b) Select a test point.
(c) Check to see whether it satisfies the inequality.

(a) Start by graphing $2x = 3y - 6$, as in Figure 7.57. When $x = 0$, then $y = 2$, so graph $(0, 2)$. When $y = 0$, then $x = -3$, so graph $(-3, 0)$. Join $(0, 2)$ and $(-3, 0)$ with a *dashed* line, since the graph of $2x = 3y - 6$ is not part of the solution set.

(b) To find the points satisfying $2x < 3y - 6$, find out if $(0, 0)$ satisfies $2x < 3y - 6$.

④ **Use** the test point to find the solution set.
What do you have to do after you check to see whether the test point satisfies the inequality $2x < 3y - 6$?

(c) When $x = 0$ and $y = 0$, $2x < 3y - 6$ becomes

$$2 \cdot 0 < 3 \cdot 0 - 6$$

or

$$0 < -6$$

which is false. Thus, (0, 0) and all points below the line $2x = 3y - 6$ are *not* in the solution set of $2x < 3y - 6$. The solution set must consist of all points *above* the line $2x = 3y - 6$.

Remember that to emphasize the fact that points on the line $2x = 3y - 6$ are *not* part of the solution set, the line itself is shown dashed in Figure 7.57.

⑤ **Verify** the solution.

The verification that the points in the shaded region satisfy the inequality $2x < 3y - 6$ is left to you.

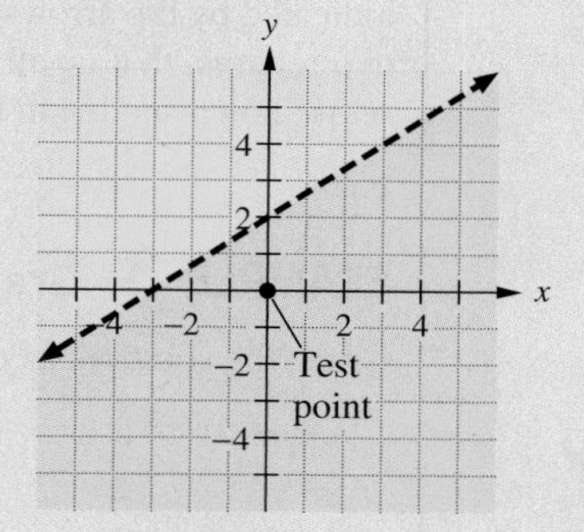

FIGURE 7.57

Try Example 1 Now

Cover the solution, write your own solution, and then check your work.

Example 1 illustrates the solution of an inequality that involves the less than or equal to sign. Notice carefully that the line corresponding to the equals sign is a part of the solution and is drawn solid in the graph.

EXAMPLE 1 Graphing Linear Inequalities

Graph the linear inequality $3x - 4y \leq 12$.

Solution

(a) We first draw the graph of the line $3x - 4y = 12$ (see Figure 7.58). We know that our answer requires one of the half-planes determined by this line.

(b) To find which of the half-planes is required, we can select any point not on the line and check whether it satisfies the original inequality. If the origin is not on the line, then (0, 0) is a good choice, because it is so easy to check.

(c) Does (0, 0) satisfy the inequality $3x - 4y \leq 12$? Yes, it does, because $3(0) - 4(0) = 0 < 12$. Thus, the half-plane containing (0, 0) is the one we need. This half-plane is shaded in Figure 7.58.

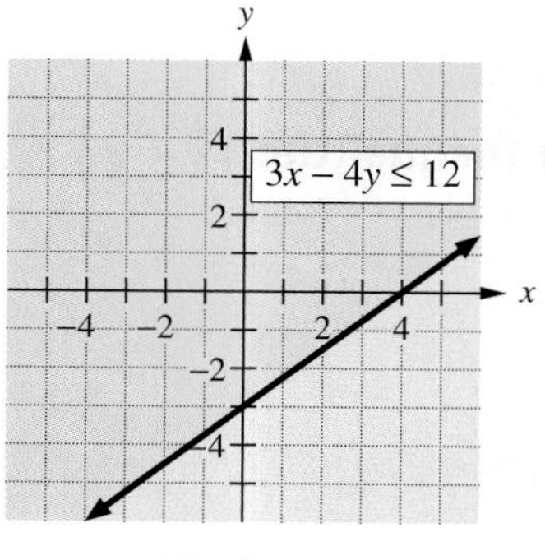

FIGURE 7.58

B Solving Systems of Inequalities by Graphing

The solution set of a system of linear inequalities in two variables can often be found as in the next example, where the individual inequalities are first solved separately and then the final shading shows the intersection of these solution sets. This intersection is the solution set of the system.

Keep in mind that the lines (boundaries) are included when the inequalities are $\leq$ or $\geq$. In this case the line is drawn solid. They are *not* included for $<$ or $>$. In that case the line is drawn dashed.

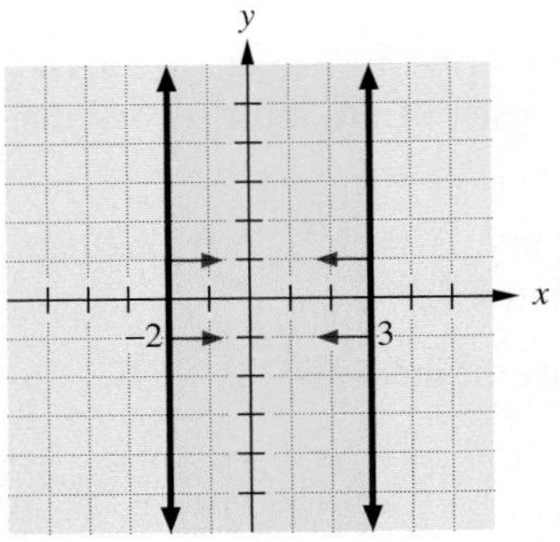

FIGURE 7.59

EXAMPLE 2 Graphing Systems of Inequalities

Graph the solution set of the system of inequalities $-2 \le x \le 3$.

Solution

Our system consists of the inequalities $-2 \le x$ and $x \le 3$. We first graph the lines $x = -2$ and $x = 3$ as shown in Figure 7.59. The inequality $-2 \le x$ is satisfied by all the points on or to the right of the line $x = -2$, as indicated by the arrows. Similarly, the inequality $x \le 3$ is satisfied by all the points on or to the left of the line $x = 3$, as indicated by the arrows. The given system is satisfied by all the points common to these two regions, that is, all the points on either line or between the two lines. The solution set is shown shaded in Figure 7.59.

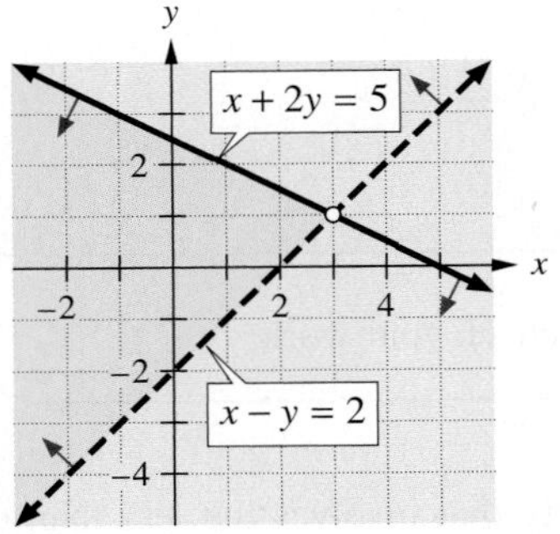

FIGURE 7.60

EXAMPLE 3 Graphing Systems with Two Inequalities

Graph the solution set of the system of inequalities

$$x + 2y \le 5$$
$$x - y < 2$$

Solution

We first graph the lines $x + 2y = 5$ and $x - y = 2$, as shown in Figure 7.60. The inequality $x + 2y \le 5$ is satisfied by the points *on or below* the line $x + 2y = 5$, as indicated by the arrows attached to the line. The inequality $x - y < 2$ is satisfied by the points *above* the line $x - y = 2$, as indicated by the arrows attached to the line. This line is drawn dashed to indicate that the points on it do *not* satisfy the inequality $x - y < 2$. The solution set of the system is shown in Figure 7.60 by the shaded region and the portion of the solid line forming one boundary of this region. The point of intersection of the two lines is *not* in the solution set.

We can also graph the solution set of a system consisting of more than two inequalities, as illustrated by the next example.

EXAMPLE 4 Graphing Systems with Four Inequalities

Graph the solution set of the system of inequalities

$$x + 2y \le 6$$
$$3x + 2y < 10$$
$$x \ge 0$$
$$y \ge 0$$

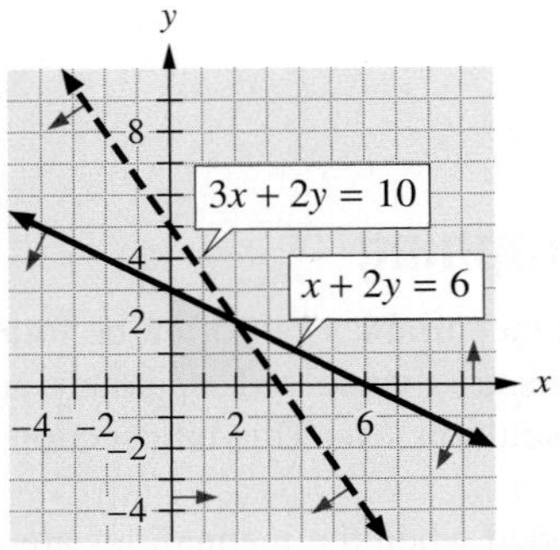

FIGURE 7.61

Solution

We first graph the lines $x + 2y = 6$, $3x + 2y = 10$, $x = 0$, and $y = 0$, as in Figure 7.61. The inequality $x + 2y \le 6$ is satisfied by the set of points on or below the line $x + 2y = 6$, as indicated by the arrows attached to the line. The inequality $3x + 2y < 10$ is satisfied by the set of points below the line $3x + 2y = 10$. Notice that this line is drawn dashed to show that it does not satisfy the given inequality. The set of inequalities $x \ge 0$ and $y \ge 0$ is satisfied by points in the first quadrant or points on the portions of the axes bounding the first quadrant. The solution set of the system can easily be identified; it is the shaded region plus the solid portions of the boundary lines.

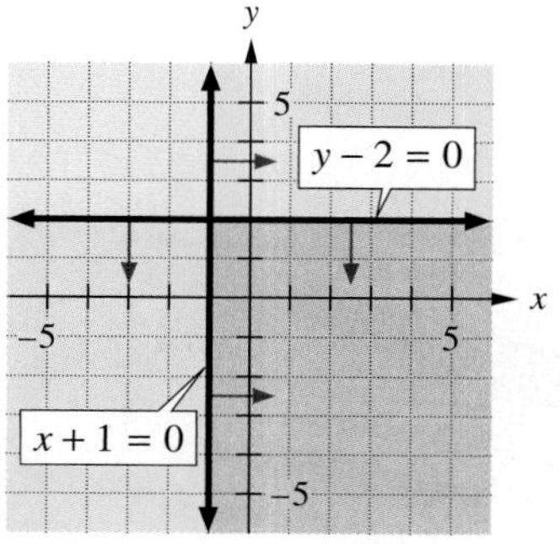

FIGURE 7.62

EXAMPLE 5 Graphing Systems Involving "Or"

Graph the solution set of the system of inequalities $x + 1 \geq 0$ or $y - 2 \leq 0$.

Solution

We first graph the lines $x + 1 = 0$ and $y - 2 = 0$, as shown in Figure 7.62. The inequality $x + 1 \geq 0$ is satisfied by the points on or to the right of the line $x + 1 = 0$, as indicated by the arrows attached to this line. The inequality $y - 2 \leq 0$ is satisfied by the points on or below the line $y - 2 = 0$, as indicated by the arrows attached to this line. Since this is an "or" set of inequalities, the solution consists of all the points that are on or to the right of the line $x + 1 = 0$ and all the points that are on or below the line $y - 2 = 0$. The shaded region and the two solid lines in Figure 7.62 show this set of points.

C Applications

In Section 7.1 the target zone used to gauge your effort when performing aerobic exercises was discussed. This target zone is determined by your pulse rate p and your age a and is found in the next example.

EXAMPLE 6 Finding the Target Zone with Inequalities

The target zone for aerobic exercise is defined by the following inequalities, in which a is the age in years and p is the pulse rate:

$$10 \leq a \leq 70$$

$$p \geq -\tfrac{2}{3}a + 150 \qquad \text{Lower limit}$$

$$p \leq -a + 190 \qquad \text{Upper limit}$$

Graph these inequalities and label the resulting target zone.

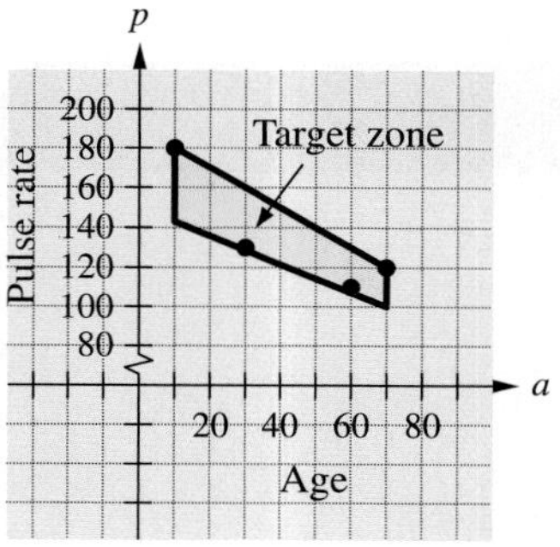

FIGURE 7.63

Solution

Since a is between 10 and 70, inclusive, it is convenient to label the horizontal axis starting at 10, using 10-unit intervals, and ending at 70. The vertical axis is used for the pulse rate p, and we start at 70 (the normal pulse rate) and go up to 200, as shown in Figure 7.63. We then graph the line $p = -\frac{2}{3}a + 150$ after finding the two points (30, 130) and (60, 110). Notice that because of the $-\frac{2}{3}a$, values of a that are divisible by 3 are most convenient to use. The inequality $p \geq -\frac{2}{3}a + 150$ is satisfied for all points that are *on or above* this line. Next, we graph the line $p = -a + 190$. Two points easy to find on this line are (10, 180) and (70, 120). The inequality $p \leq -a + 190$ is satisfied by all points that are *on or below* this line. The target zone is shown in Figure 7.63.

The United States is not the only polluting country in the world! One of the main CO_2 polluters is Russia. What are their future projections under the Kyoto Protocol, an international agreement setting targets for industrialized countries and the European communities in the reduction of greenhouse gases (GHG)? We shall see in Example 7.

EXAMPLE 7 Inequalities and Russian Goals under the Kyoto Protocol

Under the worst-case scenario, Russian emissions can be as high as $y = 60x + 1850$ and as low as $y = 30x + 1750$, where y is the number of megatons (millions of tons) of CO_2 emitted and x is the number of years after 2005. Graph the solution of the system

$$y \leq 60x + 1850$$

$$y \geq 30x + 1750$$

$$0 \leq x \leq 15$$

Solution

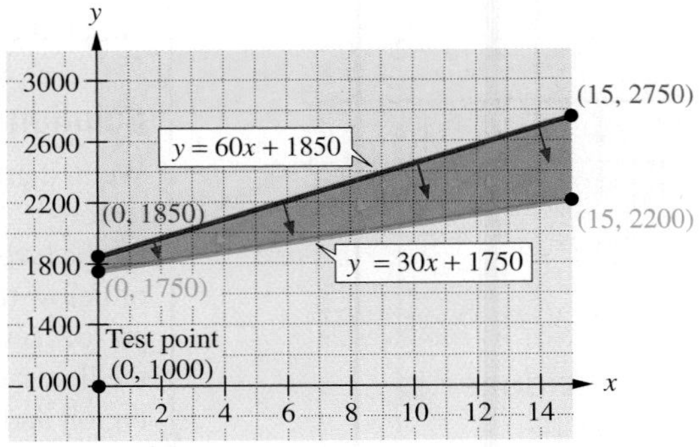

One of the challenges when graphing real-world problems is to determine the grid for the graph! We know that x must be between 0 and 15 inclusive, but what about y? If we use $x = 15$ in $y \le 60x + 1850$, we obtain $y \le 60(15) + 1850 = 2750$. For $x = 15$ in $y \ge 30x + 1750$, we get $y \ge 30(15) + 1750 = 2200$, so we let y be between 1000 and 3000 (which includes both 2200 and 2750) at 200-unit intervals.

To graph $y = 60x + 1850$, let $x = 0$, obtaining $y = 1850$. Graph $(0, 1850)$. Now, let $x = 15$ to obtain 2750. Graph the point $(15, 2750)$. Join the points $(0, 1850)$ and $(15, 2750)$ with a red line, the graph of $y = 60x + 1850$. Now, use the point $(0, 1000)$ as a test point. Because $0 \le 60(1000) + 1850$ is true, we shade the points *below and on the line* $y = 60x + 1850$. (We indicate this by using the red arrows in the graph.)

We use a similar procedure to graph $y \ge 30x + 1750$.

Letting $x = 0$ and $y = 1750$, we graph $(0, 1750)$.

Letting $x = 15$ and $y = 2200$, we graph $(15, 2200)$.

Join the points $(0, 1750)$ and $(15, 2200)$ with a blue line, the graph of $y = 30x + 1750$. Use the point $(0, 1000)$ as a test point. Because $0 \ge 30(1000) + 1750$ is false, we shade *above and on the line* $y = 30x + 1750$. We also indicate this by using the blue arrows in the graph. The solution set of the system is the area between and including the boundaries of the two lines.

7.7 EXERCISES

A Graphing Linear Inequalities

In problems 1–10, graph the given inequality.

1. $x + 2y \ge 2$ **2.** $x - 2y > 0$ **3.** $x \le 4$

4. $y \le 3$ **5.** $3x - y < 6$ **6.** $3x + 4y \ge 12$

7. $2x + y \le 4$ **8.** $2x - 3y < 0$

9. $4x + y > 8$ **10.** $x - 4y \le 4$

B Solving Systems of Inequalities by Graphing

In problems 11–26, graph the solution set of the given system of inequalities.

11. $-4 \le x < 3$

12. $2 \le y \le 5$

13. $x \le -1$ or $x > 1$

14. $y < 0$ or $y > 3$

15. $x - y \ge 2; x + y \le 6$

16. $x + 2y \le 3; x \le y$

17. $2x - 3y \le 6; 4x - 3y \ge 12$

18. $2x - 5y \le 10; 3x + 2y \le 6$

19. $2x - 3y \le 5; x \ge y; y \ge 0$

20. $x \le 2y; 2x \ge y; x + y < 4$

21. $x + 3y \le 6; x \ge 0; y \ge 0$

22. $2x - y \le 2; y \ge 1; x \ge \frac{1}{2}$

23. $x \ge 1; y \ge 1; x - y \le 1; 3y - x < 3$

24. $x - y \ge -2; x + y \le 6; x \ge 1; y \ge 1$

25. $x + y \ge 1; x \le 2; y \ge 0; y \le 1$

26. $1 < x + y < 8; x < 5; y < 5$

In problems 27–30, select the set of conditions (a) or (b) that corresponds to the shaded region in each figure.

27.

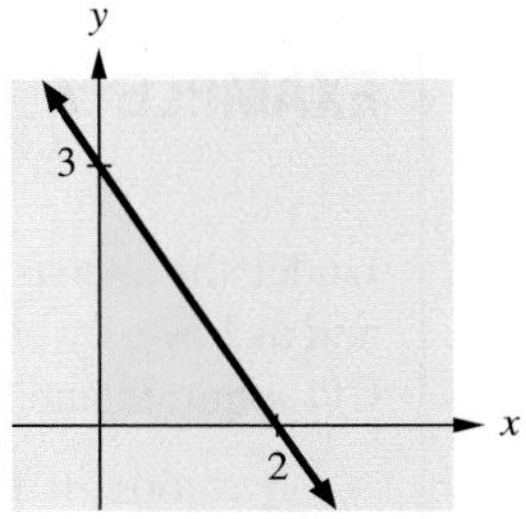

a. $3x + 2y < 6, x \le 2$ and $y \le 3$

b. $3x + 2y \le 6, x \ge 0$ and $y \ge 0$

28.

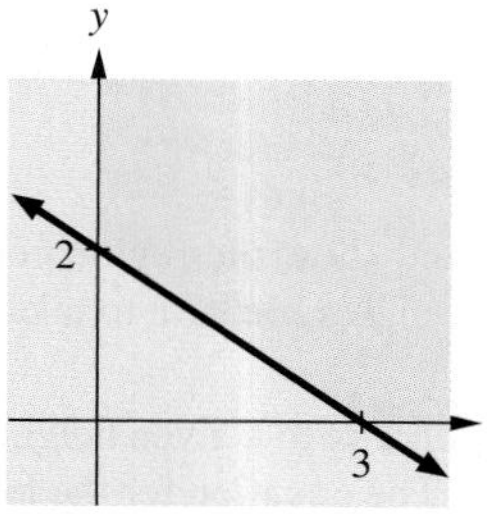

a. $2x + 3y \geq 6, x \geq 3$ and $y \geq 2$

b. $2x + 3y \geq 6, x \geq 0$ and $y \geq 0$

29.

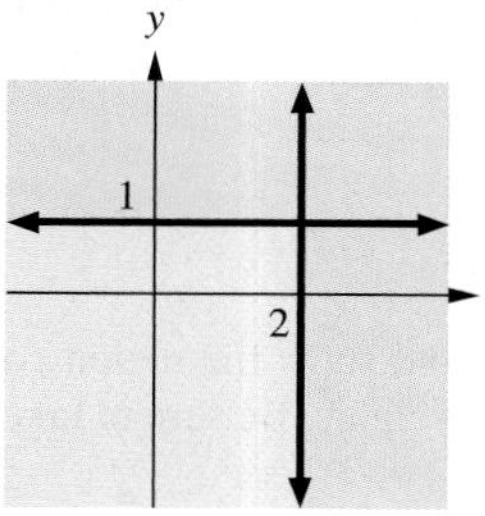

a. $x \geq 2$ or $y \geq 1$

b. $x \geq 2$ and $y \geq 1$

30.

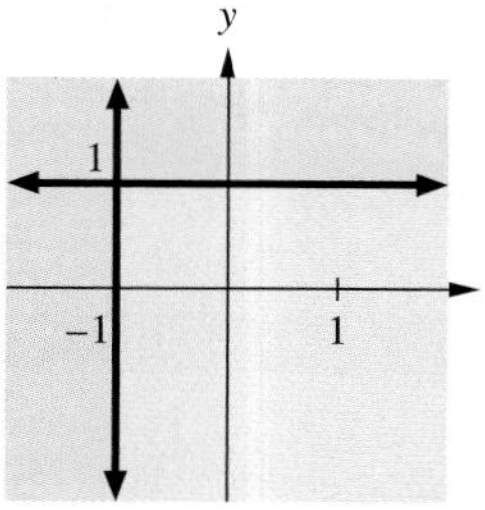

a. $x \leq -1$ and $y \geq 1$

b. $x \leq -1$ or $y \geq 1$

31. Which shaded region corresponds to the set of inequalities $x + y \geq 1$ and $x - y \leq 1$?

a.

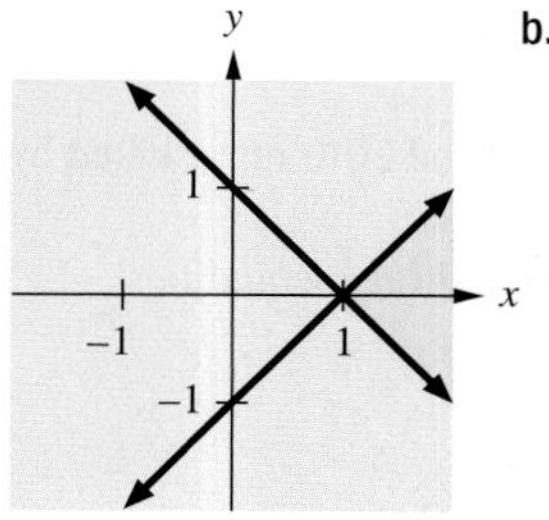

b.

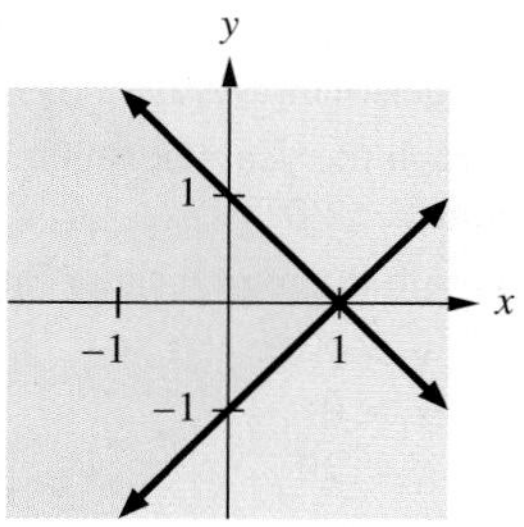

c.

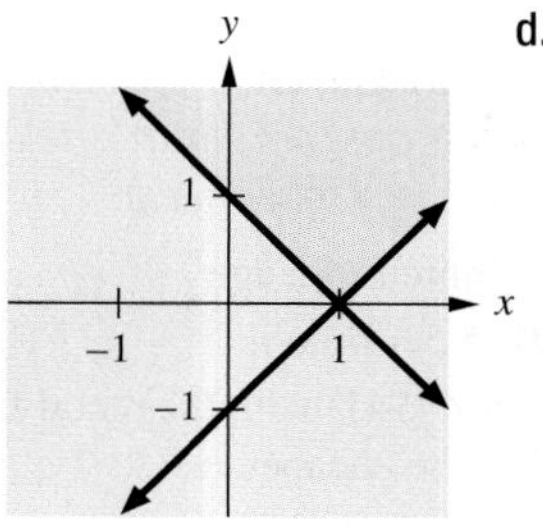

d.

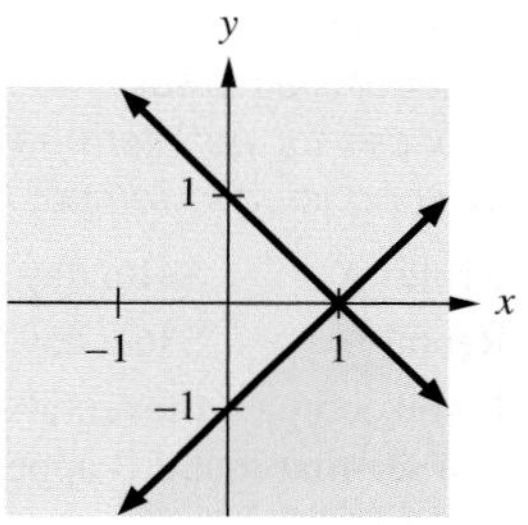

32. Write the set of inequalities that corresponds to the shaded region in the figure. Explain.

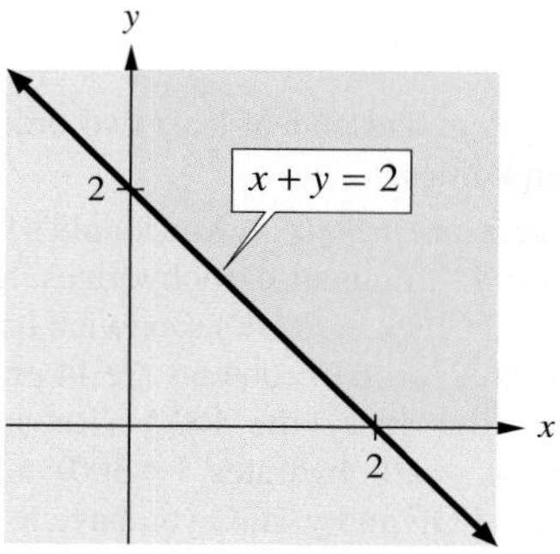

C Applications

In Example 7 you graphed three inequalities representing a region modeling a possible scenario for the Russian goals regarding CO_2 emissions for the Kyoto Protocol. In problems 33 and 34 we give you the regions and you are asked to find the inequalities corresponding to them.

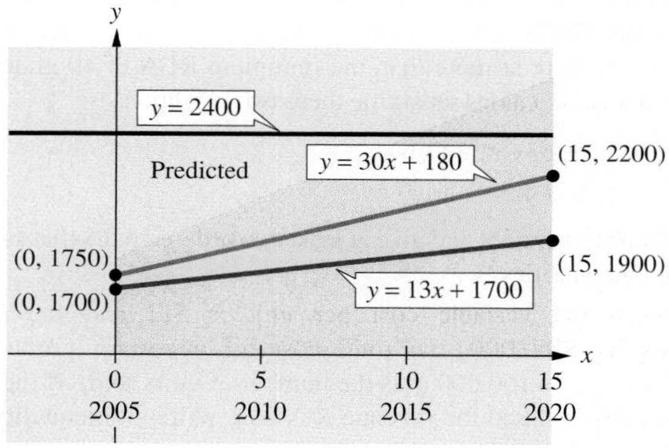

33. *Kyoto Protocol scenario 2.* Find the inequalities that define the yellow region, where x is the number of years after 2005 and y is the goal in megatons (millions of tons).

34. *Kyoto Protocol scenario* 1. Find the inequalities that define the blue region, where x is the number of years after 2005 and y is the goal in megatons (millions of tons).

35. a. In a scenario similar to the one in Example 7, Russian CO_2 emissions can be as high as 2400 megatons. Graph the line $y = 2400$ between 2005 and 2020.

b. In this scenario, emissions can be as low as $y = 15x + 1700$. Graph $y \geq 5x + 1700$, where x is the number of years after 2005.

c. Use the inequalities in parts (**a**) and (**b**) to define in words the region that describes this scenario for Russia.

36. *Sugar and protein.* A McDonald's Filet-O-Fish (FOF) has 8 grams of sugar, while a Burger King Tender Grilled Chicken (TGC) sandwich has 9 grams of sugar. You should limit your sugar intake to less than 40 grams per day. The RDA (Recommended Dietary Allowance) for protein is at least 50 grams per day: the FOF has 14 grams of protein and the TGC has 37 grams.

To satisfy your RDA's by eating x FOF and y TGC you have to satisfy the system:

$$8x + 9y < 40$$
$$14x + 37y \geq 50$$

Graph the system and give at least two ordered pairs that satisfy the inequalities.

37. *Carbohydrates and protein.* A McDonald's Filet-O-Fish (FOF) sandwich has 42 grams of carbohydrates, and a Burger King Tender Grilled Chicken (TGC) sandwich has 53 grams of carbohydrates. Their protein contents are 14 grams and 37 grams, respectively. To satisfy the RDA (Recommended Dietary Allowance) of carbohydrates (<300) and protein (≥ 50) when eating x FOF and y TGC you have to satisfy the system of inequalities:

$$42x + 53y < 300$$
$$14x + 37y \geq 50$$

Graph the system and give at least two ordered pairs that satisfy the inequalities.

38. *Carbohydrates and sugar.* A runner wants to maintain the RDA (Recommended Dietary Allowance) of carbs (< 300) by eating x McDonald's Filet-O-Fish (FOF) and y Burger King Tender Grilled Chicken (TGC). At the same time, sugar levels must be kept at more than the minimum RDA of 40 grams. A system of equaions satisfying these two conditions is:

$$42x + 53y < 300$$
$$8x + 9y \geq 40$$

Graph the system and give at least two ordered pairs that satisfy the inequalities.

39. When the variable cost per unit is \$12 and the fixed cost is \$160,000, the total cost for a certain product is $C = 12n + 160{,}000$ (n is the number of units sold). If the unit price is \$20 and the revenue R is $20n$, write an inequality for the situation and find the minimum number of units that must be sold to make a profit. (*Hint:* You need $R > C$ to make a profit.)

40. The cost of first-class mail is \$0.45 for the first ounce and \$0.20 for each additional ounce. A delivery company will charge \$6.00 for delivering a package weighing up to 2 lb (32 oz). Write an inequality indicating when the U.S. Postal Service price $P = 0.45 + 0.20(x - 1)$ (where x is the weight of the package in ounces) would be cheaper than the delivery company's price, and then solve the inequality.

41. The cost to park at a garage is $C = 1 + 0.75(h - 1)$, where h is the number of hours you park and C is the cost in dollars. Write an inequality to indicate when the cost C is less than \$10, and then solve the inequality.

42. Cigarette smoking produces air pollution. The annual number of cigarettes per person consumed in the United States is given by $N = 4200 + 70x$, where x is the number of years after 1960. How many years after 1960 will consumption be less than 1000 cigarettes per person annually? (Answer to the nearest whole year.) What year will that take place?

43. The desirable weight range corresponding to a given height for a man is shown in Table 7.7. We found the equation for the lower weights in terms of the height to be $w = 4h - 140$. The equation for the upper weights is $w = 5h - 176$. Thus, the desirable weights for men from 62 to 76 in. in height satisfy the system of inequalities

$$62 \leq h \leq 76$$
$$w \geq 4h - 140$$
$$w \leq 5h - 176$$

Graph this system of inequalities and show the region corresponding to the range of desirable weights. Be sure to take the horizontal axis as the h axis.

44. The desirable weight range corresponding to a given height for a woman is also shown in Table 7.7. The equation for the lower weights in terms of the height h is $w = 4h - 150$ and for the upper weights is $w = 5h - 187$. Thus, the desirable weights for women from 62 to 72 in. in height satisfy the system of inequalities

$$62 \leq h \leq 72$$
$$w \geq 4h - 150$$
$$w \leq 5h - 187$$

Graph this system of inequalities and show the region corresponding to the range of desirable weights. Be sure to take the horizontal axis as the h axis.

IN OTHER WORDS

45. Describe the steps you would take to graph the inequality $ax + by > c$.

46. Describe the graph of the inequality $y < mx + b$.

47. Describe the graph of the inequality $x \geq k$.

USING YOUR KNOWLEDGE

Inequalities and Hospital Stays

Did you know that hospital stays are getting shorter? Why do you think that is, better medical care or shorter insurance coverage? According to the American Hospital Association, between 1980 *and* 2010 *(inclusive), the average length of a hospital stay was* $y = 7.74 - 0.09x$ *(days), where x is the number of years after* 1980.

48. The graph of $y > 7.74 - 0.09x$ represents those longer-than-average stays. Graph $y > 7.74 - 0.09x$ representing those longer-than-average stays.

49. Graph the years between 1980 and 2010 represented by $x > 0$ and $x < 30$.

50. Graph the region satisfying the three inequalities

$$y > 7.74 - 0.09x$$
$$x > 0$$
$$x < 30$$

Instead of going to the hospital, you can use what you know about linear inequalities to save money when you rent a car. Here are the rental prices for an intermediate car obtained from a telephone survey conducted in Tampa, Florida, in a recent year.

Rental A	\$41 a day, unlimited mileage
Rental B	\$36 a day, \$0.15 per mile

51. If you compare the rental A price (\$41) with the rental B price, you see that rental B appears to be cheaper.

    a. How far can you drive a rental B car in 1 day if you wish to spend exactly \$41? (Answer to the nearest mile.)

    b. If you are planning on driving 100 mi in 1 day, which car would you rent, rental B or rental A?

52. How far can you drive a rental B car in 1 day if you wish to spend exactly \$42?

53. On the basis of your answers to problems 51 and 52, which is the cheaper rental price? (*Hint:* It has to do with the miles you drive.)

54. Will the rental prices ever be identical?

DISCOVERY

55. A **flowchart** is a type of diagram that represents an algorithm or process, showing the steps as boxes of various kinds, and their order by connecting these with arrows. This diagrammatic representation can give a step-by-step solution to a given problem. Can you discover and list three ways in which you can use a flowchart?

56. The figure in the next column is a flowchart for graphing the inequality $ax + by > c, abc \neq 0$. Explain why this works. (*Hint:* Try it for some of the problems.)

57. Can you discover what changes have to be made in the flowchart if the inequality is $ax + by < c, c \neq 0$?

58. Can you discover what changes have to be made in the flowchart if $c = 0$?

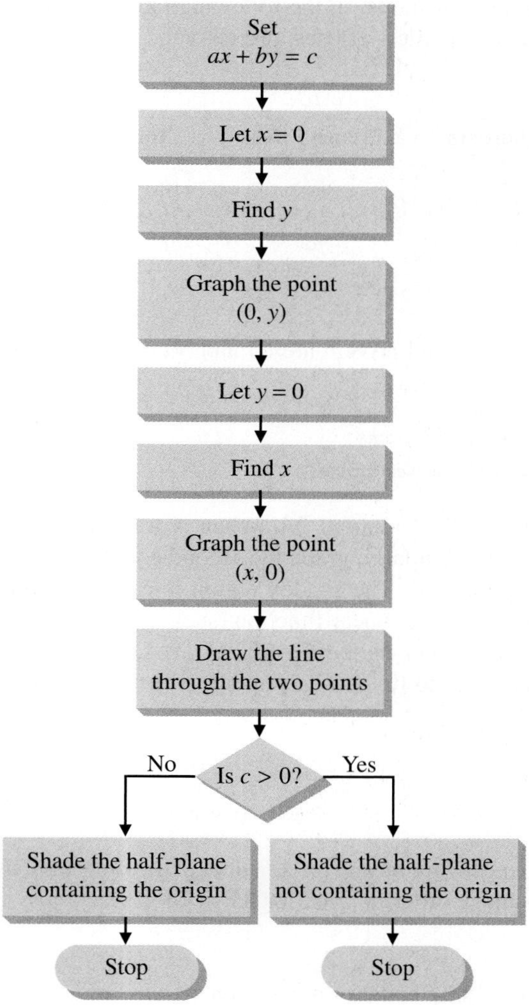

COLLABORATIVE LEARNING

As you can see in the bar graph below many fatal accidents involving drivers and pedestrians were alcohol related. The two line graphs show the effect of alcohol on males and females over a 2-hr period. Form three teams. The assignments follow.

Team 1 For the "Effects of Alcohol" below left (males), use the points $(6, 0.1)$ and $(2, 0.01)$ to find the slope of the line. Then use $(6, 0.1)$ to find the equation of the line relating B the blood alcohol level and D the number of drinks. Finally, write the inequality corresponding to the shaded region on the graph.

Team 2 For the "Effects of Alcohol" below right (females), let the slope be rise/run. What is this value? Use the point $(4, 0.1)$ and the slope to find the equation of the line relating B the blood alcohol level and D the number of drinks. Finally, write the inequality corresponding to the shaded region on the graph.

Team 3 The two graphs shown apply to 170-lb males and 137-lb females. A more general formula relating the number of drinks D and the weight W that will produce a blood alcohol level of 0.10 in 2 hr is $0.00125W - 0.01875D = 0.1$. Using W as the vertical axis and D as the horizontal axis, graph the equation and then write an inequality indicating that the blood alcohol level exceeds 0.1.

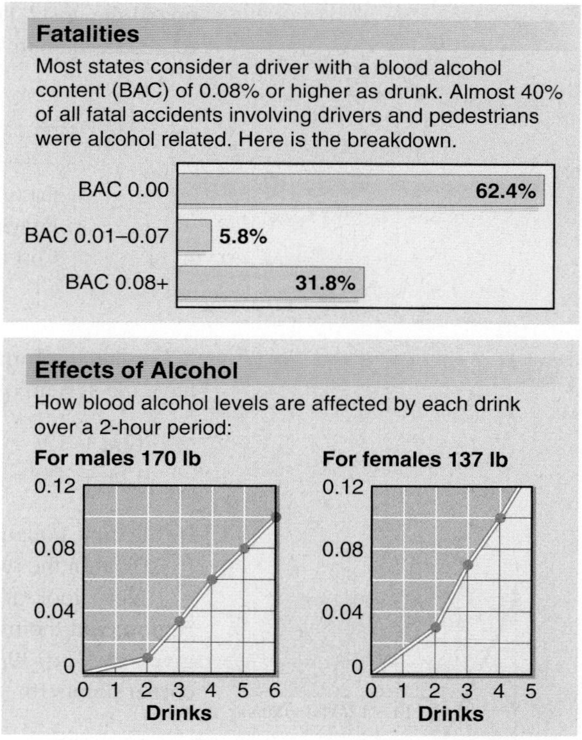

Sources: (left) http://www.alcoholstats.com/documentsVirtual/BACpiechart.pdf; (right) www.madd.org.

Blood alcohol levels.

7.8 Linear Programming

GETTING STARTED

OBJECTIVE

Solve linear programming problems by maximizing or minimizing an objective function using the specified constraints.

"YOU WANT A COKE WITH THAT?"

Are you on a steady diet of hamburgers and fries? Are you also watching your fat and protein intake? A regular hamburger contains about 11 grams of fat and 12 grams of protein. Your daily consumption of fat and protein should be about 65 g and 50 g, respectively. (RDA values for fat and protein are at http://www.netrition.com/rdi_page.html). But we are in luck: There is a special and a regular hamburger costs 39¢ and a regular order of fries is 79¢. How many of each could you eat so that you met the recommended fat and protein intake and, at the same time, minimized the cost? The given information is shown in the following table, where h and f represent the number of hamburgers and orders of fries, respectively.

	Hamburgers	French Fries	Total
Fat (g)	11	12	$11h + 12f$
Protein (g)	12	3	$12h + 3f$
Cost (¢)	39	79	$39h + 79f$

Since the recommended amounts of fat and protein are 65 and 50 g, respectively, we have the system of equations

$$11h + 12f = 65 \quad \longleftarrow \text{These are the fat grams}$$
$$12h + 3f = 50 \quad \longleftarrow \text{These are the protein grams}$$

In the first equation when $h = 0, f = \frac{65}{12}$. Graph $(0, \frac{65}{12})$. When $f = 0, h = \frac{65}{11}$. Graph $(\frac{65}{11}, 0)$. Join the two points with a line. Similarly, graph the second equation.

Now, look at the graph in Figure 7.64. The shaded region is called the **feasible region,** and the minimum or maximum for a linear function (such as the cost function given by $C = 39h + 79f$) occurs at one of the corner points. First, approximate the corner points $(0, \frac{65}{12})$, $(3.6, 2.1)$ and $(0, \frac{50}{3})$ to $(0, 5)$, $(4, 2)$ and $(0, 17)$.

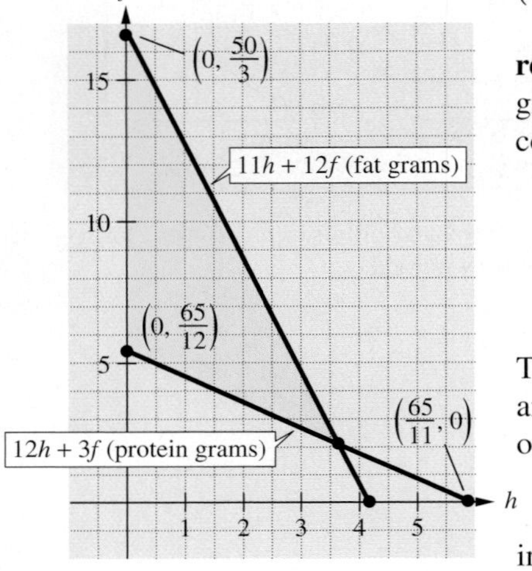

FIGURE 7.64

For $(0, 5)$, $C = 39 \cdot 0 + 79 \cdot 5 = \$3.95$
For $(0, 17)$, $C = 39 \cdot 0 + 79 \cdot 17 = \$13.43$
For $(4, 2)$, $C = 39 \cdot 4 + 2 \cdot 79 = \$3.14$ ⟵ This is the best deal!

Thus, the most economical way to meet your fat and protein intake by eating hamburgers and fries is to eat 4 hamburgers and 2 order of fries for \$3.14 (not necessarily all at once!).

Many problems and situations require better or more efficient ways of accomplishing a given objective. When studying how to conserve energy, recycle materials, or manufacture certain products, we usually want to minimize the cost. If the equations and inequalities used to model the problem are linear, we have a **linear programming problem,** usually, a two-variable problem consisting of two parts:

1. An **objective function** giving the quantity we wish to maximize or minimize (in the Getting Started the objective function is $\mathbf{C = 39h + 79f}$).
2. A system of **constraints** whose solution set is called the **feasible region** (the conditions of the problem, usually a system of linear inequalities. In the Getting Started fats and proteins have to be less than 65 and 50, respectively).

These problems are sometimes done with a computer using the **simplex algorithm** developed by George Dantzig in the late 1940s.

Although we shall not consider the simplex method, we shall solve some simple problems that illustrate the variety of applications of linear programming methods. The concepts we employ are basic even for the larger problems that are beyond the scope of this book.

As an example of a linear programming problem, let us assume that Sew & Sew, Inc., manufactures pants and vests. The profit on each pair of pants is \$6 and on each vest is \$5. The pants use 2 yd of material and the vests use 1.5 yd of material each. Because of production limitations, Sew & Sew cannot manufacture more than 10 of these garments per day and cannot use more than 18 yd of material per day. If Sew & Sew can sell all the pants and vests it makes, find the number of each garment it should produce per day to **maximize its profit.**

One way of presenting a linear programming problem so that it is easier for our minds to grasp is to put the data into tabular form. For the Sew & Sew problem, we tabulate the data and make some minor calculations as shown in the accompanying table. We can now see that the total profit P is

$$P = 6x + 5y \text{ dollars} \longleftarrow \text{This is the objective function}$$

Thus, P is a linear function of x and y, and we wish to determine x and y so that P has its maximum value.

	Pants	**Vests**
Number produced	x	y
Yards used	$2x$	$1.5y$
Profit \$	$6x$	$5y$

Next, we must express the restrictions in the problem in terms of x and y. The first restriction is that Sew & Sew produce not more than 10 garments per day. Since it produces x pants and y vests, the total number of garments is $x + y$. Thus,

$$x + y \le 10$$

A second restriction is that it use not more than 18 yd of material per day. This means that

$$2x + 1.5y \le 18$$

Another restriction is that x and y cannot be negative. This gives the **positivity conditions:**

$$x \ge 0 \qquad y \ge 0 \longleftarrow \text{These are the positivity conditions}$$

We can summarize our problem as follows: We want to maximize the linear function P given by

$$P = 6x + 5y$$

subject to the **constraints** (that is, the restrictions)

$$x + y \le 10 \qquad (1)$$
$$2x + 1.5y \le 18 \longleftarrow \text{These are the constraints} \qquad (2)$$
$$x \ge 0 \qquad y \ge 0 \qquad (3)$$

To make a start on the solution of this problem, we graph the solution set of the system of inequalities (1), (2), and (3), just as we did in the preceding section. This gives the region shown in Figure 7.65. Each point (x, y) in this region represents a combination of garments that satisfies all the constraints. For this reason, the region is called the **feasible region**.

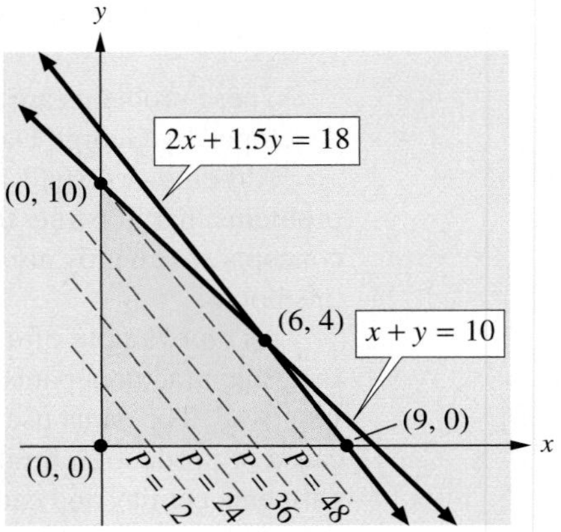

FIGURE 7.65

We need to select a point from the feasible region that will maximize the expression $6x + 5y$. In order to do this, let us examine the equation $6x + 5y = P$. For a given value of P, this is an equation of a straight line, which in slope-intercept form is

$$y = -\frac{6}{5}x + \frac{P}{5}$$

This equation shows that the slope is $-\frac{6}{5}$ regardless of the value of P. Hence, for a set of values of P, we get a set of parallel straight lines. Furthermore, for positive increasing values of P, the lines move out away from the origin. (This follows because the y intercept is $P/5$.) The dashed lines in Figure 7.65 are the graphs of $6x + 5y = P$ for the values $P = 12$, 24, 36, and 48. The smaller the value of P, the closer the line is to the origin.

These considerations make plausible the following basic theorem for feasible regions that are **convex** (non-reentrant) polygons, that is, regions such that the points of the line segment joining any two points on the boundary lie entirely inside the region or else on the boundary. See Figure 7.66.

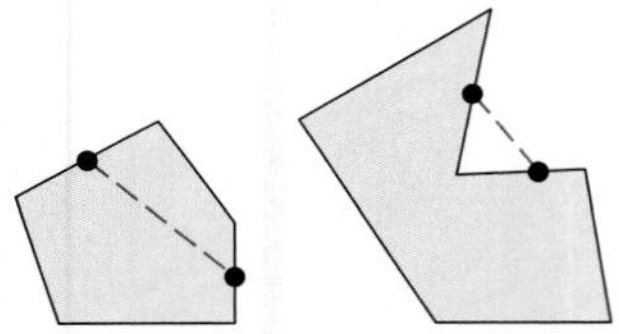

FIGURE 7.66

Theorem 7.1 Maximum or Minimum of a Linear Equation

If the feasible region is a convex (non-reentrant) polygon, then the desired maximum (or minimum) value of a linear function occurs at a corner point (vertex) of the region.

Vertex	$P = 6x + 5y$	
(0, 0)	0	
(9, 0)	54	
(6, 4)	56	← Maximum
(0, 10)	50	

To make use of this theorem, we need only check the values of P at the vertices of the polygon. These vertices are indicated in Figure 7.65 and can, of course, be found by solving the appropriate pairs of linear equations. By direct calculation, we find the values in the accompanying table. Thus, Sew & Sew should produce 6 pants and 4 vests per day to maximize its profit.

EXAMPLE 1 The Ducks and the Geese

Little Abner raises ducks and geese. He is too lazy to take care of more than 30 birds altogether but wants to make as much profit as possible (naturally). It costs him $1 to raise a duck and $1.50 to raise a goose, and he has only $40 to cover this cost. If Little Abner makes a profit of $1.50 on each duck and $2 on each goose, what is his maximum profit?

Solution

Letting x and y be the number of ducks and geese, respectively, that Little Abner should raise, we place the given information in the table.

	Ducks	Geese
Number	x	y
Cost	$1.00 each	$1.50 each
Profit	$1.50 each	$2.00 each
Total cost	$\$x$	$\$1.5y$
Total profit	$\$1.5x$	$\$2y$

It appears that Little Abner's total profit from both ducks and geese is $\$P$, where

$$P = 1.5x + 2y \quad \longleftarrow \text{This is the } \textit{objective} \text{ function}$$

The constraints are (in the order stated in the problem)

$$x + y \leq 30 \quad \text{Too lazy to raise more than 30 birds} \qquad (4)$$

$$x + 1.5y \leq 40 \quad \text{Has only \$40 to cover his costs} \qquad (5)$$

Although it is not stated, we must also obey the positivity conditions:

$$x \geq 0 \qquad y \geq 0 \qquad (6)$$

We proceed as before to find the feasible region by graphing the system of inequalities (4), (5), and (6), as shown in Figure 7.67. We then find the vertices and check them in the profit function P in the table.

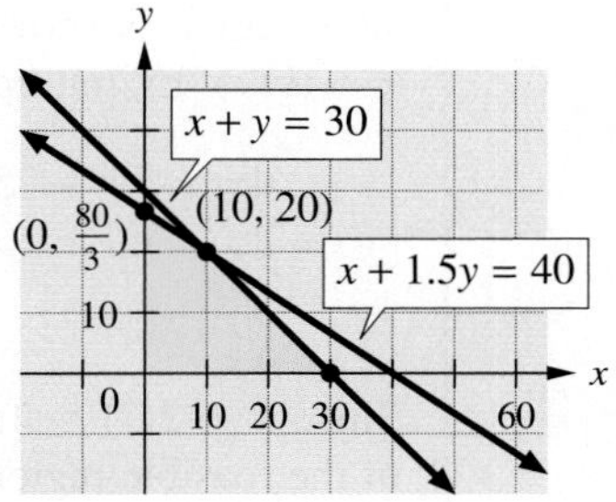

FIGURE 7.67

Vertex	$P = 1.5x + 2y$
(0, 0)	0
(30, 0)	45
(10, 20)	55 ← Maximum
$(0, \frac{80}{3})$	$53\frac{1}{3}$

By raising 10 ducks and 20 geese, Little Abner will make the maximum possible profit, $55.

The ideas we have studied are used to make decisions involving production, distribution, and advertising of many products including computers. Do you have a laptop computer or a desktop? How do companies decide which type to produce? How much profit should they try to make? Here is an example adapted from a quantitative methods course taught by Gerard Cornuejols and Michael Trick.

EXAMPLE 2 Producing Laptops and Desktops

A computer company wishes to produce laptop and desktop computers and must decide its product mix for the next quarter. It has the following constraints:

1. Each computer requires a processing chip. The supplier has allocated 10(000) chips to the company.
2. Each computer requires memory that comes in 16-MB chip sets. Laptops require 16 MB, so they take one chip, whereas desktops need 32 MB (two chips). These chips are cheaper when bought in great quantities, and 15(000) of them are available.
3. Each computer has to be assembled. A laptop computer takes 4 min versus 3 min for the desktop. There are 25(000) min of assembly time available.

Under current market conditions, material cost, and production time, each laptop produced and sold generates \$500 profit, and each desktop \$600. How many of each type computer should the company manufacture next quarter?

Solution

Suppose the company wishes to manufacture x laptop and y desktop computers. It wants to maximize its total profits P. Since the company generates \$500 for each laptop and \$600 for each desktop, $P = 500x + 600y$. The constraints are as follows:

1. $x + y \le 10$	The company only has 10(000) chips, 1 for each computer.
2. $x + 2y \le 15$	It only has 15(000) memory chips, 1 for laptops, 2 for desktops
3. $4x + 3y \le 25(000)$	It only has 25(000) min, 4 for laptops, 3 for desktops.

Graph $x + y = 10$, $x + 2y = 15$, and $4x + 3y = 25$, as shown in Figure 7.68. The feasible region is shown shaded. To find the point of intersection of $4x + 3y = 25$ and $x + 2y = 15$, multiply the second equation by -4. Then,

$$\begin{aligned} 4x + 3y &= 25 \\ -4x - 8y &= -60 \\ -5y &= -35, \quad \text{or} \quad y = 7 \end{aligned}$$

Since $x + 2(7) = 15$, $x = 1$. Thus, the point of intersection is at $(1, 7)$. The vertices of the feasible region and the profit P for each vertex are given in the following table. As you can see, the maximum profit (\$4700) occurs at $(1, 7)$, so the company should produce 1(000) laptop and 7(000) desktop computers.

Vertex	$P = 500x + 600y$	
(0, 0)	0	
(0, 7.5)	\$4500	
(1, 7)	\$4700	← Maximum
$(\frac{25}{4}, 0)$	\$3125	

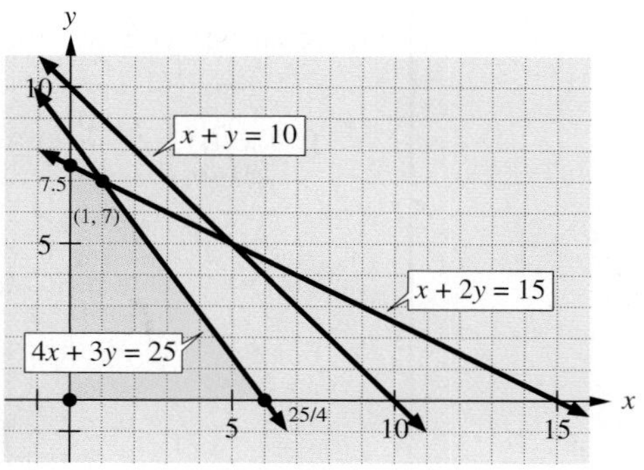

FIGURE 7.68

You have probably been wondering what to do if the desired maximum (or minimum) occurs at a vertex with noninteger coordinates. In the case of two-variable problems, if the solution must be in integers, you can try the integer points inside the feasible region that are nearest to this vertex (see Getting Started) and select the point that gives the desired maximum (or minimum). For many-variable problems, more complicated techniques, which are beyond the scope of this book, must be used.

EXAMPLE 3 Programming the Fish and Chicken Diet

Suppose you want a fish and chicken diet with less than 1000 calories but more than 50 grams of protein per day. McDonald's Filet of fish **(FOF)** has 380 calories, 15 grams of protein and costs \$3, while Burger King's Tender Grill Chicken **(TGC)** has 470 calories, 55 grams of protein and costs \$4.

How many of each would you have to eat so that you meet the recommended calorie and protein intake and, at the same time, minimize the cost?

Solution

The given information is in the table, where x and y represent the number of FOF and TGC, respectively.

	(FOF)	(TGC)	Total
Calories	380	470	$380x + 470y$
Protein	15	55	$15x + 55y$
Cost	\$3	\$4	$3x + 4y$

Since the recommended amounts of calories and protein are less than 1000 and more than 50, we have

$$380x + 470y < 1000 \quad (1)$$
$$15x + 55y > 50 \quad (2)$$

For equation (1), if $x = 0$, $y = \dfrac{1000}{470} \approx 2.1$, graph $(0, 2.1)$

If $y = 0$, $x = \dfrac{1000}{380} \approx 2.6$, graph $(2.6, 0)$

For equation (2), if $x = 0$, $y = \frac{50}{55} \approx 0.9$, graph $(0, 0.9)$

If $y = 0$, $x = \frac{50}{15} \approx 3.3$, graph $(3.3, 0)$

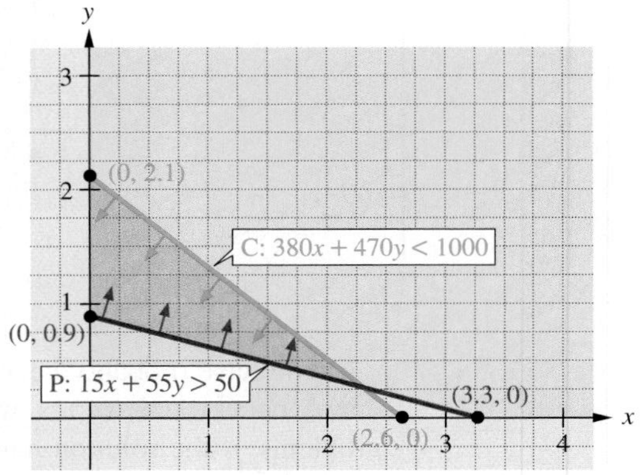

Using $(0, 0)$ as a test point

$380 \cdot 0 + 470 \cdot 0 < 1000$ is *true*, so we shade *under* the blue line, as indicated by the *down* arrows.

$15 \cdot 0 + 55 \cdot 0 > 50$ is *false*, so we shade *above* the red line, as indicated by the up arrows.

The ***feasible*** region is between the two lines as shown in the graph.

Now, we only have to **minimize** the cost $\boldsymbol{C = 3x + 4y}$.

We first approximxate the corner points in the **feasible** region so that the coordinates are integers:

$(0, 2.1) \approx (0, 2)$, $(0, 0.9) \approx (0, 1)$, but what about the point of intersection of the two lines, which is about $(2.3, 0.3)$? The closest ordered pair with integer values is $(1, 1)$ (Try others!)

so we use $(1, 1)$ as the third corner point. We then have:

For $(0, 2)$, $C = 3 \cdot 0 + 4 \cdot 2 = \$8$
For $(0, 1)$, $C = 3 \cdot 0 + 4 \cdot 1 = \$4$
For $(1, 1)$, $C = 3 \cdot 1 + 4 \cdot 1 = \$7$

Thus, the most economical way is to just buy 1 Tender Grill Chicken Sandwich (TGC) for \$4.

7.8 EXERCISES

1. Find the minimum value of $C = 2x + y$ subject to the constraints
$$x \ge 1$$
$$x \le 4$$
$$y \le 4$$
$$x - 3y \le -2$$

2. Find the maximum value of $P = x + 4y$ subject to the constraints
$$y - x \le 0$$
$$x \le 4$$
$$y \ge 0$$
$$x + 2y \le 6$$

3. Find the minimum value of $W = 4x + y$ subject to the constraints

$$\begin{aligned} x + y &\geq 1 \\ 2y - x &\leq 1 \\ x &\leq 1 \end{aligned}$$

4. Find the minimum value of $C = 2x + 3y$ subject to the constraints

$$\begin{aligned} 2x + y &\geq 18 \\ x + y &\geq 12 \\ 3x + 2y &\leq 34 \end{aligned}$$

5. Find the minimum value of $C = x + 2y$ subject to the constraints

$$\begin{aligned} 8 \leq 3x + y &\leq 10 \\ x &\geq 1 \\ y &\geq 2 \end{aligned}$$

6. Find the maximum value of $P = 2x + 3y$ subject to the constraints

$$\begin{aligned} y - x &\leq 2 \\ x + y &\leq 4 \\ 0 \leq x &\leq 3 \\ y &\geq 0 \end{aligned}$$

7. Find the maximum value of $P = x + 2y$ subject to the constraints

$$\begin{aligned} 2x + y &\geq 6 \\ 0 \leq y &\leq 4 \\ 0 \leq x &\leq 2 \end{aligned}$$

8. Find the maximum value of $P = 4x + 5y$ subject to the constraints

$$\begin{aligned} y - x &\leq 2 \qquad x \geq 0 \\ x - y &\leq 2 \qquad y \geq 0 \\ x + y &\leq 6 \end{aligned}$$

9. The E-Z-Park storage lot can hold at most 100 cars and trucks. A car occupies 100 ft^2 and a truck 200 ft^2, and the lot has a usable area of 12,000 ft^2. The storage charge is \$20 per month for a car and \$35 per month for a truck. How many of each should be stored to bring E-Z-Park the maximum revenue?

10. The Zig-Zag Manufacturing Company produces two products, zigs and zags. Each of these products has to be processed through all three of its machines, as shown in the table. If Zig-Zag makes \$12 profit on each zig and \$8 profit on each zag, find the number of each that the company should make in order to maximize its profit.

Machine	Hours Available	Hours/Piece	
		Zigs	Zags
1	Up to 100	4	12
2	Up to 120	8	8
3	Up to 84	6	0

11. The Kwik-Pep Vitamin Company wishes to prepare the following two types of vitamin tablets:

The first type tablet contains 1 mg of vitamin B_1 and 1 mg of vitamin B_2.

The second type tablet contains 1 mg of vitamin B_1 and 2 mg of vitamin B_2.

The profit on the two types of tablets is as follows:

2¢ for each tablet of the first type

3¢ for each tablet of the second type

In manufacturing two bottles of tablets, one of each type, but with the same number of tablets, Kwik-Pep wants to use no more than 100 mg of vitamin B_1 and 150 mg of vitamin B_2. How many tablets should be packed in each bottle to obtain the largest profit?

12. A nutritionist is designing a meal for one of her patients. The meal must include two vegetables, A and B, but not more than 100 g of each. Suppose that each 10-g portion of A contains 2 units of iron and 2 units of vitamin B_{12}, and each 10-g portion of B contains 1 unit of iron and 5 units of vitamin B_{12}. The number of calories in each 10-g portion of these vegetables is 5 for A and 3 for B. If the patient needs at least 20 units of iron and 36 units of vitamin B_{12} in the meal, how many grams of each vegetable should the nutritionist include to satisfy the iron and vitamin requirements while minimizing the number of calories in the meal?

13. The Jeri Tonic Company wishes to manufacture Jeri Tonic so that each bottle contains at least 32 units of vitamin A, 10 units of vitamin B, and 40 units of vitamin C. To supply the vitamins, the company uses additive X, which costs 20¢ per ounce and contains 16 units of vitamin A, 2 units of B, and 4 of C; and additive Y, which costs 40¢ per ounce and contains 4 units of vitamin A, 2 units of B, and 14 of C. If the total amount of additives is not to exceed 10 oz, how many ounces of each additive should the company put into each bottle to minimize its cost?

14. The Write-Right Paper Company operates two factories that manufacture three different grades of paper. There is a demand for each grade, and the company has contracts to supply 16 tons of low-grade, 5 tons of medium-grade, and 20 tons of high-grade paper, all in not more than 8 working days. It costs \$1000 per day to operate the first factory and \$2000 per day to operate the second factory. In 1 day's operation, factory number 1 produces 8 tons of low-grade, 1 ton of medium-grade, and 2 tons of high-grade paper, while factory number 2 produces 2 tons of low-grade, 1 ton of medium-grade, and 7 tons of high-grade paper. For how many days should Write-Right operate each factory in order to minimize its cost of filling these contracts?

15. Two oil refineries produce three grades of gasoline, A, B, and C. The refineries operate so that the various grades they produce are in a fixed proportion. Refinery I produces 1 unit of A, 3 units of B, and 1 unit of C per batch, and refinery II produces 1 unit of A, 4 units of B, and 5 units of C per batch. The price per batch is \$300 from refinery I and \$500 from refinery II. A dealer needs 100 units of A, 340 units of B, and 150 units of C. If the maximum number of batches he can get from either refinery is 100, how should he place his orders to minimize his cost?

16. A local television station is faced with a problem. It found that program A with 20 min of music and 1 min of commercials draws 30,000 viewers, whereas program B with 10 min of music and 1 min of commercials draws 10,000 viewers. The sponsor insists that at least 6 min per week be devoted to his commercials, and the station can afford no more than 80 min of music per week. How many times per week should each program be run to obtain the maximum number of viewers?

17. A fruit dealer ships her fruit north on a truck that holds 800 boxes of fruit. She must ship at least 200 boxes of oranges, which net her 20¢ profit per box; at least 100 boxes of grapefruit, which net her 10¢ profit per box; and at most 200 boxes of tangerines, which net her 30¢ profit per box. How should she load the truck for maximum profit? (*Hint:* If she ships x boxes of oranges and y boxes of grapefruit, then she ships $800 - x - y$ boxes of tangerines.)

18. Ms. Jones has a maximum of \$15,000 to invest in two types of bonds. Bond A returns 8% and bond B returns 10% per year. Because bond B is not as safe as bond A, Ms. Jones decides that her investment in bond B will not exceed 40% of her investment in bond A by more than \$1000. How much should she invest at each rate to obtain the maximum number of dollars in interest per year?

19. Growfast Nursery is adding imported fruit trees and oriental shrubs to its existing line of nursery products. The trees yield a profit of \$6 each, and the shrubs a profit of \$7 each. The trees require 2 ft^2 of display space per tree, and the shrubs require 3 ft^2 per shrub. In addition, it takes 2 min to prepare a tree for display and 1 min to prepare a shrub. The space and time constraints are as follows:

At most 12 ft^2 of display space is available.
At most 8 min of preparation time is available.

If Growfast can sell all the trees and shrubs it displays, how many trees and how many shrubs should it display each day to maximize its profit? (Assume that it is possible to arrange a display only once per day.)

20. The Excelsior Mining Company operates two mines, EMC 1 and EMC 2. EMC 1 produces 20 tons of lead ore and 30 tons of low-grade silver ore per day of operation. EMC 2 produces 15 tons of lead ore and 35 tons of low-grade silver ore per day of operation. Lead ore sells for \$14 per ton and low-grade silver ore sells for \$34 per ton. The company can sell at most 630 tons of the low-grade silver ore per month, but it can sell all the lead ore it produces. However, there is no space available for stockpiling any silver ore. The company employs one crew and operates only one of the mines at a time. Furthermore, union regulations stipulate that the crew not be worked in excess of 20 days per month. How many days per month should Excelsior schedule for each mine so that the income from the sale of the ore is at a maximum?

21. The ABC Fruit Juice Company wants to make an orange-grapefruit drink and is concerned with the vitamin content. The company plans to use orange juice that has 2 units of vitamin A, 3 units of vitamin C, and 1 unit of vitamin D per ounce, and grapefruit juice that has 3 units of vitamin A, 2 units of vitamin C, and 1 unit of vitamin D per ounce. Each can of the orange-grapefruit drink is to contain not more than 15 oz and is to have at least 26 units of vitamin A, 30 units of vitamin C, and 12 units of vitamin D. The per-ounce cost of the orange juice is 4¢, and that of the grapefruit juice 3¢.

a. How many ounces of each should be put into a can if the total cost of the can is as low as possible?

b. What is the minimum cost per can?

c. What is the vitamin content per can?

22. Joey likes a mixture of Grape-nuts, Product 19, and Raisin Bran for his breakfast. Here is some information about these cereals (each quantity in the table is per ounce).

Nutritional Value	Grape-nuts	Product 19	Raisin Bran
Calories	100	110	90
Fat	1 g	0 g	1 g
Sodium	195 mg	325 mg	170 mg

Joey is on a low-sodium diet and tries to make up 12 oz of the mixture so that the number of calories is at least 1200 but not over 1500, the total amount of fat is not more than 10 g, and the sodium content is minimized. Can he do it? If so, what are the per-ounce quantities of calories, fat, and sodium in his mixture? (*Hint:* If he uses x oz of Grape-nuts and y oz of Product 19, then he must use $12 - x - y$ oz of Raisin Bran.)

23. *Sugar and protein.* A McDonald's Filet-O-Fish (FOF) has 5 grams of sugar, while a Burger King Tender Grilled Chicken (TGC) sandwich has 7 grams of sugar. You should limit your sugar intake to less than 40 grams per day. The RDA (Recommended Dietary Allowance) for protein is at least 50 grams per day: the FOF has 15 grams of protein and the TGC has 55 grams. To satisfy your RDA's by eating x FOF and y TGC you have to satisfy the system:

$$5x + 7y < 40$$
$$15x + 55y \geq 50$$

Graph the system and approximate the corner points in the feasible region so that the coordinates are integers.

If the FOF is \$3 and the TGC is \$4, use the integer coordinates of the feasible region to minimize the total cost $C = 3x + 4y$ and satisfy the conditions of the problem.

24. *Carbohydrates and protein.* A McDonald's Filet-O-Fish (FOF) sandwich has 38 grams of carbohydrates, and a Burger King Tender Grilled Chicken (TGC) sandwich has 40 grams of carbohydrates. Their protein contents are 15 grams and 55 grams, respectively. To satisfy the RDA (Recommended Dietary Allowance) of carbohydrates (< 300) and protein (≥ 50) when eating x FOF and y TGC you have to satisfy the system of inequalities:

$$38x + 40y < 300$$
$$15x + 55y \geq 50$$

Graph the system and approximate the corner points of the feasible region so that the coordinates are integers.

If the FOF is \$3 and the TGC is \$4, use the integer coordinates of the feasible region to find the most expensive way for the total cost $C = 3x + 4y$ to satisfy the conditions of the problem.

25. *Carbohydrates and protein.* A McDonald's Filet-O-Fish (FOF) sandwich has 38 grams of carbohydrates, and a Burger King Tender Grilled Chicken (TGC) sandwich has 40 grams of carbohydrates. Their protein contents are 5 grams and 7 grams, respectively. To satisfy the RDA (Recommended Dietary Allowance) of carbohydrates (≤ 300) and protein (≥ 40) when eating x FOF you have to satisfy the system of inequalities:

$$38x + 40y \le 300$$
$$5x + 7y \ge 40$$

Graph the system and approximate the corner points in the feasible region so that the coordinates are integers.

If the FOF is \$3 and the TGC is \$4, use the integer coordinates of the feasible region to find the most expensive way for the total cost $C = 3x + 4y$ to satisfy the conditions of the problem.

IN OTHER WORDS

In a linear programming problem, describe in your own words what is meant by the following:

26. a. Constraint **b.** Feasible region

27. a. Positivity condition **b.** Convex polygon

28. Objective function

DISCOVERY

29. Suppose there is a championship prize fight. Gary the Gambler is tired of losing money and wants to hedge his bets so as to win at least \$100 on the fight. Gary finds two gambling establishments: A, where the odds are 5 to 3 in favor of the champion, and B, where the odds are 2 to 1 in favor of the champion. What is the least total amount of money that Gary can bet, and how should he place it to be sure of winning at least \$100? You can do this as a linear programming problem. First, let x dollars be placed on the champion to win with A, and y dollars on the challenger to win with B. Then, verify the following:

a. If the champion wins, Gary wins $\frac{3}{5}x$ dollars and loses y dollars, for a net gain of $\left(\frac{3}{5}x - y\right)$ dollars.

b. If the challenger wins, then Gary loses x dollars and wins $2y$ dollars, for a net gain of $(-x + 2y)$ dollars.

c. The problem now is to minimize $x + y$ subject to the constraints

$$\frac{3}{5}x - y \ge 100$$
$$-x + 2y \ge 100$$
$$x \ge 0$$
$$y \ge 0$$

Solve this problem.

30. Show that there is no feasible region if Gary reverses his bets and places x dollars on the challenger to win with A, and y dollars on the champion to win with B.

CHAPTER 7 Summary

SECTION	ITEM	MEANING	EXAMPLE
7.1A	Relation	A set of ordered pairs	$S = \{(3, 2), (5, 2), (7, 4)\}$
	Domain	The set of all possible x values of a relation	The domain of S is $\{3, 5, 7\}$.
	Range	The set of all possible y values of a relation	The range of S is $\{2, 4\}$.
	Function	A relation such that to each domain value there corresponds exactly one range value	$\{(x, y) \mid y = 2x\}$
	$f(x)$	Function notation	$f(x) = 3x + 2$
7.1C	Graph of a relation	The set of points corresponding to the ordered pairs of a relation	Function Function Not a function
	Vertical line test	The graph of a function cannot be cut in more than one point by any vertical line.	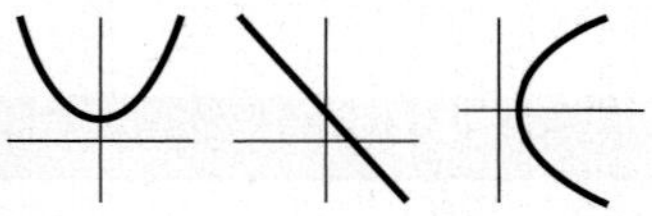

continued

CHAPTER 7 Summary – *continued*

SECTION	ITEM	MEANING	EXAMPLE
7.2B	x intercept	x coordinate of the point where the line crosses the x axis ($y = 0$)	The x intercept of $y = 2x - 4$ is 2.
	y intercept	y coordinate of the point where the line crosses the y axis ($x = 0$)	The y intercept of $y = 2x - 4$ is -4.
	Linear equation	An equation that can be written in the form $ax + by = c$	$3x + 5y = -2$; $3y = 2x - 1$
7.2C	Distance formula	$d = \sqrt{(x_2 - x_1)^2 + (y_2 - y_1)^2}$	The distance between (3, 5) and (5, 12) is $\sqrt{53}$.
7.3A	Slope of a line	$m = \dfrac{y_2 - y_1}{x_2 - x_1}$	The slope of the line through (3, 5) and (5, 12) is $\frac{7}{2}$.
7.3B	Point-slope equation	$y - y_1 = m(x - x_1)$	$y - 5 = \frac{7}{2}(x - 3)$ is the point-slope equation of the line described above.
	Slope-intercept equation	$y = mx + b$ (m is the slope, b is the y intercept).	$y = \frac{7}{2}x - \frac{11}{2}$ is the slope-intercept equation of the line described above.
	General equation of a line	$Ax + By = C$	The general equation of the line $y = 2x + 7$ is $-2x + y = 7$.
7.3C	Parallel lines	Two lines with the same slope and different y intercepts	$y = 2x + 5$ and $y = 2x - 3$ are equations of parallel lines.
7.4A	Quadratic function	A function of the form $f(x) = ax^2 + bx + c$	$f(x) = 3x^2 + 3x - 5$ is a quadratic function.
	Parabola	The graph of a quadratic function	The graph of $y = x^2 + 1$ is a parabola.
	Vertex	The lowest (or highest) point in the graph of a parabola	
7.5A	Exponential function	A function in which the variable is an exponent	$f(x) = 4^x$, $f(y) = (\frac{1}{2})^y$ and $H(z) = (1.01)^{z/2}$ are exponential functions.
7.7	Linear equation	An equation which can be written in the form $Ax + By = C$	$4x + 5y = -3$ and $3y = 4x - 1$ are linear equations.
7.8	Objective function	A function specifying the quantity to be maximized or minimized	$P = x + 2y$ is an objective function.
	Constraints	The specified conditions in a linear programming problem	$2x + y \le 4$, $0 \le y \le 3$ and $0 \le x \le 1$ may be the constraints for $P = x + 2y$.
	Feasible region	The solution set of the inequalities given in the constraints	
	Linear programming	A technique used to solve optimization problems in which we find the greatest or the least value of a function called the objective function	To maximize the objective function $P = x + 2y$ subject to the constraints $2x + y \le 4$, $0 \le y \le 3$ and $0 \le x \le 1$, evaluate $P = x + 2y$ at the corner points to obtain the maximum 6.5.

CHAPTER 7 Practice Test

1. Find the domain and range of the relation

   $R = \{(5, 3), (3, -1), (2, 2), (0, 4)\}$

2. Find the domain and range of the relation

   $R = \{(x, y) \mid y = -3x\}$

3. Which of the following relations are functions?
   a. $\{(x, y) \mid y^2 = x\}$ b. $\{(3, 1), (4, 1), (6, 1)\}$ c. $\{(x, y) \mid y = x^2\}$

4. A function is defined by $f(x) = x^2 - x$. Find the following:
   a. $f(0)$ b. $f(1)$ c. $f(-2)$

5. For a car renting for \$15 per day plus \$0.10 per mile, the cost for 1 day is

   $C(m) = 15 + 0.10m$ (dollars)

   where m is the number of miles driven. If a person paid \$35.30 for 1 day's rental, how far did the person drive?

6. Graph the relation

   $R = \{(x, y) \mid y = 3x, x \text{ is an integer between } -1 \text{ and } 3, \text{ inclusive}\}$

7. Graph the relation

   $Q = \{(x, y) \mid x + y < 3, x \text{ and } y \text{ are nonnegative integers}\}$

8. Graph the function defined by $g(x) = 2x^2 - 1$, where x is an integer and $-2 \leq x \leq 2$.

9. Graph the function defined by $f(x) = 2x - 6$.

10. Graph the equation $3x - 2y = 5$.

11. Find the distance between the two given points.
    a. $(4, 7)$ and $(7, 3)$ b. $(-3, 8)$ and $(-3, -2)$

12. Find the slope of the line that passes through the two points $(-1, -3)$ and $(9, -2)$.

13. a. Find the slope-intercept form of the equation of the line that passes through the point $(3, -1)$ and has slope -2.
    b. Find the slope-intercept form of the equation $2y = 4 - 8x$. What is the slope and what is the y intercept of the line?

14. Find the general equation of the line passing through the points $(-1, -3)$ and $(9, -2)$.

15. Determine whether the two given lines are parallel. If they are not parallel, find the coordinates of the point of intersection.
    a. $2x + y = 1$; $12x + 3y = 4$ b. $y = 2x - 5$; $4x - 2y = 7$

16. Find the general equation of the line that passes through the point $(1, -2)$ and is parallel to the line $2x - 3y = -5$.

17. Graph $y = -x^2 - 3$.

18. Graph $y = (x + 2)^2 - 1$ and give the coordinates of the vertex.

19. Graph $y = x^2 + 6x + 8$ and give the coordinates of the vertex.

20. Graph $f(x) = 3^x$ and $g(x) = (\frac{1}{3})^x$ on the same coordinate system.

21. Graph $f(x) = e^{x/2}$ and $g(x) = \ln(x/2)$ on the same coordinate system.

22. A principal of P dollars accumulates to an amount $A = Pe^{rt}$, where r is the interest rate and t is the time in years. If the interest rate is 8%, how long would it take for the money to double?

continued

CHAPTER 7 Practice Test – *continued*

23. Find the point of intersection of the lines

$$3x + 2y = 9 \qquad \text{and} \qquad 2x - 3y = 19$$

24. Solve the following system if possible. If not possible, explain why.

$$\begin{aligned} y &= 2x - 3 \\ 6x - 3y &= 9 \end{aligned}$$

25. Graph the solution set of the inequality $4x - 3y \le 12$.

26. Graph the solution set of the system of inequalities

$$x + 3y \le 6 \qquad \text{and} \qquad x - y \ge 2$$

27. Graph the solution set of the system of inequalities

$$\begin{aligned} x + 2y &\le 3 \\ x &\le y \\ x &\ge 0 \end{aligned}$$

28. Find the maximum value $C = x + 2y$ subject to the constraints

$$\begin{aligned} 3x + y &\le 8 \\ x &\le 1 \\ y &\ge 2 \\ x &\ge 0 \end{aligned}$$

29. Find the minimum value (if possible) of $P = 3y - 2x$ subject to the constraints

$$\begin{aligned} y - x &\le 2 \\ x + y &\le 4 \\ x &\le 3 \\ x &\ge 0 \\ y &\ge 0 \end{aligned}$$

30. Two machines produce the same item. Machine A can produce 10 items per hour and machine B can produce 12 items per hour. At least 420 of the items must be produced each 40-hr week, but the machines cannot be operated at the same time. If it costs \$20 per hour to operate A and \$25 per hour to operate B, determine how many hours are required per week to operate each machine in order to meet the production requirement of minimum machine cost.

ANSWERS TO PRACTICE TEST

CHAPTER 7 — What to Review *If You Missed It*

QUESTION	ANSWER	SECTION	EXAMPLE(S)	PAGE(S)
1	Domain, $\{0, 2, 3, 5\}$; range, $\{-1, 2, 3, 4\}$	7.1	1	331–332
2	Domain, the set of all real numbers; range, the set of all real numbers	7.1	1	331–332
3	**b.** and **c.**	7.1	2	332
4	**a.** 0 **b.** 0 **c.** 6	7.1	3–5	333–334
5	203 mi	7.1	6	334–335

ANSWERS TO PRACTICE TEST

CHAPTER 7

What to Review *If You Missed It*

QUESTION	ANSWER	SECTION	EXAMPLE(S)	PAGE(S)
6	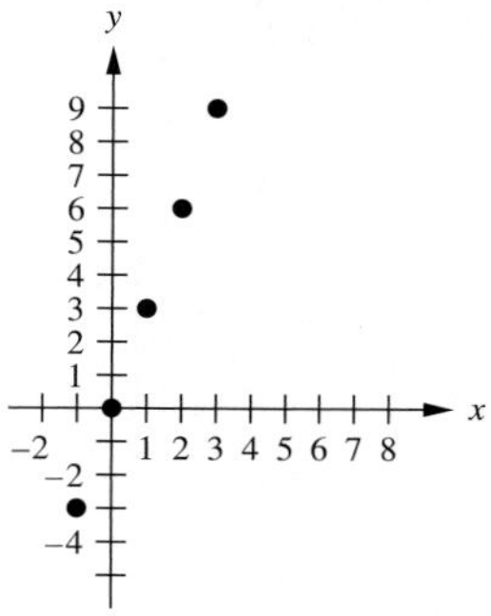	7.1	7	335
7	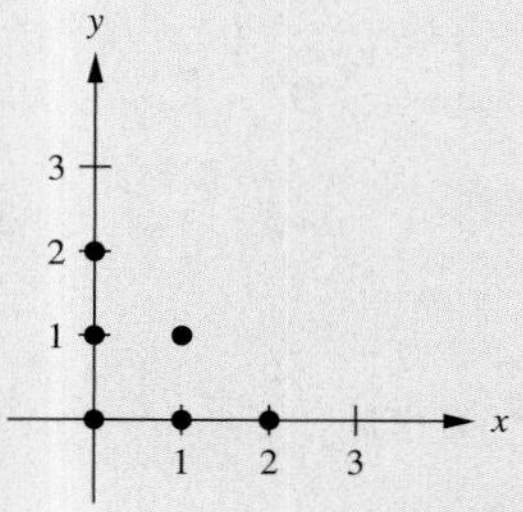	7.1	7, 8	335–336
8	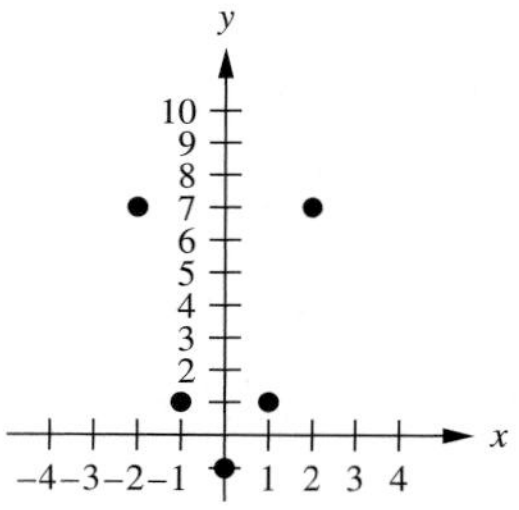	7.1	9	336
9	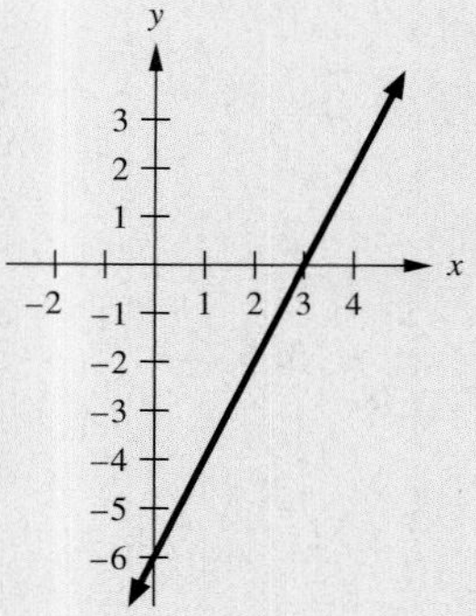	7.2	2	344
10	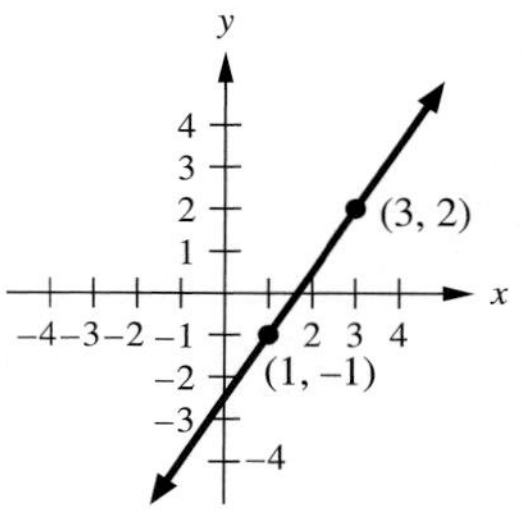	7.2	3	344

continued

ANSWERS TO PRACTICE TEST – *continued*

CHAPTER 7		What to Review *If You Missed It*		
QUESTION	**ANSWER**	**SECTION**	**EXAMPLE(S)**	**PAGE(S)**
11	**a.** 5 units **b.** 10 units	7.2	4, 5	345–346
12	$\frac{1}{10}$	7.3	1, 2	353
13	**a.** $y = -2x + 5$ **b.** $y = -4x + 2$; $m = -4$, $b = 2$	7.3	3–5	354–355
14	$x - 10y = 29$	7.3	6	356
15	**a.** Not parallel; intersect at $(\frac{1}{6}, \frac{2}{3})$ **b.** Parallel	7.3	8	358
16	$2x - 3y = 8$	7.3	9	359
17	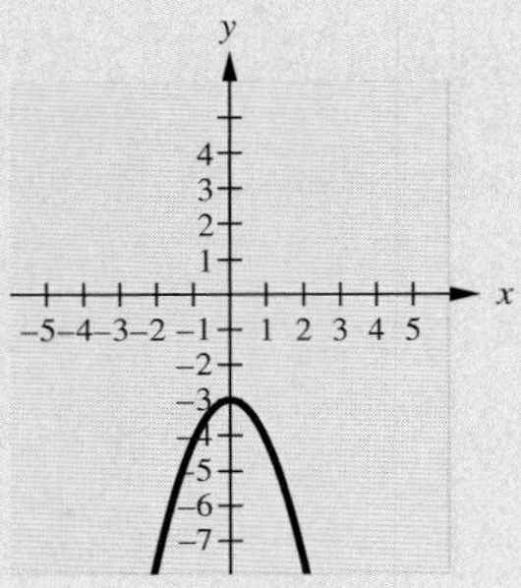	7.4	1–3	365–367
18	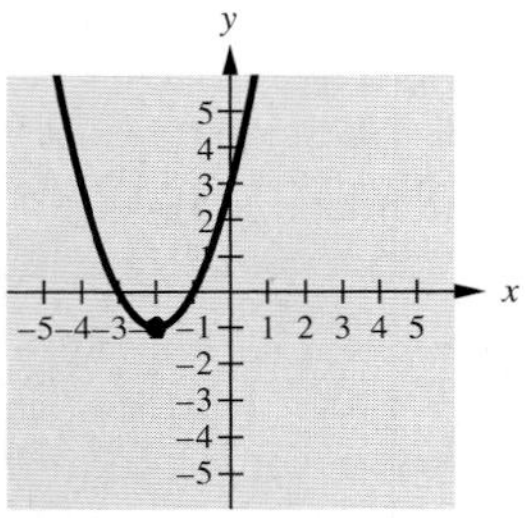 Vertex = $(-2, -1)$	7.4	4	368
19	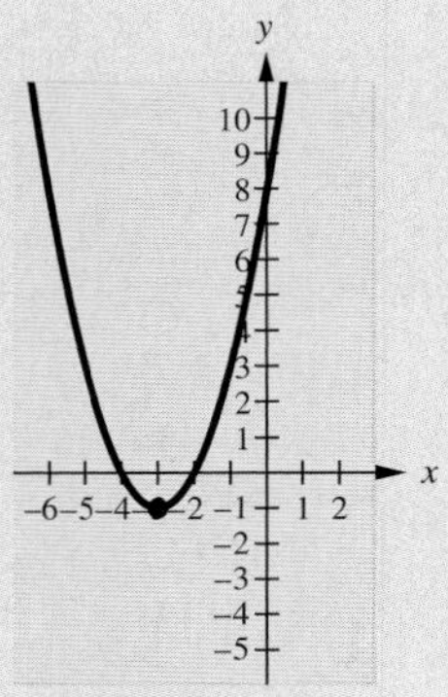 Vertex = $(-3, -1)$	7.4	5, 6	370–371

ANSWERS TO PRACTICE TEST

CHAPTER 7

What to Review *If You Missed It*

QUESTION	ANSWER	SECTION	EXAMPLE(S)	PAGE(S)
20	$g(x) = (\frac{1}{3})^x \quad f(x) = 3^x$ 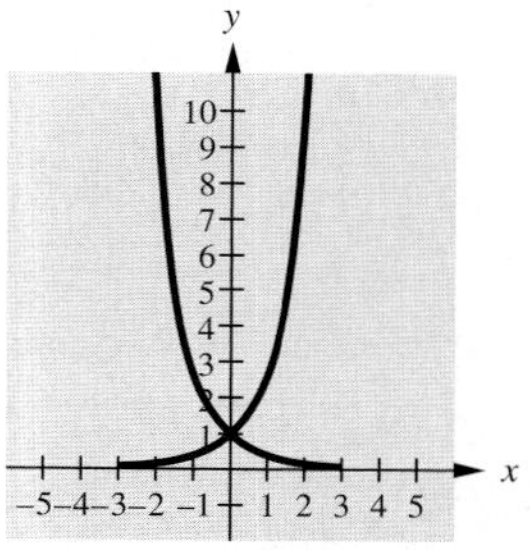	7.5	1	378
21	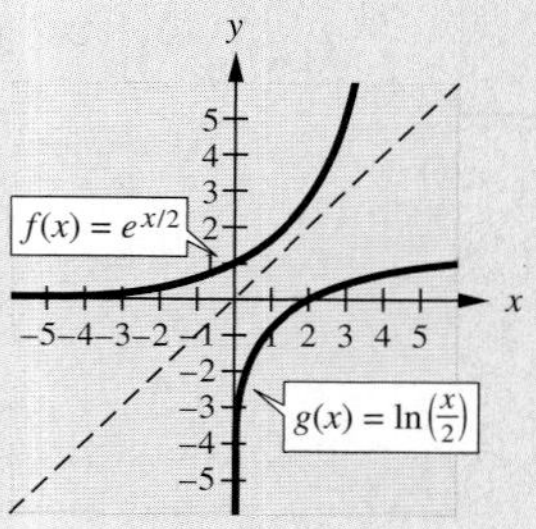	7.5	2	379
22	$\frac{\ln 2}{0.08} \approx 8.66$ years	7.5	3–5, 7–10	380–381, 383–385
23	$(5, -3)$	7.6	1, 2	391
24	The two equations represent the same line. The solution set is $\{(a, 2a - 3) \mid a \text{ is a real number}\}$.	7.6	3–6	392–393
25	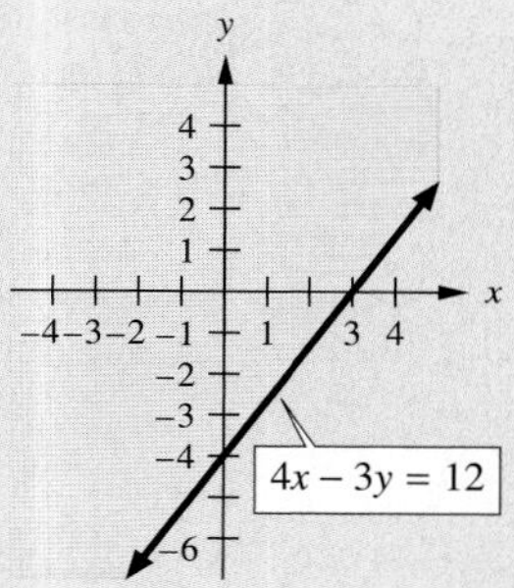	7.7	1	403
26	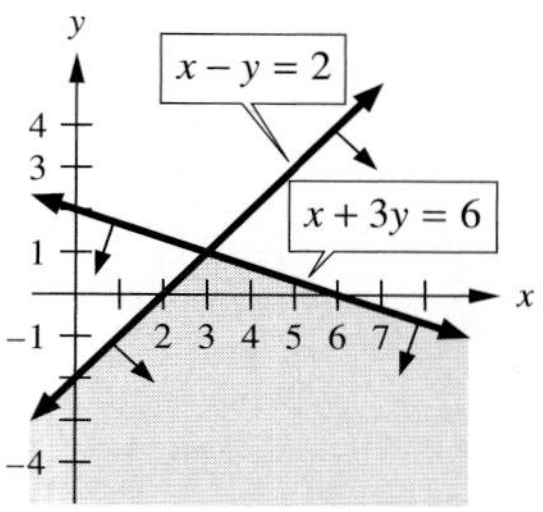	7.7	2, 3	404

continued

ANSWERS TO PRACTICE TEST – *continued*

CHAPTER 7		What to Review *If You Missed It*		
QUESTION	**ANSWER**	**SECTION**	**EXAMPLE(S)**	**PAGE(S)**
27	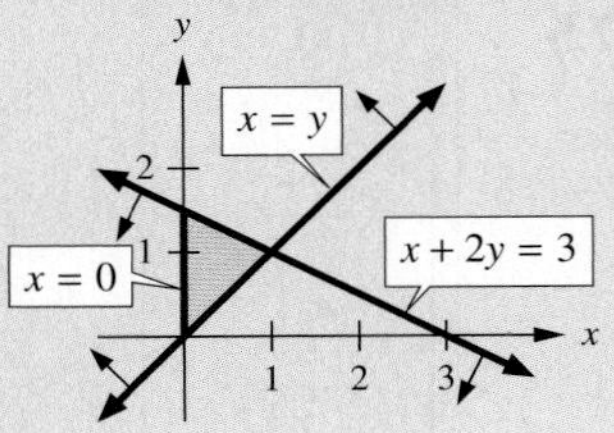	7.7	4	404
28	Maximum value 16 at (0, 8)	7.8	1, 2	413–415
29	Minimum value −6 at (3, 0)	7.8	1, 2	413–415
30	Run machine A 30 hr and machine B 10 hr.	7.8	1, 2	413–415

CHAPTER 8

Geometry

There is no royal road to Geometry. —EUCLID

© Mastering_Microstock

Satellites play an important role in advanced communication technology. Angles are critical in setting up equipment to receive signals from satellites. In Section 8.1, you will explore the use of angles in applications such as architecture and space exploration.

This chapter is devoted to the study of **geometry.** The word *geometry* literally means earth (*geo-*) measurements (*-metry*). You might have studied geometry in the past as a collection of theorems and proofs. We will not do that here. Instead, we will concentrate on measurements involving *linear, square,* and *cubic* units.

We start with some undefined terms (*points, lines, planes*), see how they relate to each other, and use linear measures to measure distances and perimeters of many-sided figures called **polygons.** We then discuss how to measure and classify *angles* by their measures, and we classify *triangles* by the number of equal sides they contain. We will relate these ideas to many other topics, including motorcycle riding, satellite trajectories, angles formed by veins in leaves, and traffic signs.

We study *similar* triangles, *similar* figures, and *circumferences* of circles and their many applications: hat sizes, ring sizes, and so on. We then study *areas* of polygons (squares, rectangles, parallelograms, and triangles) and circles and the Pythagorean theorem. Next, we look at *surface areas* and *volumes* of three-dimensional objects such as cubes, cylinders, cones, pyramids, and spheres. We then look at a classic problem, called the *Bridges of Königsberg,* solved by Leonhard Euler in 1736. Finally, we discuss non-Euclidean geometry and topology and end the chapter by studying right triangle trigonometry and chaos and fractals.

8.1 Points, Lines, Planes, and Angles

GETTING STARTED

OBJECTIVES

A. Determine the geometric figure described by the given union or intersection.

B. Introduce planes and describe the relationship between points, lines and planes.

C. Define and classify angles and find their measure.

D. Solve applications involving angles.

Human Side of Math

© Bettmann/CORBIS

(Flourished 300 B.C.)

One of the most famous mathematicians of all time is **Euclid,** who taught in about 300 B.C. at the university in Alexandria, the main Egyptian seaport.

Geometry evolved from the more or less rudimentary ideas of the ancient Egyptians (about 1500 B.C.), who were concerned with practical problems involving measurement of areas and volumes. Greek geometers, however, tried to apply the principles of Greek logic to the study of geometry and to prove theorems by a sequence of logical steps that proceeded from certain basic assumptions to a conclusion.

Euclid's greatest contribution was his collection and systematization of most of the Greek mathematics of his time. His reputation rests mainly on his work titled *The Elements,* which contains geometry, number theory, and some algebra. Most U.S. textbooks on plane and solid geometry contain the material in the geometry portions of *The Elements*. Over a thousand editions of *The Elements* have been published since the first printed edition appeared in 1482, and for more than 2000 years this work has dominated the teaching of geometry.

LOOKING AHEAD

Many of the geometric concepts that were the focus of Euclid's studies and writings also constitute the topics in this chapter.

GETTING THE RIGHT ANGLE

Have you heard the expression "I am looking at it from a new angle"? In algebra, you measured the inclination of a line by using the *slope* of a line. In geometry, you measure the inclination of a line by measuring the *angle* the line makes with the horizontal using an instrument called a **protractor.** (See Figures 8.23 and 8.24 on page 433.) Angles are everywhere. You can see angles in things as large as the cables on a suspension bridge and as small as the veins in a plant leaf. Figure 8.1 shows the angles in the flight path of the *Ranger 9* lunar probe.

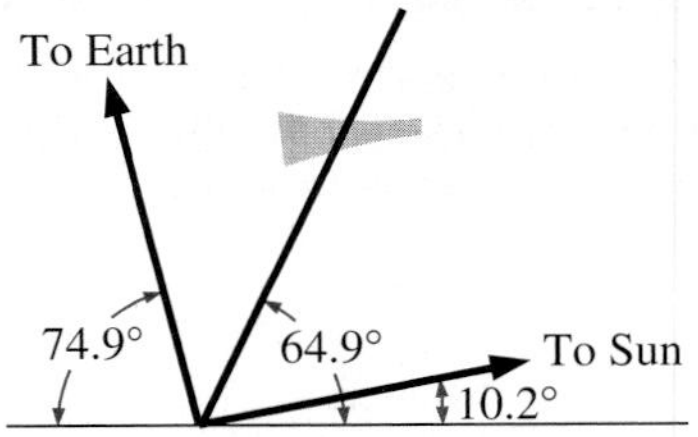

FIGURE 8.1 *Ranger 9* terminal trajectory orientation and glide path (NASA).

The Leaning Tower of Pisa has an angle of inclination of about 5° (read "5 degrees") from the vertical in the photo. Thus the tower makes an 85° *acute* angle, an angle that is less than 90°, with the ground. How do we know that? Because if the tower were completely vertical, it would make a 90° angle, that is, a *right* angle with the ground. Try to find the angle that the left side of the tower makes with the ground. Your answer will be an *obtuse* angle, an angle that measures more than 90°.

But we are getting ahead of the story! We shall see that angles are formed by *rays, rays* are part of *lines,* and *lines* are sets of *points,* and we have not discussed any of these terms yet! We shall do so in more detail in this section.

The basic elements of Euclidean geometry are **points, lines,** and **planes.** These three words cannot be precisely defined, because this would require the use of other words that are also undefined. For example,

© Fedor Selivanov/Shutterstock.com

Construction of the Tower of Pisa began in 1174, and settling was already noticeable after only three of its eight stories were built. Still leaning, the tower was completed in the fourteenth century.

we can say that a line is a set of points. But what is a point? A point is that which has no dimension. But again, what is dimension? However, since all other geometric terms are defined on the basis of these three words, we must develop an intuitive idea of their meaning.

A Points and Lines

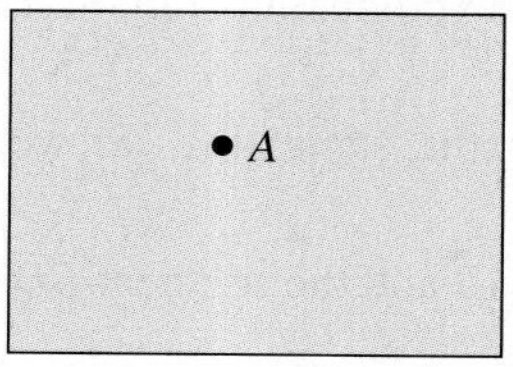

Point A

FIGURE 8.2

Line $\overleftrightarrow{AB}$

FIGURE 8.3

A **point** may be regarded as a location in space. A point has no breadth, no width, and no length. We can picture a point as a dot, such as A in Figure 8.2. (The sharper the pencil, the better the picture.)

We can think of a **line** as the path of a point moving in a fixed direction in space. A line extends without end in both its directions. If we have two points A and B, there is only *one* line that can be drawn through the two points: the line AB, denoted by $\overleftrightarrow{AB}$ (see Figure 8.3) and extending without end in both directions.

Selecting any point A on a line divides the line into *three* sets: the point A itself and two **half-lines,** one on each side of A, as shown in Figure 8.4. The half-lines *do not* include the point A, as indicated by the open circle at one end of the arrow. When the endpoint is included, the result is a **ray.** In Figure 8.5, **ray** $\overrightarrow{AB}$ has initial point A and extends in the direction of B, whereas **ray** $\overrightarrow{BA}$ has initial point B and extends in the direction of A. The **line segment** $\overline{AB}$, shown in Figure 8.5, consists of the points A and B and all the points between A and B.

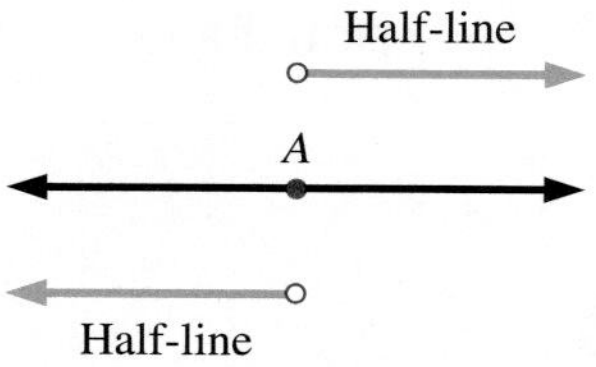

FIGURE 8.4

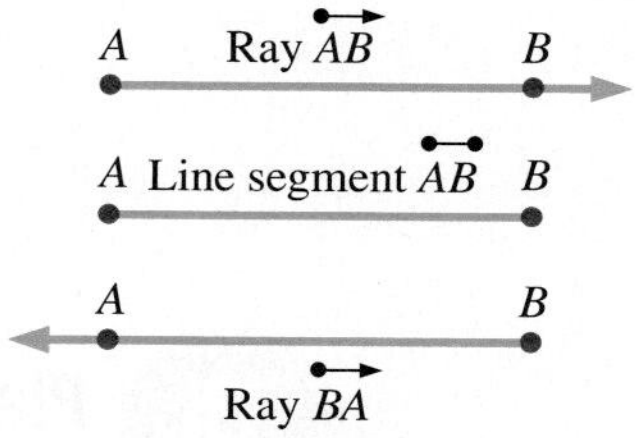

FIGURE 8.5

Figure 8.6 shows the figures and notations we have described.

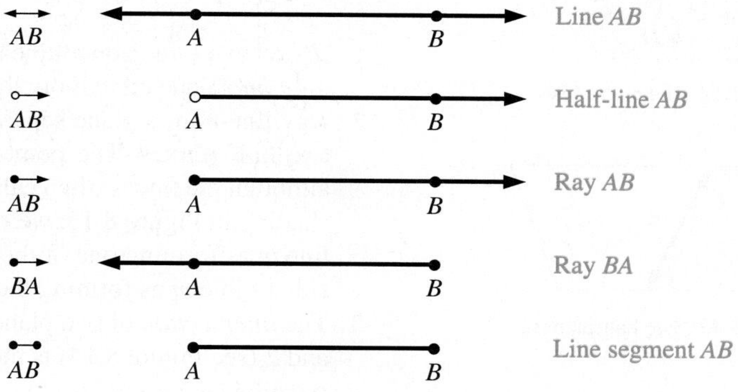

FIGURE 8.6

We can use the sets of points we have described and the set of operations of intersection ($\cap$) and union ($\cup$) to describe new sets, as shown next.

EXAMPLE 1 What Do You Get with the Descriptions?

Refer to Figure 8.7 and state what each of the following describes:

(a) $\overrightarrow{AC} \cap \overrightarrow{CA}$ (b) $\overrightarrow{AB} \cap \overrightarrow{BD}$

(c) $\overrightarrow{AC} \cup \overrightarrow{BD}$ (d) $\overline{AB} \cap \overline{CD}$

(e) $\overleftrightarrow{BC} \cap \overleftrightarrow{BA}$ (f) $\overline{AB} \cup \overline{BD}$

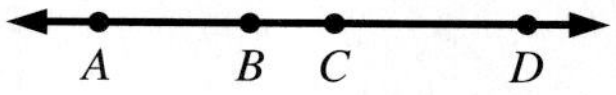

FIGURE 8.7

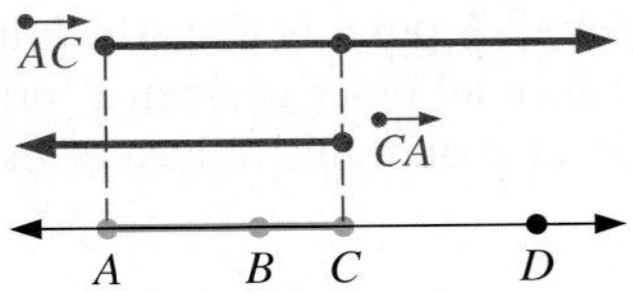

FIGURE 8.8

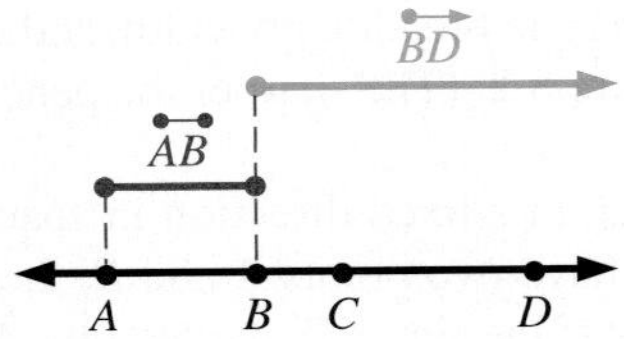

FIGURE 8.9

Solution

(a) Figure 8.8 shows the two rays $\overrightarrow{AC}$ and $\overrightarrow{CA}$. The set of points they have in common is the segment $\overline{AC}$. Thus, $\overrightarrow{AC} \cap \overrightarrow{CA} = \overline{AC}$.

(b) We can see from Figure 8.9 that the segment $\overline{AB}$ and the ray $\overrightarrow{BD}$ have only the point B in common. Therefore, $\overline{AB} \cap \overrightarrow{BD} = \{B\}$.

(c) Figure 8.10 shows that the union of the segment $\overline{AC}$ and the ray $\overrightarrow{BD}$ is the ray $\overrightarrow{AD}$. Thus, $\overline{AC} \cup \overrightarrow{BD} = \overrightarrow{AD}$.

(d) Figure 8.11 shows that the segments $\overline{AB}$ and $\overline{CD}$ have no points in common. Hence, $\overline{AB} \cap \overline{CD} = \varnothing$.

(e) In Figure 8.7, $\overleftrightarrow{BC}$, $\overleftrightarrow{BA}$, and $\overleftrightarrow{AD}$ are all symbols for the same line, so we have $\overleftrightarrow{BC} \cap \overleftrightarrow{BA} = \overleftrightarrow{AD}$.

(f) As we can see in Figure 8.7, the union of the segment $\overline{AB}$ and the segment $\overline{BD}$ is the segment $\overline{AD}$; thus, $\overline{AB} \cup \overline{BD} = \overline{AD}$.

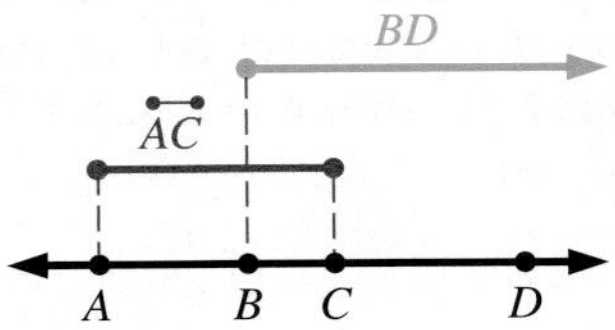

FIGURE 8.10

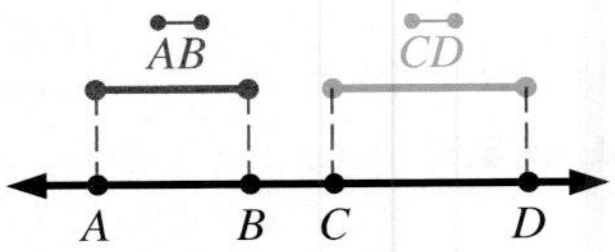

FIGURE 8.11

B Planes

As with the terms *point* and *line,* we give no formal definition of a **plane.** To help visualize a plane, we can think of the surface of a very large flat floor or of a straight wall extending indefinitely in all directions. Here are some basic properties of planes.

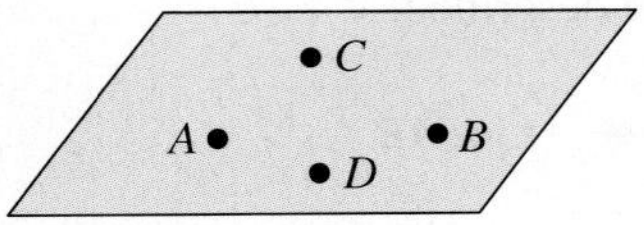

FIGURE 8.12 The plane *ABC*.

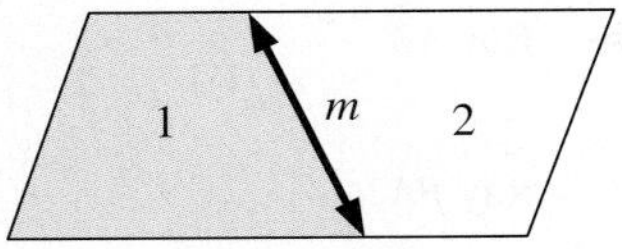

FIGURE 8.13 Two half-planes, 1 and 2.

1. If we have three noncollinear (not on the same line) points A, B, and C, there is only *one* plane containing the three points, the plane ABC (see Figure 8.12).
2. Any line m in a plane separates the plane into *three* parts: the line m itself and two **half-planes.** The points on the line m do not belong to either half-plane, although the line is often called the *edge* of both half-planes. As indicated by the shading in Figure 8.13, we regard the points of the plane that are on one side of line m as forming one of the half-planes and the points of the plane on the other side of line m as forming the other half-plane.
3. The *intersection* of two planes is a **line.** For example, the intersection of planes 1 and 2 (see Figure 8.14) is the line ℓ. Two planes that have no common point are **parallel** (see Figure 8.15).

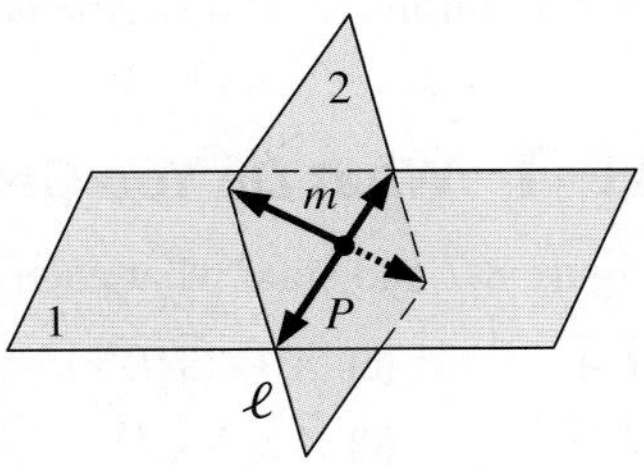

FIGURE 8.14 Intersecting planes.

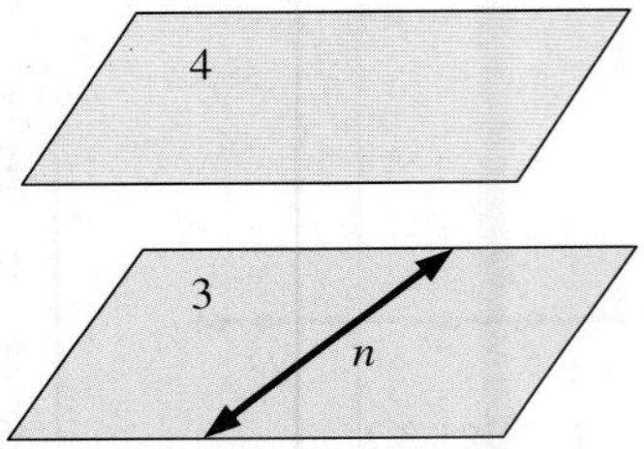

FIGURE 8.15 Parallel planes.

If a line is not in a given plane, then there are two possibilities.

1. The line **intersects** the plane in exactly one point. For instance, line m in plane 2 of Figure 8.14 intersects plane 1 in the point P.
2. The line is **parallel** to the plane. In Figure 8.15, any line such as n in plane 3 will be parallel to plane 4.

Lines that are on the same flat surface (*plane*) but never intersect (cross) are called **parallel lines,** while lines that intersect (cross) are called **intersecting lines.** The symbol || is used to indicate that two lines are **parallel.** ***Parallel*** and ***intersecting*** lines are shown in Figure 8.16 (a) and Figure 8.16 (b) respectively.

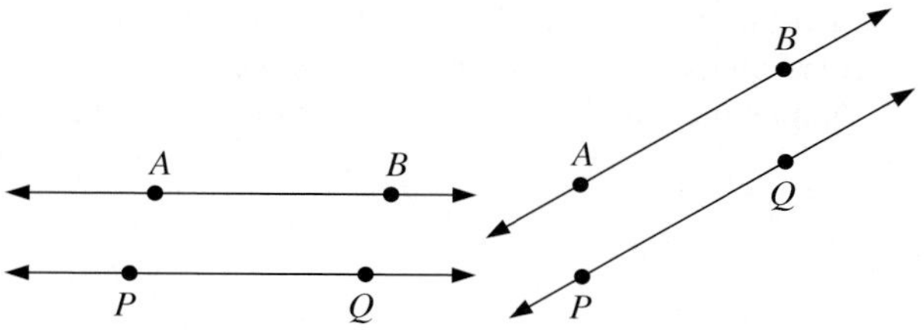

Line $\overleftrightarrow{AB} \parallel \overleftrightarrow{PQ}$

FIGURE 8.16 (a) Parallel lines.

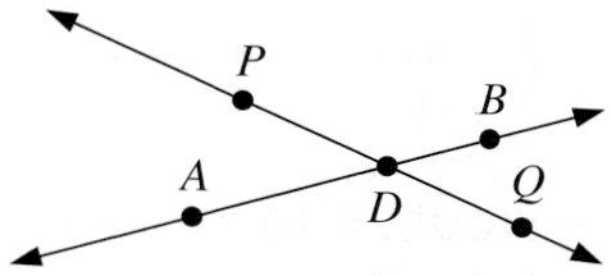

Line $\overleftrightarrow{AB}$ intersects $\overleftrightarrow{PQ}$ at point D.

FIGURE 8.16 (b) Intersecting lines.

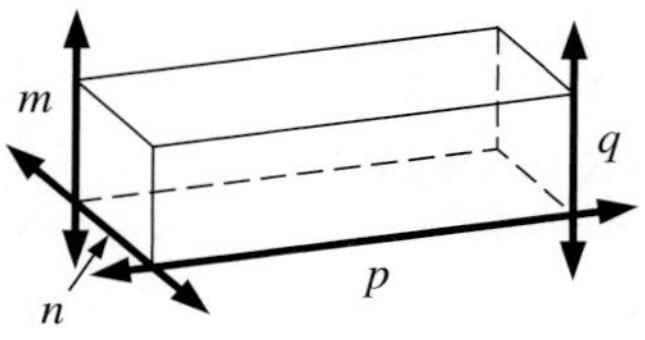

FIGURE 8.16 (c) A rectangular box. Lines m and p are skew lines. Lines m and q are parallel lines. (lines that are on the same plane but never intersect).

If the lines are neither **parallel** nor **intersecting** so that no plane can contain both lines, then they are called **skew** lines. A simple example of skew lines is the line of intersection of the ceiling and the front wall of an ordinary rectangular classroom and the line of intersection of the floor and one of the side walls. Figure 8.16(c) shows a rectangular box. The edges determine various straight lines. For instance, lines m and n intersect at a vertex (corner) of the box; m and p are skew lines, and m and q are parallel lines.

C Angles

A very important concept in mathematics is that of a *plane angle.* In elementary geometry, we think of a **plane angle** as the figure formed by two rays with a common endpoint, as in Figure 8.17. The common endpoint (A in Figure 8.17) is called the **vertex** of the angle, and the two rays ($\overrightarrow{AB}$ and $\overrightarrow{AC}$ in Figure 8.17) are called the **sides** of the angle. We often use the symbol $\angle$ (read "angle") in naming angles. The angle in Figure 8.17 can be named in the following three ways:

1. By using a letter or a number inside the angle. Thus, we would name the angle in Figure 8.17 $\angle\alpha$ (read "angle alpha").
2. By using the vertex letter only, such as $\angle A$ in Figure 8.17.
3. By using three letters, one from each ray, with the vertex letter in the middle. The angle in Figure 8.17 would be named $\angle BAC$ or $\angle CAB$.

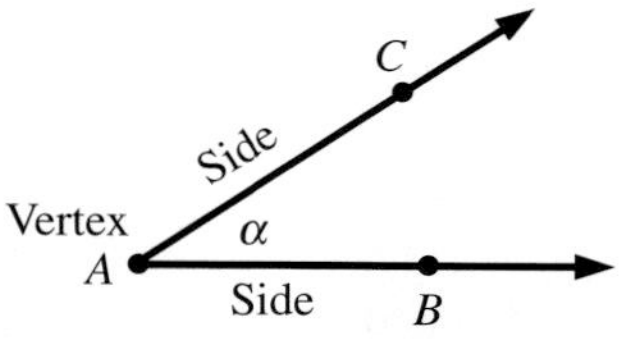

FIGURE 8.17

EXAMPLE 2 Naming Angles, Vertices, and Sides

Consider the angle in Figure 8.18.

(a) Name the angle in three different ways.

(b) Name the vertex of the angle. (c) Name the sides of the angle.

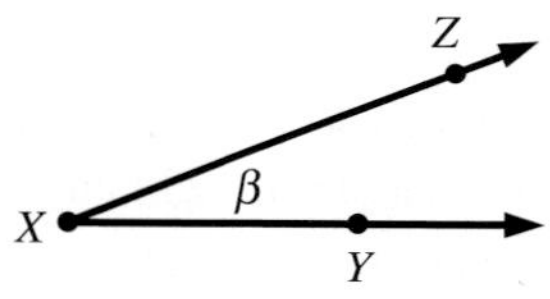

FIGURE 8.18

Solution

(a) The angle can be named $\angle\beta$ (Greek letter beta), $\angle X$, or $\angle YXZ$ (or $\angle ZXY$).

(b) The vertex is the point X. (c) The sides are the rays $\overrightarrow{XZ}$ and $\overrightarrow{XY}$.

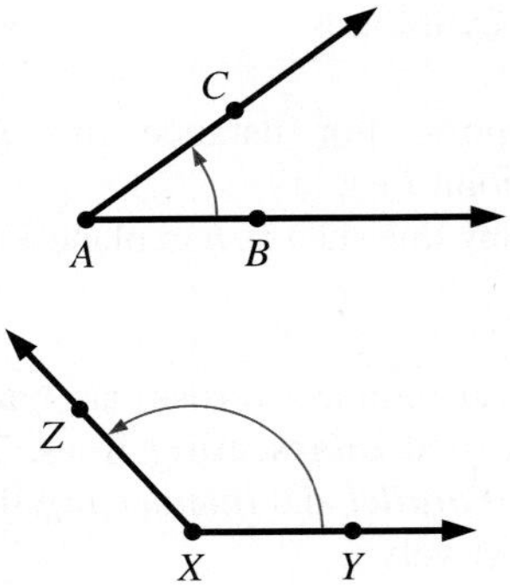

FIGURE 8.19

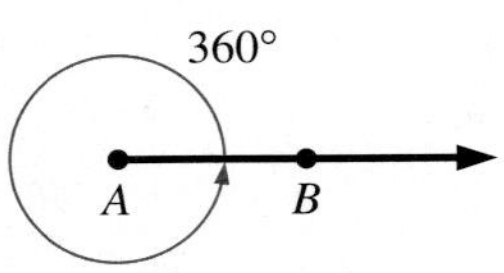

FIGURE 8.20 A complete revolution.

For most practical purposes, we need to have a way of measuring angles. We first consider the amount of **rotation** needed to turn one side of an angle so that it *coincides with* (falls exactly on top of) the other side. Figure 8.19 shows two angles, $\angle CAB$ and $\angle ZXY$, with curved arrows to indicate the rotation needed to turn the rays $\overrightarrow{AB}$ and $\overrightarrow{XY}$ so that they coincide with the rays $\overrightarrow{AC}$ and $\overrightarrow{XZ}$, respectively. Clearly, the amount needed for $\angle ZXY$ is greater than that for $\angle CAB$. To find how much greater, we have to measure the amounts of rotation.

The most common unit of measure for an angle is the *degree.* We can trace the degree system back to the ancient Babylonians, who were responsible for the base 60 system of numeration. The Babylonians considered a *complete revolution* of a ray as indicated in Figure 8.20 and divided that into 360 equal parts. Each part is **1 degree,** denoted by **1°.** Thus, a complete revolution is equal to 360°. One-half of a complete revolution is 180° and gives us an angle that is called a **straight angle** (see Figure 8.21). One-quarter of a complete revolution is 90° and gives a **right angle** (see Figure 8.22). Notice the small square at Y to denote that it is a right angle.

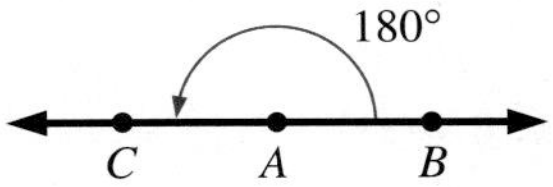

FIGURE 8.21 The straight angle *CAB*.

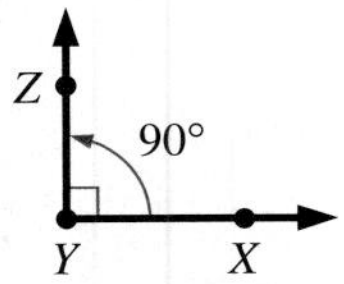

FIGURE 8.22 The right angle *XYZ*.

Definition of Perpendicular Lines

Two lines that intersect at right angles are said to be *perpendicular* to each other. The lines are called **perpendicular lines.**

For example, two adjacent outside edges of a page of this book are perpendicular to each other.

EXAMPLE 3 Time on a Clock and Degrees

Through how many degrees does the hour hand of a clock move in going through the following time intervals?

(a) 1 to 2 o'clock (b) 1 to 4 o'clock

(c) 12 to 5 o'clock (d) 12 to 9 o'clock

Solution

(a) One complete revolution is 360°, and the face of the clock is divided into 12 equal parts. Thus, the hour hand moves through

$$\frac{360°}{12} = 30°$$

in going from 1 to 2 o'clock.

(b) From 1 to 4 o'clock is 3 hr. Since a 1-hr move corresponds to 30°, a 3-hr move corresponds to $3(30°) = 90°$. (Thus, the hour hand moves through one right angle.)

(c) From 12 to 5 o'clock is 5 hr. Hence, the hour hand moves through $5(30°) = 150°$.

(d) From 12 to 9 o'clock is 9 hr, so the hour hand moves through $9(30°) = 270°$.

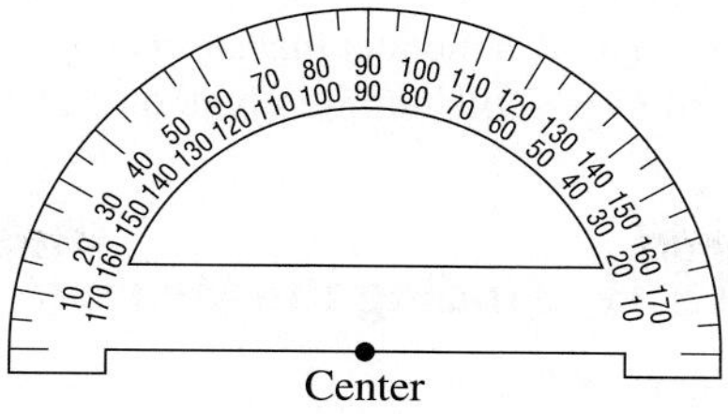

FIGURE 8.23 A protractor.

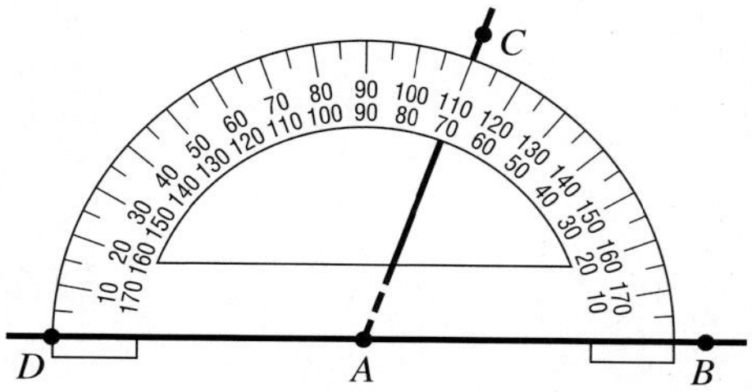

FIGURE 8.24 Measuring an angle.

In practice, the size of an angle is measured with a protractor (see Figure 8.23). The protractor is placed with its center at a vertex of the angle and the straight side of the protractor along one side of the angle, as in Figure 8.24. The measure of $\angle BAC$ is then read as 70° (because it is obviously less than 90°), and the measure of $\angle DAC$ is read as 110°. Surveying and navigational instruments, such as the sextant, use the idea of a protractor to measure angles very precisely.

We have already named two angles: a *straight angle* (180°) and a *right angle* (90°). Certain other angles are classified as follows:

Definition of Acute and Obtuse Angles

An **acute angle** is an angle of measure *greater* than 0° and *less* than 90°.
An **obtuse angle** is an angle of measure *greater* than 90° and *less* than 180°.

FIGURE 8.25

In Figure 8.24, $\angle BAC$ is an acute angle, and $\angle DAC$ is an obtuse angle.

Geometric figures frequently appear in highway signs. Do you know what the sign in the margin means? It is an advance warning for a railroad crossing. The angles B and D that are marked in Figure 8.25 are called *vertical angles.*

Definition of Vertical Angles

When two lines intersect, the opposite angles so formed are called **vertical angles.**

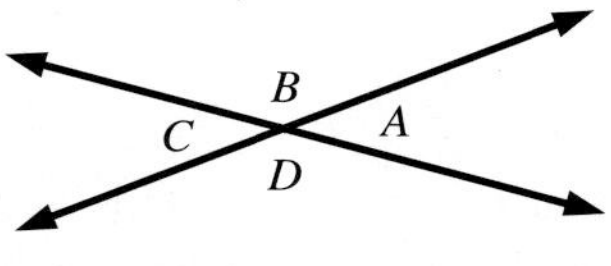

FIGURE 8.26

Two pairs of vertical angles are shown in Figure 8.26. Since the sides of angle C are just extensions of the sides of angle A, these two angles are of equal size. Similarly, angles B and D are of equal size. You complete a mathematical proof of this fact in problem 67, Exercises 8.1. Thus, in Figure 8.26, the measure of angle A, denoted by $m\angle A$, is the same as that of angle C. This fact is simply written as $m\angle A = m\angle C$. Similarly, $m\angle B = m\angle D$.

In Figure 8.26, angles A and B together form a straight angle, so the sum of their measures must be 180°. For this reason, A and B are called *supplementary angles.*

Definition of Supplementary Angles

Any two angles whose measures add up to 180° are called **supplementary angles.**

Other pairs of supplementary angles in Figure 8.26 are B and C, C and D, and A and D. Figure 8.26 illustrates the fact that *supplements of the same angle are equal.* For example, angles A and C are both supplements of $\angle B$, so $m\angle A = m\angle C$.

EXAMPLE 4 Finding the Measure of Angles

Refer to Figure 8.26.

(a) If the measure of $\angle A$ is 25°, what are the measures of the other three angles?

(b) If the two lines are to be drawn so that $\angle B$ is twice the size of $\angle A$, what should the measure of $\angle A$ be?

Solution

(a) Angles A and B are supplementary, so their measures add to 180°. Hence, the measure of $\angle B$ is 180° minus the measure of $\angle A$; that is, $180° - 25° = 155°$. Since $m\angle D = m\angle B$, the measure of $\angle D$ is also 155°. Also, $m\angle C = m\angle A$, so the measure of $\angle C$ is 25°.

(b) We let the measure of angle A be $x°$. Then the measure of angle B is $2x°$. Because angles A and B are supplementary, we must have

$$x + 2x = 180$$
$$3x = 180$$
$$x = 60$$

Thus, if we make $\angle A$ a 60° angle, $\angle B$ will be a 120° angle, twice the size of $\angle A$.

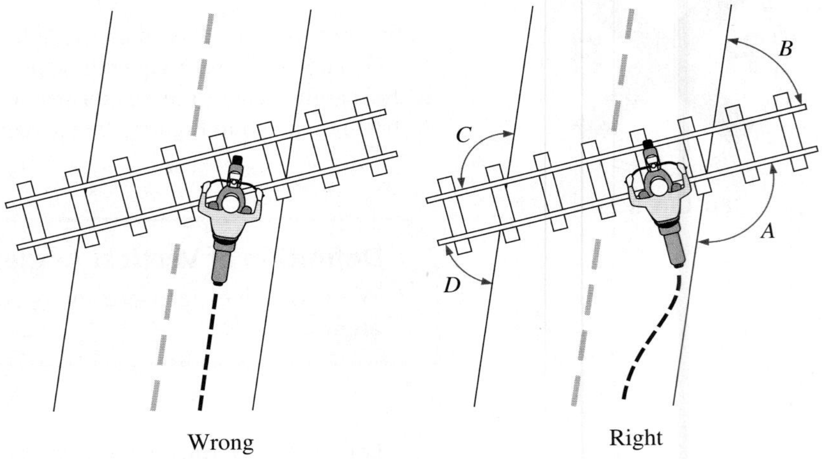

FIGURE 8.27

If you drive a motorcycle, you should look closely at Figure 8.27; it tells you to cross the railroad tracks at right angles (because there is less danger of a wheel catching in the tracks). Now look at angles A, B, C, and D marked on the right side of Figure 8.27. What can you say about angles B and D? Since they are vertical angles, they are of equal measure. (Similarly, angles A and C are of equal measure.) As you can see, the railroad track crosses the two parallel black lines in the figure. In geometry, a line that crosses two or more other lines is called a **transversal.** Thus, each railroad track is a transversal of the pair of parallel black lines. If a transversal crosses a pair of parallel lines, some of the resulting angles are of equal measure (see Figure 8.28). The exact relationships are as follows:

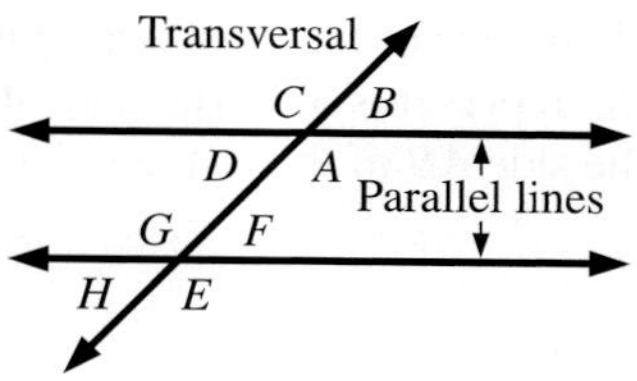

FIGURE 8.28

Corresponding angles:
A and E, B and F
C and G, D and H

Alternate interior angles:
A and G, D and F

Alternate exterior angles:
B and H, C and E

Hint: All the acute angles in the diagram have the same measure. All the obtuse angles have the same measure.

Corresponding angles are of equal measure.

$m\angle A = m\angle E$ $\quad$ $m\angle B = m\angle F$
$m\angle C = m\angle G$ $\quad$ $m\angle D = m\angle H$

Alternate interior angles are of equal measure.

$m\angle A = m\angle G$ $\quad$ $m\angle D = m\angle F$

Alternate exterior angles are of equal measure.

$m\angle B = m\angle H$ $\quad$ $m\angle C = m\angle E$

In Figure 8.28, angles A and B form a straight angle and are thus supplementary. Because $m\angle B = m\angle F$, angles A and F are also supplementary. The same idea applies to angles D and G as well as to angles B and E and angles C and H. We can summarize these facts by saying:

Parallel Lines Cut by a Transversal

Interior angles on the same side of the transversal are supplementary, and exterior angles on the same side of the transversal are also supplementary. In summary, when parallel lines are cut by a transversal,

1. All the acute angles are equal.
2. All obtuse angles are equal.
3. The sum of the measures of an acute angle and an obtuse angle is 180°.

The next example will help to make the concept clearer.

EXAMPLE 5 Finding More Measures of Angles

In Figure 8.29, find the measures of the following angles:

(a) Y (b) Z (c) X (d) R (e) S (f) T (g) U

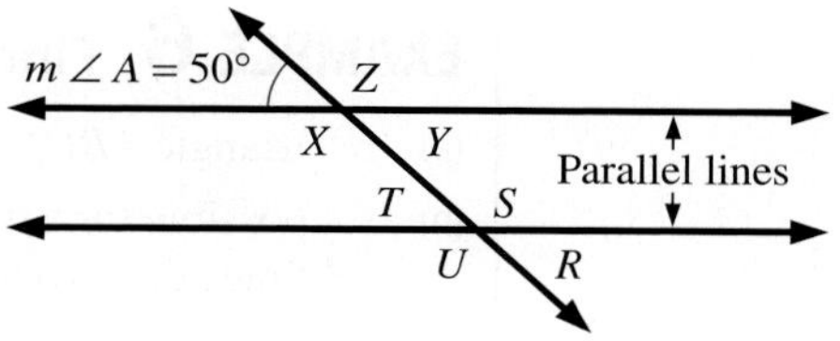

FIGURE 8.29

Solution

First, note that the measure of each acute angle ($\angle A$, $\angle Y$, $\angle T$, and $\angle R$) is 50° and the measure of each obtuse angle ($\angle Z$, $\angle X$, $\angle S$, and $\angle U$) is 130°.

(a) Since Y and A are vertical angles, $m\angle Y = m\angle A = 50°$.

(b) Angles A and Z are supplementary, so $m\angle Z = 180° - 50° = 130°$.

(c) Angles X and Z are vertical angles. Thus, $m\angle X = m\angle Z = 130°$.

(d) Angles R and A are alternate exterior angles, so $m\angle R = m\angle A = 50°$.

(e) Angles S and Y are interior angles on the same side of the transversal and so are supplementary. Therefore, $m\angle S = 180° - m\angle Y = 130°$.

(f) Angles T and A are corresponding angles. Thus, $m\angle T = m\angle A = 50°$.

(g) Angles U and A are exterior angles on the same side of the transversal. Thus, $m\angle U = 180° - m\angle A = 130°$.

Parallel lines and the associated angles allow us to obtain one of the most important results in the geometry of triangles. In Figure 8.30, *ABC* represents any triangle. The line $\overleftrightarrow{XY}$ has been drawn through the point *C* parallel to the side $\overleftrightarrow{AB}$ of the triangle. Note that $m\angle 1 = m\angle 2$ and $m\angle 3 = m\angle 4$ because they

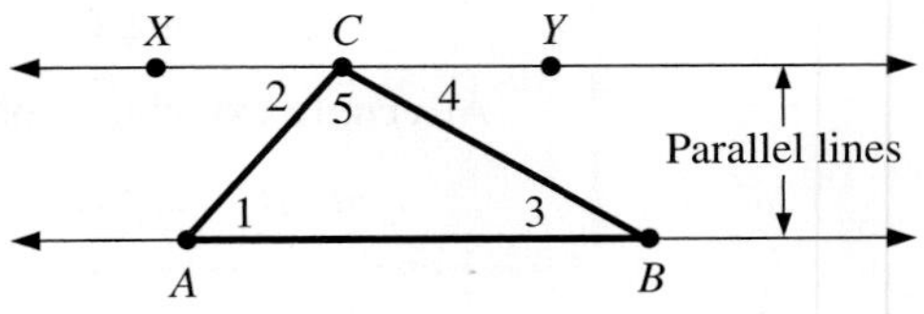

FIGURE 8.30

are respective pairs of alternate interior angles. Furthermore, angles 2, 5, and 4 form a straight angle, so

$$m\angle 2 + m\angle 5 + m\angle 4 = 180°$$

By substituting $\angle 1$ for $\angle 2$ and $\angle 3$ for $\angle 4$, we obtain

$$m\angle 1 + m\angle 5 + m\angle 3 = 180°$$

Here is a way to show this. Cut a triangle out of a sheet of paper as shown in Figure 8.31. Label the angles 1, 2, and 3 and cut them off the triangle. Place the vertices of angles 1, 2, and 3 together. Now, two of the sides form a straight line! Thus, we have shown that *the sum of the measures of the three interior angles of any triangle is 180°.*

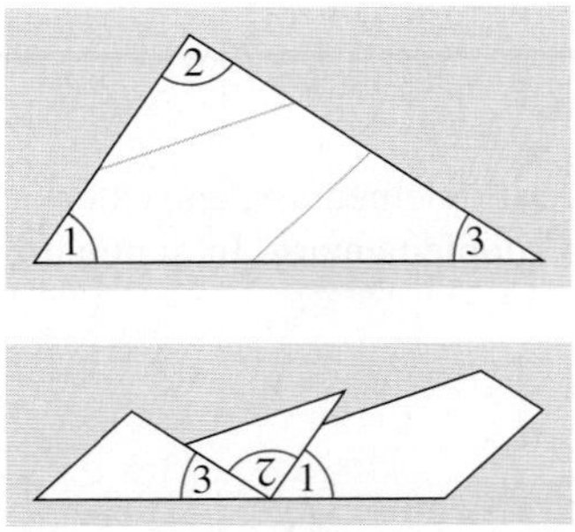

FIGURE 8.31

Sum of the Measure of the Interior Angles of a Triangle

The sum of the measures of the three **interior angles** of any triangle is **180°.**

EXAMPLE 6 Finding Measures of Angles in a Triangle

(a) In a triangle *ABC*, $m\angle A = 47°$ and $m\angle B = 59°$. Find the measure of $\angle C$.

(b) Is it possible for a triangle *ABC* to be such that $\angle A$ is 2 times the size of $\angle B$ and $\angle C$ is 3 times the size of $\angle B$?

Solution

(a) Because $m\angle A + m\angle B + m\angle C = 180°$, we have

$$47° + 59° + m\angle C = 180°$$
$$m\angle C = 180° - 47° - 59°$$
$$= 180° - 106° = 74°$$

(b) To answer this question, let $m\angle B = x°$, so $m\angle A = 2x°$ and $m\angle C = 3x°$. Then, since the sum of the angles is 180°,

$$x + 2x + 3x = 180$$
$$6x = 180$$
$$x = 30 \qquad 2x = 60 \qquad 3x = 90$$

This means that there is such a triangle, and $m\angle A = 60°$, $m\angle B = 30°$, and $m\angle C = 90°$. (Note that this is a right triangle because one of the angles is a right angle.)

In part (b) of Example 6 we found angles A and B to be of measure 60° and 30°, respectively, so $m\angle A + m\angle B = 90°$.

Definition of Complementary Angles

Two angles whose sum is 90° are called **complementary angles,** and each angle is called the **complement** of the other.

EXAMPLE 7 Finding the Complement of an Angle

(a) Find the complement of a 38° angle.

(b) Can two complementary angles be such that one is three times the size of the other?

Solution

(a) For an angle to be the complement of a 38° angle, its measure must be $90° - 38° = 52°$.

(b) Let the smaller angle be of measure $x°$, so the larger is of measure $3x°$. Since the angles are to be complementary,

$$x + 3x = 90$$
$$4x = 90$$
$$x = \frac{90}{4} = 22\tfrac{1}{2} \qquad 3x = 67\tfrac{1}{2}.$$

The answer is yes, and the angles measure $22\frac{1}{2}°$ and $67\frac{1}{2}°$.

D Applications

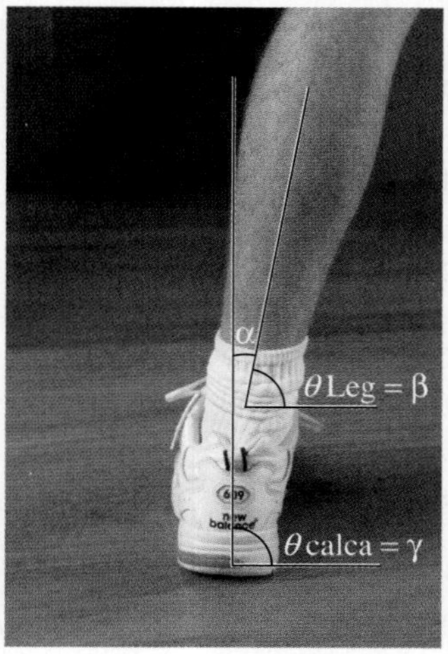

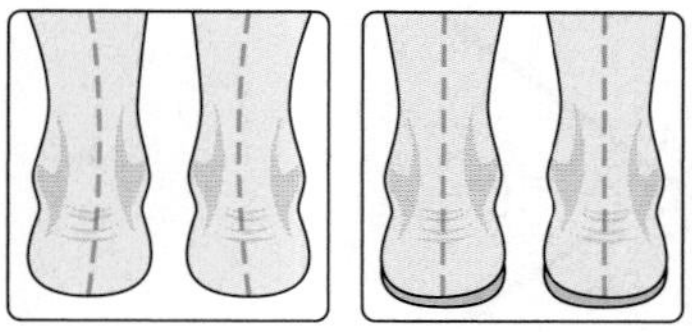

Unsupported Supported

EXAMPLE 8 Applications to Kinesiology

How far is the leg in the photo from being vertical? In physical education and kinesiology, they measure the rear foot angle α. This angle can be adjusted by using an insole as shown in the illustrations below the photo. You can find the rear foot angle if you measure angle α or angle β.

(a) What type of angles are $\angle\alpha$ and $\angle\beta$?

(b) Find $m\angle\alpha$.

(c) If $m\angle\alpha = 15°$, find $m\angle\beta$.

Solution

(a) $\angle\alpha$ and $\angle\beta$ are complementary angles, their sum is 90°.

(b) $m\angle\alpha = 90° - m\angle\beta$.

(c) Since $\angle\alpha$ and $\angle\beta$ are complementary angles,

$$m\angle\beta = 90° - m\angle\alpha$$
$$= 90° - 15° \qquad \text{Remember } m\angle\alpha = 15°.$$
$$= 75°$$

Thus, $m\angle\beta = 75°$.

8.1 EXERCISES

A Points and Lines

In problems 1 and 2, draw a line or a portion of a line that corresponds to each symbol.

1. a. $\overrightarrow{PQ}$ b. $\overset{\circ\!\longrightarrow}{QP}$ c. $\overline{QP}$
2. a. $\overset{\circ\!\longrightarrow}{PQ}$ b. $\overrightarrow{QP}$ c. $\overleftrightarrow{PQ}$

In problems 3–14, use the figure below and determine what each union or intersection describes.

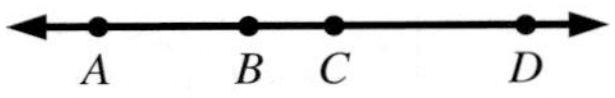

3. $\overrightarrow{AB} \cap \overline{BC}$
4. $\overrightarrow{AC} \cap \overline{BC}$
5. $\overline{AC} \cup \overrightarrow{BC}$
6. $\overline{AD} \cup \overrightarrow{CB}$
7. $\overrightarrow{AC} \cap \overrightarrow{DA}$
8. $\overrightarrow{BD} \cap \overrightarrow{DC}$
9. $\overset{\circ\!\longrightarrow}{AC} \cup \overset{\circ\!\longrightarrow}{DC}$
10. $\overset{\circ\!\longrightarrow}{AC} \cup \overset{\circ\!\longrightarrow}{DB}$
11. $\overline{BA} \cap \overline{CD}$
12. $\overline{CB} \cap \overline{CD}$
13. $AC \cap DC$
14. $AB \cap DB$

15. The figure shows a triangular pyramid.
    a. Name all the edges.
    b. Which pairs of edges determine skew lines?
    c. Do any of the edges determine parallel lines?

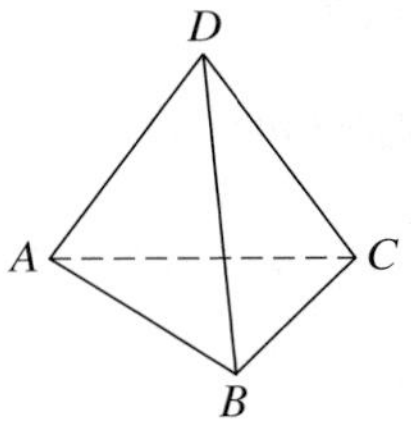

16. The figure represents a pyramid with a square base $ABCD$.
    a. Name all the edges of the pyramid.
    b. Which pairs of edges determine parallel lines?
    c. Which determine skew lines?
    d. Which lines are intersecting?

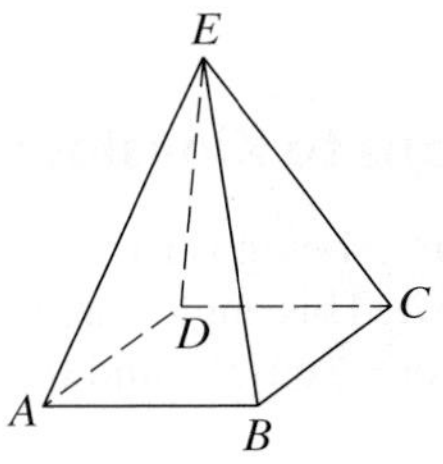

B Planes

Determine whether each of the following statements seems to be true or false in Euclidean geometry. You will find it helpful to use pencils, pieces of cardboard, walls, floors, and so on to represent lines and planes.

17. Given any plane ABC and any point P not on ABC, there is exactly one plane that contains P and is parallel to plane ABC.
18. Given any line m and any point P not on m, there is exactly one plane that contains P and is parallel to m.
19. Given any line m and any point P not on m, there is exactly one line that contains P and is parallel to m.
20. Given any plane ABC and any point P not on ABC, there are any number of lines containing P and parallel to ABC.
21. Given any line m and any point P not on m, there are any number of lines that contain P and are skew to m.
22. Given any plane ABC and any line m parallel to ABC, there is exactly one plane that contains m and intersects ABC.
23. Two nonparallel lines always determine a plane.
24. Given any line m and any point P not on m, there is exactly one plane that contains both m and P.
25. Given a plane ABC and a line m that intersects ABC, there is a plane that contains m and that does not intersect ABC.
26. If a plane intersects two parallel planes, the lines of intersection with each of the parallel planes are parallel.

C Angles

Problems 27–40 refer to the figure below. Note that perpendicular lines are indicated by small red boxes.

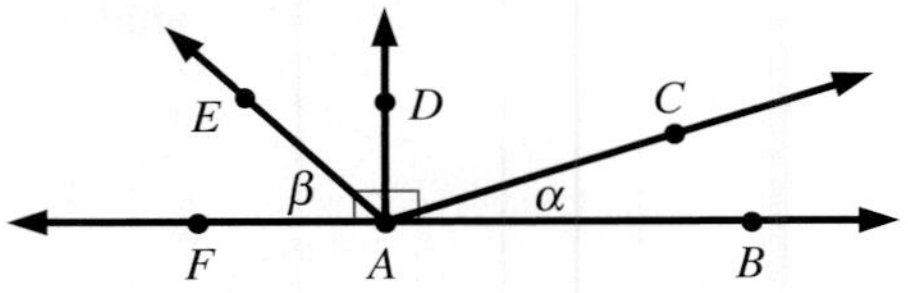

27. Name the following angles in another way:
    a. $\angle\alpha$ b. $\angle EAF$
28. Name the following angles in another way:
    a. $\angle CAB$ b. $\angle\beta$
29. List all the acute angles in the figure.
30. List all the right angles in the figure.
31. List all the obtuse angles in the figure.
32. Name an angle that is the complement of
    a. $\angle\alpha$. b. $\angle\beta$.
33. Name an angle that is the complement of
    a. $\angle EAF$. b. $\angle BAC$.
34. Name an angle that is supplementary to
    a. $\angle\alpha$. b. $\angle\beta$.
35. Name an angle that is supplementary to
    a. $\angle BAD$. b. $\angle EAF$.
36. If $m\angle\alpha = 15°$, find $m\angle CAD$.
37. If $m\angle\beta = 55°$, find $m\angle DAE$.
38. If $m\angle DAE = 35°$, find $m\angle\beta$.
39. If $m\angle CAD = 75°$, find $m\angle\alpha$.
40. If $m\angle\alpha = 15°$ and $m\angle\beta = 55°$, find $m\angle CAE$.

Problems 41–48 refer to the two intersecting lines shown in the figure.

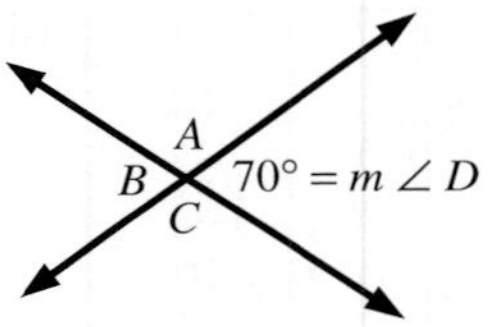

41. Name the angle that is vertical to the 70° angle.

42. Name the two angles that are each supplementary to the 70° angle.

43. Find $m \angle A$. **44.** Find $m \angle B$.

45. What is the measure of an angle complementary to the 70° angle?

46. Find the sum of the measures of angles A, B, and C.

47. Find the sum of the measures of angles A and C.

48. If $m \angle D = x°$ (instead of 70°), write an expression for the measure of $\angle A$.

Problems 49–51 refer to the two parallel lines and the transversal shown in the figure.

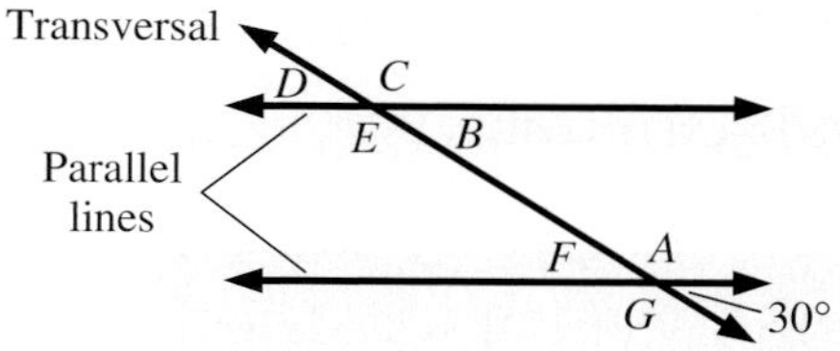

49. Find the following:

a. $m\angle A$ **b.** $m\angle B$ **c.** $m\angle C$

50. Find the following:

a. $m\angle D$ **b.** $m\angle E$ **c.** $m\angle F$

51. Name all the angles that are supplementary to $\angle B$.

52. Refer to the angles shown in the figure below.

a. If $m\angle AOB = 30°$ and $m\angle AOC = 70°$, find $m\angle BOC$.

b. If $m\angle AOB = m\angle COD$, $m\angle AOD = 100°$, and $m\angle BOC = 2x°$, find $m\angle COD$ in terms of x.

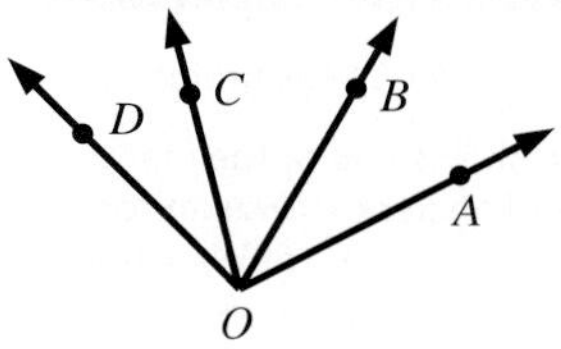

53. If $m\angle A = 41°$, find $m\angle B$ given that

a. the two angles are complementary.

b. the two angles are supplementary.

54. If $m\angle A = 19°$, find $m\angle B$ given that

a. the two angles are complementary.

b. the two angles are supplementary.

55. Given that $m\angle A = (3x + 15)°$, $m\angle B = (2x - 5)°$, and the two angles are complementary, find x.

56. Rework problem 55 if the two angles are supplementary.

In problems 57–60, the figures show the number of degrees in each angle in terms of x. Use algebra to find x and the measure of each angle.

57.

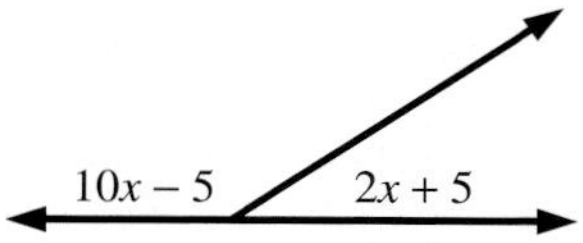

58.

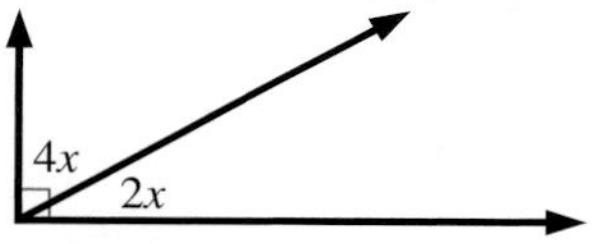

59.

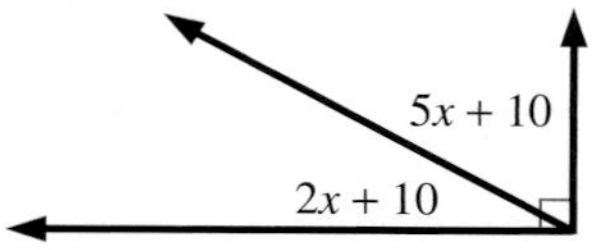

60.

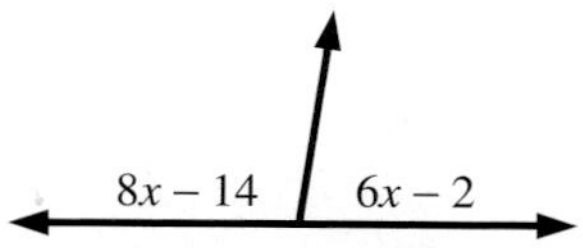

61. Through how many degrees does the hour hand of a clock move during the following time intervals?

a. 11 to 12 o'clock **b.** 11 to 5 o'clock

62. Through how many degrees does the hour hand of a clock move during the following time intervals?

a. 12 to 7 o'clock **b.** 12 back to 12 o'clock

63. In a triangle ABC, $m\angle A = 37°$ and $m\angle C = 53°$. Find $m\angle B$.

64. In a triangle ABC, $m\angle B = 67°$ and $m\angle C = 105°$. Find $m\angle A$.

65. In a triangle ABC, $m\angle A = (x + 10)°$, $m\angle B = (2x + 10)°$, and $m\angle C = (3x + 10)°$. Find x.

66. In a triangle ABC, $m\angle A$ is 10° less than $m\angle B$, and $m\angle C$ is 40° greater than $m\angle B$. Find the measure of each angle.

67. Refer to Figure 8.26. Complete the first two equations and give the reason for each step in the following proof that vertical angles are of equal measure:

a. $m\angle A + m\angle B =$ ____

b. $m\angle C + m\angle B =$ ____

c. $m\angle A + m\angle B = m\angle C + m\angle B$

d. $m\angle A = m\angle C$

D Applications

In problems 68–72, refer to the photo and classify the given angle.

68. $\angle\alpha$

69. $\angle\beta$

70. $\angle\gamma$

71. $\angle\delta$

72. Classify and name the two types of angles shown in the photo.

73. Name the type of angle you need when you want to use the phone shown in the photo below.

© Photodisc/Getty Images

74. About how many degrees is the angle shown?

75. How many degrees would the angle be when the phone is not being used and is closed?

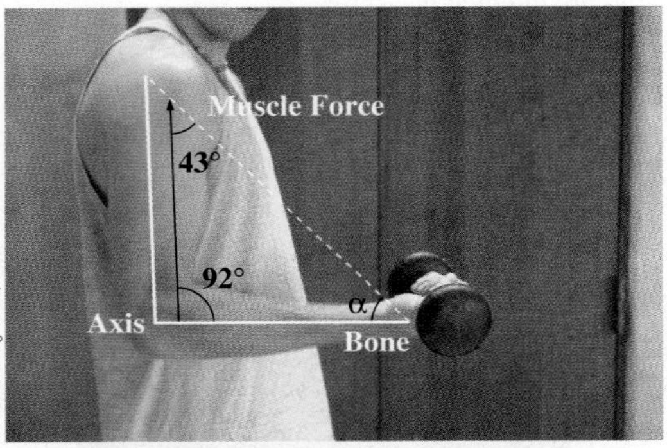

© David Young-Wolff/Photo Edit

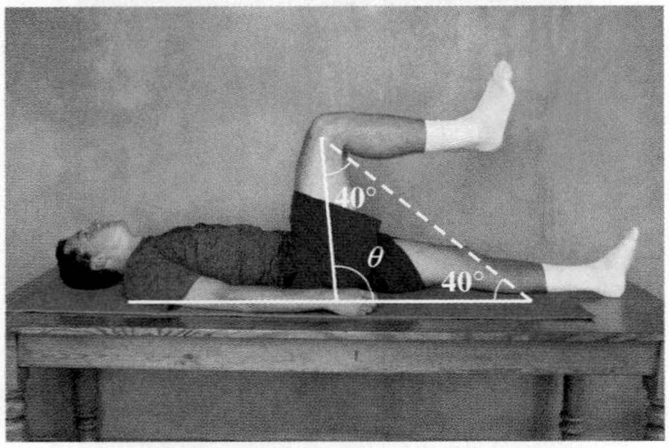

© David Young-Wolff/Photo Edit

Joint range of motion (ROM) is a common measure for students in physical education and kinesiology, and it involves the measurement of angles.

76. Find $m\angle\alpha$.

77. Find $m\angle\theta$.

IN OTHER WORDS

78. You have heard the saying "The shortest distance between two points is a straight line." Explain why this is technically incorrect.

79. Name three undefined geometric terms.

80. Find the word *point* in a dictionary. How many definitions does the word have? In your own words, give three definitions that can apply to geometry.

81. Describe the different ways in which a ray and a plane can intersect.

82. Describe the different ways in which a line and a ray can intersect.

83. We have already defined an acute and an obtuse angle. Look at the definitions of *acute* and *obtuse* in a dictionary and explain the following:
   a. What an *acute pain* means
   b. What *obtuse intelligence* means

84. Describe and show sketches of the following:
   a. How a line can intersect an angle
   b. How two angles can intersect

USING YOUR KNOWLEDGE

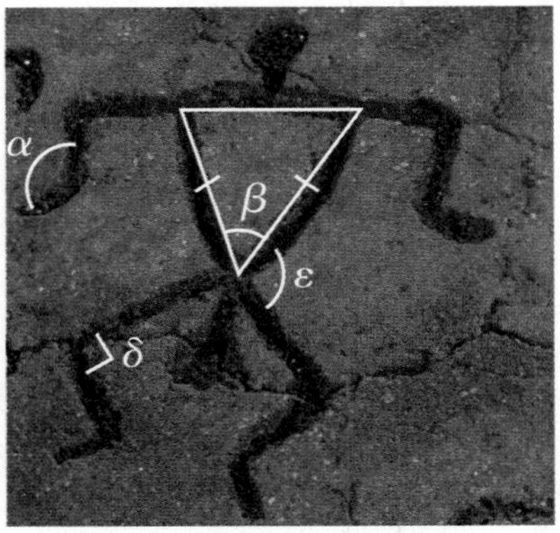

© Michael T. Sedam/CORBIS

Source: © Michael T. Sedam/Corbis;

The photo shows one of the many examples of ancient Hawaiian rock carvings (petroglyphs) at Waikoloa. These carvings contain images of the human figure varying in complexity from simple angular figures to triangular figures to muscular figures.

Use your knowledge about classifying angles to answer these questions.

Angles and triangles. For Problems 85–88, refer to the rock art drawing.

85. Classify angles α and β.

86. Classify angles δ and ε.

87. The body of the rock carving is in the shape of a triangle. Classify the triangle.

88. If the triangle is an isosceles triangle and two equal angles are 62°, what is the measure of β?

89. Why do we have solar eclipses (when the moon blocks the sun from view)? It is because the angle subtended (taken up) by the sun (0.52° to 0.54°) and the moon (0.49° to 0.55°) are almost identical. Classify these angles.

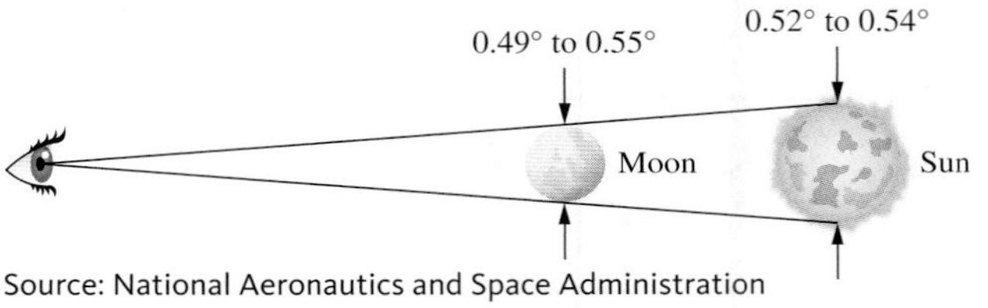

Source: National Aeronautics and Space Administration

90. The diagram shows the path of a satellite from noon to 12:03 PM. Classify angles γ, β and δ.

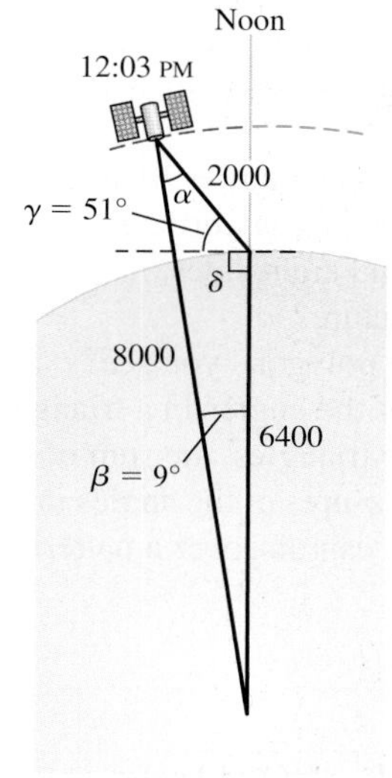

Use your knowledge about angles and percents to answer the questions about energy and renewable sources of energy in the U.S. and the U.K. Rememeber that the sum of the angles in a triangle is 360°.

91. *Energy sources for electric power.* In the United States, the three primary energy sources for generating electric power are coal, natural gas, and nuclear energy with each contributing the percent shown in the chart below.

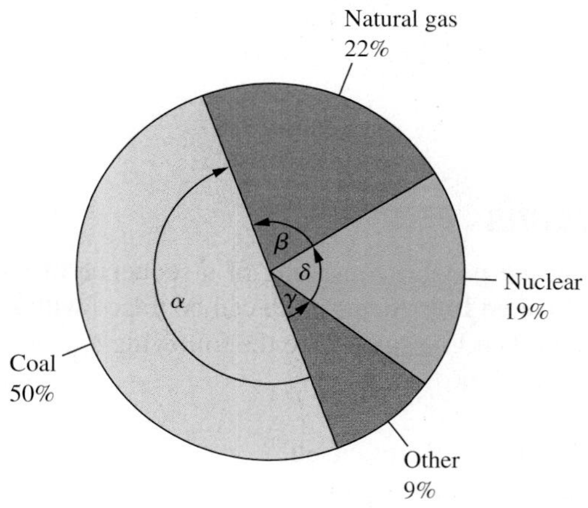

Source: U.S. Energy Information Administration.

a. What type of angle is α? What is its measure?
b. What type of angle is β? What is its measure?
c. What type of angle is δ? What is its measure?
d. What type of angle is γ? What is its measure?

92. *Renewable sources used to generate electricity.* In the United Kingdom (U.K.), the renewable sources used to generate electricity are as shown in the chart.

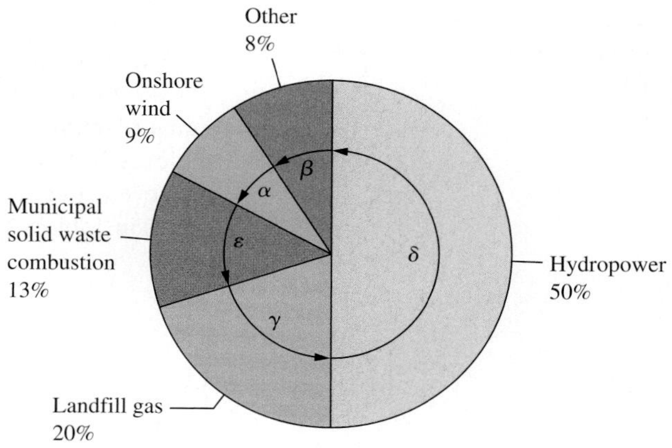

Source: http://tinyurl.com/72x57wh

a. What type of angle is δ? What is its measure?
b. What type of angle is β? What is its measure?
c. What type of angle is α? What is its measure?
d. What type of angle is ε? What is its measure?
e. What type of angle is γ? What is its measure?

8.2 Triangles and Other Polygons

GETTING STARTED

OBJECTIVES

A. Classify curves and name the sides, vertices and shapes of polygons.
B. Classify triangles and quadrilaterals by their angles or by their sides.
C. Identify and find the dimensions of similar and congruent triangles.
D. Find the measure of the angles of a convex polygon.

Soap bubbles exhibit various polygonal shapes when closely packed.

SOAP BUBBLE POLYGONS

Look at the soap bubbles in the photograph. What do you notice about the shapes shown? First, all of them are made up of line segments, and second, each shape can be traced by starting and ending at one point. You will study such shapes, called **polygons,** in this section.

Plane polygons can be named according to the number of sides. Thus, a *three-sided* polygon is a *tri*angle and a *four-sided* polygon is a *quad*rilateral. Later, you will learn how to name polygons with five, six, seven, and eight sides.

How many polygons do you see in the picture?

Can you find the sum of the angles in the polygons you see?

As you recall, the sum of the measures of the angles in a triangle is 180°. Because a quadrilateral can always be divided into two triangles, the sum of the measures of the angles is 360°. Can you find the sum of the measures of the angles in polygons with five, six, seven, and in general, n sides? See if you can discover a pattern for the sum of the angles in Table 8.1 and fill in the blank.

Table 8.1

Number of Sides	Sum of the Angles
Three-sides polygon	$1 \cdot 180°$
Four-sides polygon	$2 \cdot 180°$
Five-sides polygon	_____

The answer is $3 \cdot 180°$. Why? Read part D of this section on page 450 and you will see!

A popular children's puzzle consists of joining in order a set of numbered dots by straight line segments to form a path from the first to the last point. An example of such a puzzle and its solution is shown in Figure 8.32. (What is pictured, an antelope or a bird?)

A Broken Lines and Polygons

A **path** (such as the one shown in the puzzle) consisting of a sequence of connected straight line segments is called a **broken line.** Such a path can be traced without lifting the pencil from the paper. Certain broken line paths have the following two characteristics that are of interest to us in this section:

1. A **simple path** is a path that does *not* cross itself.
2. A **closed path** is a path that starts and ends at the same point.

Not all geometric figures are constructed using straight line segments. The following are more general concepts:

1. A **simple curve** is a curve that does not cross itself.
2. A **closed curve** is a curve that starts and ends at the same point.

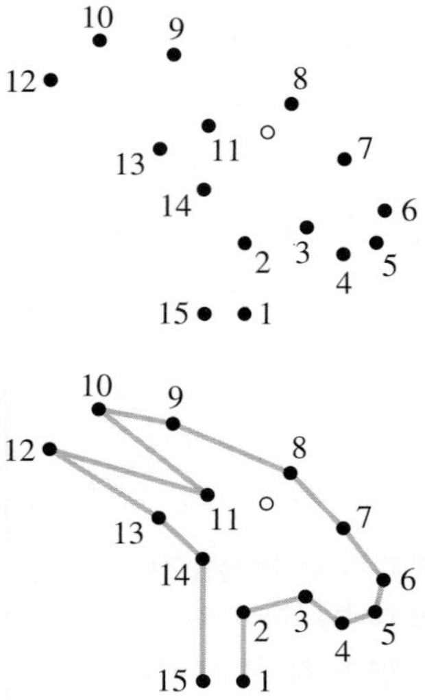

FIGURE 8.32

Most of our discussion, however, will deal with simple and closed *paths* rather than simple and closed *curves,* because simple, closed paths are used to define polygons.

The path in the solution of the puzzle in Figure 8.32 is simple but not closed. Figure 8.33 shows four broken lines. The paths in panels A and C are simple, but the paths in panels B and D are not simple. Moreover, the paths in panels B and C are closed, but the paths in panels A and D are not closed. Can you draw a path that is not simple and not closed? Can you draw a curve that is not simple and not closed? Figure 8.34 gives examples of curved paths.

Any path that consists of a simple, closed broken line is called a **polygon.** In Figures 8.35 and 8.36, paths *ABCDE* are examples of polygons. The line segments of the path are the **sides** of a polygon, and the endpoints of the sides are the **vertices.**

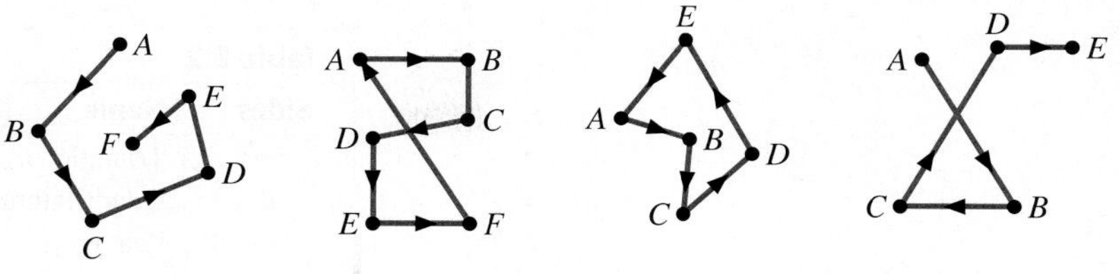

A. Simple, not closed | B. Not simple, closed | C. Simple, closed | D. Not simple, not closed

FIGURE 8.33 Broken lines.

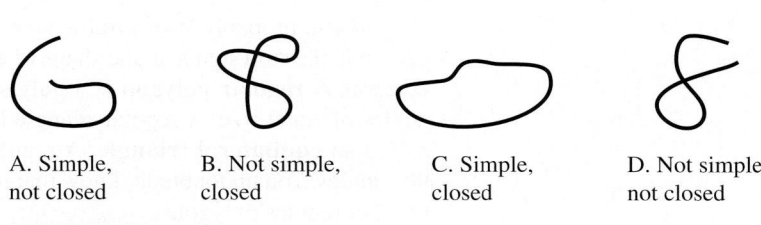

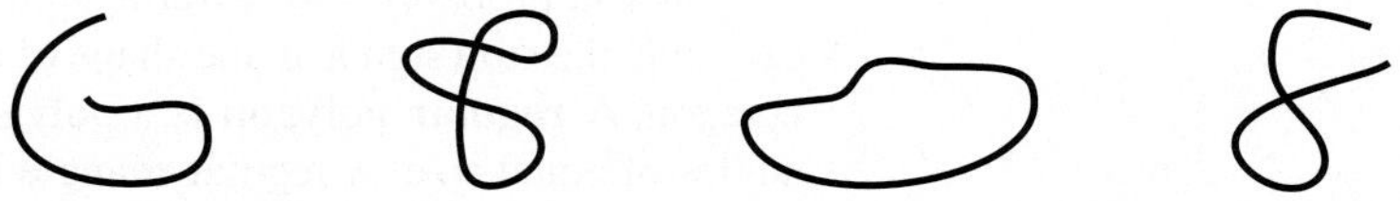

A. Simple, not closed | B. Not simple, closed | C. Simple, closed | D. Not simple, not closed

FIGURE 8.34 Curves.

A polygon is said to be **convex** if no line segment $\overline{XY}$ joining any two points on the path (boundary) ever extends outside the polygon (see Figure 8.35). The points *X* and *Y* may be any two points not on the same side of the polygon. Except for its endpoints, the line segment $\overline{XY}$ lies entirely inside the polygon. (Of course, if *X* and *Y* were on the same side, then the segment would lie on that side.)

A polygon that is not convex is called a **concave,** or **reentrant,** polygon (see Figure 8.36). Here a portion of the line segment *XY* lies outside the polygon—something that never occurs in a convex polygon.

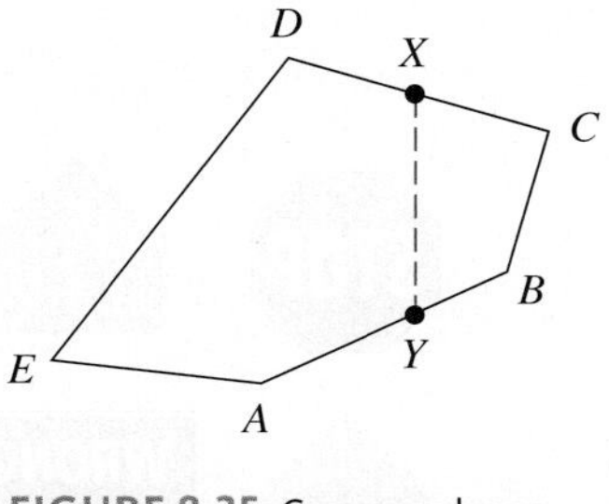

FIGURE 8.35 Convex polygon.

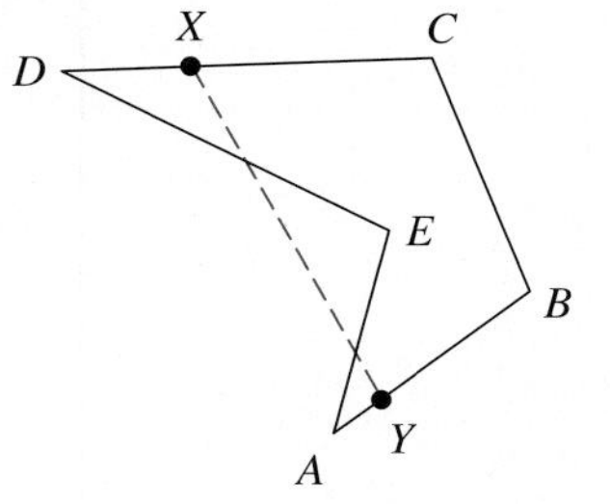

FIGURE 8.36 Concave polygon.

EXAMPLE 1 Naming Sides and Vertices of Polygons

Consider the polygon *ABCDE* in Figure 8.37.

(a) Name its sides.

(b) Name its vertices.

(c) Is this a concave or a convex polygon?

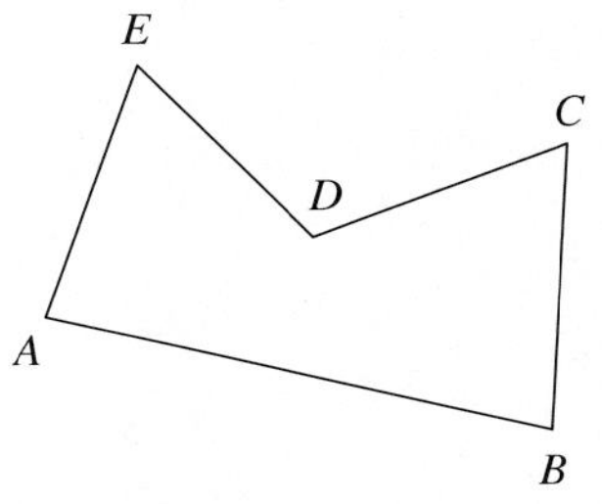

FIGURE 8.37

Solution

(a) The sides are $\overline{AB}$, $\overline{BC}$, $\overline{CD}$, $\overline{DE}$, and $\overline{EA}$.

(b) The vertices are *A*, *B*, *C*, *D*, and *E*.

(c) This is a concave, or reentrant, polygon.

Plane polygons are customarily named according to the number of sides. Table 8.2 states some of the usual names.

Table 8.2

Sides	Name	Sides	Name
3	Triangle	8	Octagon
4	Quadrilateral	9	Nonagon
5	Pentagon	10	Decagon
6	Hexagon	12	Dodecagon
7	Heptagon		

As you probably know, traffic signs are most often in the shapes of polygons. For example, the stop sign is in the shape of an octagon. In fact, it is in the shape of a *regular* octagon. A **regular polygon** is a polygon with all its sides of equal length and all its angles of equal size. A regular triangle has three equal sides and three 60° angles; it is called an **equilateral triangle.** A regular quadrilateral has four equal sides and four 90° angles. You undoubtedly know that it is called a **square.** No special names are given to other regular polygons.

EXAMPLE 2 Naming Shapes of Traffic Signs

Some standard traffic signs are shown below.

(a) Which ones are regular polygons?

(b) Name the shape of the school crossing sign.

(c) Name the shape of the yield sign.

(d) Name the shape of the warning sign.

Solution

(a) The stop sign, the yield sign, and the warning sign are all in the shape of regular polygons, a polygon with all sides of equal length and all angles of equal size.

(b) The school crossing sign has five sides, so it is in the shape of a pentagon (but not a regular pentagon).

(c) The yield sign has three equal sides; it is in the shape of an equilateral triangle.

(d) The warning sign has four equal sides and four equal angles; it is in the shape of a regular quadrilateral, a square.

FIGURE 8.38 Can you see the triangular region? It is an optical illusion. The triangle exists only in your mind.

B Triangles and Quadrilaterals

Triangles are often classified according to their angles, as shown in Table 8.3. Triangles are also classified according to the number of equal sides, as shown in Table 8.4.

Note that the angles opposite the equal sides of an **isosceles triangle** are of equal measure. (See the Using Your Knowledge section of Exercises 8.2.) Moreover, an **equilateral triangle** is also **equiangular;** it has three 60° angles. The triangle that you see in the optical illusion in Figure 8.38 is an equilateral triangle.

Certain quadrilaterals (four-sided polygons) also have special names and properties, as shown in Table 8.5 on page 446.

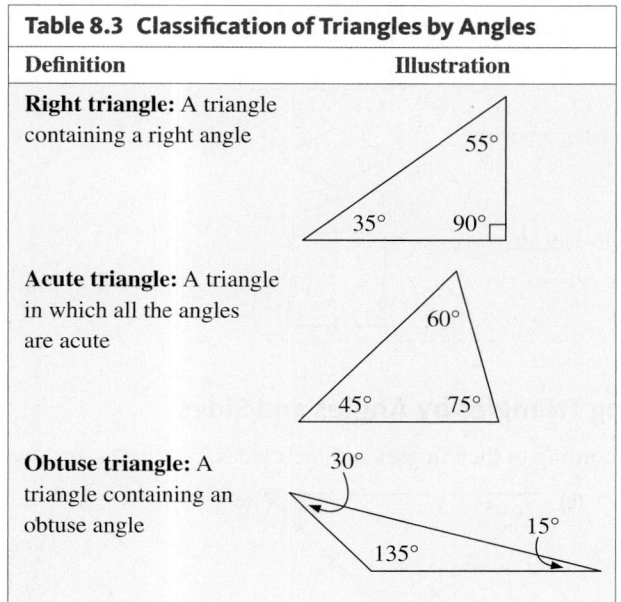

Table 8.3 Classification of Triangles by Angles

Definition	Illustration
Right triangle: A triangle containing a right angle	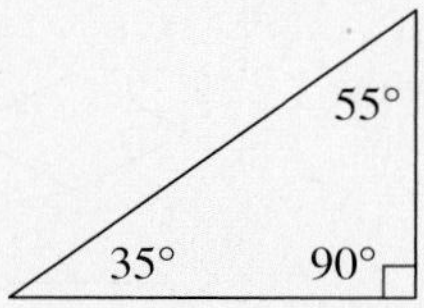
Acute triangle: A triangle in which all the angles are acute	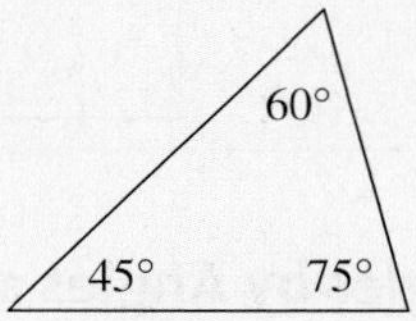
Obtuse triangle: A triangle containing an obtuse angle	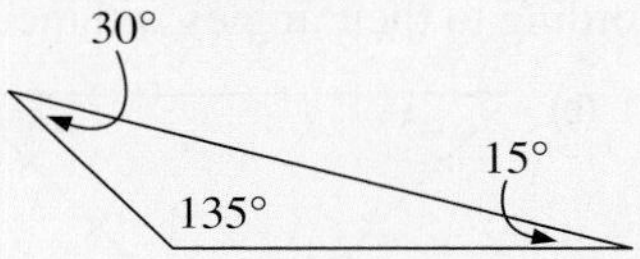

Table 8.4 Classification of Triangles by Number of Equal Sides

Definition	Illustration
Scalene triangle: A triangle with *no* equal sides (Note that the sides are labeled I, II, and III to show that the lengths of the sides are different.)	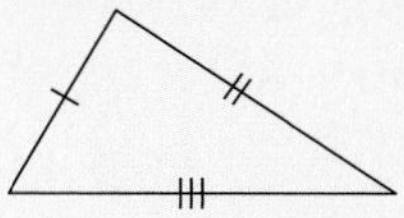
Isosceles triangle: A triangle with two equal sides	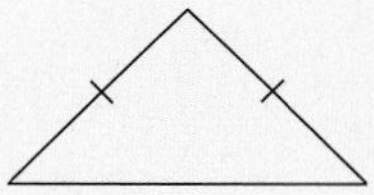
Equilateral triangle: A triangle with all three sides equal	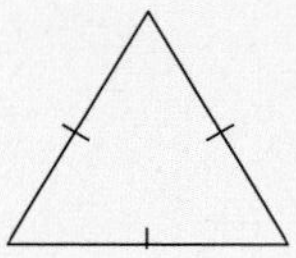

What is the most famous triangle you know? It is probably the Bermuda triangle, a 1.5-million mile triangular area with vertices at Miami, Bermuda and Puerto Rico. What kind of a triangle is the Bermuda triangle? Since all three angles in the Bermuda triangle are ***acute,*** (less than 90°), the triangle is an ***acute triangle.*** In addition, no two sides have the same length, that is, there are no equal sides, which makes it a ***scalene triangle.***

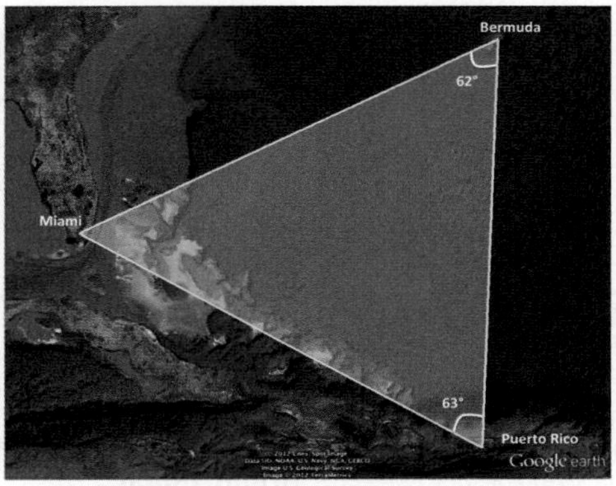

Table 8.5 Quadrilaterals

Definition	Illustration
Trapezoid: A quadrilateral with exactly one pair of parallel sides	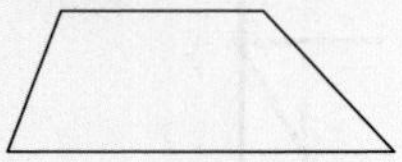
Kite: A quadrilateral with two distinct pairs of consecutive equal sides	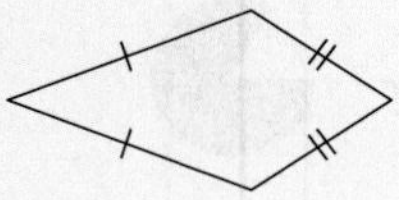
Parallelogram: A quadrilateral in which the opposite sides are parallel	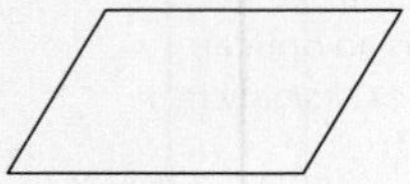
Rectangle: A parallelogram with a right angle	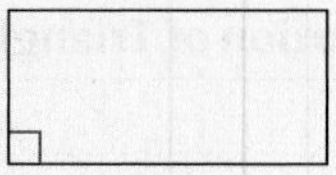
Rhombus: A parallelogram with all sides equal	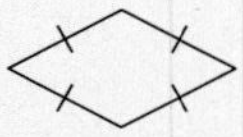
Square: A rectangle with all sides equal	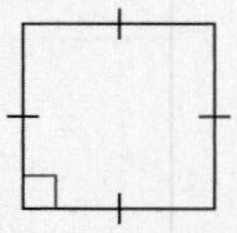

EXAMPLE 3 Classifying Triangles by Angles and Sides

Classify the given triangles according to their angles and their sides.

(a)

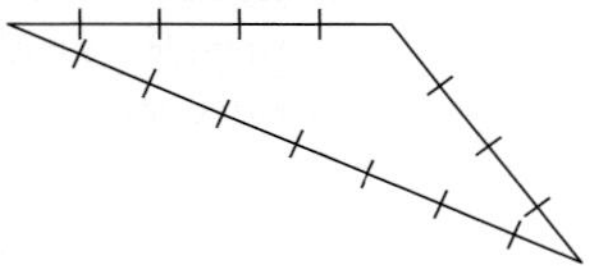

(b)

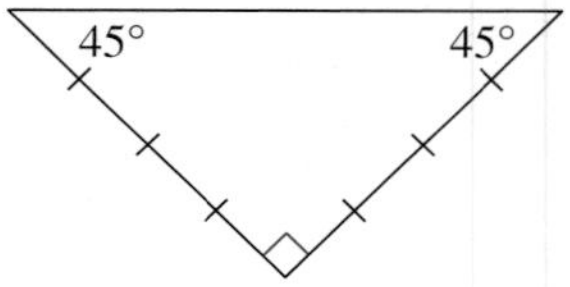

(c)

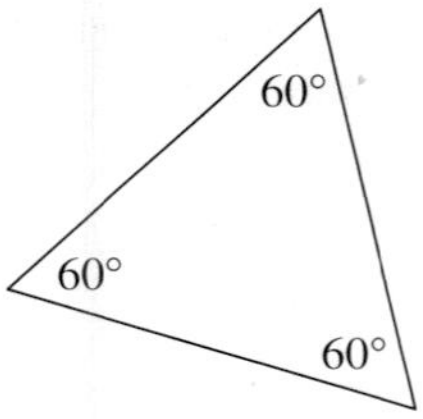

Solution

(a) The triangle has an obtuse angle and no equal sides; it is an obtuse, scalene triangle.

(b) The triangle has two equal sides and a right angle; it is an isosceles, right triangle.

(c) The triangle has three 60° angles; it is an equilateral triangle, which is also equiangular.

C Similar and Congruent Triangles

In Tables 8.3 and 8.4, we classified triangles according to their angles and their sides, respectively. Angles and sides are used to compare triangles. If two triangles have exactly the same shape (their corresponding angles are equal) but not necessarily the same size (their sides are *proportional*), then the triangles are called *similar triangles.*

The Smiley on the right is an enlargement of the Smiley on the left and exactly the same shape but not the same size. The Smileys are similar.

Definition of Similar Triangles

Triangles $\triangle ABC$ and $\triangle DEF$ are **similar** (denoted by $\triangle ABC \sim \triangle DEF$) if and only if they have **equal** corresponding angles and their corresponding sides are **proportional.**

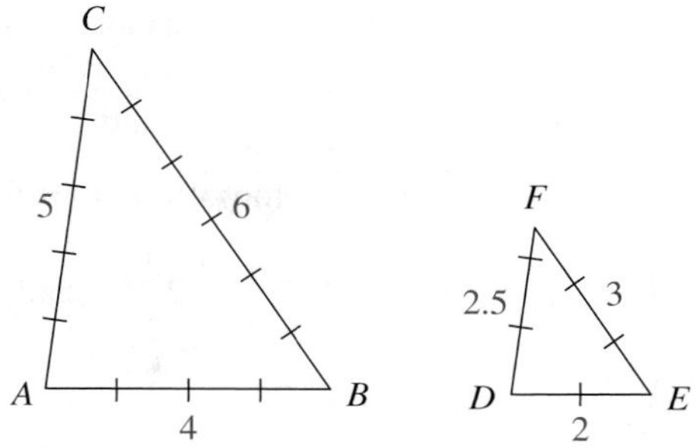

FIGURE 8.39

Look at the two similar triangles $\triangle ABC$ and $\triangle DEF$ in Figure 8.39. Because they have the same shape, the corresponding angles are equal.

Corresponding Angles of Similar Triangles

In Figure 8.39, $m\angle A = m\angle D$, $m\angle B = m\angle E$, and $m\angle C = m\angle F$. The corresponding sides of the two triangles are $\overleftrightarrow{AB}$ and $\overleftrightarrow{DE}$, $\overleftrightarrow{BC}$ and $\overleftrightarrow{EF}$, and $\overleftrightarrow{AC}$ and $\overleftrightarrow{DF}$. The length of each side of $\triangle DEF$ is one-half the length of the corresponding side of $\triangle ABC$. Recall that the ratio of two numbers a and b is the fraction a/b. For Figure 8.39, we have

$$\frac{DE}{AB} = \frac{EF}{BC} = \frac{DF}{AC} = \frac{1}{2}$$

as the ratios of corresponding sides.

We use these ideas in the next example.

EXAMPLE 4 Finding Dimensions for Similar Triangles

Two similar triangles are shown in Figure 8.40. Find d and f for $\triangle DEF$.

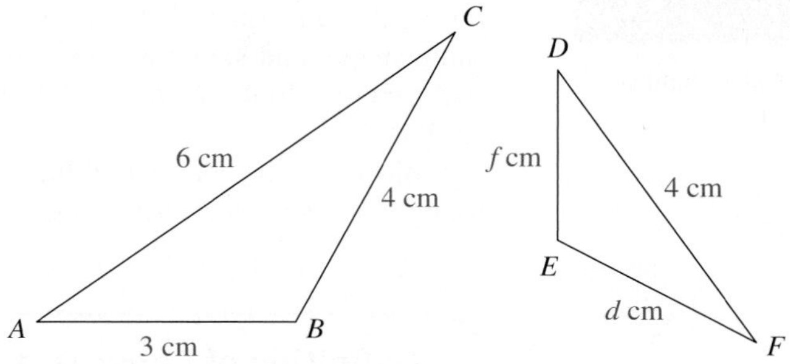

FIGURE 8.40

Solution

Since $\triangle ABC \sim \triangle DEF$, the corresponding sides must be proportional. Thus,

$$\frac{DE}{AB} = \frac{EF}{BC} = \frac{DF}{AC}$$

so that

$$\frac{f}{3} = \frac{d}{4} = \frac{4}{6}$$

Since $\frac{4}{6} = \frac{2}{3}$, we have

$$\frac{d}{4} = \frac{2}{3} \quad \text{and} \quad \frac{f}{3} = \frac{2}{3}$$

Solving these equations for d and f, we get

$$d = \frac{8}{3} = 2\frac{2}{3} \quad \text{and} \quad f = \frac{6}{3} = 2$$

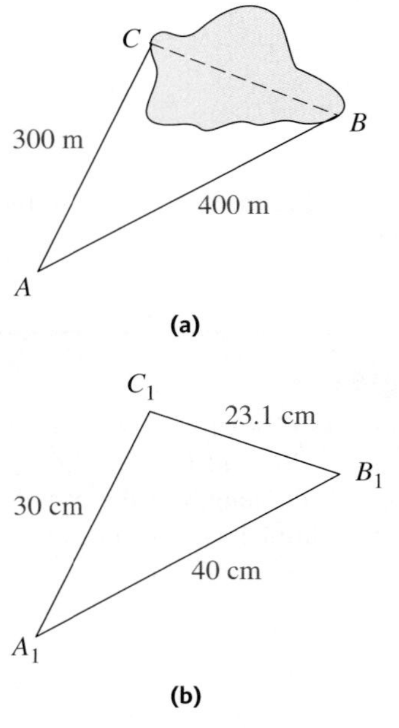

FIGURE 8.41

EXAMPLE 5 Applications of Similar Triangles

Wally wanted to find the distance across a lake, so he located a point A from which he could sight points B and C on opposite ends of the lake (see Figure 8.41a). With a surveyor's sextant, Wally found that $m\angle A = 35°$. He was able to measure $\overline{AB}$ and $\overline{AC}$ as 400 and 300 m, respectively. He took these data to his office and drew a triangle which he labeled $A_1B_1C_1$ with $m\angle A_1 = 35°$, $A_1B_1 = 40$ cm, and $A_1C_1 = 30$ cm. He then measured $\overline{B_1C_1}$ and found it to be 23.1 cm long. How could Wally use all this information to find the distance across the lake?

Solution

Since Wally made $m\angle A_1 = m\angle A$ and used the same scale (10 m/cm) for $\overline{A_1B_1}$ and $\overline{A_1C_1}$, he knows that $\triangle A_1B_1C_1 \sim \triangle ABC$ (see Figure 8.41b). Therefore, if the length of $\overline{BC}$ is x m, then

$$\frac{400}{40} = \frac{300}{30} = \frac{x}{23.1}$$

so that

$$\frac{x}{23.1} = 10 \quad \text{and} \quad x = 231$$

Thus, Wally found the distance across the lake to be 231 m.

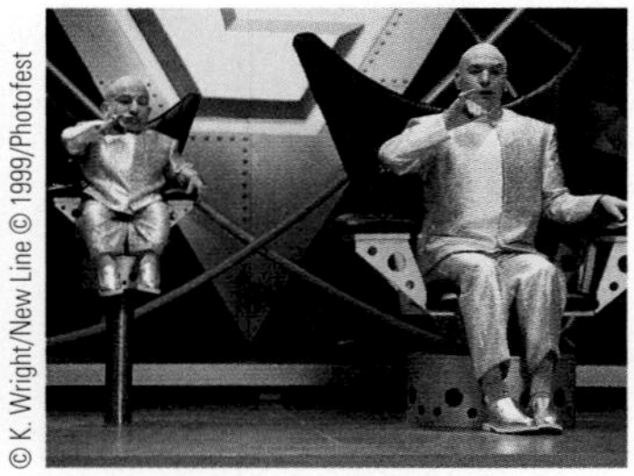

Minime and Dr. Evil are similar but not congruent.

The definition of similar triangles indicates that they have the same corresponding angles and shape but their size may be different. Triangles that have both the same shape, and size are called **congruent triangles.** This actually means that the two triangles look *identical.* Note that if two triangles are congruent, they are also similar.

Warning: The converse of the last sentence is *not* true. In other words, two similar triangles are *not* necessarily congruent. (See the photograph in the margin.)

> **Definition of Congruent Triangles**
>
> Triangles $\triangle ABC$ and $\triangle DEF$ are **congruent** (denoted by $\triangle ABC \cong \triangle DEF$) if and only if they have **equal** corresponding **angles** and **sides.**

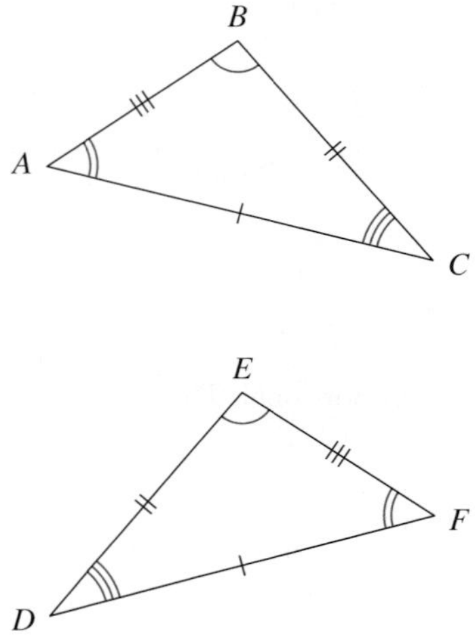

FIGURE 8.42 $\triangle ABC \cong \triangle DEF$.

Objects that are *exactly* the same shape and size are said to be **congruent.** Note that the symbol to denote congruency ($\cong$) is made up of two parts: "$\sim$" which means the same shape (similar), and "$=$," which means the same size (equal). When looking at congruent triangles, be sure that the sides are of equal (length) and corresponding angles are of equal measure (in degrees). When two triangles such as the ones in Figure 8.42 are congruent, there are six facts that are true about the triangles:

The length of side $\overline{AB}$ is the same as the length of side $\overline{EF}$.	$AB = EF$
The length of side $\overline{BC}$ is the same as the length of side $\overline{DE}$.	$BC = DE$
The length of side $\overline{AC}$ is the same as the length of side $\overline{DF}$.	$AC = DF$
The measure of angle A is the same as the measure of angle F.	$m\angle A = m\angle F$
The measure of angle B is the same as the measure of angle E.	$m\angle B = m\angle E$
The measure of angle C is the same as the measure of angle D.	$m\angle C = m\angle D$

To show graphically that two triangles are congruent, draw two triangles on a piece of paper and then carefully cut them out along their outlines. If you can place one of the triangles on top of the other so that the three vertices of the top triangle match up perfectly with the three vertices of the bottom triangle (you may have to flip and/or rotate the triangles first), then the triangles are congruent. Practice this idea by tracing out the congruent triangles in Figure 8.42.

Note: Corresponding equal sides are marked with small straight line segments, and corresponding congruent angles are marked with arcs.

You can determine whether two triangles are congruent even if you don't have all the information about the measures of their sides and angles. First, we need some definitions.

Included Side of Angles

Given any triangle, a side that lies between two angles is called the **included side** of the angles.

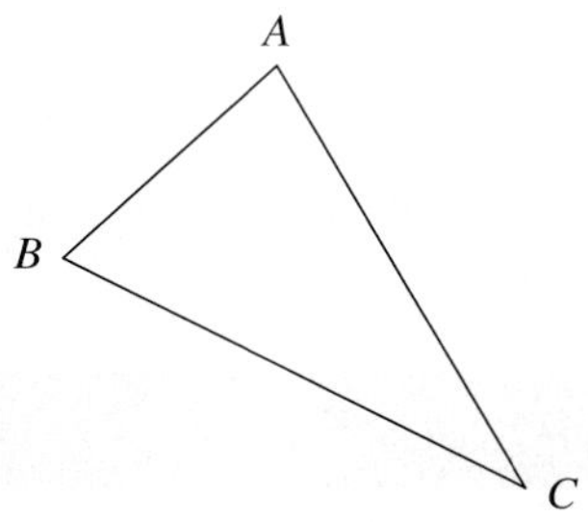

FIGURE 8.43

Similarly,

Included Angle of Sides

The angle formed by two sides is the **included angle** of the sides.

For example, $\overline{AC}$ is the included side of $\angle A$ and $\angle C$ in Figure 8.43, whereas $\angle A$ is the included angle of $\overline{AC}$ and $\overline{AB}$ in the same figure. Here are the theorems you need to prove that two triangles are congruent.

The Congruent Triangle Theorems

1. Side-Angle-Side (SAS). If two sides and the included angle of one triangle are equal to the corresponding sides and the included angle of a second triangle, then the two triangles are congruent.
2. Angle-Side-Angle (ASA). If two angles and the included side of one triangle are equal to the corresponding two angles and the included side of a second triangle, then the two triangles are congruent.
3. Side-Side-Side (SSS). If the three sides of one triangle are equal to the corresponding sides of a second triangle, then the two triangles are congruent.

EXAMPLE 6 Exploring the Congruent Triangle Theorems

(a) Show that $\triangle ABE$ and $\triangle DCE$ pictured in Figure 8.44 are congruent.

(b) Show that $\triangle ABD$ and $\triangle ACD$ pictured in Figure 8.45 are congruent.

(c) Why is there not an Angle-Angle-Angle congruent triangle theorem?

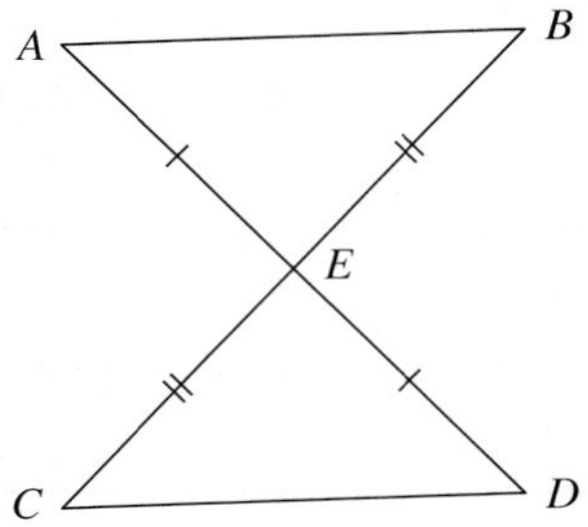

FIGURE 8.44

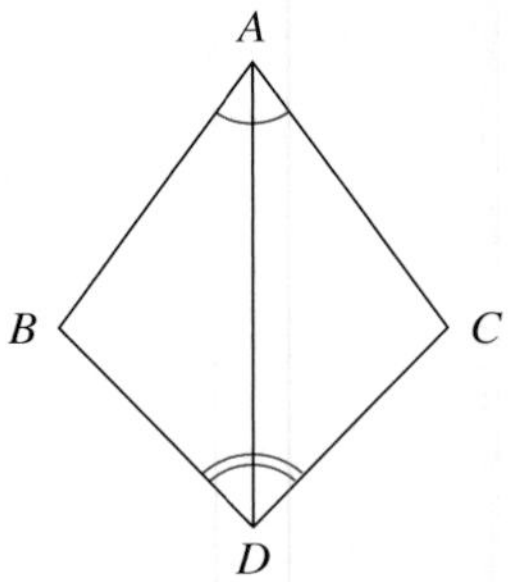

FIGURE 8.45

Solution

(a) Let $\angle X$ be the included angle of $\overleftrightarrow{AE}$ and $\overleftrightarrow{BE}$ and let $\angle Y$ be the included angle of $\overleftrightarrow{CE}$ and $\overleftrightarrow{DE}$. Since $\angle X$ and $\angle Y$ are vertical angles, $m\angle X = m\angle Y$. According to the diagram, $AE = DE$ and $BE = CE$. Thus, $\triangle ABE \cong \triangle DCE$ by SAS.

(b) Viewing $\overleftrightarrow{AD}$ as the included side in each triangle, ASA tells us that $\triangle ABD \cong \triangle ACD$.

(c) The two triangles pictured in Figure 8.46 are equilateral triangles and so all the angles are 60°. These triangles are *similar,* but not congruent.

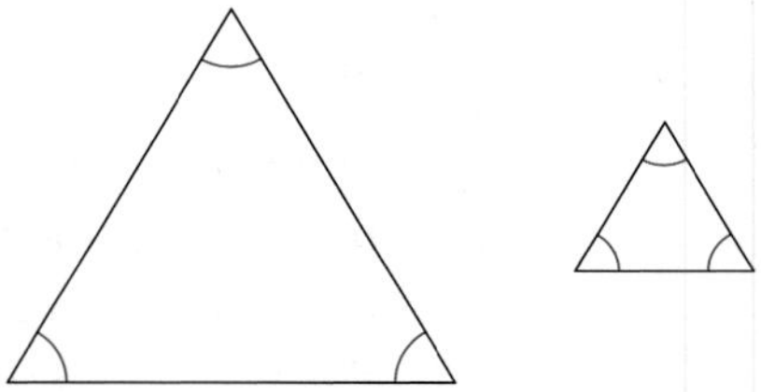

FIGURE 8.46 Triangles with all angles equal.

D Angles of a Polygon

In Example 5, Wally found the lengths of the sides of a triangle. Next, we shall examine how to find the measure of the angles of any given polygon.

PROBLEM-SOLVING

Finding the Measure of an Angle

① **Read** the problem.

Find the measure of angle β in Figure 8.47.

② **Select** the unknown.

The measure of angle β is the unknown.

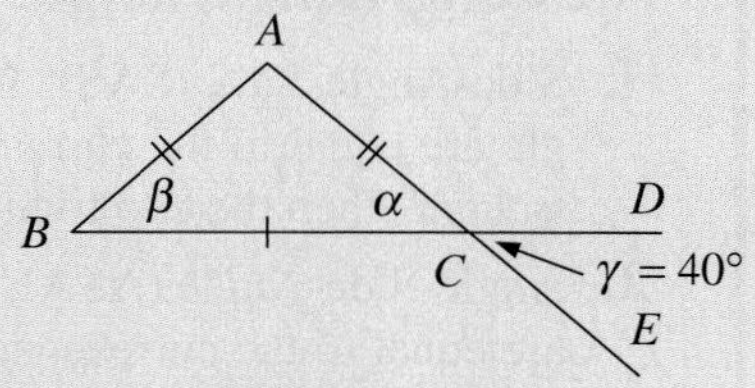

FIGURE 8.47

③ **Think** of a plan.
Find the equal sides. What angles are given? Are there any vertical angles?

You want to find the measure of angle β. According to Figure 8.47, $AB = AC$ and $m\angle\gamma = 40°$.

④ **Use** the fact that α and γ are vertical angles to find α. Look at the angles opposite the equal sides.	Since α and γ are vertical angles, they must be equal; that is, $m\angle\alpha = m\angle\gamma = 40°$. Angle α and angle β are opposite the equal sides of $\triangle ABC$ (triangle ABC); hence, they must also be of equal measure. Thus, the measure of angle β is 40°.
⑤ **Verify** the answer.	The verification is left to you.
Try Example 7 Now	Cover the solution, write your own solution, and then check your work.

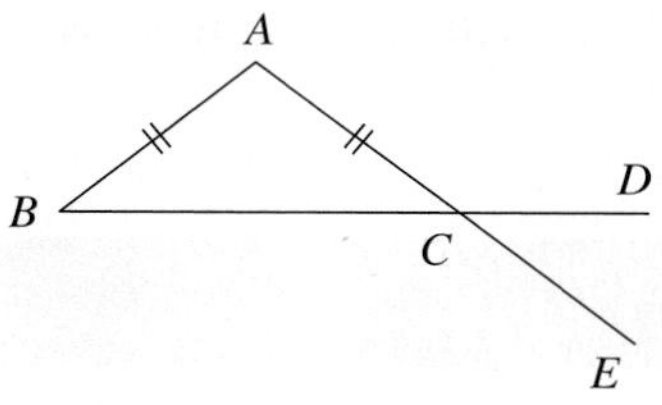

FIGURE 8.48

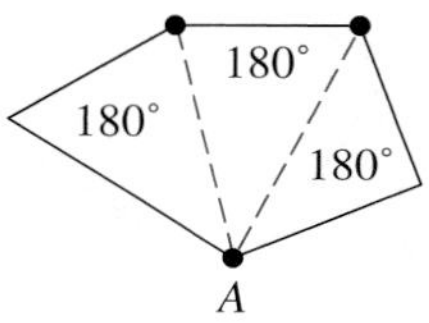

FIGURE 8.49

EXAMPLE 7 Finding Measures in a Triangle with Two Equal Sides

In $\triangle ABC$ in Figure 8.48, $AB = AC$ and $m\angle DCE = 37°$. Find $m\angle A$.

Solution

$\angle ACB$ and $\angle DCE$ are vertical angles, so $m\angle ACB = m\angle DCE = 37°$. $\angle ACB$ and $\angle B$ are opposite the equal sides of $\triangle ABC$ and are thus of equal measure. So $m\angle B = 37°$. Then,

$$m\angle A = 180° - m\angle ACB - m\angle ABC$$
$$m\angle A = 180° - 37° - 37°$$
$$= 106°$$

We have already noted that the sum of the measures of the three angles of any triangle is 180°. We can use this idea to find the corresponding sum S for any convex polygon. For example, suppose the polygon is a pentagon as shown in Figure 8.49. Select any vertex—say, A—and draw lines from A to each nonadjacent vertex, as shown by the dashed lines in Figure 8.49. The resulting number of triangles is 3 (2 fewer than the 5 sides of the polygon), and the number of degrees in the angles of these three triangles is $3 \times 180° = 540°$.

We can generalize this result to any convex polygon; if the polygon has n sides, there will be $n - 2$ triangles. We have the following result:

The Sum of the Measures of the Interior Angles of a Convex Polygon

The sum S of the measures of the interior angles of any convex polygon with n sides is given by

$$S = (n - 2)180°$$

Furthermore, if the polygon is a regular polygon, then the angles are all equal. In this case, the measure of a single angle of the polygon is just the preceding result divided by n, the total number of angles. This idea is illustrated in the next example.

EXAMPLE 8 Finding Measures of Angles in a Heptagon

Find the measure of an angle of a regular heptagon.

Solution

Since a heptagon has 7 sides, the formula gives

$$S = (7 - 2)180° = 5 \times 180° = 900°$$

Because the polygon is regular, each angle has measure

$$\frac{900°}{7} = 128\frac{4°}{7}$$

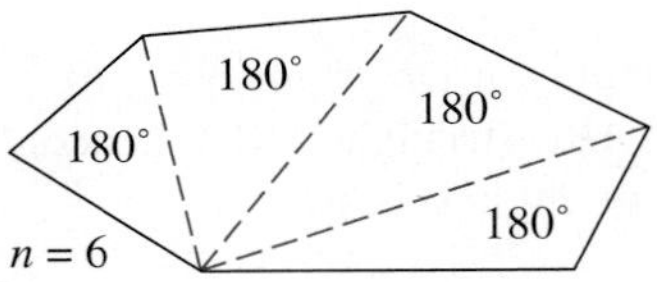

FIGURE 8.50 This hexagon breaks into four triangles, each containing 180° of angles.

That the sum S of the measures of the interior angles of any convex polygon with n sides equals $(n - 2)180°$ for the case $n = 6$ is illustrated in Figure 8.50. What if you want to know the measure of *each* of the angles in the polygon? Look at Figure 8.51 and then fill in the blank:

The measure of each of the n angles in a **regular** convex polygon with n sides is ____________.
Your Answer

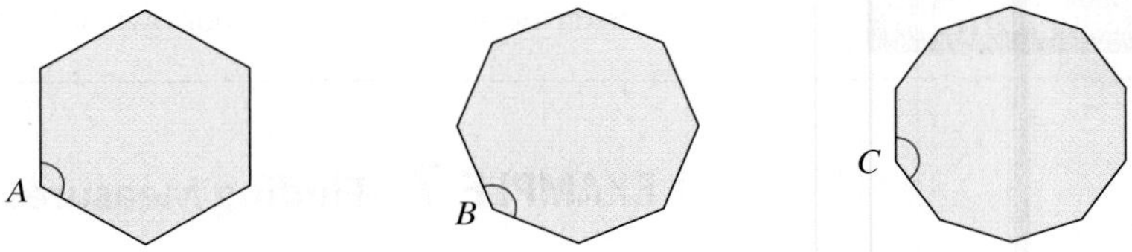

$(n = 6)$ $A = (6 - 2) \cdot 180/6 = 120°$

$(n = 8)$ $B = (8 - 2) \cdot 180/8 = 135°$

$(n = 10)$ $C = (10 - 2) \cdot 180/10 = 144°$

FIGURE 8.51

8.2 EXERCISES

A Broken Lines and Polygons

In problems 1 and 2, sketch a broken line path as described.

1. a. Closed but not simple
   b. Simple but not closed
2. a. Both simple and closed
   b. Neither simple nor closed

In problems 3–7, use the alphabet,

ABCDEFGHIJKLMNOPQRSTUVWXYZ

3. State which letters form a path or curve that is
   a. simple. b. closed.
4. State which letters form a path or curve that is
   a. closed but not simple.
   b. simple but not closed.
5. State which letters form a path or curve that is
   a. simple and closed.
   b. neither simple nor closed.
6. If the lowest points of the legs of the letter **M** are joined by a straight line segment, will the resulting polygon be concave or convex?
7. If the highest points of the legs of the letter **V** are joined by a straight line segment, will the resulting polygon be concave or convex?
8. Refer to the traffic signs in Example 2, and name the shape of the
   a. information sign. b. no passing sign.

B Triangles and Quadrilaterals

In problems 9–16, name each quadrilateral.

9.
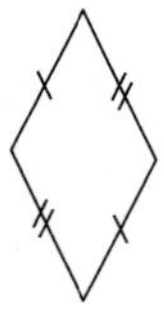

10.
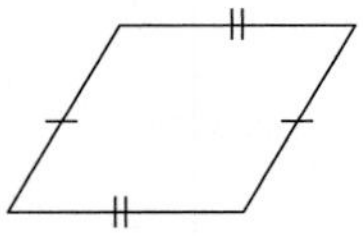

11.
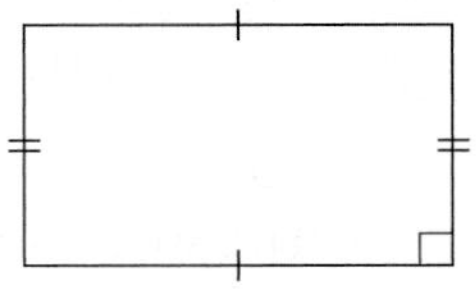

12.
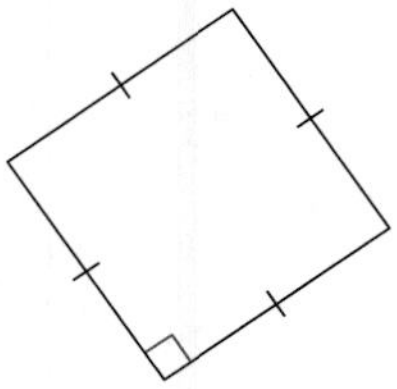

13.
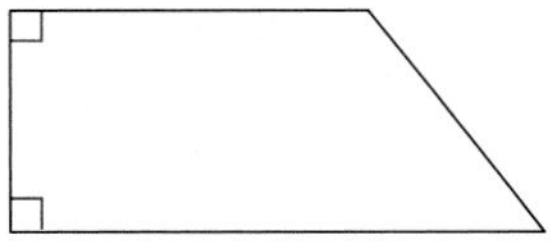

14.
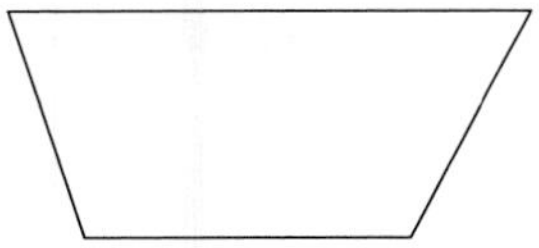

15.
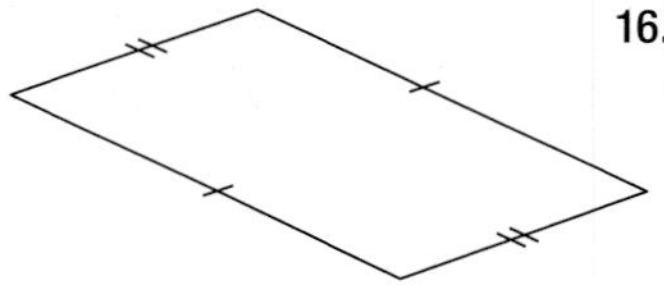

16.
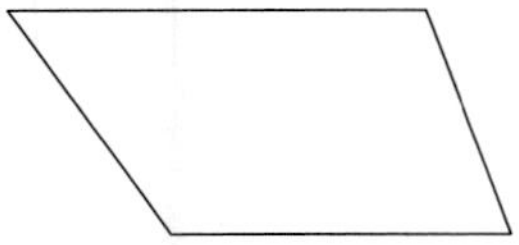

In problems 17–24, classify each triangle as scalene, isosceles, or equilateral and as acute, right, or obtuse.

17.
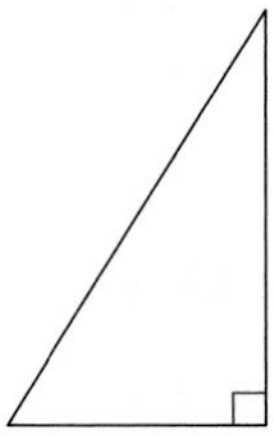

18.
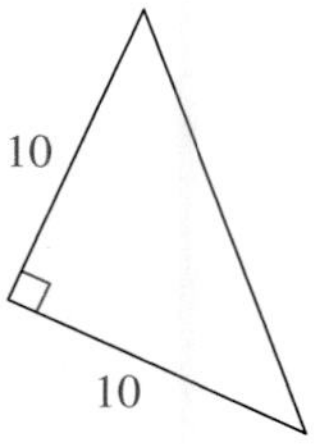

19.
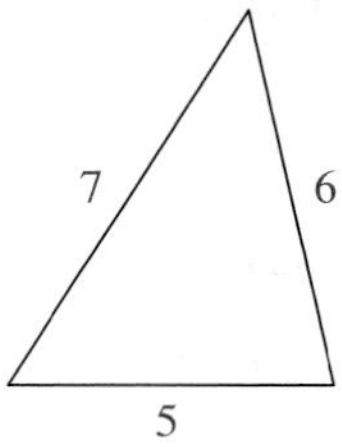

20.
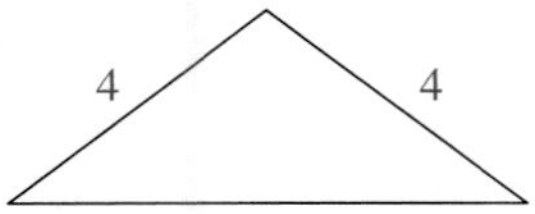

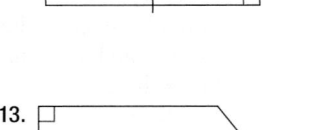

21.

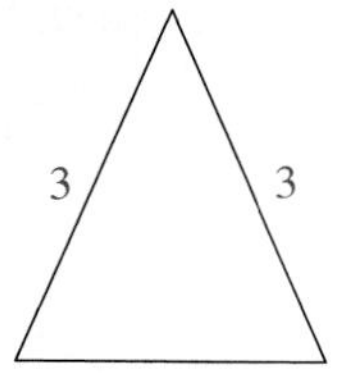

22.

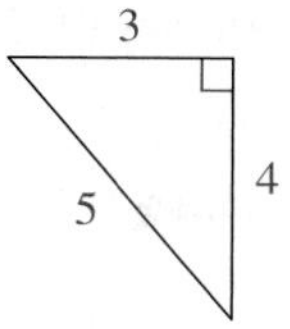

23.

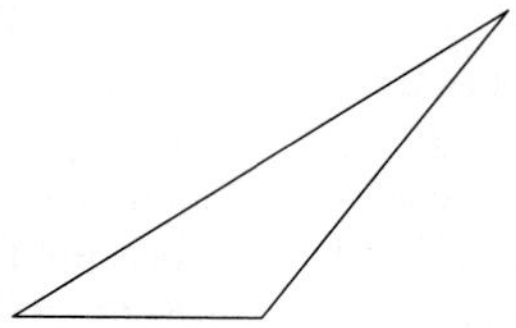

24.

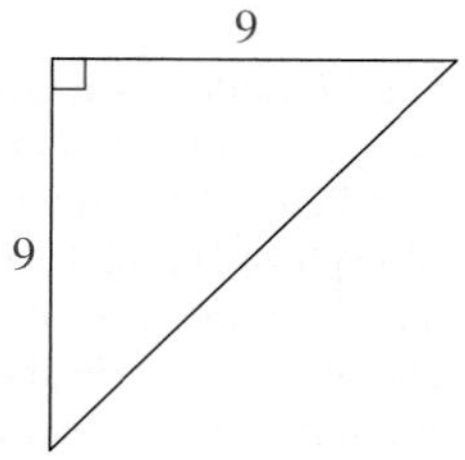

C Similar and Congruent Triangles

25. Which (if any) of the following triangles are similar?

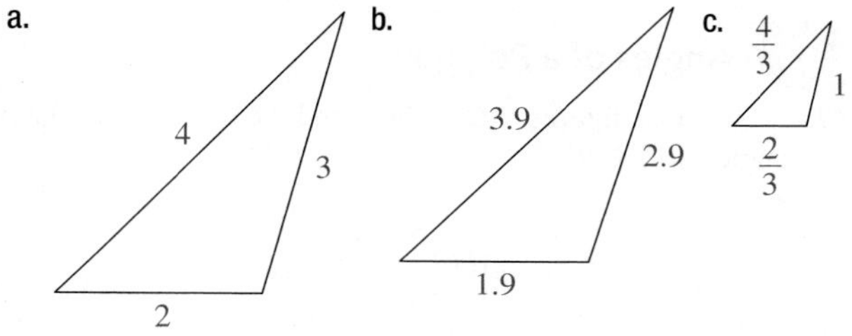

26. The marked angles in the following triangles are all equal. Which (if any) of the triangles are similar?

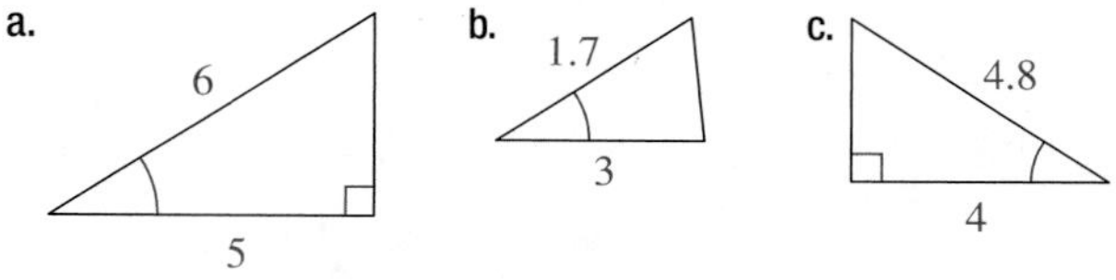

27. The following triangles are similar. Find the lengths marked x and y.

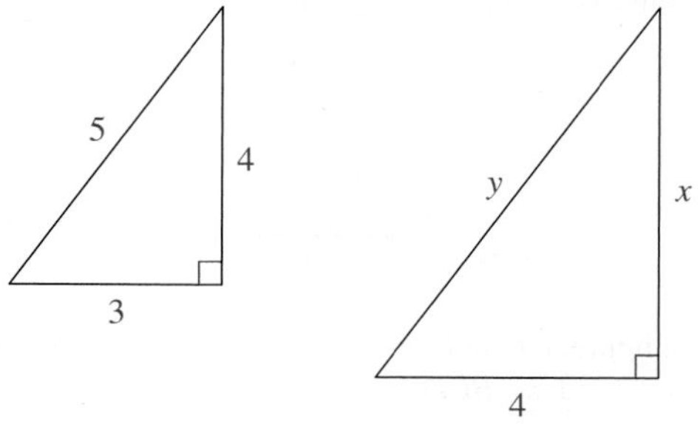

28. The following parallelograms are similar. Find the length of the diagonal $\overleftrightarrow{PR}$.

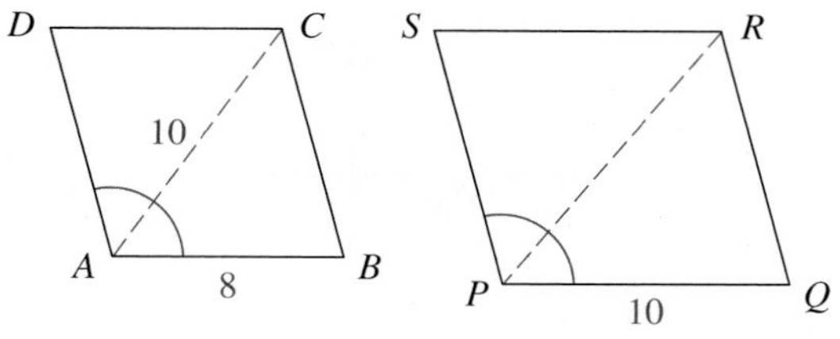

Problems 29–32 refer to the following figure. In this figure, $\overleftrightarrow{PQ}$ is parallel to $\overleftrightarrow{AB}$. In each problem, certain lengths are given. Find the missing length, indicated by a blank.

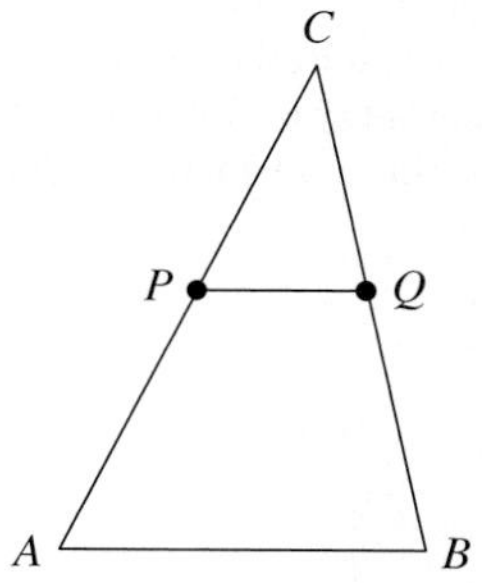

	AP	*PC*	*BQ*	*BC*
29.	3	4	6	____
30.	5	4	____	6
31.	2	____	3	5
32.	____	4	4	8

33. The sides of a triangle measure 6, 9, and 12 cm, respectively. The longest side of a similar triangle measures 7 cm. Find the lengths of the other two sides of the smaller triangle.

34. In problem 33, if the length of the shortest side of the smaller triangle is 5 cm, find the lengths of the other two sides.

35. The sides of a triangle measure 2, 3, and 4 in., respectively. The perimeter of a similar triangle is 36 in. Find the length of each side of the second triangle.

36. Jackie has a piece of wire 18 in. long. She wants to bend this into a triangle similar to a triangle whose sides are 3, 4, and 5 in., respectively. What must be the dimensions of her triangle?

37. A telephone pole casts a shadow 30 ft long at the same time that a 5-ft fence post casts a shadow 8 ft long. How tall is the telephone pole?

38. Betty wants to measure the height of a flagpole. She puts up a vertical post 8 ft tall and moves back in line with the flagpole and the post until her line of sight hits the tops of both post and pole (see the following figure). If the known distances are as shown in the figure, what is the height of the flagpole?

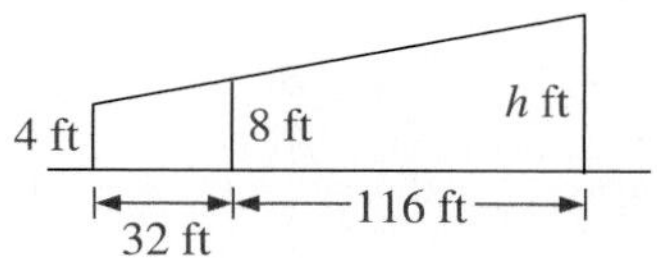

39. Ronny wants to find the height of a tree standing on level ground. He places a 5-ft stake vertically so that the sun throws a shadow of the tree and the stake as shown in the figure. He then measures the lengths of the shadows, with the results shown in the figure below. Why are the two triangles similar? What is the height of the tree?

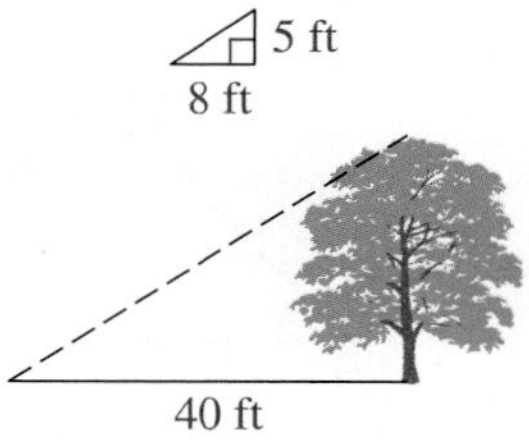

40. Gail wants to measure the distance AB across a small lake (see the figure in the next column). She walks 240 m away in a direction perpendicular to the line $\overleftrightarrow{AB}$ to a point C from which she can sight the point B. She then walks back 80 m along $\overline{CA}$ to a point P, and then walks in a direction perpendicular to $\overline{CA}$ to a point Q in line with B and C. She finds that $PQ = 60$ m. With this information, what does Gail find for the distance AB?

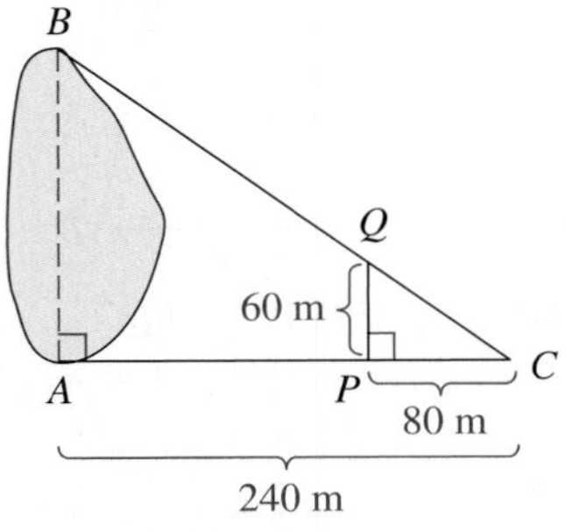

41. Sonny, the surveyor, needs to find the length of a tunnel to be bored through a small hilly area. He makes the marked angles equal and finds the measurements shown in the figure below. What length should Sonny find for the tunnel?

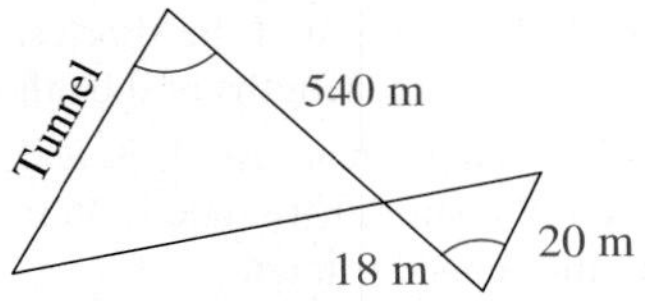

42. To find the distance between two points P and Q separated by an inaccessible area, Andy makes the measurements shown in the figure below. He returns to his office and draws $\triangle ABC$ with $m\angle A = m\angle O$, $m\angle B = m\angle P$, and $AB = 10$ cm. He then measures $\overline{BC}$ and finds it to be 18 cm. What length does Andy find for $\overline{PQ}$?

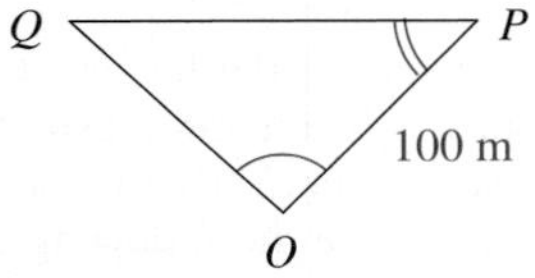

43. Use the congruent triangle theorems to show that $\triangle ABC$ is an isosceles triangle.

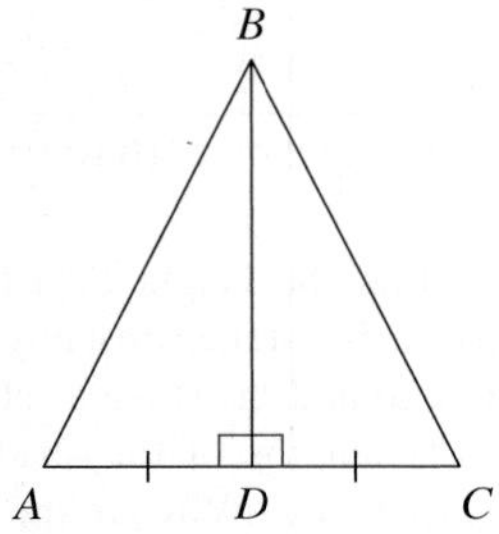

44. Show that $\triangle ABD \cong \triangle BCD$.

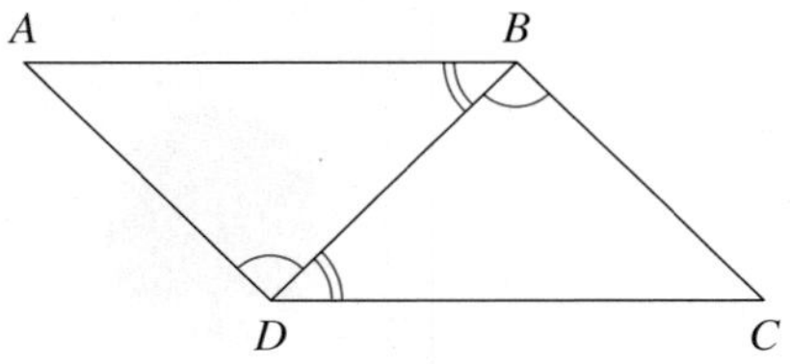

45. If $AD = BC$ and $AC = BD$, show that $\triangle ACD \cong \triangle BCD$.

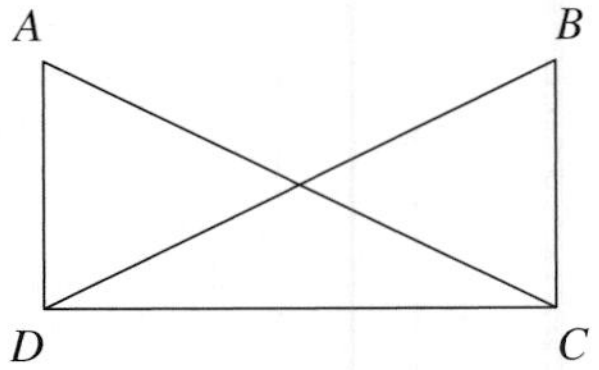

46. Old McBello has finally decided to sell his farm, which consists of two triangular plots of land (call them plot ABC and plot DEF). As an interested buyer, you inquire about the areas of each of the plots. He tells you that he has measured the lengths of the sides of each plot and that $AB = DF$, $BC = DE$, and $AC = EF$. He then declares that plot ABC has exactly the same area as plot DEF. Is Old McBello telling the truth, or is he trying to pull the wool over your eyes? (*Hint:* Draw the picture.)

D Angles of a Polygon

47. In the given figures, $AC = BC$. Find the measures of the three angles of $\triangle ABC$.

a.

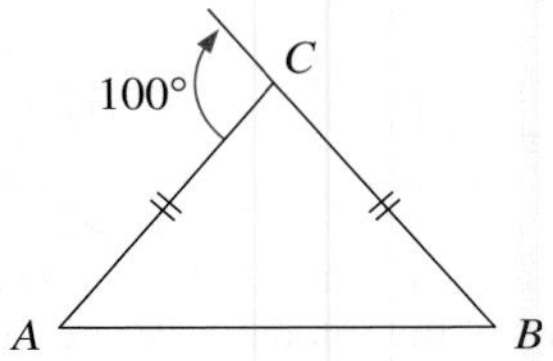

b.

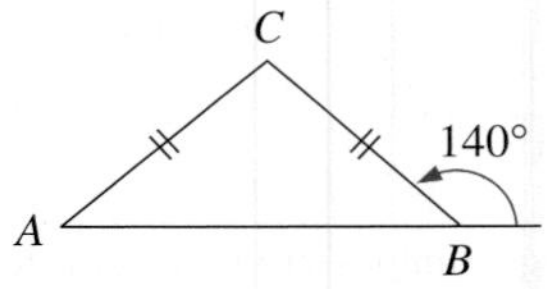

48. $ABCD$ is a parallelogram. Find the measure of $\angle BAD$.

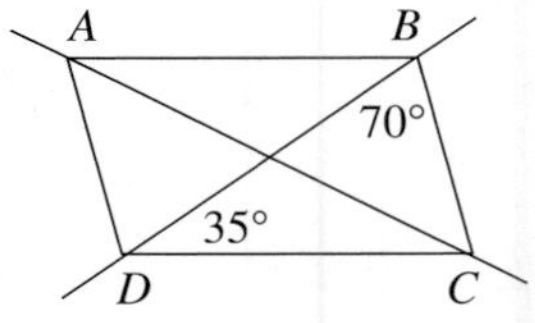

49. In the given figure, $\overleftrightarrow{AE}$ and $\overleftrightarrow{BD}$ are parallel and $\overleftrightarrow{CE}$ is perpendicular to $\overleftrightarrow{BD}$. Find $m\angle BCD$.

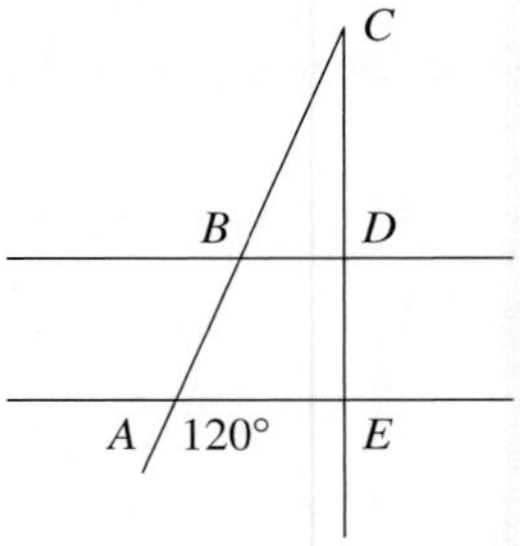

50. For the given figure, find $m\angle C$. What type of triangle is $\triangle ABC$?

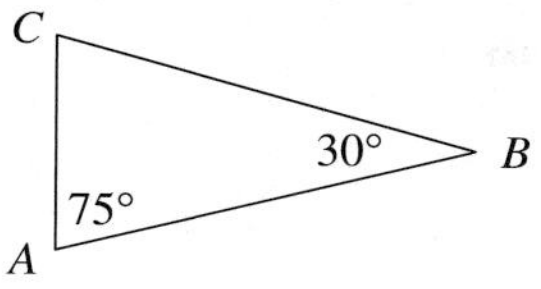

51. Find the sum of the measures of the angles of a regular polygon with 14 sides.

52. Find the sum of the measures of the angles of a regular polygon with 20 sides.

In problems 53–58, find the measure of one angle for each polygon.

53. A regular pentagon **54.** A regular hexagon

55. A regular octagon **56.** A regular nonagon

57. A regular decagon **58.** A regular dodecagon

59. The information in Table 8.5, page 446, can be represented as the **family tree** or **hierarchy** shown below, where each name includes all the shapes below it to which it is connected.

a. Use set notation to show the relationship between the set P of all polygons, the set T of all triangles, and so on.

b. Draw a Venn diagram to show the relationship between P, T, I, and E.

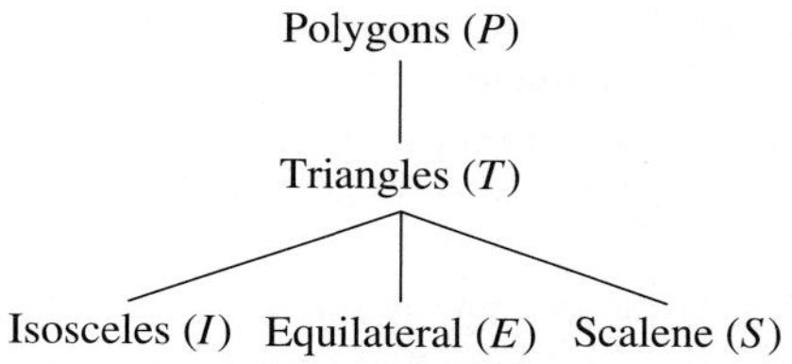

60. Show a family tree or hierarchy for the quadrilaterals in Table 8.5. Here are the first two steps.

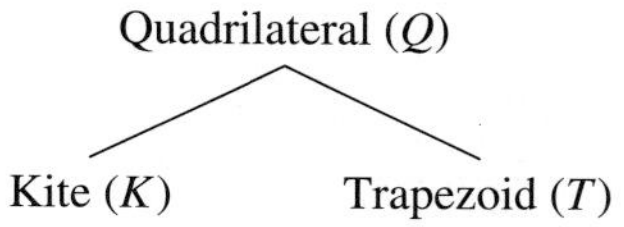

61. Draw a Venn diagram to represent the hierarchy shown in problem 60.

IN OTHER WORDS

62. When a boat, car, or plane is manufactured, a model of it is constructed first. Explain what the model and the actual structure have in common.

63. Some distances are not easy to measure directly (the distance across a lake, as for Wally and in problem 40). Describe in your own words a situation in which indirect measurements using similar triangles are used.

64. Johnny claims that he has drawn two similar triangles. He says the sides of the first triangle are 4, 5, and 7 cm long and that the corresponding sides of the second triangle are 8, 10, and 12 cm long. Betty says that Johnny is making a mistake. Write out a complete explanation and justification for Betty's claim.

USING YOUR KNOWLEDGE

In problems 65–68, use the following table, which lists all possible triangle classifications. For example, IR stands for an isosceles, right triangle, SO stands for a scalene, obtuse triangle, and so on. The problems ask you to draw certain types of triangles. In any case in which you think no such triangle exists, write "impossible."

65. Draw an example of each of the following types:

a. SA **b.** IA **c.** EA

	Acute	Right	Obtuse
Scalene	SA	SR	SO
Isosceles	IA	IR	IO
Equilateral	EA	ER	EO

66. Draw an example of each of the following types:

a. SR **b.** IR **c.** ER

67. Draw an example of each of the following types:

a. SO **b.** IO **c.** EO

68. Which of the triangles in the table are impossible?

COLLABORATIVE LEARNING

In Example 5 we saw that similar triangles and ratios can be used to find distances that cannot be measured directly because of their inaccessibility. Suppose you want to measure the height of the flagpole at your school.

1. Form several groups and find different procedures to measure the height of the flagpole.
2. The Greek mathematician Thales of Miletus was able to find the height of the Great Pyramid in Egypt by using a method called "shadow reckoning." Find out how this was done, and calculate the height of the Great Pyramid.
3. Discuss your findings with the other groups. Did they get the same answer?

8.3 Perimeter and Circumference

GETTING STARTED

OBJECTIVES

A. Find the dimensions and perimeter of a polygon.
B. Find the circumference and diameter of a circle.
C. Solve applications involving circles and polygons.

HATS, RINGS, AND CIRCUMFERENCES

Do you know your hat size? If you don't, you will be glad to know that it is supposed to be about the same as your ring size! (see *Rules of Thumb* by Tom Parker). How can that be? The ancient Greeks discovered that if they divided the circumference C of a circle by the length of its diameter d, they always obtained approximately the same number, π, regardless of the size of the circle. You can verify this by measuring the circumference of a soda can (the distance around) and dividing by its diameter. The answer should be about 3.14. The formula used to do this is the same one used by the Greeks, $C/d = \pi$. Now, back to rings and hats.

The average person's head is about 23 in. in circumference. If you divide 23 by $\pi(3.14)$—that is, $23/\pi$—the answer is the diameter $d \approx 7.32$. Unfortunately, hats are sized in increments of $\frac{1}{8}$ in. What size, to the nearest $\frac{1}{8}$ in., is the closest to 7.32 in.? You know that $7\frac{2}{8} = 7\frac{1}{4} = 7.25$ and can easily find $7\frac{3}{8} = 7.375$. Thus, $7\frac{3}{8}$ is the closest to the measure of $d \approx 7.32$ in.

Now you know that your hat size is the average diameter of your head in inches. How can this be the same as your ring size? Assume that your hat size is 7 in. in diameter. What would a 7 ring size measure? According to a jewelry handbook, the diameter d of a ring (in inches) is given by

$$d = 0.458 + 0.032s$$

where s is the ring size. When $s = 7$,

$$d = 0.458 + 0.032 \cdot 7 = 0.682 \text{ in.}$$

Since the diameter of the ring, and hence of the finger, is 0.682 in., the circumference of the finger should be $C = 3.14 \cdot 0.682 = 2.14$ in. Thus, if your hat size is 7, the circumference of your ring finger should be about 2.14 in., and of course, your ring size should be 7.

You can repeat this little experiment by measuring your own head, dividing by π, and obtaining your hat size. Now substitute your hat size for s in the formula and multiply the result by π. The answer you get should be the same as the circumference of your finger! What if it is not even close? Keep in mind that hat sizes and ring sizes should be the same for an *average* person. If you lose or gain weight, the circumference of your finger decreases or increases, respectively, but your head size does not.

In this section you study circles and the perimeters of circles, called **circumferences,** and the different applications you can solve using these ideas.

In geometry, units of length are used to measure distances along lines and are consequently called **linear measures.** Table 8.6 shows the standard units of length in the U.S. customary system and in the metric system.

Table 8.6 Standard Units of Length

U.S. System	Metric System
Inch (in.)	Millimeter (mm) = 0.001 m
Foot (ft) = 12 in.	Centimeter (cm) = 0.01 m
Yard (yd) = 3 ft	Meter (m) = base unit
Mile (mi) = 1760 yd = 5280 ft	Kilometer (km) = 1000 m

Note that the metric system is a simple decimal system in contrast to the awkward conversions in the U.S. system. Although you will not be asked to convert from one of these systems to the other in this chapter, you should know that the U.S. inch is legally defined to be exactly 2.54 cm long. Table 8.7 gives a few conversions to help you see the relationship between metric and U.S. lengths.

Table 8.7 Metric/U.S. Conversions

1 in. = 2.54 cm	1 cm = 0.39 in.
1 yd = 0.91 m	1 m = 1.09 yd
1 mi = 1.61 km	1 km = 0.62 mi

So a centimeter is about $\frac{4}{10}$ of an inch, a meter is just a bit longer than a yard, and a kilometer is about $\frac{2}{3}$ of a mile.

A Polygonal Paths and Perimeters

Many of the applications of geometry involve finding the length of a polygonal path. For instance, fencing a field, laying tile around a rectangular pool, or finding the amount of baseboard needed for a room all involve measuring around polygons. The distance around a plane figure is generally called the **perimeter** of the figure. In the case of a polygon, the perimeter is just the sum of the lengths of the sides. Table 8.8 gives the formulas for the perimeters in terms of the sides for some of the polygons we have discussed. Note that perimeters are always expressed in linear measures.

© I. Bello

How many kinds of polygons can you see in this view looking up through the center of a tower that supports power lines?

Table 8.8

Name	Geometric Shape	Perimeter
Triangle	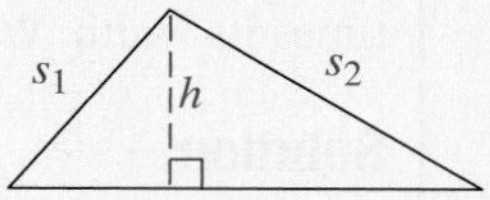	$P = s_1 + s_2 + b$
Trapezoid	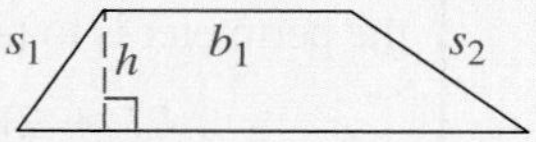	$P = s_1 + s_2 + b_1 + b_2$
Parallelogram	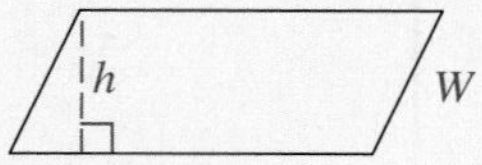	$P = 2L + 2W$
Rectangle	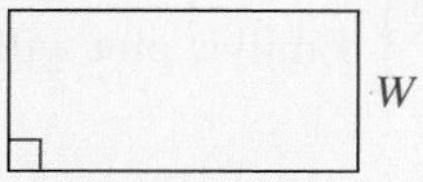	$P = 2L + 2W$
Square	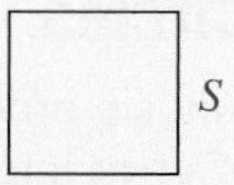	$P = 4S$

EXAMPLE 1 Perimeter for the Mona Lisa

The *Mona Lisa* by Leonardo da Vinci, assessed at $100 million for insurance purposes, measures 30.5 by 20.9 in. Find the perimeter of this picture.

Solution

Because the picture is rectangular, its perimeter is given by

$$P = 2L + 2W$$

where $L = 30.5$ and $W = 20.9$. Thus,

$$P = 2(30.5) + 2(20.9)$$
$$= 102.8 \text{ in.}$$

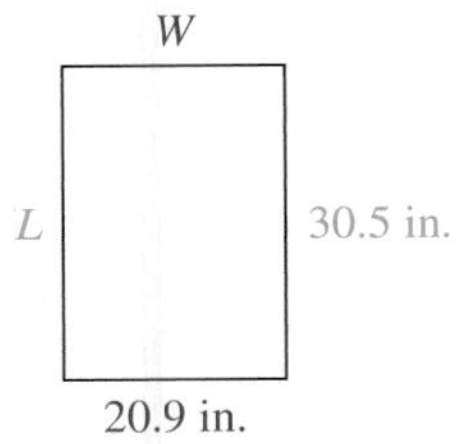

The ideas we have been studying here can be combined with the algebra you know to solve certain kinds of problems. Here is an interesting problem.

EXAMPLE 2 Width of the Largest Poster

One of the largest recorded posters was a rectangular greeting card 166 ft long and with a perimeter of 458.50 ft. How wide was this poster?

Solution

The perimeter of a rectangle is $P = 2L + 2W$, and we know that $L = 166$ and $P = 458.50$. Thus, we can write

$$2(166) + 2W = 458.50$$
$$332 + 2W = 458.50$$
$$2W = 126.50$$
$$W = 63.25$$

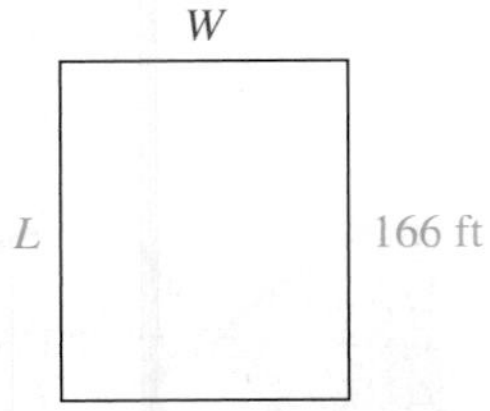

So the poster was 63.25 ft wide.

EXAMPLE 3 Finding the Dimensions of Emily's Rectangle

John and Emily Gardener want to fence in a small, rectangular plot for Emily's kitchen garden. John has 20 m of fencing and decides that the length of the plot should be $1\frac{1}{2}$ times its width. What will be the dimensions of Emily's garden plot?

Solution

We let x meters be the width of the plot. Then the length must be $\frac{3}{2}x$ m. We know the perimeter is to be 20 m, so

$$2L + 2W = P$$
$$2\left(\tfrac{3}{2}x\right) + 2x = 20$$
$$3x + 2x = 20$$
$$5x = 20$$
$$x = 4 \quad \text{and} \quad \tfrac{3}{2}x = 6$$

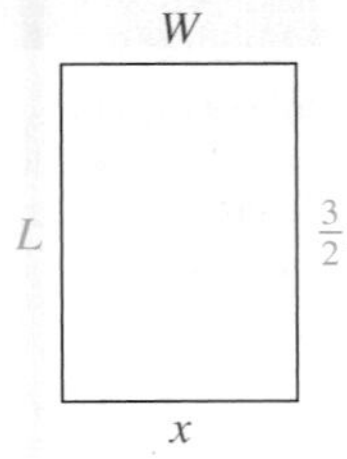

Emily's plot will be 6 m long and 4 m wide.

B Circles

You are probably familiar with the geometric figure called a *circle*. The circle has been of great interest ever since prehistoric times; it has always been used for many decorative and practical purposes. Here is a modern definition.

Definition of a Circle

A **circle** is the set of all coplanar (on the same plane) points at a given fixed distance (the **radius**) from a given point (the **center**).

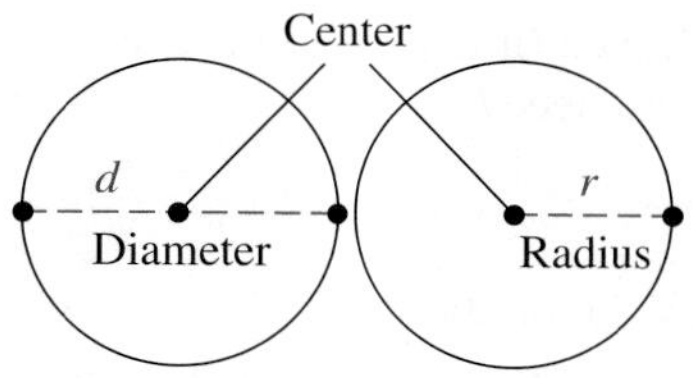

FIGURE 8.52

Figure 8.52 shows two circles with a radius and diameter indicated. Note that the **diameter** consists of two collinear radii, so that $d = 2r$; that is, the length of the diameter is twice the length of the radius, or the radius is half of the diameter. The perimeter of a circle is known as the **circumference.**

Circumference of a Circle

The **circumference** C of a circle of diameter d and radius r is given by $C = \pi d$ or $C = 2\pi r$.

The irrational number $\pi \approx 3.14159$ was discussed in an earlier chapter. Unless otherwise noted, you may use the approximate value 3.14 for the problems in this book.

EXAMPLE 4 Fencing Your Pool for Safety

Andy has a circular swimming pool with a diameter of 25 ft. To keep his little boy from falling into the water, Andy wants to put a low wire fence around the circumference of the pool. How much fencing does he need?

Solution

We use $C = \pi d$ and get

$$C \approx (3.14)(25) = 78.5 \text{ ft}$$

Since 3.14 is a little less than π, Andy should play it safe and get 79 ft of fencing.

EXAMPLE 5 Diameters of Hamburgers

According to the *Guinness Book of World Records,* one of the largest beef hamburgers had a circumference of 27.50 ft. Find the diameter of this hamburger to the nearest hundredth of a foot. Use $\pi \approx 3.14$.

Solution

Since the circumference of a circle is $C = \pi d$, we have

$$27.50 \approx 3.14\, d$$

Dividing by 3.14, we find

$$d = 8.76 \quad \text{to the nearest hundredth}$$

Thus, the diameter of this mammoth beef hamburger was about 8.76 ft. (It also weighed 2859 lb.) (*Note:* If we used a more accurate value of π, we would find the diameter to be 8.75 ft, to the nearest hundredth of a foot.)

Before we leave this section, let us shed some light on diameters and circumferences. To start, do you know how light bulbs are measured? An obvious answer is by wattage (how many watts). But there is more. Bulb shapes are identified by the letters A (typical house bulb), B (candelabra base Christmas tree bulb), and C (miniature night-light bulb). The bulb size is then given by a letter for shape followed by the bulb *maximum diameter* (in eighths of an inch). Thus, a T-8 bulb is a tubular bulb $\frac{8}{8} = 1$ in. in diameter. (Source: John Lord, *Sizes*: Harper Perennial, 1995.)

EXAMPLE 6 Circumference and Diameter of a Bulb

(a) What is the circumference and diameter of a 75-watt A-19 bulb?

(b) A bulb burns out at home. You measure its circumference (it is hard to measure the diameter!), and it is 8.25 in. Which type of bulb do you need?

Solution

(a) The diameter is $\frac{19}{8} = 2.375$ in. and $C = \pi d = \pi(2.375)$, or about 7.46 in.

(b) Since $C = \pi d$, we have $8.25 = \pi d$ and $d = 8.25/\pi \approx 2.63$. The question is, how many eighths is 0.63? We know that $\frac{1}{8} = 0.125$, so $\frac{5}{8} = 0.625$. This means that $d \approx 2.63 \approx 2\frac{5}{8} = \frac{21}{8}$. But you remember that bulbs are measured in eighths of an inch, so we need an A-21 bulb (the wattage is up to you!).

C Applications

EXAMPLE 7 Distance Traveled by Venus

The planet Venus revolves around the Sun in a nearly circular orbit whose diameter is about 100 million km. Find the distance traveled by Venus in one revolution around the Sun. Use 3.14 for π.

Solution

The distance traveled is the circumference C.

$$\begin{aligned} C &= \pi d \\ &= (3.14)(100) \text{ million km} \\ &= 314 \text{ million km} \end{aligned}$$

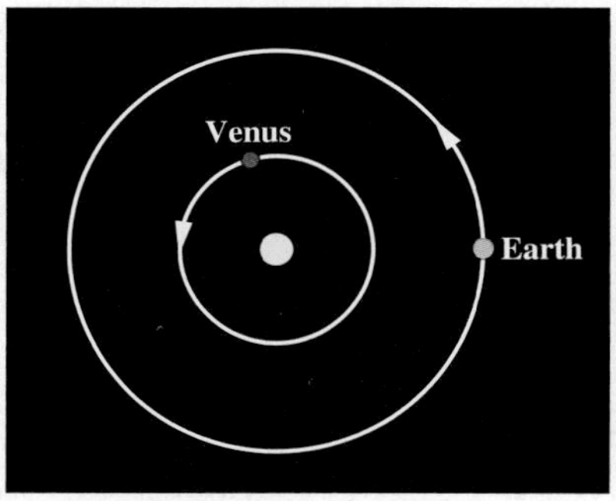

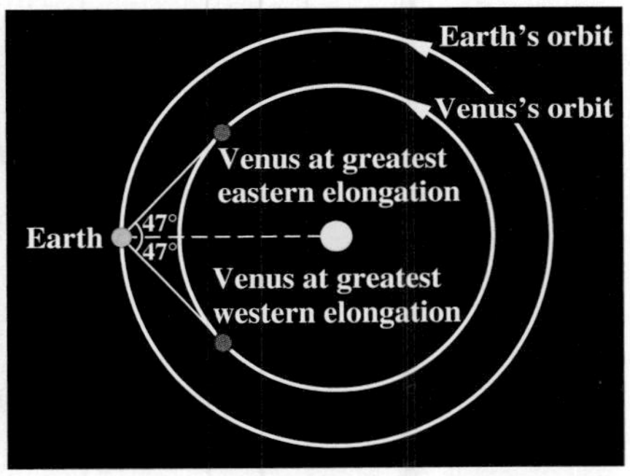

8.3 EXERCISES

A Polygonal Paths and Perimeters

In problems 1–8, find the perimeter of each polygon.

1.

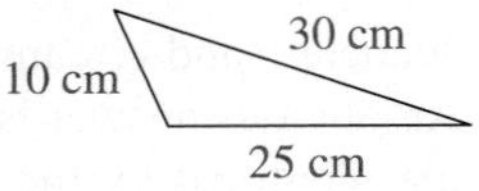

2.

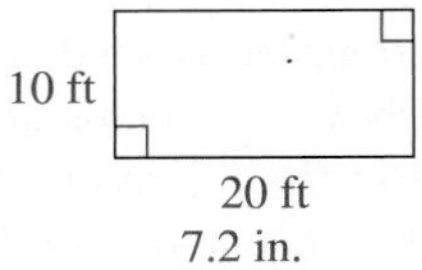

3.

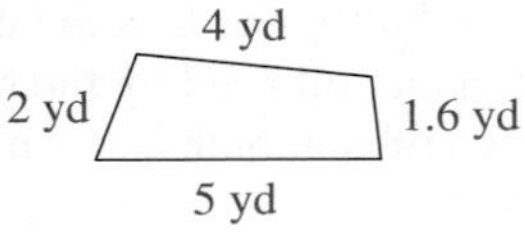

4.

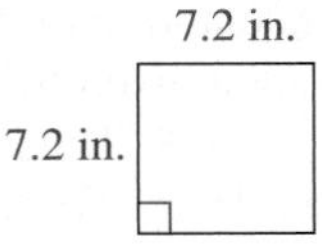

5.

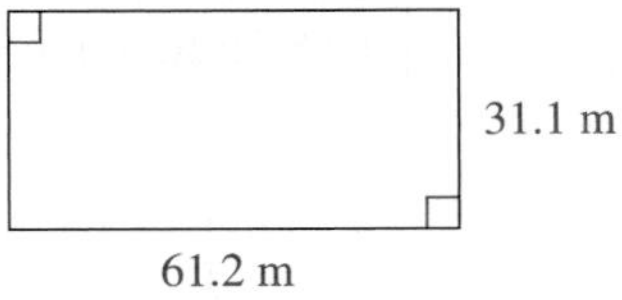

6.

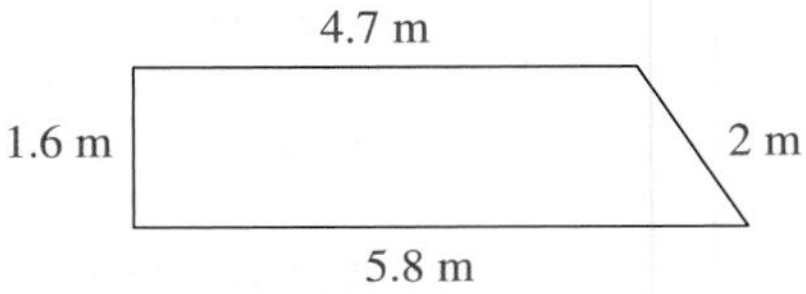

7.
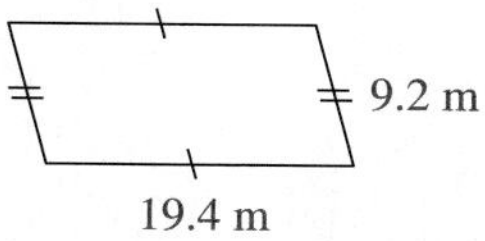

8.
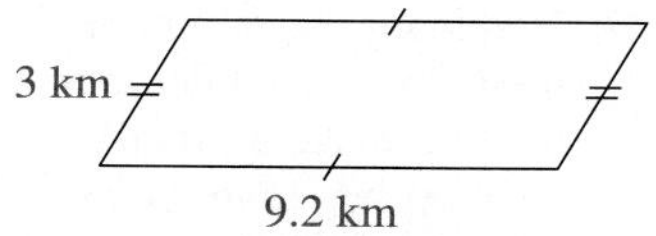

9. If one side of a regular pentagon is 6 cm long, find the perimeter of the pentagon.

10. If one side of an octagonal stop sign is 6 in. long, what is the perimeter of the stop sign?

11. The largest rectangular omelet ever cooked was 30 ft long and had an 80-ft perimeter. How wide was it?

12. Do you have a large swimming pool? If you were to walk around the largest pool in the world, in Casablanca, Morocco, you would walk more than 1 km. To be exact, you would walk 1110 m. If the rectangular pool is 480 m long, how wide is it?

13. A baseball diamond is actually a square. A batter who hits a home run must run 360 ft around the bases. What is the distance to first base?

14. The playing surface of a football field is 120 yd long. A player jogging around the perimeter of this surface covers 346 yd. How wide is the playing surface?

15. Have you seen the largest scientific building in the world? It is in Cape Canaveral, Florida. If you were to walk around the perimeter of this building, you would cover 2468 ft. If this rectangular building is 198 ft longer than it is wide, what are its dimensions?

16. The largest regular hexagon that can be cut from a circular sheet of cardboard has each side equal to the radius of the circle. If you cut such a hexagon from a sheet of radius 5 in., how much shorter is the perimeter of the hexagon than the circumference of the circle?

B Circles

In problems 17–24, find the circumference. First, give the answer in terms of π; then calculate the approximate answer using $\pi \approx 3.14$.

17.
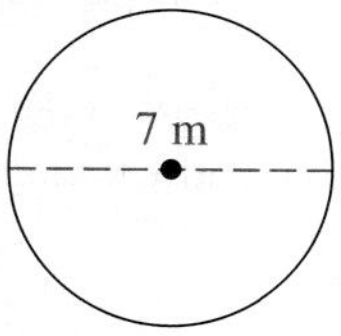

18.
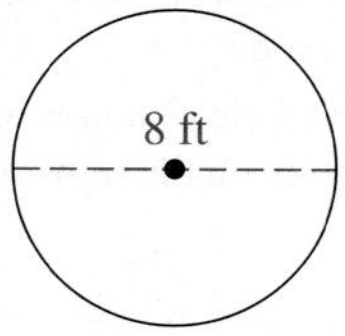

19.
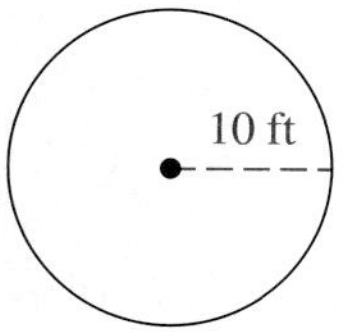

20.
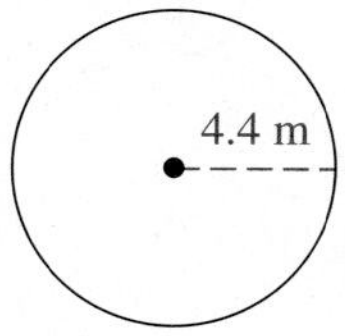

21.
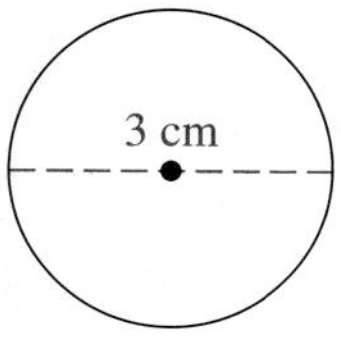

22.
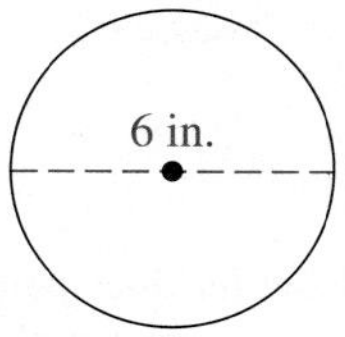

23.
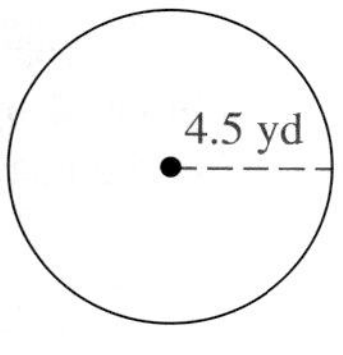

24.
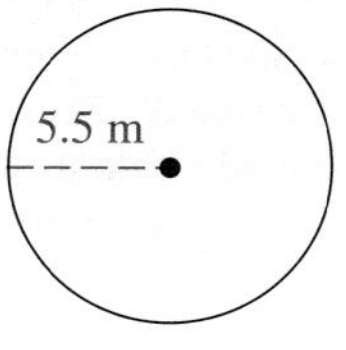

In the following problems, first give an exact answer in terms of π and then calculate the required approximate answer using $\pi \approx 3.14$:

25. The diameter of a bicycle tire is 61 cm. Through what distance does the bicycle go when the wheel makes one complete turn? Give your answer to the nearest centimeter.

26. The lid on a cylindrical garbage can has a diameter of 17 in. Find the length of the circumference of this lid. Give your answer to the nearest tenth of an inch.

27. The minute hand of a clock is 8 cm long. How far does the tip of the hand move in 1 hr? Give your answer to the nearest tenth of a centimeter.

28. The diameter of a CD is 4 in. How far does a point on the rim of this CD travel when the CD makes three-fourths of a complete revolution?

29. Shirley wants to put a low, decorative wooden border around her circular flower bed. If the radius of the bed is 4 ft, how long must the border be? Give your answer to the nearest tenth of a foot.

30. Have you seen a long-playing record? A long-playing record has a radius of 6 in. How far does a point on the rim move when the record goes around once? Give your answer to the nearest tenth of an inch.

31. The circumference of a circle is 15π cm. Find the diameter and the radius of this circle.

32. A thin metal rod 8 ft long is to be bent into a circular hoop. Find the radius of this hoop to the nearest tenth of an inch.

33. To make a wedding band for a man who wears a size 12 ring, a strip of gold 7 cm long is needed. Find the diameter of this ring.

34. One of the largest pizzas ever made had a circumference of 251.2 ft. What was its diameter?

35. You already know from problem 30 that a long-playing record has a 6-in. radius. However, do you know the circumference of the smallest functional record? It is an amazing $4\frac{1}{8}$ in.! Find the diameter of this tiny record to the nearest hundredth of an inch.

36. The outside diameter of a motorcycle tire is 26 in. How many revolutions does the tire make in one *mile*? Round the answer to the nearest whole number. (*Hint*: 1 mi = 5280 ft.)

37. A motorcycle tire is guaranteed for 20,000 mi. Use the information from problem 36 to find out for how many revolutions the tire is guaranteed.

38. The largest doughnut ever made weighed 2099 lb and had a 70-ft circumference. To the nearest whole number, what is the diameter of the smallest pan in which the doughnut could fit?

39. A circular pool is enclosed by a square deck 20 yd on each side. If the distance between the edge of the deck and the pool is 2 yd as shown on the next page, what is the distance around the pool?

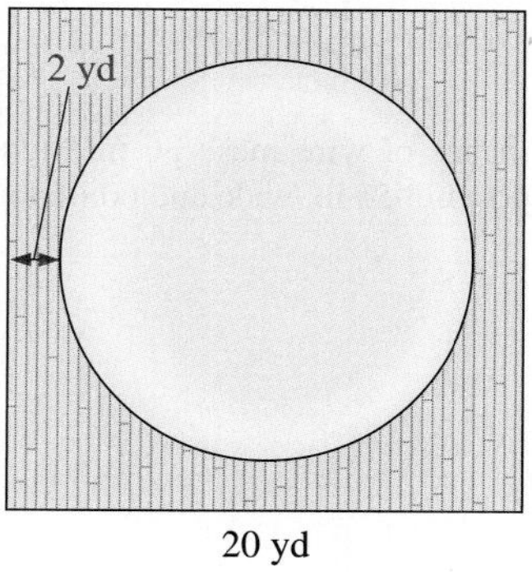

40. It takes about 15 min to walk around the Colosseum in Rome. At this rate, how long would it take you to walk straight through along a diameter? (Assume the Colosseum is perfectly round and give the answer to the nearest minute.)

C Applications

If you are traveling by car, the distance between two points is shown on travel maps.

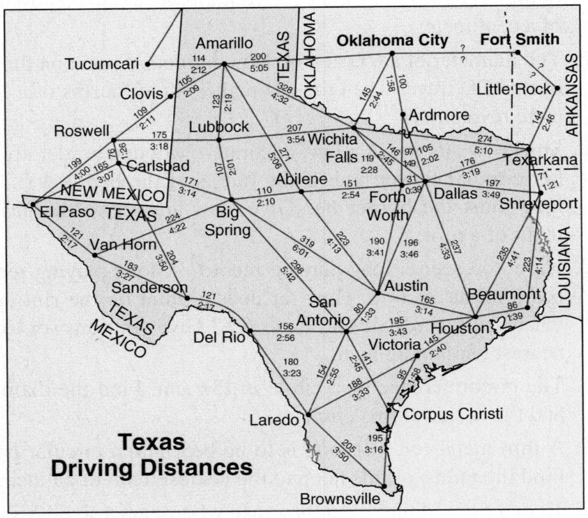

41. Find the distance traveled when going from Laredo to San Antonio to Del Rio and back to Laredo.

42. Find the distance traveled when going from Dallas to Houston to Shreveport and back to Dallas.

43. Find the distance traveled when starting at Austin, driving to Fort Worth, then to Abilene, and then back to Austin.

44. The distance from Tucumcari (New Mexico) to Fort Smith (Arkansas) is about 555 mi. How far is it from Oklahoma City to Fort Smith?

45. Suppose you want to make a rectangular compost bin with a base measuring 60 in. by 70 in. using 48-in. high wire mesh. How many inches of the 48-in. wire mesh do you need?

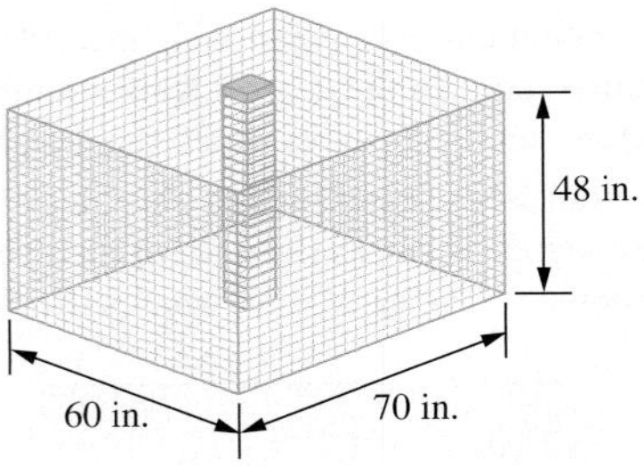

46. How many inches of wire mesh 36 in. high do you need to make a compost bin 50 in. wide and 60 in. long?

47. How many inches of wire mesh 36 in. high do you need to make a circular compost bin 30 in. in diameter?

Use 3.14 for π.

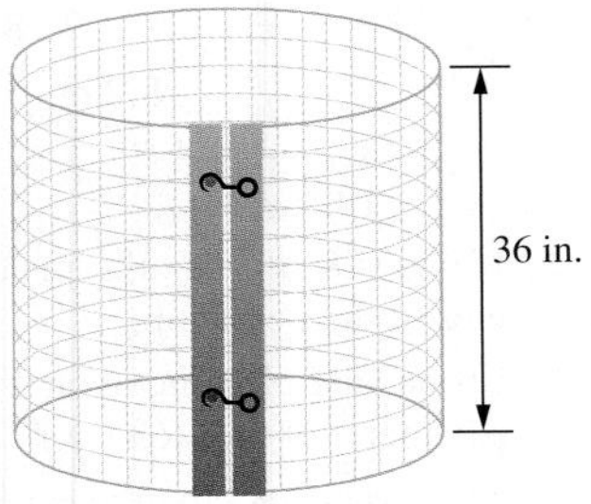

48. How many inches of wire mesh 36 in. high do you need to make a circular compost bin 48 in. in diameter?

Use 3.14 for π.

IN OTHER WORDS

49. Which do you think is the better illustration of a circle: a perfectly round penny or a bicycle tire? (See the definition of a circle.)

50. The formula $C = 1.44 + 0.1s$ gives the circumference C (in inches) of a ring of size s. Explain how you would use this formula to find your ring size.

51. If two tires, one new and one worn, are installed on a car, which one will turn more times per mile? Explain your answer.

52. If your calculator has a π key, use it to calculate the answer to problem 30. In your own words, explain the discrepancy between the answer you obtained following the instructions for problem 30 and the new answer on your calculator.

USING YOUR KNOWLEDGE

Suppose that circle A has a 3-in. circumference and circle B has a 1-in. circumference, as shown in the left diagram in the figure below. If circle B rolls around the perimeter of circle A without slipping and returns to its original position, how many revolutions will it have made? (Hint: Look at the diagram below! Using your knowledge of circumferences, can you prove your case?)

53. In the diagram on the left, what is the length of the arc shown in red?

54. If circle B makes one revolution and ends as shown in the diagram on the right, how far has point b traveled relative to circle B?

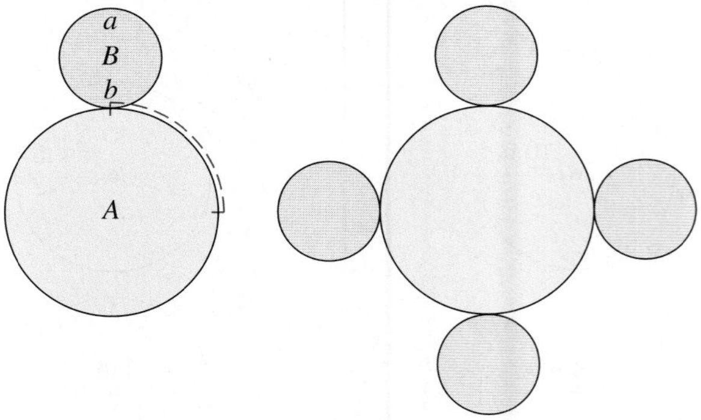

55. How far does point b travel relative to circle B when point a makes one complete revolution relative to circle B?

56. On the basis of your previous answers, ____ in. = 1 revolution of circle B. Thus, how many revolutions does circle B make around circle A, whose circumference is 3 in., to return to its original position?

CALCULATOR CORNER

Many calculators come equipped with a [π] *key (to access it, you may have to press* [2nd] [π]*) that gives a nine-decimal-place approximation for* π. *If you use this approximation to solve Example 5, the answer obtained when dividing 27.50 by* π *comes out to be 8.75352187, or 8.75 to the nearest hundredth of a foot, as mentioned in the text.*

1. Rework problems 25, 26, 30, 32, and 34 of Exercises 8.3 on your calculator.

COLLABORATIVE LEARNING

At the beginning of this section we claimed that your hat size and your ring size are identical. By the way, there is a little flaw here. This is true only of men's hat sizes. Women's hat sizes are measured differently and more logically! Women's hat sizes are simply the circumference of the inner band of the hat. Nevertheless, we would like to see if there is a relationship between men's hat sizes—for men and women—and ring sizes. Form several groups of males and females.

1. Measure the circumference of the head $C(H)$ of the participants.
2. Measure the circumference of their ring finger $C(f)$.
3. Complete the table to the right, where $C(H)$ is the circumference of the head, $C(f)$ the circumference of the finger, d the diameter of the finger, H the men's hat size, and s the ring size.

$C(H)$	$\frac{C(H)}{\pi} = H$	$C(f)$	$\frac{C(f)}{\pi} = d$	$\frac{d - 0.458}{0.032} = s$

4. Is there a relationship between H and s?
5. Is there a relationship between hat size and ring size for women? If so, what is it?

8.4 Area Measure and the Pythagorean Theorem

GETTING STARTED

OBJECTIVES

A. Find the area of polygons and circles.
B. Use the Pythagorean Theorem to find the length of the hypotenuse of a right triangle.
C. Solve applications involving areas.

PIZZA AREA

If you know areas, you can find the best pizza deal.

What is your telephone area code? What areas were severely affected by storms last year? The idea of **area** occurs in many contexts, but in geometry, **area** is measured by defining a **unit region.** For example, a square whose side is **1 unit in length** has an area of **1 square unit.** To measure larger areas, you measure how many **unit squares** are contained in the given region. This means that areas are always measured in square units. In this section you encounter formulas that give the area of several polygons as well as the area of a circle.

Now suppose you want to find the area covered by the giant 111-ft-diameter pizza made by Pizza Hut in Singapore on June 9, 1990. You will learn later that the formula for the area A of a circle of radius r is $A = \pi r^2$. Since the diameter of the pizza is 111 ft, its radius is 55.5 ft, and its area is $A = \pi \cdot 55.5^2 = 3080.25\pi$, or about 9677 square ft, usually written as 9677 ft^2.

In the same way, you can use areas to do some comparison shopping for pizzas. Suppose Pizza Hut sells medium pizzas (12 in. in diameter) with one topping for \$7.99. If you assume that the ingredients are of equal quality and the pizzas of equal thickness, is it better to buy one of these pizzas or get two 10-in. pizzas for \$4.99 each? You can compare by finding out how much you pay per square inch. The area of the \$7.99 pizza is $A = \pi(6 \text{ in.})^2 = 36\pi$, or about 113 in.^{2}. Thus, the price per square inch is $\frac{7.99}{113} \approx 0.07$, that is, about 7¢/in.^{2}. On the other hand, the area of one 10-in. pizza is $A = \pi(5)^2 = 25\pi$, or about 78.5 in.^{2}. Thus, the area of two pizzas is about 157 in.^{2}, and the price per square inch is $\frac{2 \cdot 4.99}{157}$, or about 6.36¢/in.^{2}. In this case, smaller is better; you pay less per square inch if you buy the two small pizzas.

By the way, at 7¢/in.^{2}, how much would the 111-ft-diameter pizza be worth? Close to \$100,000! Check this out by keeping in mind that 1 square foot (1 ft^2) is exactly 144 in.^{2}.

Here are two more questions for you. How many 12-in. pizzas are there in the Singapore pizza, and if you assume that a 12-in. pizza serves eight people, how many people can be served with the Singapore pizza? Think of areas and use the techniques you used here to find the answers.

Now consider the question of how much glass might be used in the construction of a skyscraper. If we think a moment, we realize that the meaning of the question is not clear. Are we looking for the number of pieces of glass, the number of pounds of glass, or what? Let us be more specific and say that we want to know the total *area* covered by the glass in this building. In order to answer questions like this, we must have a good understanding of what we mean by *area.*

A Area of a Polygon

FIGURE 8.53 The unit of area measure.

We start by choosing the **unit region** to be that of a **square,** each of whose sides is **1 unit in length,** and we say that this region has an **area of 1 square unit** (see Figure 8.53). The side of the unit square may be 1 in., 1 ft, 1 mi, 1 cm, 1 m, and so on. The corresponding units of area are the square inch (in.^{2}), the square foot (ft^2), the square mile (mi^2), the square centimeter (cm^2), the square meter (m^2), and so on.

Some of the commonly used units of area are given in Table 8.9. Note that **area** is always measured in **square** units.

Table 8.9 Standard Units of Area

U.S. System	Metric System
Square inch (in.^{2})	Square millimeter (mm^2)
Square foot (ft^2)	Square centimeter (cm^2)
Square yard (yd^2)	Square meter (m^2)
Square mile (mi^2)	Square kilometer (km^2)

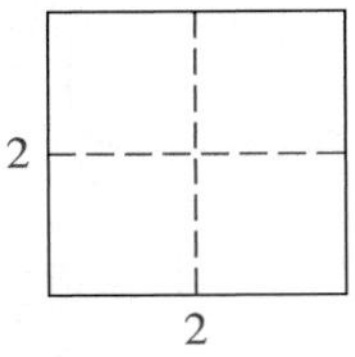

FIGURE 8.54 Area = 4 square units.

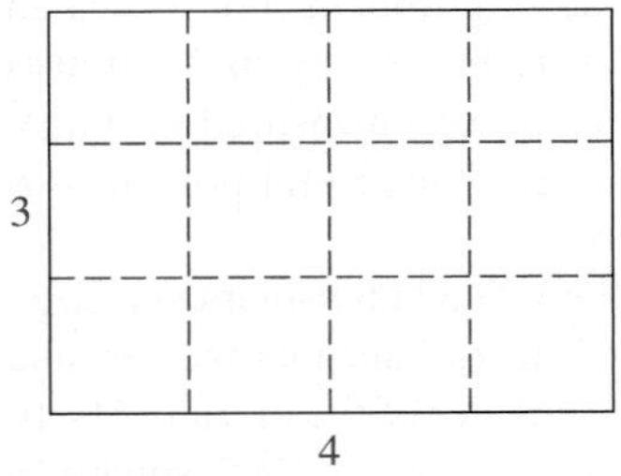

FIGURE 8.55 Area = 12 square units.

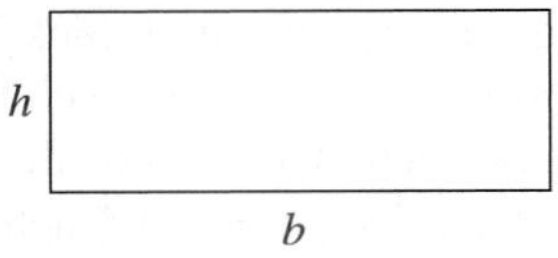

FIGURE 8.56 Area = bh.

In everyday language, the area measure of a plane region is the *number of unit regions contained in the given region.* Thus, suppose that we have a square with sides 2 units long. Then, as shown in Figure 8.54, we can draw lines joining the midpoints of the opposite sides and dividing the square into $2 \times 2 = 4$ unit squares. We say that the area of the square is 4 square units. Similarly, for a rectangle that is 3 units by 4 units, we can draw lines parallel to the sides that divide the rectangle into $3 \times 4 = 12$ unit squares (see Figure 8.55). We say that the area of the rectangle is 12 square units.

The previous illustrations show how the area measure can be found if the sides of the rectangle are whole numbers. In order to avoid a complicated mathematical argument, we define the area of a rectangle of sides b units long and h units long to be bh square units (see Figure 8.56).

Area of a Rectangle

The area of a rectangle with base length b and height h is given by $A = bh$.

Notice that we are following the usual custom of saying "area of a rectangle" to mean "area of a rectangular region." Similarly, we shall say "area of a polygon" to mean "area of a polygonal region."

Knowing the area of a rectangle, we can find the area of a parallelogram. The idea is to construct a rectangle with the same area as the parallelogram. As Figure 8.57(a) shows, we simply cut the right triangle *ADE* from one end of the parallelogram and attach it to the other end (b). This forms a rectangle *CDEF* with the same area as the parallelogram. Since the base and height are the same for both figures, the area of a parallelogram of base b and height h is bh.

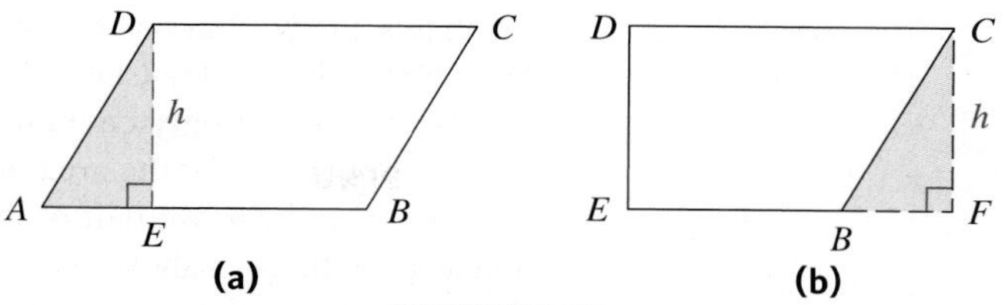

FIGURE 8.57

> ### Area of a Parallelogram
> The area A of a parallelogram with base b and height h is given by $A = bh$.

Be sure to note that h is the perpendicular height, not the length of a side of the parallelogram.

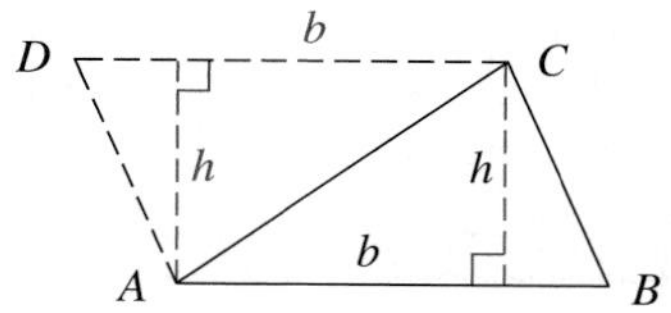

FIGURE 8.58

We can now find the area of any triangle. Suppose that triangle ABC in Figure 8.58 is given. We draw a line through C parallel to $\overleftrightarrow{AB}$ and a line through A parallel to $\overleftrightarrow{BC}$. These lines meet at a point D, and the quadrilateral $ABCD$ is a parallelogram. Clearly, the segment $\overline{AC}$ is a diagonal of the parallelogram and divides the parallelogram into two equal pieces. Because the area of parallelogram $ABCD$ is bh, the area of the triangle ABC is $\frac{1}{2}bh$. Thus, we have a formula for the area of any triangle with base b and height h.

Note: If the angle B in Figure 8.58 is a right angle, the parallelogram obtained is a rectangle. This does not change the formula for the area of a triangle.

> ### Area of a Triangle
> The area A of a triangle with base b and height h is given by $A = \frac{1}{2}bh$.

EXAMPLE 1 Finding the Area of a Triangle

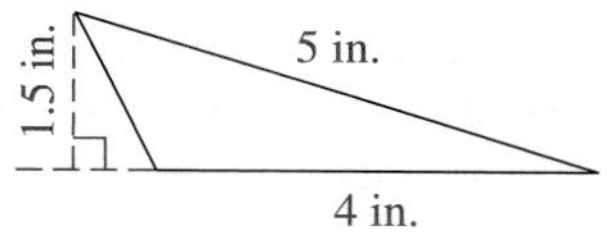

FIGURE 8.59

Find the area of the triangle shown in Figure 8.59.

Solution

This triangle has a base of 4 in. and a height of 1.5 in. Thus,

$$A = \tfrac{1}{2}(4)(1.5) = 3 \text{ in.}^2$$

> ### Area of Polygonal Regions
> The formulas we have developed can be used for finding the areas of many polygonal regions. This is done by subdividing these regions into nonoverlapping rectangular and/or triangular regions, finding the areas of these subdivisions, and adding the results. This procedure is illustrated in the next example.

EXAMPLE 2 Finding the Area of a Subdivided Region

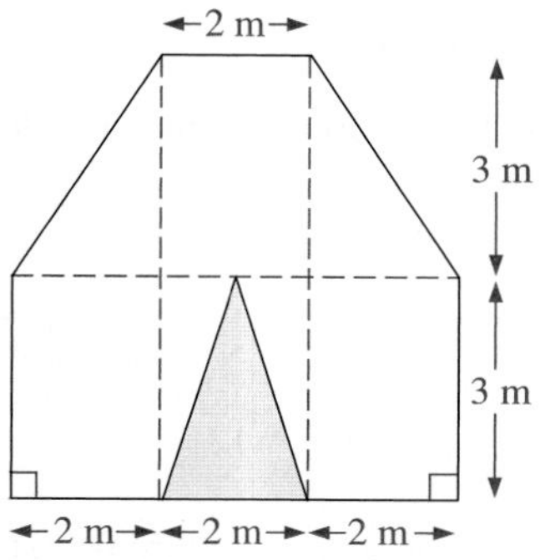

FIGURE 8.60

Find the area of the region given in Figure 8.60.

Solution

We subdivide the region as shown in Figure 8.60. The area of the lower rectangle is $6 \times 3 = 18 \text{ m}^2$. The area of the shaded triangle is $\frac{1}{2}(2 \times 3) = 3 \text{ m}^2$. The upper two triangles each have area 3 m^2, and the upper rectangle has area $2 \times 3 = 6 \text{ m}^2$. Thus, the required area is

$$18 - 3 + 3 + 3 + 6 = 27 \text{ m}^2$$

Thus far we have been concerned entirely with the areas of polygonal regions. How about the circle? Can we find the area of a circle by using one of the preceding formulas? Interestingly enough, the answer is yes. The required area can be found by using the formula for the area of a rectangle. Here is how we go about it. Look at Figure 8.61. Cut the lower half of the circular region into small equal slices called **sectors,** and arrange them as shown in Figure 8.61. Then cut the remaining half of the circle into the same number of slices, and arrange them along with the others as shown in Figure 8.62. The result is approximately a parallelogram whose longer side is of length πr (half the circumference of the circle) and whose shorter side is r (the radius of the circle).

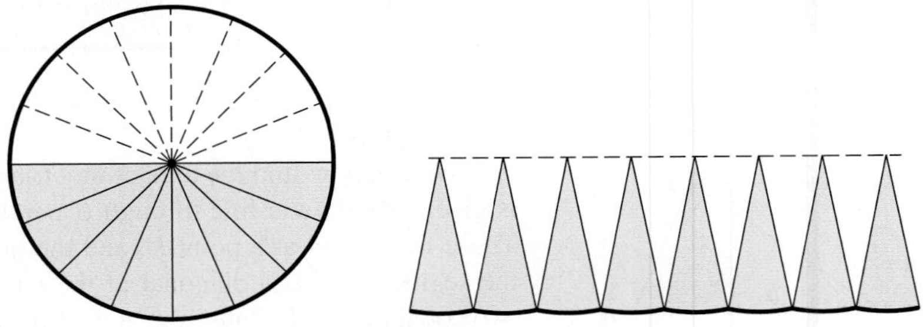

FIGURE 8.61

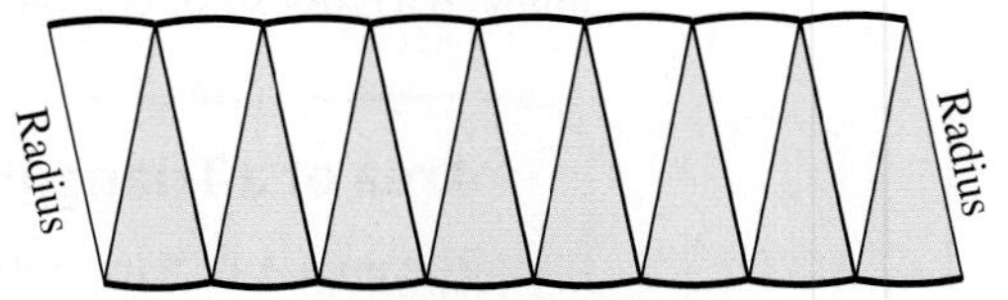

FIGURE 8.62

The more pieces we cut the circle into, the more accurate this approximation becomes. We should also observe that the more pieces we use, the more nearly the parallelogram becomes a rectangle of length πr and height r. Mathematicians have proved that the area of the circle is the same as the area of this rectangle, that is, $(\pi r)(r)$, or πr^2. Thus, we arrive at the formula for the area of a circle of radius r.

Area of a Circle

The area A of a circle with radius r is given by

$$A = \pi r^2$$

EXAMPLE 3 Area for the Arecibo Radiotelescope

The circular dish for the Arecibo radiotelescope has a radius of 500 ft. What area does the dish cover? (Use $\pi \approx 3.14$.)

Solution

Here, $r = 500$, so

$$A = \pi(500)^2$$
$$= \pi(250{,}000) \approx 785{,}000 \text{ ft}^2$$

Your knowledge of algebra can be used in conjunction with the geometric formulas you have just studied. This is illustrated in the next example.

EXAMPLE 4 Finding the Area of a Subdivided Region

The Fermi National Accelerator Laboratory has the atom smasher shown in the photograph. The smasher covers an area of 1.1304 mi^2. What is the diameter of this atom smasher? Use $\pi \approx 3.14$, and give the answer to the nearest hundredth of a mile.

The large circle is the main accelerator at the Fermi National Accelerator Laboratory at Batavia, Illinois. A proton beam travels around this circle 50,000 times a second, producing highly energized particles used in nuclear research.

Solution

The formula for the area of a circle of radius r is

$$A = \pi r^2$$

Here, $A = 1.1304$ and $\pi \approx 3.14$. Thus,

$$1.1304 \approx 3.14r^2$$

$$r^2 \approx \frac{1.1304}{3.14} = 0.36$$

$$r \approx 0.60 \text{ mi}$$

So the diameter is about 1.20 mi. If your calculator has a square root key, you can do this calculation by keying in $\boxed{1.1304}\ \boxed{\div}\ \boxed{3.14}\ \boxed{=}\ \boxed{\sqrt{x}}$.

Here is the summary of some of the area formulas for polygons.

Table 8.10 Area Formulas for Polygons

Name	Shape	Area
Rectangle	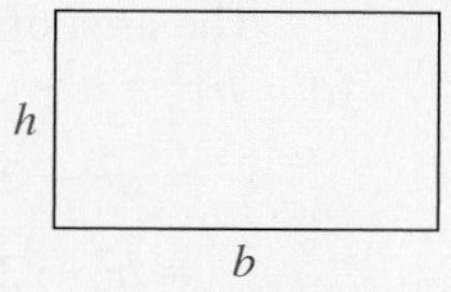	$A = bh$
Parallelogram	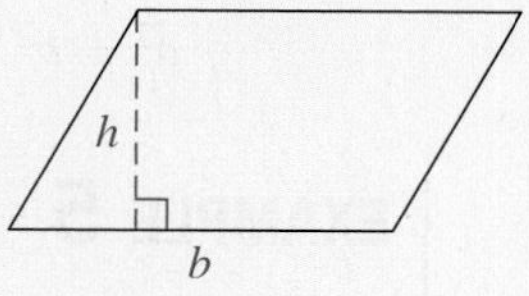	$A = bh$
Triangle	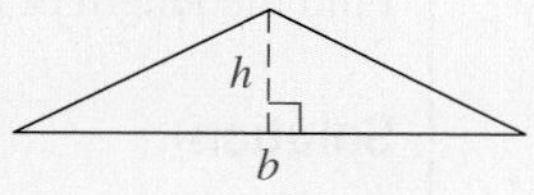	$A = \frac{1}{2}bh$
Trapezoid	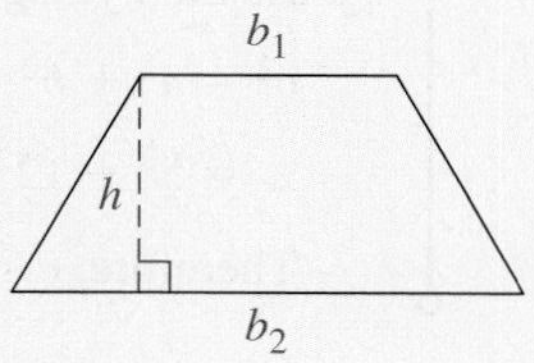	$A = \frac{1}{2}(b_1 + b_2)h$

B The Pythagorean Theorem

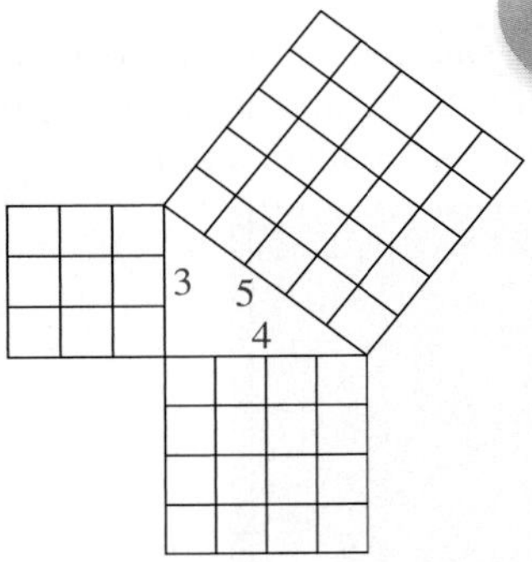

FIGURE 8.63 $5^2 = 3^2 + 4^2$.

The solution of Example 4 required taking the square root of both sides of an equation. The same technique is used in many problems involving the sides of a right triangle. One of the most famous and important theorems of all time is the Pythagorean theorem, which states that the square of the hypotenuse (the longest side) of a right triangle is equal to the sum of the squares of the other two sides. Figure 8.63 illustrates the theorem for a 3-4-5 right triangle, a triangle with sides of length 3 and 4 units and a 5-unit hypotenuse.

Theorem 8.1 Pythagorean Theorem

If the two legs of a right triangle have lengths a and b and the hypotenuse has length c, then

$$c^2 = a^2 + b^2 \quad \text{or} \quad \text{equivalently} \quad a^2 + b^2 = c^2$$

It is important to note that the converse of the Pythagorean theorem is also true. (The proof, which can be constructed with a little trigonometry, is omitted.) We can include both theorems in the statement that follows:

Generalized Pythagorean Theorem

A triangle is a right triangle if and only if the square of one of the sides is the sum of the squares of the other two sides.

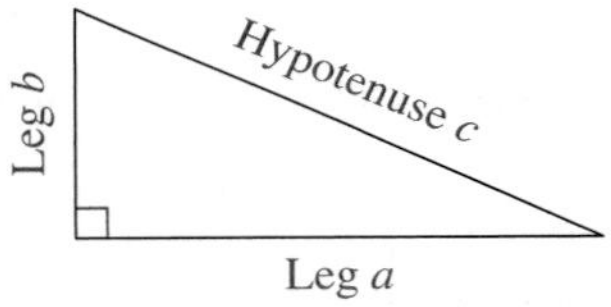

FIGURE 8.64

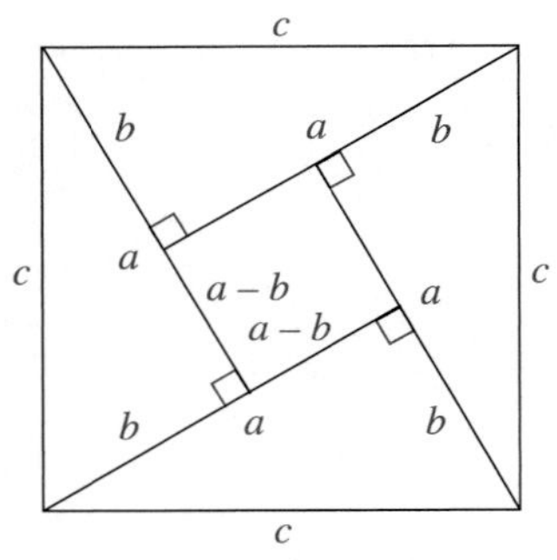

FIGURE 8.65

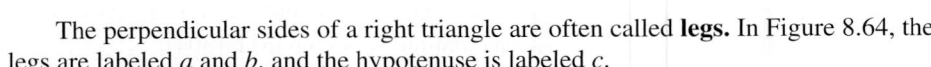

The perpendicular sides of a right triangle are often called **legs.** In Figure 8.64, the legs are labeled a and b, and the hypotenuse is labeled c.

The early Egyptians, and even the Babylonians, knew some special cases of this result; in particular, they knew the result illustrated in Figure 8.63. However, the ancient Greeks seem to have been the first to prove the general theorem. There are many different proofs of the theorem, some of which depend on areas in a simple fashion. Here is one of these proofs.

The area of the large square in Figure 8.65 is c^2. The area of the small square is $(a - b)^2 = a^2 - 2ab + b^2$, and the area of each of the four right triangles is $\frac{1}{2}ab$. Thus,

$$\begin{aligned} c^2 &= a^2 - 2ab + b^2 + 4\left(\tfrac{1}{2}ab\right) \\ &= a^2 - 2ab + b^2 + 2ab \\ &= a^2 + b^2 \end{aligned}$$

EXAMPLE 5 Finding the Hypotenuse Given Two Sides

Find the length of the hypotenuse of a right triangle whose legs are 5 and 12 units long.

Solution

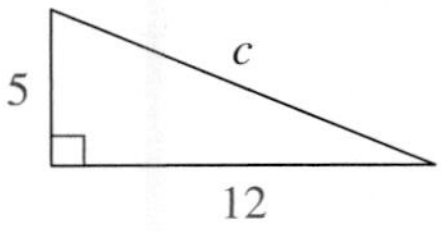

We use the Pythagorean theorem to get

$$\begin{aligned} c^2 &= a^2 + b^2 \\ &= 5^2 + 12^2 = 25 + 144 = 169 \end{aligned}$$

Therefore, $c = \sqrt{169} = 13$ units.

C Applications

EXAMPLE 6 Finding Monitor Dimensions with Pythagoras

The screen in a rectangular computer monitor shown in Figure 8.66 is 3 in. longer than it is high and its diagonal is 6 in. longer than its height. What are the dimensions of the monitor?

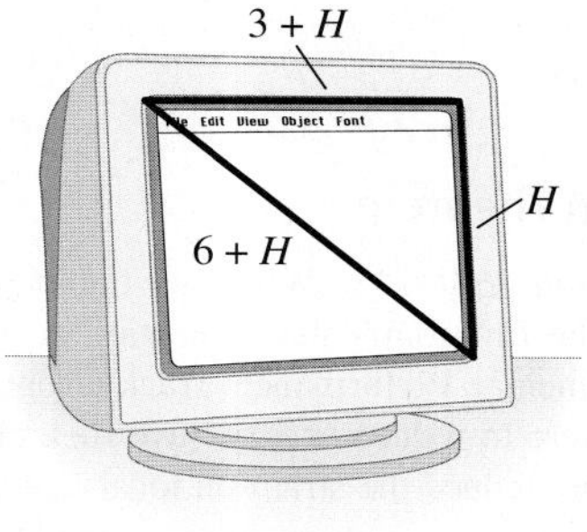

FIGURE 8.66

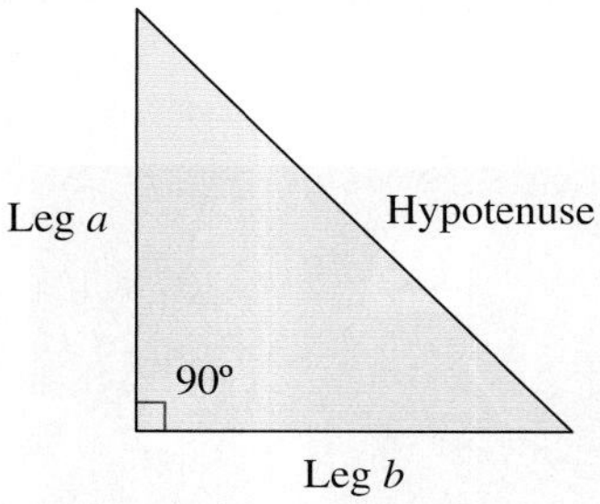

FIGURE 8.67

Solution

We are asked to find the dimensions, which involves finding the length, height, and diagonal of the screen.

Since all measurements are given in terms of the height, let H be the height.

It's a good idea to start with a picture so that we can see the relationship among the measurements. Note that the length is $3 + H$ (3 in. longer than the height), and the diagonal is $6 + H$ (6 in. longer than the height). We enter this information in Figure 8.67.

According to the Pythagorean theorem,

$$H^2 + (3 + H)^2 = (6 + H)^2$$

$$H^2 + 9 + 6H + H^2 = 36 + 12H + H^2 \quad \text{Expand } (3 + H)^2 \text{ and } (6 + H)^2.$$

$$H^2 + 9 + 6H + H^2 - 36 - 12H - H^2 = 0 \quad \text{Subtract } 36 + 12H + H^2.$$

$$H^2 - 6H - 27 = 0 \quad \text{Simplify.}$$

$$(H - 9)(H + 3) = 0 \quad \text{Factor } (-9 \cdot 3 = -27; -9 + 3 = -6).$$

$$H - 9 = 0 \quad \text{or} \quad H + 3 = 0 \quad \text{Use the principle of zero product.}$$

$$H = 9 \qquad H = -3 \quad \text{Solve each equation.}$$

Since H is the height, we discard -3, so the height of the monitor is 9 in., the length is 3 more inches, or 12 in., and the diagonal is 6 more inches than the height, or $9 + 6 = 15$ in.

Looking at the diagram and using the Pythagorean theorem, we see that $9^2 + 12^2$ must be 15^2; that is,

$$9^2 + 12^2 = 15^2$$

Since $81 + 144 = 225$ is a true statement, our dimensions are correct.

By the way, television sets claiming to be 25 in. or 27 in. (meaning that the length of the screen measured diagonally is 25 or 27 in.) hardly ever measure 25 or 27 in. This is easy to confirm using the Pythagorean theorem. For example, a 27-in. Panasonic has a screen that is 16 in. high and 21 in. long. Can it really be 27 in. diagonally? If this were the case, $16^2 + 21^2$ would equal 27^2. Is this true? Measure a couple of TV or computer screens and see whether the manufacturers' claims are true!

8.4 EXERCISES

A Area of Polygons and Circles

In problems 1–12, find the area of each region. Use 3.14 for π.

1.

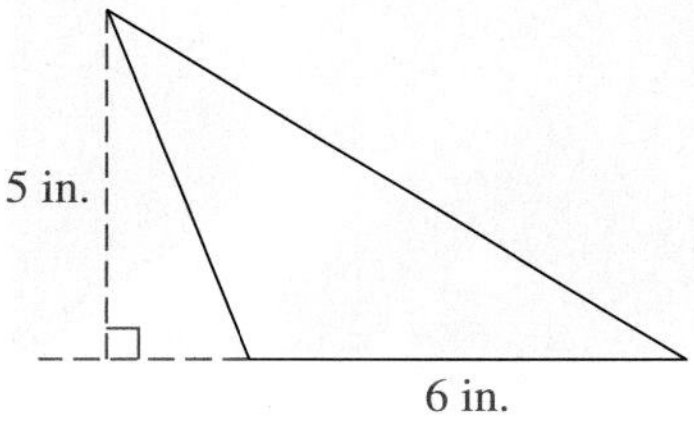

2.

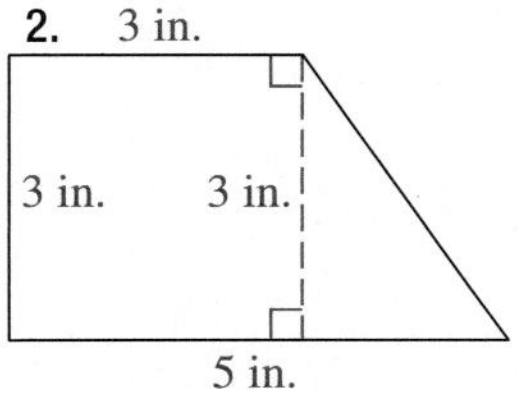

3.

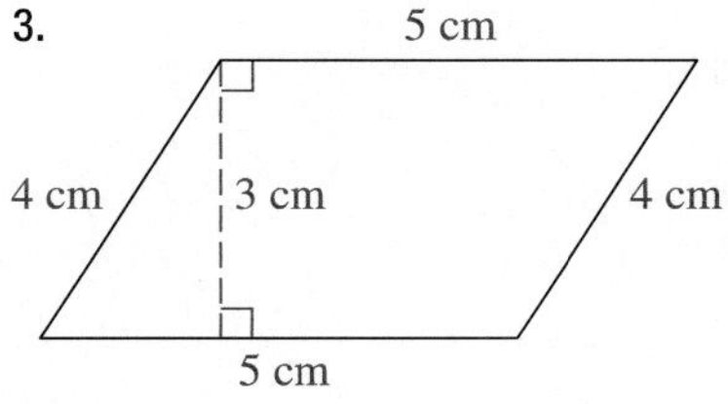

4.

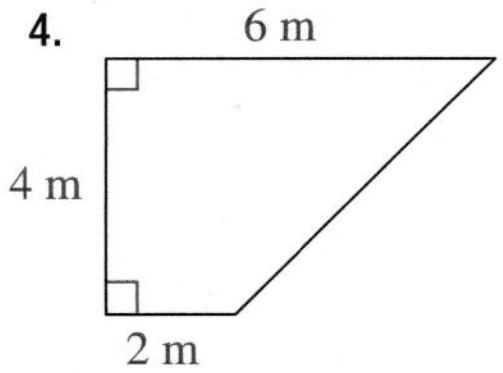

5.

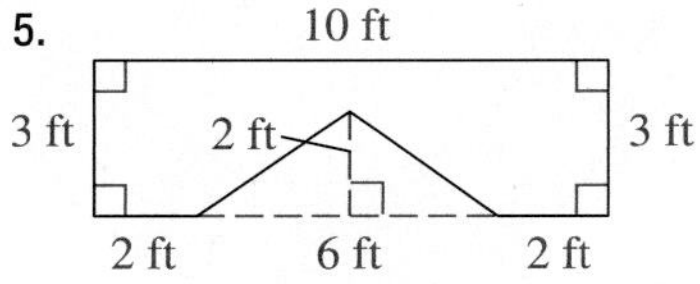

6.

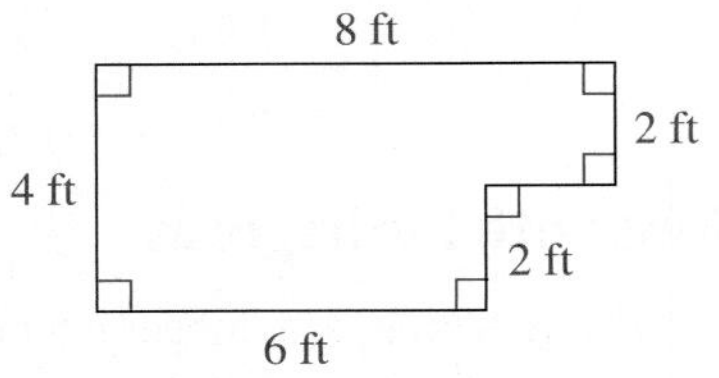

7.

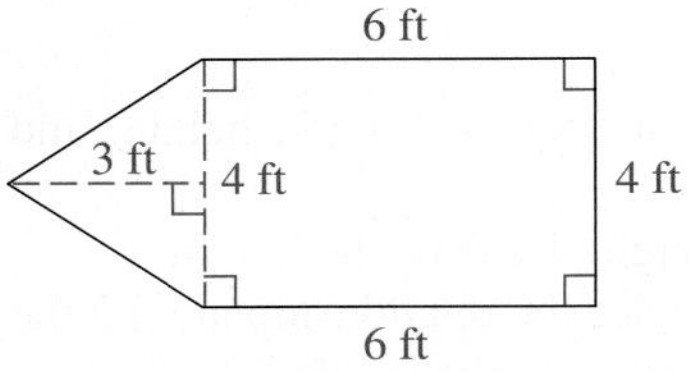

8.

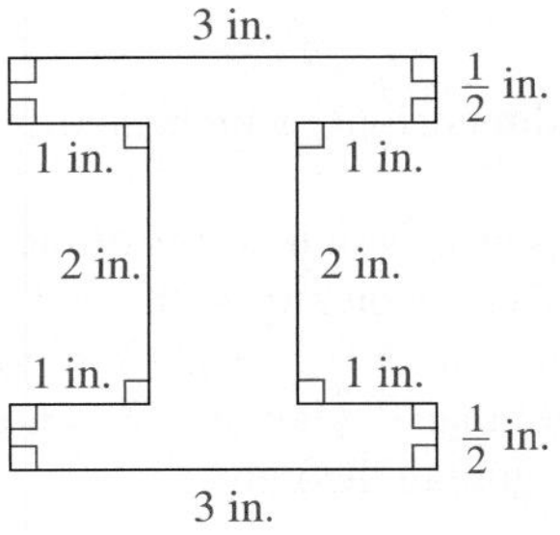

9.

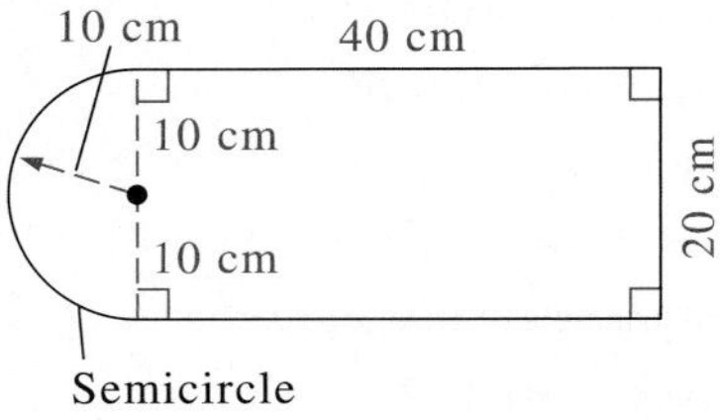

10.

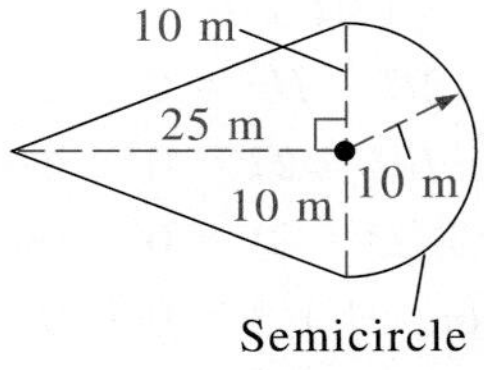

11.

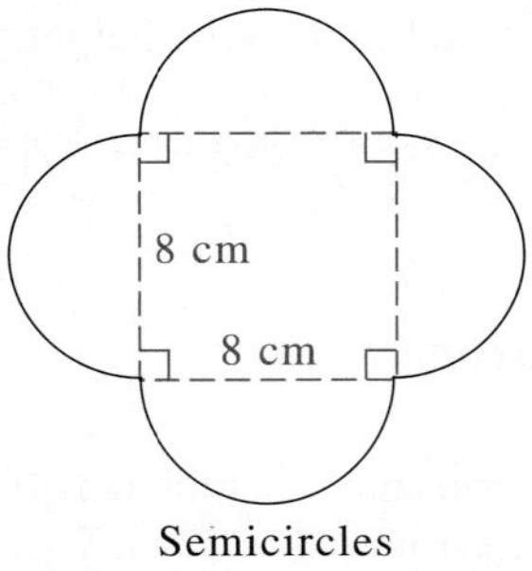

12.

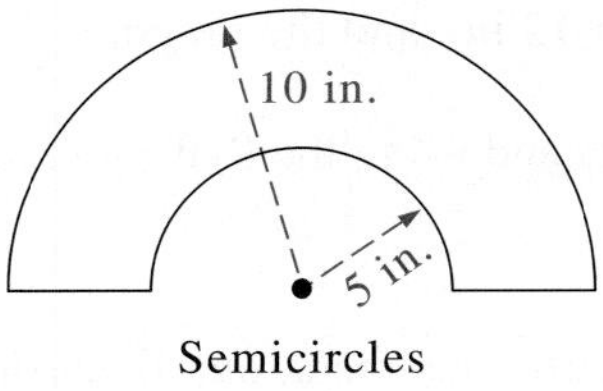

In problems 13–16, find the shaded area. Use 3.14 for π.

13.

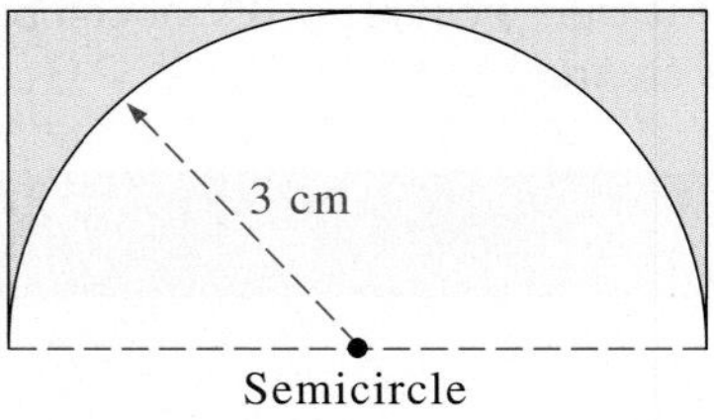

14.

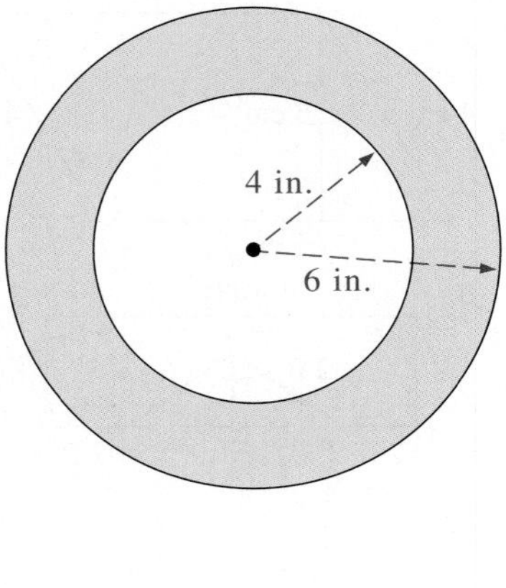

15.

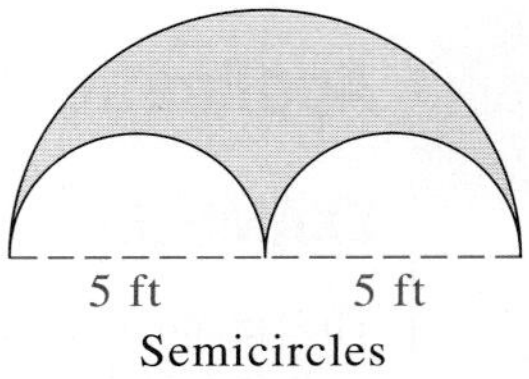

16.

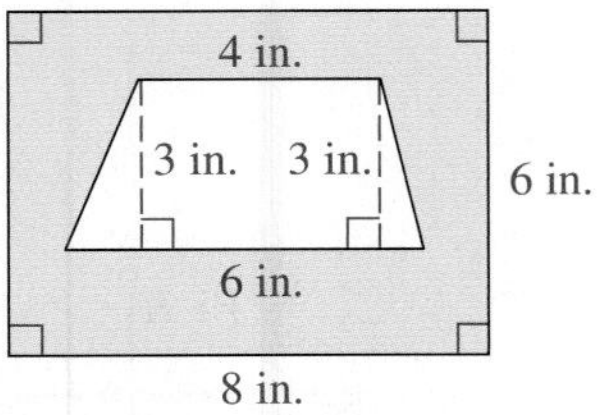

B The Pythagorean Theorem

17. *EPA-approved stadium and HD TVs.* Which is the biggest stadium recognized by the Environmental Protection Agency (EPA) National Environmental Performance Track Program, a program whose aims were to reduce energy, save fuel, clean the air, recycle solid waste, reduce the strain on local landfills, and conserve water? It is Cowboys Stadium, home of the Dallas Cowboys. The stadium boasts the two biggest HD video displays in the world, each 160 ft wide and 72 ft high. What is the diagonal measurement of each video display? Round the answer to the nearest whole number.

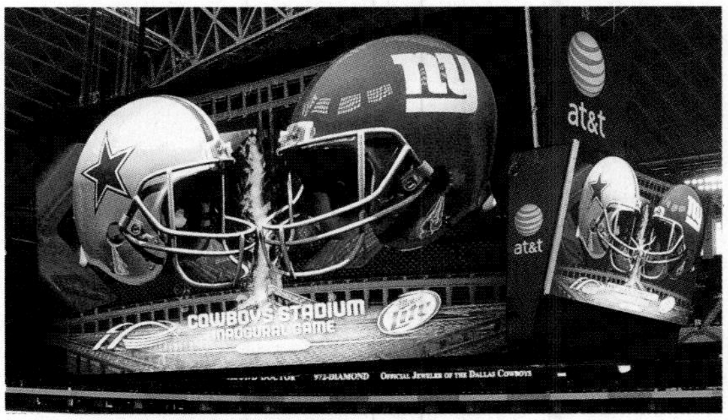

Photo: © Larry W.Smith/epa/Corbis

18. *More video boards at Cowboys Stadium.* There are two smaller video boards at Cowboys Stadium each measuring 51 ft wide and 29 ft high. What is the diagonal measurement of each of the video boards? Round the answer to the nearest whole number.

19. *Bridges.* The Dames Point Bridge spans the St. John River in Jacksonville, Florida. The longest cable supporting the bridge is 720 ft long and is secured 650 ft from the pole holding the cable as shown in the photo. What is the height h of the pole? Round the answer to the nearest whole number.

© Courtesy of HNTB

20. *Bridges.* If in problem 19 the cable was 700 ft long, how high would the pole be? Round the answer to the nearest whole number.

21. *Length of jewel case.* A rectangular DVD case is 14 cm wide and 11 cm high. What is the diagonal length of the case? Round the answer to the nearest thousandth.

22. *Length of a conveyor belt.* Pedro Mendieta operates the conveyor belt machine used to haul materials to the top of the concrete mixing container. If the belt ends 40 ft above the ground and starts 120 ft away from the base of the container, as shown in the photo, how long is the belt? Round the answer to the nearest foot.

23. *Length of a conveyor belt.* Another conveyor belt machine operated by John Taylor ends 45 ft above the ground, but it starts 118 ft away from the base of the container as shown in the photo. How far do the materials travel to get to the top of the conveyor belt? Round the answer to the nearest foot.

24. *Airplane travel.* The plane shown is ascending at a 108° angle. If the plane is 40 ft high, and the horizontal distance from the plane to the end of the runway is 220 ft as shown in the photo, how many feet has the plane traveled? Round the answer to the nearest foot.

Photo: 22-24 Ignacio Bello

C Applications

25. The playing surface of a football field is 120 yd long and $53\frac{1}{3}$ yd wide. How many square yards of artificial turf are needed to cover this surface?

26. The floors of three rooms in a certain house measure 9 by 10 ft, 12 by 12 ft, and 15 by 15 ft, respectively.
   a. How many square yards of carpet are needed to cover these three floors?
   b. If the price of the carpet is $\$14/\text{yd}^2$, how much would it cost to cover these floors?

27. A rectangular room is to have 288 ft^2 of floor space. If the room is 16 ft long, how wide must it be?

28. The Louisiana Superdome covers an area of 363,000 ft^2. Find the diameter of this round arena to the nearest foot. Use $\pi \approx 3.14$.

29. The largest cinema screen in the world is in the Pictorium Theater in Santa Clara, California; it covers 6720 ft^2. If this rectangular screen is 70 ft tall, how wide is it?

30. The area of the biggest pizza was about 5024 ft^2. What was its diameter?

31. What is the area of a circular region whose diameter is 8 cm? (Leave your answer in terms of π.)

32. Find the height of a triangle of area 70 in.^2 if its base is 20 in. long.

33. Glass for picture frames costs $\$3/\text{ft}^2$. If the cost of the glass for a rectangular frame is \$4.50 and the frame is $1\frac{1}{2}$ times as long as it is wide, find its dimensions in inches.

34. Diazinon, a toxic chemical used for insect control in grass, is banned for commercial use after 2004. Each ounce of this chemical, diluted in 3 gal of water, covers 125 ft^2. The transportation department used 32 oz of Diazinon to spray the grass in the median strip of a highway. If the strip was 16 ft wide, how long was it?

In Problems 35–43, use 3.14 for π, and give your answer to two decimal places.

35. *More crop circles.* The photo shows several of the mysterious wheat circles appearing in Rockville, California. The biggest circle is claimed to be 140 ft in diameter. What is the area of this circle?

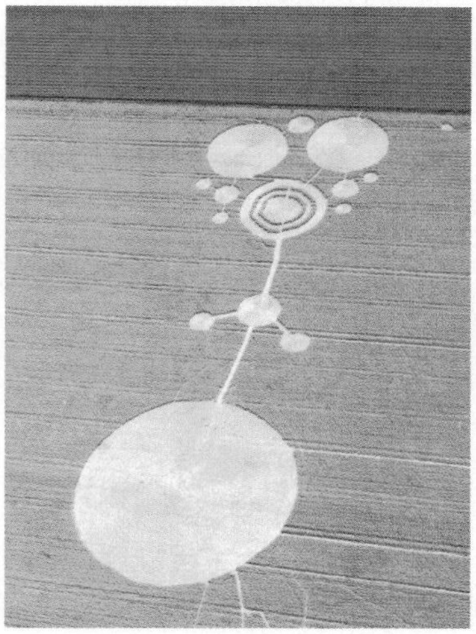

© Paul Chinn/San Francisco Chronicle/Corbis

36. *Area of a Dutch crop circle.* The diameter of the largest reported Dutch crop circle is 12 m. What is its area?

37. *Area of a hurricane's eye.* The photo shows Hurricane Katrina striking Florida the night of August 25, 2005. The diameter of the eye at landfall was 32 mi. What was the area of the eye?

© NASA/Jeff Schmaltz, MODIS Land Rapid Response Team

38. *More winds.* At Katrina's landfall, winds extended outward 120 mi from the center of the storm. What total area did Katrina cover?

39. *Comparing hurricanes.* In comparison, Hurricane Camille (1969) had a 10-mi-diameter eye at landfall. What was the difference in the area of the eye of Katrina and the eye of Camille?

40. *Mowing automatically.* A self-propelled lawnmower is tied to a pole in the backyard with a 20-ft rope. If the mower goes around in decreasing circles (because the rope is getting wrapped around the pole), what is the area the mower can mow?

41. *Area of sectors in wheel of fortune.* A wheel of fortune has six equal sectors, half of which are red and half of which are yellow. If the radius of the wheel is 3 ft, what area is covered by the red sectors?

42. *Area of Disneyland carousel.* The magical carousel in Disneyland Paris has a radius of about 27 ft. What area does it cover?

43. The recordable area on a CD is the difference between the area of the complete CD and the area covered by the opening in the middle. If the opening has a diameter of $1\frac{1}{2}$ in. and the diameter of the CD is 4.5 in., what is the recordable area for the CD?

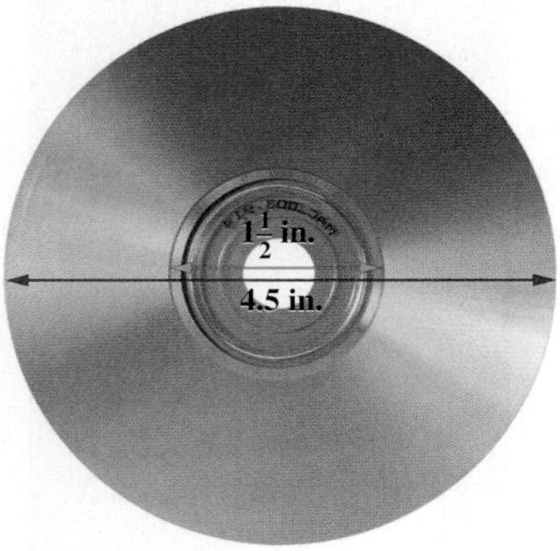

© Lawrence Manning/Corbis

IN OTHER WORDS

44. Which of the following triangles are right triangles? Explain your reasoning.

a. Sides 3, 5, 6
b. Sides 5, 12, 13
c. Sides 7, 24, 25
d. Sides 9, 10, 15

45. What would be the most appropriate U.S. units (in.^{2}, yd^2, mi^2) and metric units (cm^2, m^2, and km^2) for measuring the area of

a. a nickel.
b. your state.
c. your classroom.
d. a house.

46. Explain in your own words the difference between a 2-in. square and 2 in.^{2}.

USING YOUR KNOWLEDGE

You can use what you learned in this section to help you solve some commonly occurring problems. Do the following problems to see how:

47. A gallon of Lucite wall paint costs \$14 and covers 450 ft^2. Three rooms in a house measure 10 by 12 ft, 14 by 15 ft, and 12 by 12 ft, and the ceiling is 8 ft high.

a. How many gallons of paint are needed to cover the walls of these rooms if you make no allowance for doors and windows?
b. What will be the cost of the paint? (The paint is sold by the gallon only.)

48. The figure below shows the front of a house. House paint costs \$17/gal and each gallon covers 400 ft^2.

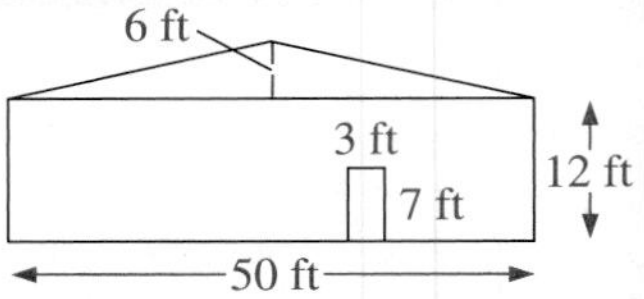

a. What is the minimum number of gallons of paint needed to cover the front of the house? (The paint is sold by the gallon only.)
b. How much will the paint for the front of the house cost?

49. A house and lot are shown in the figure that follows. The entire lot, except for the buildings and the drive, is lawn. A bag of lawn fertilizer costs \$4 and covers 1200 ft^2 of grass.

a. What is the minimum number of bags of fertilizer needed for this lawn?
b. What will be the cost of the fertilizer?

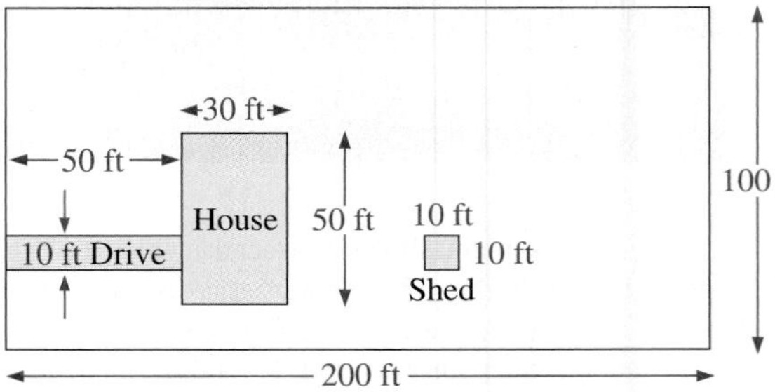

50. A small pizza (11-in. diameter) costs \$5 and a large pizza (15-in. diameter) costs \$8. Use $\pi \approx 3.14$ and find to the nearest square inch

a. the area of the small pizza.
b. the area of the large pizza.
c. Which is the better deal, two small pizzas or one large pizza?

51. A frozen apple pie of 8-in. diameter sells for \$1.25. The 10-in.-diameter size sells for \$1.85.

a. What is the unit price (price per square inch), to the nearest hundredth of a cent, of the 8-in. pie?
b. What is the unit price, to the nearest hundredth of a cent, of the 10-in. pie?
c. Which pie gives you the most for your money?

DISCOVERY

Artists and architects, past and present, have used the **Golden Ratio** *in their art and their architecture. Do you know what the Golden Ratio is? Begin with a square (shaded in the following figure). Let E be the midpoint of the base $\overline{AD}$. Put the point of your pencil compass at E and the pencil point at C, and draw the circular arc as shown. Extend $\overline{AD}$ to meet this arc and call the point of intersection F. Now draw a line perpendicular to $\overline{AF}$ at F and extend $\overline{BC}$ to meet this perpendicular at G. The rectangle ABGF is known as the* **Golden Rectangle.** *Its proportions are supposed to be particularly pleasing to the eye. The ratio of the longer to the shorter side of this rectangle is the Golden Ratio.*

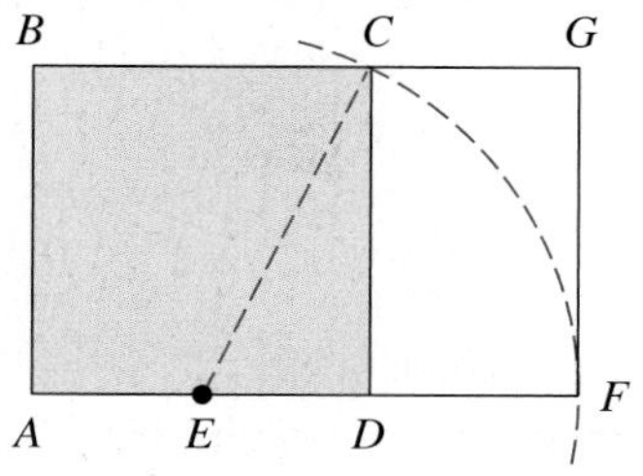

52. Can you discover the numerical value of the Golden Ratio? (*Hint:* Let the side of the square *ABCD* be $2a$. Then $\overline{EC}$ is the hypotenuse of a right triangle with legs of length a and $2a$, respectively.)

Artists are interested in the areas of their paintings and sometimes meet with the problem of drawing a rectangle of height h that will have the same area as that of a given rectangle. The figure shows the problem. The given rectangle is of length L and width W, and the artist wants a rectangle of height h that will have the same area. Of course, you could find the area LW and divide by h to get the second dimension of the desired rectangle.

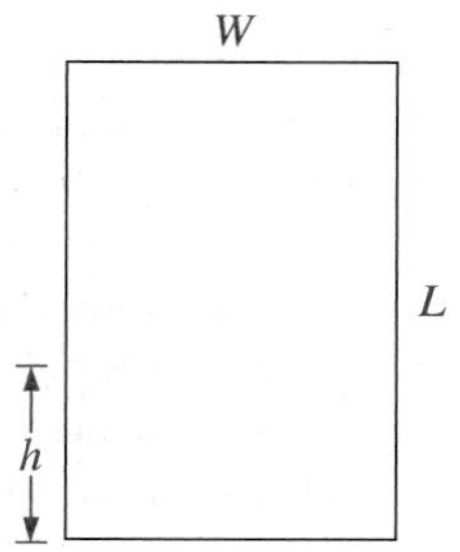

But the artist can do the job very quickly without any arithmetic at all! Here is how. Look at the following figure. Draw a line across the given rectangle at height h (line $\overleftrightarrow{BD}$ in the figure). Next, draw a line through A and C and extend the top line of the rectangle to meet line $\overleftrightarrow{AC}$ at point F. Then drop a perpendicular from F to the extended base of the given rectangle. The rectangle *ABDE* is the desired rectangle. Can you discover why? Look at the figure again. The triangles *ABC* and *FDC* are similar (have exactly the same shape). Corresponding sides of similar triangles are always in the same ratio. Thus,

$$\frac{y}{W} = \frac{x}{h}$$

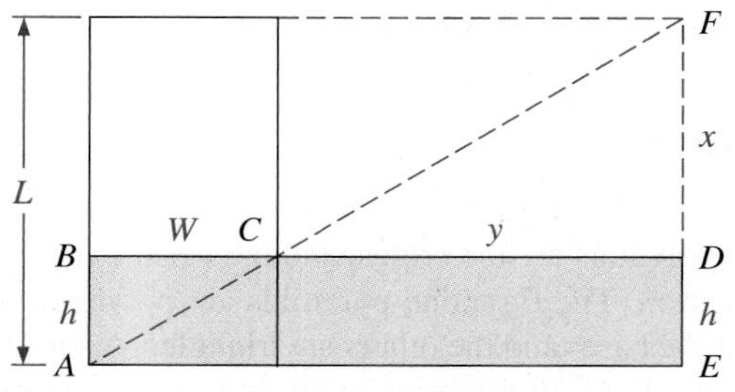

53. Use this result to show that the area of rectangle *ABDE* is equal to the area of the original rectangle. (*Hint:* What is the area of the rectangle taken away from the given rectangle? What is the area of the rectangle added on?)

54. Draw a careful diagram of a rectangle 4 cm wide and 6 cm high. Use the construction described above to find a rectangle 5 cm high with the same area. If you do this carefully, the result will help convince you that this is a neat construction.

COLLABORATIVE LEARNING

Have you heard of "squaring the circle"? The expression means trying to find the square with the same area as a circle of a given radius. The Greek mathematician Archimedes (287–212 B.C.) used this method to try to approximate the area of a circle.

Form 3 groups. Each of the groups will approximate the area of a circle according to the suggested procedure.

***Group 1** Approximating with a square*

The diagram shows a square inscribed in a circle. Triangle *ABC* is a right triangle with hypotenuse $2r$.

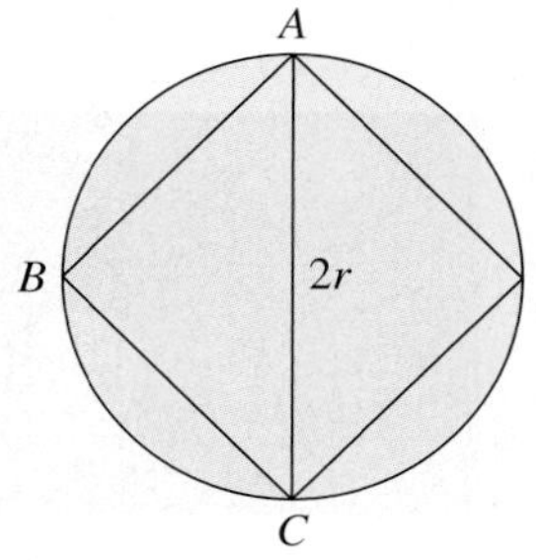

1. Find the length of the line segment $\overline{AB}$.
2. The area of the square is the length of the line segment $\overline{AB}$ squared. What is this area? How close is the area of the square to the area of a circle?

***Group 2** Approximating with a hexagon*

The diagram below shows a hexagon inscribed in a circle. The area A of the hexagon is the area of the six triangles shown; that is, $A = 6(\frac{1}{2}rh)$.

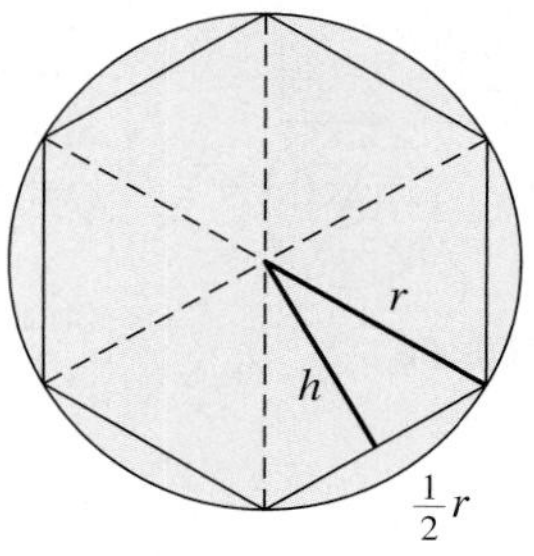

1. Find the height h in terms of r.
2. Find A.

***Group 3** Approximating with an n-sided polygon*

The following diagram shows an n-sided polygon inscribed in a circle. The area of the polygon is the area of the n triangles shown; that is, $A = n(\text{area of triangle}) = n\left(\frac{1}{2}hb\right) = \frac{1}{2}nbh$.

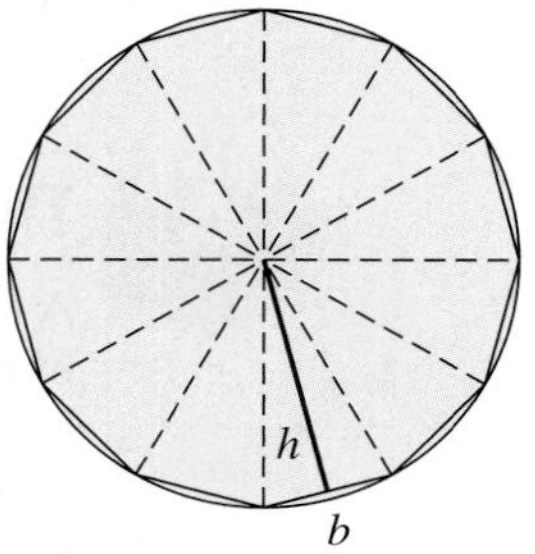

1. The polygon has n sides each of length b. What is nb?
2. When n increases, nb is the distance around the circle, the circumference. What is nb then?
3. As n increases, what is A?

8.5 Volume and Surface Area

GETTING STARTED

OBJECTIVES

A. Identify the parts of a polyhedron.
B. Find the volume and surface area of polyhedrons, cylinders, cones and spheres.
C. Solve applications involving the volume of solids.

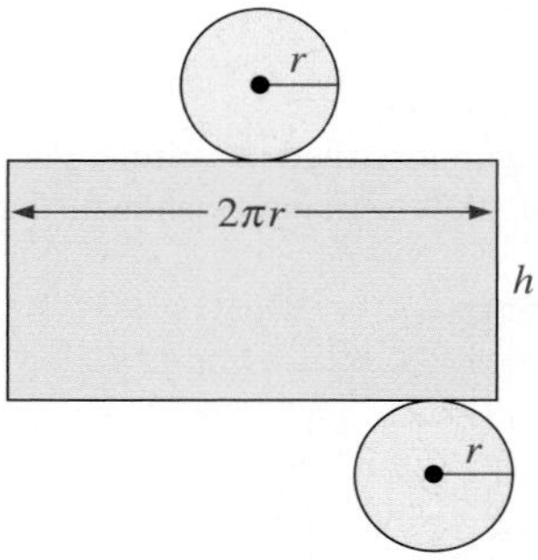

FIGURE 8.68

FROM THE GROCER'S SHELF

Which of the two bottles on the right side of the picture has more ketchup? Which has more sauce, the bottle on the left or the can? As it turns out, both ketchup bottles hold the same amount. They have the same **volume.** The volume of sauce in the can and in the bottle are also the same. One of the ketchup bottles has greater **surface area,** which in this case gives the false impression that it has greater volume and holds more. We have already studied perimeter (the length of the **boundary** of a polygon) and area (the space **enclosed** by the polygon). The counterparts of perimeter and area in three dimensions are **surface area** and **volume.** Like perimeter, **surface area** measures a **boundary,** the surface of a three-dimensional figure, whereas **volume,** like area, measures the space **enclosed** by the figure. Keep in mind, however, that perimeter is measured in **linear** units, surface area in **square** units, and volume in **cubic** units.

How can we find the surface area of the can or, in general, the surface area of a **cylinder?** If a vertical cut is made down the side of the can and the metal flattened, it forms a rectangle whose length is the same as the circumference of the can $(2\pi r)$ and whose width is the height h of the can (see Figure 8.68).

The area of this rectangle is $2\pi r \cdot h$. Then we find the area of the top and bottom lids, πr^2 for each, to obtain the total surface area for the can or, in general, for a cylinder of radius r and height h. Thus, the surface area S is given by

$$S = 2\pi rh + 2\pi r^2 \qquad \text{Surface area } S \text{ of a cylinder}$$

Now, how could you determine whether a can and a bottle hold the same volume? (No fair reading the label!) One way is to fill the can with water and then pour it into the bottle. If the bottle is exactly filled, they have the same volume. We will study volumes and surface areas in this section.

The photograph on the next page shows the Transamerica pyramid in San Francisco. At 853 ft in height (48 stories) it is the tallest building on the city's skyline. The pyramid portion of the structure is built on a square base and is thus an example of a *square pyramid.* Pyramids are one example of solids bounded by polygons.

A Three-Dimensional Figures

A solid bounded by plane polygons is called a **polyhedron.** The polygons are the **faces** of the polyhedron, the sides of the polygons are the **edges,** and the vertices of the polygons are the **vertices** of the polyhedron. The Egyptian pyramids are polyhedrons with five faces, one of which is a square (the base) and the others are triangles. A square pyramid has eight edges and five vertices. The Transamerica pyramid is a striking example of the use of a square pyramid in the design of a modern building.

A **convex polyhedron** is one that lies entirely to one side of the plane of each of its faces. A polyhedron that is not convex is called **concave,** or **reentrant.** The polyhedrons shown in Figure 8.69 are a **cube,** a **rectangular parallelepiped,** a six-sided polyhedron with triangular faces (panel C), and a seven-sided polyhedron (panel D). The first three polyhedrons are convex, and the fourth is concave (reentrant).

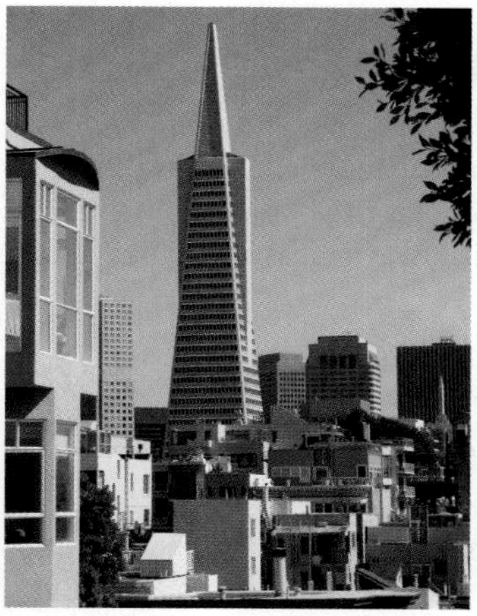

The Transamerica Corporation building in San Francisco, more commonly called the Transamerica pyramid.

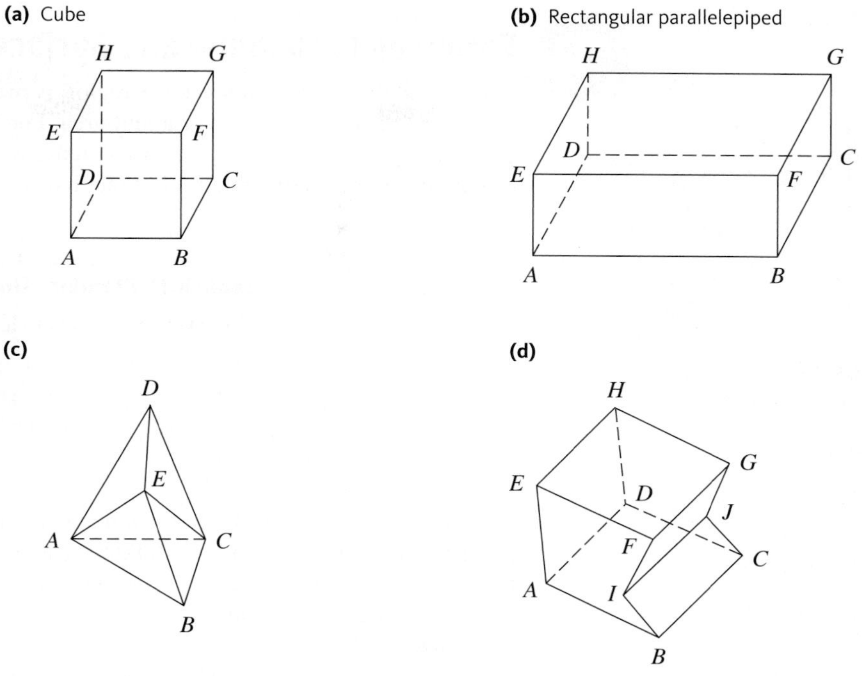

FIGURE 8.69 Polyhedrons.

If two faces of a polyhedron lie in parallel planes and if the edges that are not in these planes are all parallel to each other, then the polyhedron is called a **prism.** In Figure 8.69, panels A, B, and D all illustrate prisms. The faces of a prism that are in the two parallel planes are called the **bases.** The parallel lines joining the bases are the **lateral edges.** The two bases of a prism are congruent polygons. Figure 8.70 shows a **triangular prism.**

If all but one of the vertices of a polyhedron lie in one plane, then the polyhedron is a **pyramid.** The face that lies in this one plane is the **base,** and the remaining vertex is the **vertex of the pyramid.** Figure 8.71 shows a pentagonal pyramid; the base is a pentagon. Prisms and pyramids are named by the shapes of their bases.

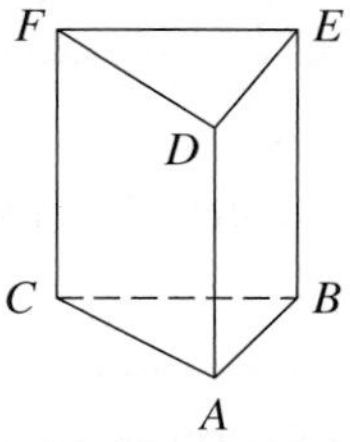

FIGURE 8.70 Triangular prism.

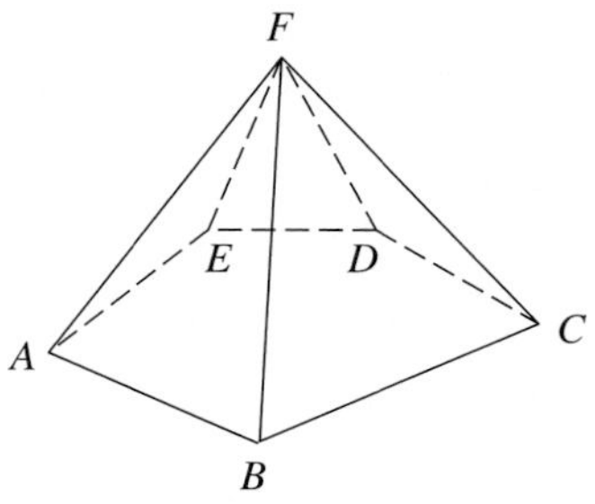

FIGURE 8.71 Pentagonal pyramid.

EXAMPLE 1 Naming the Edges and Vertices of a Pyramid

Name the edges and the vertices of the pyramid in Figure 8.71.

Solution

The edges are the line segments $\overline{AB}$, $\overline{BC}$, $\overline{CD}$, $\overline{DE}$, $\overline{EA}$, $\overline{FA}$, $\overline{FB}$, $\overline{FC}$, $\overline{FD}$, and $\overline{FE}$. The vertices are the points A, B, C, D, E, and F.

B Formulas for Volume and Surface Area

The *volume* of a three-dimensional region is measured in terms of a *unit volume,* just as area is measured in terms of a unit area. For the unit volume, we choose the region enclosed by a *unit cube,* as shown in Figure 8.72. Some of the commonly used units of volume are given in Table 8.11. Note that *volume* is always measured in *cubic* units.

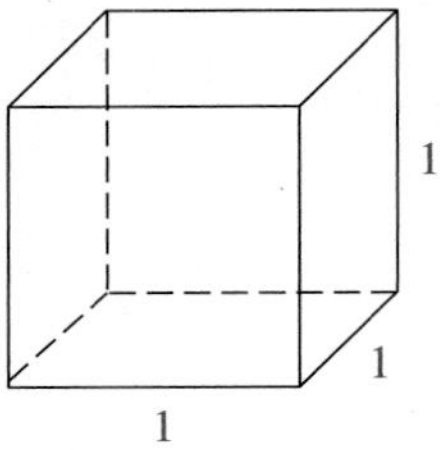

FIGURE 8.72 Unit cube; volume = 1 cubic unit.

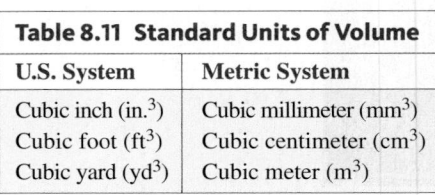

Table 8.11 Standard Units of Volume

U.S. System	Metric System
Cubic inch (in.^{3})	Cubic millimeter (mm^3)
Cubic foot (ft^3)	Cubic centimeter (cm^3)
Cubic yard (yd^3)	Cubic meter (m^3)

Volumes can be considered in a manner similar to that used for areas. If a rectangular parallelepiped (box) is such that the lengths of its edges are all whole numbers, then the region can be cut up by planes parallel to the faces, as in Figure 8.73. In general, we define the volume of a rectangular box of length l, width w, and height h to be lwh. Thus,

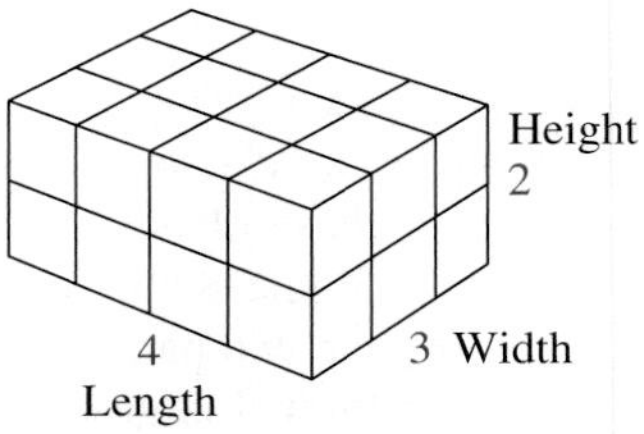

FIGURE 8.73 $V = 4 \times 3 \times 2 = 24$ cubic units.

Volume of a Rectangular Box

The volume V of a rectangular box with length l, width w, and height h is given by

$$V = lwh = \text{length} \times \text{width} \times \text{height}$$

The surface area of a rectangular box is the sum of the areas of the six faces.

Surface Area of a Rectangular Box

The surface area S of a rectangular box with length l, width w, and height h is given by

$$S = 2lw + 2lh + 2wh$$

For the rectangular box in Figure 8.73, we have

$$S = 2(4 \times 3) + 2(4 \times 2) + 2(3 \times 2)$$
$$= 24 + 16 + 12 = 52 \text{ square units}$$

© I. Bello

Which formulas do you need to find the capacity of the tank?

Table 8.12 gives the formulas for the volume and the surface area of some commonly occurring three-dimensional figures.

Table 8.12 Volumes and Surface Areas

Name	Figure	Volume (V)	Surface Area (S)
Cube	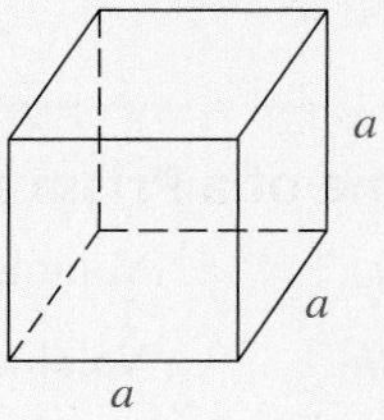	$V = a^3$	$S = 6a^2$
Rectangular box	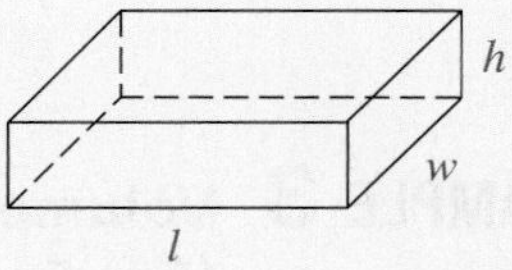	$V = lwh$	$S = 2(lw + lh + wh)$
Cylinder	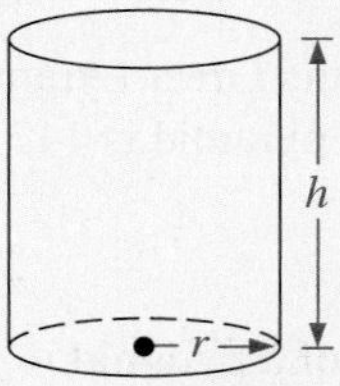	$V = \pi r^2 h$	$S = 2\pi rh + 2\pi r^2$
Cone	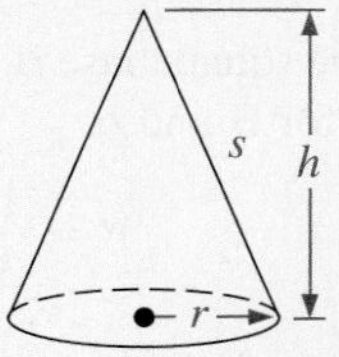	$V = \frac{1}{3}\pi r^2 h$	$S = \pi r^2 + \pi rs$
Sphere	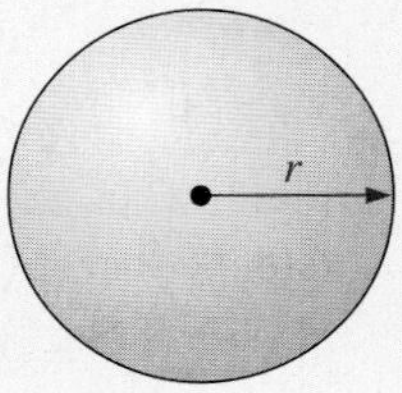	$V = \frac{4}{3}\pi r^3$	$S = 4\pi r^2$

EXAMPLE 2 Finding the Volume and Surface Area of Rubik's Cube

You are probably familiar with the Rubik's Cube puzzle like the one shown in the photograph. Each of the little cubes is $\frac{3}{4}$ in. on a side.

(a) Find the volume of Rubik's Cube.

(b) Find the surface area if no allowance is made for the dips between the small cubes.

© iStockphoto.com/Chris Hutchison

Solution

(a) Since there are three little cubes in a row, the edge of the large cube is $(3)\left(\frac{3}{4}\right) = \frac{9}{4}$ in.

Using the formula for the volume of a cube, we get

$V = a^3 = \left(\frac{9}{4}\right)^3 = \frac{729}{64}$ in.^{3}

or expressed as a decimal,

$V = 11.390625$ or about 11.4 in.^{3}

(b) The formula for the surface area of a cube gives

$S = 6a^2 = 6\left(\frac{9}{4}\right)^2 = \frac{243}{8}$ or about 30.4 in.^{2}

Do you recognize the shape of the structure in the photo? It is a **pyramid** (from the Greek word *pyra* meaning fire, light, or visible, and the word *midos* meaning measures, even though other scholars claim that the origin of the word is the Greek word *pyramis,* meaning wheat cake!). The pyramid is the Great Pyramid at Giza built by King Khufus, also known as Cheops, from 2589 to 2566 B.C. What is the volume of this pyramid?

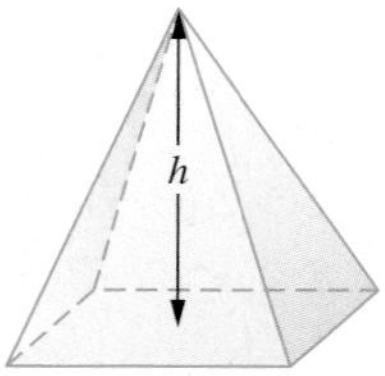

Volume of a Prism and Pyramid

$V = Bh$	Volume of a prism (B is the area of the base)
$V = \frac{1}{3}Bh$	Volume of a pyramid (B is the area of the base)

EXAMPLE 3 Volume of the Original Great Pyramid (See Exercise 20)

The base of the Great Pyramid is a square with each side measuring 230 meters. If the height of the pyramid is 147 meters, what is its volume?

Solution

The volume of a pyramid is $V = \frac{1}{3}$Bh.

The area of the square base B is 230m · 230m = 52,900 m^2 and the height h is 147 meters. Substituting for B and h,

$$\begin{aligned} V &= \frac{1}{3}Bh \\ &= \frac{1}{3}(52{,}900\ m^2)(147\ m) \\ &= (52{,}900\ m^2)\frac{(147\ m)}{3} \\ &= (52{,}900\ m^2)(49\ m) \\ &= 2{,}592{,}100\ m^3 \end{aligned}$$

Thus, the volume of the Great Pyramid is 2,592,100 cubic meters

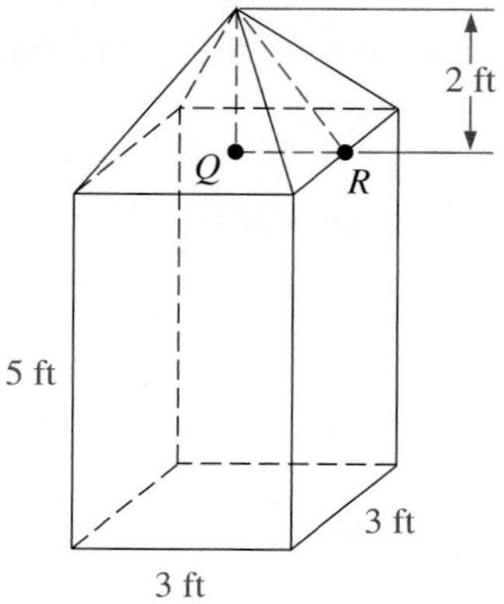

FIGURE 8.74

EXAMPLE 4 Finding the Volume and Surface Area of a Polyhedron

Figure 8.74 shows a polyhedron that consists of a rectangular box surmounted by a square pyramid with the top of the box for its base. The dimensions of the polyhedron are shown in Figure 8.74.

(a) Find the volume of the polyhedron. **(b)** Find the total surface area.

Solution

(a) The volume of the rectangular box portion in Figure 8.74 is

$V = lwh = (3)(3)(5) = 45\ ft^3$

The volume of the pyramid is

$V = \frac{1}{3}Bh = \frac{1}{3}(3 \times 3)(2) = 6\ ft^3$

Thus, the entire volume is $45\ ft^3 + 6\ ft^3$, or $51\ ft^3$.

(b) The area of the base of the figure is

$B = 3 \times 3 = 9 \text{ ft}^2$

The area of the four sides of the rectangular box portion is

$A_1 = 4(3 \times 5) = 60 \text{ ft}^2$

To find the area of the four triangular faces of the pyramid, we must first find the altitude of the triangles. To do this, we draw a line $\overleftrightarrow{PQ}$ from the top vertex and perpendicular to the base of the pyramid. This line will meet the base at its midpoint Q. Then we draw a second line $\overleftrightarrow{QR}$ from the foot of the perpendicular to the midpoint of an edge of the base. Finally, we draw the line $\overleftrightarrow{PR}$. The triangle PQR is a right triangle, whose hypotenuse $\overline{PR}$ is the desired altitude. Thus, we have

$PR = \sqrt{2^2 + (\frac{3}{2})^2} = \sqrt{4 + \frac{9}{4}} = \sqrt{\frac{25}{4}} = \frac{5}{2} \text{ ft}$

Consequently, the area of the four triangular faces of the pyramid is

$A_2 = 4 \times \frac{1}{2}bh = 4 \times \frac{1}{2}(3)(\frac{5}{2}) = 15 \text{ ft}^2$

The total surface area of the polyhedron is

$B + A_1 + A_2 = 9 + 60 + 15 = 84 \text{ ft}^2$

EXAMPLE 5 Diameters of Spheres Given Surface Area and Volume

Natasha is inflating a toy globe. Suppose that the globe is a perfect sphere. What is the diameter of the globe when the number of square inches of its surface area is equal to the number of cubic inches of its volume?

Solution

Let r in. be the radius of the globe. Then the surface area is $4\pi r^2$ in.^{2}, and the volume is $\frac{4}{3}\pi r^3$ in.^{3}. The number of units of surface area is to be equal to the number of units of volume, so

$$\frac{4}{3}\pi r^3 = 4\pi r^2$$

$$\frac{1}{3}r = 1 \qquad \text{Divide both sides by } 4\pi r^2.$$

$$r = 3$$

Since the diameter is twice the radius, the required diameter is 6 in.

C Applications

EXAMPLE 6 Finding the Volume of a Tank

The water tank for a small town is in the shape of a cone (vertex down) surmounted by a cylinder, as shown in Figure 8.75. If a cubic foot of water is about 7.5 gal, what is the capacity of the tank in gallons? (Use $\pi \approx 3.14$.)

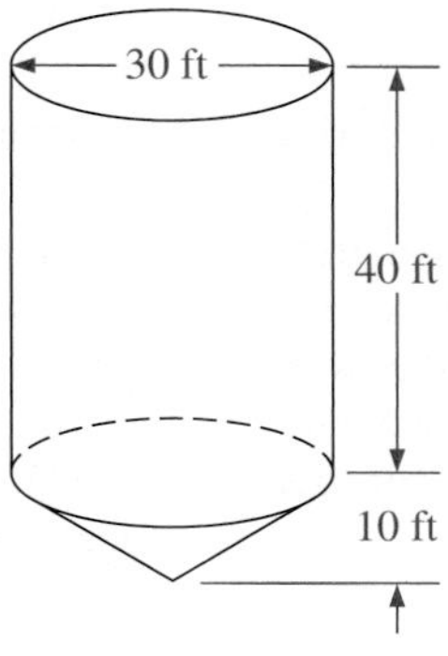

FIGURE 8.75

Solution

For the cylindrical portion of the tank, $r = 15$ and $h = 40$, so

$$V = \pi(15)^2(40) = 9000\pi \text{ ft}^3$$

For the conical portion, $r = 15$ and $h = 10$. Thus,

$$V = \frac{1}{3}\pi(15)^2(10) = 750\pi \text{ ft}^3$$

The total volume is the sum of these, that is, 9750π ft^3. Using 7.5 gal/ft^3 and 3.14 for π, we get

$$9750\pi \text{ ft}^3 \approx (9750)(3.14)(7.5)$$
$$\approx 230{,}000 \text{ gal}$$

EXAMPLE 7 How Much Water Is in the Tank?

A solid metal sphere of radius 3 m just fits inside a cubical tank. If the tank is full of water and the sphere is slowly lowered into the tank until it touches bottom, how much water is left in the tank?

Solution

The amount of water left in the tank is the difference between the volume of the tank and the volume of the sphere. Thus, since the length of any edge of the cube equals the diameter of the sphere, the required volume is

$$\begin{aligned} V &= 6^3 - \tfrac{4}{3}\pi(3^3) \\ &= 216 - 36\pi \\ &\approx 103 \text{ m}^3 \end{aligned}$$

EXAMPLE 8 Volume of a Capsule

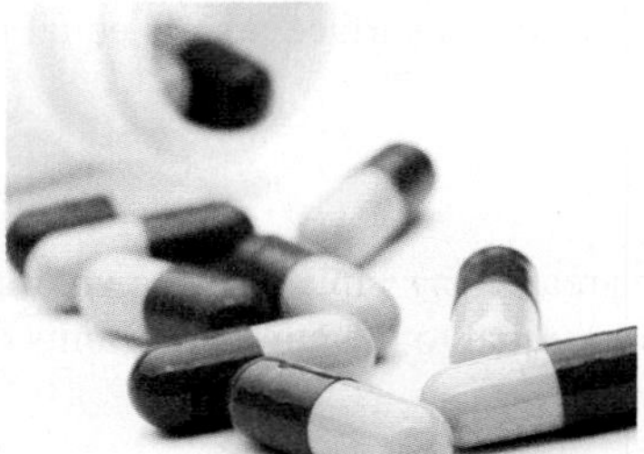

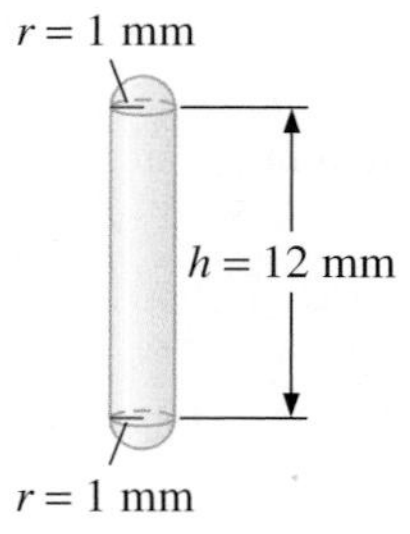

The capsules in the photo are in the shape of a cylinder 12 mm long with two half spheres with a diameter of 2 mm at each end. What is the volume of each capsule? Use 3.14 for π, and round the answer to the nearest hundredth of a cubic millimeter.

Solution

We have to find the volume V of the cylinder plus the volume of the two half spheres (which make up one whole sphere).

The volume of the cylinder is $V = \pi r^2 h$. Here, $r = 1$ mm and $h = 12$ mm, so

$$\begin{aligned} V &= (3.14)(1 \text{ mm})^2 \, (12 \text{ mm}) \\ &\approx 37.68 \text{ mm}^3 \end{aligned}$$

The volume of the sphere is

$$\begin{aligned} V &= \tfrac{4}{3}\pi r^3 \\ &= \tfrac{4}{3}(3.14)\ (1 \text{ mm})^3 \\ &= \frac{4(3.14)(1 \text{ mm})^3}{3} \\ &\approx 4.19 \text{ mm}^3 \end{aligned}$$

The volume of the whole capsule is $37.68 + 4.19 = 41.87$ mm^3.

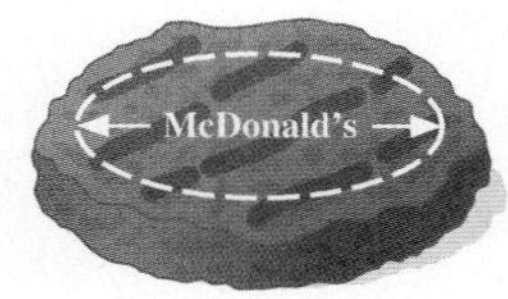

FIGURE 8.76 "The Burger King 2.8 oz. flame-broiled hamburger has 75% more beef than McDonald's hamburger."

One question students always ask is, Do we have to memorize all these formulas? Judge for yourself after reading this actual case.

Here's an example in which an incorrect formula has been used: The ad claims that the Burger King 2.8-oz. hamburger has 75% more beef than the McDonald's hamburger. Is that the idea you get from Figure 8.76? We can compare the two hamburgers by comparing the *volume* of the beef in each burger. The volume V of a burger is $V = Ah$, where A is the area of the top of the burger and h is the height. The top area of the McDonald's burger is $M = \pi r^2$, where r is the radius (half the distance across the middle) of the burger. For the McDonald's burger, $r = 1$ in., so its area is

$$M = \pi(1 \text{ in.})^2 = \pi \text{ in.}^2 \ (\pi \text{ square inches})$$

© David Young-Wolff/Photo Edit

For the Burger King burger, $r = 1.75$ *in.*, so

$$B = \pi(1.75 \text{ in.})^2 \approx 3\pi \text{in.}^2$$

This means approximately equal.

For the McDonald's burger, the volume is $V = \pi h$, and for the Burger King burger, the volume is $V = 3\pi h$. The difference in volumes is $3\pi h - \pi h = 2\pi h$, and the *percent* increase for the Burger King burger is given by

$$\text{Percent increase} = \frac{\text{increase}}{\text{base}} = \frac{2\pi h}{\pi h} = 2$$

Thus on the basis of this discussion, Burger King burgers have 200% more beef. What other assumptions must you make for this to be so? (You'll have an opportunity in In Other Words to give your opinion!)

8.5 EXERCISES

A Three-Dimensional Figures

1. Refer to Figure 8.69C on page 475, and name
   a. the vertices.
   b. the edges.
2. Refer to Figure 8.70 on page 475 and repeat problem 1.
3. Refer to Figure 8.69D on page 475, and name the bottom face.
4. Refer to Figure 8.69D on page 475, and name the left-hand back face.

In each of problems 5–8, make a sketch of the figure.

5. A triangular pyramid
6. A triangular prism surmounted by a triangular pyramid with the top base of the prism as the base of the pyramid
7. A six-sided polyhedron that is convex and is not a parallelepiped
8. An eight-sided polyhedron with triangular faces
9. a. If the edges of a cube are doubled in length, what happens to the volume?
   b. What if the lengths are tripled?

B Formulas for Volume and Surface Area

In problems 10–14, use 3.14 for π and round the answer to the nearest tenth.

10. A spherical water tank has a 24-foot radius. How many gallons of water will it hold if 1 cubic foot holds about 7.5 gallons?
11. Suppose you want to paint the outside of the water tank in Problem 10. What is the surface area of the tank?
12. A spherical water tank has a 7.2-meter radius. How many liters of water will it hold if 1 cubic meter holds 1000 liters?
13. Suppose you want to paint the outside of the water tank in Problem 12. What is the surface area of the tank?
14. A spherical Christmas ornament has a 2-inch diameter. What is its volume?
15. A pentagonal prism has a base whose area is 10 in.^{2}. If the prism is 5 in. high, what is its volume?
16. The base of a prism is a triangle whose base is 3 ft and whose height is 4 ft. If the prism is 5 ft high, what is its volume?
17. *Volume of a pyramid.* The photo shows the Pyramid of the Moon built at Teotihuacan, Mexico, between A.D. 150 and 225. Its base measures 492 feet on each side and its height is 138 feet. What is the volume of the Pyramid of the Moon?

© iStockphoto.com/Alexandra Draghici

18. A convex polyhedron consists of two pyramids with a common base that is an equilateral triangle 3 in. on a side. The height of one of the pyramids is 2 in. and the height of the other is 4 in. What is the volume of the polyhedron?
19. A container consists of a cube with 10 cm edges surmounted by a pyramid of height 15 cm and with the top face of the cube as its base. How many liters does this container hold? (*Hint:* 1 L = 1000 cm^3.)
20. Did you know that the Great Pyramid of Example 3 has shrunk? Actually, due to the loss of its outer casing stones, the base now has sides measuring 227 meters and its height is 137 meters (having lost 10 meters in height). To the nearest cubic meter, what is the volume of the pyramid now?

In problems 21–24, use the approximate value 3.14 for π to find the volume and the total surface area of

a. the circular cylinder of given radius and height.

b. the circular cone of given radius and height.

21. Radius 5 in., height 9 in.

22. Radius 10 cm, height 6 cm

23. Radius 3 ft, height 4 ft

24. Radius 6 cm, height 12 cm

25. Find the volume of a sphere of radius 6 in.

26. Find the volume of a sphere of radius 12 cm.

C Applications

27. The Peachtree Plaza Hotel tower in Atlanta, Georgia, is 70 stories high. If the height of this cylinder is 754 ft and its diameter is 116 ft, what is the volume?

28. *Volume of funnel.* The inside of a funnel is 8 cm in diameter and 7 centimeters high. What is the volume of the funnel? Use 3.14 for π and round the answer to the nearest tenth.

29. *Volume of a funnel cloud.* Funnel clouds can be 300 to 2000 feet in diameter. Assume the funnel cloud in the photo is 1000 feet in diameter and 2000 feet high. What is the volume of this funnel cloud? Use 3.14 for π and give the answer to the nearest tenth.

© Daniel Loretto/Photos.com

30. The fuel tanks on some ships are spheres of which only the top halves are above deck. If one of these tanks is 120 ft in diameter, how many gallons of fuel does it hold? Use 1 $ft^3 \approx 7.5$ gal.

31. A popular-sized can in U.S. supermarkets is 3 in. in diameter and 4 in. high (inside dimensions). About how many grams of water will one of these cans hold? (Recall that 1 cm^3 of water weighs 1 g, and 1 in. = 2.54 cm.)

32. An ice cream cone is 7 cm in diameter and 10 cm deep (see the figure below). The inside of the cone is packed with ice cream and a hemisphere of ice cream is put on top. If ice cream weighs $\frac{1}{2}$ g/cm^3, how many grams of ice cream are there in all?

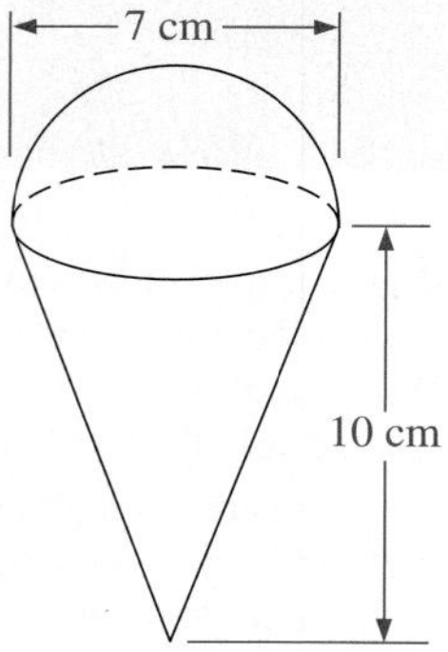

33. The circumferences of a baseball, soccer ball, and basketball are 9, 27, and 30 in., respectively.

a. Find the surface area and volume of each.

b. How does the surface area of a baseball compare to that of a basketball?

c. How does the volume of a baseball compare to that of a soccer ball?

34. A cylindrical storage tank for gasoline has a 300-ft diameter and is 200 ft high.

a. Find the capacity of this tank if one cubic foot of gasoline equals 7.5 gal.

b. How many gallons of paint are needed to paint the exterior and top of this tank with two coats of paint if a gallon of paint covers 400 ft^2?

35. A bowling ball has a 27-in. circumference and weighs 16 lb.

a. Find the volume of the ball before the holes are drilled.

b. If three cylindrical holes with diameters 1.25, 1, and 1 in., respectively, each 2.5 in. deep, are drilled into the ball, what is the weight of the ball now?

36. A basketball with a 30-in. circumference is tightly packed into a cubical box for shipment.

a. What is the volume of the ball?

b. What is the smallest possible volume for the box?

c. What percent of the space in the box is occupied by the basketball?

37. A grocery bag has a 7-by-12-in. base and is 17 in. high.

a. What is the volume of the bag?

b. What is the minimum outer surface area for the bag?

c. A ton of recycled paper will save 17 trees. If one bag weighs 2 oz, how many bags are needed to save 34 trees?

38. The Pet Kennel measures 26 in. long, 19 in. high, and 16 in. wide. What is the volume of the pet kennel?

© David Young-Wolff/Photo Edit

39. The Pet Taxi is 16 in. long, 10 in. high, and 11 in. wide. What is the volume of the Pet Taxi?

© Michael Newman/Photo Edit

40. The inside dimensions of the toaster are 11 in. wide, 8 in. deep, and 5 in. high. What is the volume of the inside of the toaster?

© Bill Aron/Photo Edit

41. The inside dimensions of the microwave are 16 in. by 11 in. by 13 in. What is the volume of the inside of the microwave?

© Felicia Martinez/Photo Edit

42. Find the volume of the large 4-ft-high, 1-ft-diameter cylinder. Use 3.14 for π, and give the answer to the nearest hundredth.

© Courtesy of Interstate Products, Inc.

43. Each sugar container is 5 in. high and 3 in. in diameter. Find the volume of one container. Use 3.14 for π, and give the answer to the nearest hundredth.

© I. Bello

44. Find the volume of the small 2-ft-high, 1-ft-diameter cylinder in the photo below on the left. Use 3.14 for π, and give the answer to the nearest hundredth.

45. Using the information in problem 43, find the volume of the sugar in the three containers. Note that one of the containers is half-full. Answer to the nearest whole number.

46. *Moving on out.* Have you moved to the dorm or to an apartment lately? You probably needed some boxes with some of the dimensions shown. Give the answer in both cubic inches and cubic feet. (1 cubic foot = 1728 cubic inches.)

a. Find the volume of the small box.

b. Find the volume of the medium box.

c. Find the volume of the large box.

d. Which of the three volumes shown for the boxes agrees exactly with your answer, the box in **a, b,** or **c?**

- **Small Box**
  16″ × 12″ × 12″ 1.5 cu/ft
- **Medium Box**
  18″ × 18″ × 16″ 3.0 cu/ft
- **Large Box**
  18″ × 18″ × 24″ 4.5 cu/ft
- **Extra-Large Box**
  24″ × 18″ × 24″ 6.0 cu/ft

47. *Does it all fit?* You probably needed a truck to move. The U-Haul truck has the dimensions shown.

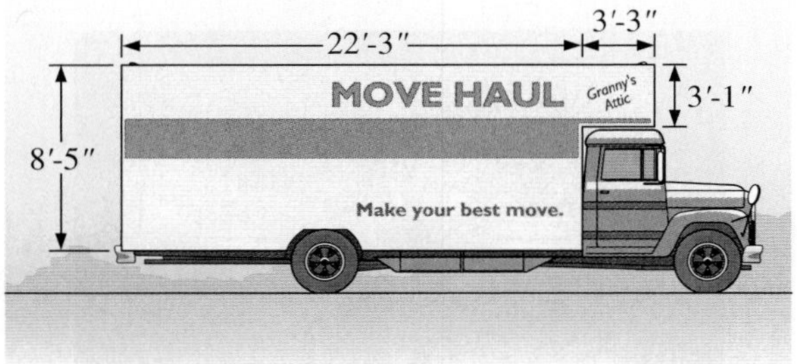

Inside dimensions: 22′-3″ × 7′-7″ × 8′-5″ ($L \times W \times H$)

Granny's Attic: 3′-3″ × 7′-7″ × 3′-1″ ($L \times W \times H$)

a. Approximate the inside dimensions of the truck to 22 ft by 7 ft by 8 ft. What is the volume?

b. Approximate the dimensions of Granny's Attic to 3 ft by 7 ft by 3 ft. What is the volume?

c. You estimate that you have a 1300 ft^3 of stuff to be moved. Does your stuff theoretically fit in the truck? Explain. *Hint:* Don't forget the space in Granny's Attic (over the truck cab).

48. *U-Haul recommendations.* If you have a two- to three-room apartment, U-Haul recommends a 1200 to 1600 ft^3 truck.

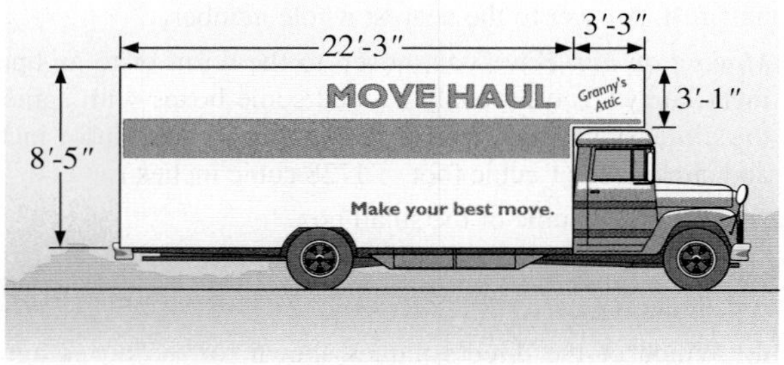

Inside dimensions: 20′-10″ × 7′-6″ × 8′-1″ ($L \times W \times H$)

Granny's Attic: 2′-10″ × 7′-6″ × 3′-1″ ($L \times W \times H$)

a. Approximate the inside dimensions of the truck to 20 ft by 7 ft by 8 ft. What is the volume?

b. Approximate the dimensions of Granny's Attic to 3 ft by 7 ft by 3 ft. What is the volume?

c. If you have a two-room apartment, U-Haul recommends a truck with a minimum of 1200 ft^3 of space. Does this truck meet that recommendation?

© I. Bello

© I. Bello

What is the volume (capacity) of the garbage cans that are used at your school? The garbage can in the photograph consists of two parts: the cylindrical bottom (2.5 ft high, 1.5 ft in diameter) and the hemisphere on top (half of a sphere).

49. What is the volume of the cylindrical part?

50. What is the volume of the hemispherical top?

51. What is the volume of the entire trash can?

52. The chemistry building has 3 floors and there are 4 trash cans on each floor. What is the total volume of the trash cans on the 3 floors of the chemistry building?

53. A garbage truck carries about 500 ft^3 of trash. How many full cans of trash can it carry?

54. If we assume that every building has 3 floors and 4 trash cans on each floor, how many buildings can the truck service? (*Hint:* How many 12-can loads fit in the truck?)

IN OTHER WORDS

55. Remember the hamburgers in Figure 8.76? Write two explanations of how the Burger King burger can have 75% more beef than the McDonald's burger and still look like the one in the picture.

56. To make a fair comparison of the amount of beef in two hamburgers, should you compare the circumferences, areas, or volumes? Explain.

57. The McDonald burger has a 2-in. diameter, whereas the Burger King burger has a 3.50-in. diameter. How much bigger (in percent) is the circumference of the Burger King burger?

58. Can you now explain the claim in the ad? Is the claim correct? Explain.

59. Explain in your own words why lengths are measured in linear units, areas in square units, and volume in cubic units.

60. Explain in your own words what happens to the volume and surface area of a sphere if the diameter is doubled.

61. Is the number of cubic units in the volume of a sphere always larger than the number of square units in its surface area? Explain in your own words why or why not.

62. Suppose the radius of a circular cone is doubled and the height is halved. Explain in your own words what happens to the volume.

DISCOVERY

63. A **regular polyhedron** is one whose faces are all congruent regular polygons, that is, regular polygons of exactly the same shape and size. The appearance of such a polyhedron at any vertex is identical with its appearance at any other vertex; the same is true at the edges. The early Greeks discovered that only five regular polyhedrons are possible. Repeat this discovery and explain why it is so.

Consider the regular polygons one at a time: equilateral triangles, squares, regular pentagons, and so on. In the case you use squares, how many squares can you put together at a vertex to form a polyhedron? Look at a cube. It is the only regular polyhedron with squares for its faces.

The regular polyhedrons are as follows:

A **tetrahedron** with 4 equilateral triangles for faces

A **cube** with 6 squares for faces

An **octahedron** with 8 equilateral triangles for faces

A **dodecahedron** with 12 pentagons for faces

An **icosahedron** with 20 equilateral triangles for faces

64. Copy the pattern of equilateral triangles in the following figure onto a piece of stiff cardboard. Cut around the outside edges and fold on the heavy lines. You can build an icosahedron by holding the cut edges together with transparent tape. There are five triangles at each vertex.

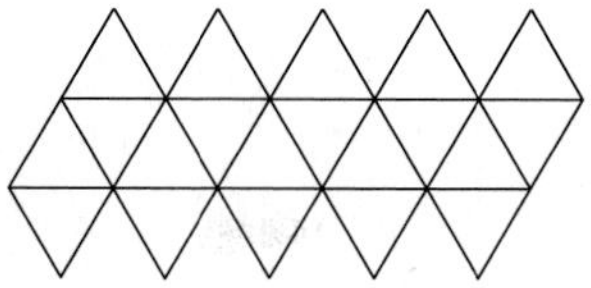

65. Count the number of faces (F), vertices (V), and edges (E) for each of the figures listed in the table below. Compare the value of E with the value of $F + V$ and discover Euler's famous formula for polyhedrons.

Figure	F	V	E	F + V
8.69B				
8.69C				
8.69D				
8.70				
8.71				

66. Can you check the formula you got in problem 65 by using the diagram in problem 64?

CALCULATOR CORNER

When higher exponents are present in an expression, calculators with a [y^x] *key are especially helpful. As the notation indicates, this key raises a number y to a power x. For instance, to perform the calculations in Example 7, we enter*

[6] [y^x] [3] [−] [4] [×] [π] [×] [3] [y^x] [3] [÷] [3] [=]

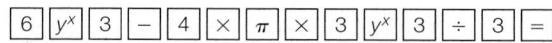

The result is given as 102.9026645, or about 103 m^3.

1. Rework problem 25 using your calculator.

COLLABORATIVE LEARNING

We have studied cubes, prisms, pyramids, cylinders, and cones. What can you build using all of these geometric figures? Your own castle, of course! Form several groups. Here is the challenge.

1. Let each group find pictures of several castles and count the number of geometric figures seen in them (prisms, pyramids, cylinders, and so on). The team that identifies the most figures wins.
2. Let each team create a drawing of a castle. The team that uses the most geometric figures in the design wins. Good luck!

8.6 Networks, Non-Euclidean Geometry, and Topology

GETTING STARTED

OBJECTIVES

A. Determine if a network is traversable and show a path indicating the beginning and the end of the path.

B. Find the measure of an angle in non-Euclidean geometries: a plane, a pseudosphere and a sphere.

C. Find topologically equivalent objects and their genus.

D. Solve applications involving networks and topology.

CROSSING THAT BRIDGE

What do you think the following activities have in common: urban engineers mapping traffic patterns, chemists modeling complex molecules, managers creating the organizational charts for a large corporation, and drawing your family tree? Each of the models consists of points (locations, atoms, job positions, and people) connected by lines. The study of these graphs is now called **graph** or **network theory.**

A famous puzzle known as the **Bridges of Königsberg** probably started the study of the traversability of networks. There was a river flowing through the city, and in the river were two islands (A and D) connected to each other and to the city by seven bridges (a, b, c, d, e, f, and g), as shown in Figure 8.77. The people of the city loved a Sunday walk and thought it would be fun to follow a route that would take them across each of the seven bridges exactly once. But they found that no matter where they started or what path they took, they could not cross each bridge exactly once.

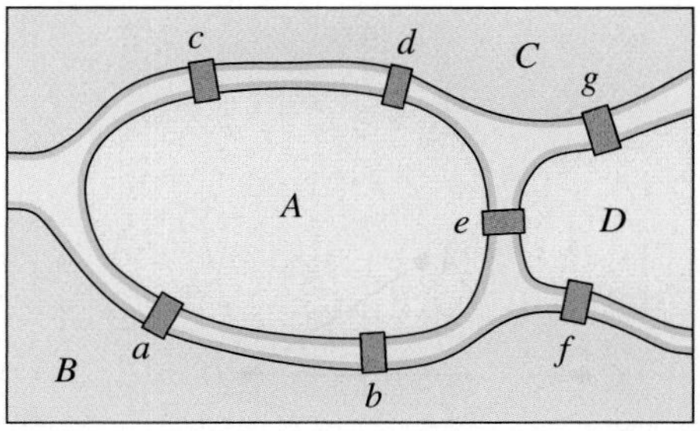

FIGURE 8.77 *A* and *D* are islands, *C* and *B* are shores. The bridges are marked *a, b, c, d, e, f, g*.

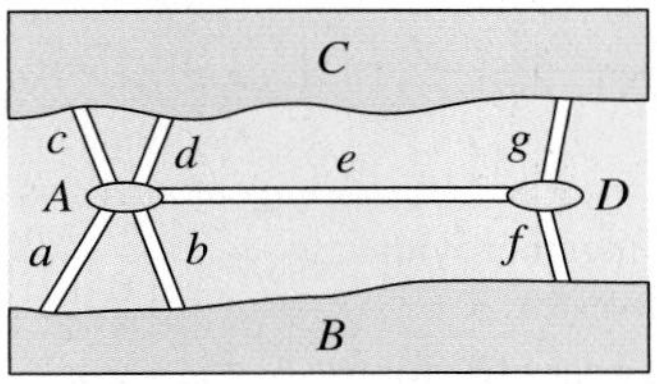

FIGURE 8.78

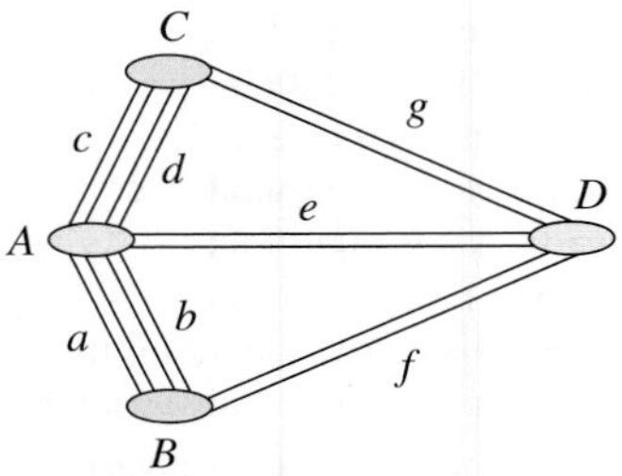

FIGURE 8.79

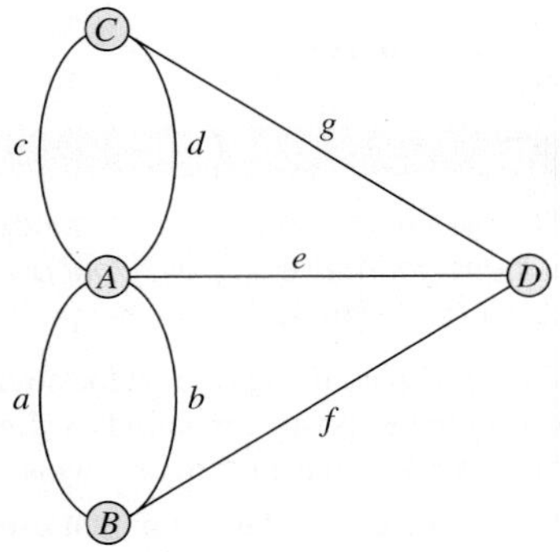

FIGURE 8.80 The network in Figure 8.80 has four vertices, **A, B, C** and **D.**
Vertex **A** has 5 edges,
Vertex **B** has 3 edges.
Vertex **C** has 3 edges
and vertex **D** has 3 edges.

The great Swiss mathematician Leonhard Euler solved the problem in 1736. First, he redrew the map by making islands *A* and *D* smaller and lengthening the bridges (Figure 8.78). He also made shores *B* and *C* smaller (Figure 8.79).

These changes distort the picture but *do not* change the problem. Then, in a stroke of genius, Euler thought of land areas *A*, *B*, *C*, and *D* as **points** and bridges *a* through *g* as **arcs** or **edges** connecting them. The resulting **network** is diagrammed in Figure 8.80. Euler's question became: *Can **all** the arcs be traced with a pencil only once without lifting the pencil off the paper?* If the answer to a problem like this is yes, the network is called **traversable.**

In a network, the points are the endpoints of arcs and are called **vertices** (singular **vertex**). Euler noticed that if a path goes through a vertex, the vertex must have two arcs: one in and one out. Thus, if a network has an odd vertex, it *must* be the starting or finishing point for a traversable path. But all four vertices in the Königsberg network are odd! Thus, the network is *not* traversable. We will study more about networks, traversability, and the bridges of New York and then end the section by considering other geometries and topology.

A Networks

Any connected set of line segments or arcs is called a **network.** (For the purposes of this section, your intuitive notion of what an arc is is sufficient.) If the network can be drawn by tracing each line segment or arc exactly once without lifting the pencil from the paper, the network is said to be **traversable.** Any simple network (one that does not cross itself) is traversable. If the network is both simple and closed, then you can choose any point of the network as the starting point, and this point will also be the terminal point of the drawing. If the network is simple but not closed, then you must start at one of the endpoints and finish at the other. Figure 8.81 shows several examples of simple networks that are either closed or not closed.

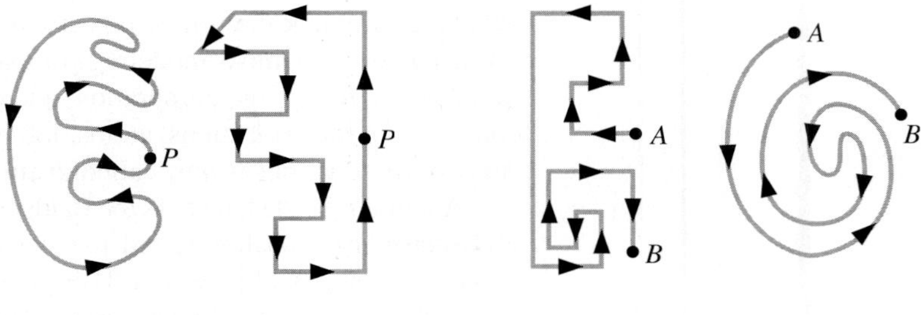

Closed

Not closed

FIGURE 8.81 Simple networks.

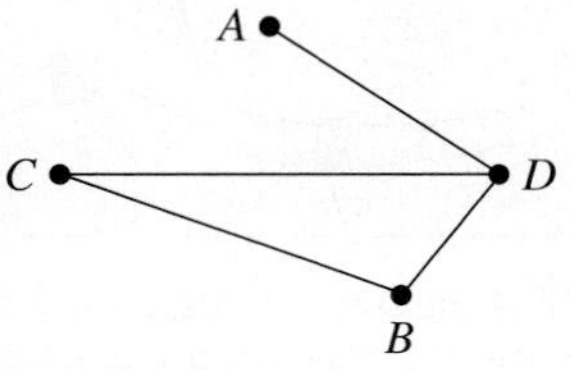

FIGURE 8.82

Let us examine the network in Figure 8.80 more closely. The number of edges for vertex *A* is 5; it is an odd vertex. As a matter of fact, all vertices in Figure 8.80 are odd. Figure 8.82 shows another network in which *A* and *D* are odd vertices but *B* and *C* are even. Since every arc has two endpoints, it is impossible for a network to have an odd number of odd vertices. Thus, a network can have 0, 2, 4, 6, . . . , any even number of odd vertices. Notice that there are four odd vertices in the Königsberg problem and two odd vertices in Figure 8.82.

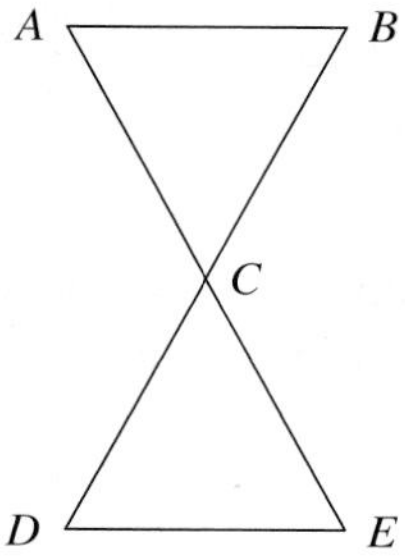

(a) No odd vertices

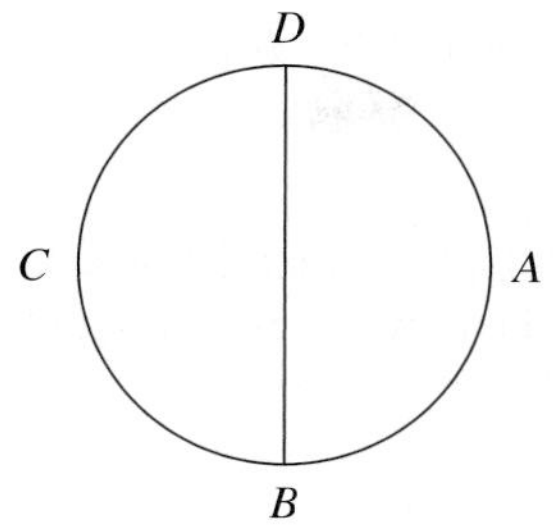

(b) Two odd vertices

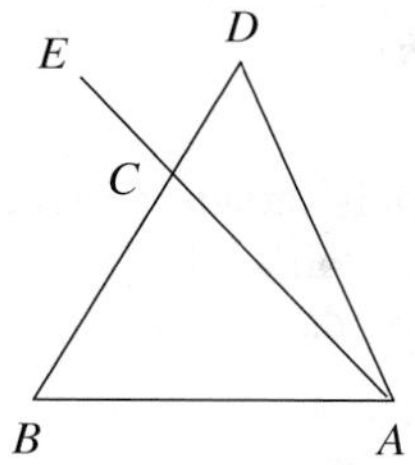

(c) Two odd vertices

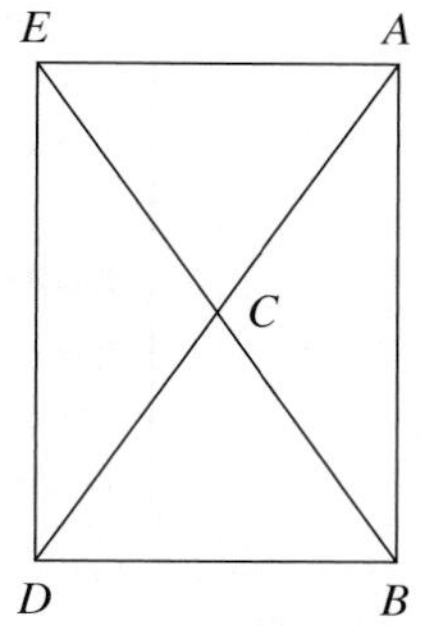

(d) Four odd vertices

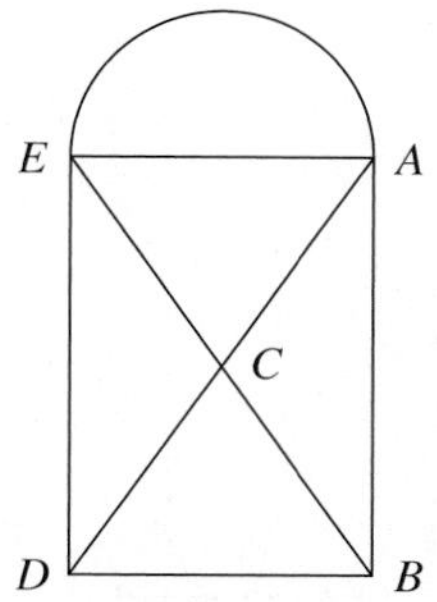

(e) Two odd vertices

EXAMPLE 1 Finding Which Network Is Traversable

Which of the following networks are traversable? If a network is traversable, indicate your beginning and ending points.

Solution

(a) The network is traversable. You can start at any point and you will end at that same point.

(b) The figure is traversable, but you must start at one of the odd vertices, *B* or *D*. If you start at *B*, you end at *D*, and if you start at *D*, you end at *B*.

(c) The figure is traversable. This time you must start at *A* or *E* (the odd vertices).

(d) The figure is not traversable. (Do you know why?)

(e) The figure is traversable. You can start at one of the odd vertices, *D* or *B*, and end at the other.

From what you have studied so far, can you make any generalizations about the traversability of a network? Here are the conclusions Euler reached.

> **Traversability Rules**
>
> 1. A network with *no* odd vertices is traversable. You can start at any point and you will end at that same point.
> 2. A network with exactly *two* odd vertices is traversable. You must start at one of the odd vertices and end at the other.
> 3. A network with *more than two* odd vertices is not traversable.

EXAMPLE 2 A New York Tour Using Networks

The city of New York is composed of five boroughs, as shown in Figure 8.83: Bronx (*B*), Brooklyn and Queens (*B-Q*), Manhattan (*M*), and Staten Island (*SI*), connected by a network of bridges and tunnels, some of them passing through Randall's Island (*RI*) and

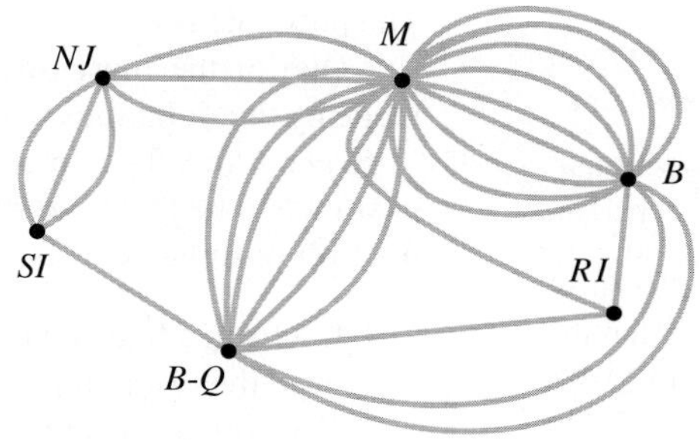

FIGURE 8.83

some leading to New Jersey (*NJ*). Determine whether you could take a tour going over each bridge and through each tunnel exactly once. (Since there is no water separating Brooklyn and Queens, we call this land mass *B*-*Q*.)

Solution

The network is shown in Figure 8.83. Note that the only *two* odd vertices are Manhattan (19) and Randall's Island (3), so the network is traversable. Your path must start at one of these two odd vertices and end at the other.

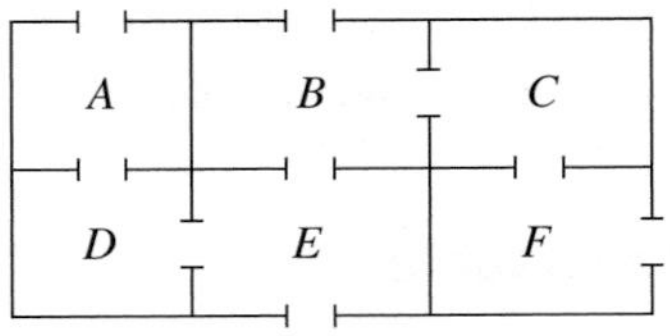

FIGURE 8.84

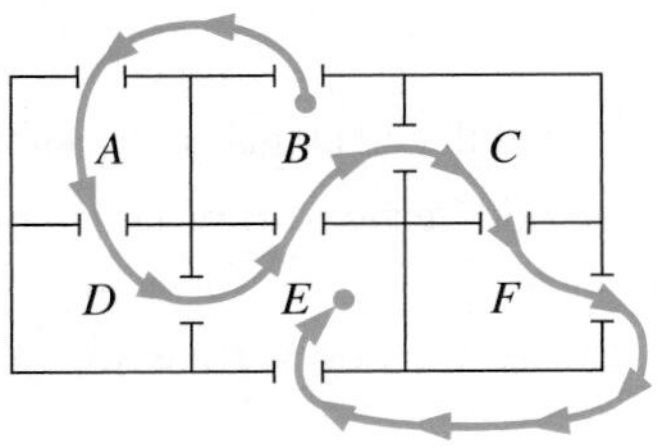

FIGURE 8.85

EXAMPLE 3 A House Tour Using Networks

Figure 8.84 shows a house floor plan with six rooms (*A*, *B*, *C*, *D*, *E*, and *F*) and with the openings representing doors. Is it possible to take a walk through the house and pass through each door exactly once?

Solution

Think of each room and the outdoors as a vertex and the corresponding number of doors as the number of paths to that vertex. Since there are only two odd vertices, *B* and *E*, the network is traversable, but you must start at one of the odd vertices and end at the other, as shown in Figure 8.85.

Network theory has many practical applications. It is of great importance in computer science and technology; it is also used to solve problems in the design of city streets, to analyze traffic patterns, to find the most efficient routes for garbage collection, and so on. Networks are further used in connection with PERT (Program Evaluation and Review Technique) diagrams in planning complicated projects. These diagrams help to determine how long a project will take and when to schedule different phases of the project.

B Non-Euclidean Geometry

The theory of networks we have studied is part of a branch of modern geometry called **graph theory.** Most of the geometry we studied earlier is based on axioms and *postulates* (statements assumed to be true) derived from Euclid's famous book, *The Elements,* written in about 300 B.C. In *The Elements,* five postulates were assumed and then used to prove many propositions about geometric figures. The fifth postulate, the parallel postulate, was quite different from the others and harder to understand until John Playfair (1748–1819), a Scottish physicist and mathematician, stated it in a logically equivalent form.

Euclid's Fifth Postulate (Parallel Postulate)

Given a line and a point not on that line, there is one and only one line through that point parallel to the original line.

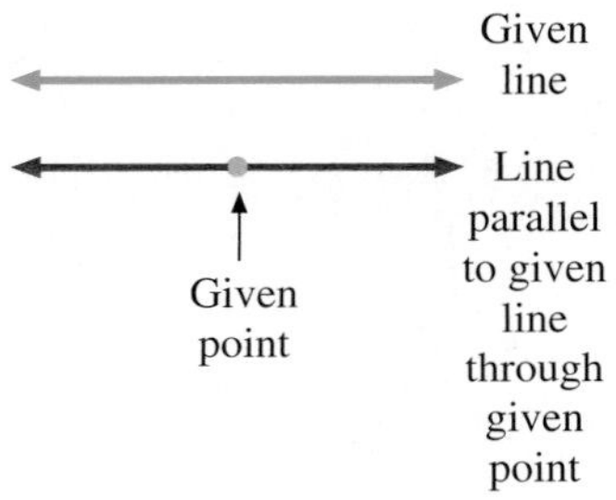

FIGURE 8.86

The postulate is illustrated in Figure 8.86.

One of the most revealing but unsuccessful attempts to prove the postulate was made by the Italian Jesuit Girolamo Saccheri (1667–1733) in a book called *Euclid Freed of Every Flaw*. The "proof" used the method of *contradiction;* that is, it assumed the postulate to be false and showed that this led to a contradiction. The negation (denial) of the fifth postulate consisted of two parts.

1. Given a line and a point not on the line, there is *no* line through the point parallel to the original line.
2. Given a line and a point not on the line, there are *at least two* lines through the point parallel to the original line.

But, to Saccheri's surprise, no contradiction could be found. Less than one hundred years later, three mathematicians, Carl Gauss, Janos Bolyai, and Nikolai Lobachevsky, used the assumptions in the negation of the parallel postulate to develop what is now called **non-Euclidean geometry.**

Carl Friedrich Gauss became interested in the parallel postulate at the age of 15. He formulated an axiom contradicting Euclid's by assuming that *more* than one parallel line could be drawn through a point not on a given line. Rather than attempting to reach a contradiction, Gauss began to see a geometry different from Euclid's but internally consistent. Unfortunately, Gauss never published his research, perhaps to avoid the inevitable public controversy.

Janos Bolyai (1802–1860) and Nikolai Lobachevsky (1792–1856) separately decided to include an *alternative* postulate. Janos Bolyai was a Hungarian army officer and son of a respected mathematician who had studied under Gauss. As Gauss had done earlier, Bolyai assumed that more than one parallel line through a point not on a given line existed, an assumption that led him to exclaim: "Out of nothing I have created a strange new world." Bolyai's work was dated 1829 but published in 1832 as an appendix to his father's two-volume book. When his father sent a copy of the work to Gauss, the reply was less than encouraging. Janos Bolyai never published again. On the other hand, Nikolai Lobachevsky published the first complete text on non-Euclidean geometry in 1829 containing one of the alternative postulates.

Lobachevsky's Alternative to the Parallel Postulate

Given a line and a point not on that line, there is *more* than one line through that point parallel to the original line.

The use of this postulate led to an entirely new type of geometry called ***hyperbolic* geometry.**

In hyperbolic geometry lines are represented by *geodesics* on a *pseudosphere*. A **pseudosphere** is formed by revolving a curve called a *tractrix* about a line *AB*, as shown in Figure 8.87. A **geodesic** is the shortest and least-curved arc between two points on a surface. Can you see why there is more than one line through a given point parallel to the given line?

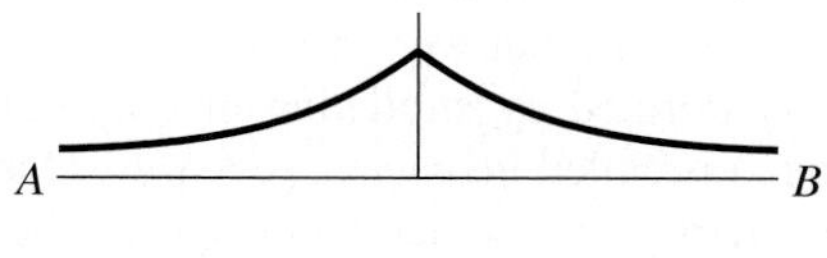

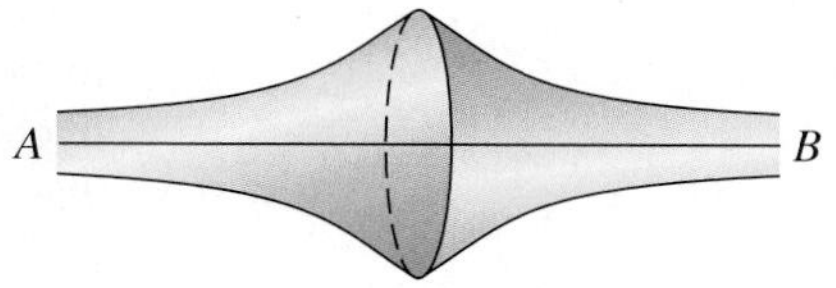

FIGURE 8.87 Lobachevskian hyperbolic model.

A generation after the discovery of hyperbolic geometry, Bernhard Riemann (1826–1866), who was a disciple of Gauss, developed ***elliptic* geometry.** In this geometry, the fifth postulate was stated as follows:

Riemann's Alternative to the Parallel Postulate

Given a line and a point not on that line, there is *no* line parallel to the original line.

Of course, if there are *no* lines parallel to a given line in elliptic, or Riemannian, geometry, every two lines must intersect! How can this be? Because the term *line* is undefined and can be interpreted differently in different geometries.

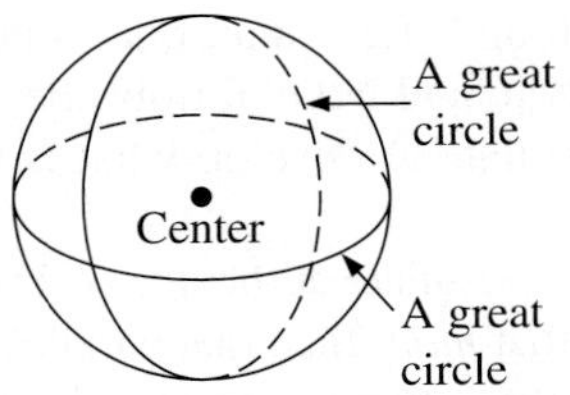

FIGURE 8.88 Riemannian spherical model.

We have already considered lines in the Euclidean plane. In elliptic, or Riemannian, geometry, lines are great circles on a sphere, as shown in Figure 8.88. A **great circle** is a circle that has its center at the center of the sphere and that divides the sphere into two equal parts. Now, can you see why any two lines (great circles) on a sphere must intersect?

EXAMPLE 4 Angle Measures of a Quadrilateral

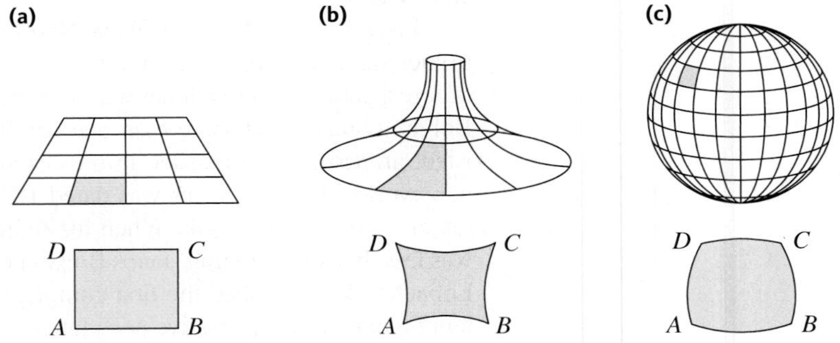

Look at the illustrations showing quadrilaterals on a plane, on a pseudosphere, and on a sphere. What can you say about the measure of the angles D?

Solution

(a) In the Euclidean plane, the measure of angle D is 90°.

(b) In the pseudosphere the measure of angle D is less than 90°.

(c) On the sphere, the measure of angle D is more than 90°.

C Topology

Another branch of modern geometry is **topology.** We have already studied properties of geometric figures that were assumed to be rigid (unchanging). If we allow the figures to be transformed by stretching or compressing, the study of properties that remain unchanged is called *geometric topology*. One of the first persons to introduce topology was the German mathematician Augustus Ferdinand Möbius (1790–1896), so topology is a relatively new branch of mathematics.

Let us look at a very simple example. Consider an ordinary rubber band as shown in Figure 8.89. Take a point on this band and call it P. If we move along the band in a fixed direction from P, we eventually return to the point P. This is a property of the band that is unaltered even if the shape of the band is changed, twisted, or tied in knots, as long as the band is not broken or cut. If the band is cut in order to get a new shape, then the cut ends must be rejoined in order to keep this property unchanged.

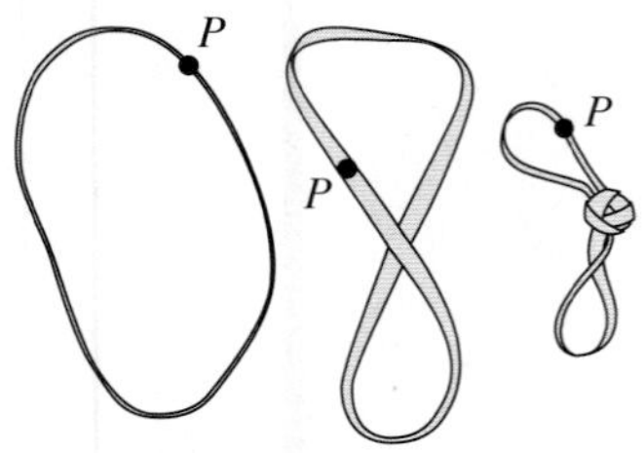

FIGURE 8.89

The three figures formed by the rubber bands in Figure 8.89 are said to be *topologically equivalent* because they can be obtained one from another by just changing the shape of the band as restricted above. Any two figures are topologically equivalent if one can be formed from the other by continuous deformation without cutting or tearing the figure. For example, a baseball and a flat solid plate are equivalent because if the ball were made of soft clay, it could be compressed into the flat plate without cutting or tearing the clay.

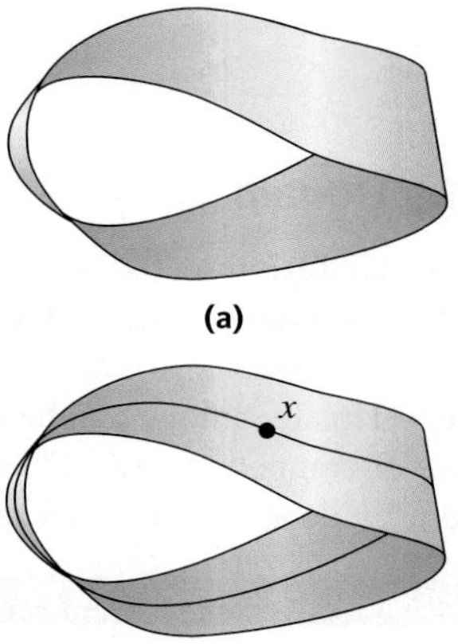

FIGURE 8.90 Möbius strip.

EXAMPLE 5 Finding Figures That Are Topologically Equivalent

Are the figures in each of the following pairs topologically equivalent?

(a) A straight line segment and the letter C

(b) A doughnut and a solid steel cylinder

Solution

(a) These are equivalent because the line would just have to be bent in the shape of the C.

(b) These are not equivalent because the doughnut would have to be cut before it could be shaped into a cylinder.

One of the things that Möbius is noted for is his study of one-sided surfaces. These surfaces include the one that is called a Möbius strip, shown in Figure 8.90(a). You can make such a strip quite easily. Take a strip of paper, give it a half-twist, and join the ends together. This connects the *opposite* sides of the original strip so that the new figure has only one side. You can check this by making an X, as in Figure 8.90(b), on the surface of the strip and then running a pencil line from the X along the strip until you come back to the starting point. Also note that the Möbius strip has only one edge. Try cutting the strip along the line you have drawn and see what you get.

The number of holes that occur in a figure are of interest to topologists. This number is called the *genus* of the figure; it gives the largest number of complete cuts that can be made without cutting the figure apart. For example, if you take a coffee cup with the usual small handle [Figure 8.91(a)], the only cut through the figure that leaves it in one piece is a cut through the handle, as in Figure 8.91(b). Note that the coffee cup is a figure with just one hole (in the handle), so its genus is 1.

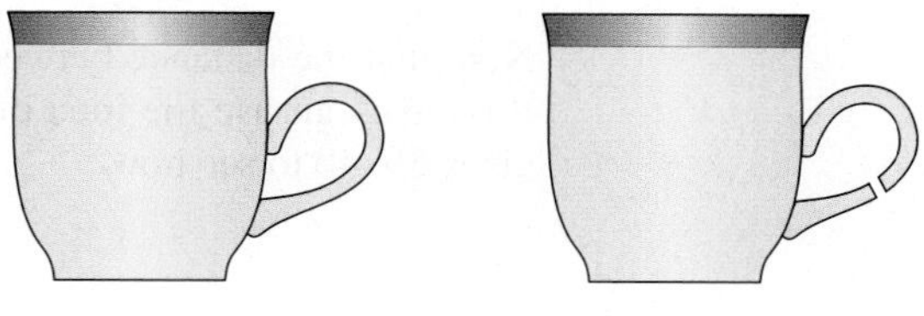

FIGURE 8.91

EXAMPLE 6 Finding the Genus of Objects

Give the genus of each of the following objects:

(a) A 25-cent coin (a quarter)

(b) This button

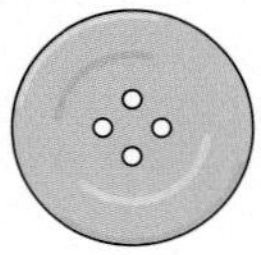

(c) This nail file

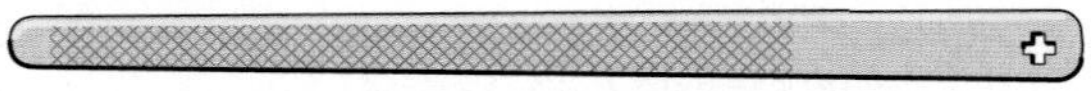

Solution

(a) There is no hole in the quarter, so the genus is zero.

(b) There are four holes in the button, so the genus is 4.

(c) There is one hole in the nail file, so the genus is 1.

D Applications

EXAMPLE 7 Applications of Geometry to McDonald's

A software program called Vertical Mapper for Surface Analysis created a Natural Neighborhood (Voroni) diagram for McDonald's restaurants (marked with stars) in San Francisco, as shown in Figure 8.92. The edges of each area (also known as a *Thiessen polygon*) are equidistant between adjacent outlets. This technique can be used to select locations that maximize distance from sister stores or competing ones. Thiessen polygons create a sense of a chain's location strategy and provide a tool to visualize the effect of potential changes in strategy.

(a) Do the edges of the areas shown (in red) form a traversable network?

(b) If you draw a line segment between two adjacent outlets (stars), where does the line segment intersect the (red) edge?

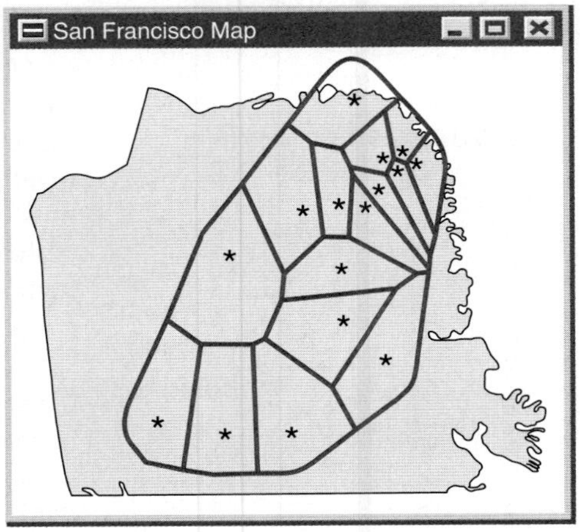

Reprinted courtesy of Tetrad Computer Applications, Inc.

FIGURE 8.92

Solution

(a) There are more than two odd vertices in the network. This means that the network is not traversable.

(b) The point of intersection of the line segment and the edge is the midpoint of the line segment.

Note that the distance between most adjacent outlets is the same. Can you generalize this? We can use the idea of a network to plan an efficient vacation! Look at Exercises 39–40 to see how.

8.6 EXERCISES

A Networks

In problems 1–10, find

a. the number of even vertices.

b. the number of odd vertices.

c. whether the network is traversable and which vertices are possible starting points if the network is traversable.

1.

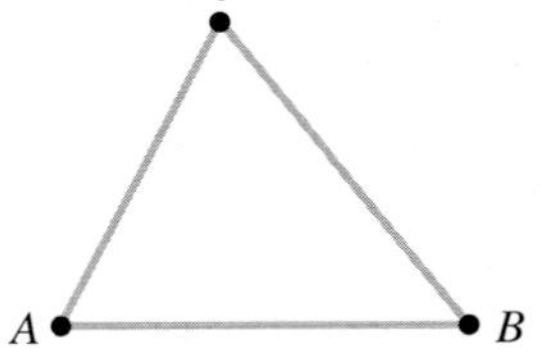

2.

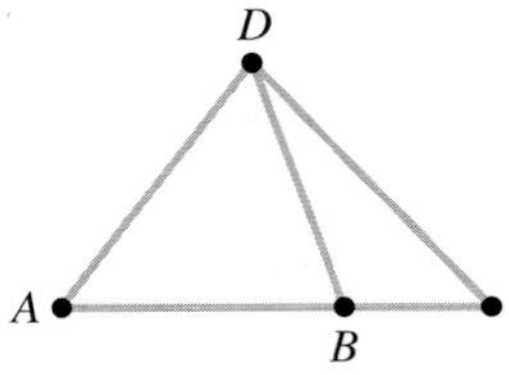

3.

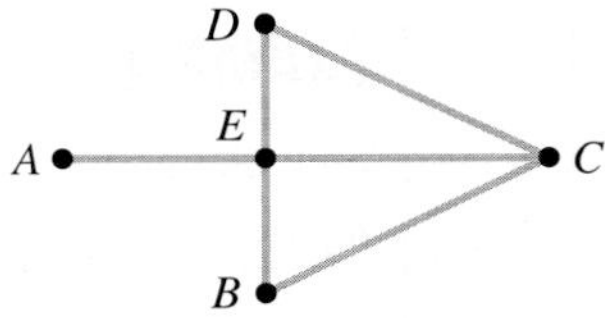

4.

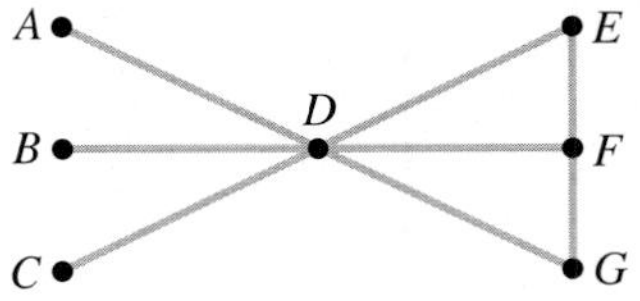

5.

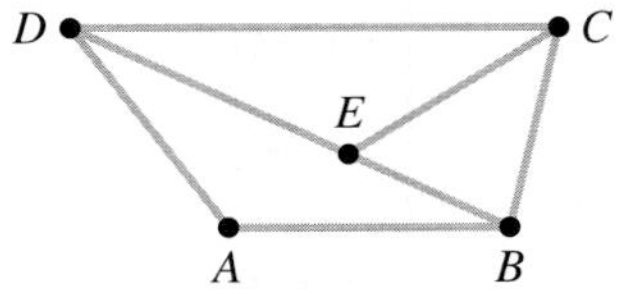

6.

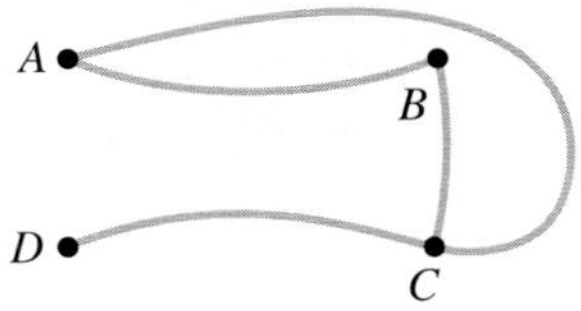

7.

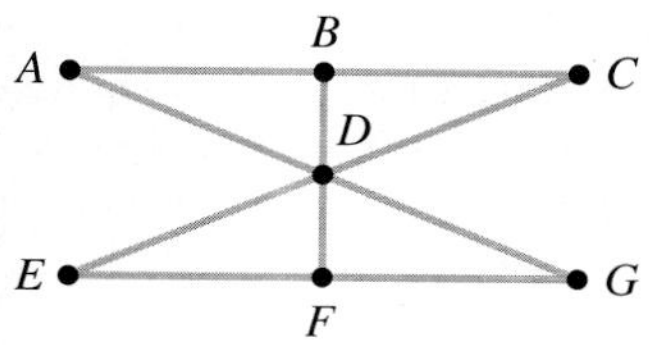

8.

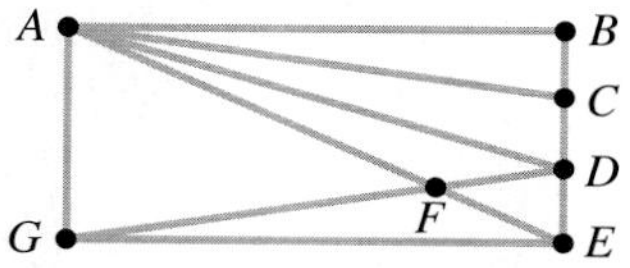

9. The network formed by the edges of a square pyramid

10. The network formed by the edges of a rectangular box

11. Use a network to find whether it is possible to draw a simple connected broken line that crosses each line segment of the figure below exactly once. The line segments are those that join successive dots.

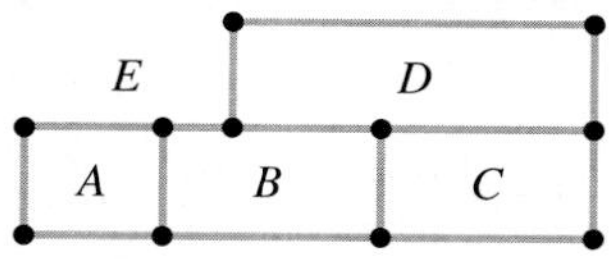

12. Repeat problem 11 for the figure below.

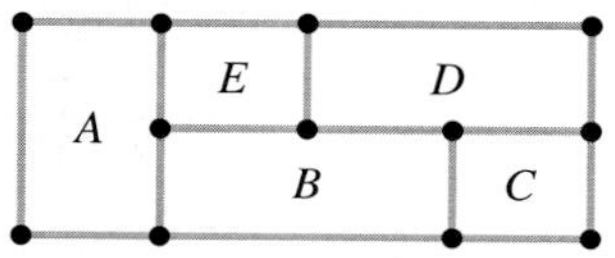

In problems 13–20, use the traversability rules to determine whether it is possible to take a walk through the house and pass through each door exactly once. Which of the paths must start and end outside?

13.

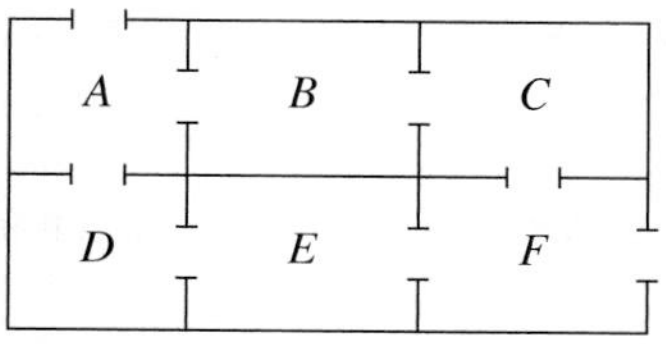

14.

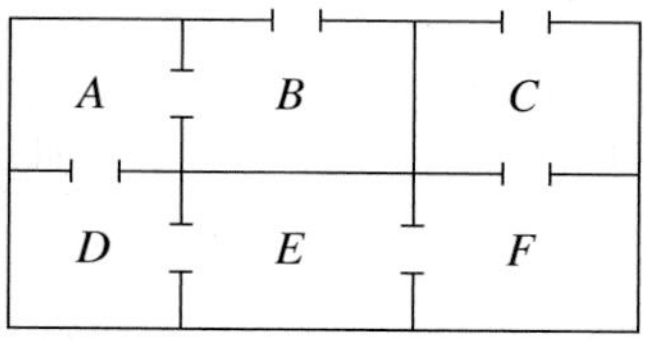

15.

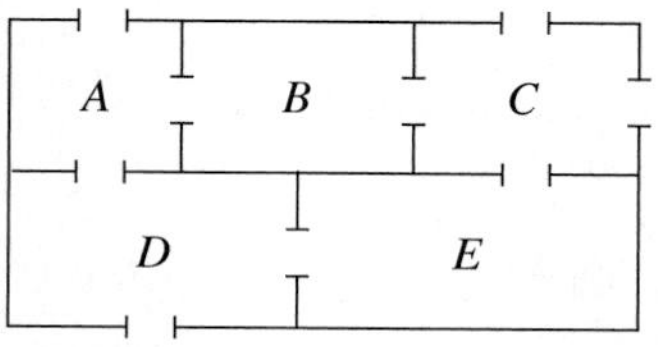

16.

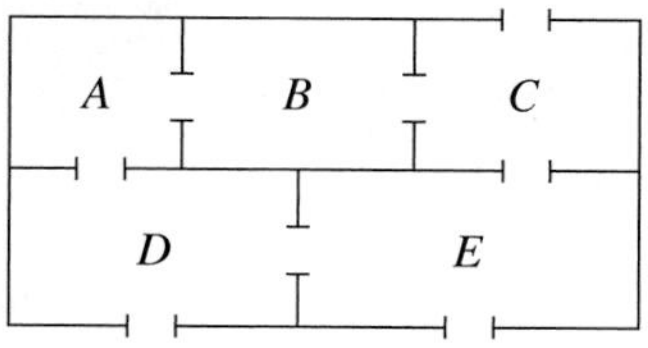

17.

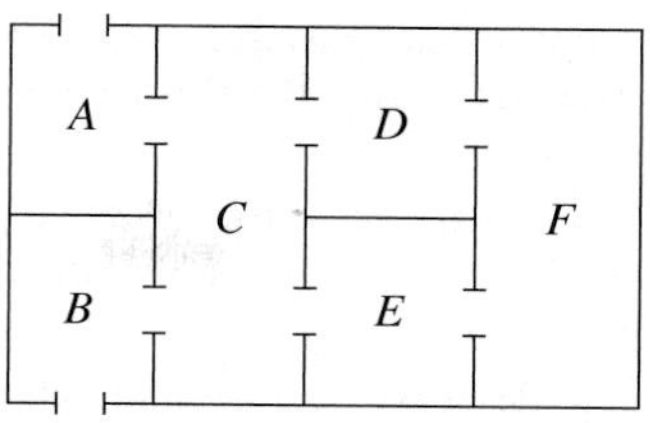

18.

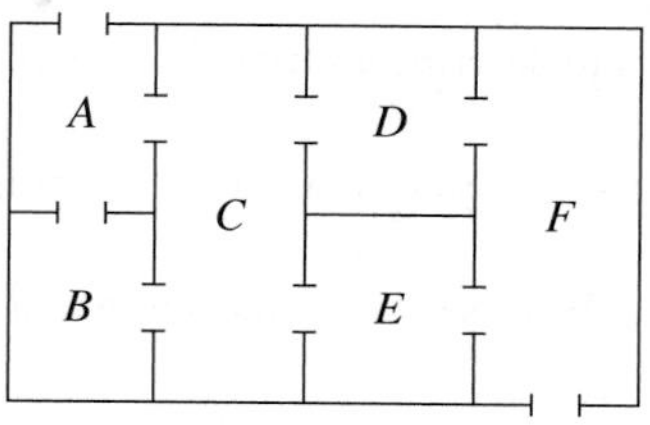

19.

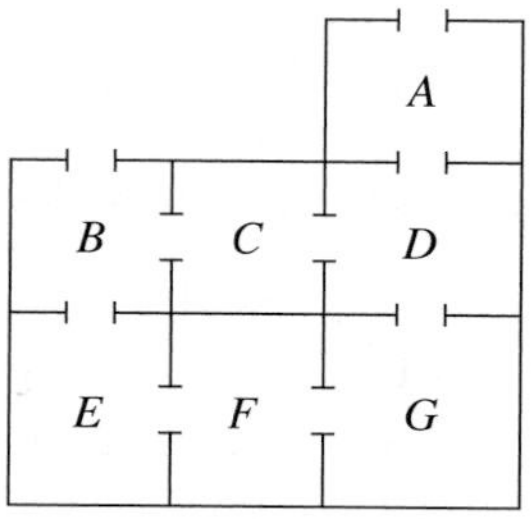

20.

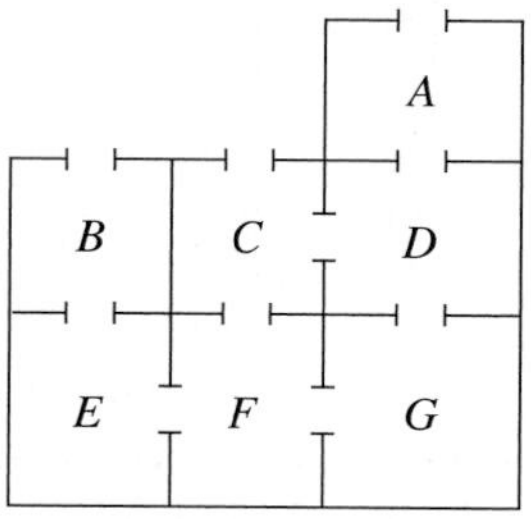

21. Use a network to find whether it is possible to take a walk through the building with the floor plan in the figure below and pass through each doorway exactly once. Is it possible if you must start and end outside?

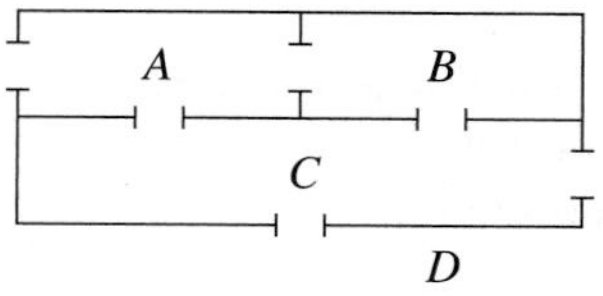

22. Repeat problem 21 for the floor plan in the figure below.

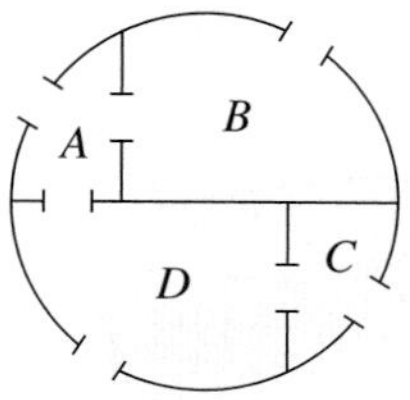

B Non-Euclidean Geometry

23. State the parallel postulate in Euclidean geometry.

24. State the parallel postulate in hyperbolic geometry.

25. State the parallel postulate in elliptic geometry.

26. In which geometry is the sum of the measures of the angles of a triangle 180°? (*Hint:* See the illustrations in Example 4.)

27. In which geometry is the sum of the measures of the angles of a triangle less than 180°? (*Hint:* See the illustrations in Example 4.)
28. In which geometry is the sum of the measures of the angles of a triangle more than 180°? (*Hint:* See the illustrations in Example 4.)
29. Which model is often used to describe a surface in Euclidean geometry?
30. Which model is often used to describe a surface in hyperbolic geometry?
31. Which model is often used to describe a surface in elliptic geometry?
32. In which geometry is a globe representing the surface of the Earth most appropriate?

C Topology

33. State which of the following saber saw and knife blades are topologically equivalent:

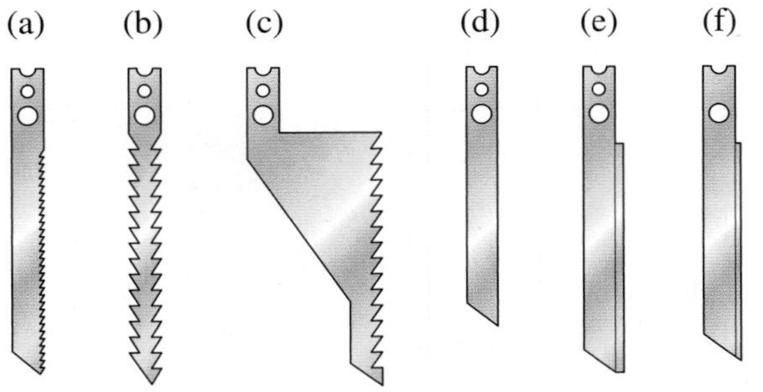

34. Which of the following statements are true and which are false?
    a. An ordinary lead pencil and a golf ball are topologically equivalent.
    b. A screw bolt and the nut that goes on it are topologically equivalent.
    c. A teacup with one handle and a teacup with two handles are topologically equivalent.
    d. An ordinary washer that goes on a bolt and the nut that screws it down are topologically equivalent.
    e. Two uncut fruits, a plum and a peach, are topologically equivalent.
35. State the genus of each of the blades shown in problem 33.
36. State the genus of each of the following:
    a. A comb

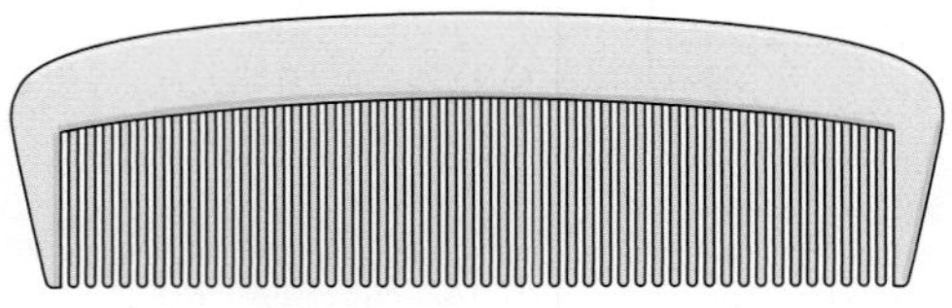

    b. A drawing aid

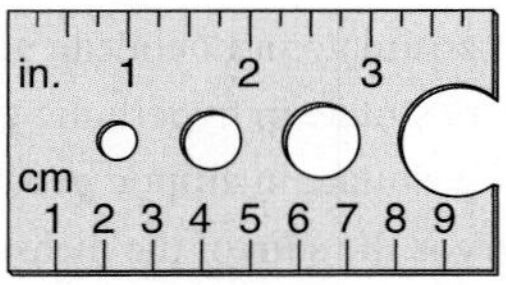

37. Assume that both of the following are made of solid cord. Student Topo claims that the two are topologically equivalent, while student Geo claims they are not equivalent. Who do you think is correct? Explain. (*Hint:* Suppose that you cut through a loop of the left-hand figure and try to unwind it.)

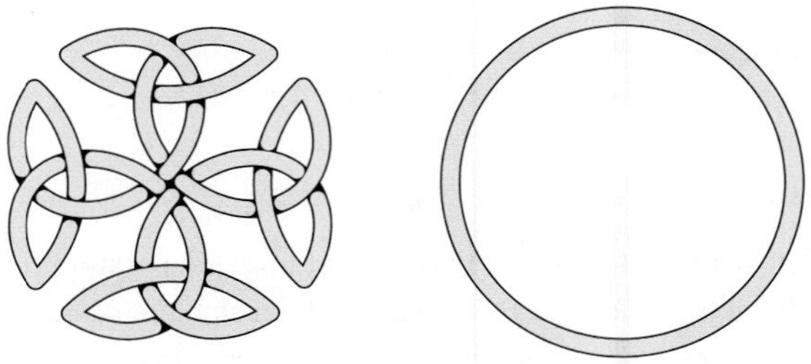

38. Are the two clips shown here topologically equivalent? Explain.

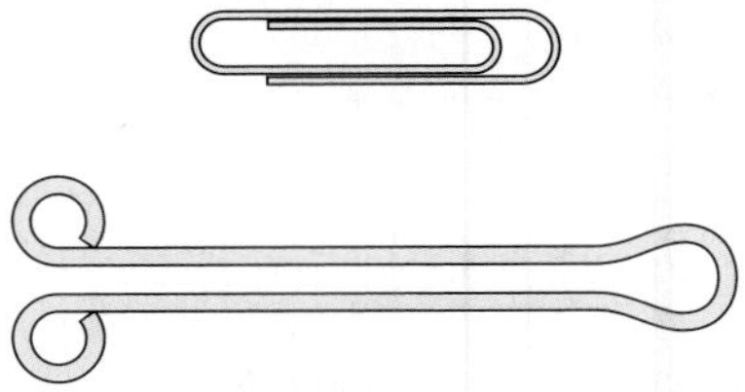

D Applications

39. Suppose you want to take a vacation and visit New York, Orlando, Texas, Los Angeles, Colorado, and St. Louis. If you want to start and end in New York, what is the most efficient way to drive to these six cities? The Web site http://www.gebweb.net/optimap can tell you. Enter the cities, starting with New York, and tell the optimizer to *Calculate the Fastest Roundtrip.*
    a. How many points are marked in the map (network)?
    b. How many edges does each point have?
    c. Is the network traversable? Why?
    d. How far have you traveled? The optimizer will tell you! Look under Computed Data.
    e. How many hours would the trip take, according to the optimizer?
    f. If you were to drive the 10,471 km continuously for 108 hr., how fast would you be going? How many mi/hr is that?

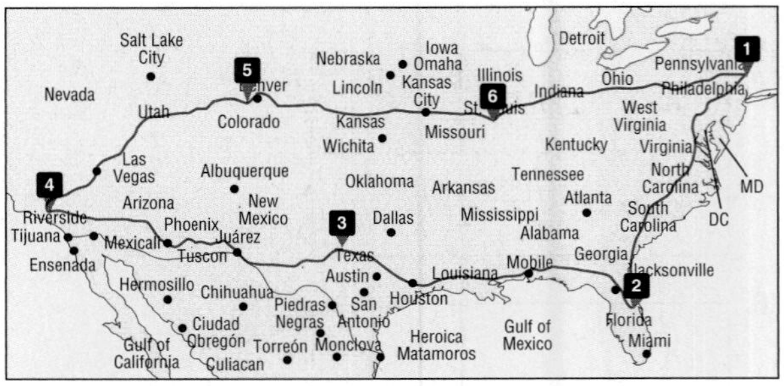

40. Suppose you want to end the vacation of Exercise 39 in Atlanta. Add Atlanta to your list and enter *Calculate Fastest A-Z trip.*

a. Draw a network representing the map you get from the optimizer.

b. Determine the number of edges for each vertex.

c. Is this network traversable? Why?

d. Show one path that traverses this network.

41. Because of budget constraints, the new mayor of Königsberg decided to close one of the bridges to avoid the traffic jams caused by tourists trying to find the route that would take them across each of the bridges only once! His solution was simple: **close one of the bridges.** But which one? He ordered his consultants to study the traversability rules.

a. Can you close any of the bridges so that the remaining 6 bridges are traversable?

b. If one of the bridges is closed, where do you have to start your journey so you can traverse the path?

c. If you start at one of the odd vertices, where would you end?

42. But times change and the mayor got some stimulus funds!

a. Can the mayor add **one more** bridge so that you have 8 bridges, forming a traversable network?

b. Does it matter where you add the bridge?

IN OTHER WORDS

43. Explain in your own words why it is impossible for a network to have an odd number of odd vertices. (Try to construct one.)

44. Explain in your own words how a network can be used to plan a bus route that can be traversed without traveling any path twice.

DISCOVERY

A plane curve that does not cross itself is called simple, *just as in the case of a broken line. A* closed curve *is one that starts and ends at the same point.* A simple closed curve divides the plane into two parts, the region interior and the region exterior to the curve. *This important statement is the* Jordan curve theorem, *a very deep theorem and one that is very difficult to prove in spite of the fact that it seems so obvious.*

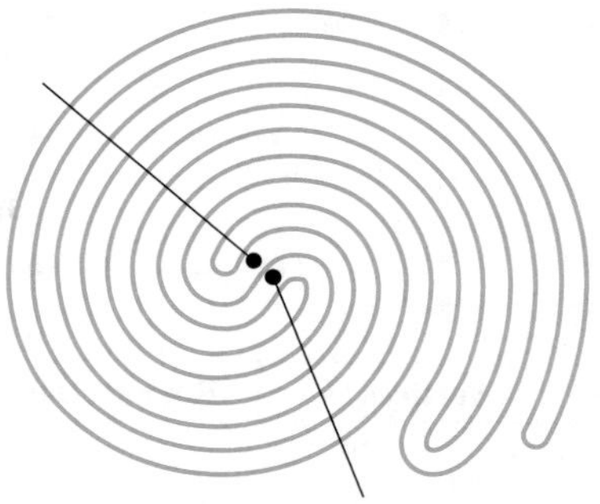

Which dot is inside?

A closed curve that is not simple divides the plane into three or more parts. We call the points where the curve crosses itself **vertices.** Any other points on the curve may also be designated as vertices. We mark the vertices with black dots as in the figure, where five vertices are indicated. The regions into which the plane is divided are numbered 1, 2, 3, and 4 in the figure. The simple curves with vertices as endpoints and containing no other endpoints are called **arcs.** In the figure, there are seven arcs. Can you count them?

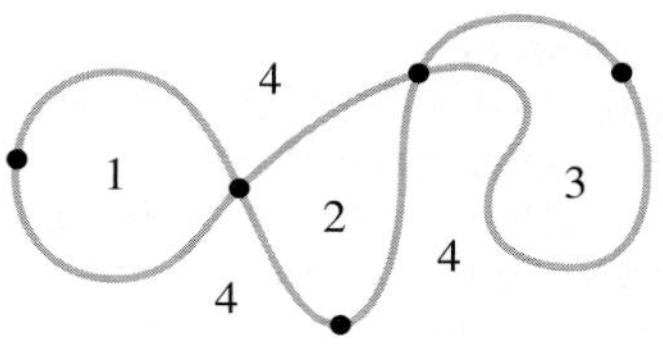

A nonsimple closed curve.

For the following networks (45–52), fill in the table on page 496 with the number of vertices (V), regions (R) into which the plane is divided, and arcs (A) for each figure. (Line segments connecting vertices are also called arcs.) See if you can discover a formula for A in terms of V and R. This formula is one form of the **Euler formula for networks.**

45.

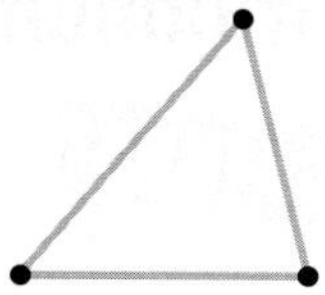

46.

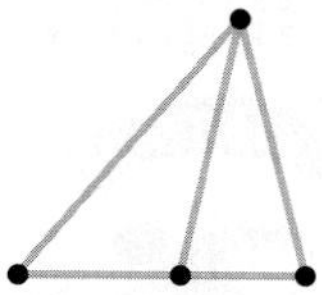

47.

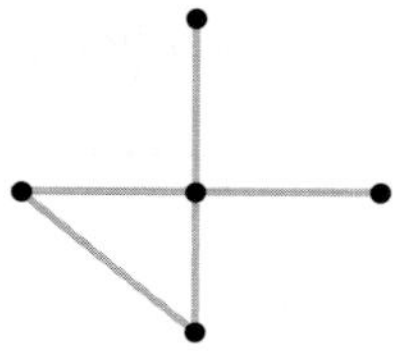

48.

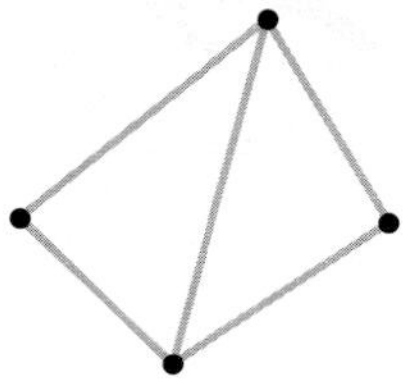

49.

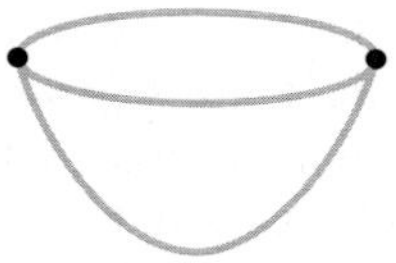

50.

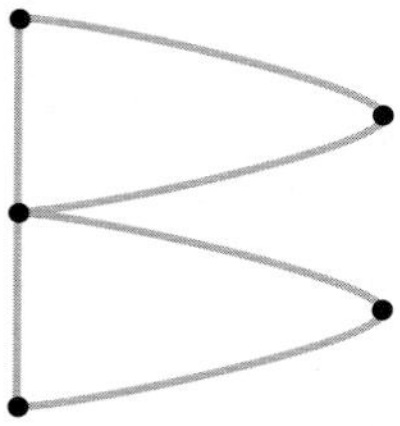

51. 

52. 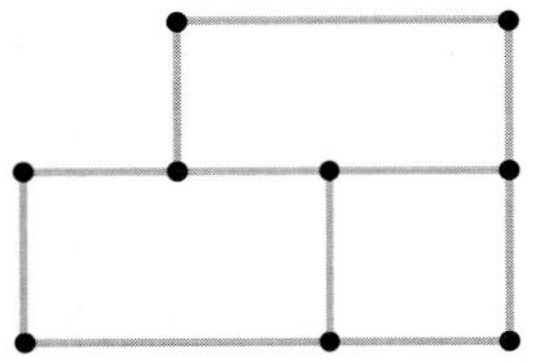

Figure	Vertices (V)	Regions (R)	Arcs (A)
45			
46			
47			
48			
49			
50			
51			
52			

WEB IT EXERCISES

All the topics discussed in this section are thoroughly discussed on the Web. In some cases you need additional software to view the animation, but usually you can download the necessary tools for free. For example, go to link http://cs.unm.edu/~joel/NonEuclid/NonEuclid.html and click on "NonEuclid Home." You can make a triangle in non-Euclidean geometry! Click on "Using NonEuclid—My First Triangle."

1. Find the definition of a parallel line in the text. According to that definition, can parallel lines intersect?

2. Now, suppose you have two lines L_1 and L_2 that are parallel to a third line L_3. What can you say about L_1 and L_2 in Euclidean geometry? What about them in hyperbolic geometry?

   Do not answer yet; look at the diagram! For more explanation, click on "Parallel lines" at link http://cs.unm.edu/~joel/NonEuclid/NonEuclid.html

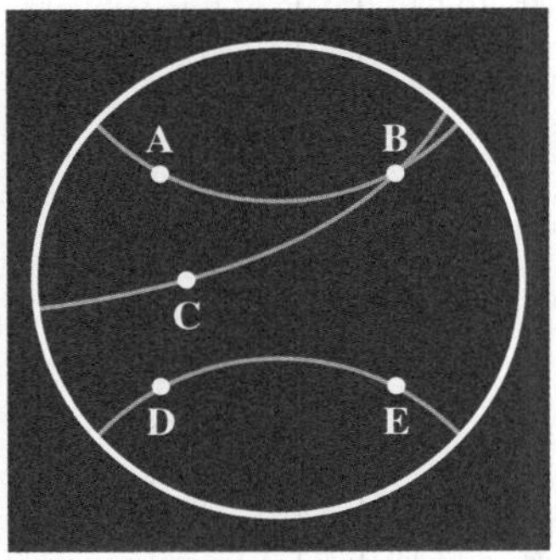

3. Remember the Cartesian coordinate system discussed in Section 7.1? Go to the site mentioned above and learn how to set up an xy coordinate system and then answer the question, How does the graph of the equation $y = x$ look in hyperbolic geometry?

8.7 Right Triangle Trigonometry

GETTING STARTED

OBJECTIVES

A. Find the sine, cosine, tangent and missing sides of a given triangle.

B. Solve applications involving the trigonometric ratios.

The origins of **trigonometry,** from the Greek *trigonon* (angle) and *metria* (measure), can be traced to the ancient Egyptian, Babylonian, and Indian civilizations more than 3000 years ago. The name *trigonometry*, however, first appeared in 1595 as the title of the book *Trigonometria* published by Bartholomeo Pitiscus. There are many applications of trigonometry: astronomy, geography, satellite navigation, and CAT scans and ultrasound, to name a few. In this section we will concentrate on three important trigonometric ratios involving the lengths of the sides of a **right** triangle: **sine** (abbreviated **sin**), **cosine** (abbreviated **cos**), and **tangent** (abbreviated **tan**). The reason for this is that when one of the acute angles and the length of one of the sides of a right triangle are known, we can solve for the length of the other two sides using these ratios. Thales of Miletus may have used similar triangles to calculate the height of the pyramids and solve simple problems. For example, how far from shore is the ship?

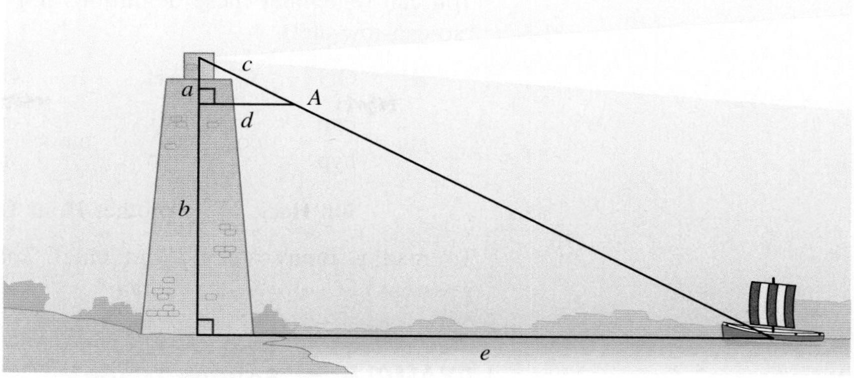
c
a
A
d
b
e

Since the two triangles are similar, their sides are proportional, and we can solve for e in

$$\frac{a}{d} = \frac{a + b}{e}$$

by cross-multiplying to obtain $ae = (a + b)d$. Dividing by a, we find the answer e. Since a, b, and d are known, the value of e from the equation is

$$e = \frac{(a + b)d}{a}$$

A Solving Triangles and the Trigonometric Ratios

The same problem can be solved using trigonometry. We define the trigonometric ratios using a right triangle with acute angle A and right angle C as shown in the figure below.

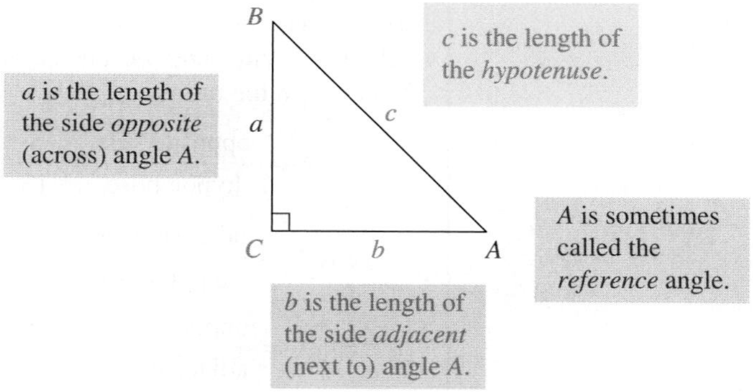
B
c is the length of the *hypotenuse*.
a is the length of the side *opposite* (across) angle A.
a
c
A is sometimes called the *reference* angle.
C
b
A
b is the length of the side *adjacent* (next to) angle A.

Trigonometric Ratios

$$\sin A = \frac{\text{opposite side}}{\text{hypotenuse}}$$

$$\cos A = \frac{\text{adjacent side}}{\text{hypotenuse}}$$

$$\tan A = \frac{\text{opposite side}}{\text{adjacent side}}$$

You can remember these definitions if you remember **SOHCATOA** (pronounced "so-cah-tow-ah"):

S OH C AH T OA

$$\sin = \frac{\text{opp}}{\text{hyp}} \qquad \cos = \frac{\text{adj}}{\text{hyp}} \qquad \tan = \frac{\text{opp}}{\text{adj}}$$

Oh Heck Another Hour Of Algebra

To read a funny story about chief Sohcahtoa visit http://www.slideshare.net/guest6ba711/soh-cah-toa-indian.

EXAMPLE 1 Solving Triangles

Find the sine, cosine, and tangent of the given triangle.

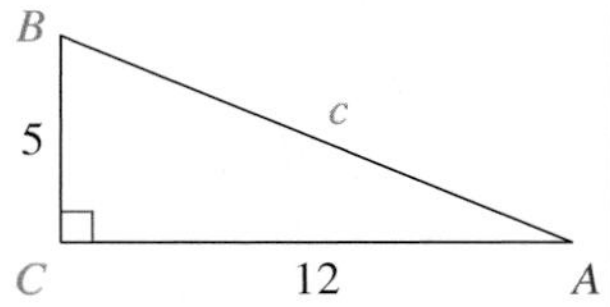

Solution

To find sin A, cos A, and tan A, we first have to find c. Using the Pythagorean theorem,

$$\begin{aligned} a^2 + b^2 &= c^2 \\ 5^2 + 12^2 &= c^2 \\ 25 + 144 &= c^2 \\ 169 &= c^2 \\ \sqrt{169} &= c \\ 13 &= c \end{aligned}$$

Next, we use the definition of the trigonometric ratios. Note that the side *opposite* angle A is 5 units, and the side *adjacent* to A is 12 units. Now substitute the numbers 5, 12, and 13 in the ratios.

$$\sin \text{A} = \frac{\text{opposite side}}{\text{hypotenuse}} = \frac{5}{13}$$

$$\cos \text{A} = \frac{\text{adjacent side}}{\text{hypotenuse}} = \frac{12}{13}$$

$$\tan \text{A} = \frac{\text{opposite side}}{\text{adjacent side}} = \frac{5}{12}$$

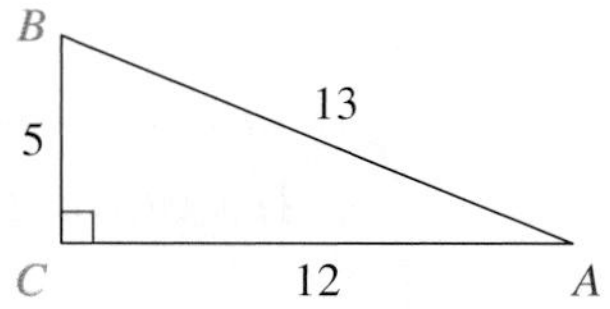

If we are given the measure of one of the acute angles in a right triangle and the length of one of the sides, we can find the length of the other two sides. To do this, we need to use a scientific calculator or a grapher to find approximations for the trigonometric ratios. For example, to find the sine, cosine, and tangent of a 50° angle rounded to *four* decimal places, we use the following keystrokes with a scientific calculator (left) and with a grapher (right).

Using a Scientific Calculator	Using a Grapher (Press MODE and Select Degrees)
50 sin = 0.7660	SIN 50 ENTER = 0.7660
50 cos = 0.6428	COS 50 ENTER = 0.6428
50 tan = 1.1918	TAN 50 ENTER = 1.1918

EXAMPLE 2 Finding a Missing Side

Find a (to the nearest whole number) in the right triangle.

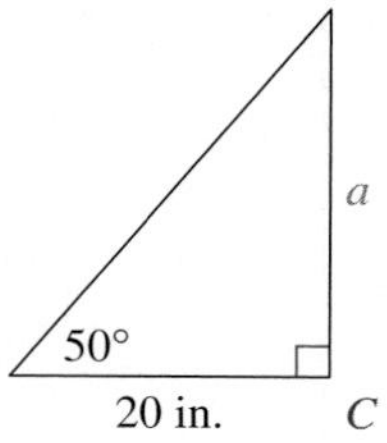

Solution

First, complete the picture by labeling all sides and angles. Note that the 50° angle is inside the triangle and must be labeled A because it is *opposite* side a. Label the remaining angle B as shown below.

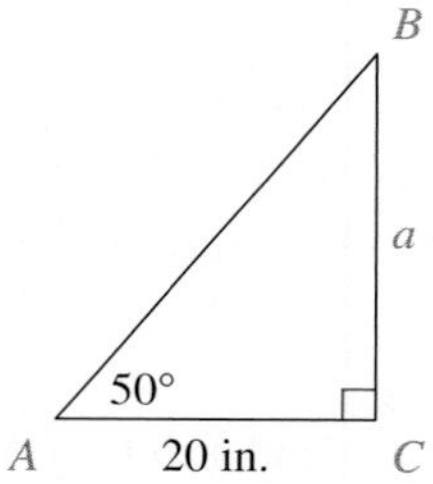

The triangle deals with a (*opposite* A) and 20 in. (*adjacent* to A), which means that we should use the tangent of A. Now,

$$\tan 50° = \frac{\text{opposite side}}{\text{adjacent side}} = \frac{a}{20}$$

Substituting for tan 50°,

$$1.1918 = \frac{a}{20}$$

Multiply by 20.

$$20(1.1918) = a$$

Thus,

$$a \approx 24$$

We already know how to find the length of the hypotenuse of a right triangle by using the Pythagorean theorem. In doing so, we need to know the length of both legs (sides) of the triangle. What about the case in which we only have the length of one side of the triangle and the measure of one of the angles? We can still do it if we use the trigonometric ratios we have just learned! Let us see how.

EXAMPLE 3 Finding the Hypotenuse When the Length of One Side and an Angle Are Given

In the right triangle ABC, the length of $\overline{BC}$ is 10 ft, and the measure of angle B is 40°. Find the length of the hypotenuse $\overline{BA}$ to the nearest whole number.

Solution

First draw triangle ABC (left), and then substitute $BC = 10$ ft, $BA = h$, and $B = 40°$ (right).

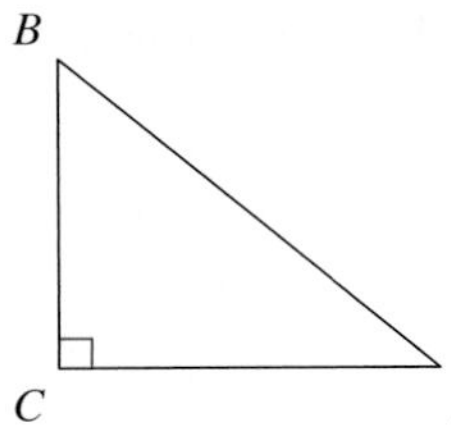

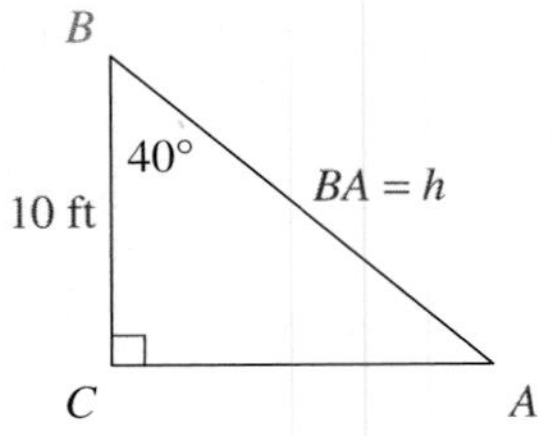

Angle B is 40°, BC is 10 ft, and $BA = h$. Since $\overline{BC}$ is *adjacent* to B and h is the *hypotenuse,* we need the ratio involving the *adjacent* side and the *hypotenuse,* that is, the cosine of $B = 40°$.

Using a calculator will tell us that

$$\cos 40° \approx 0.7660$$

Thus,

$$\cos 40° = \frac{\text{adjacent side}}{\text{hypotenuse}} = \frac{10 \text{ ft}}{h}$$

Substituting 0.7660 for cos 40°, $\quad 0.7660 = \dfrac{10 \text{ ft}}{h}$

Cross-multiplying, $\quad 0.7660h = 10 \text{ ft}$

Dividing both sides by 0.7660, $\quad h = \dfrac{10 \text{ ft}}{0.7660} \approx 13 \text{ ft}$

Can we check the answer? By the Pythagorean theorem, if $10^2 + CA^2 \approx 13^2$, we are correct. To find the length of $\overline{CA}$, we use the fact that the sum of the angles on a triangle is 180°. Since the measure of angle B is 40° and $m\angle C$ is 90°, $m\angle A = 180° - 40° - 90° = 50°$.

With this information, we can find the length of $\overline{AC}$ by using

$$\tan 50° = \frac{\text{opposite side}}{\text{adjacent}} = \frac{10 \text{ ft}}{CA}$$

Substituting 1.1918 for tan 50°, $\quad 1.1918 = \dfrac{10 \text{ ft}}{CA}$

$$CA = \frac{10 \text{ ft}}{1.1918} \approx 8$$

Our result will be correct if $10^2 + 8^2 \approx 13^2$, but $100 + 64 \approx 169$, so our answer is right!

B Applications of the Trigonometric Ratios

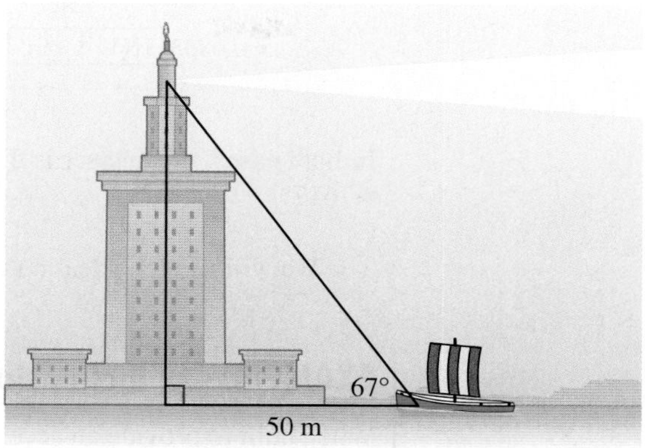

EXAMPLE 4 Finding the Height of the Alexandria Lighthouse

The figure above shows one of the Seven Wonders of the World, the Great Lighthouse at Alexandria, Egypt, whose construction started in 290 B.C. The platform on which the lighthouse stands is about 100 m wide, and the angle of elevation from the corner of the platform to the top of the lighthouse is 67°. To the nearest meter, how high is the lighthouse?

Solution

We start by making a picture. Since the platform is 100 m wide, the distance from the center of the platform to the corner is 50 m, the angle of elevation A is 67°, and the height we would like to find is x, as shown in the diagram.

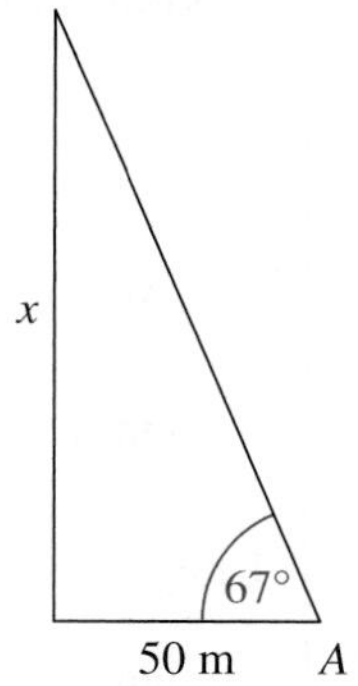

Using angle A as our reference angle, we are looking for the length x of the *opposite* side when we know the length of the *adjacent* side, so we have to use

$$\tan 67^\circ = \frac{\text{opposite}}{\text{adjacent}} = \frac{x}{50}$$

Using a calculator, $$2.3559 = \frac{x}{50}$$

Cross-multiplying, $$50(2.3559) = x$$

$$118 = x \text{ (to the nearest meter)}$$

If we know the length of two sides of a right triangle, the measures of the corresponding angles can be found by using the *inverse trigonometric keys* on a calculator. For example, suppose that $\tan A = 0.0015$. We can find the measure of angle A by using the *inverse tan* key usually labeled tan^{-1}.

Using a Scientific Calculator	Using a Grapher (Press MODE and Select Degrees)
0.0833 INV tan ($\tan^{-1}$)	2nd TAN ($\tan^{-1}$) 0.0833 ENTER

In both cases, the answer is 4.7617, which means that the measure of angle A is about 4.7617°

We will use this idea in the next example.

EXAMPLE 5 Inclination of a Ramp

When built to provide an accessible handicap entrance, the slope of a ramp should be as small as possible. The maximum slope in new construction is 1:12 (every inch of rise will require 1 ft of run). What is the maximum angle of inclination of the ramp shown in the figure?

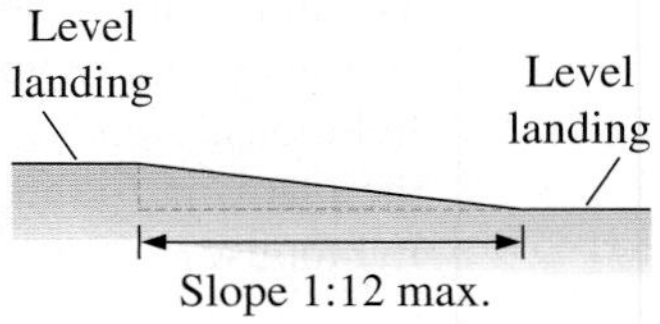

Solution

Make a diagram using the given information and labeling the unknown angle as A. We are given the length of the sides *opposite* (1) and *adjacent* (12) to A, and we are looking for the measure of angle A.

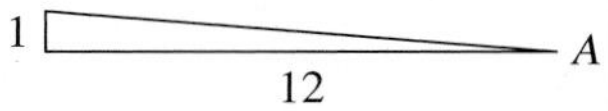

We know

$$\tan A = \frac{\text{opposite}}{\text{adjacent}} = \frac{1}{12} = 0.0833$$

Thus,

$$\tan A = 0.0833$$

Now we use the *inverse tan* key to find A. Using a scientific calculator or a grapher,

0.0833 INV tan ($\tan^{-1}$) = **4.76174498**

INV TAN ($\tan^{-1}$) 0.0833 ENTER = **4.76174498**

Thus, the measure of angle A is approximately **4.7617°.**
This means that the maximum inclination for the ramp is **4.7617°.** You can round the answer *down* to 4° (remember, 4.7617° is the *maximum* inclination, so we round *down*).

8.7 EXERCISES

A Solving Triangles and the Trigonometric Ratios

In problems 1–8, use the Pythagorean theorem to find the length of the missing side.

1. A right triangle has side lengths 3 and 4, as shown in the figure. Find the length c of the hypotenuse.

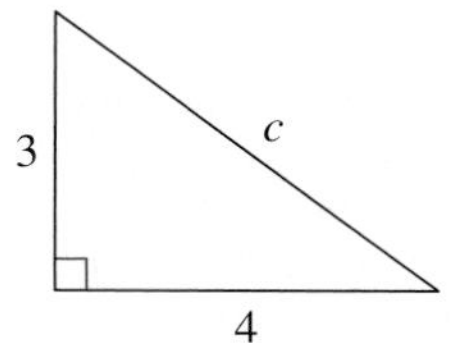

2. A right triangle has side lengths 5 and 12, as shown in the figure. Find the length c of the hypotenuse.

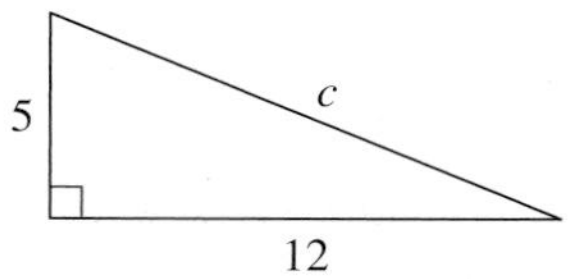

3. A right triangle has side lengths 8 and 15, as shown in the figure. Find the length c of the hypotenuse.

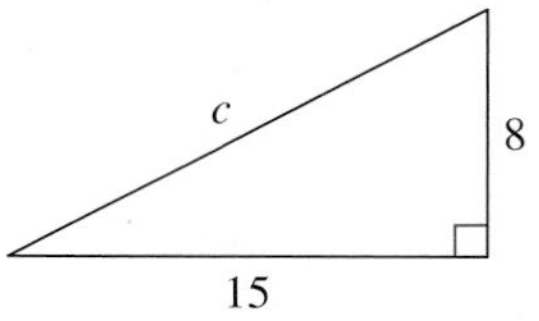

4. A right triangle has side lengths 6 and 8 as shown in the figure. Find the length c of the hypotenuse.

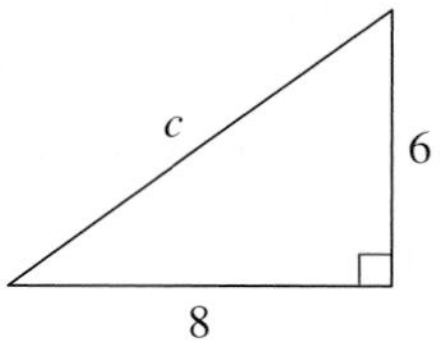

5. The length of one side of a right triangle is 9, and the length of the hypotenuse is 15, as shown in the figure. Find the length b of the other side.

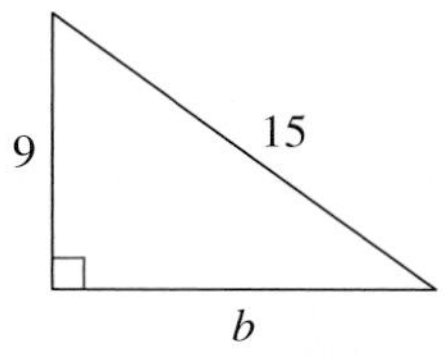

6. The length of one side of a right triangle is 12, and the length of the hypotenuse is 20, as shown in the figure. Find the length b of the other side.

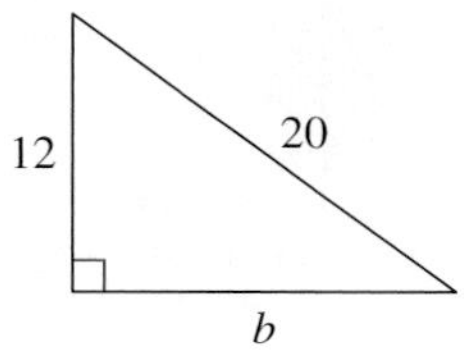

7. The length of one side of a right triangle is 24, and the length of the hypotenuse is 26, as shown in the figure. Find the length a of the other side.

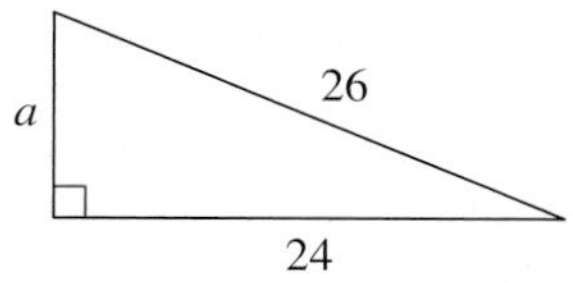

8. The length of one side of a right triangle is 20, and the length of the hypotenuse is 25, as shown in the figure. Find the length a of the other side.

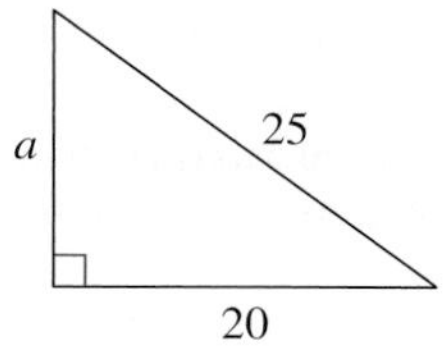

For problems 9–12, refer to the right triangle below.

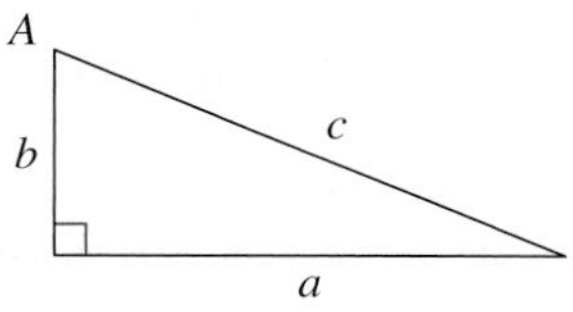

9. If $a = 4$, $b = 3$, and $c = 5$, find

a. $\cos A$.

b. $\sin A$.

c. $\tan A$.

Express your answers as reduced fractions.

10. If $a = 12$, $b = 5$, and $c = 13$, find

a. $\cos A$.

b. $\sin A$.

c. $\tan A$.

Express your answers as reduced fractions.

11. If $a = 30$, $b = 16$, and $c = 34$, find

a. $\cos A$.

b. $\sin A$.

c. $\tan A$.

Express your answers as reduced fractions.

12. If $a = 24$, $b = 10$, and $c = 26$, find

a. $\cos A$.

b. $\sin A$.

c. $\tan A$.

Express your answers as reduced fractions.

13. A right triangle has side lengths 9 and 12, as shown in the figure.

a. Use the Pythagorean theorem to find the length c of the hypotenuse.

b. Use your answer from part **(a)** to find cos A, sin A, and tan A. Express your answers as reduced fractions.

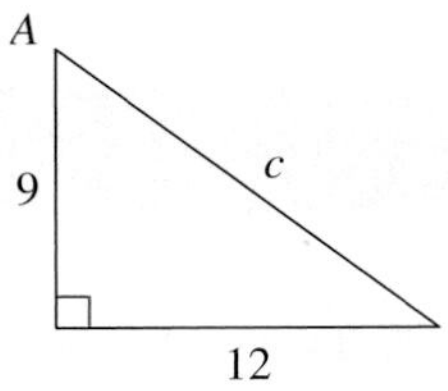

14. A right triangle has side lengths 9 and 40, as shown in the figure below.

a. Use the Pythagorean theorem to find the length c of the hypotenuse.

b. Use your answer from part **(a)** to find cos A, sin A, and tan A. Express your answers as reduced fractions.

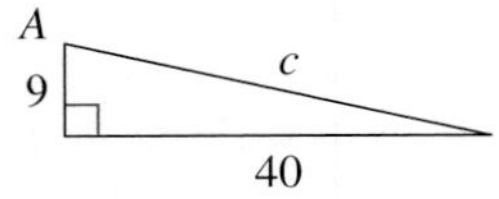

15. A right triangle has side lengths 12 and 35, as shown in the figure.

a. Use the Pythagorean theorem to find the length c of the hypotenuse.

b. Use your answer from part **(a)** to find cos A, sin A, and tan A. Express your answers as reduced fractions.

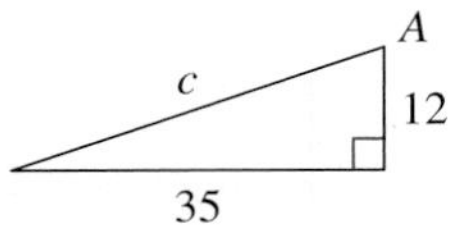

16. A right triangle has side lengths 21 and 28, as shown in the figure.

a. Use the Pythagorean theorem to find the length c of the hypotenuse.

b. Use your answer from part **(a)** to find cos A, sin A, and tan A. Express your answers as reduced fractions.

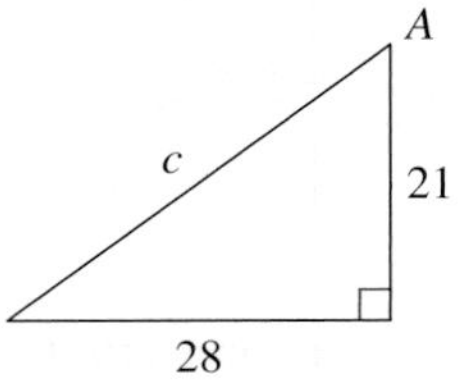

Use the following table to answer problems 17 and 18.

$\sin 55° = 0.82$
$\cos 55° = 0.57$
$\tan 55° = 1.43$

17. The length of one side of a right triangle is 16 in., as shown in the figure.

a. Find the length of side a.

b. Find the length of hypotenuse c.

Round your answers to the nearest whole number.

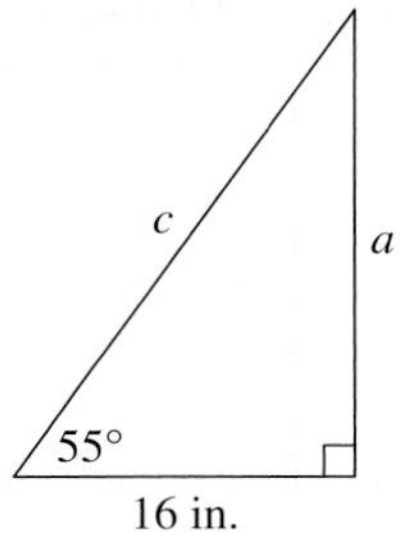

18. The length of one side of a right triangle is 25 ft, as shown in the figure.

a. Find the length of side b.

b. Find the length of the hypotenuse c.

Round your answers to the nearest whole number.

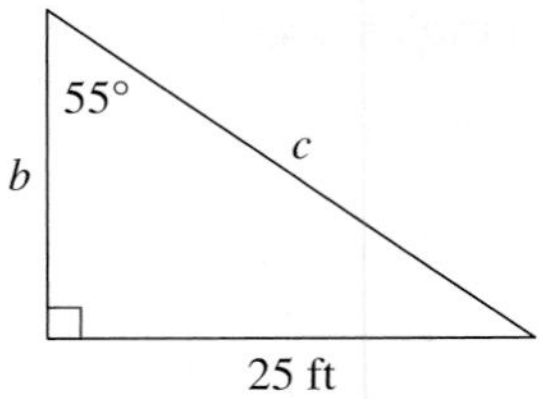

Use the following table to answer problems 19 and 20.

$\sin 20° = 0.34$
$\cos 20° = 0.94$
$\tan 20° = 0.36$

19. The length of one side of a right triangle is 24 in., as shown in the figure.

a. Find the length of side b.

b. Find the length of hypotenuse c.

Round your answers to the nearest whole number.

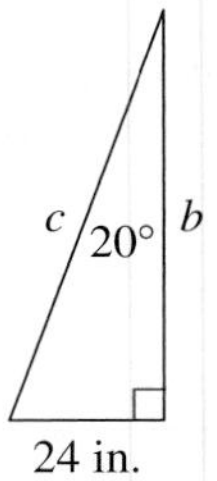

20. The length of one side of a right triangle is 40 ft, as shown in the figure.

a. Find the length of side a.

b. Find the length of hypotenuse c.

Round your answers to the nearest whole number.

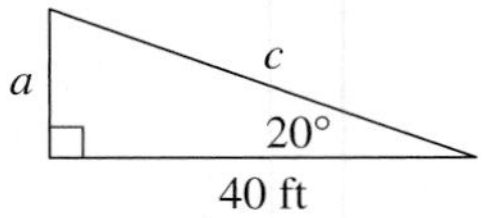

B Applications of the Trigonometric Ratios

21. A tree casts a shadow 32 ft long. A hiker estimates the angle between the Sun's rays and the ground to be 72° (see figure). Using $\tan 72° = 3$, estimate the height of the tree to the nearest whole number.

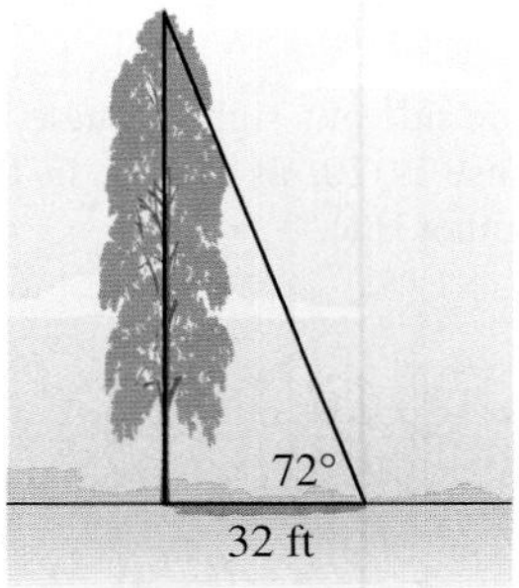

22. The Washington Monument is 555 ft tall. If the Sun's rays and the monument form an angle of 27° (see figure), how long is the shadow to the nearest whole number? (Use tan 27° = 0.5.)

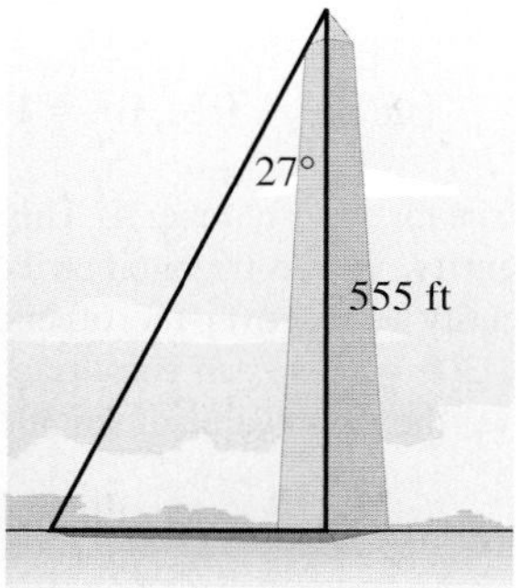

When a flying object (such as an airplane or a bird) ascends, its trajectory forms an angle with the ground, called the **angle of inclination** (see figure below).

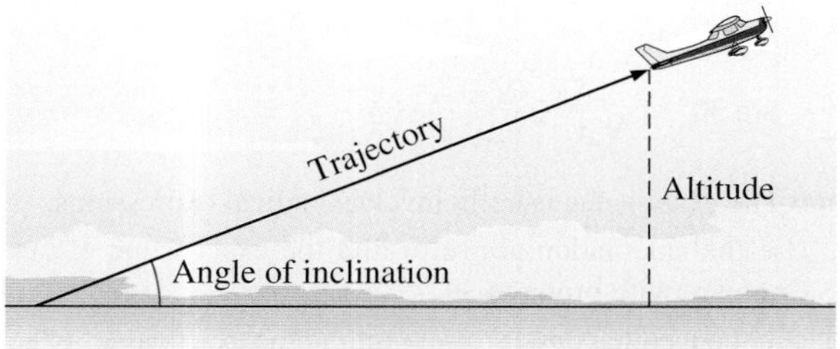

In problems 23–26, use trigonometry to find the altitudes.

23. An airplane ascends with a 30° angle of inclination. If the airplane is flying at a rate of 5 mi/min, what is the altitude after 5 min? (Use sin 30° = 0.5, and round the answer to the nearest whole number.)

24. A rocket blasts off with a 67° angle of inclination. If the rocket travels with a speed of 25 mi/min, what is the altitude after 10 min? (Use sin 67° = 0.92, and round the answer to the nearest whole number.)

25. A bird takes off with a 12° angle of inclination. If the bird is flying at a rate of 200 ft/min, how high is the bird after 7 min? (Use sin 12° = 0.21, and round the answer to the nearest whole number.)

26. A helicopter ascends with a 45° angle of inclination. If the helicopter travels at a speed of 40 mph, what is the helicopter's altitude after 15 min? (*Hint:* 15 min = $\frac{1}{4}$ hr.) (Use sin 45° = 0.7, and round the answer to the nearest whole number.)

27. The plane shown is ascending at a 10° angle. If the plane is 40 ft high, how far is the end of the runway? (Use tan 10° = 0.18, and round the answer to the nearest whole number.)

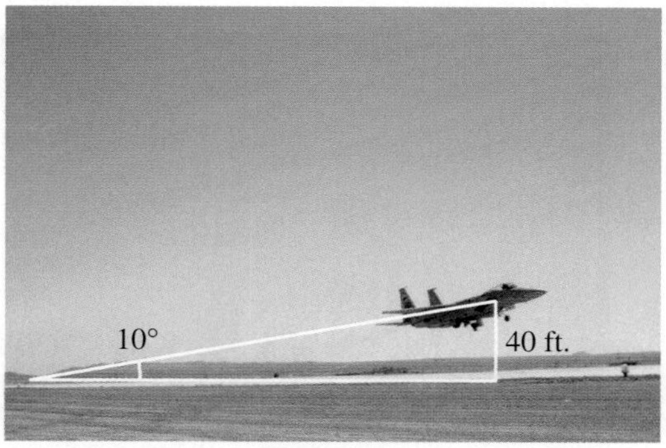

28. The Dames Point Bridge spans the St. John River in Jacksonville, Florida. The longest cable supporting the bridge is 720 ft long and makes a 25° angle with the road. What is the height h of the pole? (Use sin 25° = 0.42, and round the answer to the nearest whole number.)

29. Pedro Mendieta operates the conveyor-belt machine used to haul materials to the top of the concrete mixing container. If the belt makes a 20° angle with the horizontal and ends 40 ft above the ground, how far do the materials travel to get to the top of the conveyor belt? How long is the belt? (Use sin 20° = 0.34, and round the answer to the nearest whole number.)

30. Another conveyor-belt machine operated by John Taylor makes an 18° angle with the horizontal and ends 45 ft above the ground. How far do the materials travel to get to the top of the conveyor belt? How long is the belt? (Use sin 18° = 0.31, and round the answer to the nearest whole number.)

Caroline/zefa/Corbis

IN OTHER WORDS

31. We use the memory device **SOHCAHTOA** to remember the formulas for the sine, cosine, and tangent. Can you give other words for remembering those three trigonometric ratios?
32. Explain in your own words what it means when we say to "solve a triangle."
33. What happens to the tangent of an angle as the measure of the angle gets close to 90°? (*Hint:* Try tan 88°, tan 89°, tan 89.5°, and tan 90° with your calculator.)
34. Explain in your own words what the angle of elevation is. What would the angle of depression be?

USING YOUR KNOWLEDGE

Do you remember how to solve the equation $x^2 = a$? You extract the square root of both sides to get the answers $x = \pm\sqrt{a}$, where a is positive. What about simplifying $\sqrt{ab}$? (See Section 5.5.) Use the knowledge of these two facts to solve the following problems. A right triangle has angles 30° and 60°, as shown in the figure. Use the following table to answer problems 35–40:

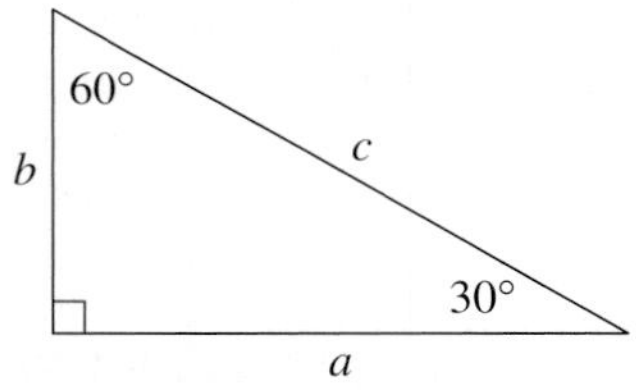

$\cos 30° = \frac{\sqrt{3}}{2}$	$\sin 30° = \frac{1}{2}$
$\cos 60° = \frac{1}{2}$	$\sin 30° = \frac{\sqrt{3}}{2}$

35. If $c = 2$, find the exact values of a and b.
36. If $b = 4$, find the exact values of a and c.
37. If $a = \sqrt{3}$, find the exact values of b and c.
38. If $c = 5$, find the exact values of a and b.
39. What is the exact value of tan 30°?
40. What is the exact value of tan 60°?

DISCOVERY

An equation relating certain trigonometric values is called a **trigonometric identity.** *For example, can you discover if the equation*

$$(\sin A)^2 + (\cos A)^2 = 1$$

is true for every number A? This equation is called the **Pythagorean identity.** If one trigonometric value is known, you can use this identity to discover the others. For example, using the fact that $\cos 30° = \frac{1}{2}$, we can substitute in the Pythagorean identity to discover the *exact* value of sin 30°.

$$(\sin 30°)^2 + (\cos 30°)^2 = 1$$

$$(\sin 30°)^2 + \left(\frac{1}{2}\right)^2 = 1$$

$$(\sin 30°)^2 + \frac{1}{4} = 1$$

$$(\sin 30°)^2 = 1 - \frac{1}{4} = \frac{3}{4}$$

$$\sin 30° = \sqrt{\frac{3}{4}} = \frac{\sqrt{3}}{2}$$

Note: The exact value usually involves radical expressions.

41. Use the calculation above to find the exact value of tan 30°. Compare with problem 39.
42. Use the fact that $\cos 45° = \frac{\sqrt{2}}{2}$ to find the exact values of sin 45° and tan 45°.
43. Use the approximation cos 15° ≈ 0.97 to approximate sin 15° and tan 15°. (Round your answers to two decimal places.)
44. Use the approximation sin 23° ≈ 0.39 to approximate cos 23° and tan 23°. (Round the answer to two decimal places.)

8.8 Chaos and Fractals

GETTING STARTED

OBJECTIVES

A. Find the attractors for a given equation.

B. Construct fractals and find the perimeter, area and length of the broken lines constituting a fractal.

ITERATIONS

Have you read the book *Jurassic Park* by Michael Crichton? In the book, a mathematician named Ian Malcolm had several quotes referring to the first, second, and third iterations of a *fractal* curve. Figure 8.93 shows the curves and his comments. Can you see that the fractals are repetitions of the first drawing?

The point being illustrated is that even though you start with very controlled and predictable patterns, the end result may be completely unexpected; that is, chaos may occur. What is chaos theory? Let us quote Ian Malcolm in *Jurassic Park*.*

> Chaos theory grew out of attempts to make models of weather in the 1960s. If I have a weather system that I start up with a certain temperature and a certain humidity and if I then repeat it with almost the same temperature, wind, and humidity the second system will not behave almost the same. It'll wander off and rapidly will become very different from the first. Thunderstorms instead of sunshine. The shorthand is the "butterfly effect." A butterfly flaps its wings in Peking and weather in New York is different.

In this section we shall draw fractals and see how chaos theory works.

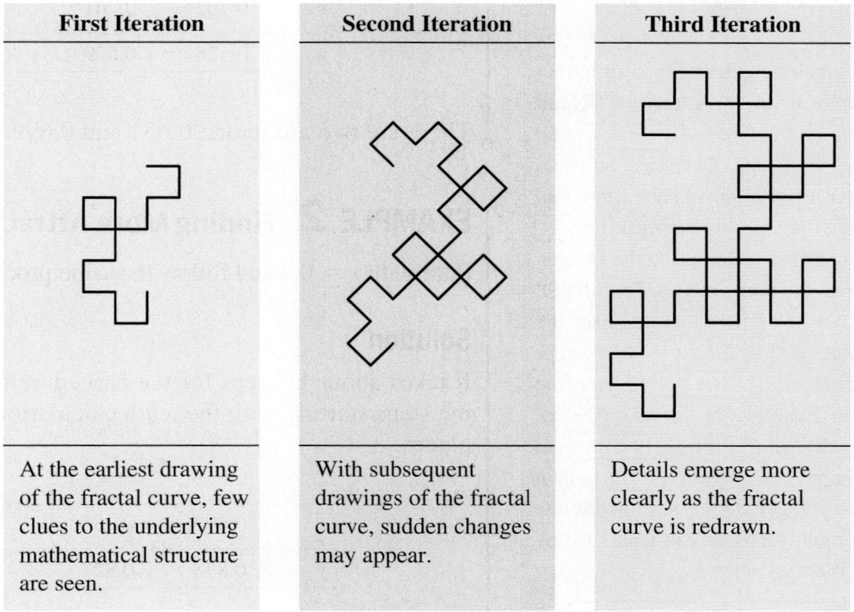
First Iteration
Second Iteration
Third Iteration
At the earliest drawing of the fractal curve, few clues to the underlying mathematical structure are seen.
With subsequent drawings of the fractal curve, sudden changes may appear.
Details emerge more clearly as the fractal curve is redrawn.

FIGURE 8.93

A Chaos

There are many things in the universe around us that are not completely understood even by the most advanced scientists. Some have asked whether our universe is not mostly chaos. The shape of the seashore, the arrangement of branches on a tree,

*Excerpt from *Jurassic Park* by Michael Crichton, copyright © 1993 by Alfred A. Knopf.

and the way tornadoes hit inhabited areas are just some of these seemingly random things that have not yielded to scientific analysis.

It was not until the 1960s that mathematicians began a serious study of what seemed to be random processes. A problem of this sort is as follows: Consider the equation $y = 2.5x(1 - x)$. Take a value of x between 0 and 1, say 0.5. Calculate the corresponding value of $y = (2.5)(0.5)(1 - 0.5) = 0.625$. Now let $x = 0.625$, and find the next corresponding value of y. A calculator gives the value 0.586 to three decimal places. Next let $x = 0.586$ and find the corresponding value of y. It is 0.607 to three decimal places. Now let $x = 0.607$, and so on. The following table shows the results of this procedure. The arithmetic can easily be done with a scientific calculator, but *be sure to round off each calculation to three decimal places before doing the next calculation.*

x	0.5	0.586	0.596	0.599	0.600	0.600
y	0.625	0.607	0.602	0.600	0.600	0.600

Note that after seven steps the resulting number seems to have settled down to 0.600. This number is called an *attractor*.

EXAMPLE 1 Finding Attractors Given an Equation

Use the equation $y = 3x(1 - x)$ starting with $x = 0.2$ and follow the procedure discussed above. Use a calculator and round your answers to three decimal places.

Solution

It takes about 43 steps for the procedure to settle down. Here are the last of these steps with three decimal place answers.

x	0.702	0.701	0.700	0.699	0.699
y	0.628	0.629	0.630	0.631	0.631

There are two attractors, 0.631 and 0.699.

EXAMPLE 2 Finding More Attractors Given an Equation

Start with $x = 0.4$ and follow the same procedure with the equation $y = 3.5x(1 - x)$.

Solution

It takes about 11 steps for the procedure to settle down to four attractors. Here are the steps starting with the tenth calculation, which gives $x = 0.498$ to three decimal places.

x	0.498	0.383	0.501	0.383	0.501
y	0.875	0.827	0.875	0.827	0.875

The four attractors are 0.383, 0.501, 0.827, and 0.875.

If slightly larger values of k are used in $y = kx(1 - x)$, it turns out that the sequence can end up by doubling the number of attractors repeatedly. However, for values of k close to 4, the sequences go on and on being totally random without any attractors. Mathematicians and scientists have called this kind of result **chaos.**

GRAPH IT

A graphing calculator is an attractive way to do attractors! Recall that x is entered as [X, T, θ, n] and that we want 3 decimals, so press [MODE], go down one line and right four spaces and press [ENTER] to specify 3 decimals in the answer. Go to the home screen. Press 0.498 [STO▸] [X] [ENTER] to use the value 0.498 for [X]. Next enter $3.5x(1 - x)$ [STO▸] [X] to let x (the y in Example 2) be $3.5x(1 - x)$. Finally, simply press [ENTER] and you get .875. Press [ENTER] again and you get .383. You can continue as many steps as you want! A few of them are shown.

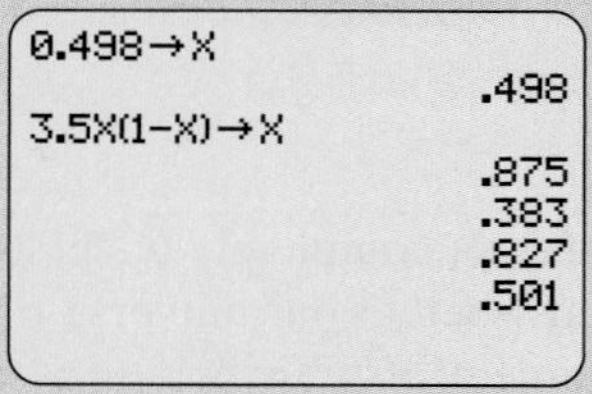

B Fractal Geometry

In our study of geometry we have come across one-, two-, and three-dimensional figures. There are many objects, however, that can hardly be classified as one-, two-, or three-dimensional. Examples of such shapes are coastlines, mountain ranges, and paths of lightning strokes. Until quite recently it was assumed that it was impossible to make realistic geometric models of these types of figures. The discovery and development of **fractal geometry** now makes this possible. This important branch of geometry has been one of the most interesting topics in the mathematics of the last 20 years.

Benoit Mandelbrot, a mathematician, applied the word *fractal* (which means "broken up, fragmented") to certain shapes such as that of the Koch snowflake, which you can construct as shown in Figure 8.94.

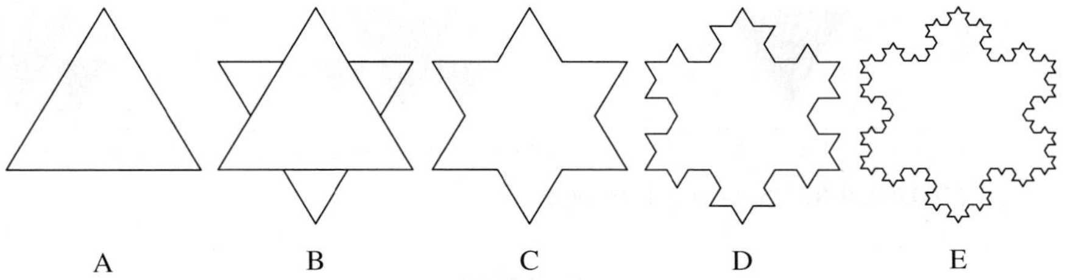

FIGURE 8.94

Step 1 Start with an equilateral triangle, as in Figure 8.94, panel A.

Step 2 On the middle part of each side, draw an equilateral triangle with side one-third the length of the side of the original triangle, as in panel B.

Step 3 Erase the side of each smaller triangle that is on a side of the original triangle, as in panel C.

Step 4 Repeat steps 1, 2, and 3 for each of the smaller triangles, as shown in panel D.

Step 5 Continue the same kind of construction on each little straight line segment of the figure. You will end up with the "snowflake" shown in panel E.

The snowflake in Figure 8.94, panel E, was named for the Swedish mathematician Helga von Koch, who was the first to discover its very remarkable properties. For example, note that the curve consists of an infinite number of small pieces of the form _/_. It can be shown that the perimeter is infinite in length, but that the area is just 1.6 times the area of the original starting triangle.

EXAMPLE 3 Finding Lengths of Lines in the Koch Snowflake

Suppose that the side of the starting triangle in the construction of the Koch snowflake is 1 in. long. In the first step of the construction, how long is the broken line that replaces one side of the triangle?

Solution

Note that the middle third of the original side is replaced by two sides of an equilateral triangle, the length of whose side is this middle third. Thus, the broken line consists of four pieces, each of length $\frac{1}{3}$ in., so that the length of the broken line is $\frac{1}{3}$ in.

The result of Example 3 shows that the perimeter of the entire figure obtained in the first step is 4 in. when the perimeter of the starting triangle is 3 in.

EXAMPLE 4 Constructing Sierpinski's Triangle

We are now ready to construct the beautiful Sierpinski triangle fractal (Figure 8.95). Inside the white equilateral triangle, we draw a second equilateral triangle pointing down (blue). Now the original triangle is divided into 4 identical equilateral triangles, 3 white and 1 blue. We repeat the process with each new equilateral triangle drawn red. If we do it two more times with yellow (iteration 3) and green (iteration 4), we obtain a total of 40 triangles.

(a) How many triangles will the fifth iteration have?

(b) What about the nth iteration?

A B C D

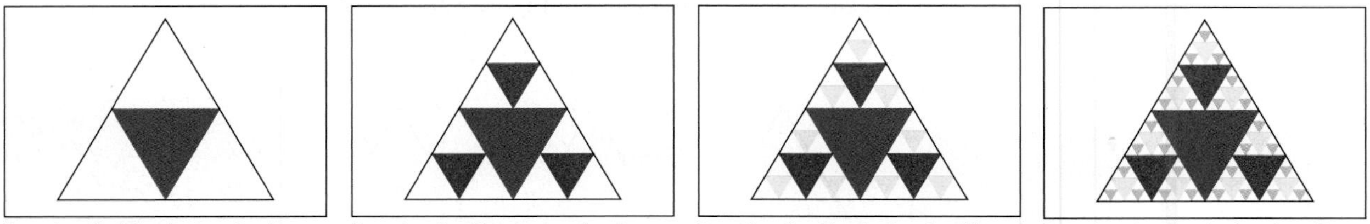

Iteration 1 Total triangles 1 — Iteration 2 Total triangles 4 — Iteration 3 Total triangles 13 — Iteration 4 Total triangles 40

FIGURE 8.95 The Sierpinski triangle.

Solution

(a) To find the fifth iteration, we have to find the pattern at each step.

The number of triangles in going from iteration 1 to iteration 2 increased by 3.
The number of triangles in going from iteration 2 to iteration 3 increased by 3^2.
The number of triangles in going from iteration 3 to iteration 4 increased by 3^3.

Thus, to go from iteration 4 to iteration 5, we should add 3^4 triangles, obtaining a total of $40 + 3^4 = 40 + 81 = 121$ triangles.

(b) Let us again look at the pattern for the number of triangles.

Iteration 1	1	$= 1$
Iteration 2	$1 + 3$	$= 4$
Iteration 3	$1 + 3 + 3^2$	$= 13$
Iteration 4	$1 + 3 + 3^2 + 3^3$	$= 40$
Iteration 5	$1 + 3 + 3^2 + 3^3 + 3^4$	$= 121$
$\vdots$		$\vdots$
Iteration n	$1 + 3 + 3^2 + 3^3 + 3^4 + \cdots + 3^{n-1}$	

Fractals have many applications but scientists have actually discovered that many of the parts of your body, for example, your lungs, can be modeled using fractal canopies. You can learn more about this in the exercises.

8.8 EXERCISES

A Chaos

In problems 1–4, follow the procedure of Example 1 to find the possible attractors.

1. In the equation $y = kx(1 - x)$, take $k = 3.5$ and a starting value of $x = 0.2$.
2. For the same k as in problem 1, take a starting value of $x = 0.7$.
3. In the equation $y = kx(1 - x)$, take $k = 3$ and a starting value of $x = 0.4$.
4. In the same equation, take $k = 2$ and a starting value of $x = 0.8$.

B Fractal Geometry

5. In the construction of the snowflake fractal, what is the perimeter after
   a. the third step? b. the fourth step?
6. Instead of an equilateral triangle, use a 3-4-5 right triangle and construct a fractal by replacing one-third of each side by a right triangle with sides respectively parallel to the other two sides of the original triangle. The first step results in the following figure:

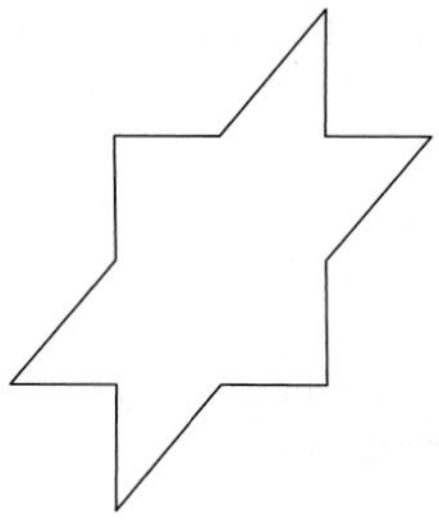

7. Instead of a triangle, use an equilateral parallelogram and construct a fractal by replacing one-third of each side by a parallelogram with its sides parallel to the sides of the original parallelogram. The first step results in the figure shown below.

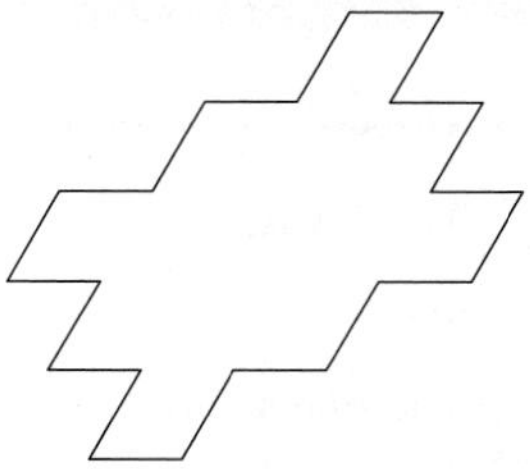

8. Consider a square of side 1 in. Note that the smallest number of complete squares that you can divide the starting square into is four. (Just draw two lines, each joining the midpoints of a pair of opposite sides of the original square.) Can you continue this procedure to show that the area of the original square can be considered as the sum of the areas of an ever-increasing number of small squares?
9. In the construction of problem 8, the area of one of the first four squares is $\frac{1}{4}$ in.^{2}. In the next step, there will be 16 small squares, each of area $\frac{1}{16}$ in.^{2}. If you go through five steps of this construction, what will be the area of one of the smallest squares?
10. a. Start with a square and develop a fractal by replacing each side, ________, by a . Repeat this procedure.
    b. If this procedure is continued indefinitely, will the perimeter of the fractal be finite? Explain why or why not.
    c. Will the area of the fractal be finite? Explain why or why not.
11. Start with a square and develop a fractal by replacing each side as in problem 10 but with the small square drawn *inside* the larger square. Then if the common segments are erased in each step, the areas of the small squares are subtracted from the area of the larger square.
12. With the procedure of problem 11, what area remains after the first step? Assume the original square to be of side s.
13. Referring to problem 12, what area remains after the second step?
14. As the procedure of problem 11 is continued, what happens to the length of the perimeter of the fractal? Does it get larger and larger—that is, does it have infinite length?
15. Referring to problems 11–13, what happens to the area enclosed by the fractal? Does it become smaller and smaller; that is, will it have zero area?
16. *Fractal canopies.* Take a vertical line segment and "split" it lengthwise into two other segments. Open the two segments forming a Y at an angle A. Take the resulting smaller segments and split them as well and open them at the same angle. If you continue this process indefinitely, you get a *fractal canopy* like the one shown. Now, to make your first fractal canopy: Take a blank sheet of paper, and draw a straight line from the center to the bottom. Draw two lines, half as long as the first, coming out at 45 degree angles ***up*** from the top of the first line, forming a Y. Do that again for each fork in the Y. That's the first iteration in your fractal. Repeat four times. The result is a fractal canopy! **Source:** http://library.thinkquest.org/26242/full/types/ch3.html

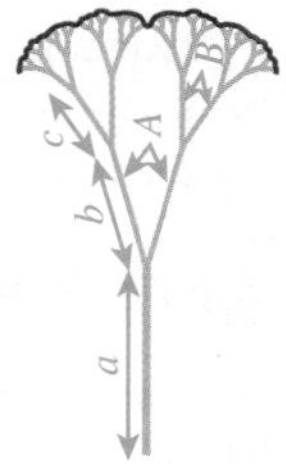

17. The pulmonary system which you use to breathe is in the shape of the *fractal canopy shown.*
    a. Retrace the first three iterations of the fractal canopy to the left (this time you start with an inverted Y).
    b. How long is the initial line segment? What about the segments emanating from it? What is their ratio?
    c. Is the ratio maintained in the next iteration?
    d. What is the measure of the angle being used?
    e. Is the measure of the angle maintained for successive iterations?

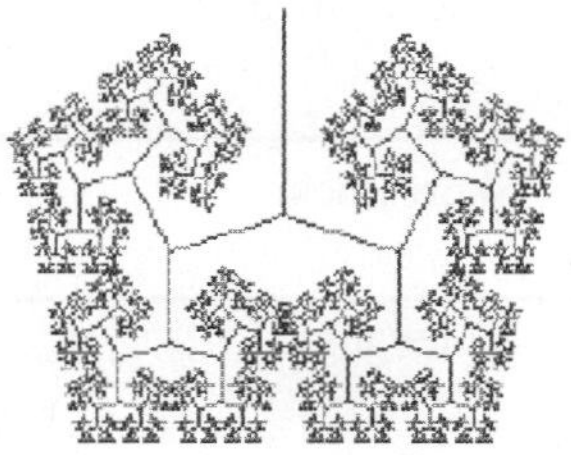

Source: http://library.thinkquest.org/26242/full/ap/ap11.html

USING YOUR KNOWLEDGE

18. You can construct an "antisnowflake" fractal by starting with an equilateral triangle as for the Koch snowflake but drawing the new triangles inside the preceding ones. This results in the area of each new triangle's being subtracted from the area enclosed by the preceding step. Carry this out for two steps. You should get a figure like the one shown below.

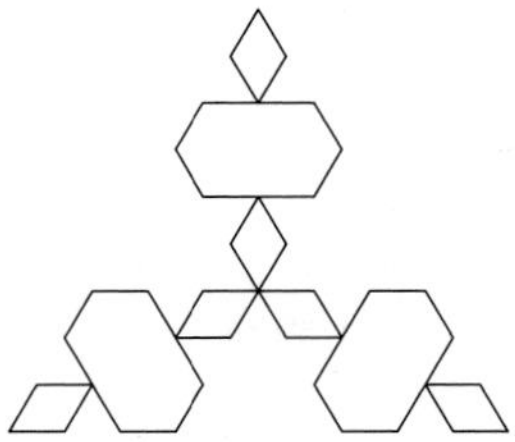

19. Use the fact that the area of an equilateral triangle of side s is $\frac{\sqrt{3}}{4}s^2$ to find the area remaining after the first step of problem 18.

20. Refer to problem 19 and find the area remaining after the second step.

IN OTHER WORDS

21. Refer to problem 18 and decide whether the perimeter of the fractal remains finite as the procedure is carried on indefinitely. Explain.
22. Refer to problem 18 and decide whether the area enclosed by the fractal tends to zero. Explain.

WEB IT EXERCISES

You can construct many of the fractals in this section (Koch, Sierspinski, and Jurassic Park) if your computer can run Java applets. Form several groups and go to link http://ejad.best.vwh.net/java/fractals/intro.shtml

Team 1

1. Does the Plus Fractal have the self-similarity property?
2. Can you find the number of line ends for each iteration?
3. Can you find the area of the rhombus?
4. Can you find its total length?

Hints are given on the Web!

Team 2

1. The length of the lines in the Koch fractal get smaller with each iteration. What about the rate of growth of the total length of the perimeter?
2. What will be the length of the 50th iteration?
3. What will happen to the length if the number of iterations increases indefinitely? (See Example 3.)

Team 3

1. Can you find the number of lines for each iteration in the Jurassic Park fractal?
2. Can you find the formula to predict the number of lines after the nth iteration in the Jurassic Park fractal?

CHAPTER 8 Summary

SECTION	ITEM	MEANING	EXAMPLE
8.1 A	$\overleftrightarrow{AB}$	The line AB	
	Ray $\overrightarrow{AB}$	A half-line and its endpoint A	The ray AB 
	Line segment $\overline{AB}$	The points A and B and the part of the line between A and B	The line segment AB 
8.1 B	Skew lines	Lines that are not on the same plane	
8.1 C	Plane angle	The figure formed by two rays with a common endpoint	
	Vertex of an angle	The common point of the two rays	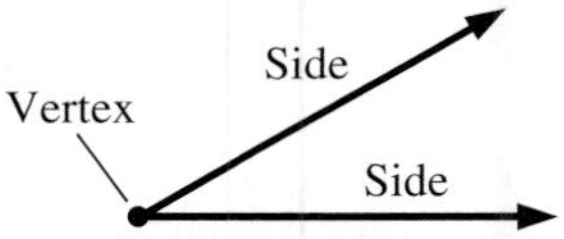
	Sides of the angles	The rays forming the angle	
	Degree	$\frac{1}{360}$th of a complete revolution	
	Straight angle	One-half of a complete revolution	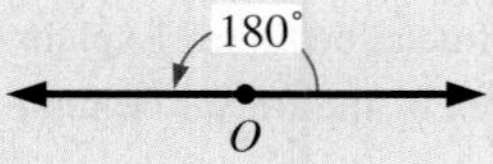
	Right angle	One-quarter of a complete revolution	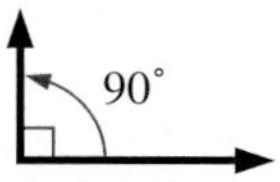
	Vertical angles	The opposite angles formed by two intersecting lines	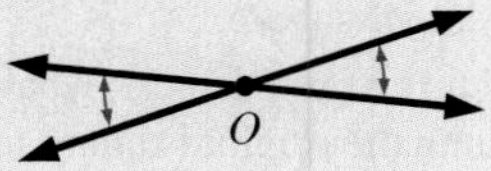

CHAPTER 8 Summary

SECTION	ITEM	MEANING	EXAMPLE
8.1 C	Supplementary angles	Angles whose measures add to 180°	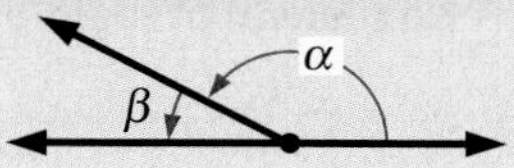
	Transversal	A line that crosses two or more other lines	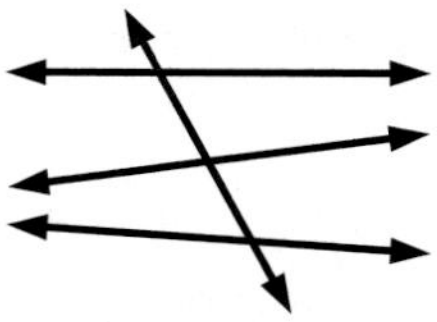
	Complementary angles	Angles whose measures add to 90°	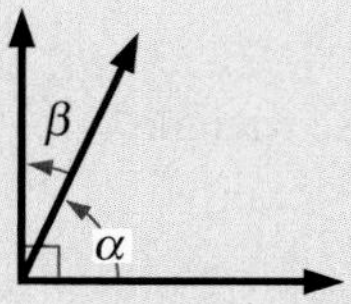
	Perpendicular lines	Lines that intersect at right angles	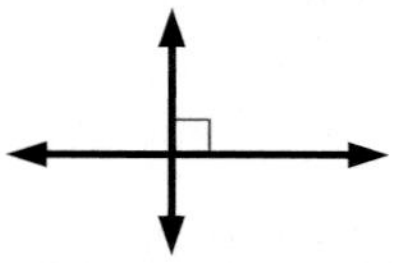
8.2 A	Broken line	A sequence of connected straight line segments	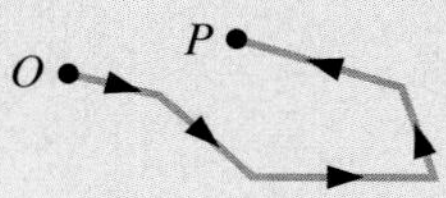
	Simple path	A path that does not cross itself	
	Closed path	A path that starts and ends at the same point	
	Polygon	A simple, closed broken line	
	Sides (of polygon)	The line segments of the path	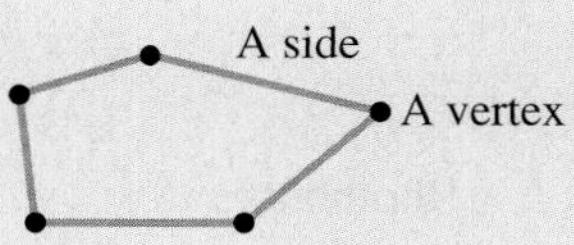
	Vertices (of polygon)	The endpoints of the sides of the polygon	
	Convex polygon	A polygon in which no line segment joining any two points on the boundary ever extends outside the polygon	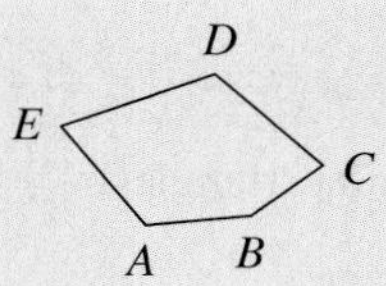
	Concave polygon	A polygon that is not convex	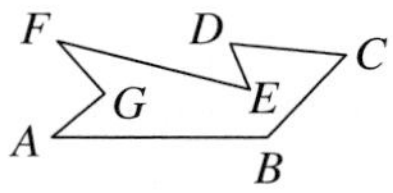
	Regular polygon	A polygon with all sides of equal length and all angles of equal size	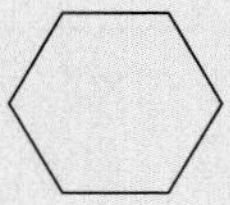

continued

CHAPTER 8 Summary – *continued*

SECTION	ITEM	MEANING	EXAMPLE
8.2 B	Equilateral triangle	A triangle with three equal sides	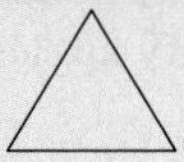
	Right triangle	A triangle with one angle that is 90°	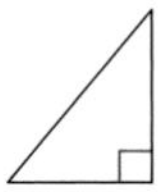
	Acute triangle	A triangle with three angles, each of which is less than 90°	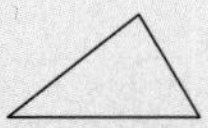
	Obtuse triangle	A triangle with one angle that is greater than 90°	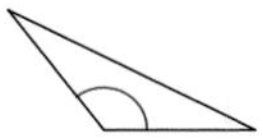
	Scalene triangle	A triangle with no equal sides	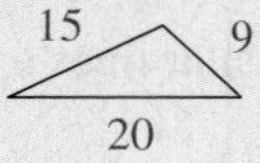
	Isosceles triangle	A triangle with two equal sides	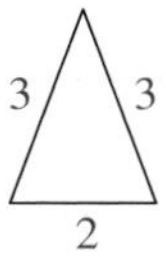
	Trapezoid	A quadrilateral with two parallel and two nonparallel sides	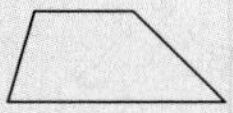
	Parallelogram	A quadrilateral with both pairs of opposite sides parallel	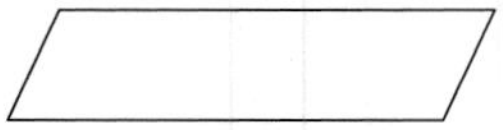
	Rectangle	A parallelogram whose angles are right angles	
	Rhombus	A parallelogram with four equal sides	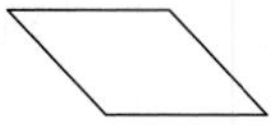
	Square	A rectangle with four equal sides	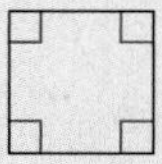
	Similar triangles	Triangles with exactly the same shape but not necessarily the same size	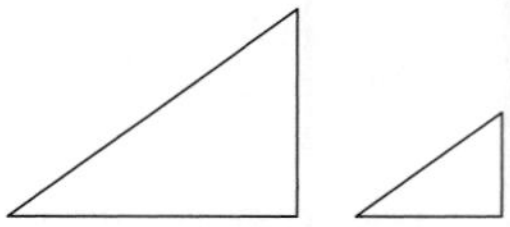
	Congruent triangles	Triangles that have both the same shape and size	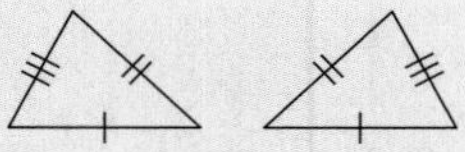
8.2 C	$S = (n - 2) \cdot 180°$	Sum of the measures of the angles of a polygon of n sides	

CHAPTER 8 Summary

SECTION	ITEM	MEANING	EXAMPLE
8.3 A	Perimeter	Distance around a polygon	
8.3 B	Circle	The set of all coplanar (on the same plane) points at a given fixed distance (the radius) from a point (the center)	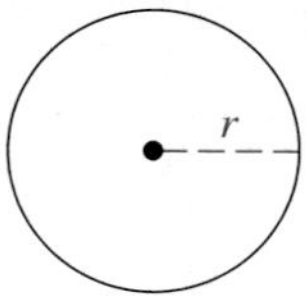
	Circumference $C = \pi d = 2\pi r$	The perimeter of a circle of diameter d (radius r)	
8.4 A	$A = bh$	The area of a rectangle of base b and height h	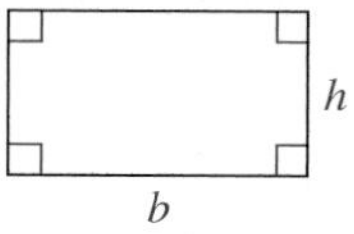
	$A = bh$	The area of a parallelogram of base b and height h	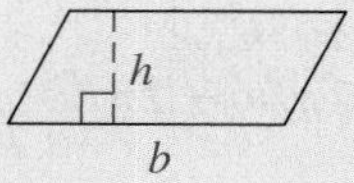
	$A = \frac{1}{2}bh$	The area of a triangle of base b and height h	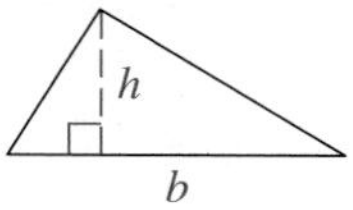
	$A = \pi r^2$	The area of a circle of radius r	
8.4 B	Pythagorean theorem $c^2 = a^2 + b^2$	The square of the hypotenuse c of a right triangle equals the sum of the squares of the other two sides, a and b.	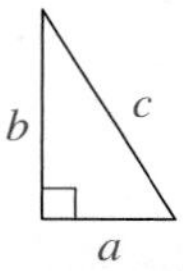
8.5 A	Polyhedron	A solid bounded by plane polygons	
	Convex polyhedron	A polyhedron that lies entirely on one side of the plane of each of its faces	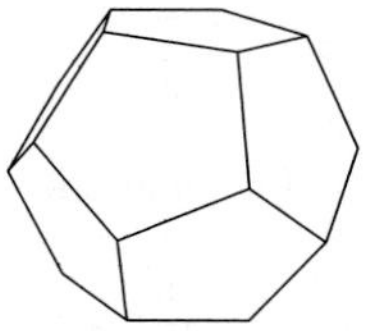
	Concave polyhedron	A polyhedron that is not convex	
	Prism $V = Bh$	A polyhedron two of whose faces are parallel and whose edges that are not on these faces are all parallel	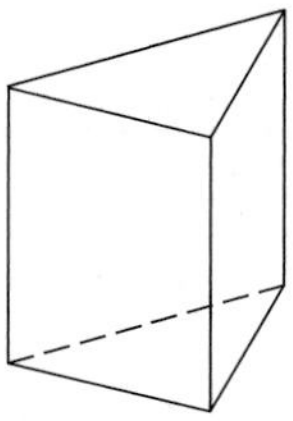
	Pyramid $A = \frac{1}{3}Bh$	A polyhedron with all but one of its vertices in one plane The volume (V) of a pyramid or prism of height h and base B	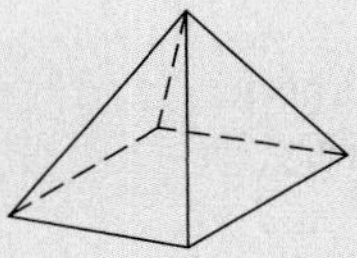

continued

CHAPTER 8 Summary – *continued*

SECTION	ITEM	MEANING	EXAMPLE
8.5 B	$V = a^3$ $S = 6a^2$	The volume (V) and surface area (S) of a cube of edge a	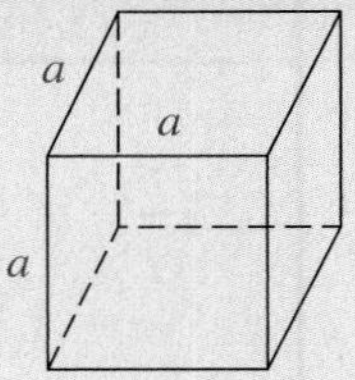
	$V = lwh$ $S = 2(hv + lh + wh)$	The volume (V) and surface area (S) of a rectangular box of length l, width w, and height h	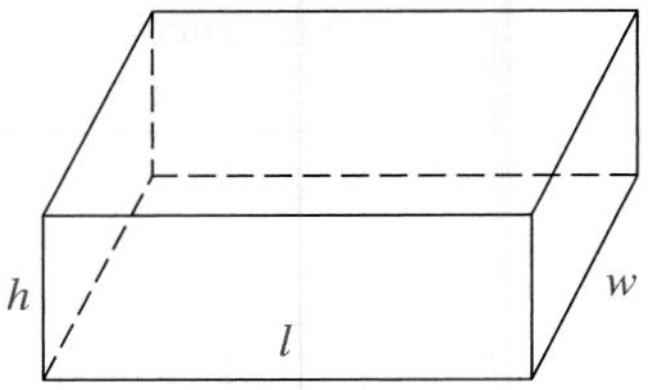
	$V = \pi r^2 h$ $S = 2\pi rh + 2\pi r^2$	The volume (V) and surface area (S) of a circular cylinder of radius r and height h	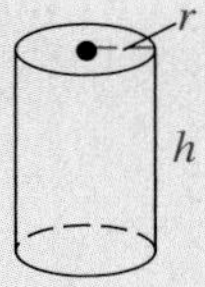
	$V = \frac{1}{3}\pi r^2 h$ $S = \pi r^2 + \pi rs$	The volume (V) and surface area (S) of a circular cone of radius r, height h, and slant height s	
	$V = \frac{4}{3}\pi r^3$ $S = 4\pi r^2$	The volume (V) and surface area (S) of a sphere of radius r	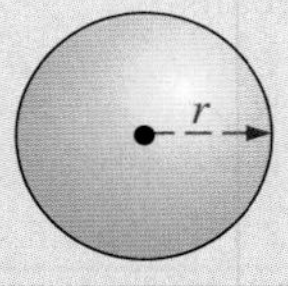
8.6 A	Network	A connected set of line segments or curves	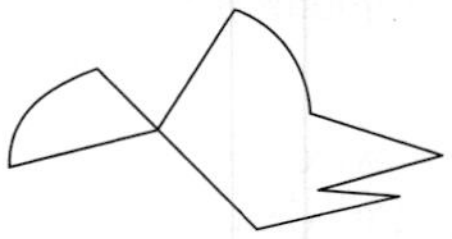
	Traversable network	A network that can be drawn by tracing each line segment or curve exactly once without lifting the pencil from the paper	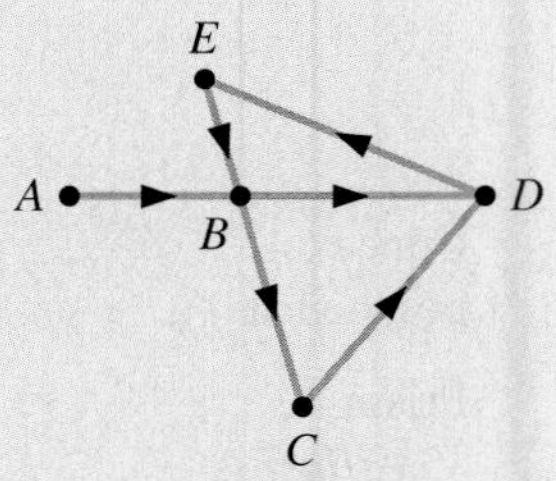
8.6 B	Euclid's fifth postulate	Given a line and a point not on that line, there is one and only one line through the point parallel to the original line.	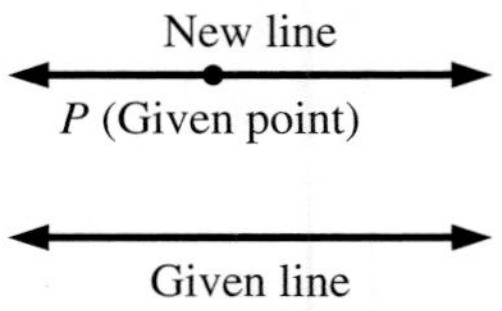
	Hyperbolic geometry	A type of geometry developed by Gauss, Bolyai, and Lobachevsky	Given a line and a point not on that line, there is *more* than one line through that point parallel to the original line.

CHAPTER 8 Summary

SECTION	ITEM	MEANING	EXAMPLE
8.6 B	Elliptic geometry	A type of geometry developed by Bernhard Riemann	Given a line and a point not on that line, there is *no* line parallel to the original line.
8.6 C	Topology	A branch of modern geometry	
	Topologically equivalent	The relation between two figures such that each can be obtained from the other by just changing the other's shape	 and  are topologically equivalent.
8.7 A	Trigonometric ratios 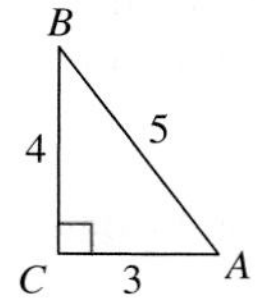 	$\sin A = \frac{\text{opposite side}}{\text{hypotenuse}}$ $\cos A = \frac{\text{adjacent side}}{\text{hypotenuse}}$ $\tan A = \frac{\text{opposite side}}{\text{adjacent side}}$	For the triangle shown $\sin A = \frac{\text{opposite side}}{\text{hypotenuse}} = \frac{4}{5}$ $\cos A = \frac{\text{adjacent side}}{\text{hypotenuse}} = \frac{3}{5}$ $\tan A = \frac{\text{opposite side}}{\text{adjacent side}} = \frac{4}{3}$
8.7 B	$\tan^{-1}$	Inverse trig key: Calculator: [INV] [tan] ($\tan^{-1}$) or Grapher: [2nd] [tan]	If tan A = 1.7321, using a calculator 1.7321 [INV] [tan] ($\tan^{-1}$) gives A = 60° Using a grapher [2nd] [tan] 1.7321 [ENTER] also gives A = 60°
8.8 A	Chaos	A field of study devoted to processes that exhibit complex, apparently random behavior	Totally random sequences
8.8 B	Fractal	Broken up or fragmented	A geometric pattern that is repeated at smaller scales and produces irregular shapes and surfaces.

CHAPTER 8 Practice Test

1. Refer to the line shown below and state what each of the following describes:
   a. $\overleftrightarrow{WY} \cap \overleftrightarrow{XZ}$ b. $\overleftrightarrow{WY} \cap \overleftrightarrow{YZ}$ c. $\overleftrightarrow{WX} \cup \overrightarrow{XZ}$

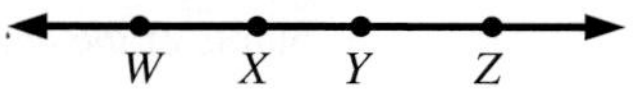

2. Sketch a triangular prism. Label the vertices; then name the edges that are
   a. parallel lines.   b. skew lines.   c. intersecting lines.

3. Through how many degrees does the hour hand of a clock turn in the following time intervals?
   a. 12 to 4 o'clock   b. 3 to 5 o'clock

4. If $\angle A$ and $\angle B$ are supplementary angles, and $m\angle A = 3 \times m\angle B$, find the measures of the two angles.

5. In the figure below, lines $\overleftrightarrow{PQ}$ and $\overleftrightarrow{RS}$ are parallel. Find
   a. $m\angle C$.   b. $m\angle E$.   c. $m\angle D$.

continued

CHAPTER 8 Practice Test – *continued*

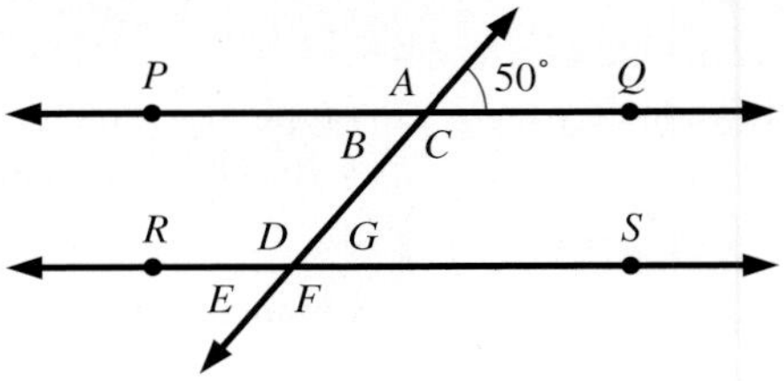

6. a. In a triangle ABC, $m\angle A = 38°$ and $m\angle B = 43°$. Find $m\angle C$.
   b. In a triangle ABC, $m\angle A = m\angle B = 2 \times m\angle C$. Find the measures of the three angles.

7. Sketch a broken line that is
   a. simple but not closed. b. closed but not simple.

8. Triangles ABC and XYZ are similar, with $m\angle A = m\angle X$ and $m\angle B = m\angle Y$. If $\overline{AB}$, $\overline{BC}$, and $\overline{AC}$ are 2, 3, and 4 in. long, respectively, and $\overline{XY}$ is 3 in. long, find the lengths of $\overline{YZ}$ and $\overline{XZ}$.

9. What is the measure of one of the interior angles of a regular polygon with
   a. 9 sides? b. 10 sides?

10. A rectangular plot of ground is to be enclosed with 120 yd of fencing. If the plot is to be twice as long as it is wide, what must be its dimensions?

11. The center of a circle is also the center of a square of side 2 cm. The circle passes through the four vertices of the square. Find the circumference of the circle. (Leave your answer in terms of π.)

12. If you rolled up an $8\frac{1}{2}$-by-11-in. sheet of paper into the largest possible cylinder $8\frac{1}{2}$ in. high, what would be the diameter of the cylinder? (Leave your answer in terms of π.)

13. In problem 11, find the area of the region that is inside the circle and outside the square. (Leave your answer in terms of π.)

14. A window is in the shape of a rectangle surmounted by a semicircle. The width of the window is 3 ft, which is also the diameter of the circle, and the height of the rectangular part is 4 ft. Find the total area of the window.

15. A circle of diameter 2 in. has its center at the center of a square of side 2 in. Find the area of the region that is inside the square and outside the circle.

16. A rectangle is 84 ft long and 13 ft wide. Find the length of its diagonal.

17. Find the total surface area of a rectangular box whose base is 3 ft wide and 5 ft long and whose height is 2 ft.

18. The triangle shown at the right is the base of a pyramid that is 4 ft high. What is the volume of this pyramid?

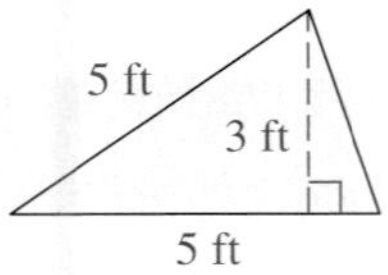

19. A solid consists of a cone and a hemisphere mounted base to base. If the radius of the common base is 2 in. and the volume of the cone is equal to the volume of the hemisphere, what is the height of the cone?

20. A sphere and a cylinder have the same radius, 10 in. If the total surface area of the cylinder equals the surface area of the sphere, what is the height of the cylinder?

21. Draw two networks, each with five vertices, such that one of them is traversable and the other is not traversable.

22. State Euclid's fifth postulate, the parallel postulate.

CHAPTER 8 Practice Test

23. **a.** Which object is *not* topologically equivalent to the rest?
b. What is the genus of the golf ball?
c. What is the genus of the button?
d. What is the genus of the paper clip?

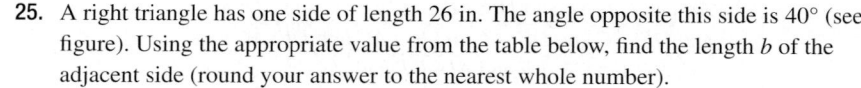

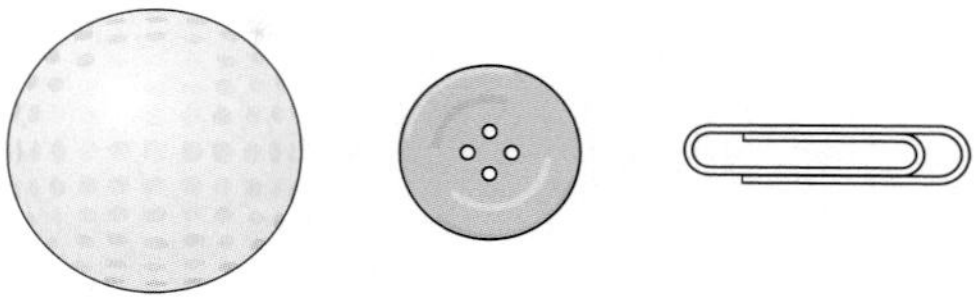

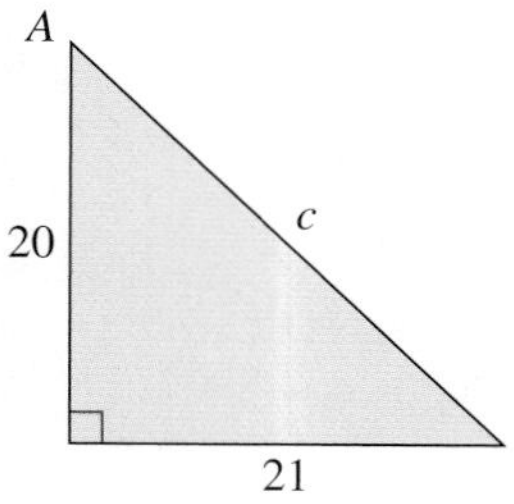

24. A right triangle has side lengths 20 and 21 as shown in the figure.
a. Find the length c of the hypotenuse.
b. Use your answer from (a) to find $\cos \boldsymbol{A}$, $\sin \boldsymbol{A}$ and $\tan \boldsymbol{A}$.

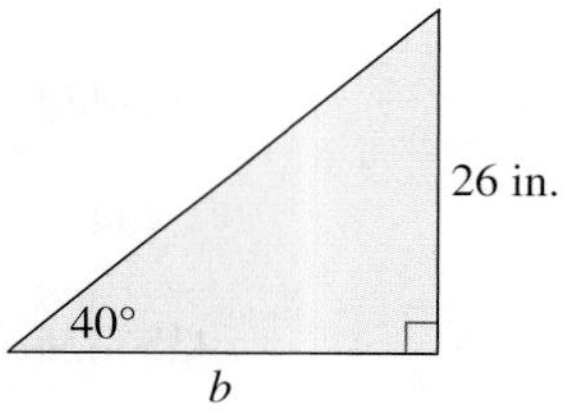

25. A right triangle has one side of length 26 in. The angle opposite this side is 40° (see figure). Using the appropriate value from the table below, find the length b of the adjacent side (round your answer to the nearest whole number).

$\cos 40° = 0.77$
$\sin 40° = 0.64$
$\tan 40° = 0.84$

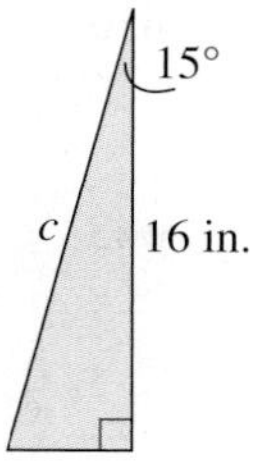

26. A right triangle has one side of length 16 in. The angle adjacent to this side is 15°. Using the appropriate value from the table below, find the length c of the hypotenuse. (Round your answer to the nearest whole number.)

$\cos 15° = 0.97$
$\sin 15° = 0.26$
$\tan 15° = 0.27$

27. When extended from the torch to the ground, a 337-ft cable forms an angle of 65° with the ground (see figure). Find the height x of the Statue of Liberty, rounded to the nearest whole number.
(*Hint*: $\sin 65° = 0.9063$)
Photo Source:
http://www.nps.gov/stli/index.htm

28. An airplane takes off with a 12° angle of inclination. If the speed of the airplane is 3 mi per min, what is the altitude 5 mins after take-off?
Round answer to the nearest whole number.

29. In the equation $y = 2x(x - 1)$, take $x = 0.1$ and find $y = y_1$. Then let $x = y_1$ and find $y = y_2$. If this procedure is taken through four steps, what is the resulting value of y?

30. Start with a 3-4-5 triangle and replace the middle half of each side by a triangle whose sides are parallel to those of the original triangle. Make a sketch of the resulting figure.

ANSWERS TO PRACTICE TEST

CHAPTER 8		What to Review *If You Missed It*		
QUESTION	**ANSWER**	**SECTION**	**EXAMPLE(S)**	**PAGE(S)**
1	a. $\overline{XY}$ b. Point Y c. $\overleftrightarrow{WZ}$	8.1	1	430
2	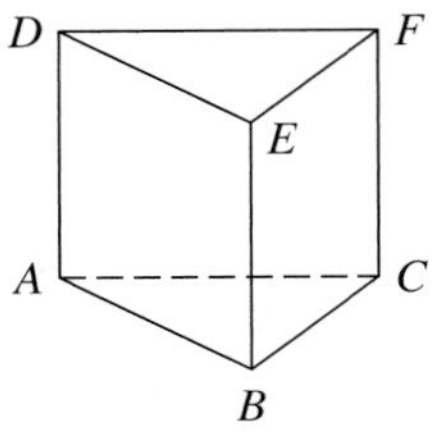 a. $\overline{AD}$, $\overline{BE}$, and $\overline{CF}$; $\overline{EF}$ and $\overline{BC}$; $\overline{DE}$ and $\overline{AB}$; $\overline{DF}$ and $\overline{AC}$ b. $\overline{AB}$ and $\overline{CF}$; $\overline{AB}$ and $\overline{DF}$; $\overline{AB}$ and $\overline{EF}$; $\overline{BC}$ and $\overline{AD}$; $\overline{BC}$ and $\overline{DE}$; $\overline{BC}$ and $\overline{DF}$; $\overline{AC}$ and $\overline{BE}$; $\overline{AC}$ and $\overline{DE}$; $\overline{AC}$ and $\overline{EF}$; $\overline{DE}$ and $\overline{CF}$; $\overline{EF}$ and $\overline{AD}$; $\overline{DF}$ and $\overline{BE}$ c. $\overline{AB}$, $\overline{AC}$, and $\overline{AD}$; $\overline{AD}$, $\overline{DE}$, and $\overline{DF}$; $\overline{BE}$, $\overline{AB}$, and $\overline{BC}$; $\overline{BE}$, $\overline{EF}$, and $\overline{ED}$; $\overline{CF}$, $\overline{AC}$, and $\overline{BC}$; $\overline{CF}$, $\overline{EF}$, and $\overline{DF}$	8.1	Fig. 8.16, 2	431–432
3	a. 120° b. 60°	8.1	3	432–433
4	$m\angle A = 135°$, $m\angle B = 45°$	8.1	4	434
5	a. $m\angle C = 130°$ b. $m\angle E = 50°$ c. $m\angle D = 130°$	8.1	5	435–436
6	a. $m\angle C = 99°$ b. $m\angle A = m\angle B = 72°$, $m\angle C = 36°$	8.1	6	436
7	a. 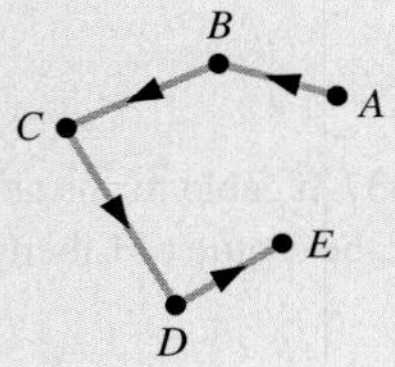 b. 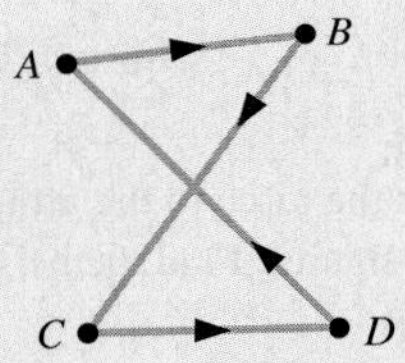	8.2	Figs. 8.33, 8.34	443
8	$\overline{XZ} = 6$ in., $\overline{YZ} = 4\frac{1}{2}$ in.	8.2	4, 5	447–448
9	a. 140° b. 144°	8.2	8	451
10	20 yd by 40 yd	8.3	1–3	458
11	$2\sqrt{2}\pi$ cm	8.3	4, 5	459
12	$\frac{11}{\pi}$ in.	8.3	5	459
13	$(2\pi - 4)$ cm^2	8.4	1–3	465–466
14	$12 + 9\pi/8 \approx 15.5$ ft^2	8.4	1–3	465–466
15	$4 - \pi \approx 0.86$ in.^{2}	8.4	1–3	465–466
16	85 ft	8.4	5, 6	468–469

ANSWERS TO PRACTICE TEST

CHAPTER 8		What to Review *If You Missed It*		
QUESTION	**ANSWER**	**SECTION**	**EXAMPLE(S)**	**PAGE(S)**
17	62 ft^2	**8.5**	**2**	**477**
18	10 ft^3	**8.5**	**3**	**478**
19	4 in.	**8.5**	**4**	**478–479**
20	10 in.	**8.5**	**5**	**479**
21	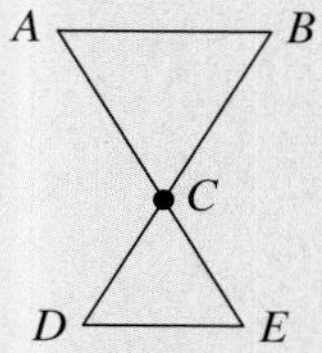 Traversable 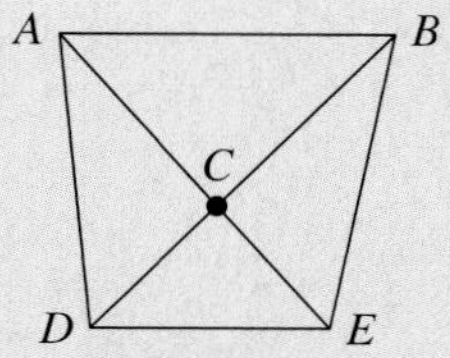 Not traversable	**8.6**	**1**	**486–487**
22	Given a line and any point not on that line, there is one and only one line through that point that is parallel to the given line.	**8.6**	**Fig. 8.86**	**488**
23	**a.** The button **b.** 0 **c.** 4 **d.** 0	**8.6**	**5, 6**	**490–491**
24	**a.** 29 **b.** cos A = 20/29, sin A = 21/29, tan A = 21/20	**8.7**	**1, 2, 3**	**498–500**
25	b = 22	**8.7**	**1, 2, 3**	**498–500**
26	c = 16	**8.7**	**1, 2, 3**	**498–500**
27	305 feet	**8.7**	**4, 5**	**501–502**
28	3 miles	**8.7**	**4, 5**	**501–502**
29	$y_4 = 1.455$	**8.8**	**1, 2**	**508**
30	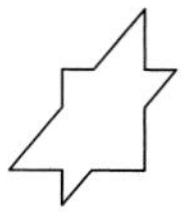	**8.8**	**3, 4**	**509–510**

CHAPTER 9

Mathematical Systems

Sophie Germain's mathematical work "is a work which few men are able to read and which only one woman was able to write." —CLAUDE-LOUIS NAVIER

As advancements in technology occur, keeping information secure becomes more important. Check digits are used in order to secure information on many items such as credit cards, money orders, and airline tickets. In Section 9.1, you will study modular arithmetic, its operations, and applications such as the use of check digits for security purposes.

Credit card numbers, bar codes, and checking account routing numbers are among the important data that businesses must transmit securely and accurately each day. To do so, companies rely on the properties of the mathematical systems that we will study in this chapter. We begin the study of mathematical systems by considering *clock arithmetic* on a 12- or 5-hour clock and generalize the idea to *modular* arithmetic. We continue with a discussion of abstract mathematical systems and will give you an opportunity to work in a new mathematical field, **Tropical Mathematics,** as well as two other mathematical structures called **groups** and **fields.** We end the chapter with a study of game theory, a subject with numerous applications to business, games of chance, and military science.

9.1 Clock and Modular Arithmetic

GETTING STARTED

OBJECTIVES

A. Perform the four fundamental operations and solve equations using clock arithmetic.

B. Perform the four fundamental operations and solve equations using modular arithmetic.

C. Solve applications using modular arithmetic.

AIRBILLS, MONEY ORDERS, CREDIT CARDS, AND CHECK DIGITS

Look at the Federal Express airbill in Figure 9.1(a) with tracking number 9048724285. Divide 904872428 (the number to the left of 5) by 7. The remainder is 5. Now try it with airbill 0054604362 Figure 9.1(b). When you divide 5460436 by 7, the remainder is 2. Next, consider the postal money order number 42888671414 in Figure 9.2. Divide the number to the left of the last 4 by 9 this time. The remainder is 4. In mathematics, when you divide a by b and the remainder is c, a is said to be **congruent** to c modulo b, written

$$a \equiv c \pmod{b}$$

The relationships in the Federal Express airbills can be written as

$$904872428 \equiv 5 \pmod{7} \quad \text{and} \quad 005460436 \equiv 2 \pmod{7}$$

and that in the money order as $4288867141 \equiv 4 \pmod{9}$.

FIGURE 9.1 (a)

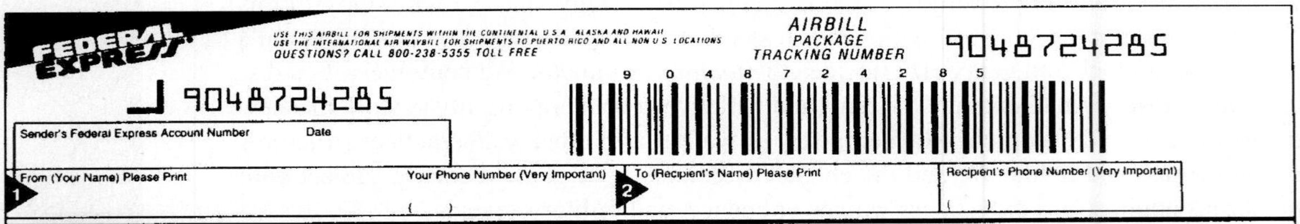

FIGURE 9.1 (b)

© I. Bello

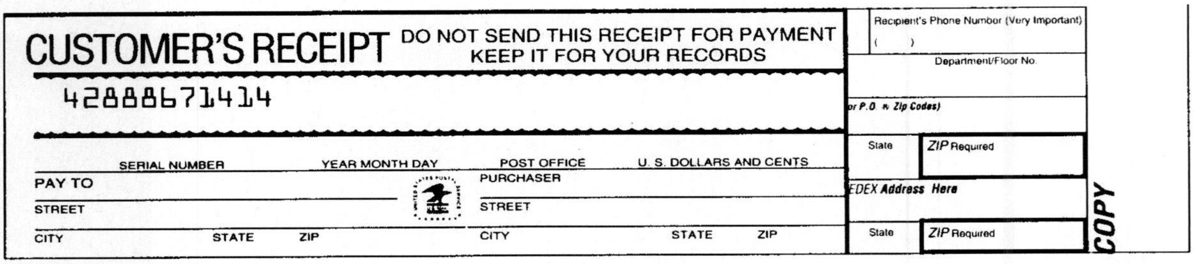

FIGURE 9.2

Human Side of Math

(1776–1831)

Sophie Germain was born in Paris in 1776. As a child, she spent many hours in her father's library. There, she came across the legend of Archimedes, who was so engrossed in the study of a geometric figure he had drawn that he failed to respond to a Roman soldier and was killed. From that point she was determined to learn all she could about mathematics.

In 1801, fascinated by Gauss's work on the theory of numbers, Germain began sending him the results of her own mathematical investigations, using the pen name M. Leblanc.

Sophie Germain won the French Academy's prize under her own name. It was the high point of her career. She died at age 55.

LOOKING AHEAD

Some of Germain's communication with Gauss involved her work in modular arithmetic, which is the focus of Section 9.1.

In this section you will study modular arithmetic, its operations and relationships, as well as some applications (see the Using Your Knowledge section of Exercises 9.1).

The last number in the first airbill (5) or the money order (4) is sometimes called the **check digit,** or **CD** for short. Check digits are used in a variety of situations. Airline tickets, UPS packages, and drivers' licenses, for example, use check digits to encode information. Why? For security reasons. Suppose you try to change the postal money order amount from \$5 to \$500. The post office *knows* that money order number 42888671414 is for \$5, so if the amount was altered, the check digit would have to be altered as well. Do you know what other numbers would work? Mathematically, you have to solve the congruence $x \equiv 4 \pmod 9$. Practically, x must somewhat resemble 42888671414. [For example, $22 \equiv 4 \pmod 9$ because when 22 is divided by 9, the remainder is 4, but money order 22 was probably used a long time ago.] Can you find "better" numbers that will work without changing the CD number? The CD number 4 is usually written under three bars ||| so that an erasure or alteration of the CD will disturb the bars and expose the fraud.

In earlier chapters of this book we made frequent reference to *mathematical systems.* For example, we defined the set of natural numbers together with the operations of addition and multiplication. We then discussed certain properties of the set of natural numbers with respect to these operations. The set of natural numbers, together with the operations of addition and multiplication, constitutes a mathematical system.

In general, a *mathematical system* consists of the following items:

1. A *set of elements*
2. One or more *operations*
3. One or more *relations* that enable us to compare the elements in the set
4. Some *rules, axioms,* or *laws* that the elements in the set satisfy

For example, when we refer to the system of integers, we have

1. *Elements.* The elements of this system are the integers in the set $I = \{\ldots, -2, -1, 0, 1, 2, \ldots\}$.
2. *Operations.* Within the system of integers, we can always perform the operations of addition, subtraction, and multiplication. We can sometimes divide, but most often the result of dividing one integer by another is not an integer. The set of integers is not closed under division.
3. *Relations.* We have three possible relations between any two integers a and b. They are

   $a < b,\qquad a > b,\qquad \text{and}\qquad a = b$
4. *Rules or laws.* Addition and multiplication in the system of integers satisfy the commutative and the associative laws, as well as the distributive law.

Most of the mathematical systems we have discussed involve an *infinite* number of elements. In this section we shall study mathematical systems that contain only a *finite* number of elements. If we are thoroughly familiar with the workings of a finite system, we can generalize this knowledge and apply it to other systems.

A Clock Arithmetic

As you are aware, the numbers on the face of a clock are used to tell the time of the day or night. The set of numbers used for this purpose is

$$S = \{1, 2, 3, 4, 5, 6, 7, 8, 9, 10, 11, 12\}$$

We shall define addition on this set by means of an addition table, but we first present some examples to justify the entries in the table. If it is now 11 A.M., and we have to be in class in 3 hours, it is obvious that we have to go to class at 2 P.M. For this reason, we

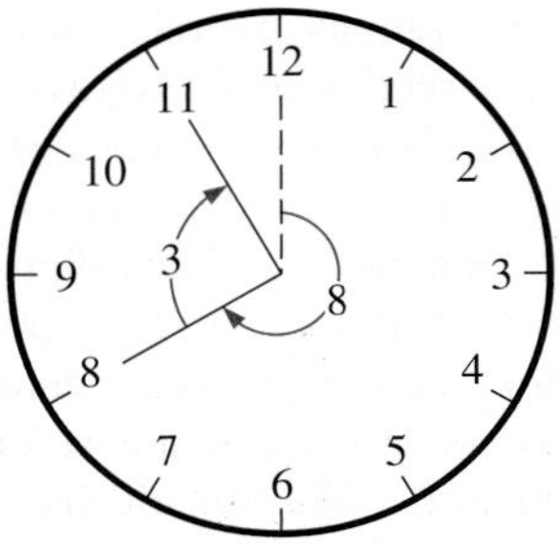

FIGURE 9.3 $8 \oplus 3 = 11$

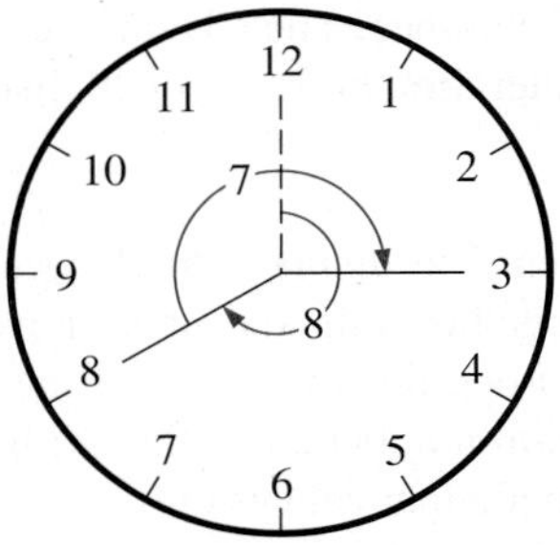

FIGURE 9.4 $8 \oplus 7 = 3$

define $11 \oplus 3 = 2$, where $\oplus$ (read "circle plus") is the operation of clock addition. If our class was to meet in 5 hours, and it was now 10 A.M., we would have to be in class at 3 P.M., so $10 \oplus 5 = 3$.

EXAMPLE 1 Addition in Clock Arithmetic

Find the following sums in clock arithmetic:

(a) $8 \oplus 3$ **(b)** $8 \oplus 7$ **(c)** $11 \oplus 12$

Solution

(a) $8 \oplus 3$ means 3 hours after 8 o'clock, so $8 \oplus 3 = 11$ (see Figure 9.3).

(b) $8 \oplus 7$ means 7 hours after 8 o'clock. Thus, $8 \oplus 7 = 3$ (see Figure 9.4).

(c) $11 \oplus 12$ means 12 hours after 11 o'clock. Thus, $11 \oplus 12 = 11$.

We can now construct Table 9.1, which shows the addition facts in clock arithmetic. Verify the entries in this table before proceeding further.

Table 9.1 Addition in Clock Arithmetic

$\oplus$	1	2	3	4	5	6	7	8	9	10	11	12
1	2	3	4	5	6	7	8	9	10	11	12	1
2	3	4	5	6	7	8	9	10	11	12	1	2
3	4	5	6	7	8	9	10	11	12	1	2	3
4	5	6	7	8	9	10	11	12	1	2	3	4
5	6	7	8	9	10	11	12	1	2	3	4	5
6	7	8	9	10	11	12	1	2	3	4	5	6
7	8	9	10	11	12	1	2	3	4	5	6	7
8	9	10	11	12	1	2	3	4	5	6	7	8
9	10	11	12	1	2	3	4	5	6	7	8	9
10	11	12	1	2	3	4	5	6	7	8	9	10
11	12	1	2	3	4	5	6	7	8	9	10	11
12	1	2	3	4	5	6	7	8	9	10	11	12

Of course, other operations can be defined on this set. For example, the clock difference $3 \ominus 4$ (read "3 circle minus 4") is a number n with the property that $3 = 4 \oplus n$. By looking at Table 9.1 we can see that the number 11 satisfies this equation because $3 = 4 \oplus 11$. Accordingly, we state the following definition:

Definition of Subtraction Using Clock Arithmetic

$a \ominus b = n$ if and only if $a = b \oplus n$

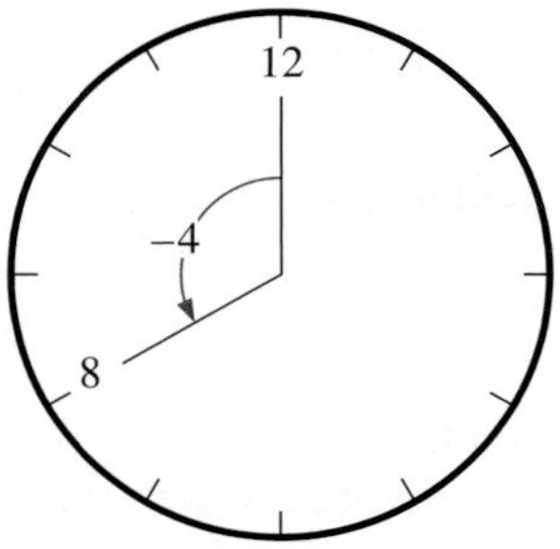

FIGURE 9.5 $-4 = 8$

With this definition, $4 \ominus 6 = 10$ because $4 = 6 \oplus 10$.

If a is a positive number, we can define $-a$ in clock arithmetic as the number obtained by going counterclockwise a hours. With this convention, it follows that

$$-a = 12 - a$$

For example, $-4 = 12 - 4 = 8$; this agrees with Figure 9.5.

With this definition of $-a$, it also follows that

$$a \ominus b = a \oplus (-b)$$

which may be regarded as an alternative way to define circle minus.

EXAMPLE 2 Solving Equations in Clock Arithmetic

Find numbers n such that the following hold:

(a) $n \oplus 5 = 3$ (b) $2 \ominus 3 = n$

Solution

(a) We inspect the fifth row in Table 9.1. We have to find a number n such that when we add n to 5, we obtain 3. The answer is 10, because $10 \oplus 5 = 3$.

(b) $2 \ominus 3 = 2 \oplus (-3) = 2 \oplus (12 - 3) = 2 \oplus 9 = 11$. (Check in the table that $3 \oplus 11 = 2$.)

As usual, multiplication can be defined in terms of addition. Thus, $3 \otimes 5 = (5 \oplus 5) \oplus 5 = 10 \oplus 5 = 3$, so $3 \otimes 5 = 3$.

Definition of Multiplication Using Clock Arithmetic

$$a \otimes b = \underbrace{b \oplus b \oplus b \oplus \cdots \oplus b}_{a \text{ times}}$$

(The symbol $\otimes$ is read "circle times.")

With this definition, $4 \otimes 3 = 3 \oplus 3 \oplus 3 \oplus 3 = 12$ and $2 \otimes 8 = 8 \oplus 8 = 4$. *Note:* A quicker way to obtain the answer is to multiply the two numbers by ordinary arithmetic, divide by 12, and take the remainder as the answer. (If the remainder is 0, the answer is 12, the zero point on a clock.) For example, $6 \otimes 5 = 6$ because $6 \times 5 = 30$ and 30 divided by 12 equals 2 with a remainder of 6. Similarly, $6 \otimes 4 = 12$ because $6 \times 4 = 24$, and 24 divided by 12 is 2 with a 0 remainder. So the answer is 12.

EXAMPLE 3 Finding Products in Clock Arithmetic

Find the following products in clock arithmetic:

(a) $3 \otimes 5$ (b) $4 \otimes 8$ (c) $9 \otimes 9$

Solution

(a) $3 \otimes 5 = 3$ because $3 \times 5 = 15$, which divided by 12 is 1 with a remainder of 3.

(b) $4 \otimes 8 = 8$ because $4 \times 8 = 32$, and 32 divided by 12 is 2 with a remainder of 8.

(c) $9 \otimes 9 = 9$ because $9 \times 9 = 81$, which divided by 12 is 6 with a remainder of 9.

Division is defined in clock arithmetic in terms of multiplication. For example, $\frac{4}{8} = 2$ because $4 = 8 \otimes 2$, and $\frac{3}{5} = 3$ because $3 = 5 \otimes 3$.

Definition of Division Using Clock Arithmetic

$$\frac{a}{b} = n \quad \text{if and only if} \quad a = b \otimes n$$

In discussing multiplication in clock arithmetic, we noted that 12 in this arithmetic corresponds to 0 in ordinary arithmetic. To show that 12 behaves further like 0 in ordinary arithmetic, let us try to find a number n such that

$$\frac{1}{12} = n$$

This equation is true only if $1 = 12 \otimes n$. But there is no n in clock arithmetic such that $12 \otimes n = 1$. So, in clock arithmetic, we cannot divide 1 by 12, just as in ordinary arithmetic we cannot divide 1 by 0.

EXAMPLE 4 Finding Quotients in Clock Arithmetic

Find the following quotients in clock arithmetic:

(a) $\frac{2}{7}$ (b) $\frac{8}{8}$ (c) $\frac{3}{4}$

Solution

(a) $\frac{2}{7} = n$ if and only if $2 = 7 \otimes n$. Thus, we wish to find an n such that $7 \otimes n = 2$ because $n = 2$ satisfies the given equation, $\frac{2}{7} = 2$. Note that the answer $n = 2$ can be found by trial and error; that is, we let $n = 1$ and see whether $7 \otimes 1 = 2$ (it does not). We then let $n = 2$ and check to see whether $7 \otimes 2 = 2$. Because $7 \otimes 2 = 2$, the desired number has been obtained.

(b) $\frac{8}{8} = n$ if and only if $8 = 8 \otimes n$, an equation that is satisfied by $n = 1$, $n = 4$, $n = 7$, and $n = 10$. Note that unlike ordinary division problems, in which the answer is unique, in clock arithmetic a division problem may have many solutions.

(c) $\frac{3}{4} = n$ if and only if $3 = 4 \otimes n$. There is no n such that $3 = 4 \otimes n$, so the problem $\frac{3}{4} = n$ has no solution.

B Modular Arithmetic

The four fundamental operations were defined on the 12-hours clock. These operations can be generalized to a type of mathematical system called **modular arithmetic.** This system can be defined on the set of integers as follows:

Definition of Congruent Modulo *m*

Two integers a and b are said to be **congruent modulo *m*,** denoted by $a \equiv b \pmod{m}$, if $a - b$ (or $b - a$) is a multiple of m (m an integer).

Thus, $14 \equiv 4 \pmod{5}$ because $14 - 4 = 10$, which is a multiple of 5, and $2 \equiv 18 \pmod{4}$ because $18 - 2 = 16$, which is a multiple of 4.

EXAMPLE 5 Truth or Falsity in Modular Arithmetic

Are the following statements true or false?

(a) $4 \equiv 1 \pmod{3}$ (b) $7 \equiv 2 \pmod{4}$ (c) $1 \equiv 6 \pmod{5}$

Solution

(a) True because $4 - 1 = 3$, a multiple of 3

(b) False because $7 - 2 = 5$ is *not* a multiple of 4

(c) True because $6 - 1 = 5$, a multiple of 5

The addition of two numbers in modular arithmetic is simple. For example, in arithmetic modulo 5, we have $3 + 3 \equiv 1$ because $3 + 3 = 6 \equiv 1 \pmod 5$. Thus, to add nonnegative numbers in a system modulo m, we proceed as follows:

Addition Modulo *m*

1. Add the numbers in the ordinary way.
2. If the sum is less than m, the answer is the sum obtained.
3. If the sum is greater than or equal to m, the answer is the remainder obtained by dividing the sum by m.

For example, in modulo 8

$3 + 4 \equiv 7 \pmod 8$ Because $3 + 4 = 7$ is less than 8

$3 + 5 \equiv 0 \pmod 8$ Because $3 + 5 = 8$, which divided by 8 leaves a 0 remainder

$3 + 7 \equiv 2 \pmod 8$ Because $3 + 7 = 10$, which divided by 8 is 1 with a remainder of 2

Table 9.2 Addition Modulo 5

+	0	1	2	3	4
0	0	1	2	3	4
1	1	2	3	4	0
2	2	3	4	0	1
3	3	4	0	1	2
4	4	0	1	2	3

We now define addition in modular arithmetic for modulo 5, as shown in Table 9.2.

When adding numbers in modular arithmetic, we may want to use the following theorem:

Addition Theorem for Congruence

If $a \equiv b \pmod m$ and $c \equiv d \pmod m$, then

$$a + c \equiv b + d \pmod m$$

For example, to add 18 and 31 (mod 5), we can use the facts that

$18 \equiv 3 \pmod 5$ and $31 \equiv 1 \pmod 5$

to obtain

$$18 + 31 \equiv 4 \pmod 5$$

Similarly, if you number the days of the week as 1 for Sunday, 2 for Monday and so on, you can use arithmetic mod 7 to predict the day of the week on which a future date will fall.

To multiply two numbers in arithmetic modulo 5, we multiply the numbers in the ordinary way. If the product is less than 5, the answer is this product. If the product is greater than 5, the answer is the remainder when the product is divided by 5. For example, $4 \times 4 \equiv 1$ because the product $4 \times 4 = 16$, which leaves a remainder of 1 when divided by 5. Multiplication modulo 5 is shown in Table 9.3.

Table 9.3 Multiplication Modulo 5

×	0	1	2	3	4
0	0	0	0	0	0
1	0	1	2	3	4
2	0	2	4	1	3
3	0	3	1	4	2
4	0	4	3	2	1

Subtraction in modular arithmetic is defined as follows:

Definition of Subtraction in Modular Arithmetic

$a - b \equiv c \pmod{m}$ if and only if $a \equiv b + c \pmod{m}$

Thus, $3 - 4 \equiv 4 \pmod{5}$ because $3 \equiv (4 + 4) \pmod{5}$, and $2 - 4 \equiv 3$ because $2 \equiv (4 + 3) \pmod{5}$.

EXAMPLE 6 Subtraction (Mod 5)

Find the following:

(a) $(4 - 1) \pmod{5}$ (b) $(2 - 3) \pmod{5}$ (c) $(1 - 4) \pmod{5}$

Solution

(a) $4 - 1 \equiv 3 \pmod{5}$

(b) $2 - 3 \equiv n \pmod{5}$ if and only if $2 \equiv (3 + n) \pmod{5}$. From Table 9.2, $3 + 4 \equiv 2 \pmod{5}$. Thus, $2 - 3 \equiv 4 \pmod{5}$.

(c) $1 - 4 \equiv n \pmod{5}$ if and only if $1 \equiv 4 + n \pmod{5}$. From Table 9.2, $1 \equiv 4 + 2 \pmod{5}$. Thus, $1 - 4 \equiv 2 \pmod{5}$.

Table 9.4 Addition Modulo 5

+	0	1	2	3	4
0	0	1	2	3	4
1	1	2	3	4	0
2	2	3	4	0	1
3	3	4	0	1	2
4	4	0	1	2	3

We examine Table 9.4 to find which properties the set $S = \{0, 1, 2, 3, 4\}$ has under the operation of addition modulo 5.

1. All entries in Table 9.4 are elements of S, so S is *closed* with respect to addition (mod 5).
2. The operation of addition (mod 5) is *associative.* (This fact is a consequence of the properties of ordinary addition because division by 5 and taking the remainder can be done after the ordinary addition is done.)
3. The operation of addition (mod 5) is *commutative;* that is, if x and y are any elements of S, then $x + y \equiv y + x \pmod{5}$. This can easily be checked by inspecting Table 9.4. As we can see, the results of the operations $2 + 4$ and $4 + 2$ appear in positions that are *symmetric* with respect to a diagonal line drawn from top left to bottom right of the table. If this type of symmetry is present for any operation table; that is, if the top half of the table is the reflection of the bottom half across the diagonal, then the operation is commutative.
4. The *identity* for addition modulo 5 is 0 because for any x in S, $x + 0 = x$; that is, $0 + 0 = 0$, $1 + 0 = 1$, $2 + 0 = 2$, $3 + 0 = 3$, and $4 + 0 = 4$.
5. Every element has an additive *inverse* (mod 5). The inverse of 0 is 0 because $0 + 0 \equiv 0 \pmod{5}$. The inverse of 1 is 4 because $1 + 4 \equiv 0 \pmod{5}$. The inverse of 2 is 3 because $2 + 3 \equiv 0 \pmod{5}$. The inverse of 3 is 2 because $3 + 2 \equiv 0 \pmod{5}$. The inverse of 4 is 1 because $4 + 1 \equiv 0 \pmod{5}$.

As we have seen in the preceding discussion, modular arithmetic is a mathematical system in which two operations are defined on the same set. For the set $S = \{0, 1, 2, 3, 4\}$, we defined addition and multiplication modulo 5 as shown in Tables 9.2 and 9.3. Are there any properties that involve both operations? The answer is yes. For example, to find $3 \times (2 + 4) \pmod{5}$, we can proceed in one of the two following ways:

1. $3 \times (2 + 4) \equiv 3 \times (1) \equiv 3 \pmod{5}$
2. $3 \times (2 + 4) \equiv (3 \times 2) + (3 \times 4) \equiv 1 + 2 \equiv 3 \pmod{5}$

To get the answer in the second way, we used a property that involves both addition and multiplication. This property is called the *distributive property;* it is true in general that if a, b, and c are elements of S, then

$$a \times (b + c) \equiv (a \times b) + (a \times c) \pmod{m}$$

because $a \times (b + c) - (a \times b) - (a \times c) = 0$ in ordinary arithmetic.

EXAMPLE 7 Solving Equations (Mod 5)

Find a replacement for n that will make the given sentence true in arithmetic modulo 5.

(a) $4 \times (3 + 1) \equiv (4 \times n) + (4 \times 1)$ **(b)** $n \times (1 + 3) \equiv (2 \times 1) + (2 \times 3)$

Solution

(a) By the distributive property, $4 \times (3 + 1) \equiv (4 \times 3) + (4 \times 1)$. Thus, $n = 3$ will make the sentence $4 \times (3 + 1) \equiv (4 \times n) + (4 \times 1)$ true.

(b) By the distributive property, $2 \times (1 + 3) \equiv (2 \times 1) + (2 \times 3)$. Thus, $n = 2$ will make the sentence $n \times (1 + 3) \equiv (2 \times 1) + (2 \times 3)$ true.

EXAMPLE 8 Solving More Equations (Mod 5)

Find a replacement for n that will make the given sentence true.

(a) $3 + n \equiv 2 \pmod 5$ **(b)** $\frac{3}{4} \equiv n \pmod 5$

Solution

(a) By inspection of Table 9.2 (or 9.4), we see that $3 + 4 \equiv 2 \pmod 5$. Thus, $n = 4$ will make the sentence $3 + n \equiv 2 \pmod 5$ true.

(b) $\frac{3}{4} \equiv n \pmod 5$ is true if and only if $3 \equiv 4 \times n \pmod 5$. By inspection of Table 9.3, we see that $4 \times 2 \equiv 3 \pmod 5$. Hence, $n = 2$ will make the sentence $\frac{3}{4} \equiv n \pmod 5$ true.

In Examples 7 and 8 we have given answers in the set $\{0, 1, 2, 3, 4\}$. If we allow n to be any integer that makes the given congruence true, then each answer can be modified by adding or subtracting any desired multiple of 5. This is justified by the addition theorem for congruency proved earlier. For instance, in Example 8(a), all the possible integer answers are given by $n \equiv 4 \pmod 5$. This means that n can have any of the values $\ldots, -6, -1, 4, 9, 14, \ldots$; each of these makes the congruence $3 + n \equiv 2 \pmod 5$ true.

C Applications

EXAMPLE 9 Finding Your Sign with Congruences

Suppose you were born in year Y. Your Chinese zodiac sign is R, where R is the remainder obtained from the formula $Y/12 = N + R$ and corresponds to monkey (0), cock (1), dog (2), boar (3), rat (4), ox (5), tiger (6), rabbit (7), dragon (8), snake (9), horse (10), and goat (11). The cock, boar, and ox are sometimes known as the rooster, pig, and buffalo.

(a) What is your sign if you were born in 1982?

(b) How can you find your Chinese zodiac sign using congruences?

Solution

(a) $\frac{1982}{12} = 165$ with a remainder R of 2, corresponding to the dog.

(b) In modular arithmetic, the remainder is the answer when a number is divided by the modulus. Thus, if Y is your birth year, to find the sign, use $Y \equiv R \pmod{12}$. Note that in part (a) $1982 \equiv 2 \pmod{12}$. Your sign is the number corresponding to R.

© I. Bello

Are you a monkey or a tiger? A ram or a dragon? Please, do not be offended! Traditional Chinese belief is that a person's year of birth holds the key to their long-life character and well-being. The Chinese zodiac is based on a 12-year cycle, and your sign depends on your year of birth. We show you how to find your sign in the Example 9.

© I. Bello

Now that you have learned about airbills, money orders, and even your horoscope, it is time for a break! Grill some spicy burgers with Bello Pepper Sauce. Horrors! The bottle is empty; there is no more. You go to the Web, get the manufacturer's phone number, and call. They want to know the UPC (Universal Product Code, or **bar code** for short) on the side of the bottle. You calmly read

0 1 2 0 6 1 1 0 1 8 5 8

The operator politely replies, "That is not a valid number." What are these Bello people, psychics? You look at the bottle again for reassurance. The operator was correct. In your hastiness, you have misread a number. The correct number is

0 1 2 0 6 1 0 0 1 8 5 8

How did the operator know that the number you gave him at first was incorrect? The Bello employees know about bar codes and check digits. The first six numbers on the bar code encode information about the manufacturer, the next five numbers have information about the product, and the last number, the 8, is the check digit. In general, how do we get the check digit c? We will tell you now.

Suppose the first 11 numbers in the bar code are $n_1, n_2, n_3, \ldots, n_{11}$. Write:

$$\begin{array}{ll}
\text{Compute} & n_1 + n_2 + n_3 + n_4 + n_5 + n_6 + n_7 + n_8 + n_9 + n_{10} + n_{11} + c \equiv 0 \pmod{10} \\
\text{In our case,} & 3n_1 + n_2 + 3n_3 + n_4 + 3n_5 + n_6 + 3n_7 + n_8 + 3n_9 + n_{10} + 3n_{11} + c \equiv 0 \pmod{10} \\
\text{Or} & 3\cdot 0 + 1 + 3\cdot 2 + 0 + 3\cdot 6 + 1 + 3\cdot 0 + 0 + 3\cdot 1 + 8 + 3\cdot 5 + c \equiv 0 \pmod{10} \\
\text{That is,} & 0 + 1 + 6 + 0 + 18 + 1 + 0 + 0 + 3 + 8 + 15 + c \equiv 0 \pmod{10} \\
 & 52 + c \equiv 0 \pmod{10}
\end{array}$$

Since $52 + 8 \equiv 0 \pmod{10}$, the check digit c is 8.

EXAMPLE 10 Finding a Check Digit

Find the check digit c for Quaker Quick grits if the first 11 numbers are

0 3 0 0 0 0 0 4 1 5 0 c

Solution

Using the scheme above, we compute the number

$$\begin{array}{ll}
 & 3\cdot 0 + 3 + 3\cdot 0 + 0 + 3\cdot 0 + 0 + 3\cdot 0 + 4 + 3\cdot 1 + 5 + 3\cdot 0 + c \equiv 0 \pmod{10} \\
\text{Or} & 0 + 3 + 0 + 0 + 0 + 0 + 0 + 4 + 3 + 5 + 0 + c \equiv 0 \pmod{10} \\
\text{That is,} & 15 + c \equiv 0 \pmod{10}
\end{array}$$

Since $15 + 5 \equiv 0 \pmod{10}$, the check digit c is 5. Remember, $15 + 5 = 20$, which leaves a remainder of 0 when divided by 10, so the check digit is correct!

Have you heard of identity theft? Identity theft occurs when someone uses your personal information, such as your credit card number, without your permission to commit fraud or other crimes. We are ready to learn more about these credit card numbers.

Look at the credit card number. The very first digit **(4)** represents the type of entity that issued the credit card. For example, a **4** means that the card was issued by a bank or financial institution. The different categories (from **0** to **9**) are shown in the accompanying table. The first *six* digits in the credit card **(427531)** identify the issuer of the card. For example, the first *six* numbers for a MasterCard may be 51xxxx, for a Visa 4xxxxx, and 34xxxx for an American Express.

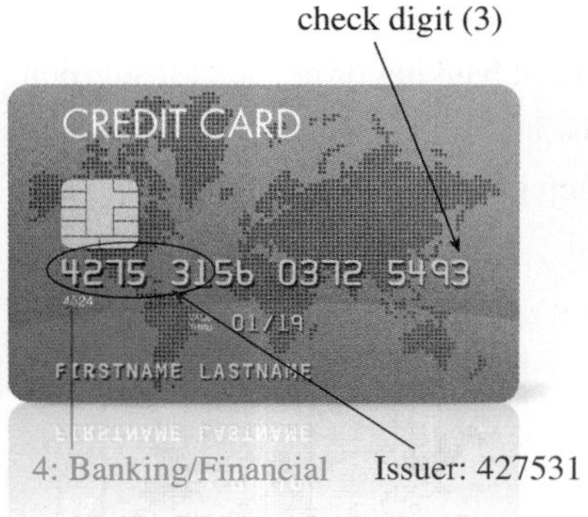

(0–9)	Card Issuer Categories
0	Special industry assignment
1, 2	Airlines
3	Entertainment
4, 5	Banking and financial
6	Merchandising/banking
7	Petroleum
8	Telecommunications
9	National assignment

CARD TYPE	Prefix	Length
MASTERCARD	51xxxx- 55xxxx	16
VISA	4xxxxx	13, 16
AMEX	34xxxx- 37xxxx 300xxx-	15
Diners Club/	305xxx	14
Carte Blanche	36xxxx 38xxxx	
Discover	6011xx	16

The *final digit* of the credit card number (8) is called the **check digit.** There is a formula, called the *Luhn algorithm,* that is used to decide if a credit card is valid. This formula was named after the IBM scientist Hans Peter Luhn (1896–1964), who was awarded U.S. Patent 2950048 ("Computer for Verifying Numbers") for inventing the technique in 1960. The Luhn algorithm is used by banks and other credit-issuing entities to combat credit-card fraud. We can decide whether or not a credit card is valid by following these three steps.

Using the Luhn Algorithm to Find Valid Credit Card Numbers

1. Starting with the second-to-last digit (the first digit to the *left* of the check digit) and moving left, **double** the value of all the alternating digits. If the result of doubling a number has two digits, add the two numbers. For example, when you double 9, you get 18, which yields 1 + 8 = 9. Now add all these numbers together.
2. Starting from the left, take all the unchanged digits (i.e., the numbers that you did *not* double in step 1) and add them together.
3. Now add the numbers obtained in steps 1 and 2. If this number ends with a zero, then the credit card number is valid. If not, then the credit card number is not valid.

EXAMPLE 11 Checking Credit Card Numbers

A credit card is numbered 4417 1234 5678 9112.

(a) What type of institution issued the card?

(b) What is the check digit of the card?

(c) Is the credit card valid? If not, what should the check digit be to make it valid?

Solution

(a) The card starts with the number 4, which denotes a banking or financial institution.

(b) The check digit is the last number in 4417 1234 5678 9112, which is 2.

(c) We check the number by following the three-step procedure. The card number is

		4	4	1	7	1	2	3	4	5	6	7	8	9	1	1	2
1.		× 2		× 2		× 2		× 2		× 2		× 2		× 2		× 2	
		8		2		2		6		10		14		18		2	
	Add:	8	+	2	+	2	+	6	+	1 (1+0)	+	5 (1+4)	+	9 (1+8)	+	2	= 35
2.	Add:		4	+	7	+	2	+	4	+	6	+	8	+	1	+	2 = 34

3. The sum of the results from steps 1 and 2 is 35 + 34 = 69, which does not end in zero, so the credit card number is not valid. If we change the check digit from a 2 to a 3, the sum will be 70, and the number will be valid.

9.1 EXERCISES

A Clock Arithmetic

In problems 1–8, find the sum in clock arithmetic.

1. $9 \oplus 7$
2. $2 \oplus 8$
3. $8 \oplus 3$
4. $5 \oplus 7$
5. $7 \oplus 8$
6. $9 \oplus 9$
7. $8 \oplus 11$
8. $12 \oplus 3$

In problems 9–14, find the difference in clock arithmetic.

9. $8 \ominus 3$
10. $5 \ominus 8$
11. $9 \ominus 12$
12. $6 \ominus 9$
13. $8 \ominus 7$
14. $1 \ominus 12$

In problems 15–22, find all n satisfying each equation in clock arithmetic.

15. $n \oplus 7 = 9$
16. $n \oplus 8 = 2$
17. $2 \oplus n = 1$
18. $7 \oplus n = 3$
19. $3 \ominus 5 = n$
20. $2 \ominus 4 = n$
21. $1 \ominus n = 12$
22. $3 \ominus 7 = n$

In problems 23–28, find the indicated products in clock arithmetic.

23. $4 \otimes 3$
24. $3 \otimes 8$
25. $9 \otimes 2$
26. $3 \otimes 9$
27. $2 \otimes 8$
28. $12 \otimes 3$
29. Make a table of multiplication facts in clock arithmetic.

In problems 30–34, find the indicated quotients in clock arithmetic.

30. $\frac{9}{7}$
31. $\frac{3}{5}$
32. $\frac{3}{9} = n$ (*Hint:* There are three answers.)
33. $\frac{1}{11}$
34. $\frac{1}{12}$

In problems 35–40, find all n satisfying the given equation in clock arithmetic.

35. $\frac{n}{5} = 8$
36. $\frac{n}{2} = 4$
37. $\frac{n}{2} \oplus 4 = 8$
38. $\frac{n}{7} = 9$
39. $\frac{2}{n} = 3$
40. $\frac{12}{12} = n$

B Modular Arithmetic

In problems 41–46, classify each statement as true or false.

41. $2 \equiv 4 \pmod 3$
42. $5 \equiv 2 \pmod 3$
43. $6 \equiv 7 \pmod 5$
44. $5 \equiv 3 \pmod 2$
45. $8 \equiv 9 \pmod{10}$
46. $12 \equiv 8 \pmod 4$

In problems 47–50, find the indicated sums.

47. $(3 + 4) \pmod 5$
48. $(2 + 9) \pmod{10}$
49. $(3 + 1) \pmod 5$
50. $(3 + 6) \pmod 7$

In problems 51–54, find the indicated products.

51. $(4 \times 2) \pmod 5$
52. $(4 \times 3) \pmod 5$
53. $(2 \times 3) \pmod 5$
54. $(3 \times 3) \pmod 5$

In problems 55–58, find the indicated differences.

55. $(2 - 4) \pmod 5$
56. $(3 - 4) \pmod 5$
57. $(1 - 3) \pmod 5$
58. $(0 - 2) \pmod 5$

In problems 59–74, find a value of n in the set {0, 1, 2, 3, 4} that will make the given congruence true.

59. $4 \times (3 + 0) \equiv (4 \times 3) + (4 \times n) \pmod 5$
60. $2 \times (1 + 3) \equiv (2 \times 1) + (n \times 3) \pmod 5$
61. $2 \times (0 + 3) \equiv (2 \times n) + (2 \times 3) \pmod 5$
62. $4 \times (1 + n) \equiv (4 \times 1) + (4 \times 2) \pmod 5$
63. $2 + n \equiv 3 \pmod 5$
64. $n + 3 \equiv 1 \pmod 5$
65. $2 \times n \equiv 4 \pmod 5$
66. $3 \equiv 2 \times n \pmod 5$
67. $n - 3 \equiv 4 \pmod 5$
68. $2 \equiv n - 1 \pmod 5$
69. $3 \equiv n - 4 \pmod 5$
70. $n - 2 \equiv 1 \pmod 5$
71. $\frac{n}{2} \equiv 4 \pmod 5$
72. $\frac{n}{3} \equiv 2 \pmod 5$
73. $\frac{3}{4} \equiv n \pmod 5$
74. $\frac{1}{2} \equiv n \pmod 5$

In problems 75–78, use Table 9.3, page 529, and multiplication modulo 5.

75. Is the set $S = \{0, 1, 2, 3, 4\}$ closed with respect to $\times$?
76. Is the set operation $\times$ commutative?
77. Is there an identity for the operation $\times$? If so, what is this identity?
78. Find the inverse (if possible) of the following:
    a. 0 b. 1 c. 2 d. 3 e. 4

C Applications

Problems 79–86 refer to the Chinese zodiac signs discussed in Example 9.

79. Find the sign for a person born in 1985.
80. Find the sign of a baby born in 2000.
81. A person tells you that his sign is the ox. Can you tell in what exact year the person was born? Can you find out if the person tells you that he is in his 20s?
82. A goat sign person tells you that she is 30 something. How old is the person?
83. A person tells you that his sign is the dragon. What additional information do you need to find his exact age?

84. A person tells you that her sign is the snake and that she was born in the 1960s. Can you determine her exact age?

85. List all the years of the rat, starting in the 1940s.

86. List all the years of the tiger, starting in the 1950s. When is the next year of the tiger?

IN OTHER WORDS

87. Find out about military, or international, or airline time. How many hours does a military clock have? Discuss the advantages of military time over regular time.

88. If you number the days of the week as 1 for Sunday, 2 for Monday and so on, you can use arithmetic mod 7 to predict on what day of the week a future date will fall. Explain why $15 \equiv 1 \equiv$ Sunday (mod 7) and predict what day of the week it will be in 15 days if today is Tuesday.

89. In your own words, write all the similarities and differences between clock arithmetic and regular arithmetic.

90. Suppose that you are tracking a package for Federal Express. The customer claims that the package number is 0005234981 or 0005234983. Which is correct? Explain your answer.

USING YOUR KNOWLEDGE

Look at the back cover of this book. What did you find? The ISBN (International Standard Book Number) is a 10-digit number that encodes certain information about the book. (Some books show the ISBN only on the copyright page.) Say that a book's ISBN is 0-669-28957-4. The following diagram shows the reference of each part of the ISBN:

But what about the 4 at the right end? This digit is a check digit that is used to verify orders. The check number is obtained from the other digits as follows: Write the numbers 10, 9, 8, 7, 6, 5, 4, 3, and 2 above the first nine digits of the ISBN, and then multiply each of these digits by the number above it and add the results (see the diagram at the bottom of this page).

To get the check number (4 in our ISBN), divide the sum 282 by 11 and take the remainder; $r = 7$. The check number c is the solution of $c + r \equiv 0$ (mod 11); that is, $c + 7 \equiv 0$ (mod 11) for the replacement set {0, 1, 2, . . . , 10}. Since $4 + 7 = 11 \equiv 0$ (mod 11), you see that the check number is $c = 4$. Note that the easy way to get the check number is to subtract the remainder r from 11.

Use these ideas to solve the following problems. Note that if the check number is 10, it is written as the Roman numeral X.

91. If the first nine digits of a book's ISBN are 0-06-040613, find the check digit.

92. If the first nine digits of a book's ISBN are 0-517-53052, find the check digit.

93. Find the check digit for ISBN 0-312-87867.

94. The last digit of the book number in the ISBN 0-060-4098■3 was blurred as indicated. What must this digit be?

95. Find what the blurred digit must be in the ISBN 0-03-0589■4-2.

96. Find what the blurred digit must be in the ISBN 0-716■-0456-0.

In problems 97–102, find the check digit.

97. G.E. light bulb
0 43168 38540 c

98. Campbell's Pork and Beans
0 51000 02952 c

99. Del Monte Fruit Cocktail
0 24000 02140 c

100. Celestial Seasonings Green Tea
0 70734 00501 c

101. Fuji Film CR-R Disk
0 74101 74010 c

102. Tylenol PM
3 00450 17615 c

In problems 103–105, find the missing number.

103. Goya Tembleque (A dessert)
0 4133□ 03183 7

104. Peanut M and M
0 40000 1213□ 9

105. Pompeian Red Vinegar
0 □0404 00100 2

In problems 106–115, decide if the given credit card number is valid. If not, find the check digit that will make it valid. You can check your work at https://wiki.openmrs.org/display/docs/Check+Digit+Algorithm.

106. 5123 4567 8901 2345

107. 5500 0100 1479 0003

108. 4111 1111 1234 0023

109. 3465 3421 7902 4679

110. 3728 5290 7342 8237

111. 3002 4456 2940 41

112. 3000 0030 0100 04

113. 3663 9023 3938 49

114. 3823 4467 2390 38

115. 6011 0030 0507 1031

10	9	8	7	6	5	4	3	2
↓	↓	↓	↓	↓	↓	↓	↓	↓
0	6	6	9	2	8	9	5	7
↓	↓	↓	↓	↓	↓	↓	↓	↓

$$(10 \cdot 0) + (9 \cdot 6) + (8 \cdot 6) + (7 \cdot 9) + (6 \cdot 2) + (5 \cdot 8) + (4 \cdot 9) + (3 \cdot 5) + (2 \cdot 7)$$
$$= 0 + 54 + 48 + 63 + 12 + 40 + 36 + 15 + 14$$
$$= 282$$

DISCOVERY

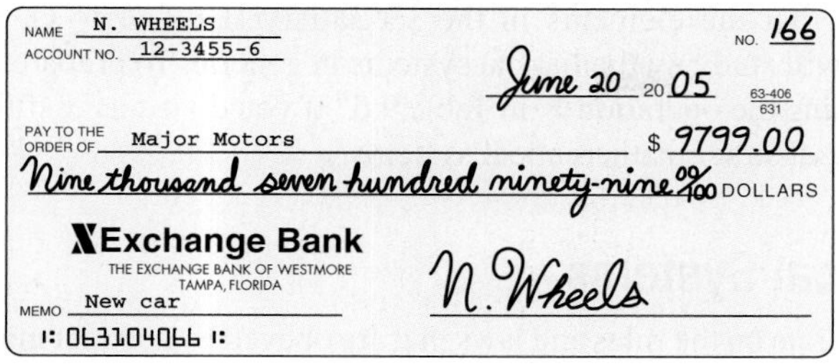

Look at the lower left-hand corner of the check. The nine-digit number in the lower left is the bank identification number, sometimes called the routing number, *and the last digit, 6, is the check digit. The scheme uses the numbers 7, 3, and 9 as multipliers to find the check digit.*

$$\begin{array}{ccccccccccccccccc} & 0 & & 6 & & 3 & & 1 & & 0 & & 4 & & 0 & & 6 & & 6 \\ & 7\cdot 0 & + & 3\cdot 6 & + & 9\cdot 3 & + & 7\cdot 1 & + & 3\cdot 0 & + & 9\cdot 4 & + & 7\cdot 0 & + & 3\cdot 6 & + & 9\cdot 6 \\ = & 0 & + & 18 & + & 27 & + & 7 & + & 0 & + & 36 & + & 0 & + & 18 & + & 54 \end{array}$$

$= 160 \equiv 0 \pmod{10}$

If the sum is not equivalent to 0 mod 10, there is an error! In problems 116–120, discover if there is an error in the given routing number.

116. 001234567 **117.** 031313562

118. 063107513 **119.** 063107514

120. 111036002

After you finish, you can verify these numbers at http://yourfavorite.com/free/verification.htm.

COLLABORATIVE LEARNING

Do you remember Pascal's triangle? The triangle is formed by starting and ending each row with the number 1. In the third row, the number 2 is obtained by adding 1 + 1 in the preceding row. Now, in the fourth row, the 3 is the sum of 1 + 2 in the preceding row. And so on.

1
1 1
1 2 1
1 3 3 1

1. Construct the next 3 rows of the triangle.

2. Now let us convert the number in each of the rows to arithmetic modulo 2. The first four rows are shown.

1	1
1 1	1 1
1 2 1	1 0 1
1 3 3 1	1 1 1 1

Complete the first 7 rows.

3. Now let a black square represent a 1 and a white square a 0. The first four rows are shown.

1
1 1
1 0 1
1 1 1 1

Complete the next 3 rows.

4. Form three or more groups of students. Each group constructs a diagram using modulo 3, 4, 5, and so on.

9.2 Abstract Mathematical Systems: Groups and Fields

GETTING STARTED

OBJECTIVES

A. Determine whether the properties of an abstract mathematical system are satisfied for a given set and operation.

B. Determine if a set together with one or two given operations forms a group and/or a field.

Table 9.5

+	E	O
E	E	O
O	O	E

EVENS, ODDS, AND MATHEMATICAL SYSTEMS

Suppose you encounter the mysterious Table 9.5. What do you think this table represents? If you think for a moment, you will see that the table exhibits the fact that if you add two even numbers, the answer is even; an even and an odd number yields an odd; an odd and an even number yields an odd, and an odd and an odd number yields an even.

Table 9.6

×	E	O
E	E	___
O	___	___

As you recall from Section 9.1, a mathematical system consists of a set of elements, {E, O} in this case, one or more operations (+ here), one or more relations (=), and some rules, axioms, or laws that the elements in the set satisfy (E + O = O, for example). In this section you will study mathematical systems in general. To prepare for this study, can you finish defining the operation × in Table 9.6? If you do it successfully, you are ready to start studying abstract mathematical systems.

A Abstract Mathematical Systems

In this section we shall concentrate on the rules and laws that are obeyed by abstract mathematical systems. To illustrate the ideas involved, we shall define a set $A = \{a, b, c, d, e\}$ and an operation $*$, which we shall call *star.* The operations on the set A can be defined by a table similar to the ones used to define the addition of natural numbers or the addition in modulo 5. Suppose that the operation $*$ is defined by Table 9.7.

To perform the operation star on any pair of elements—say, b and c—we find the element that is in the b row and the c column (rows are horizontal and columns are vertical), as shown in Table 9.8. From this table we can see that $b * c = e$. Similarly, $a * b = c$ and $c * d = b$.

Table 9.7

*	a	b	c	d	e
a	b	c	d	e	a
b	c	d	e	a	b
c	d	e	a	b	c
d	e	a	b	c	d
e	a	b	c	d	e

Table 9.8

*	a	b	c	d	e
a	b	c	d	e	a
b	c	d	e	a	b
c	d	e	a	b	c
d	e	a	b	c	d
e	a	b	c	d	e

EXAMPLE 1 Finding Results under the * Operation

Use Table 9.7 to find the result of each of the following operations:

(a) $b * e$ (b) $d * b$ (c) $(a * b) * c$

Solution

(a) $b * e$ corresponds to the entry in the b row, e column; that is, $b * e = b$.

(b) $d * b$ corresponds to the entry in the d row, b column; that is, $d * b = a$.

(c) $a * b$ is in parentheses, so we must find $a * b$ first. Thus, $(a * b) * c = c * c = a$.

By proceeding as in Example 1, we can find the result $x * y$ for all elements x and y that are in A, and it is evident that the result is also in A. The name that we give to this property is **closure.**

Definition of a Closed Set

The set A is **closed** under the operation $*$ if, for all a and b in A, $a * b$ is also in A.

Intuitively, we see that the set A is closed under the operation $*$ if the operation is always possible and if no new elements are introduced in the table defining the operation. For example, the set of natural numbers is closed under the operation of addition because for any two natural numbers a and b, $a + b$ is also a natural number. On the other hand, the set of natural numbers is not closed under subtraction because, for example, $5 - 7 = -2$, which is not a natural number.

EXAMPLE 2 Determining the Closure of Sets

Consider the sets $A = \{0, 1\}$ and $B = \{1, 2\}$. Are these sets closed under ordinary multiplication?

Solution

The set A is closed under multiplication because all possible products $0 \times 0 = 0$, $0 \times 1 = 0$, $1 \times 0 = 0$, and $1 \times 1 = 1$ are in A. On the other hand, the set B is not closed under multiplication because $2 \times 2 = 4$, which is not in B.

Another important property previously discussed in connection with the natural numbers is *associativity.*

Definition of an Associative Operation

An operation $*$ defined on a set A is **associative** if, for all a, b, and c in A,

$$(a * b) * c = a * (b * c)$$

For example, the intersection of sets that we studied in Chapter 2 is associative because for any three sets A, B, and C, we have

$$A \cap (B \cap C) = (A \cap B) \cap C$$

EXAMPLE 3 Checking Associativity under *

In Table 9.7, check to see whether each of the following is true:

(a) $(a * b) * d = a * (b * d)$ **(b)** $(c * a) * e = c * (a * e)$

Solution

(a) Table 9.7 gives $a * b = c$, so $a * b$ can be replaced by c to obtain $(a * b) * d = c * d$. Then, because the figure gives $c * d = b$, we see that $(a * b) * d = b$. Similarly, we find that $a * (b * d) = a * a = b$. The result in both cases is b, so $(a * b) * d = a * (b * d)$.

(b) Again, by using Table 9.7, we find that $(c * a) * e = d * e = d$ and $c * (a * e) = c * a = d$. Because the result is d in both cases, we have $(c * a) * e = c * (a * e)$.

Can we conclude from Example 3 that the operation $*$ is associative? The answer is no because we have not checked all the possibilities. Try some other possibilities and state whether $*$ is associative.

The next property we shall discuss is the *commutative property.*

Definition of a Commutative Operation

An operation $*$ defined on a set A is **commutative** if, for every a and b in A,

$$a * b = b * a$$

For example, the intersection of sets that we studied in Chapter 2 is commutative because for any two sets A and B, $A \cap B = B \cap A$.

EXAMPLE 4 Checking Commutativity under *

In Table 9.7, check to see whether each of the following is true:

(a) $b * d = d * b$ (b) $e * c = c * e$

Solution

(a) $b * d = a$ and $d * b = a$; thus, $b * d = d * b$.

(b) $e * c = c$ and $c * e = c$; thus, $e * c = c * e$.

Can we conclude from Example 4 that the operation $*$ is commutative? Again, the answer is no because we have not checked all the possibilities. However, there is a simple check that we can make. Since the top half of the table is the reflection of the bottom half across the diagonal going from the upper left to the lower right, the operation is commutative.

As we noted in Chapter 5, the set of integers has an additive identity (0) such that for any integer a, $a + 0 = a = 0 + a$. Similarly, 1 is the identity for multiplication because $a \cdot 1 = a = 1 \cdot a$. The idea of an *identity* can be generalized by means of the following definition:

Definition of an Identity for an Operation

An element e in a set A is said to be an **identity** for the operation $*$ if, for each element x in A,

$$x * e = x = e * x$$

For example, for the operator $*$ defined on the set $A = \{a, b, c, d, e\}$ in Table 9.7, the identity element is e, as we can easily check. Notice that the column directly under the identity element e is identical with the column at the far left, and the row opposite the element e is identical with the row across the top of the table. This appearance of the operation table is characteristic for any set that has an identity element under the operation.

EXAMPLE 5 Completing the Table for the * Operation

Let $A = \{a, b, c\}$, and let $*$ be an operation defined on A. If c is the identity element, what do you know about the table that defines the operation $*$?

Solution

From the preceding discussion, we can complete a partial table like Table 9.9. The column at the far right is identical to the column at the far left; the row across the bottom is identical to the row across the top.

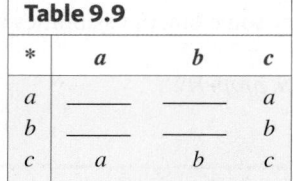

Table 9.9

*	a	b	c
a	___	___	a
b	___	___	b
c	a	b	c

Closely related to the idea of an identity is the idea of an *inverse*. For example, the additive inverse of 3 is -3 because $3 + (-3) = 0$ (the additive identity). Similarly, the multiplicative inverse of 3 is $\frac{1}{3}$ because $3 \times \frac{1}{3} = 1$ (the multiplicative identity). In order to find the inverse of a number a under addition, we need a number b such that $a + b = 0$; similarly, to find the inverse of a number a under multiplication, we need a number b such that $a \times b = 1$. These ideas can be summarized by the following definition:

Definition of Inverse

If a and b are in A, we say that ***a* is the inverse of *b*** under the operation $*$ if $a * b = e = b * a$, where e is the identity.

Table 9.10

#	a	b
a	b	a
b	a	b

EXAMPLE 6 Finding Identities and Inverses

Consider Table 9.10, which defines the operation #. Find the following:

(a) The identity (b) The inverse of a (c) The inverse of b

Solution

(a) The identity is b because the column under b is identical to the column at the far left and the row opposite b is identical to the row across the top.

(b) We have to find an element to fill the blank in a # _____ $= b$. From the table we can see that this element is a because $a \# a = b$. Thus, a is its own inverse.

(c) We have to find an element to fill the blank in b # _____ $= b$. From the table we can see that this element is b because $b \# b = b$. So, b is its own inverse.

Table 9.11

#	a	b	c
a	c	a	b
b	b	c	a
c	a	b	c

EXAMPLE 7 Checking Identities, Inverses, and Commutativity

Consider the operation # defined by Table 9.11.

(a) Is there an identity element?

(b) Do any of the elements have inverses?

(c) Is the operation commutative?

Note that this table of operations corresponds to rotations in the plane as shown in Figure 9.6.

Solution

(a) There is no column identical to the column under #, so there is no identity element.

(b) Since there is no identity element, there are no inverses.

(c) The operation is not commutative. For example,

$a \# b = a$ but $b \# a = b$

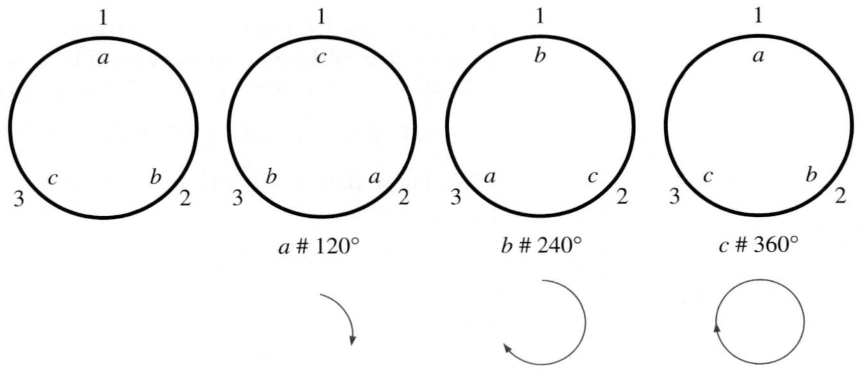

FIGURE 9.6

As in the case of modular arithmetic, there is a property that involves two operations. This property is called the *distributive property* and is defined as follows:

Definition of the Distributive Property

The operation $*$ defined on a set A is said to be **distributive** over the operation # if, for all a, b, and c in A, we have

$$a * (b \# c) = (a * b) \# (a * c)$$

For example, the operation of multiplication defined on the set of real numbers is distributive over addition because, for any real numbers a, b, and c,

$$a \times (b + c) = (a \times b) + (a \times c)$$

On the other hand, addition is *not* distributive over multiplication because

$$a + (b \times c) \neq (a + b) \times (a + c)$$

as shown by the example

$$3 + (4 \times 5) = 3 + 20 = 23$$
$$(3 + 4) \times (3 + 5) = 7 \times 8 = 56$$

Thus,

$$3 + (4 \times 5) = 23 \neq (3 + 4) \times (3 + 5) = 56$$

Now let us consider two operations, F and S, defined for any two natural numbers a and b as follows:

1. a F b means to select the *first* of the two numbers.
2. a S b means to select the *smaller* of the two numbers. (If $a = b$, then a S a is defined to be a.)

Thus, 3 F 5 = 3, 5 F 3 = 5, and 4 F 1 = 4. Similarly, 3 S 5 = 3, 5 S 3 = 3, 4 S 1 = 1, and 2 S 2 = 2.

EXAMPLE 8 Establishing Distributivity

Is the operation F distributive over S?

Solution

Recall that a F b means to select the first of the numbers and that a S b means to select the smaller of the two numbers a and b (if the numbers are the same, select the number). To show that F distributes over S, we have to show that

$$a \text{ F } (b \text{ S } c) = (a \text{ F } b) \text{ S } (a \text{ F } c)$$

We know that $a \text{ F } (b \text{ S } c) = a$ (because a is the first number). Also, $a \text{ F } b = a$ and $a \text{ F } c = a$, so

$$(a \text{ F } b) \text{ S } (a \text{ F } c) = a \text{ S } a = a$$

Thus,

$$a \text{ F } (b \text{ S } c) = (a \text{ F } b) \text{ S } (a \text{ F } c)$$

This shows that F is distributive over S.

B Groups and Fields

Interest in mathematical systems such as those we just studied started in the early nineteenth century with the study of groups.

Definition of a Group

A **group** is a mathematical system consisting of a set S and an operation $*$ with the following four properties:

1. **Closure** property
2. **Associative** property
3. **Identity** property. There is an identity element in S.
4. **Inverse** property. Each element of S has an inverse in S.

If the system also has the **commutative** property, then the group is called a **commutative** (or **abelian**) **group.**

For example, the set of integers with the operation of addition has the following properties:

Closure	The sum of two integers is always an integer.
Associative	If a, b, and c are integers, then $a + (b + c) = (a + b) + c$.
Identity	The integer 0 is the identity element such that $0 + a = a + 0 = a$ for every integer a.
Inverse	If a is an integer, then $-a$ is an integer such that $a + (-a) = 0$.
Commutative	If a and b are integers, then $a + b = b + a$.

Thus, the set of integers is a commutative group under addition.

Although group theory was developed by many mathematicians, the French mathematician Evariste Galois is usually considered the pioneer in this field. However, the origin of group theory can be traced back to the efforts of the Babylonians in solving equations of degree greater than 2. At the time of the Renaissance, the Italian mathematicians Girolamo Cardano and Nicolo de Brescia, commonly referred to as *Tartaglia* ("the Stammerer"), made the first successful attempts to solve equations of third and fourth degree. After their discoveries, it seemed natural to pursue methods to solve equations of degree 5 and higher. Galois investigated the general properties of the equations involved and the properties of their solutions. These studies led to the theory of groups.

EXAMPLE 9 Checking for a Commutative Group

Does the set $S = \{0, 1, 2, 3, 4\}$, together with the operation of multiplication modulo 5, form a commutative group?

Solution

The multiplication table for this system is shown in Table 9.12. We check the five properties as follows:

1. The set S is *closed* because all the entries in the table are elements of S.
2. The operation is *commutative* because the reflection of the bottom half of the table along the diagonal is identical to the top half.
3. The operation is *associative.* [You have to check that $(a \times b) \times c = a \times (b \times c)$, where a, b, and c are in $\{0, 1, 2, 3, 4\}$.]

Table 9.12 Multiplication Modulo 5

×	0	1	2	3	4
0	0	0	0	0	0
1	0	1	2	3	4
2	0	2	4	1	3
3	0	3	1	4	2
4	0	4	3	2	1

4. The *identity* for this system is 1.
5. All the elements, except 0, have *inverses.* Zero does not have an inverse because there is no number a in S such that $0 \times a \equiv 1$. The inverses are as follows:

   The inverse of 1 is 1 $(1 \times 1 \equiv 1)$.
   The inverse of 2 is 3 $(2 \times 3 \equiv 1)$.
   The inverse of 3 is 2 $(3 \times 2 \equiv 1)$.
   The inverse of 4 is 4 $(4 \times 4 \equiv 1)$.

Since the system does not have an inverse for 0, the system is not a group under the operation of multiplication modulo 5.

EXAMPLE 10 Checking for Another Commutative Group

If the number 0 is omitted from the set in Example 9, is the resulting system a commutative group?

Solution

The multiplication table for this system is Table 9.12 with the 0 row and the 0 column omitted. From the discussion in Example 9, we see that this system has all the required properties and is thus a commutative group.

The distributive property is the only property we have studied that involves two operations. We now turn our attention to a kind of mathematical system, called a *field,* which consists of a set S and two operations.

Definition of a Field

A **field** is a mathematical system consisting of a set S and two operations—say, $*$ and #—defined on S and having the following properties:

1. **Closure** property
2. **Associative** property
3. **Identity** property
4. **Inverse** property (except that there is no inverse for the identity with respect to $*$)
5. **Commutative** property
6. **Distributive** property of # with respect to $*$

PROBLEM-SOLVING

Groups and Fields

① **Read** the problem.

Show that the system consisting of the set $S = \{0, 1, 2, 3, 4\}$ and the operations of addition and multiplication modulo 5 is a field.

② **Select** the unknown.

You have to show that the set S together with the operations $+$ and $\times$ modulo 5 form a field.

③ **Think** of a plan.
What do we have to show?

Thus, you have to show that $+$ and $\times$ have the closure, associative, identity, inverse, commutative, and distributive properties.

④ **Use** the results of Example 9 to verify that the operations of + and × modulo 5 satisfy the properties stated in the Definition of a Field.

The operation + modulo 5 has the closure, associative, identity, inverse, and commutative properties, as shown in Table 9.4, and the operation × modulo 5 has the closure, commutative, associative, identity, and inverse properties (except that 0 has no inverse) as shown in Example 9 of this section. Finally, × is distributive over + in the set of real numbers. Thus, × is distributive over + in the set S.

⑤ **Verify** the answer.

You can examine Tables 9.2 and 9.12 and verify the properties mentioned. In general, it can be shown that if p is any prime number, then the integers modulo p form a field under + and ×.

Try Example 11 Now

Cover the solution, write your own solution, and then check your work.

EXAMPLE 11 Checking for a Field

Let S = {Odd, Even}, and let + and × be two operations defined by Tables 9.13 and 9.14. You may recognize that these operations correspond to adding or multiplying odd and even numbers. For instance, an odd number added to an even number gives an odd number; thus, Odd + Even = Odd. Similarly, Even × Even = Even. Does the set S = {Odd, Even} form a field under the + and × operations?

Table 9.13

+	Odd	Even
Odd	Even	Odd
Even	Odd	Even

Table 9.14

×	Odd	Even
Odd	Odd	Even
Even	Even	Even

Solution

1. *Closure:* The tables show that S is closed under the two operations.
2. *Associative:* Both operations are associative. For example,
   Odd + (Odd + Even) = Odd + Odd = Even, and
   (Odd + Odd) + Even = Even + Even = Even, so that
   Odd + (Odd + Even) = (Odd + Odd) + Even. (You can check the other cases in the same way.)
3. *Commutative:* The two tables show that both operations are commutative.
4. *Identity:* The identity for + is Even, because the column under Even in Table 9.13 is identical to the column at the far left, and the row adjacent to Even is identical to the top row. You can check in the same way that the identity for × is Odd.
5. *Inverse:* The inverse of Even under + is Even because Even + Even = Even. The inverse of Odd under + is Odd, because Odd + Odd = Even. The inverse of Odd under × is Odd because Odd × Odd = Odd. There is no inverse of Even under × (see the definition of a field).
6. *Distributive:* The distributive property of × over + holds because it holds for multiplication over addition for the real numbers.

Thus, the set S = {Odd, Even} with the operations + and × satisfies all the requirements of the definition of a field, so the system is a field.

We will give you an opportunity to work with these ideas in a new mathematical field, Tropical Mathematics, that will be discussed in the Using Your Knowledge section.

9.2 EXERCISES

A Abstract Mathematical Systems

In problems 1–7, consider the set $S = \{a, b, c\}$ and the operation @ defined by the following table.

@	a	b	c
a	c	a	b
b	a	b	c
c	b	c	a

1. Find the following:
   a. a @ b b. b @ c c. c @ a
2. Find the following:
   a. a @ (b @ c) b. (a @ b) @ c
   c. Are the results in parts (**a**) and (**b**) identical?
3. Find the following:
   a. b @ (a @ b) b. (b @ a) @ b
   c. Are the results in parts (**a**) and (**b**) identical?
4. Find the following:
   a. (a @ b) @ a b. a @ (b @ a)
   c. Are the results in parts (**a**) and (**b**) identical?
5. Find the following:
   a. b @ c b. c @ b
   c. Are the results in parts (**a**) and (**b**) identical?
6. Is the operation @ a commutative operation? Explain.
7. Is the set S closed with respect to the operation @? Explain.
8. Suppose a F b means to select the first of two numbers a and b, as in Example 8 of this section. Let $A = \{1, 2, 3\}$.
   a. Make a table that will define the operation F on the set A.
   b. Is A closed under the operation F?
   c. Is the operation F commutative?
   d. For any three natural numbers a, b, and c, show that
   a F (b F c) = (a F b) F c
9. Let the operation F be defined as in problem 8, and let N be the set of natural numbers.
   a. Is the set N closed under the operation F? Explain.
   b. Is the operation F associative? Explain.
   c. Is the operation F commutative? Explain.
10. Let S be the set of all nonnegative multiples of 5 (0, 5, 10, and so on).
    a. Is the set S closed with respect to ordinary multiplication?
    b. Is the operation of ordinary multiplication commutative on S? Explain.
    c. Is the operation of ordinary multiplication associative on S? Explain.
11. Are the following sets closed under the given operation?
    a. The odd numbers under addition
    b. The odd numbers under multiplication
    c. The even numbers under addition
    d. The even numbers under multiplication
12. Give an example of an operation under which the set $\{0, 1\}$ is
    a. not closed.
    b. not associative.
    c. not commutative.

Let $S = \{\varnothing, \{a\}, \{b\}, \{a, b\}\}$. The following table will be used in problems 13–18. The entries in the table represent the set intersection of the elements in the corresponding rows and columns.

$\cap$	$\varnothing$	$\{a\}$	$\{b\}$	$\{a, b\}$
$\varnothing$	$\varnothing$	$\varnothing$	$\varnothing$	$\varnothing$
$\{a\}$	$\varnothing$	$\{a\}$	$\varnothing$	$\{a\}$
$\{b\}$	$\varnothing$			
$\{a, b\}$	$\varnothing$			

13. Supply the missing entries in the table.
14. Find the following:
    a. $(\{a\} \cap \{b\}) \cap \{a, b\}$
    b. $\{a\} \cap (\{b\} \cap \{a, b\})$
    c. Are the results in parts (**a**) and (**b**) identical?
15. Find the following:
    a. $(\{b\} \cap \{a, b\}) \cap \{a\}$
    b. $\{b\} \cap (\{a, b\} \cap \{a\})$
    c. Are the results in parts (**a**) and (**b**) identical?
16. In Chapter 2 you learned that for any three sets A, B, and C, $A \cap (B \cap C) = (A \cap B) \cap C$. On the basis of this result, would you say that the operation $\cap$ defined in the table above is associative?
17. Is the set S closed with respect to the operation $\cap$? Explain.
18. Is the operation $\cap$ commutative? How can you tell?
19. Suppose that a L b means to select the larger of the two numbers a and b (if the numbers are the same, select the number).
    a. Complete the following table.
    b. If there is an identity element, what is it?

L	1	2	3	4
1				4
2			3	
3		3		
4	4			4

The following table will be used in problems 20 and 21.

S	1	2	3	4
1	1	1	1	1
2	1	2	2	2
3	1	2	3	3
4	1	2	3	4

20. Does the set $A = \{1, 2, 3, 4\}$ have an identity? If so, what is this identity?

21. Find the inverses of the following:

a. 1 **b.** 2 **c.** 3 **d.** 4

22. Consider the set $S = \{-1, 0, 1\}$ and the operation of ordinary multiplication. Complete the table.

×	−1	0	1
−1			
0			
1			

23. Does the set $S = \{-1, 0, 1\}$ of problem 22 have an identity under multiplication? If so, what is this identity?

24. For the set $S = \{-1, 0, 1\}$ of problem 22 under the operation of multiplication, find the inverses (if possible) of the following:

a. 1 **b.** −1 **c.** 0

25. If $\mathscr{U}$ is the set of all subsets of any nonempty set A,

a. find the identity element for the operation of set intersection (∩).

b. can you find more than one identity?

The following table will be used in problems 26–28.

@	0	1	2	3
0	0	1	2	3
1	1	2	3	0
2	2	3	0	1
3	3	0	1	2

26. Is the set $S = \{0, 1, 2, 3\}$ closed under the operation @?

27. Does the set S have an identity with respect to the operation @? If so, what is this identity?

28. Find the inverses (if they exist) of the following:

a. 0 **b.** 1 **c.** 2 **d.** 3

In problems 29–32, let F be defined as in problem 8 and let a L b mean to select the larger of the two numbers a and b (if a = b, assume a L b = a) as in problem 19.

29. Find the following:

a. 3 F (4 L 5) **b.** 4 F (5 L 6)

30. Find the following:

a. 4 L (4 F 5) **b.** 5 L (6 F 7)

31. Does the distributive property a F (b L c) = (a F b) L (a F c) hold for all real numbers a, b, and c? Explain.

32. Does the distributive property a L (b F c) = (a L b) F (a L c) hold for all real numbers a, b, and c? Explain.

33. In ordinary arithmetic, is multiplication distributive over subtraction?

34. In ordinary arithmetic, is division distributive over subtraction? [*Hint:* Look at the two forms $a \div (b - c) = (a \div b) - (a \div c)$ and $(a - b) \div c = (a \div c) - (b \div c)$.]

35. In the arithmetic of fractions, is multiplication distributive over addition?

36. In the arithmetic of fractions, is addition distributive over multiplication?

B Groups and Fields

37. Let $S = \{a, b, c\}$, and let $*$ be defined by the following table. Is S a group with respect to the operation $*$?

*	*a*	*b*	*c*
a	*b*	*c*	*a*
b	*c*	*a*	*b*
c	*a*	*b*	*c*

In problems 38–49, determine whether the given set forms a group under the given operation. For each set that is not a group, give one specific example of a condition that is not satisfied.

38. The odd integers under the operation of addition

39. The odd integers under the operation of multiplication

40. The even integers under the operation of addition

41. The even integers under the operation of multiplication

42. The positive integers under the operation of addition

43. The positive integers under the operation of multiplication

44. The integers under the operation of addition

45. The integers under the operation of multiplication

46. The real numbers under the operation of multiplication

47. The real numbers under the operation of addition

48. The set $\{-1, 0, 1\}$ under the operation of addition

49. The set $\{-1, 0, 1\}$ under the operation of multiplication

50. Complete the following table so that the result will be a group under the given operation:

#	*a*	*b*	*c*
a			*b*
b		*b*	*c*
c			

51. Let $S = \{a, b, c, d, e\}$, and let # be defined on S by the following table. Is the set S under the operation # a group? If not, give one specific example of a condition that is not satisfied.

#	*a*	*b*	*c*	*d*	*e*
a	*a*	*b*	*c*	*d*	*e*
b	*b*	*e*	*a*	*c*	*d*
c	*d*	*c*	*e*	*a*	*b*
d	*c*	*d*	*b*	*e*	*a*
e	*e*	*a*	*d*	*b*	*c*

In problems 52–56, determine whether the given sets form a field under the operations of addition and multiplication.

52. The set of positive odd integers

53. The set of positive even integers

54. The set of integral multiples of 5

55. The set of integral multiples of 2

56. The set of all real numbers

IN OTHER WORDS

Suppose you are given a set S and a table defining the operation ◆. For problems 57–60, explain in your own words the procedure for determining whether

57. the set S is closed under the operation ◆.

58. the operation ◆ is commutative.

59. there is an identity for the operation ◆.

60. two elements—say, a and b—are inverses of each other.

61. Explain a procedure you can use to verify that the operation $*$ of problem 37 is associative. How many cases do you have to check to be convinced that $*$ is associative?

62. Suppose that an associative operation $\cdot$ is defined for every pair of elements of a set S and that S is closed under this operation. There is a theorem that can save work when trying to show that this system is a group. This theorem says that if there is an identity element e in S such that $e \cdot x = x$ for every element x of S and if every element x of S has an inverse $\hat{x}$ in S such that $\hat{x} \cdot x = e$, then the system is a group. Explain the procedure you would follow to use this theorem to solve problem 37. How many cases do you have to check now?

USING YOUR KNOWLEDGE

Do we have to move to an exotic Caribbean location to work on this section? Fortunately, that will not be necessary. The term Tropical Mathematics *was coined by a group of French mathematicians, among them Jean Eric Pin, and was intended to honor their Brazilian and hence "tropical" colleague Imre Simon who pioneered the field. In Tropical Mathematics we have the operations of* Tropical Addition $\oplus$ *and* Tropical Multiplication $\otimes$ *defined as follows:*

$$a \oplus b = \min\{a, b\}$$
$$a \otimes b = a + b$$

This means that to find a $\oplus$ b we simply take the ***minimum*** *of the two numbers a and b. For example,*

$$2 \oplus 5 = 2$$
$$2 \oplus (-5) = -5$$
$$7 \oplus 0 = 0$$
$$(-2) \oplus 3 = -2$$

63. Construct the Tropical Addition Table for the set of numbers $\{1, 2, 3, 4, 5, 6, 7\}$.

$\oplus$	1	2	3	4	5	6	7
1							
2							
3							
4							
5							
6							
7							

a. Is the set {1, 2, 3, 4, 5, 6 and 7} closed under the operation $\oplus$?

b. Is the operation $\oplus$ commutative?

c. Is the operation $\oplus$ associative?

d. What is the identity for $\oplus$?

64. In Tropical Multiplication $a \otimes b = a + b$. For example:

$$2 \otimes 6 = 2 + 6 = 8$$
$$2 \otimes (-5) = 2 + (-5) = -3$$
$$6 \otimes 0 = 6 + 0 = 6$$
$$(-2) \otimes (-3) = (-2) + (-3) = -5$$

Construct the Tropical Multiplication Table for the set of numbers $\{0, 1, 2, 3, 4, 5, 6\}$.

a. Is the set $\{0, 1, 2, 3, 4, 5, 6\}$ closed under the operation $\otimes$?

b. Is the operation $\otimes$ commutative?

c. Is the operation $\otimes$ associative?

d. What is the identity for $\otimes$?

65. In "regular" arithmetic, multiplication is distributive over addition: $a \times (b + c) = (a \times b) + (a \times c)$. Is Tropical Multiplication distributive over Tropical Addition; that is, is $a \otimes (b \oplus c) = (a \otimes b) \oplus (a \otimes c)$? Give examples!

66. The number 0 is the identity for Tropical Multiplication because $0 \otimes x = x \otimes 0 = x$. But there is no integer that can be the identity for Tropical Addition. What should we do? If we assume that the symbol e represents the identity for Tropical Addition, we must have $e \oplus x = x$ for all integers x

a. What is the definition of $e \oplus x = x$?

b. What does $\min\{e, x\} = x$ mean?

c. In mathematics we often use the symbol ∞ to indicate a "number" larger than all other integers. So we define ∞ to be the identity for $\oplus$ (Certainly $x \le \infty$ as required!). With this definition, find $3 \oplus \infty$

d. $(-5) \oplus \infty$

e. $x \oplus \infty$

DISCOVERY

The distributive property can be used to shorten the labor in certain multiplication problems. For instance, the product of 6 and 999 can easily be found by writing

$$6 \times 999 = 6 \times (1000 - 1) = 6000 - 6 = 5994$$

Use this idea to calculate the following products.

67. 6×9999

68. 8×99

69. 7×59

70. 8×999

71. 4×9995

72. 3×9998

The distributive property can be used in an interesting way in number puzzles. Have you ever seen a magician ask a person in the audience to think of a number and perform several calculations with it? Then, without knowing the original number, the magician knows the person's final number! The following is one of these puzzles:

Think of a number.
Add 3 to it.
Triple the result.
Subtract 9.
Divide by the number with which you started.
The result is 3.

The following table presents the calculations of four persons who selected different numbers:

	First	Second	Third	Fourth
Think of a number.	4	6	8	10
Add 3 to it.	7	9	11	13
Triple the result.	21	27	33	39
Subtract 9.	12	18	24	30
Divide by the number with which you started.	3	3	3	3
The result is always 3.				

73. Why does the puzzle work? (*Hint:* Let x be the number you select, and work through the puzzle.)

74. What is the result of the following puzzle?

Think of a number.
Add 2 to it.
Double the result.
Subtract 4.
Divide by the number with which you started.
The result is ______.

COLLABORATIVE LEARNING

Here is an actual mathematical group that provides aerobic benefits. Form several groups each with a copy of the table that follows. Select a leader for each group, and let the rest of the members of the group stand at attention. Consider the set $C = \{At, R, L, A\}$, where the elements At, R, L, and A stand for the commands "Attention!" "Right face!" "Left face!" and "About face!" Let the operation FB *mean* followed by. *L followed by A has the same effect in terms of the final orientation of the group members as the single command R. So we enter R in row L column A. With this information, each group leader should give the proper commands to fill in the blanks in the table.*

FB	*At*	*R*	*L*	*A*
At				
R				
L				R
A				

1. Is the set C closed under the operation FB? Explain.
2. What is the identity element?
3. What is the inverse of At?
4. What is the inverse of R?
5. What is the inverse of L?
6. What is the inverse of A?
7. Is the operation associative? Explain.
8. Is the set consisting of the set C and the operation FB a group? Explain.
9. Is the operation FB commutative? Explain.

9.3 Game Theory

GETTING STARTED

OBJECTIVES

A. Find the value of a strictly determined game defined by a matrix.

B. Find the payoff matrix and saddle points for a specified game.

HAVE IT YOUR WAY

Have you noticed that when a fast-food chain such as McDonald's opens a restaurant, another fast-food chain, maybe Burger King, starts a competing restaurant within a couple of blocks? Why do you think this happens? Either both chains conduct extensive fast-food demand, demographic, and location surveys, reach the same conclusion, and target the same population, or one of the chains does most of the research and the other just follows. Now suppose McDonald's and Burger King wish to open restaurants. They can decide to open on opposite sides of town (O) or in a central location (C) near each

© Jeff Greenberg/Photo Edit

It is not unusual to see competing fast-food franchises in close proximity to one another.

other. If they both open on opposite sides of town (*O*) or in a central location (*C*) near each other, each will get 50% of the targeted business. If McDonald's opens in the central location (*C*) and Burger King on the other side of town (*O*), McDonald's gets 70% of the business (and Burger King 30%). However, if McDonald's opens on the other side of town (*O*) and Burger King in the central location (*C*), McDonald's gets 40% of the business (and Burger King 60%). What should each of the franchisers do to ensure their greatest incomes? The percentage gains or losses for McDonald's can be the entries in a **payoff matrix,** a rectangular array of numbers enclosed in square brackets, as shown below. The optimal strategies can be obtained by examining the rows and columns in this matrix.

$$\begin{array}{cc} & \textbf{Burger King} \\ & \begin{array}{cc} C & O \end{array} \\ \textbf{McD} & \begin{array}{c} C \\ O \end{array}\begin{bmatrix} 50 & 70 \\ 40 & 50 \end{bmatrix} \end{array}$$

To see how another simple situation can be represented by a matrix, look at the simple game of matching pennies. In this game, two players *R* and *C* each toss a penny. If they match (*HH* or *TT*), *R* keeps both pennies, but if they do not, *C* keeps both pennies. In the matrix representation for this game, the column headings *H* and *T* represent the outcomes (Heads or Tails) for *C*, the row headings represent the outcomes for *R*, and the matrix entries give the payoffs for *R*. Note that row 1, column 1, corresponds to the outcome *HH*, and since there is a match, *R* wins one penny $(+1)$. On the other hand, in row 2, column 1, the outcomes are *TH* and since there is no match, *R* loses a penny (-1) as shown in the matrix.

$$\begin{array}{cc} & \textbf{Column } (C) \\ & \begin{array}{cc} H & T \end{array} \\ \textbf{Row } (R) & \begin{array}{c} H \\ T \end{array}\begin{bmatrix} +1 & -1 \\ -1 & +1 \end{bmatrix} \end{array}$$

Now, for which of these situations (choosing a location or matching pennies) do you think it is easier to develop a winning strategy? Surprisingly enough, you will see in this section that it is easier to develop a winning strategy for the restaurant situation.

In business, economics, the sciences, and the military, decisions have to be made in competitive situations that are similar to games played according to formal rules. The branch of mathematics that deals with the analysis of competition and conflict is called **game theory** and was started because of the efforts of John von Neumann, Emil Borel, and Oskar Morgenstern. **Two-person games** (or **matrix games**) are those that have only two adversaries or players always making intelligent choices. Matching pennies and the selection of a restaurant location by two different franchises are examples of two-person games. Let us construct the **payoff matrix** denoting the percentage gains for McDonald's as described in Getting Started. The following is the information we need:

1. If McDonald's selects *O* or *C*, and Burger King chooses the same location, each will get 50% of the business.
2. If McDonald's picks *C* and Burger King *O*, McDonald's gets 70% (and Burger King 30%).
3. If McDonald's selects *O*, and Burger King *C*, McDonald's gets 40% (and Burger King 60%).

From (1), we can enter 50 in row 1, column 1 and in row 2, column 2.
From (2), we can enter 70 in row 1, column 2.
From (3), we can enter 40 in row 2, column 1.

$$\begin{array}{cc} & \textbf{Burger King} \\ & \begin{array}{cc} C & O \end{array} \\ \textbf{McD} & \begin{array}{c} C \\ O \end{array}\begin{bmatrix} 50 & 70 \\ 40 & 50 \end{bmatrix} \end{array}$$

This game and the penny-matching game are **constant-sum** games, because the sum of the payoffs is a constant (in the McDonald's–Burger King game, the McDonald's percentage plus the Burger King percentage is a constant 100%). In the penny-matching game, the sum of the payoffs is 0. Thus, matching pennies is called a **zero-sum** game.

A Saddle Points

In game theory, a player seeks an **optimal strategy,** a strategy that maximizes the player's gain or minimizes his or her loss. What should the strategy for McDonald's (the row player) be? To select row 1 or row 2? If it selects row 1, it has a chance of getting 70% of the business! But Burger King will then pick column 1, and each will end up with 50%. Certainly, row 1 is better than row 2 for McDonald's because the best it can do in row 2 is 50%, but it is also possible to end up with only 40% if Burger King picks column 1. Thus, the best strategy for McDonald's is to **select row 1.** If we think of McDonald's as player R, the row player, this discussion suggests the following method for developing an **optimal pure strategy** for player R:

Optimal Pure Strategy for Player R

1. Circle the smallest element in each row.
2. Choose the row that has the largest of the circled values.

Note that this strategy guarantees the greatest gain to R, independent of the other player's choice.

What strategy should Burger King follow? If it selects column 2, McDonald's will certainly select row 1, giving McDonald's 70% of the business. Thus, the best strategy for Burger King is to **select column 1.**

Optimal Pure Strategy for Player C

1. Box the largest element in each column.
2. Choose the column with the smallest boxed number.

In this game, the **optimal pure strategy** for McDonald's is to **select row 1,** and the **optimal pure strategy** for Burger King is to **select column 1.** Note that 50 is both the **smallest** element in its row and the **largest** element in its column. 50 is called a **saddle point,** and it is the **value** of this game.

Definition of Strictly Determined

A matrix game is **strictly determined** if there is an entry in the payoff matrix that is both the *smallest* element in its row and the *largest* element in its column. Such an entry is called a **saddle point** for the game, and the **value** of the game is the value of this saddle point.

EXAMPLE 1 Finding Values of a Game

If the entries represent payoff values for the row player, determine which of the following payoff matrices define strictly determined games and find the values of the games:

(a) $\begin{bmatrix} 1 & 3 & -2 \\ -1 & 0 & 4 \\ 2 & -3 & 1 \end{bmatrix}$ **(b)** $\begin{bmatrix} -2 & 1 & -3 \\ 3 & 4 & 1 \\ -2 & -4 & -1 \end{bmatrix}$

(c) $\begin{bmatrix} 2 & 3 & 2 & 4 \\ 1 & 4 & -3 & 3 \\ 1 & -1 & 0 & -1 \\ 2 & 4 & 2 & 5 \end{bmatrix}$

Solution

(a) For the row player, do the following:

1. Circle the smallest element in each row $(-2, -1, \text{and } -3)$.
2. The row player's optimal strategy is to choose the row that has the largest circled value, that is, the row containing -1 (*row 2*).

$$\begin{bmatrix} 1 & 3 & \enclose{circle}{-2} \\ \enclose{circle}{-1} & 0 & 4 \\ 2 & \enclose{circle}{-3} & 1 \end{bmatrix} \quad \leftarrow \text{Choose row 2.}$$

For the column player, do the following:

1. Box the largest element in each column $(2, 3, \text{and } 4)$.
2. The column player's optimal strategy is to choose the column with the smallest boxed number, that is, the column containing 2 (*column 1*).

$$\begin{bmatrix} 1 & \boxed{3} & -2 \\ -1 & 0 & \boxed{4} \\ \boxed{2} & -3 & 1 \end{bmatrix}$$

↑
Choose column 1.

Since there is no value that is both the smallest element in its row and the largest in its column, there is no saddle point. This game is *not strictly determined.*

(b) The row player circles -3, 1, and -4. Since 1 is the *largest* of the three numbers, the row player selects *row 2*. The row player's optimal strategy is to select the row containing 1 (*row 2*).

$$\begin{bmatrix} -2 & 1 & \enclose{circle}{-3} \\ 3 & 4 & \enclose{circle}{1} \\ -2 & \enclose{circle}{-4} & -1 \end{bmatrix} \quad \leftarrow \text{Choose row 2.}$$

The column player boxes 3, 4, and 1. Since 1 is the *smallest* of the three numbers, the optimal strategy for the column player is to select *column 3*, the column containing 1.

$$\begin{bmatrix} -2 & 1 & -3 \\ \boxed{3} & \boxed{4} & \boxed{\enclose{circle}{1}} \\ -2 & -4 & -1 \end{bmatrix}$$

↑
Choose column 3.

Since the 1 in the second row, third column is both the *smallest* element in its row and the *largest* element in its column (it is *circled and boxed*), this is a saddle point. The value of this strictly determined game is 1.

(c) The row player circles the *smallest* numbers in each row, *2* (twice) in row 1, *−3* in row 2, *−1* (twice) in row 3, and *2* (twice) in row 4. Since 2 is the largest of 2, −3, −1, and 2, the row player should select row 1 or row 4 (each containing 2 twice).

The column player boxes the *largest* numbers in each column, the *2*s in column 1, the *4*s in column 2, the *2*s in column 3, and *5* in column 4. The column player should select column 1 or 3.

Since the number 2 (columns 1 and 3) is both the smallest element in rows 1 and 4 and the largest element in columns 1 and 3, the game is *strictly determined* and its value is 2, occurring at four different saddle points. Note that 2 is both circled and boxed each time.

$$\begin{bmatrix} \boxed{\textcircled{2}} & 3 & \boxed{\textcircled{2}} & 4 \\ 1 & \boxed{4} & \textcircled{-3} & 3 \\ 1 & \textcircled{-1} & 0 & \textcircled{-1} \\ \boxed{\textcircled{2}} & \boxed{4} & \boxed{\textcircled{2}} & \boxed{5} \end{bmatrix}$$

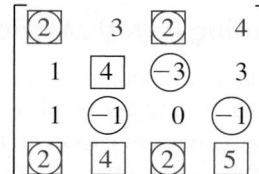

As you can see from Example 1(c), a game can have more than one saddle point (four in this case), but they must all have the same value.

B Mixed Strategies

The penny-matching game discussed in Getting Started does not have a saddle point. How can we develop a strategy to play this game a large number of times? Clearly, player *R* should not always play the same strategy (say, *H*), for if she did, player *C* might always play *T* and win! So *R* must play *H* some fraction *p* of the time and win $(+1)$ and *T* the rest, or $1 - p$, of the time and lose (-1). What can *C* do? Let us look at the payoff matrix.

Expected Payoff

If *C* always chooses *H*, *R*'s expected payoff is

$$E_H = (p)(1) + (1 - p)(-1) = 2p - 1$$

If *C* always chooses *T*, *R*'s expected payoff is

$$E_T = (p)(-1) + (1 - p)(1) = -2p + 1$$

Column

$$\textbf{Row}\quad \begin{array}{c} H \\ T \end{array}\overset{\begin{array}{cc} H & \;\;T \end{array}}{\begin{bmatrix} +1 & -1 \\ -1 & +1 \end{bmatrix}}$$

Note that these two equations can be obtained by multiplying $[p \quad 1 - p]$ by the first and second columns, respectively, in the payoff matrix. Since the expected payoff for *R* should be the same, regardless of *C*'s choice,

$$E_H = E_T$$

or

$$2p - 1 = -2p + 1$$

Solving for p,

$$p = \frac{1}{2}$$

This means that if C chooses H, R's expected payoff will be

$$E_H = 2p - 1 = 2\left(\frac{1}{2}\right) - 1 = 0$$

and if C chooses T, R's expected payoff will be

$$E_T = -2p + 1 = -2\left(\frac{1}{2}\right) + 1 = 0$$

EXAMPLE 2 Finding Payoff Matrices and Saddle Points

At the present time, some restaurants have a smoking section (S) and a nonsmoking section (N). Suppose that the average smoker spends \$15 per meal, and the average nonsmoker \$10. A customer enters a restaurant, and the manager has designated smoking and nonsmoking sections. If the person is a smoker and the smoking section is open, the restaurant makes \$15, but if only the nonsmoking section is open, the smoker leaves, and the restaurant makes nothing. If the customer is a nonsmoker and only the smoking section is available, the nonsmoker will leave, and the restaurant will make nothing, whereas if the person is a nonsmoker and the nonsmoking section is open, the restaurant will make \$10.

(a) Construct the payoff matrix for the manager.

(b) Is there a saddle point for this game?

(c) What proportion of the customers should the manager expect to be smokers and what proportion nonsmokers?

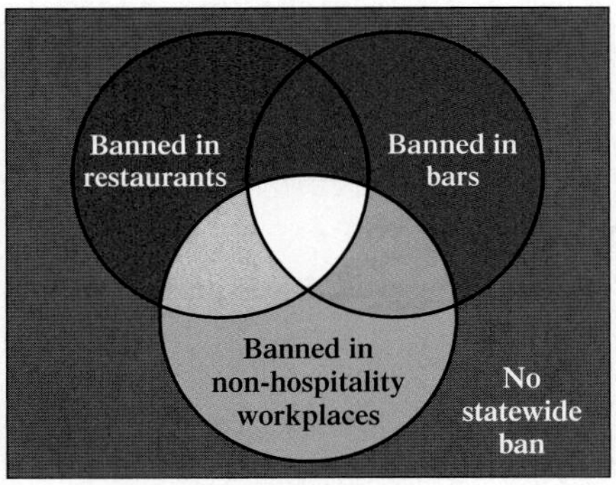

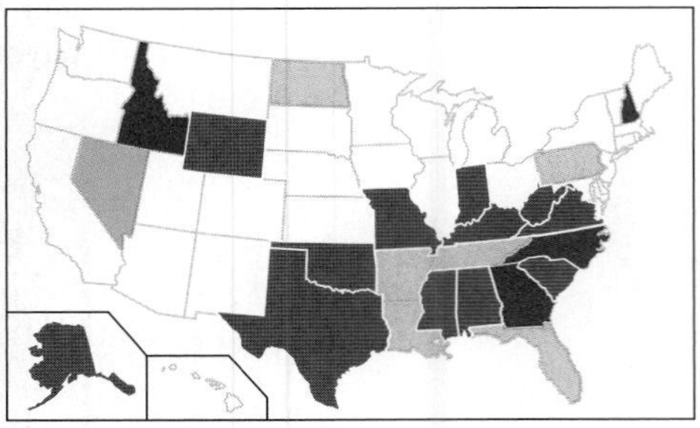

Map of current and scheduled future statewide smoking bans as of 18 June 2011

Source: Wikipedia.org

Solution

(a) If we use the rows for the manager's choice and the columns for the customer's choice, the payoff matrix is

Customer

$$\textbf{Manager}\quad \begin{matrix} & S & N \\ S & \$15 & 0 \\ N & 0 & \$10 \end{matrix}$$

(b)

Customer

$$\textbf{Manager}\quad \begin{matrix} & S & N \\ S & \boxed{\$15} & \textcircled{0} \\ N & \textcircled{0} & \boxed{\$10} \end{matrix}$$

There is no saddle point for this payoff matrix.

(c) Let p be the proportion of customers that are smokers and $1 - p$ the proportion that are nonsmokers. The manager's expectation for a smoking customer is

$$E_S = p(15) + (1 - p)(0) = 15p$$

The manager's expectation for a nonsmoking customer is

$$E_N = p(0) + (1 - p)(10) = 10 - 10p$$

To make each customer's payoff be the same, we must have

$$\begin{aligned} E_S &= E_N \\ 15p &= 10 - 10p \\ 25p &= 10 \\ p &= \tfrac{2}{5} \end{aligned}$$

Thus, the manager should expect $\frac{2}{5}$ of his customers to be smokers and $\frac{3}{5}$ to be nonsmokers.

EXAMPLE 3 Finding the Expected Test Using a Payoff Matrix

How hard do you study for your tests? It probably depends on the subject and your instructor's reputation. The payoff matrix gives the average grade expectations for students when a test that can be classified as Hard (H), Medium (M), or Easy (E) is given.

$$\textbf{Student}\quad \begin{array}{c} \\ H \\ M \\ E \end{array}\!\!\begin{array}{c} \textbf{Instructor} \\ \begin{array}{ccc} H & M & E \end{array} \\ \begin{bmatrix} 70 & 80 & 90 \\ 75 & 70 & 80 \\ 50 & 60 & 70 \end{bmatrix} \end{array}$$

On the basis of this information, what type of test should students expect?

Solution

First, we note that there is no saddle point. Think of the students and the instructor as competitors in a two-person game. Certainly the students would never choose row 3 because all the grades there are lower than the corresponding grades in row 1. Thus, the students eliminate row 3. (We say that row 1 **dominates** row 3). The result is

$$\textbf{Student}\quad \begin{array}{c} \\ H \\ M \end{array}\!\!\begin{array}{c} \textbf{Instructor} \\ \begin{array}{ccc} H & M & E \end{array} \\ \begin{bmatrix} 70 & 80 & 90 \\ 75 & 70 & 80 \end{bmatrix} \end{array}$$

On the other hand, the instructor would never let the students make 90s and 80s, that is, would never choose column 3. (Note that both columns 1 and 2 **dominate** column 3 because their corresponding values are smaller than those in column 3). Thus, we can eliminate column 3 from further consideration; this leaves the 2×2 matrix

$$\textbf{Student}\quad \begin{array}{c} \\ H \\ M \end{array}\!\!\begin{array}{c} \textbf{Instructor} \\ \begin{array}{cc} H & M \end{array} \\ \begin{bmatrix} 70 & 80 \\ 75 & 70 \end{bmatrix} \end{array}$$

Now let h be the proportion of times a hard test is given. Then $1 - h$ of the time the test will not be hard. The student's expectation for a hard test is

$$E_h = h(70) + (1 - h)(75)$$

The student's expectation for not having a hard test is

$$E_n = h(80) + (1 - h)(70)$$

Thus,

$$h(70) + (1 - h)(75) = h(80) + (1 - h)(70)$$
$$-5h + 75 = 10h + 70$$
$$h = \tfrac{1}{3}$$

Thus, on the basis of the information given, the students should expect a hard test $\frac{1}{3}$ of the time and a medium test $\frac{2}{3}$ of the time. No easy tests are given!

9.3 EXERCISES

A Saddle Points

In problems 1–8, decide whether each payoff matrix represents a strictly determined game. If the game is strictly determined, find the optimal pure strategy for each player and the value of the game.

1. $\begin{bmatrix} 4 & 5 \\ 2 & 3 \end{bmatrix}$

2. $\begin{bmatrix} 3 & 1 \\ 2 & 0 \end{bmatrix}$

3. $\begin{bmatrix} 5 & 2 \\ 3 & 4 \end{bmatrix}$

4. $\begin{bmatrix} -3 & 2 \\ 0 & -3 \end{bmatrix}$

5. $\begin{bmatrix} 6 & 6 & 4 \\ 2 & -5 & -10 \\ 8 & 5 & -15 \end{bmatrix}$

6. $\begin{bmatrix} 10 & -3 & -8 \\ 12 & -2 & 5 \\ 8 & 0 & 4 \end{bmatrix}$

7. $\begin{bmatrix} 1 & 6 & -2 \\ 3 & 5 & 2 \\ 4 & 5 & 4 \end{bmatrix}$

8. $\begin{bmatrix} 5 & 1 & 2 \\ 8 & 0 & -4 \\ 4 & 1 & 3 \end{bmatrix}$

B Mixed Strategies

In problems 9–12, do the following:

a. *Determine whether there is a saddle point.*
b. *Find the mixed strategy for the row player.*

9. $\begin{bmatrix} 2 & 1 \\ -1 & 4 \end{bmatrix}$

10. $\begin{bmatrix} 3 & 2 \\ 2 & 4 \end{bmatrix}$

11. $\begin{bmatrix} 3 & -2 \\ -1 & 0 \end{bmatrix}$

12. $\begin{bmatrix} 10 & 5 \\ 6 & 12 \end{bmatrix}$

13. Use the given payoff matrix to find the optimal mixed strategy and the value of the game for the row player.

$$\begin{bmatrix} 6 & 0 \\ 2 & 4 \\ 0 & 3 \end{bmatrix}$$

14. Use the given payoff matrix to find the optimal mixed strategy and the value of the game for the row player.

$$\begin{bmatrix} 5 & 30 \\ 0 & 20 \\ 25 & 15 \end{bmatrix}$$

15. You are preparing for a test, but you don't know whether it is an essay test or a multiple choice test. You can spend 2 or 4 hours studying for this test, and the table below shows the probable scores that you would make. On the basis of this table, what should you do?

		Essay	Multiple Choice
Study	2 hours	70	80
	4 hours	85	75

16. John must prepare for an English test and for a mathematics test. He decides to study 3 hours for one of the tests and 2 hours for the other. The table shows the probable scores he would make on each test. What should he do?

Studying Time	English	Math
English 2 hours Mathematics 3 hours	80	85
English 3 hours Mathematics 2 hours	90	75

17. Ann is planning to invest some of her savings in bonds, stocks, and money market funds. Her expected return will depend on whether interest rates rise or fall during the year. The table shows the expected returns. Find Ann's optimum investment strategy and the corresponding expected return.

	Interest Rates	
Investments	**Rise (%)**	**Fall (%)**
Bonds	6	11
Stocks	10	12
Money market	15	10

18. When stocks increase in price on a certain day, their prices tend to decrease the next day, and vice versa. The payoff matrix shows the pertinent percents. In the long run, what fraction of the time will the stock increase in price?

		Tomorrow's Price: Increase	Tomorrow's Price: Decrease
Today's Price	Increase	0.2	0.8
	Decrease	0.6	0.4

19. Two gas stations R and C are competing with each other at a certain location. The percentage of the business captured by each station is dependent on the price and is given in the payoff matrix. How should station R price its gasoline?

		Station C	
		\$1.00	\$1.10
Station R	\$1.00	60%	50%
	\$1.10	30%	70%

20. Manhattan is divided into three sectors: Uptown (U), Midtown (M), and Lower (L). The proportions of the time that a taxicab operating in Manhattan picks up a passenger in any sector and drops the passenger off in any sector are given by the payoff matrix. What is the expected percent of fares going from upper Manhattan to a different sector?

		Drop Off		
		U	M	L
Pick Up	U	0.5	0.4	0.1
	M	0.3	0.6	0.1
	L	0.2	0.3	0.1

21. Car manufacturers' ads rely on the performance or safety of the cars being advertised. Market studies show that ads based on performance are effective for 70% of the younger buyers and 20% of the older buyers, whereas ads based on safety are effective for 80% of the older buyers and 40% of the younger buyers. If this process is viewed as a game between the manufacturer and buyers, do or answer the following:
    a. Give the payoff matrix for the game.
    b. In what proportion should the two kinds of ads be mixed for maximum effectiveness?

22. You and your friend play a game with pennies and nickels. Each of you puts down a coin. If the coins match, you take both, and if they do not match, your friend takes both. Write the payoff matrix for this game. What is your optimal mixed strategy and what is your corresponding expected payoff for this game?

23. A farmer has a large acreage planted in strawberries. A freeze is predicted, and the farmer must decide whether to turn on his water sprays to protect the crop. He estimates that if there is a freeze and he turns on the sprays, he will save the crop and be able to sell it for \$6000. If there is no freeze, he will be out the \$400 in water and pumping costs. If he does not turn on the sprays and there is a freeze, he will lose \$4000, but if there is no freeze, he can sell the crop for \$4000. Make a payoff matrix to show these figures and find the farmer's optimal mixed strategy and his corresponding expected payoff.

IN OTHER WORDS

24. Why do you think the value of a strictly determined game is called a saddle point?

25. Explain why, when a row i dominates another row j in a payoff matrix, j can be eliminated.

26. Explain why, when a column i dominates a column j in a payoff matrix, j can be eliminated.

USING YOUR KNOWLEDGE

We are now ready to use your knowledge in love games. A young student is planning to send flowers, poems, or candy to his sweetheart, but there are several things to take into account. She may be allergic to flowers or on a very strict diet. The payoff matrix for the situation is

		Sweetheart's Response	
		Allergic	On a diet
He Sends	Flowers	−3	4
	Poems	2	5
	Candy	3	−2

27. Which of the rows is dominated by row 2?

28. Which row can be eliminated?

29. What is the student's optimal mixed strategy?

30. What is the student's expected value for this love game?

COLLABORATIVE LEARNING

We would be remiss if we failed to give you the opportunity to solve a classic problem: The Prisoner's Dilemma. Suppose two suspects, Bonnie and Clyde, are taken into custody and questioned separately by police. Each has the choice of confessing to the crime or not. If each confesses, both will be prosecuted and go to prison for 10 years. If neither confesses, both will serve a 1-year sentence on minor charges. However, if only one confesses and agrees to testify against the other, the one who confesses will go free and the other will go to prison for 20 years, the maximum charge. Let us write their prison sentences as ordered pairs of the form (B, C). The payoff matrix for this situation will look like this.

		Clyde	
		Confess	Don't
Bonnie	Confess		
	Don't		

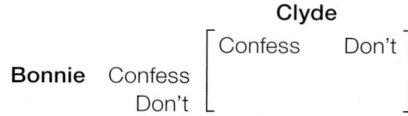

1. Fill in the entries in the payoff matrix with the four ordered pairs corresponding to the situations in which both confess, neither confesses, and one confesses and the other doesn't.
2. If Bonnie wants to minimize her time in jail, what is her best strategy: confess or not?
3. If Clyde wants to minimize his time in jail, what is his best strategy: confess or not?
4. What happens if they both reason the same way, so that both confess?
5. What happens if they both keep quiet and don't confess?
6. What do you think the "dilemma" is?

CHAPTER 9 Summary

SECTION	ITEM	MEANING	EXAMPLE
9.1	Mathematical system	A set of elements with one or more operations; relations; and rules, axioms, or laws	The set of integers with the four fundamental operations
9.1B	$a \equiv b \pmod{m}$	$a - b$ is a multiple of m.	$3 \equiv 8 \pmod{5}$
9.2A	Closure property	A set S is closed under an operation $*$ if, for all a and b in A, $a * b$ is in A.	The set I of integers is closed under the operation $+$.
	Associative property	An operation $*$ is associative if, for all a, b, and c in A, $(a * b) * c = a * (b * c)$.	The operation $+$ is associative.
	Commutative property	An operation $*$ is commutative if, for all a and b in A, $a * b = b * a$.	The operation $+$ is commutative.
	Identity	An element e is an identity for $*$ if, for every a in A, $a * e = a = e * a$.	0 is the identity for addition.
	Inverse	An element b is the inverse of a if $a * b = e = b * a$, where e is the identity for $*$.	-3 and 3 are additive inverses.
	Distributive property	The operation $*$ is distributive over the operation # if, for every a, b, and c in A, $a * (b \# c) = (a * b) \# (a * c)$.	$\times$ is distributive over $+$.
9.2B	Group	A mathematical system consisting of a set S and an operation $*$ that has the closure, associative, identity, and inverse properties	The set of integers under addition is a group.
	Commutative group	A group with the commutative property	The set of integers is a commutative group under $+$.
	Field	A set S and the operations $*$ and # with the closure, associative, commutative, and identity properties; the distributive property of # with respect to $*$; and the inverse property (except that there is no inverse for the identity with respect to $*$)	The set R of real numbers and the operations $+$ and $\times$ is a field.
9.3	Zero-sum game	A game in which the payoff to one player is the opposite of the payoff to the opposing player	
9.3A	Optimal strategy	A strategy that maximizes a player's gain or minimizes his or her loss	
	Strictly determined game	A game in which the payoff game matrix has a saddle point	
	Saddle point	A point in the payoff matrix that is both the smallest element in its row and the largest element in its column	

CHAPTER 9 Practice Test

In problems 1 and 2, find the answers in 12-hour clock arithmetic.

1. a. $3 \oplus 11$ b. $8 \oplus 9$ c. $3 \ominus 9$ d. $5 \ominus 12$
2. a. $3 \otimes 5$ b. $6 \otimes 8$ c. $\frac{3}{11}$ d. $\frac{5}{6}$
3. Are the following statements true or false?
   a. $5 \equiv 2 \pmod 3$ b. $9 \equiv 5 \pmod 4$
   c. $9 \equiv 2 \pmod 6$
4. Find the values of n in the following:
   a. $3 + 2 \equiv n \pmod 5$ b. $4 \times 3 \equiv n \pmod 5$
   c. $2 - 4 \equiv n \pmod 5$ d. $\frac{3}{2} \equiv n \pmod 5$

In problems 5 and 6, find all possible replacements for n for which each congruence is true.

5. a. $6 + n \equiv 1 \pmod 7$ b. $3 - n \equiv 4 \pmod 7$
6. a. $2n \equiv 1 \pmod 3$ b. $\frac{n}{2} \equiv 2 \pmod 3$

Problems 7–11 refer to the operation $*$ defined by the table.

*	#	$	%	¢
#	#	$	%	¢
$	$	%	¢	#
%	%	¢	#	$
¢	¢	#	$	%

7. Use the table to find the result of each of the following operations:
   a. ($ * ¢) * # b. $ * (¢ * #) c. ($ * #) * (% * ¢)
8. Is the set S = {#, $, %, ¢} closed with respect to the operation $*$? Explain.
9. Is the operation $*$ commutative? Explain.
10. Find the identity element for the operation $*$.
11. Find the inverse of each of the following:
    a. # b. $ c. % d. ¢
12. The following table defines the operation @.
    a. Find the identity element if possible.
    b. Does any element have an inverse?
    c. Is the operation commutative?

@	$	#	&
$	&	$	#
#	#	&	$
&	$	#	&

13. Suppose that a S b means to select the second of the two numbers a and b and that a L b means to select the lesser of the two numbers (if the numbers are equal, select the number).
    a. Is S distributive over L? Explain.
    b. Is L distributive over S? Explain.
14. Is the set {0, 1, 2} together with addition modulo 3 a commutative group? Explain.
15. Is the set {1, 2} together with multiplication modulo 3 a commutative group? Explain.
16. Is the set of all rational numbers along with the ordinary operations of addition and multiplication a field? Explain.

continued

CHAPTER 9 Practice Test – *continued*

Problems 17–20 refer to the set {0, 1} and the operations ⊕ and ⊗ as defined by the following tables:

⊕	0	1
0	0	1
1	1	0

⊗	0	1
0	0	0
1	0	1

17. Is the set {0, 1} together with the operation ⊕ a group?

18. Is the set {0, 1} together with the operation ⊗ a group?

19. Is the set {0, 1} together with the two operations ⊕ and ⊗ a field?

20. Determine which of the following payoff matrices represent strictly determined games and find their values:

a. $\begin{bmatrix} -2 & 0 & 8 \\ 1 & 3 & -2 \\ 2 & -3 & 1 \end{bmatrix}$ **b.** $\begin{bmatrix} -2 & -4 & -1 \\ -4 & 2 & -6 \\ 3 & 4 & 1 \end{bmatrix}$ **c.** $\begin{bmatrix} 1 & 2 & 1 & 4 \\ 1 & -1 & 0 & 1 \\ 2 & 8 & -6 & 6 \\ 2 & 3 & 2 & 4 \end{bmatrix}$

21. In the following strictly determined game, find the optimal pure strategy for the row player and give the payoff when both players use their optimal strategies:

$$\begin{bmatrix} 4 & -6 \\ 2 & -7 \end{bmatrix}$$

22. The Hills Area Rapid Transit (HART) is planning a new rapid transit system. Planners estimate that 60% of the commuters presently using HART will continue to do so next year but that 40% of them will switch to using their own cars. On the other hand, the planners predict that 30% of commuters presently using their own cars this year will switch to HART but 70% will continue to use cars.
a. Give the payoff matrix for the game.
b. What is the expected percentage of commuters using HART next year?

ANSWERS TO PRACTICE TEST

CHAPTER 9		What to Review *If You Missed It*		
QUESTION	**ANSWER**	**SECTION**	**EXAMPLE(S)**	**PAGE(S)**
1	**a.** 2 **b.** 5 **c.** 6 **d.** 5	9.1	1, 2	526, 527
2	**a.** 3 **b.** 12 **c.** 9 **d.** No solution	9.1	3, 4	527, 528
3	**a.** True **b.** True **c.** False	9.1	5	528
4	**a.** $n = 0$ **b.** $n = 2$ **c.** $n = 3$ **d.** $n = 4$	9.1	6	530
5	**a.** $n = 2 + 7k$, k any integer **b.** $n = 6 + 7k$, k any integer	9.1	8	531
6	**a.** $n = 2 + 3k/2$, k any integer **b.** $n = 1 + 3k$, k any integer	9.1	8	531
7	**a.** # **b.** # **c.** %	9.2	1, 3	538, 539
8	Yes. All the entries in the table are elements of S.	9.2	2	539

ANSWERS TO PRACTICE TEST

CHAPTER 9		What to Review *If You Missed It*		
QUESTION	**ANSWER**	**SECTION**	**EXAMPLE(S)**	**PAGE(S)**
9	Yes. The table is symmetrical across the diagonal from upper left to lower right.	9.2	4	540
10	#	9.2	5, 6	540, 541
11	**a.** # **b.** ¢ **c.** % **d.** $	9.2	6	541
12	**a.** No identity element **b.** No **c.** No	9.2	7	541
13	**a.** Yes. $a \text{ S } (b \text{ L } c) = b \text{ L } c$ and $(a \text{ S } b) \text{ L } (a \text{ S } c) = b \text{ L } c$. Therefore, S is distributive over L. **b.** Yes. $a \text{ L } (b \text{ S } c) = a \text{ L } c$ and $(a \text{ L } b) \text{ S } (a \text{ L } c) = a \text{ L } c$. Thus, L is distributive over S.	9.2	8	542
14	Yes. The system has the five properties (closure, associative, identity, inverse, and commutative), so the system is a commutative group.	9.2	9	543–544
15	Yes. The same explanation as for problem 14.	9.2	10	544
16	Yes. The system has the six properties (closure, associative, commutative, identity, distributive of multiplication over addition, and inverses, except there is no inverse for 0 with respect to multiplication), so the system is a field.	9.2	11	545
17	Yes. All the requirements of the definition of a group are satisfied.	9.2	9–11	543–545
18	No. The element 0 has no inverse.	9.2	9–11	543–545
19	Yes. All the requirements of the definition of a field are satisfied.	9.2	11	545
20	**a.** Not strictly determined **b.** Strictly determined. Value = 1. **c.** Strictly determined. Value = 2.	9.3	1	552–553
21	Row player's optimal strategy is play row 1. (Column player's optimal strategy is play column 2.) Row player's payoff when both players use their optimal strategies is -6.	9.3	2, 3	554–556
22	**a.** **This Year** $\begin{matrix} & H & C \\ H & 0.6 & 0.4 \\ C & 0.3 & 0.7 \end{matrix}$ (rows: **Next Year**) **b.** 50%	9.3	2, 3	554–556

CHAPTER 10

Counting Techniques

Music is the pleasure the human mind experiences from counting without being aware that it is counting.
—GOTTFRIED LEIBNIZ

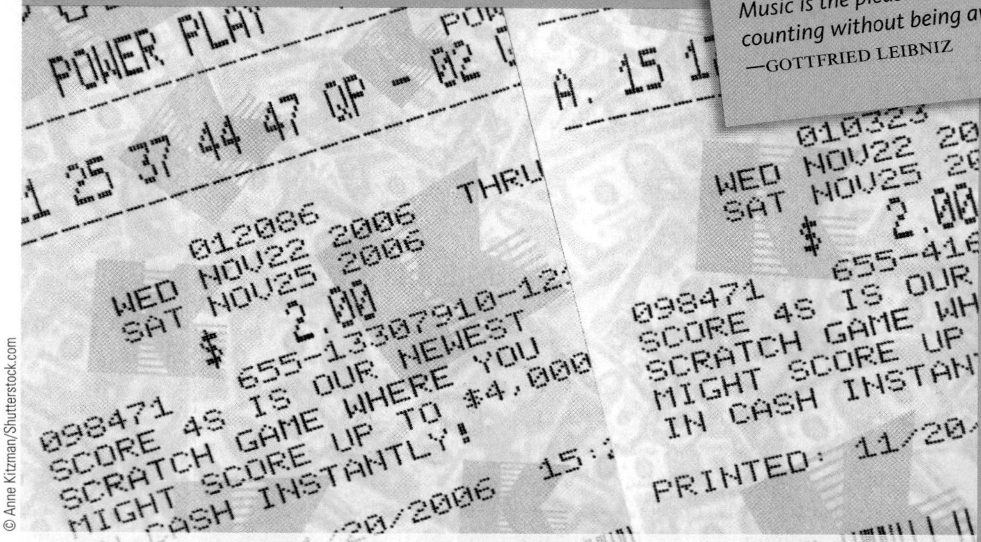

Millions of people purchase lottery tickets daily. In Section 10.4, you will study how the Sequential Counting Principle, permutations, and combinations can be used to calculate odds of events such as winning the lottery.

You use counting every day. "How many shopping days are left until Christmas?" or "How many students are in your class?" In this chapter, you will learn how to determine the number of ways in which more complicated events can occur without actually counting them. For example, do you know how many ways 6 numbers can be randomly picked from a set of 49 numbers? The answer is 13,983,816. If there are 53 numbers to pick from, it gets worse. Then you have 22,957,480 ways of selecting the 6 winning numbers! You can see that your chances of picking the right numbers to win a lottery jackpot are pretty slim. The counting methods discussed in this chapter are the following:

1. **Tree diagrams,** a useful technique when the number of outcomes is small
2. The **sequential counting principle (SCP),** a method based on generalizations made about tree diagrams
3. **Permutations,** a procedure that counts the number of ordered arrangements that can be made with r objects selected from a set of n objects when the order is important
4. **Combinations,** a method that counts the number of arrangements that can be made with r objects selected from a set of n objects when order is not important

All these counting techniques will be extremely useful when you examine probability in the next chapter. Make sure that you master the techniques in this chapter before you go on to the next.

10.1 The Sequential Counting Principle (SCP): A Problem-Solving Tool

GETTING STARTED

OBJECTIVES

A. Draw and use a tree diagram to count the number of ways a sequence of events can occur.

B. Use the sequential counting principle (SCP) to count the number of ways a sequence of events can occur.

C. Solve applications using tree diagrams and the SCP.

Human Side of Math

(1646–1716)

Gottfried Wilhelm Leibniz was born in Leipzig, Germany, in 1646. By the time he was 20, he had already begun to have ideas for a kind of *universal mathematics,* which later developed into the symbolic logic of George Boole.

In 1673, he became acquainted with some British mathematicians and exhibited his calculating machine (the first mechanical device that could do multiplication).

He made contributions to law, religion, history, literature, and logic. In 1682, he helped establish a journal, the *Acta Eruditorum*.

Leibniz's outstanding achievements in mathematics were his discovery of *calculus* (independent of Isaac Newton) and his work on *combinatorial analysis*.

LOOKING AHEAD

Leibniz's combinatorial analysis, which involves counting techniques, is the subject of this chapter.

TREES AND BREAKFAST POSSIBILITIES

Why does it seem nearly impossible to win the lottery or open a combination lock by just guessing at the numbers? Because the number of possibilities is so large! Consider another problem. At breakfast, the server asks, "How do you want your eggs? Fried (f), poached (p), or scrambled (s)? Rye (r) or white toast (w)? Juice (j) or coffee (c)?" How many choices do you have? To answer this type question, you can use a tree diagram, a picture that details the possibilities at each step. In this case, the diagram will be a *three*-step (three-event) process (pick eggs, toast, and beverage). The first step will have 3 branches indicating the 3 different ways in which you can order your eggs, as shown in Figure 10.1. Each of the 3 branches will have 2 branches (rye or white), and each of these branches will have 2 other branches (coffee or juice). The total number of possibilities corresponds to the number of branches, $3 \times 2 \times 2 = 12$. By tracing each path from left to right you can see all 12 possibilities. For example, the third choice in the list is *fwc* (fried egg, white toast, and coffee).

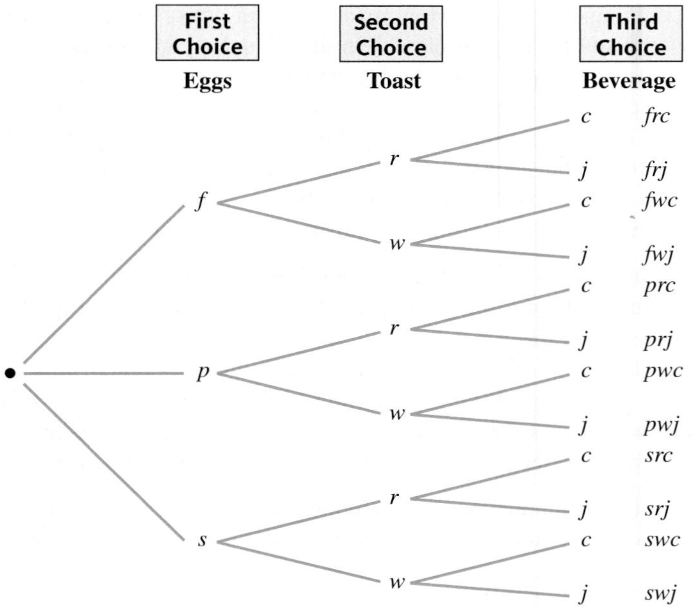

FIGURE 10.1

Now look at a lottery game called Cash 3, played with three identical urns, each containing 10 balls numbered from 0 to 9. A ball is chosen from the first urn (10 choices), then another one from the second urn (10 choices), and a third ball from the last urn

(10 choices). How many possibilities are there in all? If you drew the tree diagram, it would have $10 \times 10 \times 10 = 1000$ branches, the number of possibilities for Cash 3.

What about the combination lock? Since there are 40 possible numbers to choose as your first number, 40 for the second, and 40 for the third, the total number of possibilities is $40 \times 40 \times 40 = 64{,}000$. This is why it is nearly impossible to open the lock just by picking numbers at random!

In this section you will study tree diagrams and then develop a formula for counting the number of possibilities associated with different events.

Counting is not always as easy as 1, 2, 3. For example, can we tell in how many different ways Funky Winkerbean can answer the questions on a true/false test? There are many situations in which the answer to the question "How many?" is the first step in the solution of a problem. Earlier in the book we counted the number of subsets of a given set, and we used Venn diagrams to count the number of elements of various sets. In this chapter we shall consider a few counting techniques that are important in many applications and that we shall use when we study probability.

© FUNKY WINKERBEAN by Tom Batuik by permission of North America Syndicate, Inc.

A Tree Diagrams

Let us return to Funky Winkerbean. He is still taking a true/false test and guessing at the answers. If we assume that there are just two questions and that Funky answers both, in how many different ways can he respond?

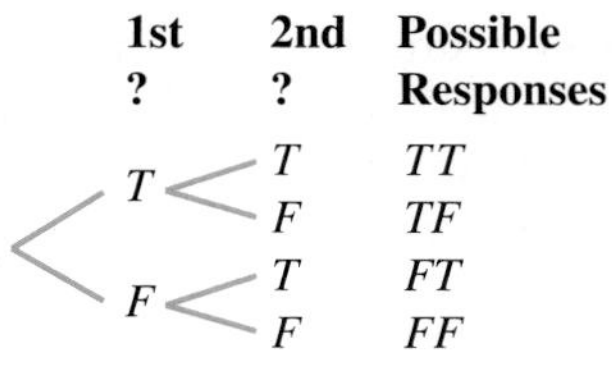

FIGURE 10.2

In order to answer this question, we have to find all the possible ways in which the two questions can be answered. We do this by constructing a **tree diagram,** as shown in Figure 10.2. In the figure, the first set of branches of the tree shows the 2 ways in which the first question can be answered (*T* for true, *F* for false), whereas the second set of branches shows the ways in which the second question can be answered. By tracing each path from left to right, we find that there are 4 end results, which correspond to the $2 \times 2 = 4$ ways in which the two questions can be answered. The 4 possibilities are *TT*, *TF*, *FT*, and *FF*.

The tree-diagram technique is used again in the next example.

EXAMPLE 1 Using Tree Diagrams to Count Choices

Here are some activities you may engage in: Sports (S), Reading (R), Watching TV (T) and Communicating and Socializing (C). Make a tree diagram listing your first and second choices among these activities.

Solution

We make a tree diagram as in the Funky Winkerbean problem. As shown in Figure 10.3 on the following page. For each of the 4 activities you can select first (S, R, T or C), there will be 3 activities left for your second choice, thus you have $4 \times 3 = 12$ choices. Which of the 12 choices do you prefer? Go to http://www.bls.gov/tus/charts/leisure.htm and find the actual time spent on an average day by people over 15 years of age.

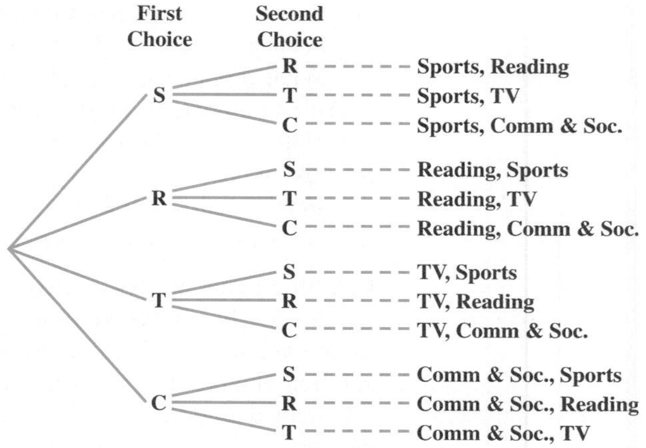

FIGURE 10.3

B Sequential Counting Principle (SCP)

In Example 1 we found that if there are 4 ways to do some event (select the first activity) and 3 ways to select a second activity, then there are $4 \times 3 = 12$ ways of doing the two events in succession in the stated order. This example illustrates a basic principle.

Sequential Counting Principle for Two Events (SCP)

If an event can occur in m ways and a second event can then occur in n ways, then the sequence of two events can occur in $m \times n$ ways.

The SCP is sometimes called the **Fundamental Counting Principle (FCP).** Note that it is assumed that the second event can occur in n ways for *each* of the ways in which the first event can occur and the second event does not influence (is independent from) the first event.

For example, the number of ways in which 2 cards can be drawn in succession and without replacement from a pack of 52 cards is $52 \times 51 = 2652$ because the first card can be drawn in 52 ways, whereas the second card can be drawn in only 51 ways (one card has been withdrawn). If the first card is returned to the deck (before the second card is drawn), then the answer is 52×52.

EXAMPLE 2 Using the SCP to Find the Number of Meals

Johnny's Homestyle Restaurant has 12 different meals and 5 different desserts on the menu. How many meal choices followed by a dessert choice does a customer have?

Solution

There are 12 choices for the meal and 5 choices for the dessert. Thus, by the SCP, there are $12 \times 5 = 60$ choices in all.

The SCP can be extended to cases in which 3, 4, or more things occur in succession. Thus, if the customer in Example 2 also has the choice of selecting a cookie (vanilla, chocolate, or almond) to go with the dessert, then the number of choices the customer has is

Meals	Dessert	Cookie ← 3 choices (vanilla, chocolate, almond)
12 ×	5 ×	3 = 180 ← Total

We now state a more general sequential counting principle.

General Sequential Counting Principle (SCP)

If an event can occur in m ways, and then a second event can occur in n ways, and then a third event can occur in r ways, and so on, then the sequence of events can occur in $m \times n \times r \times \cdots$ ways.

EXAMPLE 3 Using the SCP to Find the Number of Letters

In a Peanuts cartoon, Charlie Brown has just received a chain letter. If he sends this letter to 6 of his friends, these 6 friends send letters to 6 of their friends, and all these people send letters to 6 of their friends, how many letters will be sent starting with the ones sent by Charlie Brown?

Solution

Charlie Brown sends 6 letters, and each of the people receiving one of these sends 6 letters. Thus, by the SCP, these 6 people send a total of $6 \times 6 = 36$ letters. Then, each of the 36 people receiving one of these sends 6 letters. Again, by the SCP, these 36 people send a total of $36 \times 6 = 216$ letters. Therefore, the total number of letters is the sum

$$6 + (6 \times 6) + (36 \times 6) = 6 + 36 + 216 = 258$$

EXAMPLE 4 Hit or Miss?

Alice and Betsy agreed to meet at 2 P.M. and go shopping in one of the 3 clothing stores in their hometown. However, they forgot to specify which store. If Alice and Betsy were both on time and each went to 1 of the 3 stores, find

(a) the number of ways in which they could miss each other.

(b) the number of ways in which they could meet.

Solution

(a) Alice could go to any one of the 3 stores (first event), and Betsy could go to either of the remaining 2 stores (second event). Thus, by the SCP, there would be

$$3 \times 2 = 6$$

ways in which they could *miss* each other.

(b) In order to meet, they would both have to go to the same one of the 3 stores. Thus, there are just 3 ways in which they could *meet*.

Sometimes it is advantageous to use a diagram to represent the individual events in a sequence of events. For example, suppose we want to find out how many different telephone numbers are possible. Telephone numbers consist of a 3-digit area code, followed by a 7-digit number (10 digits in all); we must find the number of ways in which the blanks in the diagram can be filled.

(____ ____ ____) ____ ____ ____ – ____ ____ ____ ____

The answer is $10 \times 10 \times 10 \times \cdots \times 10 = 10^{10}$, or 10 billion numbers. But wait, after 1995 two restrictions were added:

1. The area code cannot begin with 0 or 1 (why?).
2. The 7-digit number after the area code cannot begin with 0 or 1.

Now, how many telephone numbers are possible? To solve this new problem, we will again use 10 blanks to represent the individual numbers to be picked.

PROBLEM-SOLVING

The Sequential Counting Principle

① **Read** the problem.

How many 10-digit telephone numbers can be made if the area code **and** the 7 digit number after the area code cannot begin with **0** or **1**.

② **Select** the unknown.

We want to find the number of telephone numbers that are possible under the given restrictions.

③ **Think** of a plan.
We have to find the number of choices we have to fill each of the 10 blanks.

The idea is to find the number of ways in which each of the 10 blanks can be filled and then use the SCP to find the total number of possibilities. Note that special restrictions apply to blank 1 (no 0s or 1s), so you have 8 choices, and blank 4 (no 0s or 1s again), so you have 8 choices for blank 4. There are 10 choices for each of the remaining blanks as shown below.

④ **Use** the SCP to carry out the plan. How many numbers can we place in the following?

The first blank
The second blank
The third blank
The fourth blank
Each of the remaining six blanks

Area Code - **Exchange Code** - **Subscriber Number**

□ □ □ □ □ □ □ □ □ □

↓ ↓ ↓ ↓ ↓ ↓ ↓ ↓ ↓ ↓

$\underline{8} \times \underline{10} \times \underline{10} \times \underline{8} \times \underline{10} \times \underline{10} \times \underline{10} \times \underline{10} \times \underline{10} \times \underline{10}$

No 0 or 1
2,3,4,5,6,7,8,9
8 choices

You can use any
digit from 0 to 9
10 choices

No 0 or 1
2,3,4,5,6,7,8,9
8 choices

You can use any of the digits from 0 to 9 in the remaining 6 spaces.
We have 10 choices (0, 1, 2, 3, 4, 5, 6, 7, 8, 9) for each space

$= 8 \times 10^2 \times 8 \times 10^2 \times 10^4$

$= 64 \times 10^{2+2+4} = 64 \times 10^8 = 6{,}400{,}000{,}000$. More than 6 billion!

⑤ **Verify** the solution.

Try Example 5 Now

Cover the solution, write your own solution, and then check your work.

EXAMPLE 5 Counting the Number of Possible Phrases

A game consists of 4 cubes, each with 6 different words or phrases inscribed, one on each face. If it is assumed that the first cube has pronouns on its faces, the second auxiliary verbs, the third verbs, and the fourth adverbs, find how many different phrases can be formed.

Solution

We draw 4 blanks representing the 4 events.

_____ _____ _____ _____

There are 6 choices for each of the blanks (each cube has 6 sides), so we enter a 6 on each line.

$\underline{6}\ \underline{6}\ \underline{6}\ \underline{6}$

The number of possibilities, by the SCP, is $6 \times 6 \times 6 \times 6 = 6^4 = 1296$.

© I. Bello

EXAMPLE 6 Counting Possibilities in a Slot Machine

A slot machine has 3 dials, each having 20 symbols, as listed in Table 10.1. The 6 symbols (bar, bell, cherry, lemon, orange, plum) are all *different.*

(a) How many symbol arrangements are possible on the 3 dials?

(b) In how many ways can we get 3 bars (the biggest payoff)?

Table 10.1

Symbol	Dial 1	Dial 2	Dial 3
Bar	1	3	1
Bell	1	3	3
Cherry	7	7	0
Lemon	3	0	4
Orange	3	6	7
Plum	5	1	5

Each dial has 20 symbols.

Solution

(a) We draw 3 blanks representing the 3 dials.

___ ___ ___

There are 20 choices for each of the blanks (each dial has 20 symbols), so we enter a 20 on each line.

$\underline{20}\ \underline{20}\ \underline{20}$

The number of possibilities is $20 \times 20 \times 20 = 8000$.

(b) The number of different ways we can get 3 bars is $1 \times 3 \times 1 = 3$, because we have 1 bar on the first dial, 3 on the second, and 1 on the third.

FREE CHANCE
COUPON
This coupon is better than all the rest! When you check out, ask the clerk to hand you the three dice. Pick your lucky number and give them a toss. If your number comes up, the room charges for your entire stay are on us!!!
(Validated Coupon Issued At Check In)

FIGURE 10.4

The Clearwater Hilton Inn had a free-chance coupon, as shown in Figure 10.4, that works like this: When you check out, ask the desk clerk to hand you the 3 dice. Pick your lucky number, and give the dice a toss. Look at the sum of the numbers on the 3 dice. If your number comes up, the room charges are canceled. Does this sound easy? Look at the next example.

EXAMPLE 7 Finding Outcomes when 3 Dice Are Thrown

Three dice are thrown.

(a) How many different outcomes are possible?

(b) If you picked 4 as your lucky number, in how many ways could you get a *sum* of 4?

Solution

(a) We draw 3 blanks, one for each die (singular of dice), to represent the possible outcomes.

___ ___ ___

There are 6 choices for each blank because a die can come up with any number from 1 to 6. So we enter a 6 on each line.

$\underline{6}\ \underline{6}\ \underline{6}$

By the SCP, there are $6 \times 6 \times 6 = 216$ outcomes possible.

© I. Bello

(b) One way to solve this part of the problem is to reason that in order to get a sum of 4, one of the 3 dice must come up 2 and the other 2 dice must come up 1. Thus, the only choice we have is which die is to come up 2. This means that there are only 3 ways to get a sum of 4 out of the 216 possible outcomes (see the tree diagram in Figure 10.5).

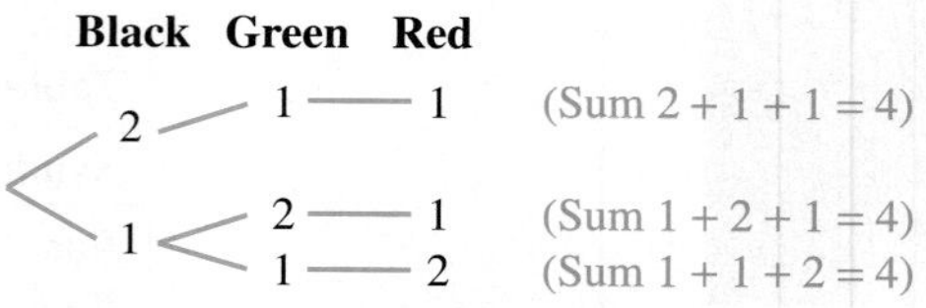

FIGURE 10.5

EXAMPLE 8 Counting Possible Zip Codes

Zip codes start with a 5-digit number.

(a) How many different 5-digit Zip codes are possible?

(b) How many are possible if 0 is not to be used as the first digit?

Solution

(a) We draw 5 blanks, each to be filled with the number of choices for that digit.

____ ____ ____ ____ ____

Since there are 10 digits (0, 1, 2, 3, 4, 5, 6, 7, 8, 9), there are 10 choices for each blank.

$\underline{10}\ \underline{10}\ \underline{10}\ \underline{10}\ \underline{10}$

Thus, by the SCP, there are $10 \times 10 \times 10 \times 10 \times 10$, that is,

$$10^5 = 100{,}000$$

different 5-digit Zip codes possible. This result gives a good estimate of the number of cities and towns in the United States. (Towns too small to have their own Zip code make up for cities and towns with more than one Zip code.)

(b) If we cannot use a 0 for the first digit, we will have only 9 choices for the first box, but the others will still have 10 choices. Again, by the SCP, there are $9 \times 10 \times 10 \times 10 \times 10$, that is,

$$9 \times 10^4 = 90{,}000$$

different possible 5-digit Zip codes that do not start with a 0.

EXAMPLE 9 Counting Choices when 2 Cards Are Drawn

Two cards are drawn in succession and *without* replacement from a deck of 52 cards. Find the following:

(a) The number of ways in which we can obtain the ace of spades and the king of hearts, *in that order*.

(b) The total number of ways in which 2 cards can be *dealt*.

(c) The total number of ways in which 2 cards can be dealt *with* replacement; that is, the first card is drawn, recorded, and placed back in the deck, and then the second card is drawn and recorded.

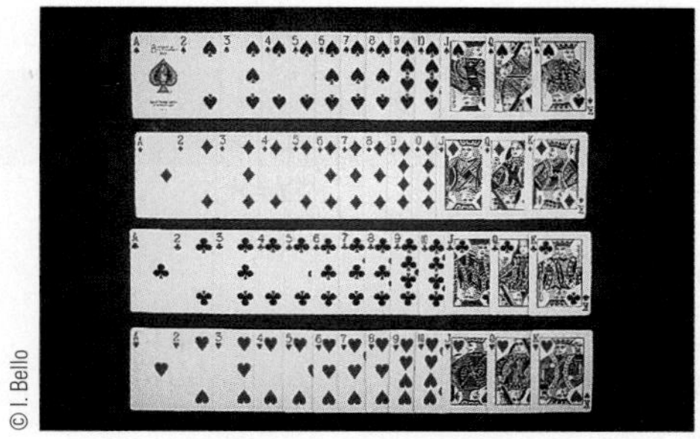

Solution

(a) There is 1 way of selecting the ace of spades and 1 way of selecting the king of hearts. Thus, there is $1 \times 1 = 1$ way of selecting the ace of spades and the king of hearts, in that order.

(b) There are 52 ways of selecting the first card and 51 ways of selecting the second card. Thus, there are $52 \times 51 = 2652$ ways in which the two cards can be dealt.

(c) There are 52 ways of selecting the first card and 52 ways of selecting the second card. Thus, there are $52 \times 52 = 2704$ ways in which the 2 cards can be dealt.

C Applications

EXAMPLE 10 Treatment Choices and Costs

The techniques we have studied can be used to determine the cost effectiveness of alternative courses of action. Suppose your doctor tells you that you can be treated with drug A or B. You may then need a second visit (or not) depending on your tolerance for the drug. The costs for drugs A and B are \$80 and \$50, respectively. Your doctor charges \$100 per visit.

(a) How many choices are possible?

(b) What are the highest and lowest possible costs for your treatment?

Solution

(a) We can use the SCP to find the number of choices. Draw two blanks representing the choice of drugs (A or B) and whether you need a second visit (Yes or No). Since there are 2 choices for each blank, there is a total of 4 choices.

$$\underset{\text{Drug}}{\underline{2}} \times \underset{\text{2nd visit}}{\underline{2}} = 4$$

(b) Let us draw a tree diagram as in Figure 10.6 and label the possible costs.

Health and drugs costs vary widely based on many factors such as type of physician (general, specialist), type of drug (generic, non-generic) and insurance status.

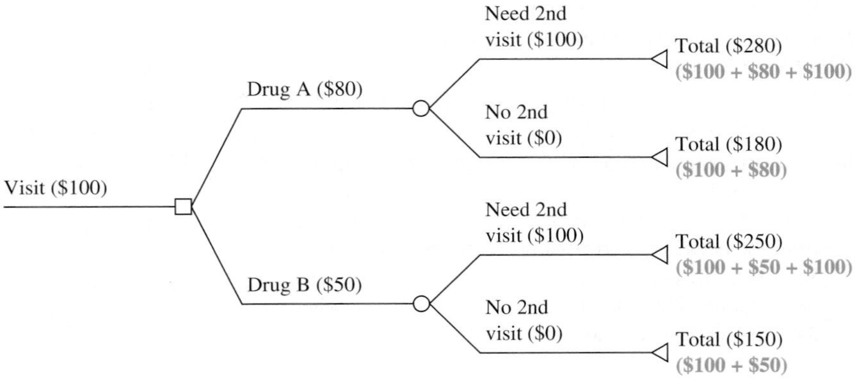

FIGURE 10.6 The highest possible cost is \$280, the lowest \$150.

10.1 EXERCISES

A Tree Diagrams

1. A man has 2 suits and 4 shirts. Use a tree diagram to find how many different outfits consisting of a suit and a shirt he can wear.
2. At the end of a meal in a restaurant, Elsie wants to have pie à la mode (pie topped with ice cream) for dessert. There are 5 flavors of ice cream—chocolate, vanilla, strawberry, peach, and coffee—and there are 2 kinds of pie—apple and cherry. Make a tree diagram to find how many choices Elsie has for dessert.
3. Kiplinger Magazine has a list of 4 items you should skip when ordering at a restaurant: No fish on Monday (M), No featured items (F), No Steak at a seafood restaurant (S) and No house Wine (W). Make a tree a diagram listing the possible first and second choices for items to skip when ordering at a restaurant.

B Sequential Counting Principle (SCP)

4. In 1935, a chain letter fad started in Denver, Colorado. The scheme worked like this. You would receive a letter with a list of 5 names, send a dime to the person at the top of the list, cross that name out, and add your name to the bottom of the list. Suppose you received one of these letters today and sent it to 5 other persons, each of whom sent it to 5 other persons, each of whom sent it to 5 others, and so on.
   a. How many letters would have your name on the list?
   b. How much money would you receive if the chain were not broken?

   Note: Don't do this! Chain letters are illegal!
5. Refer to the slot machine in Example 6, and determine in how many ways you can get
   a. 3 bells. b. 3 oranges. c. 3 plums.
6. An ordinary deck of playing cards contains 52 cards, 26 red and 26 black. If a card is dealt to each of 2 players, find in how many different ways this can be done if the following occur:
   a. Both cards are red.
   b. Both cards are black.
   c. One card is black and the other is red.
7. In poker, a pair of aces with any other pair is a good hand. (*Hint:* See Example 9.)
   a. In how many ways can you get a pair of aces when 2 cards are dealt from the deck?
   b. If the two pairs are aces and eights, the hand is considered to be unlucky! In how many ways can you get a pair of aces and then a pair of eights, in that order, when 4 cards are dealt from the deck? (This superstition dates back to 1876 when Wild Bill Hickok was shot dead by Jack McCall during a poker game. What hand was Wild Bill holding when he died? A pair of aces and a pair of eights!)
8. Mr. C. Nile and Mr. D. Mented agreed to meet at 8 P.M. in one of the Spanish restaurants in Ybor City. They were both punctual, and they both remembered the date agreed on. Unfortunately, they forgot to specify the name of the restaurant. If there are 5 Spanish restaurants in Ybor City and each man goes to one of these, find
   a. the number of ways they could miss each other.
   b. the number of ways they could meet.
9. In how many ways can 1 man and 1 woman, in that order, be selected from 5 men and 6 women?
10. How many different sets of 2 initials can be made from the letters of the English alphabet?
11. How many different sets of 3 initials can be made from the letters of the English alphabet? (*Hint:* AAA is different from BBB.)
12. A man wants to buy a ring. Suppose that he has 2 choices of metals (gold and silver) and 3 choices of stones (diamond, emerald, and ruby). How many choices does he have?
13. The Good Taste Restaurant has 7 entrees, 6 vegetables, and 9 desserts on its menu. If you want to order 1 entree, 1 vegetable, and 1 dessert, how many choices do you have?
14. Can you tell cheap water from expensive water? In a recent experiment four types of water: Ultra Purified (U), a National Brand (N), Store Brand (S) and Tap Water (T) were given to three people. In how many ways can they rank the four waters? Source: Consumer Reports, 9/2011

    The results: Only one person correctly ranked the four waters in terms of the price, one ranked two correctly while the third person only got one correct.
15. Have you had back pain lately? What did you do about it? Six popular treatments are: Over-the counter medication, Prescription Medication, Chiropractor, Massage, Yoga, Glucosamine/Chondroitin, Multivitamins
    a. In how many ways can you list these six possibilities?
    b. Unfortunately, not all of these are helpful in treating back pain. The four top-ranked treatments are: Chiropractor, Prescription Medication, Massage, Yoga. In how many ways can you rank these four treatments?
       Source: Consumer Reports, 9/2011
16. In Connecticut, auto license plates carry 3 digits followed by 3 letters.
    a. How many arrangements are possible for the 3 letters?
    b. How many arrangements are possible for the 3 numbers?
    c. How many different license plates can be made using 3 numbers followed by 3 letters?
17. How many 2-digit numbers are there in the set of natural numbers? (*Hint:* 10 is a 2-digit number, but 01 is not.)
18. How many 3-digit numbers are there in the set of natural numbers?
19. Social Security numbers consist of 9 digits.
    a. If the first digit cannot be 0, how many Social Security numbers are possible?
    b. How many Social Security numbers are possible if there are *no* restrictions?

20. Telephone numbers within the same area code consist of 7 digits. For local calls, the first digit cannot be a 0 or a 1. How many local telephone numbers are possible?

21. A combination lock has 40 numbers on its face. To open this lock, you move clockwise to a certain number, then counterclockwise to another number, and finally clockwise again to a third number.

a. If no number is used twice, what is the total number of combinations?

b. What is the total number of combinations if repetition of numbers is allowed?

22. Romano's Restaurant has 6 items you can add to your pizza. The dessert menu lists 5 different desserts. If you want a pizza with 1 of the 6 items added and a dessert, how many choices do you have for your dinner?

Problems 23–30 refer to the menu at the bottom of page.

23. How many choices does Billy have if he decides to get the following?

a. An item from group A

b. A soup

c. A dessert

d. An item from group A, a soup, and a dessert

24. How many choices does Sue have if she decides to get the following?

a. An item from group B

b. An item from group B, a soup, and a dessert

25. How many choices does Pedro have if he decides to get the following?

a. An item from group A or B

b. An item from group A or B, a soup, and a dessert

26. How many choices do Bob and Sue have if they decide to get the following?

a. One item from group A and one item from group B (no soup or dessert)

b. The family dinner, which includes soup and dessert, one item from group A, and one item from group B

27. Sam and Sally are having a family dinner, which includes soup and dessert, one item from group A, and one item from group B. If Sally decides to get an item from group A, which forces Sam to have an item from group B, how many choices do they have for dinner?

28. In problem 27, if Sam does not want to eat shrimp, how many choices do they have for dinner?

29. In problem 27, if Sam wants to avoid all the varieties of chop suey, how many choices do they have?

30. In problem 27, if Sam does not want the roast pork, how many choices do they have?

31. Write out all the different ways in which the elements of the set $\{a, b, c\}$ can be matched in pairs with the elements of the set {@, &, %} if the order in each pair is important. For example, the pair (a, @) is different from the pair (@, a).

32. Determine how many different couples Escort Dating Service can select if it has 120 men and 210 women registered with the service.

Family Dinners

(Choice of Soup and Dessert)

FOR 2 PERSONS 13.00 —— Select 1 from Group A and 1 from Group B
FOR 3 PERSONS 18.00 —— Select 1 from Group A and 2 from Group B
FOR 4 PERSONS 24.00 —— Select 2 from Group A and 2 from Group B
FOR 5 PERSONS 30.00 —— Select 2 from Group A and 3 from Group B
FOR 6 PERSONS 36.00 —— Select 3 from Group A and 3 from Group B

Entree

EGG ROLL (One Per Person)
Soup: ROAST PORK WONTON or EGG DROP
(Served Individually)

A	B
SHRIMP WITH LOBSTER SAUCE	CHICKEN CHOW MEIN
CHOW HAR KEW	SHRIMP CHOW MEIN
BUTTERFLY SHRIMP	CHICKEN CHOP SUEY
CHOW GAI KEW	SHRIMP CHOP SUEY
WOR SUE GAI	BEEF CHOP SUEY
MOO GOO GAI PAN	BEEF WITH BEAN SPROUT
LEMON CHICKEN	ROAST PORK EGG FOO YOUNG
GREEN PEPPER STEAK	ROAST PORK LO MEIN
WOR SUE OPP (PRESSED DUCK)	BARBECUED SPARERIBS
SWEET & SOUR PORK	

Served with fried rice and hot tea
Group A in Exchange for Group B——$1.50 extra

CHOICE OF DESSERTS: PINEAPPLE CHUNKS, ALMOND COOKIES, KUMQUATS, FORTUNE COOKIES

EXTRA SERVICE ON ANY FAMILY DINNER INCLUDING SOUP $1.00

C Applications

Problems 33–36 are adapted from David C. Skinner, Introduction to Decision Analysis, *3rd ed. (Florida: Probabilistic Publishing, 2006).*

33. Many investors buy stocks during a bull market (rising prices); others do so during a bear market (falling prices). You can decide to buy a risky stock or a conservative mutual fund. What is your total number of choices as to when and what you will buy?

34. When you buy insurance you can select a low premium (high deductible) or a high premium (low deductible). Then you may or may not have an accident. How many possibilities are there?

35. You inherit some money and want to invest it in mutual funds, stocks, or futures. Each of these investments can go higher or lower. How many investment possibilities are there?

36. You are in charge of a company that is about to bring its new product to market. Here are your choices: select a large, medium, or small market; then launch, license out, or sell rights to the product. How many choices do you have?

Problem 37 is adapted from Robert Clemen, Making Hard Decisions: An Introduction to Decision Analysis *(Belmont, Calif.: Wadsworth Publishing, 1996).*

37. The research and development department of a company can develop (D) or abandon (A) a certain product. If it decides to develop the product, it may obtain a patent (P) for it or not (N). If the patent is obtained, it can license (Li) the product or sell the product (S) directly. If it sells the product directly, sales can be high (H), low (L), or medium (M). Draw a tree diagram showing all the possibilities.

Problems 38 and 39 are adapted from Ann Haddix et al., Prevention Effectiveness: A Guide to Decision Analysis and Economic Evaluation *(New York: Oxford University Press, 2002).*

38. What decisions have to be made in case of a hurricane? First, you should listen to the weather forecast. The possibilities are "Will make landfall" or "Will not make landfall." Next, you have to make a decision: evacuate or not. Finally, the hurricane makes landfall or not. Draw a tree diagram showing all the possibilities.

39. A health care worker gets accidentally stuck with a needle. What are the possible courses of action? Here are some. Treat with AZT to try to prevent HIV (or not treat). If the person is treated with AZT, there may be some side effects (or no side effects) and the person may get the HIV virus (or not). Those who do not get the AZT treatment may or may not get the HIV virus. Draw a tree diagram showing all possibilities.

40. A company is considering two projects (P_1 and P_2) that must be approved (A) or rejected (R) by the Research and Development (R&D) department. If the product is approved by R&D, it can be a market success (S) or a failure (F). Draw a tree diagram showing all possibilities.

IN OTHER WORDS

41. The SCP indicates that if one event can occur in m ways *and* another event in n ways, then the sequence of events can occur in $m \times n$ ways. State a similar principle when a single event can occur in m ways *or* in n ways.

42. Many states are changing the configuration of their license plates. Florida, for example, changed from 3 digits followed by 3 letters to 3 letters followed by 2 digits and 1 letter. Explain why you think this change was made.

USING YOUR KNOWLEDGE

43. If a "word" is any arrangement of 4 different letters, how many 4-letter "words" can be formed from the letters B, O, N, and K?

44. How many 3-letter "words" can be formed from the letters B, O, N, and K, where each letter is to be used once?

45. In problem 11 we found the number of different sets of 3 initials that are possible. If a town has 27,000 inhabitants, each with exactly 3 initials, can you show that at least 2 of the inhabitants have the same initials?

DISCOVERY

In a trial in Sweden, the owner of a car was charged with overtime parking. The police officer who accused the man had noted the position of the air valves on the front and rear tires on the curb side of the car and ascertained that one valve pointed to the place occupied by 12 o'clock on a clock (directly upward), and the other one to 3 o'clock. (In both cases the closest hour was selected.) After the allowed time had elapsed, the car was still there, with the valves pointing to 12 and 3 o'clock. In court, however, the man claimed that he had moved the car and returned later. The valves just happened to come to rest in the same position as before! At this time an expert was called to compute the probability of such an event's happening.

If you were this expert and you assumed that the two wheels move independently of each other, use the SCP to find

46. the number of ways in which the front air valve could come to rest.

47. the number of ways in which the front *and* rear air valves could come to rest.

The defendant, by the way, was acquitted! The judge remarked that if all 4 wheels had been checked (assuming that they moved independently) and found in the same position as before, he would have rejected the claim as too improbable and convicted the man.

48. Again, assume you are the expert and find the number of positions in which the 4 air valves could come to rest.

49. The claim that the 2 wheels on an automobile move independently is not completely warranted. For example, if the front air valve points to 12 and the rear (on the same side) points to 3, after a complete revolution of the front wheel, where will the rear air valve be positioned? (Assume no slippage of the wheels.)

50. On the basis of your answer to problem 49, how many positions were possible for the 2 wheels on the curb side of the car if the owner did move it and return later?

COLLABORATIVE LEARNING

A tree diagram serving as a model for a certain situation can be analyzed on the basis of expected costs, effectiveness, or a combination of both. Examine the diagram at the top of the next page, where the notation $500/10 means that the cost of the treatment is $500 and the quality of the treatment 10.

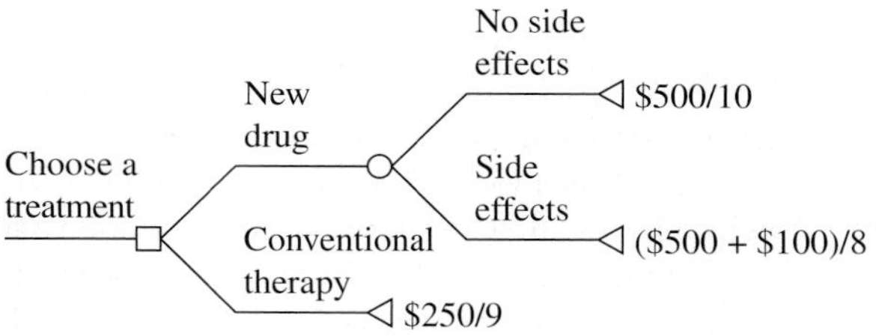

1. Which is the most inexpensive treatment? How much is it?
2. Which is the most expensive treatment? How much is it?
3. According to the diagram, which treatment offers the best quality? Discuss why you think that is.
4. According to the diagram, which treatment offers the lowest quality? Discuss why you think that is.

A decision-making model for a rental property is shown below.

5. Discuss the conditions that have to be met to maximize the amount of money made. Are the conditions realistic? Explain.
6. Discuss the conditions that have to be met to minimize the amount of money made. Are the conditions realistic? Explain.

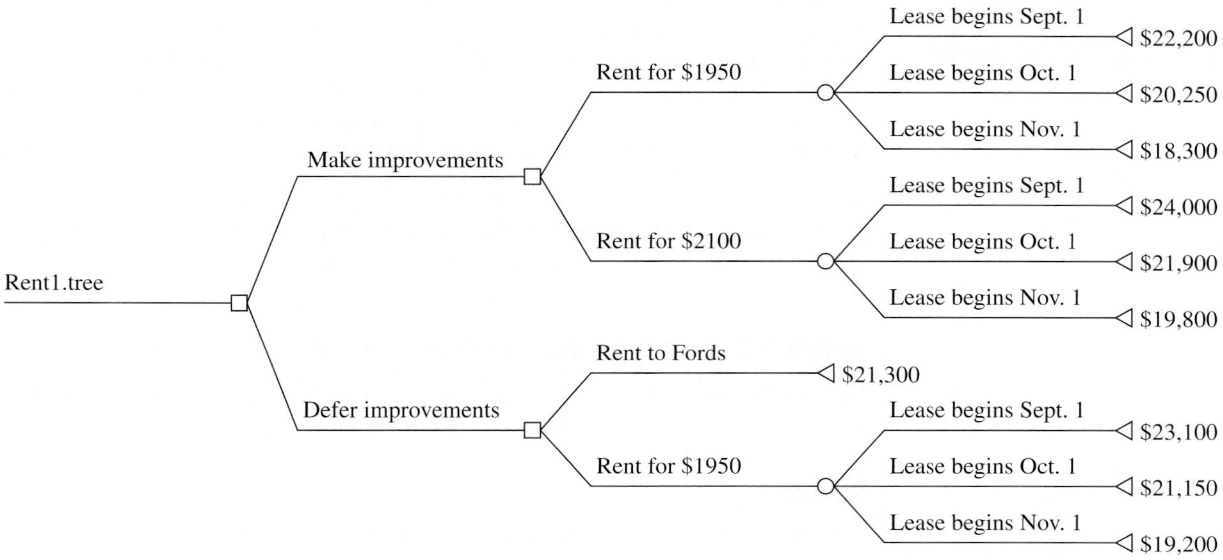

10.2 Permutations

GETTING STARTED

OBJECTIVES

A. Count the number of arrangements of n objects taken r at a time using the Permutation Formula.

B. Use the complementary counting principle to count the number of ways in which an event can occur.

C. Use the additive counting principle to count the number of ways in which an event can occur.

D. Solve applications using the SCP and permutations.

PERMUTATIONS IN THE MEDICAL LAB

Have you heard of animal research in medical labs? The possibility of adverse reactions and side effects makes experimenting with medicines risky to test on humans, so lab animals are used for these tests. For example, some patients take blood-pressure medicines, blood thinners, and cholesterol-lowering medicines. To test for adverse reactions

GRAPH IT

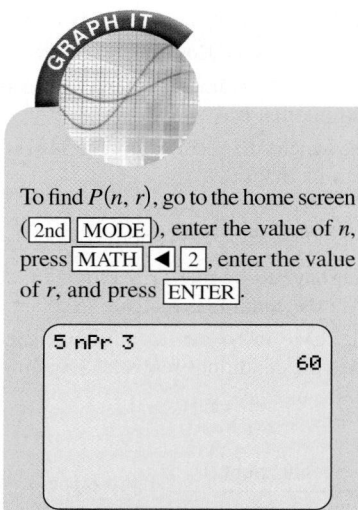

To find $P(n, r)$, go to the home screen (2nd MODE), enter the value of n, press MATH ◀ 2, enter the value of r, and press ENTER.

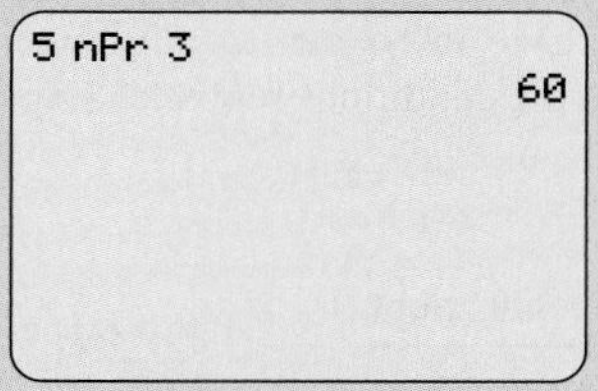

or differences in the way individual medicines work, a lab may want to experiment with animals by giving them 3 different medicines chosen from a group of 5 medicines and studying the results. How many lab animals are needed to perform the experiment?

In mathematics, an ordered arrangement of r objects selected from n objects without repetition is called a **permutation.** The number of such permutations is denoted by

$P(n, r)$ or ${}_nP_r$ Read as "permutations of n objects selected r at a time"

Available Chosen

Here we want to find $P(5, 3)$, the number of permutations of 3 of the 5 objects. To do so, we can use the sequential counting principle. Since we wish to select 3 medicines from among 5, there are 5 choices of medicines for the first selection, 4 for the second and 3 for the third. Thus, the number of ways in which we can select 3 objects from a group of 5 (in our case, the number of lab animals needed for testing) is $5 \times 4 \times 3 = 60$. Note that the first animal may be given medications A, B, and C in that *order.* If the researcher decides to use medications A, C, and B, a different animal is needed because the order in which medicines is given is extremely important. Thus, we have found that the number of permutations of 5 objects, taken 3 at a time, is 60, that is, $P(5, 3) = 5 \times 4 \times 3 = 60$. We will study permutations in this section and develop a new type of notation, called **factorial** notation, that will help us write and compute permutations more efficiently.

In Section 10.1 we used the sequential counting principle (SCP) to determine the number of ways in which a sequence of events could happen. A special case of this principle occurs when we want to count the possible *arrangements* of a given set of elements.

EXAMPLE 1 Counting Arrangements with No Repetitions

How many different lists containing **4** different items can we make from the set of 8 items listed in the article "8 Expenses You Can Cut Out Of Your Life"?

Solution

We have **8** choices for the first item, **7** for the second, **6** for the third and **5** for the fourth. By the SCP, the number of arrangements is $\mathbf{8 \times 7 \times 6 \times 5} = 1680$. Two of the items are ***Home Phones*** and ***Cable TV*** but you can see the complete list at http://tinyurl.com/4sdlwgz

A Permutations

Now, pick 3 items a, b, c from the list. Can you show all the possible arrangements we can make containing these 3 items? We can draw the tree diagram shown in Figure 10.7, in which each path corresponds to one such arrangement. There are 6 paths, so the total number of arrangements is 6. Notice that in this example abc and acb are treated as different arrangements, because the **order** of the letters is not the same in the two arrangements. This type of arrangement, in which the *order is important,* is called a *permutation.*

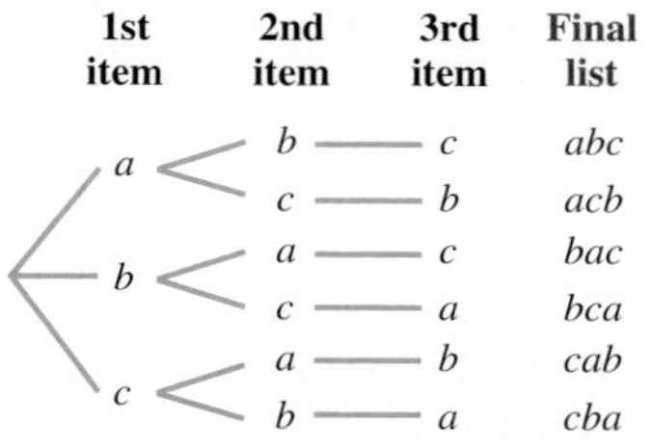

FIGURE 10.7

Definition of Permutation

An ordered arrangement of n distinguishable objects, taken r at a time and with no repetitions, is called a **permutation** of the objects. The **number of permutations** or arrangements of n distinct objects taken r at a time is denoted by $\boldsymbol{P(n, r)}$.

The notation ${}_nP_r$ is sometimes used instead of $P(n, r)$.

Note:
$0! = 1$ (See page 579.)
$1! = 1$
$2! = 2$
$3! = 6$
$4! = 24$
$5! = 120$
$6! = 720$
$7! = 5040$
$8! = 40{,}320$
$9! = 362{,}880$
$10! = 3{,}628{,}800$

Figure 10.7 shows that the number of permutations of the letters in the set $\{a, b, c\}$ is $3 \times 2 \times 1 = 6$. Thus, $P(3, 3) = 6$. A notation that is convenient to represent $3 \times 2 \times 1$ is 3! (read "3 factorial").

Definition of Factorial

The symbol $\boldsymbol{n!}$ (read **"*n* factorial"**), where n is a positive integer, represents the product of n and every positive integer less than n.

$$n! = n \times (n - 1) \times (n - 2) \times \cdots \times 3 \times 2 \times 1$$

Thus,

$$4! = 4 \times 3 \times 2 \times 1 = 24$$

and

$$5! = 5 \times 4 \times 3 \times 2 \times 1 = 120$$

EXAMPLE 2 Computations Involving Factorials

Compute the following:

(a) $6!$ (b) $7!$ (c) $\frac{6!}{3!}$

Solution

By the definition of a factorial,

(a) $6! = 6 \times 5 \times 4 \times 3 \times 2 \times 1 = 720$

(b) $7! = 7 \times 6 \times 5 \times 4 \times 3 \times 2 \times 1 = 5040$

(c) $\frac{6!}{3!} = \frac{6 \times 5 \times 4 \times \not{3} \times \not{2} \times \not{1}}{\not{3} \times \not{2} \times \not{1}} = 120$

Note that $\frac{6!}{3!} \neq 2!$.

EXAMPLE 3 Using Permutations to Count Outcomes

Dale Earnhardt Jr. (**E**), Tony Stewart (**S**), Jeff Gordon (**G**), Kyle Busch (**B**) and Jimmy Johnson (**J**) are drivers in the Nascar Sprint Cup Series standings. If there are no ties:

(a) In how many ways can they finish in the standings?

(b) In how many ways can **3** of the **5** drivers finish in the standings?

Solution

(a) The number of ways in which they can finish if there are no ties is the number of permutations of 5 things taken 5 at a time. By the definition of a permutation, this number is $P(5, 5)$, so, by the SCP,

$$P(5, 5) = 5 \cdot 4 \cdot 3 \cdot 2 \cdot 1 = 5! = 120$$

(b) Here we need the number of ordered arrangements of 3 out of the 5 drivers—that is, the number of permutations of 5 things taken 3 at a time. Again, by the definition of permutation, this number is $P(5, 3)$, and by the SCP,

$$P(5, 3) = 5 \cdot 4 \cdot 3 = 60$$

GRAPH IT

To find 5! with your grapher, go to the home screen, enter 5, and press [MATH] [◄] [4] [ENTER]. The result 120 is shown.

By the definition of permutation, $P(n, r)$ is the number of permutations of n objects using r of these objects at a time. We can now obtain formulas to compute these numbers.

___	___	___	…	___
First blank	Second blank	Third blank		nth blank

FIGURE 10.8

1. If we use all n of the objects, we must find $P(n, n)$. We can think of n blanks to be filled with n objects, as shown in Figure 10.8. We have n choices for the first blank, $(n - 1)$ choices for the second blank, $(n - 2)$ choices for the third blank, and so on, until we come to the last blank, for which there is only 1 object left. By the SCP, we have

> **Permutations Formula (n at a Time)**
>
> The number of permutations of n objects, taken n at a time, is
>
> $$P(n, n) = n(n - 1)(n - 2) \cdots (3)(2)(1) = n!$$

2. The procedure used to evaluate $P(n, n)$ can be applied to $P(n, r)$. We think of r blanks to be filled by r of the n objects. There are n choices for the first blank, $n - 1$ choices for the second blank, $n - 2$ choices for the third blank, and so on, until there are $n - r + 1$ choices for the rth blank. Thus, by the SCP, we have

Note that the permutation formula is used when the *order* is important.

> **Permutations Formula (r at a Time)**
>
> The number of permutations of n objects, taken r at a time, is
>
> $$P(n, r) = n(n - 1)(n - 2) \cdots (n - r + 1)$$

You should keep in mind that the n in $P(n, r)$ is the number of objects available and the r is the number of spaces to be filled. (Notice that if $r = n$, then the preceding two formulas agree exactly.)

The symbols ${}_nP_r$, $P_{n,r}$, and P^n_r are sometimes used to represent the number of permutations of n things, r at a time.

Some calculators have a factorial ($n!$) key and a $P(n, r)$ or ${}_nP_r$ key. By following the instructions for the calculator, you can get answers to many of the following examples and problems without having to do all the detailed arithmetic.

EXAMPLE 4 Using the Permutations Formulas

Compute the following:

(a) $P(6, 6)$ **(b)** $P(7, 3)$ **(c)** $P(6, 2)$

Solution

(a) Here we use the formula for $P(n, n)$ with $n = 6$.

$$P(6, 6) = 6 \cdot 5 \cdot 4 \cdot 3 \cdot 2 \cdot 1 = 6! = 720$$

(b) We wish to find the number of permutations of 7 objects, taken 3 at a time. We use the formula for $P(n, r)$ with $n = 7$ and $r = 3$ (n choices, r blanks).

$$P(7, 3) = 7 \cdot 6 \cdot 5 = 210$$

(c) We proceed as in part (b), but with $n = 6$ and $r = 2$.

$$P(6, 2) = 6 \cdot 5 = 30$$

GRAPH IT

To do Example 4(b), go to the home screen and enter 7 [MATH] [◄] [2] 3 [ENTER]. You obtain 210.

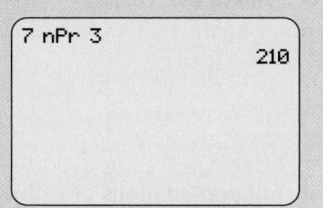

```
7 nPr 3
                 210
```

By using the definitions of $n!$ and $(n - r)!$, we can obtain the useful formula

A Factorial Formula for Permutations

The number of permutations of n objects taken r at a time is given by

$$P(n, r) = \frac{n!}{(n-r)!}, \; r \le n$$

We can verify this formula as follows:

$$\frac{n!}{(n-r)!} = \frac{n(n-1)(n-2)\cdots(n-r+1)\cancel{(n-r)}\cdots(\cancel{3})(\cancel{2})(\cancel{1})}{\cancel{(n-r)}\cdots(\cancel{3})(\cancel{2})(\cancel{1})}$$

$$= n(n-1)(n-2)\cdots(n-r+1) = P(n, r)$$

as the formula states. Notice that for $r \le n$,

$$P(n, n) = n(n-1)(n-2)\cdots(n-r+1)[(n-r)!]$$

$$= P(n, r)[(n-r)!]$$

We want this formula to hold also in the case $n = r$; that is, we want

$$P(n, n) = P(n, n)(0!)$$

For this reason, 0! is defined to be 1.

Here is the definition.

Zero Factorial

$0! = 1$

EXAMPLE 5 Using the Formula for $P(n, r)$

Use the factorial formula for $P(n, r)$ to compute the answer to part (b) of Example 4.

Solution

$$P(7, 3) = \frac{7!}{(7-3)!} = \frac{7!}{4!}$$

$$= \frac{7 \times 6 \times 5 \times \cancel{4} \times \cancel{3} \times \cancel{2} \times \cancel{1}}{\cancel{4} \times \cancel{3} \times \cancel{2} \times \cancel{1}}$$

$$= 7 \times 6 \times 5$$

$$= 210$$

Note that it is easier to compute $P(7, 3)$ as in Example 4(b); that is, $\underline{7} \times \underline{6} \times \underline{5}$. Similarly, $P(8, 2) = \underline{8} \times \underline{7} = 56$ and $P(5, 3) = \underline{5} \times \underline{4} \times \underline{3} = 60$.

8 objects Pick 2 **5 objects Pick 3**

B The Complementary Counting Principle

The number of elements in a set A can sometimes be calculated more easily by an indirect rather than a direct method. If $\mathcal{U}$ is the universal set, the number of elements in A can be obtained by subtracting the number of elements in A' from the number in $\mathcal{U}$. This gives us the **complementary counting principle.**

Complementary Counting Principle

$n(A) = n(\mathcal{U}) - n(A')$

Now, you are ready to complement your household by adding pets, and you actually want 4 puppies. What choices do you have?

EXAMPLE 6 Selecting Puppies

How many ways are there to select *at least* 1 male puppy if 4 puppies are available?

Solution

The only alternative to selecting at least 1 male puppy is selecting no male puppies; that is, the 4 puppies are all females. This is just one of all the possible cases. There are 4 places to fill, with 2 possible choices for each place (male or female). The total number of possible arrangements is

$$n(\mathcal{U}) = 2 \times 2 \times 2 \times 2 = 2^4 = 16$$

Thus,

$$\begin{aligned} n(\text{at least 1 male}) &= 16 - n(\text{no males}) \\ &= 16 - 1 = 15 \end{aligned}$$

So there you have it, 15 happy puppy choices!

C The Additive Counting Principle

Another useful counting principle is the **additive counting principle,** giving the number of elements in the union of two sets, which we obtained earlier in the book.

The additive counting principle is sometimes called the principle of inclusion–exclusion (PIE for short).

Additive Counting Principle

If A and B are two sets, then

$$n(A \cup B) = n(A) + n(B) - n(A \cap B)$$

The use of this formula is illustrated in the next example.

EXAMPLE 7 Divisibility Involving *Or*

How many 2-digit counting numbers are divisible by 2 or by 5?

Solution

Let A be the set of 2-digit numbers divisible by 2, and let B be the set of 2-digit numbers divisible by 5. We are looking for the number of digits that are divisible by 2 or 5, that is, $n(A \cup B)$. Using the SCP, for 2-digit numbers divisible by 2, the first digit can be any digit from 1 to 9 (9 choices), and the second digit can be 0, 2, 4, 6, or 8 (5 choices). Thus,

$$n(A) = \underline{9} \times \underline{5} = 45$$

For 2-digit numbers divisible by 5, the first digit can be any digit from 1 to 9 (9 choices), and the second digit can be 0 or 5 (2 choices). Thus,

$$n(B) = 9 \times 2 = 18$$

Since $A \cap B$ is the set of numbers divisible by both 2 and 5, the first digit can still be any digit from 1 to 9 (9 choices), and the second digit can only be 0 (1 choice). Thus,

$$n(A \cap B) = 9 \times 1 = 9$$

and the desired number is

$$\begin{aligned} n(A \cup B) &= n(A) + n(B) - n(A \cap B) \\ &= 45 + 18 - 9 = 54 \end{aligned}$$

That is, the number of 2-digit numbers divisible by either 2 or 5 is 54.

We will use this formula more extensively when we study surveys in the statistics chapter.

D Applications

Now that you have learned about permutations, you have to be careful using the formulas because there are teachers watching. As a matter of fact, Bob Swain, a Souderton High School mathematics teacher, found a mistake in a Boston Market (a restaurant chain) ad. The ad, featuring a famous quarterback, claimed that there are 3360 combinations of 3-item meals available to customers. (Actually, it was determined later that what the ad intended to convey was the fact that you could have 3360 three-item *side dishes* to accompany your main meal.) Anyway, Mr. Swain proved this statement wrong and in the process got a free lunch for himself and 30 of his students! (Who says there is no free lunch anymore?)

© I. Bello

EXAMPLE 8 Counting Outcomes at Boston Market

Suppose Boston Market has 16 side dishes.

(a) In how many ways can you *select* 3 different dishes?

(b) How many permutations of 16 objects taken 3 at a time are there?

(c) Suppose you select carrots, potatoes, and broccoli. If you had selected broccoli, potatoes, and carrots, would the *end result* be different?

(d) Is the order in which you select your side dishes important?

Solution

(a) You can use the SCP by filling in the 3 blanks below. Since you have 16 choices for the first vegetable, 15 for the next, and 14 for the last, the number of ways in which you can *select* the 3 side dishes (no repetitions) is

$$\underline{16} \times \underline{15} \times \underline{14} = 3360$$

(b) The number of permutations of 16 items taken 3 at a time is

$$P(16, 3) = \frac{16!}{(16-3)!} = \frac{16 \cdot 15 \cdot 14 \cdot 13!}{13!} = \underline{16} \cdot \underline{15} \cdot \underline{14} = 3360$$

(c) You end up with the same 3 side dishes, so the end result is the same.

(d) The order is not important, so this is *not* a permutation.

10.2 EXERCISES

A Permutations

1. In how many different orders can the letters in the set $\{a, b, c, d\}$ be written?
2. In how many different ways can 4 people be seated in a row?
3. If 6 horses are in a race and they all finish with no ties, in how many ways can the horses finish the race?
4. In how many different ways can 7 people be lined up at the checkout counter in a supermarket?
5. You may be able to save time if you scan your own purchases at the supermarket. Five top reasons (not necessarily in order) people hate this method: Difficult to use, monitored like a criminal, bar scanner does not work, accidental double scanning, mandatory placing of items in the bag. In how many ways can you list these 5 items?
6. An insurance agent has a list of 5 prospects and decides to telephone 3 of the prospects today and the other 2 prospects tomorrow. In how many different ways can the agent telephone the prospects?

In problems 7–20, compute the given number.

7. 8!
8. 10!
9. 9!
10. $\frac{10!}{7!}$
11. $\frac{11!}{8!}$
12. $\frac{8!}{2!6!}$
13. $\frac{9!}{5!4!}$
14. $P(9, 4)$
15. $P(10, 2)$
16. $\frac{P(6, 3)}{4!}$
17. $\frac{P(5, 2)}{2!}$
18. $2 \cdot P(8, 3)$
19. $3 \cdot P(8, 5)$
20. $4 \cdot P(3, 3)$
21. A student is taking 5 classes, each of which requires 1 book. In how many ways can she stack the 5 books she must carry?
22. Suppose 10 people are entered in a race. If there are no ties, in how many ways can the first 3 places come out?
23. The Mateland building is a very special building where you can select the qualities for your significant other. The instructions state that you can only visit once. The building is 6 stories tall and the value of the significant other increases as you go higher. You can select a quality for your significant other at any floor or go on to the next floor but you can't go down, except to leave. The floors are labeled with the qualities you desire:
    1. Has a job
    2. Loves kids
    3. Good looking
    4. Helps with housework
    5. Romantic

    a. How many permutations of these 5 qualities can you make?

    b. If you decide to build a new 3 story building selecting the floor names from the list of 5, how many different buildings are possible?

    c. But what happened to the 6th floor? An unsatisfied person, not content with having selected a significant other with the great 5 qualities listed, decided to go up one more floor:

    The 6th floor had a sign: You are visitor 7,601,445 and we built this floor to demonstrate how hard it is to please people. Thanks for visiting!

    By the way, is 7,601,445 divisible by 3? By 5?
24. A basketball coach must choose 5 players to play in a particular game. If there are 10 players available and they can play any position, in how many ways can the 5 positions be filled?

In problems 25–28, assume the cards are drawn sequentially and without replacement. (Hint: See Example 9, Section 10.1)

25. In how many ways can 3 hearts be drawn from a standard deck of 52 cards?
26. In how many ways can 2 kings be drawn from a standard deck of 52 cards?
27. In how many ways can 2 red cards be drawn from a standard deck of 52 cards?
28. In how many ways can 4 diamonds be drawn from a standard deck of 52 cards?
29. How many 3-digit numbers can be formed from the digits 1, 3, 5, 7, and 9 with no repetitions allowed?
30. How many even 3-digit numbers can be formed from the digits 2, 4, 5, 7, and 9 with no repetitions allowed? (*Hint:* Try filling the units place first.)
31. A red die and a green die are tossed. In how many ways is it possible for both dice to come up even numbers? (Distinguish between the 2 dice.)
32. In problem 31, in how many ways is it possible for one of the dice to come up an odd number and the other to come up an even number?

B The Complementary Counting Principle

33. Out of 5 children, in how many ways can a family have *at least* 1 boy?
34. If 2 dice are tossed, in how many ways can at least one of the dice come up a 6? (*Hint:* There are 5 ways a single die can come up not a 6.)

Six coins are tossed; in how many ways can you have

35. no tails.
36. at least 1 tail.
37. at least 2 heads.
38. at most 1 head.

C The Additive Counting Principle

39. How many of the first 100 natural numbers are multiples of 2 or multiples of 5?
40. How many of the first 100 natural numbers are multiples of 2 or multiples of 3?

D Applications

41. How many license plates using 6 digits can the state of Vermont issue if repetition of digits is

a. permitted?

b. *not* permitted?

c. In the 2000 census the population of Vermont was 608,827. Why do you think Vermont allows repetition of digits in its license plates? (It now uses three letters and three numerals.)

42. How many license plates using 1 digit followed by 3 letters and then 3 digits can the state of California issue if

a. repetition of letters *and* numbers is permitted?

b. no repetition of letters *or* numbers is permitted?

43. Most radio stations licensed after 1927 use 4 call letters starting with K or W—for example, WFLA in Tampa or KROW in Huntsville, Missouri. Assuming no repetitions, how many 4-letter sets are possible?

44. Your 9-digit Social Security number is divided into 3 parts: area (XXX), group (XX), and serial (XXXX). The area indicates the state on the original application, the group has no special significance, and the serial represents a straight numerical progression.

a. How many Social Security numbers are possible if repetitions of digits are permitted?

b. How many if repetitions of digits are not permitted?

c. How many if repetitions of digits are not permitted and groups under 10 have never been assigned?

IN OTHER WORDS

45. Give at least two reasons why 0! had to be defined as 1.

46. How would you define $P(n, 0)$? Verify your answer by finding $P(n, 0)$ using the formula for $P(n, r)$.

47. In your own words, what is the additive counting principle?

48. Explain under what circumstances it is advantageous to use the additive counting principle.

USING YOUR KNOWLEDGE

If you are interested in horse racing, here are some problems for you.

49. Five horses are entered in a race. If there are no ties, in how many ways can the race end?

50. In problem 49, if we know that 2 horses (A and B) are going to be tied for first place, in how many ways can the race end?

51. It seems unlikely that if 5 horses are entered in a race, 3 of them will be tied for first place. However, this actually happened! In the Astley Stakes, at Lewes, England, in August 1880, Mazurka, Wandering Nun, and Scobell triple dead-heated for first place. If it is known that these 3 horses tied for first place, in how many ways could the rest of the horses finish?

52. You probably answered 2 in response to problem 51, because it is unlikely that there will be a tie for fourth place. However, the other 2 horses, Cumberland and Thora, *did* tie for fourth place. If ties are allowed, in how many different ways could Cumberland and Thora have finished the race in the preceding problem?

DISCOVERY

In this section you learned that the number of permutations of n distinct objects is n!. Thus, if you wish to seat 3 people across the table from you, the number of possible arrangements is 3!. However, if 3 persons are to be seated at a circular table, the number of possible arrangements is only 2! = 2. If the persons are labeled A, B, and C, the two arrangements look like those in the figure.

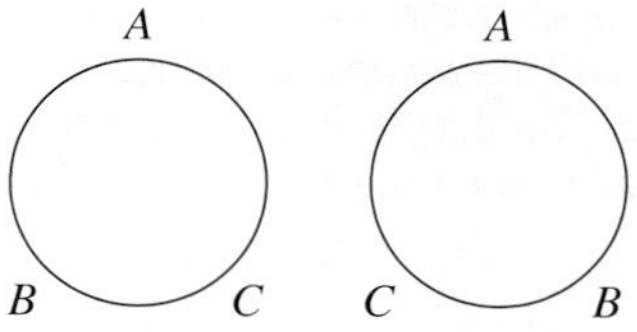

At first glance it may seem that there should be 3! = 6 different arrangements, like those in the next figure.

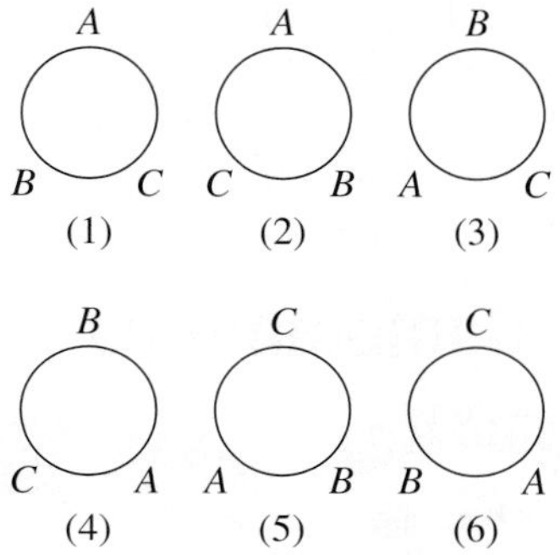

However, a closer look will reveal that arrangements (1), (4), and (5) are identical; in all of them B is to the right and C to the left of A. Similarly, (2), (3), and (6) are identical, because in every case C is to the right and B is to the left of A. To avoid this difficulty, if you have, say, 4 persons to be seated at a circular table, you seat one of them and use this person as a reference. The rest of the people can be seated in 3! ways. You have the following relationship:

Number of Persons	Number of Different Ways They Can Be Seated Around a Circular Table
3	2!
4	3!

53. From this discussion, can you discover in how many ways n persons can be seated around a circular table?

54. In how many ways can 4 people (including A and B) be seated at a circular table so that A and B are facing each other?

55. In problem 54, find the number of ways in which the people can be seated so that A and B are *not* facing each other.

56. In problem 54, find the number of ways in which the people can be seated so that A and B are next to each other.

CALCULATOR CORNER

Many calculators have a factorial [x!] *or* [n!] *key. Thus, to find 6!, you first enter the number 6 and then activate the factorial key. The steps are*

[6] [2nd] [x!] *or* [6] [inv] [x!]

In addition, some calculators even have a key that will calculate P(n, r), the [$_nP_r$] *key. To enter the n and the r, you must use other special keys. If the* [a] *and the* [b] *keys are those special keys on your calculator and you wish to find P(7, 3), as in Example 4(b), you enter*

[7] [a] [3] [b] [2nd] [$_nP_r$] The answer is 210.

1. Use your calculator to check the answers to problems 7 and 14.

COLLABORATIVE LEARNING

In Example 8 we discussed the number of ways in which the 3 side dishes could be selected, *the number of* permutations *of the 3 side dishes possible, and the number of* different choices *you had for the 3 side dishes. The 3 important words here are* selected, permutations, *and* different choices. *Let us discuss this further.*

Form 3 groups and consider the set

$A = \{a, b, c, d, e\}$.

Group 1

1. In how many ways can you *select* 3 letters from the set A?
2. Make a list to confirm your answer.
3. Is the order in which you *select* the letters important? Explain why or why not.

Group 2

4. How many *permutations* of 3 letters can be made using the letters in set A?
5. Make a list to confirm your answer.
6. Is the order in which you *select* the letters important? Explain why or why not.

Group 3

7. How many *different choices* consisting of 3 letters can be made using the letters in set A?
8. Make a list to confirm your answer.
9. Is the order in which you *select* the letters important? Explain why or why not.

Now, discuss your findings among the members of all 3 groups and establish a procedure to solve problems involving the words select, permutations, and different choices.

10.3 Combinations

GETTING STARTED

OBJECTIVE

Count the number of arrangements or the number of subsets of n objects taken r at a time using the Combinations Formula.

PLANETARY CONJUNCTIONS AND COMBINATIONS

Have you heard of planetary conjunctions? When 2 or more planets are in line with Earth and the Sun, as shown in Figure 10.9, you have what is known as a **planetary conjunction.** In certain cultures, planetary conjunctions were believed to exert special influences on events. According to Hindu tradition, a special dreaded conjunction was that of the 7 planetary bodies known to man at that time (Sun, Moon, Mercury, Venus, Mars, Jupiter, and Saturn), an event that was supposed to occur in 26,000 years and result in the end of the world.

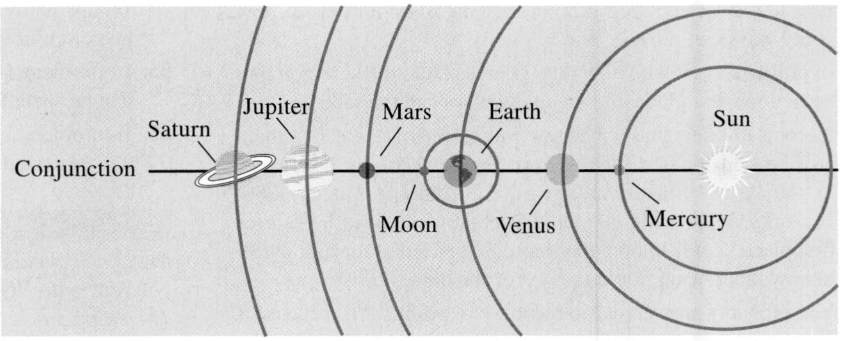

FIGURE 10.9

Rabbi Ben Ezra, a Jewish scholar, used an original computational method to show that the number of possible conjunctions of 2 or more of these planetary bodies was 120. How did he do it? Using *permutations* and *combinations,* Ben Ezra reasoned that the number of conjunctions of 2 planets was $P(7, 2) = 42$, but a conjunction of the Sun and Moon, for example, was the same as a conjunction of the Moon and Sun. Since there were 2! ways of arranging 2 planets, he divided $P(7, 2)$ by 2! to obtain the correct result, 21. For 3 planets, the number of conjunctions was $P(7, 3) = 210$, but this number had to be divided by $3! = 6$ to account for repetitions; thus the number of possible conjunctions involving 3 planets was $\frac{P(7, 3)}{6} = \frac{210}{6} = 35$.

In mathematics, a set of objects that can be selected disregarding their order is called a **combination** of the objects. The number of combinations of n objects taken r at a time is denoted by $C(n, r)$, read "the number of combinations of n objects taken r at a time" or "n choose r." In our example,

$$C(7, 2) = \frac{P(7, 2)}{2!} \quad \text{and} \quad C(7, 3) = \frac{P(7, 3)}{3!}$$

In general,

$$C(n, r) = \frac{P(n, r)}{r!}$$

Now, can you help Ben Ezra find how many different planetary conjunctions are possible? You need to find $C(7, 2) + C(7, 3) + C(7, 4) + \cdots + C(7, 7)$. If you arrive at a total of 120, you are on the way to understanding the formula for combinations.

Here is another way of thinking about the concept itself. $C(n, r)$ counts the number of subsets of r objects that can be made from a set of n objects. Thus, $C(4, 2)$ counts all the subsets of 2 objects that can be formed from a set of 4 objects. (If the set is $\{a, b, c, d\}$, the subsets are $\{a, b\}$, $\{a, c\}$, $\{a, d\}$, $\{b, c\}$, $\{b, d\}$, and $\{c, d\}$, a total of 6.) By the formula,

$$C(4, 2) = \frac{P(4, 2)}{2!} = \frac{12}{2} = 6$$

Now, you have both the concept and the formula for combinations!

In Section 10.2, we found the number of ordered arrangements that are possible with n distinguishable objects. Sometimes we may wish to count the number of subsets of these objects that can be selected if we *disregard the order* in which the objects are selected. Such subsets are called **combinations.** We use the symbol $C(n, r)$ to denote the number of combinations of r objects that can be formed from a set of n objects. The symbols ${}_nC_r$, $C_{n,r}$, C^n_r, and $\binom{n}{r}$ are also used to represent $C(n, r)$.

EXAMPLE 1 Using Combinations to Find Sums of Money

How many different sums of money can be made from a set of coins consisting of a penny, a nickel, and a dime if exactly 2 coins are selected?

Solution

Because the *order* in which we select the coins is *not* important (selecting a nickel and then a dime gives the same sum as selecting a dime and then a nickel), the question asked is equivalent to finding $C(3, 2)$, the number of combinations of 2 things that can be formed using a set of 3 things. One of the sums is 6¢ (it makes no difference whether the penny is selected first and then the nickel, or vice versa), the second sum is 11¢, and the third sum is 15¢. Hence, $C(3, 2)$, the number of combinations of 3 objects taken 2 at a time, is 3.

EXAMPLE 2 Combinations and Smartphones

Here are 4 incentives to buy a Smartphone:

(a) Decreasing price

(b) Increased job productivity

(c) Help you stay organized

(d) Best platform for social networking
Source: http://www.techrepublic.com/blog/10things/10-reasons-to-invest-in-new-smartphones/620

Consider the set of four incentives $S = \{a, b, c, d\}$.

(a) How many combinations of 2 incentives are possible using elements of the set S?

(b) How many permutations of 2 incentives are possible using elements of the set S?

(c) Which will give you more incentives, the permutations of 2 incentives or the combinations of 2 incentives?

(d) How many subsets of 2 elements does the set S have?

Solution

(a) The 6 possible combinations are shown in Table 10.2. Hence, $C(4, 2) = 6$.

(b) $P(4, 2) = 4 \times 3 = 12$. The 12 permutations are shown in Table 10.2.

(c) The permutations. There are 12 permutations and only 6 combinations.

(d) This problem is equivalent to finding the number of combinations that can be made from the 4 incentives using 2 at a time; hence, the answer is 6, as in part (a).

Table 10.2

Combinations	Permutations
ab	*ab*, *ba*
ac	*ac*, *ca*
ad	*ad*, *da*
bc	*bc*, *cb*
bd	*bd*, *db*
cd	*cd*, *dc*

We can see from Table 10.2 that every combination determines 2! permutations, so $P(4, 2) = 2! \cdot C(4, 2)$. We use a similar argument to solve Example 3.

GRAPH IT

To find $C(n, r)$ with your grapher, go to the home screen (2nd MODE) enter the $n(26)$ MATH ◀ 3 and the $r(3)$. When you press enter, the answer 2600 will appear.

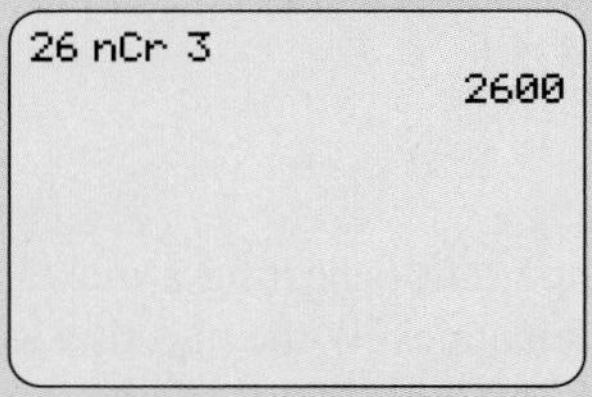

EXAMPLE 3 Combinations and Sets of 3 Letters

How many sets of 3 letters can be made from the English alphabet?

Solution

Here we want to find $C(26, 3)$. One of the possible combinations is, for example, $\{A, B, C\}$. This choice determines $3! = 6$ permutations (ABC, ACB, BAC, BCA, CAB, and CBA). If we were to make a table similar to Table 10.2, we would see that to each combination there corresponds $3! = 6$ permutations. Hence, there are 6 times as many permutations as there are combinations. That is, $P(26, 3) = 6 \cdot C(26, 3)$; but $P(26, 3) = 26 \times 25 \times 24 = 15{,}600$, so $15{,}600 = 6 \times C(26, 3)$, or $C(26, 3) = 2600$.

The number of ways in which we can select a combination of r objects from a set of n objects is $C(n, r)$. The r objects in any one of these combinations can be arranged (permuted) in $r!$ ways. By the SCP, the total number of permutations is $r! \times C(n, r)$; but this number is $P(n, r)$. Hence,

$$P(n, r) = (r!)C(n, r)$$

so dividing both sides by $r!$, we have

Combinations Formula

The number of combinations of n objects, taken r at a time, is

$$C(n, r) = \frac{P(n, r)}{r!} \qquad 0 \leq r \leq n$$

By substituting for $P(n, r)$, we obtain

$$C(n, r) = \frac{P(n, r)}{r!} = \frac{n!}{(n - r)!} \div r! = \frac{n!}{r!(n - r)!}$$

Factorial Formula for Combinations

The number of combinations of n objects, taken r at a time, is

$$C(n, r) = \frac{n!}{r!(n - r)!}$$

EXAMPLE 4 Reasons NOT to buy a Smartphone

In Example 2, we gave 4 reasons to buy a Smartphone, but many people disagree. Here is a list of 4 reasons **NOT** to buy one:

1. Expensive
2. Tied down by contract
3. Not as convenient as you may think
4. Too much technology in your life

Source: http://blog.creditkarma.com/step-by-step/personal-finance/5-reasons-not-to-buy-a-smartphone/

(a) Find the number of combinations of these 4 reasons taken 2 at a time.

(b) Form all possible subsets of 2 reasons taken from the list.

(c) How many subsets did you get in part (**b**)?

Solution

(a) The number of combinations of 4 objects, taken 2 at a time is $C(4, 2) = \frac{4!}{2!2!} = 6$.

(b) The subsets containing two reasons are: {expensive, tied down by contract}, {expensive, not as convenient as you may think}, {expensive, too much technology in your life}, {tied down by contract, not as convenient as you may think}, {tied down by contract, too much technology in your life}, {not as convenient as you may think, too much technology in your life}.

(c) 6.

Note that the number of subsets of 2 elements that can be formed from a set of 4 elements is 6 (part **b**), which is the same as $C(4, 2)$ (part **a**).

More generally, the meaning of $C(n, r)$ can also be stated in terms of a set of n elements.

Combinations as Subsets

$C(n, r)$ is the number of subsets of r elements each that can be formed from a set of n elements.

Note that this is just a repetition of the statement made at the beginning of this section. In general, we have the following:

Interpretations of $C(n, r)$

1. The number of ways to select r different objects from n different objects when the order is ***not*** important.
2. The number of combinations of r different objects from n different objects
3. The number of subsets with r elements of a set with n elements
4. $C(n, r) = \dfrac{n!}{r!(n - r)}$

EXAMPLE 5 Finding the Number of Subsets

How many subsets of *at least* 3 elements can be formed from a set of 4 elements?

Solution

If we wish to have *at least* 3 elements in the subset, we can have either 3 or 4 elements. Using the preceding statement, the number of subsets of 3 elements that can be formed from a set of 4 elements is

$$C(4, 3) = \frac{4!}{3!1!} = 4$$

and the number of subsets of 4 elements that can be formed from a set of 4 elements is

$$C(4, 4) = \frac{4!}{4!0!} = 1$$

Thus, the number of subsets of at least 3 elements that can be formed from a set of 4 elements is $4 + 1 = 5$. (Try it with the set $\{a, b, c, d\}$.)

GRAPH IT

To do Example 6, go to the home screen ([2nd] [MODE]) and press 26 [MATH] [◄] [3] 3 [ENTER]. To find $C(8, 2)$, press 8 [MATH] [◄] [3] 2 [ENTER] as shown.

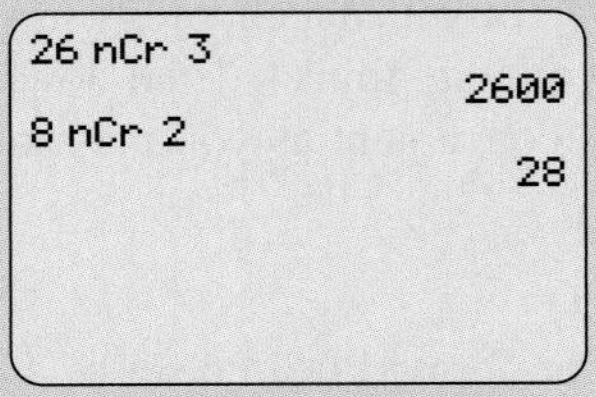

EXAMPLE 6 Computations Involving the Combinations Formula

Compute the following: **(a)** $C(26, 3)$ **(b)** $C(8, 2)$

Solution

(a) From the second formula for $C(n, r)$, we get

$$C(26, 3) = \frac{26!}{3!23!} = \frac{26 \times 25 \times 24 \times \cancel{23!}}{3!\cancel{23!}} = 2600$$

(b) Similarly,

$$C(8, 2) = \frac{8!}{2!6!} = \frac{8 \times 7 \times \cancel{6!}}{2!\cancel{6!}} = 28$$

You can make your work easier by noting possible cancellations, as done in the solutions for Example 6.

EXAMPLE 7 Finding the Number of Different 2-Card Hands

How many different 2-card hands are possible if we use an ordinary deck of 52 cards?

Solution

Since the order in which you receive the cards is not important, the question asked is equivalent to "How many combinations are there of 52 elements, 2 at a time?" Using the first formula for $C(n, r)$, we find

$$C(52, 2) = \frac{P(52, 2)}{2!} = \frac{52 \cdot 51}{2 \cdot 1} = 1326$$

Suppose you are asked to find the number of combinations of 10 objects, 8 at a time. You can see that if you take away any combination of 8 of the objects, a combination of 2 of the objects is left. This shows that $C(10, 8) = C(10, 2)$. This result can be verified directly as follows:

$$C(10, 8) = \frac{P(10, 8)}{8!} = \frac{10 \cdot 9 \cdot 8 \cdot 7 \cdot 6 \cdot 5 \cdot 4 \cdot 3}{8 \cdot 7 \cdot 6 \cdot 5 \cdot 4 \cdot 3 \cdot 2 \cdot 1} = \frac{10 \cdot 9}{2 \cdot 1}$$

and

$$C(10, 2) = \frac{P(10, 2)}{2!} = \frac{10 \cdot 9}{2 \cdot 1}$$

Therefore,

$$C(10, 8) = C(10, 2)$$

In general,

Alternative Formula for Combinations

The alternative formula for finding combinations is

$$C(n, r) = C(n, n - r)$$

You can verify this result if you note that

$$\begin{aligned} C(n, n - r) &= \frac{n!}{(n - r)![n - (n - r)]!} \\ &= \frac{n!}{(n - r)!(n - n + r)!} = \frac{n!}{(n - r)!r!} = C(n, r) \end{aligned}$$

ROMANO'S
Greek - Italian Restaurant
Menu For Lunch & Take Out
555-6666

PIZZA

OUR SPECIAL DOUGH LIGHT AND CRISPY TO YOUR EXPECTATION ONE-SIZE ONLY 10"-6 PIECES

PLAIN CHEESE	5.95
ANY 1 ITEM	6.95
ANY 2 COMBINATIONS	7.95
ANY 3 COMBINATIONS	8.95
SPECIAL (All Items)	9.95

ITEMS

PEPPERONI, ONION, PEPPERS, MUSHROOMS, SAUSAGE, AND MEATBALL

SOFT DRINKS

	Sm.	Lg.
COKE, 7-UP	.75	.95
TAB, ROOT BEER	.75	.95
COFFEE or ICE TEA		.95

DESSERTS

Try Our Delicious Homemade Desserts

RICE PUDDING	1.50
GALACTOBURICO Greek Custard with Fillo	1.50
BAKLAVA Walnuts, Honey, and Fillo	2.50
BOUGATZA Walnuts, Honey, Cinnamon, and Fillo	2.50
SPUMONI Italian-style Ice Cream	2.50

FIGURE 10.10

EXAMPLE 8 Counting Pizzas

Romano's Restaurant offers the pizza menu in Figure 10.10. Find how many different pizzas you can order with the following:

(a) 1 item (b) 2 items (c) 3 items (d) 4 items

Solution

(a) Because there are exactly 6 different items available, there are 6 different pizzas with 1 item. Note if you use the formula for $C(6, 1)$, it gives $\frac{6}{1} = 6$.

(b) The *order* in which the items are added is *not* important. (If you order pepperoni and onion, you get the same pizza as if you order onion and pepperoni.) Thus, you need to find the number of combinations of 6 things, taken 2 at a time.

$$C(6, 2) = \frac{P(6, 2)}{2!} = \frac{6 \cdot 5}{1 \cdot 2} = 15$$

(c) Here, you need $C(6, 3)$.

$$C(6, 3) = \frac{P(6, 3)}{3!} = \frac{6 \cdot 5 \cdot 4}{3 \cdot 2 \cdot 1} = 20$$

(d) The answer is $C(6, 4)$, which is the same as $C(6, 2) = 15$

EXAMPLE 9 Counting Possibilities Selecting 3 Side Dishes

Let us go back to the problem of selecting 3 side dishes from 16 available dishes (Section 10.2, Example 8) and count the number of choices we have for our 3 side dishes

(a) without any repetitions (we have to pick 3 different dishes).

(b) with one repetition (say *aba* or *ccd* or *eff*).

(c) with 3 repetitions (say *aaa*, *bbb*, or *ccc*).

Solution

(a) Without repetition, there are

$$C(16, 3) = \frac{16!}{3!13!} = \frac{16 \cdot 15 \cdot 14}{6} = 560 \text{ choices}$$

(b) With one repetition there are 16 choices for the first dish, 1 choice for the second (it has to be the same as the first), and $C(15, 1)$ for the last dish, a total of

$$\underline{16} \cdot \underline{1} \cdot \underline{C(15, 1)} = 16 \cdot \frac{15!}{1 \cdot 14!} = 16 \cdot 15 = 240 \text{ choices}$$

1st dish 2nd 3rd

(c) With three repetitions, we have a total of 16 choices (say, 3 macaroni or 3 broccoli or 3 whatever!).

Note that the total number of choices is $560 + 240 + 16 = 816$ and that is the total number of choices we have to select our 3 side dishes, which is what Mr. Swain said!

Before you go to the exercises, you should know that some calculators have a $C(n, r)$ or a ${}_nC_r$ key so you can work most of the problems without doing all the detailed arithmetic.

10.3 EXERCISES

In problems 1–6, evaluate each of the following:

1. $C(5, 2)$ and $P(5, 2)$
2. $C(6, 4)$ and $P(6, 4)$
3. $C(7, 3)$ and $P(7, 3)$
4. $C(5, 0)$ and $P(5, 0)$
5. $C(9, 6)$ and $P(9, 6)$
6. $C(7, 0)$ and $P(7, 0)$

Do you want to help save the environment? Try these 5 tips at home:

1. *Turn off unneeded lights*
2. *Set refrigerator at 36–38°F*
3. *Clean lint-filter in dryer*
4. *Use compact fluorescent lights*
5. *Insulate your home*

7. How many combinations can you make with 4 of the 5 tips given in the list?
8. How many combinations can you make with 2 of the 5 tips given in the list?
9. How many combinations are possible if the 5 tips in the list are taken 3 at a time?
10. How many combinations are possible if 3 of the 5 tips are used?
11. How many subsets of 2 elements can be made from a set of 8 elements?
12. How many subsets of 5 elements can be made from a set of 7 elements?
13. How many different 8-element subsets can be made from a set of 12 elements?
14. How many different 10-element subsets can be made from a set of 15 elements?
15. According to Kiplinger Magazine, there are 12 things that college students don't need. To find out what they are go to http://tinyurl.com/lrp3u9. Now, let T be the set of 12 things that college students don't need.
    a. How many subsets of 3 elements does T have?
    b. How many subsets of less than 3 elements does T have?
    c. How many subsets of no elements does T have?
    d. How many subsets of more than 9 elements does T have?
16. How many different sums of money can be formed from a penny, a nickel, a dime, a quarter, and a half-dollar if exactly 3 coins are used?
17. Rework problem 16 using 4 coins.
18. Rework problem 16 using at least 2 coins.
19. Let $A = \{1, 2, 3, 4, 5\}$.
    a. How many subsets of 3 elements does the set A have?
    b. How many subsets of A have no more than 3 elements?
20. If 20 people all shake hands with each other, how many handshakes are there?
21. The Greek alphabet has 24 letters. In how many ways can 3 different Greek letters be selected if the order does not matter?
22. The mathematics department is sending 5 of its 10 members to a meeting. How many different sets of 5 members can be selected?
23. Congressional leaders have to appoint 3 members to the Debt Super Committee. If there are 4 men and 6 women available to serve on this committee, how many different committees can be formed?
24. The Book of the Month Club offers a choice of 3 books from a list of 40. How many different selections of 3 different books each can be made from this list?
25. How many different 5-card poker hands are possible using a deck of 52 cards?
26. A restaurant offers 8 different kinds of sandwiches. How many different sets of 2 sandwiches could you select?
27. The U.S. Senate has 100 members. How many different 5-member committees can be formed from the Senate?
28. The U.S. Congress Debt Super Committee consists of 12 members. In how many ways can a subcommittee of 7 be formed from the 12?
29. Johnny has a \$1 bill, a \$5 bill, a \$10 bill, and a \$20 bill in his pocket. How many different sums of money can Johnny make with these bills if he uses at least 1 bill each time?
30. Desi has 6 coins: a penny, a nickel, a dime, a quarter, a half-dollar, and a dollar. How many different sums of money can Desi form using just 2 of these coins for each sum?
31. Refer to problem 30. How many different sums of money can Desi form if she uses at least 1 coin each time?
32. How many different committees can be formed from 8 people if each committee must consist of at least 3 people?
33. In how many ways can 8 people be divided into 2 equal groups?
34. A diagonal of a polygon is a line segment joining 2 nonadjacent vertices. How many diagonals does a polygon of
    a. 8 sides have?
    b. n sides have?

    (*Hint:* Think of *all* the lines joining the vertices two at a time. How many of these lines are sides and not diagonals?)

IN OTHER WORDS

35. Write in your own words the difference between a permutation of 3 objects and a combination of 3 objects.
36. You know that a *combination* for your locker uses the numbers 1, 2, 3.
    a. Will the combination 1, 2, 3 necessarily open the locker?
    b. What are the permutations of 1, 2, and 3? Will one of these open the locker? Explain.
37. Discuss why a *combination lock* should really be called a *permutation lock.*
38. Consider $P(n, r)$ and $C(n, r)$.
    a. Discuss the conditions under which $P(n, r) = C(n, r)$ and explain why.
    b. Is $P(n, r)$ greater than or less than $C(n, r)$? Explain.

USING YOUR KNOWLEDGE

The following figure shows the famous Pascal's triangle. The triangle counts the number of subsets of k elements that can be made from a set of n elements, that is, C(n, k). If you consider n to be the row number and k the diagonal number, you can find C(5, 2) by going to the fifth row, second diagonal. The answer is 10. Note that the value 10 is obtained by adding the 4 and 6 above 10 in the triangle. Similarly, the 5 in the fifth row, first diagonal is found by adding the 1 and 4 above 5 in the preceding row.

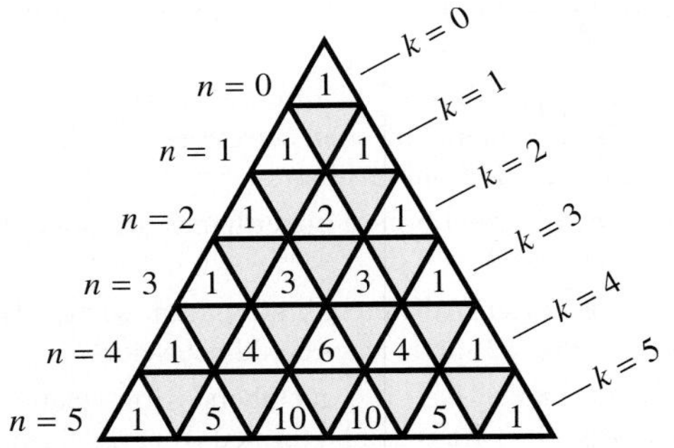

39. Construct the next two rows of Pascal's triangle.

40. Use Pascal's triangle to find the following:

a. $C(6, 4)$ **b.** $C(7, 3)$

41. You might have learned in algebra that

$$(a + b)^0 = \mathbf{1}$$
$$(a + b)^1 = \mathbf{1}a + \mathbf{1}b$$
$$(a + b)^2 = \mathbf{1}a^2 + \mathbf{2}ab + \mathbf{1}b^2$$
$$(a + b)^3 = \mathbf{1}a^3 + \mathbf{3}a^2b + \mathbf{3}ab^2 + \mathbf{1}b^3$$

Compare Pascal's triangle with the given expressions and then find the following:

a. $(a + b)^4$ **b.** $(a + b)^5$

42. Use Pascal's triangle to find $(a + b)^6$.

DISCOVERY

Suppose a fair coin is flipped 5 times in succession. How many different outcomes are possible? Since the coin can fall in either of 2 ways (heads or tails), the number of different outcomes is $2^5 = 32$.

In how many different ways can the outcome be 2 heads and 3 tails? If you think a moment, you will realize that the answer is the number of combinations of 5 things, taken 2 at a time. (Look at the 5 tosses and determine in how many ways you can select 2 of them when the order is unimportant.) Thus, the correct answer is

$$C(5, 2) = \frac{5 \cdot 4}{2 \cdot 1} = 10$$

See if you can discover the answers to the following questions:

43. In how many different ways can the outcome be 0 heads and 5 tails? Call this number $C(5, 0)$.

44. Rework problem 43 for 1 head and 4 tails.

45. Rework problem 43 for 3 heads and 2 tails.

46. Rework problem 43 for 4 heads and 1 tail.

47. Rework problem 43 for 5 heads and 0 tails.

48. Add the answer you found for 2 heads and 3 tails and your answers for problems 43–47. You should come out with

$$C(5, 0) + C(5, 1) + C(5, 2) + C(5, 3) + C(5, 4) + C(5, 5) = 32$$

Explain why.

49. The result of problem 48 is a special case of the general result

$$C(n, 0) + C(n, 1) + C(n, 2) + \cdots + C(n, n) = 2^n$$

Can you tell why this must be a correct result? (*Hint:* Think of the coin's being flipped n times.)

CALCULATOR CORNER

Some calculators can evaluate C(n, r). To do this, you must enter n and r using special keys, say [a] *and* [b]*, on your calculator. Thus, to evaluate C(26, 3), as in Example 6(a), press* [26] [a] [3] [b] [2nd] [$_nC_r$]*. As before, the answer is 2600.*

1. Check the answers to Examples 6, 7, and 8 using your calculator.

COLLABORATIVE LEARNING

Suppose that your group is in charge of designing license plates for the Department of Motor Vehicles.

1. If you use the numbers 0–9 to create a 6-digit plate, as Washington, D.C. did, how many license plates are possible? Go to http://www.licencepl8s.com/dcpass.html to see the different types of plates issued by Washington, D.C.

2. Go to an almanac or the *Statistical Abstract of the United States* and determine the states in which your answer to the first question might provide enough license plates.

3. The population of Wyoming is about 568,158. If you created a 6-digit plate, using the digits 0–9, do you think there would be enough license plates for all motorists? (*Hint:* Suppose you have two cars!)

4. If you were in charge of designing license plates for the state of California, which method would you use to make sure that there were enough license plates available: a digit, 3 letters and 3 digits, or 3 letters and 3 digits?

5. How can you make sure that there are enough license plates available?

6. At the present time there are 2 types of license plates in California: 1 digit, 3 letters and 3 digits; and 3 letters followed by 3 digits.

a. How many license plates are possible using each of the 2 schemes?

b. Which one do you think is more likely to be used? Explain why.

10.4 Miscellaneous Counting Methods

GETTING STARTED

OBJECTIVES

A. Count the number of arrangements using either the permutation or the combination formula.

B. Find the number of distinct arrangements (permutations) that can be made with *n* objects of various types.

C. Solve applications using tree diagrams.

"COUNTING" ON WINNING THE LOTTERY

In Section 10.1 you were asked, "Why does it seem so difficult to win the lottery?" The answer, you found, is because there are so many possible *permutations* or so many *combinations,* depending on the game you play. For example, suppose you play a lottery in which you pick 4 digits and you win if the digits are drawn in the *exact* order you have chosen. To find your chance of winning, you must find in how many ways you can select the 4 digits. The number of ways in which you can fill the 4 blanks.

STRAIGHT. You win when the number drawn is exactly the same as your selection.

$$\underline{\qquad}\ \underline{\qquad}\ \underline{\qquad}\ \underline{\qquad}$$

using the sequential counting principle and the 10 digits (0 to 9) to fill each blank, is

$$\underline{10} \times \underline{10} \times \underline{10} \times \underline{10}$$

or 10,000 ways. Only one number will win, so your chance is 1 in 10,000. (If you pick 1345 and the number selected is 5431, you are out of luck.) Here the sequential counting principle (SCP) was used as the counting method.

24-WAY BOX. You win when the number drawn matches your selection in any order.

You can also play this game by selecting the 24-way box. In this case, you select a set of 4 numbers and win if the numbers come out *in any order.* How many ways can you win now? Since there are $P(4, 4)$, or 24, ways of permuting the 4 numbers you choose, your chances are increased to 24 in 10,000. Here permutations were used as the counting method.

The number of correct numbers you have to pick to win, as well as the numbers to choose from, vary by state. In Florida you need 6 numbers out of 53 to win the jackpot. Your chances to win are 1 in 22,957,480 = $C(53, 6)$.

Other lottery games are even more challenging. For example, in many state lotteries you pick 6 different numbers from a set of 49 numbers. You win the jackpot if you match *(in any order)* the 6 winning lottery numbers. How many chances of winning do you have now? To find out, you must find the number of ways in which 6 numbers can be selected from a set of 49 numbers when the order is not important; that is, you must find $C(49, 6)$. If you have a calculator or if you are patient, you can compute $C(49, 6)$ and obtain 13,983,816. Your chances are only 1 in almost 14 million. Here combinations were used as the counting method.

The examples and problems in this section will use the SCP, permutations, and combinations. The question you must consider is when to use which method. You begin this section by considering a diagram that may help you to make this choice.

In the preceding sections we discussed the use of the SCP, permutations, and combinations in simple counting problems. Very often, the most difficult step in dealing with a counting problem is to decide which method or formula to use. We shall try to make this decision easier in the following discussion.

A Permutations and Combinations

As you recall, if the problem involves two or more events that are to occur in succession, you must use the SCP. For problems that involve choosing r items from a set of n different items, with no repetitions allowed, remember the diagram shown in Figure 10.11.

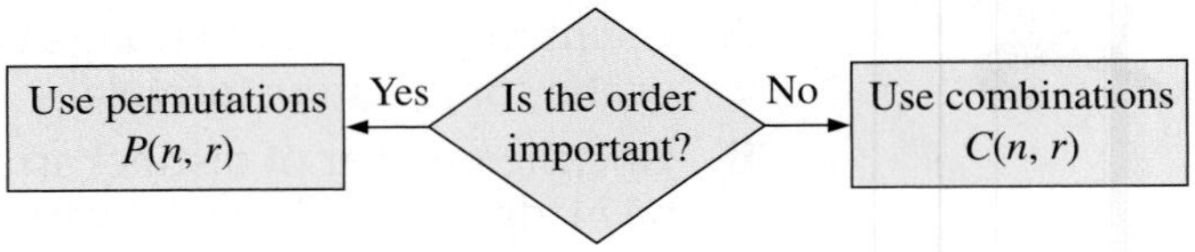

FIGURE 10.11

The next example will help to clarify this idea.

EXAMPLE 1 Combinations or Permutations?

An employment agency has 5 highly skilled workers listed. Find in how many ways 2 of these workers can be selected given the following:

(a) The first one is to be in charge, and the second one is to help.

(b) They are simply to do a job.

Solution

In both parts of this problem, 2 workers are to be selected from 5.

(a) If the first worker is to be in charge and the second to help, then the *order* in which they are picked is important. Hence, we must use *permutations.* The answer is

$$P(5, 2) = 5 \cdot 4 = 20$$

(b) Here the order is *not* important. (It makes no difference if Joe and Sally, or Sally and Joe are picked; both will do the job.) Thus, we must use *combinations,* and the answer is

$$C(5, 2) = \frac{5 \cdot 4}{2 \cdot 1} = 10$$

Sometimes we must combine more than one principle in solving a counting problem. We illustrate this in the next example.

EXAMPLE 2 Choices to Select 3 Programs from 6

A television network has 6 different half-hour programs during prime time (7 to 10 P.M.). You want to watch 3 programs in one evening.

(a) How many choices do you have?

(b) If exactly 1 of the programs must be after 9 P.M., how many choices do you have?

Solution

In this problem you can choose the programs, but you must watch them at the times when they are presented. No permutations are allowed. Thus, to answer the questions, you must use combinations.

(a) Here, you simply need to select 3 of the 6 programs. This means

$$C(6, 3) = \frac{6 \cdot 5 \cdot 4}{3 \cdot 2 \cdot 1} = 20 \text{ choices}$$

(b) Divide the problem into two parts as follows:

1. Select 1 program *after* 9 P.M. Since there are two half-hours between 9 p.m. and 10 p.m., there are 2 choices.
2. Select 2 other programs from 4 *before* 9 P.M. There are

$$C(4, 2) = \frac{4 \cdot 3}{2 \cdot 1} = 6 \text{ choices}$$

Now use the SCP to combine the two sets of choices. This gives

$$\underset{\text{Before 9}}{\underline{6}} \cdot \underset{\text{After 9}}{\underline{2}} = 12 \text{ choices}$$

Tips for the Office
1. Copy and print on both sides of paper
2. Reuse items (envelopes, paper clips)
3. Use e-mail instead of regular mail
4. Use ceramic mugs instead of paper cups

Tips to Save Water
5. Check and fix water leaks
6. Use water-saving devices on faucets
7. Install low-flow shower head
8. Wash and dry only full loads
9. Replace toilets with efficient ones

EXAMPLE 3 Making Choices to Save the Environment

Do you want to save the environment? See the margin for tips you can use. Source: http://www.duluthmerchants.com/100ways.html

(a) How many priority lists can you make if you pick one tip from each list?

(b) How many different lists can you make if you pick 2 Tips for the Office and then 2 Tips to Save Water?

(c) In how many ways can you prioritize (order) the 4 items in the Tips for the Office?

(d) How many sets of tips can you make with the 5 items on the Tips to Save Water list?

(e) How many sets of tips can you make if you pick 3 tips from the second list?

(f) There is one more tip you can use for the office: Set up a bulletin board for messages instead of hard copies. If you decide to make lists with 1, 2, 3 and 4 tips and post them in successive days, how many days would it take to post all possible lists?

Solution

(a) We divide the problem into 3 parts: pick a list, pick one item from one list, pick another item from the other list. Now, fill in the blanks:

$$\frac{2}{\text{Pick a list}} \times \frac{4}{\text{Pick a tip}} \times \frac{5}{\text{Pick another tip}} = 40$$

(b) This time we need only two blanks:

$$\frac{P(4, 2)}{\text{Pick from office tips}} \times \frac{P(5, 2)}{\text{Pick from water tips}} = \frac{4 \cdot 3}{} \times \frac{5 \cdot 4}{} = 240$$

(c) The ***order*** is important and there are **4** items to ***order.*** The answer is $P(\mathbf{4}, \mathbf{4}) = 4 \cdot 3 \cdot 2 \cdot 1 = 24$.

(d) If we are making **sets** of **5** priorities using all of them, the order is **not** important, so we have $C(5, 5) = 1$ possible set (you can only have **one** set using the 5 tips to save water. Remember, when forming a subset, the order in which you list the elements is not important!).

(e) Here the order is **not** important. We have to pick 3 items from 5 so the answer is $C(5, 3) = \frac{5 \cdot 4 \cdot 3!}{3!\, 2!} = \mathbf{10.}$

(f) We are actually looking for all the non-empty subsets we can make from a set of 4 elements, that is, $2^4 - 1 = 15$. Thus, it will take 15 days to post all possible lists. If you want to convince yourself, try making all 15 lists.

EXAMPLE 4 Number of Choices Selecting from a Menu

Roy and Rosie are eating out at an Asian restaurant (see the menu on page 573). They select a special family dinner that allows an individual choice of 1 of 2 soups, 1 entree from 10 items in group A, 1 entree from 9 items in group B, and an individual choice of 1 of 4 desserts. How many different possibilities are there for dinner?

Solution

We consider the following two cases:

1. Roy picks an entree from group A and Rosie picks one from group B. Thus, Roy has a choice of 2 soups, 10 entrees, and 4 desserts, so by the SCP, he has $2 \cdot 10 \cdot 4 = 80$ choices. At the same time, Rosie has a choice of 2 soups, 9 entrees, and 4 desserts, so she has $2 \cdot 9 \cdot 4 = 72$ choices. Hence, by the SCP, together they have $\underline{80} \cdot \underline{72} = 5760$ different choices available.
   Roy ↑ ↑ Rosie
2. Roy picks an entree from group B and Rosie picks one from group A. This simply exchanges the choices we found in case 1, so the number of choices for both is again 5760.

Thus, the total number of possibilities is $2 \cdot 5760 = 11{,}520$.

B Permutations of Nondistinct Objects

In the preceding examples, all the objects considered were distinct (you could tell them apart). Here is a different type of problem. If you go to Madison, Wisconsin, and look at the white pages of the telephone book, you might find that the last name listed is Hero Zzyzzx (pronounced "Ziz-icks"). Can you find in how many different ways the letters in Mr. Zzyzzx's last name can be arranged? Before tackling this problem, look at a simpler one. It is conceivable that no one calls Mr. Zzyzzx by his proper last name; perhaps he is named Zzx (Zicks) for short. In how many different ways can the letters in the name Zzx be arranged? To do this problem, you ignore the capitalization and rewrite the name as z_1z_2x so that you now have three distinct things. Then look at all the possible arrangements of z_1, z_2, and x. After this step, erase the subscripts and look at the arrangements again. Table 10.3 shows the two sets of arrangements. Notice that with the

Table 10.3

With Subscripts		Without Subscripts
z_1z_2x	z_2z_1x	zzx zzx
z_1xz_2	z_2xz_1	zxz zxz
xz_1z_2	xz_2z_1	xzz xzz

subscripts you have 3 distinct objects, which can be ordered in $P(3, 3) = 3! = 6$ ways. The second half of the table, with subscripts erased, shows that two permutations of z_1, z_2, and x, in which the 2 z's are simply interchanged, become identical. Hence, to find the number of distinct arrangements without subscripts, you must divide the number with subscripts by the number of ways in which the identical letters can be permuted. Because there are 2 z's, they can be permuted in 2! ways, so the number of arrangements of zzx is

$$\frac{3!}{2!} = 3$$

A similar argument leads to the general result.

Distinct Arrangements

Suppose that a set of n objects consists of r different types, objects of the same type being indistinguishable. If there are n_1 objects of type 1, n_2 objects of type 2, . . . , and n_r objects of type r, then the total number of *distinct* arrangements of the n objects is

$$\frac{n!}{n_1!n_2! \ldots n_r!}$$

With this formula, you can find the number of distinct arrangements of the letters in the name Zzyzzx. Now regard the Z and the z as distinct, so there are 6 letters, 1 Z, 3 z's, 1 y, and 1 x. The formula gives

$$\frac{6!}{1!3!1!1!} = 6 \cdot 5 \cdot 4 = 120$$

EXAMPLE 5 Arranging Minnie's Letters

In how many different ways can the letters in the name Minnie be arranged?

Solution

There is a total of $n = 6$ letters in the name: 1 M, 2 i's, 2 n's, and 1 e. Thus, $n_1 = 1$, $n_2 = 2$, $n_3 = 2$, and $n_4 = 1$. Hence, the number of distinct arrangements is

$$\frac{6!}{1!2!2!1!} = \frac{6 \cdot 5 \cdot 4 \cdot 3 \cdot 2 \cdot 1}{1 \cdot 1 \cdot 2 \cdot 1 \cdot 2 \cdot 1} = 180$$

EXAMPLE 6 Que Zzzzzzzzzra Zzzzzzzzzra

The last name in the San Francisco phone book used to be (are you ready?) Zachary Zzzzzzzzzra. (Please, don't ask how to pronounce it!) In how many distinguishable ways can the letters in Zzzzzzzzzra be arranged?

Solution

Here, $n = 11$, $n_1 = 1$ (1 Z), $n_2 = 8$ (8 z's), $n_3 = 1$ (1 r), and $n_4 = 1$ (1 a). Thus, the number of distinct arrangements is

$$\frac{11!}{1!8!1!1!} = \frac{11 \cdot 10 \cdot 9 \cdot 8!}{8!} = 11 \cdot 10 \cdot 9 = 990$$

C Applications

There is one counting technique that has not been discussed in this section: tree diagrams. These diagrams can be used to "help make better decisions in litigation management." Let us see how. (Source: TreeAge Software.)

EXAMPLE 7 An Application to Law

A lawyer handling legal cases "first identifies the factual and legal uncertainties in a case and then decides: Should we litigate or settle?" If we litigate, we can lose or win a summary judgment. If we lose, the jury finds liability (high, medium, or low) or there may not be any liability. Draw a tree diagram and show all the possibilities for the case.

Solution

We draw the tree shown in Figure 10.12 and label the branches.

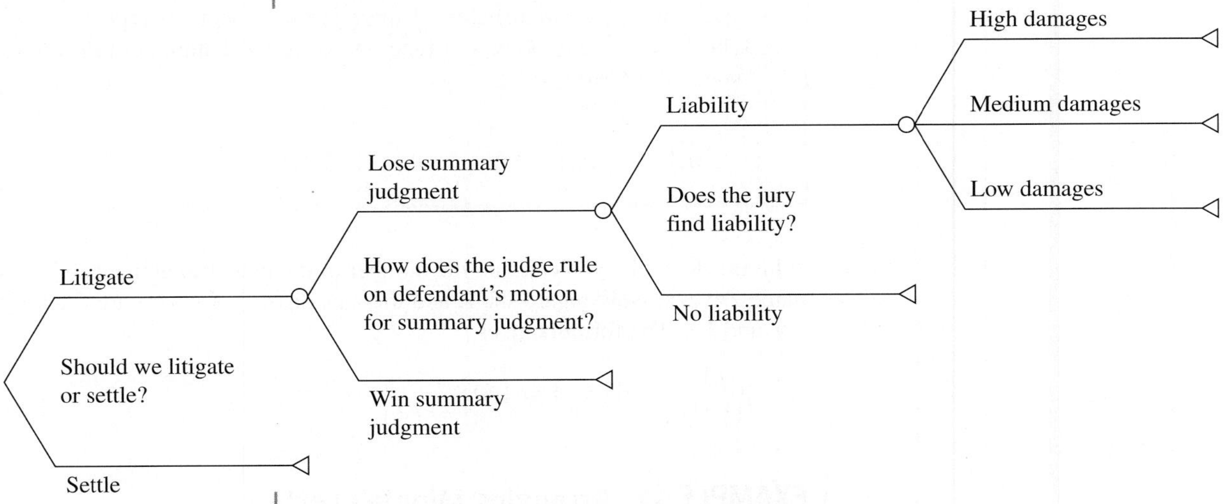

FIGURE 10.12

As you can see, there are 6 distinct possibilities identified by the ◁ symbol. In the next chapter we will be able to assign probabilities to each of the events involved. For example, "The reality is that more than 90% of all cases end up being resolved through settlement, rather than trial."

10.4 EXERCISES

A Permutations and Combinations

1. Three cards are dealt in succession and without replacement from a standard deck of 52 cards.
   a. In how many different orders can the cards be dealt?
   b. How many different 3-card hands are possible?
2. An employment agency has 6 temporary workers.
   a. In how many ways could 4 of them be assigned to the research department?
   b. In how many ways could 3 of them be assigned to 3 different companies?
3. The playbook for the quarterback of the Dallas Cowboys contains 50 plays.
   a. In how many different ways could the quarterback select 3 plays to use in succession in the next 3 downs?
   b. In how many different ways could he select a set of 3 plays to study?
4. A student must take 3 different courses on Mondays. In how many different ways can the student do this given the following:
   a. There are 6 different courses, all available at each of the 3 hours 8, 9, and 10 A.M.
   b. There are 6 different courses, and only 1 course is available at each of the hours between 8 A.M. and 2 P.M. (6 hours).
5. Rework problem 4(**b**) if the student wants to keep the hour from 12 noon to 1 P.M. free for lunch.
6. A student wishes to schedule mathematics, English, and science. These classes are available every hour between 9 A.M. and noon (3 hours).
   a. How many different schedules are possible?
   b. How many schedules are possible if this student wants to take mathematics at 11 A.M. with her favorite instructor, Mr. Eldridge?
7. Peter must select 3 electives from a group of 7 courses.
   a. In how many ways can Peter do this?
   b. If all 7 of these courses are available each of the 4 hours from 8 A.M. to noon, from how many different schedules (hours and what course at each hour) can Peter choose?
8. At the University of South Florida, a student must take at least 2 courses from each of 5 different areas in order to satisfy the general distribution requirement. Each of the areas has the number of courses indicated in the table.

Area	I	II	III	IV	V
Courses	2	50	20	40	100

   a. If Sandy has satisfied all the requirements except for area V, and she wishes to take 3 courses in this area, how many choices does she have?
   b. Bill has already satisfied his requirements in areas I, II, and III. Now he wishes to take the minimum number of courses in areas IV and V. How many choices does he have?

9. A class consists of 14 boys and 10 girls. They want to elect officers so that the president and secretary are girls, and the vice president and treasurer are boys.
   a. How many possibilities are there?
   b. How many are there if 2 of the boys refuse to participate?
10. A company has 6 officers and 4 directors (10 different people). In how many ways can a committee of 4 be selected from these 10 people so that the following hold?
    a. 2 members are officers and 2 are directors.
    b. 3 members are officers and 1 is a director.
    c. All the members are officers.
    d. There are no restrictions.
11. There are 4 vacancies on the scholarship committee at a certain university. In order to balance the men and women on the committee, 1 woman and 3 men are to be appointed. In how many ways can this be done if the following are available to serve?
    a. 7 men and 8 women
    b. 5 men and 2 women
12. Romano's Restaurant has the menu shown in Example 8 of Section 10.3. In how many ways can a meal consisting of a pizza with 3 toppings, 2 beverages, and a dessert be chosen? The menu shows that there are 6 toppings for the pizza, 6 beverages, and 5 desserts offered.

B Permutations of Nondistinct Objects

13. How many distinct arrangements can be made with the letters in the word TALLAHASSEE?
14. How many distinct arrangements can be made with the letters in the word MISSISSIPPI?
15. Do you know what a *palindrome* is? It is a word or phrase with the same spelling when written forward or backward. The longest single-word palindrome in the English language is the word REDIVIDER. How many distinct arrangements can be made with the letters in this word?
16. There is a place in Morocco with a name that has 8 vowels in a row in its spelling! Do you know what place this is? It is spelled IJOUAOUOUENE. How many distinct arrangements can be made with the letters in this name?
17. A contractor needs to buy 7 electronic components from 3 different subcontractors. The contractor wants to buy 2 of the components from the first subcontractor, 3 from the second, and 2 from the third. In how many ways can this be accomplished?
18. An advertiser has a contract for 20 weeks that provides 3 different ads each week. If it is decided that in no 2 weeks will the same 3 ads be shown, how many different ads are necessary? [*Hint:* You need to find the least n such that $C(n, 3) \geq 20$.]
19. A cable television network wishes to show 5 movies every day for 3 weeks (21 days) without having to show the same 5 movies any 2 days in the 3 weeks. What is the least number of movies the network must have in order to do this? (See the hint in problem 18.)
20. Repeat problem 19 but assume the network wants to show the movies for 8 weeks.
21. Polly needs to take biology, English, and history. All these are available every hour between 9 A.M. and 3 P.M. (6 hours). If Polly must schedule 2 of these courses between 9 A.M. and 1 P.M. and 1 course between 1 and 3 P.M., how many schedules (hours and course each hour) are available to her?
22. Roy must elect 3 courses from among 4 courses in group I and 3 courses in group II. If he must take at least 1 of his 3 electives from each group, how many choices does he have? (*Hint:* First find how many choices he has if he elects only 1 course from group I. Then find how many choices he has if he elects 2 courses from group I. Since he must do one or the other of these, the final answer is the sum of the two answers.)

C Applications

Problems 23–25 are adapted from David C. Skinner, Introduction to Decision Analysis *(Florida: Probabilistic Publishing, 1996).*

23. Suppose you wish to invest \$1000 for a year. You have *three* choices: a mutual fund, a management company, or a CD. Each of the investments may have a *high* or a *low* yield. Mutual funds return 6–10%, management companies 5–10%, and CDs 3–4%.
    a. Make a tree diagram showing all possibilities. At the end of each branch write the amount of money expected from the investment.
    b. Based on your tree diagram, what is the highest value for the investment?
    c. Based on your tree diagram, what is the lowest value for the investment?
24. Do you bet at all? Let us look at a hypothetical problem and perhaps you won't. Suppose you are considering betting on the horses. You can either place the bet or not. If you place a \$200 bet, you can win \$50,000 or lose your \$200 (−\$200).
    a. Make a tree diagram showing all possibilities. At the end of each branch write the amount associated with that branch.
    b. Based on your diagram, what is the highest (best) amount you can get?
    c. Based on your diagram, what is the lowest (worst) amount you can get?
25. A company is considering the introduction of a new product. The market size for the product can be extremely high or low. If the market size is extremely high, sales can be high (\$2000), medium (\$1000), or low (\$750). If the market size is low, sales can be high (\$750), medium (\$500), or low (\$300).
    a. Make a tree diagram showing all possibilities. At the end of each branch, write the amount expected from that outcome.
    b. Based on your tree diagram, what is the highest amount of money you can get and under what conditions?
    c. Based on your tree diagram, what is the lowest amount of money you can get and under what conditions?
26. Here is a personal investment decision. You can buy high-risk, low-risk, or preferred stocks. For each of these types of stocks, the market can go up, stay the same, or go down. In the case of the high risk stocks, if the markets go up, you get \$1500; if it stays the same, you get \$100; but if it goes down, you lose \$1000 (−\$1000). With the low-risk stock, you get \$1000 when the market goes up and \$200 if it stays the same, but you lose \$100 (−\$100) if the market goes down. The preferred stock will always pay \$500 regardless of market conditions.
    a. Make a tree diagram showing all possibilities. At the end of each branch, write the amount associated with the outcome corresponding to that branch.
    b. Based on your tree diagram, what is the highest amount of money you can expect and under what conditions?
    c. Based on your tree diagram, what is the lowest amount of money you can expect and under what conditions?

IN OTHER WORDS

27. Describe in your own words how you would decide which of the formulas to use (SCP, permutations, combinations) in a counting problem.
28. Which formula would you use in a counting problem involving indistinguishable objects? Explain.

USING YOUR KNOWLEDGE

Do you know an easy way of finding how many positive integers are exact divisors of a given positive integer? For example, how many exact divisors does 4500 have? The easy way to answer this question is to write 4500 first as a product of its prime divisors.

$$4500 = 2^2 3^2 5^3$$

Now you can see that every exact divisor of 4500 must be of the form $2^a 3^b 5^c$, where a is 0, 1, or 2; b is 0, 1, or 2; and c is 0, 1, 2, or 3. Because there are 3 choices for a, 3 choices for b, and 4 choices for c, the SCP tells you that the number of exact divisors of 4500 is $3 \cdot 3 \cdot 4 = 36$. Notice that the exponents in the prime factorization of 4500 are 2, 2, and 3, and the number of exact divisors is the product $(2 + 1)(2 + 1)(3 + 1)$. Try this out for a small number, say 12, for which you can check the answer by writing out all the exact divisors.

29. How many exact divisors does 144 have?
30. How many exact divisors does 2520 have?
31. If the integer $N = 2^a 3^b 5^c 7^d$, how many exact divisors does N have?
32. How many exact divisors does the number $2^4 3^2 7^3$ have?

COLLABORATIVE LEARNING

The following tree shows a model of a decision whether to vaccinate for a specific disease. The numbers appearing on individual branches indicate the probability that the event associated with that branch will occur. For example, if the decision is made to vaccinate, the probability that there are no complications is 0.99, or 99%. In addition, different numbers are given at the end of each branch. Those numbers represent the quality of that particular course of action. Thus, if the decision is made not to vaccinate and there is no disease, the quality number is 10 (see the bottom branch).

1. What is the best quality number in the diagram, and what course of action has to be taken to obtain that number?
2. Discuss which one of the two courses of action associated with the highest quality number is, in your opinion, best for the patient.
3. What is the worst quality number in the diagram and under which conditions does it occur?
4. Why do you think there are two courses of action that merit a 5 for their quality number? What actions could be taken to get a 5?

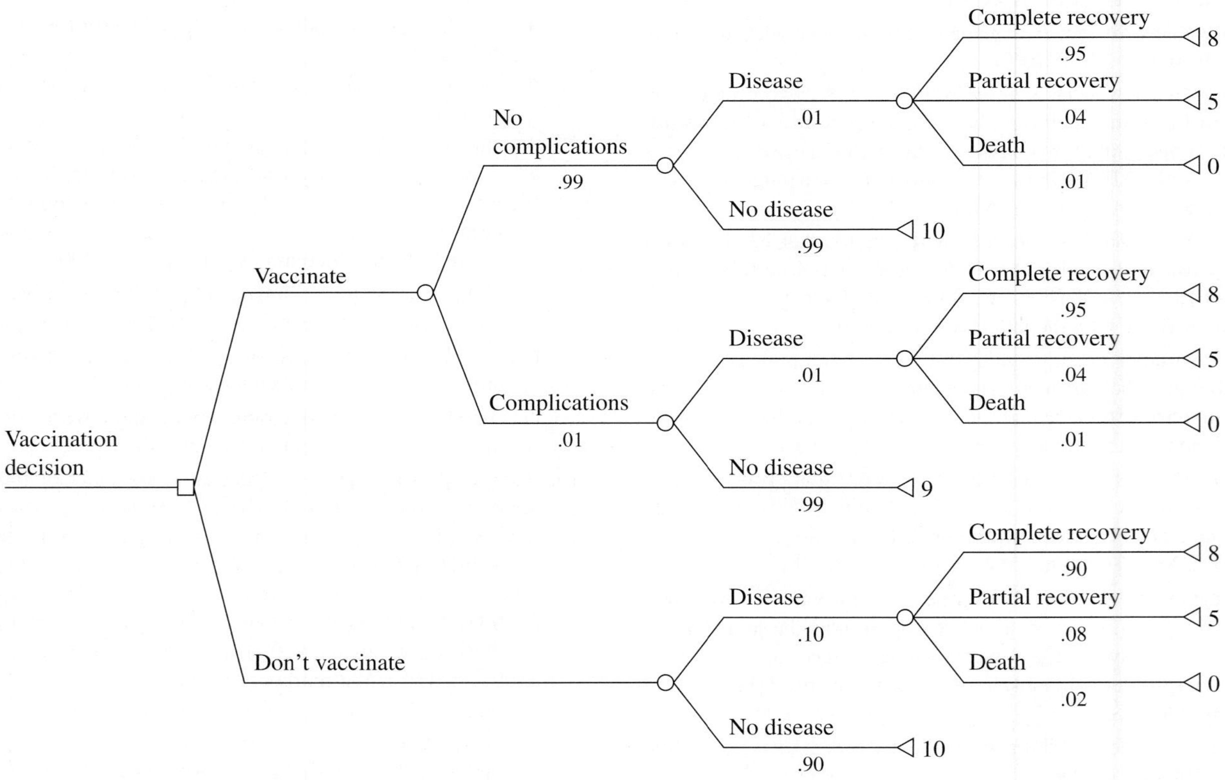

This tree models a decision of whether to vaccinate for a specific disease and is to be used in the Collaborative Learning exercises.

CHAPTER 10 Summary

SECTION	ITEM	MEANING	EXAMPLE
10.1B	SCP	Sequential counting principle: If one event can occur in m ways, a second event can then occur in n ways, a third event can occur in r ways, and so on, then the sequence of events can occur in $m \times n \times r \times \cdots$ ways.	If there are 3 roads to go to the beach and 2 dates are available, then you have $3 \times 2 = 6$ different choices.
10.2A	Permutation	An ordered arrangement of n distinguishable objects, taken r at a time with no repetitions	$P(3, 2) = 3 \times 2 = 6$
	$n!$ (n factorial)	$n(n-1)(n-2)\cdots(3)(2)(1)$	$3! = 3 \cdot 2 \cdot 1 = 6$
	$P(n, r)$	$n(n-1)(n-2)\cdots(n-r+1)$ or $\dfrac{n!}{(n-r)!}$	$P(6, 2) = \dfrac{6!}{(6-2)!}$ or $6 \times 5 = 30$
	$0!$	1	
10.2B	Complementary counting principle	$n(A) = n(\mathcal{U}) - n(A')$	If $\mathcal{U} = \{a, b, c, d\}$ and $A = \{a, c, d\}$, then $A' = \{b\}$ and $n(A) = n(\mathcal{U}) - n(A')$; or $3 = 4 - 1$.
10.2C	Additive counting principle	$n(A \cup B) = n(A) + n(B) - n(A \cap B)$	If $A = \{a, b, c\}$ and $B = \{b, c, d\}$, then $A \cup B = \{a, b, c, d\}$, $A \cap B = \{b, c\}$, and $n(A \cup B) = n(A) + n(B) - n(A \cap B)$; or $4 = 3 + 3 - 2$.
10.3	Combination	A selection of r objects without regard to order, taken from a set of n distinguishable objects	The combination of 2 letters that can be made from the letters in $\{a, b, c\}$ are *ab*, *ac*, and *bc*.
	$C(n, r)$	$\dfrac{n!}{r!(n-r)!} = \dfrac{P(n, r)}{r!}$	$C(6, 2) = \dfrac{6!}{214!}$
	$C(n, r)$	The number of subsets of r elements that can be formed from a set of n elements	$C(5, 2) = \dfrac{5!}{2!3!} = 10$ is the number of subsets of 2 elements that can be formed from a set of 5 elements.
10.4B	The total number of distinct arrangements of n objects, n_1 of type 1, n_2 of type 2, . . . , and n_r of type r, is given by the formula	$\dfrac{n!}{n_1!n_2!\cdots n_r!}$	The number of arrangements of the letters aabbbc is $\dfrac{6!}{2!3!1!}$.

CHAPTER 10 Practice Test

1. A student wants to take two courses, A and B, both of which are available at 9, 10, and 11 A.M. Make a tree diagram to show all the possible schedules for that student. Use a notation like (A, 9) to mean course A at 9 A.M., (B, 11) to mean course B at 11 A.M., and so on.

2. A restaurant offers a choice of 2 soups, 3 entrees, and 5 desserts. How many different meals consisting of a soup, an entree, and a dessert are possible?

continued

CHAPTER 10 Practice Test – *continued*

3. a. Two dice are thrown. How many different outcomes are possible?
   b. In how many ways could you get a sum of 5?

4. Two cards are drawn in succession and without replacement from a standard deck of 52 cards. In how many ways could these be a black jack and a red card, in that order?

5. An airline has 3 flights from city A to city B and 5 flights from city B to city C. In how many ways could you fly from city A to city C using this airline?

6. Compute the following: a. $7!$ b. $\frac{7!}{4!}$

7. Compute the following: a. $3! \times 4!$ b. $3! + 4!$

8. Find the following: a. $P(5, 5)$ b. $P(6, 6)$

9. Find the following: a. $P(8, 2)$ b. $P(7, 3)$

10. In how many ways can 4 people be arranged in a row for a group picture?

11. Three married couples are posing for a group picture. They are to be seated in a row of 6 chairs, with each husband and wife together. In how many ways can this be done? (*Hint:* First count the number of ways in which the couples can be arranged.)

12. Bobby has 6 pigeons: 2 white, 2 gray, and 2 gray and white. In how many ways can Bobby select 3 of his pigeons and include exactly 1 white bird?

13. How many counting numbers less than 50 are divisible by 2 or 5?

14. How many different sums of money can be made from a set of coins consisting of a penny, a nickel, a dime, and a quarter if exactly 2 coins are selected?

15. How many subsets of 3 elements does the set $\{a, b, c, d, e, f\}$ have?

16. Find the following: a. $C(5, 2)$ b. $C(6, 4)$

17. Find the following: a. $C(6, 0)$ b. $\frac{C(5, 4)}{C(5, 3)}$

18. Two cards are drawn in succession and without replacement from a standard deck of 52 cards. How many different sets of 2 cards are possible?

19. A student wants to schedule mathematics, English, science, and economics. These 4 classes are available every hour between 8 A.M. and noon (4 hours). How many different schedules are possible?

20. Billy has 5 coins: a penny, a nickel, a dime, a quarter, and a half-dollar. How many different sums of money can Billy form by using 1, 2, or 3 of these coins?

21. The A-1 Company needs 3 skilled employees, 1 to be in charge and 2 to help. If the company has 5 competent applicants, in how many ways can the employees be selected?

22. On a certain night, there are 8 half-hour programs scheduled on a television station. How many choices do you have if you want to watch 4 of these programs?

23. How many distinct arrangements can you make with the letters in the word *boogaboo?*

24. How many distinct arrangements can be made with the letters in the palindrome "Madam I'm Adam"? (Disregard the apostrophe and capitalization.)

25. On a particular day, a total of 1977 stocks were traded on the New York Stock Exchange for a volume of 137,350,000 shares. Of the 1977 stocks traded, 1189 advanced (a), 460 declined (d), and 328 were unchanged (n). Suppose at the end of the day, you marked a, d, or n after each stock traded. How many distinct arrangements of all the a's, d's, and n's are possible? (Do not try to simplify your answer.)

ANSWERS TO PRACTICE TEST

CHAPTER 10		What to Review *If You Missed It*		
QUESTION	**ANSWER**	**SECTION**	**EXAMPLE(S)**	**PAGE(S)**
1	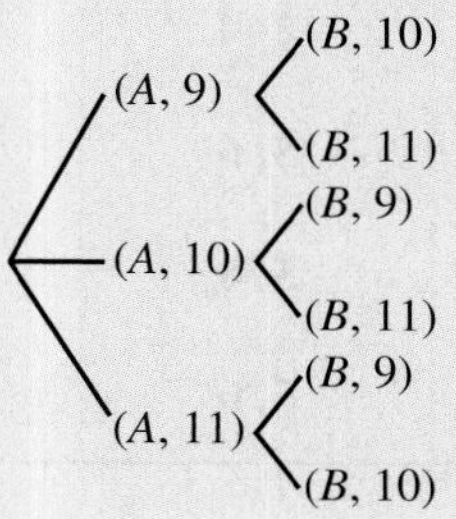	**10.1**	**1**	**565–566**
2	30	**10.1**	**2**	**566**
3	**a.** 36 **b.** 4	**10.1**	**3, 4**	**567**
4	52	**10.1**	**5–9**	**568–571**
5	15	**10.1**	**10**	**571**
6	**a.** 5040 **b.** 210	**10.2**	**2**	**577**
7	**a.** 144 **b.** 30	**10.2**	**2**	**577**
8	**a.** 120 **b.** 720	**10.2**	**3, 4**	**577, 578**
9	**a.** 56 **b.** 210	**10.2**	**4**	**578**
10	24	**10.2**	**5**	**579**
11	48	**10.2**	**5**	**579**
12	72	**10.2**	**6**	**580**
13	29	**10.2**	**7**	**580–581**
14	6	**10.3**	**1**	**585**
15	20	**10.3**	**2, 3, 5**	**586, 588**
16	**a.** 10 **b.** 15	**10.3**	**6**	**588–589**
17	**a.** 1 **b.** $\frac{1}{2}$	**10.3**	**6**	**588–589**
18	1326	**10.3**	**7**	**589**
19	24	**10.4**	**1**	**594**
20	25	**10.4**	**1**	**594**
21	30	**10.4**	**1**	**594**

continued

ANSWERS TO PRACTICE TEST – *continued*

CHAPTER 10		What to Review *If You Missed It*		
QUESTION	**ANSWER**	**SECTION**	**EXAMPLE(S)**	**PAGE(S)**
22	70	10.4	2–4	594–596
23	840	10.4	5, 6	597
24	34,650	10.4	5, 6	597
25	$\frac{1977!}{1189!460!328!}$	10.4	5, 6	597

Probability

Probability is the very guide of life. —CICERO

Advertising new products is a key marketing strategy that increases the probability of sales. In Section 11.4, you will study conditional probability, which can be used to determine the conditions under which sales may be made.

In this chapter we will examine probability, the science of determining the likelihood or chance that an event will occur.

The study of probability dates back to the Assyrians and Sumerians who had games similar to dice. The Egyptians even had dicelike objects called *tali* made from the heel bones of animals, polished and engraved so that, when thrown, they could land on any of four different sides with different probabilities because the *talis* were not uniformly shaped.

In Section 11.1 we shall study how to assign probabilities to events. We will use the ideas of Chapter 10 (tree diagrams, the sequential counting principle, permutations, and combinations) to handle more complex problems and consider some of the theories and formulas that facilitate the computations in probability. Because probability is heavily dependent on arithmetic, the absence of these formulas and methods long hampered the development of the theory of probability. It was not until the contributions of Blaise Pascal, Pierre Fermat, and Pierre-Simon Laplace that the theory was fully developed.

Sections 11.4 and 11.5 are devoted to the study of conditional probability and independent events, ideas that are used in medicine, law, and insurance.

We end the chapter by studying odds and mathematical expectation. If a state has a lottery, we can verify the odds of the game and the probability of obtaining different prizes. But our applications of mathematical expectation are not limited to gambling. We also use the idea to predict the number of postseason baseball games, how much insurance policies are expected to cost and as a management tool to determine which way to proceed when confronted with different business decisions involving outcomes with given probabilities and to consider the results that can be expected when these outcomes occur.

11.1 Sample Spaces and Probability

GETTING STARTED

OBJECTIVES

A. Find the probability of an event.
B. Find the empirical probability of an event.

Human Side of Math

(1623–1662)

Blaise Pascal was born in the French province of Auvergne in June of 1623. His most original contribution was to the theory of probability, but this notoriety was shared by the famous French mathematician Pierre Fermat.

By the age of 17, Pascal had written an amazing essay on conic sections (parabolas, circles, ellipses, and hyperbolas), including new and deep theorems on the properties of these curves. At the age of 18, Pascal had invented the world's first calculating machine and had begun to work in physics and mechanics. But he continued his scientific work for only a few years and quit at the age of 27 to devote himself to religious contemplation.

At the age of 31, a problem was proposed to him on the division of the pot in an unfinished gambling game. Pascal wrote to Fermat about the problem, and in the ensuing correspondence these two men shared equally in establishing basic results in the theory of probability.

LOOKING AHEAD

Mathematicians' interest in probability theory grew because of Pascal's and Fermat's writings and prompted the thorough development of the theories contained in this chapter.

PROBABILITY AND THE *TONIGHT SHOW WITH JAY LENO*

Which is more probable, appearing on the *Tonight Show with Jay Leno* or winning the jackpot in your state lottery with a single ticket? (If there is no lottery in your state, the probability of winning it is, of course, 0.) According to a book called *What Are the Chances,* the probability of appearing on the *Tonight Show with Jay Leno* is 1 in 490,000, that is, $\frac{1}{490,000}$. What is the probability of winning the jackpot in your state lottery? In the 6 from 49 lotteries, you buy a $1 ticket and pick 6 numbers from 1 to 49. (In Florida you pick numbers from 1 to 53.) If you match all 6 numbers, you win the jackpot. How probable is that? Since there is only 1 set of winning numbers and $C(49, 6)$ possible number combinations, your probability is 1 in $C(49, 6)$, that is, 1 in 13,983,816. It is much more probable that you will appear on the *Tonight Show with Jay Leno!* If you are playing the Florida lottery, the probability that you hold a winning ticket is even smaller because there are more possible number combinations, namely, $C(53, 6)$ instead of $C(49, 6)$. This makes the probability of winning the Florida jackpot 1 in 22,957,480.

Probability theory was developed by mathematicians studying gambling games. In 1654, Antoine Gombaud, better known as the Chevalier de Méré, offered even money that in 4 rolls of a die, at least one 6 would be rolled. He reasoned that since the chance that a 6 will be rolled when a die is tossed is $\frac{1}{6}$, in 4 rolls, the chances of getting at least one 6 should equal $\frac{4}{6} = \frac{2}{3}$. Do you think that he was right? You will be able to give the answer after you read this section!

Here are some probabilities that may be of interest to you.

EVENT	PROBABILITY
Struck by lightning	1/576,000
Audited by IRS	1/175
Identity Stolen	1/200
Having Stroke	1/6
Getting Arthritis	1/7
Getting the flu this year	1/10
Cancer (lifetime, man)	1/2
Cancer (lifetime, woman)	1/3

Source: http://funny2.com/odds.htm

To try to verify the probability that you are struck by lightning, find the number of deaths plus injuries caused by lightning (400) and divide by the U.S. population (310,000,000). The result is different from 1/576,000. It is $\frac{400}{310,000,000} = \frac{1}{775,000}$. Source: http://www.lightningsafety.noaa.gov/medical.htm.

The theory of probability is an important tool in the solution of many problems in the modern world. Although the most obvious applications are in gambling games, important applications occur in many situations involving an element of uncertainty. Probability theory is used to estimate whether a missile will hit its target, to determine premiums on insurance policies, and to make important business decisions such as where to locate a supermarket or how many checkout clerks to employ so that customers will not be kept waiting in line too long. Various sampling techniques, which are used in opinion polls and in the quality control of mass-produced items, are based on the theory of probability.

We want the **probability** of a given event to be a mathematical estimate of the likelihood that this event will occur. The following examples show how a probability can be assigned to a given event.

A Theoretical Probabilities

The odds of appearing on the *Tonight Show with Jay Leno* are better than the odds of winning the lottery in your state (if there is one).

EXAMPLE 1 Finding the Probability of Heads

A fair coin is tossed; find the probability of getting heads.

Solution

Even though we have not officially defined the term *probability,* our intuition tells us the following:

1. When a fair coin is tossed, it can turn up in one of 2 ways. Assuming that the coin will not stand on edge, heads and tails are the only 2 possible **outcomes.**
2. If the coin is balanced (and this is what we mean by saying "the coin is fair"), the 2 outcomes are considered **equally likely.**
3. The probability of obtaining heads when a fair coin is tossed, denoted by $P(H)$, is 1 out of 2. That is, $P(H) = \frac{1}{2}$.

Activities such as tossing a coin (as in Example 1), drawing a card from a deck, or rolling a pair of dice are called **experiments.** The set $\mathcal{U}$ of all possible outcomes for an experiment is called the **sample space** for the experiment. These terms are illustrated in Table 11.1.

Table 11.1 Experiments and Sample Spaces

Experiment	Possible Outcomes	Sample Space $\mathcal{U}$
A penny is tossed.	Heads or tails are equally likely outcomes.	$\{H, T\}$
There are 3 beige and 3 red balls in a box; 1 ball is drawn at random.	A beige or a red ball is equally likely to be drawn.	$\{b_1, b_2, b_3, r_1, r_2, r_3\}$
A penny and a nickel are tossed.	**Penny** **Nickel** H H H T T H T T	$\{(H, H), (H, T), (T, H), (T, T)\}$
One die is rolled.	The numbers from 1 to 6 are all equally likely outcomes.	$\{1, 2, 3, 4, 5, 6\}$
The pointer is spun, as shown in Figure 11.1. 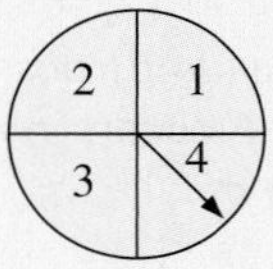 FIGURE 11.1	The pointer is equally likely to point to 1, 2, 3, or 4.	$\{1, 2, 3, 4\}$
An integer between 1 and 50 (inclusive) is selected at random.	The integers from 1 to 50 are all equally likely to be selected.	$\{1, 2, 3, \ldots, 50\}$

© Owen Franken

Returning to Example 1, we see that the set of all possible outcomes for the experiment is $\mathscr{U} = \{H, T\}$. But there are only two subsets of $\mathscr{U}$ that can occur, namely, $\{H\}$ and $\{T\}$, and each of these is called an **event.** If we get heads—that is, if the event $E = \{H\}$ occurs—we say that we have a **favorable outcome** or a **success.** Since there are 2 equally likely events in $\mathscr{U}$ and 1 of these is E, we assign the value $\frac{1}{2}$ to the event E. But what if the coin is *not* fair?

Here is a quote from an article appearing in the English newspaper *The Guardian* on Friday, January 4, 2002: "When spun on edge 250 times, a Belgian one-euro coin came up heads 140 times and tails 110. 'It looks very suspicious to me,' said Barry Blight, a statistics lecturer at the London School of Economics." Does it look suspicious to you?

On the basis of that experiment, what would the probability of heads be for *that* coin? This time, the number of favorable outcomes for $E = \{H\}$ is 140 and the total number of outcomes is 250. Thus, $P(H) = \frac{140}{250} = \frac{14}{25}$, not $\frac{1}{2}$! Can you consider this coin fair?

We now expand on the problem discussed in Example 1. Suppose that a fair coin is tossed 3 times. Can we find the probability that 3 heads come up? As before, we proceed in three steps as follows:

1. The set of all possible outcomes for this experiment can be found by drawing a tree diagram, as shown in Figure 11.2. As we can see, the possibilities for the first toss are labeled H and T, and likewise for the other two tosses. The number of outcomes is 8.

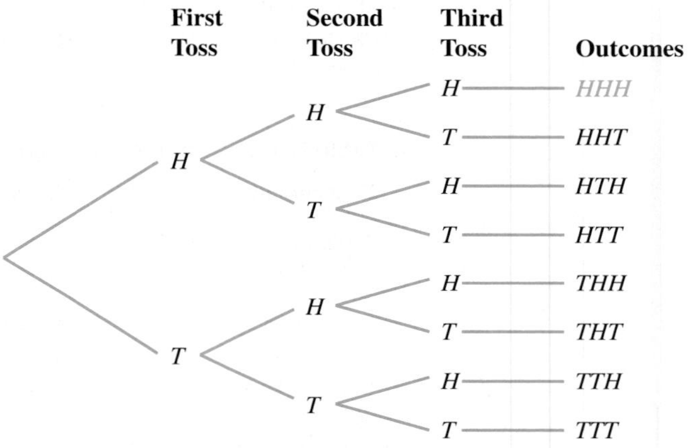

FIGURE 11.2 Tree diagram.

2. The 8 outcomes are equally likely.
3. We conclude that the probability of getting 3 heads, denoted by $P(HHH)$, is 1 out of 8; that is, $P(HHH) = \frac{1}{8}$.*

If we want to know the probability of getting *at least* 2 heads, the 4 outcomes HHH, HHT, HTH, and THH are favorable out of the 8 outcomes shown in Figure 11.2, so the probability of getting at least 2 heads is $\frac{4}{8} = \frac{1}{2}$.

In examples such as these, in which all the possible outcomes are equally likely, the task of finding the probability of any event E can be simplified by using the following definition:

Definition of the Probability of an Event

Suppose an experiment has $n(\mathscr{U})$ possible outcomes, **all equally likely.** Suppose further that the event E occurs in $n(E)$ of these outcomes. Then, the **probability** of event E is given by

$$P(E) = \frac{\text{number of ways } E \text{ can occur}}{\text{number of possible outcomes}} = \frac{n(E)}{n(\mathscr{U})} \tag{1}$$

*Technically, we should write $P(\{HHH\})$ instead of $P(HHH)$. However, we shall write $P(HHH)$ whenever the meaning is clear.

In the previous example, $n(\mathcal{U}) = 8$ and $n(E) = 4$, so

$$P(E) = \frac{n(E)}{n(\mathcal{U})} = \frac{4}{8} = \frac{1}{2}$$

We illustrate the use of equation (1) in the following examples. Note that $0 \leq P(E) \leq 1$ because $0 \leq n(E) \leq n(\mathcal{U})$.

PROBLEM-SOLVING

Computing Probability

① **Read** the problem.

There are 75 possible numbers in Bingo. Find the probability that the first number selected is the following:

(a) 25 (b) 80 (c) An odd number (d) A number less than 80

② **Select** the unknown.

We want to find the probability of four events: (a), (b), (c), and (d).

③ **Think** of a plan. We have to find out how many outcomes are possible when the first number is selected and in how many ways each of the four given events (a), (b), (c), and (d) can occur.

If we select a number from a group of 75 numbers, there are 75 equally likely outcomes; that is, the universal set is

$$\mathcal{U} = \{1, 2, 3, \ldots, 75\} \quad \text{and} \quad n(\mathcal{U}) = 75$$

Let T be the event that number 25 is selected.
Let E be the event that number 80 is selected.
Let O be the event that an odd number is selected.
Let L be the event that a number less than 80 is selected.

④ **Use** equation (1) on page 608 to find the probability of each event. In how many ways can we do the following?

(a) Select number 25.

(a) There is only one way of selecting number 25; thus,

$$P(T) = \frac{n(T)}{n(\mathcal{U})} = \frac{1}{75}$$

(b) Select number 80.

(b) There is no way number 80 can be selected; thus, $P(E) = \frac{0}{75} = 0$. This event is *impossible*.

(c) Select an odd number.

(c) There are 38 odd numbers $\{1, 3, 5, 2 \cdot 38 - 1 = 75\}$ that are 75 or less; thus, $P(O) = \frac{38}{75}$.

(d) Select a number that is less than 80.

(d) All 75 numbers in Bingo are less than 80; thus, $P(L) = \frac{75}{75} = 1$. This event is *certain* (a "sure thing"!).

⑤ **Verify** the solution.

Are all the probabilities we have computed between 0 and 1, inclusive?

Try Example 2 Now

Cover the solution, write your own solution, and then check your work.

EXAMPLE 2 Probabilities with 1 Die

A single die is rolled. Find the probabilities of obtaining the following:

(a) A number greater than 4

(b) An odd number

Solution

(a) Let E be the event in which a number greater than 4 appears. When a die is rolled, there are 6 equally likely outcomes, so $n(\mathscr{U}) = 6$. There are two outcomes (5 and 6) in E; that is, $n(E) = 2$. Hence,

$$P(E) = \frac{n(E)}{n(\mathscr{U})} = \frac{2}{6} = \frac{1}{3}$$

(b) Let O be the event in which an odd number appears. Three outcomes (1, 3, 5) are in O. Thus, $P(O) = \frac{3}{6} = \frac{1}{2}$.

EXAMPLE 3 Urn Probabilities

Ten balls numbered from 1 to 10 are placed in an urn. If 1 ball is selected at random, find the probabilities of the following:

(a) An even-numbered ball is selected (event E).

(b) Ball number 3 is chosen (event T).

(c) Ball number 3 is *not* chosen (event T').

Solution

(a) There are 5 outcomes (2, 4, 6, 8, 10) in E out of 10 equally likely outcomes. Hence, $P(E) = \frac{5}{10} = \frac{1}{2}$.

(b) There is only 1 outcome (3) in the event T out of 10 equally likely outcomes. Thus, $P(T) = \frac{1}{10}$.

(c) There are 9 outcomes (all except the 3) in T' out of the 10 possible outcomes. Hence, $P(T') = \frac{9}{10}$.

In Example 3 we found $P(T) = \frac{1}{10}$ and $P(T') = \frac{9}{10}$, so $P(T') = 1 - P(T)$. This is a general result because $T \cup T' = \mathscr{U}$ and $T \cap T' = \varnothing$. Thus,

$$n(T \cup T') = n(T) + n(T') = n(\mathscr{U})$$

Therefore,

$$\frac{n(T)}{n(\mathscr{U})} + \frac{n(T')}{n(\mathscr{U})} = \frac{n(\mathscr{U})}{n(\mathscr{U})}$$

or, by the definition of the probability of an event,

$$P(T) + P(T') = 1$$

Thus, the probability $P(T')$ of an event not occurring is $1 - P(T)$.

Probability of an Event Not Occurring

The probability $P(T')$ of an event not occurring is

$$P(T') = 1 - P(T)$$

The next example illustrates the use of this idea.

EXAMPLE 4 Probability of at Least 1 Head

A coin is thrown 3 times. Find the probability of obtaining at least 1 head.

Solution

Let E be the event that we obtain at least 1 head. Then E' is the event that we obtain 0 heads; that is, that we obtain 3 tails. From the preceding discussion, $P(E) = 1 - P(E')$. Here, $P(E')$ is the same as $P(TTT) = \frac{1}{8}$; hence, $P(E) = 1 - P(TTT) = 1 - \frac{1}{8} = \frac{7}{8}$.

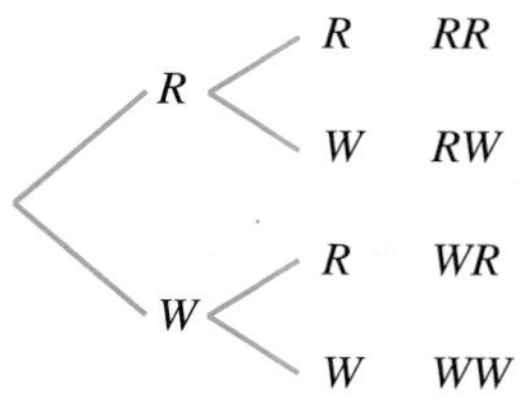

FIGURE 11.3

EXAMPLE 5 Heredity and Probability

The science of heredity uses the theory of probability to determine the likelihood of obtaining flowers of a specified color when crossbreeding. Suppose we represent with letters the genes that determine the color of an offspring flower. For example, a white offspring has genes *WW*, a red offspring has genes *RR*, and a pink offspring has genes *RW* or *WR*. When we crossbreed 2 pink flowers, each plant contributes one of its color genes to each of its offspring. The tree diagram in Figure 11.3 shows the 4 possibilities. Assuming that these possibilities are all equally likely, what are the probabilities of obtaining the following?

(a) A white flower **(b)** A pink flower **(c)** A red flower

Solution

(a) We see from the tree diagram that the probability of obtaining a white flower (*WW*) is $\frac{1}{4}$.

(b) The probability of obtaining a pink flower (*RW* or *WR*) is $\frac{2}{4} = \frac{1}{2}$.

(c) The probability of obtaining a red flower (*RR*) is $\frac{1}{4}$.

EXAMPLE 6 Probabilities with 2 Dice

Two dice are rolled. Find the following:

(a) The sample space for this experiment.

(b) The probability that the sum of the two numbers facing up is 12.

(c) The probability that the sum of the two numbers facing up is 7.

Solution

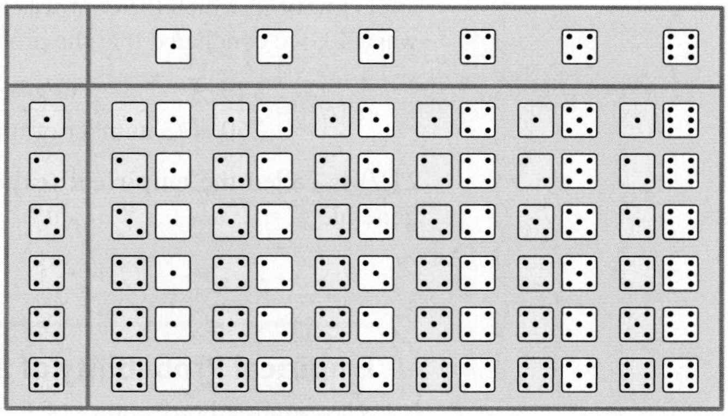

FIGURE 11.4

(a) Figure 11.4 shows the 36 possible outcomes. The sample space for this experiment follows.

$$\begin{Bmatrix} (1, 1) & (1, 2) & (1, 3) & (1, 4) & (1, 5) & (1, 6) \\ (2, 1) & (2, 2) & (2, 3) & (2, 4) & (2, 5) & (2, 6) \\ (3, 1) & (3, 2) & (3, 3) & (3, 4) & (3, 5) & (3, 6) \\ (4, 1) & (4, 2) & (4, 3) & (4, 4) & (4, 5) & (4, 6) \\ (5, 1) & (5, 2) & (5, 3) & (5, 4) & (5, 5) & (5, 6) \\ (6, 1) & (6, 2) & (6, 3) & (6, 4) & (6, 5) & (6, 6) \end{Bmatrix}$$

Note: Since we want the sum of the two numbers, we can think of the sample space as

$$\begin{Bmatrix} 2 & 3 & 4 & 5 & 6 & 7 \\ 3 & 4 & 5 & 6 & 7 & 8 \\ \vdots & \vdots & \vdots & \vdots & \vdots & \vdots \\ 7 & 8 & 9 & 10 & 11 & 12 \end{Bmatrix}$$

(b) The probability that the sum of the two numbers facing up is 12 is $\frac{1}{36}$ because there is only 1 favorable case, (6, 6), and there are 36 possible outcomes, all equally likely.

(c) There are 6 favorable cases to obtain a sum of 7 [(6, 1), (5, 2), (4, 3), (3, 4), (2, 5), and (1, 6)] out of 36 possible. Thus, the probability is $\frac{6}{36} = \frac{1}{6}$.

© I. Bello

EXAMPLE 7 Finding the Probability of 1 King

Find the probability of getting a king when drawing 1 card at random from a standard deck of 52 playing cards. (See the photo in Section 10.1, Example 9.)

Solution

A standard deck of playing cards consists of 4 suits (clubs, diamonds, hearts, and spades) of 13 cards each. The clubs and spades are printed in black; the diamonds and hearts are printed in red. Each suit contains 9 cards numbered from 2 to 10, an ace, and 3 face (picture) cards: a jack, a queen, and a king. Since 4 of the 52 cards are kings, the probability of drawing a king is $\frac{4}{52} = \frac{1}{13}$.

B Empirical Probability

Because the probabilities in the preceding examples are based on the **theory** that the outcomes are equally likely (a balanced coin, fair dice), they are called **theoretical probabilities.** What about the Belgian euro coin (see page 608)? After performing an **experiment** in which the coin was tossed 250 times and the number of heads observed was 140, we concluded that the probability of heads for this coin was

$$P(H) = \frac{140}{250} \begin{matrix} \leftarrow \text{number of times heads occurred} \\ \leftarrow \text{number of times the experiment is performed} \end{matrix}$$

$P(H)$ is called the **empirical (expected** or **experimental) probability** of heads. In general,

Empirical Probability of an Event *E*

The empirical probability of E is

$$P(E) = \frac{\text{number of times } E \text{ has occurred}}{\text{total number of times the experiment is performed}}$$

EXAMPLE 8 Empirical Probability

A spinner has 5 equal-sized sectors colored red, orange, yellow, green, and blue. If in 20 spins we get 3 red, 4 orange, 6 yellow, 4 green, and 3 blue outcomes, what is the empirical probability of

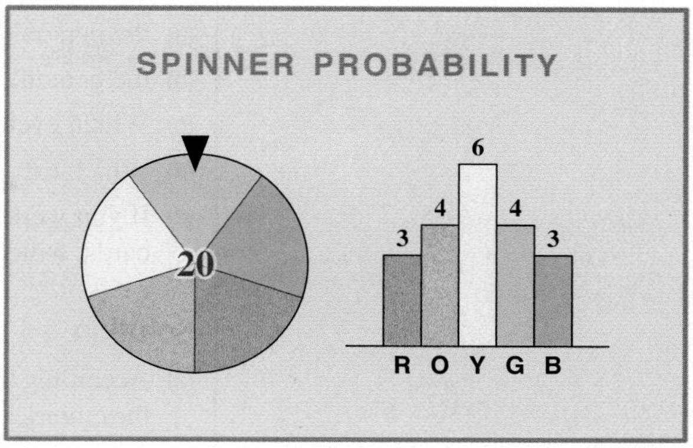

(a) getting orange (O) in 20 spins?

(b) getting yellow (Y) in 20 spins?

(c) getting green (G) in 20 spins?

(d) getting blue (B) in 20 spins?

Solution

(a) $P(O) = \frac{4}{20} = \frac{1}{5} = \frac{\text{orange outcomes}}{\text{total number of spins}}$

(b) $P(Y) = \frac{6}{20} = \frac{3}{10} = \frac{\text{yellow outcomes}}{\text{total number of spins}}$

(c) $P(G) = \frac{4}{20} = \frac{1}{5} = \frac{\text{green outcomes}}{\text{total number of spins}}$

(d) $P(B) = \frac{3}{20} = \frac{\text{blue outcomes}}{\text{total number of spins}}$

You can play a similar game and get the theoretical and empirical probabilities of different numbers of spins at http://Shodor.org/interactivate/Activities/BasicSpinner.

EXAMPLE 9 Applications of Empirical Probability to Credit Card Choices

An online survey of 324 people conducted by Insight Express asked the question, "What is your primary credit card?" The results are shown in the bar graph. (Source: http://insightexpress.com.)

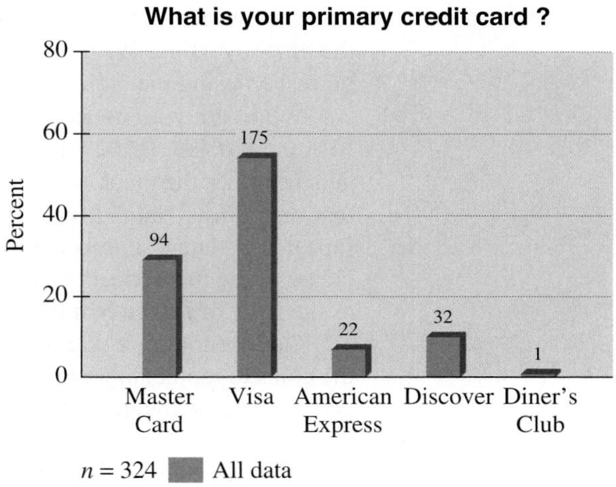

If a person is selected at random from the 324 surveyed, what is the empirical probability that

(a) the person's primary card is MasterCard?
(b) the person's primary card is Visa?
(c) Which event has the highest empirical probability? What is that probability?
(d) Which event has the lowest empirical probability? What is that probability?
(e) If you were the manager of a retail store and you can only accept two types of credit cards, which two cards would you accept?

Solution

(a) According to the graph, 94 out of 324 people use MasterCard as their primary card; thus, the empirical probability of selecting a person whose primary card is a MasterCard is

$$P(MC) = \frac{94}{324} = \frac{47}{162}$$

(b) Similarly, 175 people use Visa as their primary card; thus,

$$P(V) = \frac{175}{324}$$

(c) The event with the highest empirical probability (longest bar in the graph) corresponds to the selection of a person who uses Visa as his or her primary card. The probability is

$$P(V) = \frac{175}{324}$$

(d) The event with the lowest empirical probability (shortest bar in the graph) corresponds to the selection of a person who uses Diner's Club as his or her primary card. The probability of that is

$$P(DC) = \frac{1}{324}$$

(e) Visa and MasterCard (those are the cards that most people in the survey use as their primary card)

For information about credit cards, industry facts, and debt statistics go to http://tinyurl.com/6hdtv6.

The formulas to find the theoretical or empirical probability of an event are very similar. Is there a relationship between the numerical results obtained when using the formulas? Suppose somebody claims to have a "fair" coin. Can we determine if the coin is indeed fair? (Remember the Belgian euro coin!) We can do it by performing an experiment in which we toss the coin 1, 10, 100, 1000, and 10,000 times. But who has the time to do this? We used a "coin-toss simulator" (see Figure 11.5). You can get similar results using the one at http://argyll.epsb.ca.

What do you notice about the decimal value of the **empirical** probabilities (0.7, 0.54, 0.493, 0.5022, and 0.49875)? As the number of tosses gets bigger, the value gets near 0.5, the theoretical probability. This is a good indication (though not a proof) that the coin is "fair." More importantly, it illustrates the fact that as an experiment is repeated a "large" number of times, the empirical probability of an event tends to get closer to the theoretical probability of the event. This principle is appropriately known as the **Law of Large Numbers.**

Oddly enough, if you stand 100 coins on edge on a table and slam the table causing the coins to topple, more than half of the coins will show heads! As the number of tosses gets bigger, the theoretical probability for heads is still higher than 0.5! Try it!*

*From *The Heart of Mathematics* by E. B. Burger and Michael Starbird.

NUMBER OF TOSSES	NUMBER OF HEADS	PROBABILITY	
		EXPERIMENTAL $P(H)$	THEORETICAL $P(H)$
1	1	1	$\frac{1}{2} = 0.5$
10	7	$\frac{7}{10} = 0.7$	$\frac{1}{2} = 0.5$
100	54	$\frac{54}{100} = 0.54$	$\frac{1}{2} = 0.5$
1000	493	$\frac{493}{1000} = 0.493$	$\frac{1}{2} = 0.5$
10,000	5022	$\frac{5022}{10000} = 0.5022$	$\frac{1}{2} = 0.5$
100,000	49,875	$\frac{49875}{100000} = 0.49875$	$\frac{1}{2} = 0.5$

FIGURE 11.5

11.1 EXERCISES

A Probabilities

On a single toss of a die, what is the probability of obtaining the following?

1. The number 5
2. An even number
3. A number greater than 4
4. A number less than 5

A single ball is taken at random from an urn containing 10 balls numbered 1 through 10. What is the probability of obtaining the following?

5. Ball number 8
6. An even-numbered ball
7. A ball different from 5
8. A ball whose number is less than 10
9. A ball numbered 12
10. A ball that is either less than 5 or odd

In problems 11–16, assume that a single card is drawn from a well-shuffled deck of 52 cards. Find the probability of the following:

11. An ace is drawn.
12. The king of spades is drawn.
13. A spade is drawn.
14. One of the face (picture) cards (jack, queen, or king) is drawn.
15. A face (picture) card or a spade is drawn.
[*Hint:* $P(F \text{ or } S) \neq P(F) + P(S)$]
16. A red card or a face (picture) card is drawn.
[*Hint:* $P(R \text{ or } F) \neq P(R) + P(F)$]
17. An executive has to visit 1 of his 5 plants for an inspection. If these plants are numbered 1, 2, 3, 4, and 5, and if he selects the plant he will visit at random, find the probability that he will
a. visit plant number 1.
b. visit an odd-numbered plant.
c. not visit plant number 4.
18. Four fair coins are tossed.
a. Draw a tree diagram to show all the possible outcomes.
b. Find the probability that 2 or more heads come up.
c. Find the probability that exactly 1 head comes up.
19. A disk is divided into 3 equal parts numbered 1, 2, and 3, respectively (see the figure below). After the disk is spun and comes to a stop (assuming it will not stop on a line), a fixed pointer points to 1 of the 3 numbers. Suppose that the disk is spun once. Find the probabilities that the disk stops on
a. the number 3.
b. an even number.

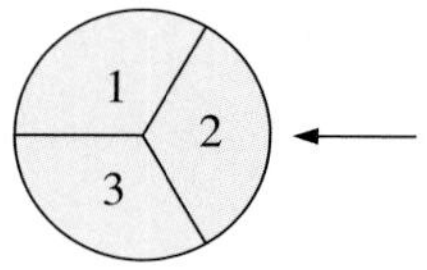

Do you know how many packages are mailed daily? UPS ships nearly 16 million packages every day while Federal Express handles 7 million. Assume that a person can select from 8 delivery services A, B, C, D, E, F, G, and H. Assuming one of the services is to be selected at random to mail a package, do problems 20–23.

20. Find the probability that company A is selected.
21. Find the probability that company G is selected.
22. Find the probability that company C is not used to mail the package.
23. Find the probability that 1 of the first 3 companies is selected.

24. The genetic code of an organism is the self-reproducing record of the protein pattern in that organism. This code is formed by groups of small molecules that can be of 4 kinds: adenine (A), cytosine (C), guanine (G), and thymine (T).

a. Draw a tree diagram to find all possible groups of 2 molecules. *Note:* It is possible for both molecules to be of the same kind.

b. Assume that all the outcomes in part (**a**) are equally likely. Find the probability of obtaining 2 adenine molecules in a row.

c. Find the probability of obtaining a guanine molecule and a cytosine molecule, in that order.

d. Find the probability of obtaining two cytosine molecules in a row.

In problems 25–30, find the probability on a single toss of a pair of dice of obtaining (see Example 6)

25. a sum of 7.

26. a sum of 2.

27. the same number on both dice.

28. different numbers on the two dice.

29. an even number for the sum.

30. an odd number for the sum.

B Empirical Probability

In problems 31–44, write the answers as a fraction in reduced form.

31. A spinner has 4 equal sectors colored yellow, blue, green, and red. If in 100 spins we get 25 blue, 28 red, 24 green, and 23 yellow outcomes, find the empirical probability of

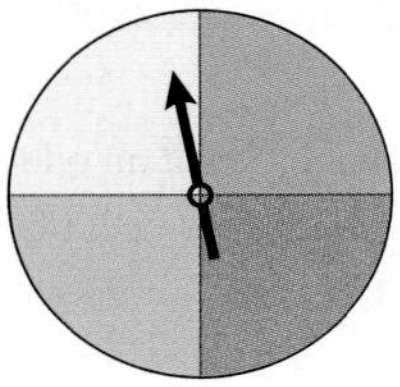

a. getting blue $P(B)$.

b. getting red $P(R)$.

c. getting green $P(G)$.

d. getting yellow $P(Y)$.

e. What are the theoretical probabilities of $P(B)$, $P(R)$, $P(G)$, and $P(Y)$?

f. Which outcome has the same empirical and theoretical probability?

32. A spinner has 6 equal sectors colored yellow, blue, green, white, orange, and red. If in 100 spins we get 15 yellow, 18 blue, 20 green, 13 white, 15 orange and 19 red outcomes, find the empirical probability of

a. getting yellow $P(Y)$.

b. getting blue $P(B)$.

c. getting green $P(G)$.

d. getting white $P(W)$.

e. getting orange $P(O)$.

f. getting red $P(R)$.

33. A spinner has 5 unequal sectors: $\frac{1}{6}$ red, $\frac{1}{9}$ blue, $\frac{5}{18}$ green, $\frac{2}{9}$ white and $\frac{2}{9}$ yellow. In 100 spins we get these results.

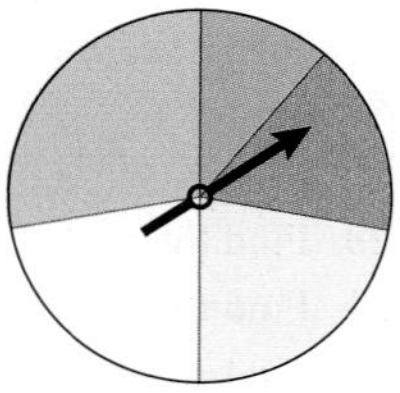

Spins	Red	Blue	Green	White	Yellow
100	24	9	29	20	18

Fill in the blanks with the appropriate reduced fractions.

Outcome	Empirical Probability	Theoretical Probability
a. Red	$P(R) =$	$P(R) =$
b. Blue	$P(B) =$	$P(B) =$
c. Green	$P(G) =$	$P(G) =$
d. White	$P(W) =$	$P(W) =$
e. Yellow	$P(Y) =$	$P(Y) =$

34. When 2 dice are thrown, the 36 possible outcomes are as shown (see Example 6). Now, suppose that 2 dice are thrown 100 times, and the following sums occur the indicated number of times. (A sum of 2 occurs 3 times, a sum of 3 occurs 4 times, and so on.)

Sum 2	Sum 3	Sum 4	Sum 5	Sum 6	Sum 7	Sum 8	Sum 9	Sum 10	Sum 11	Sum 12
3	4	9	12	14	17	15	13	5	6	2

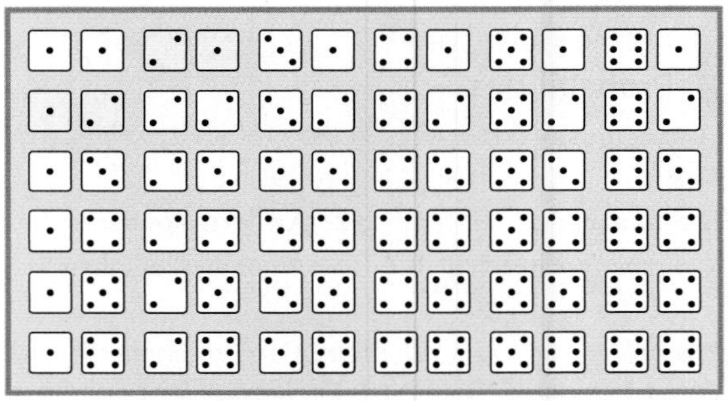

Note that there are 2 ways of getting a sum of 3, (1, 2) and (2, 1), as shown.

Fill in the blanks with the appropriate reduced fractions.

Outcome	Empirical Probability	Theoretical Probability
a. The sum is 2.	$P(\text{sum } 2) =$	$P(\text{sum } 2) =$
b. The sum is 5.	$P(\text{sum } 5) =$	$P(\text{sum } 5) =$
c. The sum is 7.	$P(\text{sum } 7) =$	$P(\text{sum } 7) =$
d. The sum is 9.	$P(\text{sum } 9) =$	$P(\text{sum } 9) =$
e. The sum is 12.	$P(\text{sum } 12) =$	$P(\text{sum } 12) =$
f. The sum is greater than 10.	$P(\text{sum } G\ 10) =$	$P(\text{sum } G\ 10) =$
g. The sum is less than 4.	$P(\text{sum } L\ 4) =$	$P(\text{sum } L\ 4) =$
h. The sum is greater than 2.	$P(\text{sum } G\ 2) =$	$P(\text{sum } G\ 2) =$
i. The sum is less than 12.	$P(L\ 12) =$	$P(L\ 12) =$

35. Suppose that 2 dice are rolled 50 times and that the results are as shown in the bar graph. Find the empirical probability of
   a. $P(11)$, the sum is 11.
   b. $P(7)$, the sum is 7.
   c. $P(O)$, the sum is odd.
   d. $P(\sim O)$, the sum is not odd.
   e. Which outcome has the highest empirical probability?
   f. Which outcome has the lowest empirical probability?
   g. Which 3 outcomes have the same empirical probability?
   h. Do these 3 outcomes have the same empirical and theoretical probability?

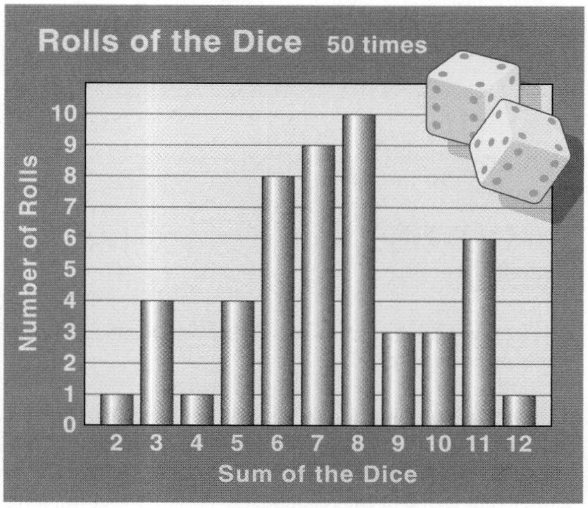

36. This time 2 dice are rolled 36 times, and the results are shown in the bar graph. What is the empirical probability of obtaining
   a. a sum of 2 or 12?
   b. a sum that is odd and greater than 8?
   c. a sum that is even and less than 5?
   d. a sum less than 12?
   e. a sum of 1?
   f. Which of the sums have the same empirical and theoretical probability? (See the sample space for the theoretical probability in Example 6.)

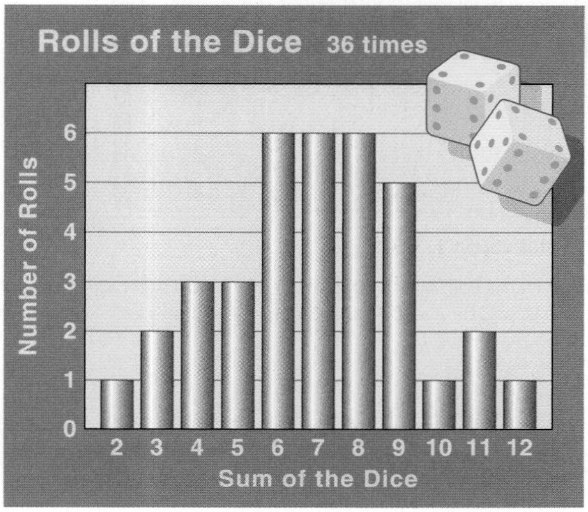

37. An online survey of 502 persons conducted by Insight Express asked the question, "How many credit cards do you own (credit cards only, no debit cards)?" The results are shown in the bar graph. If a person is selected at random from the 502 surveyed, what is the empirical probability that
   a. the person owns no credit cards?
   b. the person owns exactly one credit card?
   c. What is the outcome with the lowest empirical probability?
   d. What is the outcome with the highest empirical probability?
   e. What is the empirical probability that the person owns at least one credit card?

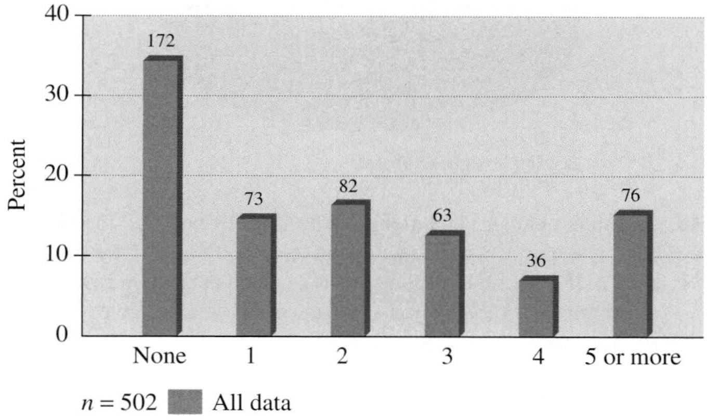

Source: Insight Express.

38. In a recent study conducted by Impulse Research for Oreida, half of 1510 moms with kids at home say that "When they serve French fries, they also cook hamburgers." Find the empirical probability that a mom selected at random from the 1510 French fry–serving moms surveyed also will cook
   a. hot dogs.
   b. sandwiches.
   c. chicken.
   d. fish sticks or sandwiches.

What goes with French fries?

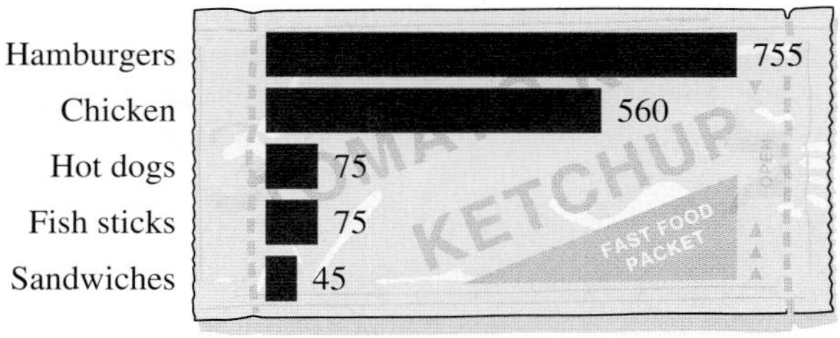

Source: www.theallineed.com/family/05062502.htm.

39. In a survey conducted by Insight Express, 500 Americans were asked if they have been a victim of identity theft. The results were as shown in the graph. If a person is chosen at random from the group of 500 Americans, what is the empirical probability that
   a. the person was a victim of identity theft?
   b. the person was not a victim of identity theft?
   c. the person was not sure if he or she was a victim of identity theft?

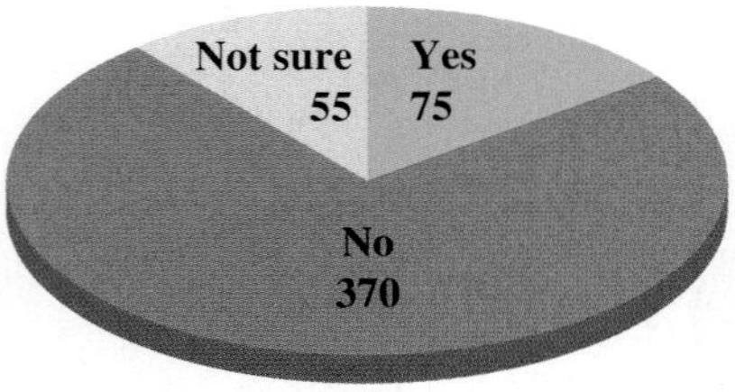

Source: Insight Express.

40. In a statistical survey among adults 18–49 years old, the percent of respondents unwilling to give up certain activities is as shown. If one of the respondents is selected at random, what is the empirical probability that the person would not give up
   a. exercise? b. drinking coffee?
   c. Which activity are the respondents least likely to give up?

Activities We Won't Give Up

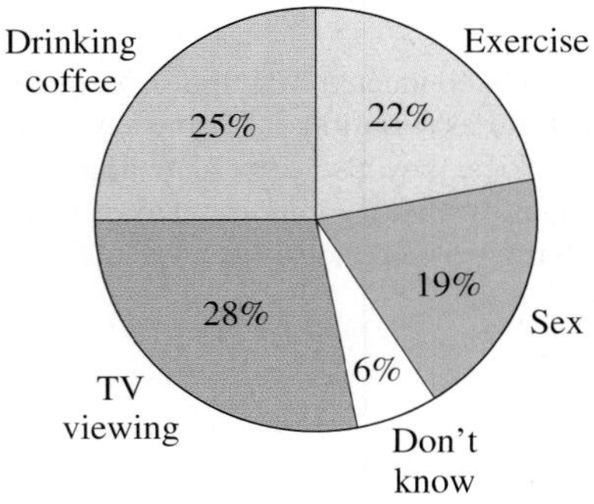

Source: Opinion Research for Dunkin Donuts.

41. Which activity is your favorite thing to do on a flight? A survey of 239 respondents planning to fly revealed their favorite in-flight activity was as shown in the graph. If you are flying with these 239 people and select one of them at random, what is the empirical probability that
   a. he or she will be reading?
   b. he or she will be watching a movie?
   c. he or she will not be watching a movie?
   d. he or she will be sleeping?

Things to Do at 35,000 Feet

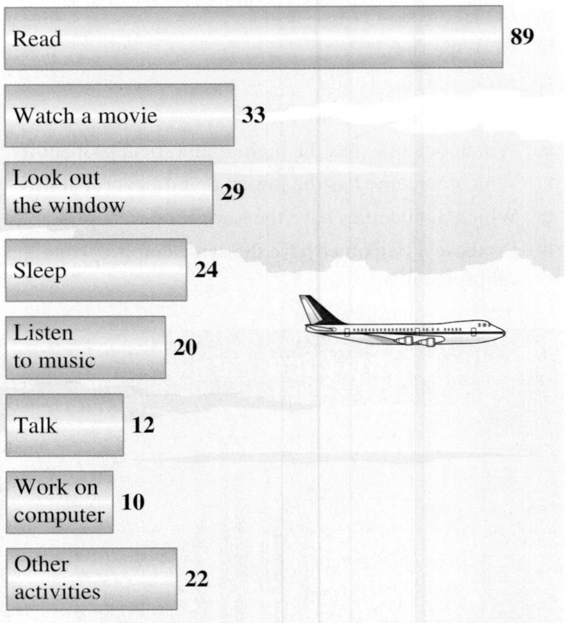

Source: Survey conducted by ORC's CARAVAN Omnibus Services, http://tinyurl.com/9ey32.

42. Are you a conservationist, an environmentalist or "green" (environmentally friendly)? The responses from a recent survey of 1323 adults are as shown. What is the empirical probability that if one of the respondents is selected at random, the respondent is:
   a. A conservationist? b. An environmentalist? c. Green?

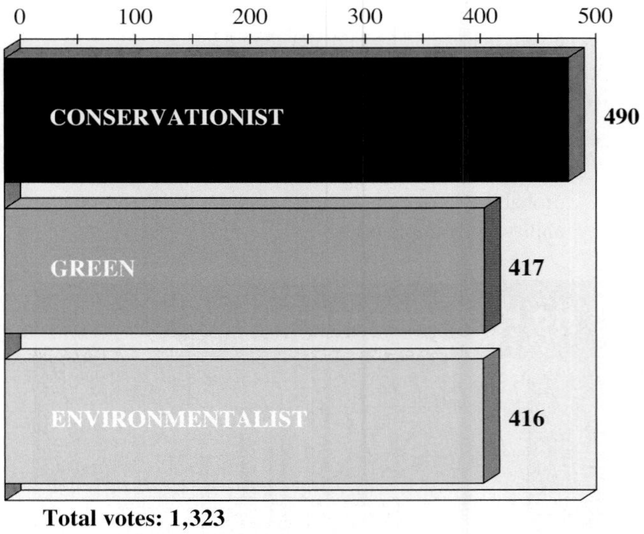

Source: Harris Poll, March 2012, http://www.harrisinteractive.com/vault/Harris%20Poll%2041%20-Green_4.18.12.pdf.

43. Do you know what *regifting* is? It is loosely defined as "giving someone a gift that was originally given to you without telling the recipient the origin of the gift." Now that you know, how often do you engage in regifting? In a survey of 5543 persons, the answers to that question were as follows. If one of the persons is selected at random, what is the empirical probability that the person

 a. very often engages in regifting?

 b. never engages in regifting?

 c. If you get a gift and you assume that the results of the survey apply to that gift, what is the probability that you are getting a regift? Assume that the people who give regifts are the ones who did not answer "Never."

Response to the question: How often do you engage in regifting?

Very often → 140 votes
Every now and then → 817 votes
Not very often → 1755 votes
Never → 2804 votes
I'm not sure → 27 votes
Total number of voters: 5543

Source: Excite.com

44. Do you clip coupons? What do you do with them? A survey conducted by Excite.com asked the question, "How often do you clip and redeem coupons?" The response from 8523 persons is as shown. What is the empirical probability that a person selected at random from those surveyed clips and redeems coupons

 a. rarely? b. very often? c. never?

How often do you clip and redeem coupons?

Very often → 2137 votes
Every now and then → 2386 votes
Rarely → 2443 votes
Never → 1532 votes
I'm not sure → 25 votes
Total number of voters: 8523

Source: Excite.com

45. In a survey conducted on a Friday at Quick Shop Supermarket, it was found that 650 of 850 people who entered the supermarket bought at least 1 item. Find the probability that a person entering the supermarket on a Friday will purchase

 a. at least 1 item. b. no item.

46. Two common sources of nicotine are cigarettes and cigars. Suppose that 35% of the adults in the United States smoke cigarettes but not cigars and 10% smoke both cigarettes and cigars. Find the probability that a randomly selected adult does not smoke cigarettes. (*Hint:* Draw a Venn diagram.)

The following table shows the average number of At Bats (AB) and Home Runs (HR) in the National League (NL), American League (AL) and the actual At Bats and HR for the two Home Run Leaders in each league during the 2010 baseball Season.

	AB	HR
NL	5493	150
AL	5533	158
Jose Bautista	559	54
Albert Pujols	587	42

The quotient **HR/AB** gives the probability that a player hits a home run when he comes to bat. Note that walks, sacrifices, and hit batters are not included.

Source: http://espn.go.com/mlb/stats/team/_/stat/batting/year/2010.

In Problems 47–50, find the probability that:

47. a. A player in the NL hits a home run

 b. A player in the AL hits a home run

48. a. Jose Bautista hits a home run

 b. Albert Pujols hits a home run

49. On the basis of your answers for Problem 47, which players have the highest probability of hitting a home run? Why?

50. On the basis of your answers for Problem 48, which of the two players is more likely to hit a home run when coming to bat? Why?

IN OTHER WORDS

51 Explain, in your own words the difference between experimental and theoretical probability.

52. Explain in your own words what is meant by a probability experiment and the corresponding sample space. Give an example.

53. Explain under what circumstances the probability formula

$$P(E) = \frac{n(E)}{n(\mathcal{U})}$$

does *not* apply. Give an example.

54. Which of the following is an outcome and which an experiment?

 a. Rolling a pair of dice

 b. Choosing two cards from a deck of cards

 c. Landing on black when a roulette wheel is spun

 d. Choosing 2 marbles from a jar

 Explain your answers.

55. Which of the following experiments do not have equally likely outcomes?

 a. Choose a number at random from 1 to 7.

 b. Toss a coin.

 c. Choose a letter at random from the word *MISSISSIPPI.*

 d. Choose a number at random from 1 to 10.

 Explain your answers.

56. Two dice are rolled. One student claims that there are only 3 ways in which a sum of 7 can occur. Explain what is wrong.

USING YOUR KNOWLEDGE

Do you have to have surgery soon? The chances are that you will have no trouble at all! The following table gives the statistics for the numbers of certain operations and the numbers of successes in a recent year. Using these statistics, estimate the probability of

57. a gallbladder operation's being successful.

58. an appendectomy's being successful.

59. a hernia operation's being successful.

Type	Number of Operations	Number of Successes
Gallbladder	472,000	465,300
Appendectomy	784,000	781,000
Hernia	508,000	506,000

COLLABORATIVE LEARNING

Have you read the column "Ask Marilyn" in Parade *magazine? Sometimes a great deal of controversy is generated by the answers given. Here are a couple of instances you can discuss.*

1. You're at a party with 199 other guests when robbers break in and announce they're going to rob one of you. They put 199 blank pieces of paper in a hat, plus one marked "you lose." Each guest must draw a piece, and the person who draws "you lose" gets robbed. The robbers think you're cute, so they offer you the option of drawing first, last, or any time in between. (Source: Reprinted with permission from PARADE and Marilyn vos Savant, copyright © 1999, 1996, and 1992, respectively.)
   a. Marilyn said she would choose to draw first, explaining, "It would make no difference to my chances of losing—any turn is the same—but at least I'd get to leave this party as soon as possible." What is the probability that you pick the paper marked "you lose" if you are the first person who draws? Is the probability different if you are the 100th person who draws? Explain why or why not.
   b. One letter argues for drawing first: "You said any turn is the same, but I believe that would be true only if the partygoers all had to replace the papers they drew before another selection was made. But if they keep the papers (the scenario intended by the question), wouldn't the odds of losing increase as more blanks were drawn? If so, drawing first is best." If 100 blanks have been drawn, the chance that the next slip says "you lose" is indeed 1 in 100. Why doesn't this mean you should draw early if you have the choice?
   c. The first letter mentions the distinction between sampling with replacement and without replacement, which Marilyn does not directly address. Is the answer really the same in both scenarios? Discuss your answer.
   d. When would you choose to make your draw? Why?
2. Here is another problem that appeared in Marilyn's column. Given that a family has 2 children and at least 1 is a boy, what is the probability that the family has 2 boys? (Source: Reprinted with permission from PARADE and Marilyn vos Savant, copyright © 1999, 1996, and 1992, respectively.)
   a. Marilyn said the answer was $\frac{1}{3}$. Can you prove this?
   b. Readers said that it was easy to give stories for which the answer would be $\frac{1}{2}$. Can you make up one such story?

11.2 Counting Techniques and Probability

GETTING STARTED

OBJECTIVES

A. Draw and use a tree diagram to find the probability of an event.
B. Use permutations and combinations to find the probability of an event.
C. Solve applications involving probability.

POKER IMPROBABILITIES

Have you ever played poker? John Scarne's *Complete Guide to Gambling* claims that 95 out of 100 adults have played the game! In his book *Poker Stories* (1896) John F. B. Lillard tells the story of a professional gambler stopping for a beer at a saloon in Butte, Montana. As luck would have it, a poker game was in progress, so the hustler decided to join in and make some money. After playing for a while, the hustler dealt himself four aces.

© Huntington Library/SuperStock

GRAPH IT

To verify the answer (getting four aces), go to the home screen (2nd MODE) and press 48 MATH ◄ 3 1 ENTER ÷ 52 MATH ◄ 3 5 ENTER . The answer is a decimal. How do you know the answer is equivalent to $\frac{1}{54,145}$? Press 1 ÷ 54,145 ENTER . You get the same answer, so you are correct!

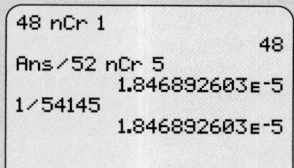

```
48 nCr 1
                    48
Ans/52 nCr 5
      1.846892603E-5
1/54145
      1.846892603E-5
```

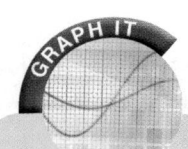

Do you know the probability of getting four aces in a 5-card poker hand? Since there are four aces in a deck, there is only 1 way of getting four aces if the fifth card can be any of the 48 remaining; hence, there are $1 \cdot C(48, 1) = 48$ ways of getting four aces of the $C(52, 5) = 2,598,960$ possible poker hands (see Example 6 for the computation). Thus, the probability of four aces in poker is only

$$\frac{48}{2,598,960} = \frac{1}{54,145}$$

Assured of winning, the hustler made a fair-sized bet that forced every player to drop out except for one old stalwart with gray whiskers and a deadpan poker face. The old cowboy didn't blink; he merely shoved all his chips into the pot and called. The hustler showed his four aces and reached for the pot.

"Not so fast, sonny," said the cowboy, laying down three clubs and two diamonds. Can you find the probability of getting three clubs and two diamonds? It is

$$\frac{C(13, 3) \cdot C(13, 2)}{C(52, 5)} = \frac{22,308}{2,598,960} = \frac{143}{16,660}$$

"What do you mean, not so fast?" the hustler said. "My four aces have a lower probability, and they should win."

"Of course they should—ord'narily," the cowboy said, "But in this town a Lollapalooza beats anythin', and that's what I've got, three clubs and two diamonds, a Lollapalooza."

The hustler knew he had just been out-hustled, but he figured he could still change his "luck." On the next deal, the hustler dealt himself a Lollapalooza and gave four aces to the old cowboy with the gray whiskers. Again, he made a fair-sized bet, and again, the old cowboy stayed while the rest dropped out. The hustler pushed all his chips to the center of the table. The cowboy called again.

"Well," the hustler said grinning, "This time I can't lose. Seems I've got the Lollapalooza!"

But the old cowboy was already bellied-up to the table, raking in the pot. "Sorry, pardner," he said, as the hustler looked on, "Only one Lollapalooza per night!"

In this section you will use the sequential counting principle (SCP), permutations, and combinations to find the probabilities of many events, including different poker hands.

The counting techniques that we studied in Chapter 10 play a key role in many probability problems. We now see how these techniques are used in such problems.

A Using Tree Diagrams

EXAMPLE 1 Stock Probabilities Using a Tree

Have you heard of the witches of Wall Street? These are people who use astrology, tarot cards, or other supernatural means to predict whether a given stock will go up, go down, or stay unchanged. Not being witches, we assume that a stock is equally likely to go up (U), go down (D), or stay unchanged (S). A broker selects two stocks at random from the New York Stock Exchange list.

(a) What is the probability that both stocks go up?

(b) What is the probability that both stocks go down?

(c) What is the probability that one stock goes up and one goes down?

Solution

In order to find the total number of equally likely possibilities for selecting the two stocks, we draw the tree diagram shown in Figure 11.6.

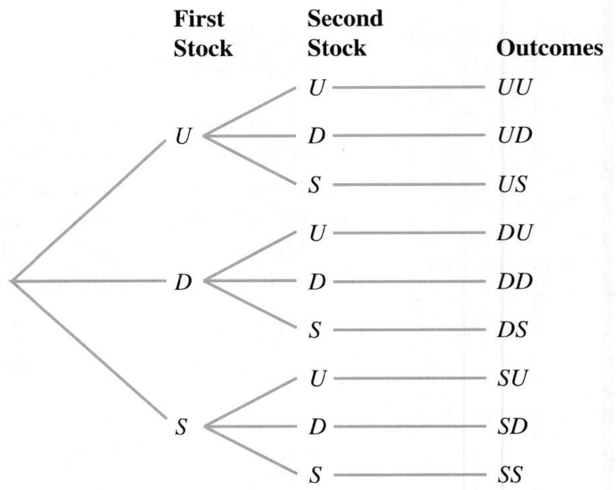

FIGURE 11.6

(a) There is only 1 outcome (UU) out of 9 in which both stocks go up. Thus, the probability that both stocks go up is $\frac{1}{9}$.

(b) There is only 1 outcome (DD) in which both stocks go down, so the probability that both go down is $\frac{1}{9}$.

(c) There are 2 outcomes (UD, DU) in which one stock goes up and one down. Hence, the probability of this event is $\frac{2}{9}$.

(Notice that the tree diagram shows that there are 4 outcomes in which one stock stays unchanged and the other goes either up or down. The probability of this event is thus $\frac{4}{9}$.)

B Using Permutations and Combinations

In many games of chance, probability is used to determine payoffs. For example, a slot machine has three dials with 20 symbols on each dial, as listed in Table 11.2. In the next example we shall find the probability of getting certain arrangements of these symbols on the 3 dials.

Table 11.2

	Dial		
Symbol	1	2	3
Bar	1	3	1
Bell	1	3	3
Cherry	7	7	0
Lemon	3	0	4
Orange	3	6	7
Plum	5	1	5

EXAMPLE 2 Slot Machine Probabilities

Refer to the slot machine described in Table 11.2 to answer the following questions.

(a) What is the probability of getting 3 bars?

(b) What is the probability of getting 3 bells?

(c) What is the probability of getting 3 oranges?

(d) What is the probability of getting 3 plums?

(e) On the basis of your answers to these questions, which outcome should have the greatest payoff and which the least?

Solution

(a) We draw 3 blanks representing the 3 dials.

_____ _____ _____

Dial 1 Dial 2 Dial 3

There are 20 choices for each of the blanks (each dial has 20 symbols), so we enter a 20 on each blank.

$\underline{20}$ $\underline{20}$ $\underline{20}$

The total number of possibilities is $20 \times 20 \times 20 = 8000$. Now, the number of ways to get 3 bars is $1 \times 3 \times 1 = 3$ because the first dial has 1 bar, the second has 3 bars, and the third has 1 bar. Thus,

$$P(3 \text{ bars}) = \frac{\text{number of favorable cases}}{\text{number of possible outcomes}} = \frac{3}{8000}$$

(b) The number of ways of getting 3 bells is $1 \times 3 \times 3 = 9$. Thus,

$$P(3 \text{ bells}) = \frac{9}{8000}$$

(c) The number of ways of getting 3 oranges is $3 \times 6 \times 7 = 126$. Thus,

$$P(3 \text{ oranges}) = \frac{126}{8000} = \frac{63}{4000}$$

(d) The number of ways of getting 3 plums is $5 \times 1 \times 5 = 25$. Thus,

$$P(3 \text{ plums}) = \frac{25}{8000} = \frac{1}{320}$$

(e) Since 3 bars is the outcome with the lowest probability and 3 oranges is the outcome with the highest probability, the greatest payoff should be for 3 bars and the least for 3 oranges. (This is how payoffs are actually determined.)

EXAMPLE 3 Probability of Being in a Committee

Suppose you are a member of a committee of 10 people, of whom 2 are to be chosen for a particular task. If these are selected by drawing names out of a hat, what is the probability that you will be 1 of the 2 selected?

Note that if you draw the names of A and B out of the hat in that order, it is not the same as drawing B and A, so the order is important and we will use **permutations.**

Solution

It is easier to first calculate the probability that you will *not* be selected. Since there are 9 people not including you, there are $P(9, 2)$ ways of selecting 2 *not* including you. Also there are $P(10, 2)$ ways of selecting 2 people from the entire 10. Hence, the probability P' that you will *not* be selected is

$$P' = \frac{P(9, 2)}{P(10, 2)} = \frac{9 \times 8}{10 \times 9} = \frac{4}{5}$$

So the probability that you *will* be selected is

$$P = 1 - P' = 1 - \frac{4}{5} = \frac{1}{5}$$

The next example deals with a problem involving ordinary playing cards. Note that in solving part (a), you can use combinations, permutations, or the SCP. The important thing is to be **consistent** in the computation.

EXAMPLE 4 Probabilities When 2 Cards Are Chosen

Two cards are drawn in succession and without replacement from an ordinary deck of 52 cards. Find the probability that

(a) the cards are both aces. (b) an ace and a king, in that order, are drawn.

Solution

(a) Here, the **order is not important** because we are simply interested in getting 2 aces. We can find this probability by using **combinations.** The number of ways to draw 2 aces is $C(4, 2)$ because there are 4 aces and we want a combination of any 2 of them. The number of combinations of 2 cards picked from the deck of 52 cards is $C(52, 2)$. Thus, the probability of both cards being aces is

$$\frac{C(4, 2)}{C(52, 2)} = \frac{4 \cdot 3}{52 \cdot 51} = \frac{1}{221}$$

(b) In this part of the problem, we want to consider the **order** in which the 2 cards are drawn, so we use **permutations.** The number of ways of selecting an ace is $P(4, 1)$ and the number of ways of selecting a king is $P(4, 1)$. By the SCP, the number of ways of doing these two things in succession is $P(4, 1)P(4, 1)$. The total number of ways of drawing 2 cards is $P(52, 2)$, so the probability of drawing an ace and a king, in that order, is

$$\frac{P(4, 1)P(4, 1)}{P(52, 2)} = \frac{4 \cdot 4}{52 \cdot 51} = \frac{4}{663}$$

EXAMPLE 5 Not Picking Aces, Kings, Queens, or Jacks

Suppose we take all the cards from one suit—say, hearts—out of a standard deck of 52 cards. Shuffle the 13 hearts and then draw 3 of them. What is the probability that none of the 3 will be an ace, king, queen, or jack?

Solution

Here the **order does not matter,** so we use **combinations.** The number of combinations of 13 things taken 3 at a time is $C(13, 3)$. There are 9 cards not including the ace, king, queen, or jack, and the number of combinations of these taken 3 at a time is $C(9, 3)$. Thus, the required probability is

$$\frac{C(9, 3)}{C(13, 3)} = \frac{\dfrac{9 \cdot 8 \cdot 7 \cdot 6!}{3!\,6!}}{\dfrac{13 \cdot 12 \cdot 11 \cdot 10!}{3!\,10!}} = \frac{9 \cdot 8 \cdot 7}{13 \cdot 12 \cdot 11} = \frac{42}{143}$$

EXAMPLE 6 Probability of 4 Aces and 1 King

A poker hand consists of 5 cards. What is the probability of getting a hand of 4 aces and 1 king?

Solution

Here, the **order is not to be considered** because any order of getting the aces and the king will result in a hand that consists of 4 aces and 1 king. Now, the number of ways in which 4 aces can be selected is $C(4, 4)$, and the number of ways in which 1 king can be selected is $C(4, 1)$. Hence, by the SCP, the number of ways of getting 4 aces and

1 king is $C(4, 4)C(4, 1)$. Furthermore, the total number of 5-card hands is $C(52, 5)$, so the required probability is

$$\frac{C(4, 4)C(4, 1)}{C(52, 5)} = \frac{1 \cdot 4}{C(52, 5)}$$

Since

$$C(52, 5) = \frac{52 \cdot 51 \cdot 50 \cdot 49 \cdot 48}{5 \cdot 4 \cdot 3 \cdot 2 \cdot 1} = 2{,}598{,}960$$

the probability of getting 4 aces and 1 king is

$$\frac{C(4, 4)C(4, 1)}{C(52, 5)} = \frac{4}{2{,}598{,}960} = \frac{1}{649{,}740}$$

which is very small indeed!

EXAMPLE 7 Probability of 1 Ace and No Face Card

Five cards are drawn from a standard deck. What is the probability of getting exactly 1 ace and no face cards?

Solution

Since there are 4 aces, the number of ways of getting exactly 1 ace is $C(4, 1)$. There are 36 cards that are not aces or face cards. The number of ways of getting 4 of these is $C(36, 4)$. Thus, the number of ways of getting 1 ace and 4 of the 36 cards is, by the SCP,

$$C(4, 1)C(36, 4)$$

The total number of ways that 5 cards can be drawn from the entire deck is $C(52, 5)$, so the required probability is

$$\frac{C(4, 1)C(36, 4)}{C(52, 5)} = \frac{4 \cdot 36 \cdot 35 \cdot 34 \cdot 33}{4 \cdot 3 \cdot 2 \cdot 1 \cdot C(52, 5)}$$

$$= \frac{235{,}620}{2{,}598{,}960} \quad \text{(See Example 6 to get the denominator.)}$$

$$= \frac{33}{364}$$

Do we always use the SCP and/or permutations and/or combinations in solving a probability problem? Not necessarily; sometimes it is easier just to look at the possible outcomes or to reason the problem out directly. This is illustrated in the next example.

EXAMPLE 8 Stuffing Envelopes at Random

A careless clerk was supposed to mail 3 bills to 3 customers. He addressed 3 envelopes but absent mindedly paid no attention to which bill he put in which envelope.

(a) What is the probability that exactly 1 of the customers received the proper bill?

(b) What is the probability that exactly 2 of the customers received the proper bills?

Solution

In Table 11.3, the headings C_1, C_2, and C_3 represent the customers, and the numbers 1, 2, and 3 below represent the bills for the customers with the corresponding subscripts. Thus, the rows represent the possible outcomes.

Table 11.3

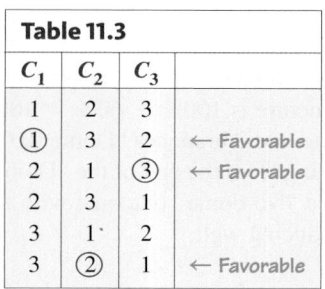

C_1	C_2	C_3	
1	2	3	
(1)	3	2	← Favorable
2	1	(3)	← Favorable
2	3	1	
3	1	2	
3	(2)	1	← Favorable

(a) Table 11.3 shows that there are 6 possibilities and 3 cases in which exactly 1 (that is, 1 and only 1) of the customers received the proper bill. Therefore, the required probability is $P = \frac{3}{6} = \frac{1}{2}$.

(b) Here the probability is 0 because if 2 customers received their proper bills, then the third one did also. This means that there is no case in which 2 and only 2 received the proper bills.

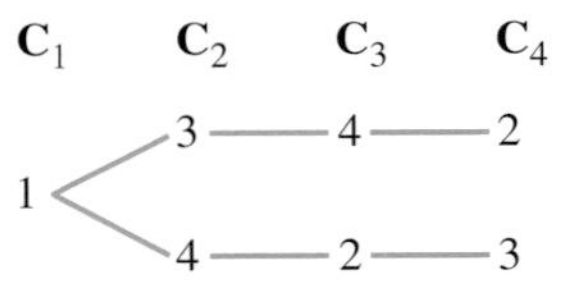

FIGURE 11.7

In Example 8, if there were 4 customers and 4 bills, then there would be a total of $P(4, 4) = 24$ cases in all. (This is just the number of ways in which the bills could be permuted.) You can see that it would be quite cumbersome to list all these cases. Instead, draw a tree showing the possible favorable cases if 1 customer, C_1, receives the proper bill (see Figure 11.7). This shows the 1 (representing the bill for C_1) under C_1; then C_2 can have only the 3 or the 4. If C_2 has the 3, then C_3 must have the 4 and C_4 the 2. (Otherwise, more than 1 customer would receive the proper bill.) If C_2 has the 4, then C_3 must have the 2 and C_4 the 3. These are the only 2 favorable cases possible if C_1 gets bill 1. The same argument holds if one of the other customers gets the proper bill; there are just 2 ways in which none of the other customers gets a proper bill. Since there are 4 customers, the SCP shows that there are only $4 \times 2 = 8$ favorable cases. Thus, the probability that exactly 1 of the customers gets the proper bill is $\frac{8}{24} = \frac{1}{3}$.

C Applications

EXAMPLE 9 An Application to Oil Drilling

An oil company is considering drilling an exploratory oil well. If the rocks under the drilling site are characterized by what geologists call a "dome" structure, the chances of finding oil are 60%. The well can be **dry,** a **low** producer, or a **high** producer of oil. The probabilities for these outcomes are given in the table.

Production	Dome (60%)	No Dome (40%)
Dry	0.6	0.85
Low producer	0.25	0.125
High producer	0.15	0.025

Source: Robert T. Clemen and Terry Reilly, *Making Hard Decisions with Decisions Tools Suite.* (Pacific Grove, CA: Brooks Cole Publishing, 2004).

(a) Draw a tree diagram for the data given in the table.

(b) What is the probability that the well is dry?

Solution

(a) Since the probability of finding oil when there is a dome structure is 60%, the probability of finding oil when there is **no** dome structure is $100\% - 60\% = 40\%$. We draw the tree diagram in Figure 11.8 and label the first 2 branches "Dome (0.6)" and "No dome (0.4)." We then label 3 branches starting from the end of the "Dome" outcome and 3 branches starting from the end of the "No dome" outcome with the probabilities for a dry, low-producing, and high-producing well.

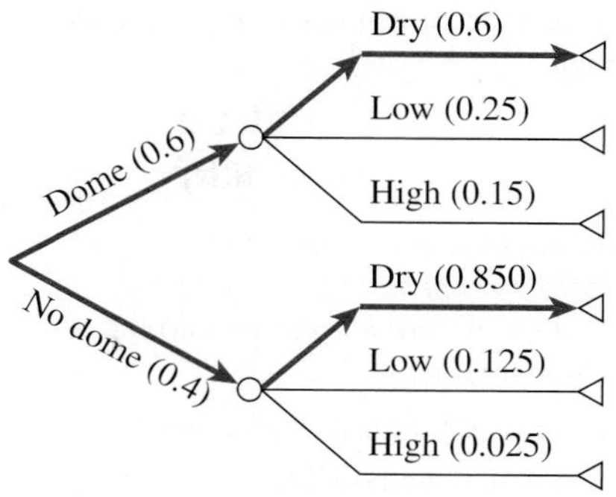

FIGURE 11.8 The total probability for a dry well is $0.6 \times 0.6 + 0.4 \times 0.850 = 0.70$.

(b) To find the probability that the well is dry, we start at the branch in Figure 11.8 labeled "Dome (0.6)" and continue through the branch labeled "Dry (0.6)." The probability of that path is $0.6 \times 0.6 = 0.36$. The other possibility for a dry well is to start at the branch labeled "No dome (0.4)" and continue through the branch labeled Dry (0.850). The probability for that branch is $0.4 \times 0.850 = 0.34$. The total probability for a dry well is the sum of the two probabilities, $0.36 + 0.34 = 0.70$.

11.2 EXERCISES

A Using Tree Diagrams

1. A man has 3 pairs of shoes, 2 suits, and 3 shirts. If he picks a pair of shoes, a suit, and a shirt at random, what is the probability that he picks his favorite shoes, suit, and shirt?

2. At the end of a meal in a restaurant, a person wants to have pie à la mode (pie topped with ice cream) for dessert. There are 5 flavors of ice cream—chocolate, vanilla, strawberry, peach, and coffee—and there are 2 kinds of pie—apple and cherry. If the waiter picks the pie and ice cream at random, what is the probability that the person will get apple pie with vanilla ice cream?

3. A fair die is rolled 3 times in succession. What is the probability that even numbers are rolled all 3 times?

B Using Permutations and Combinations

4. Jim belongs to a club of 40 members. A committee of 3 is to be selected at random from the 40 members. Find the probability that Jim is 1 of the 3 selected members.

5. Helen and Patty both belong to a club of 25 members. A committee of 4 is to be selected at random from the 25 members. Find the probability that both Helen and Patty will be selected.

6. Two cards are drawn at random, in succession and without replacement, from a deck of 52 cards.

a. Find the number of ways in which the ace of spades and a king can be selected, in that order.

b. What is the probability of drawing the ace of spades and a king, in that order?

7. Mr. C. Nile and Mr. D. Mented agreed to meet at 8 P.M. in one of the Spanish restaurants in Ybor City. They were both punctual, and they both remembered the date agreed on. Unfortunately, they forgot to specify the name of the restaurant. If there are 5 Spanish restaurants in Ybor City, and the 2 men each go to 1 of these, find the probability that they

a. meet each other. **b.** miss each other.

8. P.U. University offers 100 courses, 25 of which are mathematics. All these courses are available each hour, and a counselor randomly selects 4 different courses for a student. Find the probability that the selection will not include a mathematics course. (Do not simplify your answer.)

9. A piggy bank contains 2 quarters, 3 nickels, and 2 dimes. A person takes 2 coins at random from this bank. Label the coins $Q_1, Q_2, N_1, N_2, N_3, D_1$, and D_2 so that they can all be regarded as different. Then find the probabilities that the values of the 2 coins selected are the following:

a. 35¢ **b.** 50¢

10. A committee of 2 is chosen at random from a population of 5 men and 6 women. What is the probability that the committee will consist of 1 man and 1 woman?

In problems 11–15, assume that 2 cards are drawn in succession and without replacement from an ordinary deck of 52 cards. Find the probability that

11. 2 kings are drawn.

12. 2 spades are drawn.

13. 1 spade and 1 king other than the king of spades (in that order) are drawn.

14. 1 spade and 1 king other than the king of spades (not necessarily in that order) are drawn.
15. 2 red cards are drawn.

In problems 16 and 17, assume that there is an urn containing five \$50 bills, four \$20 bills, three \$10 bills, two \$5 bills, and one \$1 bill and that the bills all have different serial numbers so that they can be distinguished from each other. A person reaches into the urn and withdraws one bill and then another.

16. a. In how many ways can two \$20 bills be withdrawn?
    b. How many different outcomes are possible?
    c. What is the probability of selecting two \$20 bills?
17. a. In how many ways can a \$50 bill and a \$10 bill be selected in that order?
    b. What is the probability of selecting a \$50 bill and a \$10 bill in that order?
    c. What is the probability of selecting two bills, one of which is a \$50 bill and the other a \$10 bill?
18. If 2% of the auto tires manufactured by a company are defective and 2 tires are randomly selected from an entire week's production, find the probability that neither is defective.
19. In problem 18, find the probability that at least 1 of the 2 selected tires is defective.
20. A box contains 10 CD-R disks and 2 are defective. If 2 disks are randomly selected from the box, find the probability that both are defective.
21. According to the National Collegiate Athletic Association (NCAA), about 6% of all high school senior boys playing interscholastic football will go on to play football at a NCAA member institution and eight in 10,000 of high school senior boys playing interscholastic football will eventually be drafted by an NFL team. Find the probability that a randomly selected high school senior interscholastic football player will play both football at an NCAA member institution and be drafted by an NFL team.
22. An urn contains 5 white balls and 3 black balls. Two balls are drawn at random from this urn. Find the probability that
    a. both balls are white.
    b. both balls are black.
    c. 1 ball is white and the other is black.
23. In this problem, do not simplify your answers. What is the probability that a 5-card poker hand will contain the following?
    a. 2 kings, 2 aces, and 1 other card
    b. 3 kings and 2 aces
24. 70 of the 315 houses that Habitat for Humanity built in New Orleans since Hurricane Katrina hit the city have tested positive for corrosion problems caused by defective Chinese drywall. If 3 houses are selected at random, what is the probability that 2 test positive for corrosion problems and 1 does not? http://tinyurl.com/3ljlq3a
25. The crew of the last shuttle mission consisted of 3 men and 1 woman. If 2 of them are selected at random for a space walk, what is the probability that the woman is included?
26. Low-calorie food is required to contain no more than 40 calories per serving. The Food and Drug Administration (FDA) suspects that a company is marketing illegally labeled low-calorie food. If an inspector selects 3 cans at random from a shelf holding 10 cans (3 legally labeled and 7 illegally labeled), what are the probabilities that the following are legally labeled?
    a. All 3 cans selected
    b. Only 2 of the 3 cans selected

In problems 27–32 a poker hand consisting of 5 cards is drawn. Find the probability of obtaining

27. a royal flush (ten, jack, queen, king, ace of the same suit).
28. a straight flush (5 consecutive cards of the same suit).
29. 4 of a kind (4 cards of the same face value).
30. a full house (one pair and one triple of the same face value).
31. a flush (5 cards of the same suit but not a straight or royal flush).
32. a straight (5 consecutive cards, not all of the same suit).
33. Referring to Example 9, what is the probability of drilling a low-producing well?
34. Referring to Example 9, what is the probability of drilling a high-producing well?
35. On the basis of the answers to Example 9 and problems 33 and 34, what is the outcome with the highest probability? Explain.

C Applications

Problems 36–40 refer to the following table showing the death penalty and racial status distribution for 326 convicted murderers.

Death Penalty	White	Black
Yes	19	17
No	141	149
Total	160	166

Source: M. Radelet, "Racial Characteristics of the Death Penalty," *American Sociological Review* 46: 918–927.

36. a. Start a tree diagram similar to that in Example 9 with two branches labeled white and black.
    b. What is the probability that a person selected at random from the 326 convicts is white? Write the answer on the appropriate branch.
    c. What is the probability that a person selected at random from the 326 convicts is black? Write the answer on the appropriate branch.

37. The first set of branches for the tree corresponding to the table were labeled "White" and "Black." The second set of branches should be labeled "Yes" and "No" for whites and "Yes" and "No" for blacks.

a. What is the probability that a white convict received the death penalty? Write the answer on the appropriate branch.

b. What is the probability that a black convict received the death penalty? Write the answer on the appropriate branch.

38. Using a tree diagram, find the probability that a convict (either race) did not receive the death penalty.

39. Using the table, find the probability that a convict (either race) did not receive the death penalty.

40. Is your answer to problem 39 the same as your answer to problem 38? Explain why or why not.

IN OTHER WORDS

Three people, a mathematician, a statistician, and a fool, observed 10 tosses of a coin. Heads came up 10 times. Do you agree with statements 41–43? Explain why or why not.

41. Tails are "due." Bet on tails.

42. Heads are "hot." Bet on heads.

43. It is a random fluke. Don't bet.

44. Explain which strategy you think

a. the statistician will pick.

b. the mathematician will pick.

c. the fool will pick.

If you do this correctly, you will answer the classic riddle, "How do you tell the difference between a mathematician, a statistician, and a fool?"

USING YOUR KNOWLEDGE

Dr. Benjamin Spock, a famous pediatrician, was accused of violating the Selective Service Act by encouraging resistance to the Vietnam War. In his trial, the defense challenged the legality of the method used to select the jury. In the Boston District Court, jurors are selected in three stages, as follows:

45. The clerk of the court selects 300 names at random from the Boston City Directory. If the directory lists 76,000 names (40,000 women and 36,000 men), what is the probability of selecting 150 men and 150 women? (Do not simplify.)

46. The 300 names are placed in a box, and the names of 30 potential jurors are drawn. If the names in the box correspond to 160 women and 140 men, find the probability that 15 men and 15 women are selected. (Do not simplify.)

47. The subgroup of 30 is called a *venire*. From the venire, 12 jurors are selected. If the venire consists of 16 women and 14 men, what is the probability that the final jury consists of 6 men and 6 women? (Do not simplify.)

By the way, it was shown that the Spock trial judge selected only about 14.6% women, whereas his colleagues selected about 29% women. This showed that the trial judge systematically reduced the proportion of women and had not selected a jury legally.

CALCULATOR CORNER

You can use a calculator to compute expressions such as $C(52, 5)$ *in Example 6. To do this, enter*

[52] [a] [5] [b] [2nd] [$_nC_r$]

COLLABORATIVE LEARNING

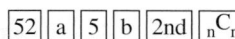

Have you heard of the birthday problem? Here it is. Discuss or prove why this is so: In a group of 23 people, at least 2 *have the same birthday with probability higher than* $\frac{1}{2}$. *Divide into groups and discuss this problem.* (Hint: *It is easier to find the answer to the related question: In a group of 23 people, what is the probability that all of them have* different *birthdays?)*

1. Suppose your group consists of 5 students. What is the probability that all 5 students have different birthdays? Assume there are 365 days in a year. *Hint:* The birthday for the first student falls on any one of the 365 days in the year, with probability $\frac{365}{365}$, so the probability that the second student has a different birthday is $\frac{364}{365}$. For the third student, the probability is $\frac{363}{365}$, for the fourth $\frac{362}{365}$, and for the fifth $\frac{361}{365}$. Thus, the probability that all 5 students have different birthdays is

$$\frac{365}{365} \times \frac{364}{365} \times \frac{363}{365} \times \frac{362}{365} \times \frac{361}{365} \approx 0.97$$

Check this!

2. If you follow the pattern in problem 1, the probability that in a group consisting of 10 students all have different birthdays is

$$\frac{365}{365} \times \frac{364}{365} \times \frac{363}{365} \times \frac{362}{365} \times \cdots \times \frac{365 - 10 + 1}{365}$$

What is the probability that in a group of 23 students all have different birthdays?

3. If the probability that all 23 students in the group of problem 2 have different birthdays is q, the probability that at least 2 have the same birthday is $1 - q$. Find this probability.

4. Is the answer to problem 3 more than 50%?

11.3 Computation of Probabilities

GETTING STARTED

OBJECTIVE

Use the 4 properties given in the text to solve probability problems.

ADVERTISING AND PROBABILITY

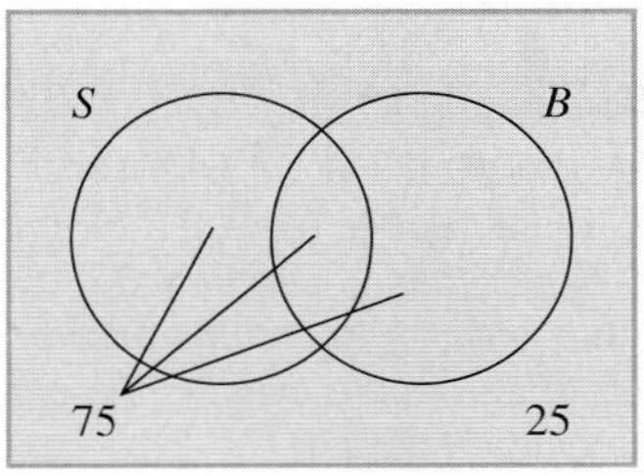

(a)

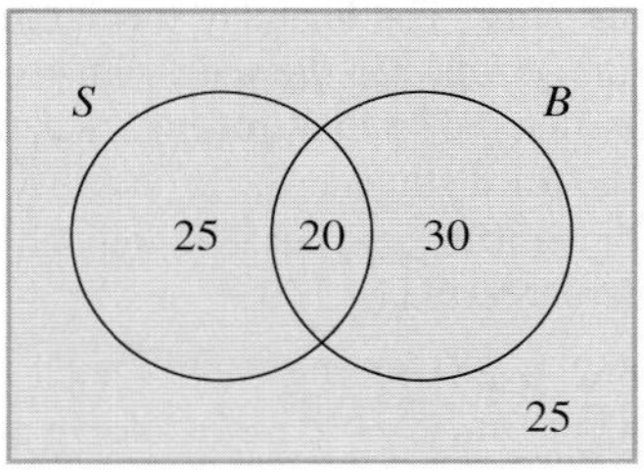

(b)

FIGURE 11.9

Does advertising influence a consumer's decision when buying a car? A car dealership conducted a survey of people inquiring about a new model car. Of the people surveyed, 45% had seen an advertisement for the car in the paper, 50% eventually bought one of these cars, and 25% had neither seen the ad nor bought a car. What is the probability that a person selected at random from the survey read the ad *and* bought a car?

At this time, we are unable to answer this question. However, let us assume that 100 persons were surveyed. The information from the survey is as follows:

45 saw the ad (S).
50 bought a car (B).
25 neither saw the ad nor bought a car ($S' \cap B'$).

We can draw a Venn diagram, as in Figure 11.9(a), using the sets S and B. Since 25 persons neither saw the ad nor bought a car, we place 25 persons outside both circles. This means that we must have 75 persons in $S \cup B$. Since S has 45 persons and B has 50 ($45 + 50 = 95$), there must be 20 persons in $S \cap B$, as shown in Figure 11.9(b). Thus, the number of persons who saw the ad *and* bought a car is 20.

If we generalize this idea to probability (see Example 3), the probability that a person selected at random read the ad and bought a car is $\frac{20}{100} = \frac{1}{5}$. Compare this with the probability that a person bought a car without even seeing the ad. Did seeing the ad make a lot of difference?

In this section we will formalize some of the ideas we have used. What do we think the probability for an impossible event should be? What about the probability of an event that is certain to occur? The answers to these questions are given in properties 1 and 2 that follow. The letters E, A, and B stand for events in a sample space $\mathcal{U}$.

Property 1 (Impossible Events)

An impossible event E has a probability of 0.

$$P(E) = 0 \quad \text{if and only if} \quad E = \varnothing \tag{1}$$

Property 1 states that an **impossible event** has a probability 0. For example, the probability of winning the lottery in Alabama is 0 because there is no lottery in Alabama and 6 other states. Do you know which states?

EXAMPLE 1 Impossible Probabilities

A die is rolled. What is the probability that a 7 comes up?

Solution

The sample space for this experiment is

$$\mathcal{U} = \{1, 2, 3, 4, 5, 6\}$$

so it is impossible for a 7 to be rolled. Thus, $P(7) = 0$.

Property 2 (Range of Probability)

The probability of any event E is a number between 0 and 1, inclusive.

$$0 \leq P(E) \leq 1 \tag{2}$$

Property 2 says that the probability of any event is a number between 0 and 1, inclusive. This follows because the number of favorable cases cannot be less than 0 or more than the total number of possible cases. Thus, $P(E) = 1$ means that the event E is *certain* to occur (a "sure thing"). For example, if you buy 22,957,480 distinct tickets for the Florida Lottery, one of your tickets is certain to be the winning ticket; it is a "sure thing" since there are only 22,957,480 combinations of numbers possible. Of course, you may have to share the jackpot with somebody who plays the lottery every week and happens to also have picked the winning number!

Property 3 (Probabilities with *Or*)

The probability of A or B is given by

$$P(A \cup B) = P(A) + P(B) - P(A \cap B) \tag{3}$$

Property 3 says that the probability of event A *or* B is the probability of event A plus the probability of event B, decreased by the probability of events A *and* B. Note the key words *or* and *and*. The subtraction of $P(A \cap B)$ is to ensure that events belonging to both A *and* B are not counted twice.

EXAMPLE 2 Tossing Two Coins

A penny and a nickel are tossed. What is the probability that one *or* the other of the coins will turn up heads?

Solution

If we use subscripts p and n for penny and nickel, respectively, we can list the possible cases as follows: (H_p, H_n), (H_p, T_n), (T_p, H_n), and (T_p, T_n). Since there are 3 favorable cases out of the 4 possible,

$$P(H_p \cup H_n) = \tfrac{3}{4}$$

We can check that equation (3) gives

$$\begin{aligned} P(H_p \cup H_n) &= P(H_p) + P(H_n) - P(H_p \cap H_n) \\ &= \tfrac{1}{2} + \tfrac{1}{2} - \tfrac{1}{4} = \tfrac{3}{4} \end{aligned}$$

as before.

EXAMPLE 3 Probability of an Ace or a Red Card

A card is drawn from a deck of 52 playing cards. Find the probability that the card is either an ace or a red card.

Solution

Let A be the event in which the card drawn is an ace, and let R be the event in which the card drawn is red. Then by equation (3),

$$P(A \cup R) = P(A) + P(R) - P(A \cap R)$$

Now, $P(A) = \frac{4}{52}$, $P(R) = \frac{26}{52}$, and $P(A \cap R) = \frac{2}{52}$, so

$$P(A \cup R) = \frac{4}{52} + \frac{26}{52} - \frac{2}{52} = \frac{7}{13}$$

Equation (3), in case all outcomes in the sample space are equally likely, is derived from the fact that

$$P(E) = \frac{n(E)}{n(\mathcal{U})}$$

Hence,

$$\begin{aligned} P(A \cup B) &= \frac{n(A \cup B)}{n(\mathcal{U})} = \frac{n(A) + n(B) - n(A \cap B)}{n(\mathcal{U})} \\ &= \frac{n(A)}{n(\mathcal{U})} + \frac{n(B)}{n(\mathcal{U})} - \frac{n(A \cap B)}{n(\mathcal{U})} \\ &= P(A) + P(B) - P(A \cap B) \end{aligned}$$

If the outcomes are not equally likely, then the same result follows by replacing $n(E)$ and $n(\mathcal{U})$ by $w(E)$ and $w(\mathcal{U})$, where these mean the sum of the weights of the outcomes in E and $\mathcal{U}$, respectively.

EXAMPLE 4 Probability of a Red or Yellow Ball

An urn contains 5 red, 2 black, and 3 yellow balls. Find the probability that a ball selected at random from the urn will be red or yellow.

Solution

By equation (3),

$$\begin{aligned} P(R \cup Y) &= P(R) + P(Y) - P(R \cap Y) \\ &= \frac{5}{10} + \frac{3}{10} - 0 = \frac{4}{5} \end{aligned}$$

In Example 4, notice that $P(R \cap Y) = 0$. This means the events of selecting a red ball and selecting a yellow ball cannot occur simultaneously, that is, $R \cap Y = \varnothing$. We say that A and B are **mutually exclusive** if $A \cap B = \varnothing$. For any two mutually exclusive events A and B, it follows that $P(A \cap B) = 0$, and property 3 becomes

Property 4 (Mutually Exclusive Events)

For any two mutually exclusive events A and B,

$$P(A \cup B) = P(A) + P(B); \quad \text{that is,} \quad P(A \cap B) = 0 \qquad (4)$$

EXAMPLE 5 Determining Mutually Exclusive Events

Why do you work? Is it because you need the money (N) or because you want to work (W) or both? A Pew Research study concluded that the answer depends on your age! Forty-nine percent of persons in the 16–64 age group worked because they needed the money (N), 20% because they wanted to work (W) and 31% because of both N and W.

(a) If a person aged 16–64 is selected at random, find $P(N \cup W)$, the probability that the person works because they need the money (N) or want to work (W).

(b) Are N and W mutually exclusive?

To see how opinions depend on age, go to http://pewresearch.org/pubs/1330/american-work-force-is-graying.

Solution

(a) According to equation (3), substituting $P(N) = 49\%$, $P(W) = 20\%$ and $P(N \cap W) = 31\%$

$$P(N \cup W) = P(N) + P(W) - P(N \cap W)$$
$$= 49\% + 20\% - 31\% = 38\%$$

(b) No, $P(N \cap W) = 31\%$, not 0. The 16–64 group worked mostly because they needed the money!

EXAMPLE 6 Determining Mutually Exclusive Events

In a game of blackjack (also called twenty-one), a player and the dealer each get 2 cards. Let A and B be the events defined as follows:

A The player gets an ace and a face card for 21 points.
B The dealer gets an ace and a 10 for 21 points.

Are A and B mutually exclusive events?

Solution

No. Both player and dealer can get 21 points. (In the game of blackjack, 21 points wins, and in most casinos, the dealer would be the winner with this tie score.)

EXAMPLE 7 Probability that a State Regulates Smoking

The diagram shows the number of states regulating smoking in various areas. If you select one of the 50 states at random, what is the probability that smoking is regulated in:

(a) Restaurants, $P(R)$
(b) Bars **and** Restaurants, $P(B \cap R)$
(c) Restaurants only, $P(RO)$
(d) Bars, $P(B)$
(e) Restaurants **or** Bars, $P(R \cup B)$

If you want to find out which states regulate smoking go to http://tinyurl.com/2evsr3.

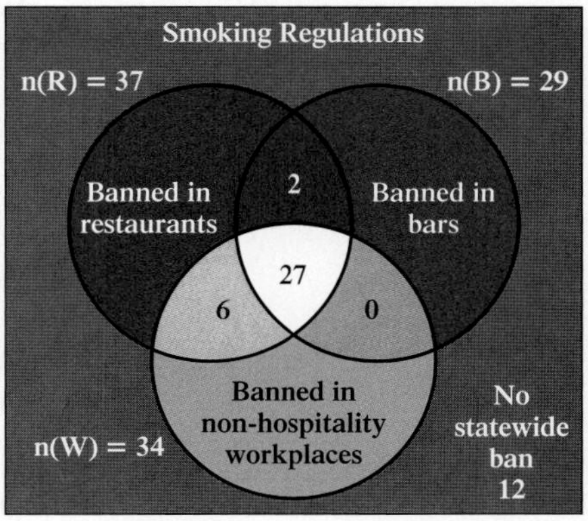

Solution

(a) **37** out of 50 states regulate smoking in restaurants, so $P(R) = \frac{37}{50}$.

(b) $27 + 2 =$ **29** states regulate smoking in Bars **and** Restaurants, so $P(B \cap R) = \frac{29}{50}$.

(c) Refer to the diagram: $P(RO) = P(R) - P(B \cap R) - \frac{6}{50} = \frac{37}{50} - \frac{29}{50} - \frac{6}{50} = \frac{2}{50} = \frac{1}{25}$.

(d) Note that there are 0 elements in the blue area (there are 50 states, and they are all accounted for, so there are **no** elements in the blue area), so $P(B) = \frac{2+27}{50} = \frac{29}{50}$.

(e) Using formula **(3)** with $P(R) = \frac{37}{50}$, $P(B) = \frac{29}{50}$ and $P(R \cap B) = P(B \cap R) = \frac{29}{50}$

$$P(R \cup B) = P(R) + P(B) - P(R \cap B)$$
$$= \frac{37}{50} + \frac{29}{50} - \frac{29}{50}$$
$$= \frac{37}{50}$$

We have used the formula $P(T') = 1 - P(T)$ to calculate the probability of the complement of an event. For example, if the probability that it will rain today is $\frac{1}{4}$, the probability that it will not rain today is $1 - \frac{1}{4} = \frac{3}{4}$, and if the probability of a stock going up in price is $\frac{3}{8}$, the probability that the stock will not go up in price is $1 - \frac{3}{8} = \frac{5}{8}$. We now see how this property is used in the field of life insurance.

Table 11.4 Table of Mortality for 100,000 Americans

	Males		Females	
Exact Age	**Number of Lives***	**Life Expectancy**	**Number of Lives***	**Life Expectancy**
0	100,000	75.38	100,000	80.43
10	99,065	66.08	99,228	71.04
20	98,541	56.40	98,983	61.20
30	97,147	47.13	98,466	51.50
40	95,525	37.84	97,586	41.91
50	92,224	28.99	95,530	32.69
60	85,227	20.92	91,220	23.97
70	72,066	13.73	81,944	16.05
80	47,974	7.90	61,930	9.43
90	15,722	3.92	27,333	4.69
100	754	2.07	2,411	2.39
110	2	1.15	11	1.22

*Number of survivors out of 100,000 born alive.
Source: www.ssa.gov/OACT/STATS/table4c6.html.

According to Table 11.4, of 98,541 males alive at age 20 (column 2, row 3), 754 were still alive at age 100, and only 2 were left at age 110! Females get a better deal. Of 98,983 females alive at age 20 (column 4, row 3), 2411 were still alive at age 100, and 11 were still around at age 110!

A table similar to this one is used to calculate a portion of the premium on life insurance policies. Use Table 11.4 to do the next example.

EXAMPLE 8 Longevity Probabilities from a Table

Find the probability that a person who is alive at age 20 is

(a) still alive at age 70 if the person is a female.

(b) not alive at age 70 if the person is a female.

(c) still alive at age 70 if the person is a male.

(d) not alive at age 70 if the person is a male.

Solution

(a) Based on Table 11.4, the probability that a female alive at age 20 is still alive at age 70 is given by

$$P(\text{female alive at 70}) = \frac{\text{number of females alive at 70}}{\text{number of females alive at 20}} = \frac{81{,}944}{98{,}983}$$

(b) The probability of a female not being alive at age 70 is

$$1 - \frac{81{,}944}{98{,}983} = \frac{17{,}039}{98{,}983}$$

(c) $P\,(\text{male alive at 70}) = \dfrac{\text{number of males alive at 70}}{\text{number of males alive at 20}} = \dfrac{72{,}066}{98{,}541} = \dfrac{24{,}022}{32{,}847}$

(d) $1 - \dfrac{72{,}066}{98{,}541} = \dfrac{26{,}475}{98{,}541}$

11.3 EXERCISES

In problems 1–4, find the answer to each question and indicate which of the four properties presented in this section you used to solve the problem.

1. A die is rolled. Find the probability that the number that comes up is a 0.

2. A die is rolled. Find the probability that an odd or an even number occurs.

3. Two dice are rolled. Find the probability that the sum of the two faces that turn up is between 0 and 13.

4. Five cards are drawn in succession and without replacement from a regular deck of 52 cards. What is the probability that you get 5 aces?

A single ball is drawn from an urn containing 10 *balls numbered* 1 *through* 10. *In each of problems 5–8, find the probability that the ball chosen is*

5. an even-numbered ball or a ball with a number greater than 7.

6. an odd-numbered ball or a ball with a number less than 5.

7. an even-numbered ball or an odd-numbered ball.

8. a ball with a number that is greater than 7 or less than 5.

In problems 9–13, a single card is drawn from a deck of 52 cards. Find the probability the card chosen is

9. the king of hearts or a spade.

10. the ace of hearts or an ace.

11. the ace of diamonds or a diamond.

12. the ace of clubs or a black card.

13. the king of hearts or a picture card (jack, queen, or king).

14. The U.S. Weather Service reports that in a certain northern city it rains 40 days and snows 50 days in the winter. However, it rains and snows on only 10 of those days. Based on this information, what is the probability that it will rain or snow in that city on a particular winter day? (Assume that there are 90 days of winter.)

15. Among the first 50 stocks listed in the New York Stock Exchange transactions on a certain day (as reported in the *Wall Street Journal*), there were 26 stocks that went down, 15 that went up, and 9 that remained unchanged. On the basis of this information, find the probability that a stock selected at random from this list would not have remained unchanged.

The following table shows the probability that there is a given number of people waiting in line at a checkout register at Dear's Department Store.

Number of Persons in Line	Probability
0	0.10
1	0.15
2	0.20
3	0.35
4 or more	0.20

In problems 16–20, find the probability of having

16. exactly 2 persons in line.

17. more than 3 persons in line.

18. at least 1 person in line.

19. more than 3 persons or fewer than 2 persons in line.

20. more than 2 persons or fewer than 3 persons in line.

In solving problems 21–25, refer to Table 11.4.

21. What is the probability that a person who is alive at age 20 will not be alive at age 60

a. if the person is a male?

b. if the person is a female?

22. What is the probability that a person who is alive at age 30 will be alive at age 70

a. if the person is a male?

b. if the person is a female?

23. What is the probability that a person who is alive at age 30 will not be alive at age 70

a. if the person is a male?

b. if the person is a female?

24. What is the probability that a person who is alive at age 50 will live 80 more years

a. if the person is a male?

b. if the person is a female?

(Assume that none of the persons in Table 11.4 attained 130 years of age.)

25. What is the probability that a person who is alive at age 50 will live less than 80 more years? (See problem 24.)
   a. if the person is a male?
   b. if the person is a female?

Problems 26–30 refer to the following table. This table shows the number of correctly and incorrectly filled out tax forms obtained from a random sample of 100 returns examined by the Internal Revenue Service (IRS) in a recent year.

	Short Form (1040A)	**Long Form (1040)**		
	No Itemized Deductions	**No Itemized Deductions**	**Itemized Deductions**	**Totals**
Correct	15	40	10	65
Incorrect	5	20	10	35
Totals	**20**	**60**	**20**	**100**

26. Find the probability that a form was a long form (1040) or an incorrectly filled out form.
27. Find the probability that a form had no itemized deductions and was correctly filled out.
28. Find the probability that a form was not filled out incorrectly.
29. Find the probability that a form was not a short form (1040A).
30. Find the probability that a form was a long form (1040) with no itemized deductions and filled out incorrectly.

31. A traffic light follows the pattern green, yellow, red for 60, 5, and 20 seconds, respectively. What is the probability that a driver approaching this light will find it green or yellow?
32. A driver approaching the green light decides to go ahead through the intersection whether the light changes or not. If it takes the driver 6 seconds to get through the intersection, what is the probability that the driver makes it through the intersection before the light turns red? See problem 31.

IN OTHER WORDS

33. Explain, in your own words, what it means to say "The probability of an event is 0."
34. Explain, in your own words, what it means to say "The probability of an event is 1."
35. Explain, in your own words, the circumstances under which you can use the formula

$$P(A \cup B) = P(A) + P(B)$$

36. Explain why the probability of an event cannot be negative.

USING YOUR KNOWLEDGE

In this section you used a mortality table to calculate the probability that a person alive at a certain age will be alive at a later age. There are other tables that give the probabilities of different events. For example, many mortgage companies use a credit-scoring table to estimate the likelihood that an applicant will repay a loan. One such table appears below.

A Hypothetical Credit-Scoring Table

Age	Under 25 (12 pts)	25–29 (5 pts)	30–34 (0 pts)	35–39 (1 pt)	40–44 (18 pts)	45–49 (22 pts)	50 + (31 pts)
Time at Address	1 yr or less (9 pts)	1–2 yr (0 pts)	2–3 yr (5 pts)	3–5 yr (0 pts)	5–9 yr (5 pts)	10 yr + (21 pts)	
Age of Auto	None (0 pts)	0–1 yr (12 pts)	2 yr (16 pts)	3–4 yr (13 pts)	5–7 yr (3 pts)	8 yr + (0 pts)	
Monthly Auto Payment	None (18 pts)	\$1–\$80 (6 pts)	\$81–\$99 (1 pt)	\$100–\$139 (4 pts)	\$140 + (0 pts)		
Housing Cost	\$1–\$125 (0 pts)	\$126–\$274 (10 pts)	\$275 + (12 pts)	Owns clear (12 pts)	Lives with relatives (24 pts)		
Checking and Savings Accounts	Both (15 pts)	Checking only (2 pts)	Savings only (2 pts)	Neither (0 pts)			
Finance Company Reference	Yes (0 pts)	No (15 pts)					
Major Credit Cards	None (0 pts)	1 (5 pts)	2 + (15 pts)				
Ratio of Debt to Income	No debts (41 pts)	1–5% (16 pts)	6–15% (20 pts)	16% + (0 pts)			

In the table on page 636 your score depends on the number of points you get on the nine tabulated items. To obtain your score, you add the scores (shown in color) on the individual items. For example, if your age is 21, you get 12 points. If you have lived at your present address for less than a year, you get 9 more points. Moreover, if your car is 2 years old, you get another 16 points. So far your score is 12 + 9 + 16. This should give you the idea.

A lender using the scoring table selects a cutoff point from a table, such as the following table that gauges the probability that an applicant will repay a loan:

Total Score	Probability of Repayment	Total Score	Probability of Repayment
60	0.70	100	0.92
65	0.74	105	0.93
70	0.78	110	0.94
75	0.81	115	0.95
80	0.84	120	0.955
85	0.87	125	0.96
90	0.89	130	0.9625
95	0.91		

37. John Dough, 27 years old, living for 3 years at his present address, has a 2-year-old automobile on which he pays \$200 monthly. He pays \$130 per month for his apartment and has no savings account, but he does have a checking account. He has no finance company reference. He has one major credit card, and his debt-to-income ratio is 12%. On the basis of the credit-scoring table, what is the probability that Mr. Dough will repay a loan?

38. What is the probability in problem 37 if Mr. Dough pays off his car, sells it, and rides the bus to work?

39. Find the probability that you will repay a loan, based on the information in the table.

DISCOVERY

The Venn diagrams we studied in Chapter 2 can often be used to find the probability of an event by showing the number of elements in the universal set and the number of elements corresponding to the event under consideration. For example, if there are 100 employees in a certain firm and it is known that 82 are males (M), 9 are clerk typists (C), and 2 of these clerk typists are male, we can draw a diagram corresponding to this situation.

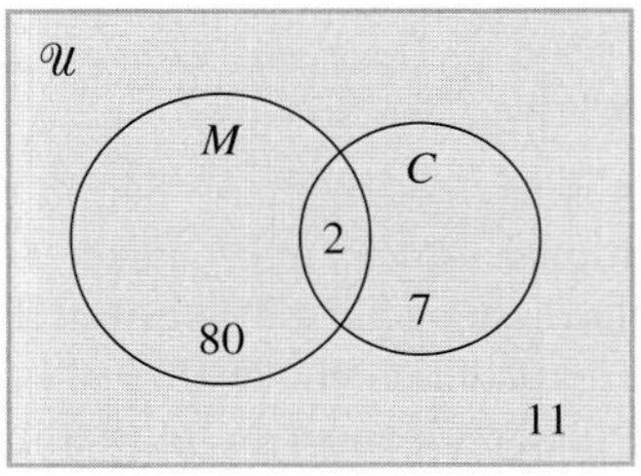

From this diagram, we can conclude that

$$P(M) = \frac{82}{100}, \quad P(C) = \frac{9}{100}, \quad P(M \cap C) = \frac{2}{100},$$

$$\text{and } P(M \cup C) = \frac{82}{100} + \frac{9}{100} - \frac{2}{100} = \frac{89}{100}$$

Use this technique to solve the following problems. In problems 40–42, assume that of the 100 persons in a company, 70 are married, 80 are college graduates, and 60 are both married and college graduates. Find the probability that if a person is selected at random from this group, the person will be

40. married and a college graduate.

41. married or a college graduate.

42. not married and not a college graduate.

In a recent election, voters were asked to vote on two issues, A and B. A Gallup poll indicated that of 1000 eligible voters, 600 persons voted in favor of A, 500 persons voted in favor of B, 200 persons voted in favor of both A and B, and 50 persons voted against both issues. If an eligible voter is selected at random, find the probability that he or she voted

43. for A but not B.

44. for B but not A.

45. for both A and B.

46. against both A and B.

47. not at all.

COLLABORATIVE LEARNING

In order to see how credit ratings are done at Fair, Isaac and Co. (FICO), go to http://www.myfico.com/crediteducation/whatsinyourscore.aspx. The scores there are between 300 and 800. Higher than 660 it is OK, between 620 and 660 is fair, and below 620 you may be in trouble. To reach these scores, they consider past delinquency, how you used credit in the past, the age of the credit file, the number of times you ask for credit, and your mix of credit (cards, installment, and revolving). Discuss how these five factors can affect your creditworthiness.

11.4 Conditional Probability

GETTING STARTED

OBJECTIVES

A. Use the definition of conditional probability to solve problems.
B. Solve applications involving conditional probability.

SURVEYS AND CONDITIONAL PROBABILITY

Have you ever been to a car dealership and taken a look at consumer magazines that rank different automobiles? If you are the manager of a dealership, you want to know whether people who read the reports in *Consumer Reports* or *Car and Driver* are more likely to buy a car from you. The first step is to conduct a survey of potential buyers. Suppose the results of such a survey are as follows:

70% of the people read the report (R).
45% bought a car from you, the dealer (B).
20% neither read the report nor bought a car from you, the dealer.

You want to find the effect of reading the report (R) on buying a car from you (B). Thus, you must compare the probability that the person bought a car $P(B)$ with the probability that the person bought a car given that the person read the report, denoted by $P(B|R)$ and read as "the probability of B given R."

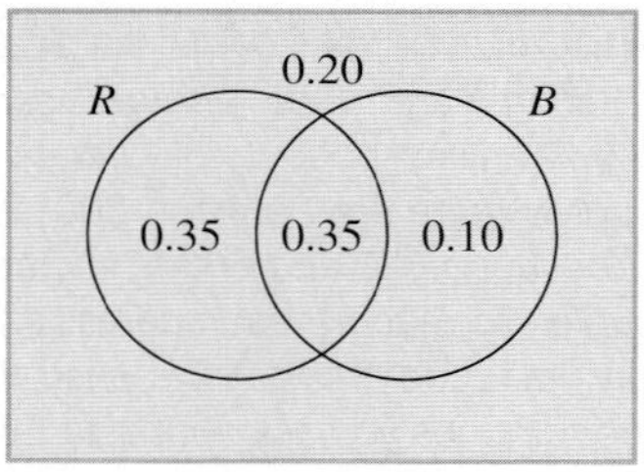

FIGURE 11.10

You first make a Venn diagram of the situation. Label two circles R and B and place 20%, the percentage of people who neither read the report nor bought a car, outside these two circles. This means that 80% of the people must be inside the two circles. But 70% + 45% = 115%, so 35% (115% − 80%) of the people must be in $B \cap R$, as shown in Figure 11.10.

You can see from Figure 11.10 that $P(B) = 0.35 + 0.10 = 0.45$. To find $P(B|R)$, you have to look at all the people who bought cars *given* that they read the report; that is, you must look inside the circle labeled R. Inside this circle, 35% of the people out of the 70% who read the report bought a car; that is,

$$P(B|R) = \frac{P(B \cap R)}{P(R)} = \frac{0.35}{0.35 + 0.35} = \frac{0.35}{0.70} = 0.50$$

Thus, $P(B) = 0.45$ and $P(B|R) = 0.50$; this means that people are more likely to buy a car from you, the dealer, if they have read the report. For this reason many dealers give copies of consumer magazine articles to potential customers. In this section you will study *conditional* probability, that is, probability computed using a subset of the sample space.

A Conditional Probability

As the "Wizard of Id" cartoon shows, it is sometimes the case that in considering the probability of an event A, we obtain additional information that may suggest a revision of the probability of A. For example, assume that in Getwell Hospital, 70 of the patients have lung cancer (C), 60 of the patients smoke (S), and 50 have cancer and smoke. If there are 100 patients in the hospital, and 1 is selected at random, then $P(C) = \frac{70}{100}$ and $P(S) = \frac{60}{100}$. But suppose a patient selected at random tells us that he or she smokes. What is the probability that this patient has cancer? In other words, what is the probability that a patient has cancer, given that the patient smokes? The expression

The WIZARD OF ID by permission of Johnny Hart and Creator's Syndicate, Inc.

"given that the patient smokes" means that we must restrict our attention to those patients who smoke. We have thus added a **restrictive condition** to the problem. Essentially, the condition that the person smokes requires that we use S as our sample space.

To compute $P(C|S)$ (read "the probability of C, given S"), we recall that there are 50 favorable outcomes (people who have lung cancer and smoke) and 60 elements in the new sample space (people who smoke). Hence, $P(C|S) = \frac{50}{60} = \frac{5}{6}$.

We note that

$$P(C|S) = \frac{n(C \cap S)}{n(S)}$$

$$= \frac{n(C \cap S)/n(\mathcal{U})}{n(S)/n(\mathcal{U})} = \frac{P(C \cap S)}{P(S)}$$

This discussion suggests the following definition:

Definition of Conditional Probability

If A and B are events in a sample space $\mathcal{U}$ and $P(B) \neq 0$, the **conditional probability of A, given B,** is denoted by $P(A|B)$ and is defined by

$$P(A|B) = \frac{P(A \cap B)}{P(B)} \tag{1}$$

Notice that the conditional probability of A, given B, results in a new sample space consisting of the elements in $\mathcal{U}$ for which B occurs. This gives rise to a second method of handling conditional probability, as illustrated in the following five examples:

EXAMPLE 1 Probability of a 3 When an Odd Number Turns Up

A die is rolled. Find the probability that a 3 comes up if it is known that an odd number turns up.

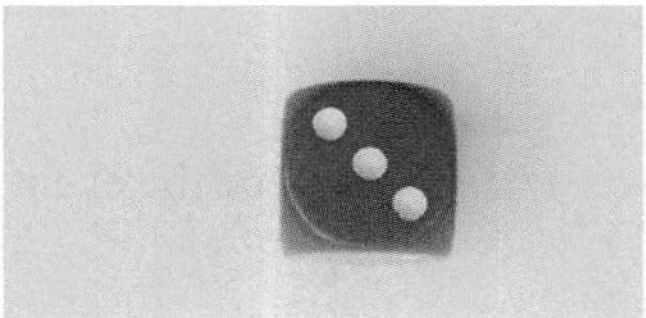

Solution

Method 1 Let T be the event in which a 3 turns up and Q be the event in which an odd number turns up. By equation (1),

$$P(T|Q) = \frac{P(T \cap Q)}{P(Q)} = \frac{\frac{1}{6}}{\frac{3}{6}} = \frac{1}{3}$$

Method 2 We know that an odd number turns up, so our new sample space is $\mathcal{U} = \{1, 3, 5\}$. Only one outcome (3) is favorable, so

$$P(T|Q) = \tfrac{1}{3}$$

© I. Bello

EXAMPLE 2 Probability of a 6 After Heads

A coin is tossed; then a die is rolled. Find the probability of obtaining a 6, given that heads comes up.

Solution

Method 1 Let S be the event in which a 6 is rolled, and let H be the event in which heads comes up.

$$P(S|H) = \frac{P(S \cap H)}{P(H)} = \frac{\frac{1}{12}}{\frac{1}{2}} = \frac{1}{12} \cdot 2 = \frac{1}{6}$$

Method 2 We know that heads comes up, so our new sample space is $\mathcal{U} = \{(H, 1), (H, 2), (H, 3), (H, 4), (H, 5), (H, 6)\}$. Only one outcome is favorable, $(H, 6)$, so $P(S|H) = \frac{1}{6}$.

EXAMPLE 3 Probability of 4 After Different Outcomes

Two dice were thrown, and a friend tells us that the numbers that came up were different. Find the probability that the sum of the two numbers was 4.

Solution

Method 1 Let D be the event in which the two dice show different numbers, and let F be the event in which the sum is 4. By equation (1),

$$P(F|D) = \frac{P(F \cap D)}{P(D)}$$

Now, $P(F \cap D) = \frac{2}{36}$ because there are two outcomes, (3, 1) and (1, 3), in which the sum is 4 and the numbers are different, and there are 36 possible outcomes. Furthermore,

$$P(D) = \frac{36 - 6}{36} = \frac{30}{36} \quad \text{so} \quad P(F|D) = \frac{P(F \cap D)}{P(D)} = \frac{\frac{2}{36}}{\frac{30}{36}} = \frac{1}{15}$$

Method 2 We know that the numbers on the two dice were different, so we have $36 - 6 = 30$ (36 minus 6 outcomes that show the same number on both dice) elements in our sample space. Of these, only two, (3, 1) and (1, 3), have a sum of 4. Hence, $P(F|D) = \frac{2}{30} = \frac{1}{15}$.

EXAMPLE 4 Probability of 7 After 6

Two dice are rolled, and a friend tells you that the first die shows a 6. Find the probability that the sum of the numbers showing on the two dice is 7.

Solution

Method 1 Let S_1 be the event in which the first die shows a 6, and let S_2 be the event in which the sum is 7. Then

$$P(S_2|S_1) = \frac{P(S_2 \cap S_1)}{P(S_1)} = \frac{\frac{1}{36}}{\frac{6}{36}} = \frac{1}{6}$$

Method 2 We know that a 6 comes up on the first die, so our new sample space is $\mathcal{U} = \{(6, 1), (6, 2), (6, 3), (6, 4), (6, 5), (6, 6)\}$. Hence, $P(S_1|S_2) = \frac{1}{6}$ because there is only one favorable outcome, (6, 1).

B Applications

EXAMPLE 5 Genes and Probability

Suppose we represent with the letters B and b the genes that determine the color of a person's eyes. If the person has two b genes, the person has blue eyes; otherwise, the person has brown eyes. If it is known that a man has brown eyes, what is the probability that he has two B genes? (Assume that both genes are equally likely to occur.)

Solution

The tree diagram for the four possibilities appears in Figure 11.11.

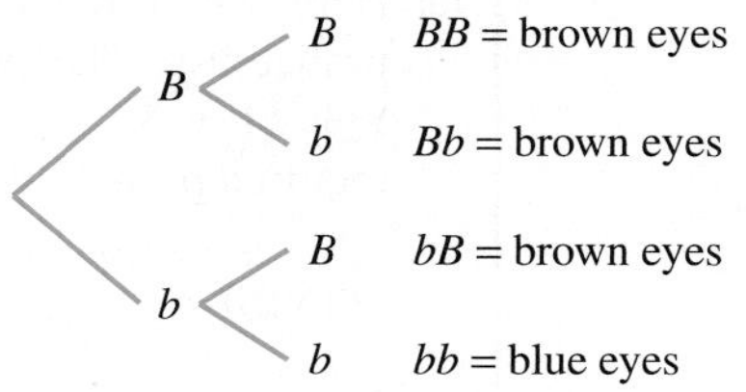

FIGURE 11.11

Method 1 Let T be the event in which the man has two B genes, and let B be the event in which the man has brown eyes. By the definition of conditional probability,

$$P(T|B) = \frac{P(T \cap B)}{P(B)} = \frac{\frac{1}{4}}{\frac{3}{4}} = \frac{1}{3}$$

Method 2 It is known that the man has brown eyes, so we consider the 3 outcomes corresponding to these cases (BB, Bb, and bB). Because only 1 of these equally likely outcomes (BB) is favorable, the probability that a man has two B genes if it is known that he has brown eyes is $\frac{1}{3}$.

Table 11.5 Strokes, per 1000 People Aged 45–74

Blood Pressure	Number	Strokes
Normal	390	8
Borderline	315	14
High	295	31

Other important applications also make use of conditional probability. For example, the Framingham Heart Disease Study focused on strokes and heart failure. Table 11.5 is based on this study and shows the number of adults (per 1000) aged 45–74 with certain blood pressure types and the number of strokes in each category. As we can see, the incidence of stroke for people aged 45–74 increases almost fourfold as blood pressure goes from normal to high (from 8 per 1000 to 31 per 1000). Note that the numbers in the body of Table 11.5 are all per 1000. This means that Table 11.5 gives approximate conditional probabilities. The number 31 in the last line of Table 11.5 means that the probability that a person will have a stroke and has high blood pressure is about $\frac{31}{1000}$. We look at some other aspects of this study in the next example.

EXAMPLE 6 Blood Pressure and Probability

Assume that numbers in Table 11.5 are accurate, and find the probability that

(a) a person in the 45–74 age group has a stroke (S), given that the person has normal blood pressure (N).

(b) a person in the 45–74 age group has a stroke (S), given that the person has borderline blood pressure (B).

(c) a person in the 45–74 age group has a stroke (S).

(d) a person has normal blood pressure (N), given that the person had a stroke (S).

Solution

(a) There were 8 strokes among the 390 who have normal blood pressure, so

$$P(S|N) = \frac{8}{390} = \frac{4}{195}$$

(b) The idea is similar to that of part (a); in the second row there are 14 people who had a stroke out of 315; thus,

$$P(S|B) = \frac{14}{315}$$

(c) There are three mutually exclusive sets, *N, B,* and *H,* so the required probability is the sum of the probabilities for the three sets, that is,

$$\frac{8}{1000} + \frac{14}{1000} + \frac{31}{1000} = \frac{53}{1000}$$

(d) Here, we know the person has had a stroke, so we can use the idea of conditional probability. The population for this condition (having a stroke) consists of the $8 + 14 + 31 = 53$ people. Of these, 8 have normal blood pressure. Thus, the required probability is $\frac{8}{53}$. You also can use the formula

$$P(N|S) = \frac{P(N \cap S)}{P(S)}$$

$$= \frac{\frac{8}{1000}}{\frac{53}{1000}} = \frac{8}{53}$$

Same answer!

EXAMPLE 7 Monty Hall Probabilities

Have you heard of the Monty Hall Problem? It goes like this: In the game show *Let's Make a Deal,* contestants are presented with 3 doors (A, B, C), only one of which has a big prize behind it (the others are empty). You do not know what is behind any of the doors. You choose a door. Monty then counters by showing you what is behind one of the other doors (which is empty) and asks you if you would like to stick with the door you have or switch to the other unknown door.

(a) What is the probability that you win given that you decide to **stay?**

(b) What is the probability that you win given that you decide to **switch?**

Solution

(a) Since there are 3 doors, the probability that you win by selecting the door with the prize is $\frac{1}{3}$.

(b) The winning prize (W) can be behind door A, B, or C. Two of the doors are empty (E). Here are the three possibilities.

	A	B	C
1.	*W*	*E*	*E*
2.	*E*	*W*	*E*
3.	*E*	*E*	*W*

Now, suppose that you select door A (it really does not matter which door you select), and you decide to **switch.** (Remember, Monty has to show you the empty door!)

In case 1, you will certainly lose.
In case 2, Monty will have to show you door C and you pick B and win.
In case 3, Monty will have to show you door B and you pick C and win.

Thus, you win 2 out of 3 times by switching!

EXAMPLE 8 Why Do People Work?

The table shows the reasons that people work. Suppose you select a person at random and they tell you that "they work because they want to" **(W).** What is the probability that the person is:

(a) 65 + ? **(b)** 16–64?

(c) Now, suppose that the person tells you that they are 16–64. What is the probability that the person is working "because they want to", **(W)?**

Reason to Work	AGE 16-64	AGE 65+
Need Money (N)	49%	17%
Wants to (W)	20%	54%
Both (B)	31%	27%

Solution

(a) We want the probability that the person is 65+ given that they work "because they want to" **(W),** that is, $P(65+|W)$. The total percent of persons that want to work **(W)** is 20% + 54%, (second row) and of those 54% are 65+ (last column). Thus,

$$P(65+|W) = \frac{54}{20 + 54} = \frac{54}{74} = \frac{27}{37}$$

(b) This time we want $P(16\text{–}64|W)$ so we go to the second row **(W)** that has a total of 20% + 54% of people that want to work. Of those, 20% are 16–64 (second row, second column), thus

$$P(16\text{–}64|W) = \frac{20}{20 + 54} = \frac{20}{74} = \frac{10}{37}$$

(c) We want $P(W|16\text{–}64)$. Since we know that the person is 16–64, we look in column 2 and select the 20% in the second row.

Source: http://pewresearch.org/pubs/1330/american-work-force-is-graying.

11.4 EXERCISES

A Conditional Probability

1. A die was rolled. Find the probability that a 5 came up, given that an even number turned up.
2. A coin was tossed; then a die was rolled. Find the probability of obtaining a 7, given that tails came up.
3. Two dice were rolled, and a friend tells us that the numbers that came up were identical. Find the probability that the sum of the numbers was
   a. 8. **b.** 9.
   c. an even number. **d.** an odd number.

4. Referring to Example 5 of this section, find the probability that a person has two b genes, given that the person has
   a. brown eyes. b. blue eyes.
5. For a family with 2 children, the sample space indicating boy (B) or girl (G) is BB, BG, GB, and GG. If each of the outcomes is equally likely, find the probability that the family has 2 boys, given that the first child is a boy.
6. A family has 3 children. If each of the outcomes in the sample space is equally likely, find the probability that the family has 3 girls given that
   a. the first child is a girl. b. the first child is a boy.
7. Referring to problem 6, find the probability that the family has exactly 2 girls, given that the first child is a girl.
8. The following table gives the approximate number of suicides per 100,000 persons, classified according to country and age for 1 year:

	Country		
Age	**United States**	**Canada**	**Germany**
15–24	10	10	20
25–44	20	15	30
45–64	30	13	50
65 or over	40	14	50

Based on the table, find the probability that
   a. a person between 25 and 44 years of age committed suicide, given that the person lived in the United States. (For national suicide rates per 100,000 by gender and age, see www.who.int/mental_health/en.)
   b. a person between 25 and 44 years of age committed suicide, given that the person lived in Canada.
   c. a person committed suicide, given that the person lived in Germany.
9. The personnel director of Gadget Manufacturing Company has compiled the following table, which shows the percent of men and women employees who were absent the indicated number of days. Suppose there are as many women as men employees.

	Sex	
Absences (Days)	**Men**	**Women**
0	20%	20%
1–5	40%	20%
6–10	40%	20%
11 or more	0%	40%
Total	100%	100%

   a. Find the probability that an employee missed 6–10 days, given that the employee is a woman.
   b. Find the probability that an employee is a woman, given that the employee missed 6–10 days.
10. The following table describes the student population in a large college:

Class	Male	Female
Freshman (%)	25	15
Sophomore (%)	13	10
Junior (%)	12	8
Senior (%)	10	7

   a. Find the probability that a randomly selected student is female.
   b. Find the probability that a randomly selected student is a junior.
   c. If the selected student is a junior, find the probability that the student is female.
11. The table shows the reasons to work (as a percent) for people age **16–64** and **65+**. Suppose you select a person at random and they tell you that "they work because they need the money," (N). What is the probability that the person is:
   a. 65+?
   b. 16–64?
   c. Now, suppose that the person tells you that they are 65+. What is the probability that the person is working "because they need money" (N)?

Reason to Work	AGE	
	16–64	**65+**
Need Money (N)	49%	17%
Wants to (W)	20%	54%
Both (B)	31%	27%

Source: http://pewresearch.org/pubs/1330/american-work-force-is-graying.

In problems 12–14, assume that 2 cards are drawn in succession and without replacement from a standard deck of 52 cards. Find the probability that

12. the second card is the ace of hearts, given that the first card was the ace of spades.
13. the second card is a king, given that the first card was a king.
14. the second card is a 7, given that the first card was a 6.

B Applications

The following information will be used in problems 15 and 16.

The Merrilee Brokerage House studied two groups of industries (computers and petroleum) and rated them as low risks or high risks, as shown.

Industry	Low	High
Computers	5	10
Petroleum	20	15

15. If a person selected one of these stocks at random (that is, each stock had probability $\frac{1}{50}$ of being selected), find the probability that the person selected a computer stock, given that the person selected a low-risk stock.

16. If a person selected one of the stocks at random, find the probability that the person selected a petroleum stock, given that the person selected a high-risk stock.

17. A stock market analyst figures the probabilities that two related stocks, A and B, will go up in price. She finds the probability that A will go up to be 0.6 and the probability that both stocks will go up to be 0.4. What should be her estimate of the probability that stock B goes up, given that stock A goes up?

18. The Florida Tourist Commission estimates that a person visiting Florida will visit Disney World, Busch Gardens, or both with probabilities 0.5, 0.3, and 0.2, respectively. Find the probability that a person visiting Florida will visit Busch Gardens, given that the person did visit Disney World.

© I. Bello

19. A recent survey of 400 instructors at a major university revealed the data shown in the following table. Based on the data, what are the probabilities of the following?

a. An instructor received a good evaluation, given that the instructor was tenured.

b. An instructor received a good evaluation.

Status	Good Evaluations	Poor Evaluations
Tenured	72	168
Nontenured	84	76

20. Referring to the data in problem 19, find the probability that an instructor received

a. a poor evaluation, given that the instructor was tenured.

b. a poor evaluation.

21. Do you own a cell phone? If you are 25–34 years old you probably do! But what about older people, say people in the 65+ category? A Pew Research survey revealed the data shown in the table.

Age Bracket	Smartphone Ownership by Age		
	Smart	Other	None
18–24	108	101	11
25–34	144	87	17
35–44	124	127	31
45–54	110	227	55
55–64	95	255	82
65+	70	287	280

Source: http://www.pewinternet.org/~/media//Files/Reports/2011/PIP_Smartphones.pdf.

Based on this information find, to the nearest percent, the probability that

a. you have no cell phone given that you are 65+.

b. you have no cell phone given that you are in the 18–24 age bracket.

22. Refer to the table in problem 21. Find, to the nearest percent, the probability that

a. you are in the 65+ bracket given that you have a smartphone.

b. you are in the 18–24 bracket given that you have a smartphone.

23. A doctor for a pharmaceutical company treats 100 patients with an experimental drug and another 100 patients with a conventional drug. The results of the experiment are given in the following table. What is the probability that

Type	Improved (I)	Same (S)
Experimental (E)	70	30
Conventional (C)	65	35

a. a patient chosen at random from the group of 200 patients has improved, $P(I)$?

b. a patient taking the experimental drug has improved, $P(I|E)$?

24. The University Apartments has 1000 units classified by size and location as shown in the following table. What is the probability of selecting at random

a. a first-floor apartment?

b. a first-floor, three-bedroom apartment?

c. a second-floor apartment, given that it is a one-bedroom?

d. a two- or three-bedroom apartment, given that it is located on the first floor?

Floor	Bedrooms		
	One	Two	Three
First floor	20%	30%	10%
Second floor	15%	20%	5%

Problems 25–27 refer to the following table showing the death penalty and racial distribution for 326 convicted murderers.

Death Penalty	White	Black
Yes	19	17
No	141	149
Total	**160**	**166**

Source: M. Radelet, "Racial Characteristics of the Death Penalty," *American Sociological Review* 46: 918–927.

Let D be the person gets the death penalty, W the person is white, and B the person is black.

25. Find $P(D|W)$.

26. Find $P(D|B)$.

27. On the basis of your answers to problems 25 and 26, is there much difference between outcomes for whites and blacks? Explain.

Problems 28–32 refer to the following table showing the death penalty, racial status, and race of the victim distribution for the same 326 murderers.

Race of Victim	Death Penalty	White	Black
White	Yes	19	11
	No	132	52
	Total	**151**	**63**

Race of Victim	Death Penalty	White	Black
Black	Yes	0	6
	No	9	97
	Total	**9**	**103**

28. Find $P(D|WW)$, where WW means that the defendant is white and the victim is white.

29. Find $P(D|BW)$.

30. Find $P(D|WB)$.

31. Find $P(D|BB)$.

32. On the basis of your answers to problems 28–31, is there much difference between outcomes for whites and blacks? Explain and compare your answer with problem 27.

IN OTHER WORDS

33. Of the two methods of solving conditional probability problems, which do you prefer? Why?

34. Can you find two events A and B such that $P(A|B) = P(A)$? What is the relationship between A and B? Explain.

USING YOUR KNOWLEDGE

The Statistical Abstract of the United States *gives the number of crime victims per 1000 persons, 12 years old and over, as shown in the following table:*

Sex	Robbery	Assault	Personal Larceny
Male	5	18	52
Female	2	9	42

Use the information in this table to do the following problems:

35. **a.** Find the probability that the victim of one of the three types of crime was a male.

b. Find the probability that the victim of one of the three types of crime was a female.

c. Considering your answers to parts (**a**) and (**b**), which sex would you say is more likely to be the victim of one of these three types of crime?

36. If it is known that an assault was committed, what is the probability that the victim was a

a. male? **b.** female?

37. If it is known that the victim was a female, what is the probability that the crime was assault?

38. If it is known that the victim was a male, what is the probability that the crime was robbery?

COLLABORATIVE LEARNING

The study cited in problems 25–32 was done several years ago. Go to the Statistical Abstract of the United States *or to the Web and find more recent and similar statistics to the ones given in the tables of problems 25–32. Discuss any changes in the outcomes.*

11.5 Independent Events

GETTING STARTED

OBJECTIVES

A. Determine if two events are independent and find the probability of independent events.

B. Solve probability problems involving "and".

© I. Bello

A water tower advertises bingo on a Florida Seminole Native American reservation.

PROBABILITIES IN BINGO AND BIRTHDAYS

Have you played Bingo lately? The world's biggest Bingo contest was held in Cherokee, North Carolina, and offered a \$200,000 prize to any player who could fill a 24-number card by the 48th number called (there are 75 possible numbers in Bingo). What is the probability that you would win this game? The probability that any given number on your 24-number card is drawn is $\frac{48}{75}$, the probability of drawing a second number on your card is $\frac{47}{74}$, and so on. To win, you must get *all* 24 numbers on your card in 48 draws. The probability is

$$\frac{48}{75} \cdot \frac{47}{74} \cdot \frac{46}{73} \cdot \cdots \cdot \frac{25}{52} = \frac{1}{799{,}399}$$

Note that the individual probabilities have been multiplied to find the final answer. In this section, you will study **independent** events. If two events A and B are independent, $P(A \cap B) = P(A) \cdot (B)$.

A classic use of this formula is the birthday problem. Given a group of people, what is $P(L)$, the probability that *at least* two people have the same birthday? It is easier to find $P(L')$, the probability that *no* two people have the same birthday, and then to compute $P(L) = 1 - P(L')$. Assuming that all birthdays are equally likely, the probability that a second person has a different birthday than a first is $\frac{364}{365}$, the probability that a third person has a different birthday than the other two is $\frac{363}{365}$, and the probability that an nth person has a different birthday than all the others is

$$\frac{365 - n + 1}{365}$$

Thus,

$$P(L) = 1 - \frac{364}{365} \cdot \frac{363}{365} \cdot \frac{362}{365} \cdot \cdots \cdot \frac{365 - n + 1}{365}$$

Now, compute some of these probabilities and note some others. When there are two people in the room, $n = 2$,

$$P(L) = 1 - \frac{364}{365} \approx 1 - 0.997 = 0.003$$

When there are three people in the room, $n = 3$,

$$P(L) = 1 - \frac{364}{365} \cdot \frac{363}{365} \approx 1 - 0.992 = 0.008$$

When $n = 10$, $P(L) = 0.117$; when $n = 22$, $P(L) = 0.476$; and when $n = 23$, $P(L) = 0.507$. Thus, with 22 people in a room, the probability that at least 2 have the same birthday is slightly under $\frac{1}{2}$; add one more person and it becomes slightly better than $\frac{1}{2}$.

One of the more important concepts in probability is that of **independence.** In this section we shall define what we mean when we say that two events are independent. For example, the probability of obtaining a sum of 7 when two dice are rolled *and* it is known that the first die shows a 6 is $\frac{1}{6}$; that is $P(S|6) = \frac{1}{6}$. It is of interest that the probability of obtaining a 7 when two dice are rolled is also $\frac{1}{6}$, so $P(S|6) = P(S)$. This means that the additional information that a 6 came up on the first die does not affect the probability of the sum's being 7. It can happen, in general, that the probability of an event A is not affected by the occurrence of a second event B. Hence, we state the following definition:

Definition of Independent Events

Two events A and B are said to be **independent** if and only if

$$P(A|B) = P(A) \tag{1}$$

If A and B are independent, we can substitute $P(A)$ for $P(A|B)$ in the equation

$$P(A|B) = \frac{P(A \cap B)}{P(B)}$$

See Section 11.4, equation (1).

to obtain

$$P(A) = \frac{P(A \cap B)}{P(B)}$$

Then, multiplying by $P(B)$, we get

$$P(A \cap B) = P(A) \cdot P(B)$$

Consequently, we see that an equivalent definition of independence is as follows:

Alternate Definition of Independent Events

Two events A and B are **independent** if and only if

$$P(A \cap B) = P(A) \cdot P(B) \tag{2}$$

A Independent Events

The preceding ideas can be applied to experiments involving more than two events. We define independent events to be such that the occurence of any one of these events does not affect the probability of any other. The most important result for applications is that if n events, $E_1, E_2, \ldots, E_n$, are known to be independent, then the following multiplication rule holds:

Multiplication Rule for Independent Events

$$P(E_1 \cap E_2 \cap E_3 \cap \ldots \cap E_n) = P(E_1) \cdot P(E_2) \cdot \ldots \cdot P(E_n) \tag{3}$$

The next examples illustrate these ideas.

EXAMPLE 1 Determining If Events Are Independent

Two coins are tossed. Let E_1 be the event the first coin comes up tails, and let E_2 be the event the second coin comes up heads. Are E_1 and E_2 independent?

Solution

Because $P(E_1 \cap E_2) = \frac{1}{4}$, $P(E_1) = \frac{1}{2}$, $P(E_2) = \frac{1}{2}$, and $\frac{1}{2} \cdot \frac{1}{2} = \frac{1}{4}$, we see that $P(E_1 \cap E_2) = P(E_1) \cdot P(E_2)$. Hence, E_1 and E_2 are independent.

EXAMPLE 2 Probability of 2 Black Balls

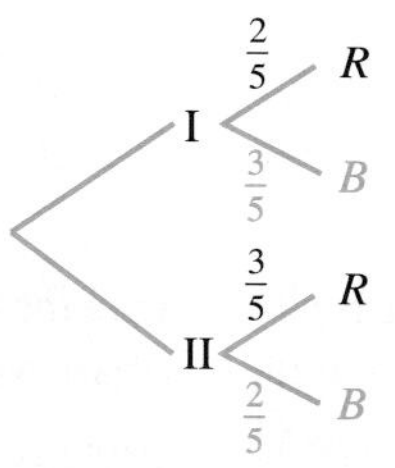

FIGURE 11.12

We have two urns, I and II. Urn I contains 2 red and 3 black balls, whereas urn II contains 3 red and 2 black balls. A ball is drawn at random from each urn. What is the probability that both balls are black?

Solution

Let $P(B_1)$ be the probability of drawing a black ball from urn I, and let $P(B_2)$ be the probability of drawing a black ball from urn II. Clearly, B_1 and B_2 are independent events. Thus, $P(B_1) = \frac{3}{5}$ and $P(B_2) = \frac{2}{5}$, so $P(B_1 \cap B_2) = \frac{3}{5} \cdot \frac{2}{5} = \frac{6}{25}$ (see Figure 11.12).

EXAMPLE 3 Grades and Probability

Bob is taking math, Spanish, and English. He estimates that his probabilities of receiving A's in these courses are $\frac{1}{10}$, $\frac{3}{10}$, and $\frac{7}{10}$, respectively. If he assumes that the grades can be regarded as independent events, find the probability that Bob makes

(a) all A's (event A).

(b) no A's (event N).

(c) exactly two A's (event T).

Solution

(a) $P(A) = P(M) \cdot P(S) \cdot P(E) = \frac{1}{10} \cdot \frac{3}{10} \cdot \frac{7}{10} = \frac{21}{1000}$, where M is the event in which he makes an A in math, S is the event in which he makes an A in Spanish, and E is the event in which he makes an A in English (see the tree diagram in Figure 11.13).

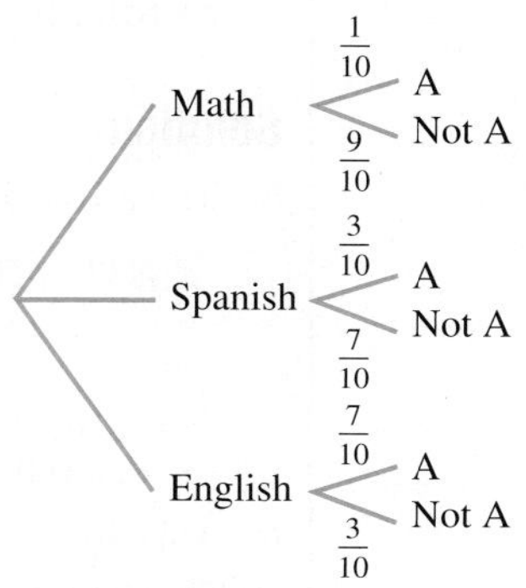

FIGURE 11.13

(b) $P(N) = P(M') \cdot P(S') \cdot P(E') = \frac{9}{10} \cdot \frac{7}{10} \cdot \frac{3}{10} = \frac{189}{1000}$

(c) There are three ways of getting exactly two A's:

1. Getting A's in math and Spanish and not in English. The probability of this event is

$$P(M) \cdot P(S) \cdot P(E') = \frac{1}{10} \cdot \frac{3}{10} \cdot \frac{3}{10} = \frac{9}{1000}$$

2. Getting A's in math and English and not in Spanish. The probability of this event is

$$P(M) \cdot P(S') \cdot P(E) = \frac{1}{10} \cdot \frac{7}{10} \cdot \frac{7}{10} = \frac{49}{1000}$$

3. Getting A's in Spanish and English and not in math. The probability of this event is

$$P(M') \cdot P(S) \cdot P(E) = \frac{9}{10} \cdot \frac{3}{10} \cdot \frac{7}{10} = \frac{189}{1000}$$

Since the three events we have just considered are mutually exclusive, the probability of getting exactly two A's is the sum of the probabilities we calculated. Thus,

$$P(T) = \frac{9}{1000} + \frac{49}{1000} + \frac{189}{1000} = \frac{247}{1000}$$

where T is the event of getting exactly two A's.

Have you been to a baseball game lately? Did anybody hit a home run? What are the chances of that? In a recent year, the number of home runs in major league baseball was 5386 and the number of plate appearances 188,052, thus, $P(HR) = \frac{\text{Home Runs}}{\text{Plate Appearances}} = \frac{5386}{188{,}052}$, about 1 in 35 times, or more precisely, 0.02864. But what about the probability of four home runs **in a row?** This actually happened on April 22, 2007 in a game between the New York Yankees and the Boston Red Sox, imagine that! Manny Ramirez came to bat with two outs in the third inning and hit a home run! Then, the incredible happened: J.D. Drew, Mike Lowell and Jason Varitek followed Ramirez and each of them hit a home run! What is the probability of that? We will find out in the next example. Source: Mathematics and Sports, Joseph A. Gallian, Editor.

EXAMPLE 4 Probability of Four Home Runs in a Row!

Assume that each players' at bat is ***independent*** of each other and that the probability of a home run is $P(HR) = 0.02864$

(a) What is the probability that four home runs are hit consecutively?

(b) If instead of using 0.02864 as the probability of hitting a home run by *each* of the players, use the *individual* probability that each of the players hit a home run, 0.0608, 0.0403, 0.0369 and 0.0324, for Ramirez, Drew, Lowell and Varitek, respectively. What is the probability now that four home runs are hit consecutively?

(c) There have been about 170,000 major league baseball games since 1900 and only 5 times have four home runs been hit in a row. Based on this information, what is the probability, written as a fraction, that four home runs are hit in a row?

Solution

(a) The probability of four consecutive home runs is:

$$\begin{aligned} P(HR) \cdot P(HR) \cdot P(HR) \cdot P(HR) &= \mathbf{0.02864 \cdot 0.02864 \cdot 0.02864 \cdot 0.02864} \\ &= 0.0000006728 \end{aligned}$$

This gives the probability at about 1 in 1.5 million (Go to http://tinyurl.com/yujb to see that 0.0000006728 is about 1 in 1.5 million!)

(b) This time the probability is $0.0608 \cdot 0.0403 \cdot 0.0369 \cdot 0.0324 = 0.0000029294$. Now the probability is larger, about 1 in 341,366.

(c) The probability that four home runs are hit in a row is 5/170,000 or 1 in 34,000 Which of the three probabilities is right? They all are, it depends on the assumptions you make regarding the independence of each of the at bats!

B Stochastic Processes

A **stochastic process** is a sequence of experiments in which the outcome of each experiment depends on chance. For example, the repeated tossing of a coin or of a die is a stochastic process. Tossing a coin and then rolling a die is also a stochastic process.

In the case of repeated tosses of a coin, we assume that on each toss there are two possible outcomes, each with probability $\frac{1}{2}$. If the coin is tossed twice, we can construct a tree diagram corresponding to this sequence of experiments (see Figure 11.14).

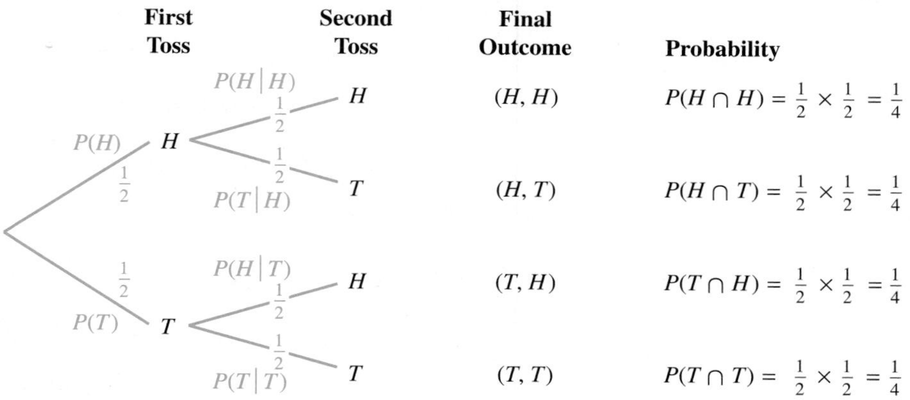

FIGURE 11.14

In Figure 11.14 we have put on each branch the probability of the event corresponding to that branch. To obtain the probability of, say, a tail and then a head, $P(T \cap H)$, we multiply the probabilities on each of the branches going along the path that leads from the start to the final outcome, as indicated in Figure 11.14. This multiplication gives $\left(\frac{1}{2}\right)\left(\frac{1}{2}\right) = \frac{1}{4}$, in agreement with the results we have previously obtained.

It is possible to show, by means of the SCP, that the terminal probabilities are always correctly obtained by using this multiplication technique. Notice that Figure 11.14 illustrates that

$$P(H \cap T) = P(H|T) \cdot P(T)$$

EXAMPLE 5 Probability of a Head and a 5

© I. Bello

A coin and a die are tossed. What is the probability of getting a head and a 5?

Solution

Since the outcomes depend only on chance, this is a stochastic process for which the multiplication procedure can be used. Since the probability of getting a head on the coin is $\frac{1}{2}$, and the probability of getting a 5 on the die is $\frac{1}{6}$, the probability of getting a head and a 5 is

$$P(H, 5) = \frac{1}{2} \times \frac{1}{6} = \frac{1}{12}$$

EXAMPLE 6 Outcomes from an Unbalanced Coin

Jim has two coins, one fair (F) and the other unbalanced (U) so that the probability of its coming up heads is $\frac{2}{3}$. He picks up one of the coins and tosses it, and it comes up heads. What is the probability that the outcome came from the unbalanced coin?

Solution

We draw a tree diagram as shown in Figure 11.15. The probabilities at the ends of the branches are obtained by the multiplication technique. The asterisked probabilities (*) may be taken as weights for the corresponding events.

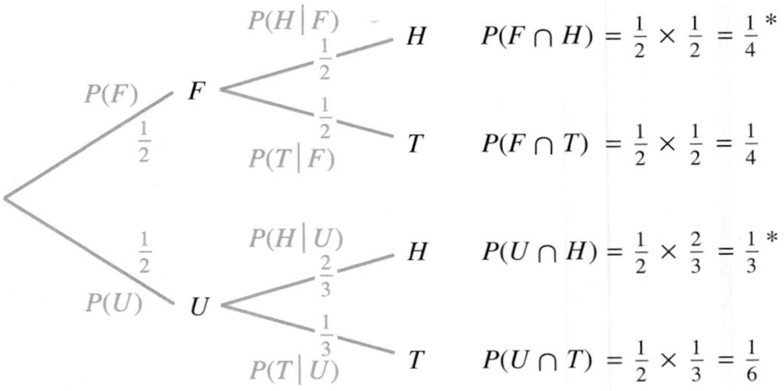

FIGURE 11.15

Thus, the probability that you picked the unbalanced coin (U) given that the outcome was heads (H) can be found by using

$$P(U|H) = \frac{P(U \cap H)}{P(H)} = \frac{\frac{1}{3}}{\frac{1}{4}+\frac{1}{3}} = \frac{4}{7}$$

EXAMPLE 7 Predicting Storms and Hurricanes in the Atlantic

In a recent year 16 named storms formed in the Atlantic. Of those, 5 became hurricanes and 3 (Don, Lee and Irene) hit the U.S. Based on this information, what is the probability that a named storm:

(a) will become a major hurricane?

(b) hits the U.S. in any single year?

(c) hits the U.S. in 3 consecutive years?

(d) does not hit the U.S.?

(e) does not hit the U.S. in the next 3 years?

(f) hits the U.S. at least once in the next 3 years ?

SOLUTION

(a) There were 16 named storms and 5 became major hurricanes, so the probability is $\frac{5}{16}$

(b) **3** of the 16 named storms hit the U.S., so the probability is $\frac{3}{16}$

(c) The probability of a named storm hitting the U.S. in **3** consecutive years is $\frac{3}{16} \cdot \frac{3}{16} \cdot \frac{3}{16} = \frac{27}{4096}$

(d) Since the probability that a named storm hits the U.S. in any single year is $\frac{3}{16}$, the probability that it does **not** is $1 - \frac{3}{16} = \frac{13}{16}$

(e) Since the probability that a named storm does **not** hit the U.S. is $\frac{13}{16}$, the probability that it does **not** hit in the next **3** years is $\frac{13}{16} \cdot \frac{13}{16} \cdot \frac{13}{16} = \frac{2197}{4096}$

(f) $P(\text{at least once in the next 3 years}) = 1 - P(\text{does not hit in the next 3 years})$

$$= 1 - \frac{2197}{4096} = \frac{1899}{4096}$$

EXAMPLE 8 Pancakes, Hats, and Marilyn

The following problem appeared in the "Ask Marilyn" question-and-answer column in *Parade* magazine:

> You have a hat in which there are three pancakes: One is golden on both sides, one is brown on both sides, and one is golden on one side and brown on the other. You withdraw one pancake, look at one side, and see that it is brown. What is the probability that the other side is brown?
>
> Robert Batts
> Acton, Massachusetts

> Source: Reprinted with permission from PARADE and Marilyn vos Savant, copyright © 1999, 1996, and 1992, respectively.

So, what do you think? There are several ways of solving the problem; we shall use a tree diagram.

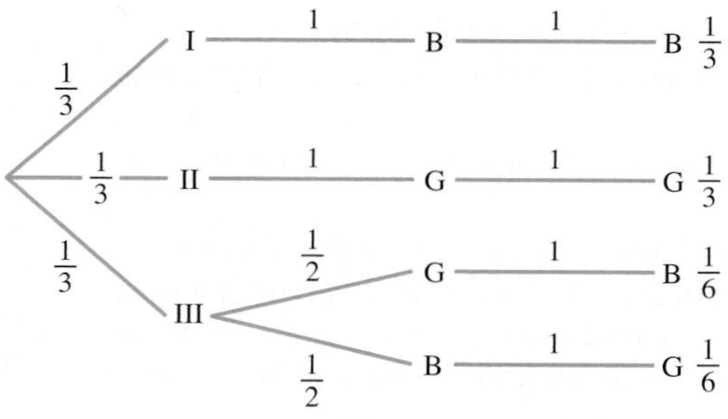

FIGURE 11.16

Solution

Let us make a tree diagram as in Figure 11.16 and label the pancakes and their sides I(B, B), II(G, G), and III(G, B). Let S be the second side is brown, and F the first side is brown. We want

$$P(S|F) = \frac{P(S \cap F)}{P(F)}$$

For both sides to be brown, we must select I(B, B) with probability $\frac{1}{3} = P(S \cap F)$. To find $P(F)$, let us study the tree.

If we select I(B, B), both sides are certainly brown, with probability 1.
If we select II(G, G), both sides are certainly golden with probability 1.

Finally, for III(G, B), the first side can be G or B each with probability $\frac{1}{2}$. If you picked G first, the second side is B with probability 1. If you picked B first, the second side is G with probability 1. Thus, the required probability is

$$\frac{\frac{1}{3}}{\frac{1}{3} + \frac{1}{6}} = \frac{\frac{2}{6}}{\frac{3}{6}} = \frac{2}{3}$$

11.5 EXERCISES

A Independent Events

1. Two coins are tossed. Let E_1 be the event in which the first coin comes up heads, and let E_2 be the event in which the second coin comes up tails. Are E_1 and E_2 independent?

2. According to a survey by the Pew Research Center, the rankings for the job the education system is doing in providing value for your money, are as shown in the graph. If two people are selected at random, and they said the education system was good or excellent, what is the probability that

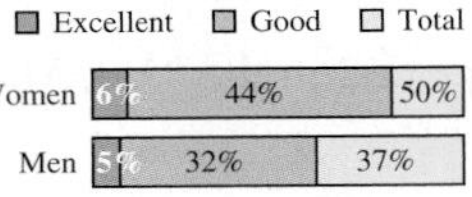

   a. both are women.
   b. the first is a woman, the second a man.
   c. both are women giving excellent ratings.
   d. both are men giving excellent ratings.
   e. one is a woman giving a good rating and the second is a man giving an excellent rating.

3. A computer repair shop has estimated the probability that a computer sent to the shop has a bad modem is $\frac{1}{4}$, the probability that the computer has a bad CPU is $\frac{1}{8}$, and the probability that it has a bad drive is $\frac{1}{3}$. If we assume that modems, CPUs, and drives are independent, find the probability that
   a. a modem, CPU, and a drive in a computer sent to the shop are bad.
   b. only a modem and a CPU in a computer sent to the shop are bad.
   c. none of the three parts (modem, CPU, or drive) is bad.

4. The following graph gives the reason people 16–64 or 65 and older work. Suppose you select two persons, one 16–64 and the other 65+. Written as a decimal, what is the probability that
   a. they both work because they need the money?
   b. the younger one works because they need the money and the older one because they want to work?
   c. one works because they need the money the other one because they want to work?

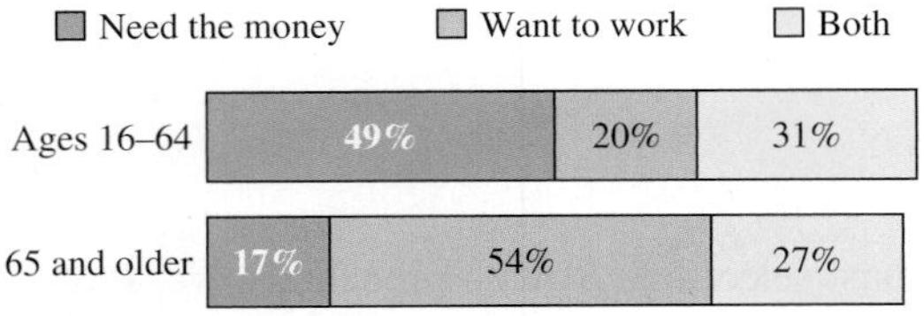

5. A coin is tossed 3 times. Find the probability of obtaining
   a. heads on the first and last toss, and tails on the second toss.
   b. at least 2 heads.
   c. at most 2 heads.

6. A die is rolled 3 times. Find the probability of obtaining
   a. an odd number each time.
   b. 2 odd numbers first and an even one on the last roll.
   c. at least 2 odd numbers.

7. A card is drawn from an ordinary deck of 52 cards, and the result is recorded on paper. The card is then returned to the deck and another card is drawn and recorded. Find the probability that
   a. the first card is a spade.
   b. the second card is a spade.
   c. both cards are spades.
   d. neither card is a spade.

8. Rework problem 7, assuming that the 2 cards are drawn in succession and without replacement. (*Hint:* Make a tree diagram and assign probabilities to each of the branches.)

9. A family has 3 children. Let M be the event "the family has at most 1 girl," and let B be the event "the family has children of both sexes."
   a. Find $P(M)$.
   b. Find $P(B)$.
   c. Find $P(B \cap M)$.
   d. Determine whether B and M are independent.

10. Two cards are drawn in succession and without replacement from an ordinary deck of 52 cards. What is the probability that
   a. the first card is a king and the second card is an ace?
   b. both cards are aces?
   c. neither card is an ace?
   d. exactly 1 card is an ace?

In problems 11–15, assume the spinner has 5 unequal sectors $\frac{1}{6}$ red, $\frac{1}{9}$ blue, $\frac{5}{18}$ green, $\frac{2}{9}$ white, and $\frac{2}{9}$ yellow as shown. If the spinner is spun twice, find the probability (as a reduced fraction) that the spinner will

11. land in the green and then in the red sector.
12. land in the white and then in the blue sector.
13. land twice on green.
14. not land on the white sector.
15. land in a sector other than red.

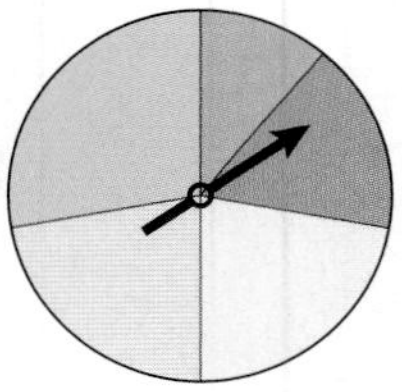

Do you know what the message below says? If the 20 marbles used to spell the word are placed in a glass jar and two marbles are chosen at random in succession and without replacement, what is the probability (as a reduced fraction) of choosing

16. 2 red marbles?
17. a red and then a blue marble?
18. a marble other than red each time?
19. a green and then a yellow marble?
20. 2 marbles of the same color?

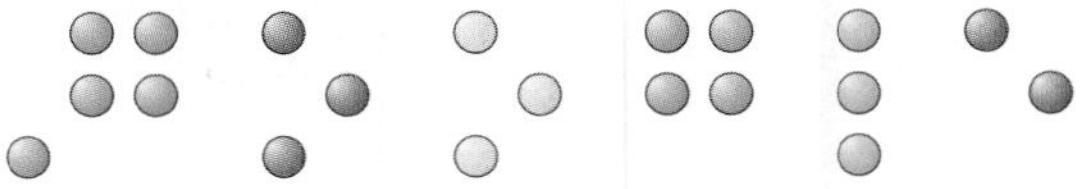

Think braille!

A jar contains 7 red, 6 green, 8 blue, and 4 yellow marbles. A marble is chosen at random from the jar. After replacing it, a second marble is chosen. What is the probability of choosing

21. a red and then a yellow marble?
22. 2 yellow marbles?
23. no blue marbles?
24. 2 marbles of the same color?
25. at least one red marble?

The circle graph below will be used in problems 26–30. In a survey of different spam categories conducted by Clearswift, the percent of each type of spam was as shown in the graph. Suppose 3 spam messages from the ones included in the survey are selected at random. Find the probability (written as a decimal) that

26. all of them were about healthcare.
27. none of them was about healthcare.
28. the first one was about healthcare, the second one about finance, and the third regarded direct products.
29. there was no direct product spam among the 3.
30. If you were to regulate spamming, which category would you investigate first?

Spam Categorization Breakdown

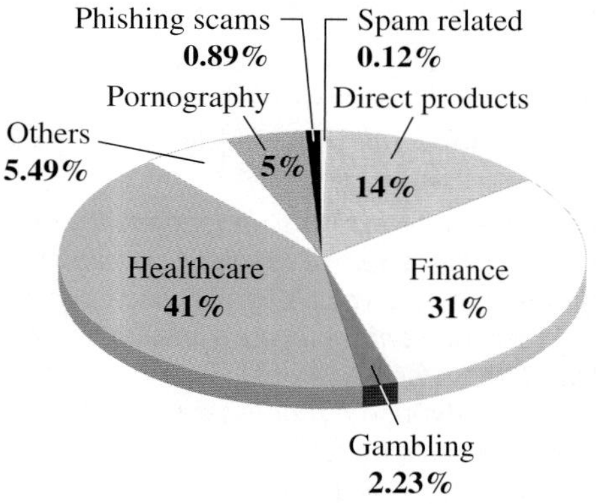

Note: Results do not add to 100% because of rounding.

31. A company has estimated that the probabilities of success for 3 products introduced in the market are $\frac{1}{4}$, $\frac{2}{3}$, and $\frac{1}{2}$, respectively. Assuming independence, find the probability that
    a. the 3 products are successful.
    b. none of the products is successful.
32. In problem 31, find the probability that exactly 1 product is successful.
33. A coin is tossed. If heads comes up, a die is rolled; but if tails comes up, the coin is thrown again. Find the probability of obtaining
    a. 2 tails.
    b. heads and the number 6.
    c. heads and an even number.
34. In a survey of 100 persons, the data in the following table were obtained:

Type of Person	Lung Cancer (L)	No Lung Cancer (L')
Smoker (S)	42	28
Nonsmoker (S')	18	12

    a. Are S and L independent?
    b. Are S' and L' independent?
35. Referring to Table 11.4 (page 634), find the probability that two females, one 30 years old and the other 40 years old, will live to be 60.
36. In problem 35, find the probability that both females will live to be 70.
37. The Apollo module has five components: the main engine, the propulsion system, the command service module, the lunar excursion module (LEM), and the LEM engine. If each of the systems is considered independent of the others and the probability that each of the systems performs satisfactorily is 0.90, what is the probability all the systems will perform satisfactorily?
38. A die is loaded so that 1, 2, 3, and 4 each has probability $\frac{1}{8}$ of coming up, while 5 and 6 each has probability $\frac{1}{4}$ of coming up. Consider the events $A = \{1, 3, 5\}$ and $B = \{2, 4, 5\}$. Determine whether A and B are independent.
39. On one of the experimental flights of a space shuttle, the mission was cut short due to a malfunction of a battery aboard the ship. The batteries in the shuttle are guaranteed to have a failure rate of only 1 in 20. The system of 3 batteries is designed to operate as long as any one of the batteries functions properly. Find the probability that
    a. all 3 batteries fail. b. exactly 2 fail.
40. In a certain city, the probability of catching a burglar is 0.30, and the probability of convicting a caught burglar is 0.60. Find the probability that a burglar will be caught and convicted.
41. In a recent year the average number of at bats in the National League postseason was 254 including 54 hits, while in the American League, the number of at bats in the postseason was 274 with 66 hits. Based on this information, find the probability that
    a. a batter gets a hit in the postseason in the National and in the American League.
    b. In which league is the probability of getting a hit in the postseason higher?
    c. Find the probability of getting four hits in a row in the National and in the American League postseason.
42. In the 2010 baseball season the New York Yankees earned a wild card spot to play in the American League Division series against the Minnesota Twins. During the regular season it did not matter where the game was played: the Yankees beat the Twins 2 out of 3 times at home and 2 out of 3 away. In the series, however, the Yankees won all 3 games! Based on this information, what is the probability that:
    a. the Yankees beat the Twins at home.
    b. the Yankees beat the Twins away.
    c. the Yankees sweep the Twins by winning 3 games in a row (2 away, 1 at home).

B Stochastic Processes

43. Three boxes, labeled *A*, *B*, and *C*, contain 1 red and 2 black balls, 2 red and 1 black ball, and 1 red and 1 black ball, respectively. First a box is selected at random, and then a ball is drawn at random from that box. Find the probability that the ball is red. (*Hint:* Draw a tree diagram, assign the probabilities to the separate branches, and compute the terminal probabilities by using the multiplication technique. Then add the terminal probabilities for all the outcomes in which the ball is red.)

44. There are 3 filing cabinets, each with two drawers. All the drawers contain letters. In one cabinet, both drawers contain airmail letters; in a second cabinet, both drawers contain ordinary letters; and in the third cabinet, one drawer contains airmail and the other contains ordinary letters. A cabinet is selected at random, and then a drawer is picked at random from this cabinet. When the drawer is opened, it is found to contain airmail letters. What is the probability that the other drawer of this cabinet also contains airmail letters? (*Hint:* Use the same procedure as in problem 43.)

45. John has 2 coins, one fair and the other unbalanced so that the probability of its coming up heads is $\frac{3}{4}$. He picks one of the coins at random, tosses it, and it comes up heads. What is the probability that he picked the unbalanced coin?

46. A box contains 3 green balls and 2 yellow balls. Two balls are drawn at random in succession and without replacement. If the second ball is yellow, what is the probability that the first one is green?

IN OTHER WORDS

47. a. Explain, in your own words, what is meant by the statement "Two events *A* and *B* are independent."

b. If *A* and *B* are independent events and you know $P(A)$ and $P(B)$, how can you calculate $P(A \cap B)$?

48. In 2010 for the first time in recorded history, 12 hurricanes formed in the Atlantic basin without a single one hitting the U.S., according to experts at Colorado State University. Thus, based on this information, the probability that a hurricane in the Atlantic basin hit the U.S. in 2010 was **0**, and the probability that at least one hurricane hits the Atlantic basin at least once the next year was **1.** Explain why.

USING YOUR KNOWLEDGE

Suppose that a fair coin is flipped 10 times in succession. What is the probability that exactly 4 of the flips turn up heads? This is a problem in which repeated trials of the same experiment are made, and the probability of success is the same for each of the trials. This type of procedure is often called a ***Bernoulli trial,*** *and the final probability is known as a* ***binomial probability.***

Let us see if we can discover how to calculate such a probability. We represent the 10 flips and one possible success like this:

H	*T*	*T*	*H*	*H*	*T*	*T*	*T*	*H*	*T*
1	2	3	4	5	6	7	8	9	10

Because each flip is independent of the others, the probability of getting the particular sequence shown is $(\frac{1}{2})^{10}$. *All we need do now is find in how many ways we can succeed, that is, in how many ways we can get exactly 4 heads. This is the same as the number of ways we can select 4 of the 10 flips, that is,* $C(10, 4)$. *The successful ways of getting 4 heads are all mutually exclusive, so the probability of getting exactly 4 heads is*

$$\frac{C(10, 4)}{2^{10}}$$

Let us suppose now that the coin is biased so that the probability of heads on any one toss is p and the probability of tails is $q = 1 - p$. *The probability of getting the arrangement we have shown is now* p^4q^6. *(Why?) Hence, the probability of getting exactly 4 heads is*

$$C(10, 4)p^4q^6$$

You should be able to convince yourself that if n is the number of trials, p is the probability of success in each trial, and $q = 1 - p$ *is the probability of failure, then the probability of exactly x successes is*

$$C(n, x)p^xq^{n-x}$$

49. Suppose that a fair coin is tossed 50 times in succession. What is the probability of getting exactly 25 heads? (Do not multiply out your answer.)

50. If a fair coin is tossed 6 times in succession, what is the probability of getting at least 3 heads?

51. Suppose that the coin in problem 50 is biased 2 to 1 in favor of heads. Can you calculate the probability of getting at least 3 heads?

52. Suppose that a fair coin is tossed an even number of times, 2, 4, 6, ... What happens to the probability of getting heads in exactly half the tosses as the number of tosses increases?

53. A fair die is tossed 5 times in succession. What is the probability of getting exactly two 3s?

54. In problem 53, what is the probability of obtaining at least two 3s?

In the case of security systems, independent components in series are the most reliable. For example, consider a triple-threat security system that uses voice patterns, fingerprints, and handwriting to screen persons entering a maximum security area. Here is how the system operates. To enter a secure area, a person must pass through a room that has a door at each end and contains three small booths. In the first booth, the person punches in his or her 4-digit identification number. This causes the machine inside the booth to intone 4 words, which the person must repeat. If the voice pattern matches the pattern that goes with the identification number, the machine says "Thank you" and the person goes to the next booth. After entering his or her number there, the person signs his or her name on a Mylar sheet. If the signature is acceptable, the machine flashes a green light and the person goes to the third booth. There, he or she punches in the identification number once more and then pokes a finger into a slot, fingerprint down. If a yellow light flashes "IDENTITY VERIFIED," the door opens and the person can enter the high-security area.

55. Assume each of the machines is 98% reliable. What is the probability that a person fools the first machine?

56. What is the probability that a person fools the first 2 machines?

57. What is the probability that a person fools all 3 machines?

58. On the basis of your answer to problem 57, how would you rate the reliability of this security system?

11.6 Odds and Mathematical Expectation

GETTING STARTED

OBJECTIVES

A. Given the probability of an event find the odds "for" and "against" the event.

B. Find the expected value of an event.

C. Solve applications involving maximizing or minimizing the results of an event.

LOTTERY ODDS

Look at the information in Table 11.6. The odds of winning the first prize by picking 6 out of 6 numbers (there are 49 numbers to pick from) are said to be1 in 13,983,816. But in Section 11.1 we found that the *probability* of winning the first prize is $\frac{1}{13,983,816}$. Isn't there a difference between odds and probability? Of course there is! What most state lotteries mistakenly report as *odds* are actually the *probabilities* of winning.

To explain further, the **probability** of an event is a fraction whose numerator is the number of times the event can occur and whose denominator is the total number of possibilities in the sample space. Thus, if we throw a die, the probability of getting a number greater than 4 is $\frac{2}{6}$ because there are two favorable outcomes of numbers greater than 4 (5 and 6) out of 6 total possibilities (1, 2, 3, 4, 5, and 6.) The **odds** in favor of an event are defined as the **ratio** of favorable to unfavorable occurrences for the event. Thus, the odds for getting a number greater than 4 are *2 to 4* because there are 2 favorable outcomes (5 and 6) and 4 unfavorable ones (1, 2, 3, and 4). These odds are sometimes written as 2 : 4 (read "2 to 4"). Now, back to the lottery ticket. Since the probability of winning the first prize is 1 to 13,983,816, the odds of winning the first prize are 1 to 13,983,815, not 1 to 13,983,816.

Table 11.6 State Lottery with 49 Numbers

Prize Divisions and Odds of Winning

Matching Numbers	Odds
6 of 6 numbers	1 in 13,983,816
5 of 6 numbers	1 in 54,200.84
4 of 6 numbers	1 in 1032.4
3 of 6 numbers	1 in 56.66
Overall odds	1 in 53.66

Some probabilities are given in Table 11.7. What are the corresponding odds?

Table 11.7

Situations	Probability	Odds in Favor
Getting married if you are 18 or older	0.64	64 : 36
Having 3 or more children	0.11	
Developing high blood pressure	$\frac{2}{5}$	
Getting accepted to medical school	$\frac{6}{10}$	
Never eating candy	$\frac{1}{33}$	

Note that if the odds for the event are 64 to 36, the probability of the event should be

$$\frac{64}{64 + 36} = \frac{64}{100} = 0.64$$

We shall study more about the relationship between odds and probability in this section.

In this chapter we have several times used games of chance to illustrate the concepts of probability. In connection with these games, we often encounter such statements as "The odds are 1 to 5 for rolling a 1 with a die" or "The odds are 12 to 1 against picking an ace from a deck of cards." When a person gives us 1 to 5 odds for rolling a 1 with a die, it usually means that if a 1 does occur, we pay \$5 and, if a 1 does not occur, the person pays \$1. These statements simply compare the number of favorable outcomes to the number of unfavorable outcomes. Thus, odds of 1 to 5 mean that there are 5 times as many unfavorable as favorable outcomes.

A Odds

Odds in Favor of an Event

If an event E is such that the total number of favorable outcomes is f and the total number of unfavorable outcomes is u, the **odds in favor of E are f to u.** Moreover, the Odds Against the Event are ***u* to *f*.**

For instance, there are 4 aces in a standard deck of 52 cards. Thus, if a single card is drawn from the deck, there are 4 ways of getting an ace (favorable) and 48 ways of not getting an ace (unfavorable). Thus, the odds in favor of drawing an ace are 4 to 48, or 1 to 12, when written in ***reduced*** form by dividing both 4 and 48 by 4.

Favorable (4) Unfavorable (48)

Note that the odds *against* drawing an ace are 48 to 4, or 12 to 1.

EXAMPLE 1 Odds When Rolling 1 Die

A fair die is rolled. What odds should a person give

(a) in favor of a 1 turning up?

(b) against a 1 turning up?

Solution

(a) In this case, there is 1 favorable outcome, so $f = 1$, and there are 5 unfavorable outcomes, so $u = 5$. Thus, the odds are 1 to 5.

(b) There are 5 ways in which 1 does not turn up (favorable) and 1 way in which 1 turns up (unfavorable), so the odds against a 1 turning up are 5 to 1.

EXAMPLE 2 Probabilities Based on a Record

A horse named Camarero has a record of 73 wins and 4 losses. Based on this record, what is the probability of a win for this horse?

Solution

Here, $f = 73$ and $u = 4$, since the probability of an event is

$$\frac{\text{Number of favorable outcomes}}{\text{Number of possible outcomes}}$$

Favorable ⟶ Possible ⟶

$$\frac{f}{f+u} = \frac{73}{73+4} = \frac{73}{77}$$

Note that since $f = 73$ and $u = 4$, the **odds** for Camarero to win 73 races and lose 4 are 73 to 4. In general, we have:

Probability and Odds

If the probability for an event is $P = \dfrac{\text{Favorable Outcomes}}{\text{Total Outcomes}} = \dfrac{f}{f+u}$, the odds in *favor* of the event are f to u and the odds ***against*** are **u** to f.

An equivalent definition of odds in favor of the event E is

$P(E)$ to $P(\text{not } E)$

or, since $P(\text{not } E) = 1 - P(E)$,

$P(E)$ to $1 - P(E)$

In the case of the die in Example 1(a), the odds are $\frac{1}{6}$ to $\frac{5}{6}$, which is the same as 1 to 5. Note that if $P(E)$ and $P(\text{not } E)$ are expressed as fractions with the same denominator, we can compare just the numerators. For example, if $P(E) = \frac{2}{7}$, then $P(\text{not } E) = 1 - \frac{2}{7} = \frac{5}{7}$, so the odds in favor of E are 2 to 5.

EXAMPLE 3 From Probability to Odds

A horse named Blue Bonnet has won 5 of her last 8 races and is thus assigned a probability of $\frac{5}{8}$ of winning her ninth race. Assuming this probability is correct, what are the odds *against* Blue Bonnet's winning that race?

Solution

Since $P(\text{winning}) = \frac{5}{8}$, we know $P(\text{not winning}) = 1 - \frac{5}{8} = \frac{3}{8}$. Thus, the odds in favor of Blue Bonnet are 5 to 3, and the odds *against* her are 3 to 5.

EXAMPLE 4 Odds for the Florida Lottery

To play Lotto in Florida you select 6 numbers from 1 to 53 and pay \$1. To win, you must match (in any order) 3, 4, 5, or 6 of the winning numbers drawn in the official drawing for the date played.

(a) What is the probability that you match 6 out of the 6 numbers?

(b) What are the odds in favor of matching 6 out of 6 numbers?

(c) What is the probability that you match exactly 5 out of the 6 numbers?

(d) What are the odds in favor of matching exactly 5 out of 6 numbers?

GRAPH IT

If you want to calculate $C(53, 6)$ the long way, try

$$\frac{53 \cdot 52 \cdot 51 \cdot 50 \cdot 49 \cdot 48}{6 \cdot 5 \cdot 4 \cdot 3 \cdot 2 \cdot 1}$$

Simplify!

With a grapher, enter 5 3 [MATH] [◄] 3 6. Then press [ENTER]. The answer is shown.

```
53 nCr 6
                22957480
```

Solution

Recall that the probability of an event is

$$\frac{\text{Favorable outcomes}}{\text{Total outcomes}}$$

(a) Since there are 53 numbers to choose from and we have to select 6 of them, the total number of outcomes is $C(53, 6)$. Of these, only 1 is favorable, thus

$$\frac{\text{Favorable outcomes}}{\text{Total outcomes}} = \frac{1}{C(53, 6)} = \frac{1}{22{,}957{,}480}$$

(b) The odds in favor are 1 to 22,957,479.

(c) To match 5 out of the 6 numbers, we have to select 5 numbers from the 6 winning numbers. This can be done in $C(6, 5)$ ways. We then have to select one more number from the 47 $(53 - 6 = 47)$ remaining numbers. This can be done in 47 different ways. Thus, we have $C(6, 5) \cdot 47$ favorable outcomes out of $C(53, 6)$. The probability is

$$\frac{C(6, 5) \cdot 47}{C(53, 6)} = \frac{6 \cdot 47}{22{,}957{,}480} = \frac{282}{22{,}957{,}480}$$

(d) The odds in favor of this are 282 to 22,957,198.

Table 11.8 Florida Lotto Odds and Estimated Prizes

Prize Level	Estimated Prize*	Odds of Winning
6-of-6	Jackpot†	1:22,957,480
5-of-6	$5,000	1:81,409.50
4-of-6	$70	1:1,415.82
3-of-6	$5	1:70.79
Overall		1:67.36

*The estimated prize payouts to each winner are based on averages of previous payouts. FLORIDA LOTTO is a parimutual game. Actual prize amounts vary depending on sales and the number of winners in each prize category.

†If no FLORIDA LOTTO ticket matches all six winning numbers, the jackpot rolls over, and the cash in the jackpot prize pool is carried over to the next drawing.

Source: Florida Lottery.

The official Florida Lotto table (Table 11.8) confuses *odds* with probability, erroneously stating that the *odds* of winning the jackpot are 1:22,957,480 when, as we have shown, the *probability* of winning the jackpot is $\frac{1}{22{,}957{,}480}$. Can you figure out how they obtained the odds for getting 5 of 6 numbers?

B Expected Value

In many games of chance we are concerned with betting. Suppose that a given event E has probability $P(E) = f/n$ of occurring and $P(\text{not } E) = u/n$ of not occurring. If we now agree to pay f dollars if E does not occur in exchange for receiving u dollars if E does occur, then we can calculate our "expected average winnings" by multiplying $P(E)$ (the approximate proportion of the times we win) by u (the amount we win each time). Similarly, our losses will be $P(\text{not } E) \times f$, because we lose f dollars approximately $P(\text{not } E)$

of the times. If the bet is to be fair, the average net winnings should be 0. Let us see if this is the case. Our net winnings will be

$$\underbrace{P(E) \times u}_{\text{Our gain}} - \underbrace{P(\text{not } E) \times f}_{\text{Our loss}} = \frac{f}{n} \times u - \frac{u}{n} \times f$$

$$= \frac{fu - uf}{n} = 0$$

as they should be. Since the odds in favor of E are f to u, we state the following definition:

Definition of a Fair Bet

If the probability that event E will occur is f/n and the probability that E will not occur is u/n, where n is the total number of possible outcomes, then the odds of f to u in favor of E occurring constitute a **fair bet.**

EXAMPLE 5 Odds for a Fair Bet

A woman bets that she can roll a 7 in one roll of a pair of dice. What odds should she give for the bet to be fair?

Solution

$P(7) = \frac{6}{36} = \frac{1}{6}$. Here $1 = f$ and $f + u = 6$, so $u = 5$. Hence, the odds should be 1 to 5.

Sometimes we wish to compute the *expected value,* or *mathematical expectation,* of a game. For example, if a woman wins \$6 when she obtains a 1 in a single roll of a die and loses \$12 for any other number, we can see that if she plays the game many times, she will win \$6 one-sixth of the time and she will lose \$12 five-sixths of the time. We then expect her to gain $(\$6)(\frac{1}{6}) - (\$12)(\frac{5}{6}) = -\$9$, that is, to lose \$9 per try on the average.

For another example, if a fair die is rolled 600 times, we would expect $(\frac{1}{6})(600) = 100$ ones to appear. This does not mean that exactly 100 ones *will appear* but that this is the *expected average* number of ones for this experiment. In fact, if the number of ones were far away from 100, we would have good reason to doubt the fairness of the die.

Definition of Expected Value

If the k possible outcomes of an experiment are assigned the values $a_1, a_2, \ldots, a_k$ and they occur with probabilities $p_1, p_2, \ldots, p_k$, respectively, then the **expected value** of the experiment is given by

$$E = a_1p_1 + a_2p_2 + a_3p_3 + \cdots + a_kp_k$$

A casino game called Keno is played with 80 balls numbered 1 through 80. Twenty winning balls are chosen at random. A popular bet is the \$2, 10-number bet in which you select 10 numbers and the casino will pay you, say, \$4 if exactly 5 of the numbers you picked match 5 of the 20 that were selected. What is the probability of that happening?

There are 80 numbers altogether, 10 you pick and 70 you do not. There are $C(10, 5)$ ways to pick the 5 matching numbers from your 10. That leaves $C(70, 15)$ for the numbers you do not pick.

Thus, the number of ways of matching 5 numbers from the 10 is

$C(10, 5) \cdot C(70, 15)$

The number of combinations when 20 balls are picked from 80 is $C(80, 20)$. Thus,

$$P(\text{match } 5) = \frac{C(10, 5) \cdot C(70, 15)}{C(80, 20)}$$
$$\approx 0.0514277$$

Table 11.9 gives the payoffs and probabilities for a \$2, 10-number bet.

Table 11.9

Match	Pays	Probability
5	\$ 4	0.0514277
6	\$ 40	0.0114794
7	\$ 280	0.0016111
8	\$ 1800	0.0001354
9	\$ 8000	0.0000061
10	\$50,000	0.0000001

PROBLEM-SOLVING

Mathematical Expectation

① **Read** the problem.

Find the mathematical expectation for a \$2, 10-number bet in Keno.

② **Select** the unknown.

You want to find the mathematical expectation of a \$2 bet.

③ **Think** of a plan.
Find how much you can expect to get if you match 5, 6, 7, 8, 9, or 10 numbers. Subtract the \$2 cost of the ticket.

To find how much you can expect to get for matching 5, 6, 7, 8, 9, or 10 numbers, multiply the payoffs by their probabilities and add to get your winnings. Then, subtract \$2.

④ **Use** Table 11.9 to find the expected value of the winnings for matching the following:

Here are the payoffs times the probabilities rounded to two decimal places.

5 numbers	$\$4 \cdot 0.0514277 = \$0.21$
6 numbers	$\$40 \cdot 0.0114794 = \$0.46$
7 numbers	$\$280 \cdot 0.0016111 = \$0.45$
8 numbers	$\$1800 \cdot 0.0001354 = \$0.24$
9 numbers	$\$8000 \cdot 0.0000061 = \$0.05$
10 numbers	$\$50{,}000 \cdot 0.0000001 = \$0.01$
	$\$1.42$

Subtract the cost of the \$2 ticket to find *E*.

$E = \$1.42 - \$2.00 = -\$.58$

Thus, your expected value is $-\$.58$. (You lose 58 cents!)

⑤ **Verify** the solution.

Do this with a calculator!

Try Example 6 Now

Cover the solution, write your own solution, and then check your work.

Table 11.10	
Claim Amount	**Probability**
0	0.83
500	0.06
1000	0.05
2000	0.02
5000	0.02
8000	0.01
10,000	0.001

Source: http://tinyurl.com/3nxnr2y

EXAMPLE 6 Determining Insurance Premiums Using Expected Value

Statewide Insurance has determined the probability of paying various claim amounts as shown in Table 11.10. Find the expected value of a claim with Statewide Insurance.

Solution

Let $a_1 = 0, a_2 = \$500, a_3 = \$\,1000, a_4 = \$\,2000, a_5 = \$\,5000, a_6 = \$8000, a_7 = \$10{,}000$ and p_1, p_2 and so on be the corresponding probabilities. The expected value E of a claim is

$$\begin{aligned} E &= (\$0)(0.83) + (\$500)(0.06) + (\$1000)(0.05) + (\$2000)(0.02) + (\$5000)(0.02) + (\$8000)(0.01) + (\$10{,}000)(0.001) \\ &= 0 + \$30 + \$50 \quad \$40 + \$100 + \$80 + \$10 \\ &= \$310 \end{aligned}$$

Note that to be **fair** the premium (amount you pay) for a policy based on this information should be \$310.

EXAMPLE 7 Fair Price for Annual Premium

A 35-year-old female buys a \$200,000 one-year term life insurance policy. Based on a U.S. government mortality table, the probability that she will live for one year is 0.999104. Find **(a)** the expected value of the policy, **(b)** a fair price for the annual premium, **(c)** the monthly payment that covers the expected value of the policy.

Solution

(a) The expected value is $E = a_1 p_1$, where $a_1 = \$200{,}000$ and the probability of death is $p_1 = 1 - 0.999104 = 0.000896$, so $E = \$200{,}000(0.000896) = \$179.20$.

(b) A fair price for the annual premium is the expected value of the policy, \$179.20.

(c) The monthly payment would be \$179.20/12 or \$14.93 http://www.jdpower.com/content/study/zOtfWKH/everyone-can-afford-term-life-insurance.htm.

Definition of a Fair Game

A game is **fair** if its expected value is 0.

EXAMPLE 8 Payment for a Fair Game

A die is rolled. A person receives double the number of dollars corresponding to the dots on the face that turns up. How much should a player pay for playing in order to make this a fair game?

Solution

The player can win \$2, \$4, \$6, \$8, \$10, and \$12, each with probability $\frac{1}{6}$, so expected winnings (the player does not lose) are

$$E = 2\left(\tfrac{1}{6}\right) + 4\left(\tfrac{1}{6}\right) + 6\left(\tfrac{1}{6}\right) + 8\left(\tfrac{1}{6}\right) + 10\left(\tfrac{1}{6}\right) + 12\left(\tfrac{1}{6}\right) = \tfrac{42}{6} = \$7$$

A person paying \$7 can expect winnings of 0. Thus, \$7 is a fair price to pay for playing this game.

C Applications

EXAMPLE 9 Maximizing Business Expectations

Dear's Department Store wishes to open a new store in one of two locations. It is estimated that if the first location is chosen, the store will make a profit of \$100,000 per year if successful and will lose \$50,000 per year otherwise. For the second location, it is estimated that the annual profit will be \$150,000 if successful; otherwise, the annual loss will be \$80,000. If the probability of success at each location is $\frac{3}{4}$, which location should be chosen in order to maximize the expected profit?

Solution

For the first location, $a_1 = \$100{,}000$, $p_1 = \frac{3}{4}$, $a_2 = -\$50{,}000$, and $p_2 = \frac{1}{4}$. Thus, the expected profit is

$$E_1 = \$100{,}000(\tfrac{3}{4}) - \$50{,}000(\tfrac{1}{4}) = \$75{,}000 - \$12{,}500 = \$62{,}500$$

For the second location, $a_1 = \$150{,}000$, $p_1 = \frac{3}{4}$, $a_2 = -\$80{,}000$, and $p_2 = \frac{1}{4}$. Thus, the expected profit is

$$E_2 = \$150{,}000(\tfrac{3}{4}) - \$80{,}000(\tfrac{1}{4}) = \$112{,}500 - \$20{,}000 = \$92{,}500$$

The expected profit from the second location (\$92,500) is greater than that for the first location (\$62,500), so the second location should be chosen.

Decision problems that depend on mathematical expectation require three things for their solutions: *options, values,* and *probabilities.* From Example 9 we have the information given in Table 11.11. With this information we can find the expected value for each option and hence make the desired decision.

Table 11.11

	Options			
	Site 1		Site 2	
Values	\$100,000	−\$50,000	\$150,000	−\$80,000
Probabilities	$\frac{3}{4}$	$\frac{1}{4}$	$\frac{3}{4}$	$\frac{1}{4}$

However, sometimes it is easier to write all the information using a tree diagram as we shall show next.

EXAMPLE 10 Maximizing Personal Decisions

Suppose you have two choices for a personal decision. Let us call these choices *A* and *B*. With choice *A*, you can make \$20 with probability 0.24, \$35 with probability 0.47, and \$50 with probability 0.29. With choice *B* you can **lose** \$9 with probability 0.25, make nothing (\$0) with probability 0.35, and make \$95 with probability 0.40. Make a tree diagram and determine what your decision should be if you want to maximize your profit.

Solution

We first draw the tree diagram for this situation as in Figure 11.17 with the branches labeled with their respective probabilities and the monetary outcomes indicated at the end of the corresponding branches.

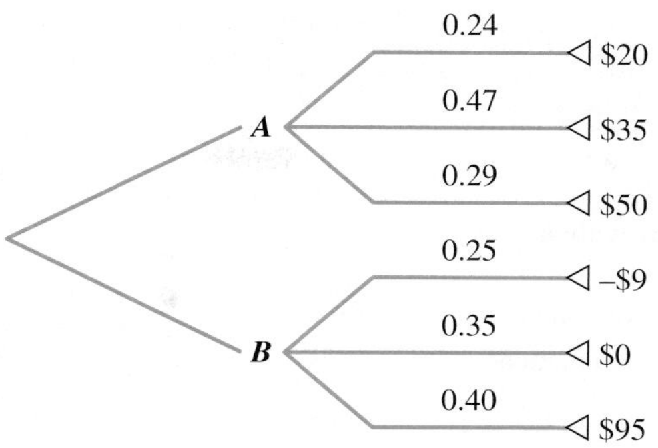

FIGURE 11.17

The expected value E_A for A is

$$E_A = (0.24)(\$20) + (0.47)(\$35) + (0.29)(\$50)$$
$$= \$4.80 + \$16.45 + \$14.50$$
$$= \$35.75$$

The expected value E_B for B is

$$E_B = (0.25)(-\$9) + (0.35)(\$0) + (0.40)(\$95)$$
$$= -\$2.25 + \$0 + \$38$$
$$= \$35.75$$

Both decisions have the same expected value! We will discuss possible courses of action in Collaborative Learning in the exercises.

11.6 EXERCISES

A Odds

In problems 1–7, find the odds in favor of obtaining

1. a 2 in one roll of a single die.
2. an even number in one roll of a single die.
3. an ace when drawing 1 card from an ordinary deck of 52 cards.
4. a red card when drawing 1 card from an ordinary deck of 52 cards.
5. 2 tails when an ordinary coin is tossed twice.
6. at least 1 tail when an ordinary coin is tossed twice.
7. a vowel when 1 letter is chosen at random from among the 26 letters of the English alphabet.

In problems 8–12, find the odds against obtaining

8. a 4 in one roll of a single die.
9. an odd number in one roll of a single die.
10. the king of spades when drawing 1 card from an ordinary deck of 52 cards.
11. one of the face (picture) cards (jack, queen, king) when drawing 1 card from an ordinary deck of 52 cards.
12. at most 1 tail when an ordinary coin is tossed twice.
13. Using the information in Table 11.8 on page 660, what is the probability of winning \$5 when you buy one Florida Lottery ticket? Write the answer as a proper fraction. What are the odds in favor of winning \$5? (*Hint:* The table is wrong!)
14. Using the information in Table 11.8, what is the probability of winning \$70 when you buy one Florida Lottery ticket? Write the answer as a proper fraction. What are the odds in favor of winning \$70? (*Hint:* The table is wrong!)
15. If the correct odds in favor of Johnny's winning a race are 3 to 2, what is the probability that Johnny wins?

The information for problems 16–25 was taken from the book What Are the Chances? *by Bernard Siskin, Jerome Staller, and David Rorvik. Find the missing numbers.*

	Event	*Probability*	*Odds*
16.	Being the victim of a serious crime in your lifetime	$\frac{1}{20}$	______
17.	Being the victim of a serious crime in San Antonio, where there are 630 violent crimes per 100,000 population	______	______
18.	Having complications during surgery in June	______	1 to 4
19.	Having complications during surgery in July when new interns and residents are brought in	$\frac{1}{2}$	______
20.	Having high cholesterol levels	$\frac{1}{4}$	______

Event	*Probability*	*Odds*
21. Publishing 1 of the 10 best-selling novels of the year	_____	10 to 4867
22. Getting rich by hard work	_____	41 to 9
23. Being a top executive of a major company without going to college	_____	3 to 21
24. Completing 4 years of college	0.19	_____
25. Growing up being incompetent in math	0.33	_____

B Expected Value

26. A coin is tossed twice. If heads comes up either time, we get \$2; but if heads does not occur, we lose \$4. What is the expected value of this game?

27. Two dice are rolled. If the sum of the dots showing is even, we get \$10; otherwise, we lose \$20. What is the expected value of this game?

28. A die is rolled. A person receives the number of dollars corresponding to the dots on the face that turns up. How much should a player pay in order to make this game fair?

29. A 35-year-old male buys a \$300,000 one-year term life insurance policy. Based on a U.S. government mortality table, the probability that he will live for a year is 0.998349. Find:

a. the expected value of the policy.

b. a fair price for the annual premium.

c. the monthly payment that covers the expected value of the policy.

30. A 65-year-old female buys a \$200,000 one-year term life insurance policy. Based on a U.S. government mortality table, the probability that she will live for a year is 0.989302. Find:

a. the expected value of the policy.

b. a fair price for the annual premium.

c. The annual profit the insurance company makes if the premium is \$200/month

31. Have you been following postseason baseball games? Those are the 5 or 7 game series after the regular season in October. How long are they going to last? The following table assumes that each game is a 50-50 proposition, that is, each team has a 50% chance of winning each game and gives the probability that a 5 game series lasts 3, 4, or 5 games. You can predict how long the series are going to last if you extend the idea of **expected value** to the number of postseason games in a 5 game series. Remember, in a 5 game series, the team that wins 3 games first is the winner!

5 Game Series	Probability
3	25%
4	37.5%
5	37.5%

32. Assuming that each game is a 50-50 proposition (each team has a 50% chance of winning each game) the probabilities for a 4, 5, 6 or 7 game series are shown. Which one will it be? Find the expected number of postseason games in a **7** game series. Here the team that wins 4 games first, is the winner!

7 Game Series	Probability
4	12.5%
5	25%
6	31.25%
7	31.25%

Source: http://tinyurl.com/6hedjbv.

C Applications

33. If in Example 9 of this section the probabilities of success in the first and second locations are $\frac{2}{3}$ and $\frac{2}{5}$, respectively, what location should be chosen in order to have a maximum expected profit? See Table 11.11 on page 664.

34. Gadget Manufacturing Company is debating whether to continue an advertising campaign for a new product. Its research department has predicted the gain or loss to be derived from the decision to continue or discontinue the campaign, as summarized in the following table. The president of the firm assigns odds of 4 to 1 in favor of the success of the advertising campaign. Find

a. the expected value for the company if the advertising campaign is continued.

b. the expected value for the company if the advertising campaign is discontinued.

c. the best decision based on the answers to parts (**a**) and (**b**).

Advertising Campaign	Successful	Unsuccessful
Continue	\$20,000	−\$10,000
Discontinue	\$30,000	\$ 5000

35. Repeat problem 34 assuming the president of the firm assigns odds of 4 to 1 against the success of the advertising campaign.

36. An oil drilling company is considering 2 sites for its well. The probabilities for getting a dry, a low-producing, or a high-producing well at site *A* are 0.6, 0.25, and 0.15, respectively. The costs for the 3 eventualities are −\$100,000, \$150,000, and \$500,000. For site *B*, the probability of finding a dry well, resulting in a \$200,000 loss, is 0.2. The company estimates that the probability of a low-producing well is 0.8, and in that case it would make \$50,000. Make a tree diagram for this situation and find the expected value for

a. site *A*. b. site *B*.

c. On the basis of your answers to (**a**) and (**b**), which site should the company select?

37. Suppose you have the choice of selling hot dogs at 2 stadium locations. At location *A* you can sell 100 hot dogs for \$4 each, or if you lower the price and move to location *B*, you can sell 300 hot dogs for \$3 each. The probability of being assigned to *A* or *B* is equally likely. Make a tree diagram for this situation and find the expected value for

a. *A*. b. *B*.

c. Which location has the better expected value?

IN OTHER WORDS

38. Explain the difference between the probability of an event and the odds in favor of an event.

39. Explain why betting in Keno is not a fair bet.

40. Explain in your own words what information is needed to solve a decision problem that depends on mathematical expectation.

USING YOUR KNOWLEDGE

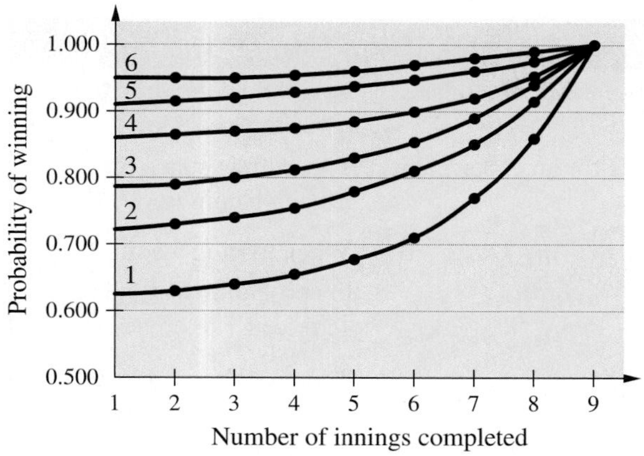

Curves represent the number of runs by which the team is ahead.

The graph shows the probabilities that a baseball team that is ahead by 1, 2, 3, 4, 5, or 6 runs after a certain number of innings goes on to win the game. As you can see, if a team is leading by 1 run at the end of the first inning, the probability that this team wins is about 0.62. If a team is ahead by 2 runs at the end of the first inning, then the probability of this team's winning the game is about 0.72.

Suppose a team is ahead by 1 run at the end of the first inning. The probability that this team wins the game is about 0.62, which can be written

$$\frac{62}{100} = \frac{31}{50}$$

Therefore, the odds in favor of this team's winning the game should be 31 to 19 (50–31). Use the graph shown above to solve the following problems:

41. Find the probability that a team leading by 2 runs at the end of the sixth inning
    a. wins the game. b. loses the game.
42. For the same situation as in problem 41, find the odds
    a. in favor of this team's winning the game.
    b. against this team's winning the game.
43. At the end of the sixth inning, a team is ahead by 4 runs. A man offers to bet \$10 on this team. How much money should be put up against his \$10 to make a fair bet?

DISCOVERY

In American roulette, the wheel has 38 compartments, 2 of which, the 0 and 00, are colored green. The rest of the compartments are numbered from 1 through 36, and half of them are red and the other half black. The wheel is spun in one direction, and a small ivory ball is spun in the other direction. If the wheel is fair, all the compartments are equally likely and hence the ball has probability $\frac{1}{38}$ of landing in any one of them. If a player bets, say, \$1 on a given number and the ball comes to rest on that number, the player receives from the croupier 36 times his or her stake, that is, \$36. In this case, the player wins \$35 with probability $\frac{1}{38}$ and loses \$1 with probability $\frac{37}{38}$. The expected value of this game is

$$E = \$35\left(\tfrac{1}{38}\right) - \$1\left(\tfrac{37}{38}\right) = -5\tfrac{5}{19}¢$$

This may be interpreted to mean that in the long run, for every dollar that you bet in roulette, you are expected to lose $5\frac{5}{19}$¢.

A second way to play roulette is to bet on red or black. Suppose a player bets \$1 on red. If the ball stops on a red number (there are 18 of them), the player receives twice his or her stake; in this case the player wins \$1. If a black number comes up, the player loses his or her stake. If a 0 or 00 turns up, then the wheel is spun again until it stops on a number different from 0 and 00. If this is black, the player loses the \$1, but if it is red, the player receives only his or her original stake (gaining nothing).

44. What is the expected value of this game?
45. If you place 50¢ on red and 50¢ on black, what is the expected value of the game? (*Hint:* The answer is not 0.)

COLLABORATIVE LEARNING

In Example 10 the expected values for choices A and B were the same. We may rely on conditional probability to make our decision. Form two groups. One will study choice A and the other choice B.

Group A

1. What is the probability that you lose money given that you choose *A*?
2. What is the probability that you make more than \$50 given that you choose *A*?
3. Based on your answers to 1 and 2, make an argument in favor of choosing *A*.

Group B

4. What is the probability that you do not make any money given that you choose *B*?
5. What is the probability that you make more than \$50 given that you chose *B*?
6. Based on your answers to 4 and 5, make an argument in favor of choosing *B*.

Now, one more debate. Which do you think is best: to play \$50 one week in the lottery or to play \$1 for 50 weeks? (The possible number of combinations for the lottery is C(n, r), where n is how many numbers you can select and r is how many correct numbers you need to win.) Assume tickets cost \$1.

7. What is the probability that you win your state lottery with one ticket? What about with 50 tickets?
8. What is the probability that you lose in the state lottery? What about losing 50 times in a row?
9. What is the probability that you win at least once when playing the lottery 50 weeks in a row?
10. On the basis of your answers to 7 and 9, which is best: \$50 one week or \$1 for 50 weeks?

CHAPTER 11 Summary

SECTION	ITEM	MEANING	EXAMPLE
11.1A	Experiment	An activity that generates well-defined outcomes	Tossing a coin, drawing a card from a deck
	Sample space	The set of all possible outcomes for an experiment	The sample space for tossing a coin is $\{H, T\}$.
	$P(E)$	The probability of event E, $P(E) = \dfrac{n(E)}{n(\mathscr{U})}$	When tossing a coin, the probability of tails is $P(T) = \frac{1}{2}$.
	$P(T')$	$1 - P(T)$	The probability of a 3 when rolling a die is $\frac{1}{6}$. The probability of not rolling a 3 is $\frac{5}{6}$.
11.1B	Empirical probability of an event E	$P(E) = \dfrac{\text{number of times } E \text{ occurred}}{\text{number of times experiment is performed}}$	If a coin is thrown 890 times and heads come up 451 times, $P(H) = \frac{451}{890}$.
11.3	$P(E) = 0$	E is an impossible event.	Rolling a 7 on a die
	$P(E) = 1$	E is a certain event.	Rolling less than 7 on a die
	$P(A \cup B)$	$P(A) + P(B) - P(A \cap B)$	
	Mutually exclusive events	Two events that cannot occur simultaneously; $P(A \cap B) = 0$	Getting a 5 and a 6 on one roll of a die
11.4A	$P(A \mid B)$, the probability of A, given B	$\dfrac{P(A \cap B)}{P(B)}$	The probability that a die turns up 3 (T) when rolled, given that an odd number (O) comes up is $\dfrac{P(T \cap O)}{P(O)} = \dfrac{\frac{1}{6}}{\frac{1}{2}} = \dfrac{1}{3}$.
11.5	Independent events	$P(A \cap B) = P(A) \cdot P(B)$	Rolling a 6 with a die and tossing tails with a coin are independent events.
11.5A	$P(E_1 \cap E_2 \cap \ldots \cap E_n)$	$P(E_1) \cdot P(E_2) \cdot \ldots \cdot P(E_n)$, when the events are independent	The event H: obtaining heads when a coin is tossed, and the event S: obtaining a 6 when a die is rolled, are independent because $P(H \cap S) = P(H) \cdot P(S)$.
11.5B	Stochastic process	A sequence of experiments in which the outcome of each experiment depends on chance	
11.6A	Odds in favor	The ratio of favorable to unfavorable occurrences	The odds for a 3 when rolling a die are 1 to 5.
11.6B	Expected value	$E = a_1p_1 + a_2p_2 + \cdots + a_np_n$, where the a's are the values that occur with probability $p_1, p_2,$ and so on	The expected value of getting heads when a coin is tossed and you are paid \$2 is $E = 2 \cdot \frac{1}{2} = \$1$.
	Fair game	A game is fair if its expected value is 0.	Tossing a coin and getting \$1 if heads come up and losing \$1 if tails come up is a **fair** game.

CHAPTER 11 Practice Test

1. A single fair die is rolled. Find the probability of obtaining
   a. a number different from 7. b. a number greater than 2.

2. A box contains 5 balls numbered from 1 to 5. If a ball is taken at random from the box, find the probability that it is
   a. an even-numbered ball. b. ball number 2. c. not ball number 2.

3. A box contains 2 red balls, marked R_1 and R_2, and 3 white balls, marked W_1, W_2, and W_3.
   a. If 2 balls are drawn in succession and without replacement from this box, find the number of elements in the sample space for this experiment. (We are interested in which balls are drawn and the order in which they are drawn.)
   b. Do part (**a**) assuming the balls are drawn in succession *with* replacement.

4. Two cards are drawn at random and without replacement from a standard deck of 52 cards. Find the probability that
   a. both cards are red. b. neither card is an ace.

5. A card is drawn at random from a standard deck of 52 cards and then replaced. Then another card is drawn. Find the probability that
   a. both cards are red. b. neither card is red.

6. A fair coin is tossed 5 times. What is the probability of obtaining at least 1 head?

7. An urn contains 5 white, 3 black, and 2 red balls. Find the probability of obtaining in a single draw
   a. a white or a black ball. b. a ball that is not red.

8. Three cards are drawn in succession and without replacement from a standard deck of 52 cards. What is the probability that they are all face cards (jack, queen, king)?

9. A student estimates that the probability of his passing math or English is 0.9, the probability of his passing English is 0.8, but the probability of his passing both is 0.6. What should be his estimate of the probability of his passing math?

10. Two dice are rolled. Find the probability that the sum turning up is 11, given that the first die showed a 5.

11. Two dice are rolled. Find the probability that the sum turning up is 11, given that the second die showed an even number.

12. Two dice are rolled.
    a. Find the probability that they show a sum of 10.
    b. Find the probability that the first die comes up an odd number.
    c. Are these two events independent? Explain.

13. A certain drug used to reduce hypertension (high blood pressure) produces side effects in 4% of the patients. Three patients who have taken the drug are selected at random. Find the probability that
    a. they all had side effects. b. none of them had side effects.

14. Roland has to take an English course and a history course, both of which are available at 8 A.M., 9 A.M., and 3 P.M. If Roland picks a schedule at random, what is the probability that he will have English at 8 A.M. and history at 3 P.M.?

15. The probability that a digital tape is defect-free is 0.97. If 2 tapes are selected at random, what is the probability that both are defective?

16. A card is selected at random from a deck of 52 cards. What are the odds in favor of the card's being
    a. a king? b. not a king?

17. The probability of an event is $\frac{3}{7}$. Find
    a. the odds in favor of this event occurring.
    b. the odds against this event occurring.

continued

CHAPTER 11 Practice Test – *continued*

18. The odds in favor of an event occurring are 3 to 7.
    a. What are the odds against this event occurring?
    b. What is the probability that the event will not occur?

19. A coin is tossed twice. If exactly 1 head comes up, we receive \$5, and if 2 tails come up, we receive \$5; otherwise, we get nothing. How much should we be willing to pay in order to play this game?

20. The probabilities of being an "instant winner" of \$2, \$5, \$25, or \$50 in the Florida lottery are $\frac{1}{10}$, $\frac{1}{50}$, $\frac{1}{600}$, and $\frac{1}{1200}$, respectively. What is the mathematical expectation of being an "instant winner"?

ANSWERS TO PRACTICE TEST

CHAPTER 11				What to Review *If You Missed It*	
QUESTION	**ANSWER**			**SECTION**	**EXAMPLE(S)**	**PAGE(S)**
1	a. 1	b. $\frac{2}{3}$		11.1	1, 2	607, 609–610
2	a. $\frac{2}{5}$	b. $\frac{1}{5}$	c. $\frac{4}{5}$	11.1	3	610
3	a. 20	b. 25		11.1	4, 5	611
4	a. $\frac{25}{102}$	b. $\frac{188}{221}$		11.1	6	611–612
5	a. $\frac{1}{4}$	b. $\frac{1}{4}$		11.1	6	611–612
6	$\frac{31}{32}$			11.1	4	611
7	a. $\frac{4}{5}$	b. $\frac{4}{5}$		11.2	1–4	621–624
8	$\frac{11}{1105}$			11.2	5–8	624–626
9	0.7			11.3	2, 7	631, 633–634
10	$\frac{1}{6}$			11.4	1	639
11	$\frac{1}{18}$			11.4	2, 3	640
12	a. $\frac{1}{12}$	b. $\frac{1}{2}$	c. No. $P(A \cap B) = \frac{1}{36} \neq P(A)P(B)$	11.4	3, 4	640
13	a. 0.000064	b. 0.884736		11.5	1–4	649–650
14	$\frac{1}{6}$			11.5	5	651
15	0.0009			11.5	6, 7	652
16	a. 1 to 12	b. 12 to 1		11.6	1	658
17	a. 3 to 4	b. 4 to 3		11.6	3, 4	659–660
18	a. 7 to 3	b. $\frac{7}{10}$		11.6	3	659
19	\$3.75			11.6	8	663
20	$-61\frac{2}{3}$ cents			11.6	6–8	663

CHAPTER 12

Statistics

There are three kinds of lies: Lies, Damn Lies, and Statistics.
—MARK TWAIN'S AUTOBIOGRAPHY

Statistics play a major role in our everyday lives. Statistics can be used to measure team performances, rainfall, economic trends, and test scores. Throughout this chapter we will analyze data with the use of statistical tools. One such tool is the normal distribution curve, which we use as a problem-solving tool in Section 12.4.

Americans are fascinated by numbers. Consider the *Guinness Book of World Records,* almanacs, surveys, and so on. But what are the meanings of all these numbers, and how can we interpret them? In this chapter we discuss different ways of organizing and reporting data. The simplest way is to use the **frequency distribution** of Section 12.1, which is a type of table that tells us how many objects of different types we have in each of several categories. Such a distribution can then be represented by a graph called a **histogram.**

When we want to describe an entire sample or population by a number, we use an **average.** The three most common averages are the **mean,** the **median,** and the **mode.** Each of these averages, which are presented in Section 12.2, uses one number to try to tell us where the "middle" of a set of data is. However, averages cannot tell us how far data values are spread out away from this "middle." For this we use the **range** and the **standard deviation.** Using means, standard deviations, and **z-scores,** we can compute how far a data point is from the "middle." These topics are covered in Sections 12.3 and 12.4.

In real life, your smartphone, the Internet, newspapers, and magazines present data using many varieties of graphs, including line, bar, and circle graphs. We examine these in Section 12.5.

An important aspect of statistics is predicting the likelihood of future outcomes based on data gathered from earlier observations. For example, can we predict winning Olympic times based on athletes' past performances, college costs based on current tuition data, or the incidence of cancer based on exposure to ultraviolet sunlight? We will make predictions and study **scattergrams** and **correlations** in the last two sections of the chapter.

12.1 Sampling, Frequency Distributions, and Graphs

GETTING STARTED

OBJECTIVES

A. Find the population of a simple random sample.
B. Make a frequency distribution for a data set.
C. Make a histogram and a frequency polygon for a data set.
D. Solve applications involving frequency distributions, histograms, and frequency polygons.

Human Side of Math

© Photos.com
Bills of Mortality

Statistical analysis emerged in London, where in 1662 John Graunt published a remarkable book, *Natural and Political Observations upon the Bills of Mortality.*

At that time, the population of London had already reached approximately 100,000. Overcrowding, prevalence of disease, and the many plague years all made Londoners exceedingly interested in reports of births and deaths. After the great plague in 1603, these reports were published weekly. The causes of death were reported in the *Bills of Mortality,* published regularly starting in 1629.

After this somewhat morbid beginning for statistical analysis, many mathematicians, including Laplace (1749–1827) and Gauss (1777–1855), made important contributions to the basic ideas of statistics. The analysis of numerical data is fundamental to so many different fields such as biology, geology, genetics, and evolution. Charles Darwin (1809–1882), Gregor Mendel (1822–1884), and Karl Pearson (1857–1936) contributed greatly to these subjects.

LOOKING AHEAD

We start this chapter by studying what is usually called *descriptive statistics,* which consists of summarizing in a concise way the information collected. We end the chapter by discussing *inferential statistics*—using methods that generalize the results obtained from a sample to the population and measure their reliability.

COMPARISON SHOPPING FOR JEANS

A buyer for a large department store or a budget-conscious college student wanted to compare prices of high-quality jeans for men and women. One way to do this is to search for "Jeans Prices" on the Internet or look in a consumer magazine at the 15 best-rated jeans for men and women and their prices. The prices appear in Table 12.1. How can we organize the information so that we can make meaningful comparisons? Let us look at prices for women's jeans.

Table 12.1 Jeans' Prices

Women's Jeans		**Men's Jeans**	
Sears Jeans That Fit	$19+	Wrangler Prorodeo	$20
Wrangler Prorodeo	26	Wrangler American Hero	17
Chic Heavenly Blues	48+	Levi's 509	31
P.S. Gitano	21	Wrangler Rustler	15
Gap Straight Leg	30	J. C. Penney Long Haul	23+
Lee Easy Rider	33	Guess/Georges Marciano	60
L. L. Bean Stretch	36	Wrangler American Hero L	23
Lands' End Square Rigger	26+	Levi's 550	45
L. L. Bean Double L	27	Lands' End Square Rigger	20+
Levi's 501	35	Levi's 501	34
Lee Relaxed Rider	29	Gap Tapered Leg	34
Calvin Klein	52	L. L. Bean Double L	27
Levi's 902	34	Sears Roebucks	14+
Bonjour	20	Gap Easy Fit	32
Gap Classic Contour	30	Lee Riders Straightleg	20

Table 12.2 Women's Jeans' Prices by Classes

Step 1		Step 2	Step 3
Lower Limit	*Upper Limit*	*Tally*	*Frequency*
19	30	𝍸||	7
30	41	𝍸|	6
41	52*	||	2

*Note that 52 *must* go in the third class because there are no classes above it.

Note: Unless otherwise specified, data values falling on class upper limits are included in the next *higher* class.

Since these prices range from \$52 to \$19, we will break them down into 3 **classes** (you could as easily make it 4 or 5). To do this, we divide the range of prices by the number of classes to get the **width** of each class.

$$\frac{52 - 19}{3} = \frac{33}{3} = \mathbf{11} \text{ (width)}$$

The **lower limits** for our classes will be 19, 19 + **11** = 30, and 30 + **11** = 41, as shown in Table 12.2. The corresponding **upper limits** are 29, 40, and 51. Notice that there is a gap between the end of one class and the beginning of the next (from 29 to 30, for example). We can fix this by making the upper limits of the classes 30, 41, and 52 (instead of 29, 40, and 51). See *step 1* in table 12.2. Now, in which class will the \$30 price go?

With this convention we can tally the prices falling in each class (*step 2*) and note their frequency (*step 3*). We can then make a picture of this information, called a **histogram,** in which each of the classes is represented by a bar whose width is 11 units, the **class width,** and whose height is given by the **frequency** as shown in Figure 12.1. Note that this histogram does not show the lower and upper limits. Rather, each class is described by a single value called its **midpoint.** Sometimes the lower and upper limits are shown as well (see the Problem Solving section).

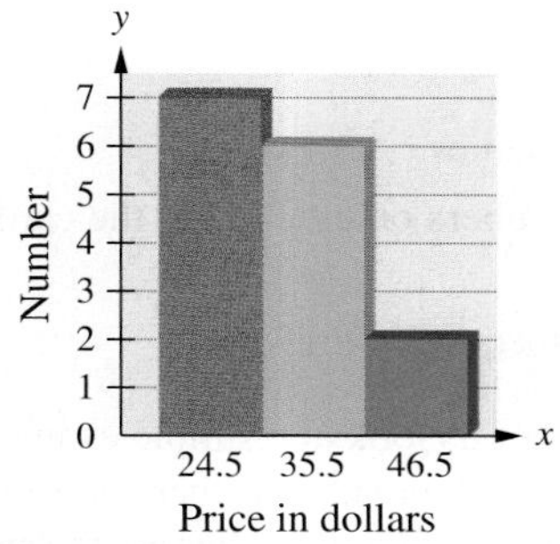

FIGURE 12.1 Women's jeans' prices histogram.

To see a misuse of statistics when constructing a histogram, look at the Discovery section.

The word *statistics* brings to the minds of most people an image of a mass of numerical data. **Statistics** can be defined as the science of collecting, organizing, and summarizing data (*descriptive statistics*) so that valid conclusions can be drawn from them (*inferential statistics*).

A Sampling

Who will be the next governor in your state? What about the next president of the United States? A veritable army of statisticians, analysts, and *pollsters* (people who conduct surveys or *polls*) spend a lot of time and money to try to determine what percent of the vote each candidate will receive. How do they do it? Obviously, it is impossible to ask each registered voter (the **target population**) for whom he or she plans to vote, so analysts concentrate on a select, smaller number of people (a **sample population**) to represent the entire group and then project the result to all registered voters. In order for the conclusions reached to be valid, a **simple random sample** must be used.

Definition of a Simple Random Sample

A **simple random sample** of a given population is a sample for which

1. Each member is selected at random.
2. Every member of the population has the same chance of being chosen.

Thus, to pick a simple *random* sample of 100 students from a college with 5000 students, number the students from 1 to 5000 and write these numbers on cards. Then mix up the cards and draw 100 numbers. The result will be a *simple random sample* consisting of the 100 students corresponding to the drawn cards. Note that if you decide to select only *even*-numbered cards, this would **not** be a random sample because only the students numbered 2, 4, 6, and so on would be chosen. Similarly, if you decide to select the first 100 students arriving at school, this would **not** be a random sample.

In general, the term **sample** refers to a ***portion*** of the population which is *representative* of the **total** population from which it was selected.

EXAMPLE 1 Finding Customer Population and Sample

The owner of the Latin Grill wants to determine if the items on his new menu satisfy the demands and tastes of his customers. He has a list of 1000 past customers who have visited the restaurant but because of budget and time constraints he cannot contact all of them, so he decides to make a simple random sample of 50 customers.

(a) What is the population?

(b) What procedure can you use to select the simple random sample?

(c) What is the sample?

Solution

(a) The population consists of the 1000 past customer's names.

(b) Number the customers from 1 to 1000, write their numbers on cards, mix the cards, and draw 50 numbers.

(c) The sample consists of the 50 customers whose numbers were drawn.

How do these ideas relate to each other and to you? Let us look at a simple example that you may have encountered and even avoided! You go to the mall, and there is somebody conducting a survey. To simplify things, suppose that the person conducting the survey selects the first 10 people who walk in and asks each of them if he or she owns a cell phone. Each person falls into one of two categories: yes (Y) or no (N). The responses are

1 Y, 2 N, 3 Y, 4 Y, 5 N, 6 Y, 7 N, 8 Y, 9 Y, 10 Y

© D. Thomas Porter, Photos at Your Place

1. What do you think the target population and the sample population are? Are they the same?
2. Do we have a simple random sample?
3. How can we summarize the data?

1. The **target** or implied population may be cell phone owners in the United States, the state, or this particular mall. The **sample** population consists of the 10 people surveyed. The target and the sample populations are **not** the same.
2. We do not have a simple random sample. The definition of simple random sample requires that every member of the population have the same chance of being chosen. A mall survey leaves out anyone not visiting the mall that day.
3. There are several ways we can summarize the data. One is using a table or we can even make a picture (graph) of the results, as shown below. The table is called a **frequency distribution;** the graph is a **histogram,** which can be converted easily into a **frequency polygon,** as we will show in the next sections.

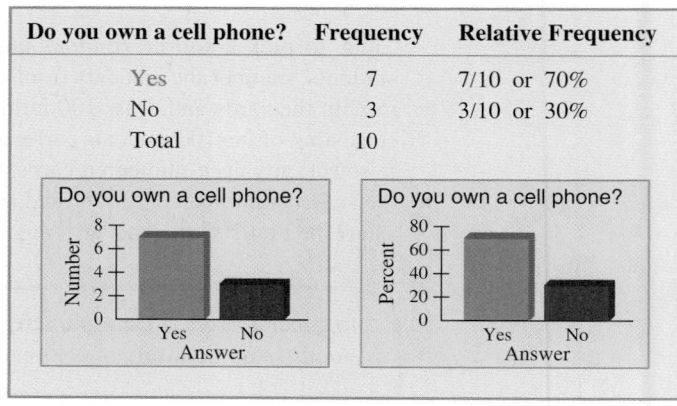

Do you own a cell phone?	Frequency	Relative Frequency
Yes	7	7/10 or 70%
No	3	3/10 or 30%
Total	10	

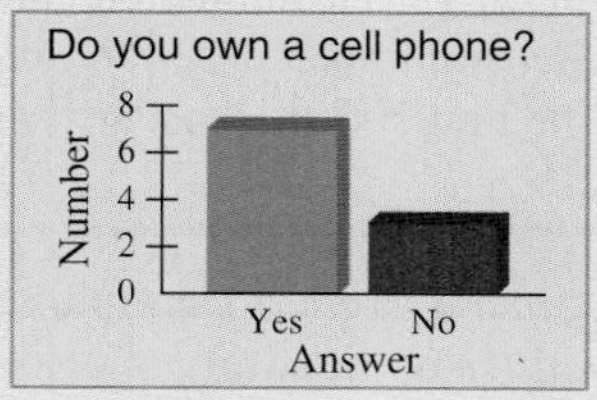

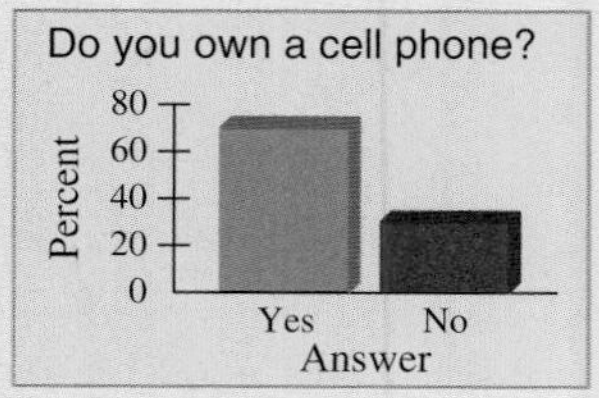

B Frequency Distributions

Statistical studies start by collecting data. In order to *organize* and *summarize* these data to detect any trends that may be present, we can use three types of tools: *frequency distributions, histograms,* and *frequency polygons*.

Let us look at a statistics problem that should interest a teacher and students, both of whom might wonder how well the students are learning a certain subject. Out of 10 possible points, the class of 25 students made the following scores:

6	5	4	0	9
2	0	8	8	1
10	6	8	5	5
8	7	9	10	9
6	5	8	4	7

Table 12.3 Frequency Distributions for Class Scores

Score	Tally Marks	Frequency
0	||	2
1	|	1
2	|	1
3		0
4	||	2
5	||||	4
6	|||	3
7	||	2
8	~~||||~~	5
9	|||	3
10	||	2
		25 Total

This listing shows at once that there were some good scores and some poor ones, but because the scores are not arranged in any particular order, it is difficult to conclude anything else from the list.

A **frequency distribution** is often a suitable way of organizing a list of numbers to show what patterns are present. First, the scores from 0 through 10 are listed in order in a column (see Table 12.3). Then, by going through the original list in the order in which it is given, we can make tally marks on the appropriate lines of our table. Finally, in a third column we can list the number of times that each score occurs; this number is the **frequency** of the score.

It is now easier to see that a score of 8 occurred more times than any other number. This score was made by

$$\frac{5}{25} = \frac{1}{5} = 20\% \text{ of the students}$$

Ten of the students, or 40% of the class, received scores of 8 or better. Only 6, or 24%, received scores less than 5.

If there are very many items in a set of numerical data, then it is usually necessary to shorten the frequency distribution by grouping the data into intervals. For instance, in the preceding distribution, we can group the scores in intervals of 2 to obtain the listing in Table 12.4.

Of course, some of the detailed information in the first table has been lost in the second table, but for some purposes a condensed table may furnish all the information that is required.

Table 12.4 Frequency Distribution with Grouped Data for Class Scores

Score	Frequency
0–1	3
2–3	1
4–5	6
6–7	5
8–9	8
10–11	2

C Histograms and Frequency Polygons

It is also possible to present the information contained in Table 12.3 by means of a special type of graph called a **histogram,** consisting of vertical bars with no space between bars. In the histogram of Figure 12.2 on the following page, the units on the y axis represent the frequencies, whereas those on the x axis indicate the scores.

From the histogram in Figure 12.2 we can construct a **frequency polygon** (or line graph) by connecting the midpoints of the tops of the bars, as shown in Figure 12.3. It is customary to extend the graph to the baseline (x axis) using the midpoints of the extended intervals at both ends. This "ties the graph down" but has no predictive significance.

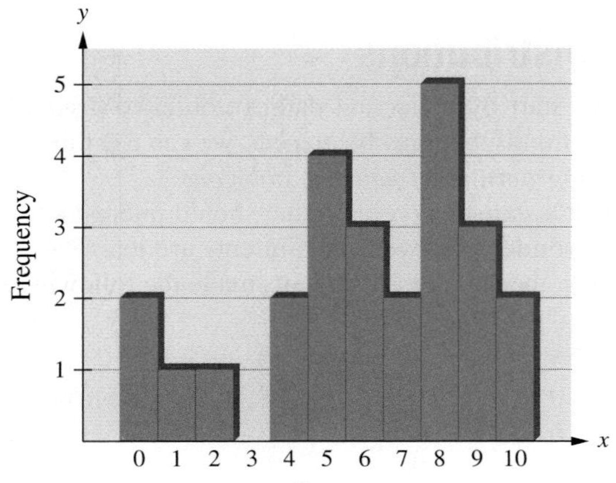

FIGURE 12.2 Histogram for Table 12.3.

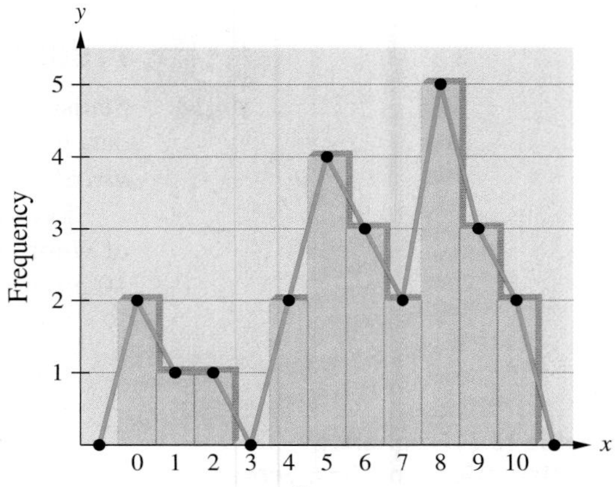

FIGURE 12.3 Frequency polygon.

EXAMPLE 2 Frequency Distribution and Histogram for Wages

Here are the hourly wages of a group of 30 workers who are performing similar tasks but, because of differences in seniority and skill, are paid at different rates:

\$8.00	\$7.90	\$8.00	\$8.10	\$7.90	\$7.90
7.90	7.80	7.90	8.00	7.80	8.00
8.10	7.70	7.90	7.80	8.10	8.00
8.00	8.10	8.20	7.80	8.20	8.10
7.70	8.00	7.80	7.70	7.80	8.00

(a) Make a frequency distribution of these rates.

(b) What is the most frequent rate?

(c) How many workers are being paid less than \$8 per hour?

(d) Make a histogram of the wage rate distribution.

(e) Make a frequency polygon of the distribution.

Table 12.5

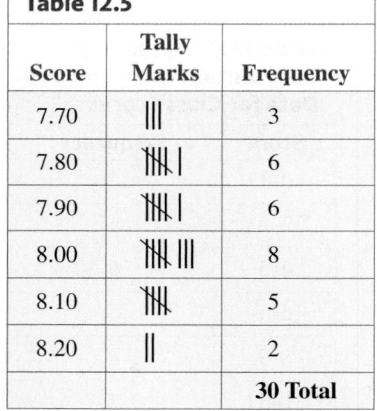

Score	Tally Marks	Frequency
7.70	|||	3
7.80	~~||||~~ |	6
7.90	~~||||~~ |	6
8.00	~~||||~~ |||	8
8.10	~~||||~~	5
8.20	||	2
		30 Total

Solution

(a) Table 12.5 lists the wage rates from the lowest (\$7.70) to the highest (\$8.20). We tally these from the given data and obtain the desired frequency distribution.

(b) From the frequency distribution, we read off the most frequent rate to be \$8 per hour.

(c) Again, we read from the frequency distribution that 15 workers are being paid less than \$8 per hour.

(d) The desired histogram appears in Figure 12.4.

(e) Figure 12.4 also shows the frequency polygon.

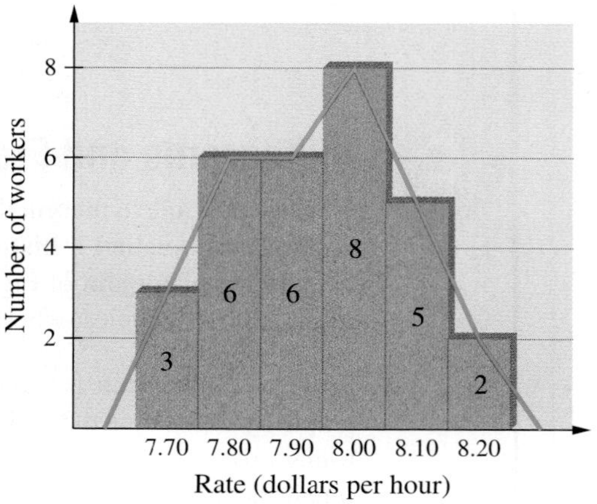

FIGURE 12.4

GRAPH IT

You can use a grapher to do histograms, but you have to be extremely careful with class widths and endpoints.

To produce the histogram in Figure 12.4, enter the values in Example 2 as a list. To do this, press STAT 1 and enter the numbers. Tell the grapher you want to plot data by pressing 2nd STAT PLOT 1. On the next screen, select ON and the histogram icon. Now press Window and select 7.7 for the minimum, 8.3 for the max (if you select 8.2 for the maximum, you will not see the last bar), and .1 for the Xscl. Finally, select 0 for Ymin, 10 for Ymax, 1 for Yscl, and 1 for Xres. Press GRAPH. If you followed these steps faithfully, you will be rewarded with the graph shown below.

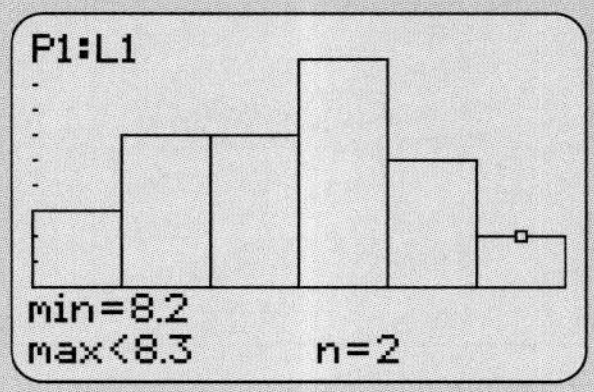

Note that the last bar goes from a min of 8.2 to a max < 8.3 and is $n = 2$ units high.

In making a frequency distribution in which the data are to be grouped, we can use the following procedure:

Procedure for Making a Frequency Distribution

1. Decide on the number of classes into which the data are to be grouped. This depends on the number of items that have to be grouped but is usually between 3 and 15.
   (a) The *width* of each class is given by

$$\textbf{Class width} \approx \frac{\text{largest data value} - \text{smallest data value}}{\text{desired number of classes}}$$

   The symbol $\approx$ means "approximately." If we want the class width to be a whole number, we round *up* to the nearest whole number.
   (b) The lowest and highest values in each class are called the **lower class limit** and **upper class limit,** respectively. Note that the difference between the lower class limit of one class and that of the next should be the class width.
   (c) The center of the class is called the **midpoint.**
   (d) To make sure that the bars in a histogram touch, we can do either of the following:
      (i) Use the halfway points between the upper limit of one class and the lower limit of the next class, the **class boundaries,** as the endpoints of the bars.
      (ii) Use the upper class limit of the first class as the lower class limit of the second class and stipulate that values falling on class limits will be included in the next higher class.
2. Sort or tally the data into the appropriate classes.
3. Count the number of items in each class.
4. Display the results in a table.
5. If desired, make a histogram and/or frequency polygon of the distribution.

By following the procedure for making a frequency distribution, we will see that it is really not very difficult to tabulate a frequency distribution and construct a histogram or frequency polygon.

Note: Sometimes the upper-class boundaries are included in the corresponding lower class, as in the next example and in problems 23 and 27 of Exercises 12.1. You will see that the inequalities in the distribution tables show this.

PROBLEM-SOLVING

Making Histograms

① **Read** the problem.

Make a frequency distribution with three classes, and construct the corresponding histogram for the men's jeans' prices shown in the Getting Started section.

② **Select** the unknown.

We want to make a frequency distribution and then a histogram for the men's jeans' prices.

③ **Think** of a plan.

We need to create three classes and determine their frequencies.

④ **Use** the procedure we have studied to carry out the plan. What is the class width? What are the class limits? What are the class boundaries? Are these boundaries convenient for this problem?

Since the highest price is 60 and the lowest 14, the class width is

$$\frac{60 - 14}{3} \approx 15.3$$

which is rounded *up* to 16. The lower limits for our classes are 14, 30, and 46, making the upper limits 29, 45, and 61. Thus, the class boundaries are the halfway points between 29 and 30 (29.5), 45 and 46 (45.5), and 45.5 + 16 = 61.5. However, these boundaries are not convenient or natural, so we choose to make our class limits 14 to 30, 30 to 46, and 46 to 62. The classes can be described by the inequalities shown in Table 12.6, where p represents the price. The tallies and frequencies are shown in Table 12.6 and the histogram in Figure 12.5.

Make the frequency distribution.

Draw the histogram.

Table 12.6

Class	Tally	Frequency
$14 \le p < 30$	𝍸 ||||	9
$30 \le p < 46$	𝍸	5
$46 \le p < 62$	|	1

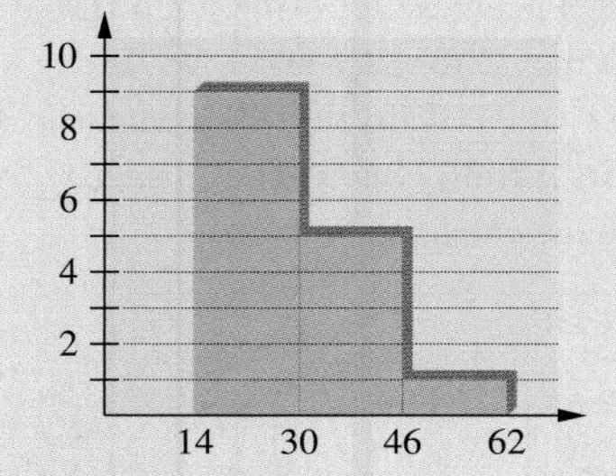

FIGURE 12.5

⑤ **Verify** the answer.

Try Example 3 Now Cover the solution, write your own solution, and then check your work.

Did you vote in the last general election? The percent of eligible voters actually voting in the 2008 general election was about 61.6%.

EXAMPLE 3 Frequency Distribution and Histograms for Voters

In a study of voter turnout in 20 cities with populations of over 100,000 in the United States, the following data were found:

Turnout Rate as a Percent of the Voting-Age Population

85.2	72.4	81.2	62.8	71.6
72.1	87.2	76.6	58.5	70.0
76.5	74.1	70.0	80.3	65.9
74.9	70.8	67.0	72.5	73.1

Inspection of the data shows that the smallest number is 58.5 and the largest is 87.2. This time we go from 55 to 90, with the convenient class width of 5 units.

(a) Make a frequency distribution of the data on voting rate (r) using a class interval of 5% so that the classes will be $55 < r \le 60$, $60 < r \le 65$, . . . , $85 < r \le 90$.

(b) Make a histogram and a frequency polygon of this distribution.

(c) In what percent of the cities was the voting rate greater than 80%?

(d) In what percent was the voting rate less than or equal to 70%?

Solution

(a) The required frequency distribution appears in Table 12.7. (You should check this table.)

(b) The histogram and frequency polygon are shown in Figure 12.6. These are constructed from the frequency distribution, just as before with ungrouped data.

(c) In 4 out of 20 cities, the voting rate was greater than 80%. Thus, the required percent is $\frac{4}{20} = 20\%$.

(d) In 6 out of 20 cities, the voting rate was less than or equal to 70%. Thus, in 30% of the cities, no more than 70% of the voting-age population voted.

Table 12.7

Voting Rate r %	Tally Marks	Frequency
$55 < r \le 60$	|	1
$60 < r \le 65$	|	1
$65 < r \le 70$	||||	4
$70 < r \le 75$	~~||||~~ |||	8
$75 < r \le 80$	||	2
$80 < r \le 85$	||	2
$85 < r \le 90$	||	2

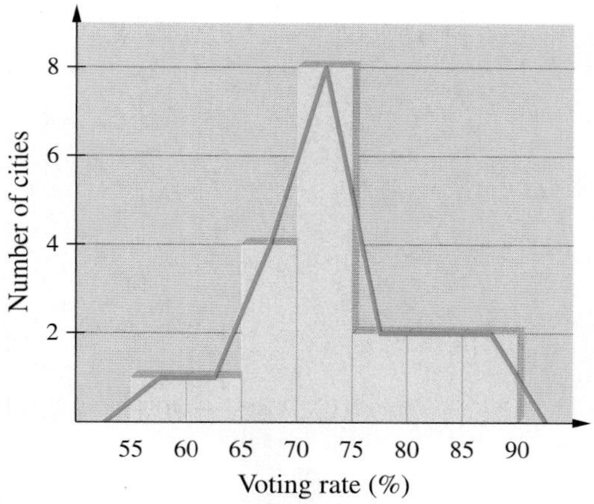

FIGURE 12.6

D Applications

The data in Table 12.8 represent the number and percent of homes that were owner occupied, renter occupied, or vacant.

Table 12.8

Housing Tenure	1302	1303	1304	1305	1404	1405
Owner occupied	524 (77%)	850 (44%)	35 (30%)	879 (39%)	1454 (62%)	594 (44%)
Renter occupied	130 (19%)	981 (51%)	76 (66%)	1240 (55%)	836 (36%)	702 (52%)
Vacant	25 (4%)	89 (5%)	5 (4%)	132 (6%)	56 (2%)	56 (4%)
Total Housing Units	**679**	**1920**	**116**	**2251**	**2346**	**1352**

Source: U.S. Census Bureau, Census 2000, Summary File 1.

A better visual representation of this information can be obtained by using histograms. A software program created by Tetrad Computer Applications translates the information into the histograms shown in Figure 12.7 on the following page.

EXAMPLE 4 Applications of Histograms to Housing

An investment banker is studying the histograms in Figure 12.7.

(a) Which tract has the most owner-occupied homes?

(b) Which tract has the most vacant homes?

(c) If you are the banker, in which tract would you invest your money?

Solution

(a) Tract 1404 has the most owner-occupied homes (1454).

(b) Tract 1305 has the most vacant homes (132).

(c) The banker wants to find out which tract has the most owner-occupied houses. Unfortunately, the histograms only give the relative frequency (**percent**) of owner-occupied homes, so we have to use Table 12.8. Since tract **1404** has the most owner-occupied homes (1454), a smart banker will select tract 1404, even though the relative frequency (percent) of owner-occupied homes in tract 1302 is higher (77%) than in tract 1404 (62%).

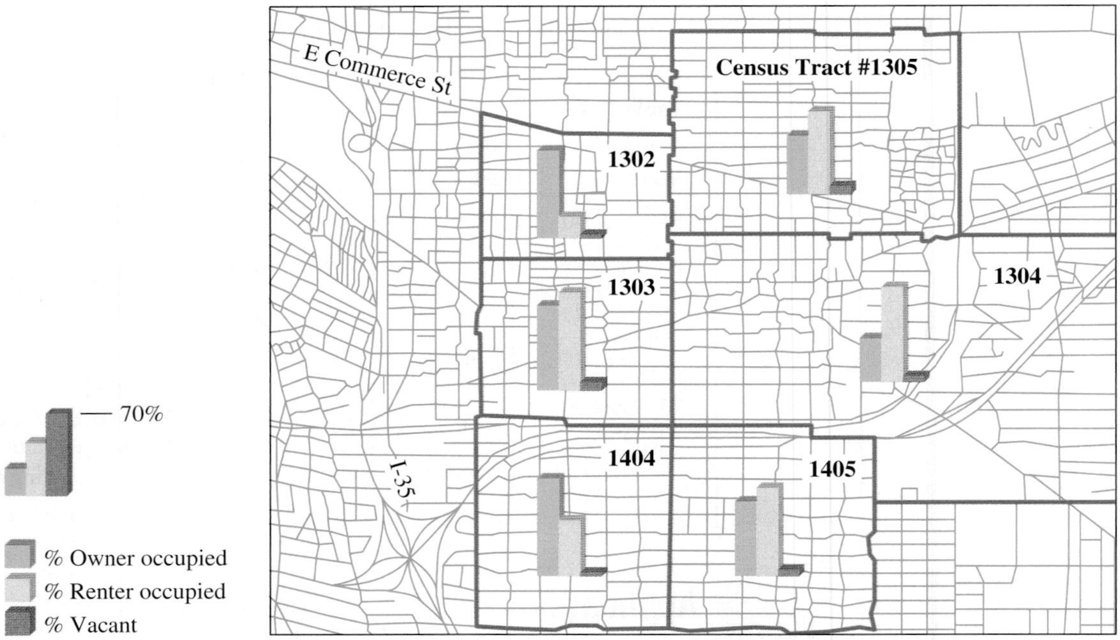

FIGURE 12.7 Housing by tenure.

12.1 EXERCISES

A Sampling

1. What is descriptive statistics?
2. What is inferential statistics?
3. What is the difference between a target population and a sample population?
4. What is the number-one-rated TV program at this time? The Nielsen Company can tell us! (http://www.nielsen.com/us/en/insights/top10s/television.html). They have between 20,000 and 25,000 National People Meter (NPM) households that measure the viewing habits in any one of the 116 million TV households.
   a. What is the population for these ratings?
   b. What is the sample for these ratings?
5. A survey in *USA Today* reports that 29% of the 1006 households surveyed stated that their favorite shopping day was Saturday.
   a. What is the implied population?
   b. What is the sample?
6. The students in a statistics class took a random sample of 50 colleges and universities regarding student fees at the 50 institutions and concluded that their own student fees were higher than at most colleges in the country.
   a. What is the population?
   b. What is the sample?
7. A television station asked viewers to respond either yes or no to a certain question by calling a 900 number to respond yes and a different 900 number to respond no. Each call or text message cost $0.50.
   a. Is this a simple random sample?
   b. Explain why or why not.
8. Who is the best U.S. president? That depends on who you ask! A Gallup poll about presidential greatness, asked 1015 adults in the United States, "Who do you regard as the greatest United States president?"
   a. What was the population?
   b. What was the sample?
   c. Was the sample a random sample? Explain.

   By the way, the answer is Ronald Reagan (or Abraham Lincoln if you believe C-Span or ABC news) Check it out!

   Source: http://tinyurl.com/7jcltcs.

9. Consider the population of all students in your class.
   a. How could you get a random sample of 10 students from this population?
   b. List three ways of getting samples from this population that are *not* random samples.

10. The Current Population Survey (CPS) is a monthly survey of about 50,000 households (out of about 120 million total households) conducted by the Bureau of the Census for the Bureau of Labor Statistics. The survey includes employment, unemployment, earnings, hours of work, and other economic indicators.
    Source: http://www.census.gov/cps.
    a. What is the sample for the CPS?
    b. What is the population?

11. Do you surf the Net? Have you been annoyed by the pop-up ads? An ad from an educational Web site asks you to participate in a survey to determine how people feel about educational television.
    a. What is the target population?
    b. What is the sample population?
    c. Are these two populations the same? Explain.

12. Do you buy your books at the bookstore or online? The finance department of a college conducted a survey at the bookstore, where students were selected at random and asked to participate in the survey.
    a. Is this a random sample?
    b. What is the target population?
    c. What is the sample population?
    d. Are these two populations the same? Explain.

© Colin Young-Wolff / Photo Edit

13. Do you buy your vegetables and bakery products at a regular or a specialty store? The owner of El Mirasol wanted to know how many people would buy fresh tortillas at his market, so he surveyed the first 100 people who entered the store and he received 50 responses. He then conducted a second survey of 75 people who had actually bought some goods at the store and also received 50 responses. Which survey do you think would produce more accurate results, and why?

© I. Bello

14. A politician wants to introduce a bill in Congress and uses the results of a survey of his constituents to help sell the bill to his colleagues. He introduces the bill by saying, "All American patriots really want this bill."
    a. What are the target and sample populations?
    b. Is it reasonable to assume that the target and sample populations are the same? Explain.

B Frequency Distributions

15. The athletic department asks 1000 students if they have been to a football game in the last year. The results indicate that 720 students said yes (Y), 160 said no (N), and 120 did not respond (**NR**).
    a. Display the results in a frequency distribution.
    b. Why do you need to include the people who did not respond?

16. Use the information in problem 15 to make a relative frequency distribution showing the percentage of students in each of the three categories.

17. How many hours do you spend daily in leisure and sports? According to the Census Time Use Survey, Americans spend about 5.18 hr daily in leisure and sports. The following data represent the number of hours spent daily in leisure and sports by 20 people.
    Source: http://www.bls.gov/tus/tables/a1_2010.pdf.

4	3	4	0	4	3	6	3	1	6
6	5	2	7	5	5	6	2	2	7

    a. Make a frequency distribution of the number of hours spent daily in leisure and sports. Label the columns "Number of Hours," "Tally Marks," and "Frequency."
    b. What is the most frequent number of hours spent in leisure and sports?
    c. How many people spend more hours daily in leisure and sports than the 5.18 hr daily average? What percent is that?
    d. How many people spend fewer hours daily in leisure and sports than the 5.18 hr daily average? What percent is that?

18. What are the top social media tools? Facebook, Twitter, LinkedIn, and blogs. These tools are used by marketers to promote their products on the Internet. A significant 58% of marketers are using social media for an average of **6** hr or more each week and 34% for **11** or more hours weekly.
    Source: http://tinyurl.com/3exua89.
    The following data represent the number of weekly hours spent online by 30 social media marketers.

12	13	4	0	14	3	15	13	11	13
6	5	12	7	5	5	6	2	10	12
12	3	10	13	9	11	14	1	11	8

a. Make a frequency distribution for the number of hours spent online per person. Label the columns "Number of Hours," "Tally Marks," and "Frequency."

b. What is the most frequent number of hours spent online per person?

c. How many people are online more than 11 hr? What percent is that?

d. How many people are online fewer than 6 hr? What percent is that?

19. The following data show the results of 30 rolls of a die that has had the edges on the 1-face rounded (sometimes called a **loaded die**). In 30 rolls, the 6, which is opposite the 1, showed only once!

3	6	3	1	2
1	1	1	1	1
5	5	5	5	3
3	1	2	5	4
5	3	1	5	1
5	1	3	4	1

a. Make a frequency distribution for the outcomes. Label the columns "Outcome," "Tally Marks," and "Frequency."

b. Which outcome is the most frequent? How many times did it occur?

c. Which outcome is the least frequent? How many times did it occur?

20. Another loaded die is rolled several times, and the results are as shown in the histogram.

a. Make a relative frequency histogram of the results.

b. What percent of the time does the 1 occur?

c. What percent of the time does the 4 occur?

d. In part (**a**) you made a *relative* frequency histogram from a frequency histogram. Can you make a frequency histogram from a relative frequency histogram? Explain.

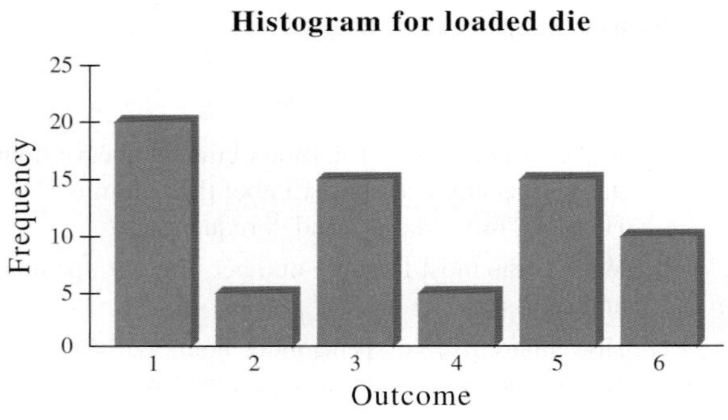

21. Thirty students were asked to list the television programs each had watched during the preceding week. From this list, the number of hours each had spent watching television during the week was calculated. The results are

1	5	4	7	10	8	2	3	9	6
6	12	8	14	3	4	8	7	2	1
0	3	5	8	10	12	0	15	1	4

a. Make a frequency distribution of the number of hours of television watched per student. Label the three columns "Number of Hours," "Tally Marks," and "Frequency."

b. What is the most frequent number of hours watched per student?

c. How many students watched television more than 10 hr?

d. How many students watched television 5 hr or less?

e. What percent of the students watched television more than 7 hr?

C Histograms and Frequency Polygons

22. Make a histogram for the data given in problem 21.

23. Have you read online or in the newspapers or magazines about cases in which individuals became so disgusted with the amount of time they had to wait to see a doctor or a dentist that they sued for lost wages? The waiting times for 50 patients are given in the table.

Waiting Time t (min)	Number of Patients
$0 < t \leq 3.5$	10
$3.5 < t \leq 7.0$	8
$7.0 < t \leq 10.5$	6
$10.5 < t \leq 14.0$	16
$14.0 < t \leq 17.5$	6
$17.5 < t \leq 21.0$	4

a. Make a histogram for this set of data.

b. What percent of the patients waited 7.0 min or less?

c. What percent of the patients had to wait more than 10.5 min?

24. General Foods, in testing a new product, which it called Solid H, had 50 people (25 men and 25 women selected at random) taste the product and indicate their reactions on the picture ballot shown. The boxes on the ballot were then assigned scores of +3, +2, +1, 0, −1, −2, and −3 in order from left to right, top to bottom.

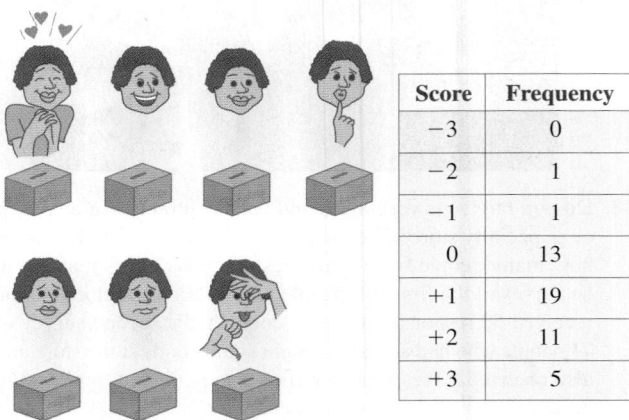

Score	Frequency
−3	0
−2	1
−1	1
0	13
+1	19
+2	11
+3	5

Please check the box under the picture that expresses how you feel about the product you have just tasted.

The table shows the frequencies for this taste test. (Incidentally, no significant difference was found between the men's and women's reactions.)

a. Make a histogram of these data.

b. What percent of the tasters liked Solid H?

c. What percent were undecided?

25. Would you like to be a writer? Look at the following list of authors whose books were published at the ages given:

	Age
Allen Dulles (*The Boer War: A History*)	8
Hilda Conkling (*Poems by a Little Girl*)	9
Betty Thorpe (*Fioretta*)	10
Nathalia Crane (*Janitor's Boys*)	10
David Statler (*Roaring Guns*)	9
Erlin Hogan (*The Four Funny Men*)	8
Minou Drouet (*First Poems*)	8
Dorothy Straight (*How the World Began*)	6
Kali Diana Grosvenor (*Poems by Kali*)	7
Benjamin Friedman (*The Ridiculous Book*)	9

a. Make a frequency distribution showing the number of authors for each age.

b. Make a histogram for the distribution in part (**a**).

c. What percent of the authors were less than 8 years old when they published their first books?

26. How tall are you? The following are 10 famous people and their heights:

	Height (in.)
Honoré de Balzac (Fr. novelist)	62
Napoleon Bonaparte (Fr. emperor)	66
Yuri Gagarin (Soviet cosmonaut)	62
Hirohito (Japanese emperor)	65
Nikita Khrushchev (Soviet leader)	63
James Madison (U.S. president)	64
Margaret Mead (U.S. anthropologist)	62
Pablo Picasso (Spanish painter)	64
Mickey Rooney (U.S. actor)	63
Tutankhamen (Egyptian king)	66

a. Make a frequency distribution showing the number of people for each height.

b. Make a histogram for the distribution in part (**a**).

27. Have you gained a few pounds lately? One of the most challenging health crises the country has ever faced is obesity. Two-thirds of adults and nearly one-third of children and teens are currently obese or overweight, putting them at increased risk for type 2 diabetes, heart disease, and cancer. But who is at risk and more likely to be obese? Read on!

The Behavioral Risk Factor Surveillance System (BRFSS) of the U.S. Center for Disease Control and Prevention has determined that obesity is related to income and education. Here is a chart showing the data relating household income and obesity, but you can get a better visual representation with a histogram.

Household Income and Obesity	
Household Income	**Percent of Obese Adults (BMI ≥ 30) (Based on 2008–2010 Combined Data)**
Less than \$15,000	33.8%
\$15,000 to less than \$25,000	31.8%
\$25,000 to less than \$35,000	29.7%
\$35,000 to less than \$50,000	29.5%
\$50,000 or more	24.6%

a. Make a histogram for this data using 5 categories:
1 = Less than \$15,000
2 = \$15,000 to less than \$25,000
3 = \$25,000 to less than \$35,000
4 = \$35,000 to less than \$50,000
5 = \$50,000 or more

b. According to the histogram, which of the 5 categories has the highest percentage of obese adults?

c. What is the obesity rate for adults making \$50,000 or more (Category 5)?

d. Based on the histogram, what seems to be the relationship between household income and obesity?

Source: http://healthyamericans.org/assets/files/TFAH2011 FasInFat10.pdf, page 19. Note slash after files. Also comma after pdf, page 19 black.

28. Has your weight increased since you started attending college? As you can see from the chart, there is a relationship between education and obesity.

Education and Obesity	
Level of Schooling	**Percent of Obese Adults (BMI ≥ 30) (Based on 2008–2010 Combined Data)**
Did not graduate High School	32.8%
Graduated High School	30.4%
Attended College or Technical School	29.6%
Graduated from College or Technical School	21.5%

a. Make a histogram for this data using the 4 categories shown in the chart.

b. According to the histogram, which of the four categories has the most obese people?

c. What is the obesity rate for people who attended College or Technical School?

d. Based on the histogram, what seems to be the relationship between education and obesity?

29. Do you know that certain isotopes (different forms) of the elements are used in nuclear reactors and for medical purposes such as the treatment of cancer? At the present time, about 1400 isotopes have been observed, but of these only 332 occur naturally. The following table lists the number of elements having 1–10 naturally occurring isotopes. For instance, there are 22 elements having only 1 such isotope but only 1 element having the maximum number, 10. Make a histogram and a frequency polygon for these data.

Number of Naturally Occurring Isotopes	Number of Elements
1	22
2	21
3	9
4	6
5	7
6	9
7	11
8	3
9	1
10	1

30. Twenty apprentices were asked to measure the diameter of a steel rod with a **micrometer** (an instrument that can measure to thousandths of an inch). Their results (in inches) were

0.254	0.245	0.253	0.251
0.249	0.252	0.251	0.252
0.247	0.251	0.250	0.247
0.251	0.249	0.246	0.249
0.250	0.248	0.249	0.253

a. Make a frequency distribution of these measurements.

b. What single measurement has as many measurements above it as below it?

c. What percent of the measurements are between 0.249 and 0.251 in., inclusive?

d. What would you take as the best estimate of the diameter? Why?

31. The following is a quotation from *Robinson Crusoe,* which many of you have probably read:

> Upon the whole, here was an undoubted testimony that there was scarce any condition in the world so miserable, but was something negative or something positive, to be thankful for in it.

a. There are 151 letters in this quotation. Make a frequency distribution of the 151 letters.

b. Which letter occurs most frequently?

c. What percent of the letters are vowels?

32. Four coins were tossed 32 times, and each time the number of heads occurring was recorded, as follows:

1	2	2	1
2	3	0	3
3	1	3	2
2	3	2	1
2	1	2	3
4	3	3	4
1	2	2	1
2	0	1	2

Label three columns "Number of Heads," "Tally Marks," and "Frequency," and prepare a frequency distribution for these data.

33. a. Make a histogram for the data in problem 32.

b. Now make a frequency polygon for the data in problem 32.

34. A high school class was asked to roll a pair of dice 3000 times. The sums of the top faces of the dice, the frequency of these sums, and the theoretical number of times the sums should have occurred appear in the following table. Make a histogram for these data showing the actual frequency with a solid line and the theoretical frequency with a dotted line (perhaps of a different color).

Sum	Actual Frequency	Theoretical Frequency
2	79	83
3	152	167
4	252	250
5	312	333
6	431	417
7	494	500
8	465	417
9	338	333
10	267	250
11	129	167
12	91	83

35. Sulfur dioxide is a pollutant resulting from fuel combustion at power plants. At the present time, a 75 ppb (part per billion) or 0.075 ppm maximum is mandated by the EPA.

In a study of air pollution in a certain city, the following concentrations of sulfur dioxide in the air (in parts per million) were obtained for 30 days:

0.04	0.17	0.18	0.13	0.10	0.07
0.09	0.16	0.20	0.22	0.06	0.05
0.08	0.05	0.11	0.07	0.09	0.07
0.08	0.02	0.08	0.08	0.18	0.01
0.03	0.06	0.12	0.01	0.11	0.04

a. Make a frequency distribution for these data grouped in the intervals 0.00–0.04, 0.05–0.09, 0.10–0.14, 0.15–0.19, and 0.20–0.24.

b. For what percent of the time was the concentration of sulfur dioxide more than 0.14 part per million?

c. What percent of the time was the concentration more than 0.075, the highest allowed by law?

36. Make a histogram and a frequency polygon for the data in problem 35.

37. The following are the minimum weekly salaries (rounded to the nearest hundred dollars) for persons engaged in film production:

$7800	$5200	$4600	$1900	$1800	$1600
$1500	$1400	$ 800	$ 700	$ 700	$ 600

a. Make a frequency distribution using four classes with the upper class limit of the first class as the lower class limit of the second.

b. Make a histogram and a frequency polygon from your frequency distribution.

38. The following numbers represent the salaries of the 15 best-paid players in the National Hockey League (in millions of dollars):

$10,000,000	$10,000,000	$9,000,000
$ 9,000,000	$ 9,000,000	$8,000,000
$ 8,000,000	$ 8,000,000	$8,000,000
$ 8,000,000	$ 7,900,000	$7,800,000
$ 7,775,000	$ 7,775,000	$7,650,000

Source: http://tinyurl.com/84415pu.

a. Make a frequency distribution using three classes with the upper class limit of the first class as the lower class limit of the second.

b. Make a histogram and a frequency polygon from your frequency distribution.

39. Who was the best-paid baseball player in 2012? Alex Rodriguez of the New York Yankees, who makes 27.5 million per year, which is more than the combined salaries of the 25 best-paid players in 1947. Their salaries (in meager thousands of dollars) are as shown.

$90	$75	$65	$60	$44	$30	$30	$28	$26	$25
$23	$23	$20	$20	$20	$20	$20	$20	$20	$20
$20	$20	$20	$20	$20					

a. Make a frequency distribution using five classes with the upper-class limit of the first class as the lower-class limit of the second.

b. Make a histogram and a frequency polygon from your frequency distribution.

40. How do you use the Internet? Is there a difference between the activities you do on the Internet and the activities your professors (academics) do? A survey conducted by BSA-Ipsos indicated the following relative frequencies of Internet use among students and academics:

	Students	*Academics*
Personal	63%	11%
School	34%	0
Work	3%	89%

Source: BSA-Ipsos-Education Survey.

a. Make a relative frequency histogram for the students' data.

b. Make a relative frequency histogram for the academics' data.

c. Which category has the shortest bar (frequency) in the histogram for the students? What does that mean?

d. Which category has the longest bar (frequency) in the histogram for the academics? What does that mean?

41. Do you want to get your e-mail and browse the Web? You may consider a netbook, a lightweight and inexpensive laptop computer. The following are the list prices (in dollars) of the 15 best-rated netbooks:

$500	$300	$475	$280	$550	$265	$300	$310
$250	$240	$300	$250	$190	$290	$180	

a. Find the class width using five classes.

b. Make a frequency table with the five classes showing the class boundaries and frequencies.

c. Make a histogram showing the boundaries.

42. One of the top-grossing films of all time is *Titanic,* which grossed more than $600 million by 1999. But which films are the losers? The following are the amounts lost by the 10 biggest movie failures (in millions):

$35	$25	$23.3	$20	$20
$18.5	$17	$16.6	$15	$14

a. Find the class width using three classes.

b. Make a frequency table with the three classes showing the class boundaries and frequencies.

c. Make a histogram showing the boundaries.

43. Do you think you're getting old? Still, you're probably not nearly as old as Shigechiyo Izumi of Japan, who claimed to be an unverified 121 years old. As of this writing, the following were the authenticated ages of the 25 oldest people, rounded to the nearest year:

122	119	118	118	117	117	116	116	116	116
116	116	116	116	115	115	115	115	115	115
115	115	115	115	115					

Source:http://en.wikipedia.org/wiki/Wiki_List_of_the_verified_oldest_people.

a. Find the class width using four classes.

b. Make a frequency table with the four classes showing the class boundaries and frequencies.

c. Make a histogram showing the boundaries.

D Applications

Problems 44–47 refer to the data in Example 4.

44. Which tract has the most renter-occupied homes?

45. Which tract has the fewest renter-occupied homes?

46. Which tract has the fewest vacant homes?

47. On the basis of your previous answers, which tract would you select to sell renter's insurance on?

Problems 48 and 49 refer to the following table. An ad for a home pregnancy test claimed 99.5% accuracy as shown in the table.

Status	**Actually Pregnant**	**Actually Not Pregnant**
Test says pregnant	197	0
Test says not pregnant	1	2
Total	**198**	**2**

48. a. What was the sample size?

b. How many times was the test incorrect?

c. What percent is that?

49. Look at the definition of a simple random sample. Do you think that a simple random sample was used to obtain the data in the table? Why or why not?

50. Midway Airlines published ads in the *New York Times* and the *Wall Street Journal* claiming that "84 percent of frequent business travelers to Chicago prefer Midway Metrolink to American, United, and TWA." If it is known that Midway only has 8% of the traffic between New York and Chicago, can you explain how it may have arrived at this figure?

51. At the bottom of the ad cited in problem 50, the fine print stated that the survey was "conducted among Metrolink passengers between New York and Chicago." Is the sample used a representative random sample? (See the definition of a simple random sample on page 673.) Why or why not?

IN OTHER WORDS

52. When making a histogram, why is it necessary to make the class boundaries the endpoints of the bar?

53. Explain the difference between class limits and class boundaries.

54. A survey of the weight of 200 persons and a histogram of the last digit of each weight show that 0 occurred 130 times and 5 occurred 123 times. What might be wrong with the survey?

USING YOUR KNOWLEDGE

Around 1940 *it was estimated that it would require approximately* 10 *years of computation to find the value of the number* π *(pi) to* 1000 *decimal places. But in the early* 1960s, *a computer calculated the value of* π *to more than* 100,000 *decimal places in less than* 9 *hours! Since then,* 1.24 *trillion decimal places for* π *have been calculated. Here are the first* 40 *decimal places for* π.

3.14159	26535	89793	23846
26433	83279	50288	41971

55. Make a frequency distribution of the digits after the decimal point. List the digits from 0 to 9 in your first column.

56. What are the most and the least frequently occurring digits?

Mathematicians are interested in knowing whether the digits after the decimal point all occur with the same frequency. This question can hardly be answered with so few decimal places. You should notice that only two of the digits occur with a frequency more than one unit away from what you should expect in 40 decimal places.

DISCOVERY

Misuses of Statistics *In this section we have shown an honest way of depicting statistical data by means of a histogram. But you can lie with statistics! Here is how. In a newspaper ad for a certain magazine, the circulation of the magazine was as shown below. The heights of the bars in the diagram seem to indicate that sales in the first* 9 *months were tripled by the first quarter of the next year (a whopping* 200% *rise in sales!).*

57. Can you discover what was the approximate jump in sales from the first 9 months to the first quarter of the next year? If so, what was it?

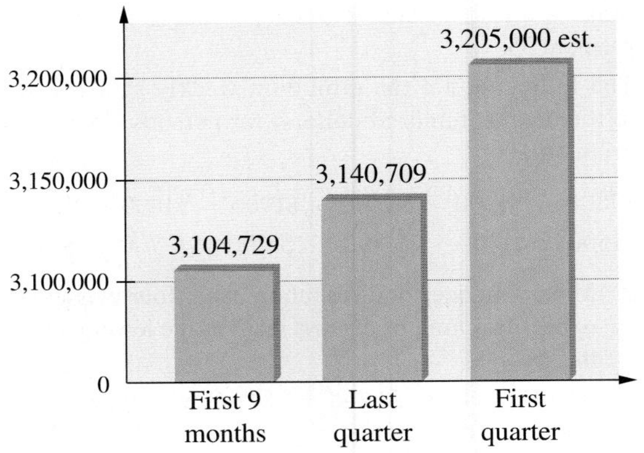

58. Can you discover what was the approximate percent rise in sales? If so, what was it?

59. Can you discover what is wrong with the graph? If so, what was it?

60. Here is a more recent actual misuse of statistics:

The *Terri Schiavo* case was a legal battle in the United States between the legal guardians and the parents of Teresa Marie "Terri" Schiavo. At issue was whether to forgo further life-prolonging procedures for Terri.

According to a poll conducted on March 18–20, 2005, when asked if they "agree[d] with the court's decision to have the feeding tube removed" (from Terri Schiavo), 62% of Democratic respondents agreed, compared with 54% of Republicans and 54% of Independents. The results of the poll are shown in the graph.

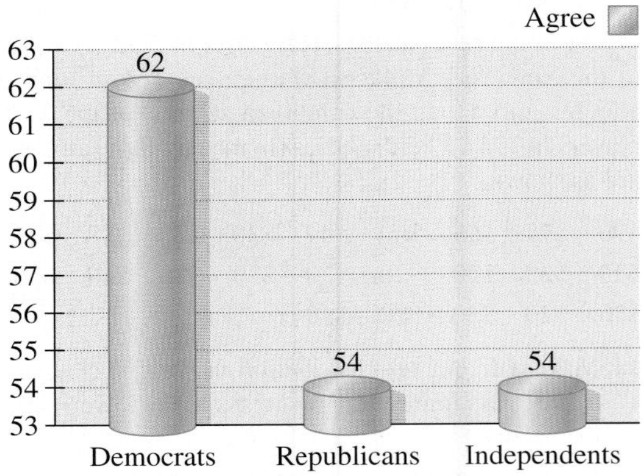

Results by Party

Sample: Interviews conducted by telephone on March 18–20, 2005, with 909 adults in the United States.
Sampling error: $\pm 7\%$ pts.

Source: Adapted from http://mediamatters.org/items/200503220005.

a. The categories are clearly labeled, but the frequencies are not. Should they be "frequencies" or "relative frequencies"? Can you discover how to label the units on the y axis?

b. Can you discover the actual percent difference between Republicans and Democrats?

c. Note that the sampling error is $\pm 7\%$ points. Keeping this in mind, can you discover how close the opinion of the Republicans and the Democrats could be? Explain.

d. Can you discover how to redraw the graph to show a more accurate presentation of the poll's findings? CNN has updated its graphic. You can see the updated version at the link provided in the source note.

COLLABORATIVE LEARNING

Many of the problems in the Discovery section deal with the misuses of statistics. Now, it is your turn to find some of these misuses. Form two or more groups.

1. Discuss how statistics can be misused or misleading. Concentrate on examples involving sampling and histograms.
2. Get the book *How to Lie with Statistics* by Darrell Huff and find some other misuses of statistics involving sampling and histograms.

The chart shows cosmetic products that cause allergies.

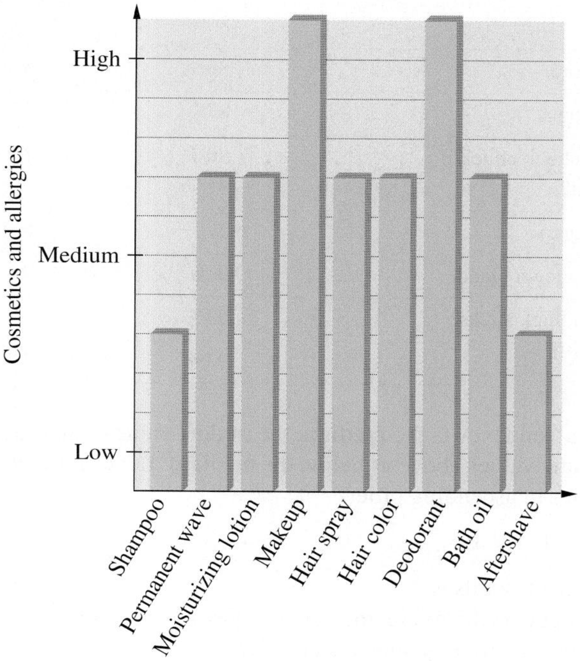

3. Which two products cause the most allergies? Suppose you want to sell hypoallergenic products. On the basis of the chart, which products would you concentrate on manufacturing? Discuss why.
4. Look at the definition of *histogram* given in the text. According to that definition, is the chart a histogram? Discuss why or why not. If not, what type of chart is it? Does the chart convey the idea that some products are more likely to produce allergic reactions, and if so, do you think it makes a difference whether or not the chart is a histogram?
5. A type of chart called a *Pareto* chart is used in quality control programs. The chart is used to improve quality control in production and service industries. In a Pareto chart, the tallest bar is placed on the left and the rest of the bars in descending order by height, so the chart highlights the major causes of problems. Convert the chart to a Pareto chart. Is it clearer now which products produce allergies?

12.2 Measures of Central Tendency: The Mean, Median, and Mode

GETTING STARTED

OBJECTIVE

Find the mean, median, and mode for a set of data.

TONGUE TWISTER AVERAGES

Is there a relationship between the number of words in a tongue twister and the difficulty in reciting it? Table 12.9 shows several tongue twisters and the percentage of successful attempts out of 30 total attempts at reciting each. What is the average number of words in each? It depends on what we mean by *average*.

The most commonly used measure of central tendency of a set of n numbers is the mean (the arithmetic average), which is obtained by *adding* all the numbers in the set and *dividing* by n. The mean of the number of words in the given tongue twisters is thus

$$\frac{11 + 7 + 5 + 4 + 10 + 6 + 6 + 5 + 13 + 35 + 9 + 8 + 4}{13} = \frac{123}{13} = 9.5$$

Table 12.9 Tongue Twisters

Phrase	Success Rate	Words
The seething sea ceaseth and thus the seething sea sufficeth us.	3%	11
The sixth sick sheik's sixth sheep's sick	30%	7
The Leith police dismisseth us.	67%	5
Sixty-six sick chicks	77%	4
Toy boat (said five times fast)	67%	10
Tie twine to three tree twigs	80%	6
She sells seashells by the seashore.	83%	6
Long slim slick sycamore saplings	87%	5
How much wood could a woodchuck chuck if a woodchuck could chuck wood?	80%	13
Peter Piper . . . (you know this one)	57%	35
Three new blue beans in a new-blown bladder	90%	9
Twixt six thick thumbs stick six thick sticks.	93%	8
Better baby buggy bumpers	97%	4

Another measure of central tendency is the **median,** the middle value of an ordered set of numbers (there are as many values above as below the median). Let us arrange the number of words in each twister in ascending order.

4 4 5 5 6 6 $\underline{7}$ 8 9 10 11 13 35

In this case, the median number of words is 7.

The easiest average to compute is the **mode,** the value occurring most often. We see that 4, 5, and 6 are modes for these numbers; they occur twice each. If Peter Piper were replaced by "Zack zapped Zeus zinc," the most common number of words (the **mode**) would then be 4.

So what is the **average** number of words in these tongue twisters? Either 4, 5, 6, 7, or 9.5. Which of the numbers is most representative? In this section we shall study these three types of **averages**—the mean, the median, and the mode—and how they can be used and misused (see the Discovery section) in different situations.

Alberto and Barney have just gotten back their test papers. There are 9 questions, and each one counted 10 points. Their scores are given in Table 12.10.

Table 12.10 Alberto's and Barney's Scores

	Questions									
Person	1	2	3	4	5	6	7	8	9	*Total*
Alberto	10	7	10	7	7	10	9	10	2	72
Barney	10	8	10	7	7	7	10	7	7	73

Who do you think wrote a better paper? As you can see, Alberto's **average** score is $\frac{72}{9} = 8$, and Barney's **average** score is $\frac{73}{9} = 8.1$. Barney clearly has the higher average and concludes that he wrote the better paper. Do you agree?

Alberto does not agree because he did as well as or better than Barney on 6 of the 9 questions. Alberto thinks that Barney's higher average does not tell the whole story, so he tries something else. First, he makes a frequency distribution of the two sets of scores, as shown in Table 12.11.

Table 12.11 Frequency Table

Score	Alberto	Barney
2	1	0
7	3	5
8	0	1
9	1	0
10	4	3

On inspecting this list, Alberto says, "I did better than you did, Barney, because I scored 10 more often than any other number, and you scored 7 more often than any other number." Would you agree with Alberto?

The first given averages, 8 and 8.1, are the *means*. These are the ones that most of us think of as the averages.

Definition of the Mean

The **mean** of a set of n numbers is the sum of the numbers divided by n. The mean is usually denoted by $\bar{x}$ (read "x bar"). Thus,

$$\bar{x} = \frac{\text{sum}}{n}$$

Alberto used a different kind of measure, called the *mode*.

Definition of the Mode

The **mode** of a set of numbers is that number of the set that occurs most often. If no number in the set occurs more than once, there is **no** mode. if several numbers all occur an equal number of times and more than all the rest, then all these several numbers are *modes*.

Thus, it is possible for a set of numbers to have more than one mode or no mode at all.

The mean and the mode are useful because they give an indication of a sort of center of the set. For this reason, they are called **measures of central tendency.**

EXAMPLE 1 Mean and Mode of Golf Scores

Ten golf professionals playing a certain course scored 69, 71, 72, 68, 69, 73, 71, 70, 69, and 68. Find the following:

(a) The mean (average) of these scores **(b)** The mode of these scores

Solution

(a) $$\bar{x} = \frac{69 + 71 + 72 + 68 + 69 + 73 + 71 + 70 + 69 + 68}{10} = \frac{700}{10} = 70$$

(b) The score that occurred most often—the mode—is 69 (3 times).

There is a third commonly used measure of central tendency, called the *median*.

Definition of the Median

The **median** of a set of numbers is the middle number when the numbers are arranged in order of magnitude. If there is no single middle number, then the median is the mean (average) of the two middle numbers.

Let us list Alberto's and Barney's scores in order of magnitude as follows:

Alberto	2	7	7	7	⑨	10	10	10	10
Barney	7	7	7	7	⑦	8	10	10	10

The median is circled in each case.

Table 12.12 Measures of Central Tendency

Measure	Alberto	Barney
Mean	8	8.1
Mode	10	7
Median	9	7

Now look in Table 12.12 for the three measures we have found for the scores. The mode and the median in this case would appear to some people to be evidence that perhaps Alberto did write a better paper than Barney.

But Barney is not convinced, and he does not give up easily. He concedes that Alberto had a better **mode** but claims that in many practical situations the mode does not even exist! Look at the prices of gas. "What?" says Alberto. Most gas station signs always show the mean and the median but rarely the mode. The mode is not a good indicator. Go out and check for yourself! Here are some samples.

Mean:

$$\frac{3.29 + 3.39 + 3.49}{3} = \mathbf{3.39}$$

Median: 3.39
No mode

Mean:

$$\frac{3.31 + 3.41 + 3.51}{3} = \mathbf{3.41}$$

Median: 3.41
No mode

Mean:

$$\frac{3.35 + 3.45 + 3.55}{3} = \mathbf{3.45}$$

Median: 3.45
No mode

"Si, si!" Alberto says, "but look at the prices I found" in the next example.

EXAMPLE 2 Mean, Median, and Mode of Gas Prices

Find the mean, median, and mode of the gas prices. Which is the most representative of the actual prices?

Solution

Mean: $\frac{3.31 + 3.39 + 3.49}{3} \approx \mathbf{3.3967}$

Median: 3.39
No mode

This time probably the median represents the actual prices better. Do you agree?

GRAPH IT

To do Example 3(a), clear any lists by pressing [2nd] [+] [4] [ENTER], and tell your grapher that you want to do statistics by pressing [STAT] [1]. Enter the values as the list L_1 by pressing 300 [ENTER] 250 [ENTER], and so on. Now you have the list {300, 250, . . . , 400}. To find the mean of the numbers in L_1, go to the home screen ([2nd] [MODE]) and press [2nd] [STAT] [◄] [3]. What mean do you want? The mean of the numbers in L_1, so enter [2nd] [L_1] [ENTER].

What if you want the median? Press [2nd] [STAT] [►] [4] [2nd] [L_1] [ENTER].

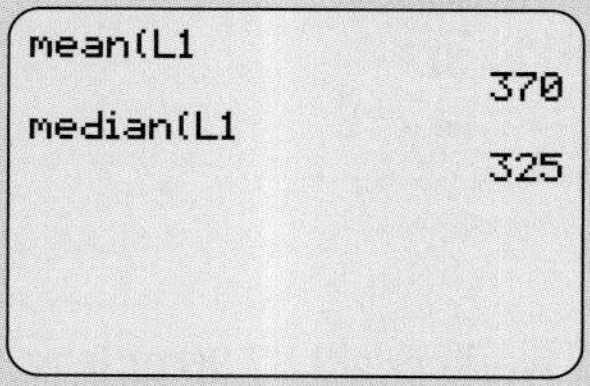

You can close parentheses after L_1 if desired!

EXAMPLE 3 Mean, Median, and Mode of Calorie Loss

Have you been exercising lately? You must exercise if you want to keep your weight down. The following are 10 different activities with the corresponding hourly energy expenditures (in calories) for a 150-lb person:

Activity	*Calories/Hour*	*Activity*	*Calories/Hour*
Fencing	300	Square dancing	350
Golf	250	Squash	600
Running	900	Swimming	300
Sitting	100	Volleyball	350
Standing	150	Wood chopping	400

(a) Find the mean of these numbers.

(b) Find the median number of calories spent in these activities.

(c) Find the mode of these numbers.

Solution

(a) The mean $\bar{x}$ is obtained by adding all the numbers and dividing the sum by 10. Thus,

$$\bar{x} = \frac{\text{sum}}{n}$$

$$= \frac{300 + 250 + 900 + 100 + 150 + 350 + 600 + 300 + 350 + 400}{10}$$

$$= 370 \text{ calories per hour}$$

(b) To find the median, we must first arrange the numbers in order of magnitude, as follows:

Sitting	100	
Standing	150	
Golf	250	
Fencing	300	
Swimming	300	← Median = $\frac{300 + 350}{2} = 325$
Square dancing	350	
Volleyball	350	
Wood chopping	400	
Squash	600	
Running	900	

We have an even number of items, and there is no "middle" value. the median is the mean (average) of the two middle items.

(c) The mode is the number with the greatest frequency if there is one such number. In this case, the numbers 300 and 350 both occur twice, whereas all other numbers occur just once. Thus, there are two modes, 300 and 350; the data are *bimodal*.

Wage	Tally Marks	Frequency
7.70	|||	3
7.80	𝍸 |	6
7.90	𝍸 |	6
8.00	𝍸 |||	8
8.10	𝍸	5
8.20	||	2
		30 Total

GRAPH IT

To do Example 4(a), enter the numbers in the first column as list L_1 and the frequencies as L_2. Go to the home screen ([2nd] [MODE]) and press [STAT] [▶] [1]. This means that you are doing one-variable statistics. But on which variables? It should be on the variables you entered, L_1 and L_2. Press [2nd] L_1 [,] [2nd] L_2 [ENTER]. The mean is 7.94 as before. If you scroll down by pressing [▼], the median is given as 7.95.

EXAMPLE 4 Mean, Median, and Mode for Wages

How much do you make an hour? Effective July 24, 2009, the federal minimum wage was increased to \$7.25 per hour. For the frequency distribution of wage rates given in the table, find the following:

(a) The mean rate (b) The mode (c) The median rate

Solution

(a) Referring to the table below, make the calculation shown in Table 12.13; the mean rate is \$7.94 per hour.

Table 12.13

Wage Rate	Frequency	Frequency × Rate
7.70	3	23.10
7.80	6	46.80
7.90	6	47.40
8.00	8	64.00
8.10	5	40.50
8.20	2	16.40
	Total 30	$30\overline{)238.20}$
		$7.94 = \bar{x}$

(b) The mode is the most frequent rate, \$8 per hour.

(c) By adding down the frequency column, we see that 15 workers get \$7.90 or less, and the other 15 get \$8.00 or more per hour. The median rate is the mean of \$7.90 and \$8.00, that is, \$7.95 per hour. Note that the mean, median, and mode are all more than the \$7.25 minimum wage.

EXAMPLE 5 Median and Mean for Student Scores Distributions

Table 12.14 shows the distribution of scores made by a large number of students taking a five-question true/false test.

(a) Which is the median score? (b) What is the mean score?

Solution

(a) Table 12.14 gives the proportion of students making each score, so the sum of these proportions must be 1. To find the median (the middle value 0.5), we add the proportions starting from the top until we get a sum of 0.5 or more. This occurs when we add the first four items. Thus the median score is 3.

(b) To find the mean score, we add the products of the scores and their proportions as follows:

$0 \times 0.05 = 0$
$1 \times 0.05 = 0.05$
$2 \times 0.10 = 0.20$
$3 \times 0.35 = 1.05$
$4 \times 0.25 = 1.00$
$5 \times 0.20 = 1.00$
$\text{Sum} = 3.30$

Since the sum of the proportions is 1, the mean score is the sum 3.30.

Table 12.14

Score (Number Correct)	Proportion of Students
0	0.05
1	0.05
2	0.10
3	0.35
4	0.25
5	0.20

2011 Team Payrolls		
No.	**Team**	**Payroll**
1.	New York Yankees	$201
2.	Philadelphia Phillies	$173
3.	Boston Red Sox	$161
4.	Los Angeles Angels	$139
5.	Chicago White Sox	$129
6.	Chicago Cubs	$125
7.	New York Mets	$120
8.	San Francisco Giants	$118
9.	Minnesota Twins	$113
10.	Detroit Tigers	$106

EXAMPLE 6 Finding the Mean, Median, and Mode

The 10 largest payrolls in Major League Baseball, approximated to the nearest million, are in the last column of the table.

(a) Find the mean of the payrolls. **(b)** Find the median of the payrolls.

(c) Find the mode of the payrolls. **(d)** Why is the mean higher than the median?

Solution

(a) The mean of the 10 payrolls is:

$$\frac{201 + 173 + 161 + 139 + 129 + 125 + 120 + 118 + 113 + 106}{10} = \frac{1385}{10} \approx 139 \text{ million}$$

(b) The numbers are: 201 173 161 139 129 | 125 120 118 113 106

5 numbers — 5 numbers

$$\text{Median: } \frac{129 + 125}{2} = 127$$

(c) There is no mode.

(d) The mean (139) is higher than the median (127) because of the New York Yankees' large payroll. If the New York Yankees' $201 million is excluded from the calculations, the mean is about $133 million, an amount closer to the median.

EXAMPLE 7 True Statements about the Mean, Median, and Mode

Figure 12.8 shows the distribution of scores on a placement test for students at South High School. In the chart, x is the score and y is the frequency. Which of the following statements is true?

(a) The mode and the mean are the same.

(b) The mode and the median are the same.

(c) The median is less than the mode.

(d) The median is greater than the mode.

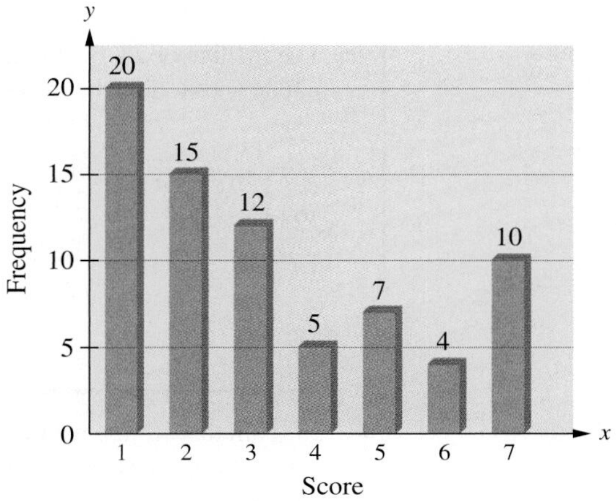

FIGURE 12.8

Solution

The chart shows that the mode is $x = 1$. It also shows that more than 20 students scored higher than 1. Hence, the median must be greater than 1 (the mode) and therefore statement (d) is correct.

EXAMPLE 8 Mean and Median of the Number of Rooms

Remember the housing units we studied in Section 12.1? Averages are used to find the number of rooms per unit. For example, in tract 1302 (column 1), the average (mean) number of rooms per unit is 4.8 (see Table 12.15).

(a) Find the average (mean) number of one-room houses in the four tracts.

(b) Find the average (mean) number of two-room houses in the four tracts.

(c) Find the median number of two-room houses in the four tracts.

Table 12.15

Housing Tenure (by Number of Rooms)	Tract 1302		Tract 1303		Tract 1304		Tract 1305	
1 room	43	6%	19	1%	39	2%	20	1%
2 rooms	28	4%	67	5%	98	4%	137	7%
3 or 4 rooms	247	32%	481	35%	817	32%	764	37%
5 or 6 rooms	367	47%	611	45%	1315	51%	900	44%
7 or 8 rooms	64	8%	160	12%	246	10%	235	11%
9 or more rooms	27	3%	19	1%	56	2%	4	0%
Total housing units	776		1357		2571		2060	
Rooms per unit	4.8		4.9		4.9		4.7	
Persons per occupied unit	2.1		2.5		2.7		2.4	
Persons per occupied room	0.4		0.5		0.6		0.5	

Solution

(a) The average (mean) number of one-room houses is the sum of the numbers in the first row divided by 4, the number of tracts; that is,

$$\frac{43 + 19 + 39 + 20}{4} = \frac{121}{4} = 30.25, \text{ or approximately } 30$$

(b) This time we add the numbers in the second row and divide by 4.

$$\frac{28 + 67 + 98 + 137}{4} = \frac{330}{4} = 82.5, \text{ or approximately } 83$$

(c) The median of 28, 67, 98, and 137 is obtained by arranging the numbers in order of magnitude and finding the mean (average) of the two middle numbers as shown.

$$\begin{matrix} 28 \\ \left.\begin{matrix} 67 \\ 98 \end{matrix}\right\} \dfrac{67 + 98}{2} = 82.5, \text{ or about } 83 \\ 137 \end{matrix}$$

In this section we introduced three **measures of central tendency.** The following shows how they compare:

1. The **mean** (arithmetic average) is the most commonly used of the three measures. A set of data always has a unique mean, and this mean takes account of each item of the data. On the negative side, finding the mean takes the most calculation of the three measures. Another bad feature of the mean is its sensitivity to extreme values. For instance, the mean of the data 2, 4, 6, and 8 is $\frac{20}{4} = 5$, but the mean of 2, 4, 6, and 28 is $\frac{40}{4} = 10$, a shift of 5 units toward the extreme value 28.

2. The **mode** has the advantage of requiring no calculation. However, the mode may not exist, as in the case of the data 2, 4, 6, and 8. On the other hand, the mode may be most useful. For example, suppose a shoe manufacturer surveys 100 women to see which of three styles, A, B, or C, of shoes each one prefers and finds style A selected by 30 women, style B by 50, and style C by 20. The mode is 50, and there is not much doubt about which style the manufacturer will feature.

3. The **median** always exists and is unique, as in the case of the mean. However, the median requires very little computation and is not sensitive to extreme values. Of course, in order to find the median, the data must be arranged in order of magnitude, and this may not be practical for large sets of data. But the most important disadvantage of the median is its failure to take account of each item of data. Hence, in many statistical problems, the median is not a reliable measure.

12.2 EXERCISES

1. Find the mean and the median for each set of numbers.
   a. 1, 5, 9, 13, 17
   b. 1, 3, 9, 27, 81
   c. 1, 4, 9, 16, 25
   d. For which of these sets are the mean and the median the same? Which measure is the same for all three sets? Which (if any) of the sets has a mode?
2. Show that the median of the set of numbers 1, 2, 4, 8, 16, 32 is 6. How does this compare with the mean?
3. Out of 10 possible points, a class of 20 students made the following test scores:

   0, 0, 1, 2, 4, 5, 5, 6, 6, 6, 7, 8, 8, 8, 8, 9, 9, 9, 10, 10

   Find the mean, the median, and the mode. Which of these three measures do you think is the least representative of the set of scores?
4. Find the mean and the median of the following set of numbers:

   0, 3, 26, 43, 45, 60, 72, 75, 79, 82, 83
5. An instructor gave a short test to a class of 25 students. The scores on the basis of 10 were

Score	Number of Students
3	2
4	1
5	3
6	2
7	6
8	4
9	4
10	3

   The instructor asked two students, Agnes and Betty, to calculate the mean (average) score. Agnes made the calculation

$$\frac{3 + 4 + 5 + 6 + 7 + 8 + 9 + 10}{8} = \frac{52}{8} = 6.5$$

   and said the mean (average) score is 6.5. Betty calculated a *weighted average* by multiplying each score by the number of students attaining that score, adding the results, and dividing by the total number of students as shown.

$$\frac{2 \cdot 3 + 1 \cdot 4 + 3 \cdot 5 + 2 \cdot 6 + 6 \cdot 7 + 4 \cdot 8 + 4 \cdot 9 + 3 \cdot 10}{25} = \frac{177}{25} = 7.08$$

   She then said the mean (average) was 7.08. Who is correct, Agnes or Betty? Why?
6. An investor bought 150 shares of Fly-Hi Airlines stock. He paid \$60 per share for 50 shares, \$50 per share for 60 shares, and \$75 per share for 40 shares. What was his average cost per share? (Compare with problem 5.)
7. Make a frequency distribution of the number of letters per word in the following quotation: "For seven days seven priests with seven trumpets invested Jericho, and on the seventh day they encompassed the city seven times."
   a. Find the mode(s) of the number of letters per word.
   b. Find the median. (You can use your frequency distribution to do this.)
   c. Find the mean of the number of letters per word.
   d. Do you think your answers would give a good indication of the average length of words in ordinary English writing? Why or why not?
8. The following are the temperatures at 1-hour intervals in Denver, Colorado, from 1 P.M. on a certain day to 9 A.M. the next day:

1 P.M.	90	8 P.M.	81	3 A.M.	66
2 P.M.	91	9 P.M.	79	4 A.M.	65
3 P.M.	92	10 P.M.	76	5 A.M.	66
4 P.M.	92	11 P.M.	74	6 A.M.	64
5 P.M.	91	12 M	71	7 A.M.	64
6 P.M.	89	1 A.M.	71	8 A.M.	71
7 P.M.	86	2 A.M.	69	9 A.M.	75

   a. What was the mean temperature? The median temperature?
   b. What was the mean temperature from 1 P.M. to 9 P.M.? The median temperature?
   c. What was the mean temperature from midnight to 6 A.M.? The median temperature?

9. Suppose that a dime and a nickel are tossed. They can fall in four different ways: (H, H), (H, T), (T, H), and (T, T), where the first letter indicates how the dime falls and the second letter, the nickel. How many tosses do you think it would take, on average, to get all four possibilities at least once? A good way to find out is by experimenting. Take a dime and a nickel and toss them to get your data. For example, on the first trial it took 11 tosses to get all four possibilities, (H, H), (H, T), (T, H), and (T, T). You can keep track of what happens with a frequency distribution like the following:

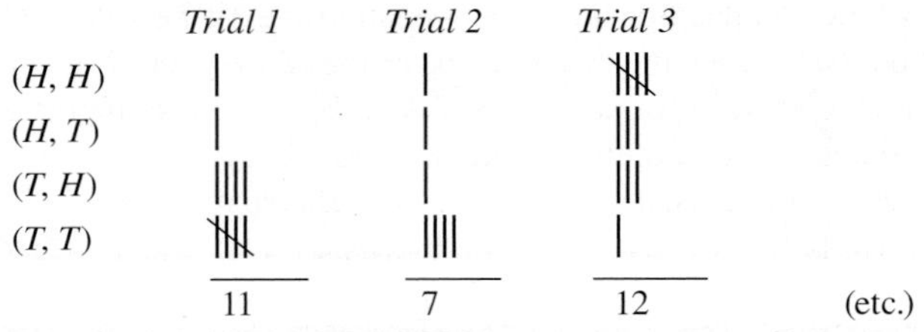

You will need to make tally marks in the trial column until there is at least one mark for each possibility. Then write the total number of tosses at the bottom of the column. A new column will be needed for each trial, of course. Do 20 trials.

a. When you finish the 20 trials, make a frequency distribution of the number of tosses required to give all four possibilities.

b. Use the frequency distribution you obtained in part (a) to find the median number of tosses.

c. Find the mean number of tosses needed to obtain all four possibilities.

10. The mean score on a test taken by 20 students is 75; what is the sum of the 20 test scores?

11. A mathematics professor lost a test paper belonging to one of her students. She remembered that the mean score for the class of 20 was 81 and that the sum of the 19 other scores was 1560. What was the grade on the paper she lost?

12. If in problem 11 the mean was 82 and the sum of the 19 other scores was still 1560, what was the grade on the lost paper?

13. The mean salary for the 20 workers in company A is \$90 per week, whereas in company B the mean salary for its 30 workers is \$80 per week. If the two companies merge, what is the mean salary for the 50 employees of the new company?

14. A student has a mean score of 88 on five tests taken. What score must she obtain on her next test to have a mean (average) score of 80 on all six tests?

15. The following table shows the distribution of families by income in a particular urban area.

Annual Income (\$)	Proportion of Families
0–9999	0.02
10,000–14,999	0.09
15,000–19,999	0.25
20,000–24,999	0.30
25,000–34,999	0.11
35,000–49,999	0.10
50,000–79,999	0.07
80,000–119,999	0.05
120,000+	0.01

a. What proportion of the families have incomes of at least \$25,000?

b. What is the median income range?

c. Find the mean of the lower limits for the annual incomes.

d. Find the amount below which 36% of the families have lower incomes.

16. a. Find the mean, median, and mode of the five most expensive gasoline prices.

b. Are the mean, median, and mode close?

c. Which of the three do you think is most representative of the prices?

d. Delete Hong Kong and answer part (c) again.

17. a. Find the mean, median, and mode of the five least expensive gasoline prices.

b. Are the mean, median, and mode close?

International Gasoline Prices	
Most Expensive	
Location	**Price per Gallon**
Hong Kong	\$5.34
London, England	\$4.55
Paris, France	\$4.41
Amsterdam, Neth	\$4.38
Seoul, S. Korea	\$4.35
Least Expensive	
Location	**Price per Gallon**
Caracas, Venezuela	\$0.28
Jakarta, Indonesia	\$0.74
Cairo, Egypt	\$0.75
Kuwait City, Kuwait	\$0.77
Manama, Bahrain	\$0.82

c. Which of the three do you think is most representative of the prices?

d. Delete Caracas and answer part (c) again.

18. The following graph shows the distribution of scores on a placement test given to juniors at West High School. Which of the following statements applies to this distribution? *Hint:* See Example 7.

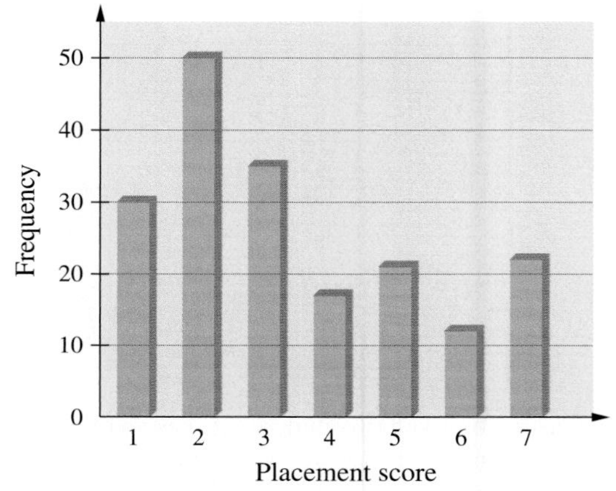

a. The mode and the mean are the same.

b. The mode is greater than the mean.

c. The mode and the median are the same.

d. The mode is less than the median.

19. Can you name the 5 best-paying jobs for **women** in America? The 5 best-paying jobs for women in America and their **weekly** salaries are as follows: Chief Executive: $1553, Pharmacist: $1475, Lawyer: $1449, IT manager $1411, Software engineer: $1311.

Source: http://tinyurl.com/2dndrlt.

a. Find the mean, median and mode of the 5 salaries

b. Which is higher, the mean or the median?

20. What is the salary of **men** in the same positions as those listed in Problem 19? Here they are: Chief Executive: $2085, Pharmacist: $1954, Lawyer: $1935, IT manager $1788, Software engineer: $1550.

a. Find the mean, median and mode of the 5 salaries

b. Which is higher, the mean or the median?

21. Refer to Table 12.15 and find the mean and median number of three- or four-room houses in the four tracts.

22. Refer to Table 12.15 and find the mean and median number of five- or six-room houses in the four tracts.

The *ABC Consumer Comfort Index* rates the economy, the buying climate, and personal finances. The three resulting numbers are added and divided by 3. For a particular week the results were as follows:

General Population	
Overall index	25
State of economy	42
Personal finances	34
Buying climate	0

Note that

$$\frac{42 + 34 + 0}{3} = \frac{76}{3} \approx \boxed{25}$$

Find the mean of the following overall indexes classified by

23. *Income*

Under $15K	−18
$15K–$24.9K	8
$25K–$39.9K	5
$40K–$49.9K	46
Over $50K	62

24. *Education*

< High school	−13
High school grad.	16
College +	45

The table that follows will be used in problems 25–29.

Type of Spam	July	August
Internet	14	22
Other	28	32
Scams	18	20
Products	40	40
Spiritual	2	2
Financial	30	28
Leisure	16	14
Adult	28	24
Health	24	18

Source: Data from Brightmail Probe Network.

The table shows the number and type of spam (unsolicited "junk" e-mail sent to large numbers of people to promote products or services) received by the same 200 persons in July and August.

25. Find the mean number of spams received in July.

26. Find the median number of spams received in July.

27. Find the mode (if it exists) of the number of spams received in July.

28. Name the categories in which the number of spams received did not change from July to August.

29. Which category increased the most from July to August?

Attendance at Top Five Amusement/Theme Parks in the United States (in millions)*

Name	Year 1	Year 2	Year 3	Year 4	Current
The Magic Kingdom at Walt Disney World Lake Buena Vista, FL	11.2	12.9	13.8	17.0	16.9
Disneyland Anaheim, CA	10.3	14.1	15.0	14.3	16
Epcot at Walt Disney World Lake Buena Vista, FL	9.7	10.7	11.2	11.8	10.8
Disney-MGM Studios at Walt Disney World Lake Buena Vista, FL	8.0	9.5	10.0	10.5	9.7
Universal Studios Florida Orlando, FL	7.7	8.0	8.4	8.9	6.59

Source: From THE WALL STREET JOURNAL ALMANAC 1999 by Wall Street Journal Staff, copyright © 1998 by Dow Jones & Company, Inc. Used by permission of Ballantine books, a division of Random House.

*For the latest figures, try http://en.wikipedia.org/wiki/List_of_amusement_park_attendance_figures#.

The table shows the attendance (in millions) of the top five amusement/theme parks in the United States for five successive years. Find the mean (average) and median attendance and determine if they are greater than the current attendance at:

30. the Magic Kingdom. **31.** Disneyland. **32.** Epcot.

33. Disney-MGM. **34.** Universal Studios Florida.

Do you surf or shop on the Web? The following tables give the 10 most visited Web sites and the top education sites.

35. What is the average number of visitors to the top 10 Web sites overall?

Top 10 Web Sites Overall

Rank	Site	Unique Visitors (MILLIONS)
1	facebook.com	880
2	youtube.com	800
3	yahoo.com	590
4	live.com	490
5	msn.com	440
6	wikipedia.org	410
7	blogspot.com	340
8	baidu.com	300
9	microsoft.com	250
10	qq.com	250

Source: http://www.google.com/adplanner/static/top1000.

36. What is the average number of visitors to the top 10 education sites?

Top 10 Education Sites

Rank	Education Web Sites	Unique Visitors* (millions)	Rank	Education Web Sites	Unique Visitors* (millions)
1	Fastweb	4.06	6	UMich.edu	2.53
2	Learning Network Property	3.67	7	Cornell.edu	2.49
3	Berkeley.edu	3.05	8	Harvard.edu	2.44
4	UTexas.edu	2.87	9	MIT.edu	2.39
5	UIUC.edu	2.68	10	Thinkquest site	2.32

*Unique visitors over 1-month period.

37. The following table shows the average annual salary for 5 consecutive years for a person with an associate degree:

1	39,468
2	39,276
3	40,827
4	46,778
5	49,733

a. Find the mean, median, and mode of the person's salary for the 5 years.

b. Which is the most representative of the person's salary: the mean, the median, or the mode?

38. The following table shows the average annual salary for 5 consecutive years for a person with less than a high school diploma:

1	20,484
2	19,935
3	21,611
4	22,679
5	23,845

Source: Bureau of Labor Statistics.

a. Find the mean, median, and mode of the person's salary for the 5 years. Compare with the person in problem 37!

b. Which is the most representative of the person's salary: the mean, the median, or the mode?

IN OTHER WORDS

39. Explain in your own words what is meant by the median of a set of scores. Is the median a good measure of a set of scores?

40. What is meant by the mode of a set of scores? Is this a good measure? If so, for what purpose? Give an example.

USING YOUR KNOWLEDGE

Have you ever been in the checkout line at a supermarket or department store for so long that you were tempted to walk out? There is a mathematical theory called ***queuing*** *(pronounced "cueing") theory that studies ways in which lines at supermarkets, department stores, and so on can be reduced to a minimum. The following problems show how a store manager can estimate the average number of people waiting at a particular counter:*

41. Suppose that in a 5-min interval customers arrive as indicated in the following table. (Arrival time is assumed to be at the beginning of each minute.) In the first minute, A and B arrive. During the second minute, B moves to the head of the line (A was gone because it took 1 min to serve him), and C and D arrive, and so on. From the figure, find

a. the average (mean) number of people in line.

b. the mode of the number of people in line.

Time	Customers
1	*A, B*
2	*C, D*
3	
4	*E, F*
5	

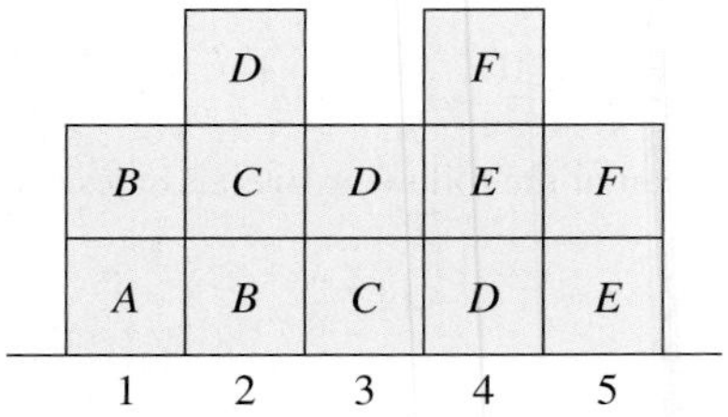

42. Use the ideas of problem 41 and suppose that the list of arrivals is as shown in the following table. (Assume it takes 1 min to serve the first customer in line and that the customer leaves immediately.)

a. Draw a diagram showing the line during each of the first 5 min.

b. Find the mean of the number of people in line during the 5 min.

c. Find the mode of the number of people in line.

Time	Customers
1	*A*
2	*B*
3	*C, D, E*
4	*F*
5	

DISCOVERY

Misuses of Statistics *We have just studied three measures of central tendency: the mean, the median, and the mode. All these measures are frequently called averages. Suppose that the following chart shows the salaries at Scrooge Manufacturing Company.*

43. Scrooge claims that the workers should not unionize; after all, he says, the "average" salary is \$21,000. Can you discover what "average" this is?

44. Manny Chevitz, the union leader, claims that Scrooge Manufacturing really needs a union. Just look at their salaries! A meager $6000 on the average. Can you discover what "average" he means?

45. B. Crooked, the politician, wants both union and management support. He says that the workers are about average as far as salary is concerned. You can figure it out. The company's "average" salary is $8000. Can you discover what "average" B. Crooked has in mind?

CALCULATOR CORNER

If you have a calculator with [Σ+] *(read "sigma plus") and* [$\bar{x}$] *keys, you are in luck. The calculation for the mean is done automatically for you. First, place the calculator in the statistics mode (press* [mode] [stat] *or* [2nd] [stat]*). To find the mean of the numbers in Example 2, enter* [300] [Σ+] [250] [Σ+] [900] [Σ+] [100] [Σ+] [150] [Σ+] [350] [Σ+] [600] [Σ+] [300] [Σ+] [350] [Σ+] [400] [Σ+] [2nd] [$\bar{x}$]*. The display gives the mean* [$\bar{x}$] = *370.*

COLLABORATIVE LEARNING

Form two groups. One group will investigate race discrimination complaints and the other sex discrimination complaints, as shown in the following table. Then answer the questions.

1. What was the average number of complaints for race and for sex in the 5-year period?
2. What was the average number of resolutions for race and for sex in the 5-year period?
3. What were the average monetary benefits for race and for sex per resolved case in the 5-year period?

Discussion Which average monetary benefits per resolved case were greater, race or sex discrimination? Why?

Discrimination Complaints: Number of Complaints Received, Number of Cases Resolved, and Amount of Monetary Benefits for Different Types of Workplace Discrimination in a 5-Year Period

	Year 1	Year 2	Year 3	Year 4	Year 5
Race					
Complaints received	31,695	31,656	29,986	26,287	29,199
Resolutions	27,440	25,253	31,674	35,127	36,419
Monetary benefits (millions)	$ 33.3	$ 39.7	$ 30.1	$ 37.2	$ 41.8
Sex					
Complaints received	23,919	25,860	26,181	23,813	24,728
Resolutions	21,606	21,545	26,726	30,965	32,836
Monetary benefits (millions)	$ 44.0	$ 44.1	$ 23.6	$ 47.1	$ 72.5

Source: U.S. Equal Employment Opportunity Commission.

12.3 Measures of Dispersion: The Range and Standard Deviation

GETTING STARTED

OBJECTIVE

Find the range and standard deviation for a set of data.

RATINGS DEVIATIONS FOR MOVIES AND TV

Which programs get the best television ratings, weekly series or movies? The ratings for the 10 best series and 10 best movies according to the *Top 10 Almanac* are shown in Table 12.16. If you were a manufacturer selling your product to consumers, would you buy television advertisement time during a series or during a movie? Before you make up your mind, look at Table 12.16 and note that the series' ratings **range** from 18 to 24 (6 points), whereas the movies' ratings **range** from 19 to 25 (also 6 points). Since the range is the same in both distributions, you might look next at the mean rating in each category. But the mean is 21 in both cases. What else can you look at to try to determine the best air time for an advertiser? There is a measurement that indicates how the data differ from the mean, and it is called the **standard deviation (s).** The standard deviation, like the range, is a measure of the spread of data. To obtain the standard deviation of a set of numbers, start by computing the difference between each measurement and the mean, that is, $x - \bar{x}$, as shown in Table 12.17 for the movie ratings data.

Unfortunately, if you add the $x - \bar{x}$ values, you get a sum of 0. (This will always be true when finding standard deviations. Can you figure out why?) Therefore, you square each $x - \bar{x}$ value before you do the addition and then arrive at a sum of 32. If you were looking at the entire population of movies on TV, you would then divide this number by the population size to get a type of "average squared difference" of ratings from the mean. However, this sample does not include the entire population, so, as a rule, divide instead by 1 less than the number in the sample (here, that number is $10 - 1 = 9$) to make the final value of the standard deviation a bit larger. You then have $s^2 = \frac{32}{9}$, in units

Table 12.16

	Ratings	
Rank	**Series**	**Movies**
1	24	25
2	23	23
3	23	22
4	22	21
5	21	21
6	20	20
7	20	20
8	20	20
9	19	19
10	18	19
Total	**210**	**210**

Table 12.17

Rank	Movie Ratings (x)	$x - \bar{x}$	$(x - \bar{x})^2$
1	25	$25 - 21 = 4$	16
2	23	$23 - 21 = 2$	4
3	22	$22 - 21 = 1$	1
4	21	$21 - 21 = 0$	0
5	21	$21 - 21 = 0$	0
6	20	$20 - 21 = -1$	1
7	20	$20 - 21 = -1$	1
8	20	$20 - 21 = -1$	1
9	19	$19 - 21 = -2$	4
10	19	$19 - 21 = -2$	4
Total	**210**		**32**

of squared ratings points. What kind of unit is that? To return to ratings points, you need to take the square root of $\frac{32}{9}$.

$$s = \sqrt{\frac{32}{9}} \quad \text{or} \quad \frac{4\sqrt{2}}{3}$$

(Remember that $\sqrt{32} = \sqrt{16 \cdot 2} = 4\sqrt{2}$.) A calculator or square root table gives $s \approx 1.89$. For the series data, $s \approx 1.94$ (try it); this means that series ratings are slightly more dispersed, or spread out. You might like advertising time during movies because their ratings are closer together and slightly less variable.

In this section you will learn how to find the range and calculate the standard deviation of a set of sample data.

Most of the time we want to know more about a set of numbers than we can learn from a measure of central tendency. For instance, the two sets of numbers {3, 5, 7} and {0, 5, 10} both have the same mean and the same median, 5, but the two sets of numbers are quite different. Clearly, some information about how the numbers vary will be useful in describing the set.

A number that describes how the numbers of a set are spread out, or dispersed, is called a **measure of dispersion.** A very simple example of such a measure is the range.

Definition of the Range

The **range** of a set of numbers is the difference between the greatest and the least of the numbers in the set.

The two sets {3, 5, 7} and {0, 5, 10} have ranges $7 - 3 = 4$ and $10 - 0 = 10$, respectively. Because the range is determined by only two numbers of the set, it gives very little information about the other numbers of the set. The range gives only a general notion of the spread of the given data.

As noted in Getting Started, if we add all the deviations from the mean, the $x - \bar{x}$ values, we always get a sum of 0. Accordingly, the most commonly used measure of dispersion, the *standard deviation,* uses the squares of the deviations $x_k - \bar{x}$ in the following definition:

Definition of the Standard Deviation

Let a set of n numbers be denoted by $x_1, x_2, x_3, \ldots, x_n$, and let the mean of these numbers be denoted by $\bar{x}$. Then the **standard deviation** s is given by

$$s = \sqrt{\frac{(x_1 - \bar{x})^2 + (x_2 - \bar{x})^2 + (x_3 - \bar{x})^2 + \ldots + (x_n - \bar{x})^2}{n - 1}}$$

If the standard deviation is to be calculated for an **entire** population, then the sum of the squared differences is divided by N, the size of the entire population. For a **sample** drawn from a population (as in this book), $n - 1$ is used, where n is the sample size.

Finding the Standard Deviation

In order to find the standard deviation, we have to find the following:

1. The mean $\bar{x}$ of the set of numbers
2. The difference (deviation) between each number of the set and the mean
3. The squares of these deviations
4. The sum of the squared deviations divided by $n - 1$
5. The square root s of this quotient

The last four steps motivate the name **root-mean-square deviation,** which is often used for the standard deviation. As we shall see, the number s gives a good indication of how the data are spread about the mean.

GRAPH IT

To do Example 1, erase any lists first (press [2nd] [+] [4] [ENTER]). The grapher says "Done." Press [STAT] [1] and enter 7, 9, 10, 11, and 13 (press [ENTER] after each entry). To find the standard deviation, go to the home screen ([2nd] [MODE]) and press [2nd] [STAT] [◄] [7] [2nd] [L_1] and [ENTER]. The answer is shown.

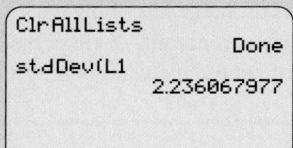

```
ClrAllLists
                Done
stdDev(L1
         2.236067977
```

EXAMPLE 1 Standard Deviation of Children's Ages

The ages of five schoolchildren were found to be 7, 9, 10, 11, and 13. Find the standard deviation s for this set of ages.

Solution

We follow the five steps given at the bottom of page 701, as shown in Table 12.18.

1. The mean of the 5 ages is

$$\bar{x} = \frac{7 + 9 + 10 + 11 + 13}{5} = \frac{50}{5} = 10 \qquad \text{(Column 1)}$$

2. We now find the difference (deviation) between each number and the mean (column 2).
3. We square the numbers in column 2 to get column 3.

Table 12.18 Calculation of the Standard Deviation

Age x	Difference from Mean $x - \bar{x}$	Square of Difference $(x - \bar{x})^2$
7	−3	9
9	−1	1
10	0	0
11	1	1
13	3	9
50 Sum of ages		20 Sum of squares
$\bar{x} = \frac{50}{5} = 10$ Mean of ages		$\frac{20}{5-1} = 5$

4. We find the sum of the squares in column 3 divided by $5 - 1$.

$$\frac{9 + 1 + 0 + 1 + 9}{5 - 1} = \frac{20}{5 - 1} = 5$$

5. The standard deviation is the square root of the number found in step 4. Thus, $s = \sqrt{5} \approx 2.2$. Note that $\sqrt{5}$ can be found from the table at the end of the book or with a calculator.

The number s, although it seems complicated to compute, is a most useful number to know. In many practical applications, about 68% of the data are within 1 standard deviation from the mean. That is, 68% of the numbers lie between $\bar{x} - s$ and $\bar{x} + s$. Also, about 95% of the data are within 2 standard deviations from the mean; that is, 95% of the numbers lie between $\bar{x} - 2s$ and $\bar{x} + 2s$.

For example, if the mean of a set of 1000 numbers is 200 and the standard deviation is 25, then approximately 680 of the numbers lie between 175 and 225, and all but about 50 of the numbers lie between 150 and 250. Thus, even with no further information, the number s gives a fair idea of how the data are spread about the mean. These ideas are discussed more fully in Section 12.4.

EXAMPLE 2 Mean, Median, Mode, and Standard Deviation

A consumer group checks the price of 1 dozen large eggs at 11 chain stores, with the following results:

Store Number	1	2	3	4	5	6	7	8	9	10	11
Price (cents)	70	68	72	60	63	75	66	65	72	69	68

Find the mean, median, mode, and standard deviation. What percent of the data are within 1 standard deviation from the mean?

Note: To compare prices per ounce for different size eggs go to http://tinyurl.com/7mkpsqx.

Solution

In Table 12.19, the data are arranged in order of magnitude. The mean is found to be 68¢. The median is the middle price, 68¢. The modes are 68¢ and 72¢. The calculation of the standard deviation is shown in the table. The result is $s = 4.3$. To find the percent of the data within 1 standard deviation from the mean, we first find $\bar{x} - s = 63.7$ and $\bar{x} + s = 72.3$. By examining the data, we see that 8 of the prices are between these two numbers. Thus, 73% of the prices are within 1 standard deviation from the mean price.

Note that you are not expected to calculate square roots. Use Table I in the back of the book or a calculator. Both forms of the answer, $\sqrt{18.8}$ and 4.3, are given in the answer section.

Table 12.19

x	$x - \bar{x}$	$(x - \bar{x})^2$
60	−8	64
63	−5	25
65	−3	9
66	−2	4
68	0	0
68	0	0
69	1	1
70	2	4
72	4	16
72	4	16
75	7	49
748		**188**
$\bar{x} = \frac{748}{11} = 68$		$\frac{188}{10} = 18.8$ $s = \sqrt{18.8} \approx 4.3$

We have been studying for some time now. I think we need a vacation. Let us go from New York to Honolulu. What do we need to do? Book a flight, a hotel, and a car. Figure 12.9 on the following page gives the prices we found.

We can ask a lot of questions about these prices. Some have a simple answer, and others are harder to compute (unless you have a calculator!). We shall answer some questions now and leave some for the exercises.

Flight Price	Hotel Price	Rental	Price
734.20 (US Dollars)	**CORAL REEF** 247 Rooms / 15 Floors USD 70.00 — USD 150.00*	Omala	US $21.99 /Day US $23.99 /Day
816.20 (US Dollars)	**WAIKIKI BEACHCOMBER** 500 Rooms USD 105.00 — USD 495.00*	BUCKS	US $24.99 /Day US $26.99 /Day
837.20 (US Dollars)	**RADISSON ALA MOANA** 1168 Rooms / 36 Floors USD 215.00 — USD 215.00*	International	US $31.98 /Day US $34.98 /Day
837.20 (US Dollars)	**WAIKIKI PARKSIDE** 247 Rooms / 15 Floors USD 59.00 — USD 148.00*	Davis	US $33.99 /Day US $37.99 /Day
837.20 (US Dollars)	**PAGODA HOTEL** 360 Rooms / 12 Floors USD 68.00 — USD 145.00*	–Widget–	US $34.99 /Day US $36.99 /Day

* Prices depend on time of travel.

FIGURE 12.9

EXAMPLE 3 Vacation Price Ranges, Modes, Means, and Deviations

(a) What is the range of prices for the flight? What is the mode?

(b) In the last column, there are two prices for a rental car. The first price is the price of renting an economy model for one day, the second for renting a compact. What is the range of prices for the economy model?

(c) What is the mean rental price for an economy model?

(d) What is the standard deviation of the prices of an economy model?

Solution

(a) The range is the difference between the highest price ($837.20) and the lowest price ($734.20), which is $837.20 − $734.20 = $103. The mode is the price that occurs most often, $837.20.

(b) The prices for the economy model range from $21.99 to $34.99. Thus, the range is $34.99 − $21.99 = $13.00.

(c) To find the mean for the economy model, it is much more practical (and expedient) to use whole numbers. The mean of the numbers is

$$\bar{x} = \frac{22 + 25 + 32 + 34 + 35}{5} = \$29.60 \approx \$30.00$$

(d) To find the standard deviation, use the following table.

x	$x - \bar{x}$	$(x - \bar{x})^2$
22	−7.60	57.76
25	−4.60	21.16
32	2.40	5.76
34	4.40	19.36
35	5.40	29.16
148		**133.20**
$\bar{x} = \frac{148}{5} = 29.60$		$\frac{133.20}{4} = 33.3$ $s = \sqrt{33.3} \approx 5.8$

OK, vacation is over; back to work on the exercises!

12.3 EXERCISES

In problems 1–10, do the following:

a. State the range.

b. Find, to two decimal places, the standard deviation s.

1. 3, 5, 8, 13, 21
2. 1, 4, 9, 16, 25
3. 5, 10, 15, 20, 25
4. 6, 9, 12, 15, 18
5. 5, 6, 7, 8, 9
6. 4, 6, 8, 10, 12
7. 5, 9, 1, 3, 8, 7, 2
8. 2, 0, 4, 6, 8, 10, 8, 2
9. −3, −2, −1, 0, 1, 2, 3
10. −6, −4, −2, 0, 2, 4, 6
11. Out of 10 possible points, a class of 20 students made the following test scores:

    0, 0, 1, 2, 4, 4, 5, 6, 6, 6, 7, 8, 8, 8, 8, 9, 9, 9, 10, 10

    a. What is the mode?
    b. What is the median?
    c. What is the mean?
    d. Calculate the standard deviation to the nearest hundredth.
    e. What percent of the scores lie within 1 standard deviation from the mean?
    f. What percent of the scores lie within 2 standard deviations from the mean?
12. Suppose that the 4 students who scored lowest on the test in problem 11 dropped the course. Answer the same questions as in problem 11 for the remaining students.
13. How much time do you spend doing educational activities? According to the American Time Use Survey, full-time University and college students spend about 100 hours a month (3.3 hr per day) in educational activities. The number of hours spent per month by a student for the last 10 months of this academic year are as shown:

    103, 110, 113, 102, 105, 110, 111, 110, 106, and 110

    a. What is the mode for the number of hours?
    b. What is the median?
    c. What is the mean?
    d. Calculate the standard deviation of the hours to the nearest hundredth.
    e. Which of the values are more than 1 standard deviation from the mean score? What percent of the values is this?
14. Answer the same questions as in problem 13 for the lowest 8 of the student's 10 scores.
15. How much garbage do you generate daily? In the last few years, the average daily amount *per person* is 4.5 pounds. The daily numbers of pounds of garbage for six different persons were

    6, 2, 17, 3, 5, 9

    Find the range, mean, and standard deviation of the weights.
16. Most domestic U.S. airlines have a 40-lb limit on carry-on luggage. The carry-on luggage weights (in pounds) for a random sample of 10 passengers during a domestic flight were

    30, 30, 32, 35, 37, 40, 40, 40, 42, 44

    Find the range, mean, and standard deviation of the weights. By the way, there may be a limit on the number of free bags and the weight! The weight and number vary among airlines!
17. Do you know how long it takes firefighters to respond to a fire? A FEMA study indicates that response times were less than 5 min nearly 50% of the time and less than 8 min about 75% of the time.

    Source: http://www.usfa.fema.gov/downloads/pdf/tfrs/v5i7.pdf.

    The response times of six emergency fire calls were measured to the nearest minute and found to be 6, 7, 9, 12, 3, and 5 min. Find the range, mean, and standard deviation for the calls.
18. From 1918 to 1931, Babe Ruth was the American League home-run champion 12 times (he did not win in 1922 and 1925). The numbers of home runs he hit to earn the titles were

11	29	54	59	41	46
47	60	54	46	49	46

    Find the range, mean, and standard deviation for the number of home runs.

Problems 19–26 refer to Figure 12.9 on page 704.

19. There are two prices (low and high) given for each of the five hotels. Find the range between the high and the low price for each of the hotels.
20. Calculate the average (mean) price between the low and the high price for each of the five hotels.
21. Calculate the average (mean) of the answers in problem 20.
22. a. Calculate the standard deviation of the prices in problem 20.
    b. What percent of the prices lie within 1 standard deviation of the mean?
    c. What percent of the prices lie within 2 standard deviations of the mean?
23. The second price for each of the rental cars in Figure 12.9 is the price for renting a compact car for 1 day. Find the range of the prices.
24. Calculate the average (mean) of the prices for renting a compact car for 1 day.
25. Calculate the standard deviation of the prices for renting a compact car for 1 day.
26. What percent of the prices for renting a compact car for 1 day lie
    a. within 1 standard deviation of the mean?
    b. within 2 standard deviations of the mean?

IN OTHER WORDS

27. Suppose the standard deviation of a set of numbers is 0. What does this tell you about the numbers? Explain.
28. In problem 27 we assumed that the standard deviation for a set of numbers was 0. In general, what types of numbers can you obtain as an answer when calculating the standard deviation? Explain.
29. Suppose you are allowed to choose four numbers from 1 to 5. If repetitions are allowed, what is the largest possible result for the standard deviation? Explain.
30. Two classes, each with 100 students, took an examination with a maximum possible score of 100. In the first class, the mean score was 75, and the standard deviation was 5. In the second class, the mean score was 70, and the standard deviation was 15. Which of the two classes do you think had more scores of 90 or better? Why?

USING YOUR KNOWLEDGE

A **binomial experiment** is one that consists of a number of identical trials, each trial having only two possible outcomes (like tossing a coin that must fall heads or tails). Let us consider one of the outcomes as a success and the other as a failure. If p is the probability of success, then $1 - p$ is the probability of failure.

Suppose the experiment consists of n trials; then the theoretical expected number of successes is pn. For instance, if the experiment consists of tossing a fair coin 100 times, then the expected number of heads is $(\frac{1}{2})(100) = 50$. This means that if the experiment of tossing the coin 100 times is repeated many times, then the average number of heads is theoretically 50. In general, if a binomial experiment is repeated many times, then the theoretical mean (average) number of successes is pn, where p is the probability of success in one trial and n is the number of trials in the experiment.

If we let P_k denote the probability of k successes and $n - k$ failures in a binomial experiment with n trials, then the set of numbers $P_0, P_1, P_2, \ldots, P_n$ constitutes a **binomial frequency distribution.** The following simple formula has been obtained for the standard deviation of such a distribution:

$$s = \sqrt{np(1 - p)}$$

For example, if the experiment consists of tossing a fair coin 10,000 times and tallying the number of heads, then $n = 10{,}000$, $p = \frac{1}{2}$, $\bar{x} = 5000$, and

$$s = \sqrt{10{,}000(\tfrac{1}{2})(1 - \tfrac{1}{2})} = \sqrt{2500} = 50$$

If this experiment (tossing the coin 10,000 times) were repeated many times, then we would expect the average number of heads to be close to 5000. Although we are not justified in expecting the number of heads in any one experiment to be exactly 5000, we may expect that about 68% of the time the number of heads will be between 4950 and 5050.

31. If a fair die is rolled, the probability that it comes up 2 is $\frac{1}{6}$, and the probability that it comes up not 2 is $\frac{5}{6}$. If we regard 2 as a success and any other number as a failure, what is the standard deviation for the experiment of rolling the die 180 times?
32. Suppose that in rolling a die we regard a 3 or a 4 as a success and any other number as a failure. What is the standard deviation for the experiment of rolling the die 18 times? How far away from the mean would the number of successes have to be before we became suspicious of the die's honesty?
33. Suppose a die is loaded so that the probability that a 6 comes up is $\frac{1}{4}$. If we regard a 6 as a success and any other number as a failure, what is the standard deviation for the experiment of rolling the die 400 times?

DISCOVERY

34. According to *The Education Reporter*, the mean salary of teachers in Maryland is about $64,000 a year. Suppose all teachers in Maryland get a $1000 raise. What happens to the standard deviation? Explain.
35. This time, suppose all teachers in Maryland get a 10% raise (remember, their average salary is $64,000 annually). What happens to the standard deviation this time? Explain.

CALCULATOR CORNER

If you have a calculator with a $\boxed{\sigma_{n-1}}$ *key, it will compute the standard deviation for a set of data at the push of a button. For example, to find the standard deviation of Example 1, set the calculator in the statistics mode and enter*

$\boxed{7}\ \boxed{\Sigma+}\ \boxed{9}\ \boxed{\Sigma+}\ \boxed{10}\ \boxed{\Sigma+}\ \boxed{11}\ \boxed{\Sigma+}\ \boxed{13}\ \boxed{\text{2nd}}\ \boxed{\sigma_{n-1}}$

The result is given as 2.2.

COLLABORATIVE LEARNING

The table shows the percent of women in managerial/administrative positions.

Women in Managerial/Administrative Positions

Anglo	*African American*	*Hispanic*	*Asian/Other*
85.7%	6.6%	5.2%	2.5%

Source: "Women of Color in Corporate Management: A Statistical Picture," American Catalyst.

1. Calculate the mean, median, and range of the numbers.

Discussion Which of the three measurements gives a better indication of the wide variability of the scores? Explain.

2. Round the percents to the nearest whole number and find the standard deviation of the four numbers.
3. What percent of the numbers obtained in part 2 are within 1 standard deviation of the mean?
4. What percent of the numbers obtained in part 2 are within 2 standard deviations of the mean?

Discussion What does the information obtained in parts 3 and 4 tell you? Does the information indicate that there is a wide variability in the numbers? Explain.

12.4 The Normal Distribution: A Problem-Solving Tool

GETTING STARTED

OBJECTIVES

A. Find the mean and standard deviation from a normal curve.

B. Find the z-score of a measurement from a normally distributed set of data.

C. Know the distribution of z-scores and their relationship to the probability of an event under a normal curve.

S.A.T. DEVIATIONS

Do you remember your S.A.T. writing and mathematics scores? In a recent year, the mean score for the writing portion was μ (read "mu") = 489 with a standard deviation of σ (read "sigma") = 113, whereas the mathematics scores had a mean of 514 and a standard deviation of 117. Suppose you scored **603** on the verbal portion and your friend scored 631 on the mathematics portion. Which is the better score? It might not be the 631. Statistically, you may still beat your friend but to see how, you have to learn about the *normal curve* shown in Figure 12.10.

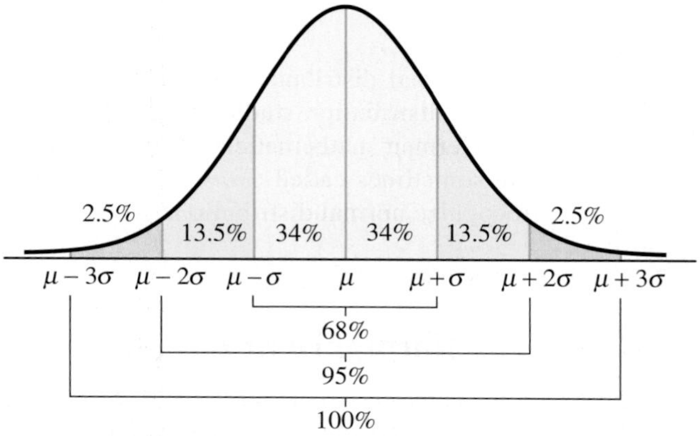

Note: Nearly 100% of the scores lie within 3 standard deviations of the mean. Thus, the normal curve is not sketched outside this domain.

FIGURE 12.10 Area under a normal curve.

(Some books give these values as 34.1%, 13.6%, and 2.3%; we use the approximate values 34%, 13.5%, and 2.5% for convenience.)

A normal curve describes data that have a very large (or infinite) number of values distributed among the population in a **bell shape.** A large number of the values are near the middle with a few values trailing off in either direction. Statisticians call a distribution with a bell-shaped curve a **normal distribution.**

Properties of a Normal Curve

The **normal curve** is a bell-shaped curve with the following four important properties:

1. It is smooth and symmetric (if you fold the graph in half along the center line, the two parts of the curve coincide exactly).
2. Its highest point occurs over the mean μ of the *entire* population.
3. It levels out and approaches the x axis but never touches it.
4. The total area under any normal curve is 1 and the proportion of data values between 1, 2, and 3 standard deviations to either side of the mean is as shown in Figure 12.10.

Now, for the rest of the story. If we assume that scores on the writing and mathematics portions of the S.A.T. are normally distributed and have the means and standard deviations mentioned, we can label the curves in Figures 12.11 and 12.12 with their respective means, $\mu = 489$ and 514. Remember that $\bar{x}$ is the mean of a sample population and s is its standard deviation, but μ is the mean of the entire population and σ is its standard deviation. In Figure 12.11, 1 standard deviation to the right of the mean will be $\mu + \sigma$, or $489 + 113 = 602$, whereas in Figure 12.12, 1 standard deviation to the right of the 514 mean will be 631 $(514 + 117)$. Now, a score of **603** on the writing will be slightly to the right of 1 standard deviation (602), whereas a score of 631 on the mathematics will be **exactly** 1 standard deviation from the mean. Believe it or not, a **603** writing score is comparatively better than a 631 mathematics score!

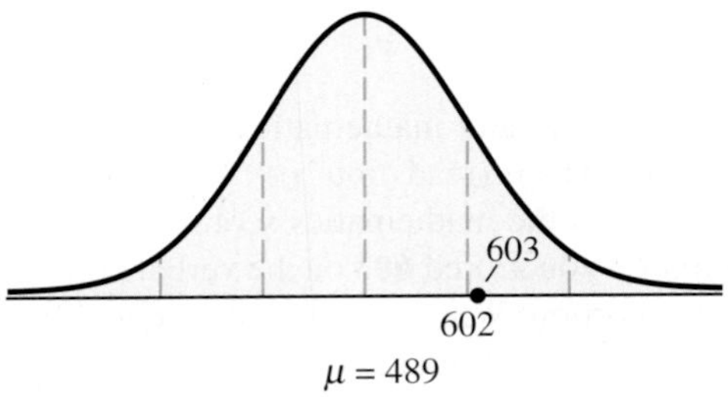

FIGURE 12.11 Writing S.A.T. scores.

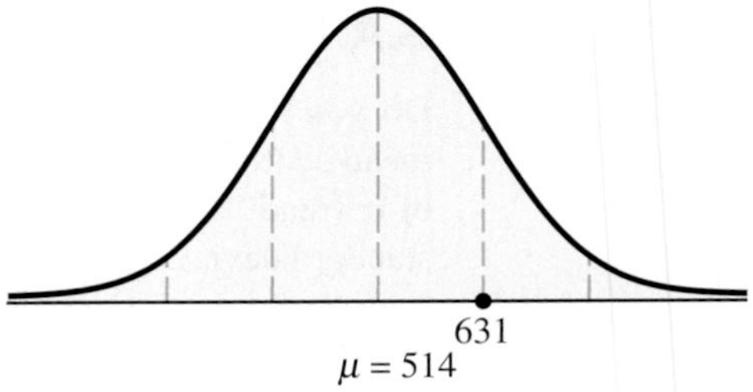

FIGURE 12.12 Math S.A.T. scores.

Note: We are using μ and σ, the mean and standard deviation of the *entire* population, instead of $\bar{x}$ and s, the mean and standard deviation of a sample.

The normal distribution we have mentioned is an example of a continuous probability distribution studied by the French mathematician Abraham De Moivre and the German mathematician Carl Gauss (as a matter of fact, normal distributions are sometimes called *Gaussian* distributions in his honor). First, we must learn to recognize normal distributions.

A The Normal Distribution

Look at the curves in Figure 12.13. They are *not* normal distributions! The curve labeled (a) is not symmetric, (b) is not bell shaped, (c) crosses the x axis, and (d) has tails turning up away from the x axis. We show some normal curves in Figure 12.14.

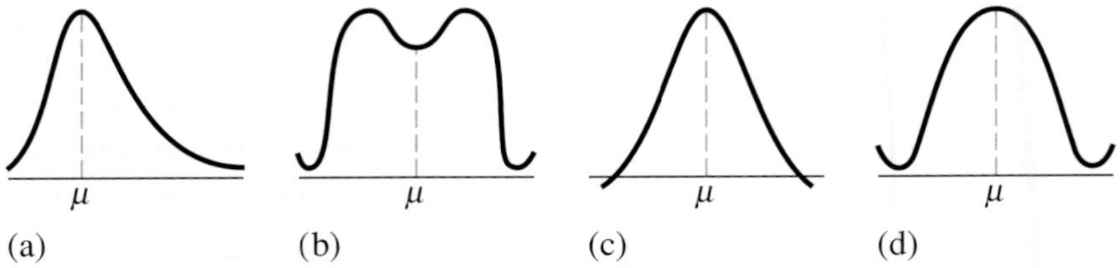

FIGURE 12.13

EXAMPLE 1 Mean and Standard Deviations in Normal Curve

Consider the normal curves in Figure 12.14.

(a) What is the mean for A?

(b) What is the mean for B?

(c) What is the standard deviation for A?

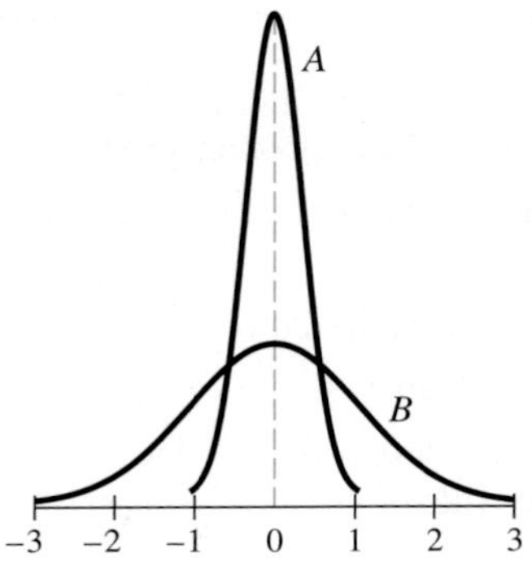

FIGURE 12.14

(d) What is the standard deviation for B?

(e) What percent of the values would you expect to lie between -3 and -1 in B?

(f) What percent of the values would you expect to lie between 0 and 1 in A?

Solution

(a) The mean for A is 0 (under the highest point).

(b) The mean for B is also 0.

(c) The interval from 0 to 1 must have 3 standard deviations, so each of them must be $\frac{1}{3}$ unit.

(d) The standard deviation for B is 1 (there are 3 to the right of 0).

(e) Since there are 2 standard deviations between -3 and -1, $2.5\% + 13.5\% = 16\%$ of the values would be in that region. (Refer to Figure 12.10 on page 707, for the values.)

(f) Half (50%) of the values should be between 0 and 1.

PROBLEM-SOLVING

The Normal Distribution

① **Read** the problem.

Refer to the S.A.T. data given in Getting Started and Figure 12.10 on page 707.

(a) What percent of the scores would you expect to be under 425 on the writing portion of the S.A.T.?

(b) What percent of the scores would you expect to be between 350 and 475 on the mathematics portion of the S.A.T.?

(c) If 1000 students took the S.A.T., how many students should score more than 600 on the mathematics portion?

② **Select** the unknown. Where do we find the different percentages under the normal curve?

We are asked several questions about S.A.T. scores. There are two things that are essential: the information in Figure 12.10 (Memorize it!) and the corresponding information given in Figures 12.11 and 12.12 on page 708.

③ **Think** of a plan. Look at Figure 12.10. What percentage of the values are in the following locations?

(a) To the left of μ

(b) Between $\mu - \sigma$ and μ

(c) To the right of $\mu + \sigma$

If we examine Figure 12.10, we see the following:

50% of the values are to the left of μ.

34% of the values are between $\mu - \sigma$ and μ.

$13.5\% + 2.5\% = 16\%$ of the values are to the right of $\mu + \sigma$.

④ **Use** the values shown in Figures 12.11 and 12.12 to answer the questions.

Thus, we have the following:

(a) In Figure 12.11, $\mu = 489$, so we expect 50% of the scores to be to the left of μ and to be less than 489 on the writing portion.

(b) In Figure 12.12, $\mu = 514$ and $\mu - \sigma = 397$. Thus, 34% of the scores are between $\mu - \sigma = 397$ and $\mu = 514$.

(c) In Figure 12.12, 16% of the values are to the right of $\mu + \sigma$. Since 16% of $1000 = 160$, 160 students should score higher than 631 on the mathematical portion.

⑤ **Verify** the solution.

Try Example 2 Now

Cover the solution, write your own solution, and then check your work.

EXAMPLE 2 Heights and Standard Deviations for Women

According to a survey by the National Center for Health Statistics, adult women in the United States have a mean height of 65 in. with a standard deviation of 2.5 in. If the heights of 1000 women are measured and found to be normally distributed:

(a) About how many of the women are over 70 in. tall?

(b) About how many are between 60 and 65 in. tall?

(c) About how many are between 62.5 and 66 in. tall?

Solution

We refer to Figure 12.10 on page 707 for the required percentages; then draw your own curve and label it.

(a) Because 70 in. is 2 standard deviations above the mean, about 2.5%, or 25 of the women are over 70 in. tall.

(b) We see that 65 in. is the mean, and 60 in. is exactly 2 standard deviations below the mean; hence, we add 13.5% and 34% and find that 47.5% of the women are between 60 and 65 in. tall. This represents 47.5% of 1000, or 475 women.

(c) Because 62.5 in. is 1 standard deviation below the mean, and 67.5 in. is 1 standard deviation above the mean, we add 34% and 34% to find that about 68% of 1000, or 680 women are between these two heights.

EXAMPLE 3 Normal Distributions and Reading Tests

A standardized reading comprehension test is given to 10,000 high school students. The scores are found to be normally distributed, with a mean of 500 and a standard deviation of 60. If a score below 440 is considered to indicate a serious reading deficiency, about how many of the students are rated as seriously deficient in reading comprehension?

Solution

Since 440 is exactly 1 standard deviation below the mean, scores below 440 are more than 1 standard deviation below the mean. By referring to the percentages in Figure 12.10 on page 707, we see that we must add 13.5% and 2.5% to get the total percentage of students who scored more than 1 standard deviation below the mean. Thus, 16% of the 10,000 students, or 1600 students, are rated as seriously deficient in reading comprehension.

In Getting Started we were able to compare two scores on two different tests by referring to the normal curve. Now suppose Rudie earned a score of 80 on her U.S. history test and a score of 80 on her geometry test. Which of these is the better score? Without additional information, we cannot answer this question. However, if we are told that the mean score in the U.S. history test was 60, with a standard deviation of 25.5, and the mean score in the geometry test was 70, with a standard deviation of 14.5, then we can use a technique similar to the one used in Getting Started to compare Rudie's two scores.

B z-Scores

In order to make a valid comparison, we have to restate the scores on a common scale. A score on this scale is known as a **standardized score** or a ***z*-score.**

Definition of z-Score (Standardized Score)

If x is a given score and μ and σ are the mean and standard deviation of the entire set of scores, then the **corresponding *z*-score** is

$$z = \frac{x - \mu}{\sigma}$$

Since the numerator of z is the difference between x and the mean, the *z-score gives the number of standard deviations that x is from the mean.*

EXAMPLE 4 z-Scores for Rudie

Compare Rudie's scores in U.S. history and geometry, given all the preceding information.

Solution

Rudie's z-scores are

U.S. history $\quad z = \dfrac{80 - 60}{25.5} \approx 0.78$

Geometry $\quad z = \dfrac{80 - 70}{14.5} \approx 0.69$

Thus, Rudie did better in U.S. history than in geometry.

C Distribution of z-Scores

For a normal distribution of scores, if we subtract μ from each score, the resulting numbers will have a mean of 0. If we then divide each number by the standard deviation σ, the resulting numbers will have a standard deviation of 1. Thus, the z-scores are distributed as shown in Figure 12.15. For instance, 34% of the z-scores lie between 0 and 1, 13.5% lie between 1 and 2, and 2.5% are greater than 2. For such a distribution of scores, the probabilities of randomly selecting z-scores between 0 and a given point to the right of 0 have been calculated and appear in tables such as Table II in the back of the book. To read the probability that a score falls between 0 and 0.25 standard deviation above the mean, we go down the column under z to 0.2 and then across to the column under 5; the number there is 0.099, the desired probability. This probability is actually the area under the curve between 0 and 0.25.

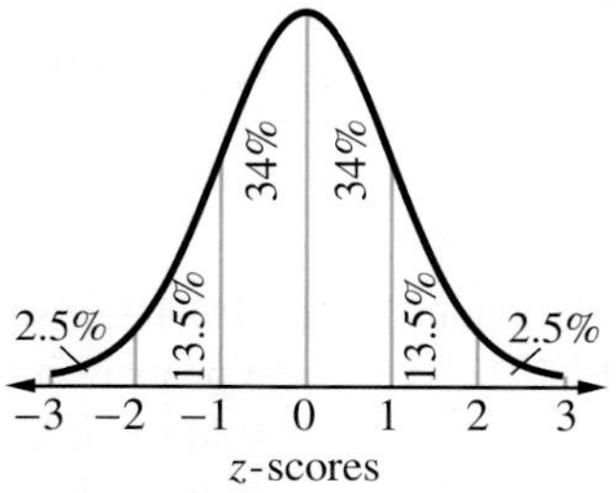

FIGURE 12.15 Distribution of z-scores.

EXAMPLE 5 Probabilities Under the Normal Curve

For the normally distributed population shown in Figure 12.16 the mean is $\mu = 100$ and the standard deviation is 15. Find the probability that a randomly selected item of the data falls between 100 and 120.

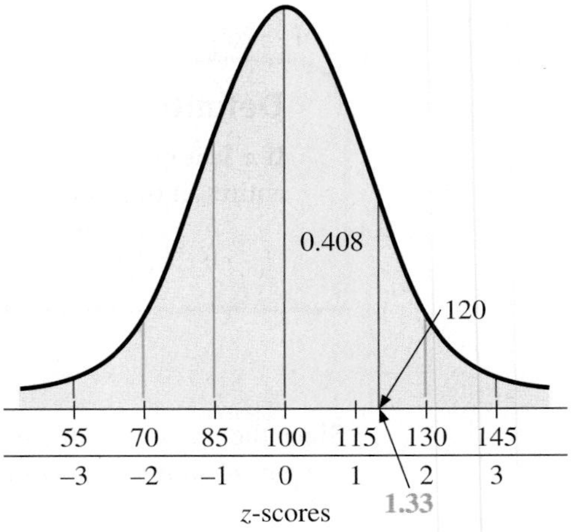

FIGURE 12.16

Solution

We first find the z-score for 120.

$$z = \frac{x - \mu}{\sigma} = \frac{120 - 100}{15} = \frac{4}{3} \approx 1.33$$

We then refer to Table II and read down the column under z to the number 1.3 and then across the column under 3 to the desired probability, 0.408.

EXAMPLE 6 Reading Tables

Refer to Table II. In the column under 5 and across from 2.0, the entry 0.480 appears. What does this mean?

Solution

This means that if an item is selected at random from a normally distributed set of data, the probability that this item is within 2.05 standard deviations from the mean is 0.480.

EXAMPLE 7 Finding Probabilities Using Tables

Referring to Example 5, find the probability that a randomly selected item is less than 110.

Solution

The probability that a randomly selected item of the data is less than 100 is 50% because 50% of the scores are to the left of the mean (see Figure 12.17). To find the probability that a randomly selected item is less than 110, we can find the probability that the item is between 100 and 110 and add this probability to 50% = 0.50. The z-score for 110 is

$$z = \frac{x - \mu}{\sigma}$$

$$= \frac{110 - 100}{15} \approx 0.67$$

The value by 0.6 and under 7 in Table II is 0.249. Thus, the probability that a randomly selected item of the data is less than 110 is

$$0.50 + 0.249 = 0.749$$

(See Figure 12.17.)

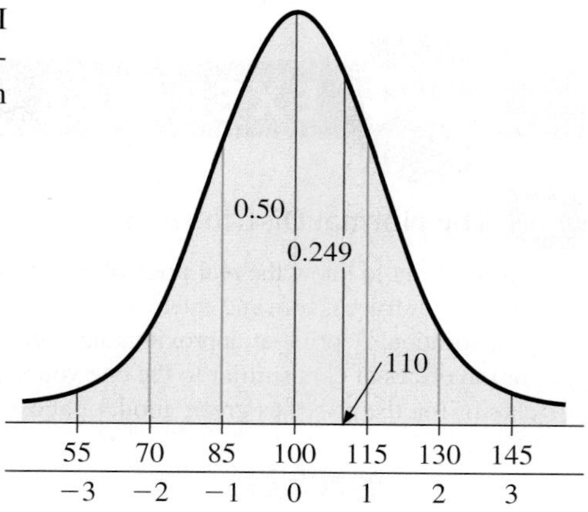

FIGURE 12.17

EXAMPLE 8 We Scream for More Ice Cream

Time for a break: We are headed to the ice cream parlor! The combined weight of the two scoops on a double-dip ice cream cone satisfies a normal distribution with a mean of 8 oz and a standard deviation of $\frac{1}{4}$ oz. But one double-dip looks a little bit larger. As a matter of fact, it weighs 8.5 oz, and you picked it! What is the probability that a randomly selected cone is smaller than yours?

Solution

To find the answer, we find the probability that the amount of ice cream in a randomly selected cone is less than yours, that is, that the z-score for the other cones is less than the z-score of yours. The z-score for your 8.5-oz ice cream cone is

$$z = \frac{x - \mu}{\sigma} = \frac{8.5 - 8}{0.25} = \frac{0.50}{0.25} = +2$$

Now refer to Table II. The value for $z = +2$ is 0.477 (red area), and the total value for all dips with z-scores under 2 is the yellow area plus the red area, that is, $0.50 + 0.477 = 0.977$. This means that the probability that the other dips are smaller than yours is 97.7%. You have a good eye for ice cream!

You also can do this problem by looking at Figure 12.15 on page 711 and observing that the area under the curve to the left of $z = +2$ is approximately $1 - 0.025 = 0.975$, or 97.5%.

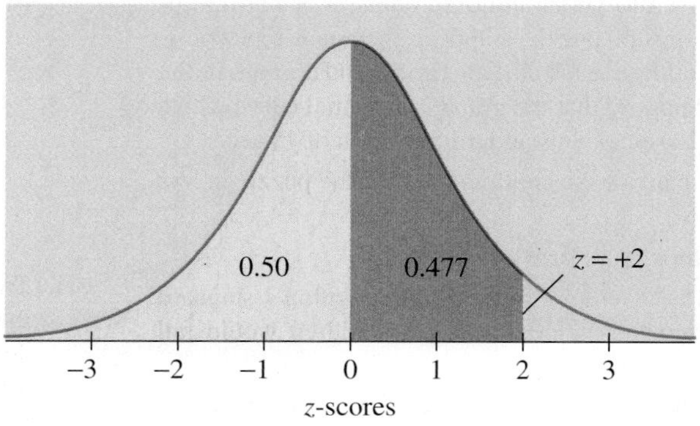

12.4 EXERCISES

A The Normal Distribution

1. Do you want to know the real price of the car you want to buy? Go to www.truecar.com and enter the the make, model, year, and your location. A printout approximating a ***normal distribution*** for the prices of cars similar to the one you want is then given, classifying the prices as great, good, or above market.

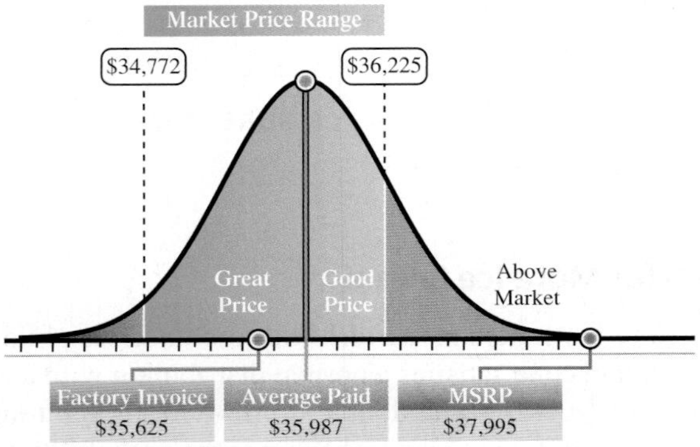

   a. What is the mean (average) price?
   b. What is the standard deviation?
   c. What percent of the cars had a price between $34,772 and $35,987?

2. Suppose you were informed that the annual income of teachers is normally distributed, with a mean of $40,000 and a standard deviation of $10,000.
   a. What would you estimate for the percent of teachers with incomes over $50,000?
   b. What percent of teachers would you estimate have an annual income of less than $20,000?
   c. If a teacher were selected at random, what would be the probability that his or her annual income was more than $60,000?
   d. If the information given here were correct, would you think it very likely that 50% of all teachers have annual incomes of over $50,000? Why or why not?

3. Part of a test given to young children consists of putting together a simple jigsaw puzzle. Suppose that such a puzzle is given to 1000 children, each child is timed, and a graph of the times is made. Suppose that the graph is a normal curve with a mean time of 120 sec and a standard deviation of 15 sec.
   a. About how many of the children finished the puzzle in less than 90 sec?
   b. How many took more than 150 sec?
   c. If you rated as "average" all the children within 1 standard deviation from the mean, how many children would fall into this classification?

4. For a certain standardized placement test, it was found that the scores were normally distributed, with a mean of 200 and a standard deviation of 30. Suppose that this test is given to 1000 students.
   a. How many are expected to make scores between 170 and 230?
   b. How many are expected to score above 260?
   c. What is the expected range of all the scores?

5. A psychology teacher gave an objective-type test to a class of 500 students and, after seeing the results, decided that the scores were normally distributed. The mean score was 50, and the standard deviation was 10. The teacher assigned a grade of A to all scores of 70 or over, B to scores of 60 to 69, C to scores of 40 to 59, D to scores of 30 to 39, and F to scores below 30. About how many of each grade did the teacher assign?

6. The diagram in problem 1 analyzes car sales normally distributed, with a mean (average) price of $35,987 and a standard deviation of $607.50.
   a. Is the MSRP more than 3 standard deviations from the mean?
   b. What percent of the cars were priced below $35,987?
   c. What percent of the cars had a "great price"?
   d. What was the starting price for "great price" cars?

7. The lifetimes of a random sample of 200 automobile tires were found to be normally distributed, with a mean of 26,000 mi and a standard deviation of 2500 mi. About how many of these tires gave out before 21,000 mi?

8. The mean price of 20,000 cars purchased during the past 6 months at ABC Auto was normally distributed with a mean of $25,000 and a standard deviation of $600. If you want to buy a car from ABC, what price range can you expect 95% of the time?

In Problems 9–13 assume that the results are normally distributed.

9. Suppose that 10 measurements of the length of a wooden beam have a mean of 20 ft and a standard deviation of 0.5 in. Between what limits do almost all the measurements fall?

10. An experiment consists of tossing 100 dimes repeatedly and noting the number of heads each time. The graph of the number of heads turns out to be very nearly a normal curve, with a mean of 50 and a standard deviation of 5.
    a. Within what limits would you expect the number of heads to be 95% of the time?
    b. What percent of the time would you expect the number of heads to be between 45 and 55?
    c. Suppose that a particular dime arouses your suspicion by turning up heads too often. You toss this dime 100 times. How many times will it have to turn up heads in order for you to be almost 100% certain that it is not a fair coin? (*Hint:* Most of the data in a normal distribution fall within 3 standard deviations of the mean.)

11. The purchasing director of Druid Enterprises is considering the purchase of 8000 ball bearings. The purchase is dependent on receiving at least a dozen ball bearings that will last 40 days. If the manufacturer claims that the lifetime of each ball bearing is 30 days, with a standard deviation of 5 days, what will be the decision of the purchasing director and why?

12. The Department of Transportation (DOT) counted the number of vehicles using a certain road for a period of 50 days. The mean number of vehicles using the road was 350, and the standard deviation was 10.
    a. How many days was the road used by more than 360 vehicles?
    b. How many days was the number of vehicles using the road between 340 and 380?
    c. What is the lowest number of vehicles you would expect on this road on any given day?
    d. What is the highest number of vehicles you would expect on this road on any given day?
13. In a recent year, the scores on the mathematics portion of the Scholastic Assessment Test (S.A.T.) had a 514 mean and a 117 standard deviation. This same year, the mathematics portion of the American College Test (A.C.T.) had a mean of 21 and a standard deviation of 5.2. A student scored 635 on the S.A.T., whereas another student scored 26.2 on the A.C.T. Which student has the higher score relative to the test?
14. Suppose you are the manager of a cereal packing company. Every box must contain at least 16 oz of cereal. Your packing machine has a normal distribution for the weights of the cereal with a standard deviation of 0.05 oz and a mean equal to the setting on the machine. What will you make this setting to ensure that all of the packages contain at least 16 oz of cereal?

B *z*-Scores

15. Examine the normal distributions shown.

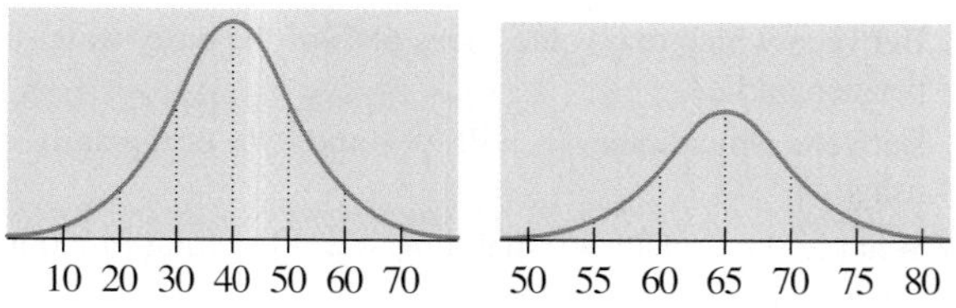

    a. What is the standard deviation for the first?
    b. What is the standard deviation for the second?
    c. What is the mean for the first distribution?
    d. What is the mean for the second distribution?
    e. In the first distribution, what value corresponds to a z-score of $+2$? What about a z-score of -1?
    f. In the second distribution, what value corresponds to a z-score of $+2$? What about a z-score of -1?
16. Examine the normal distribution below and determine what percent of the scores you would expect to be
    a. between 40 and 50.
    b. between 20 and 50.
    c. between 10 and 70.

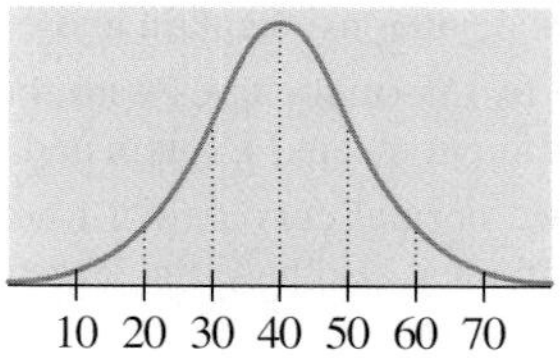

17. You are still managing the cereal packing company of problem 14, and now you know that the weights of the boxes have a normal distribution with a mean of 16.15 oz and a standard deviation of 0.05 oz. What is the weight of a box with a z-score of 0?

In Problems 18–24 assume that the results are normally distributed.

18. Now we are going to the dogs, but not literally! According to the St. Bernard club, your 170-lb Bernie is too hefty compared with other dogs his age. (Source: http://svennesandcompany.com/The%20Breed.html.)

    Bernie goes on a diet, and his z-score decreases from $+2$ to -2. If the standard deviation for St. Bernards' weight is 5 lb,
    a. what is the mean weight for Bernie's breed and age?
    b. what is Bernie's weight after the diet?
19. Pedro took an exam in a class in which the mean was 70 with a standard deviation of 10. If his z-score was $+2$, what was his exam score?
20. If you take an exam and your score is the same as the mean score for the class, what is your z-score for the exam?
21. In a certain normal distribution of scores, the mean is 5, and the standard deviation is 1.25. Find the z-score corresponding to a score of
    a. 6. b. 7. c. 7.5.
22. The car sales in problem 1 have a mean of \$19,310 and a standard deviation of 574. What is the z-score for a car priced at \$19,482?
23. Gretchen scored 85 on a test in German and also on a test in English. If the mean in the German test was 75, with a standard deviation of 20, and the mean in the English test was 80, with a standard deviation of 15, which of Gretchen's 85s was the better score?
24. Juan scored 88 on a Spanish test and 90 on an algebra test. If the mean on the Spanish test was 78, with a standard deviation of 7.5, and the mean on the algebra test was 82, with a standard deviation of 6.5, which of Juan's scores was the better score?

C Distribution of *z*-Scores

25. A student's commute to school is normally distributed with a mean of 30 min and a standard deviation of 5 min. What is the probability that the student gets to school in 20 to 30 min?
26. An express workout at the gym is normally distributed with a mean of 30 min and a standard deviation of 5 min. What is the probability that Latasha completes the workout in 30 to 35 min?
27. Elias at La Cubanita restaurant says he will *always* serve you within 5 min! If service at the restaurant is normally distributed with a mean of 4.5 min and a standard deviation of 1.5 min, what is the probability that Elias is right?

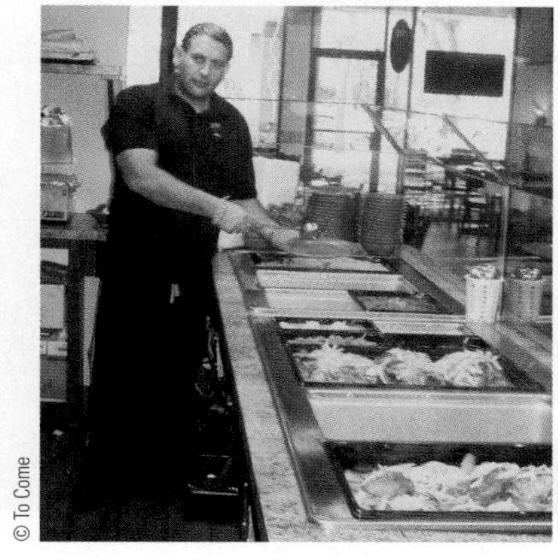

28. Referring to problem 27, within what time period will you be certain (100% probability) of being served?

In problems 29–33 assume a normally distributed set of test scores with a mean of $\mu = 100$ and a standard deviation of 15.

29. Find the probability that a person selected at random will have a score between
    a. 100 and 110. b. 100 and 130.

30. Find the probability that a person selected at random will have a score between 80 and 120. [*Hint:* In Example 5 we found the probability that the score is between 100 and 120 to be 0.408. The probability that the score is between 80 and 100 is also 0.408. (Recall the symmetry of the normal curve.)]

31. Find the probability that a person selected at random will have a score
    a. between 55 and 145. b. less than 60.

32. Find the probability that a person selected at random will have a score
    a. between 75 and 100. b. more than 80.

33. Find the probability that a person selected at random will have a score between 110 and 130. (*Hint:* In problem 29 you found the probability that the score will be between 100 and 110 and the probability that the score will be between 100 and 130. You should be able to see how to combine these two results to get the desired probability.)

34. In problem 10 it was noted that the distribution of heads if 100 dimes are tossed repeatedly is approximately a normal distribution, with a mean of 50 and a standard deviation of 5. Find the probability of getting 60 heads if 100 fair coins are tossed. [*Hint:* To use the normal curve, consider 60 to be between 59.5 and 60.5 and proceed as in problem 23. This will give a very good approximation and is much easier to calculate than the exact probability, which is $C(100, 60) \cdot 2^{100}$.]

35. The heights of the male students in a large college were found to be normally distributed, with a mean of 5 ft 7 in. and a standard deviation of 3 in. Suppose these students are to be divided into five equal-sized groups according to height. Approximately what is the height of the shortest student in the tallest group?

© iStockphoto.com/technotr

36. If 10 of the boys who show up for the basketball team are over 6 ft 3 in. tall, about how many male students are there in the college mentioned in problem 35?

37. What is your major, and how much money do you think you will make? The monthly income of budget analysts is normally distributed with a mean μ of \$4200 and a standard deviation σ of \$200. (Source: *College Graduates Average Salaries Report.*)

    Find the z-value for a monthly income of \$4400. Explain what the z-value you obtained means.

38. Referring to problem 37, find the z-value for a \$3800 monthly income and explain what it means.

39. Remember the ice cream of Example 8? Within what weight will you be certain (100% probability) that the ice cream will be?

40. A professor's commute is normally distributed with a mean of 45 minutes and a standard deviation of 10 minutes.
    a. What is the probability that the professor gets to work in 30 min or less?
    b. If the professor has a 9 A.M. class and leaves home at 8 A.M., how often is the professor late for class?

41. According to e-medicine, sleeping 8 to 8.4 hr per night is considered fully restorative for adults. Suppose Caruca sleeps an average of 8 hr per night with a standard deviation of 15 min. What is the probability that Caruca will get her restorative sleep (between 8 and 8.4 hr)? (*Hint:* 15 min = 0.25 hr.)

42. Suppose you know your test score in this class is above the mean, but you don't know by how much. How many students scored less than you on this test?

The following information will be used in problems 43–48. In Florida, the daily water usage per person is normally distributed with a mean of 110 gal and standard deviation of 10 gal.

43. Between which two values does 68% of the daily water usage per person lie?

44. Between which intervals will 95% and 99% of the daily water usage lie?

45. What is the probability that a person selected at random will use less than 110 gal per day?

46. What is the probability that a person selected at random will use more than 110 gal per day?

47. What percent of the people use between 100 and 110 gal?

48. What percent of the people use between 100 and 120 gal?

49. The amount of daily tips waiters receive at a famous restaurant is normally distributed with a mean of \$100 and a standard deviation of \$20. A statistically inclined waitress has decided that her service is *poor* if her daily tips are less than \$70. On the basis of her theory, what is the probability that she has provided poor service?

50. Referring to problem 49, if the standard deviation is \$10, what is the probability that she has provided poor service?

IN OTHER WORDS

51. Can you have two normal curves with the same mean and different standard deviations? Explain and make a sketch.

52. Can you have two normal curves with the same standard deviation and different means? Explain and make a sketch.

53. If you have two normal curves, is it true that the curve with the larger mean must also have the larger standard deviation? Explain your answer.

54. Explain in your own words the meaning of a z-score.

USING YOUR KNOWLEDGE

Standardized, or z, scores provide a way of making comparisons among different sets of data. To compare scores within one set of data, we use a measurement called a **percentile.** *Percentiles are used extensively in educational measurements and enable us to convert raw scores into meaningful comparative scores. If you take an exam and are told that you scored in the 95th percentile, it does not mean that you scored 95% on the exam but rather that you scored higher than 95% of the persons taking the exam. The formula used to find the percentile corresponding to a particular score is as follows:*

$$\text{Percentile of score } x = \frac{\text{number of scores less than } x}{\text{total number of scores}} \cdot 100$$

Thus, if 80 students take a test and 50 students score less than you do, you will be in the $\frac{50}{80} \cdot 100 = 62.5$ *percentile. Use this knowledge to solve the following problems:*

55. A student took a test in a class of 50 students, and 40 of the students scored less than she did. What was her percentile?

56. A student took a test in a class of 80, and only 9 students scored better than he did. What was his percentile?

57. The scores in a class were as follows:

83, 85, 90, 90, 92, 93, 97, 97, 98, 100

a. What percentile corresponds to a score of 90?
b. What percentile corresponds to a score of 97?
c. What percentile corresponds to a score of 100?
d. What percentile corresponds to a score of 83?

58. The scores on a placement test were scaled so that some of the scores and the corresponding percentiles were as follows:

Score	*Percentile*
119	98th
150	85th
130	72nd
90	50th
60	26th
30	10th
20	1st

What percent of the scores fell between 30 and 90? (*Hint:* Look at the definition of the percentile. The percentile gives the percent of what?)

DISCOVERY

We have discovered that we can make fairly accurate predictions about the dispersion of the measurements in a normal distribution. For instance, 68% of the measurements fall between $\mu - \sigma$ *and* $\mu + \sigma$*, 95% between* $\mu - 2\sigma$ *and* $\mu + 2\sigma$*, and nearly 100% between* $\mu - 3\sigma$ *and* $\mu + 3\sigma$*. But what can we say in the case the distribution is not normal?*

The great Russian mathematician Pafnuti Lvovich Chebyshev (1821–1894) discovered the following remarkable result:

Chebyshev's Theorem

For any distribution with a finite number N of measurements and for any h such that $h > 1$, the number of measurements within h standard deviations of the mean is **at least** equal to

$$\left(1 - \frac{1}{h^2}\right)N$$

For example, if $h = 2$, then $1 - 1/h^2 = \frac{3}{4}$, so at least $\frac{3}{4}N$, or 75%, of the measurements fall between $\mu - 2\sigma$ and $\mu + 2\sigma$. This is not as large a percentage as for a normal distribution, but the amazing thing is that this result holds for any kind of distribution at all—as long as there is only a finite number of measurements!

Suppose we have 20 numbers with a mean of 8 and a standard deviation of 2. How many of the numbers can we *guarantee* to fall between 2 and 14? Because 2 and 14 are each 3 standard deviations from the mean, we take $h = 3$ in Chebyshev's theorem and obtain

$$\left(1 - \tfrac{1}{3^2}\right)(20) = \left(\tfrac{160}{9}\right) \approx 17.8$$

Thus, the theorem guarantees that at least 17 of the 20 numbers fall between 2 and 14.

In the same way, by taking $h = 1.5$, we find that

$$\left(1 - \tfrac{1}{1.5^2}\right)(20) = \left(\tfrac{5}{9}\right)(20) \approx 12.1$$

Hence, we can guarantee that at least 11 of the 20 numbers fall within 1.5 standard deviations from the mean, that is, between 5 and 11.

Notice that Chebyshev's theorem makes no claim at all for the case in which $h \le 1$.

59. If 100 measurements have a mean of 50 and a standard deviation of 5, how many of the measurements must be between

a. 40 and 60? **b.** 35 and 65? **c.** 43 and 57?

60. What is the smallest value of h that is large enough to guarantee that of a set of measurements at least the following percentages will be within h standard deviations from the mean?

a. 96% **b.** 91% **c.** 64%

61. Find the mean and the standard deviation of the following numbers: 1, 1, 1, 2, 6, 10, 11, 11, 11. How many of these numbers lie within 1 standard deviation from the mean? How many lie within 2 standard deviations from the mean? How do these results compare with those predicted by Chebyshev's theorem?

62. Do you think it is possible for all the items in a population to be *less* than 1 standard deviation from the mean? Justify your answer. *Hint:* The formula for the standard deviation shows that $n\sigma^2 = (x_1 - \bar{x})^2 + (x_2 - \bar{x})^2 + \ldots + (x_n - \bar{x})^2$

63. Can Chebyshev's theorem be used to find the percentage of the measurements that must fall between 2 and 3 standard deviations from the mean? What can you say about this percentage?

CALCULATOR CORNER

You can find the probability that a randomly selected item will fall between the mean and a given z-score by using the key sequence [2nd] [VARS] [2] *and as in Example 5 enter* (100, 120, 100, 15)*—the left number* (100)*, the right number* (120)*, the mean* (100)*, and the standard deviation* (15)*. Press* [ENTER].

The result is given as 0.4087887176. Note that there is a slight difference (due to rounding) between this answer and the one in the text.

1–6. Use a calculator to rework problems 29–34.

COLLABORATIVE LEARNING

The figure on page 718 shows intelligence quotient (IQ) scores under the normal curve. A raging controversy, fueled by a book titled The Bell Curve*, claiming that intelligence is largely inherited, has sparked new interest in IQ tests. Form several groups.*

1. One group's assignment is to get a copy of *The Bell Curve* and find out what the book's actual claims are.
2. A second group can find a copy of the winter 1998 issue of *Scientific American* (where the following figure was found) and find out what the *g* (global, general) factor is and how it measures intelligence.

Now, for the math questions.

3. If IQ scores are normally distributed as shown in the diagram, what are the mean, median, and mode for the scores?

Discussion Do you think that IQ scores are normally distributed? For example, the percentages given for the total population distribution apply to "young white adults in the United States."

4. What is the standard deviation suggested in the figure?
5. What is the z-score for a person with a score of 120?
6. What is the z-score for a person with a score of 80?
7. If scores are normally distributed, for what percent of the people should IQ scores fall between 90 and 110? What percent of the total population distribution is shown in that range? Are the percents different? Why do you think that is?
8. If scores are normally distributed, for what percent of the people should IQ scores fall between 125 and 130? What percent of the total population distribution is shown in that range? Are the percents different? Why do you think that is?

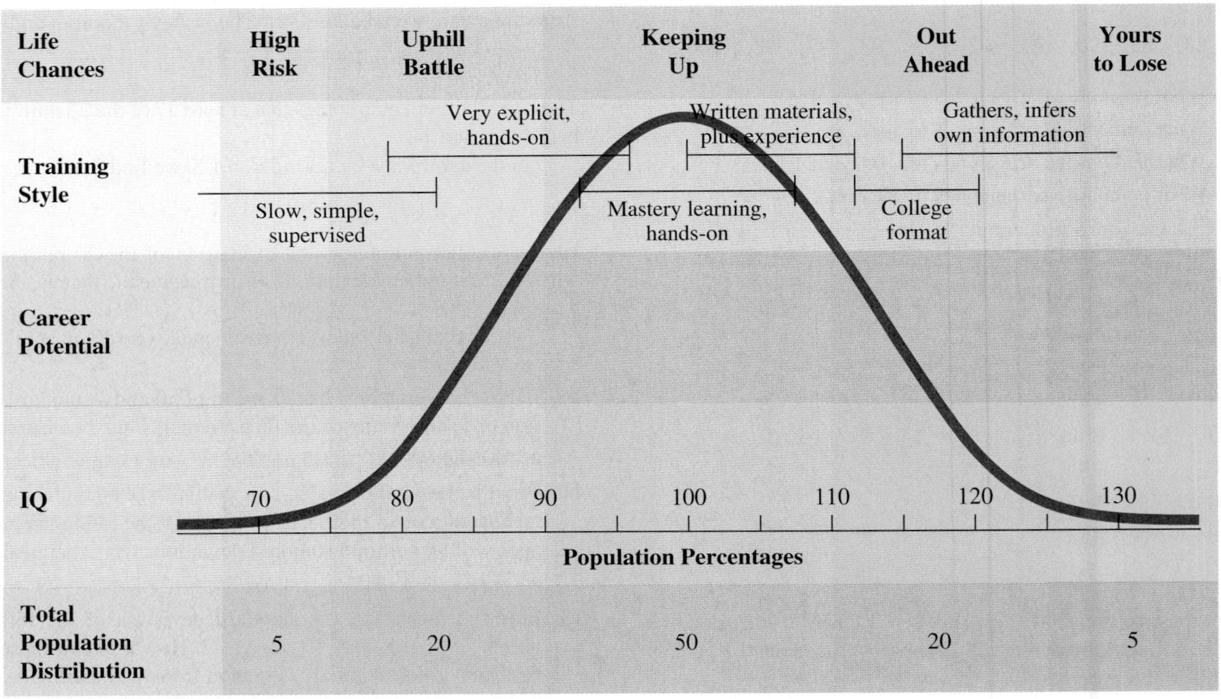

Measure of intelligence.

12.5 Statistical Graphs: A Problem-Solving Tool

GETTING STARTED

OBJECTIVES

Given a set of data:

A. Make and interpret a linear graph.
B. Make and interpret a horizontal or linear bar graph.
C. Make and interpret a circle graph.

GASSING UP AND PIE CHARTS

Americans are often fascinated with numbers. Many of the facts of American life are expressed in books such as *The First Really Important Survey of American Habits, The Top 10 Almanac, The Day America Told the Truth, The Great Divide,* and *On an Average Day*. These books are devoted to surveys of American habits using numbers, tables, and graphs. For example, do you gas up your car when it is $\frac{3}{4}$ full, $\frac{1}{2}$ empty, $\frac{3}{4}$ empty, or almost empty? As you would expect, different age groups of different sexes behave differently. Thus, 2%, 42%, 38%, and 18% of males in the 21–34 age group fill their tanks when they are $\frac{3}{4}$ full, $\frac{1}{2}$ empty, $\frac{3}{4}$ empty, or almost empty, respectively. For females, the corresponding percentages are 1%, 2%, 6%, and 91%. Why do you think this difference exists? Whatever the reason, you can compare the data better if the information is contained in a table with a caption and column headings such as Table 12.20. This table enables you to instantly compare differences based on sex.

Table 12.20 Percent of People Who Gas Up Car When It Is . . .

	$\frac{3}{4}$ Full		$\frac{1}{2}$ Empty		$\frac{3}{4}$ Empty		Almost Empty	
Age	**Male**	**Female**	**Male**	**Female**	**Male**	**Female**	**Male**	**Female**
21–34	2	1	42	2	38	6	18	91

You can also show the division of a total quantity (100%) into its component parts by using a **circle graph** or **pie chart.** If you are interested only in a rough sketch, use the four-step procedure shown in Figure 12.18. Now here is a word of caution. Mathematicians and statisticians use the starting point shown in step 4 and move counterclockwise (see Figure 12.19a on page 720). Computer-generated pie charts start at the 12 o'clock point and move clockwise (see Figure 12.19b). Both are correct, and both methods are used in this book.

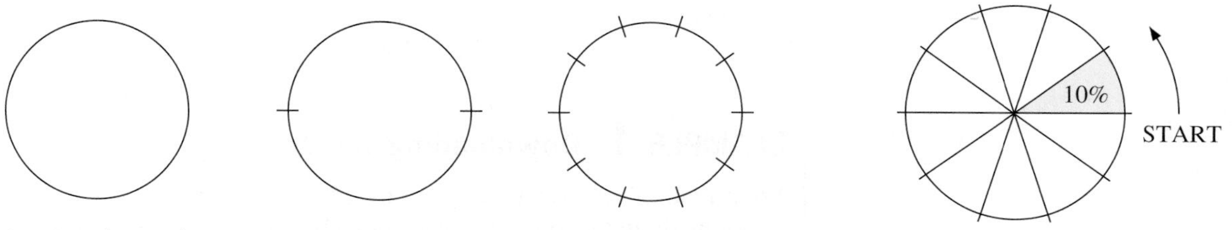

Step 1. Make a circle.

Step 2. Divide it into 2 equal parts.

Step 3. Subdivide each of the 2 parts into 5 equal parts.

Step 4. Each of the subdivisions represents $\frac{1}{10}$, or 10%.

FIGURE 12.18

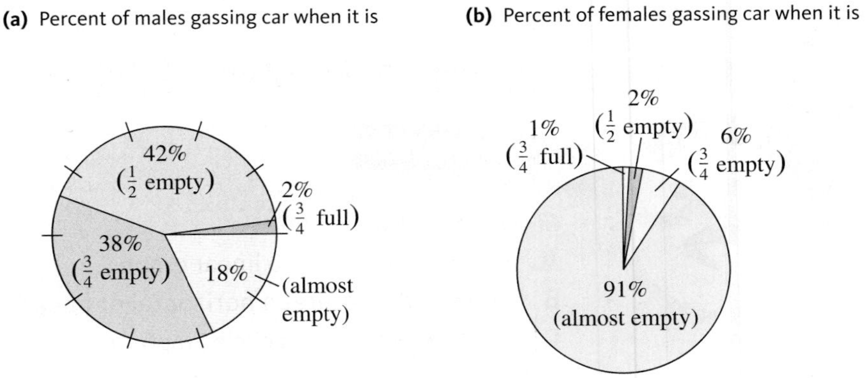

FIGURE 12.19

A graph of a set of data can often provide information at a glance that might be difficult and less impressive when gleaned from a table of numbers. No table of numbers would make the visual impact created by the graph in Figure 12.20, for example.

It is almost always possible to alter the appearance of a graph to make things seem better (or worse) than they are. For instance, Figure 12.21 is a portion of Figure 12.20 but with a compressed vertical scale. Obviously, things look better on this graph! Can you see why an economist might feel it politically advantageous to publish one of these graphs rather than the other?

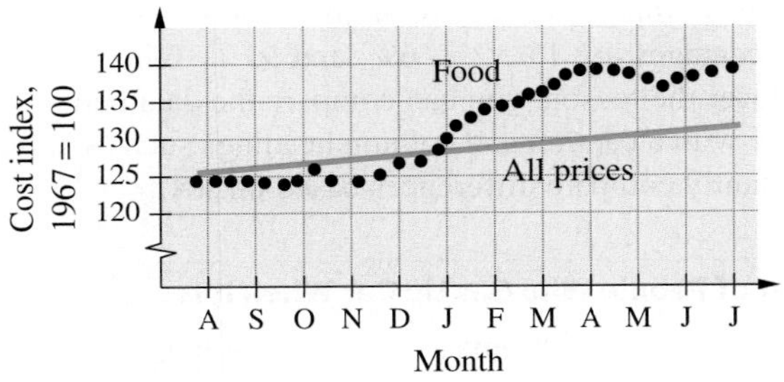

FIGURE 12.20 The high cost of eating.

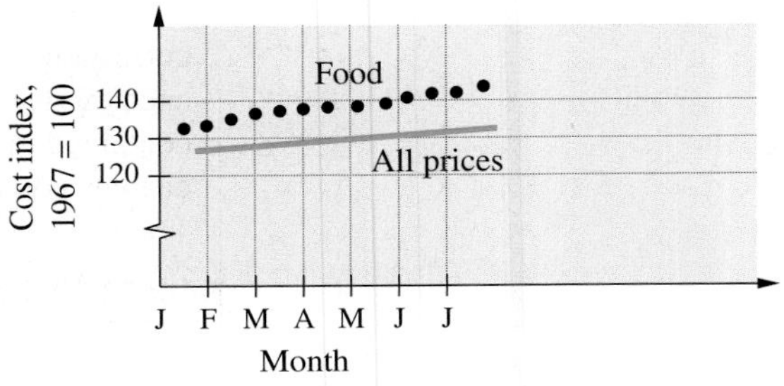

FIGURE 12.21

A Line Graphs

The construction of line graphs is similar to the type of graphing we did in Chapter 7. As before, we draw two perpendicular lines called *axes*. The horizontal line is still the x axis, and the vertical line the y axis. Each of these lines has equally spaced points with numbers or other identifying information assigned to it. For example, the numbers on the x axis may represent the number of hours a person has worked, whereas those on the y axis may indicate the earnings for that person. We make our first line graph next.

EXAMPLE 1 Downloading or CDs

What kind of recordings do you buy, physical (CDs and vinyl) or online digital recordings? Sales of CDs have been decreasing worldwide, but recording industry revenues for online music in the last four years (to the nearest billion) have increased as shown in the chart. Make a line graph for these data.

Source: http://grabstats.com/statcategorymain.asp?StatCatID=9.

Year	Billions
2008	4
2009	6
2010	7
2011	11

Solution

The categories (years 2008, 2009, 2010, and 2011) are on the *horizontal* axis, and the amounts or *frequencies* ($4, $6, $7, and $11 billion) are on the *vertical* axis. For convenience, we use a $1 billion scale on the vertical axis. To graph the first point corresponding to 2008, we start at 2008, go up 4 units, and graph the point. For 2009, we go to 2009, go up 6 units, and graph the point. We do the same for 2010 and 2011. Finally, we join the points with line segments as shown.

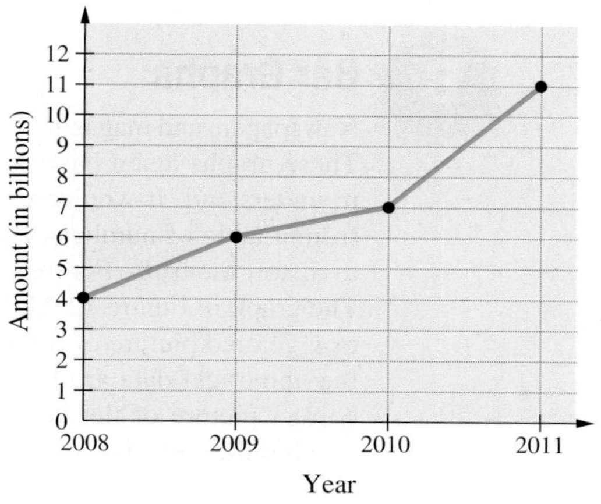

Sometimes, we draw more than one line on the same graph, as shown next.

Table 12.21

	Unemployment Rate	
Month	**Women**	**Men**
January	7.9%	8.8%
February	8.0%	8.7%
March	7.7%	7.6%

Seasonally adjusted, 20 years and over

EXAMPLE 2 Unemployment Line Graph

Construct a line graph for the data in Table 12.21.

Solution

In Figure 12.22 we start by making a time scale and labeling the points January, February, and March. (Time is usually shown on the x axis.) We then label the y axis with the percents from 1 to 9, or you can label the y axis using the percents from 7.0 to 9.0 as shown in the second graph.

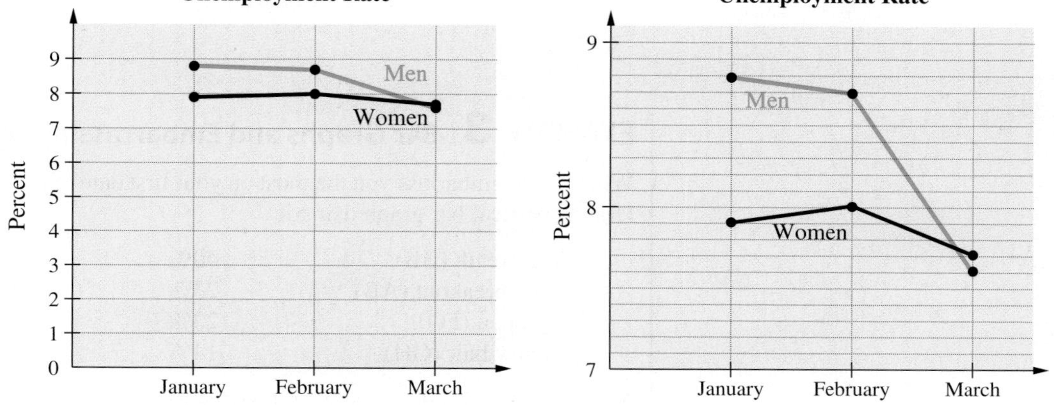

FIGURE 12.22 Unemployment rate.

To graph the point corresponding to the unemployment rate for women in January, go to January on the horizontal scale and move 7.9 units up. Mark the point with a dot. Now go to February on the horizontal axis and move 8.0 units up. Make a dot. Finally, starting at March, go 7.7 units up and mark the point. Now join the first point to the second and the second to the third with two black line segments. Note that we made a grid of horizontal and vertical lines to make the work easier to read. The same result can be obtained by doing the graph on graph paper. We use a similar procedure to add the men (shown in blue).

B Bar Graphs

Newspapers and magazines often publish **bar graphs** of the type shown in Figure 12.23. These graphs again have the advantage of displaying the data in a form that is easy to understand. It would be difficult for most people to obtain the same information from a table of numbers. As in the case of line graphs, bar graphs can also be made to distort the truth. For example, consider the two graphs in Figures 12.24 and 12.25. The graph in Figure 12.24 does not have the bars starting at 0, so it gives a somewhat exaggerated picture of the proportion of gasoline saved at lower speeds, even though the numerical data are the same for both graphs. The graph in Figure 12.25 gives a correct picture of the proportion of gasoline saved. Why do you think the first bar graph rather than the second would be published?

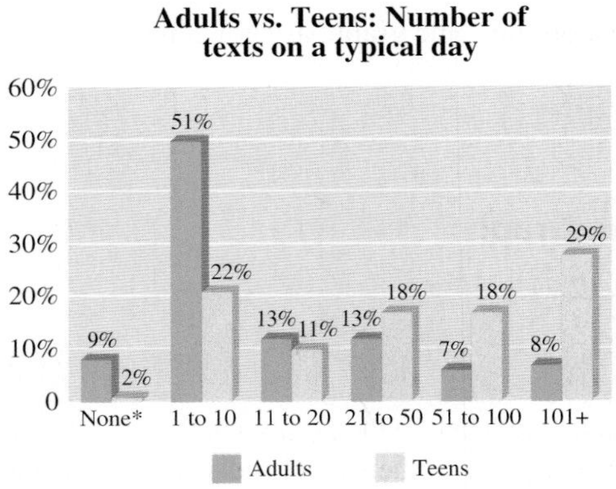

FIGURE 12.23 The bar graph shows that adults send more text messages than teens when the number of messages sent is less than 20.
Source: Copyright © 2012 Pew Internet & American Life Project. http://pewinternet.org/~/media//Files/Reports/2010/PIP_Adults_Cellphones_Report_2010.pdf.

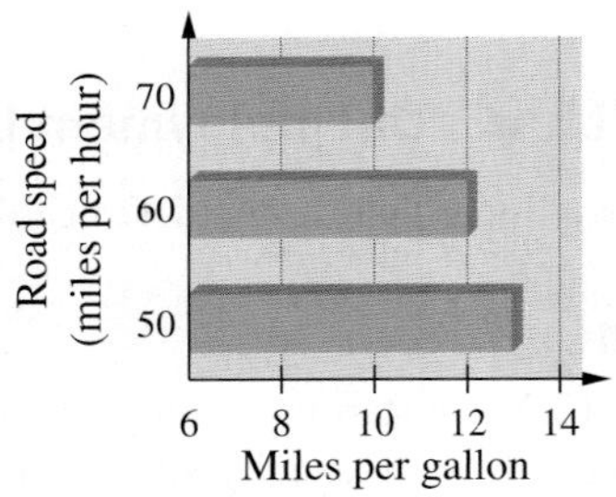

FIGURE 12.24

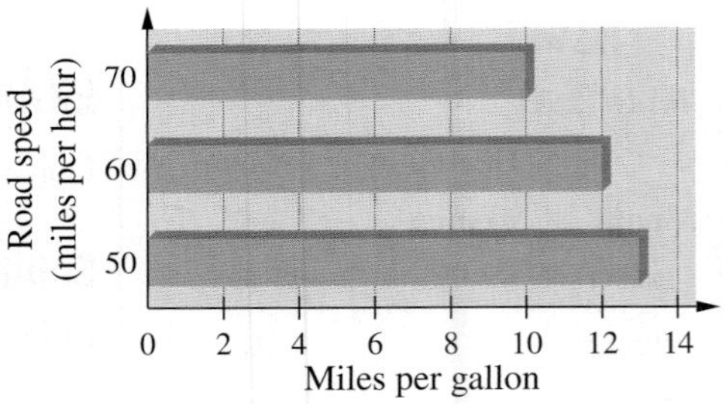

FIGURE 12.25

EXAMPLE 3 Bar Graphs and Embarrassing Moments

What would embarrass you the most on your first date? See the data below from Listerine! Draw a vertical bar graph using it.

Bad breath (BB)	40%
Acne breakout (AB)	23%
Fly open (FO)	22%
Greasy hair (GH)	14%

Note: Percentages do not sum to 100 due to rounding.
Source: Data from Wirthline Worldwide for Listerine.

Solution

To identify the graph, we label it "First-Date Blunders." We have four categories represented on the *horizontal* axis. The *frequencies* go from 14 to 40, so we make the *vertical* axis go from 0 to 50 at 10-unit intervals as shown. The bars are 40, 23, 22, and 14 units long, corresponding to the percents given in the table. How does it look when done by a graphic artist? The result is shown below.

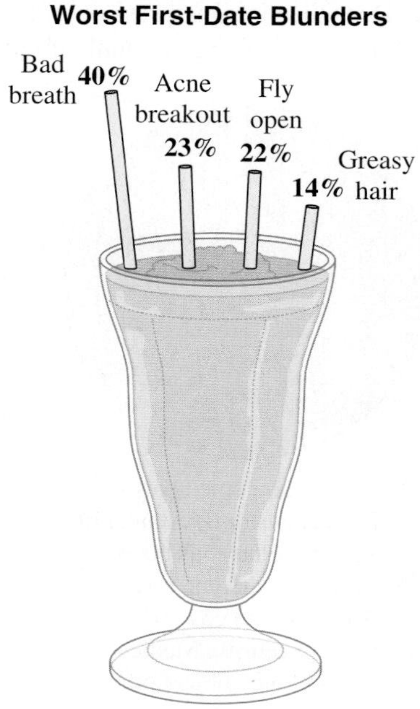

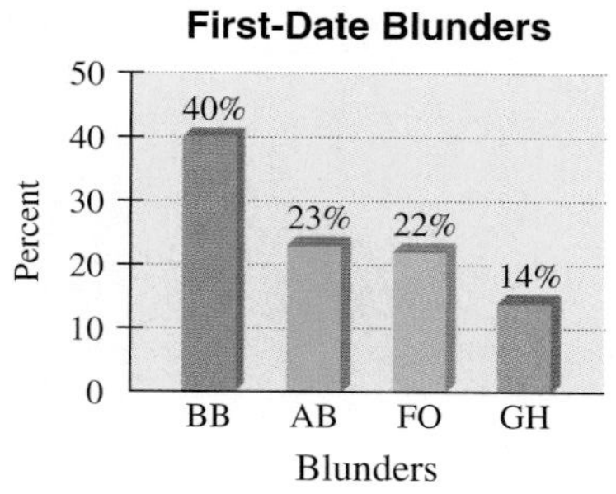

EXAMPLE 4 Horizontal Bar Graphs at a Restaurant

A recent poll listed the features patrons liked in a restaurant as follows:

Self-service salad bar	57%	All-you-can-eat specials	37%
Varied portion sizes	47%	Self-service soup bar	30%
More varied menu	42%		

Use horizontal bars to make a bar graph of this information.

Solution

We label the x axis with percents equally spaced and at intervals of 10 as in Figure 12.26. However, since the highest percent used in the problem is 57, we can shorten the x axis and stop at 60%. We find the points on the graph just as we did for the line graphs, but instead of connecting the dots with a line, we draw a bar. The labels can be placed alongside the vertical axis or inside the bars as shown.

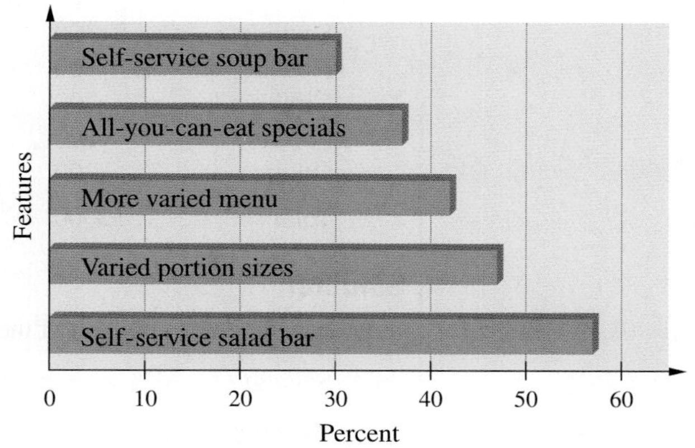

FIGURE 12.26 Restaurant preferences.

C Circle Graphs

Graphs like those in Figures 12.27 and 12.28 are called **circle graphs** or **pie charts.** Such graphs are a very popular means of displaying data, and they are also susceptible to being drawn to make things look better (or worse) than they are. For instance, compare the graph in Figure 12.27 with the version of the same data that was published by the Internal Revenue Service. Does the visual impression of Figure 12.28 make you feel that individual income taxes are not quite so large a chunk of federal income as Figure 12.27 indicates?

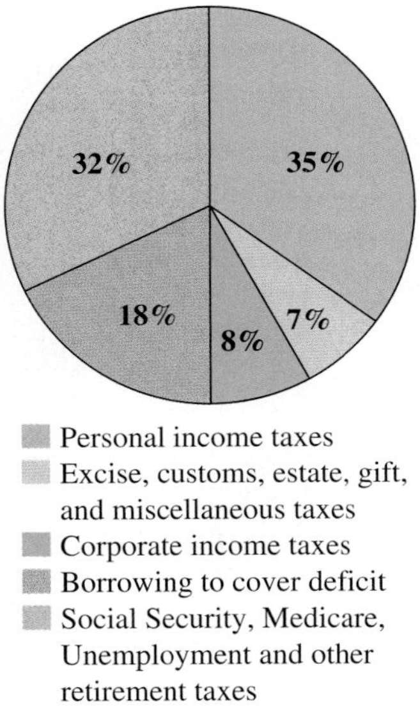

FIGURE 12.27 Circle graph.

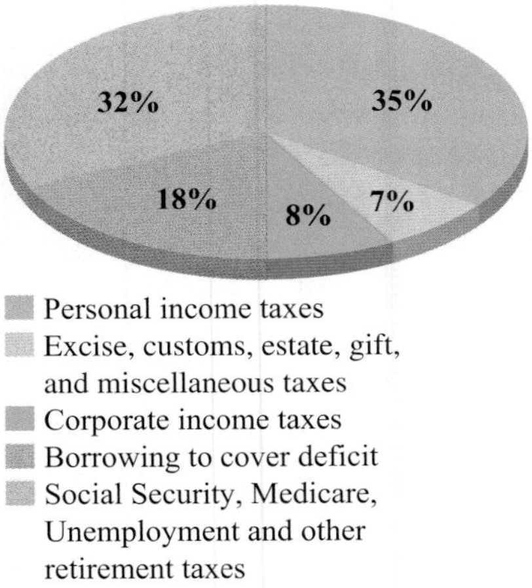

Source: www.irs.gov/pub/irs-pdf/i1040.pdf.

FIGURE 12.28 Income.

Circle graphs are quite easy to draw if you know how to use a simple compass and a protractor. For the graph in Figure 12.27, which shows where the typical dollar of federal money comes from, 23¢ is 23% of a dollar. The entire circle corresponds to 360°, so you would use 23% of 360°, or 82.8° ≈ 83°, for the slice that represents 23¢, and likewise for the other slices. This is the most accurate and honest way to present data on a circle graph.

EXAMPLE 5 Circle Graphs and Budgets

A marketing executive for a food manufacturer wants to show that food is an important part of a family budget. She finds that the typical budget is as follows. Make a circle graph for these data. Keep in mind that this is the executive's idea of a budget. To see how real Americans spend their money, go to http://tinyurl.com/7q4mnuw.

Monthly Family Budget	
Savings	$ 300
Housing	500
Clothing	200
Food	800
Other	200
Total	$2000

Solution

First determine what *percent* of the total amount each of the items represents.

Savings $\frac{300}{2000} = \frac{3}{20} = 15\%$ Food $\frac{800}{2000} = \frac{2}{5} = 40\%$

Housing $\frac{500}{2000} = \frac{1}{4} = 25\%$ Other $\frac{200}{2000} = \frac{1}{10} = 10\%$

Clothing $\frac{200}{2000} = \frac{1}{10} = 10\%$

Then find out how many degrees each slice covers.

$$15\% \text{ of } 360° = 0.15 \times 360° = 54°$$
$$25\% \text{ of } 360° = 0.25 \times 360° = 90°$$
$$10\% \text{ of } 360° = 0.10 \times 360° = 36°$$
$$40\% \text{ of } 360° = 0.40 \times 360° = 144°$$
$$10\% \text{ of } 360° = 0.10 \times 360° = 36°$$

Now measure the required number of degrees with a protractor, and label each of the slices as shown in Figure 12.29. As a check, make sure the sum of the percentages is 100 and the sum of the degrees for the slices is 360.

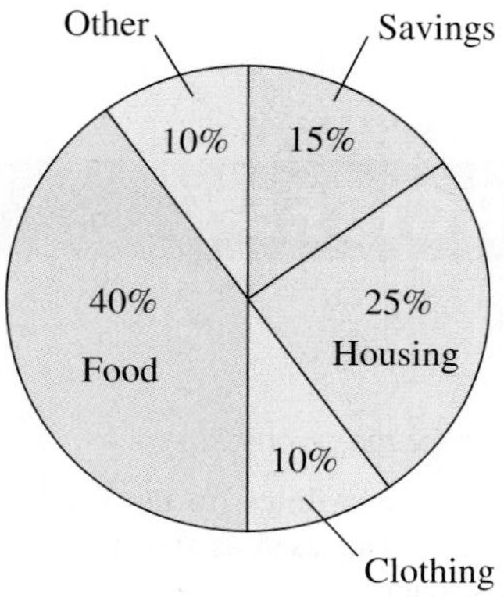

FIGURE 12.29 Monthly family budget.

In Example 2 we drew two lines on the same graph. Sometimes we have to draw more than one circle graph to solve a problem, as shown in Example 6.

EXAMPLE 6 Predictions about El Niño, La Niña, and Normal Years

Can you predict the probability of rainfall using a circle graph or pie chart on the next page? The Bureau of Meteorology does in Australia. Rainfall predictions can be given using numerical data, either in a table or as a circle graph. The following table gives the probability of dry, wet, or normal weather based on the type of year (El Niño, normal, or La Niña). The information from the table can be summarized by using three circle graphs. Make three different circle graphs corresponding to the three columns in the table.

El Niño Year	Normal Year	La Niña Year
50% dry	33.3% dry	17% dry
17% wet	33.3% wet	50% wet
33% normal	33.3% normal	33% normal

Solution

The third circle graph on the next page shows the information for a La Niña year. The easiest category to graph is wet because wet represents 50%, or half of the circle. The top half of the circle shows dry (17%) and normal (33%). Because 17 is about one-half of 33, the tan region representing the dry weather is about half the size of the normal region. Can you see how the first and second circle graphs were done?

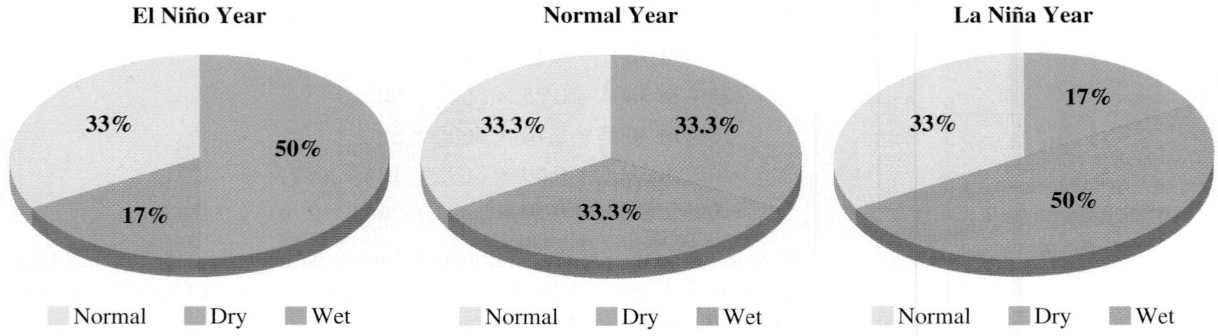

Source: Australian Government Bureau of Meteorology.

12.5 EXERCISES

A Line Graphs

In problems 1–6, make a line graph for the given data.

1. Worldwide revenues for physical recordings (to the nearest billion) in the last four years have decreased as shown in the table. Make a line graph for these data.

Year	Billions
2008	28
2009	25
2010	22
2011	20

2. Are you trying to lose weight? Here are the daily calories needed to maintain weight for females in given age intervals.

11–14	2200 calories
15–18	2100 calories
19–22	2050 calories
23–50	2000 calories
51–75	1800 calories
75+	1500 calories

3. Have you ever joined a social networking site (Facebook, MySpace or LinkedIn)? 65% of adults have! The table shows the percent of adults who have used a social networking site, according to a Pew Research Survey. Make a line graph for the data.

2005	8%
2006	16%
2007	NA
2008	29%
2009	46%
2010	61%
2011	65%

4. Percent of males squeezing the toothpaste tube from top or bottom

Age	*Bottom*	*Top*
21–34	37	63
35–44	33	67
45–54	10	90
55+	10	90

5. Percent of females squeezing the toothpaste tube from top or bottom

Age	*Bottom*	*Top*
21–34	33	67
35–44	43	57
45–54	30	70
55+	45	55

6. Projected percent of age ranges in the United States

	1950	1990	2010	2030	2050
0–14	27%	22%	18%	19%	19%
15–64	65%	66%	68%	62%	62%
65+	8%	12%	13%	20%	19%

7. How much candy do you eat? According to the Census Bureau, the per capita consumption of candy for five consecutive years is as follows:

Year	1	2	3	4	5
Pounds	25.1	23.6	24	24.6	24.7

Make a line graph for the data using 1–5 as the years and 20–25 as the amount (in pounds).

8. Does your Internet use interfere with your TV watching? A Stanford group survey shows the percent of persons reporting less time watching television based on the number of hours they spent using the Internet.

Internet time	< 1 hour	1–5 hours	5–10 hours	> 10 hours
Percent watching less TV	27%	43%	56%	65%

Make a line graph for the data using the four categories in the horizontal axis and the percents from 0 to 70 at intervals of 10 units.

In problems 9–20, make a line graph for the given data representing a recent 5-year period. (Source: U.S. Department of Labor. Bureau of Labor Statistics, www.bls.gov/data/home.htm.) How do you compare with these averages? Note that because of economic conditions the price of housing may have gone up and the amount spent on entertaining may be down.

9. *Men's Clothing.* The following data show the average amount of money spent on apparel by men between the ages of 16 and 25:

1	247
2	221
3	209
4	294
5	262

Graph the data using 1–5 as the years and 200–300 as the amounts at $10 intervals.

10. *Women's Clothing.* The following data show the average amount of money spent on apparel by women between the ages of 16 and 25:

1	434
2	382
3	377
4	405
5	359

Graph the data using 1–5 as the years and 350–450 as the amounts at $10 intervals.

11. *Food in general.* The following data show the average amount of money spent on food by persons under 25:

1	2838
2	3075
3	3354
4	3213
5	3724

Graph the data using 1–5 as the years and 2600–4000 as the amounts at $200 intervals.

12. *Food at home.* The following data show the average amount of money spent on food at home by persons under 25:

1	2758
2	2547
3	2890
4	2951
5	2936

Graph the data using 1–5 as the years and 2500–3000 as the amounts at $100 intervals.

13. *Housing.* The following data show the average amount of money spent on housing by persons under age 25:

1	5860
2	6151
3	6585
4	7109
5	7585

Graph the data using 1–5 as the years and 5000–8000 as the amounts at $500 intervals.

14. *Housing.* The following data show the average amount of money spent on housing by persons between the ages of 25 and 34:

1	11,774
2	12,015
3	12,519
4	13,050
5	13,828

Graph the data using 1–5 as the years and 11,000–14,000 as the amounts at $500 intervals.

15. *Entertainment.* The following data show the average amount of money spent on entertainment by persons under age 25:

1	1051
2	974
3	1149
4	1091
5	1152

Graph the data using 1–5 as the years and 900–1200 as the amounts at $50 intervals.

16. *Entertainment.* The following data show the average amount of money spent on entertainment by persons between the ages of 25 and 34:

1	1865
2	1757
3	1776
4	1876
5	2001

Graph the data using 1–5 as the years and 1700–2100 as the amounts at $50 intervals.

17. *Health Care.* The following data show the average amount of money spent on health care by persons under age 25:

1	425
2	445
3	551
4	504
5	530

Graph the data using 1–5 as the years and 400 to 600 as the amounts at $50 intervals.

18. *Health Care.* The following data show the average amount of money spent on health care by persons between the ages of 25 and 34:

1	1236
2	1185
3	1170
4	1256
5	1286

Graph the data using 1–5 as the year and 1000–3000 as the amounts at $50 intervals.

19. *Wages-salaries.* The following data show the average amount of annual wages-salaries earned by persons between the ages of 25 and 34:

1	37,455
2	38,548
3	39,372
4	42,770
5	46,301

Graph the data using 1–5 as the years and 37,000–47,000 as the amounts at $1000 intervals.

20. *Wages-salaries.* The following data show the average amount of annual wages-salaries earned by persons under age 25:

1	13,098
2	14,553
3	16,210
4	16,908
5	17,650

Graph the data using 1–5 as the years and 12,000–18,000 as the amounts at $1000 intervals.

B Bar Graphs

In problems 21–23, draw a bar graph based on the data provided.

21. According to Merrill Lynch Relocation Management, Inc., hundreds of people accepted a transfer from their company. The following are the numbers of employees relocated in various industries:

Industry	*Number*
Computers	803
Petroleum	324
Transportation	271
Public utilities	265
Retail/wholesale	231

Use horizontal bars to make a graph of this information.

22. A manager in the food industry had to predict future consumption of major food commodities. The following are the data:

Food	*Increase*
Chicken	70%
Turkey	60%
Fish	30%
Cheese	90%
Dairy Products	10%

a. Use horizontal bars to make a graph that displays this information.

b. If you were to be in a growing business, which industry would you choose to own or manage in the future? Which business would you avoid?

23. The personnel department of a major corporation was asked to make a vertical bar graph indicating the percent of salary to be replaced by pension and Social Security income for married persons who worked for 40 years. The following is the information supplied by the Bureau of Labor Statistics:

Salary at Time of Retirement	*Percent Received from Pension and Social Security*
$20,000	93%
$30,000	74%
$40,000	64%

a. Make the graph.

b. If you retired at $20,000, what amount would you expect from your pension and Social Security?

24. Does the gender of a person influence the decision to purchase or delay the purchase of an item? The information gives the percent of people in New Zealand (by gender) and their decision to purchase an item this year (Year 1) or delay the purchase until next year (Year 2).

Purchase Year 1		Purchase Year 2		Delay Year 1		Delay Year 2	
Male	**Female**	**Male**	**Female**	**Male**	**Female**	**Male**	**Female**
29	23	33%	23%	57%	57%	26%	27%

Use side-by-side vertical bars and make a histogram comparing the percent of consumers planning to buy an item year 1 with the percent of those that will delay the purchase until year 2. **Source:** http://tinyurl.com/7gfxo6c.

25. In a survey conducted by *Chain Store Age*, respondents indicated where their cameras were bought. Some of the responses were

Source of Purchase	*This Year*	*2 Years Ago*
Discount stores	18.6%	23.7%
Sears	11.4%	6.2%
Department stores	15.7%	4.1%
Specialty stores	30.0%	29.9%

a. Use side-by-side vertical bars to compare the given percents during the specified time periods.

b. On the basis of the graph, where do most people now buy their 35-mm cameras?

c. On the basis of the graph, which store category lost the most sales in the 2-year interval?

d. On the basis of the graph, which stores would you say had the most consistent camera sales over the 2-year period?

26. In another survey conducted by *Chain Store Age*, respondents indicated which store provided the best value for home electronics. The following are some of the results:

Source for Best Values	*Last Year*	*This Year*
Department stores	15%	20%
Electronic stores	31%	20%
Sears	17%	14%
Discount stores	8%	10%

a. Use the same horizontal bars to include each of the four categories for the given time periods.

b. On the basis of the graph, which stores provided the best value for home electronics?

27. Do you go to the movies often? The chart shows the average number of movies seen by the U.S./Canada population in different age brackets in two successive years.

Categories Age Bracket	*Frequencies Year 2*	*Year 1*
2–11	3.4	4.1
12–17	7.6	7.9
18–24	7.0	8.4
25–39	5.0	4.3
40–49	3.0	3.9
50–59	2.9	3.0
60+	2.4	2.4

Source: http://tinyurl.com/6y4pxoa.

a. Draw a vertical bar graph for the data.

b. What age bracket goes to the movies the most frequently and in what year?

c. What age bracket goes to the movies the least?

d. What is the only age bracket in which attendance ***increased*** from **Year 1 to Year 2**?

28. How many unwanted calls do you get daily? The number of unwanted calls received by the given percent of the people is shown below.

Unwanted Calls	*Frequencies*
0	15%
1–2	41%
3–5	28%
6 and up	12%

Source: Data from Bruskin/Goldring Research for Sony Electronics.

a. Draw a vertical bar graph for the data.

b. Which is the most common number of calls received?

c. What percent of the people received no unwanted calls?

29. Which branch of the military has the most women? A Defense Department survey shows the following numbers:

Branch	*Frequencies*
Air Force	19.4%
Army	15.4%
Navy	14.4%
Marines	6%

a. Draw a horizontal bar graph of the data.

b. Which branch has the highest percent of women?

c. Which branch has the lowest percent of women?

d. Can you use the information to find out if there are more women in the Air Force than in the Army? Explain.

30. Who has the most Internet knowledge? A survey of *USA Today* adult respondents answering the question, "Who has the most Internet knowledge?" revealed the following data:

Response	*Percent*
Kids	72%
Adults	21%
Both the same	2%

a. Draw a horizontal bar graph for the data.

b. According to the survey, who has the most knowledge?

c. What percent of the people think that kids and adults have the same knowledge?

C Circle Graphs

In problems 31–36, make a circle graph for the data.

31. Have you been to a meeting lately? The following are the numbers of hours per week spent in meetings by chief marketing executives:

Hours	*Percent*	*Hours*	*Percent*
Fewer than 5	2	20–24	22
5–9	10	25–29	16
10–14	17	29+	17
15–19	16		

32. Clairol, Inc., reports that the percent of industry sales for favorite hair colorings are

Blond	40%	Black	8%
Brunette	38%	Other	1%
Red	13%		

33. Have you looked in your refrigerator and found some UFOs (unidentified food objects)? The makers of Saran Wrap found the following information from survey respondents:

9% don't have leftovers.
61% have leftovers that are 6 days old or less.
23% have leftovers that are 1–4 weeks old.
5% have leftovers that are more than 4 weeks old.
2% don't know.

34. Where do you think you use the most water in the home? According to *National Wildlife Magazine*, the percents of water used in different parts of the home are as follows:

Toilet	40%	Laundry	12%
Shower/bath	20%	Kitchen	10%
Bathroom sink	15%	Outside	3%

35. Do you have a Facebook account? How many "friends" do you have? A survey by *Pew Research* indicates that the average Facebook user has **never** met in-person with **7%** of their Facebook friends. An additional **3%** of their friends are people they have only met in-person **one** time. The rest, **89%,** they have met **more than once.** Totals do not add to 100% because of rounding.

Source: Pew Research Center.

36. How often do you wash your car? The following are the results of a survey of 1000 drivers:

220 wash them weekly.
180 wash them every 2 weeks.
230 wash them once a month.
370 never wash them!

37. The National Restaurant Association surveyed 500 customers at fast-food restaurants serving breakfast and compiled the following figures:

Who Eats Breakfast Out?

Age	*Number*	*Age*	*Number*
18–24	80	50–64	90
25–34	130	65+	50
35–49	150		

a. Make a circle graph for these data.

b. If you were the manager of a fast-food restaurant serving breakfast, which age group would you cater to?

38. Where does money used for advertising go? For every dollar spent in advertising, it goes as follows:

27¢ to newspapers
21¢ to television
16¢ to direct mail
7¢ to radio
6¢ to magazines
3¢ to business publications
20¢ to other sources

Make a circle graph for these data.

39. A company specializing in leisure products surveyed 500 people and found their favorite activities were as follows:

75 read.
250 watched TV.
50 watched movies.
60 had family fun.
65 had other activities.

Make a circle graph for these data.

40. Here are the top five frozen pizza brands. Make a circle graph for the dollar sales in the data.

Brand Name	**Dollar Sales (in millions)**	**Unit Sales (in millions)**
DiGiorno	$591.3	100
Tombstone	$270.4	70
Red Baron	$256.3	63
California Pizza Kitchen	$175.6	33
Totino's	$162.6	117

Source: https://secure.aibonline.org/php/web-search.php.

41. The U.S. Department of Labor updated its theoretical budget for a retired couple. The high budget for such a couple is apportioned approximately as follows:

Food	22%
Housing	35%
Transportation	11%
Clothing	6%
Personal care	3%
Medical care	6%
Other family costs	7%
Miscellaneous	7%
Income taxes	3%

Make a circle graph to show this budget.

42. The pie chart shown here appeared side by side with the one in Figure 12.28 on page 724. Make a circle graph to represent the same data. Compare the impression made by your circle graph with that made by the pie chart.

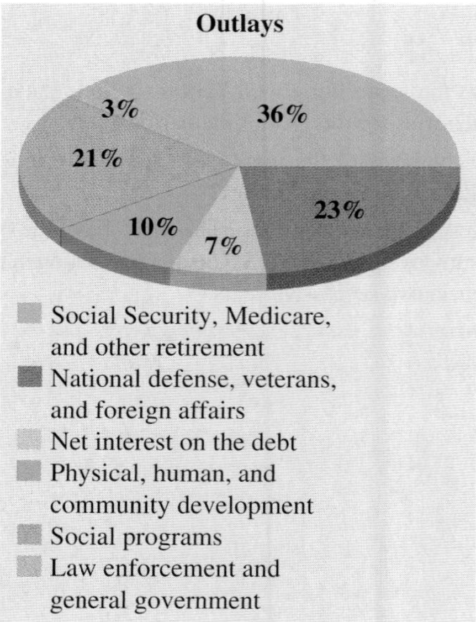

Source: http://www.irs.gov/pub/irs-pdf/i1040.pdf.

43. According to an advertisement for a color television, the top six brands of television sets were voted as best by the following percentages of about 2700 people:

Brand	Percent	Brand	Percent
1	50.1	4	8.5
2	21.1	5	5.8
3	8.8	6	5.7

a. Make a circle graph to illustrate this information.

b. Make a bar graph for the same data.

c. Which of these do you think makes the stronger impression? Why?

44. A survey conducted by the University of Michigan's Institute for Social Research showed that many of the women surveyed enjoy keeping house. The survey found that about 67% of the women who responded had an unqualified liking for housework, while only 4% had an unqualified dislike for housework. Make a bar graph to illustrate these data.

45. The Mighty Midget Canning Company wants to impress the public with the growth of Mighty Midget business, which it claims has doubled over the previous year. It publishes the following pictorial graph.

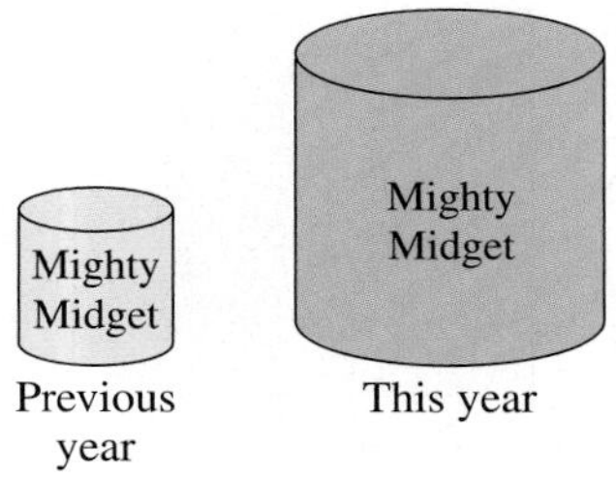

a. Can you see something wrong with this picture? (*Hint:* Your mind compares the volumes pictured here. The volume of a cylinder is $\pi r^2 h$. What happens if you double the radius r and the height h?)

b. Draw a bar graph that correctly represents the situation.

46. The U. B. Wary Company wants to give its stockholders a very strong impression of the rapid rate at which earnings have grown and prints the histogram shown in the following figure in its annual report. Redraw this graph to give a more honest impression.

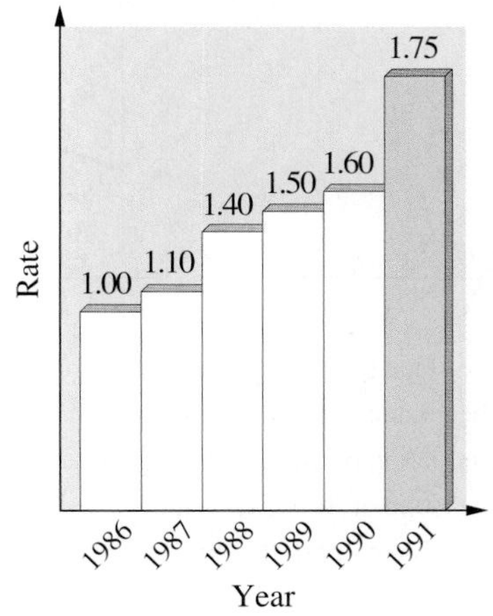

47. Do you know that playing golf is not a particularly good way to lose weight? Here is the calorie consumption per hour for five popular activities. Make a bar graph with horizontal bars, with each bar identified at the left side of your graph.

Activity	*Calories Consumed per Hour*
Bicycling (15 mph)	730
Running (6 mph)	700
Swimming (40 yd/min)	550
Walking (4 mph)	330
Golf (walking and carrying your clubs)	300

(These figures apply to a person weighing 150 lb; you have to add or subtract 10% for each 15-lb difference in weight.)

48. Women are generally lighter than men, so they require fewer calories per day. Here are three occupations and their energy-per-day requirements. Make a vertical bar graph with the bars for male and female side by side for comparison. On the average, about what percent more calories does the male require than the female for these three occupations?

Occupation	*Calories Required per Day*
University student, male	2960
University student, female	2300
Laboratory technician, male	2850
Laboratory technician, female	2100
Office worker, male	2500
Office worker, female	1900

49. Although the best a cold remedy can do is ease the discomfort (without curing the cold), the relief seems to be worth plenty to victims. Here is how people in the United States spent money on cold remedies in a recent year. Make a bar graph with the horizontal bars representing the data. Be sure to identify the bars.

Cold Remedy	*Millions Spent*
Cough drops and sore throat remedies	\$130
Nasal sprays, drops, and vaporizers	\$160
Aspirin substitutes	\$275
Cold and cough syrups	\$310
Aspirin	\$575

50. The more you learn, the more you earn! The following are the median incomes by educational attainment for persons 25 years or older:

Education	*Men*	*Women*
Not high school	\$ 22,636	\$13,217
High school	32,024	19,156
Some college	39,031	23,015
AA degree	40,608	26,104
Bachelor's degree	56,779	32,816
Master's degree	67,202	41,270
Professional degree	115,931	63,904
Doctoral degree	91,982	56,807

Source: http://www.census.gov/prod/2002pubs/p23-210.pdf. For the latest figures go to http://trends.collegeboard.org/.

Make a side-by-side vertical bar graph for these data. Find the women's income as a percentage of the men's in each category.

51. This chart shows the annual sales for the ABC Bookstore for a 10-year period.
   a. Approximately what were the sales in year 4?
   b. When did the sales start to level off?

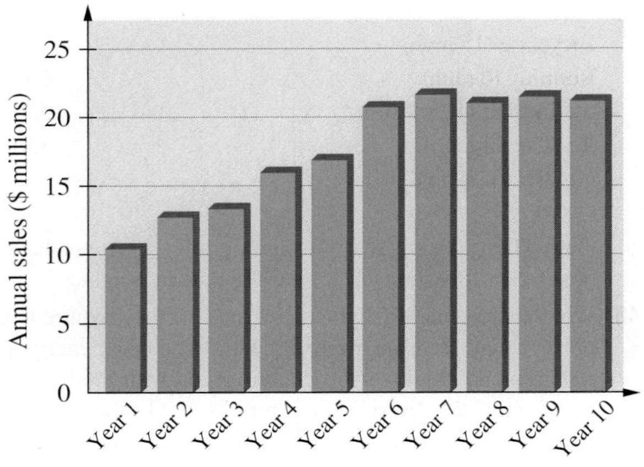

52. The circle graph shows Harry's time allotment for Mondays, Wednesdays, and Fridays. What percent of the time is Harry allowing for classes and study?

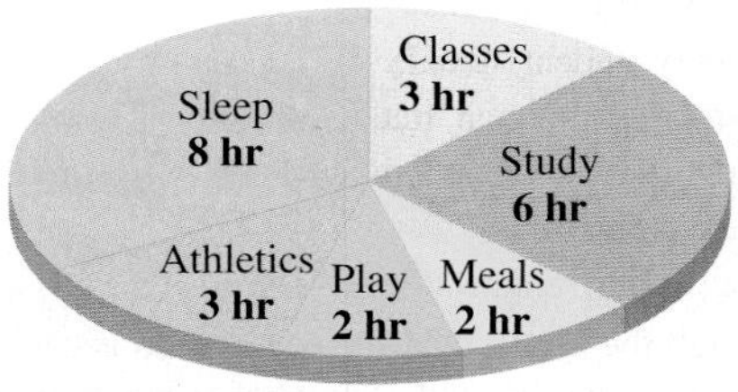

Harry's activities.

For the latest time-use statistics for university and college students go to: http://www.bls.gov/tus/charts/students.htm.

IN OTHER WORDS

You are the manager of a store whose sales (in millions) for January, February, and March were $20, $21, and $23 million, respectively.

53. Explain how to make a line graph that would
   a. make sales look better.
   b. make sales look flat.
54. Explain how to make a bar graph that would
   a. make sales look better.
   b. give the impression that sales are not increasing.
55. Explain in your own words the difference between a bar graph and a histogram.
56. When is a pie chart especially useful?

DISCOVERY

Misleading graphs can be used in statistics to accomplish whatever deception you have in mind. The graphs shown here and on the following page, for example, give exactly the same information. However, the following graph seems to indicate a steep increase in government payrolls, whereas the graph beneath it shows the stability of the same payrolls!

57. Can you discover what is wrong?

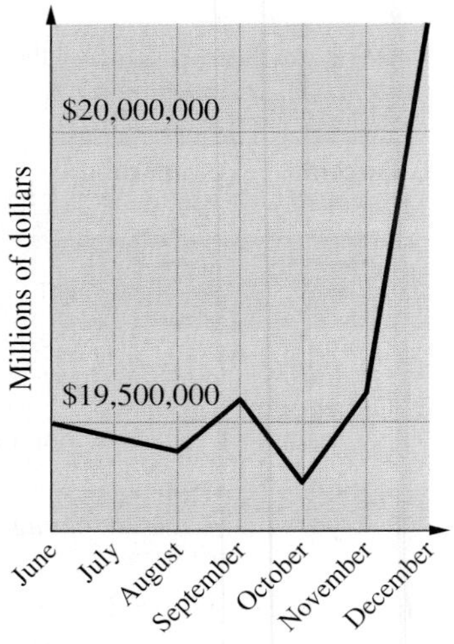

Government payrolls up.

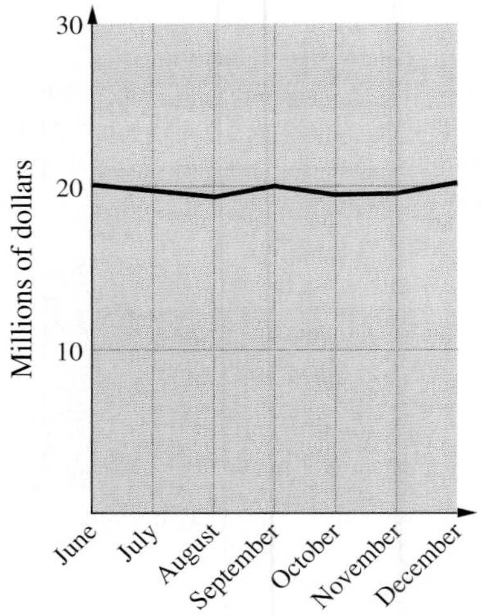

Government payrolls stable.

SKILL CHECKER

In the next section we will be finding the equations of certain lines called "best fit" or "least-squares" lines. Write an equation in the slope-intercept form $y = mx + b$, where m is the slope and b the y intercept. Answer the questions referring to the lines in the following figure.

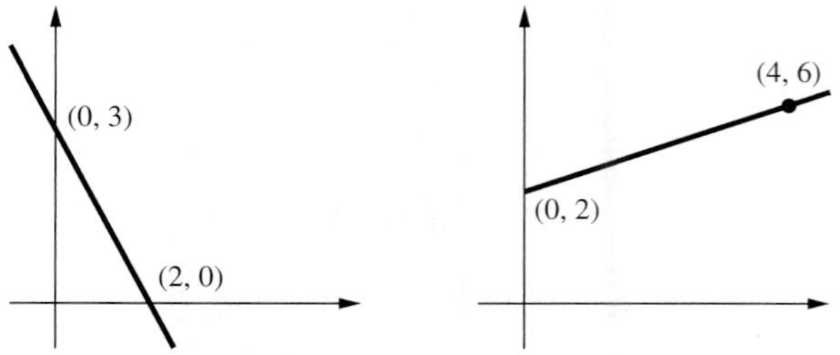

1. What is the slope of the first line in the figure?
2. What is the y intercept of this line?
3. Write the equation of this line in slope-intercept form.
4. What is the slope of the second line in the figure?
5. What is the y intercept of this line?
6. Write the equation of this line in slope-intercept form.

12.6 Making Predictions: Linear Regression

GETTING STARTED

OBJECTIVE

Given a set of data for an event:

Make a graph, draw the line of best fit, find the equation of the regression line, and make predictions about the event.

OLYMPIC PREDICTIONS

© AF/AFP/Getty Images

Source: http://tinyurl.com/y9lllen

Table 12.22 gives the winning times (in seconds) for the men's 200-m dash in the Olympic Games from 1984 to 2004. The points in Figure 12.30 (a scattergram) are the graphs of the corresponding number pairs (1984, 19.80), (1988, 19.75), and so on. As we can see, the points do not lie on a straight line. However, we can draw a straight line that goes "between" the points and seems to fit the data fairly well. Such a line, called the **line of best fit,** has been drawn in Figure 12.30. Statisticians sometimes use lines like this to make predictions. But what happened in the 1996 Olympic 200-m race was hard to predict. Michael Johnson entered the Olympic finals donning a custom-designed pair of golden-colored Nike racing spikes made with Zytel, the left one a U.S. size 10.5 and the right one a U.S. size 11 and weighing between 3 and 3.3 grams each! But that was not all. With an astounding burst of speed, he actually won the 200-m, setting a world record time of 19.32 sec. His record would endure for 12 years until another incredible event happened in the Beijing Olympics of 2008. The table shows the time for the new record holder (19.30 sec) for a man with the unpredictable name of Usain St. Leo Bolt.

In this section you will learn how to make predictions by drawing lines to fit given data.

Table 12.22

Year	1984	1988	1992	1996	2000	2004	2008
Time (sec)	19.80	19.75	20.01	19.32	20.09	19.79	**19.30**
	Carl Lewis U.S.	Joe DeLoach U.S.	Mike Marsh U.S.	Michael Johnson U.S.	Konstantinos Kenteris Greece	Shawn Crawford U.S.	Usain Bolt Jamaica

© Pete Niesen / Shutterstock.com

Source: http://zh.wikipedia.org/wiki File:Usain_Bolt_Olympics_cropped.jpg
Usain Bolt won the 200-m dash in the 2008 Olympics with a time of 19.30 sec.

How do we draw a line to fit data such as those in Table 12.22? One way is just to use our best visual judgment, but a better way is to calculate a *least-squares line*. If we have n points, say $(x_1, y_1), (x_2, y_2), \ldots, (x_n, y_n)$, in the xy plane, a line $y = mx + b$ is called the **least-squares (regression) line** for these points if the sum of the squares of the differences between the actual y values of the points and the corresponding y values on the line is as small as possible. The line in Figure 12.30 is the least-squares line for the data in Table 12.22, using **1** for 1984, **2** for 1988, and so on, and excluding the extreme times of Johnson and **Bolt.** In Figure 12.30, when we excluded Johnson's and **Bolt's** scores the trend was for ***higher*** scores, and that is one of the reasons **Bolt's 19.30** time was so unexpected. In Example 3 we shall see what happens to predictions when Johnson's and **Bolt's** times are also included.

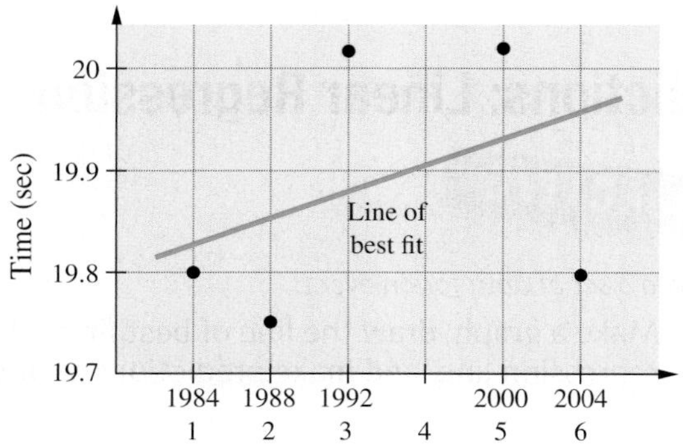

FIGURE 12.30 Olympic men's winning times: 200-m dash.

Until Usain Bolt's record time in 2008, the results for the 200-m dash were getting **worse,** except for the 1996 Olympic record set by Michael Johnson in 1996 (not in the graph). See the slope of the line going up from left to right?

To enter the data in Example 1 as a set of ordered pairs $(x, y) =$ (year, time), it is easier to let $1988 = 1$, $1992 = 2$, and so on. Clear any lists in your grapher (2nd + 4 ENTER), go to the home screen (2nd MODE), press STAT 1 , and enter 1, 2, 3, 4, 5 under L_1 and 48.63, 49.02, 48.74, 48.3, 48.17 under L_2. To find the relationship between the two, press STAT ▶ 4 ENTER . * This means $y = -0.164x + 49.064$. Thus, in 1988 ($x = 1$), the equation predicts a time of 48.9 sec. For 1992 ($x = 2$), time would be $y = -0.164(2) + 49.064 = 48.74$ sec, very close to the value in the graph!

```
LinReg
y=ax+b
a=-.164
b=49.064
```

To see the graph, press Y= VARS 5 ▶ ▶ 1 . This copies the equation and makes it equal to Y_1. Next, make a window like Figure 12.31. Press WINDOW and enter Xmin = 0, Xmax = 7, Xscl = 1, Ymin = 47, Ymax = 49, and Yscl = 1. Press GRAPH . Voila! *You also can enter Y= CLEAR VARS 5 ▶ ▶ 1 . This will find the regression equation and copy it to Y= .

EXAMPLE 1 Predicting Olympic Times for the Men's 100-m Freestyle Swim

Table 12.23 gives the winning times in seconds for the men's 100-m freestyle swim in the Olympic Games from 1988 to 2004. Make a graph of these data, and then draw a line "between" the points and predict the winning time for this event in the 2008 and 2012 Olympics.

Table 12.23 Times for the Men's 100-m Freestyle Swim

Year	1988	1992	1996	2000	2004
Time (sec)	48.63	49.02	48.74	48.30	48.17

Solution

The required graph for the men's 100-m freestyle swim is shown in Figure 12.31. The line in Figure 12.31 is the least-squares line for the given data. From this line we can read the predicted time for the 2008 Olympics as about **48.1** sec. The actual winning time was 47.21 sec, so the predicted time is off by less than 1.9%. The prediction for the 2012 Olympics is **47.9** sec; see how close you come!

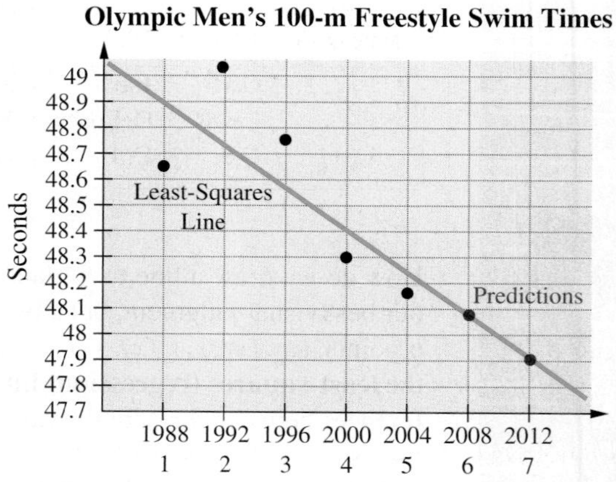

FIGURE 12.31 Winning times: Olympic men's 100-m freestyle swim.

EXAMPLE 2 Best-Fit Line for Sales and Advertising

Suppose we have the data for sales and advertising shown in Figure 12.32. By looking at the scattergram, it is clear that sales increase as advertising is increased. Can we find a best-fitting line? This time we draw the *two* lines shown. What are their equations, and how did we get them?

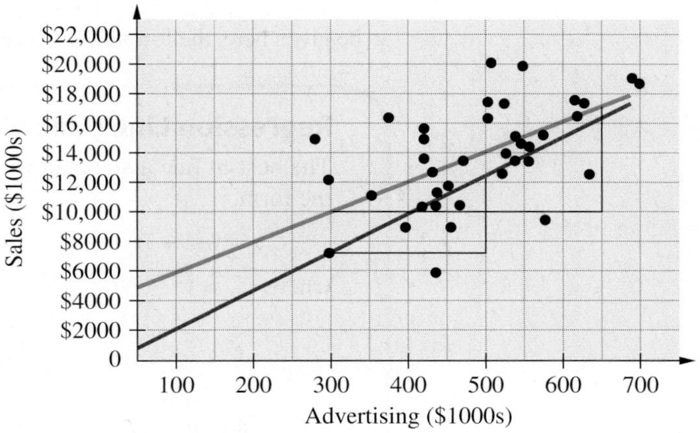

FIGURE 12.32 Sales and advertising.

Solution

As you recall, m = slope = rise/run. For the red line, m is about

$$\frac{12{,}000 - 7000}{500 - 300} = \frac{5000}{200} = 25$$

The intercept b is about 1000. Thus, $y = 25x + 1000$ (thousands).

For the blue line,

$$m = \frac{17{,}000 - 10{,}000}{650 - 300} = \frac{7000}{350} = 20$$

and $b = 4500$. Hence, $y = 20x + 4500$ (thousands).

This means that if we spend $400 in advertising and use the red line as our predictor, we can expect $y = 25(400) + 1000 = \$11{,}000$ (thousands) in sales. On the other hand, if we use the blue line for our estimation, expected sales are $y = 20(400) + 4500 = \$12{,}500$ (thousands).

Which is the best approximation? The one that is done using the method of "least squares." Look at Figure 12.33, showing all times between 1984 and 2008 for the men's 200-m dash. In Figure 12.33, d_1 and d_2 represent the difference between the y coordinate of the data point and the corresponding y coordinate on the line itself. Since d_1 is above

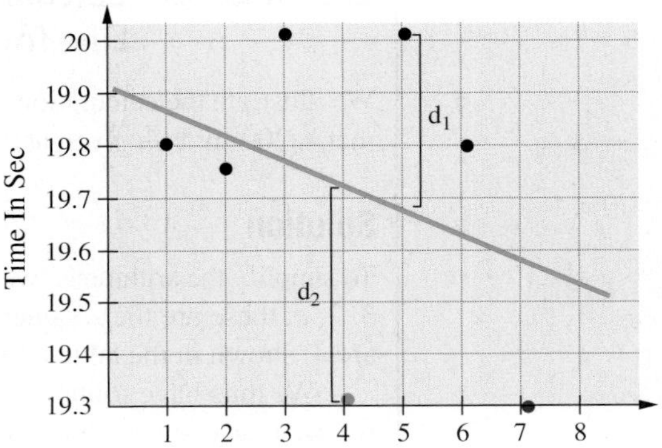

FIGURE 12.33 Winning times: Olympic men's 200-m dash. The blue dot corresponds to Michael Johnson's 1996 record, and the red dot belongs to Usain Bolt's 2008 record.

the line, d_1 is positive. On the other hand, since d_2 is below the line, d_2 is negative. If we simply add d_1 and d_2, the result may be 0. However, the squares of d_1 and d_2 cannot be negative. To construct a line that is as close as possible to the one shown, our job is to "minimize" the sum of the squares of the d's for all data points, thus the name "least-squares" line. To facilitate writing the formulas for the calculation of such a line, we shall use the symbol Σ to indicate a sum.

Although the derivation of the least-squares formula for the best-fit line is too advanced to be given here, the formulas themselves are not difficult to describe, as shown next.

Regression Line (Line of Best Fit)

The best-fit line associated with the n points $(x_1, y_1), (x_2, y_2), \ldots, (x_n, y_n)$ has the form

$$y = mx + b \tag{1}$$

where

$$\text{Slope} = m = \frac{n\Sigma(xy) - (\Sigma x)(\Sigma y)}{n(\Sigma x^2) - (\Sigma x)^2} \tag{2}$$

Same denominator

$$\text{Intercept} = b = \frac{(\Sigma x^2)(\Sigma y) - (\Sigma x)(\Sigma xy)}{n(\Sigma x^2) - (\Sigma x)^2}$$

or

$$b = \frac{\Sigma y - m(\Sigma x)}{n} \tag{3}$$

Total number of points → n

Σxy = sum of products = $x_1y_1 + x_2y_2 + \cdots + x_ny_n$
Σx = sum of x values = $x_1 + x_2 + \cdots + x_n$
Σy = sum of y values = $y_1 + y_2 + \cdots + y_n$
Σx^2 = sum of squares of x values = $x_1^2 + x_2^2 + \cdots + x_n^2$

Note: You can use either formula for b in equation (3)
The denominator in equations (2) and (3) are identical.

To use these formulas efficiently, we make a table with the headings x, y, x^2, and xy, as shown on page 737. The first two columns simply list the x's and y's, the third column lists the x^2's, and the last column gives the xy products. After filling out the table, we add the four columns to get Σx, Σy, Σx^2, and Σxy, the four sums that are required in equations (2) and (3).

EXAMPLE 3 Calculating the Least-Squares (Regression) Line for 200-m Dash

We illustrate the calculation of the least-squares (regression) line for the data for the entire men's 200-m dash given at the beginning of this section.

Solution

To simplify the arithmetic, we designate the successive Olympics starting with 1984 as 1, 2, 3, . . . ; these are the x values. The y values are the times in seconds, and our calculations are as shown in the table on page 737.

We thus have found $\Sigma x = 28$, $\Sigma y = 138.06$, $\Sigma x^2 = 140$, and $\Sigma xy = 550.9$, and we are ready to use equations (2) and (3). Since there are 7 points, $n = 7$, and we get

$$m = \frac{(7)(550.9) - (28)(138.06)}{(7)(140) - (28)^2} = -0.048$$

and

$$b = \frac{(140)(138.06) - (28)(550.9)}{(7)(140) - (28)^2} = 19.914$$

Year	x	y	x^2	xy
1984	1	19.80	1	19.80
1988	2	19.75	4	39.50
1992	3	20.01	9	60.03
1996	4	19.32	16	77.28
2000	5	20.09	25	100.45
2004	6	19.79	36	118.74
2008	7	19.30	49	135.1
Totals	**28**	**138.06**	**140**	**550.9**

(These answers are rounded to three decimal places.) The required line has the equation

$$y = -0.048x + 19.914$$

If we put $x = 8$ in this equation, we get $y = 19.53$. Thus, the predicted winning time for the 2012 Olympics is 19.53 sec, about the same as predicted by the line in Figure 12.33.

The best way to find m and b in the least-squares line $y = mx + b$ is to organize your work into a table as we have done. Also, your answers to the exercises may differ from ours depending on how you round during the intermediate steps. One last word of warning: Please do not confuse Σx^2 and $(\Sigma x)^2$. For Σx^2, we *first square* each x value and then find the total sum. For $(\Sigma x)^2$, we *first sum* the x values and then square the total as in the table. Finally, $n(\Sigma xy)$ and $n(\Sigma x^2)$ mean we multiply n by the appropriate sums. We illustrate this in Example 4.

EXAMPLE 4 Regression Line for Predicting Birth Weight

What is the relationship between the age of the mother and low birth weight for the child? Of course, they are related (the older the mother, the lower the birth weight of the child). But what happens if, in addition, the mother smokes during pregnancy? The following table shows the age x of seven pregnant women who smoked during their pregnancy and the percent y who had a low-birth-weight baby (defined as infants weighing less than 2500 g, or 5 lb 8 oz). Find the regression line and predict the percent of low-birth-weight babies for 30-year-olds. If your instructor allows it, do it with a grapher; the answer will be exactly the same!

Solution

Women	x	y	x^2	xy
1	16	12	256	192
2	18	11	324	198
3	23	10	529	230
4	27	11	729	297
5	33	13	1089	429
6	38	16	1444	608
7	46	19	2116	874
Totals	**201**	**92**	**6487**	**2828**

From the table, $\sum x = 201$, $\sum y = 92$, $\sum x^2 = 6487$, and $\sum xy = 2828$. Since there are $n = 7$ points, using equations (2) and (3),

$$m = \frac{(7)(2828) - (201)(92)}{(7)(6487) - (201)^2} \approx 0.260$$

Using the second formula for b,

$$b = \frac{92 - (0.260)(201)}{7} \approx 5.677$$

Thus,

$$y = 0.260x + 5.677$$

For 30-year-olds the percent of low-birth-weight babies is

$$y = 0.260(30) + 5.677 = 13.477\%$$

Can you make weather predictions? Groundhogs are supposed to, but the National Hurricane Center does it better! The following graph was the first advisory for Hurricane Twenty-Four and shows the National Hurricane Center (NHC) maximum 1-minute wind speed forecast as a broad blue line on a chart of wind speed versus forecast period. Examining the blue line, we can see from its inception (marked NOW in the graph) until 72 hours later, the hurricane was growing in intensity (the wind speed at the beginning was about 30 mph, and 72 hours later it had reached 90 mph). Can we find an equation for the blue line and predict the wind speed? Suppose we concentrate on the period starting at 48 hours and ending at 72 hours marked with the two blue dots. If we let x be the hours and y the wind speed, the first dot has coordinates $(48, 80)$, and the second has coordinates $(72, 90)$. To find the equation of this line, we first find the slope

$$m = \frac{y_2 - y_1}{x_2 - x_1} = \frac{90 - 80}{72 - 48} = \frac{10}{24} = \frac{5}{12}$$

Then we use the point-slope formula $y - y_1 = m(x - x_1)$ to obtain

$$y - 80 = \frac{5}{12}(x - 48)$$

Multiplying by 12,

$$12y - 960 = 5(x - 48) = 5x - 240$$

Adding 960,

$$12y = 5x + 720$$

Dividing by 12,

$$y = \frac{5}{12}x + 60$$

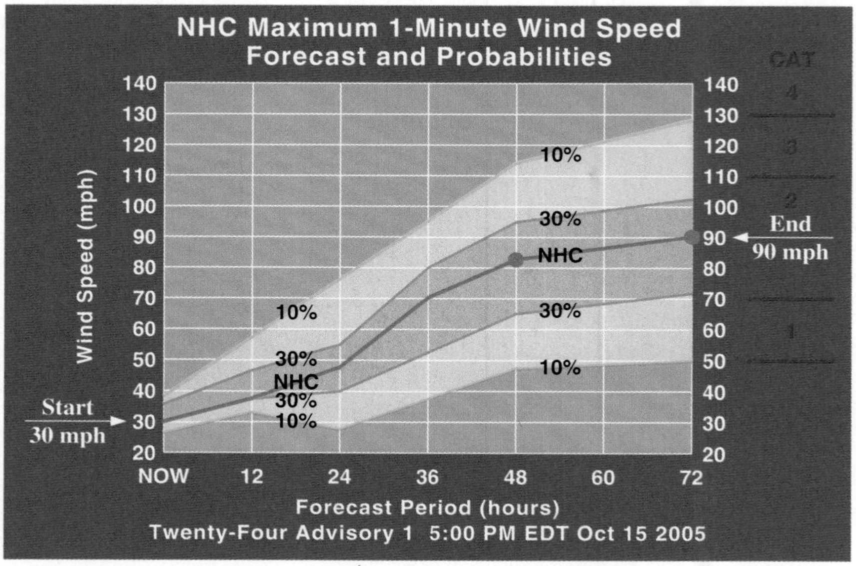

If you want to find the wind velocity y at any point x between 48 and 72 hours, simply substitute for x in the equation! For example, if you want to know the wind velocity 60 hours after the beginning of the forecast, let $x = 60$ in the equation $y = \frac{5}{12}x + 60$, obtaining

$$y = \frac{5}{12}(60) + 60 = 85$$

This means that the wind velocity 60 hours after the beginning of the forecast was 85 mph.

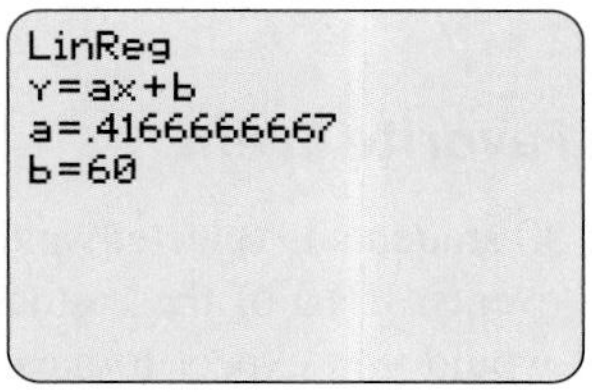

The work we have done is the same as obtaining the **regression line** for the points (48, 80) and (72, 90). With a graphing calculator (see the Graph It, page 734), press STAT 1 and enter 48 and 72 under L_1 and enter 80 and 90 under L_2. Now press STAT ▶ 4 ENTER. The grapher says $y = ax + b$, where $a = 0.4166666667 \approx 0.417$ and $b = 60$. Note that $\frac{5}{12} \approx 0.417$.

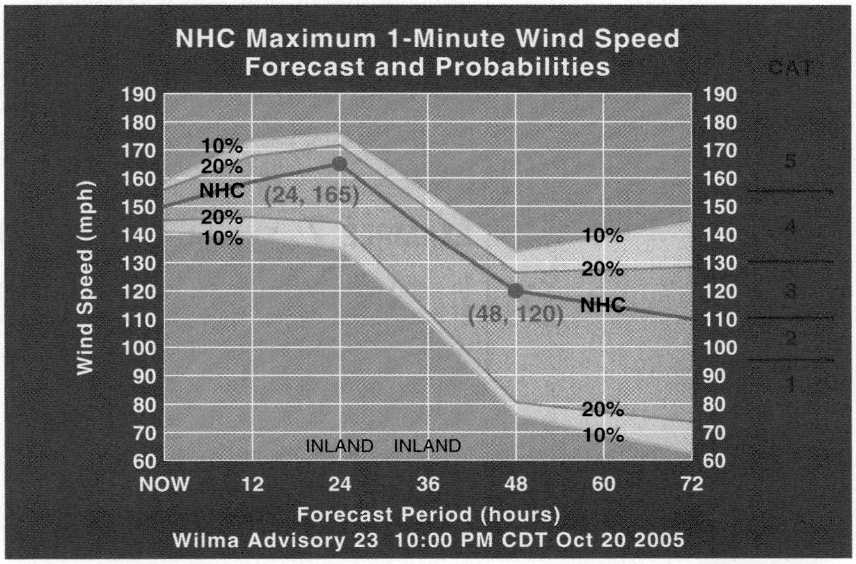

EXAMPLE 5 Hurricane Predictions

The graph shows the twenty-third advisory for Hurricane Wilma.

(a) What was the wind speed at the beginning of the advisory?

(b) In what interval of time was the hurricane increasing in intensity?

(c) In what interval of time was the hurricane decreasing in intensity?

(d) Find the regression line for the points between (24, 165) and (48, 120).

(e) What was the wind velocity 32 hours after the beginning of the forecast?

Solution

(a) 150 mph

(b) The slope of the line is positive (going up from left to right) from the beginning (NOW) of the forecast to 24 hours later.

(c) From 24 to 72 hours

(d) Use a grapher and follow the procedure we used before. Enter 24 and 48 for L_1 and 165 and 120 for L_2. Then press STAT ▶ 4 ENTER. The grapher says $y = ax + b$, where $a = -1.875$ and $b = 210$. Note that since the wind intensity is *decreasing*, the slope is negative.

(e) To find the wind velocity 32 hours after the beginning of the forecast, let $x = 32$ in $y = -1.875x + 210$, obtaining $y = -1.875(32) + 210 = 150$ mph.

By the way, look at the scale to the right of the graph (under CAT for category); at 150 mph, Wilma was classified as a category 4 hurricane!

Another way in which statisticians make predictions is based on a **sampling procedure.** The idea is quite simple. The statistician takes data from a **random sample** of the population and assumes that the entire population behaves in the same way as the sample. The difficulties lie in making certain that the sample is random and represents the population in a satisfactory manner. We shall not discuss the different ways in which a sample is selected but only mention that one of these ways uses a table of random numbers. (Such tables can be generated by a computer.)

EXAMPLE 6 Expected Number with Same Favorite Event

A certain school has 3000 students. A random sample of 50 students is selected, and the students are asked to name their favorite track and field events. If 10 of these students name the 100-m dash, how many students in the school would you expect to have the same favorite event?

Solution

You should expect $\frac{10}{50}$, or 20%, of the student body to favor the 100-m dash. Thus, the required number is 20% of 3000, or $(0.20)(3000) = 600$.

EXAMPLE 7 Expected Number of Failures

In a certain county, 15% of the eleventh-grade students failed a required literacy test. If 60 of the eleventh-grade students in this county were selected at random, how many of these would we expect to have failed the test?

Solution

We would expect 15% of the 60 students to have failed the test; that is, $(0.15)(60) = 9$ students.

12.6 EXERCISES

Much has been written about the relationship between S.A.T. scores and test-takers' family income. But can you predict your future income (in thousands) based on your S.A.T. scores? We shall try it! In problems 1-3 use a 450 to 550 x-scale with 10 unit increments and a \$30 to \$150 y-scale with 20 unit increments.

a. Graph the scores. b. Find and graph the regression line.

c. Predict the salary of a person scoring 500 and another person scoring 540 in the S.A.T.

1.

Math S.A.T. (x)	475	497	512	528	538	542	550
Salary (y)	\$30	\$50	\$70	\$90	\$110	\$130	\$150

2.

Reading S.A.T. (x)	462	488	503	517	525	529	536
Salary (y)	\$30	\$50	\$70	\$90	\$110	\$130	\$150

3.

Writing S.A.T. (x)	453	476	491	505	516	520	527
Salary (y)	\$30	\$50	\$70	\$90	\$110	\$130	\$150

4. The following table shows the world records for the women's 200 m-dash from 1984 to 2008. Compare to the men's records of Example 3. Are they close?

Year	Time	Name	Country
1984	21.81	Valerie Brisco	U.S.
1988	21.34	Florence Griffith	U.S.
1992	21.81	Gwen Torrence	U.S.
1996	22.12	Marie-Jose Perec	FRA
2000	VACANT	Marion Jones	Disqualified
2004	22.05	Veronica Campbell	JAM
2008	21.74	Veronica Campbell	JAM

Follow the procedure of Example 3.

a. Make a graph of these data.

b. Find and graph the regression line.

c. Use the line to predict the time for the 2000 Olympics.

d. Use the formula to predict the time for the 2012 Olympics.

5. In the Shell Marathon, a Japanese experimental vehicle achieved the equivalent of 6409 mi/gal! Of course, the mileage you get depends on your speed. The following table shows the speed x in miles per hour and the distance y a car ran on 1 gal of gas.

x	30	35	40	45
y	34	31	32	30
x	50	55	60	65
y	29	30	28	27

a. Make a graph of these data.
b. Draw a line between the points and predict how many miles per gallon you would get if your speed were 70 mph.
c. Find the equation for the regression line and repeat part (**b**).

6. The following table shows the number x of television ads Top Flight Auto ran during a certain week and the number (y) of cars it sold during the same week.

x	3	10	0	7	13	8	14
y	7	15	10	8	14	10	20

a. Make a graph of these data.
b. If the management decides that it can afford only 6 ads per week, can you predict how many cars will be sold?
c. Find the equation for the regression line and repeat part (**b**).

7. Does the number of student absences in a course influence the number of failures? The following table shows the average number x of absences per student in a certain course and the number y of students failing the course.

x	5	7	2	4	3
y	16	20	9	12	10

a. Make a graph of these data.
b. Can you predict how many students would fail the course if the average number of absences per student were 6?
c. Find the equation for the regression line and repeat part (**b**).

8. The manager of the concession stand at a baseball stadium is trying to predict the number of hot dogs that must be bought for an upcoming game. The number x (in thousands) of advance tickets sold and the number y (in thousands) of hot dogs sold the day of the game for the last five games are shown in the following table:

x	23	32	19	29	20
y	16	23	13	22	16

a. Find the equation for the regression line.
b. If advance ticket sales are 26,000 tickets, how many hot dogs should the concessionaire buy?

9. The following table shows the serving size (in grams) and number of calories recently given for different sandwiches at Burger King:

Item	Serving Size (in grams)	Calories
Total Bacon Cheeseburger (1)	168 g	450
Total BK 1/4 lb BURGER™ (1)	222 g	590
Total DOUBLE WHOPPER® with Cheese Sandwich (1)	418 g	1120
Total KING SUPREME™ Sandwich (1)	209 g	625
Total Chicken WHOPPER® (1)	231 g	430

Source: http://www.bk.com/cms/en/us/cms_out/digital_assets/files/pages/MenuNutritionInformation.pdf.

a. Draw the graph for these data.
b. Find the equation of the regression line for the data.
c. Use the equation to predict the caloric intake when you consume 300 grams of a Burger King sandwich.

10. The following table shows the serving size (in grams) and number of calories for various McDonald's sandwiches.

Item	Serving Size (in grams)	Calories
Hamburger	102 g	280
Cheeseburger	116 g	330
Quarter Pounder +	166 g	430
Quarter Pounder with Cheese +	194 g	530
Big Mac	215 g	590

Source: http://nutrition.mcdonalds.com/getnutrition/nutritionfacts.pdf.

a. Draw the graph for these data.
b. Find the equation of the regression line for the data.
c. Use the equation to predict the caloric intake when you consume 300 grams of McDonald's sandwiches. Compare with problem 9(**c**).

11. The following table shows the current wind chill estimate when the air temperature is 10°F.

Weather Revisions May Warm Up Cold

The current wind-chill estimate when the temperature of air is 10 degrees above zero and a proposed revision		
Wind Speed (mph)	**Current Wind Chill**	**Proposed Wind Chill**
5	6	10
10	−9	0
15	−18	−8
20	−24	−14

Source: www.usatoday.com/weather/windchil.htm.

a. Draw the graph for these data.
b. Find the equation for the regression line for the data.
c. Use the equation to predict the wind chill when the wind speed is 25 mph.

12. The third column in the table shows the new proposed wind chill when the air temperature is 10°F.
a. Draw the graph for this data.
b. Find the equation of the regression line for the data.
c. Use the equation to predict the new wind chill when the wind speed is 25 mph.
d. Is it lower or higher than the current wind chill?

13. The following table shows the approximate amount of trash produced in the United States from 1980 to 2000. Let x represent the year after 1980 (1980 is year 0) and y represent the amount of trash (millions of tons).

Year	Million Tons
1980	150
1990	200
2000	220

Source: http://science.howstuffworks.com/environmental/green-science/landfill2.htm.

a. Draw the graph for this data.
b. Find the equation of the regression line for the data.
c. Use the equation to predict the amount of trash y that will be produced in 2010 and 2015.

14. How much of the trash is recycled? The table shows the amount of paper and paperboard recycled from 1980 to 2000. Let x represent the year after 1990 (1990 is year 0) and y represent the amount of trash (millions of tons).

Year	Million Tons
1980	55
1990	70
2000	90

a. Draw the graph for these data.
b. Find the equation of the regression line for the data.
c. Use the equation to predict the amount of paper and paperboard that will be recycled in 2010 and 2015.

15. The table shows the Actual Manufacturer's Suggested Retail Price for a Chevrolet Camaro and the invoice price (the price that the manufacturer supposedly charges its franchised dealers). First, round all numbers to the nearest thousand and let x be the MSRP and y be the invoice price in thousands of dollars.

Chevrolet Camaro

Model Trim Name	MSRP	Invoice Price
Camaro Coupe 1LS	$23,200	$22,272
Camaro Convertible 1LT	$30,100	$28,896
Camaro Convertible 1SS	$37,900	$36,384
Camaro Convertible 2LT	$34,100	$32,736
Camaro Convertible 2SS	$40,600	$38,976

Source: http://consumerguideauto.howstuffworks.com/2012-chevrolet-camaro-trim-options.htm.

a. Draw the graph for these data.
b. Find the equation of the regression line for the data rounded to two digits.
c. Use the equation to predict the invoice price for a car with a $30,000 MSRP.

Note: The invoice price is really not the net price paid by the dealer to the manufacturer because of "holdbacks"—moneys that the manufacturer will refund the dealer.

16. Suppose you want to buy a Sony Carousel CD or DVD changer. You can go online and find the MSRP for several models as well as the lowest price for that day.

The table shows several models with their MSRP and actual price. First, round all numbers to the nearest 10 dollars, and let x be the MSRP and y be the invoice price.

Model	MSRP	Actual Price
Sony DVP CX995V	$500.00	Check Prices $399
Sony wx-4500x	$700.00	Check prices $248
Sony 10 Disc Changer	$ 99.95	Check prices $89
Sony 10 Disc Changer Recorder	$170.00	Check prices $199
Sony SCD-CE595	$129.95	Check prices $116
Sony CDP-CX355	$149.95	Check prices $99.88

Source: Adapted from http://auto.consumerguide.com/cp/electronics/browse/index.cfm/type/prod/id/11275.htm.

a. Draw the graph for these data.
b. Find the equation of the regression line for the data.
c. Use the equation to predict the actual price for a changer with a $300 MSRP.

17. Before we end regression problems, let us go and get some gourmet potato chips. The following table shows the brands, the number of chips per serving, and the number of calories in one serving. Let x be the number of chips in a serving and y the number of calories.

© I. Bello

Brand	Chips/Serving	Calories
Terra	10	140
Taro	10	140
Sweet Potato	17	160
Glenny's	12	160
Sesame	9	150

a. Draw the graph for these data.
b. Find the equation of the regression line for the data.
c. Use the equation to predict the number of calories in a serving of 15 chips.

18. What about the price you pay per chip? Refer to the following table. Let x be the number of chips in a bag and y the price.

Brand	Chips	Price
Terra	80	\$5.00
Taro	60	\$3.25
Sweet Potato	100	\$3.25
Glenny's	60	\$3.00
Sesame	70	\$3.00

a. Draw the graph for these data.
b. Find the equation of the regression line for the data.
c. What should the price of a bag with 90 chips be?

19. Of 50 students selected at random at a school, 12 said they preferred their hamburgers plain. How many of the 3000 students enrolled in the school would you expect to prefer their hamburgers plain?

20. A state welfare department selected 150 people at random from its welfare roll of 10,000 people. On investigation, it was found that 9 of the 150 had gotten on the welfare roll through fraud. About how many of the 10,000 people on the roll would you expect to be guilty of fraud?

21. An automobile tire manufacturer selected a random sample of 150 tires from a batch of 10,000 tires. It was found that 3 of the 150 tires were defective. How many of the 10,000 tires should the manufacturer expect to be defective?

22. An automobile manufacturer selected a random sample of 150 of its cars and found a defective steering assembly in 5 of the 150 cars. If the manufacturer had turned out 5000 cars under the same conditions, how many of these should it expect to have defective steering assemblies?

23. The best shooting percent for one basketball season is 72.7% and belongs to Wilt Chamberlain. If he attempted 586 baskets, how many would you expect him to have made?

24. A recent study indicates that 9 out of 50 males and 19 out of 50 females squeeze their toothpaste tubes from the bottom. In a group of 200 males and 200 females, how many males and how many females would you expect to be squeezing their toothpaste tubes from the bottom?

25. Can you predict the weather? Groundhogs are supposed to be able to! On February 2 of every year several famous groundhogs emerge from hibernation. If they see their shadows, that means 6 more weeks of winter. The following are the records of six famous groundhogs for varying numbers of years:

Punxsutawney Phil (15 years)	10 right, 5 wrong
Sun Prairie (7 years)	3 right, 4 wrong
West Orange, NJ (13 years)	7 right, 6 wrong
Staten Island, NY (7 years)	6 right, 1 wrong
Lilburn, GA (7 years)	6 right, 1 wrong
Chicago (6 years)	1 right, 5 wrong

If these six groundhogs predict the weather for the next 20 years, how many times would you expect

a. Punxsutawney Phil to be right?
b. Sun Prairie to be right?
c. West Orange to be wrong?
d. Staten Island to be wrong?
e. Lilburn to be wrong?
f. Chicago to be right?

26. The dropout rate (defined as "neither enrolled in school nor working") for 16–19-year-old African Americans is about 14%. The rate for whites is 9%. (Source: U.S. Bureau of Labor Statistics.)

A school has 500 African American and 1500 white students. How many African Americans and how many whites would you expect to drop out?

27. In a recent year 20% of Americans identified themselves as liberal and 32% as conservative. (Source: CBS News Poll.) If 500 Americans are chosen at random, how many people who identified themselves as liberals and how many as conservatives would you expect?

28. The following table shows the marriage rate y for 1000 Americans from 1980 to 1995.

x	1980	1985	1990	1995	2000
y	10.5	10	9.5	9	8.5

Source: U.S. National Center for Health Statistics.

a. Make a graph for these data.
b. Follow the pattern in the table and predict the marriage rate for the years 2010 and 2015.
c. If you select a representative sample of 5000 Americans in the year 2015, how many would you expect to marry? (*Hint:* Follow the pattern!)

29. It has been said that cats and dogs age the equivalent of seven human years for each year of life. Actually, their rate of development is more variable than that as you can see in the table where x represents the cat's age and y the equivalent human years.

x	$\frac{1}{2}$	1	2	3	4
y	10	15	24	28	32

Source: http://www.cats.alpha.pl/catsagechart.htm.

a. Make a graph for the data.
b. Find the regression line for the data in the chart.
c. According to the graph a 2-year-old cat is 24 in human years. How old is the cat, according to the formula?

30. We need equal time for dogs! Some people claim that the dog's age in human years is simply obtained by multiplying the dogs age by 7. This is not quite true, according to the age conversion graph.

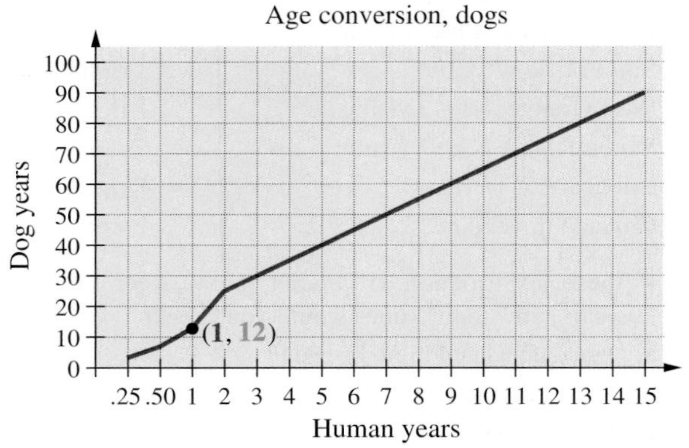

Source: http://tinyurl.com/6mawrwh.

a. If a dog is 9 years old in human years, how old is it in dog years?

b. If retirement age is 65 for humans, what is the equivalent retirement age for dogs in human years? (Answer to the nearest whole number.)

31. Referring to the Dog's Age conversion graph, if the drinking age for humans is 21, what is the equivalent drinking age for dogs in human years? (Answer to the nearest whole number.)

32. Use the points (1, 12), (3, 30), (4, 40), (9, 60) and (11, 70) to find the equation of the regression line for a dog's age y in human years x.

33. a. According to the formula in problem 32, what is the age y of a dog 15 years old in human years?

b. What is the age of the dog according to the graph?

34. Graph the points and the regression line of problem 32.

35. a. What are the coordinates of the point closest to being on the line?

b. Use the the formula in problem 32 to find the coordinates of the point.

The following graph will be used in problems 36 and 37:

36. a. What was the wind speed at the beginning of the advisory?

b. In what interval of time was there no change in the hurricane intensity?

c. In what interval of time was the hurricane decreasing in intensity?

37. a. Find the regression line for the points between (0, 75) and (36, 60).

b. What was the wind velocity 24 hr after the beginning of the forecast?

c. What was the wind velocity between 48 and 72 hr after the beginning of the forecast?

d. What is the equation of the regression line between 48 and 72 hr?

38. The following graph represents the average monthly temperatures for the first 6 months of the year. What would you predict to be the increase in the average temperature from February to May?

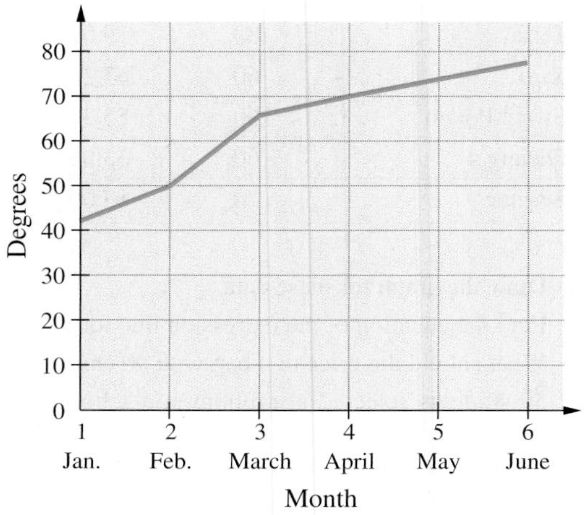

39. The publisher of a science fiction magazine wants to determine which features of the magazine are the most popular with its readers and decides to make a survey. Which of the following procedures would be the most appropriate for obtaining a statistically unbiased sample?

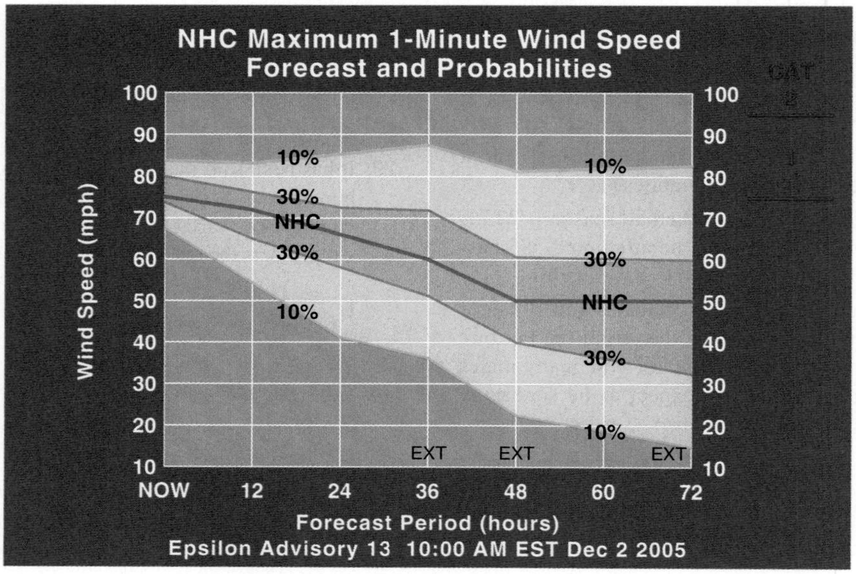

a. Survey the first 100 subscribers from an alphabetical listing of all the subscribers.

b. Survey a random sample of people from the telephone directory.

c. Have the readers voluntarily mail in their preferences.

d. Survey a random sample of readers from a list of all subscribers.

40. A tax committee in a small city wants to estimate the average county tax paid by the citizens of its city and decides to make a survey. Which of the following procedures would be the most appropriate for obtaining a statistically unbiased sample?

a. Survey all the residents of one section of the city.

b. Survey a random sample of people at the largest shopping mall in the city.

c. Survey a random sample of all the people in the city.

d. Survey all the people who work for the largest employer in the city.

IN OTHER WORDS

41. To make predictions, statisticians take data from random samples. Discuss why the following procedures might not yield a random sample of the population of California:

a. Every third woman shopper on Rodeo Drive is selected.

b. Every third man in Berkeley is selected.

c. Every third person leaving a baseball game in Oakland is selected.

42. If you use a sampling procedure to make a prediction, what do you assume about the sample? How can you make sure that you have a satisfactory sample?

USING YOUR KNOWLEDGE

The least-squares (regression) line in Example 3 is $y = -0.048x + 19.914$. Can we find another approximation for this line without all the calculations? Refer to Figure 12.33 on page 735. Let us concentrate on the first and last points on the line, which can be approximated as (0, 19.9) and (7, 19.58). Answers may vary!

43. What is the y intercept b of the line?

44. What is the slope m of the line?
(*Hint:* Slope = rise/run)

45. What is the equation of the line?

46. Use the equation of the line obtained in problem 45 to predict the winning time in the year 2012.

47. What is the predicted winning time in the year 2012 using $y = -0.048x + 19.914$?

48. Compare your answers for problems 46 and 47. What is the difference between the answers?

12.7 Scattergrams and Correlation

GETTING STARTED

OBJECTIVES

Given a set of data:

A. Make a scattergram and determine if there is a positive, a negative, or no correlation for the data.

B. Find and interpret the coefficient of correlation r for the data.

CORRELATION OF CANCER TO SOLAR RADIATION

You have probably heard the expression "What does that have to do with the price of tea in China?" In many practical applications of mathematics such as business, medicine, social sciences, and economics, you find pairs of variables that have to be considered simultaneously. (Perhaps tea production and tea prices!) In general, you are looking for certain patterns or co-relations. For example, in Norway, the annual herring catch has dwindled from more than a million tons to fewer than 4000, and the rates of breast and colon cancer have nearly doubled. Is there a connection? Is there a relationship between herring catch and cancer? Yes, if you consider the fact that herring is rich in vitamin D, a nutrient that you can get from sunlight, and there is not too much sunlight in Norway! If this were the case, people living in sunny areas, where they receive greater amounts of sunlight, and hence more vitamin D, should have less breast and colon cancer.

Drs. Frank and Cedric Garland have shown that a population's vitamin D intake can be a predictor of breast and colon cancer. How can they make this claim? They looked at the number of deaths per 1000 women in places where there was not too much sunlight (say, New York, Chicago, and Boston) and the number of deaths per thousand in sunny places (Las Vegas, Honolulu, and Phoenix, for example). The graph of the results, called a **scattergram,** is shown in Figure 12.34. As you can see, the sunnier it is, the fewer deaths from breast cancer there are. It is said that there is a **negative correlation** between the amount of solar radiation (sunshine) received and the number of breast-cancer deaths. On the other hand, there is a **positive correlation** (not shown) between the amount of solar radiation received and the number of skin cancers. In this section you will study positive and negative correlations and how "good" these correlations are by means of a correlation coefficient devised by Karl Pearson.

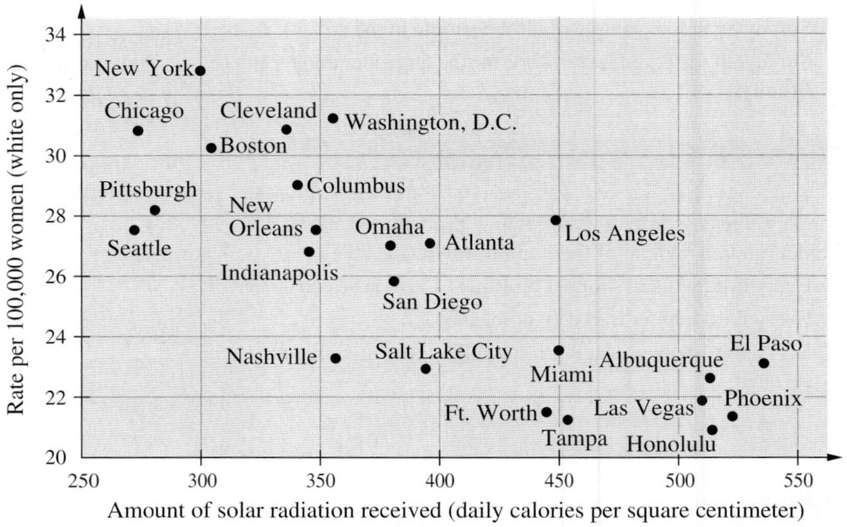

Source: Frank Garland.

FIGURE 12.34 Deaths from breast cancer (negative correlation).

A Correlation

In general, three kinds of correlations are possible. The scattergrams in Figure 12.35 illustrate typical cases. A good illustration of a negative correlation appears in Section 12.6, Example 1.

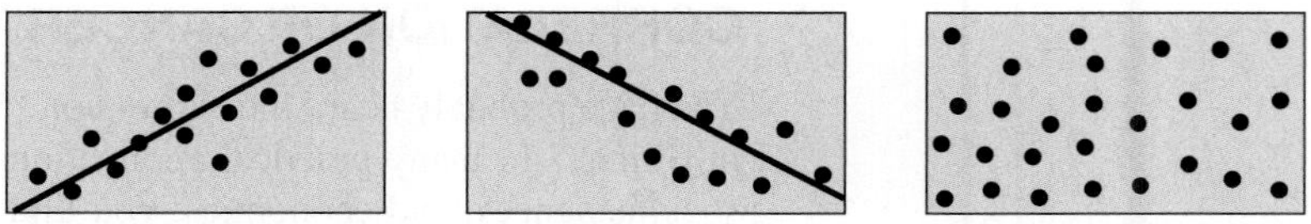

Positive correlation (Line slopes upward) | Negative correlation (Line slopes downward) | No correlation (No particular pattern)

FIGURE 12.35 Different types of correlations.

How can we best represent the data in a scattergram by a line? We use this rule: The slope of the line should show the direction of the data and have approximately the same number of points above as below the line.

EXAMPLE 1 Determining Accurate Representation of Data

For each of the following graphs, determine if the line is an accurate representation of the data. Explain your reasoning.

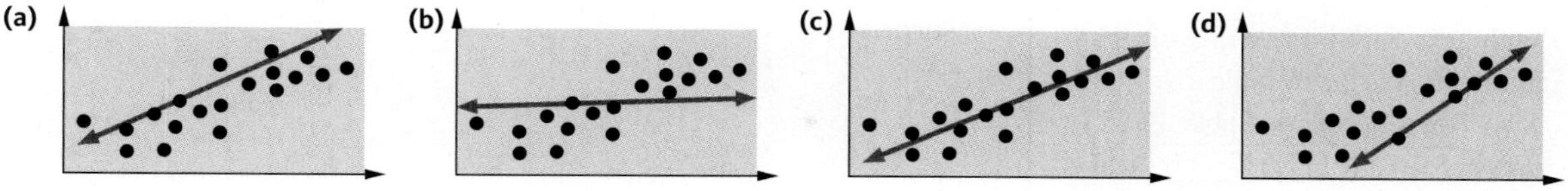

Solution

(a) No. There are too many points below the line.

(b) No. The slope of the line does not show the direction of the data, even though there are 9 points above and 9 points below the line.

(c) Yes. The slope follows the direction of the line and has about the same number of points above and below the line.

(d) No. There are too many points above the line.

GRAPH IT

To do Example 1, clear all lists by pressing [2nd] [+] [4] [ENTER]. Press [STAT] [1] and enter the numbers in the left column of Table 12.25 as L_1 and the numbers in the right column as L_2. To make a window corresponding to Figure 12.37 on page 748, press [WINDOW] and enter X min = 0, X max = 4.4, X scl = 0.4, Y min = 1.6, Y max = 4.4, and Y scl = 0.4. Now press [2nd] [STAT PLOT] [1] [ENTER] [▼] [ENTER] and [GRAPH].

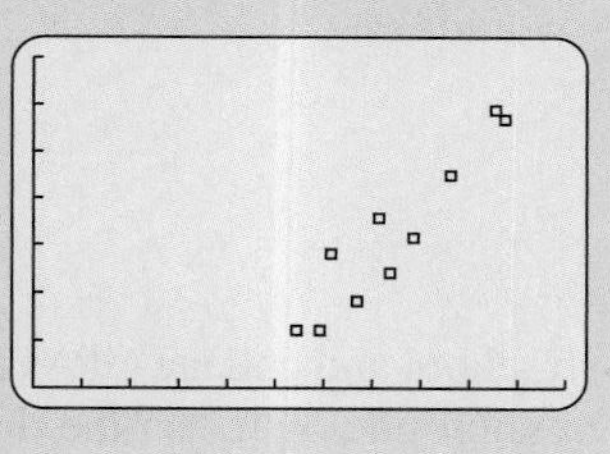

Now suppose 20 students tried out for the basketball team at West Side High. The coach listed their heights and weights as in Table 12.24. We have graphed the ordered pairs (height, weight) as shown in Figure 12.36. The scattergram indicates how the height and weight are related. As we might expect, in any group of boys (or girls), the greater height usually corresponds to the greater weight.

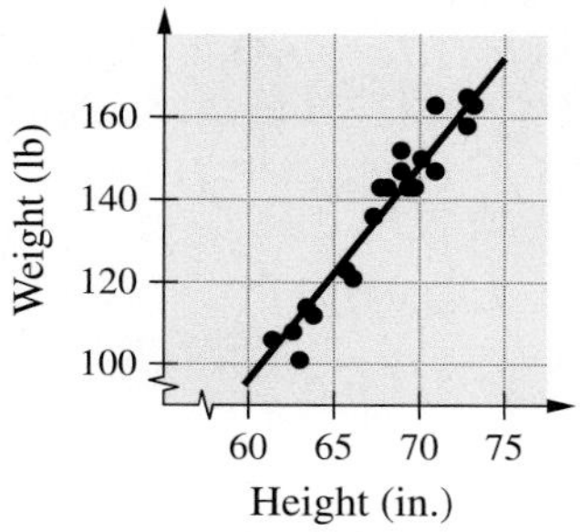

FIGURE 12.36 Height/weight.

The line drawn "between" the points in Figure 12.36 is the least-squares line for the data in Table 12.24. Notice that most of the points lie close to the line and that we have about the same number of points above the line as below. Because this line slopes upward, we say that the scattergram shows a **positive correlation** between the heights and the weights of the 20 students.

Table 12.24 Height/Weight for 20 Students

Height (in.)	61.4	62.6	63.0	63.4	63.8	65.7	66.1	67.3	67.7	68.1
Weight (lb)	106	108	101	114	112	123	121	136	143	143
Height (in.)	68.9	68.9	69.3	69.7	70.1	70.9	70.9	72.8	72.8	73.2
Weight (lb)	147	152	143	143	150	147	163	158	165	163

Table 12.25

High School GPA	College GPA
2.2	2.0
2.4	2.0
2.5	2.7
2.7	2.3
2.9	3.0
3.0	2.5
3.2	2.8
3.5	3.4
3.9	4.0
4.0	3.9

EXAMPLE 2 Scattergram and Correlation for GPAs

Ten students were selected at random, and a comparison was made of their high school grade-point averages (GPAs) and their grade-point averages at the end of their first year in college (see Table 12.25).

(a) Make a scattergram and decide what kind of correlation is present.

(b) Find the equation for the regression line.

(c) If a student has a 2.5 high school GPA, what would be the predicted college GPA?

GRAPH IT

With a TI-83, you can find all the information in the formula after you enter the values from Table 12.25. Press STAT ▶ 2 ENTER and the values in the formula will be displayed.

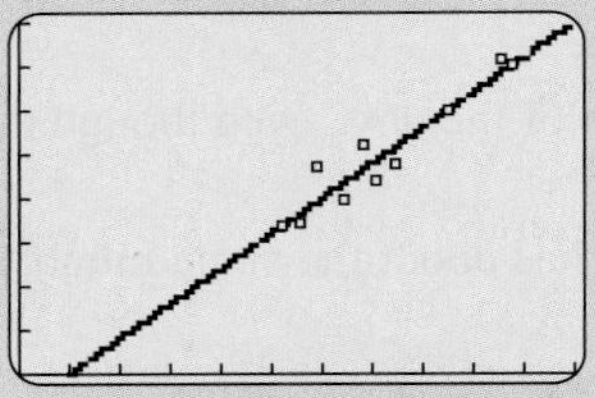

Points in Table 12.25 and the regression line
$y = 1.09x - 0.443$.

Solution

(a) Graph the given ordered pairs as shown in Figure 12.37. This scatter gram indicates a *positive* correlation between the high school and college GPAs. Are you surprised?

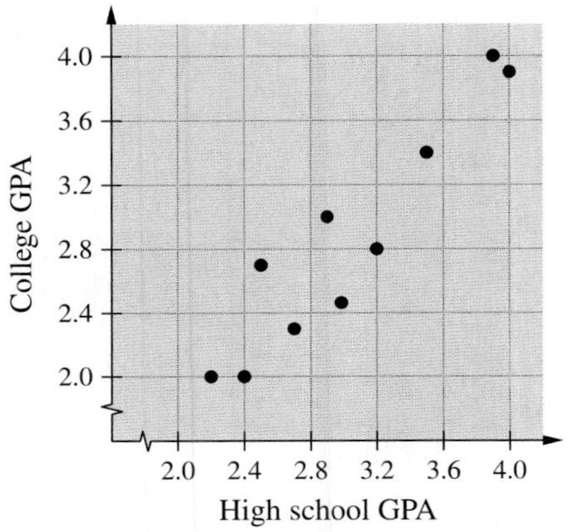

FIGURE 12.37

(b) To find the equation for the regression line, we follow equations (2) and (3) of Section 12.6 and use a TI-83.

$$m = \frac{n\Sigma(xy) - (\Sigma x)(\Sigma y)}{n(\Sigma x^2) - (\Sigma x)^2} \tag{2}$$

$$= \frac{10(90.42) - (30.3)(28.6)}{10(95.25) - (30.3)^2} \approx 1.09$$

$$b = \frac{\Sigma y - m(\Sigma x)}{n} \tag{3}$$

$$= \frac{28.6 - (1.09)(30.3)}{10} \approx -0.443$$

Thus, the regression formula is $y = 1.09x - 0.443$.

(c) When the high school GPA $x = 2.5$, the college GPA would be $y = 1.09\,(2.5) - 0.443 = 2.282$.

B Coefficient of Correlation

In Example 2 we found a **positive** correlation between high school and college GPAs and drew their regression line. How accurately does their regression line represent the data? The points in the calculator screen fit the line closely, so the predictions we make should be fairly accurate. If the points are widely scattered, the predictions are not likely to be accurate. The closer the *sample* data points are (like the ones in Table 12.25) to the *regression* line, the more likely the entire *population* of predicted points (x, y) forms a line. The better the fit, the more confident we are that our regression line is a "good" estimator of the entire population line. But can we quantify how good? One common measure of the "goodness" of the linear relationship in the sample is called the **sample coefficient of correlation,** denoted by r. This coefficient is obtained from the sample data as shown.

Coefficient of Correlation

The **coefficient of correlation** for n points $(x_1, y_1), (x_2, y_2), \ldots, (x_n, y_n)$ is

$$r = \frac{n\Sigma(xy) - (\Sigma x)(\Sigma y)}{\sqrt{n(\Sigma x^2) - (\Sigma x)^2}\sqrt{n(\Sigma y^2) - (\Sigma y)^2}} \tag{4}$$

The value of r is between -1 (a perfect **negative** correlation) and $+1$ (a perfect **positive** correlation). When r is close or near 0, there is *no linear* correlation. *Note:* The numerator for r is the same as that for m in equation (3). The denominator is also very similar to that for m.

Table 12.26

High School GPA	College GPA
2.2	2.0
2.4	2.0
2.5	2.7
2.7	2.3
2.9	3.0
3.0	2.5
3.2	2.8
3.5	3.4
3.9	4.0
4.0	3.9

Table 12.27

	Critical Values for r	
n	95%	99%
4	.950	.999
5	.878	.959
6	.811	.917
7	.754	.875
8	.707	.834
9	.666	.798
10	.632	.765
11	.602	.735
12	.576	.708
13	.553	.684
14	.532	.661
15	.514	.641
16	.497	.623
17	.482	.606
18	.468	.590
19	.456	.575
20	.444	.561

EXAMPLE 3 Finding the Coefficient of Correlation

Find the coefficient of correlation (r) for the data shown in Table 12.26.

Solution

Almost all the values in equation (4) were already computed in Example 2. Thus, $n = 10$, $\Sigma(xy) = 90.42$, $\Sigma x = 30.3$, $(\Sigma y) = 28.6$, $\Sigma x^2 = 95.25$, and $(\Sigma x)^2 = (30.3)^2$. The only missing value is $\Sigma y^2 = 86.44$.

Using the formula, or a calculator, we find $r = 0.94$ (to two decimal places). This value, which is "close" to 1, shows that the GPAs in high school and college are highly correlated.

Is there a way of quantifying *how* highly correlated our variables are? If r is $+1$, we have a **perfect positive** correlation. For $r = -1$, a **perfect negative** correlation. For other values of r we use Table 12.27, which contains a list of critical values that can be used to decide whether there is a *significant* correlation between two variables at the 95% or 99% confidence level. Use the table like this.

Interpreting *r*

1. Find r for n points of data.
2. Go to line n in Table 12.27.
3. If the absolute value of r is greater than the number in the column labeled 95% on line n, we can be 95% confident that there is a *significant* linear correlation between the variables.*
4. If the absolute value of r is greater than the number in the column labeled 99% on line n, we can be 99% confident that there is a *significant* linear correlation between the variables.

*For the definition of absolute value, see page 284 in Section 6.3A.

Remember, **regression** gives the equation of a line that quantifies the relationship between two variables. The **correlation coefficient** measures the direction and strength of the linear relationship.

Now let us go back to Example 3 and interpret r by following these steps.

1. We found $r = 0.94$ with $n = 10$.
2. See the line corresponding to $n = 10$ in Table 12.27.
3. The absolute value of $r = |0.94| = 0.94$, which exceeds the 0.765 in line 10 and column 99%. Thus, we can be 99% confident that there is a *significant* correlation between the variables.

EXAMPLE 4 Finding the Correlation Coefficient

Use the data from Section 12.6, Example 4 (see Table 12.28 on page 750), to find r and then interpret the results.

Solution

Referring to the data in the table, $n = 7$, $\Sigma x = 201$, $\Sigma y = 92$, $\Sigma x^2 = 6487$, and $\Sigma xy = 2828$. The only missing value is $\Sigma y^2 = 1272$.

Equation (4) states

$$r = \frac{n\Sigma(xy) - (\Sigma x)(\Sigma y)}{\sqrt{n(\Sigma x^2) - (\Sigma x)^2}\sqrt{n(\Sigma y^2) - (\Sigma y)^2}}$$

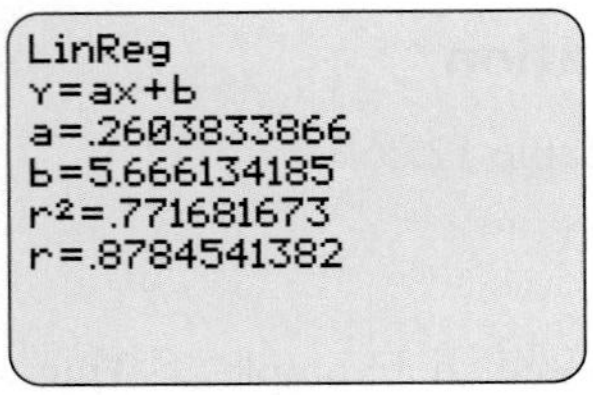

Note: If r^2 and r are not showing, press 2ND 0 and ▼ until you get to Diagnostic On; then press ENTER. Repeat the procesure and this time you will see r^2 and r.

Table 12.28

Women	x	y	x^2	xy
1	16	12	256	192
2	18	11	324	198
3	23	10	529	230
4	27	11	729	297
5	33	13	1089	429
6	38	16	1444	608
7	46	19	2116	874
Total	**201**	**92**	**6487**	**2828**

So for the data of Example 4,

$$r = \frac{7(2828) - (201)(92)}{\sqrt{7(6487) - (201)^2}\sqrt{7(1272) - (92)^2}}$$

$$\approx 0.88$$

(You can calculate this with your grapher. See the grapher screen in the margin.) To interpret the value $r = 0.88$, go to Table 12.27.

1. $n = 7, r = 0.88$
2. Go to the line labeled 7.
3. $|0.88| = 0.88$ is larger than 0.875 (barely!), so we can be 99% confident that there is a *significant* correlation between the age of a smoking pregnant woman and low birth weight for the baby.

What would the relationship be if the mother did not smoke? Figure 12.38 shows that relationship. In order to simplify computations, round to the nearest percent.

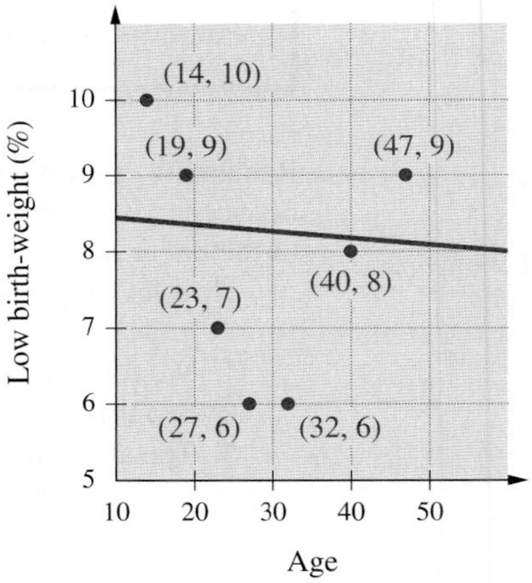

Source: www.uvm.edu/~dhowell/gradstat/psych340/Lectures/CorrelReg/correl1.html.

FIGURE 12.38

EXAMPLE 5 Finding the Equation for a Regression Line

Use the data in Figure 12.38 to

(a) find the equation for the regression line.

(b) find the coefficient of correlation r.

(c) provide an interpretation for the value r found in part (b).

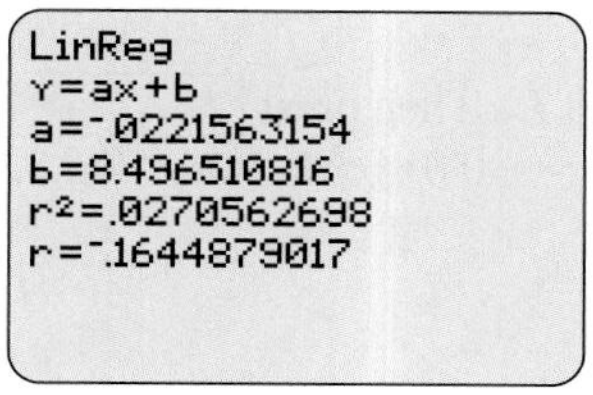

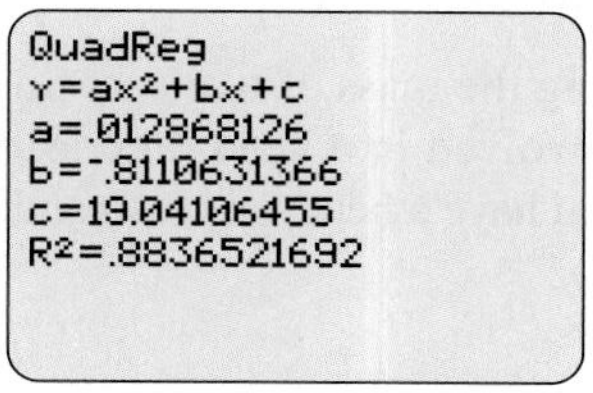

The quadratic regression.

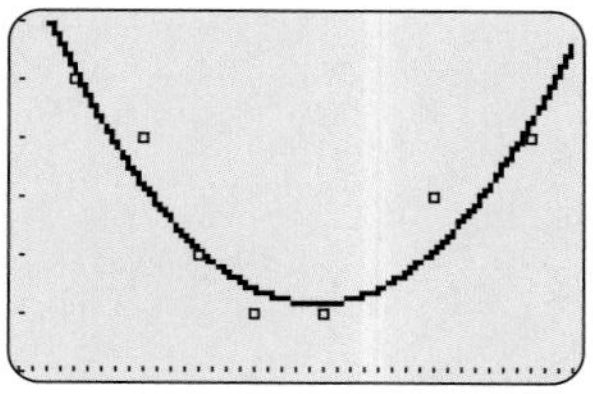

$y = 0.013x^2 - 0.811x + 19.04$

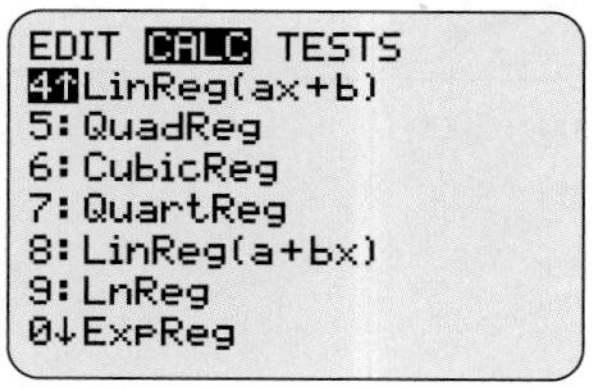

Solution

Enter the ages 14, 19, 23, 27, 32, 40, and 47 under L_1 and the corresponding percent of low birth weight 10, 9, 7, 6, 6, 8, and 9 under L_2. Now press STAT ▶ 4 ENTER. (See the grapher screen in the margin.)

(a) The regression line is $y = -0.022x + 8.5$.

(b) $r = -0.16$

(c) There is a negative correlation between low birth weight and age for nonsmoking mothers (as age increases, the percent of low-birth-weight babies decreases). However, Table 12.27 shows that for $n = 7$, r is less (not more) than the numbers under 95% and 99%, so we conclude that there is no *significant* linear correlation between the variables. You would not expect that the percent of low-birth-weight babies would decrease as the mother's age increases!

If we look at the graph of the data for Example 5, you may realize that the quantities are not linearly related. As a matter of fact, the data are closer to a **quadratic** model (parabola). Can we get a regression curve for a parabola? With a TI-83, press STAT ▶ 5 ENTER and you will get the ordered pairs relating age and percent of low-birth-weight babies, as well as the parabola $y = 0.013x^2 - 0.811x + 19.04$ graphed. A TI-83 grapher can compute best-fit curves of the type shown. (Just press STAT ▶ and you will see them!)

General Forms of Equations

Type of Curve	*Equation*
Linear	$y = ax + b$
Quadratic	$y = ax^2 + bx + c$
Cubic	$y = ax^3 + bx^2 + cx + d$
Quartic	$y = ax^4 + bx^3 + cx^2 + dx + e$
Linear	$y = a + bx$
Logarithmic	$y = a + b \ln x$
Exponential	$y = a \cdot b^x$
Power	$y = a \cdot x^b$

EXAMPLE 6 Creating and Interpreting Scattergrams

Table 12.29 shows the relationship between the speed of a car and its gas mileage (mpg).

(a) Make a scattergram for the data.

(b) Show that the linear correlation between speed and gas mileage is $r = 0$.

Table 12.29

Speed	20	30	40	50	60
Mpg	24	28	30	28	24

(c) From the shape of the scattergram, what type of curve will give a best-fit regression curve?

(d) Find the equation of the curve.

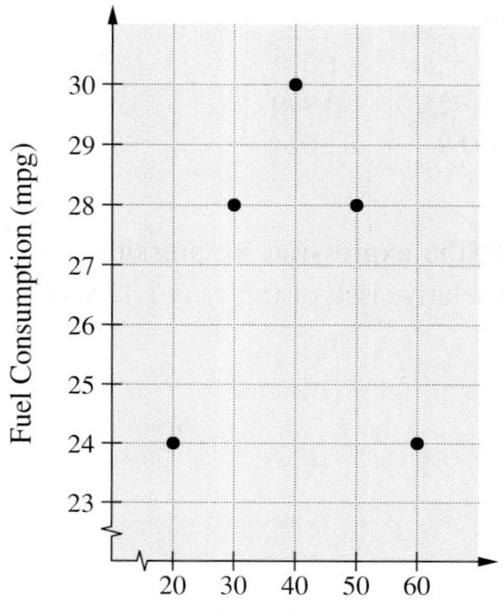

FIGURE 12.39

Solution

(a) The scattergram is shown in Figure 12.39.

(b) $$r = \frac{n\Sigma(xy) - (\Sigma x)(\Sigma y)}{\sqrt{n(\Sigma x^2) - (\Sigma x)^2}\sqrt{n(\Sigma y^2) - (\Sigma y)^2}}$$

$$= \frac{5(5360) - 200(134)}{\sqrt{n(\Sigma x^2) - (\Sigma x)^2}\sqrt{n(\Sigma y^2) - (\Sigma y)^2}} = 0$$

(c) A parabola

(d) Using a TI-83, enter the speeds as list L_1 and the mpgs as list L_2. Then press STAT ▶ 5 ENTER and you will get the equation of the parabola $y = -0.014x^2 + 1.14x + 6.8$.

The size or the mass of a vehicle has the largest effect on the risk of injuries to those traveling in it. The relative risk of driver injury or fatality when cars of similar mass crash head-on declines as the mass of the cars increases (see Tables 12.30 and 12.31). The five data sets were collected from real crashes on U.S. and German roads. (Sources: Evans and Wasielewski, 1987 and Ernst et al., 1993.)

Table 12.30

Mass	Risk of Injury
700	2.5
800	2.1
900	2.0
1100	1.7
1200	1.5
1400	1.3
1600	1.0

EXAMPLE 7 Using a Grapher to Find a Curve of Best Fit

Use a grapher to find a reasonable curve to fit the data relating the mass of five cars (in kilograms) and the relative risk of injury or fatality when involved in a head-on crash (Figure 12.40). Then predict the risk of injury or fatality if you have a head-on crash and your car weighs 1500 kg.

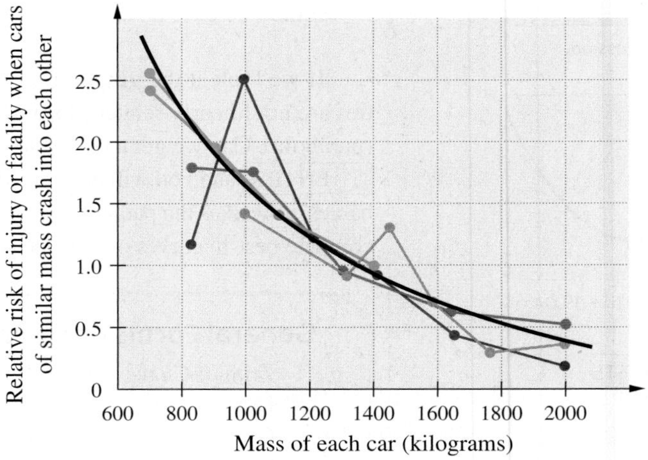

Source: *American Scientist* 90: 248.

FIGURE 12.40

Solution

Start by entering the mass as list L_1 and the risk of injury as list L_2. From the graph, the relationship is not linear. We try three possibilities: logarithmic, exponential, and power. The results are shown in the margin. All curves give a good correlation (close to -1), but the best fit is the exponential curve ($r = -0.994$). Try it! In particular, the best exponential curve is given by $y = 4.725 \cdot (0.999)^x$.

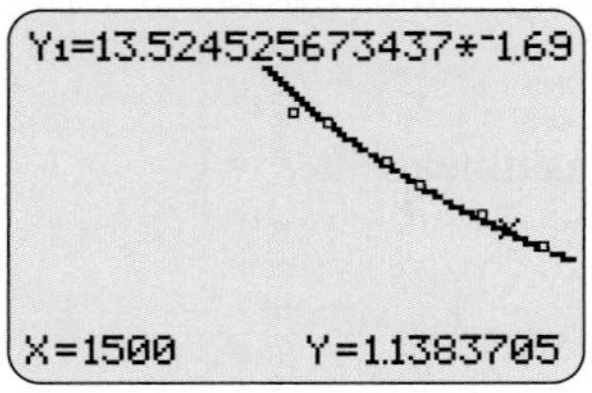

Table 12.31

Type of Curve	r	a	b
Logarithmic	−0.994	13.525	−1.694
Exponential	−0.994	4.725	0.999
Power	−0.986	2080.69	−1.024

When your car weighs $x = 1500$ kg, we evaluate the expression by pressing 2nd CALC 1, then entering 1500 and ENTER. Your relative risk of injury is 1.138. (See the graph in the margin.)

12.7 EXERCISES

A Correlation

In problems 1–4, determine if the line is a good representative of the data. Explain why or why not.

1. 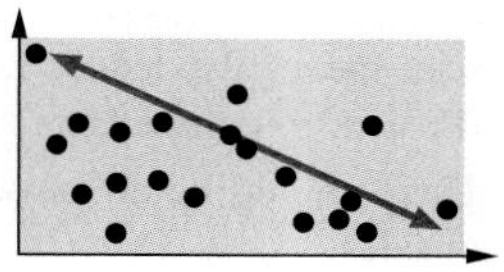

2. 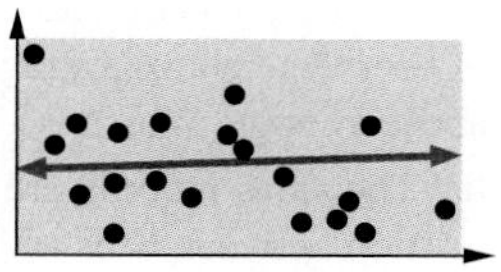

3. 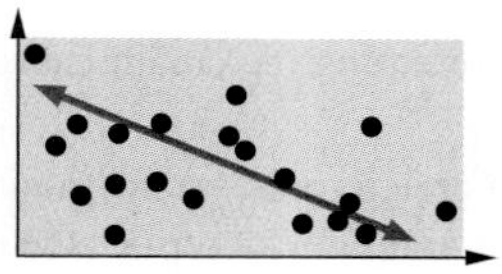

4. 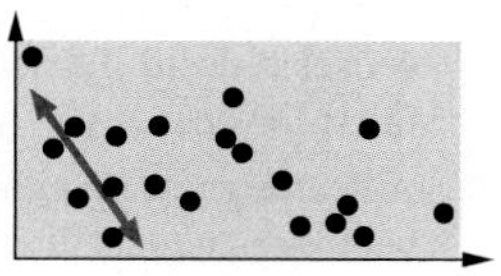

In problems 5–12, state which kind of correlation you would expect in a scattergram for the indicated ordered pairs.

5. (Length of person's leg, person's height)
6. (Outdoor temperature, cost of air conditioning a house)
7. (Student's weight, student's score on mathematics test)
8. (Person's salary, cost of person's home)
9. (Altitude, atmospheric pressure)
10. (Weight of auto, miles per gallon of fuel)
11. (Student's score on college aptitude test, student's GPA)
12. (Speed of auto, miles per gallon)

In problems 13–20, select the phrase that correctly completes the sentence.

13. The value of the linear correlation coefficient r is always
    - a. close to 0.
    - b. close to 1.
    - c. between -1 and 1, inclusive.
    - d. positive.
14. The linear correlation coefficient r measures
    - a. whether a cause-and-effect relationship exists between two variables.
    - b. whether a scattergram shows an interesting pattern.
    - c. whether two variables are related.
    - d. the direction and strength of the linear relationship.
15. A linear regression line $y = 10 + 0.9x$ is computed to predict the final exam score y on the basis of the first score x on the first test. Suppose Maria scores a 90 on the first test. What would be the predicted value of her score on the final exam?
    - a. 81
    - b. 89
    - c. 91
    - d. Cannot be determined
16. The scattergram shows the calories and sodium content of several brands of meat hot dogs.

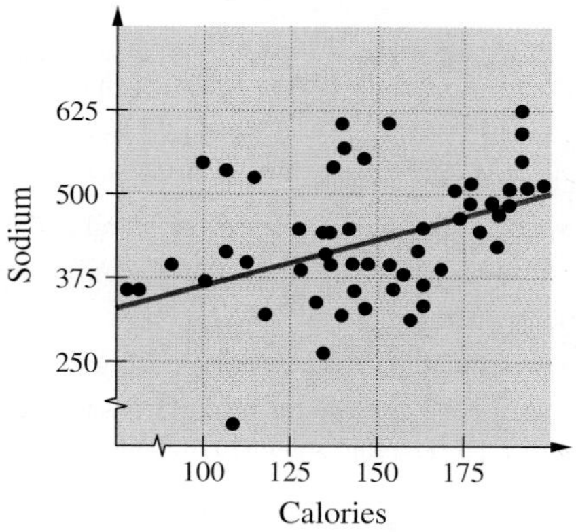

On the basis of the least-squares regression line shown, a hot dog containing 100 calories would have a sodium content of about
    - a. 70.
    - b. 350.
    - c. 400.
    - d. 600.
17. The scattergram shows the amount of carbon monoxide and nitrogen oxide emitted in the exhaust of cars per mile driven.

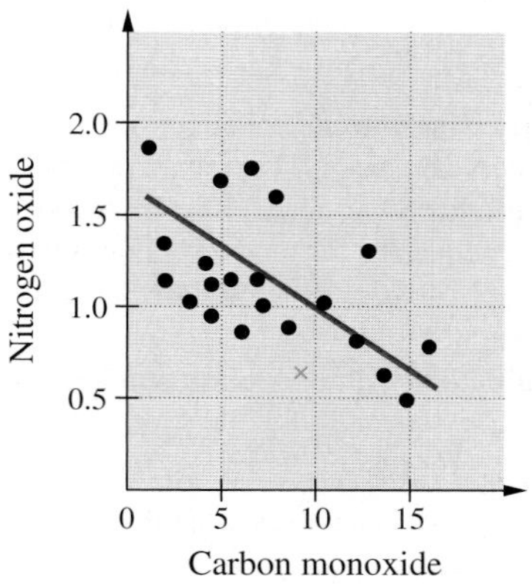

On the basis of the scattergram, the least-squares line would predict that a car emitting 10 g of carbon monoxide per mile driven would emit how many grams of nitrogen oxide per mile driven?
    - a. 1.1
    - b. 2.2
    - c. 10
    - d. 1.4

18.

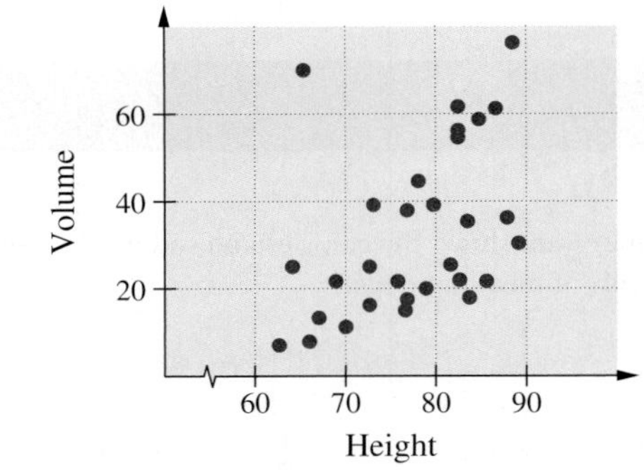

The scattergram indicates

a. a positive association between height and volume.

b. a negative association between height and volume.

c. neither (**a**) nor (**b**).

d. no association between height and volume.

19. A plausible value r for the correlation between vehicle weight and miles per gallon (mpg) shown in the following scattergram is

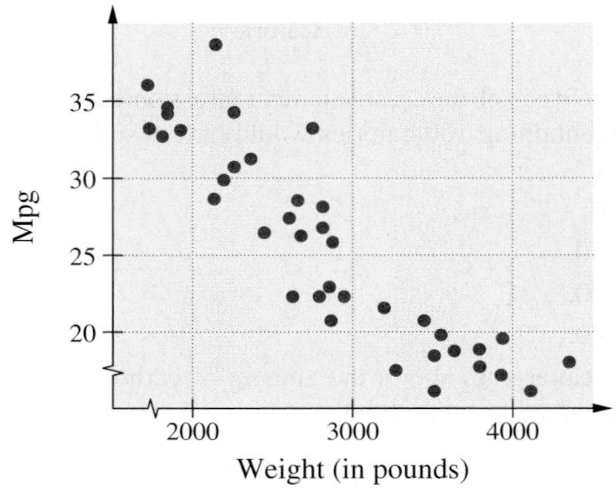

a. -1.0. b. $+0.8$. c. -0.9. d. 1.0.

20. A researcher wishes to determine whether the rate of water flow y (in liters per second) over an experimental soil bed can be used to predict the amount of soil x washed away (in kilograms). If the equation for the regression line is

$y = 1.3x + 0.4$

the correlation between amount of eroded soil and flow rate would be

a. $\frac{1}{1.3}$. b. 1.3.

c. positive, but we cannot say what the exact value would be.

d. either positive or negative. It is impossible to say anything about the correlation from the information given.

21. Do people of similar heights tend to date each other? A student measures herself, her roommate, and three women in adjoining dorm rooms. She then measures the height of their dates. Here are the results.

Women	65	63	65	69	64
Men	71	67	69	73	68

Which statement is true?

a. The correlation makes no sense because there is always a correlation between genders.

b. There is a strong positive correlation between the heights of men and women, since the women are always smaller than the men they date.

c. There is a positive correlation between the heights of men and women on a date.

d. There is a strong positive correlation between the heights of men and women on a date, since the men are always taller than the women they date.

22. Is there a positive correlation between beer sales and ice cream sales? The owner of a deli store noticed that in seasons when sales of beer were above average, sales of ice cream also tended to be above average. Which is a valid conclusion from these facts?

a. The sales records are wrong. There should be no association between beer and ice cream sales.

b. For a significant proportion of customers, drinking beer causes a desire for ice cream or eating ice cream causes a thirst for beer.

c. A scattergram of monthly ice cream sales versus monthly beer sales would show that a straight line describes the pattern in the graph, but it would have to be a horizontal line.

d. None of the above.

B Coefficient of Correlation

In problems 23–30,

a. make a scattergram for the data.

b. find the equation of the regression line.

c. find r, the coefficient of correlation.

d. interpret the results for r (see Table 12.27 on page 749).

23.

x	2	4	7	3	1	5
y	1	3	8	4	2	2
x	8	10	6	9		
y	6	7	6	4		

24.

x	9	10	8	8	6	4
y	4	2	3	6	4	8
x	5	5	3	2		
y	7	5	8	10		

25. The following table gives the weights and the highway miles per gallon for eight automobiles:

Weight (lb)	2800	1900	2000
Miles per gallon	19	34	28
Weight (lb)	3300	3100	2900
Miles per gallon	19	24	23
Weight (lb)	400	2600	
Miles per gallon	16	24	

26. The following table gives the scores of 10 students on an English exam and their corresponding scores on an economics exam:

English	50	95	55	20
Economics	75	95	70	35
English	85	75	45	20
Economics	70	80	40	15
English	80	90		
Economics	60	90		

e. What would the predicted economics score be for a student with a 70 in English?

27. Does Education pay? For a complete report see http://trends.collegeboard.org.

In the meantime here are some recent statistics on years of schooling successfully completed and average annual salaries (in thousands of dollars) for men over 25:

Years of schooling	8	12
Average salary	$16.800	$23.300
Years of schooling	15	16
Average salary	$25.800	$33.900

e. A man (over 25) has 10 years of schooling. What is his predicted salary?

28. The following table gives the gain in reading speed for students in a speed-reading program:

Weeks in program	2	3	3
Speed gain (words per minute)	40	60	80
Weeks in program	4	5	6
Speed gain (words per minute)	100	110	150
Weeks in program	8	9	
Speed gain (words per minute)	190	220	

e. If a student spent 7 weeks in the program, what is the expected gain in reading speed?

29. A student was curious about the effect of antifreeze on the freezing point of a water–antifreeze mixture. He went to the chemistry lab, where he made the measurements in the following table:

Percent antifreeze (by volume)	10	20	30
Freezing point (degrees C)	−4	−10	−20
Percent antifreeze (by volume)	40	50	
Freezing point (degrees C)	−24	−36	

e. If the percent of antifreeze by volume is 25%, what is the freezing point of the mixture?

30. The following table gives the heights of students and their scores on an English test.

Height (in.)	62	67	70	64
Test score	85	60	75	70
Height (in.)	72	68	65	61
Test score	95	35	60	80
Height (in.)	73	67		
Test score	45	100		

e. What would the score be for a 66-in. student?

31. The following power chart shows the number of power outages experienced by the Central Power Company during the 12 weeks starting June 1.

a. During which week was there no outage?

b. Which week had the most outages?

c. When did the decline in the number of outages seem to start?

d. Is any kind of correlation shown by the chart?

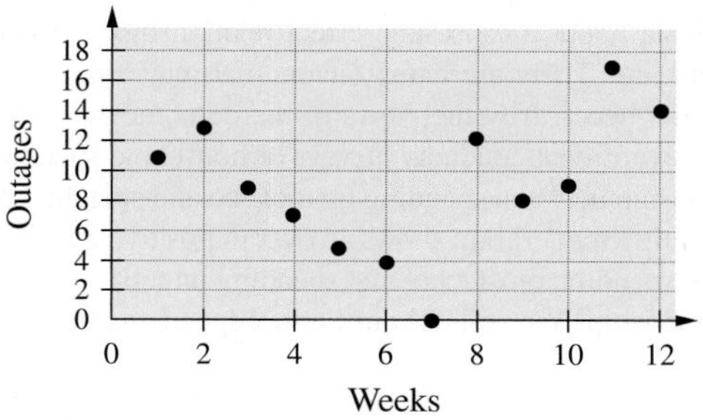

32. The following chart shows the hours studied by 10 students and their grades on an examination.

a. Which kind of correlation (if any) is shown?

b. If a student studied for 12 hours, about what grade would you expect her to make?

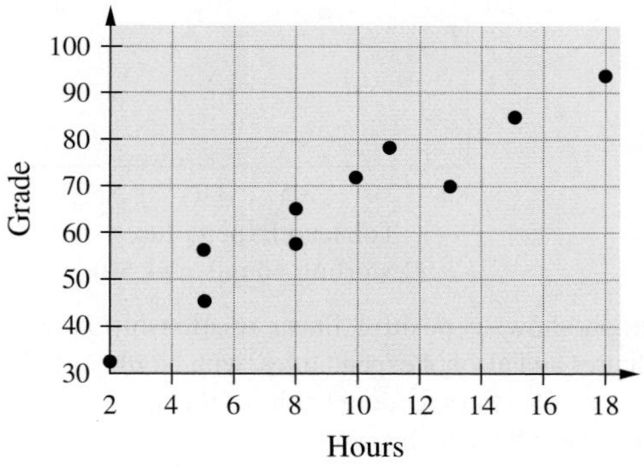

IN OTHER WORDS

33. During the past 10 years there has been a positive correlation between the number of cars with air bags sold in Florida and the number of traffic accidents.

a. Do air bags cause traffic accidents?

b. What other factors may cause traffic accidents and the number of cars with air bags to increase together?

34. Describe what happens to the related items of data if the corresponding scattergram shows

a. a positive correlation.

b. a negative correlation.

USING YOUR KNOWLEDGE

You should not assume that there is any cause-and-effect relationship between two variables simply because the correlation is high.

© Dario Sabljak/Shutterstock.com

Is there a correlation between the number of storks and the number of babies born?

A classic example of a high positive correlation is that of the number of storks found in English villages and the number of babies born in these villages. Do you think there is a cause-and-effect relationship here? What about a cause-and-effect relationship between smoking and drinking? There are many factors that may *influence* outcomes, but are not necessarily the *cause* of the outcomes. For example, the British government conducts surveys of household spending. Is there a relationship between spending on tobacco and spending on alcohol? The resulting scattergram shows an overall positive linear relationship between spending on alcohol and spending on tobacco. How strong is the relationship? We will use our knowledge to answer the question.

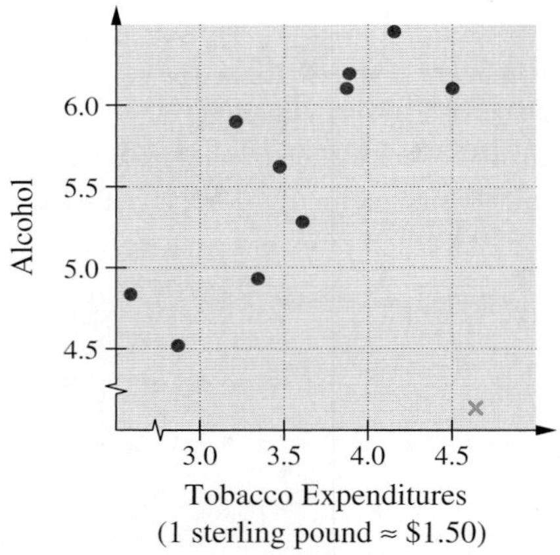

This graph shows a positive linear relationship between tobacco expenditures and alcohol expenditures, with Northern Ireland (blue *x*) as an *outlier.* Can the spending habits of the inhabitants of Northern Ireland alone influence the results?

Region	Alcohol	Tobacco
North	6.47	4.03
Yorkshire	6.13	3.76
Northeast	6.19	3.77
East Midlands	4.89	3.34
West Midlands	5.63	3.47
East Anglia	4.52	2.92
Southeast	5.89	3.20
Southwest	4.79	2.71
Wales	5.27	3.53
Scotland	6.08	4.51
N. Ireland	4.02	4.56

35. Use the table above and a grapher to find the coefficients of correlation r for the 11 regions of Great Britain and interpret the results (use Table 12.27 on page 749).

36. Do the same as in problem 35, but delete Northern Ireland from the sample.

37. Notice the difference between the coefficient of correlation *r* obtained in problems 35 and 36. Do the different values of *r* mean that Ireland caused the correlation?

38. As we have mentioned, the point corresponding to Northern Ireland and shown with a blue *x* in the graph is called an **outlier.** When do you think you can ignore this point in the calculations?

COLLABORATIVE LEARNING

Do you know the difference between ***correlation*** *and* ***causation?*** *Let us examine some examples. Divide the class into* ***four*** *groups.*

Find how many calories **c** each member of group *one* consumes each day and their weight **w** in pounds. Make a graph of the ordered pairs **(c, w)**

Find the weight **w** in pounds of each member of group *two* and how many calories **c** they consume each day. Make a graph of the ordered pairs **(w, c)**

1. Is there a ***correlation*** between food consumption in calories and weight in pounds.
2. Is there a ***correlation*** between weight in pounds and food consumption in calories.

What about ***causation?*** Here are two possibilities.

❶ F(food consumption) could ***cause*** more W(weight) or ❷ the other way around

Do you think food consumption F ***causes*** weight gain **W** or does weight gain **W** ***causes*** F?

But there is a third possibility ❸. There could be a hidden factor, ***causing*** both more weight (**W**) **and** more food consumption (F). Blame it all on your height H! (the person's height). Taller people usually weigh more **and** eat more.

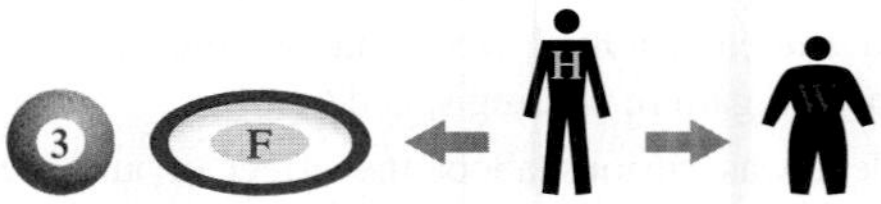

Make a graph of the ordered pairs **(h, c)** of each member of group *three.*

What about group *four?* Make a graph of the ordered pairs **(h, w)** of the members of group *four.*

3. Do you think that your height H ***causes*** you to eat more F or to weigh more **W**?

What if there isn't an obvious cause? You could run an experiment: use a control group F and measure how **W** changes. Of course, if the height H of the people in the group also varies, the cause of the weight is hard to determine.

CHAPTER 12 Summary

SECTION	ITEM	MEANING	EXAMPLE
12.1	Statistics	The science of collecting, organizing, and summarizing data so that valid conclusions can be drawn from them	
12.1 A	Population	The entire collection of elements to be studied	In a shipment of 1000 shoes, the set of 1000 shoes is the population.
	Random sample	A subset of a population	If the 1000 shoes are numbered and 10 are chosen at random, the random sample consists of the 10 shoes chosen.
12.1B	Frequency distribution	A way of organizing a list of numbers	
	Frequency	Number of times an entry occurs	In the set of numbers {1, 4, 4, 7} the number 4 appears with frequency 2.
12.1C	Histogram	A special type of graph consisting of vertical bars with no space between the bars	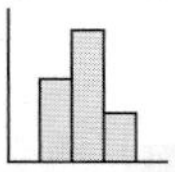
12.1D	Frequency polygon	A line graph connecting the midpoints of the tops of the bars in a histogram	
12.2	Mean, $\bar{x}$	The sum of the scores divided by the number of scores	The mean of 3, 7, and 8 is 6.
	Mode	The number that occurs most often	The mode of 1, 2, 2, and 3 is 2.
	Median	If the numbers are arranged in order of magnitude for an odd number of scores, the median is the middle number; for an even number of scores, the median is the average of the two middle numbers.	Median ↓ 1 3 ⑧ 15 19 1 2 5 9 11 18 $\frac{5+9}{2} = 7$ ← Median
12.3	Range	The difference between the greatest and the least numbers in a set	The range of 2, 8, and 19 is 17.
	Standard deviation, s	$\sqrt{\dfrac{(x_1-\bar{x})^2+\cdots+(x_n-\bar{x})^2}{n-1}}$, where $\bar{x}$ is the mean and n is the number of items	
12.5B	z-score	$z = \dfrac{x-\mu}{\sigma}$, where x is a score, μ is the mean, and σ is the standard deviation of the population	
12.6	Regression (best-fit) line	The best-fit line associated with the n points $(x_1, y_1), (x_2, y_2), \ldots, (x_n, y_n)$ has the form $y = mx + b$ where $m = \dfrac{n\Sigma(xy) - (\Sigma x)(\Sigma y)}{n(\Sigma x^2) - (\Sigma x)^2}$ and $b = \dfrac{(\Sigma x^2)(\Sigma y) - (\Sigma x)(\Sigma xy)}{n(\Sigma x^2) - (\Sigma x)^2} = \dfrac{\Sigma y - m(\Sigma x)}{n}$	The regression line for the points (1, 3), (2, 5), and (3, 7) is $y = 2x + 1$, where $m = 2$ and $b = 1$.

continued

CHAPTER 12 Summary – *continued*

SECTION	ITEM	MEANING	EXAMPLE
12.7A	Correlation	A measure of the direction and strength of a straight-line relationship between two variables	A + 1.0 is a perfect positive correlation, and a −1.0 is a perfect negative correlation.
12.7B	Coefficient of correlation	The coefficient of correlation for n points $(x_1, y_1), (x_2, y_2), \ldots, (x_n, y_n)$ is $r = \dfrac{n\Sigma(xy) - (\Sigma x)(\Sigma y)}{\sqrt{n(\Sigma x^2) - (\Sigma x)^2}\sqrt{n(\Sigma y^2) - (\Sigma y)}}$	The coefficient of correlation for the points (1, 3), (2, 5), and (3, 7) is 1.

CHAPTER 12 Practice Test

1. A college president wants to find out which courses are popular with students. The president decides to conduct a survey of a sample of 30 students from the English department. Will these 30 students correspond to a simple random sample of the whole student body? Explain your answer.

The following scores were made on a scholastic aptitude test by a group of 25 high school seniors:

85	65	89	83	98
67	88	87	88	90
95	77	91	73	88
99	67	91	72	86
79	83	61	70	75

Use these data for problems 2 and 3.

2. Group the scores into intervals of $60 < s \le 65$, $65 < s \le 70$, $70 < s \le 75$, and so on. Then make a frequency distribution with this grouping.

3. **a.** Make a histogram for the frequency distribution in problem 2.
   b. Make a frequency polygon for the distribution in problem 2.

4. During a certain week, the following maximum temperatures (in degrees Fahrenheit) were recorded in a large eastern city: 78, 82, 82, 71, 69, 73, and 70.
   a. Find the mean of these temperatures.
   b. Find the mode of the temperature readings.
   c. Find the median high temperature for the week.

5. **a.** Find the range of temperatures in problem 4.
   b. Find, to two decimal places, the standard deviation of the temperatures in problem 4.

6. A fair coin is tossed 256 times. If this experiment is repeated many times, the numbers of heads will form an approximately normal distribution, with a mean of 128 and a standard deviation of 8.
   a. Within what limits can we be almost 100% confident that the total number of heads in 256 tosses will lie?
   b. What is the probability that heads will occur fewer than 112 times?

CHAPTER 12 Practice Test

7. A normal distribution consists of 1000 scores, with a mean of 100 and a standard deviation of 20.
   a. About how many of the scores are above 140?
   b. About how many scores are below 80?
   c. About how many scores are between 60 and 80?

8. A testing program shows that the breaking points of fishing lines made from a certain plastic fiber are normally distributed, with a mean of 10 lb and a standard deviation of 1 lb.
   a. What is the probability that one of these lines selected at random has a breaking point of more than 10 lb?
   b. What is the probability that one of these lines selected at random has a breaking point of less than 8 lb?

9. On a multiple choice test taken by 1000 students, the scores were normally distributed, with a mean of 50 and a standard deviation of 5. Find the z-score corresponding to a score of
   a. 58. b. 62.

10. Agnes scored 88 on a French test and 90 on a psychology test. The mean score in the French test was 76, with a standard deviation of 18, and the mean score in the psychology test was 80, with a standard deviation of 16. If the scores were normally distributed, which of Agnes's scores was the better score?

11. With the data in problem 9, find the probability that a randomly selected student will have a score between 50 and 62. (Use Table II in the back of the book.)

12. The following are the amounts (to the nearest billion) the federal government has spent on education for selected years:

1984	1988	1989	1990
17	21	24	26

   a. Make a line graph for this information.
   b. Use your graph to estimate how much was spent on education in 1986.

13. Here is a list of five of the most active stocks on the New York Stock Exchange in a recent year. Make a bar graph of the yield rates of these stocks.

Stock	Price ($)	Dividend ($)	Yield Rate (%)
Fed DS	60.25	1.48	2.5
Ford M	44.75	2.00	4.5
Noes Ut	20.75	1.76	8.5
Exxon	42.75	2.00	4.7
Gen El	43.25	1.40	3.2

14. In a recent poll, the features that patrons liked in a restaurant were

Low-calorie entrees	67%	All-you-can-eat specials	27%
Varied portion sizes	47%	Self-service soup bar	35%
Cholesterol-free entrees	52%		

Use horizontal bars and make a bar graph of this information.

continued

CHAPTER 12 Practice Test – *continued*

15. The bar graph in the figure shows the 2000 sales and the projected 2004 sales of the Wesellum Corporation. Read the graph, and estimate the percentage increase that was projected for 2004 over 2000.

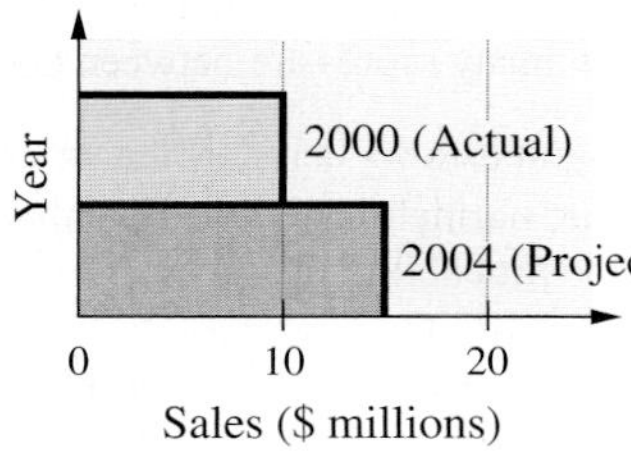

16. The typical family budget is as follows:

Monthly Family Budget	
Savings	\$ 200
Housing	600
Clothing	300
Food	800
Other	100
Total	\$2000

Make a circle graph for these data.

17. Graph the five points given in the following table. Draw the best line you can "between" these points, and estimate the value of y for $x = 6$.

x	1	2	3	4	5
y	10.2	7.6	5.8	4.4	2.0

18. Find the equation for the best-fit line for the points you have just graphed and estimate the value of y for $x = 6$.

19. The testing department of Circle Tire Company checks a random sample of 150 of a certain type of tire that the company makes and finds a defective tread on 3 of these tires. In a batch of 10,000 of these tires, how many are expected to have defective treads?

20. In a large county, 50,000 high school students took a reading comprehension test, and 4000 of these students got a rating of excellent. In a random sample of 100 of these students, how many should be expected to have gotten an excellent rating on this test?

21. Which of the graphs shows the best representation for the data and why?

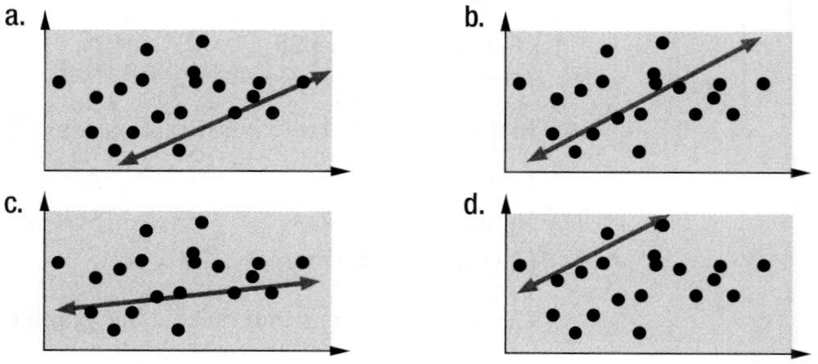

CHAPTER 12 Practice Test

22. Which kind of correlation would you expect for the indicated ordered pairs?
a. (Value of a family's home, family's annual income)
b. (Number of hours of training, number of minutes in which runner can do the mile run)
c. (Person's shoe size, person's salary)
d. (Number of children getting polio immunization, number of children contracting polio)

23. The coefficient of correlation r for the regression line shown is about

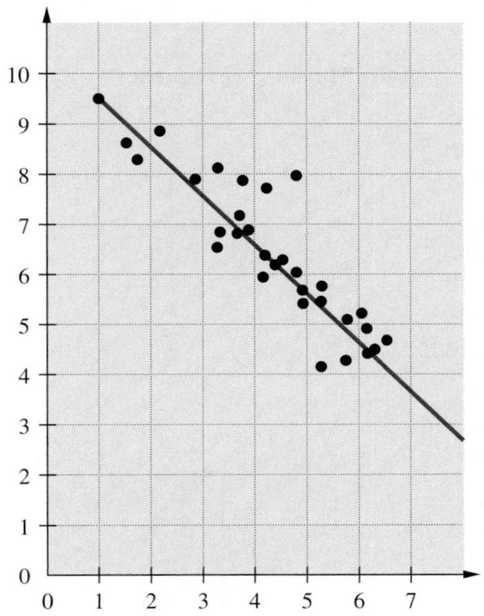

a. $+0.94$. **b.** 94. **c.** -0.94. **d.** -94.

24. Business intelligence software is one of the fastest-growing segments in the software market. If x represents the year and y the product sales (in billions of dollars), find the line of best fit (regression line) for the data.

Year	x	y
2002	2	4
2003	3	4.2
2004	4	5
2005	5	5.8

25. What is the coefficient of correlation r to the data in problem 24 and what does it represent? (Use this table.)

n	95%	99%
4	.950	.999
5	.878	.959
6	.811	.917
7	.754	.875

ANSWERS TO PRACTICE TEST

<table>
<tr><th colspan="2">CHAPTER 12</th><th colspan="3">What to Review *If You Missed It*</th></tr>
<tr><th>QUESTION</th><th>ANSWER</th><th>SECTION</th><th>EXAMPLE(S)</th><th>PAGE(S)</th></tr>
<tr><td>1</td><td>No. Not every member of the student body had the same chance of being chosen (only the ones in the English department).</td><td>12.1</td><td>Definition of a simple random sample</td><td>673</td></tr>
<tr><td>2</td><td><table><tr><th>Score</th><th>Tally Marks</th><th>Frequency</th></tr><tr><td>$60 < s \le 65$</td><td>||</td><td>2</td></tr><tr><td>$65 < s \le 70$</td><td>|||</td><td>3</td></tr><tr><td>$70 < s \le 75$</td><td>|||</td><td>3</td></tr><tr><td>$75 < s \le 80$</td><td>||</td><td>2</td></tr><tr><td>$80 < s \le 85$</td><td>|||</td><td>3</td></tr><tr><td>$85 < s \le 90$</td><td>𝍸 ||</td><td>7</td></tr><tr><td>$90 < s \le 95$</td><td>|||</td><td>3</td></tr><tr><td>$95 < s \le 100$</td><td>||</td><td>2</td></tr></table></td><td>12.1</td><td>2(a)</td><td>676</td></tr>
<tr><td>3</td><td>a. –b. 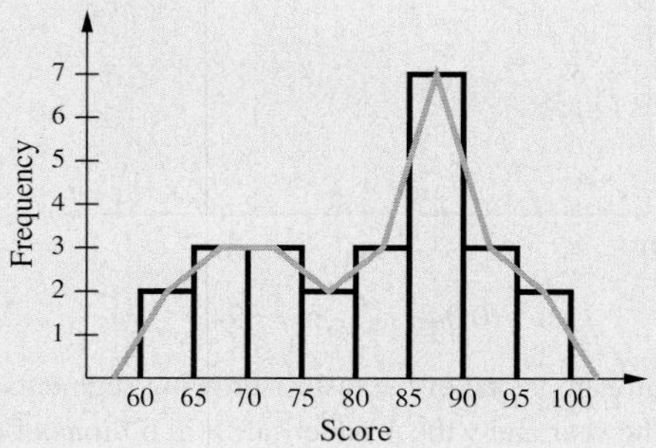</td><td>12.1</td><td>2(d), (e); 3</td><td>676, 678–679</td></tr>
<tr><td>4</td><td>a. 75°F b. 82°F c. 73°F</td><td>12.2</td><td>1–5</td><td>689–692</td></tr>
<tr><td>5</td><td>a. 13°F b. 5.60°F</td><td>12.3</td><td>1–3</td><td>702–704</td></tr>
<tr><td>6</td><td>a. 104–152 b. 0.025</td><td>12.4</td><td>1</td><td>708–709</td></tr>
<tr><td>7</td><td>a. 25 b. 160 c. 135</td><td>12.4</td><td>2</td><td>710</td></tr>
<tr><td>8</td><td>a. 0.5 b. 0.025</td><td>12.4</td><td>3</td><td>710</td></tr>
<tr><td>9</td><td>a. 1.6 b. 2.4</td><td>12.4</td><td>4</td><td>711</td></tr>
<tr><td>10</td><td>The score in French was the better score.</td><td>12.4</td><td>4</td><td>711</td></tr>
<tr><td>11</td><td>0.492</td><td>12.4</td><td>5</td><td>712</td></tr>
<tr><td>12</td><td>a. 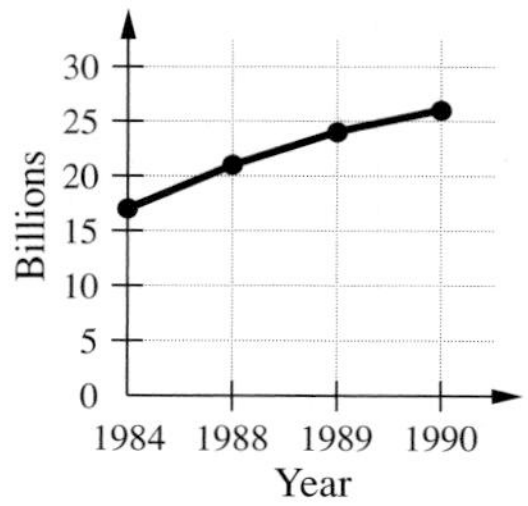 b. About $19 billion</td><td>12.5</td><td>1, 2</td><td>720–721</td></tr>
</table>

ANSWERS TO PRACTICE TEST

CHAPTER 12		What to Review *If You Missed It*		
QUESTION	**ANSWER**	**SECTION**	**EXAMPLE(S)**	**PAGE(S)**
13	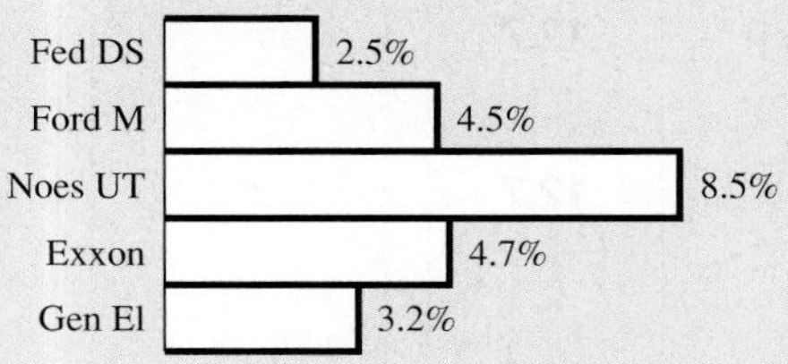	**12.5**	**3, 4**	**722–723**
14	Features that Patrons Liked 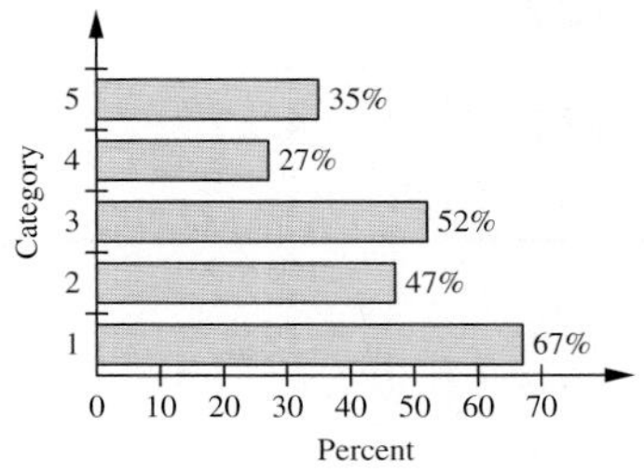 **1** Low-calorie entrees **2** Varied portion sizes **3** Cholesterol-free entrees **4** All-you-can-eat specials **5** Self-service soup bar	**12.5**	**3, 4**	**722–723**
15	About 50%	**12.5**	**3, 4**	**722–723**
16	Typical Family Budget 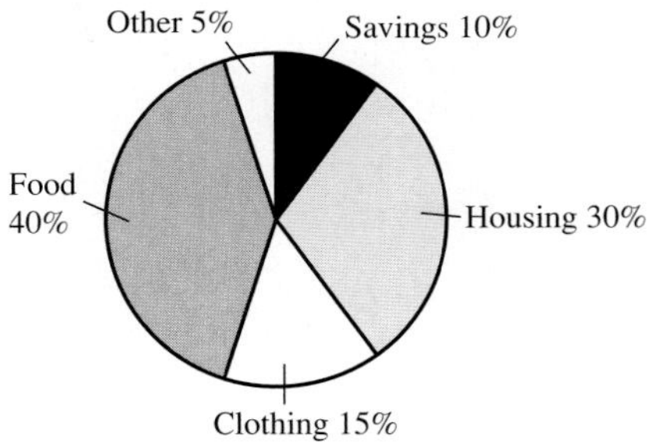	**12.5**	**5, 6**	**724–725**
17	**a.** For $x = 6$, $y \approx 0$. 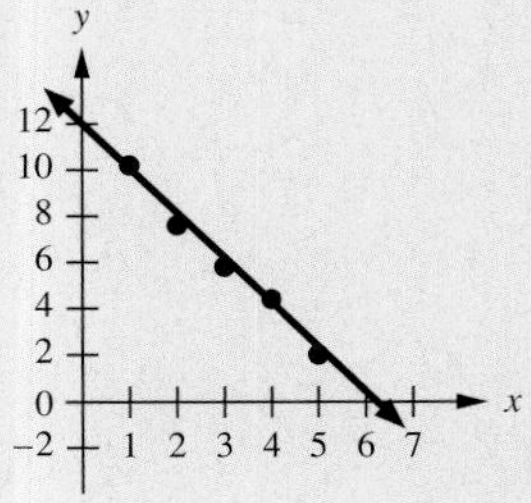	**12.6**	**1, 3**	**734–735, 736–737**
18	$y = -1.96x + 11.88$; for $x = 6$, $y = 0.12$	**12.6**	**1, 3, 4**	**734, 736–738**
19	About 200	**12.6**	**6**	**740**
20	About 8	**12.6**	**6**	**740**

continued

ANSWERS TO PRACTICE TEST – *continued*

CHAPTER 12		What to Review *If You Missed It*		
QUESTION	**ANSWER**	**SECTION**	**EXAMPLE(S)**	**PAGE(S)**
21	**(b)** The slope follows the direction of the line and has about the same number of points above and below the line.	12.7	1	746–747
22	**a.** Positive **b.** Negative **c.** None **d.** Negative	12.7	2	247–248
23	**(c)** -0.94	12.7	1, 2	746–748
24	$y = 0.62x + 2.58$	12.7	3	749
25	$r \approx 0.97$. We can be 95% confident that there is a significant *correlation* between the year x and sales y.	12.7	4, 5	749–751

CHAPTER 13

Your Money and Your Math

"For I don't care too much for money, for money can't buy me love." —THE BEATLES

© Stephen Chernin/Getty Images

Many people invest money throughout their lives in order to obtain additional income, to save for retirement, or to help save money for their children's education. In Section 13.5, you will study long-term investments, their cost, and their potential for profitability.

If you have a checking or savings account or a mortgage, you should be familiar with ***interest*** rates. These rates may be *simple* or *compound,* and the compounding may be *monthly, quarterly, or* even *daily*. It is important to know the **APY** (Annual Percentage Yield) for your accounts. With it you can compare rates and see which one is best for you. Moreover, interest rates can be used to find sales taxes and discounts. All of these topics will be covered in Section 13.1.

What about your credit cards? How much interest do you pay on them? What are their annual fees? Can you get some cards *without* an annual fee? The most important question is: which credit card is best for you? Credit cards and other types of credit such as **revolving charge accounts** and **add-on interest** are studied in Section 13.2.

As a consumer, you do have certain rights regarding credit purchases. In Section 13.3 you study the **Truth-in-Lending Act,** its provisions, and the benefits afforded you as a consumer under the act.

Section 13.4 discusses the American dream: buying a house. It starts by discussing how much you can afford, how much of a down payment you should make, the different types of loans available to you, and how monthly payments are estimated. It also discusses an expense often overlooked when buying a home: the closing costs. What do they entail and when do they have to be paid? When you study this section, you will gain a wealth of information regarding the mechanics and strategies for buying a home. Finally, after discussing how to manage charge accounts and credit cards and even buying a house, you may have money left for **investing** so you can make even more money. In Section 13.5 we learn how to **invest** money in stocks, bonds, and mutual funds.

13.1 Interest, Taxes, and Discounts

GETTING STARTED

OBJECTIVES

A. Find the simple interest and the total amount to be paid on a loan.
B. Find the tax and total cost of an item.
C. Find the discount and total cost of an item.
D. Find the future value and APY for an account.

SIMPLE AND COMPOUND INTEREST

Do you know the difference between simple and compound interest? First, you should know that **interest** is the amount paid for using borrowed money. When you deposit money in a savings account, buy a certificate of deposit, or loan money to someone, the person or institution receiving the money will pay you *interest* for the use of your money. On the other hand, if you borrow money from a bank, you must pay interest for the money you borrow.

How is interest computed? It depends! **Simple interest** I depends on the **principal** P (the amount borrowed or invested), the **interest rate** r (the portion of the principal charged for using the principal and usually expressed as a percent), and the **time** or **term** t (the number of years during which the borrower or investor has the use of all or part of the money). To calculate simple interest, use the formula

$$I = Prt$$

Now suppose you invest \$1000 at 6% simple interest for 1 year. Here, $P = \$1000$, $r = 6\% = 0.06$, and $t = 1$. Thus,

$$I = \$1000 \times 0.06 \times 1 = \$60$$

At the end of the year, you get your \$1000 back plus \$60 in interest; that is, \$1000 + \$60 = \$1060.

But suppose you invest the \$1000 at the same nominal rate of 6% and the interest is **compounded** quarterly (this means the interest is calculated four times a year instead of just once). How much money would you get at the end of the year? This information is shown in Table 13.1.

You can see current interest rates at http://tinyurl.com/cjul5vq.

Table 13.1

Quarter	Interest	New Principal*
1st	$\$1000 \times 0.06 \times \frac{1}{4} = \$15$	$\$1000 + \$15.00 = \$1015.00$
2nd	$\$1015 \times 0.06 \times \frac{1}{4} = \$15.23$	$\$1015 + \$15.23 = \$1030.23$
3rd	$\$1030.23 \times 0.06 \times \frac{1}{4} = \$15.45$	$\$1030.23 + \$15.45 = \$1045.68$
4th	$\$1045.68 \times 0.06 \times \frac{1}{4} = \$15.69$	$\$1045.68 + \$15.69 = \$1061.37$

*Banks round *up* when collecting money, *down* when paying it.

Thus, at the end of the year, you get \$1061.37, which is \$1.37 more than the simple interest amount. If you invested the same \$1000 at 1% compounded quarterly, you will get \$1010.04. You can repeat the calculations using 0.01 instead of 0.06 to prove that.

Human Side of Math

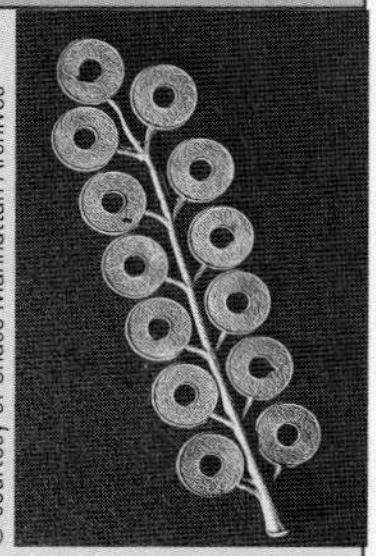

Have you ever wished for a money tree? The picture shows an **East Indian money tree**. The tin coins, used by the people of the Malay Peninsula in the nineteenth century, were broken off as needed.

The first coins were probably made about 2500 years ago in Lydia, now part of western Turkey. The coins were of a natural mixture of gold and silver called *electrum,* and they were stamped with a design showing that the king guaranteed them to be of uniform size. These coins were accepted by traders as a convenient medium of exchange and inspired other countries to make their own coins.

The first paper money was used in China about 1400 years ago. Europeans were skeptical about a piece of paper having any value, and it was not until the seventeenth century that paper money was accepted.

Until 1863, most of the currency in the United States consisted of notes issued by various state banks. Then Congress established national banks with the authority to issue bank notes. In 1913, the Federal Reserve System was established, and Federal Reserve notes gradually replaced national bank notes and became the official currency of the United States.

LOOKING AHEAD

In this chapter you will study many financial applications.

A word of warning: interest rates for saving accounts or certificates of deposit are now as low as 1% or lower (0.75% or 0.89% are common), so be very careful when writing these percents (0.75% = 0.0075 and 0.89% = 0.0089). In this section you will study simple interest and compound interest and their applications.

Some of these applications involve calculating best buys, checking credit account statements, comparing interest rates, using credit cards, and purchasing a home or a car. In this chapter, you investigate these activities.

Realistic problems dealing with personal finances are usually solved with the aid of a calculator. Hence, the examples will show how a calculator can be used to obtain the answer. Of course, a calculator is not absolutely necessary but is just a tool to help you do the arithmetic faster and more easily.

Let us start with a concept that occurs in most financial transactions: interest. In general, there are two types of interest, simple and compound. We shall study simple interest first.

A Simple Interest

How much money would you get if you received 12% interest on $1 million for 10 years? The answer depends on how this interest is calculated!

The **simple interest** for 1 year on a principal P at the rate r is just the principal times the rate, that is, Pr. The simple interest for t years is obtained by multiplying by t.

Simple Interest

The formula for calculating simple interest I on a principal P at the rate r for t years is

$$I = Prt$$

Notice that in the calculation of simple interest, the principal is just the original principal; the periodic interest that you earned does *not* earn further interest. Thus, if on $1 million ($P = \$1{,}000{,}000$) you receive 12% interest ($r = 12\% = 0.12$) for 10 years ($t = 10$), the simple interest is

$$\begin{aligned} I &= \overbrace{P}^{} \times \overbrace{r}^{} \times \overbrace{t}^{} \\ &= \$1{,}000{,}000 \times 0.12 \times 10 \\ &= \$1{,}200{,}000 \end{aligned}$$

Of course, at the end of the 10 years, you would also get your \$1,000,000 back, so you would receive \$1,000,000 + \$1,200,000 = \$2,200,000 at simple interest. At today's rates, however, you would probably get 1.75% or maybe 2% on your investment, so the simple interest for 10 years would be \$1,000,000 × 0.0175 × 10 or \$175,000, and you would then receive \$1,175,000, not \$2,200,000.

Final Amount

The final amount A is given as $A = P + I$.

However, if your annual interest were calculated on your original \$1,000,000 principal *plus* all previously earned interest—that is, if your interest were **compounded annually at 12%**—you would receive the much greater amount of \$3,105,848 (to the nearest dollar). At the lower 1.75% interest rate, you would only get \$1,189,444. We will see how this works when we study compound interest later in the section.

As a consumer, you will be interested in three important applications of simple interest: loans and deposits, taxes, and discounts. These applications are considered next.

Of course, you know that borrowing money from (or depositing money in) a bank or lending institution involves interest. Here is an example.

EXAMPLE 1 Finding Interest and Total Amount

A loan company charges 32% simple interest for a 2-year, \$600 loan.

(a) What is the total interest on this loan?

(b) What is the interest for 3 months?

(c) What is the total amount A that must be paid to the loan company at the end of 2 years?

Solution

(a) The interest is given by $I = Prt$, where $P = \$600$, $r = 32\% = 0.32$, and $t = 2$. Thus,

$$I = \$600 \times 0.32 \times 2 = \$384$$

On a calculator with a percent key [%], press

[6] [0] [0] [×] [3] [2] [%] [×] [2] [=]

The interest for the 2 years is \$384.

(b) Here, $P = \$600$, $r = 32\% = 0.32$, and $t = \frac{3}{12} = \frac{1}{4}$ because 3 months is $\frac{3}{12}$ of a year. Thus,

$$\begin{aligned} I &= \$600 \times 0.32 \times \tfrac{1}{4} \\ &= \$600 \times 0.08 \qquad (0.32 \times \tfrac{1}{4} = 0.08) \\ &= \$48 \end{aligned}$$

The interest for 3 months is \$48.

(c) At the end of 2 years, the loan company must be paid the original \$600 plus the interest of \$384; that is,

$$A = \$600 + \$384 = \$984$$

The company must be paid \$984.

B Taxes

You have probably heard the saying "There is nothing certain but death and taxes." Here is a simple problem "it is certain" you can do.

EXAMPLE 2 Finding Tax and Total Cost

A state has a 6% sales tax. Mary Rios buys an item priced at \$84.

(a) What is the sales tax on this item?

(b) What is Mary's total cost for this item?

Solution

(a) The sales tax S is 6% of \$84; that is,

$$S = 0.06 \times \$84 = \$5.04$$

The tax is \$5.04.

(b) The total cost is the price, \$84, plus the tax.

$$\$84 + \$5.04 = \$89.04$$

A calculator with a percent key [%] will give the total cost automatically if you press [8] [4] [+] [6] [%] [=].

C Discounts

In Examples 1 and 2, the consumer had to pay interest or taxes. But there is some hope! Sometimes you can obtain a **discount** on certain purchases. Such a discount is usually stated as a percent. For example, a coupon may entitle you to a 20% discount on certain purchases. Many stores, restaurants, Web sites, and other companies provide student discounts. If you have a student ID, you can get anywhere from 25% off to free shipping from many merchants. Examples of Web sites that offer student discounts are http://tinyurl.com/6wcnrok and www.studentbistro.com.

EXAMPLE 3 Finding Discounts and Cost

Ralph McWaters purchased a \$42 item and used his coupon to get 20% off.

(a) How much was his discount?

(b) How much did he have to pay for the item?

Solution

(a) His discount rate d was 20% of \$42. So in money his discount was

$$d = 0.20 \times \$42 = \$8.40$$

(b) Since he had a discount of \$8.40, he had to pay

$$\$42 - \$8.40 = \$33.60$$

for the item. A calculator with a percent key [%] will obtain the final price if you press [4] [2] [−] [2] [0] [%] [=].

D Compound Interest

When interest is **compounded,** the interest is calculated not only on the original principal but also on the earned interest. For example, if you deposit \$1000 in a savings account that pays 6% interest compounded annually, then in the first year, the account will earn interest calculated as

$$\begin{aligned} I &= Prt \\ &= \$1000 \times 0.06 \times 1 = \$60 \end{aligned}$$

If you make no withdrawals, then at the beginning of the second year the accumulated amount will be

$$\$1000 + \$60 = \$1060$$

which is the new principal. In the second year, this new principal will earn interest

$$\begin{aligned} I &= Prt \\ &= \$1060 \times 0.06 \times 1 = \$63.60 \end{aligned}$$

Thus, at the beginning of the third year, the accumulated amount will be

$$\$1060 + \$63.60 = \$1123.60$$

and so on.

You can see that when interest is compounded, the earned interest increases each year (\$60, \$63.60, and so on, as in the preceding illustration). This is so because the interest at the end of a year is calculated on the accumulated amount (principal plus interest) at the beginning of that year. Piecewise calculation of the accumulated amount is a very time-consuming procedure, but it can be avoided by developing a general formula for the amount A_n accumulated after n interest periods and the use of special tables or a calculator. To develop the formula for A_n, let I be the compound interest, P be the original principal, r be the rate per period, and A_1 be the compound amount at the end of the first period.

$$\begin{aligned} I &= Pr && \text{Interest for the first period} \\ A_1 &= P + I \\ &= P + Pr && \text{Substitute } Pr \text{ for } I. \\ &= P(1 + r) && \text{Use the distributive property.} \end{aligned}$$

After the end of the second period, the compound amount A_2 is

$$\begin{aligned} A_2 &= A_1 + A_1 r \\ &= A_1(1 + r) && \text{Use the distributive property.} \\ &= P(1 + r)(1 + r) && \text{Substitute } P(1 + r) \text{ for } A_1. \\ &= P(1 + r)^2 && \text{Substitute } (1 + r)^2 \text{ for } (1 + r)(1 + r). \end{aligned}$$

If you continue this procedure, after n periods you will derive the formula for the future value A_n.

Amount after Compounding for n Periods (Future Value A_n)

If P dollars are deposited at an interest rate r and compounded n times, the **future value** A_n is

$$A_n = P(1 + r)^n$$

Thus, if you deposit \$1 at 6% compounded annually for 20 years,

$$A_{20} = \$1(1 + 0.06)^{20}$$

GRAPH IT

Some graphers can calculate finances. If your grapher has a FINANCE key (under x^{-1}) then your calculator can calculate finances. Press 2nd FINANCE 1 or APPS 1 to reach the TVM (**T**ime **V**alue of **M**oney) solver. The meanings of the variables are

- N = number of payments
- $I\%$ = annual interest rate
- PV = present value (how much it is worth *now*)
- PMT = payment amount
- FV = future value (how much it is worth *later*)
- P/Y = periods per year
- C/Y = compoundings per year
- PMT = END BEGIN (when the payment is made)

To find the compound amount in 20 years when you deposit \$1 at 6% at the end of each year, press 2nd FINANCE 1 or APPS 1 ENTER and enter 20, 6, 1, 0, 0, 1, 1 END. Press ▲ ▲ ▲ ALPHA ENTER. You get −3.207135472. The negative sign indicates that the amount is a future value.

```
N=20
I%=6
PV=1
PMT=0
FV=-3.207135472
P/Y=1
C/Y=1
PMT:END BEGIN
```

Table 13.2 Amount (in dollars) to Which $1 Will Grow in *n* Periods Under Compound Interest

n	1%	2%	3%	4%	5%	6%	7%	8%	9%	10%	11%	12%
1	1.0100	1.0200	1.0300	1.0400	1.0500	1.0600	1.0700	1.0800	1.0900	1.1000	1.1100	1.1200
2	1.0201	1.0404	1.0609	1.0816	1.1025	1.1236	1.1449	1.1664	1.1881	1.2100	1.2321	1.2544
3	1.0303	1.0612	1.0927	1.1249	1.1576	1.1910	1.2250	1.2597	1.2950	1.3310	1.3676	1.4049
4	1.0406	1.0824	1.1255	1.1699	1.2155	1.2625	1.3108	1.3605	1.4116	1.4641	1.5181	1.5735
5	1.0510	1.1041	1.1593	1.2167	1.2763	1.3382	1.4026	1.4693	1.5386	1.6105	1.6851	1.7623
6	1.0615	1.1262	1.1941	1.2653	1.3401	1.4185	1.5007	1.5869	1.6771	1.7716	1.8704	1.9738
7	1.0721	1.1487	1.2299	1.3159	1.4071	1.5036	1.6058	1.7138	1.8280	1.9487	2.0762	2.2107
8	1.0829	1.1717	1.2668	1.3686	1.4775	1.5938	1.7182	1.8509	1.9926	2.1436	2.3045	2.4760
9	1.0937	1.1951	1.3048	1.4233	1.5513	1.6895	1.8385	1.9990	2.1719	2.3579	2.5580	2.7731
10	1.1046	1.2190	1.3439	1.4802	1.6289	1.7908	1.9672	2.1589	2.3674	2.5937	2.8394	3.1058
11	1.1157	1.2434	1.3842	1.5395	1.7103	1.8983	2.1049	2.3316	2.5804	2.8531	3.1518	3.4785
12	1.1268	1.2682	1.4258	1.6010	1.7959	2.0122	2.2522	2.5182	2.8127	3.1384	3.4985	3.8960
13	1.1381	1.2936	1.4685	1.6651	1.8856	2.1329	2.4098	2.7196	3.0658	3.4523	3.8833	4.3635
14	1.1495	1.3195	1.5126	1.7317	1.9799	2.2609	2.5785	2.9372	3.3417	3.7975	4.3104	4.8871
15	1.1610	1.3459	1.5580	1.8009	2.0789	2.3966	2.7590	3.1722	3.6425	4.1772	4.7846	5.4736
16	1.1726	1.3728	1.6047	1.8730	2.1829	2.5404	2.9522	3.4259	3.9703	4.5950	5.3109	6.1304
17	1.1843	1.4002	1.6528	1.9479	2.2920	2.6928	3.1588	3.7000	4.3276	5.0545	5.8951	6.8660
18	1.1961	1.4282	1.7024	2.0258	2.4066	2.8543	3.3799	3.9960	4.7171	5.5599	6.5436	7.6900
19	1.2081	1.4568	1.7535	2.1068	2.5270	3.0256	3.6165	4.3157	5.1417	6.1159	7.2633	8.6128
20	1.2202	1.4859	1.8061	2.1911	2.6533	3.2071	3.8697	4.6610	5.6044	6.7275	8.0623	9.6403
21	1.2324	1.5157	1.8603	2.2788	2.7860	3.3996	4.1406	5.0338	6.1088	7.4002	8.9492	10.8038
22	1.2447	1.5460	1.9161	2.3699	2.9253	3.6035	4.4304	5.4365	6.6586	8.1403	9.9336	12.1003
23	1.2572	1.5769	1.9736	2.4647	3.0715	3.8197	4.7405	5.8715	7.2579	8.9543	11.0263	13.5523
24	1.2697	1.6084	2.0328	2.5633	3.2251	4.0489	5.0724	6.3412	7.9111	9.8497	12.2392	15.1786
30	1.3478	1.8114	2.4273	3.2434	4.3219	5.7435	7.6123	10.0627	13.2677	17.4494	22.8923	29.9599
36	1.4308	2.0399	2.8983	4.1039	5.7918	8.1473	11.4239	15.9682	22.2512	30.9127	42.8181	59.1356
42	1.5188	2.2972	3.4607	5.1928	7.7616	11.5570	17.1443	25.3395	37.3175	54.7637	80.0876	116.7231
48	1.6122	2.5871	4.1323	6.5705	10.4013	16.3939	25.7289	40.2106	62.5852	97.0172	149.7970	230.3908

Just press (1 + .06)^20 [ENTER] on your grapher or (1 + .06) [y^x] 20 [=] on your calculator and you get 3.2071. There are tables that give the value of the accumulated amount for a $1 initial deposit at compound interest r for n time periods. Table 13.2 is such a table. To find the value of the accumulated amount $(1 + 0.06)^{20}$ in Table 13.2, go down the column headed n until you reach 20, and then go across to the column headed 6%. The accumulated amount given there is $3.2071. If you wish to know the accumulated amount for an original deposit of $1000 instead of $1, multiply the $3.2071 by 1000; you obtain $3207.10.

In using Table 13.2, there is a warning: *The entries in this table have been rounded to four decimal places from more accurate values.* Consequently, you should not expect answers to be accurate to more than the number of digits in the table entry. If more accuracy is needed, you must use a table with more decimal places or a calculator. To find $(1 + 0.06)^{20}$, press [(] [1] [.] [0] [6] [)] [y^x] [2] [0] [=] and obtain 3.207135472, or 3.2071.

Many financial transactions call for interest to be compounded more often than once a year. In such cases, the interest rate is customarily stated as a nominal annual rate, it being understood that **the actual rate per interest period is the nominal rate divided by the number of periods per year.** For instance, if interest is at 18%, compounded monthly, then the actual interest rate is $\frac{18}{12}\% = 1.5\%$ per month because there are 12 months in a year.

EXAMPLE 4 Finding the Accumulated Amount and Interest

Find the accumulated amount and the interest earned for the following:

(a) \$8000 at 8% compounded annually for 5 years.

(b) \$3500 at 2% compounded semiannually for 10 years.

Solution

(a) Here, $P = 8000$ and $n = 5$. In Table 13.2, we go down the column under n until we come to 5 and then across to the column under 8%. The number there is 1.4693. Hence, the accumulated amount will be

$\$8000 \times 1.4693 = \$11{,}754$ to the nearest dollar.

With a calculator, press [8] [0] [0] [0] [×] [(] [1] [+] [.] [0] [8] [)] [y^x] [5] [=].
The interest earned is the difference between the \$11,754.63 and the original deposit; that is, $\$11{,}754.63 - \$8000 = \$3754.63$.

(b) Because *semiannually* means twice a year, interest is compounded every 6 months, and the actual rate per interest period is the nominal rate, 2% divided by 2, or 1%. In 10 years, there are $2 \times 10 = 20$ interest periods. Hence, we go down the column under n until we come to 20 and then across to the column headed 1% to find the accumulated amount 1.2202. Since this is the amount for \$1, we multiply by \$3500 to get

$\$3500 \times 1.2202 = \$4271$ to the nearest dollar.

The amount of interest earned is $\$4271 - \$3500 = \$771$.

With a calculator, press [3] [5] [0] [0] [×] [(] [1] [+] [.] [0] [1] [)] [y^x] [2] [0] and obtain \$4270.67. The interest earned is $\$4270.67 - \$3500 = \$770.67$, which, rounded to the nearest dollar, yields the same answer, \$771. Note that we used $r = \frac{2}{2}\% = 1\%$.

GRAPH IT

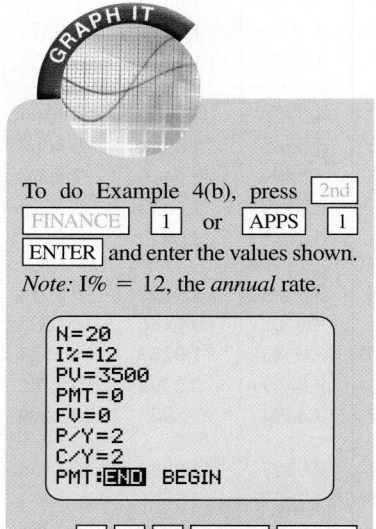

To do Example 4(b), press [2nd] [FINANCE] [1] or [APPS] [1] [ENTER] and enter the values shown.
Note: I% = 12, the *annual* rate.

```
N=20
I%=12
PV=3500
PMT=0
FV=0
P/Y=2
C/Y=2
PMT:END BEGIN
```

Press [▲] [▲] [▲] [ALPHA] [ENTER] to get the *FV* − \$11,224.97.

> **Future Value for Compound Interest**
>
> If P dollars are deposited at an annual interest r, compounded m times a year, and the money is left on deposit for n periods, the **future value** (or final amount) A_n is
>
> $$A_n = P\left(1 + \frac{r}{m}\right)^n$$

The interest can also be compounded *continuously* for n years.

> **Future Value for Continuously Compounded Interest**
>
> If P dollars are deposited and earn continuously compounded interest at an annual rate r for n years, then the **future value** A_n is
>
> $$A_n = Pe^{rn}$$

EXAMPLE 5 Finding Compound Interest

Suppose you invest \$1000 at 8%. How much interest will you earn in 5 years if the money is compounded.

(a) quarterly? **(b)** continuously?

Solution

(a) Here $P = \$1000$, $r = 8$, $m = 4$, $r/m = 8/4 = 2$, and $n = 4 \times 5 = 20$. From Table 13.2 with $n = 20$ and under the heading 2%, we find 1.4859. Thus, $A_5 = 1000 \times 1.4859 = \$1485.90$. The interest is $\$1485.90 - \$1000 = \$485.90$. With a calculator, press [1] [0] [0] [0] [×] [(] [1] [+] [.] [0] [2] [)] [y^x] [20] [=] and obtain \$1485.95.

(b) In this case, $A_n = Pe^{rn} = 1000e^{(0.08)(5)} = 1000e^{0.40}$. With a calculator with an [e^x] key, press [1] [0] [0] [0] [×] [(] [.] [4] [0] [2nd] [e^x] [)] [=] and get \$1491.82, which is a little bit more than the \$1485.95 you get when compounding quarterly. Caution: When entering quantities involving [e^x] using a scientific calculator, you must enter the exponent x first and then press [2nd] [e^x].

The type of comparison made in Example 5 can be generalized by looking at the **APY** (**A**nnual **P**ercentage **Y**ield, sometimes called **effective rate**) of two investments. For example, if the nominal interest is r compounded k times a year, the **future value** of \$1 is given by

$$1\left(1 + \frac{r}{k}\right)^k = \left(1 + \frac{r}{k}\right)^k$$

and the APY is your future value minus the original \$1, that is,

Formula for APY (Effective Rate)

$$\textbf{APY} = \left(1 + \frac{r}{k}\right)^k - 1$$ k the number of compoundings per year, r the nominal rate

$$\textbf{APY} = e^r - 1$$ for continuous compounding

EXAMPLE 6 Comparing Investments Using APY

Find the APY for an 8% investment when the money is compounded

(a) quarterly. **(b)** continuously.

Solution

(a) The nominal rate $r = 8\%$, and the number of compoundings $k = 4$. Thus,

$$\begin{aligned} \text{APY} &= \left(1 + \frac{0.08}{4}\right)^k - 1 \\ &= (1 + 0.02)^4 - 1 \\ &= (1.02)^4 - 1 \\ &= 1.08243216 - 1 && \text{Using a calculator} \\ &= 0.08243216 \\ &= 8.24\% && \text{To two decimal places} \end{aligned}$$

(b) The nominal rate is still $r = 8\%$, but the interest is compounded continuously. Thus,

$$\begin{aligned} \text{APY} &= e^r - 1 \\ &= e^{0.08} - 1 \\ &= 1.083287068 - 1 && \text{Using a calculator} \\ &= 8.33\% && \text{To two decimal places} \end{aligned}$$

EXAMPLE 7 Purchasing Power and Inflation

Suppose you are earning \$30,000 a year. How much salary would you need to earn 10 years from now to maintain your purchasing power if the inflation rate is 2.5%?

Solution

We assume that the inflation rate is growing continuously, so your \$30,000 salary P in $n = 10$ years at $r = 2.5\%$ will have to amount to $A = \$30{,}000e^{(0.025)(10)} = 30{,}000e^{0.25}$. With a calculator, press [3] [0] [0] [0] [0] [×] [(] [.] [2] [5] [2nd] [e^x] [)] [=] and get \$38,520.76.

13.1 EXERCISES

A Simple Interest

In problems 1–10, find the simple interest.

	Principal	*Rate*		*Time*
1.	\$3000	a. 8%	b. 4%	1 year
2.	\$4500	a. 7%	b. 3.5%	1 year
3.	\$2000	a. 9%	b. 4.5%	3 years
4.	\$6200	a. 8%	b. 4%	4 years
5.	\$4000	a. 10%	b. 3.5%	6 months
6.	\$6000	a. 12%	b. 1.5%	4 months
7.	\$2500	a. 10%	b. 2.5%	3 months
8.	\$12,000	a. 9%	b. 2%	1 month
9.	\$16,000	a. 7%	b. 3%	5 months
10.	\$30,000	a. 8%	b. 1.5%	2 months

B Taxes

11. The state sales tax in Florida is 6%. Desiree Cole bought \$40.20 worth of merchandise.
    a. What was the tax on this purchase?
    b. What was the total price of the purchase?
12. The state sales tax in Alabama is 4%. Beto Frias bought a refrigerator priced at \$666.
    a. What was the sales tax on this refrigerator?
    b. What was the total price of the purchase?
13. Have you seen the FICA (Federal Insurance Contribution Act, better known as Social Security) deduction taken from your paycheck? For 2011; the tax was temporarily lowered to 5.65% of your annual salary; otherwise, the FICA rate is fixed at 7.65%. Find the FICA tax for a person earning \$24,000 a year:
    a. in 2011 b. at the 7.65% rate
14. Except for the year 2011, the FICA tax for 1990 and subsequent years is 7.65% of your annual salary. Walter Snyder makes \$30,000 a year. What would his FICA tax deduction be based on this rate?

Refer to the following table for problems 15 and 16.

Schedule X—Use if your 2011 filling status is Single			
If line 5 is:		**The tax is:**	**of the amount**
Over—	**But not over—**		**over—**
\$0	\$8,500	.... 10%	\$0
8,500	34,500	\$850.00 + 15%	8,500
34,500	83,600	4,750.00 + 25%	34,500
83,600	174,400	17,025.00 + 28%	83,600
174,400	379,150	42,449.00 + 33%	174,400
379,150	....	110,016.50 + 35%	379,150

15. Mabelle was single and had a taxable income of \$25,850. How much was her estimated income tax?
16. Bob was single and had a taxable income of \$9500. What was his estimated income tax?

For current tax information go to www.irs.gov.

C Discounts

17. An article selling for \$200 was discounted 20%.
    a. What was the amount of the discount?
    b. What was the final cost after the discount?
    c. If the sales tax was 5%, what was the final cost after the discount and including the sales tax?
18. A Sealy mattress sells regularly for \$900. It is offered on sale at 50% off.
    a. What is the amount of the discount?
    b. What is the price after the discount?
    c. If the sales tax rate is 6%, what is the total price of the mattress after the discount and including the sales tax?
19. A jewelry store is selling rings at a 25% discount. The original price of a ring was \$500.
    a. What is the amount of the discount?
    b. What is the price of the ring after the discount?

20. If you have a Magic Kingdom Club Card from Disneyland, Howard Johnson's offers a 10% discount on double rooms. A family stayed at Howard Johnson's for 4 days. The rate per day was $45.
   a. What was the price of the room for the 4 days?
   b. What was the amount of the discount?
   c. If the sales tax rate was 6%, what was the total bill?
21. Some oil companies are offering a 5% discount on the gasoline you buy if you pay cash. Anita Gonzalez filled her gas tank, and the pump registered $28.40.
   a. If she paid cash, what was the amount of her discount?
   b. What did she pay after her discount?
22. U-Mart had Comfort bicycles selling regularly for $350. The bicycles were put on sale at 20% off. The manager found that some of the bicycles were dented or scratched, and offered an additional 10% discount.

   a. What was the price of a dented bicycle after the two discounts? (Careful! This is not a 30% discount, but 20%, followed by 10%.)
   b. Would it be better to take the 20% discount followed by the 10% discount or to take a single 28% discount?

D Compound Interest

In problems 23–26, use Table 13.2 or a calculator to find the final accumulated amount and the total interest if interest is compounded annually. (Give answers to five significant digits.) Answers may vary because of rounding or calculator use.

23. a. $100 at 6% for 8 years.
   b. $100 at 4% for 8 years.
24. a. $1000 at 9% for 11 years.
   b. $1000 at 3% for 11 years.
25. a. $2580 at 12% for 9 years.
   b. $2580 at 2% for 9 years.
26. a. $6230 at 11% for 12 years.
   b. $6230 at 2% for 12 years.

In problems 27–32, use Table 13.2 or a calculator to find the final accumulated amount and the total interest. (Give answers to the same number of digits as the table entry or to the nearest dollar.)

27. a. $12,000 at 10% compounded semiannually for 8 years.
   b. $12,000 at 4% compounded semiannually for 8 years.
28. a. $15,000 at 14% compounded semiannually for 10 years.
   b. $15,000 at 4% compounded semiannually for 10 years.
29. a. $20,000 at 8% compounded quarterly for 3 years.
   b. $20,000 at 2% compounded semiannually for 3 years.
30. a. $30,000 at 12% compounded quarterly for 4 years.
   b. $30,000 at 4% compounded quarterly for 4 years.
31. a. $40,000 at 20% compounded semiannually for 24 years.
   b. $40,000 at 4% compounded semiannually for 24 years.
32. a. $50,000 at 16% compounded semiannually for 15 years.
   b. $50,000 at 6% compounded semiannually for 15 years.
33. When a child is born, grandparents sometimes deposit a certain amount of money that can be used later to send the child to college. Mary and John Glendale deposited $1000 when their granddaughter Anna was born. The account was paying 6% compounded annually.
   a. How much money will there be in the account when Anna becomes 18 years old?
   b. How much money would there be in the account after 18 years if the interest had been compounded semiannually?
34. When Natasha was born, her mother deposited $100 in an account paying 6% compounded annually. After 10 years, the money was transferred into another account paying 10% compounded semiannually.
   a. How much money was in the account after the first 10 years?
   b. How much money was in the account at the end of 18 years? (Give answers to the nearest cent.)
35. Jack loaned Janie $3000. She promised to repay the $3000 plus interest at 10% compounded annually at the end of 3 years.
   a. How much did she have to pay Jack at the end of 3 years?
   b. How much interest did she pay?
36. Bank A pays 8% interest compounded quarterly; bank B pays 10% compounded semiannually. If $1000 were deposited in each bank, how much money would there be at the end of 5 years in
   a. the bank A account.
   b. the bank B account.
   c. In which bank would you deposit your money?
37. How much more would there be at the end of 5 years if $1000 were invested at 12% compounded quarterly rather than semiannually?
38. Suppose you can invest $1000 in a fund that pays 6% compounded annually or into a fund that pays 6.5% annually but does not reinvest the interest. How long would it be before the accumulated interest in the first fund exceeded the total interest paid out by the second fund? Make a table to show what happens and explain.
39. Find the compound amount when $2000 is compounded continuously at 8% for 6 months.
40. Find the compound amount when $3000 is invested at 8% compounded continuously for 5 years.
41. An investor can buy a 2-year, $10,000 certificate of deposit paying 11% compounded semiannually or place the money in an account paying $10\frac{1}{2}$% compounded continuously. Which of the two investments will yield the most interest, and how much extra interest will the investor get by making the correct choice?

42. The president of a bank is considering changing savings account interest to continuous compounding. At the present time, the bank pays 5% interest compounded daily. How much difference in interest will there be in a $1000 deposit left in an account for 180 days? How much difference in interest payments will there be in a 6-month period if the bank has $2 million deposited in savings accounts? (*Hint:* $e^{0.025} = 1.0253151$.) Assume a year has 360 days.

In problems 43–52, find the APY (effective annual rate).

43. 2% compounded daily.
44. 3% compounded daily.
45. 6%, compounded semiannually.
46. 6%, compounded monthly.
47. 8%, compounded quarterly.
48. 12%, compounded monthly.
49. 9%, compounded quarterly.
50. 15%, compounded semiannually.
51. 18%, compounded monthly.
52. 15%, compounded monthly.

IN OTHER WORDS

53. Discuss the difference between simple and compound interest.
54. If you increase the price of a product by 10% and then decrease that price by 10%, would the new price be the same as the original price? Explain.

USING YOUR KNOWLEDGE

In problems 55–58, check the APY approximate to two decimal places for the given nominal rate.

High Yield Rates for 1-Year CD, Rates May be Different

	Institution	Date	Rate	CM	APY	Min. Deposit
55.	Imperial Capital Bank, LaJolla, CA	8/2	3.98	M	4.06	2000
56.	Net Bank Alpharetta, GA	8/2	3.92	W	4.00	1000
57.	ING DIRECT Wilmington, DE	8/2	3.90	S	3.98	1
58.	Interwest Natl Bank New York, NY	8/2	3.88	D	3.96	2500

Source: http://www.free-online-calculator-use.com/apy-calculator.html#calculator.

COLLABORATIVE LEARNING

Form three groups. The objective is to answer the question: What is the rule of 70 (or 72)?

Group 1 Call a bank, an investment company, or a financial planner and ask.

Group 2 Go to the Internet and find the answer.

Group 3 Go to the library and use an encyclopedia or other reference materials to answer the question.

Discuss your findings.

If you invest P dollars at r percent compounded continuously, the amount A you will receive after t years is $A = Pe^{rt}$. If you want to double your money, $A = 2P$ and $2P = Pe^{rt}$.

1. Solve for t.
2. If $\ln 2 \approx 0.069315$, what is t?
3. How long would it take P dollars to double at
   a. 4%? b. 8%? c. 12%?

Can you see where the name rule of 70 (or 72) came from? Restate the rule.

13.2 Credit Cards and Consumer Credit

GETTING STARTED

OBJECTIVE

Understand the requirements and terms of a credit card and find the finance charge, interest, balance, minimum and monthly payment.

EVERYTHING YOU ALWAYS WANTED TO KNOW ABOUT CREDIT CARDS*

Do you have a credit card, or are you planning to get one soon? You can save money if you know the **interest rate** (the percent you pay on the card balance), the **annual fee** (the amount paid for the privilege of having the card), and the **grace period** (the interest-free period between purchases and billing given to consumers who pay off their balances entirely) on your cards. The interest rate can be **fixed** or **variable** (depending on the amount you owe or some standard such as the **prime rate,** the rate banks charge their best customers). How can you save money? First, you can get a card with no annual fee for a savings of \$20 to \$50. Next, you can eliminate interest payments by paying off your entire balance each month. Note that if a balance of *any amount* is carried over from the previous month, most banks will charge interest from the date of each new purchase, even *before* the monthly statement arrives.

The type of card you should have to maximize savings depends on your monthly balance. If you plan to pay your balance in full each month, the annual fee is the largest expense. Get a card with no annual fee and the longest grace period available. If you plan to have a high monthly balance, choose a card with a low interest rate. (For example, if your average balance is \$1000, you will pay \$180 annually on an 18% annual percentage rate (APR) card but only \$120 on a 12% APR card, a savings of \$180 − \$120, or \$60.) Now, suppose you already have a credit card. How can you decide on your best course of action? Follow these steps.

1. Find the annual fee and interest rate on your card.
2. Look at your past statements and find your average monthly balance.
3. Figure your annual cost by multiplying the interest rate by the monthly balance and add the annual fee.

Here is an example. Suppose you have a card with a \$25 annual fee and an 18% APR. If the average monthly balance on your card is \$500 and you can get a card with a 14% APR and no annual fee, you will be saving 4% (18% − 4%) of \$500, or \$20, in interest and the \$25 annual fee, a total of \$45. On the other hand, if your annual fee is \$20 and your APR is 14%, changing to another card with no annual fee and 19% APR makes no sense. (You pay 14% of \$500, or \$70, plus the \$20 fee, \$90 in all with the first card and 19% of \$500, or \$95, with the other.) How do you find the interest rate and annual fee on credit cards? Find a consumer magazine or an organization (such as BankCard Holders of America) that publishes the latest information regarding annual fees and interest rates for credit cards, or look in the World Wide Web (Internet).

To obtain a credit card, you have to meet requirements set by the institution that issues the card. These requirements will vary but are illustrated in the next example. Moreover,

*For more information regarding credit cards, their benefits, and the amount of time or the payments needed to pay off a card, you may search the Internet.

banks sometimes have promotions in which credit cards are offered under other special conditions.

Company A will issue a credit card to an applicant who meets the following requirements:

1. The applicant must have a good credit rating.*
2. If single, the applicant must have a gross annual income of at least $30,000.
3. If married, the couple's combined gross annual income must be at least $40,000.

EXAMPLE 1 Qualifying for a Credit Card

Using the three preceding requirements, determine which of the following applicants qualifies for a credit card from company A:

(a) Annie Jones is single, has a good credit rating, and earns $25,000 per year.

(b) John Smith has an excellent credit rating and earns $35,000 per year. His wife has no paying job.

(c) Don and Daryl Barnes each earn $24,000 per year and have a good credit rating.

(d) Bill Spender is single, earns $40,000 per year and has only a fair credit rating.

Solution

Only Don and Daryl Barnes meet the requirements of company A. They have a good credit rating, and their combined annual income is $48,000.

One of the costs associated with credit cards is the **finance charge** that is collected if you decide to pay for your purchases later than the allowed payment (grace) period. Usually, if the entire balance is paid within a certain period of time (25–30 days), there is no charge. However, if you want more time, then you will have to pay the finance charge computed at the rate printed on the monthly statement you receive from the company issuing the card. Figure 13.1 shows the top portion of such a statement. As you can see,

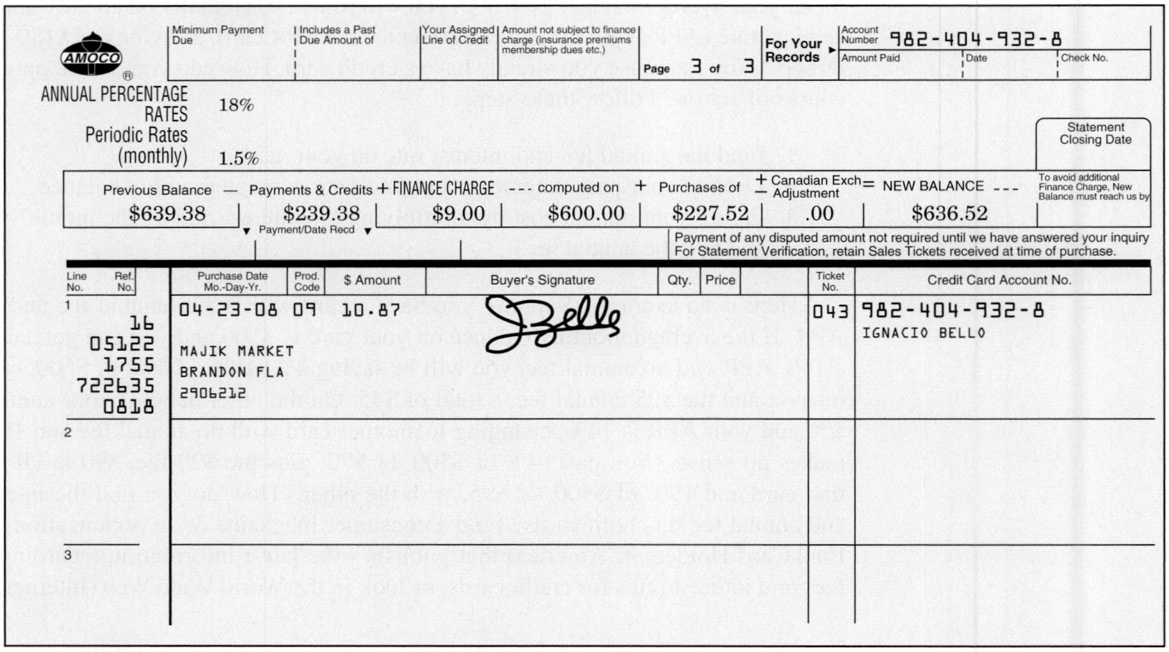
AMOCO

Minimum Payment Due | Includes a Past Due Amount of | Your Assigned Line of Credit | Amount not subject to finance charge (insurance premiums membership dues etc.) | Page 3 of 3

For Your Records ▸ Account Number 982-404-932-8 | Amount Paid | Date | Check No.

ANNUAL PERCENTAGE RATES 18%

Periodic Rates (monthly) 1.5%

Statement Closing Date

Previous Balance	— Payments & Credits	+ FINANCE CHARGE	--- computed on	+ Purchases of	± Canadian Exch Adjustment	= NEW BALANCE ---	To avoid additional Finance Charge, New Balance must reach us by
$639.38	$239.38	$9.00	$600.00	$227.52	.00	$636.52	

▾ Payment/Date Recd ▾

Payment of any disputed amount not required until we have answered your inquiry For Statement Verification, retain Sales Tickets received at time of purchase.

Line No.	Ref. No.	Purchase Date Mo.-Day-Yr.	Prod. Code	$ Amount	Buyer's Signature	Qty.	Price	Ticket No.	Credit Card Account No.
1	16 05122 1755 722635 0818	04-23-08 MAJIK MARKET BRANDON FLA 2906212	09	10.87				043	982-404-932-8 IGNACIO BELLO
2									
3									

FIGURE 13.1

*Your credit rating is usually determined by a credit bureau, an organization that tracks the history of individuals' spending and repayment habits.

the periodic (monthly) rate is 1.5%. This rate is used to calculate the charge on \$600. Where does the \$600 come from? The back of the statement indicates that "The Finance Charge is computed on the Average Daily Balance, which is the sum of the Daily Balances divided by the number of days in the Billing Period." Fortunately, the computer calculated this average daily balance and came out with the correct amount. In Example 2, we shall verify only the finance charge.

EXAMPLE 2 Minimum Payments and Finance Charges

Find the finance charge (interest) to be paid on the statement in Figure 13.1 if the monthly rate is 1.5% computed on the average daily balance of \$600.

Solution

The finance charge is 1.5% of \$600, that is,

$$0.015 \times \$600 = \$9$$

Next, let us look at a different problem. Suppose you wish to obtain a credit card. First, you have to apply to the issuing bank for such a card (sometimes the bank will preapprove you). If your application is accepted, then you must pay a fee. (Most credit unions and banks issue cards free.) After some time, the card finally arrives in the mail. Now suppose you wish to use your card at a restaurant where these cards are accepted. Instead of collecting cash, the cashier will "swipe" your card in a machine that will print on a receipt certain information that is encoded in the black strip on the back of the card: the card number, your name, and the expiration date of the card; it will also print the name and identification numbers of the restaurant as well as the date of the transaction and an authorization code issued by the bank owning the card. You will sign the receipt and be given a copy for your records. Figure 13.2 shows such a receipt.

At the end of the billing period, a statement is sent to you. If the balance due is \$10 or less, you must pay the account *in full.* Otherwise, you must make a minimum payment of \$10 or 5% of the balance due, *whichever is greater.* (Terms vary from one bank to another.)

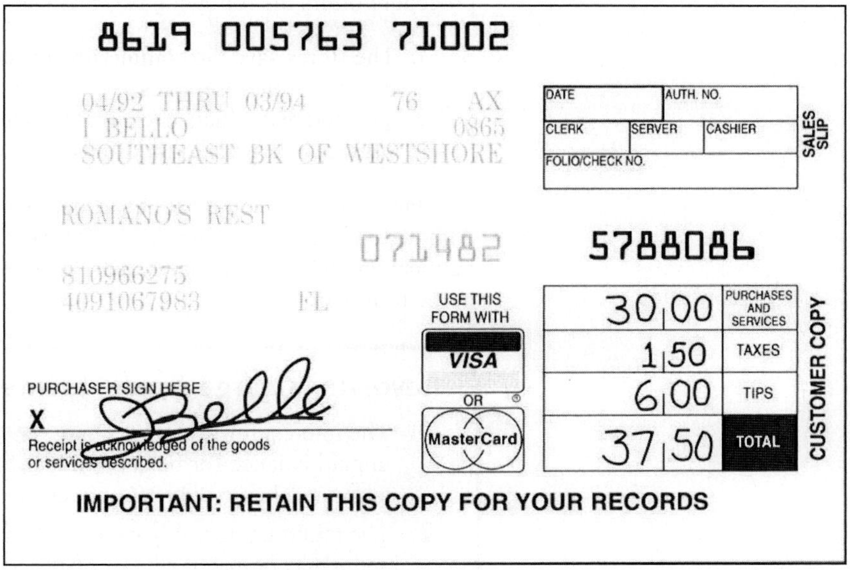

FIGURE 13.2

EXAMPLE 3 Finding Finance Charges

The customer who signed the receipt in Figure 13.2 received a statement at the end of the month. The new balance was listed as \$37.50. Find the following:

(a) The minimum payment due.

(b) The finance charge that will be due the next month if only the minimum payment is made now.

Solution

(a) Because the new balance is \$37.50 and 5% of \$37.50 is \$1.875, the minimum payment is \$10. (Remember, you pay \$10 or 5% of the new balance, whichever is greater.)

(b) After paying the \$10, the customer's new balance is

$\$37.50 - \$10 = \$27.50$

The finance charge is 1.5% of \$27.50, or

$0.015 \times \$27.50 = \$0.4125$

Thus, if no additional credit card purchases are made, the finance charge will be \$0.41.

Note: The finance charge is *not* the only profit made by the credit card company. Credit card companies charge the businesses that accept your credit card 1% to 3% of each sale. (Rates vary and are based on the average charge per transaction.)

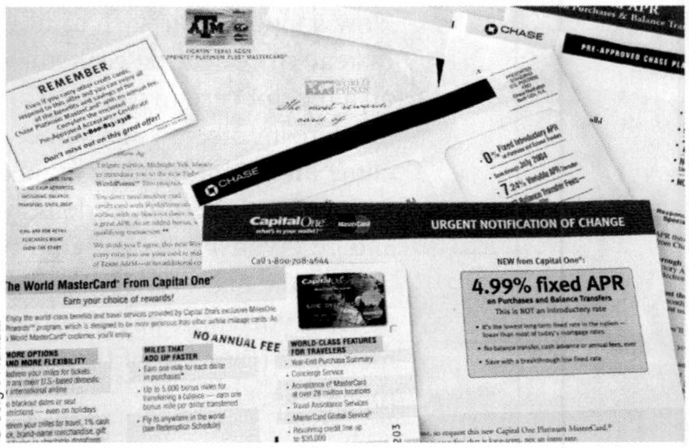

© Sergio Piumatti

Many large department stores prefer to handle their own credit card business. This procedure offers the following two main advantages to the stores:

1. The stores save the commission on sales that the national credit card companies charge for their services.
2. The interest (finance charges) collected from their customers is a welcome source of revenue to the stores.

Most charge accounts at department stores are called **revolving charge accounts.** Although the operational procedure for these accounts is similar to that employed by the national credit card companies, there may be some differences between them, as noted in the following list:

Revolving Charge Accounts Interest and Payments

1. The interest for revolving charge accounts is $1\frac{1}{2}\%$ to $1\frac{3}{4}\%$ per month on the unpaid balance for balances under \$500. If the balance is over \$500, some accounts charge only 1% interest per month on the amount over \$500.
2. The minimum monthly payment may be established by the department store, and it may or may not be similar to that of the national credit card companies.

EXAMPLE 4 Finance Charges, Balance, and Payments

Mary Lewis received her statement from Sears, where she has a revolving charge account. Her previous balance was \$225.59, and she charged an additional \$288.09 to her account. She also had \$105.97 in credits. Find the following:

(a) The finance charge for the month (Sears charges interest on the average daily balance of \$222.95, as described in the form shown in Figure 13.3.).

(b) The new balance.

(c) The minimum monthly payment.

SEARS Card
BOX 34577
Anytown, US 12345

Ms. Mary Lewis
123 Anywhere Street
Hometown, US 55555

Account Number: 12 34567 89012 3
Billing date: January 13

ACCOUNT SUMMARY

Previous balance		\$225.59
Total charges	+	288.09
Total credits	−	105.97
FINANCE CHARGE	+	3.91
New balance		\$411.62
Scheduled payment:		35.00
Minimum due:		**35.00**
Due date:		**February 12**

TRANSACTIONS

Dec 15 PANT, 1 PC DRESS, 2PC DRESS, 2PC DRESS........\$98.96
Dec 16 SHIRT, SHIRT, 2PC DRESS, 1PC DRESS,
1PC DRESS, EARS, EARRS 14K....................... \$178.02
Dec 16 PARTS, REPAIRS.. 6.88
Dec 16 SEASONAL/OUTDOOR SHOP................................ 4.23
Dec 17 *CREDIT - RETURN, CREDIT - RETURN.................−43.98*
Dec 17 *BLOUSE,*
CREDIT - CANCELLATION: LADIES DRESSES,
CREDIT - CANCELLATION: LADIES SPORTSWEAR
CREDIT - CANCELLATION: LADIES SPORTSWEAR,
NET AMOUNT FOR TRANSACTION.....................−31.99
Dec 31 *CREDIT - RETURN, CREDIT - RETURN.................−30.00*

HELPFUL INFORMATION
Available Credit: **\$5,445**

If the amount of Available Credit is not sufficient, or you have a question, call:
1–800–000–0000
M - S 9-9, SUN 12-5 ET

Mail any billing error notices to:
BOX 35065
Realtown, US 88888
Please include your account number with any correspondence.

SEARS BONUS CLUB
CONGRATULATIONS! You have earned a Bonus Certificate worth \$3.33 in savings at Sears. You will find it enclosed with this statement.

FINANCE CHARGE SCHEDULE	Average Daily Balance	**ANNUAL PERCENTAGE RATE**	Monthly Periodic Rate	Average Daily Balance	**FINANCE CHARGE**
All	Over \$0.00	21.0%	1.75%		
	\$222.95			Total	\$3.91

NOTE: See other side for important information

R

On a Sears Revolving Charge Account your monthly payments decrease as your account balance decreases . . . and, likewise your monthly payments increase as your account balance increases. Payments are flexible with your balance, as shown on the table below. Any premiums for Group Insurance, for which you may have contracted, other than Accidental Death and Disability Insurance, are in addition to your minimum monthly payments.

New Balance	*Minimum Payment*
\$ .01 to \$ 10.00	Balance
10.01 to 200.00	\$10.00
200.01 to 250.00	15.00
250.01 to 300.00	20.00
300.01 to 350.00	25.00
350.01 to 400.00	30.00
400.01 to 450.00	35.00
450.01 to 500.00	40.00
Over \$500.00	1/10 of New Bal.

Source: Courtesy of Sears, Roebuck & Co.

FIGURE 13.3

Solution

(a) Since the average daily balance was \$222.95, the finance charge is $1\frac{3}{4}\%$ (21% annual rate) of the \$222.95, that is,

$$0.0175 \times \$222.95 = \$3.91 \qquad \text{(rounded up)}$$

(b) The new balance is calculated as follows:

Previous balance	\$225.59
Finance charge	3.91
New purchases	288.09
Total credits	−105.97
New balance	\$411.62

(c) The minimum monthly payment is found by using the information given at the bottom of Figure 13.3. (This is a copy of the table that appears on the back of the statement.) Because the new balance is between \$400.01 and \$450, the minimum payment is \$35.

Some stores charge interest on the unpaid balance. How do we find the new balance under this method? The next example will tell you.

EXAMPLE 5 Finance Charges and New Balance

Ms. Spoto received a statement from a department store where she has a charge account. Her previous balance was \$280. She made a \$20 payment and charged an additional \$30.12 to her account. If the store charges 1.5% of the unpaid balance, find the following:

(a) The finance charge (b) The new balance

Solution

(a) The unpaid balance is \$280 − \$20 = \$260, so the finance charge is 1.5% of \$260, which is $0.015 \times \$260 = \$3.90$.

(b) The new balance is computed as follows:

Unpaid balance	\$260.00
Finance charge	3.90
Purchases	30.12
New balance	\$294.02

There is another way of charging interest when consumers buy on credit, the **add-on interest** used by furniture stores, appliance stores, and car dealers. For example, suppose you wish to buy some furniture costing \$2500 and you make a \$500 down payment. The amount to be financed is \$2000. If the store charges a 10% add-on rate for 5 years (60 monthly payments), the interest will be

$$\begin{aligned} I &= Prt \\ &= \$2000 \times 0.10 \times 5 = \$1000 \end{aligned}$$

Thus, the total amount to be paid is \$2000 + \$1000 = \$3000. The monthly payment is found by dividing this total by the number of payments.

$$\text{Monthly payment} = \frac{\$3000}{60} = \$50$$

Note that the add-on interest is charged on the *entire* \$2000 for the 5 years, but the customer does *not* have the full use of the entire amount for the 5 years. It would be fairer to charge interest on the *unpaid balance only.*

EXAMPLE 6 Total Interest and Monthly Payments

A used car costing \$8500 can be bought with \$2500 down and a 12% add-on interest rate to be paid in 48 monthly installments. Find the following:

(a) The total interest charged (b) The monthly payment

(c) The total interest charged and the monthly payment if the loan is at 12% **compound** interest.

Solution

(a) The amount to be financed is \$8500 − \$2500 = \$6000. The interest is 12% of \$6000 for 4 years. Thus,

$$\text{Interest} = 0.12 \times \$6000 \times 4 = \$2880$$

(b) Total amount owed = \$6000 + \$2880 = \$8880

$$\text{Monthly payment} = \frac{\$8880}{48} = \$185$$

(c) Go to http://www.onlineloancalculator.org and enter the information as shown. Press Calculate and a Loan Summary report is provided.

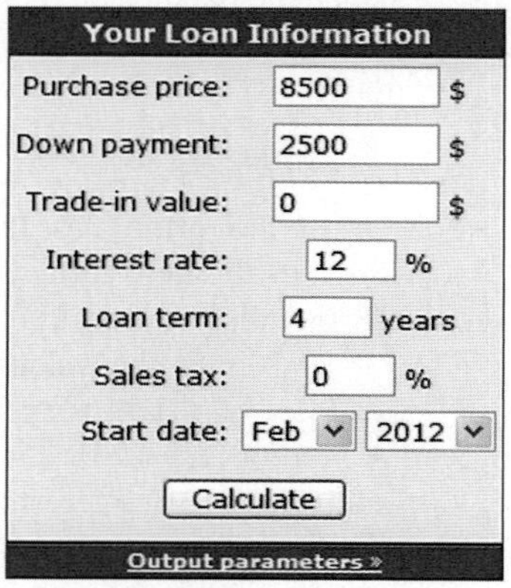

Loan Summary	
\$158.00 Monthly Payment	**\$7,584.14** Total of 48 Payments
\$1,584.14 Total Interest Paid	

The total interest paid is **\$1584.15** and the monthly payment is **\$158.** Compare with the add-on interest! We will talk more about auto loans in the next section.

Now suppose you receive this notice in the mail:

> Limited-time 0% APR
> Your credit line has been increased to \$26,200!

with this fine print added at the end:

> Effective on or after the first day following your statement closing date in October, the Daily Periodic Rate (DPR) for new cash advances and for new purchases posting to your account through your April statement closing date is 0% (corresponding **ANNUAL PERCENTAGE RATE (APR)** of 0%). Thereafter, the DPR for these promotional cash advance balances will be .035589% (corresponding **APR** of 12.99%), and the DPR for these promotional purchase balances will be .035589% (corresponding **APR** of 12.99%). **Important Reminder:** The transaction fee for credit card access checks, including the enclosed checks, is 3% of each transaction (Min. \$5, Max. \$50). See your Credit Card Agreement for any other applicable transaction fees.

If you have two credit cards with a \$1000 and a \$500 balance, respectively, each charging 9% APR, should you take this deal? Before you do, you should read the fine print. The limited time at 0% is 6 months (from the end of October to April) and after that your interest rate on the new card will be 12.99% (which we round to 13%). Let us compare the total amounts you would pay.

PROBLEM-SOLVING

Comparing Credit Card Options

① **Read** the problem.

We have two credit cards now. We have to compare the total amount these two cards cost with the total amount we would pay for a new card at 0% interest for 6 months and 13% thereafter.

② **Select** the unknown.

We have two unknowns: (1) the amount to pay on the two old (9%) credit cards and (2) the amount to pay on the new 13% credit card with the limited 0% interest.

③ **Think** of a plan.

Let us figure the amount we have to pay for the two 9% credit cards and the amount we have to pay for the new 13% card and compare the results.

④ **Use** the techniques you are studying to carry out the plan.

Since the balance on the old cards is \$1500(\$1000 + \$500), find the amount we pay on these two cards when $n = 2$ and $r = 9\%$. In Table 13.2, go to the 9% column and the $n = 2$ row. The entry there is 1.1881; thus, the amount to be paid is

$$1500 \cdot 1.1881 = \$1782.15$$

```
N=1.5
I%=13
PV=1500
PMT=0
FV=0
P/Y=1
C/Y=1
PMT:END BEGIN
```

Or use the formula for the amount $A = 1500(1 + 0.09)^2 = \$1782.15$.

For the new card, you do not pay interest for 6 months and then pay 13% for 18 months. To find the amount with a grapher, press [2nd] [FINANCE] [1] or [APPS] [1] and enter the values on the screen in the margin. As usual, press [▲] [▲] [▲] [ALPHA] [ENTER] to get FV, the future value of the loan, as \$1801.81, or use $A = 1500(1 + .13)^{1.5} =$ **\$1801.81.** Thus, this new card with no interest for 6 months and with a 13% interest thereafter is more expensive: \$1801.81 versus \$1782.15.

But there is more. To pay off the two 9% cards you have to write two checks, one for \$1000 and one for \$500. The **Important Reminder** tells you that the fee is 3% of each transaction—that is, \$30 and \$15—for an additional \$45 cost. Definitely, stay with the old cards unless you intend to pay off the new card in 6 months at 0% interest.

⑤ **Verify** the answer.

The verification (with a calculator if you wish) is left to you.

Cover the solution, write your own solution, and then check your work.

Remember, you have rights too! *Credit Cardholders' Bill of Rights of 2009.*

Credit Cardholders' Bill of Rights of 2009

1. Stop raising rates in the first year after an account is opened and require that promotional rates last at least 6 months.
2. Stop issuers from charging fees for spending beyond credit limits, unless approved by the cardholder.
3. Post credit card agreements on the Internet and let customers pay their bills online or by phone without adding a fee.
4. Give a 45-day notice and explanation before increasing interest rates. To read the entire bill, go to http://tinyurl.com/ygbvsto.

13.2 EXERCISES

1. Chad and Susan Johnson are married and have a good credit rating. Chad earns $25,000 per year. What is the least that Susan must earn for the couple to qualify for a card from company A? (See Example 1.)
2. Jim and Alice Brown are married and have an excellent credit rating. They both work and earn the same salaries. What is the least that each salary must be for the Browns to qualify for a card from company A? (See Example 1.)

In problems 3–7, find the new balance, assuming that the bank charges $1\frac{1}{2}$% per month on the unpaid balance.

	Previous Balance	Payment	New Purchases
3.	$100	$ 10	$50
4.	$300	$190	$25
5.	$134.39	$ 25	$73.98
6.	$145.96	$ 55	$44.97
7.	$378.93	$ 75	$248.99

In problems 8–17, find the following:

a. The finance charge for the month.

b. The new balance.

c. The minimum monthly payment.

Use the following rates and payments table:

Monthly Rate	$1\frac{1}{2}$%	1%
Unpaid balance	Up to $500	Over $500
New balance	Under $200	Over $200
Minimum payment	$10	5% of new balance

	Previous Balance	New Purchases
8.	$ 50.40	$173
9.	$ 85	$150
10.	$154	$ 75
11.	$344	$ 60
12.	$666.80	$ 53.49
13.	$ 80.45	$ 98.73
14.	$ 34.97	$ 50
15.	$ 55.90	$ 35.99
16.	$ 98.56	$ 45.01
17.	$ 34.76	$ 87.53

18. Phyllis Phillips has a revolving charge account that charges a finance charge on the unpaid balance using the following schedule:

    $1\frac{1}{2}$% per month of that portion of the balance up to $300.

    1% per month on that portion of the balance over $300.

    If the previous month's balance was $685, find the finance charge.

19. Daisy Rose has a credit card that charges a finance charge on the previous balance according to the following schedule:

    2% per month on balances up to $100.

    $1\frac{1}{2}$% per month on balances between $100 and $200.

    1% per month on balances of $200 or over.

    If the previous month's balance was $190, find the finance charge.

20. Mr. Dan Dapper received a statement from his clothing store showing a finance charge of $1.50 on a previous balance of $100. Find the monthly finance charge rate.
21. Paul Peters received a statement from the ABC Department Store showing a previous balance of $90. If the ABC store's finance charge is 1.5% on the previous balance, find the finance charge for the month.
22. In problem 21, if the monthly rate were 1.25%, what would be the finance charge for the month?
23. A $9000 used car can be purchased with $1600 down, the balance plus a 9% add-on interest rate to be paid in 36 monthly installments. Find
    a. the total interest charged.
    b. the monthly payment, rounded to the nearest dollar.
    c. the interest and monthly payment if the loan is at compound interest.
24. The Ortegas move into their first apartment and decide to buy furniture priced at $400 with $40 down, the balance plus 10% add-on interest to be paid in monthly installments in 1 year. Find
    a. the total interest charged.
    b. the monthly payment.
25. Wayne Pinski wishes to buy a stove and a refrigerator from an appliance dealer. The cost of the two items is $2400, and Wayne pays $400 down and finances the balance at 15% add-on interest to be paid in 18 monthly installments. Find
    a. the total interest charged.
    b. the monthly payment, to the nearest dollar.
26. Bill Seeker bought a boat costing $8500 with $1500 down, the balance plus add-on interest to be paid in 36 monthly installments. If the add-on interest rate was 18%, find
    a. the total interest charged.
    b. the monthly payment, to the nearest dollar.
27. Felicia Johnson bought a freezer costing $500 on the following terms: $100 down and the balance plus a 10% add-on interest rate to be paid in 18 monthly installments. Find
    a. the total interest to be paid by Ms. Johnson.
    b. the amount of her monthly payment, to the nearest dollar.
28. Cissie owes $1000 to a department store that charges a monthly interest rate of 1.5% on the unpaid balance. Cissie considers paying off this debt at the rate of $200 at the end of each month for 5 months and then paying off the balance at the end of the sixth month. She also considers making payments of $200 plus the month's interest at the end of each month for 5 months. Make a table showing the monthly payments and the interest

under each scheme. How much would Cissie save by using her second scheme? How do you account for this savings? Explain fully.

IN OTHER WORDS

29. An article in *Money* magazine states, "If you pay in full each month, you can get the most from the grace period by making big credit purchases just after your statement closing date and paying your bill on time at the last minute." Explain why.
30. The same article says to "buy bigger ticket items toward the end of the billing cycle and pay as much of the bill as possible as soon as you get your bill." Explain why.

USING YOUR KNOWLEDGE

A table shows that a monthly payment of $61 *(to the nearest dollar) for* 18 *months will repay* $1000 *with interest at* 1% *per month on the unpaid balance. Can we find the equivalent add-on interest rate? Yes; here is how to do it. Eighteen payments of* $61 *make a total of* $1098 (18 × $61), *which shows that the total interest paid is* $98. *As this is the interest for* 18 *months* ($1\frac{1}{2}$, *or* $\frac{3}{2}$, *years), the equivalent add-on interest rate is*

$$\frac{98}{(1000)(\frac{3}{2})} = \frac{98}{1500} \approx 0.065$$

or 6.5%, *to the nearest tenth of a percent.*

A table shows that the following monthly installment payments will repay $1000 *in the stated term and at the stated rate of interest on the unpaid balance. Find the equivalent add-on interest rate to the nearest tenth of a percent.*

	Monthly Payment	Term	Rate per Month on Unpaid Balance
31.	$47	2 years	1%
32.	$64	18 months	$1\frac{1}{2}$%
33.	$50	2 years	$1\frac{1}{2}$%
34.	$48	2 years	$1\frac{1}{4}$%

WEB IT EXERCISES

The questions in this section require access to the Internet. For help with exercises 1–3, *access links* http://tinyurl.com/d7ycxwf *or* http://www.cardweb.com.

1. Find and discuss the difference between a "bank card," a "travel and entertainment card," and a "house card."
2. What are secured, unsecured, guaranteed, and debit cards?
3. How do credit companies calculate your credit card interest each month?

13.3 Annual Percentage Rate (APR) and the Rule of 78

GETTING STARTED

OBJECTIVES

A. Find the APR of a loan.
B. Use the rule of 78 to find the refund and payoff of a loan.
C. Find the monthly payment for a loan using an online calculator.

TRUTH-IN-LENDING: APR TO Z

In the preceding section we studied several types of consumer credit: credit cards, revolving charges, and add-on interest. Before 1969, it was almost impossible to compare the different types of credit accounts available to consumers. In an effort to standardize the credit industry, the government enacted the federal Truth-in-Lending Act of 1969. A key feature of this law is the inclusion of the **total payment,** the **amount financed,** and the **finance charges** in credit contracts. In conjunction with this law, the Board of Governors of the Federal Reserve System issued Regulation Z requiring all lenders that make consumer loans to disclose certain information regarding the cost of consumer credit.

How can we compare loans? To do so, two items are of crucial importance: the **finance charge** and the **annual percentage rate (APR).** A look at annual percentage rates will enable us to compare different credit options.

For example, suppose you can borrow $200 for a year at 8% add-on or get the same $200 by paying $17.95 each month. Which is the better deal? In the first instance, you borrow \$200 at 8% add-on, which means that you pay 8% of \$200, or \$16, in finance charges. The charge you pay per \$100 financed is $\frac{16}{200} \times 100 = \$8$. On the other hand, if you pay \$17.95 per month for 12 months, you pay a total of \$215.40. Here the finance charge per \$100 financed is $\frac{15.40}{200} \times 100 = \$7.70$. Obviously, the second loan is a better deal.

Can we find the APR for each loan? To help in doing so, tables have been prepared so that we can translate the finance charge per \$100 to the APR (see Table 13.3). In this section we shall discuss the APR and one of the methods that will enable us to get a refund on our interest in case we decide to pay off our loan early.

As you have seen in Sections 13.1 and 13.2, there are many ways of stating the interest rates used to compute credit costs. A few examples are 12% *simple interest,* 12% *compounded annually,* 12% *add-on interest,* and 1% *per month on the unpaid balance.* How can you compare various credit costs? Without some help, it is difficult to do this. In response, Congress enacted the Truth-in-Lending Act on July 1, 1969. This law helps the consumer to know exactly what credit costs. Under this law, all sellers (car dealers, banks, credit card companies, and so on) must disclose to the consumer.

1. the finance charge.
2. the *annual percentage rate* (APR).

Table 13.3 True Annual Interest Rate (APR)

Number of Payments	14%	$14\frac{1}{2}$%	15%	$15\frac{1}{2}$%	16%	$16\frac{1}{2}$%	17%	$17\frac{1}{2}$%	18%
6	\$ 4.12	\$ 4.27	\$ 4.42	\$ 4.57	\$ 4.72	\$ 4.87	\$ 5.02	\$ 5.17	\$ 5.32
12	7.74	8.03	8.31	8.59	8.88	9.16	9.45	9.73	10.02
18	11.45	11.87	12.29	12.72	13.14	13.57	13.99	14.42	14.85
24	15.23	15.80	16.37	16.94	17.51	18.09	18.66	19.24	19.82
30	19.10	19.81	20.54	21.26	21.99	22.72	23.45	24.18	24.92
36	23.04	23.92	24.80	25.68	26.57	27.46	28.35	29.25	30.15
42	27.06	28.10	29.15	30.19	31.25	32.31	33.37	34.44	35.51
48	31.17	32.37	33.59	34.81	36.03	37.27	38.50	39.75	41.00

Note: Numbers in the body of the table are finance charges per \$100 of amount financed.

A APR

Recall that the finance charge is the total dollar amount you are charged for credit. It includes interest and other charges such as service charges, loan and finder's fees, credit-related insurance, and appraisal fees. The **annual percentage rate (APR)** is the charge for credit stated as a percent.

In general, the lowest APR corresponds to the best credit buy regardless of the amount borrowed or the period of time for repayment. For example, suppose you borrow \$100 for a year and pay a finance charge of \$8. If you keep the entire \$100 for the whole year and then pay \$108 all at one time, then you are paying an APR of 8%. On the other hand, if you repay the \$100 plus the \$8 finance charge in 12 equal monthly payments (8% add-on), you do not have use of the \$100 for the whole year. What, in this case, is your APR? The formulas needed to compute the APR are rather complicated, and as a consequence, tables such as Table 13.3 have been constructed to help you find the APR. These tables are based on the cost per \$100 of the amount financed. To use Table 13.3, you must first find the finance charge per \$1 of the amount financed and then multiply by 100. Thus, to find the APR on the \$100 borrowed at 8% add-on interest and repaid in 12 equal payments of \$9, first find the finance charge per \$100 as follows:

GRAPH IT

Want to find the exact interest with your grapher? Go to the TVM solver by pressing 2nd FINANCE 1 or APPS 1. Next, enter the values for $N(30)$, $I\%(0)$, $PV(1200)$, $PMT(-48.80)$, $FV(0)$, $P/Y(12)$, $C/Y(12)$, and END. Move the cursor up to $I\%$. Press ALPHA ENTER. The APR is about 16%, as shown by the $I\%$.

```
N=30
I%=16.00944902
PV=1200
PMT=-48.8
FV=0
P/Y=12
C/Y=12
PMT:END BEGIN
```

1. The finance charge is \$108 − \$100 = \$8.
2. The charge per \$100 financed is

$$\frac{\text{Finance charge}}{\text{Amount financed}} \times 100 = \frac{\$8}{\$100} \times 100 = \$8$$

Since there are 12 payments, look across the row labeled 12 in Table 13.3 until you find the number closest to \$8. This number is \$8.03. Then read the heading of the column in which the \$8.03 appears to obtain the APR. In this case, the heading is $14\frac{1}{2}\%$. Thus, the 8% add-on rate is equivalent to a $14\frac{1}{2}\%$ APR. (Of course, Table 13.3 gives the APR only to the nearest $\frac{1}{2}\%$.)

EXAMPLE 1 APR on Furniture

Mary Lewis bought some furniture that cost \$1400. She paid \$200 down and agreed to pay the balance in 30 monthly installments of \$48.80 each. What was the APR for her purchase?

Solution

We first find the finance charge per \$100 as follows:

Payments	30 × \$48.80 =	\$1464
Amount financed		−1200
Finance charge		\$ 264
Finance charge per \$100	$\frac{\$264}{\$1200} \times \$100 = \$22$	

We now turn to Table 13.3 and read across the row labeled 30 (the number of payments) until we find the number closest to \$22. This number is \$21.99. We then read the column heading to obtain the APR, 16%.

Note: There is also a formula to approximate the APR. The formula is discussed in problems 37–46.

B The Rule of 78

In all the preceding examples it has been assumed that the consumer will faithfully make the payments until the debt is satisfied. But what if you wish to pay in full before the final due date? (Perhaps your rich aunt gave you some money.) In many cases you are entitled to a partial refund of the finance charge! The problem is to find how much you should get back. One way of calculating the refund is to use the **rule of 78.** This rule assumes that the final payment includes a portion, say, \$$a$, of the finance charge, the payment before that includes \$$2a$ of the finance charge, the second from the final payment includes \$$3a$ of the finance charge, and so on. If the total number of payments is 12, then the finance charge is paid off by the sum of $a + 2a + 3a + 4a + 5a + 6a + 7a + 8a + 9a + 10a + 11a + 12a = 78a$ dollars. If the finance charge is F dollars, then

$$78a = F$$

so $a = \frac{1}{78}F$. This is the reason for the name "rule of 78." Now suppose you borrow \$1000 for 1 year at 8% add-on interest. The interest is \$80, and the monthly payment is one-twelfth of \$1080, that is, \$90. If you wish to pay off the loan at the end of 6 months, are you entitled to a refund of half the \$80 interest charge? Not according to the rule of 78. Your remaining finance charge payments, according to this rule, are

$$\tfrac{1}{78}F + \tfrac{2}{78}F + \tfrac{3}{78}F + \tfrac{4}{78}F + \tfrac{5}{78}F + \tfrac{6}{78}F = \tfrac{21}{78}F$$

Since $F = \$80$, you are entitled to a refund of $\frac{21}{78} \times \$80$, or \$21.54. There are six payments of \$90 each for a total of \$540, so you would need to pay \$540 − \$21.54 = \$518.46 to cover the balance of the loan.

Notice that to obtain the numerator of the fraction $\frac{21}{78}$, we had to add $1 + 2 + 3 + 4 + 5 + 6$. If there were n payments remaining, then to find the numerator, we would have to add.

$$1 + 2 + 3 + \cdots + (n - 2) + (n - 1) + n$$

There is an easy way to do this. Let us call the sum S. Then we can write the sum S twice, once forward and once backward.

$$S = 1 + 2 + 3 + \cdots + (n - 2) + (n - 1) + n$$
$$S = n + (n - 1) + (n - 2) + \cdots + 3 + 2 + 1$$

If we add these two lines, we get

$$2S = (n + 1) + (n + 1) + (n + 1) + \cdots + (n + 1) + (n + 1) + (n + 1)$$

and because there are n terms on the right,

$$2S = n(n + 1)$$
$$S = \frac{n(n + 1)}{2}$$

Thus, for $n = 6$, we obtain

$$S = \frac{6 \times (6 + 1)}{2} = \frac{6 \times 7}{2} = 21$$

as before. For $n = 12$, we find $S = (12 \times 13)/2 = 78$, which again agrees with our previous result.

Now suppose the loan is for 15 months, and you wish to pay it off in full after 10 payments, so that there are 5 payments remaining. By arguing in the same way as for the 12-month loan, you can see that you are entitled to a refund of a fraction a/b of the finance charge, where the numerator is

$$a = 1 + 2 + 3 + 4 + 5 = \frac{5 \times 6}{2} = 15$$

and the denominator is

$$b = 1 + 2 + 3 + \cdots + 15 = \frac{15 \times 16}{2} = 120$$

Thus, you are entitled to $\frac{15}{120} = \frac{1}{8}$ of the total finance charge.

In general, if the loan calls for a total of n payments and the loan is paid off with r payments remaining, then the unearned interest is a fraction a/b of the total finance charge, with the numerator

$$a = 1 + 2 + 3 + \cdots + r = \frac{r(r + 1)}{2}$$

and the denominator

$$b = 1 + 2 + 3 + \cdots + n = \frac{n(n + 1)}{2}$$

Thus,

$$\frac{a}{b} = \frac{r(r + 1)}{n(n + 1)}$$ The 2s cancel.

Thus, the unearned interest u is as shown in the box on the next page.

Formula for the Unearned Interest u

$$u = \frac{r(r+1)}{n(n+1)} \times F$$

where F is the finance charge.

For example, if an 18-month loan is paid off with 6 payments remaining, the amount of unearned interest u is

$$u = \frac{6 \times 7}{18 \times 19} \times F = \frac{7}{57}F$$

Although the denominator is no longer 78 (except for a 12-payment loan), the rule is still called the rule of 78.

EXAMPLE 2 Refunds and Payoffs

Cal Olleb purchased a television set on a 15-month installment plan that included a \$60 finance charge and called for payments of \$25 monthly. If Cal decided to pay off the loan at the end of the eighth month, find

(a) the amount of the interest refund u using the rule of 78.

(b) the amount needed to pay off the loan.

Solution

(a) Here, $n = 15$ and $r = 7$. We substitute into the formula to obtain

$$u = \frac{7 \times 8}{15 \times 16} \times \$60 = \frac{7}{30} \times \$60 = \$14$$

(b) There are 7 payments of \$25 each left, that is, \$175. Thus, Cal needs

$$\$175 - \$14 = \$161$$

to pay off the loan.

There is another way of calculating refunds and payoffs: by using a formula.

Actuary Formulas for the Refund u and the Payoff

The refund u is given by

$$u = \frac{r \cdot \text{PMT} \cdot V}{100 + V}$$

where r is the number of remaining payments, PMT is the payment, and V is the value from the APR table corresponding to r.

The payoff is given by

$$\text{PMT}\left[\frac{1-(1+i)^{-r}}{i}\right]$$

where PMT is the payment, r is the number of remaining payments, and $i = \frac{\text{APR}}{12}$.

EXAMPLE 3 Refunds and Payoffs Using Formulas

Refer to Example 1, where Mary Lewis bought furniture costing \$1400 with \$200 down and 30 payments of \$48.80. Assume that Mary wants to pay off the loan after 24 payments. Find

(a) the refund using the rule of 78.
(b) the refund using the formula.
(c) the payoff using the rule of 78.
(d) the payoff using the formula.

Solution

(a) Using the rule of 78, the refund is

$$u = \frac{r\,(r+1)}{n\,(n+1)} \times F$$

where $r = 30 - 24 = 6$, $n = 30$, and $F = \$264\ (30 \times \$48.60 - \$1200)$. Thus, the refund using the rule of 78 is

$$u = \frac{6\,(6+1)}{30\,(30+1)} \times 264$$

$$= \frac{42}{930} \times 264$$

$$= \$11.92$$

(b) The refund using the formula is

$$u = \frac{r \cdot \text{PMT} \cdot V}{100 + V}$$

where $r = 6$, PMT $= \$48.80$, and V is the value from the APR table corresponding to 6 and an APR of 16% (recall that the APR in Example 1 was 16%). This value is \$4.72. Thus, the refund is

$$u = \frac{6 \cdot 48.80 \cdot 4.72}{100 + 4.72} = \$13.20$$

(c) The payoff using the rule of 78 is

$$r \cdot \text{PMT} - u = 6 \cdot \$48.80 - \$11.92 = \$280.88$$

(d) The payoff using the formula is

$$\text{PMT} \cdot \left[\frac{1 - (1+i)^{-r}}{i}\right]$$

where $i = \dfrac{\text{APR}}{12}$. Since in Example 1 the APR $= 16\%$,

$$i = \frac{\text{APR}}{12} = \frac{0.16}{12}$$

and the payoff is

$$\$48.80 \cdot \left[\frac{1 - \left(1 + \frac{0.16}{12}\right)^{-6}}{\frac{0.16}{12}}\right] = \$279.60$$

C Applications

Realistically, there are more factors associated with loans than the APR and the rule of 78. In most cases you need a calculator to do the work! Such a calculator can be found online at http://tinyurl.com/3shsp2c. We illustrate the use of such a calculator in Example 4.

EXAMPLE 4 Monthly Payments from the Net

Suppose that the purchase price of a car is $15,000. There is no cash rebate, your trade-in is $4000, you do not owe any money on your trade-in, the down payment is $2000, and you want to finance the car at 10% for 36 months. What is your monthly payment?

Solution

Steps **1** and **2** (see Figure 13.4) are to enter your zip code and the vehicle sales price: ($15,000). Skip the sales tax ($0) and the title and registration ($0) for now. Next enter the value of your trade-in ($4000), the amount you owe on your trade in ($0), and the cash down payment ($2000).

In step **4,** enter the Loan Term in months (36) and the Finance Rate (10%). Press CALCULATE.

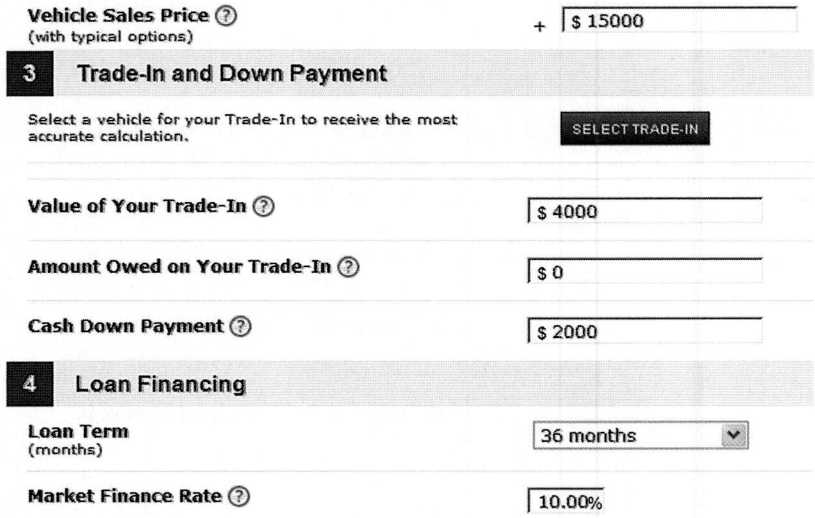

Used with permission from Edmunds.com.

FIGURE 13.4

As you can see in Figure 13.5, your monthly payment will be $290. By the way, you can also find out about your maintenance costs and leasing. You can even figure out what car you can afford by selecting the topic!

Used with permission from Edmunds.com.

FIGURE 13.5

13.3 EXERCISES

A APR

In problems 1–10, find the APR.

	Amount Financed	Finance Charge	Number of Payments
1.	$2500	$ 194	12
2.	$2000	$ 166	12
3.	$1500	$ 264	24
4.	$3500	$ 675	24
5.	$1500	$ 210	18
6.	$4500	$1364	36
7.	$4500	$1570	48
8.	$4000	$ 170.80	6
9.	$5000	$1800	48
10.	$4000	$ 908.80	30

B The Rule of 78

In problems 11–15, find the following:

a. *The unearned finance charge.*

b. *The amount needed to pay off the loan.*

	Finance Charge	Number of Payments	Frequency	Amount	Number of Payments Left
11.	$15.60	12	Monthly	$25	4
12.	$23.40	12	Monthly	$35	5
13.	$31.20	12	Monthly	$45	6
14.	$52.00	18	Weekly	$10	9
15.	$58.50	20	Weekly	$10	5

In problems 16–19, find

a. *the refund using the rule of 78.*

b. *the refund using the formula.*

c. *the payoff using the rule of 78.*

d. *the payoff using the formula.*

	Amount Financed	Finance Charge	No. of Payments	Payments Left
16.	$2500	$194	12	6
17.	$1500	$264	24	6
18.	$1500	$210	18	12
19.	$4500	$1570	48	12

(*Hint:* The APR was found in problems 1, 3, 5, and 7.)

20. Alfreda Brown bought a car costing $6500 with $500 down and the rest to be paid in 48 equal installments of $173.

a. What was the finance charge?

b. What was the APR?

21. Gerardo Norega bought a dinette set for $300, which he paid in 12 monthly payments of $27.

a. What was the finance charge?

b. What was the APR on this sale?

22. Yu-Feng Liang bought a used car for $6500. He made a down payment of $1000 and paid off the balance in 48 monthly payments of $159 each.

a. What was the finance charge? **b.** What was the APR?

23. A used sailboat is selling for $1500. The owner wants $500 down and 18 monthly payments of $63.

a. What finance charge does the owner have in mind?

b. What is the APR for this transaction?

24. Natasha Gagarin paid $195 interest on a $2000 purchase. If she made 12 equal monthly payments to pay off the account, what was the APR for this purchase?

25. Virginia Osterman bought a television set on a 12-month installment plan that included a $31.20 finance charge and called for payments of $50 per month. If she decided to pay the full balance at the end of the eighth month, find the following:

a. The interest refund.

b. The amount needed to pay off the loan.

26. Marie Siciliano bought a washing machine on a 12-month installment plan that included a finance charge of $46.80 and called for monthly payments of $70. If Marie wanted to pay off the loan after 7 months, find the following:

a. The interest refund.

b. The amount needed to pay off the loan.

27. A couple buys furniture priced at $800 with $80 down and the balance to be paid at 10% add-on interest. If the loan is to be repaid in 12 equal monthly payments, find

a. the finance charge. **b.** the monthly payment.

c. the interest refund if the couple decides to pay off the loan after 8 months.

d. the amount needed to pay off the loan.

28. Dan Leizack is buying a video recorder that costs $1200. He paid $200 down and financed the balance at 15% add-on interest to be repaid in 18 monthly payments. Find the following:

a. The finance charge. **b.** The monthly payment.

c. The interest refund if he pays off the loan after 9 months.

d. The amount needed to pay off the loan.

29. Joe Clemente bought a stereo costing $1000 with $200 down and 10% add-on interest to be paid in 18 equal monthly installments. Find

a. the finance charge.

b. the monthly payment.

c. the interest refund if he pays off the loan after 15 months.

d. the amount needed to pay off the loan.

C Applications

The following information will be used in problems 30–35. (Internet access is required. See http://tinyurl.com/6lt2puv, "Calculate Car Payment and Purchase Cost.") If you are buying a car, one of the factors to consider (but by no means the only one!) is the monthly payment. What are your options? Assume you are buying a $20,000 car, your trade-in is worth $2000, you have $1000 to give down, the sales tax is 6%, and you want to finance the car for 36 months at 8%.

30. a. To the nearest dollar, what is the total purchase cost?

b. What is the monthly payment?

c. If you want a $510 monthly payment, how much car can you afford? Try http://tinyurl.com/bu9bex5.

31. You can lower the monthly payment by getting a lower interest rate. What is the payment if the interest rate is

a. 7%? b. 6%?

32. On the basis of your answers to problems 30 and 31,

a. by how much is the payment lowered when you lower the rate by 1%?

b. if you want a monthly payment of about $536, what rate of interest will you have to negotiate?

33. What is the total cost to purchase the car when your finance rate is

a. 4%? b. 5%? c. 6%?

d. To the nearest dollar, by about how much is the total cost to purchase increased when the rate is increased by 1%?

34. An alternative plan to buying a car is leasing it. How do the costs of buying and leasing compare? A calculator at http://tinyurl.com/c2wjlfb will help us answer that question. Assume the purchase price of the car is $20,000 with a $1000 down payment and a 6% sales tax rate; the car is to be financed for 3 years at 8% with an annual depreciation of 15%. At the end of the 3 years the residual value of the car when you trade it in will be 50%, and you can assume a 1% rate of return on your investment. If we assume no other extra expenses, what would the lease payment and the net cost of the lease be?

35. Under the same conditions as problem 34, what would be the loan payment and the net cost for buying the car?

IN OTHER WORDS

36. Do you think the rule of 78 gives the debtor a fair break? In your own words, explain why or why not.

USING YOUR KNOWLEDGE

Approximating the APR by Formula *The APR for the loans just discussed can also be approximated (however, not within the $\frac{1}{4}$ of 1% accuracy required by Regulation Z*) by using the following formula:*

$$\text{APR} = \frac{2mI}{P(n+1)}$$

where m = the number of payment periods per year

I = the interest (or finance charge)

P = the principal (amount financed)

n = the number of periodic payments to be made

Thus, in Example 1, $m = 12$, $I = \$264$, $P = \$1200$, $n = 30$, and

$$\text{APR} = \frac{2mI}{P(n+1)} = \frac{2 \times 12 \times 264}{1200 \times 31} = 17\%$$

In problems 37–46, use the APR formula to find the APR to one decimal place in the specified problem. In each case, state the difference between the two answers.

37. Problem 1

38. Problem 2

39. Problem 3

40. Problem 4

41. Problem 5

42. Problem 6

43. Problem 7

44. Problem 8

45. Problem 9

46. Problem 10

WEB IT EXERCISES

The exercises in this section require access to the Internet. See http://tinyurl.com/c2wjlfb.

1. Look at Example 4 and discuss some expenses that have been omitted from the calculation.

2. Instead of buying a car you can lease (rent) one, but you should understand several new terms before you do so. Discuss the meaning and importance of the following terms applicable to leasing a car:

a. Residual value

b. Sales tax

c. Rate of return on investment

3. Suppose you wish to buy a $15,000 car to be financed at 7% for 36 months with a $1000 down payment and a 1% rate of return on your investment. Assume the sales tax is 6% of the car price, the residual value is 50 % of the $15,000 car less 3 years depreciation, at 15% per year, and you will buy the leased car for its residual price at the end of the 3 years.

a. What is the depreciation the first year? See http://tinyurl.com/c2wjlfb.

b. What is the net cost of leasing a $15,000 car every 3 years?

c. What is the net cost of buying a $15,000 car every 3 years?

d. Which is cheaper?

4. On the basis of the results in these problems, discuss the benefits of leasing versus purchasing a car.

*Regulation Z limits the use of this formula for approximating APRs to the "exceptional instance where circumstances may leave a creditor with no alternative."

13.4 Buying a House

GETTING STARTED

OBJECTIVE

Find how much mortgage you can afford, the down payment, the maximum amount you can borrow, and the monthly payment for a conventional or FHA loan.

HOUSES: HOW MUCH DOWN? HOW MUCH A MONTH?

As for most people, the single largest credit purchase (and investment) of your life will be buying a house. This purchase will require many decisions in what may be unfamiliar areas. This section will help you make these decisions wisely. The first question is: How much house can you afford? Look at the rules on the next page to figure this out. Next, what type of loans are available? See the discussion after Example 1 and the Using Your Knowledge section of Exercises 13.4. The information there is accurate, except for the rates. What will be the difference in the monthly payment amount if the interest rate is 1% higher? From Table 13.4 on page 798, you will see that for each \$1000 borrowed, the payment difference between a 7%, 30-year loan (first row, last column) and an 8% loan (third row, last column) is \$7.32 − \$6.64 = \$.68. Now, this does not seem like much, but if you are borrowing \$100,000, the difference in your monthly payment will be \$68! Can you figure out how much the payment difference per \$1000 will be on a 30-year loan if the rate is lowered from 13% to 12%? (Current rates may be lower than those appearing in the Using Your Knowledge section of Exercises 13.4.)

Of course, your monthly payment should not be the only consideration when buying a house. You must consider the amount of **down payment** required, the **interest rate,** the number of **years taken to pay off** the loan, whether there are any **penalties** for prepayment (paying the loan early), the **loan application fee** covering the cost of appraisal and credit report (\$250–\$300), and one of the most overlooked items when buying a home: the **closing costs.** These may include, but not be limited to, any or all of the following:

Points, Origination Fees and PMI

Points are fees lenders charge to increase profits. *Each point is equivalent to 1% of the loan amount*, so if you are borrowing \$80,000 and are paying 1 point, you have to pay \$800 at closing.

The **loan origination fee** is typically 1% of the loan amount (\$700 on a \$70,000 loan).

Private Mortgage Insurance (PMI) is insurance to protect the lender and is required if your down payment is less than 20% of the purchase price. Fees vary, but typically first-year premiums are 1% of the loan amount with a 5% down payment, 0.4% with a 10% down payment, and 0.3% with a 15% down payment, plus a monthly fee. You must prepay the first year's premium at closing, or you can decide to make a lump-sum payment of 2.95% of the mortgage amount with a 10% down payment or 2.30% with a 15% down payment.

Many homeowners say that buying a house is both a harrowing experience and a rewarding one at the same time.

What else must be paid at closing? First monthly mortgage payment, title search and title insurance, property survey, deed recording, document preparation, homeowners insurance, prorated property taxes, and lawyers' fees. These expenses can add 4 to 5% to the immediate price of the home. For an excellent article dealing with closing costs and a calculator to estimate them, go to http://tinyurl.com/7wwot7d. In this section you will learn all about mortgages!

One of the first decisions, if not the first, you must make when buying a house is how much to spend. Certain rules of thumb are used as guidelines in order to help people decide how much they should spend on a home. The following are three such rules:

Guidelines for Purchasing a Home

1. Spend no more than 2 to $2\frac{1}{2}$ times your annual income.
2. Limit housing expenses (the amount going to the mortgage payment) to 1 week's pay out of each month's gross pay (before deductions).
3. Do not let the amount of the monthly payment of principal, interest, taxes, and insurance exceed 28% of your monthly gross pay.

EXAMPLE 1 Can You Afford It?

John and Pat Harrell are graduate students and earn a total of \$35,000 annually. Can they afford an \$80,000 home with a \$60,000 mortgage that requires monthly payments of \$710 including principal, interest, taxes, and insurance (PITI)?

Solution

The following are the maximum amounts they can spend according to the three criteria given above:

1. $2.5 \times \$35{,}000 = \$87{,}500$
2. If the Harrells earn \$35,000 annually, in 1 week they earn

$$\frac{\$35{,}000}{52} = \$673.08$$

3. The Harrells's gross pay is \$35,000. Their monthly gross pay is

$$\frac{\$35{,}000}{12} = \$2916.67 \text{ per month}$$

and 28% of \$2916.67 = \$816.67.

Thus, the Harrells qualify under the first and third criteria but not under the second. Of course, they must come up with the \$20,000 down payment!

Now that you know how much house you can afford, you need to borrow money to buy it. How do you do that? By getting a **mortgage loan,** a contract in which the lender agrees to lend you money to buy a specific house or property. The contract creates a lien (a charge against the property making it security for payment) and you, in turn, agree to repay the money according to the terms of the contract. There are many different types of mortgage loan plans (see the Using Your Knowledge section of Exercises 13.4); two of these will be considered here: **conventional loans** and **Federal Housing Authority (FHA) loans** (Figure 13.6).

Today's Mortgage Rates

Loans up to \$417,000	Rate	APR
30 Year Fixed	3.250	3.516
15 Year Fixed	2.750	2.950
7 Year ARM	1.875	3.039
5 Year ARM	1.375	3.035
3 Year ARM	2.000	3.432
FHA Rates	Rate	APR
30 Year Fixed	3.250	3.937
15 Year Fixed	2.750	3.038

Rate Details as of 02/28/2012

APPLY NOW

Source: www.AmeriSave.com/Mortgage-Rates.

FIGURE 13.6

Conventional loans are arranged between you and a private lender. In these loans, the **amount of the down payment,** the **repayment period,** and the **interest rate** are agreed on by the **borrower** and the **lender.** The lender usually requires taxes and insurance to be paid in advance through a reserve **(escrow)** account. Lenders sometimes require borrowers to pay for private mortgage insurance (PMI) if the down payment is less than 20% of the loan amount. In addition, they may require that the buyer do the following:

Note: Interest rates vary. To get the best current rates in your state go to http://www.interest.com/mortgage/rates.

Conventional Loan Requirements

1. Be steadily employed and a resident of the state in which the property is located.
2. Have enough savings to make one or two mortgage payments.
3. Have the necessary down payment in hand (not borrowed).

Maximum amounts for conventional loans are set by individual lenders. Loans up to 80% of the value of the property are quite common, and loans of 90 to 95% can often be obtained.

FHA loans are made by private lenders and are insured by the Federal Housing Administration. The FHA does *not* make loans; it simply insures the lender against loss in case you, the borrower, fail to repay the loan in full. To pay expenses and cover this insurance, the FHA charges (at closing) an insurance premium of 3.8% of the loan for 30-year loans, 2.4% for 15-year loans, or an additional 0.5% is added to the interest rate to pay the insurance. To qualify for an FHA loan, a buyer must have the following:

FHA Loan Requirements

1. A total housing expense less than 29% of the buyer's gross income.
2. Total monthly payments (all debts with 12 or more payments plus total housing expenses) less than 41% of the gross income.

Interest rates on these loans are sometimes 1 or 2 percentage points lower than conventional loan rates. The FHA loan maximum for a single-family dwelling depends on its location and range from $172,632 to $312,895.

These limits were established by the FHA Down Payment Simplification Act of 2002, which requires that the borrower makes a cash investment of at least 3% of the purchase price (or appraised value). This 3% can be a down payment or a combination of 2.25% down payment and 0.75% closing costs. The maximum FHA loans are based on the location of the property, as shown in Table 13.4. To find the loan limits in your area, see the FHA guidelines at http://tinyurl.com/2x4vsm.

Table 13.4 FHA Maximum Loan Values by State

Low Closing Cost States	High Closing Cost States
Arizona, California, Colorado, Guam, Idaho, Illinois, Indiana, New Mexico, Nevada, Oregon, Utah, Virgin Islands, Washington, Wisconsin, Wyoming	All other states
98.75% if price is ≤$50,000	98.75% if price is ≤$50,000
97.65% if price is $50,001–$125,000	97.75% if price is >$50,000
97.15% if price is >$125,000	

EXAMPLE 2 Conventional and FHA Loans

A family wishes to buy a \$164,000 house in a state with high closing costs.

(a) If a conventional lender is willing to loan the family 90% of the price of the house, what will be the amount of the loan?

(b) What will be the down payment with that loan?

(c) If the family decides to obtain an FHA loan instead, what will be the minimum cash investment?

(d) What will be the maximum FHA loan the family can get?

Solution

(a) 90% of \$164,000 = \$147,600

(b) \$164,000 − \$147,600 = \$16,400 (which is 10% of \$164,000)

(c) With an FHA loan, in a high-closing-cost state, the minimum cash investment the family will have to pay down is 3% of \$164,000 = \$4920. Why didn't we use 97.75% of \$164,000 = \$160,310, making the down payment \$3690 (\$164,000 − \$160,310)? Because \$3690 is less than the required \$4920 minimum cash investment of 3%.

(d) The maximum FHA loan the family can get is

\$164,000 − \$4920 = \$159,080

Here is the procedure we shall use to determine the maximum loan amount and cash investment for an FHA loan.

Finding Down Payment and FHA Loan Amount

Step 1. Calculate the minimum cash investment: 3% of price.
Step 2. Calculate the FHA down payment:

Acquisition price − FHA loan amount

Down payment: Higher value between steps 1 and 2
Loan amount: Acquisition price − down payment

EXAMPLE 3 Finding Down Payment and FHA Loan Amount

Marcus McWaters is buying a \$100,000 home in Florida (a high-closing-cost state) and paying \$2500 in closing costs.

(a) What is the minimum cash investment?

(b) What is the maximum FHA loan he can get?

Solution

(a) The minimum cash investment is 3% of \$100,000, or \$3000.

(b) ***Step 1.*** The minimum cash investment is \$3000.
Step 2. The FHA down payment is

Acquisition price − FHA loan amount
= (\$100,000 + \$2500) − (97.75% of \$100,000)
= \$102,500 − \$97,750
= \$4750

Step 3. The down payment is \$4750 (the higher value in steps 1 and 2). The loan amount is

$$\begin{aligned}&\text{Acquisition price} - \text{down payment}\\&\quad = \$102{,}500 - \$4750\\&\quad = \$97{,}750\end{aligned}$$

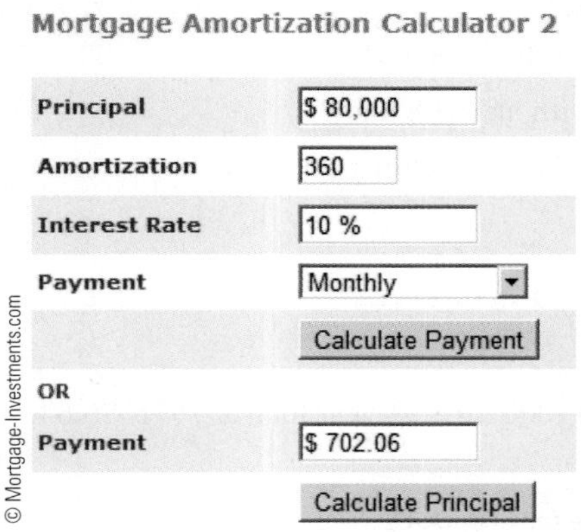

The last item we shall discuss in connection with mortgages is the **actual amount** of the monthly payment. This amount depends on three factors.

1. The amount borrowed.
2. The interest rate.
3. The number of years taken to pay off the loan.

Table 13.5 shows the monthly payments for \$1000 borrowed at various rates and for various times. To figure the actual monthly payment, find the appropriate interest rate and the payment period, and then multiply the amount shown in Table 13.5 by the number of thousands of dollars borrowed. Thus, to figure the monthly payment on an \$80,000 mortgage at 10% for 30 years, look down the column for 30 years until you come to the row labeled 10%. The amount per \$1000 is \$8.78. Multiply this amount by 80 (there are 80 thousands in \$80,000) to obtain \$702.40 for the required monthly payment. There is a calculator that will show you the monthly payments at http://tinyurl.com/87fpr8s (see the margin).

Table 13.5 Monthly Payments (Principal and Interest) for Each \$1000 Borrowed

	Payment Period				
Interest Rate (%)	**10 Years**	**15 Years**	**20 Years**	**25 Years**	**30 Years**
5	10.61	7.91	6.60	5.85	5.37
$5\frac{1}{2}$	10.85	8.17	6.88	6.14	5.68
6	11.10	8.44	7.16	6.44	6.00
$6\frac{1}{2}$	11.36	8.71	7.46	6.75	6.32
7	11.60	8.97	7.75	7.05	6.64
$7\frac{1}{2}$	11.86	9.26	8.04	7.37	6.98
8	12.12	9.54	8.35	7.70	7.32
$8\frac{1}{2}$	12.38	9.83	8.66	8.04	7.67
9	12.67	10.14	9.00	8.39	8.05
$9\frac{1}{2}$	12.94	10.44	9.32	8.74	8.41
10	13.22	10.75	9.65	9.09	8.78
$10\frac{1}{2}$	13.49	11.05	9.98	9.44	9.15
11	13.78	11.37	10.32	9.80	9.52
$11\frac{1}{2}$	14.06	11.68	10.66	10.16	9.90
12	14.35	12.00	11.01	10.53	10.29
$12\frac{1}{2}$	14.64	12.33	11.36	10.90	10.67
13	14.93	12.65	11.72	11.28	11.06
$13\frac{1}{2}$	15.23	12.98	12.07	11.66	11.45
14	15.53	13.32	12.44	12.04	11.85
$14\frac{1}{2}$	15.83	13.66	12.80	12.42	12.25
15	16.13	14.00	13.17	12.81	12.64
$15\frac{1}{2}$	16.44	14.34	13.54	13.20	13.05
16	16.75	14.69	13.91	13.59	13.45
$16\frac{1}{2}$	17.06	15.04	14.29	13.98	13.85
17	17.38	15.39	14.67	14.38	14.26

GRAPH IT

To solve part (c), press 2nd FINANCE 1 or APPS 1, enter the values for $N(360)$, $I(7\%)$, $PV(-95{,}500)$, $PMT(0)$, $FV(0)$, $P/Y(12)$, and $C/Y(12)$, and enter END. Now press ▲ ▲ ▲ ▲ ALPHA ENTER. The payment is given as \$635.36. For part (e), enter the values $N = 360, I = 9\%, PV = -97{,}000$, $PMT = 0$, $FV = 0$, $P/Y = 12$, and $C/Y = 12$ and enter END. Finally, press ▲ ▲ ▲ ▲ ALPHA ENTER. The payment is given as \$780.48.

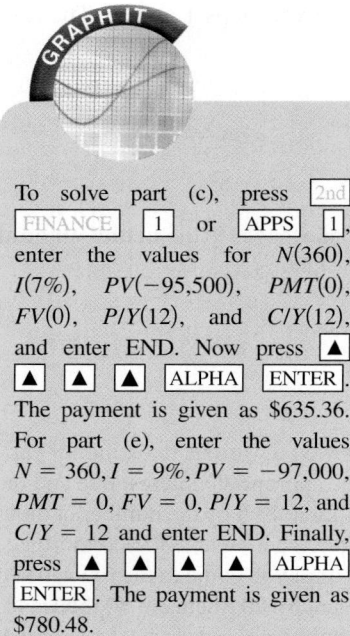

EXAMPLE 4 Payments and FHA Loans

Athanassio and Gregoria Pappas wish to obtain a 30-year loan to buy a \$100,000 house in Tarpon Springs, Florida, a high-closing-cost state.

(a) If they can get a loan of 95% of the value of the house, what is the amount of the loan?

(b) What will be the down payment with that loan?

(c) If the interest rate is 7%, what will be the monthly payment?

(d) What will be the minimum cash investment with an FHA loan?

(e) If the FHA loan carries 9% interest, what will be the monthly payment?

Solution

(a) 95% of \$100,000 = \$95,000

(b) \$100,000 − \$95,000 = \$5000

(c) We read from Table 13.5 that the amount per \$1000 on a 30-year loan at 7% is \$6.64. Thus, the monthly payment will be

95 × \$6.64 = \$630.80 *The mortgage loan is for \$95,000.*

(d) With an FHA loan, the minimum cash investment will be

3% of \$100,000 = \$3000

Note that 97.75% of \$100,000 = \$97,750, leaving a down payment of \$2250, less than the 3% required minimum cash investment.

(e) In Table 13.5 we find the amount per \$1000 on a 30-year loan at 9% to be \$8.05. The amount to be financed is \$97,000 (\$100,000 − \$3000). Thus, the monthly payment will be

97 × \$8.05 = \$780.85

Note: This is not the entire payment because for an FHA loan, interest, insurance, and taxes must be added to this amount.

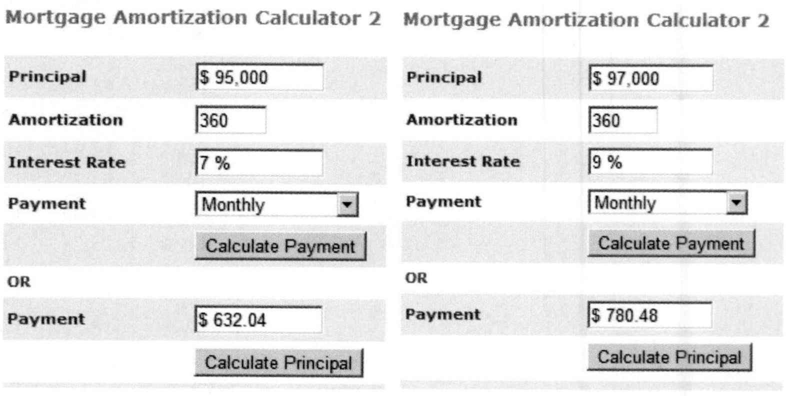

With the calculator at http://tinyurl.com/87fpr8s we enter the data shown above and the payments are \$632.04 and \$780.48, respectively.

What if we don't have Table 13.5 to find the monthly payment? There is a formula that will do it for us. Here it is, but be warned that you need a calculator to use it!

Formula to Find the Monthly Payment for a Loan

The monthly payment M for a loan of P dollars for n months at monthly rate i is

$$M = \frac{Pi}{1 - (1 + i)^{-n}}$$

For example, the monthly payment M on the 30-year, 9%, \$97,000 loan of part (e) is

$$M = \frac{Pi}{1 - (1 + i)^{-n}}$$

Here, $P = 97{,}000$, $i = \frac{9\%}{12} = 0.0075$, and $n = 12 \times 60 = 360$ months. Substituting, we obtain

$$M = \frac{(97{,}000)(0.0075)}{1 - (1 + 0.0075)^{-360}}$$

Using a calculator,

$$M = \$780.48$$

This figure is very close to the \$780.85 we obtained in part (e) but be very careful when using your calculator! Make sure that you enter the denominator as $[1 - (1 + 0.0075)^{-360}]$.

EXAMPLE 5 Finding the Monthly Payment Using the Formula

Use the formula to find the monthly payment M on a \$175,000 loan at 6% for 15 years.

Solution

In this case, $P = \$175{,}000$, $i = \frac{6\%}{12} = 0.005$, and $n = 12 \times 15 = 180$ months. Substituting,

$$M = \frac{(175{,}000)(0.005)}{1 - (1 + 0.005)^{-180}}$$
$$= \$1476.75$$

Your screen should look like the one in the margin where the -180 is entered by pressing the gray key $\boxed{(-)}$, indicating the additive inverse, or negative, of 180.

13.4 EXERCISES

1. A family has a \$40,000 annual salary. Can they afford an \$80,000 house with a \$70,000 mortgage requiring payments of \$750 per month, including principal, interest, taxes, and insurance?
   a. Use the first criterion given in the text.
   b. Use the second criterion given in the text.
   c. Use the third criterion given in the text.

2. A family earns \$36,000 annually. Can they afford a \$95,000 house with a \$60,000 mortgage requiring monthly payments of \$570, including principal, interest, taxes, and insurance?
   a. Use the first criterion given in the text.
   b. Use the second criterion given in the text.
   c. Use the third criterion given in the text.

3. The Browning family of Colorado wants to buy a $77,000 house.
   a. If they can get a loan of 80% of the value of the house, what is the amount of the loan?
   b. What will be the down payment on this loan?
   c. If they decide to obtain an FHA loan, what will be the minimum cash investment? (Do not forget that the maximum FHA loan for this location has to be determined using Table 13.4 on page 797.)
4. The Scotdale family of Arizona wants to buy a $60,000 house.
   a. If they can get a conventional loan of 95% of the purchase price, what will be the amount of the loan?
   b. What will be the down payment with this loan?
   c. If they use an FHA loan, what will be the minimum cash investment?

In problems 5–10, find the total monthly payment, including taxes and insurance, for the given mortgage loan using Table 13.5. Calculator answers may be slightly different.

	Amount	Rate	Time (Years)	Annual Taxes	Annual Insurance
5.	$60,000	6%	20	$800	$360
6.	$80,000	$6\frac{1}{2}$%	30	$1200	$380
7.	$90,000	9%	25	$1200	$960
8.	$80,000	$9\frac{1}{2}$%	20	$1400	$740
9.	$173,000	$5\frac{1}{2}$%	30	$2400	$1200
10.	$80,000	$10\frac{1}{2}$%	15	$1000	$390

In problems 11–14, find
   a. the minimum cash investment.
   b. the maximum FHA loan amount.

	Sale Price	State
11.	$45,000	Ajo, Arizona
12.	$150,000	Orlando, Florida
13.	$75,000	Eola, Oregon
14.	$95,000	Bath, Maine

15. Assume that the buyer in problem 11 is paying closing costs of $1200.
   a. What is the acquisition cost?
   b. What is the maximum FHA loan amount?
   c. Use the formula to find the monthly payment if the loan is at 6% for 15 years.
16. Assume that the buyer in problem 12 is paying closing costs of $6000.
   a. What is the acquisition cost?
   b. What is the maximum FHA loan amount?
   c. Use the formula to find the monthly payment if the loan is at 6% for 30 years.
17. Assume that the buyer in problem 13 is paying a promotionally reduced $100 in closing costs.
   a. What is the acquisition cost?
   b. What is the maximum FHA loan amount?
   c. Use the formula to find the monthly payment if the loan is at $7\frac{1}{2}$% for 25 years.
18. Assume that the buyer in problem 14 is paying a reduced $500 in closing costs.
   a. What is the acquisition cost?
   b. What is the maximum FHA loan amount?
   c. Use the formula to find the monthly payment if the loan is at 9% for 10 years.

In problems 19–28, use Table 13.4 on page 797 or table 13.5. Calculator answers may be slightly different.

19. The Aikido family wants to obtain a conventional loan for 30 years at 11%. Suppose it finds a lender that will lend 95% for the $60,000 house it has selected, and its taxes and insurance amount to $1500 per year.
   a. What will be their down payment on the loan?
   b. What will be their total monthly payment, including taxes and insurance?
20. The Perez family is planning to buy a $90,000 house. Suppose the family gets a loan of 80% of the price of the house, and this is a 25-year loan at 10%.
   a. What will be the family's down payment on the loan?
   b. If the family's taxes and insurance amount to $810 annually, what will be the monthly payment, including taxes and insurance?
21. The Green family of Kansas obtained a 30-year FHA loan at $6\frac{1}{2}$% to buy a $100,000 house. The family made the minimum required down payment, and taxes and insurance amounted to $2400 annually.
   a. What was the family's down payment?
   b. What was the total monthly payment?
22. A family was planning to buy a $95,000 house with an FHA loan carrying $9\frac{1}{2}$% interest over a 20-year period. If the family could get the largest possible loan, $75,000 for this location, and taxes and insurance amounted to $1200 annually, find
   a. the family's down payment.
   b. the total monthly payment.
23. The Bixley family has a $50,000 mortgage loan at 10% for 30 years.
   a. What is the family's monthly mortgage payment?
   b. How many payments will the family have to make in all?
   c. What is the total amount the family will pay for principal and interest?
   d. What is the total interest the family will pay?
   e. If the loan was 80% of the price of the house, is the price more or less than the total interest?
24. The Peminides have a $35,000 mortgage loan at 9% for 30 years.
   a. What is their monthly mortgage payment?
   b. How many payments will they have to make in all?
   c. What is the total amount they will pay for principal and interest?
   d. If their loan was 80% of the price of the house, is the price more or less than the total interest?

25. If you think house prices are high, there is bad news! The costs mentioned so far are not all-inclusive. You also have to pay **closing costs.** These costs include various fees and are usually paid at the time of closing, that is, when the final mortgage contract is signed. They are in addition to the agreed-on down payment. The following are some typical closing costs for a $50,000 house with the buyer making a 20% down payment (prices vary):

Credit report fee	$ 45	
$\frac{3}{12}$ estimated taxes of $600	$150	To escrow account
Insurance premium for 1 year	$300	
$\frac{2}{12}$ insurance premium	$ 50	To escrow account
Title insurance	$220	
Mortgage recording fee	$ 20	
Loan fee, 1 point (1% of loan amount)	$?	
Total closing costs	$?	

a. What would be the total cash payment, down payment plus closing costs, at the time of closing?

b. If the buyer had to make escrow account (an account maintained by the mortgage company and used to pay property taxes and insurance) deposits each month for taxes and insurance, what would be the combined monthly payment under mortgage terms of 14% for 30 years?

c. Suppose the lender agreed to add the closing costs to the loan amount instead of asking for cash. What would be the combined monthly payment with the same terms as in part (**b**)?

Remember to read all about closing costs at http://tinyurl.com/7wwot7d.

26. The following are some different closing costs for a $75,000 house with a 10% down payment (prices vary):

Credit report fee	$ 45
Mortgage recording fee	$ 15
Lot survey	$250
Loan fee (1.5% of loan amount)	$?
Insurance premium for 1 year	$210
Total closing costs	$?

a. What would be the total cash payment, down payment plus closing costs, at the time of closing?

b. If no escrow account was required, what would be the monthly payment for a 25-year, 10% loan?

c. If the lender added the closing costs to the loan amount instead of asking for cash, what would be the monthly payment under the same terms as in part (**b**)?

27. The following are some closing costs for a $120,000 home with 20% down (prices vary):

Credit fee	$ 45
Mortgage recording fee	$ 25
Plot plan	$250
1-point loan fee	$?
Title insurance	$350
Total closing costs	$?

a. Find the cash payment, down payment plus closing costs, at the time of closing.

b. If the buyer had to make escrow account deposits each month for $1200 taxes and insurance, what would be the combined monthly payment under mortgage terms of 9% for 30 years?

c. Suppose the lender agrees to add the closing costs to the loan amount instead of asking for cash. What would be the combined monthly payment with the same terms as in part (**b**)?

28. The following are some closing costs for a $150,000 home with 25% down (prices vary):

Credit fee	$ 45
Mortgage recording fee	$ 25
Lot survey	$300
$1\frac{1}{2}$-point loan fee	$?
Title insurance	$420
Total closing costs	$?

a. Find the cash payment, down payment plus closing costs, at the time of closing.

b. If the buyer had to make escrow account deposits each month for $1500 taxes and insurance, what would be the combined monthly payment under mortgage terms of 8% for 20 years?

c. Suppose the lender agrees to add the closing costs to the loan amount instead of asking for cash. What would be the combined monthly payment with the same terms as in part (**b**)?

The following information about closing costs for an $84,000 house with a 10% down payment will be used in problems 29–30:

2 points	2% of loan contract
Appraisal and credit report	$235 conventional loan ($200 FHA)
Recording fee	$ 25
Title insurance	$295

29. Assume you are getting a 15-year conventional loan with a 10% interest rate. Use the given information to find the following:

a. The total cash payment, down payment plus closing costs, at the time of closing.

b. The monthly payment (assuming no escrow account).

30. Assume you are getting a 30-year FHA loan with an 8% interest rate. Use the given information to find the following:

a. The total cash payment, down payment plus closing costs, at the time of closing.

b. The monthly payment (assuming no escrow account).

IN OTHER WORDS

31. Write in your own words the advantages and disadvantages of an FHA loan.

32. Write in your own words the advantages and disadvantages of a conventional loan.

33. Suppose you obtain a $100,000 conventional loan and finance it at 9% for 30 years. Which is greater, the price of the house or the interest you pay on the loan? Answer the same question for a $50,000 loan. Explain your answers.

USING YOUR KNOWLEDGE

There are so many different types of loans available that we cannot discuss all the possible financing alternatives you may have when you buy a house. The accompanying information derived from Money *magazine might help you to make some sense out of the existing confusion. Most of the types of loans mentioned are still used, but interest rates are much* lower *in many cases!*

A Gallery of Loans The following chart will help you shop for the housing loan that's best for you. Your choice should be determined by your income and your expectations about inflation and interest rates. As they rise and fall, so will rates for inflation-indexed and adjustable-rate mortgages. Fixed-rate loans don't fluctuate, but they can be expensive. All the loans listed are widely available, except for the adjustable-balance mortgages. They have been offered so far only in Utah, but they may become more common in the future if inflation develops.

34. Find the current rates for the type loans in the chart. To find some of these rates, access link http://tinyurl.com/cpmrc68.

Type of Loan	Typical Minimum Down Payment	Initial Interest Rate (Rates Vary)	Interest Rate After 5 Years	Who Should Consider This Type Loan
Fixed rate				
Conventional	10–20%	5–8%	Unchanged	High-income people who believe interest rates won't drop much
Graduated payment	5%	5–8%	Unchanged	People who feel certain their incomes will rise substantially
Growing equity	10%	5–7%	Unchanged	Borrowers who can afford high payments and want to pay off their loans early
Adjustable rate				
Typical adjustable rate	10%	5–$6\frac{1}{2}$%	Unknown	People who expect interest rates to drop
Dual rate	10%	5–7%	Unknown	Borrowers who, in return for lower monthly payments, are willing to give some of their equity to lenders if interest rates rise
Balloon payment	20%	5–7%	Loan is usually repaid by then	Borrowers who believe they'll be able to refinance their loans at lower rates in the future
Equity sharing				
Shared equity	10%	7–8%	Unchanged	People who are willing to give investors part of their houses' tax benefits and future appreciation in return for help in raising down payments and making monthly loan payments
Partnership mortgage	10%	7–8%	Unchanged	Low-income people who are willing to give investors most of the tax deductions a home generates and some of the future appreciation in exchange for down payments and help in monthly payments
Inflation indexed				
Adjustable balance	10%	$6\frac{1}{2}$%	Unknown	Borrowers who are confident that their incomes will keep pace with inflation

WEB IT EXERCISES

The questions in this section require access to the Internet.

1. Discuss the following questions:
   a. By how many years would a mortgage be reduced if you make biweekly rather than monthly payments? What does the answer depend on?
   b. Which is better, biweekly payments or extra money in each regular payment?

Now, do the problems and find out some facts. Assume you are considering a $100,000 *mortgage at* 8% *for* 30 *years.*

2. For the $100,000 mortgage at 8% for 30 years,
   a. what would the payment be?
   b. what is the total amount of interest you will pay?
   c. if you decide to make biweekly payments, how many years will it take to pay off the entire mortgage?
3. Which do you think is better, to make biweekly payments or to pay $60 extra on each payment? (*Hint:* Find out how many years it will take to pay off the entire mortgage when you add the extra $60 in each payment.)
4. If you want to consider a 15-year mortgage with the same payment as the 8%, 30-year mortgage, what interest rate do you need?

13.5 Investing in Stocks, Bonds, and Mutual Funds

GETTING STARTED

OBJECTIVES

A. Find the cost and returns on a stock.
B. Find the cost and returns on a bond.
C. Find the Net Asset Value (NAV) and the percent return of a mutual fund.

TYPES OF INVESTMENTS

Now that we have learned how to handle interest, taxes, credit cards, and mortgages, what can we do if we have some money left? We can invest it! **Investing** is the art of committing money or capital to an endeavor with the expectation of obtaining additional income or profit. Your investments may be **short term** [bank savings accounts, money-market funds, certificates of deposit (CDs)] or **long term** (stocks, bonds, and mutual funds). We shall concentrate on long-term investments and, in particular, on their cost and profitability (or lack thereof).

A Becoming an Owner: Investing in Stocks

When you buy stocks (shares) in a company, you become part owner of the company in which you have invested. What do you get then? The right to vote at the shareholder's meeting and receive **dividends** (profits) that the company allocates its owners.

To buy or sell stocks this of a **broker,** an individual or firm that charges a fee or **commission** for executing (doing) buy and sell orders submitted by an investor like you. Here are three types of brokers you may use:

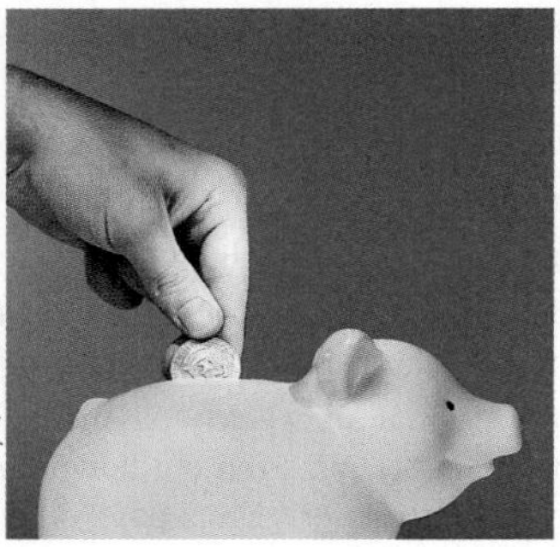

© Stockbyte/Photos.com

Types of Stock Brokers

Full service: Gives investment and financial advice. Charges a commission on the number of shares you buy or sell. The charges are usually a percent of the transaction and typically range from \$100 to \$300 per trade.
Discount: Charges a reduced commission, typically \$30 to \$55 per transaction, and usually does not provide investment advice. (If it does, they will charge you for it!)
Deep discount: Only executes (does) stock and option trades at a flat rate (say, \$25, but as low as \$10) regardless of the size of the trade.

We are now ready to learn how to buy and sell stocks. How much will it cost, and how much money (return on your investment) can you make? The cost of one share of stock and related information can be found in newspapers in stock tables similar to Table 13.6.

Table 13.6

52W high	52W low	Stock	Ticker	Div	Yield %	P/E	Vol 00s	High	Low	Close	Net chg
s45.39	19.75	ResMed	RMD			52.5	3831	42.00	39.51	41.50	-1.90
11.63	3.55	Revlon A	REV				162	6.09	5.90	6.09	+0.12
77.25	55.13	RioTinto	RTP	2.30	3.2		168	72.75	71.84	72.74	+0.03
31.31	16.63	RitchieBr	RBA			20.9	15	24.49	24.29	24.49	-0.01
8.44	**1.75**	**RiteAid**	**RAD**				**31028**	**4.50**	**4.20**	**4.31**	**+0.21**
s38.63	18.81	RobtHalf	RHI			26.5	6517	27.15	26.50	26.50	+0.14
51.25	27.69	Rockwell	ROK	1.02	2.1	14.5	6412	47.99	47.00	47.54	+0.24
Highest and lowest levels at which the stock traded the last 52 weeks		Company name	Ticker symbol	Dividend per share	Percent return on dividend	Price to earnings ratio	Total number of shares traded	Price range the stock traded throughout the day		Last trading price recorded when the market closed	Dollar value change in the stock price from the previous day closing price

Source: Copyright © 1999-2012 Investopedia, Inc. http://www.investopedia.com.

EXAMPLE 1 Finding the Cost and Return for Stocks

Mida Lariz bought 100 shares of Any-Cola at \$42.50 per share and paid a \$50 commission on the transaction. A year later she sold the 100 shares at \$47.75 per share and paid a 2% commission on the sale. If Any-Cola paid \$1.12 per share in dividends, find

(a) the total cost of the 100 shares.

(b) the total dividend.

(c) the commission when selling the 100 shares.

(d) the capital gain (profit) after she sold the 100 shares.

(e) the total return for the year.

(f) the percent of return.

Solution

(a) Total cost $= (\$42.50 \text{ per share}) \times (100 \text{ shares}) + \text{commission}$

$$= \$4250 + \$50 = \$4300$$

Thus, the total cost was \$4300.

(b) Total dividend = (\$1.12 per share) × (100 shares) = \$112
Thus, the total dividend was \$112.

(c) The commission on the sale was

$$\begin{aligned} 2\% \times (\text{sale price}) &= 0.02 \times (\$47.75 \times 100) \\ &= 0.02 \times \$4775 \\ &= \$95.50 \end{aligned}$$

Thus, the commission on the sale was \$95.50.

(d)
$$\begin{aligned} \text{Capital gain} &= (\text{change in price per share}) \times 100 - (\text{commissions}) \\ &= (\$47.75 - \$42.50) \times 100 - \$50 - \$95.50 \\ &= \$525 - \$50 - \$95.50 \\ &= \$379.50 \end{aligned}$$

The capital gain (profit) was \$379.50.

(e)
$$\begin{aligned} \text{Total return} &= \text{capital gain} + \text{dividends} \\ &= \$379.50 + \$112 \\ &= \$491.50 \end{aligned}$$

Thus, the total return was \$491.50.

(f)
$$\begin{aligned} \text{The percent of return PR} &= \frac{\text{total return}}{\text{total cost of entire transaction}} \\ &= \frac{\$491.50}{\$4250 + \$50 + \$95.50} \\ &= \frac{\$491.50}{\$4395.50} \\ &= 11.18\% \end{aligned}$$

A Return on Investment Calculator can be found at http://tinyurl.com/bundr35. (You have to figure the commission on the sale by hand and then enter the rest of the information.) The profits for capital gain (\$379.50), dividends (\$112), return on investment (\$491.50), and period yield (11.430%) are then provided by the calculator.

B Becoming a Lender: Investing in Bonds

Instead of becoming part owner of a company by becoming a stockholder, you may decide to lend money to the company or even the government. What do you get then? You get **interest** on your money, and eventually, you get all your money back. A **bond** is nothing more than an IOU ("I owe you") from a company or government to you, the lender. When you invest in bonds, the bond you buy shows the amount of money being borrowed (**face value**), the interest rate (**coupon rate** or **yield**) that the borrower has to pay, the interest payments (**coupon payments**), and the deadline for paying the money back (**maturity dates**).

For example, you can buy a bond with a **face value** of \$1000, a **coupon rate** of 7%, and a **maturity** of 10 years. This means that you will get \$70 (7% of \$1000) each year for the next 10 years. After the 10 years, the bond **matures,** and you get your \$1000 back.

Many bonds pay interest semiannually, so you will receive *two* payments of \$35 a year for 10 years (the interest is **not** compounded because you are not reinvesting the money). As with stocks, there are **bond tables** in the newspaper similar to Table 13.7 on the next page showing the **issuer,** the **coupon** (rate), the **maturity** date, the bid **price** and the **yield** of **bonds.**

Table 13.7.

	Coupon	Mat. date	Bid $	Yld %
Corporate				
AGT Lt	8.800	Sep 22/25	100.46	8.75
Air Ca	6.750	Feb 02/04	94.00	9.09
AssCap	5.400	Sep 04/01	100.01	5.38
Avco	5.750	Jun 02/03	100.25	5.63
Bell	6.250	Dec 01/03	101.59	5.63
Bell	6.500	May 09/05	102.01	5.95
BMO	7.000	Jan 28/10	106.55	6.04
BNS	5.400	Apr 01/03	100.31	5.24
BNS	6.250	Jul 16/07	101.56	5.95
CardTr	5.510	Jun 21/03	100.52	5.27
Cdn Pa	5.850	Mar 30/09	93.93	6.83
Clearn	0.000	May 15/08	88.50	8.61
CnCrTr	5.625	Mar 24/05	99.78	5.68
Coke	5.650	Mar 17/04	99.59	5.80

Company or country issuing the bond

Fixed interest rate that the issuer pays the lender

Date on which the borrowers will pay the investors their principal back

Price someone is willing to pay for the bond. Always quoted in relation to 100.

The annual return until the bond matures

EXAMPLE 2 Finding the Cost and Returns for Bonds

Mile wants to invest \$10,000 for his children's education in a 5-year Toys Corporation bond. If the coupon rate of the bond is 7.5% paid semiannually,

(a) how much will Mile receive semiannually?

(b) what is the total return on the investment?

Solution

(a) The formula for simple interest is $I = Prt$. In this example, $P = \$10{,}000$, $r = 7.5\% = 0.075$, and $t = \frac{1}{2} = 0.5$ year. Therefore,

$$I = \$10{,}000 \times 0.075 \times 0.5$$
$$= \$375$$

Mile will receive a check of \$375 semiannually (twice a year) for 5 years.

(b) To find the total return, we let $t = 5$ in the formula $I = Prt$. Thus,

$$I = \$10{,}000 \times 0.075 \times 5$$
$$= \$3750$$

Mile's total return, assuming that he kept the bond for the 5 years, is \$3750.

Now that we have seen how stocks and bonds work, would you invest in stocks or in bonds? Here are some advantages and disadvantages to help you decide.

Advantages and Disadvantages of Stocks and Bonds

Stocks

Advantages Long historical track record of outperforming bank savings, money-market funds, CDs, and real estate investments. You have voting rights! (Bondholders and depositors do not.)

Disadvantages Stock prices fluctuate (go up and down). If the stock price drops, you may lose part or all of your money.

Bonds

Advantages Higher interest rates compared with short-term investments. Less risk (compared to stocks).

Disadvantages If you sell the bond before **maturity,** you may incur a loss (politely called a **discount**). If the issuer declares bankruptcy, you may lose money.

So what is your decision? You may decide to invest in **mutual funds** instead.

C Investing in Mutual Funds

A **mutual fund** is a pool of many investors who pay a professional manager to purchase a variety of investments. There are literally thousands of mutual funds to suit a variety of needs and objectives. You can find tables of mutual funds similar to Table 13.8 in the newspaper.

The most common type of mutual fund is the **open-ended** fund, in which an unlimited number of shares can be issued. The more money investors put into the fund, the

Table 13.8

52W high	52W low	Fund	Spec.	Fri. NAVPS $chg	Fri. NAVPS %chg	Wkly NAVPS high	Wkly NAVPS low	Wkly NAVPS cls	Wkly NAVPS $chg	Wkly NAVPS %chg
Montrusco Bolton Funds										
11.71	10.12	Bal Plus	*N	-0.08	-0.76	10.58	10.50	10.50	0.02	0.15
12.50	10.25	Growth Plus	*N	-0.10	-0.96	10.89	10.78	10.78	0.02	0.22
31.39	24.78	Quebec Growth	*FR	0.05	0.17	26.97	26.75	26.97	0.43	1.61
13.78	7.24	RSP Intl Growth	*N	-0.08	-1.01	7.45	7.36	7.36	-0.03	-0.41
11.16	9.09	Value Plus	*N	-0.07	-0.75	9.39	9.32	9.32	0.01	0.14
9.65	8.90	World Inc	*N	-0.04	-0.40	9.52	9.39	9.48	0.04	0.43
Montrusco Select Funds C$(n)										
12.87	10.49	Balanced	*N	-0.04	-0.37	10.85	10.80	10.81	0.05	0.45
16.32	12.11	Balanced +	*N	-0.05	-0.43	12.57	12.52	12.52	0.06	0.45
10.36	9.86	Bond Index +	X*N	-0.03	-0.32	10.35	10.30	10.30	0.04	0.37

- 52W high / 52W low: Highest and lowest prices for the fund during the last 52 weeks
- Fund: Name of the mutual fund. Name of the company that manages the fund is written above in **bold type**.
- Spec.: Fund specifics. * Retirement eligible, N no load, F front load, B both front and back end fees
- Fri. NAVPS $chg: Dollar change from previous day
- Fri. NAVPS %chg: Percent change from previous day
- Wkly NAVPS high / low: Highest and lowest prices the fund traded at during the last week
- cls: The last price at which the fund traded
- $chg: The dollar change in price over the previous week
- %chg: The percent change in price over the previous week

more shares it issues (the fund company absorbs the shares of sellers). The price of each share, called the **net asset value (NAV),** is calculated every day (that's where the name "open-ended fund" comes from) by using the formula

$$NAV = \frac{A - L}{N}$$

where A = total fund assets
L = total fund liabilities
N = total number of outstanding shares

EXAMPLE 3 Finding the Cost of a Share in the ABC Mutual Fund

The ABC Mutual Fund has \$400 million worth of stock, \$200 million in bonds, and \$500,000 in other assets. Total liabilities amount to \$10 million, and there are 20 million shares outstanding.

(a) Find the NAV of one share.

(b) How many shares can you buy with \$100,000?

Solution

(a) Here,

$$A = \$400{,}000{,}000 + \$200{,}000{,}000 + \$500{,}000 = \$600{,}500{,}000$$
$$L = \$10{,}000{,}000$$
$$N = 20{,}000{,}000 \text{ shares}$$

Thus,

$$\begin{aligned} NAV &= \frac{A - L}{N} \\ &= \frac{600{,}500{,}000 - 10{,}000{,}000}{20{,}000{,}000} \\ &= \frac{590{,}500{,}000}{20{,}000{,}000} \\ &= \$29.525 \end{aligned}$$

(b) The number of shares that can be bought with \$100,000 at \$29.525 per share is

$$\frac{\$100{,}000}{\$29.525} = 3386.96, \text{ or } 3386 \text{ shares}$$

We have already learned how to make money in stocks and bonds, but how do you make money with mutual funds? There are at least three ways.

How to Make Money with Mutual Funds

1. By **capital appreciation,** an increase in the NAV of the fund.
2. By receiving a portion of the **dividends** paid by the stocks in the fund.
3. By receiving a **capital gain distribution,** the profits made by selling stocks or bonds that have gone up in price in the fund.

For convenience in tracking fund performance, we express each outcome as an annual percent by using the following formulas:

Fund Performance Terminology

1. $\text{Capital appreciation } (\%) = \dfrac{\text{change in NAV}}{\text{number of shares}}$

2. $\text{Yield } (\%) = \dfrac{\text{distribution per share}}{\text{NAV (at time of sale)}}$

3. $\%\ \text{Return} = \dfrac{\text{increase in value} + \text{distribution}}{\text{cost of initial investment}}$

Source: *Wall Street Journal Guide to Understanding Money and Investing* and http://tinyurl.com/7ft7we8.

EXAMPLE 4 Finding Annual Returns on a Mutual Fund

An investor buys 100 shares of the Math Fund at \$80 per share. A year later she sells them at \$90 per share. If she received an income distribution of \$2.50 per share, find

(a) the capital appreciation. **(b)** the yield. **(c)** the return.

Solution

(a) $\text{Capital appreciation } (\%) = \dfrac{\text{change of NAV}}{\text{number of shares}} = \dfrac{\$90 - \$80}{100} = \dfrac{10}{100} = 10\%$

(b) $\text{Yield } (\%) = \dfrac{\text{distribution per share}}{\text{NAV (at time of sale)}} = \dfrac{\$2.50}{\$90.00} = 2.78\%$

(c) The increase in value is $(\$90 - \$80) \times 100 = \$1000$. The distribution is $\$2.50 \times 100 = \$250$. Thus,

$$\text{Return } (\%) = \frac{\text{increase in value} + \text{distribution}}{\text{cost of initial investment}}$$

$$= \frac{\$1000 + \$250}{\$8000} = 15.63\%$$

We have calculated **annual** returns on a mutual fund. How can we calculate returns, in general, for a mutual fund? A good answer can be found by accessing http://personalfinance.byu.edu/?q=node/813.

It would be easy to calculate your returns on mutual funds if you invested only on the first business day of every year and you sold on the last business day of the year. But calculating a compound rate of return when distributions are reinvested is considerably more complicated than that because most people buy and sell mutual funds at other times. In addition, when calculating the return of your mutual funds, you should consider the fees charged when buying and selling the fund, as well as the taxes involved. If you want specific instructions on how to calculate a mutual fund's annual return, you can visit http://tinyurl.com/6rh698p.

EXAMPLE 5 Finding the Return on a Mutual Fund When Reinvesting Dividends

Suppose the investor of Example 4 bought 100 shares of the Math Fund at \$80 per share and that, for the sake of simplicity, we only consider the returns the fund earns and automatically reinvests at the rate of 1% per month. Find

(a) the beginning value of the fund.

(b) the monthly return.

(c) the annual rate of return.

Solution

(a) The beginning value of the fund is

$$\text{NAV} \times \text{number of shares} = \$80 \times 100 = \$8000$$

(b) The monthly return is 1% of \$8000 = \$80.

(c) Since the money is reinvested (compounded) at 1% per month, we need to find the future value A_n of 1 compounded n times at interest rate r. In this case, $n = 12$ and $r = 1\% = 0.01$. From page 770, this value is

$$A_n = (1 + r)^n = (1 + 0.01)^{12} = (1.01)^{12} \approx 1.13$$

Since we started with 1, the return is $1.13 - 1 = 0.13 = 13\%$. Thus, the annual rate of return is 13%.

Can you see the advantages of mutual funds? Here are some advantages and disadvantages:

Advantages and Disadvantages of Mutual Funds

Advantages	*Professional management* of your money.
	Diversification—your risk is spread out, and losses in any particular investment may be minimized by gains in other investments.
	Liquidity—you can request that your shares be converted to cash at any time.
Disadvantages	*Professional management* costs you money.
	Cost—sometimes hidden and hard to understand.
	Taxes—when making decisions, managers don't consider your personal tax situation. Sometimes you incur unwanted tax liabilities.

Source: Copyright 1999-2012 Investopedia, Inc. http://www.investopedia.com.

13.5 EXERCISES

A Finding the Cost and Returns for Stocks

The following lists the six New York Stock Exchange volume leaders on June 24:

NYSE VOLUME LEADERS

Symbol	Name	Last Trade	Change	Dividend
GE	GEN ELECTRIC CO	34.78 Jun 24	↑ 0.12 (0.35%)	\$1.06
NWS-A	NEWS CORP CL A	16.90 Jun 24	↑ 0.26 (1.56%)	\$0
PFE	PFIZER INC	28.52 Jun 24	↓ 0.38 (1.31%)	\$0.72
GDT	GUIDANT CORP	63.90 Jun 24	↓ 4.70 (6.85%)	\$0.40
LU	LUCENT TECH INC	3.02 Jun 24	↓ 0.09 (2.89%)	\$0
XOM	EXXON MOBIL CP	58.15 Jun 24	↓ 0.87 (1.47%)	\$1.10

In problems 1–6, find

a. *the total cost.*
b. *the total dividend.*
c. *the commission when selling the shares.*
d. *the capital gain when selling the shares.*
e. *the total return for the year.*
f. *the percent of return (round your answer to two decimal places).*

1. An investor buys 100 shares of GE at the Last Trade price, pays a \$50 commission on the purchase, and sells the 100 shares a year later for \$36.78 per share with a 2% commission on the sale.
2. An investor buys 100 shares of NWS-A at the Last Trade price, pays a \$50 commission on the purchase, and sells the 100 shares a year later for \$18.40 per share with a 2% commission on the sale.
3. An investor buys 200 shares of PFE at the Last Trade price, pays a \$50 commission on the purchase, and sells the 200 shares a year later for \$30 per share with a 2% commission on the sale.
4. An investor buys 200 shares of GDT at the Last Trade price, pays a \$50 commission on the purchase, and sells the 200 shares a year later for \$64 per share with a 2% commission on the sale.
5. An investor buys 200 shares of LU at the Last Trade price, pays a 2% commission on the purchase, and sells the 200 shares a year later for \$3.00 per share with a \$50 commission on the sale.
6. An investor buys 200 shares of XOM at the Last Trade price, pays a 2% commission on the purchase, and sells the 200 shares a year later for \$68 per share with a \$50 commission on the sale.

Problems 7–12 refer to the following chart. An investor (a day trader) always buys 1000 shares of stock at the market close price and sells them at the last sale price, paying a \$25 commission per transaction. Find

a. *the total cost.*
b. *the return for the day.*
c. *the percent of return if the stock the trader bought is*

7. MSLV.
8. PWOD.
9. NEON.
10. SDIX.
11. XXIA.
12. MKTY.

NASDAQ - After Hours 10 Most Advanced

Symbol	Company Name	Market Close	Last Sale (after hours)	% Change (after hours)	Share Volume (after hours)
MSLV	MetaSolv Inc.	\$2.21	\$2.60	17.65%	500
PWOD	Penns Woods Bancorp, Inc.	\$41.17	\$44.62	8.38%	1,500
NEON	NEON Systems, Inc.	\$3.01	\$3.25	7.97%	1,000
SDIX	Strategic Diagnostics Inc.	\$3.50	\$3.70	5.71%	7,200
XXIA	Ixia	\$18.96	\$19.90	4.96%	57,965
MKTY	Mechanical Technology Incorporated	\$3.61	\$3.78	4.59%	100

Source: http://dynamic.nasdaq.com/dynamic/afterhourma.stm.

Order	Ratings	Qty	Min	Ticker	Description	Coupon	Maturity	YTC/YTM	Price
Buy	Baa3/BB	100		GM	General Mtrs Corp 370442BB0 Global Nt Make-Whole	7.200	01-15-2011	9.254	91.242
Buy	A3/A−	100		DOW	Dow Chem Co 260543BL6 Nt Non-Callable	6.125	02-01-2011	4.257	109.195
Buy	Baa3/BBB	100		TYC	Tyco Intl Group S A 902118AY4 Nt Make-Whole	6.750	02-15-2011	4.405	111.564
Buy	A1/AA	100		ABT	Abbott Labs 002824AP5 Nt Make-Whole	3.750	03-15-2011	4.145	98.005
Buy	Aa3/A+	100		KO	Coca Cola Co 191216AH3 Nt Make-Whole	5.750	03-15-2011	4.120	108.209
Buy	Baa1/BBB+	100		K	Kellogg Co 487836AS7 Nt Make-Whole	6.600	04-01-2011	4.359	111.285

For a sample of today's bond offerings, go to http://bernardisecurities.com/html/offerings_inventory.asp.

B Finding the Cost and Returns for Bonds

In problems 13–18 use the information in the table above to find

a. *the amount you will receive semiannually*

b. *the total return on the investment if you bought*

13. $5000 in General Motors bonds and kept them for 5 years until maturity.

14. $5000 in Dow Chem bonds and kept them for 5 years until maturity.

15. $10,000 in Tyco Intl Group bonds and kept them for 2 years until maturity.

16. $10,000 in Abbott Labs bonds and kept them for 2 years until maturity.

17. $20,000 in Coca-Cola bonds and kept them for 5 years until maturity.

18. $20,000 in Kellogg Co bonds and kept them for 5 years until maturity.

C Finding the Cost and Returns of a Mutual Fund

In problems 19–24, find

a. *the NAV of one share.*

b. *the number of shares you can buy when you invest the amount of money shown in the last column of the table below.*

	Name	Stocks	Bonds	Other Assets	Liabilities	Outstanding Shares	Amount to Invest
19.	ABC	$200 million	$100 million	$250,000	$10 million	10 million	$ 50,000
20.	XYZ	$100 million	$ 50 million	$200,000	$10 million	20 million	$ 40,000
21.	Grand	$500 million	$250 million	$1.5 million	$25 million	25 million	$100,000
22.	MathRUs	$100 million	$ 50 million	$100,000	$ 5 million	5 million	$ 25,000
23.	Liberty	$400 million	$200 million	$1 million	$20 million	20 million	$100,000
24.	Freedom	$250 million	$125 million	$750,000	$10 million	10 million	$ 75,000

In problems 25–30 find

a. *the capital appreciation.*

b. *the yield.*

c. *the return for the indicated mutual fund when the given number of shares is bought and sold 1 year later after receiving the distribution shown in the following table.*

	Name	Shares Bought	Shares Sold	Distribution
25.	Bolting	100 at $70	100 at $80	$3 per share
26.	TrustCo	200 at $90	200 at $100	$2.50 per share
27.	NorthCo	300 at $75	300 at $80	$1.25 per share
28.	SouthCo	500 at $30	500 at 40	$0.50 per share
29.	EastCo	400 at $40	400 at $50	$4.00 per share
30.	WestCo	1000 at $20	1000 at $25	$0.75 per share

IN OTHER WORDS

31. Describe in your own words what stocks, bonds, and mutual funds are.

32. Explain the difference between stocks, bonds, and mutual funds.

33. Explain in your own words what a dividend is.

34. Explain in your own words what liquidity means to you.

USING YOUR KNOWLEDGE

*The **current yield** for an investment can be defined in many ways. Here is a formula for the current yield of a bond.*

$$\text{Current yield} = \frac{\text{coupon rate}}{\text{market price}} \times 100$$

Find the current yield of the following bonds using the information in the table accompanying problems 13–18 at the top of page 814:

35. The General Motors bond

36. The Dow Chemical bond

37. The Tyco International bond

38. The Abbot Labs bond

39. The Coca-Cola bond

40. The Kellogg Co bond

PREMIUM AND DISCOUNT PRICES

*If you sell a bond prematurely, the bond price will change depending on the **current** interest rate and the **fixed coupon payment.** For example, suppose you have a bond with a face value of $1000, a 10% coupon rate, and a $100 fixed coupon payment (10% × 1000 = $100). If interest rates go down, say, to 8%, your bond is worth more (because it pays 10%, but the interest rate is now only 8%). You must pay a **premium** for the bond. How much?*

Suppose the premium price of the bond is P. You have to pay the fixed coupon payment of $100 at the new rate of 8%. Thus,

$$8\% \text{ of } P = 100$$
$$0.08\,P = 100$$
$$P = \frac{100}{0.08} = \$1250$$

*The **premium price** of the bond is $1250 (you make a **premium** of $1250 − $1000 = $250).*

*On the other hand, if interest rates go up, say, to 12%, your bond is worth less (because it pays only 10%, but interest rates went up to 12%). You must **discount** your bond. How much?*

Suppose that the discount price of the bond is D. You have to pay the fixed coupon payment of $100 at the new rate of 12%. Thus,

$$12\% \text{ of } D = 100$$
$$0.12D = 100$$
$$D = \frac{100}{0.12} = \$833.33$$

*The **discount price** of the bond is $833.33 (the **discount** is $1000 − $833.33 = $166.66.*

In problems 41–46, find the price of a $1000 bond with a 10% coupon rate when

41. interest rates go down to 7%.

42. interest rates go down to 6%.

43. interest rates go down to 5%.

44. interest rates go up to 11%.

45. interest rates go up to 12%.

46. interest rates go up to 13%.

WEB IT EXERCISES

Problems 47–62 require access to the Internet. Use your favorite search engine and look for the topic under discussion.

Investing in Bonds

47. What different types of bonds are there?

48. What are some factors that determine the price of a bond?

49. What are some of the possible credit ratings for bonds?

50. How can you evaluate a broker?

How to Read Bond Tables

51. What does **bid** and **ask** price mean?

52. What does a bid of 105:12 mean? What do the numbers after the colon represent?

Trading Stocks

53. What is a market order? A limit order? A stop order?

54. What are online, after hours, day, and active traders?

55. What is a common stock?

56. What is a preferred stock?

57. What is a bull market? What is a bear market?

How to Read Stock Tables in Detail

58. What is the P/E ratio?

59. What does the YLD column mean, and how can the value be approximated?

Fundamental Analysis

60. What is fundamental analysis?

61. What is PEG?

62. What is ROE?

CHAPTER 13 Summary

SECTION	ITEM	MEANING	EXAMPLE
13.1A	$I = Prt$	Simple interest equals *Prt,* where *P* is the principal, *r* is the rate, and *t* is the time in years.	The interest on a \$500 2-year loan at 12% is $I = \$500 \cdot 0.12 \cdot 2 = \$120$.
13.1A	$A = P + I$	Amount equals principal plus interest.	The amount *A* you have to pay on a \$500, 2-year loan at 12% simple interest is $A = \$500 + \$120 = \$620$.
13.1D	$A_n = P(1 + r)^n$	Compound amount equals $P(1 + r)^n$, where *P* is the principal, *r* is the rate per period, and *n* is the number of periods.	The compound amount A_2 paid on a 2-year loan of \$500 compounded annually at 12% is $A_2 = \$500(1 + 0.12)^2 = \$500(1.12)^2 = \$627.20$
13.3A	APR	Annual percentage rate	
13.3B	Rule of 78	The unearned interest rate on a loan of *n* periods with *r* remaining periods is $\frac{r(r+1)}{n(n+1)} \times F$, where *F* is the finance charge.	The unearned interest rate on a 15-month loan with a \$120 finance charge and monthly payments of \$50 at the end of the eighth month is $\frac{7 \times 8}{15 \times 16} \times \$120 = \frac{7}{30} \times \$120 = \$28$
13.5A	Stock	A share in the ownership of a company	You may own stock (shares) of Coca Cola or Dell Computer.
13.5A	Dividend	The profits that the company allocates to the owners	The dividend of company ABC may be \$2.50 per quarter.
13.5A	Broker	An individual or firm that charges a commission for executing orders submitted by investors	The commission on a transaction may be a percent of the value of the transaction or a fixed fee.
13.5B	Bond	An IOU from a company or government to a lender	Treasury bonds, corporate bonds, municipal bonds
13.5C	Mutual fund	A pool of many investors who pay a professional manager to purchase investments	Merrill Lynch, Smith Barney, and T. Rowe Price have mutual funds.
13.5C	NAV	Net asset value	$\text{NAV} = \frac{A - L}{N}$ where A = assets, L = liabilities, and N = number of outstanding shares
13.5C	Capital appreciation	An increase of the NAV of a fund	The capital appreciation of a fund may be 10%.
13.5C	Yield	The amount the fund produces	$\frac{\text{Distribution per share}}{\text{NAV}}$
13.5C	Percent of return	The quotient of the sum of the increase in value plus distributions and the cost of the initial investment	$\frac{\text{Increase in value + distribution}}{\text{Cost of initial investment}}$

CHAPTER 13 Practice Test

1. The Ready-Money Loan Company charges 28% simple interest (annual) for a 2-year, \$800 loan. Find the following:
   a. The total interest on this loan
   b. The interest for 3 months
   c. The total amount to be paid to the loan company at the end of 2 years

2. A state has a 6% sales tax.
   a. What is the sales tax on a microwave oven priced at \$360?
   b. What is the total cost of this oven?

3. In a sale, a store offers a 20% discount on a freezer chest that is normally priced at \$390.
   a. How much is the discount?
   b. What is the sale price of the freezer?

4. The following table is a portion of a compound interest table to use in this problem. Find the accumulated amount and the interest earned for the following:
   a. \$100 at 8% compounded semiannually for 2 years
   b. \$100 at 8% compounded quarterly for 2 years

Amount (in dollars) to Which \$1 Will Grow in *n* Periods Under Compound Interest

n	2%	4%	6%	8%	10%
1	1.0200	1.0400	1.0600	1.0800	1.1000
2	1.0404	1.0609	1.1236	1.1664	1.2100
3	1.0612	1.1249	1.1910	1.2597	1.3310
4	1.0824	1.1699	1.2625	1.3605	1.4641
5	1.1041	1.2167	1.3382	1.4693	1.6105
6	1.1262	1.2653	1.4185	1.5869	1.7716
7	1.1487	1.3159	1.5036	1.7138	1.9487
8	1.1717	1.3686	1.5938	1.8509	2.1436

5. A credit card holder is obligated to pay the balance in full if it is less than \$10. Otherwise, the minimum payment is \$10 or 5% of the balance, whichever is more. Suppose a customer received a statement listing the balance as \$185.76.
   a. Find the minimum payment due.
   b. The finance charge is 1.5% per month. What will be the amount of this charge on the next statement if the customer makes only the minimum payment?

6. JoAnn Jones received a statement showing that she owed a balance of \$179.64 to a department store where she had a revolving charge account. JoAnn made a payment of \$50 and charged an additional \$23.50. If the store charges 1.5% per month on the unpaid balance, find the following:
   a. The finance charge for the month
   b. The new balance

7. A car costing \$6500 can be bought with \$1500 down and a 12% add-on interest to be paid in 48 equal monthly installments.
   a. What is the total interest charge?
   b. What is the monthly payment?

8. The following is a table for you to use in this problem:

True Annual Interest Rate for a 12-Payment Plan

Finance Charge	14%	14%	15%	$15\frac{1}{2}$%	16%
Finance charge (per \$100 of the amount financed)	7.74	8.03	8.31	8.59	8.88

continued

CHAPTER 13 Practice Test – *continued*

Sam Bear borrows \$200 and agrees to pay \$18.10 per month for 12 months.

a. What is the APR for this transaction?

b. If Sam decided to pay off the balance of the loan after 5 months (with 7 payments remaining), use the rule of 78 to find the amount of the interest refund.

c. Find the amount needed to pay off the loan.

9. The Mendoza family wants to buy a \$50,000 house in New Mexico.

a. If a bank was willing to loan the family 75% of the price of the house, what would be the amount of the loan?

b. What would be the down payment for this house?

c. If the family decided to obtain an FHA loan instead, what would be the minimum cash investment?

d. What would be the maximum FHA loan the family could get?

10. Refer to problem 9. Suppose the Mendoza family contracted for a 15-year mortgage at 12% with the bank that loaned the family 75% of the price of the house. What is the family's monthly payment for principal and interest? (Use the following table.)

Monthly Payment (in dollars) for Each \$1000 Borrowed

Rate	10 years	15 years	20 years
11%	13.78	11.37	10.32
12%	14.35	12.00	11.01
13%	14.93	12.65	11.72

11. Scott McWaters bought 100 shares of Kiwi-Cola at \$52.50 per share and paid a \$50 commission on the transaction. A year later he sold the 100 shares at \$57.75 per share and paid a 2% commission on the sale. If Kiwi-Cola paid \$1.22 per share in dividends, find

a. the total cost of the 100 shares.

b. the total dividend.

c. the commission when selling the 100 shares.

d. the capital gain (profit) after he sold the 100 shares.

e. the total return for the year.

f. the percent of return.

12. Fernando wants to invest \$10,000 for his children's education in a 5-year Kiddies Corporation bond. If the coupon rate of the bond is 6.5% paid semiannually,

a. how much will Fernando receive semiannually?

b. what is the total return of the investment?

13. The XYZ Mutual Fund has \$200 million worth of stock, \$100 million in bonds, and \$250,000 in other assets. Total liabilities amount to \$10 million, and there are 20 million shares outstanding.

a. Find the NAV of one share.

b. How many shares can you buy with \$100,000?

14. An investor buys 100 shares of the Geo Fund at \$70 per share. A year later she sells them at \$80 per share. If she received an income distribution of \$1.50 per share, find

a. the capital appreciation.

b. the yield.

c. the return.

15. Suppose that the investor of problem 14 bought 100 shares of the Geo Fund at \$70 per share and that, for the sake of simplicity, we only consider the returns the fund earns and automatically reinvests at the rate of 2% per month. Find

a. the beginning value of the fund.

b. the monthly return.

c. the annual rate of return.

ANSWERS TO PRACTICE TEST

CHAPTER 13		What to Review *If You Missed It*		
QUESTION	**ANSWER**	**SECTION**	**EXAMPLE(S)**	**PAGE(S)**
1	a. \$448 b. \$56 c. \$1248	13.1	1	768
2	a. \$21.60 b. \$381.60	13.1	2	769
3	a. \$78 b. \$312	13.1	3	769
4	a. \$116.99; \$16.99 b. \$117.17; \$17.17	13.1	4	771–772
5	a. \$10 b. \$2.64	13.2	2, 3	779, 780
6	a. \$1.94 b. \$155.08	13.2	4, 5	781, 782
7	a. \$2400 b. \$154.17	13.2	6	783
8	a. $15\frac{1}{2}\%$ b. \$6.17 c. \$120.53	13.3	1, 2	788, 790
9	a. \$37,500 b. \$12,500 c. \$1500 d. \$48,500	13.4	2	798
10	\$450	13.4	3	798–799
11	a. \$5300 b. \$122 c. \$115.50 d. \$359.50 e. \$481.50 f. 8.89%	13.5	1	806–807
12	a. \$325 b. \$3250	13.5	2	808
13	a. \$14.5125 ≈ \$14.51 b. 6891.8 or 6891 shares	13.5	3	810
14	a. 10% b. 1.875% c. \$16.43%	13.5	4	811
15	a. \$7000 b. \$140 c. 27%	13.5	5	812

CHAPTER 14

Voting and Apportionment

The ballot is stronger than the bullet.
—ABRAHAM LINCOLN

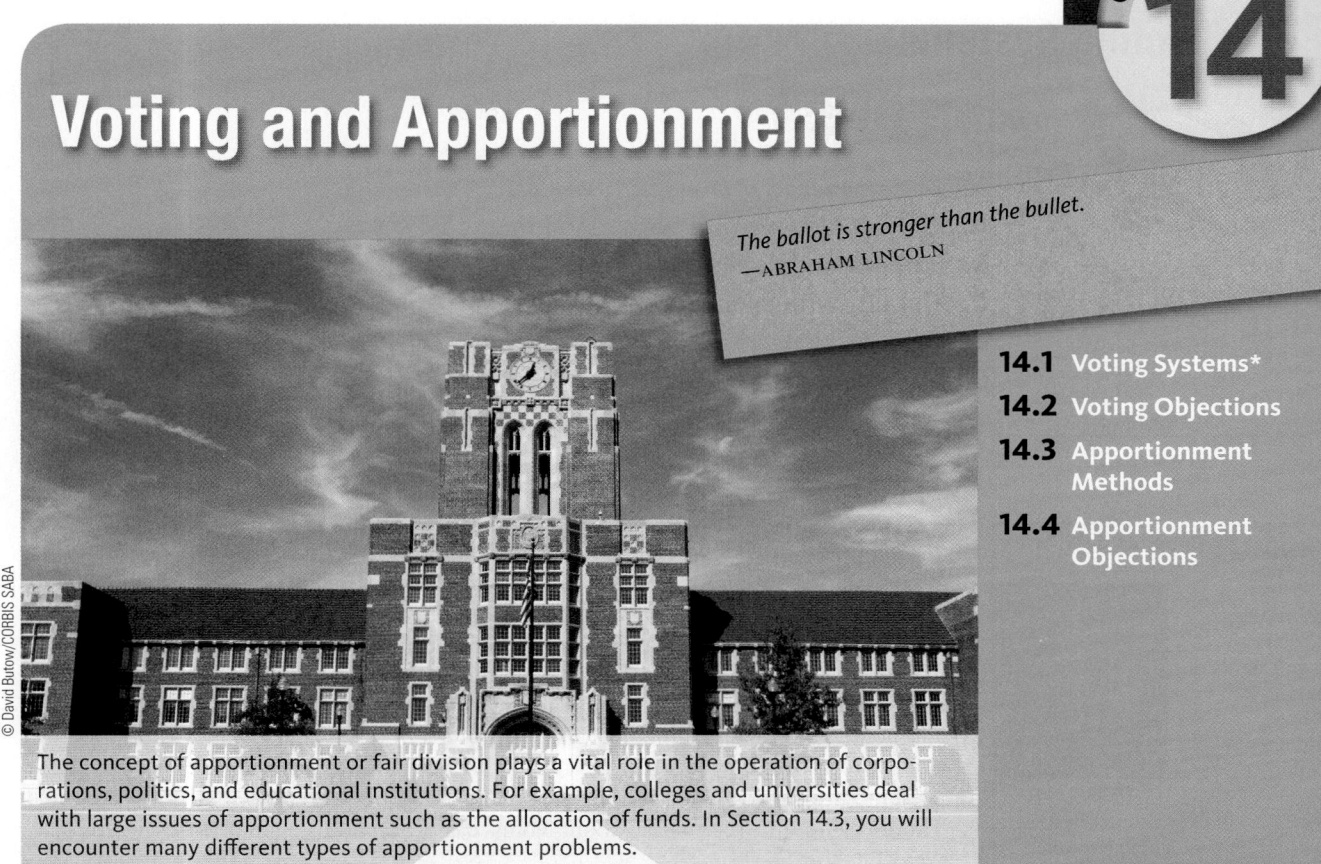

The concept of apportionment or fair division plays a vital role in the operation of corporations, politics, and educational institutions. For example, colleges and universities deal with large issues of apportionment such as the allocation of funds. In Section 14.3, you will encounter many different types of apportionment problems.

One of the most precious rights in our democracy is the right to vote. We have elections to select the president of the United States, senators and representatives, members of the United Nations General Assembly, baseball players to be inducted into the Baseball Hall of Fame, and even "best" performers to receive Oscar and Grammy awards. There are many ways of making the final decision in these elections, some simple, some more complex.

Electing senators and governors is simple: Have some primary elections and then a final election. The candidate with the most votes in the final election wins. Elections for president, as attested by the controversial 2000 presidential election, are complicated by our Electoral College system. Under this system, each state is allocated a number of electors selected by their political parties and equal to the number of its U.S. senators (always two), plus the number of its U.S. representatives (which may change each decade according to the size of each state's population as determined in the census). These state electors cast their **electoral** votes (one for president and one for vice president) and send them to the president of the Senate who, on the following January 6, opens and reads them before both houses of Congress. The candidate for president with the most electoral votes, provided that it is an absolute majority (one over half the total), is declared president. Similarly, the vice presidential candidate with the absolute majority of electoral votes is declared vice president. At noon on January 20, the duly elected president and vice president are finally sworn into office.

In this chapter we will look at several voting methods, the "fairness" of these methods, how votes are apportioned or divided among voters or states, and the fairness of these apportionments.

*Portions of this section were developed by Professor William Webb of Washington State University and funded by a National Science Foundation grant (DUE-9950436) awarded to Professor V. S. Manoranjan.

14.1 Voting Systems

GETTING STARTED

OBJECTIVES

Determine the winner of an election using the:

A. Plurality and plurality with runoff methods.
B. Borda count method.
C. Plurality with elimination method.
D. Pairwise comparison method.
E. Approval voting method.

Human Side of Math

(1743–1794)

Marie-Jean Antoine Nicolas de Caritat, **Marquis de Condorcet,** was born September 17, 1743, in Ribemont, France. Condorcet distinguished himself as a writer, administrator, and politician. His most important work was the *Essay on the Application of Analysis to the Probability of Majority Decisions* (1785), in which he tried to combine mathematics and philosophy to apply to social phenomena. One of the major developments in this work is known as the *Condorcet paradox,* a topic covered in this chapter.

LOOKING AHEAD

In this chapter we shall study different **voting systems,** the "flaws" or objections that can be raised about such systems, the methods used to fairly apportion resources among different groups, and the objections to these apportionment methods.

MONSIEUR BUTTERFLY AND PIZZA TOO

When you vote in a presidential election, you are not directly voting for the president! You are actually voting for **electors,** individuals who cast the *electoral votes* on behalf of their party and states. *They* are the ones who elect the president. Originally, electors were free to cast their votes as they pleased, but many of today's electors are "bound" or "committed" by state law (25 states have such laws) to vote for the candidate who received the most *popular* votes in their state. In a typical U.S. election, voters vote for their first choices by using a **ballot.** A so-called butterfly ballot used in Palm Beach County, Florida, during the 2000 presidential election is shown. There was some confusion about votes cast for Pat Buchanan (second hole) or Al Gore (third hole).

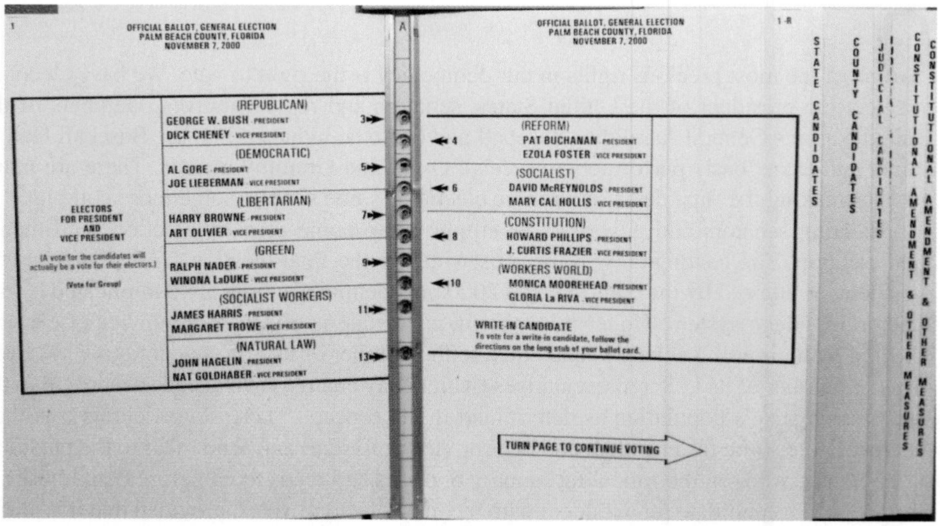

A butterfly ballot used in Palm Beach County, Florida, during the 2000 presidential election.

About 460,000 votes were cast in Palm Beach County, and of those, 3400 were for Buchanan. Assuming that the remaining precincts in Florida would yield the same proportion of votes for Buchanan, how many of the approximately 6 million votes cast in Florida would you project for Buchanan? Think about it before you answer!

The proportion of votes for Buchanan in Palm Beach was

$$\frac{3400}{460{,}000} = \frac{34}{4600}$$

If the same proportion applies to Florida,

$$\frac{F}{6{,}000{,}000} = \frac{34}{4600}$$

or equivalently

$$4600F = 34 \times 6{,}000{,}000$$
$$F \approx 44{,}348$$

Thus, you would *expect* about 44,347 Florida votes for Buchanan. (He actually got about 17,000 votes in Florida.) Moreover, the number of registered voters for Buchanan's Reform Party in Palm Beach County was a mere 304 voters! What might be some of the reasons for this discrepancy?

There are two fundamentally different types of voting methods: **preferential** and **non-preferential.** As the name suggests, a preferential voting system asks a voter to state a **preference** by ranking alternatives. This is usually done using a **preference ballot.**

For example, suppose the Math Club wants to order some pizzas for the end-of-year party. The Pizza House offers a special: three different one-topping pizzas—one jumbo, one large, and one medium—for only \$20. The question is, Which topping to order on which pizza? The club members decide that the most popular topping should go on the jumbo pizza, the second-choice topping on the large pizza, and the third choice on the medium pizza; the topping choices are pepperoni, sausage, mushrooms, or anchovies. Each club member fills out a **preference ballot,** and the results for the ballots might be summarized as in Table 14.1.

Table 14.1

Choice	Joan	Richard	Suzanne
First	Sausage	Sausage	Pepperoni
Second	Pepperoni	Pepperoni	Mushrooms
Third	Mushrooms	Anchovies	Sausage
Fourth	Anchovies	Mushrooms	Anchovies

If you were only considering each person's first choice, and Joan, Richard, and Suzanne were the only voters, sausage would win 2 votes to 1. We say that sausage received a **majority** (2 out of 3) of the first-place votes. A candidate with a *majority* of the votes is the one with more than half, or 50%, of the vote. Looking at the table, you might argue that pepperoni is a better choice because each voter has it listed as *first* or *second* choice.

If all of the Math Club members were voting, listing every ballot might take up a lot of space. Instead, we can make a **preference table,** which shows how many voters cast *identical* ballots. Here are the steps for making one.

Table 14.2

6	4	2
S	P	S
P	M	P
M	S	A
A	A	M

Making a Pizza Preference Table

1. **Replace** the word *sausage* with the letter S, *pepperoni* with the letter P, and so on.
2. If several ballots have exactly the same list of preferences, **group** them together.
3. **Create** a column for each of the groups. The top entry is the *number* of ballots in the group, followed by the corresponding *list of preferences*. For example, if all 12 members of the Math Club voted and 6 chose S, P, M, A; 4 chose P, M, S, A; and 2 chose S, P, A, M, then the resulting preference table would appear as in Table 14.2.

Now we are ready to analyze the results of elections using different voting systems: plurality, plurality with runoff, plurality with elimination, Borda count, and pairwise comparison.

A The Plurality Method

As you can see from the results of the 2000 presidential election in Table 14.3, if there are three or more candidates it is possible that no candidate receives a **majority** (more than 50%) of the votes. In this case, one method of selecting the winner is to select the candidate with the *most* votes. This method is called the **plurality method.** In a U.S. presidential election, the candidate with the *most* popular votes does *not* necessarily win!

Table 14.3

Candidates	Votes	Vote (%)
D Gore	50,999,897	48.4
R Bush	50,456,002	47.9
G Nader	2,882,955	2.7
RF Buchanan	448,895	0.4

Source: Federal Election Commission.

Plurality Method

Each voter votes for one candidate. The candidate with the *most* first-place votes is the winner.

Now let us go back to our pizza ballots.

EXAMPLE 1 Using the Plurality Method

The Math Club conducted an election to determine the top-rated pizza topping. The results are summarized in Table 14.4.

Table 14.4

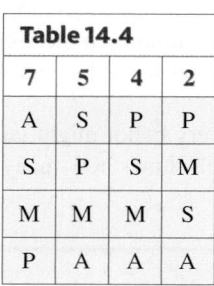

7	5	4	2
A	S	P	P
S	P	S	M
M	M	M	S
P	A	A	A

(a) Did any of the toppings get the majority of the first-place votes?
(b) Which topping is the plurality winner?
(c) Which topping comes in second?
(d) Which topping comes in last?

Solution

Since plurality counts only first-place votes, we can see that A got 7 votes (see column 1, with 7 at the top), S got 5 votes (column 2), and P got $4 + 2 = 6$ votes. Mushroom was never at the top, so it got no votes.

(a) *None* of the toppings got a majority of the votes. Since there are $7 + 5 + 4 + 2 = 18$ voters, more than $18/2 = 9$ votes are needed for a majority.
(b) A (anchovies) is the *plurality* winner with 7 votes.
(c) P (pepperoni) comes in second with 6 votes.
(d) M (mushrooms) comes in last with no votes.

As we saw in Example 1, a *plurality* is not necessarily a *majority.* There may be a situation with a large number of alternative choices where the winner might not get even 10% of the votes! Many political elections have only two candidates (or at least only two with a chance of winning). With only *two* choices, a plurality is necessarily a majority. However, there are also numerous instances with *many* candidates, including primary elections, electing members to the Baseball Hall of Fame, ranking football teams, and so on.

In Example 1, the jumbo pizza ended up with anchovies (A) as the topping, but you may have noticed that anchovies was the last choice of 5 + 4 + 2 = 11 voters. Since many people who don't like anchovies really *hate* anchovies, it could well be the case that these 11 people—a clear majority—might not even want any of the jumbo pizza. Although this means more pizza for the 7 people who like anchovies, it doesn't seem like the fairest way to choose. How can we overcome these difficulties? One way is to begin by eliminating all but the top two candidates and then make a head-to-head comparison between these two. Now the winner will have a majority! This variation of the plurality method is called **plurality with runoff.**

Plurality with Runoff Method

Each voter votes for one candidate. If a candidate receives a **majority** of votes, that candidate is the winner. If *no* candidate receives a majority, **eliminate** all but the *two* top candidates and hold a runoff election. The candidate that receives a *majority* in the **runoff** election is the winner.

EXAMPLE 2 Using the Plurality with Runoff Method

As you recall from Example 1, the election results were A, 7 votes; P, 6 votes; S, 5 votes; and M, 0 votes. Find the winner using the plurality with runoff method.

Solution

Table 14.5

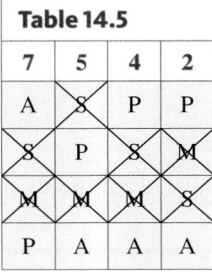

7	5	4	2
A	S	P	P
S	P	S	M
M	M	M	S
P	A	A	A

Since the top two vote getters were A and P, all others are eliminated, and we run an election between A and P. Look at Table 14.5 and mentally (or you can actually do it with a pencil) cross out all the S and M entries. Now look at the first column. There are 7 people who prefer A to P. The second, third, and fourth columns have 5 + 4 + 2 = 11 people who prefer P to A. (Note that in these columns we are only concerned with the fact that P is preferred over A, not the particular value of the preference.) Eleven is the *majority* of the 7 + 5 + 4 + 2 = 18 people voting in the election. Thus, A has 7 votes against P's 11, and P is the new winner using the plurality with runoff method. The jumbo pizza will now have pepperoni!

So far we have looked at the methods of plurality and plurality with runoff, two of the most widely used methods for political elections in many countries. Although they can be used to obtain a complete ranking of many alternatives, they are really designed to choose an overall winner. A major problem with both methods is that candidates who do not get either the *most* or *second most* first-place votes are immediately eliminated. Do we really want to place so much emphasis on first-place votes?

A fairly natural way to correct this emphasis on first-place votes is to use some kind of system that assigns a point value to each of the rankings and then counts points instead of votes. This kind of method is widely used in ranking sports teams such as in football polls, as well as in scoring track meets or selecting winners in music or television award shows. Historically, this method goes back to the eighteenth century and is named for Jean-Charles Borda (1733–1799), a French mathematician and nautical astronomer.

B The Borda Count Method

The Borda Count Method

Voters rank candidates from most to least favorable. Each last-place vote is awarded no point; each next-to-last-place vote is awarded one point, each third-from-last-place vote is awarded two points, and so on.* The candidate who receives the **most points** is the winner.

EXAMPLE 3 Using the Borda Count Method

Find the winner of the election in Example 1 using the Borda count method.

Solution

Award 0, 1, 2, and 3 points to last, next to last, and so on. Counting the points for anchovies (A) in column 1 of Table 14.6, you get 7 first-place votes, worth 3 points each, a total of $3 \times 7 = 21$ points. Sausage (S) gets 2×7 in column 1, 3×5 in column 2, 2×4 in column 3, and 1×2 in column 4 for a total of $14 + 15 + 8 + 2 = 39$ points. Pepperoni (P) gets 10 points in column 2, 12 in 3 and 6 in 4 for a total of 28 points. Finally, mushrooms (M) get 7 points in column 1, 5 in 2, 4 in 3, and 4 in 4 for a total of 20 points. Thus, using the Borda count method, the rankings are S (winner), P, A, and M with 39, 28, 21, and 20 points, respectively.

Table 14.6

Points	7	5	4	2
3	A	S	P	P
2	S	P	S	M
1	M	M	M	S
0	P	A	A	A

C The Plurality with Elimination Method

This method is a variation of the plurality method and may involve a series of elections.

Plurality with Elimination (The Hare Method)

Each voter votes for one candidate. If a candidate receives a **majority** of votes, that candidate is the winner. If no candidate receives a majority, **eliminate** the candidate with the *fewest* votes and hold another election. (If there is a **tie** for *fewest* votes, eliminate all candidates tied for *fewest* votes.) Repeat this process until a candidate receives a majority.

EXAMPLE 4 Using the Plurality with Elimination Method

Consider the familiar pizza voting results. Which topping wins the election using the plurality with elimination method?

*Sometimes the last-place vote is awarded one point, next-to-last vote two points, and so on.

Solution

First, let us count the number of first-place votes in Table 14.7 to see if there is a majority.

Table 14.7

7	5	4	2
A	S	P	P
S	P	S	M
M	M	M	S
P	A	A	A

Table 14.8

7	5	4	2
A	S	P	P
S	P	S	S
P	A	A	A

Table 14.9

7	5	6
A	P	P
P	A	A

A has 7 votes (first column).
S has 5 votes (second column).
P has $4 + 2 = 6$ votes (third and fourth columns).
M has no votes.

Since there are $7 + 5 + 4 + 2 = 18$ voters, we need 10 votes for a majority. None of the toppings has a majority of the votes, but M received the fewest first-place votes, so M is **eliminated,** and all selections in each column below M move up one place, as shown in Table 14.8.

Now A still has 7 votes, S has 5, and P has $4 + 2 = 6$. Since S has the *fewest* votes, S is *eliminated,* and we are down to just P and A, as shown in Table 14.9.

Now P is the clear majority winner with $5 + 6 = 11$ votes. Thus, P is the winner of the election when we use the **plurality with elimination** method.

If we look at Examples 1–4, we can see that A is the winner using the plurality method, P is the winner using the plurality with runoff method, S is the winner using the Borda count method, and P is the winner using the plurality with elimination method. If a voting method is to indicate a group's preference, the method used should not change the winner. This situation points out the importance of deciding on the voting system to be used *before* the election takes place. Of course, elections with only two candidates are easy because the winner will get at least half the votes—not only a *plurality* but also a *majority.* The difficulty arises when we have three or more candidates. If this is the case, we can compare candidates the easiest way we know: two at a time. This is the basis of the next voting method.

D The Pairwise Comparison Method

Pairwise Comparison Method

Voters rank candidates from most to least favorable. Each candidate is then compared with each of the other candidates. If candidate A is preferred to candidate B, then A receives one point. If candidate B is preferred to candidate A, then B receives one point. If there is a tie, each candidate receives one-half point. The candidate who receives the most overall points is the winner.

For example, suppose we have three candidates: Alice, Bob, and Carol. We have to compare Alice versus Bob, Alice versus Carol, and Bob versus Carol. We could hold three separate elections, but it is possible to use the information in the preference tables we have used before. As the number of candidates grows, so do the number of head-to-head comparisons that need to be made. For n candidates, there are

$$\frac{n(n-1)}{2} = C(n, 2)$$

such comparisons. Thus, for $n = 10$ candidates, we would need $(10 \times 9)/2 = 45$ head-to-head comparisons. Let us use our preference tables to calculate the winner of all the possible head-to-head comparisons. The one clear-cut case is when one candidate beats all the others. This case even has a special name: A candidate who beats all the others in head-to-head comparisons is the **Condorcet** winner (named after the Marquis de Condorcet mentioned in the Human Side of Mathematics at the beginning of the chapter, who, like Borda, was an eighteenth-century Frenchman). As you might suspect, a big problem with using Condorcet winners is that often there is *no* such winner, as we shall see in the following example.

EXAMPLE 5 Using the Pairwise Comparison Method

Table 14.10

2	3	4
A	B	C
B	C	A
C	A	B

The results of an election involving three candidates, A, B, and C, are shown in Table 14.10. Who wins the election using the pairwise comparison method?

Solution

To determine the winner using the pairwise comparison method, we have to compare A and B, A and C, and B and C.

Suppose the election is between just A and B (leave C out).

A: 2 votes from column 1 and 4 from column 3, a total of 6 votes
B: 3 votes from column 2, a total of 3 votes

Thus, A beats B 6 votes to 3, and A is awarded one point.

Now, let us compare A and C (leave B out).

A: 2 votes from column 1, a total of 2 votes
C: 3 votes from column 2 and 4 votes from 3, a total of 7 votes

Thus, C beats A 7 votes to 2, and C is awarded one point.

Finally, let us compare B and C (leave A out).

B: 2 votes from column 1 and 3 from column 2, a total of 5 votes
C: 4 votes from column 3, a total of 4 votes

Thus, B beats C 5 votes to 4, and B is awarded one point.

What a dilemma! All the candidates have one point. There is *no* Condorcet winner in this election.

As we mentioned at the beginning of the section, there are two fundamentally different types of voting methods: *preferential* (those using a preference table) and *nonpreferential*. We will now discuss a nonpreferential voting method: approval voting.

E Approval Voting Method

Approval voting uses a different kind of preference table. The good news is that the table is much simpler in one respect: Each voter does not have to **rank** all the candidates first, second, third, and so on. Instead, each voter simply approves (A) or disapproves (D) each candidate. Thus, if you are a voter, you can vote for one candidate, two candidates, three candidates, and so on. Voting for two or more candidates doesn't dilute your vote; each candidate that you approve of gets one full vote. When the votes are counted, the candidate with the most **approval** votes wins.

EXAMPLE 6 Using Approval Voting

In Table 14.11, each row corresponds to a different candidate (W, X, Y, and Z), and each column corresponds to a different voter. An A means "approve" and a D means "disapprove." Which of the candidates wins using approval voting?

Table 14.11

Candidate	Voter 1	Voter 2	Voter 3	Voter 4	Voter 5	Voter 6	Voter 7	Voter 8
W	A	D	A	A	D	D	D	D
X	A	A	D	D	A	D	A	A
Y	D	D	A	D	D	A	A	A
Z	D	D	A	D	A	A	D	A

Solution

We examine each of the rows and count only the A's.

Row W has 3 A's.
Row X has 5 A's.
Row Y has 4 A's.
Row Z has 4 A's.

This means that candidate X (row 2) wins with 5 votes. Y and Z are tied with 4 votes each, and W is in last place with only 3 votes.

Like all voting methods, approval voting has its deficiencies, but it has a number of good features, too. It is simpler than the Borda count or plurality with elimination method, although not as simple as the plurality method. However, unlike the plurality method, it doesn't rely only on first-place votes. It works well when voters can easily divide the candidates into "good" and "bad" categories. Approval voting is also good in situations where more than one winner is allowed. This occurs, for example, in electing players to the Baseball Hall of Fame. To be elected, an eligible player has to be named on 75% of the ballots. The voters are members of the Baseball Writers' Association of America. They add one extra requirement: No one can vote for more than 10 players.

14.1 EXERCISES

A The Plurality Method

1. The results of the 2008 presidential election are as shown in the table.

Candidate	Votes
L Barr	523,686
R McCain	59,934,814
I Nader	738,475
D Obama	69,456,897
Other candidates	603,456

Source: Federal Election Commission.

a. How many votes were cast?
b. What percentage of the vote was captured by McCain? By Obama? Round your answers to the nearest percent.
c. Did either candidate receive a majority of the votes?

2. The results of the 2004 presidential election are as shown in the table.

Candidate	Votes
R Bush	62,040,610
D Kerry	59,028,444
I Nader	465,650
Other candidates	760,641

Source: Federal Election Commission.

a. How many votes were cast in the 2004 election?
b. What percentage of the vote was captured by Bush? By Kerry? Round your answers to the nearest percent.
c. Did either candidate receive a majority of the votes?

3. Why did they have a vote recount in Florida during the 2000 presidential election? Because Florida law requires a *recount* when the winning margin in votes is less than 0.5% of the total number of votes cast.

Candidate	Votes
R Bush	2,911,872
D Gore	2,910,942
G Nader	97,419
RF Buchanan	17,472

a. What is the total number of votes shown in the table?
b. What is the difference between the number of votes obtained by Bush and by Gore?
c. What percent difference (to 3 decimal places) is that?
d. Does the difference require a recount?

4. Who is the winner in Florida under the plurality method?

5. Four candidates, A, B, C, and D, are running for class president and receive the number of votes shown in the table.

6	7	3	4
D	C	A	B
C	B	D	A
B	D	B	C
A	A	C	D

a. How many votes were cast in the election?
b. How many first-place votes are needed for a majority?
c. Did any candidate receive a majority of first-place votes?
d. Who is the winner using the plurality method?

6. Five hundred registered voters cast their preference ballots for four candidates, P, T, R, and S. The results are summarized in the preference table below.

	Number of Voters			
Place	130	120	100	150
First	P	T	T	S
Second	R	R	R	R
Third	S	S	P	P
Fourth	T	P	S	T

a. How many first-place votes are needed for a majority?
b. Did any candidate receive a majority of first-place votes?
c. Who is the winner by the plurality method?

7. Refer to the preference table in problem 6.
a. Which two candidates have the most first-place votes?
b. Which candidate is the winner using the plurality with runoff method?

8. This preference table shows the rankings for four brands of auto tires, A, B, C, and D.

	Number of Voters		
Place	13	12	10
First	A	C	D
Second	B	B	A
Third	D	D	B
Fourth	C	A	C

a. How many votes were cast in the election?
b. How many first-place votes are needed for a majority?
c. Did any brand receive a majority of first-place votes?
d. Who is the winner by the plurality method?

9. Refer to the preference table in problem 8.
a. Which two brands have the most first-place votes?
b. Which brand is the winner using the plurality with runoff method?

In problems 10–12, *use the following table. A survey was conducted at Tampa International Airport to find the favorite vacation destination in Florida. The rankings for four destinations—Busch Gardens* (B), *Disney World* (D), *Epcot* (E), *and Sea World* (S)*—are shown in the table.*

	Number of Voters		
Place	20	15	10
First	D	E	S
Second	B	B	B
Third	E	D	D
Fourth	S	S	E

B The Borda Count Method

10. Find the winner and runner-up using the Borda count method.

C The Plurality with Elimination Method

11. Find the winner using the plurality with elimination method.

D The Pairwise Comparison Method

12. Find the winner using the pairwise comparison method.

In problems 13–17, use the following information: A group of patients suffering from a severe cold were informed that they needed at least 60 mg of vitamin C daily. The possible sources of vitamin C were 1 orange (O), 2 green peppers (G), 1 cup of cooked broccoli (B), or $\frac{1}{2}$ cup of fresh orange juice (J). The rankings for the group are given in the table which follows.

	Number of Voters			
Place	**5**	**11**	**8**	**6**
First	B	O	G	J
Second	J	J	J	G
Third	G	G	O	O
Fourth	O	B	B	B

13. Which source wins using the plurality method?

14. Which source wins using the plurality with runoff method?

15. Which source wins using the Borda count method?

16. Which source wins using the plurality with elimination method?

17. Which source wins using the pairwise comparison method?

E Approval Voting

18. The results of a hypothetical election using approval voting are summarized in the following table. An X indicates that the voter approves of the candidate; a blank indicates no approval. Who is the winner using approval voting?

	Voters							
Candidates	**Richard**	**Sally**	**Thomas**	**Uma**	**Vera**	**Walter**	**Yvette**	**Zoe**
Adams	X		X	X	X		X	X
Barnes			X		X	X		
Collins	X				X	X	X	

19. In problem 18, who is the winner using approval voting if Collins drops out of the race?

20. Have you seen the rankings for sugary drinks advertising? You can, if you go to http://www.sugarydrinkfacts.org. Coca-Cola, 5-hour Energy, Gatorade, Dr Pepper, and Pepsi spent the most advertising money in sugary and energy drinks. A separate survey of social media subjects asked participants to vote for his or her favorite drink using approval voting. Following is a summary of the results.

12 participants voted for 5-hour Energy drinks.
7 participants voted for 5-hour Energy drinks and Pepsi.
20 participants voted for Gatorade and Coca-Cola.
18 participants voted for Dr Pepper, Gatorade, and Coca-Cola.
23 participants voted for Pepsi and Dr Pepper.
25 participants voted for Coca-Cola.

Use approval voting to determine the voter's favorite drink.

21. A college class has decided to take a vote to determine which coffee flavors are to be served in the cafeteria. The choices are latte, cappuccino, mocha, and Americano. The winning coffee flavor will be determined using approval voting on the basis of the following responses:

12 students voted for latte and cappuccino.
5 students voted for cappuccino, mocha, and Americano.
10 students voted for mocha and cappuccino.
13 students voted for Americano and cappuccino.

The flavor with the most votes wins.

a. How many total votes did latte receive?
b. How many total votes did cappuccino receive?
c. How many total votes did mocha receive?
d. How many total votes did Americano receive?
e. Which coffee is selected by the class using approval voting?

22. The Math Club uses approval voting to choose a faculty adviser for the upcoming year on the basis of the following responses:

Anne and Fran voted for Mr. Albertson.
Peter, Alex, and Jennifer voted for Ms. Baker and Ms. Carr.
William, Sam, Allison, and Betty voted for Mr. Albertson, Ms. Baker, and Mr. Davis.
Joe, Katie, and Paul voted for Ms. Carr and Mr. Davis.
Jonathan voted for Mr. Davis.

a. How many total votes did Mr. Albertson receive?
b. How many total votes did Ms. Baker receive?
c. How many total votes did Ms. Carr receive?
d. How many total votes did Mr. Davis receive?
e. Which teacher is selected as faculty adviser using approval voting?

Do you know where the 2000 Olympics were held and why? Let us find out! On September 23, 1993, 88 members of the International Olympics Committee (IOC) met in Monte Carlo to choose a site for the 2000 Summer Olympics. Five cities made bids: Beijing, (BC), Berlin (BG), Istanbul (I), Manchester (M), and Sydney (S). In the table on page 832 is a summary of the site preferences of the committee members; use this information in problems 23–32.

	Number of Votes								
Choice	**3**	**2**	**32**	**3**	**3**	**1**	**8**	**30**	**6**
First	I	I	BC	M	BG	I	M	S	BG
Second	BC	BC	I	BC	BC	S	S	M	S
Third	M	BG	BG	BG	I	BC	BG	BG	M
Fourth	BG	M	M	S	S	M	I	I	BC
Fifth	S	S	S	I	M	BG	BC	BC	I

23. Does any city have a majority of the first-place votes? If so, which city?

24. Which city has the most first-place votes? How many does it have?

25. Which city is selected if the committee decides to use the plurality method?

26. Which city is selected if the committee decides to use the plurality with elimination method?

27. Suppose the committee decides to give 5 points to each city for every first-place selection it gets, 4 points for every second-place selection, 3 points for every third-place selection, 2 points for every fourth-place selection, and 1 point for every fifth-place selection. If the winning city will be the city with the most points, which city will be selected?
28. Which city is selected if the committee decides to use the "regular" 4-3-2-1-0 Borda count method?
29. Which city is selected if the committee decides to use the pairwise comparison method?
30. Rank the cities from first to last using the "regular" Borda count method. (Remember, you found the Borda count winner in problem 26.)
31. Which city is selected if the committee decides to use approval voting? (Assume that each voter approves only his or her first two choices.)
32. Rank the cities from first to last using approval voting.

The following information will be used in problems 33–37. In October 2009, members of the International Olympic Committee (IOC) met in Copenhagen, Denmark, to choose the site of the 2016 Olympics. Four cities made bids: Madrid (M), Rio de Janeiro (R), Tokyo (T), and Chicago (C). The results of the election, which used the plurality with elimination method, are shown in the table. (IOC members from countries with candidate cities were ineligible to vote while their nation's city was still in the running.)

	M	R	T	C
First Round	28	26	22	18
Second Round	29	46	20	
Third Round	32	66		

Source: www.olympic.org.

33. Which city won the election?
34. Did any city receive a majority of votes in the first round?
35. Did any city receive a majority of votes in the second round?
36. If the plurality with runoff method were used instead, which cities would have faced off in the runoff election?
37. If the plurality method was used, which city hosts the 2016 Olympics?
38. The candidate cities to host the 2012 Olympics were: London, Madrid, Moscow, New York, and Paris. Madrid, Moscow, and New York were eliminated, and the fourth vote to decide between London and Paris was about to take place whereupon French president Jacques Chirac declared: "We can't trust people [the British] who have such bad food. After Finland, it's the country with the worst food." Unfortunately, two current members of the International Olympic Committee are from Finland.
    a. After these two facts, who do you think will win?
    b. At the end of the fourth round of voting, London had 54 votes and Paris 50, so who actually won?

USING YOUR KNOWLEDGE

Ace Cola has decided to begin a multimillion-dollar ad campaign to increase its lagging sales. The ads are to be based on consumers' preferring the taste of Ace Cola to its major competitors, Best Cola, Coala Cola, and Dkimjgo Cola.

An independent testing agency conducted a carefully controlled taste test on 50 randomly selected cola drinkers. Their results are summarized in the table. (In the table, A represents Ace, B represents Best, and so on.)

10	13	8	7	12
A	B	C	C	D
B	A	D	B	A
C	D	B	A	B
D	C	A	D	C

39. Use the plurality method to find the preferred cola.
40. Use the plurality with runoff method to find the preferred cola.
41. Use the Borda count method to find the preferred cola.
42. As an expert in the mathematics of voting, you are approached by Ace and offered a $25,000 consulting fee if you can show that Ace is really the number one cola. Find a point assignment for the Borda count method in which Ace comes in first. (*Hint:* A gets a lot of second-place votes, so we want to make second place worth proportionally more. Remember, first place must still be worth more than second, so make the gap between second and third place larger.)

14.2 Voting Objections

GETTING STARTED

OBJECTIVES

Compare voting methods using:

A. The majority criterion.
B. The head-to-head criterion.
C. The monotonicity criterion.
D. The irrelevant alternatives criterion.

DISASTER 2000

In the preceding section we studied five preferential voting systems: plurality, plurality with runoff, Borda count, plurality with elimination, and pairwise comparison. We also studied a nonpreferential voting system: approval voting. As we pointed out, all these systems have advantages and disadvantages and sometimes can produce different winners. Let us look at an actual example—the 2000 presidential election (Table 14.12).

Table 14.12 2000 U.S. Presidential Election Results

Candidate	Votes	Vote (%)	States Won	EV*	EV (%)
D Gore	50,999,897	48.38	21**	266	49.44
R Bush	50,456,002	47.87	30	271	50.37
G Nader	2,882,955	2.74	0	0	0
Other candidates	1,066,246	1.01	0	0	0

*One elector from Washington DC, abstained from voting.
**Includes Washington DC, which has 3 electoral votes.
Source: Federal Election Commission.

As you can see, Gore received a **plurality** of the votes, but no candidate received a **majority** of the votes. Why then did George Bush become the 43rd president? Because elections for U.S. president rely on the **Electoral College** to determine the winner: to become president, a candidate must receive a majority of the 538 **electoral votes (EV).** Since

$$\frac{538}{2} = 269$$

a candidate needs at least 270 electoral votes to be declared the winner 271 vs 266. From Table 14.12 we see that Bush did indeed win a majority of the electoral votes and thus he won the election.

Is this fair? By what criteria? Clearly, more voters chose Gore as their preferred candidate, but next we will introduce four criteria that mathematicians and political scientists have identified as the **fairness criteria** for a voting system: the **majority criterion,** the **head-to-head (Condorcet) criterion,** the **monotonicity criterion,** and the **irrelevant alternatives criterion.**

A The Majority Criterion

It seems fair that if a candidate is the *first* choice of a majority of voters, then that candidate should be declared the winner. If this is not the case, then that voting method violates the **majority criterion.** Under this criterion (total number of votes), Gore should have been the winner. But as we know, Bush won the election.

> **Majority Criterion**
>
> If a candidate receives a **majority** of first-place votes, then that candidate should be the winner.

EXAMPLE 1 Using the Majority Criterion

La Cubanita Restaurant is conducting a survey to find out which is the most popular omelet among the western (W), bacon (B), and ham (H) omelets. The results of the survey are shown in Table 14.13.

BREAKFAST 7AM TO 11AM
CUBAN TOAST $ .99
CHEESE TOAST $1.45
WESTERN OMELETTE $2.95
CHEESE OMELETTE $2.50
HAM OMELETTE $2.80
PLAIN OMELETTE $2.25
BACON OMELETTE $2.80
CAFE CON LECHE SM.$1.40 LG.$1.70
HOT CHOCOLATE SM.$1.40 LG.$1.70
SERVED ON CUBAN BREAD CHEESE 45¢

Table 14.13

	Number of Votes		
Place	**60**	**25**	**15**
First	W	B	B
Second	B	H	W
Third	H	W	H

(a) Which omelet is the winner using the Borda count method?

(b) Does the winner have a majority of votes?

Solution

Using the Borda count method, W has $2(60) + 1(15) = 135$ points
B has $1(60) + 2(25) + 2(15) = 140$ points
H has $1(25) = 25$ points

(a) Using the Borda count method, the winner is B, the bacon omelette, with 140 points.

(b) No. A majority of the people, 60 out of 100, chose the western omelette.

Note that although a majority of the people (60 out of 100) preferred the western omelet, under the Borda count method, the bacon omelet wins. Thus, in this example, the Borda count method *violates* the *majority* criterion; that is, a candidate with a *majority* of first-place votes can lose the election!

Table 14.14

	Number of Votes		
Place	**8**	**6**	**18**
First	A	A	B
Second	B	C	A
Third	C	B	C

EXAMPLE 2 Using the Majority Criterion

An election to select their favorite airline, A, B, or C, is conducted among 32 students. The results are shown in Table 14.14. Which airline should be selected under the specified method, and does the method satisfy the majority criterion?

(a) The plurality method

(b) The Borda count method

(c) The plurality with elimination method

(d) The pairwise comparison method

Solution

(a) Using the plurality method, B is the winner with 18 out of 32 votes. Note that B received a majority of the votes, so the method of plurality does not violate the majority criterion. In general, a candidate who holds a majority of first-place votes also holds a plurality of first-place votes.

> The plurality method **never** violates the majority criterion.

Note that the converse is not true: If you have a plurality of the votes, you do not necessarily have a majority of the votes.

(b) Under the Borda count method we assign 0, 1, and 2 points to the third, second, and first places, respectively. The points for each airline are as follows:

A: $2(8) + 2(6) + 1(18) = 46$ points
B: $1(8) + 2(18) = 44$ points
C: $1(6) = 6$ points

Thus, A is the winner under the Borda count method.

Since airline B is the one holding the majority of first-place votes (18 out of 32), the Borda count method violates the majority criterion. Of course, the Borda count method does not *always* violate the majority criterion; it just has the potential to do so.

> The Borda count method has the **potential** for violating the majority criterion.

(c) Since B has the majority of the votes (18 out of 32), B is the winner under plurality with elimination, so the *majority* criterion is not violated. In general, a candidate who holds a *majority* of first-place votes wins the election without having to hold a second election.

> The plurality with elimination method **never** violates the majority criterion.

(d) Using the pairwise comparison involves the following cases and outcomes:

A versus B (eliminate C)
A: $8 + 6 = 14$ B: 18 B wins 18 to 14. B is awarded 1 point.
A versus C (eliminate B)
A: $8 + 6 + 18 = 32$ C: 0 A wins 32 to 0. A is awarded 1 point.
B versus C (eliminate A)
B: $8 + 18 = 26$ C: 6 B wins 26 to 6. B is awarded 1 point.

Since B has 2 points, B wins the election under the pairwise comparison method. In general, if a candidate holds a *majority* of first-place votes, this candidate *always* wins every pairwise (head-to-head) comparison.

> The pairwise comparison method **never** violates the majority criterion.

Even though the Borda count method is the only method studied that violates the *majority* criterion, it does take into account the voters' preferences by having all candidates ranked.

B The Head-to-Head (Condorcet) Criterion

Suppose four candidates, A, B, C, and D, are running for chair of the mathematics department. There are 20 voting members in the department, and the student newspaper performed a postelection survey of each of the 20 members in the department. Among other things, the survey asked the voters whom they preferred in a two-way race between candidate C (the one endorsed by students) and each of the other candidates. Here are the results.

11 voters preferred candidate C over candidate A.
11 voters preferred candidate C over candidate B.
17 voters preferred candidate C over candidate D.

So, in head-to-head competition, candidate C won against each of the other candidates. Wouldn't it seem unfair if candidate C was not declared the winner of the election? When the actual votes were tabulated, candidate A got 9 first-place votes, candidate B got no first-place votes, candidate C got 8 first-place votes, and candidate D got 3 first-place votes. If candidate C is not declared the winner, this would be a violation of the head-to-head, or **Condorcet criterion** because C certainly wins when compared with every other candidate.

> **Head-to-Head (Condorcet) Criterion**
> If a candidate is favored when compared **head-to-head** with every other candidate, then that candidate should be the winner.

EXAMPLE 3 Using the Head-to-Head Criterion

Which sandwich is the most popular? La Cubanita restaurant conducted a survey among its customers to select the favorite sandwich from Cuban (C), pork (P), turkey (T), and vegetarian (V). The number of votes for each is shown in Table 14.15. Which sandwich should be selected under the specified method, and does the method satisfy the head-to-head criterion?

(a) Head-to-head
(b) Plurality
(c) Borda count
(d) Plurality with elimination
(e) Pairwise comparison

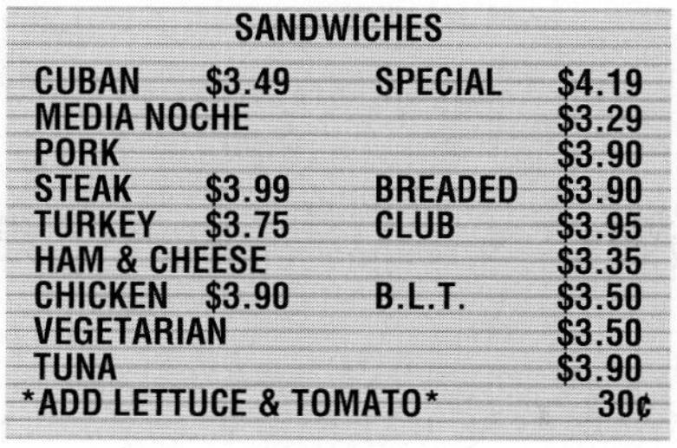
SANDWICHES
CUBAN $3.49
SPECIAL $4.19
MEDIA NOCHE $3.29
PORK $3.90
STEAK $3.99
BREADED $3.90
TURKEY $3.75
CLUB $3.95
HAM & CHEESE $3.35
CHICKEN $3.90
B.L.T. $3.50
VEGETARIAN $3.50
TUNA $3.90
ADD LETTUCE & TOMATO 30¢

Table 14.15

	Number of Voters				
Place	**30**	**50**	**58**	**60**	**90**
First	V	V	T	P	C
Second	T	T	V	V	P
Third	P	C	P	T	T
Fourth	C	P	C	C	V

Solution

(a) We need a total of six head-to-head comparisons. A further look seems to indicate that P is the winner. Let us see why.

P beats C in columns 1, 3, and 4 for $30 + 58 + 60 = 148$ points, whereas C beats P in columns 2 and 5 for $50 + 90 = 140$ points. Thus, P beats C.

Comparing P and T, we see that P beats T in columns 4 and 5, obtaining $60 + 90 = 150$ points, and T beats P in columns 1, 2, and 3, obtaining $30 + 50 + 58 = 138$ points. Thus, P beats T 150 to 138.

Comparing P and V, we see that P beats V in columns 4 and 5, and V beats P in columns 1, 2 and 3, so the score is the same as in the preceding comparison: P beats V 150 to 138.

Thus, P is the favored candidate when compared head-to-head with every other candidate.

(b) Using the plurality method, C wins with 90 votes.

> The plurality method has the **potential** for violating the head-to-head criterion.

(c) Using the Borda count method, we assign 0, 1, 2, and 3 points to the fourth-, third-, second-, and first-place winners. The total points are

C: $1(50) + 3(90) = 320$ points
P: $1(30) + 1(58) + 3(60) + 2(90) = 448$ points
T: $2(30) + 2(50) + 3(58) + 1(60) + 1(90) = 484$ points
V: $3(30) + 3(50) + 2(58) + 2(60) = 476$ points

Using the Borda count method, T wins with 484 points.

> The Borda count method has the **potential** for violating the head-to-head criterion.

(d) Using plurality with elimination, T is eliminated in the first round, P in the second round, and C in the third round. (Check this!) Thus, V is the winner 198 to 90 over C.

> The plurality with elimination method has the **potential** for violating the head-to-head criterion.

(e) As you recall, in the pairwise comparison method each candidate is ranked and compared with each of the other candidates. Each time, the preferred candidate gets 1 point. Let us look at the comparisons.

C and P		
C: 50 + 90 = 140	P: 30 + 58 + 60 = 148	P wins and gets 1 point.
C and T		
C: 90	T: 30 + 50 + 58 + 60 = 198	T wins and gets 1 point.
C and V		
C: 90	V: 30 + 50 + 58 + 60 = 198	V wins and gets 1 point.
P and T		
P: 60 + 90 = 150	T: 30 + 50 + 58 = 138	P wins and gets 1 point.
P and V		
P: 60 + 90 = 150	V: 30 + 50 + 58 = 138	P wins and gets 1 point.
T and V		
T: 58 + 90 = 148	V: 30 + 50 + 60 = 140	T wins and gets 1 point.

Thus, using the pairwise comparison method, P is the winner with 3 points.

> The pairwise comparison method **never** violates the head-to-head criterion.

This example shows that the *plurality, Borda count,* and *plurality with elimination* methods may *potentially* violate the head-to-head criterion. Next, we shall introduce a third criterion called the **monotonicity criterion** that can be used to evaluate the fairness of an election and explore the possibility that the plurality with elimination method may have some further flaws.

C Monotonicity Criterion

When the outcome of a first election is not binding—for example, when a **straw poll** or **survey** is taken before the election—voters may change their preferences before the actual election. If a leading candidate gains votes at the expense of another candidate, the chances of winning for the leading candidate *should* increase because of the additional votes. However, this is not always the case! This strange result is a violation of the monotonicity criterion.

> ### The Monotonicity Criterion
> If a candidate is the winner of a first *nonbinding* election and then gains additional support without *losing* any of the original support, then the candidate should be the winner of the second election.

We shall now discuss an example in which the winner of the first election (straw vote) gains additional votes before the actual election and still loses.

EXAMPLE 4 Using the Monotonicity Criterion

Months before the actual vote to select the Heisman Trophy winner, it was claimed that one of the contenders was too old to win the trophy. A straw vote (first election) was conducted among 105 sportswriters, and the results were as shown in Table 14.16. After several weeks of heated discussion, five writers decided to change their ballots and award their first-choice votes to JH. The results of the new election are shown in Table 14.17.

Table 14.16 First Election

	Number of Voters			
Place	**42**	**30**	**23**	**10**
First	JH	CW	DB	DB
Second	DB	JH	CW	JH
Third	CW	DB	JH	CW

Table 14.17 New Election

	Number of Voters			
Place	**47**	**30**	**23**	**5**
First	JH	CW	DB	DB
Second	DB	JH	CW	JH
Third	CW	DB	JH	CW

Using the plurality with elimination method,

(a) who is the winner of the first election?

(b) who is the winner of the new election?

(c) is the monotonicity criterion violated?

Solution

(a) Using the plurality with elimination method, the first election results in the elimination of CW and then a win by JH over DB with a majority vote of 72 to 33. Thus, JH is the winner.

(b) In the new election, using the plurality with elimination method, DB, with $23 + 5 = 28$ points, is eliminated, and CW gets a majority of $30 + 23 = 53$ votes over JH's $47 + 5 = 52$ votes. This time CW is the winner.

(c) Although 5 voters changed from DB to JH in the new election, adding 5 votes to JH's total, JH's win in the first election was *not* repeated in the second election.

The plurality with elimination method has the **potential** for violating the monotonicity criterion.

By the way, a similar situation actually occurred in 2000 when selecting the Heisman winner among Chris Weinke (CW), Josh Heupel (JH), and Drew Brees (DB). The election, however, was actually conducted using the Borda count method, awarding each candidate 1, 2, and 3 points for third, second, and first place, respectively. Even though Weinke had reached the ripe old age of 28, he won by collecting 1628 points.

D The Irrelevant Alternatives Criterion

The fourth and last criterion we will study involves the removal (or introduction) of a candidate who has *no chance* of winning the election. For example, let us assume that we have an election among candidates A, B, and C with the results shown in Table 14.18.

Table 14.18			
	Number of Voters		
Place	**4**	**3**	**9**
First	A	A	B
Second	B	C	A
Third	C	B	C

It is easy to see that B is the winner using plurality, plurality with runoff, or pairwise comparison. But let us use the Borda count method. When we add up the points, we find

A: 23 points B: 22 points C: 3 points

The race is close, but A wins out using the Borda count method.

It seems that in deciding between A and B, what people think of C shouldn't matter; after all, C is completely out of the running. But look at the 3 voters represented in column 2. Suppose that after thinking it over a little more, they all decide that candidate C is even *worse* than they thought before and should be dropped to the bottom of their ballots or even dropped out of the election altogether! Note that the relative positions of A and B have not changed. With C at the bottom, the results are shown in Table 14.19.

Table 14.19			
	Number of Voters		
Place	**4**	**3**	**9**
First	A	A	B
Second	B	B	A
Third	C	C	C

Our Borda point count now becomes

A: 23 points B: 25 points C: 0 points

B is now the winner using the Borda count method.

In other words, because some voters changed their minds about C, or because C dropped out of the race, the rankings of A and B were reversed. But the rankings of A and B should depend on how voters view A and B and not on what they think of some other alternative. We call C an **irrelevant alternative** in ranking A and B.

The Irrelevant Alternatives Criterion

If a candidate is the winner of an election, and in a second election one or more of the losing candidates is removed, then the winner of the *first* election should be the winner of the *second* election.

All the methods we have studied have the **potential** to violate the irrelevant alternatives criterion.

EXAMPLE 5 Movie Critics and the Four Fairness Criteria

The top-selling movie of the 1980s was *ET: The Extraterrestrial* (ET), the top-selling movie of the 1990s was *Titanic* (T), and the top-selling movie of the 2000s was *Avatar* (A). A group of 50 movie critics was asked to rank them by preference, and the results are shown in Table 14.20. If the plurality method is used to select the top movie, does the method satisfy the four fairness criteria we have studied?

Table 14.20			
	Number of Voters		
Place	**28**	**12**	**10**
First	ET	T	A
Second	T	ET	T
Third	A	A	ET

Using the plurality method, ET is the winner with 28 votes, which is a majority (56%) of the 50 votes cast. Thus, the **majority criterion** is satisfied. If we use the pairwise comparison method, we see that ET beats A 40 to 10, ET beats T 28 to 22, and T beats A 40 to 10, so ET *wins* two points and the **head-to-head criterion** is satisfied.

The **monotonicity criterion** is satisfied if we assume that a second election is held in which ET picks up additional votes. ET will certainly win the second election by plurality. Finally, if A or T drops out, ET *still* wins by the plurality method, satisfying the **irrelevant alternatives criterion.** Thus, this particular election satisfies *all four* fairness criteria we have studied. Of course, each of the voting methods can be made to violate at least one of the fairness criteria.

Can we find a method that will satisfy all four criteria all the time? This question led to a long and futile search. In 1950, Kenneth Arrow, a U.S. economist, made a very surprising discovery. He found that no voting method could ever satisfy these four conditions *all the time.* This idea it not restricted to the voting methods we know of now, but *any* voting method anybody might think of in the future as well. This fact is known as **Arrow's Impossibility Theorem.** This discovery was a major factor in Arrow's winning the Nobel Prize in economics.

Theorem 14.1 Arrow's Impossibility Theorem

There is no possible voting method that will always *simultaneously* satisfy each of the four fairness criteria:

1. The majority criterion
2. The head-to-head criterion
3. The monotonicity criterion
4. The irrelevant alternatives criterion

In simple terms, Arrow's discovery means that we can never find a voting method that does everything we want.

Before you attempt the exercises, we summarize in Table 14.21 the four fairness criteria and indicate in Table 14.22 on page 842, which of the voting methods we have studied satisfies a particular criterion.

Table 14.21

Majority criterion	If a candidate receives a *majority* of first-place votes, then that candidate should be the winner.
Head-to-head (Condorcet) criterion	If a candidate is favored when compared *head-to-head* with every other candidate, then that candidate should be the winner.
Monotonicity criterion	If a candidate is the winner of a first election and then gains additional support without losing any of the original support, then that candidate should be the winner of the second election.
Irrelevant alternatives criterion	If a candidate is the winner of an election and in a second election one or more of the losing candidates is removed, then the winner of the first election should be the winner of the second election.

Table 14.22

Fairness Criterion	Plurality Method	Borda Count Method	Plurality with Elimination Method	Pairwise Comparison Method
Majority criterion	Always satisfies	May not satisfy	Always satisfies	Always satisfies
Head-to-head criterion	May not satisfy	May not satisfy	May not satisfy	Always satisfies
Monotonicity criterion	Always satisfies	Always satisfies	May not satisfy	Always satisfies
Irrelevant alternatives criterion	May not satisfy	May not satisfy	May not satisfy	May not satisfy

14.2 EXERCISES

A The Majority Criterion

1. Who makes the best Cuban sandwich in Tampa? According to a panel of *Tampa Tribune* judges who rated each sandwich anywhere from 1 (low) to 5 (high), the best three Cuban sandwiches are produced at Wrights Gourmet (W), Puccetti's Market (P), and La Segunda Central Bakery (S). Here is a table simulating the points in the voting.

	Number of Points		
Place	**25**	**5**	**20**
First	W	S	P
Second	P	W	S
Third	S	P	W

   a. Who is the winner using the plurality method?
   b. Who is the winner using the Borda count method?
   c. Does the Borda count method violate the majority criterion?
   d. Who is the winner using the pairwise comparison method?

2. Of course, you cannot rely solely on professional judges, so the *Tribune* had *readers* vote for their favorite Cuban sandwich, and the outcome was different! According to the people, the three best Cuban sandwiches are produced at La Septima (L), West Gate Bakery (G), and the Cuban Sandwich Shop (C). The approximate number of votes is shown in the following table.

	Number of Voters		
Place	**600**	**300**	**200**
First	L	G	C
Second	G	C	L
Third	C	L	G

   a. Who is the winner using the plurality method?
   b. Who is the winner using the Borda count method?
   c. Does the Borda count method violate the majority criterion?
   d. Who is the winner using the pairwise comparison method?

3. Do you drink coffee? Which kind do you prefer? Starbucks coffee offers latte (L), cappuccino (C), mocha (M), and Americano (A). The preferences of 70 students surveyed at the University of South Florida are shown in the table.

	Number of Voters			
Place	**10**	**20**	**30**	**10**
First	C	C	L	L
Second	A	M	C	C
Third	M	A	M	A
Fourth	L	L	A	M

   a. Which flavor is the winner using the Borda count method?
   b. Is the majority criterion satisfied? Explain your answer.

B The Head-to-Head (Condorcet) Criterion

4. The Performing Arts Center Board is considering showing three different plays this season: *Cats* (C), *A Chorus Line* (L), and *Les Miserables* (M). The 10 members of the board rank the plays according to the following preference table.

	Number of Voters		
Place	**2**	**5**	**3**
First	L	C	M
Second	C	L	C
Third	M	M	L

a. In a head-to-head comparison, is there a play that is preferred to all others?

b. Is the head-to-head criterion satisfied if the plurality method is used to determine the most popular play?

5. Did you watch the Super Bowl this year? Which commercials do you remember? Four of the all-time most memorable are Staples (S), 7 Up (U), Honda (H), and Budweiser (B). One hundred viewers were asked to watch and vote on the commercial they preferred. The results are in the following preference table.

	Number of Voters			
Place	**50**	**25**	**15**	**10**
First	S	H	B	U
Second	U	S	H	B
Third	H	U	S	S
Fourth	B	B	U	H

a. In a head-to-head comparison, is there a commercial preferred to all others?

b. Is the head-to-head criterion satisfied if the plurality method is used to find the preferred commercial? Explain your answer.

C The Monotonicity Criterion

6. A company is planning to relocate to one of the larger counties in the United States: Los Angeles (L), Cook (C), or Harris (H). The Committee of 100 is to use the plurality with elimination method to select the county, and their preferences are shown in the table. After careful deliberation, the 10 voters who voted C, L, H changed their vote to L, C, H. Is the monotonicity criterion satisfied? Explain your answer.

	Number of Voters			
Place	**25**	**30**	**10**	**35**
First	C	H	C	L
Second	H	L	L	C
Third	L	C	H	H

D The Irrelevant Alternatives Criterion

7. Which of the following has the highest cost of living: Washington, DC (D), Alaska (A), or Hawaii (H)? The table shows the responses of 50 people who were asked that question. If Hawaii (H) is eliminated, is the irrelevant alternatives criterion satisfied? Explain your answer.

	Number of Voters		
Place	**20**	**18**	**12**
First	D	A	H
Second	A	H	D
Third	H	D	A

8. Suppose that in problem 7 the responses of the 50 people are as shown in the table. If Alaska (A) is eliminated, is the irrelevant alternatives criterion satisfied? Explain your answer.

	Number of Voters		
Place	**20**	**16**	**14**
First	D	A	H
Second	A	H	D
Third	H	D	A

9. The following preference table gives the results of an election among three candidates, A, B, and C.

	Number of Voters		
Place	**27**	**24**	**2**
First	A	B	C
Second	C	C	B
Third	B	A	A

a. Who wins using the plurality method?

b. Does any candidate get a majority of the first-place votes? If so, which one?

c. Who wins using the pairwise comparison method?

d. Does any candidate beat every other candidate one-on-one, that is, in a head-to-head comparison? If so, which one?

e. Who wins using the Borda count method?

f. Which fairness criteria, if any, are violated? Explain.

g. Suppose candidate B drops out, but the winner is still chosen using the Borda count method. Is the winner the same as in part (**e**)? If not, which candidate does win?

h. Which fairness criteria, if any, are violated? Explain.

10. The following preference table gives the results of an election among three candidates, A, B, and C.

	Number of Voters		
Place	**20**	**19**	**5**
First	A	B	C
Second	B	C	B
Third	C	A	A

a. Who wins using pairwise comparisons?

b. Does any candidate beat every other candidate one-on-one, that is, in a head-to-head comparison? If so, which one?

c. Who wins using the plurality method?

d. Which fairness criteria, if any, are violated? Explain.

e. Suppose candidate C drops out, but the winner is still chosen using the plurality method. Is the winner the same as in part (**c**)? If not, which candidate does win?

f. Which fairness criteria, if any, are violated? Explain.

g. Who wins using the plurality with elimination method? (Assume candidate C is now back in.)

h. Now suppose candidate A drops out, but the winner is still chosen using the plurality with elimination method. Is the winner the same as in part (**g**)? If not, which candidate does win?

i. Which fairness criteria, if any, are violated? Explain.

11. The following preference schedule gives the results of an election among four candidates, A, B, C, and D.

	Number of Voters				
Place	**14**	**4**	**10**	**1**	**8**
First	A	B	C	C	D
Second	B	D	B	D	C
Third	C	C	D	B	B
Fourth	D	A	A	A	A

a. Who wins using the plurality with elimination method?

b. Who wins using the pairwise comparison method?

c. Does any candidate beat every other candidate one-on-one, that is, in a head-to-head comparison? If so, which one?

d. Which fairness criteria, if any, are violated? Explain.

12. The following preference table gives the results of an election among three candidates, A, B, and C.

	Number of Voters			
Place	**7**	**8**	**10**	**4**
First	A	B	C	A
Second	B	C	A	C
Third	C	A	B	B

a. Who wins using the plurality with elimination method?

b. Suppose that the Election Commission invalidates the results of the election, and everyone must revote. As it happens, everyone votes exactly as before except for the 4 voters in the last column of the table. These 4 voters, who originally voted A, C, B, decide to switch the order of their votes for A and C so that their new preference ballots are C, A, B. Who wins this new election using the plurality with elimination method?

c. Which fairness criteria, if any, are violated? Explain.

13. This preference table gives the results of an election among three candidates, A, B, and C.

	Number of Voters		
Place	**20**	**19**	**5**
First	A	B	C
Second	B	C	B
Third	C	A	A

a. Who wins using the plurality with elimination method?

b. Suppose candidate A drops out, but the winner is still chosen using the plurality with elimination method. Is the winner the same as in part (**a**)? If not, which candidate does win?

c. Which fairness criteria, if any, are violated? Explain.

14. The following preference table gives the results of an election among five candidates, A, B, C, D, and E.

	Number of Voters							
Place	**3**	**3**	**1**	**1**	**3**	**3**	**1**	**1**
First	B	A	C	C	B	A	B	E
Second	A	C	B	E	A	D	A	D
Third	C	D	A	B	D	E	E	A
Fourth	D	E	D	D	E	C	C	C
Fifth	E	B	E	A	C	B	D	B

a. Who wins using pairwise comparisons?

b. Suppose candidate C drops out, but the winner is still chosen using the pairwise comparison method? Is the winner the same as in part (**a**)? If not, which candidate does win?

c. Which fairness criteria, if any, are violated? Explain.

15. When using the pairwise comparison method, how many comparisons need to be made if there are

a. three candidates? b. four candidates?

c. five candidates? d. n candidates?

16. When using the pairwise comparison method, how many comparisons must a candidate (say A) win to guarantee winning the election if there are

a. three candidates? b. four candidates?

c. five candidates? d. n candidates?

IN OTHER WORDS

17. Explain the majority criterion in your own words.
18. Explain why the plurality method always satisfies the majority criterion.
19. Explain why the pairwise comparison method always satisfies the majority criterion.
20. Explain the monotonicity criterion in your own words.
21. Explain why the plurality with elimination method always satisfies the monotonicity criterion.
22. Explain the Condorcet criterion in your own words.
23. Explain why the pairwise comparison method always satisfies the head-to-head (Condorcet) criterion.
24. Explain the irrelevant alternatives criterion in your own words.
25. Which of the five election techniques that we have studied is most likely to end in a tie? Explain.

14.3 Apportionment Methods

GETTING STARTED

OBJECTIVES

A. Find the standard divisor and standard quota for apportionment problems.
B. Use the Hamilton method of apportionment.
C. Use the Jefferson method of apportionment.
D. Use the Webster method of apportionment.
E. Use the Adams method of apportionment.

In 1787, at the Constitutional Convention in Philadelphia, delegates of the 13 original states created a system of government with three branches: **executive, legislative,** and **judicial.** One of the most important issues was the representation of the states in the legislative branch. *Smaller states* wanted *equal* representation. In response, a **Senate** in which two senators represent each state was created. *Larger states* preferred *proportional* representation. Thus, a **House of Representatives,** in which each state receives a number of representatives proportional to its population, was created. Unfortunately, the founding fathers did not decide on the *exact* number of representatives for each state. In fact, Article 1, Section 2, of the Constitution states:

> Representatives shall be apportioned among the several states . . . according to their respective numbers. The number of representatives shall not exceed one for every thirty thousand, but each state shall have at least one representative.

Historically, at least four apportionment methods have been implemented.

1792–1841: The Jefferson method
1842–1851, 1901–1941: The Webster method
1852–1900: The Hamilton (Vinton) method
1941–present: The Hill–Huntington method

We shall study the Hamilton, Jefferson, and Webster methods and omit the Hill–Huntington method because of its complexity. Instead, we will examine a similar method known as the John Quincy Adams method. The various methods will be presented in order of mathematical complexity rather than chronological order. Keep in mind that apportionment methods are not limited to governing bodies. Budget allocations, Super Bowl tickets, faculty and student senate seats, and many other items have to be fairly distributed, or *apportioned.*

FUNDING THE FLORIDA EDUCATION SYSTEM

The Florida College System consists of 28 colleges. In 2009–2010, the general budget allocation for the system amounted to almost 2 billion dollars—\$1,794,111,471 to be exact. How can we fairly distribute the money among the 28 colleges? Here are some possibilities.

1. Divide the funds *equally* among the 28 colleges. Each college gets

$$\frac{\$1{,}794{,}111{,}471}{28} = \$64{,}075{,}409.68$$

   Is this fair? Consider this: Miami-Dade had 139,942 students, whereas the Florida Keys had 3166. Under this equal allocation method, each will get the same amount, despite the disparity in their student populations.

2. We can also base funding on the number of students attending. In the same year, the total student population in the Florida College System was 907,753, so funding for each college would be *proportional* to the number of students attending that college. The amount for each college would be

$$\frac{\text{Number of students in the college}}{907{,}753} \times \$1{,}794{,}111{,}471$$

   Is this method fair? Keep in mind that a college with, say, 1000 students each taking a 3-hour course will need to fund $3 \times 1000 = 3000$ student semester hours, whereas a college with 1000 **full-time** equivalent students (FTEs) will have to fund $40 \times 1000 = 40{,}000$ student semester hours. *Note:* One FTE is equivalent to 40 student semester hours.

3. Perhaps a fairer distribution would be to allocate the money on the basis of the number of FTEs in each college. The formula for the allocation to each college would then be

$$\frac{\text{Number of FTEs in the college}}{\text{Total number of FTEs}} \times \$1{,}794{,}111{,}471$$

Can you think of any other way of fairly apportioning the \$1,794,111,471 to the 28 colleges?

Source: Florida Department of Education.

A Apportionment Problems

In Getting Started, we considered several methods for apportioning money. To make these methods more standard and the resulting allocation quotas more precise, we define the standard divisor (SD) and the standard quota (SQ) as follows:

Formula for Standard Divisor

$$\text{SD} = \frac{\text{total population}}{\text{total number to be apportioned}}$$

Formula for Standard Quota

$$\text{SQ} = \frac{\text{population in the group}}{\text{SD}}$$

EXAMPLE 1 Finding the Standard Divisor

In a recent year, the five largest colleges in the Florida College System received about \$820 million in total general education and general fund revenues. The number of FTEs (to the nearest 1000) in each of the five colleges is shown in Table 14.23.

Table 14.23

Miami	Jacksonville	Broward	Valencia	Hillsborough	Total
57,000	29,000	28,000	29,000	21,000	164,000

Find the standard divisor SD and the standard quota SQ for each college.

Solution

$$\text{SD} = \frac{\text{total population}}{\text{total number to be apportioned}}$$

The total population is the total number of FTEs, that is, 164,000. The total number to be apportioned is \$820,000,000. Thus,

$$\text{SD} = \frac{164{,}000}{\$820{,}000{,}000} = \frac{1}{5000} = 0.0002$$

$$\left(\frac{1}{5000} \text{ means that 1 FTE gets \$5000}\right)$$

The standard quota SQ for each college is given in Table 14.24.

Table 14.24

Miami	$\text{SQ} = \frac{\text{population in the group}}{\text{SD}} = \frac{57{,}000}{1/5000} = \$285{,}000{,}000$
Jacksonville	$\text{SQ} = \frac{\text{population in the group}}{\text{SD}} = \frac{29{,}000}{1/5000} = \$145{,}000{,}000$
Broward	$\text{SQ} = \frac{\text{population in the group}}{\text{SD}} = \frac{28{,}000}{1/5000} = \$140{,}000{,}000$
Valencia	$\text{SQ} = \frac{\text{population in the group}}{\text{SD}} = \frac{29{,}000}{1/5000} = \$145{,}000{,}000$
Hillsborough	$\text{SQ} = \frac{\text{population in the group}}{\text{SD}} = \frac{21{,}000}{1/5000} = \$105{,}000{,}000$

You may have noticed that since each FTE gets \$5000, each college's allocation will be (\$5000 × number of FTEs).

B The Alexander Hamilton Method of Apportionment

One of the earliest *apportionment* methods was the Hamilton method. Proposed to President George Washington in 1791, the method was promptly vetoed by the president—the first presidential veto in U.S. history! First, we give the procedure for apportioning a number of items into various groups using the Hamilton method and then discuss the presidential objections to the method.

Hamilton's Method

1. Find $$\text{SD} = \frac{\text{total population}}{\text{total seats to be apportioned}}$$
2. Find $$\text{SQ} = \frac{\text{state population}}{\text{SD}}$$
3. Round SQ down to the nearest integer (lower quota). Each state should get at least that many seats but must get *at least one* seat.
4. Apportion additional seats one at a time to the states with the *largest* fractional part of the standard quotas.

EXAMPLE 2 Using the Hamilton Method

Table 14.25 shows the population of the 15 states in the Union according to the 1790 census. Use the Hamilton method to apportion the 105 seats in the House of Representatives.

Table 14.25

State	Population	SQ	Rounded Down	Seats
Virginia	630,560	18.31	18	18
Massachusetts	475,327	13.80	13	**14**
Pennsylvania	432,879	12.57	12	**13**
North Carolina	353,523	10.27	10	10
New York	331,589	9.63	9	**10**
Maryland	278,514	8.09	8	8
Connecticut	236,841	6.88	6	**7**
South Carolina	206,236	5.99	5	**6**
New Jersey	179,570	5.21	5	5
New Hampshire	141,822	4.12	4	4
Vermont	85,533	2.48	2	2
Georgia	70,835	2.06	2	2
Kentucky	68,705	2.00	2	2
Rhode Island	68,446	1.99	1	**2**
Delaware	55,540	1.61	1	**2**
Total	3,615,920		**98**	**105**

Solution

We use the four steps.

1. Since the total population is 3,615,920 and we have to apportion 105 seats,

$$\text{SD} = \frac{3{,}615{,}920}{105} = 34{,}437.33$$

2. We first find SQs for Virginia, Massachusetts, and Delaware.

$$\text{For Virginia,} \quad SQ = \frac{630{,}560}{34{,}437.33} = 18.31$$

$$\text{For Massachusetts,} \quad SQ = \frac{475{,}327}{34{,}437.33} = 13.80$$

$$\text{For Delaware,} \quad SQ = \frac{55{,}540}{34{,}437.33} = 1.61$$

   The SQ for all states, to two decimal places, is shown in column 3 of Table 14.25.

3. The SQs rounded *down* to the nearest integer are in column 4 of Table 14.25. Accordingly, Virginia, Massachusetts, and Delaware will get 18, 13, and 1 seat, respectively. Note that the total seats in column 4 add up to 98. What about the $105 - 98 = 7$ seats that are left over? See step 4!

4. The additional seats are apportioned, one at a time, to the states with the *largest* fractional parts (South Carolina, Rhode Island, Connecticut, Massachusetts, New York, Delaware, and Pennsylvania). The *actual* number of seats apportioned is in column 5 of Table 14.25.

Note that the Hamilton method assigns 2 seats to Delaware, a state with a population of 55,540. However, it was stipulated in the Constitution that each seat in the House would represent a population of at least 30,000. Logically, 2 seats would have to represent 60,000 people, but Delaware only had a population of 55,540! Partially on the basis of this flaw, President Washington vetoed use of the Hamilton plan to apportion the first House of Representatives. Instead, the Jefferson method, which assigned an extra seat to Virginia, Jefferson's home state, was used.

We shall use the Jefferson method to apportion the 105 seats in the original House of Representatives after we give one more example using the Hamilton method.

EXAMPLE 3 Using the Hamilton Method

The second floor of Brandon Hospital houses five intensive care units: Medical (M), Surgical (S), Cardiac (C), Transitional (T), and Progressive (P). The maximum number of patients that each unit can house is shown in Table 14.26. The total for all units is 90. The hospital has bought 50 recliners to be distributed among the five units. Use the Hamilton method to apportion the 50 recliners on the basis of the number of patients in each unit.

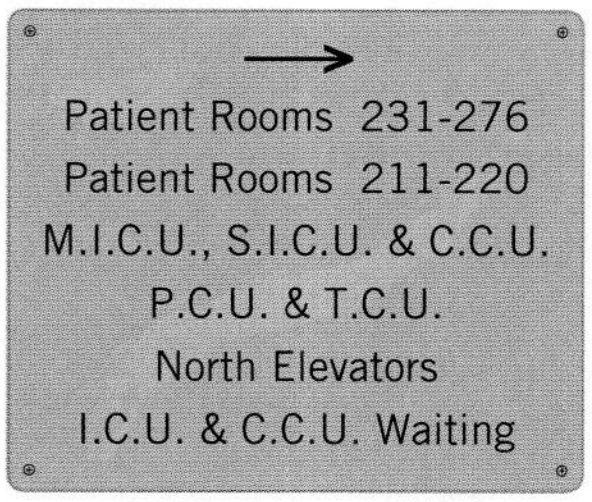

Table 14.26

Unit	Patients	SQ	Rounded Down	Actual Number
Medical	15	$15/1.8 = 8.33$	8	8
Surgical	30	$30/1.8 = 16.67$	16	$16 + \mathbf{1} = \mathbf{17}$
Cardiac	12	$12/1.8 = 6.67$	6	$6 + \mathbf{1} = \mathbf{7}$
Transitional	8	$8/1.8 = 4.44$	4	4
Progressive	25	$25/1.8 = 13.89$	13	$13 + \mathbf{1} = \mathbf{14}$
Totals	**90**	**50**	**47**	**50**

Solution

The standard divisor $SD = 90/50 = 1.8$, and the standard quota SQ is the number of patients in each unit divided by 1.8, as shown in column 3. Next, we **round down** each SQ and enter the result in column 4. Note that the sum of all the rounded-down numbers in column 4 is 47. We apportion the 3 remaining recliners, one by one, to the units with the highest fractional parts: 0.89 (P), 0.67 (C), and 0.67 (S). Column 5 shows the actual number of recliners apportioned to each unit, with the bold numbers reflecting the extra recliner. Note that the sum of the numbers in column 5 is 50, the total number of recliners.

Now you know how to apportion recliners as well as seats!

C The Thomas Jefferson Method of Apportionment

In Examples 2 and 3 some of the groups (Delaware and the Surgical Care Unit, for example) received additional items when applying step 4 in Hamilton's method. Can we modify the standard quota SQ to overcome the possible inequity? Jefferson's method attempts to do this by using a **modified divisor MD** that is *slightly lower* than the standard divisor SD to obtain a **modified quota MQ** that is *slightly higher* than the standard quota SQ. Does this sound confusing? Just remember that if you have the fraction

$$SQ = \frac{\text{population in the group}}{SD}$$

and you make the denominator SD *slightly lower,* the new modified quota MQ will be *slightly higher.* Here are the steps to apportion items using Jefferson's method.

Jefferson's Method

1. Find a modified divisor MD such that when each modified quota MQ is *rounded down* to the nearest integer, the sum of the resulting integers equals the number of items to be apportioned.
2. The apportionment for each group corresponds to the *rounded down* MQs found in step 1.

As we shall see, the challenge is to find that "magical" MD!

EXAMPLE 4 Using the Jefferson Method

Use the Jefferson method to apportion the 50 recliners of Example 3.

Solution

Table 14.27 shows the first four columns in Example 3. The standard divisor in Example 3 was 1.8, so let us make the modified divisor MD slightly *lower*—say, **1.7**—to obtain the modified quotas shown in column 5 (rounded to two decimal places). We show the rounded down numbers corresponding to the actual number of recliners apportioned in the last column.

Table 14.27

Unit	Patients	SQ	Rounded Down	Modified Quota	Rounded Down
Medical	15	$\frac{15}{1.8} = 8.33$	8	$\frac{15}{1.7} = 8.82$	8
Surgical	30	$\frac{30}{1.8} = 16.67$	16	$\frac{30}{1.7} = 17.65$	17
Cardiac	12	$\frac{12}{1.8} = 6.67$	6	$\frac{12}{1.7} = 7.06$	7
Transitional	8	$\frac{8}{1.8} = 4.44$	4	$\frac{8}{1.7} = 4.71$	4
Progressive	25	$\frac{25}{1.8} = 13.89$	13	$\frac{25}{1.7} = 14.71$	14
Total	**90**	**50**	**47**		**50**

Note that the sum of the rounded-down numbers in the last column adds up to **50** as required.

EXAMPLE 5 Using the Jefferson Method

Use the Jefferson method to apportion the 1794 House of Representatives shown in Table 14.28. Note that the total U.S. population was 3,615,920, 105 seats were to be apportioned, and

$$MQ = \frac{\text{total population}}{MD}$$

Table 14.28

State	Population	MQ	Rounded Down
Virginia	630,560	19.11	19
Massachusetts	475,327	14.40	14
Pennsylvania	432,879	13.12	13
North Carolina	353,523	10.71	10
New York	331,589	10.05	10
Maryland	278,514	8.44	8
Connecticut	236,841	7.18	7
South Carolina	206,236	6.25	6
New Jersey	179,570	5.44	5
New Hampshire	141,822	4.30	4
Vermont	85,533	2.59	2
Georgia	70,835	2.15	2
Kentucky	68,705	2.08	2
Rhode Island	68,446	2.07	2
Delaware	55,540	1.68	1
Total	3,615,920	109.57	**105**

Solution

The modified divisor MD = 33,000 was mercifully supplied by Congress. We calculate some modified quotas and show the rest in the table.

For Virginia, $\dfrac{630{,}560}{33{,}000} \approx 19.11$

For Massachusetts, $\dfrac{475{,}327}{33{,}000} \approx 14.40$

For Delaware, $\dfrac{55{,}540}{33{,}000} \approx 1.68$

The rounded-down quotas corresponding to the number of seats under the Jefferson method are shown in the last column of Table 14.28.

D The Daniel Webster Method of Apportionment

The feasibility of the Jefferson method hinges on finding the "magic" modified divisor MD and was attacked on constitutional grounds. However, Jefferson pointed out that the Constitution only required that apportionment be based on population, and the modified divisor MD produced quotas that indeed reflected the population and, moreover, did so equally, since all states used the *same* divisor. The Jefferson method was used without incident until after the 1820 census, when a major flaw (to be discussed in the next section) was uncovered. When the same flaw appeared again following the 1830 census, the method was replaced by one proposed by Daniel Webster in 1832. By that time, the country had grown from 15 states with 3,615,920 people to 24 states with 12,860,702 people.

The appeal of Webster's method was its mathematical simplicity. Modified quotas are *not* rounded *down* to the nearest integer. Instead, they are rounded to the *nearest* integer using the mathematical rules we have studied: round *up* for fractions of $\frac{1}{2}$ or more and *down* for fractions that are less than $\frac{1}{2}$. The bad news is that *you still have to find that modified "magic" divisor MD.* The good news is that the MD is usually supplied for us.

Webster's Method

1. Find MD, the modified divisor.
2. Find MQ, the modified quota for each group.

$$\text{MQ} = \frac{\text{total population}}{\text{MD}}$$

3. Round MQ in the **usual** manner for each group (*up* for 0.5 or more, *down* for less than 0.5).
4. The apportionment for each group corresponds to the values obtained in step 3, and the sum of the apportionments for all groups must equal the total number of items to be apportioned.

EXAMPLE 6 Using the Webster Method

Use the Webster method to apportion the five states shown with their respective populations in the 1830 census in Table 14.29. The modified divisor MD selected by Webster was 49,800, and the total population was 12,860,702.
(Source: www.census.gov/population/censusdata/table-16.pdf.)

Solution

The modified quota MQ is found by dividing the state population by 49,800.

For New York, MQ = 1,918,608/49,800 = 38.53, or 39
New York gets **39** seats.

For Pennsylvania, MQ = 1,348,233/49,800 = 27.07, or 27
Pennsylvania gets **27** seats.

For Kentucky, MQ = 687,917/49,800 = 13.81, or 14
Kentucky gets **14** seats.

For Vermont, MQ = 280,652/49,800 = 5.64, or 6
Vermont gets **6** seats.

For Louisiana, MQ = 215,739/49,800 = 4.33, or 4
Louisiana gets **4** seats.

The final results are shown in Table 14.29.

Table 14.29

State	Population	$\text{MQ} = \frac{\text{Population}}{49{,}800}$	Apportionment
New York	1,918,608	38.53	**39**
Pennsylvania	1,348,233	27.07	**27**
Kentucky	687,917	13.81	**14**
Vermont	280,652	5.64	**6**
Louisiana	215,739	4.33	**4**

E The John Quincy Adams Method of Apportionment

As we have mentioned, by 1830, politicians were once again struggling over the apportionment method to be used. The debate was so intense that former president John Quincy Adams, at the time a representative from Massachusetts, wrote in his memoirs:

> I passed an entirely sleepless night again. The iniquity of the Apportionment bill, and the disreputable means by which so partial and unjust a distribution of the representation had been effected, agitated me so that I could not close my eyes.

Mr. Adams was referring to a proposal by James K. Polk of Tennessee, which used Jefferson's method of apportionment with an *increased* divisor of 47,700. This increase favored the representation of some states but hurt the representation of some of the New England states. As a consequence, Adams proposed a new apportionment method that was similar to Jefferson's but *rounded up* instead of down and, unfortunately, still used a "magic" divisor. Here is the procedure for Adams's apportionment method.

Adams's Method

1. Find a modified divisor MD such that when each group's modified quota MQ is *rounded up* to the nearest integer, the sum of the resulting integers equals the number of items to be apportioned.
2. The apportionment for each group corresponds to the rounded up MQs found in step 1.

EXAMPLE 7 Using the Adams Method

Use Adams's method to apportion the recliners of Example 3.

Solution

We have to find the modified "magic" divisor. Recall that in Example 4 the standard divisor 1.8 was slightly *lowered* to 1.7 to obtain the desired modified quotas. If the modified quotas are *rounded up,* the sum will be $9 + 18 + 8 + 5 + 15 = 55$. To reduce this number, let us *increase* the divisor to 1.9 and *round up* the quota as shown in Table 14.30.

Table 14.30

Unit	Patients	Modified Quota	Rounded Up
Medical	15	$\frac{15}{1.9} = 7.89$	**8**
Surgical	30	$\frac{30}{1.9} = 15.79$	**16**
Cardiac	12	$\frac{12}{1.9} = 6.32$	7
Transitional	8	$\frac{8}{1.9} = 4.21$	5
Progressive	25	$\frac{25}{1.9} = 13.16$	**14**
Totals	**90**		**50**

Our modified "magic" divisor 1.9 did the trick; the *rounded-up* values, which correspond to the number of recliners each unit will get, add up to **50.**

Before you attempt the exercises, Table 14.31 on the next page gives a summary of the apportionment methods we have studied and their important features.

Table 14.31

Method	Divisor	Round the Quota	Apportionment
Hamilton's	$SD = \dfrac{\text{total population}}{\text{seats to be apportioned}}$	*Down* to the nearest integer	Distribute leftover items to the groups with the *largest* fractional part until all items are distributed.
Jefferson's	MD is less than SD.	*Down* to the nearest integer	Apportion to each group its modified *lower* quota.
Webster's	MD is less than, greater than, or equal to SD.	*To* the nearest integer	Apportion to each group its modified *rounded* quota.
Adams's	MD is greater than SD.	*Up* to the nearest integer	Apportion to each group its modified *upper* quota.

As you can see from Table 14.31, Hamilton's method rounded the *standard* quotas *down* to the nearest integer, Jefferson's method rounded the *modified* quotas *down* to the nearest integer, Webster's method rounded the *modified* quotas *to* the nearest integer, and Adams's method rounded the *modified* quotas *up* to the nearest integer.

14.3 EXERCISES

A Apportionment Problems

In problems 1–7, use the following table:

University	Headcount	FTE
University of Florida	41,652	29,646
Florida State University	30,389	21,195
Florida A&M University	11,324	8064
University of South Florida	31,555	18,176
Florida Atlantic University	19,153	10,725
University of West Florida	7790	4556
University of Central Florida	30,009	18,312
Florida International University	30,096	17,434
University of North Florida	11,360	6697
Florida Gulf Coast University	2893	1558
Subtotal E & G	**216,221**	**136,363**

1. The university system in the State of Florida consists of the 10 universities listed in the table. In a recent year, the general budget allocation for the system amounted to more than 2 billion dollars: $2,001,102,854.
   a. If the state decides to apportion the money *equally* among the 10 universities, how much will each university get? Answer to the nearest dollar.
   b. How much money will each student be allocated if the money is apportioned *equally* among all the students? Answer to the nearest dollar.
   c. How much money will each FTE (full-time equivalent) be allocated if the money is apportioned equally among all FTEs? Answer to the nearest dollar.
2. The University of Florida has 41,652 students, whereas Florida Gulf Coast University has 2893. How much money will each of these two universities receive if the money is allocated according to the *number of students* in each institution? Answer to the nearest dollar.
3. The University of South Florida has 18,176 FTEs, whereas the University of West Florida has 4556. How much money will each of these two universities receive if the money is allocated according to the *number of FTEs* in each institution? Answer to the nearest dollar.

B The Alexander Hamilton Method of Apportionment

4. Suppose that the state decides to apportion 200 new teaching positions on the basis of the *number of students* in each university.
   a. Use the Hamilton method to find the standard divisor SD.
   b. Use the Hamilton method to find the standard quota SQ for Florida Atlantic and the University of Central Florida. Answer to three decimal places.
5. Suppose the state decides to apportion 200 new teaching positions on the basis of the *number of FTEs* in each university.
   a. Use the Hamilton method to find the standard divisor SD.
   b. Use the Hamilton method to find the standard quotient SQ for Florida Atlantic and the University of Central Florida. Answer to 3 decimal places.

6. Use the Hamilton method to apportion the 200 new teaching positions to each of the 10 universities on the basis of the *number of students*.
7. Use the Hamilton method to apportion the 200 new teaching positions to each of the 10 universities on the basis of the *number of FTEs*. Is the number of positions for each university the same as that obtained in problem 6?
8. Let us go back to the five intensive care units of Example 3. Suppose the hospital buys 75 new intravenous (IV) pumps to be distributed among the five units on the basis of the *number of patients* in each unit. Use the Hamilton method to fill in the blanks in the table below and apportion the 75 IV units.

Unit	Patients	SQ	Rounded Down	Actual Number
Medical	15			
Surgical	30			
Cardiac	12			
Transitional	8			
Progressive	25			
	90			

9. According to the Centers for Disease Control and Prevention, the states reporting the highest annual number of AIDS cases in a recent year are as shown in the table. In that same year, federal spending on AIDS research amounted to $9,988 million.

California	5637
Florida	5683
New York	7655
Texas	3715
New Jersey	2061

Suppose the federal government wishes to allocate an additional $100 million for AIDS research on the basis of the *number of cases* in each of these states.

a. Find each state's standard quota.

b. Find each state's apportionment using Hamilton's method.

10. A university consists of five colleges: Agriculture, Arts, Business, Engineering, and Science. The student council is made up of 100 members, with the number of delegates from each college allocated on the basis of the number of students in each college. Use the Hamilton method to complete the following table.

College	Students	SQ	Rounded Down	Delegates
Agriculture	2500			
Arts	500			
Business	3000			
Engineering	4000			
Science	3000			

C The Thomas Jefferson Method of Apportionment

11. What leisure activities do you participate in? In the table are five activities and the approximate number of participants (in millions) in each.

Exercise	150
Sports	90
Charity work	85
Home repair	130
Computer hobbies	80

Sources: National Endowment for the Arts; *Statistical Abstract of the United States.*

Suppose you wish to allocate $100 million to promote leisure activities on the basis of the *number of participants.*

a. Find the modified quota for each activity using the divisor 5.25.

b. Find how much money should be apportioned to each activity using Jefferson's method.

12. In the following table, the five U.S. charities receiving the highest donations (in millions) in a recent year are shown.

Salvation Army	$1230
YMCA	$ 630
Fidelity Investments	$ 570
American Cancer Society	$ 560
American Red Cross	$ 540

Source: *The Chronicle of Philanthropy.*

Suppose you are a philanthropist willing to donate $150 million to these five charities on the basis of *received donations.*

a. Find the modified quota for each charity using the divisor 23.3.

b. Find how much money should be apportioned to each charity using Jefferson's method.

D The Daniel Webster Method of Apportionment

13. How much do you spend on your pet annually? In the following table are the average annual costs (to the nearest $10) spent per household for several types of pets.

Dogs	$190
Cats	$110
Birds	$ 10
Horses	$230

Source: *U.S. Pet Ownership and Demographic Sourcebook.*

For every $500 spent on each of these four types of pets,

a. find the modified quota using the divisor 1.08.

b. how much money should be apportioned to each pet category using Webster's method?

14. What continents do immigrants to the United States come from? The table shows the number of immigrants from each continent admitted to the United States in a recent year.

Europe	90,000
Asia	220,000
North America	255,000
South America	45,000
Africa	40,000

Source: U.S. Immigration and Naturalization Service.

Suppose the Immigration and Naturalization Service is planning to grant 700,000 visas next year.

a. Find the modified quota using the divisor 0.928.

b. How many visas should be allocated to each continent using Webster's method?

E The John Quincy Adams Method of Apportionment

15. The acreage of five county parks in Hillsborough County is shown in the following table. Suppose the county wishes to distribute 75 new park rangers among these five parks.

Lake Park	600
E. G. Simmons	470
Lettuce Lake	240
Lithia Springs	160
Eureka Springs	30

a. Find the modified quota for each park using the divisor 20.5.

b. Find the number of rangers that should be allocated to each park using Adams's method.

16. Has your telephone area code been changed lately? With the popularity of cell phones increasing, more area codes are needed. The table shows the number of existing area codes in five states. Unfortunately, there are a limited number of area codes that can be allocated to states. Suppose we wish to allocate 25 new area codes to the five states listed on the basis of the number of area codes they already have.

Texas	21
California	20
Florida	12
Ohio	10
Colorado	7

a. Find the modified quota for each state using the divisor 3.08.

b. Find the number of area codes allocated to each state using Adams's method.

In problems 17–20, use the headcount enrollment by county in the Florida State University System (to the nearest thousand) given in the following table:

County	Dade	Broward	Hillsborough	Orange	Pinellas
Headcount	33,000	21,000	17,000	11,000	11,000

Suppose the state decides to allocate $100 *million to these five counties.*

17. a. Find the standard divisor.

b. Find each county's standard quota.

c. Find each county's apportionment using Hamilton's method.

18. a. Find each county's modified quota using the divisor 916.05.

b. Find each county's apportionment using Jefferson's method.

19. a. Find each county's modified quota using the divisor 948.60.

b. Find each county's apportionment using Adams's method.

20. Find each county's apportionment using Webster's method with the standard quota.

In problems 21–24, use the top-rated AIDS treatment hospitals and their scores given in the table.

Hospital	**Points**
San Francisco General	100
Johns Hopkins Hospital	72
Massachusetts General	62
Univ. of Calif. at San Francisco	56
Memorial Sloan-Kettering	50

Source: *U.S. News and World Report.*

Suppose the best 200 AIDS specialists are to be assigned to these five hospitals on the basis of the number of points in the survey.

21. a. Find the standard divisor.
b. Find each hospital's standard quota.
c. Find each hospital's apportionment using Hamilton's method.

22. a. Find each hospital's modified quota using the divisor 1.6745.
b. Find each hospital's apportionment using Jefferson's method.

23. a. Find each hospital's modified quota using the divisor 1.7238.
b. Find each hospital's apportionment using Adams's method.

24. Find each hospital's apportionment using Webster's method with the modified divisor 1.6983.

USING YOUR KNOWLEDGE

Students have suggested that many of the apportionment problems can be done using ratio and proportion. Suppose you have four sports, A, B, C, and D, and the Student Government Association wishes to distribute $200,000 *among the four on the basis of their average attendance of* 2000, 4000, 6000, *and* 8000 *spectators, respectively.*

25. a. How much will each sport get if the $200,000 is distributed *proportionately* to its *attendance?*
b. How much will each sport get if the $200,000 is apportioned using Hamilton's, Jefferson's, Adams's, and Webster's methods?
c. Are the answers the same in parts (**a**) and (**b**)?

IN OTHER WORDS

Describe in your own words how to calculate

26. a standard divisor.

27. a standard quota.

28. Look at Table 14.31 on page 854. Name the method we have studied that rounds the modified quota
a. up. **b.** down. **c.** in the usual manner.

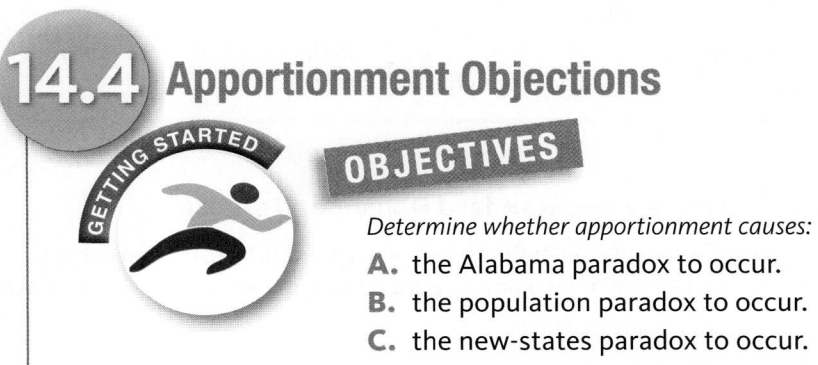

14.4 Apportionment Objections

GETTING STARTED

OBJECTIVES

Determine whether apportionment causes:

A. the Alabama paradox to occur.
B. the population paradox to occur.
C. the new-states paradox to occur.

As we saw in Section 14.2, there were several objections, or flaws, associated with the voting methods we studied. Similarly, there are several objections, or flaws, associated with Hamilton's apportionment method. These objections are paradoxical and depend mainly on three factors: the number of items to be apportioned (objection: the **Alabama paradox**), the population in the group (objection: the **population paradox**), and the addition of one or more new groups that require apportionment (objection: the **new-states paradox**).

The main objection to Jefferson's, Webster's, and Adams's methods is that each has the potential of violating the **quota rule.**

The Quota Rule

The apportionment for *every* group under consideration should always equal either the group's **upper quota** (rounding up) or its **lower quota** (rounding down).

Even though Hamilton's method will *always* satisfy the quota rule and Jefferson's, Webster's, and Adams's methods will not, the method has equally serious flaws. The three main objections to Hamilton's method are the *Alabama paradox,* the *population paradox,* and the *new-states paradox.*

SWEET HOME ALABAMA

The Alabama paradox first surfaced after the 1870 census. With 270 members in the House of Representatives, Rhode Island got 2 representatives, but when the house size was increased to 280, Rhode Island *lost* a seat. After the 1880 census, C. W. Seaton (chief clerk of the U.S. Census Office) computed apportionments for all house sizes between 275 and 350 members. He then wrote a letter to Congress pointing out that if the House of Representatives had 299 seats, Alabama would get 8 seats, but if the House of Representatives had 300 seats, Alabama would only get 7 seats! Again, this meant a *loss* of 1 seat for Alabama, even though the total number of house seats could be increased from 299 to 300. This objection or flaw has come to be known as the *Alabama paradox.*

A The Alabama Paradox

The Alabama Paradox

The **Alabama paradox** occurs when an *increase* in the total number of items to be apportioned results in a *loss* of items for a group.

EXAMPLE 1 Finding the Standard Divisor and Quota

In the 1880 census, the population of the United States was 50,189,209, and the population of Alabama was 1,262,505. Find the standard divisor and the standard quota when

(a) 299 seats are to be apportioned.

(b) 300 seats are to be apportioned.

Solution

(a) The standard divisor is

$$\frac{50{,}189{,}209}{299} \approx 167{,}856.89$$

and the standard quota is

$$\frac{1{,}262{,}505}{167{,}856.89} \approx 7.52$$

(b) The standard divisor is

$$\frac{50{,}189{,}209}{300} \approx 167{,}297.36$$

and the standard quota is

$$\frac{1{,}262{,}505}{167{,}297.36} \approx 7.55$$

Does Example 1 prove that Alabama would get 8 seats when 299 seats were apportioned and only 7 when 300 seats were apportioned? The answer is *no.* To prove this, we would have to find the standard quotas for all the states and then assign the leftover seats to the states with the largest fractional parts. Unfortunately, there were a total of 38 states in 1880, so the task would be monumental indeed.

For now, let us try a simple example.

EXAMPLE 2 The Alabama Paradox and the Hamilton Method

Consider a country with a population of 50,000 and three states, A, B, and C, with the populations shown in Table 14.32. Using Hamilton's apportionment method, show that the Alabama paradox occurs if the number of seats is increased from 50 to 51.

Solution

When the number of seats to be apportioned is 50, the standard divisor is $\frac{50,000}{50} = 1000$. The standard quotas SQs and the rounded-down values RDs are shown in columns 3 and 4 of Table 14.32. The state with the *largest* fractional part (0.5) is C. Thus, C gets the extra seat.

Table 14.32

State	Population	SQ	RD	Extra	Final
A	25,200	$\frac{25,200}{1000} \approx 25.2$	25	0	**25**
B	23,300	$\frac{23,300}{1000} \approx 23.3$	23	0	**23**
C	1500	$\frac{1500}{1000} \approx 1.5$	1	1	**2**
Total	**50,000**		**49**		**50**

If we repeat the apportionment in Table 14.33 using 51 seats, the standard divisor is $\frac{50,000}{51} \approx 980.39$. Again, we show the standard quotas SQs and the rounded-down values in columns 3 and 4. The states with the *largest* fractional parts are B (0.77) and A (0.70), so each gets an extra seat.

Table 14.33

State	Population	SQ	RD	Extra	Final
A	25,200	$\frac{25,200}{980.39} = 25.70$	25	1	**26**
B	23,300	$\frac{23,300}{980.39} = 23.77$	23	1	**24**
C	1500	$\frac{1500}{980.39} = 1.53$	1	0	**1**
Total	**50,000**		**49**		**51**

Here we go again! Even though we *increased* the number of seats from 50 to 51, state C, formerly with 2 seats, ended up *losing* 1 seat—the Alabama paradox!

Note that this paradox can *only* occur when the number of objects to be apportioned *increases.* Thus, it seems reasonable to expect that if we hold the size of the House of Representatives to 435, as it has been for many years, no objections or paradoxes should surface. Unfortunately, this is not the case. If the population of one or more states changes, one state could *lose* a seat to another state, even if its population is *growing* at a faster rate than the state that loses the seat. This paradox is known as the *population paradox.*

B The Population Paradox

The Population Paradox

The **population paradox** occurs when the population of group A is *increasing* faster than the population of group B, yet A *loses* items to group B.

The population paradox was discovered around 1900, when it was shown that a state could *lose* seats in the House of Representatives as a result of an *increase* in its population. (Virginia was growing much faster than Maine—about 60% faster—but Virginia *lost* a seat in the house, whereas Maine *gained* a seat.)

EXAMPLE 3 The Population Paradox and the Hamilton Method

Table 14.34 shows the number of students taking mathematics, English, and science courses during the fall and spring semesters. If 100 full-time teaching positions are to be apportioned among the three departments on the basis of their respective course enrollments,

(a) how many positions will each department get in the fall using Hamilton's method?

(b) how many positions will each department get in the spring using Hamilton's method?

(c) is the apportionment fair? Explain your reasoning

(d) is this apportionment an example of the population paradox?

Solution

Since there are 10,000 students and 100 positions, the standard divisor for the fall is 10,000/100 = 100. The standard quotas SQs and the number of positions for each department during the fall are shown in columns 3 and 4 of Table 14.34. The number of students for the spring is 10,030, so the standard divisor SQ is 10,030/100 = 100.3. The new standard quotas New SQs and the number of positions per department for the spring are shown in columns 6 and 7.

Table 14.34

	Fall Semester			Spring Semester		
Subject	**Number**	**SQ**	**Positions**	**Number**	**New SQ**	**Positions**
Math	951	9.51	**10**	961	961/100.3 = 9.58	**9**
English	1949	19.49	**19**	1969	1969/100.3 = 19.63	**20**
Science	7100	71.00	**71**	7100	7100/100.3 = 70.79	**71**
Total	**10,000**		**100**	**10,030**		**100**

(a) In the fall, mathematics gets 10 positions, English 19, and science 71.

(b) In the spring, mathematics gets 9 positions, English 20, and science 71.

(c) No. The rate of growth for mathematics was $\frac{961 - 951}{951} = \frac{10}{951} \approx 1.05\%$.

The rate of growth for English was $\frac{1969 - 1949}{1949} = \frac{20}{1949} \approx 1.03\%$.

Thus, mathematics was growing at a faster rate (1.05%) than English (1.03%), but despite this, mathematics *lost* 1 position (from 10 to 9), whereas English *gained* 1 position (from 19 to 20).

(d) Yes. In this instance the mathematics population was increasing faster than the English population, yet mathematics *lost* one position to English.

C The New-States Paradox

As we have mentioned before, the objections to Hamilton's apportionment method occur when the number of items to be apportioned changes (Alabama paradox) and when the population in the group changes (population paradox). We consider one more paradox that occurs when we add one or more groups that require apportionment (*new-states paradox*). The **new-states paradox** means that adding a new state with its fair share of seats can affect the number of seats due to other states. This has actually happened! The paradox was discovered in 1907 when Oklahoma became a state. Before Oklahoma became a state, the House of Representatives had 386 seats. Comparing Oklahoma's population with that of other states, it was clear that Oklahoma should have 5 seats, so the house size was increased by 5 to 391 seats. The intent was to leave the number of seats unchanged for the other states. However, when the apportionment was mathematically recalculated, Maine gained a seat (from 3 to 4), and New York lost a seat (from 38 to 37).

The New-States Paradox

The **new-states paradox** occurs when the *addition* of a new group *changes* the apportionment of another group.

EXAMPLE 4 The New-States Paradox and the Hamilton Method

Suppose that in Example 3 the art department enrolls 600 students in the fall and that 5 additional positions are allocated, bringing the total number of students to 10,600 and the total number of positions to 105.

(a) Use the Hamilton method to find the new fall apportionment for mathematics, English, science, and art.

(b) How does the new fall apportionment compare with the original fall apportionment of Example 3?

(c) Does the new apportionment seem fair?

(d) Show that the new apportionment results in an occurrence of the new-states paradox.

Solution

(a) To find the new fall semester apportionment, note that there are now 10,600 students and 105 positions, so the new standard divisor is $\frac{10{,}600}{105} = 100.95$. The standard quotas and the final number of positions are shown in Table 14.35.

Table 14.35

	New Fall Semester			Original Fall Semester		
Subject	**Number**	**SQ**	**Positions**	**Number**	**SQ**	**Positions**
Math	951	9.42	**10**	951	9.51	**10**
English	1949	19.31	**19**	1949	19.49	**19**
Science	7100	70.33	**70**	7100	71.00	**71**
Art	**600**	**5.94**	**6**			
Total	**10,600**		**105**	**10,000**		**100**

(b) The right side of Table 14.35 shows the original fall semester apportionments. As you can see, the science department *lost* 1 position (from 71 to 70) in the new apportionment, even though it did not lose any students. Presumably, the art department should have gotten the 5 new positions, but it got 6 instead.

(c) The new apportionments do not seem fair because science *lost* 1 position to art.

(d) The addition of one group (art) changed the apportionment of another group (science) and, by definition, is an occurrence of the *new-states paradox*.

Now we have seen that Hamilton's method satisfies the quota rule but can produce the paradoxes we have studied in this section. Jefferson's, Webster's, and Adams's methods *can* violate the quota rule because they are based on the philosophy that quotas can be conveniently modified. On the other hand, they do not produce the paradoxes we have studied. Can we find a perfect apportionment method that not only satisfies the quota rule but also avoids these paradoxes? Two mathematicians, Michael Balinski and H. Payton Young, proved in 1980 that there is no such method. Their result is called **Balinski and Young's Impossibility Theorem.**

Balinski and Young's Impossibility Theorem

There is *no* apportionment method that satisfies the quota rule and avoids paradoxes.

Table 14.36 shows which methods violate the quota rule or produce some of the paradoxes studied.

Table 14.36

Characteristic	Hamilton's	Jefferson's	Adams's	Webster's
May violate the *quota rule*	No	Yes	Yes	Yes
May result in the *Alabama paradox*	Yes	No	No	No
May result in the *population paradox*	Yes	No	No	No
May result in the *new-states paradox*	Yes	No	No	No

So there we have it. Just as we could find *no* perfect voting method, there is also *no* perfect apportionment method!

14.4 EXERCISES

A The Alabama Paradox

1. Three Greek letter societies, α, β, and γ, have the numbers of members as shown in the table. If Hamilton's method is used to apportion seats in the Pan Hellenic Council, does the *Alabama paradox* occur if the number of seats is increased

   a. from 30 to 31?

   b. from 60 to 61?

Society	Members
α	3220
β	5000
δ	9780
Total	**18,000**

2. A country consists of four states, A, B, C, and D, with the populations shown in the table. If Hamilton's method is used to apportion the legislature, does the *Alabama paradox* occur if the number of seats is increased

   a. from 104 to 105?

   b. from 114 to 115?

City	Population
A	1800
B	3720
C	2330
D	2150
Total	**10,000**

3. Which are the four best theme parks in the United States? According to *Inside Track,* a publication that rates theme parks and attractions, the four best parks are Busch Gardens (B), King's Island (K), Walt Disney World (W), and Six Flags Magic Mountain (S). The number of votes received by each of the parks in a survey of 1020 persons is as shown in the table. Suppose Hamilton's method is used to apportion 71 free tickets to visit the parks on the basis of the number of votes obtained in the survey. Does the *Alabama paradox* occur if the number of tickets is increased to 72? If so, which park loses a ticket?

Park	Votes
B	405
K	306
W	204
S	105
Total	**1020**

4. The total number of minority students (in thousands) studying allopathic medicine in a recent year is as shown in the following table. If Hamilton's method is used to allocate scholarships on the basis of enrollment, does the *Alabama paradox* occur when the number of scholarships is increased from 24 to 25?

Race	Students
White	44
Black	5
Hispanic	4
Asian	12
Total	**65**

Source: National Center for Health Statistics.

a. Which group(s) lose 1 scholarship?
b. Which group(s) gain 1 scholarship?
c. Which group(s) stay the same?

B The Population Paradox

5. The number of Medicare enrollees (in thousands) for Delaware (D), Nebraska (N), and Kansas (K) in a recent year and the estimated *projection* for a future year are as shown in the table. Suppose the federal contribution is $11 million for each year and Hamilton's method is used to apportion the money on the basis of the number of enrollees.

State	Number	Projection
Delaware	110	122
Nebraska	250	300
Kansas	380	428
Total	**740**	**850**

Source: Health Care Financing Administration.

a. How much will each state get in the most recent year? (Answer to the nearest million.)
b. How much will each state get using the projected population? (Answer to the nearest million.)
c. Which state has the higher percent increase of enrollees, Delaware or Kansas?
d. Does the *population paradox* occur when Hamilton's method is used to allocate the $11 million? Explain.

6. A state consists of three counties, A, B, and C, with the present populations and in 10 years shown in the following table. Suppose 100 seats are to be apportioned on the basis of population using Hamilton's method.

County	Now	10 Years
A	89,000	97,000
B	12,500	14,500
C	22,500	24,700
Total	**124,000**	**136,200**

a. How many seats will each of the counties get now?
b. How many seats will each of the counties get in 10 years?
c. Does the *population paradox* occur? Explain.

7. The populations of three counties, A, B, and C, at present and in 10 years are shown in the table. "Lucky" Fulano, the state governor, suggested a 13-seat legislature apportioned according to population using Hamilton's method.

County	Now	10 Years
A	89,000	97,000
B	125,000	145,000
C	225,000	247,000
Total	**439,000**	**489,000**

a. How many seats will each of the counties get now?
b. How many seats will each of the counties get in 10 years?
c. Does the *population paradox* occur? Explain.
d. Which of the three counties will be unhappy with reapportionment and why?

8. A nation consists of five states, A, B, C, D, and E, with populations 300, 156, 346, 408, and 590, respectively. Suppose 50 seats are to be apportioned on the basis of population using Hamilton's method.

a. How many seats will each state receive?
b. If the populations of states C and E were to increase by 16 and 2, respectively, how many seats would each state receive then?
c. Does the *population paradox* occur? Explain.
d. Which of the five states will be unhappy with reapportionment and why?

C The New-States Paradox

9. A company has two divisions: production (P) and sales (S). The number of employees in each is shown in the table. There are 41 managers to be apportioned between the two divisions P and S.
   a. Find each division apportionment using Hamilton's method.
   b. Suppose a new advertising division (A) with 114 employees and 8 new managers is to be added. Does the *new-states paradox* occur using Hamilton's method? Explain.

Division	Number
P	402
S	156
A	114
Total	**672**

10. A country has two states, A and B, with the populations (in thousands) shown in the table and 30 seats in the legislature.
   a. Find the apportionments for A and B using Hamilton's method.
   b. Suppose a third state C with a population of 76 (thousand) is added with 6 additional seats. Does the *new-states paradox* occur using Hamilton's method? Explain.

State	Population
A	268
B	104
C	76
Total	**448**

11. A country has two states, A and B, with the population (in hundreds) shown in the table and 100 seats in the legislature.
   a. Find the apportionments for A and B using Hamilton's method.
   b. Suppose a third state C with a population of 263 (hundred) is added with 6 additional seats. Does the *new-states paradox* occur using Hamilton's method? Explain.

State	Population
A	4470
B	520
C	263
Total	**5253**

IN OTHER WORDS

12. Describe in your own words the *Alabama paradox.*
13. Describe in your own words the *population paradox.*
14. Describe in your own words the *new-states paradox.*

CHAPTER 14 Summary

SECTION	ITEM	MEANING
14.1	Plurality method	Each voter votes for one candidate, and the candidate with the *most* first-place votes is the winner.
	Plurality with runoff method	Each voter votes for one candidate. If the candidate receives a *majority* of votes, that candidate is the winner. Otherwise, eliminate all but the two top candidates and hold a runoff election. The candidate who receives a *majority* is the winner.
	Borda count method	Each voter ranks the candidates from most to least favorable, with each last-place vote awarded *no* point; each next to last place is awarded *one* point; each third from last place is awarded *two* points; and so on. The candidate who receives the *most* points is the winner.
	Plurality with elimination method	Each voter votes for one candidate. If a candidate receives a *majority* of votes, that candidate is the winner. If no candidate receives a majority, *eliminate* the candidate with the fewest votes and hold another election. (If there is a tie for fewest votes, eliminate all candidates tied for fewest votes.) Repeat this process until a candidate receives a *majority.*

CHAPTER 14 Summary

SECTION	ITEM	MEANING
14.1D	Pairwise comparison method	Each voter ranks candidates from most to least favorable. Each candidate is then compared with each of the other candidates. If A is preferred to B, A gets 1 point. If B is preferred to A, B gets 1 point. If there is a tie, each candidate receives $\frac{1}{2}$ point. The candidate with the *most* overall points is the winner.
14.1E	Approval voting	Voters approve or disapprove each candidate. The candidate with the *most* approval votes wins.
14.2A	Majority criterion	If a candidate receives a *majority* of first-place votes, then that candidate should be the winner.
14.2B	Head-to-head criterion	If a candidate is favored when compared *head-to-head* with every other candidate, then that candidate should be the winner.
14.2C	Monotonicity criterion	If a candidate is the winner of a first election and then gains additional support without losing any of the original support, then the candidate should be the winner of the second election.
14.2D	Irrelevant alternatives criterion	If a candidate is the winner of an election, and in a second election one or more of the losing candidates are removed, then the winner of the *first* election should be the winner of the *second* election.
	Arrow's Impossibility Theorem	There is *no* voting method that will always simultaneously satisfy *all* of the four fairness criteria.
14.3A	Standard divisor (SD)	Total population in a group/total number to be apportioned.
	Standard quota (SQ)	Population in the group/standard divisor.
14.3B	Hamilton's method	A method in which the standard quota is rounded *down* and additional seats are apportioned to the states with the largest fractional part of the standard quotas.
14.3C	Jefferson's method	A method using a modified divisor so that when each group's modified quota is rounded *down* to the nearest integer, the sum of the integers equals the number of items to be apportioned.
14.3D	Webster's method	A method using a modified divisor so that when each group's modified quota is rounded in the *usual* manner, the sum of the integers equals the number of items to be apportioned.
	Adams's method	A method using a modified divisor so that when each group's modified quota is rounded *up* to the nearest integer, the sum of the integers equals the number of items to be apportioned.
14.4	Quota rule	The apportionment for *every* group under consideration should always equal either the group's *upper quota* or its *lower quota.*
14.4A	Alabama paradox	Occurs when an *increase* in the total number of items to be apportioned results in a *loss* of items for a group.
14.4B	Population paradox	Occurs when the population of group A *increases* faster than the population of group B, yet A *loses* items to group B.
14.4C	New-states paradox	Occurs when the *addition* of a new group *changes* the apportionment of another group.
	Balinski and Young's Impossibility Theorem	There is *no* apportionment method that satisfies the quota rule and *avoids* paradoxes.

CHAPTER 14 Practice Test

10	8	7	5
A	C	D	D
C	D	C	B
B	B	B	C
D	A	A	A

1. The results of an election involving four candidates, A, B, C, and D, are shown in the table to the left.
   a. Did any of the candidates receive a majority?
   b. Which candidate is the plurality winner?
   c. Which candidate comes in second?
   d. Which candidate comes in last?

2. Using the *plurality with runoff method,* who is the winner of the election in problem 1?

3. Using the *Borda count method,* who is the winner of the election in problem 1?

4. Using the *plurality with elimination method,* who is the winner of the election in problem 1?

5	3	9
A	B	C
B	C	A
C	A	B

5. The results of an election involving three candidates, A, B, and C, are shown in the table to the left. Using the pairwise comparison method, who is the winner
   a. between A and B?
   b. between A and C?
   c. between B and C?
   d. of the election?

6. The results of a hypothetical election using approval voting are summarized in the table. An X indicates that the voter approves of the candidate; a blank indicates no approval.

	Voters					
Candidates	**Thomas**	**Uma**	**Vera**	**Walter**	**Yvette**	**Zoe**
Adams	X	X	X		X	X
Barnes	X		X	X		
Collins			X		X	

   a. Who is the winner using approval voting?
   b. Who is the winner if Adams drops out of the race?

	Number of Voters		
Place	**36**	**16**	**12**
First	B	A	A
Second	A	B	C
Third	C	C	B

7. An election to select their spring break destination, Aruba (A), Bahamas (B), or Cancun (C), is conducted among 64 students. The results are as shown in the table to the left. Which destination should be selected under the specified method? Does the method satisfy the majority criterion?
   a. The plurality method
   b. The Borda count method
   c. The plurality with elimination method
   d. The pairwise comparison method

8. A restaurant conducted a survey among its customers to select their favorite entree from chicken (C), pork (P), turkey (T), and vegetarian (V). The number of votes for each was as shown in the table. Which entree should be selected under the specified method, and does the method satisfy the head-to-head criterion?
   a. Head-to-head
   b. Plurality
   c. Borda count
   d. Plurality with elimination
   e. Pairwise comparison

	Number of Voters				
Place	**15**	**25**	**29**	**30**	**45**
First	V	V	T	P	C
Second	T	T	V	V	P
Third	P	C	P	T	T
Fourth	C	P	C	C	V

CHAPTER 14 Practice Test – *continued*

	Number of Voters		
Place	**56**	**24**	**20**
First	C	B	A
Second	B	C	B
Third	A	A	C

9. A group of 100 students ranked the three courses they liked best as shown in the table to the left. If the plurality method is used to select the top course, does the plurality method satisfy
   a. the majority criterion? Explain.
   b. the head-to-head criterion? Explain.

10. As in problem 9, does the plurality method satisfy
    a. the monotonicity criterion if we assume a second election is undertaken and C gains additional support without losing any of the original support? Explain.
    b. the irrelevant alternatives criterion if we assume that either A or B drops out and a second election is undertaken? Explain.

11. Explain in your own words the meaning of Arrow's Impossibility Theorem.

12. Five universities received \$162 million in total general education and general fund revenues. The number of FTEs (to the nearest 1000) in each of the five universities is as shown in the table.

A	B	C	D	E	Total
15,000	8500	6500	6000	4500	**40,500**

Find the standard divisor SD and the standard quota SQ for each university.

13. A college is composed of five departments: mathematics (M), English (E), languages (L), art (A), and chemistry (C), with the number of faculty members shown in the table. If 100 new positions are to be apportioned using Hamilton's method and on the basis of the number of faculty in each department, what is the actual number of positions apportioned to each of the departments?

Department	Faculty	MQ	Actual Number
Mathematics	30		
English	60		
Language	24		
Art	16		
Chemistry	50		
Totals	**180**		**90**

14. Use the Jefferson method to apportion 90 (instead of 100) positions in problem 13. (*Hint:* The modified divisor must be slightly *less* than 2.)

15. In 1830, the population of Florida was 34,730. Use Webster's method to find the number of seats for Florida if the modified divisor was 49,800.

16. Use Adams's method to apportion 90 faculty positions in problem 13. (*Hint:* The modified divisor must be slightly *more* than 2.)

17. Consider a country with a population of 100,000 and three states in the legislature, A, B, and C, with the populations shown in the following table. Suppose 50 seats are apportioned using Hamilton's method as shown in the first table. Fill in the blanks in the *second* table and determine if the Alabama paradox occurs when the number of seats is increased from 50 to 51 using Hamilton's apportionment method. Explain your answer.

continued

CHAPTER 14 Practice Test – *continued*

State	Population	SQ	RD	Extra	Final
A	50,400	50,400/2000 = 25.2	25	0	25
B	46,600	46,600/2000 = 23.3	23	0	23
C	3000	3000/2000 = 1.5	1	1	2
Total	**100,000**		**49**		**50**

State	Population	SQ	RD	Extra	Final
A	50,400				
B	46,600				
C	3000				
Total	**100,000**				**51**

18. The following table shows the number of students taking mathematics, English, and science courses during the fall and spring semesters. Suppose that 100 full-time teaching positions were apportioned during the fall semester using Hamilton's method with the results shown.

a. How many positions will each department get in the spring using Hamilton's method?
b. Is the apportionment fair? Explain your answer.
c. Is this apportionment an example of the population paradox? Explain.

	Fall Semester			Spring Semester		
Subject	**Number Fall**	**SQ**	**Positions**	**Number Spring**	**New SQ**	**Positions**
Math	476	9.5180	**10**	484	9.6338	**9**
English	975	19.4961	**19**	990	19.7054	**20**
Science	3550	70.9858	**71**	3550	70.6608	**71**
Total	**5001**		**100**	**5024**		**100**

State	Population
A	804
B	312
C	228
Total	**1344**

19. A country has two states, A and B, with the population (in thousands) shown in the table to the left and 41 seats in the legislature.

a. Find the apportionments for A and B using Hamilton's method.
b. Suppose a third state C with a population of 228 (thousands) is added with 8 additional seats. Does the new-states paradox occur using Hamilton's method? Explain.

20. Explain the meaning of Balinski and Young's Impossibility Theorem in your own words.

ANSWERS TO PRACTICE TEST

<table>
<tr><th colspan="2">CHAPTER 14</th><th colspan="3">What to Review If You Missed It</th></tr>
<tr><th>QUESTION</th><th>ANSWER</th><th>SECTION</th><th>EXAMPLE(S)</th><th>PAGE(S)</th></tr>
<tr><td>1</td><td>a. No b. D c. A d. B</td><td>14.1</td><td>1</td><td>824</td></tr>
<tr><td>2</td><td>D wins the runoff 20 to 10.</td><td>14.1</td><td>2</td><td>825</td></tr>
<tr><td>3</td><td>C wins with 63 points.</td><td>14.1</td><td>3</td><td>826</td></tr>
<tr><td>4</td><td>D</td><td>14.1</td><td>4</td><td>826–827</td></tr>
<tr><td>5</td><td>a. A wins 14 to 3. b. C wins 12 to 5.
c. C wins 9 to 8. d. C is the winner.</td><td>14.1</td><td>5</td><td>828</td></tr>
<tr><td>6</td><td>a. Adams b. Barnes</td><td>14.1</td><td>6</td><td>828–829</td></tr>
<tr><td>7</td><td>a. B. Yes
b. A. No. B has the majority but A wins under the Borda count method.
c. B. Yes d. B. Yes</td><td>14.2</td><td>2</td><td>835–836</td></tr>
<tr><td>8</td><td>a. P. Yes b. C. No c. T. No d. V. No
e. P. Yes</td><td>14.2</td><td>3</td><td>836–838</td></tr>
<tr><td>9</td><td>a. Yes. C has the majority and wins under the plurality method.
b. Yes. C has the majority and wins head-to-head against all other candidates.</td><td>14.2</td><td>5</td><td>840–841</td></tr>
<tr><td>10</td><td>a. Yes. C will still win the second election under the plurality method.
b. Yes. C will still win the second election under the plurality method when either A or B drops out.</td><td>14.2</td><td>5</td><td>840–841</td></tr>
<tr><td>11</td><td>There is no voting method that will always simultaneously satisfy each of the four fairness criteria.</td><td>14.2</td><td></td><td>841</td></tr>
<tr><td>12</td><td>SD = 40,500/162,000,000 = 0.00025
Standard Quotas (in millions)
For A, 15,000/0.00025 = 60
For B, 8500/0.00025 = 34
For C, 6500/0.00025 = 26
For D, 6000/0.00025 = 24
For E, 4500/0.00025 = 18
Note that the total is $162 million.</td><td>14.3</td><td>1</td><td>846–847</td></tr>
<tr><td>13</td><td><table>
<tr><th>SQ</th><th>RD</th><th>Actual Number</th></tr>
<tr><td>30/1.8 ≈ 16.67</td><td>16</td><td>16 + 1 = 17</td></tr>
<tr><td>60/1.8 ≈ 33.33</td><td>33</td><td>33</td></tr>
<tr><td>24/1.8 ≈ 13.33</td><td>13</td><td>13</td></tr>
<tr><td>16/1.8 ≈ 8.89</td><td>8</td><td>8 + 1 = 9</td></tr>
<tr><td>50/1.8 ≈ 27.78</td><td>27</td><td>27 + 1 = 28</td></tr>
<tr><td>100</td><td>97</td><td>100</td></tr>
</table></td><td>14.3</td><td>3</td><td>849</td></tr>
</table>

continued

ANSWERS TO PRACTICE TEST – *continued*

<table>
<tr><th colspan="2">CHAPTER 14</th><th colspan="3">What to Review If You Missed It</th></tr>
<tr><th>QUESTION</th><th>ANSWER</th><th>SECTION</th><th>EXAMPLE(S)</th><th>PAGE(S)</th></tr>
<tr><td>14</td><td>Use 1.95 as the modified divisor, then round down.
<table>
<tr><th>MQ</th><th>Actual</th></tr>
<tr><td>30/1.95 ≈ 15.38</td><td>15</td></tr>
<tr><td>60/1.95 ≈ 30.77</td><td>30</td></tr>
<tr><td>24/1.95 ≈ 12.31</td><td>12</td></tr>
<tr><td>16/1.95 ≈ 8.21</td><td>8</td></tr>
<tr><td>50/1.95 ≈ 25.64</td><td>25</td></tr>
</table></td><td>14.3</td><td>4</td><td>850</td></tr>
<tr><td>15</td><td>34,730/49,800 ≈ 0.6974, or 1</td><td>14.3</td><td>6</td><td>852</td></tr>
<tr><td>16</td><td>Use 2.05 as the modified divisor, then round up.
<table>
<tr><th>MQ</th><th>Actual</th></tr>
<tr><td>$\frac{30}{2.05} \approx 14.63$</td><td>15</td></tr>
<tr><td>$\frac{60}{2.05} \approx 29.27$</td><td>30</td></tr>
<tr><td>$\frac{24}{2.05} \approx 11.71$</td><td>12</td></tr>
<tr><td>$\frac{16}{2.05} \approx 7.80$</td><td>8</td></tr>
<tr><td>$\frac{50}{2.05} \approx 24.39$</td><td>25</td></tr>
</table></td><td>14.3</td><td>7</td><td>853</td></tr>
<tr><td>17</td><td>
<table>
<tr><th>SQ</th><th></th><th>Extra</th><th>Final</th></tr>
<tr><td>$\frac{50{,}400}{1960.78} \approx 25.70$</td><td>25</td><td>1</td><td>26</td></tr>
<tr><td>$\frac{46{,}600}{1960.78} \approx 23.77$</td><td>23</td><td>1</td><td>24</td></tr>
<tr><td>$\frac{3000}{1960.78} \approx 1.53$</td><td>1</td><td>0</td><td>1</td></tr>
</table>
The Alabama paradox occurs because even though the number of seats was increased from 50 to 51, state C lost 1 seat, from 2 to 1.</td><td>14.4</td><td>2</td><td>859</td></tr>
<tr><td>18</td><td>a.
<table>
<tr><th>Position</th><th>Number</th><th>New SQ</th><th>Positions</th></tr>
<tr><td>10</td><td>484</td><td>9.6338</td><td>9</td></tr>
<tr><td>19</td><td>990</td><td>19.7054</td><td>20</td></tr>
<tr><td>71</td><td>3550</td><td>70.6608</td><td>71</td></tr>
</table>
b. No.
c. Yes. Mathematics lost 1 position and English gained 1 even though mathematics was growing at a faster rate, $\frac{8}{476} \approx 0.01681$, than English, $\frac{15}{975} \approx 0.01538$.</td><td>14.4</td><td>3</td><td>860</td></tr>
<tr><td>19</td><td>a. A gets 30 seats, and B 11.
b. Yes. The addition of the new state C caused A to lose 1 seat (from 30 to 29) and B to gain 1 (from 11 to 12).</td><td>14.4</td><td>4</td><td>861</td></tr>
<tr><td>20</td><td>There is no apportionment method that satisfies the quota rule and avoids all paradoxes.</td><td>14.4</td><td></td><td>862</td></tr>
</table>

CHAPTER 15

Graph Theory

"Read Euler, read Euler, he is the master of us all."
— PIERRE-SIMON LAPLACE

Electrical engineers use concepts of graph theory in order to set up systems of computers and communication lines for businesses. In Section 15.1, you will discover how graph theory is used to obtain optimal solutions for certain problems.

How many airplane flights connect a given number of cities? How can we create a schedule for visiting these cities using an efficient and cost-effective schedule? How many ways can you connect your company's computers so they communicate with each other efficiently and inexpensively? These types of problems are extremely important and are sometimes called **routing problems.** A routing problem is one whose solution provides an efficient way of routing among different destinations and can be solved using special diagrams called **graphs.** The theory associated with these graphs (**graph theory**) is used to reach cost-effective solutions by individuals and businesses. In this chapter we study graphs and two types of paths that have applications to routing problems: Euler and Hamilton paths. The last section deals with trees, which are connected graphs that have no circuits.

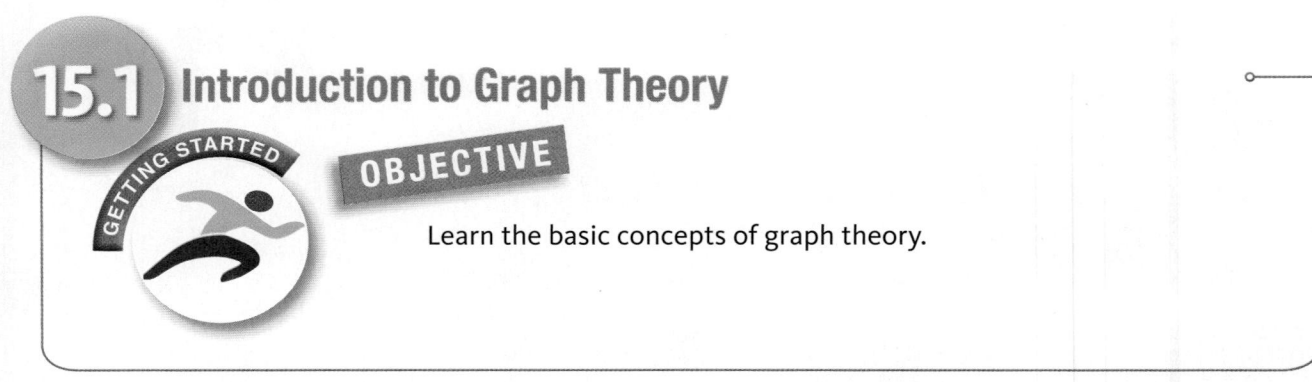

15.1 Introduction to Graph Theory

GETTING STARTED

OBJECTIVE

Learn the basic concepts of graph theory.

BRIDGES, THE WEB, MAPS, AND TRAVELING

As you recall from Chapter 8, the Bridges of Königsberg problem was solved by Leonhard Euler in 1736. The question was: Can we follow a route that would take us across each of the seven bridges of the Pregel River exactly once? Euler provided the conditions that are necessary and sufficient to permit such a stroll. Here is a more modern problem. Suppose you are given the task of deciding how to link 12 computers together. Since linking each of them to all the others is too expensive, you decide that each computer will be connected to three other computers in such a way that messages don't have to pass through more than two of the computers on their way to their destination. How would you decide on the best way to connect these computers together? You can do it by representing each computer as a dot called a *vertex* and the connecting wires as lines or *edges!* We will tell you exactly how to do it later, but first let us start with some definitions.

A Graphs, Paths, and Circuits

The reader should note that graphs as defined here are *not* the same as the graphs of *functions* as discussed in Chapter 7.

Definition of a Graph

A **graph** is a collection of points called **vertices** and arcs or line segments called **edges,** that join pairs of vertices. A *vertex* may be an endpoint of any number of edges, or it may stand alone in a graph. The **degree** of a vertex is the *number* of edges that have it as a common endpoint.

When discussing a particular graph, it is often helpful to provide labels for the edges and vertices of the graph. We will label the edges of a graph with lowercase letters $(a, b, c, \ldots)$ and the vertices with uppercase letters $(A, B, C, \ldots)$. Typical graphs are depicted in Figure 15.1.

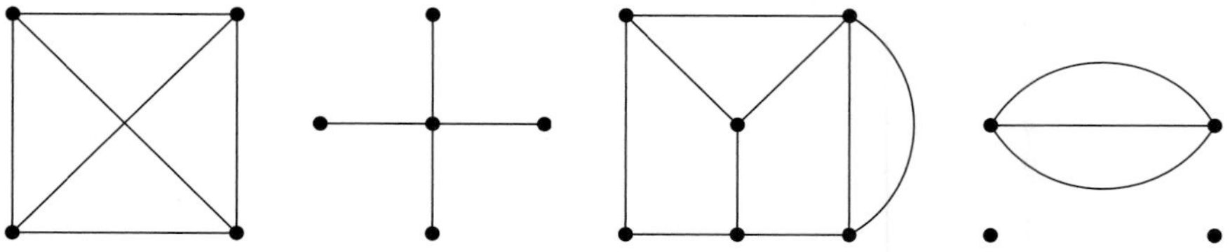

FIGURE 15.1

Human Side of Math

(1805–1865)

William Rowan Hamilton was an Irish mathematician and astronomer who developed the theory of quaternions, a landmark in the development of algebra. Hamilton became interested in mathematics after a meeting in 1820 with Zerah Colburn, an American who could calculate mentally with fantastic speed. In 1823, he entered Trinity College and obtained the highest honors in both classics and mathematics. Even today, Hamiltonian mechanics is used commercially to determine the orbital trajectories of satellites. ■

LOOKING AHEAD

Hamilton circuits have a wide range of applications in today's business world and are one of the topics in this chapter.

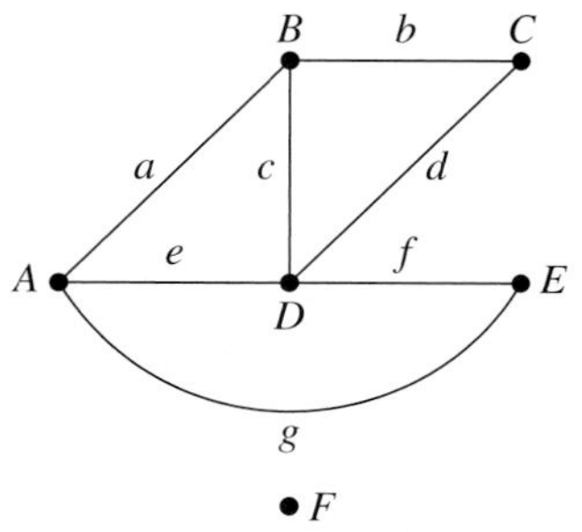

FIGURE 15.2

An example of a graph with its labels is given in Figure 15.2.

EXAMPLE 1 Finding the Degrees of Vertices

What are the degrees of each of the vertices in Figure 15.2?

Solution

To find the *degree* of each vertex, we merely count the number of edges that meet the vertex. Thus, the degrees of vertices *A*, *B*, *C*, *D*, *E*, and *F* are 3, 3, 2, 4, 2, and 0, respectively.

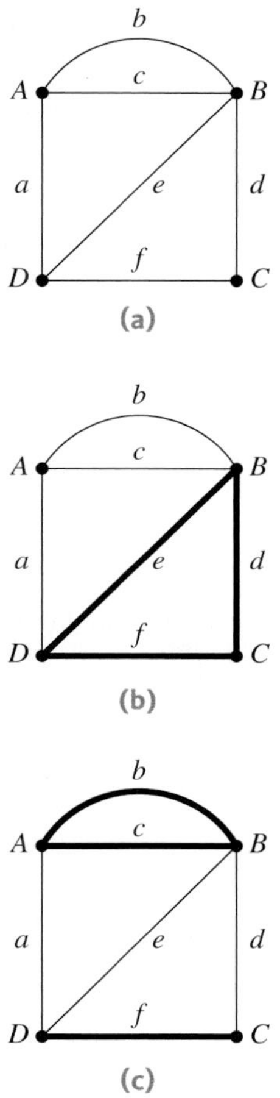

FIGURE 15.3

A graph that consists of some of the vertices and edges of another graph is called a **subgraph.** We emphasize that a subgraph must be a graph itself. In particular, each edge must join two vertices. Figure 15.3(a) shows a graph; two of its subgraphs are depicted in bold in Figures 15.3(b) and 15.3(c). Thus, the subgraph in Figure 15.3(b) consists of the vertices *B*, *C*, and *D* and the edges *d*, *e*, and *f*. The subgraph in Figure 15.3(c) consists of the vertices *A*, *B*, *C*, and *D* and the edges *b*, *c*, and *f*.

Definition of Path

Let *V* and *W* be vertices of a graph. A **path** from *V* to *W* is a *sequence* of edges in the graph for which

1. *V* is a vertex of the first edge of the sequence.
2. *W* is a vertex of the last edge of the sequence.
3. starting at *V*, you can trace along each consecutive edge of the sequence without lifting your pencil.

Notice that consecutive edges of a path *must have a common endpoint.*

Whenever we describe a path, we will enclose the sequence of edges in square brackets. For example, the sequence [*a, b, c, d, b, e*] in Figure 15.4(a) describes the path from *A* to *D* indicated. The sequence [*a, b, c, d, i*] indicated in Figure 15.4(b) does *not* define a path because edges *d* and *i* have no endpoint in common. Notice that edges may be traversed more than once in a given path (as in Figure 15.4a). A path that has no repeated edges is called a **simple path.**

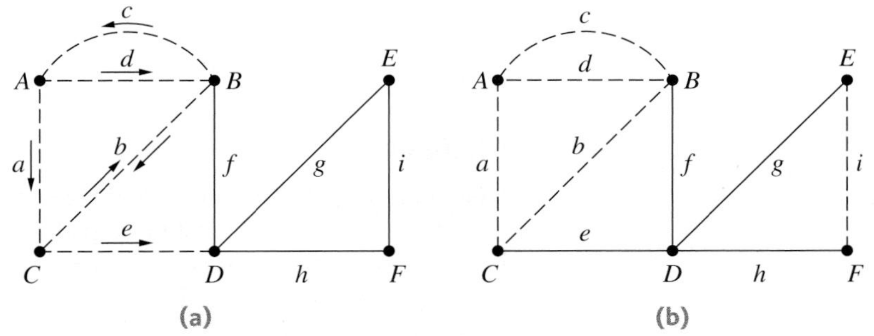

FIGURE 15.4

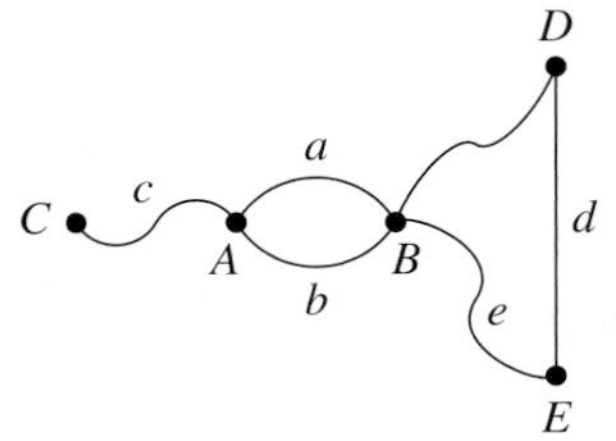

FIGURE 15.5

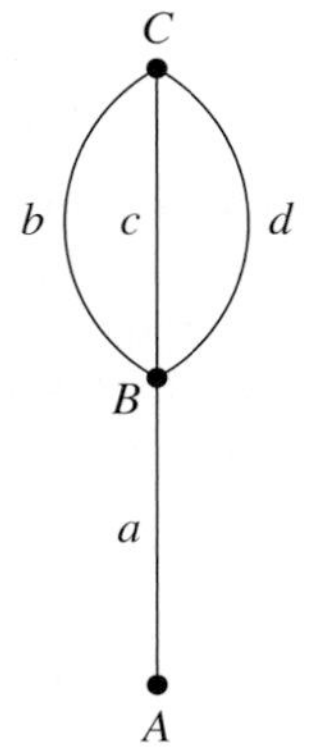

FIGURE 15.6

In certain cases, there will be some ambiguity when describing a path by listing successive edges. For instance, does the path [*a, b*] in Figure 15.5 start at vertex *A* and end at *B*, or vice versa? In such situations we will clarify the matter by specifying the intended order of the vertices or by indicating the intended order with arrows. Note that the path [*a, b, c*] in Figure 15.5 clearly starts at vertex *A* and ends at vertex *C*.

A path that begins and ends at the same vertex is called a **circuit.** A circuit beginning and ending at the vertex *A* is said to be **based** at *A*. For example, the path [*a, b, c, a*] in Figure 15.6 is a circuit based at *A*, while the path [*a, b, d*] is *not* a circuit (the path begins at vertex *A* and ends at vertex *B*).

A graph for which every pair of vertices can be joined by a path is said to be **connected** (otherwise, it is **disconnected**). In a visual sense, a graph is *disconnected* if there are any vertices for which we are required to lift our pencil in order to travel between them. Figure 15.7(a) depicts a connected graph, while Figure 15.7(b) is an example of a disconnected graph.

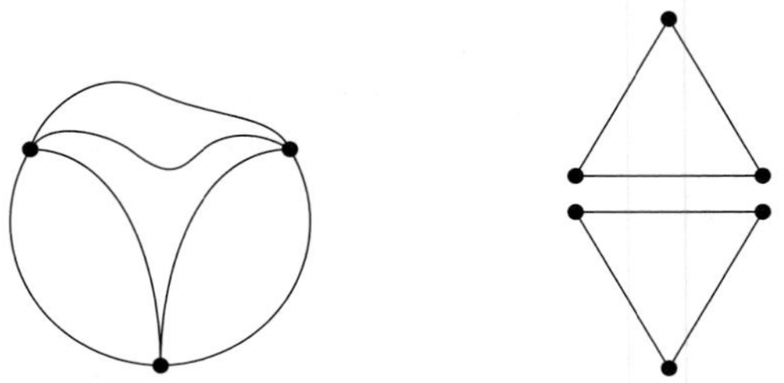

Connected (a)

Disconnected (b)

FIGURE 15.7

EXAMPLE 2 Identifying Paths and Circuits

For which of the graphs in Figure 15.8, parts (a), (b), and (c), does the sequence of edges *a, b, c, d* represent a path? A circuit? Which graphs are connected?

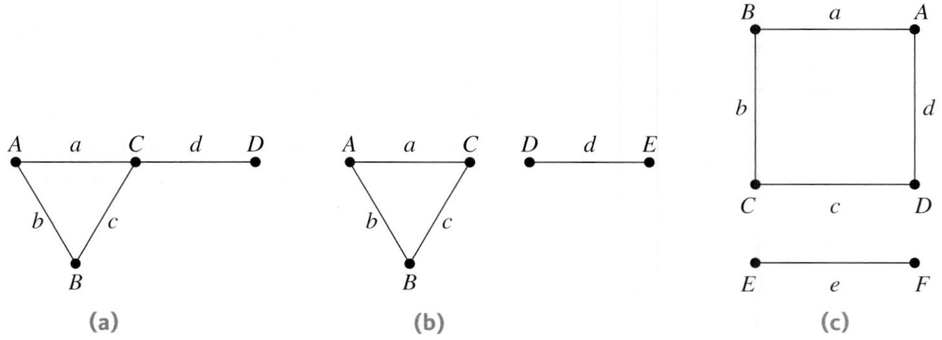

FIGURE 15.8

Solution

(a) Starting at *C*, we can trace along each of the edges listed in the sequence, ending at *D*, so the sequence defines a path from *C* to *D*. Since this path begins and ends at different vertices, it is *not* a circuit. The graph is *connected*. Indeed, it is easy to find a path between any pair of vertices, so the path is *connected*.

(b) Edges *c* and *d* have no endpoints in common, so the sequence does *not* define a path (or a circuit, for that matter). Since there is no way to reach vertex *D* from vertex *C* without leaving the graph, we conclude that the graph is *disconnected*.

(c) The sequence [*a, b, c, d*] is a circuit based at *A*. The graph is *disconnected*. For example, there is no way to travel from vertex *C* to vertex *E* without lifting our pencil.

A **complete** graph is one in which every pair of vertices is joined by exactly *one* edge. A complete graph with n vertices will be denoted by K_n. Complete graphs will be especially important in future applications (Section 15.3). The first five complete graphs are given in Figure 15.9.

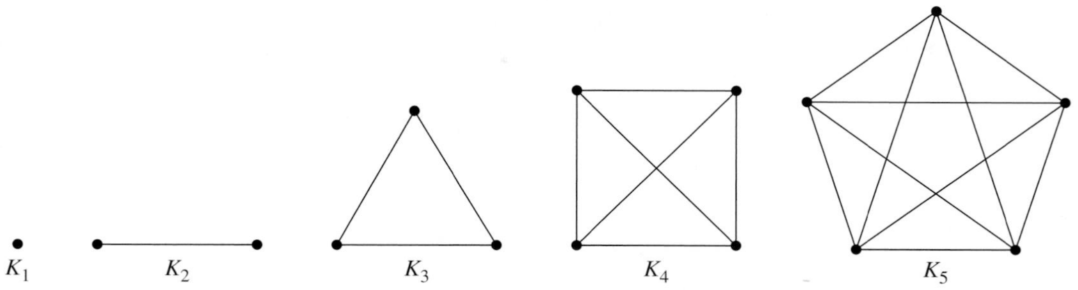

FIGURE 15.9

15.1 EXERCISES

A Graphs, Paths, and Circuits

In problems 1–4, find the degree of each vertex of the graph.

1.

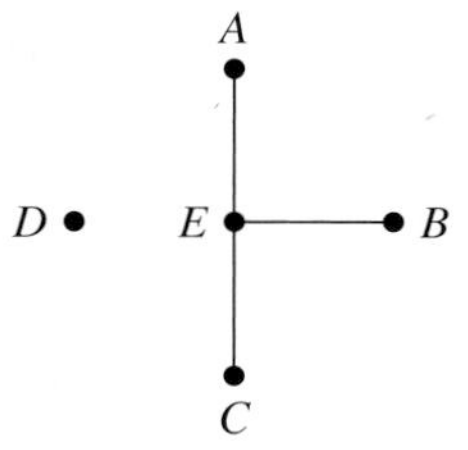

2.

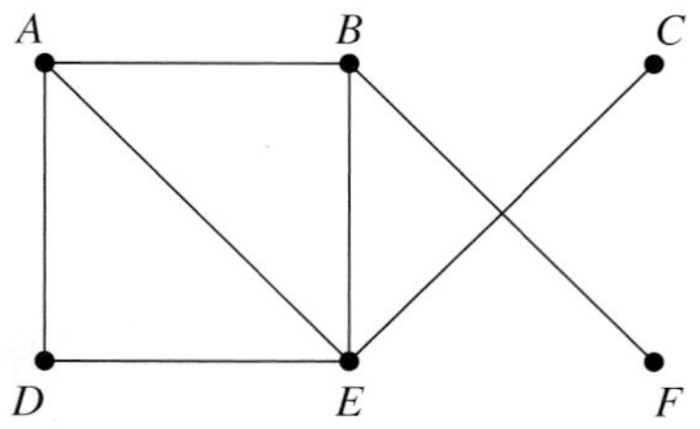

3.

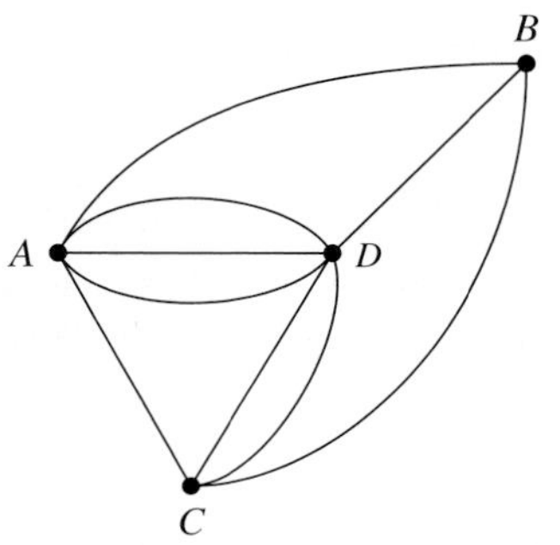

4.

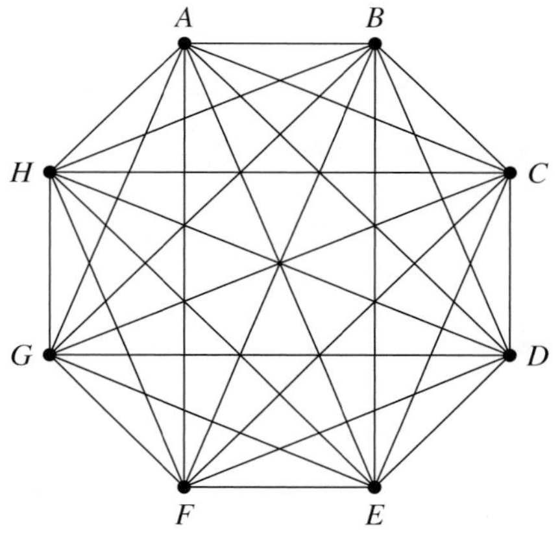

In problems 5–8, refer to the graph below. Decide whether the collection of vertices and edges listed in each problem determines a subgraph of the graph.

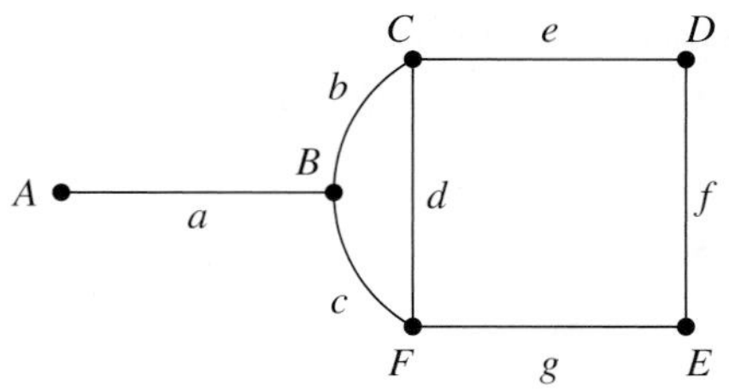

5. Vertices $\{A, B, D\}$; edges $\{a, b, e\}$

6. Vertices $\{A, B, C, D\}$; edges $\{a, b, e\}$

7. Vertices $\{A, E, F\}$; edge $\{g\}$

8. Vertices $\{A, B, D, E\}$; edges $\{a, f, c\}$

For problems 9–16, refer to the following graph and determine whether the given sequence of edges represents a path, a circuit, or neither. Explain your answers.

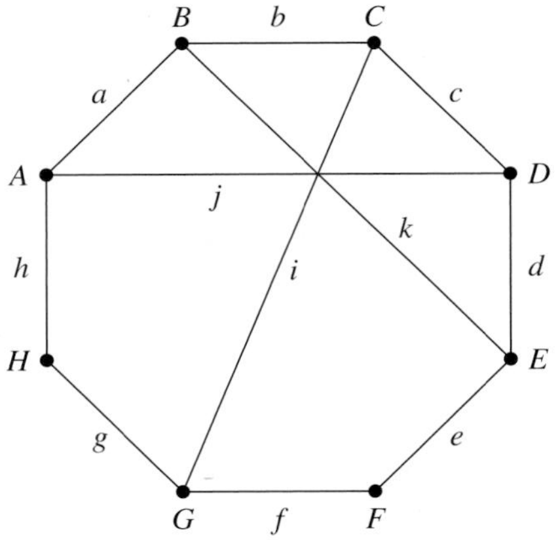

9. $[a, b, c]$

10. $[a, k, d, b]$

11. $[j, d, k, a]$

12. $[a, b, i, g, f]$

13. $[h, g]$

14. $[i, c, d, k, a, j, c, i]$

15. $[h, f, g]$

16. $[f, i, b, k, e]$

In problems 17–20, decide whether the graph pictured is connected or disconnected.

17.

18.
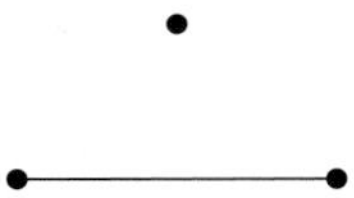

19.
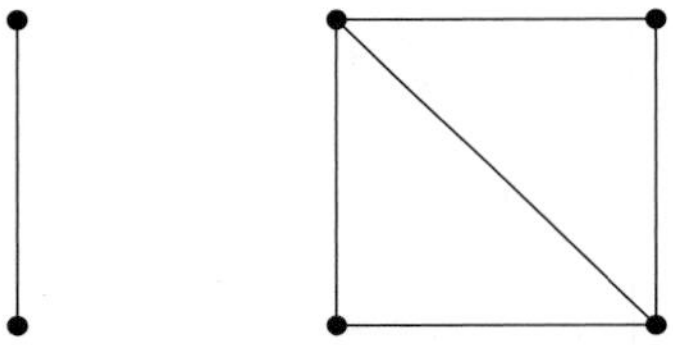

20.
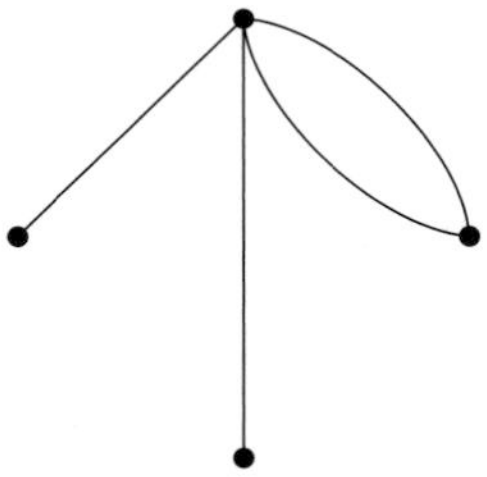

For problems 21–26, determine whether the graph pictured is complete. Explain your reasoning.

21.
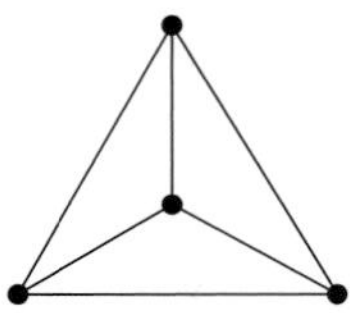

22.

23.
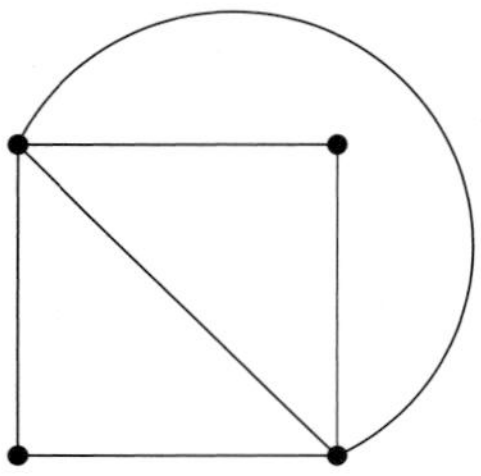

24.
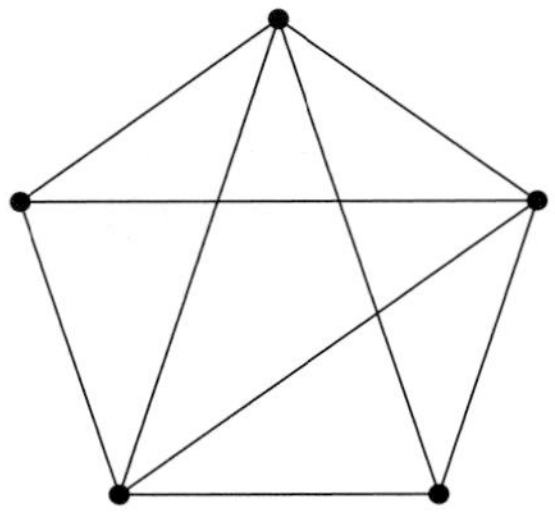

25.
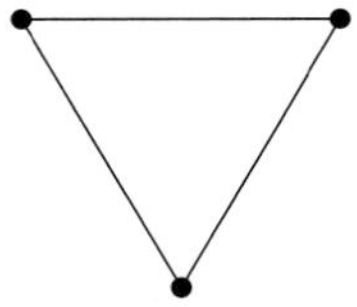

26.
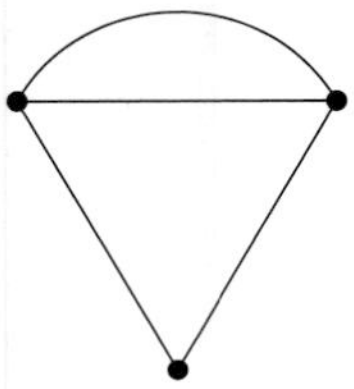

A graph is said to be **simple** *if each pair of vertices is joined by at most one edge. In problems 27–30, determine whether the graph pictured is simple. Explain your reasoning.*

27.
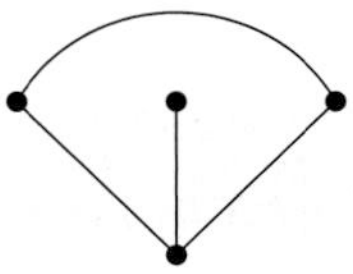

28.
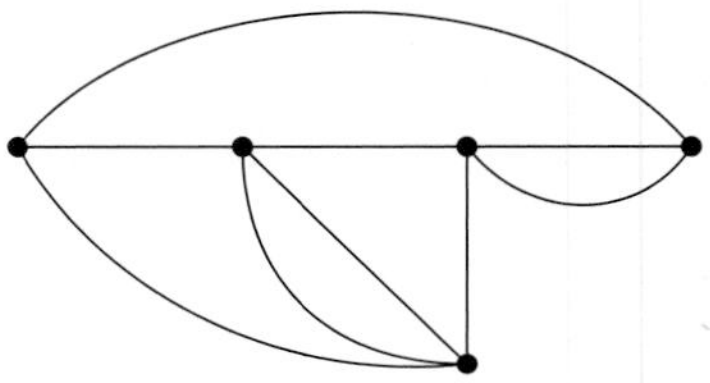

29.
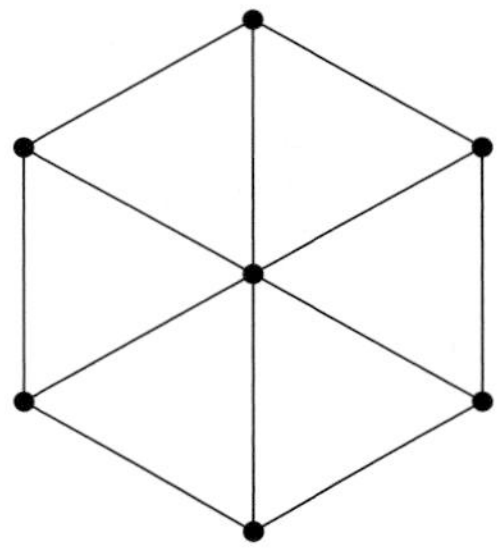

30.
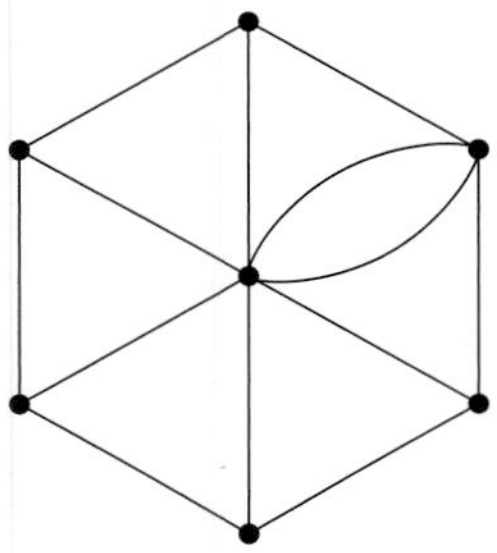

IN OTHER WORDS

31. Describe in your own words the difference between a connected graph and a disconnected graph.

32. Describe in your own words the difference between a circuit and a path.

USING YOUR KNOWLEDGE

Do you remember the problem in the Getting Started regarding linking 12 computers together? Can you solve it now? Here is a restatement of the problem.

33. Suppose you are given the task of deciding how to link 12 computers together. Since linking each of them to all the others is too expensive, we decide that each computer will be connected to three other computers in such a way that messages don't have to pass through more than two of the computers on their way to their destination. How would you decide how to connect these computers together?

15.2 Euler Paths and Euler Circuits

GETTING STARTED

OBJECTIVES

A. Identify Euler paths and circuits in a given graph.
B. Use Fleury's algorithm to find Euler circuits.

The Granger Collection
Leonhard Euler (1707–1783).

ANOTHER BRIDGE TO CROSS

As you recall, the great Swiss mathematician Leonhard Euler (1707–1783; pronounced "oiler") was one of the first to recognize the utility of graph theory and put it to work for him in solving the famous Bridges of Königsberg problem (Section 8.6). Euler solved this problem by representing certain objects as vertices and representing the relationships between these objects as edges. In Euler's case the vertices represented various land masses, and the edges represented the bridges joining the islands and the mainland. Euler's technique is a powerful tool for applying the mathematical theory of graphs to problems in the world around us. Time and again we will put this technique to work for us.

A Euler Paths and Circuits

The reader should recognize that the definition of **traversability** given here is the same as that given in Section 8.6. As with ordinary circuits, a Euler circuit that begins and ends at vertex *A* is said to be **based** at *A*.

Euler Paths, Circuits, and Traversability

A path that uses *every* edge of a graph *once and only once* is called an **Euler path.** An **Euler circuit** is an Euler path that begins and ends at the same vertex. A graph that has an Euler path (or circuit) is said to be **traversable.**

EXAMPLE 1 Defining an Euler Path or Circuit

For which of the graphs in Figure 15.10, parts (a), (b), and (c), does the sequence of edges $[a, b, c, d, e]$ define an Euler path? An Euler circuit?

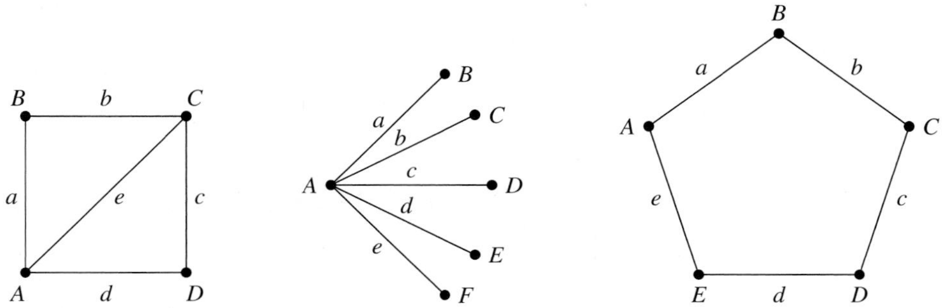

(a) (b) (c)

FIGURE 15.10

Solution

(a) The sequence $[a, b, c, d, e]$ defines an Euler path from A to C.

(b) Although every edge is listed, this sequence does not even define an ordinary path.

(c) The sequence $[a, b, c, d, e]$ describes an Euler circuit based at the vertex A.

EXAMPLE 2 Finding an Efficient Route

The city of Pittsburgh, known as the "City of Bridges," lies at the point where the Allegheny and Monongahela Rivers join to form the Ohio River. This divides the city into three parts: the North Side (NS), the South Side (SS), and the East End (EE). A bridge safety inspector has recently been hired by the city to ensure that each bridge is properly maintained. To perform a safety inspection, he must travel over each bridge and, as you can see from the map, he has many bridges to cross (20 bridges, to be exact). To do his job efficiently, he would prefer to travel over each bridge exactly one time. How can graph theory aid the inspector in planning an efficient route?

Source: http://www.iiofpitt.org/UserFiles/Image/Pittsburgh.jpg

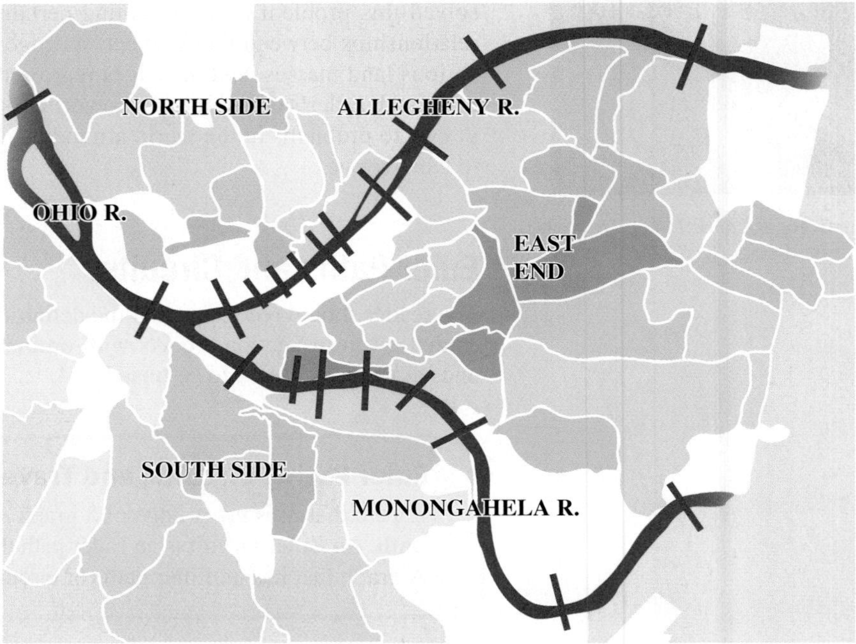

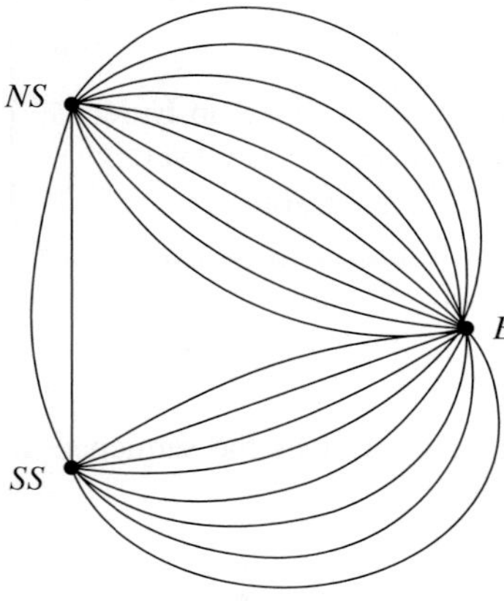

FIGURE 15.11

Solution

Following Euler's technique, we construct a graph to represent the problem. In the graph, each of the city's three sections will be represented by a vertex and each bridge will be an edge. To determine whether is it possible to travel over each bridge exactly one time, we must determine whether the graph in Figure 15.11 is *traversable*. In other words, does the graph have an Euler circuit and if so, can we find one? We will return to this question shortly.

B Finding Euler Paths and Circuits

We have seen that it is possible to represent real-world problems with graphs. Once we have represented a problem with a graph, finding a solution to the problem may sometimes involve finding an Euler path or circuit.

Before we begin searching for an Euler path or circuit, it would be helpful to know if any exist. The **traversability rules** are just the tools we need for this, so we'll review them now, restating them in the language of graph theory.

Traversability Rules

1. A *connected* graph with *no* vertices of odd degree is *traversable.* You can start at any point, and you will end up at that same point. In other words, a connected graph with *no* vertices of odd degree *always* has an Euler *circuit.*
2. A *connected* graph with exactly *two* vertices of odd degree is *traversable.* You must start at one of the odd vertices and end at the other. In other words, a connected graph with *two* vertices of odd degree *always* has an Euler *path.*
3. A graph with *more than two* vertices of odd degree is *not* traversable. In other words, no matter how hard we try, we will *never* be able to find an Euler path or circuit if our graph has *more than two* vertices of odd degree.

EXAMPLE 3 Deciding Whether Graphs Are Traversable

Determine whether each of the graphs in Figure 15.12, parts (a), (b), and (c), is traversable.

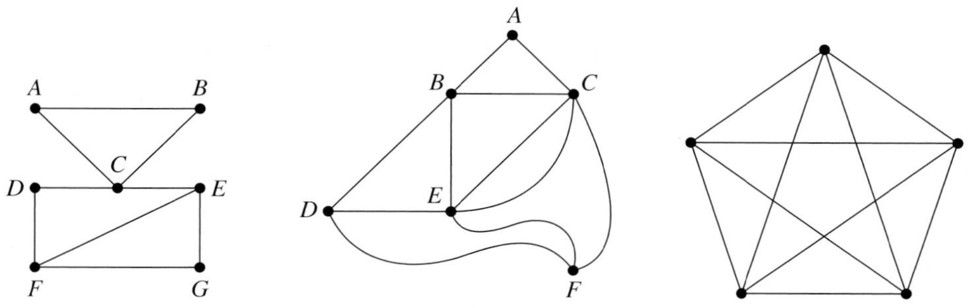

(a) (b) (c)

FIGURE 15.12

Solution

(a) Vertices *A, B, D,* and *G* have degree 2, vertex *C* has degree 4, and vertices *E* and *F* have degree 3. According to traversability rule 2, the graph is traversable because we have exactly *two* vertices of odd degree, *E* and *F.* In other words, there exists an Euler *path* that starts at vertex *E* and ends at vertex *F* (or vice versa).

(b) Vertices *C* and *E* have degree 5, whereas vertex *F* has degree 3. According to traversability rule 3, the graph is *not* traversable because we have more than *two* vertices of odd degree.

(c) Each vertex has degree 4. According to traversability rule 1, the graph is traversable because we have *no* vertices of odd degree. There is an Euler *circuit* based at each of the vertices.

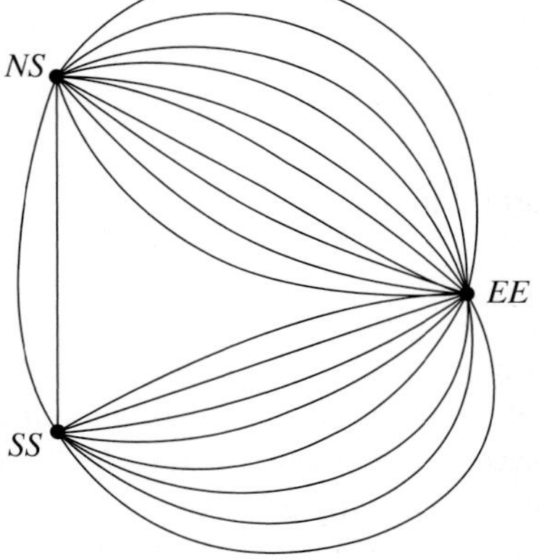

FIGURE 15.13

EXAMPLE 4 Finding an Efficient Route

Remember the Pittsburgh bridge inspector from Example 2? We return to the problem of deciding whether there is an efficient way for him to complete his inspection. As we saw, this means that we need to determine whether the graph in Figure 15.13 has an Euler circuit. How can the traversability rules help us?

Solution

The graph in Figure 15.13 is connected and has three vertices, which we labeled NS, SS and EE. By counting the edges emanating from each vertex, we see that NS has degree 12, SS has degree 10, and EE has degree 18. Since there are no vertices of odd degree, traversability rule 1 tells us that the graph has an Euler circuit. From this we can conclude that there is an efficient route for our inspector: He can start at any of the three sections of the city, travel over each of the bridges exactly one time, and end up back at his starting point. We will return to the process of actually *finding* such a route in Example 8.

We've seen how to use the traversability rules to determine whether a graph is traversable, but these rules don't provide us with a method for actually *finding* the particular path that traces out every edge. Using trial and error, we will eventually find an Euler path, but this is not a very efficient way to proceed, and if our graph is complicated, the search could take a very long time. What we would like is a process that, when applied, *guarantees* that we will find an Euler path (and preferably with a minimal amount of effort). Such a process is called an **algorithm.** Fortunately, when searching for Euler *circuits,* there is just such an algorithm. Before describing it, we need to introduce one more concept.

Definition of a Bridge

A **bridge** is an edge in a graph that, when removed, creates a *disconnected* graph.

EXAMPLE 5 Finding Bridges

Find the bridges in the graphs in Figure 15.14, parts (a), (b), and (c).

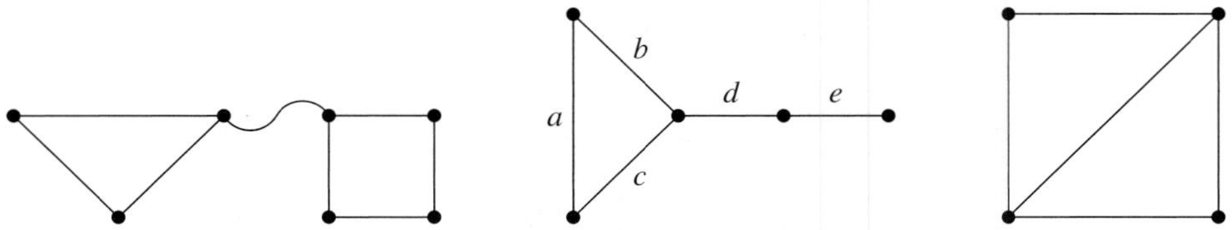

(a) (b) (c)

FIGURE 15.14

Solution

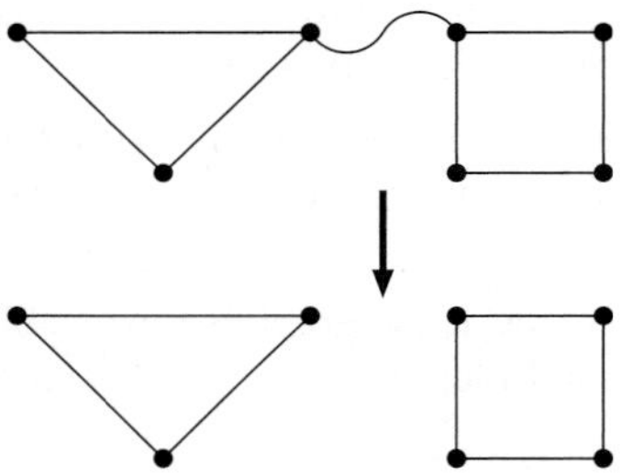

FIGURE 15.15

(a) By removing the indicated edge as shown in Figure 15.15, we obtain a disconnected graph; this edge is a bridge. Removing any other edge does not disconnect the graph.

(b) Edges *d* and *e* are bridges. Figure 15.16 shows the result of removing edge *e*, while Figure 15.17 shows the result of removing edge *d*.

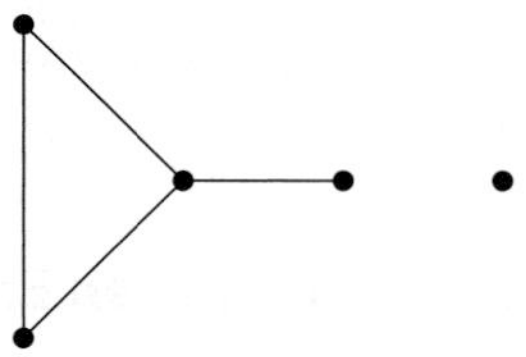

FIGURE 15.16

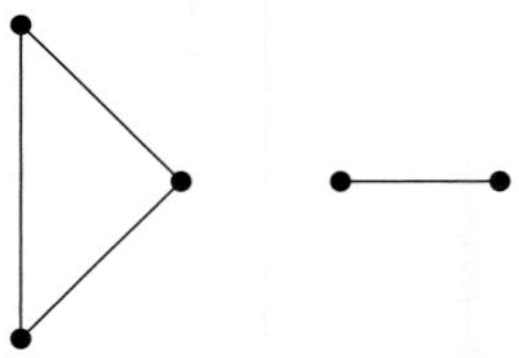

FIGURE 15.17

(c) The graph has no bridges. It remains connected after removing any edge.

Remember that we are currently interested in Euler circuits. This means that we intend to start at some vertex of our graph and travel along every edge *once and only once* until we return to our starting point. In the process, we will need to keep track of the edges we have already traced (otherwise, we might accidentally travel along an edge more than once!). We will do this by first replacing the edges we have already traveled over with dotted line segments or arcs. We will then remove them from the graph (see Example 6). Notice that the untraveled part of the graph is a *subgraph* of the original graph called the **untraveled subgraph.** Each time we trace along a new edge, we create a new *untraveled subgraph.*

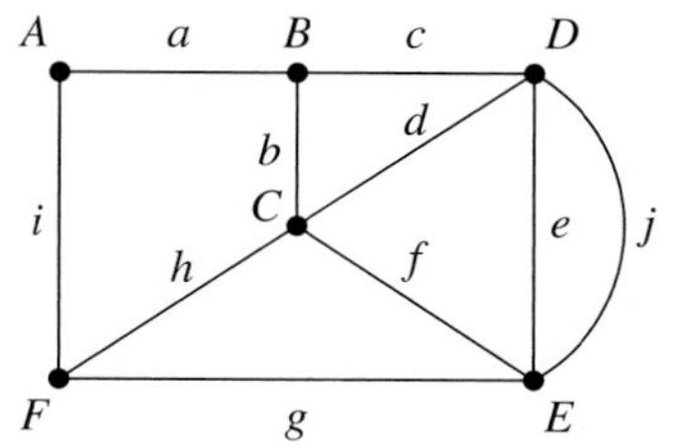

FIGURE 15.18

EXAMPLE 6 Finding the Untraveled Subgraph

Consider the path $[a, b, d]$ from A to D in Figure 15.18. What is the untraveled subgraph corresponding to this path?

Solution

By replacing the edges indicated by dashed line segments, we obtain Figure 15.19(a). The edges that remain (together with their endpoints) constitute the untraveled subgraph (Figure 15.19b).

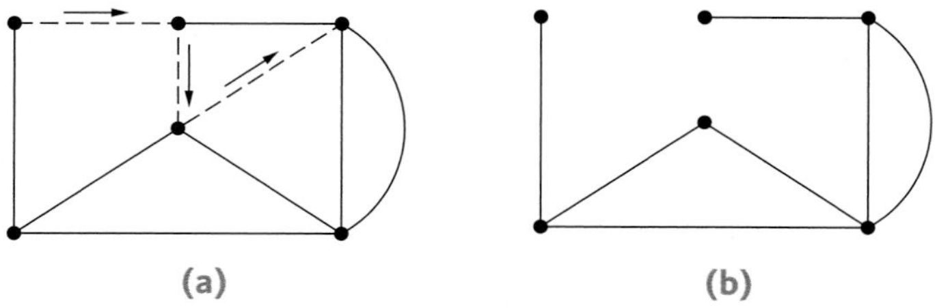

FIGURE 15.19

We now have all the tools needed to describe the algorithm for finding Euler circuits. The method is called **Fleury's algorithm,** and the basic idea is as follows: First, notice that if a graph is disconnected, then it cannot have an Euler circuit. Consequently, for the remainder of this discussion we consider *connected* graphs only. We also need to decide whether the (connected) graph we are interested in even *has* an Euler circuit. Traversability rule 1 provides the answer: If every vertex of our graph has *even* degree, the graph is guaranteed to have an Euler circuit; if any one of the vertices of our graph has *odd* degree, no matter how hard we try, we will never be able to find an Euler circuit.

Fleury's Algorithm

Assume that the graph we are interested in *has* an Euler circuit. Pick any vertex as a starting point. This vertex will have an even number of edges extending from it. The basic idea behind Fleury's algorithm can be summarized as "don't cross a bridge until you *have* to." In other words, from our starting point, we can trace along any edge to a new vertex as long as

It is *not* a bridge. or It *is* a bridge *but* there is no other alternative.

In either case we have now arrived at a new vertex. Once again, we may have numerous choices as to which edge to trace along, and we may choose any of them as long as

The edge is *not* a bridge for the *untraveled* subgraph or the edge *is* a bridge for the *untraveled* subgraph, *but* there is no other alternative.

We now repeat this process, avoiding bridges for the untraveled subgraph whenever possible, until we eventually end up at our starting point, completing an Euler circuit as desired.

EXAMPLE 7 Using Fleury's Algorithm

Determine whether each of the graphs in Figure 15.20, parts (a), (b), and (c), has an Euler circuit. If so, use Fleury's algorithm to find one.

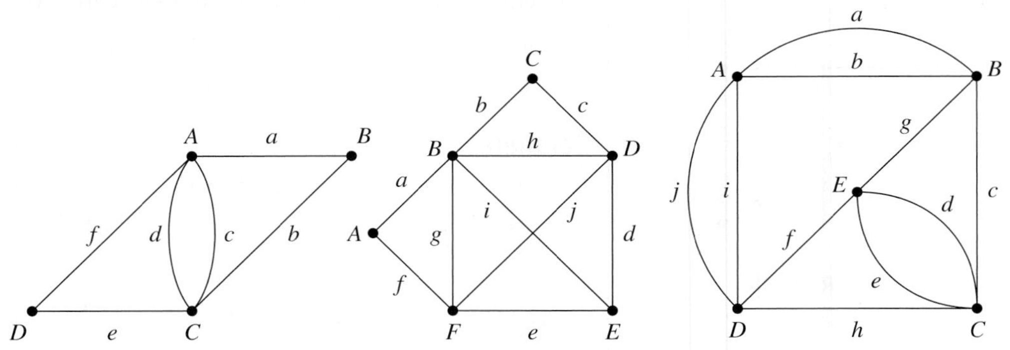

(a) (b) (c)

FIGURE 15.20

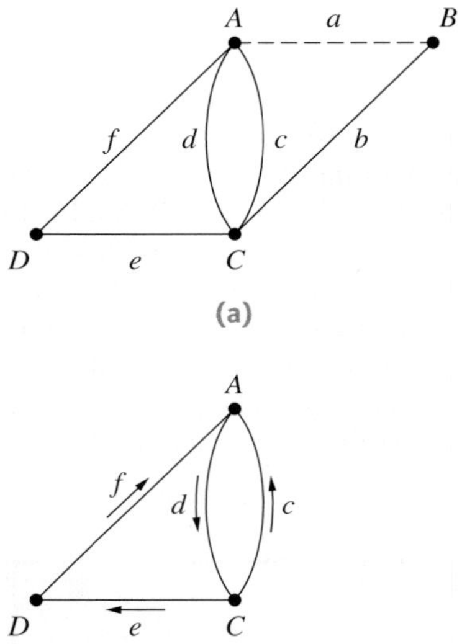

(a)

(b)

FIGURE 15.21

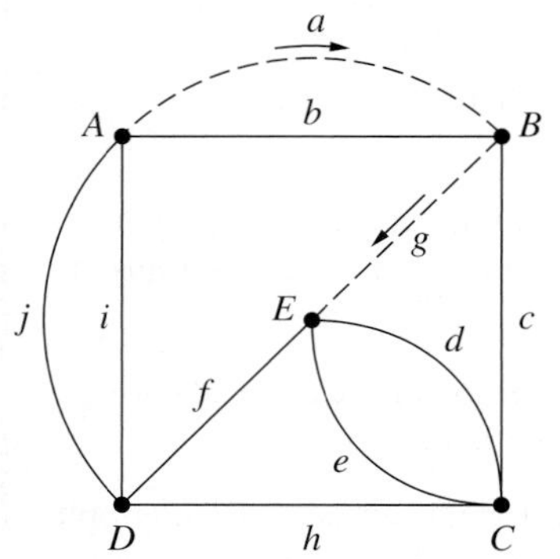

(a)

FIGURE 15.22

Solution

(a) Since each vertex has even degree, traversability rule 1 tells us that the graph has an Euler circuit.

(i) We will choose vertex *A* as our starting point (this choice is arbitrary; according to traversability rule 1, *any* vertex can serve as a starting point). Note that none of the edges meeting *A* are bridges. This means that we may choose any of them as the first edge of our circuit.

(ii) We choose to proceed to vertex *B* along edge *a*. Note that edge *b* is a bridge for the untraveled subgraph (Figure 15.21a); however, we have no alternative but to travel along this edge until we reach vertex *C*. From *C* we have three options: Travel along edge *c, d,* or *e.*

(iii) Observing the untraveled subgraph (Figure 15.21b), we note that none of these edges are bridges and decide to travel along edge *e* until we arrive at vertex *D*. Though edge *f* is a bridge for the untraveled subgraph, there is no other option: we proceed to vertex *A* along edge *f.*

(iv) It is now clear that by traveling from *A* to *C* along edge *d* and returning to *A* along edge *c,* we complete an Euler circuit, [*a, b, e, f, d, c*], as desired.

(b) Since vertices *B* and *E* are of odd degree, the graph has no Euler circuit (it does, however, have an Euler *path*) according to traversability rule 2.

(c) Every vertex has degree 4, so the graph has an Euler circuit.

(i) We pick *A* as our starting point and, noting that edge *a* is not a bridge, travel along edge *a,* arriving at *B*. We have three options for the next edge in our circuit: *b, c,* or *g*. Since none of these edges are bridges for the untraveled subgraph (see Figure 15.22a), we choose edge *g* arbitrarily and travel to vertex *E*.

(ii) Once again we have three options: edge *d, e,* or *f.* Observing Figure 15.22(b), we see that none of these edges is a bridge for the untraveled subgraph and decide to travel along *f* to *D*. The untraveled subgraph up to this point is given in Figure 15.22(c).

(iii) Since edge *i* is not a bridge for this subgraph, we proceed back to *A* along *i*. With edges *b* or *j* as our options for the next edge, we check Figure 15.22(d) and determine that neither is a bridge for the untraveled subgraph.

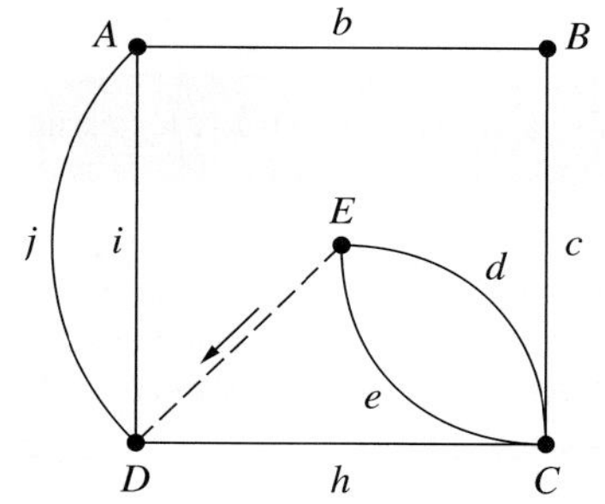

(b)

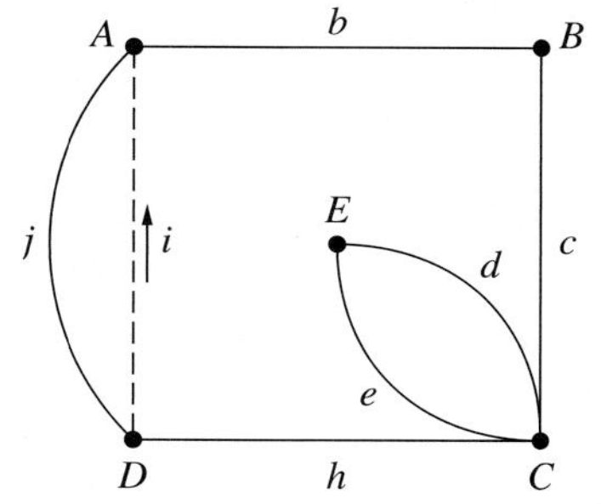

(c)

(iv) We pick edge j and return to D. Our only option at this point is to travel to C along edge h. The untraveled subgraph at this point is provided in Figure 15.22(e). From this subgraph we determine that edge c *is* a bridge, while edges d and e are not. We avoid c and travel along d to E. From the untraveled subgraph of Figure 15.22(f) it is clear how to proceed from here: travel along the path given by the sequence of edges $[e, c, b]$, which takes us back to our original starting point and completes the Euler circuit $[a, g, f, i, j, h, d, e, c, b]$.

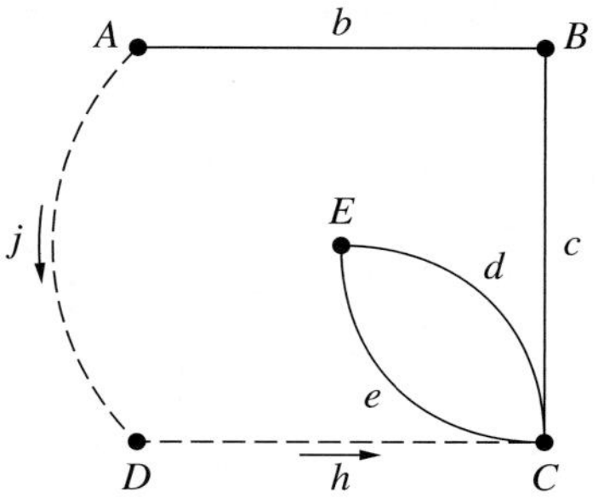

(d)

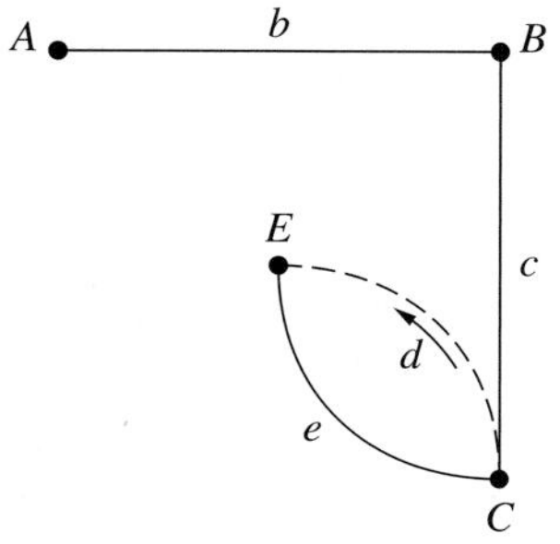

(e)

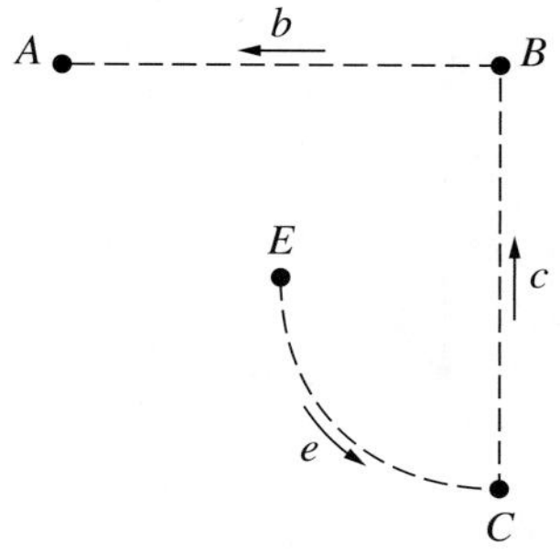

(f)

FIGURE 15.22 (continued)

EXAMPLE 8 Finding an Efficient Route

We now return to the Pittsburgh bridge inspector. We saw in Example 4 that the graph of Figure 15.13 has an Euler circuit, which means that an efficient bridge inspection route exists. Figure 15.23(a) shows the same graph with edge labels added. Find an efficient route for the inspector.

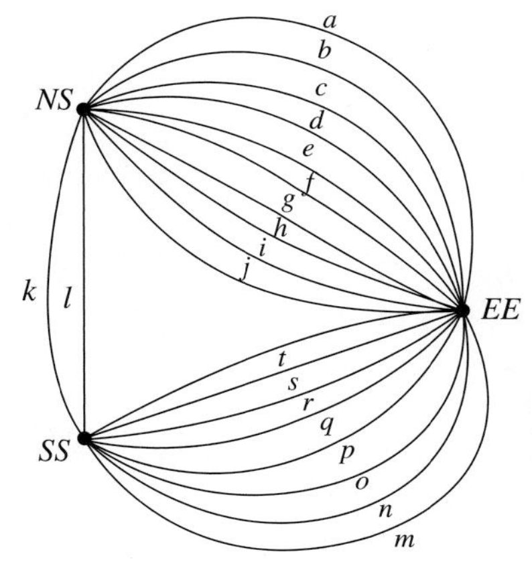

(a)

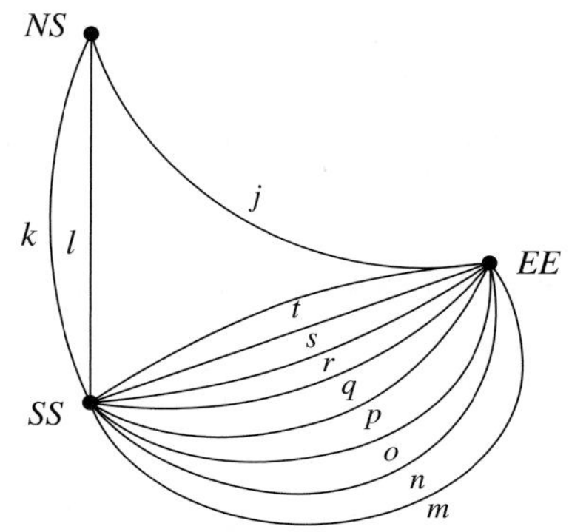

(b)

Solution

We will use Fleury's algorithm to find an Euler circuit. Let's assume that the inspector starts out in the East End of the city (vertex EE). The path $[a, b, c, d, e, f, g, h, i]$ corresponds to a journey that alternates between EE and NS. Figure 15.23(b) shows the corresponding untraveled subgraph. At this point we are at vertex NS and notice that edge j is now a bridge for the untraveled subgraph, so we must now go to SS say, along edge k. Figure 15.23(c) shows the corresponding untraveled subgraph. Since edge l is now a bridge for the untraveled subgraph, we must proceed to EE and, since edge j is also a bridge, we must go back and forth between EE and SS. The path $[m, n, o, p, q, r, s]$ is such a journey, and we are now at vertex EE. Figure 15.23(d) shows the untraveled subgraph. Completing the inspection route by traveling the path $[j, l, t]$ takes us to NS, then SS and finally back to EE. Putting all of this together, we have that $[a, b, c, d, e, f, g, h, i, k, m, n, o, p, q, r, s, j, l, t]$ is an Euler circuit that gives an efficient route for the Pittsburgh bridge inspector.

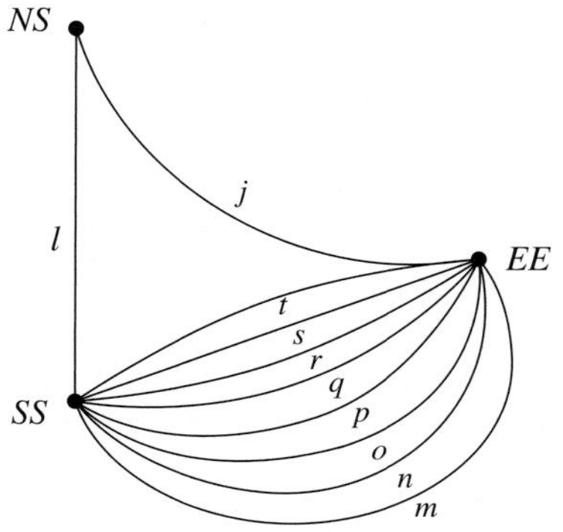

(c)

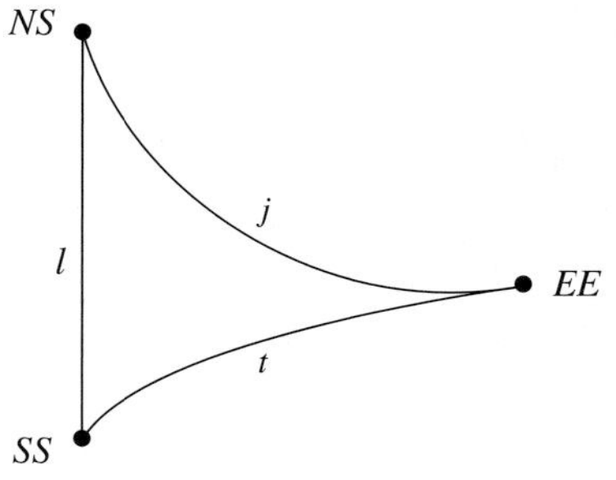

(d)

FIGURE 15.23

15.2 EXERCISES

A Euler Paths and Circuits

In problems 1–4, determine whether the sequence of edges [a, b, c, d, e] is an Euler path, an Euler circuit, or neither.

1.

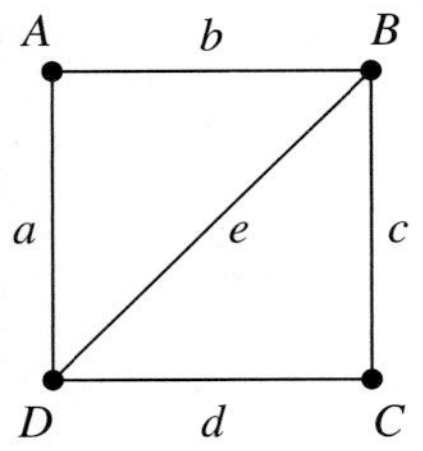

2.

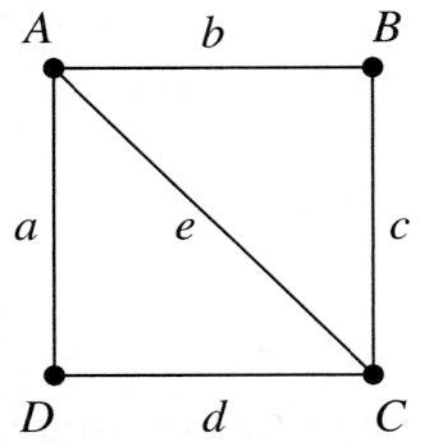

3.

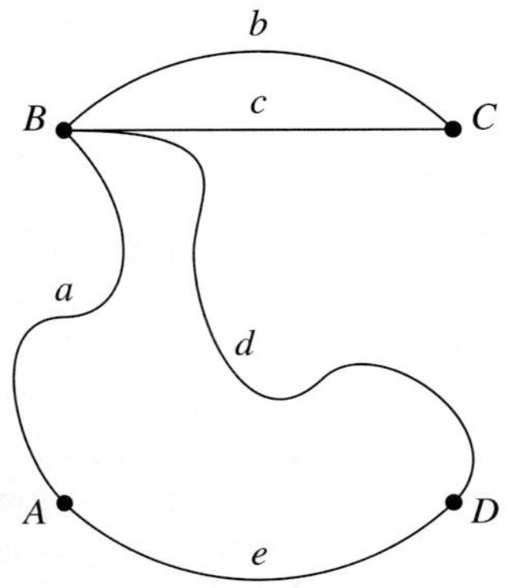

4.

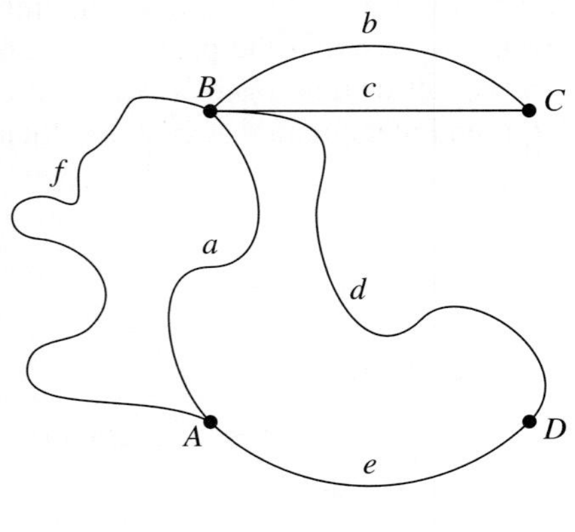

In problems 5–10, use the traversability rules to determine whether the following graphs have an Euler path, an Euler circuit, or neither. You do not need to actually find the path or the circuit.

5.

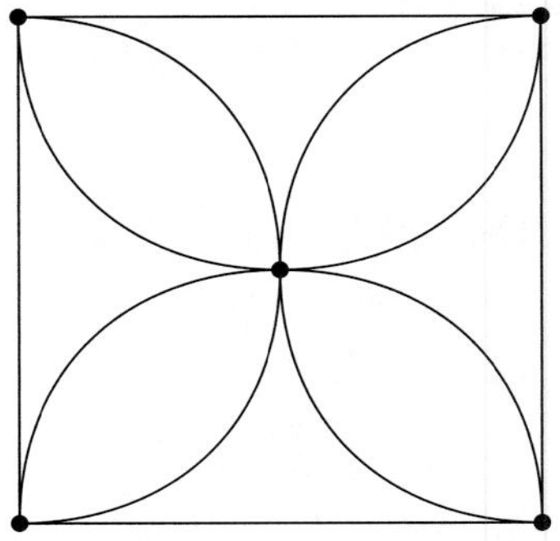

6.

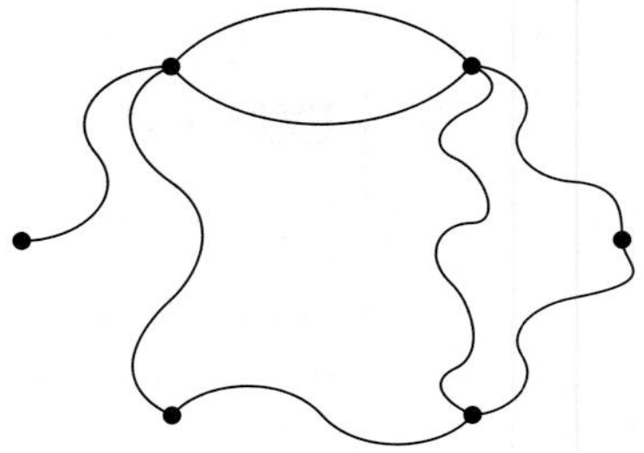

7.

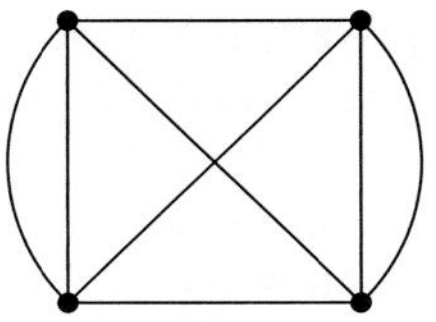

8.

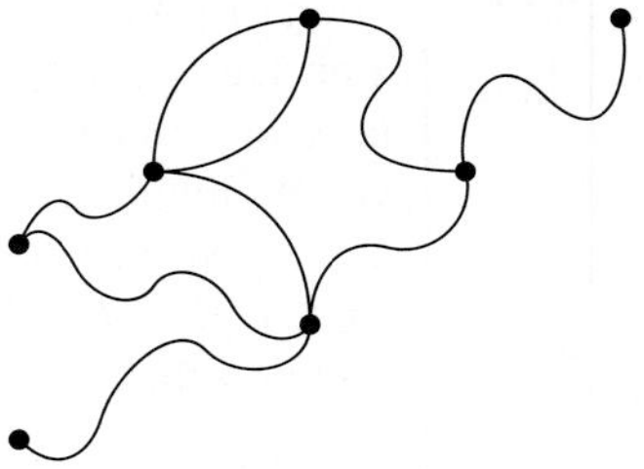

9.

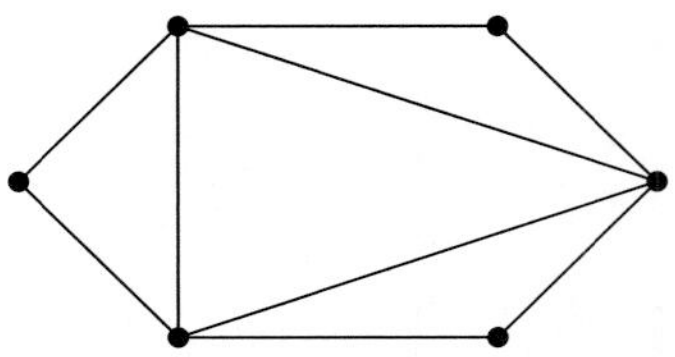

10.

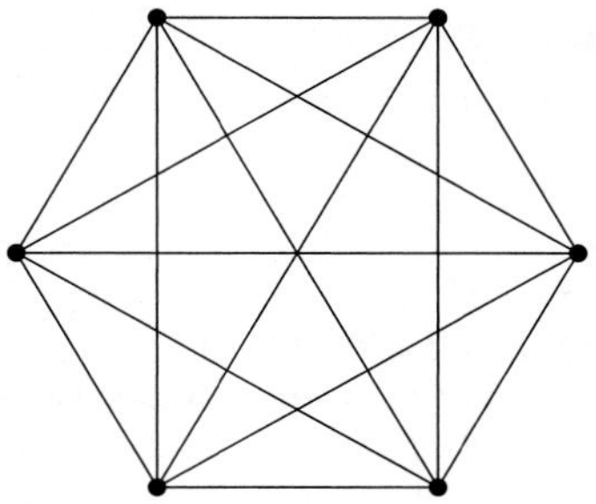

B Finding Euler Paths and Circuits

In problems 11–18, *use Fleury's algorithm to find an Euler circuit in the given graph. (According to the traversability rules, each of the graphs has at least one Euler circuit.)*

11.

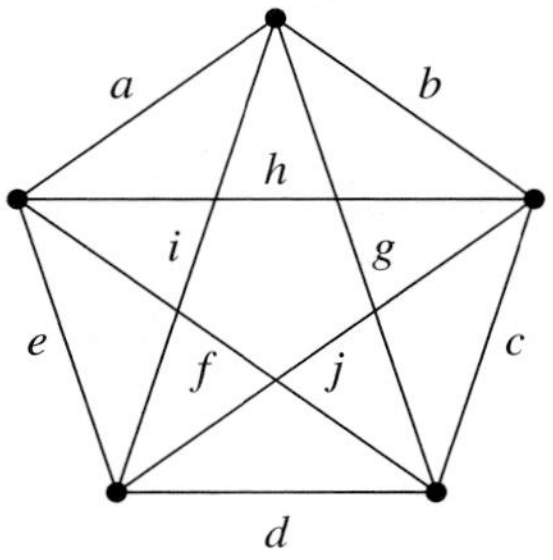

12.

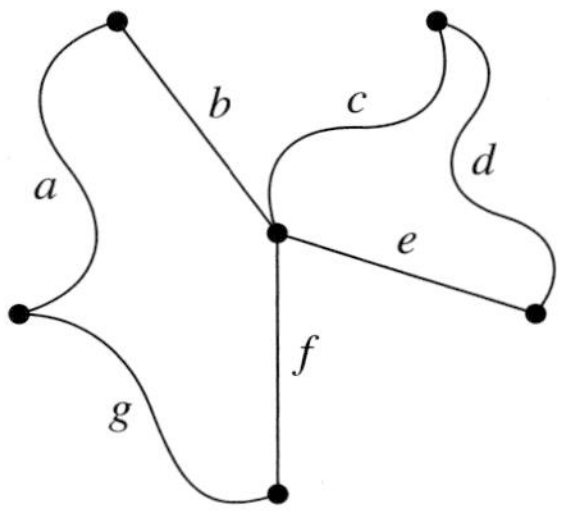

13.

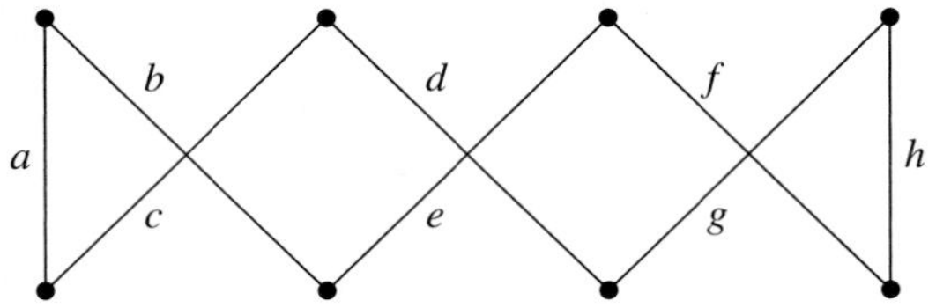

14.

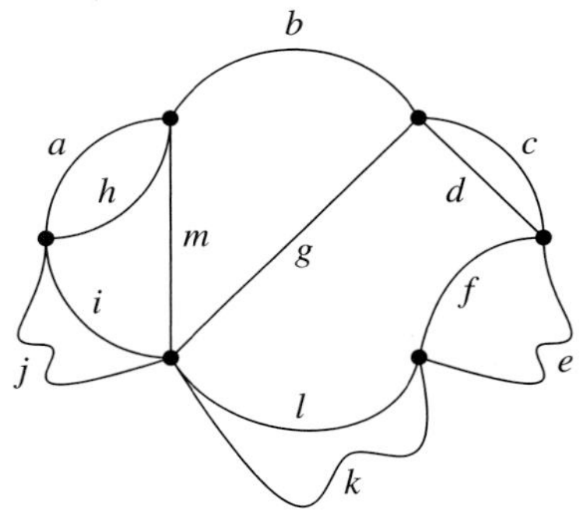

15.

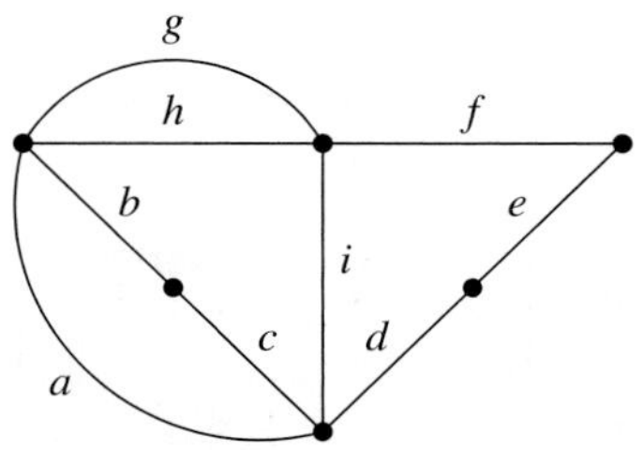

16.

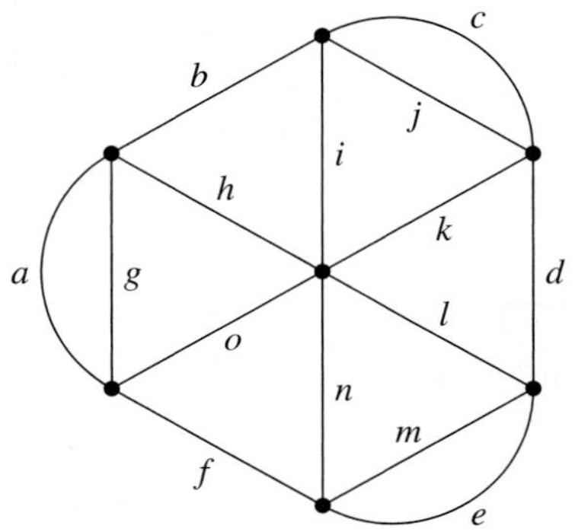

17.

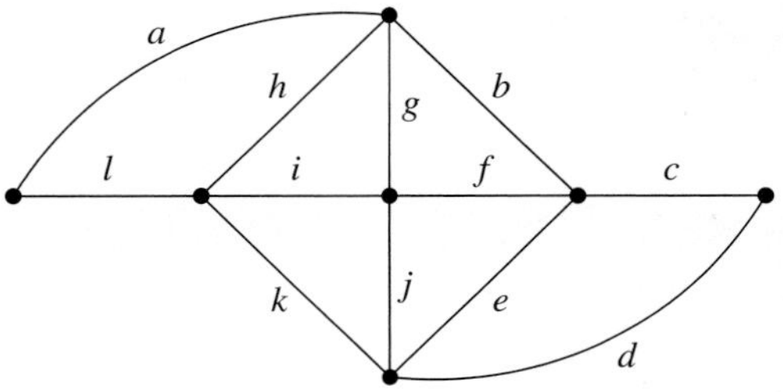

18.

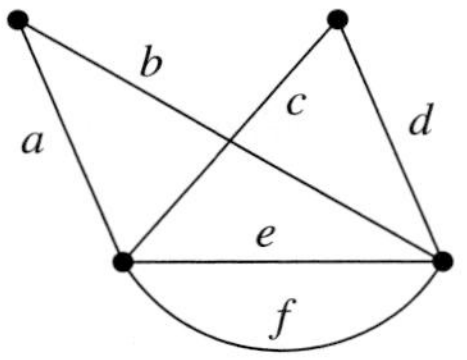

Applications

In problems 19–22, use Fleury's algorithm to design a traversable mail route for the given neighborhood.

19.

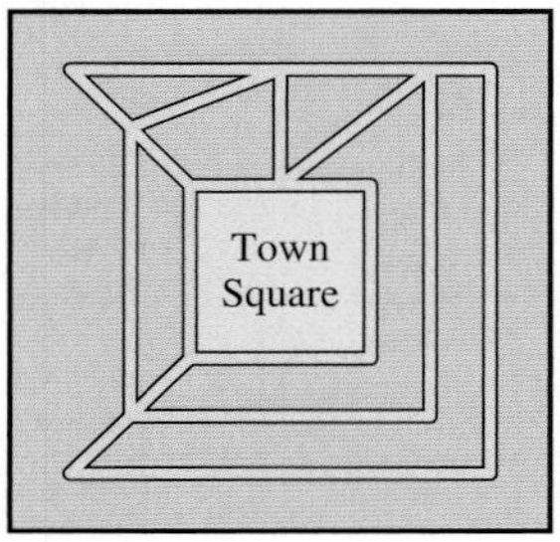

20.

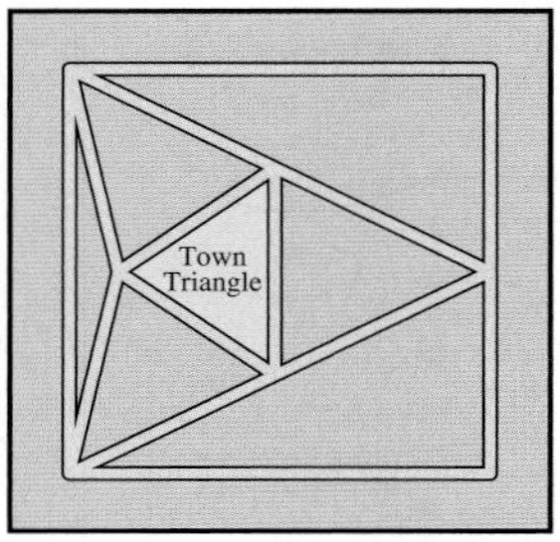

21.

22.

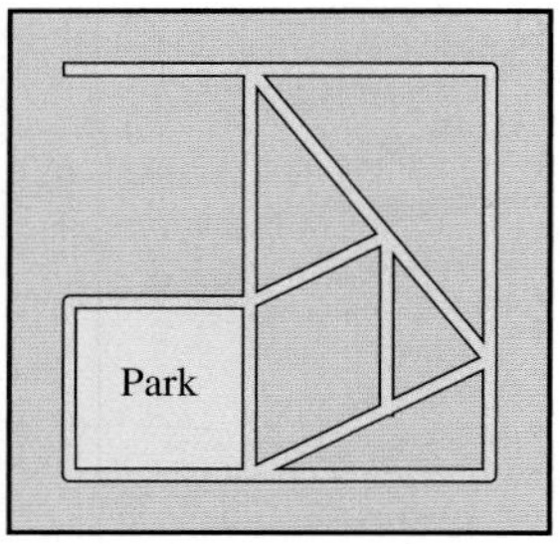

IN OTHER WORDS

23. Describe the following terms in your own words:
   a. Traversable graph
   b. Euler circuit
   c. Euler path
   d. Bridge
24. Describe the Bridges of Königsberg problem in your own words.

USING YOUR KNOWLEDGE

*The following definition will be needed in problems 25–30. A connected graph is **planar** if it can be drawn so that any two edges intersect only at vertices. For example, the graph in problem 9 is planar, whereas the graph in problem 10 is not planar. Notice that a planar graph divides the page into various regions so that you must cross over at least one edge to get from one region to another. For example, the graph in problem 1 divides the page into three regions: the two triangular regions "inside" and the single region "outside." If G is a planar graph, the Euler characteristic of G is given by the formula*

$$X(G) = R - E + V$$

where R is the number of regions, E is the number of edges, and V is the number of vertices.

25. Calculate $X(G)$, where G is the graph in problem 1.
26. Calculate $X(G)$, where G is the graph in problem 4.
27. Calculate $X(G)$, where G is the graph in problem 5.
28. Calculate $X(G)$, where G is the graph in problem 9.
29. Calculate $X(G)$, where G is the graph in problem 7. *Hint:* First redraw G so that none of the edges intersect.
30. What do you notice about $X(G)$ for each of the calculations in problems 25–29?

15.3 Hamilton Paths and Hamilton Circuits

GETTING STARTED

OBJECTIVES

A. Find Hamilton paths and circuits in a given graph.
B. Find the length of a path in a weighted graph.
C. Apply the nearest neighbor method to find a nearly minimal Hamilton circuit.

THE TRAVELING HITCHHIKER

Have you been to Yellowstone Park? If you decide to park your car at one of the four entrances and visit certain locations in the park once and only once, can you do it? It depends on which locations you choose! If you go to Example 2, we will show you how a hiker did it, and then you can visit on your own.

A Hamilton Paths and Circuits

In Section 15.2 we considered the problem of finding paths or circuits that use each edge of a graph once. Now we will investigate a similar problem: Given a graph such as the one in Figure 15.24, can we find a path that meets each *vertex* once (and only once)? Such a path is called a **Hamilton path.**

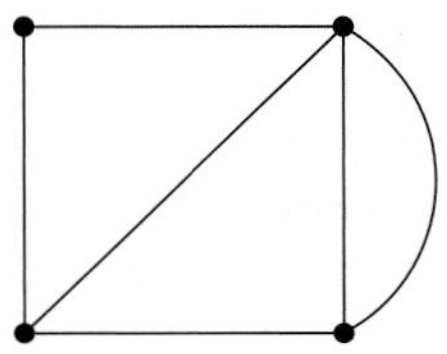

FIGURE 15.24

Hamilton Circuit

A path that meets every vertex once and then returns to the starting point is called a **Hamilton circuit.**

As usual, if a Hamilton circuit begins and ends at vertex *A,* we say that the circuit is **based** at *A*. Figure 15.25 gives some examples of Hamilton paths, whereas Figure 15.26 provides examples of Hamilton circuits.

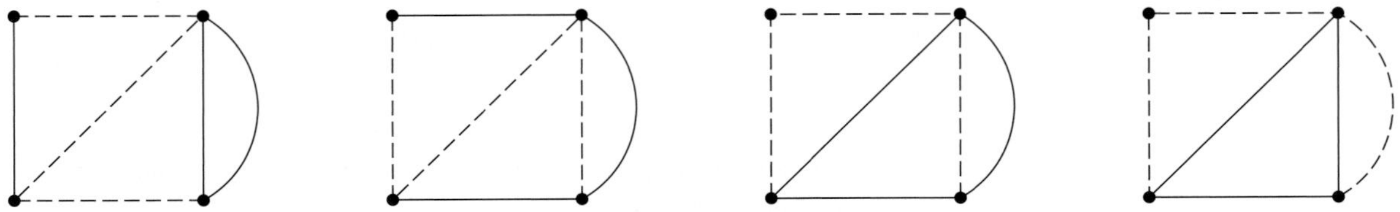

FIGURE 15.25

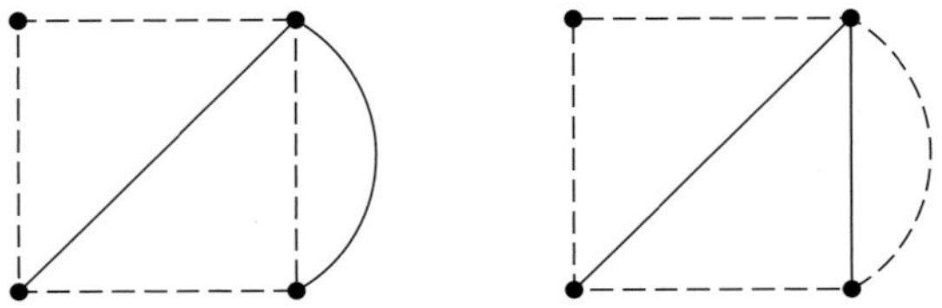

FIGURE 15.26

Naturally, we are led to the problem of determining whether a particular graph has a Hamilton path or circuit. In the case of finding Euler circuits, we had a rule for deciding whether a graph has an Euler circuit (the *traversability rules*) and a method for actually finding one (*Fleury's algorithm*). Unfortunately, there is no efficient algorithm for finding Hamilton circuits. In fact, there is at present *no* theorem that provides necessary and sufficient conditions for determining whether a graph even *has* a Hamilton circuit. In other words, when faced with a particular graph, the only way to find a Hamilton circuit is by trial and error.

Although there is no efficient algorithm for finding Hamilton circuits, this shouldn't prevent us from attempting to find them. In many cases, finding a Hamilton circuit in a graph is quite simple.

EXAMPLE 1 Finding a Hamilton Circuit

Find a Hamilton circuit in each of the graphs in Figure 15.27.

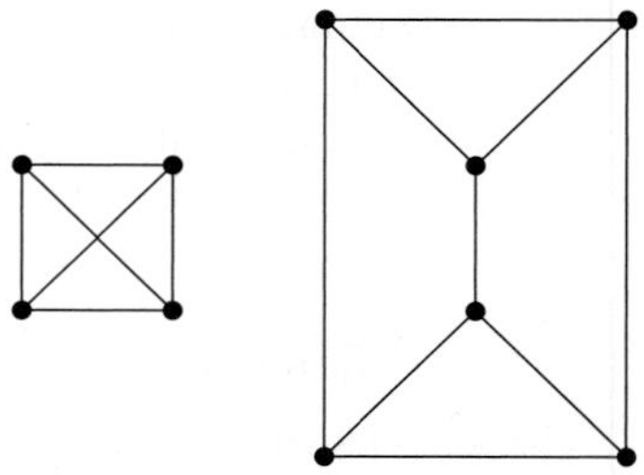

FIGURE 15.27

Solution

Starting at any vertex and following the indicated edges in either direction completes a Hamilton circuit in each of the graphs, as shown in Figure 15.28. Of course, those are not the only ones. Can you find any others?

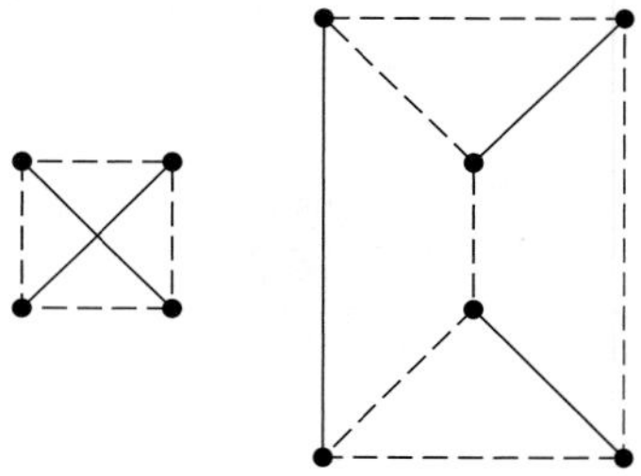

FIGURE 15.28

Not surprisingly, the theory of Hamilton circuits has numerous applications to real life, as illustrated in Example 2.

EXAMPLE 2 Finding a Hamilton Circuit

A hiker plans to visit Yellowstone National Park, entering at the West Entrance. Beginning at Madison Junction, he would like to visit each of the locations indicated on the Yellowstone map (Figure 15.29) once and only once and then return to Madison Junction. Can the hiker accomplish this goal?

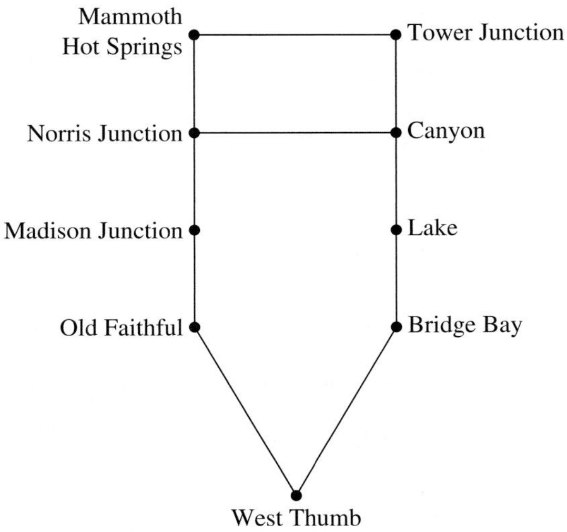

FIGURE 15.30

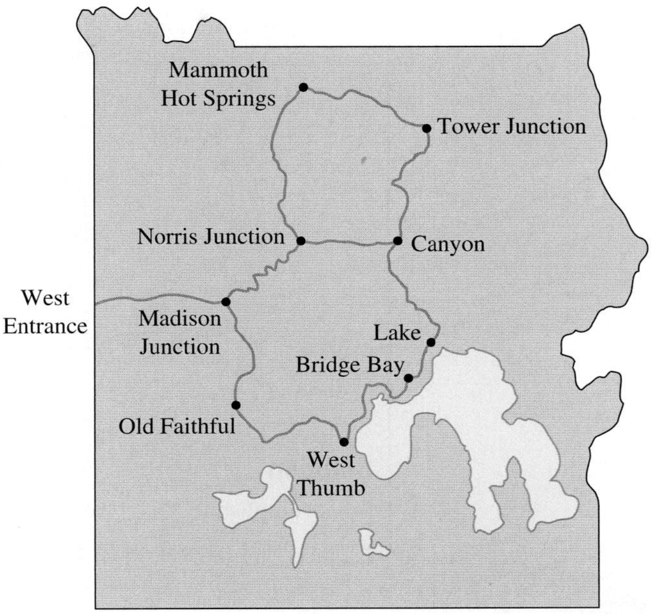

FIGURE 15.29

Solution

By now we know that this question can be restated in terms of graph theory. By representing each destination as a vertex and the roads joining them as edges (as in Figure 15.30), the hiker will be able to visit each destination once and only once if we can find a Hamilton circuit on the graph. Can you find one?

B Weighted Graphs

Weighted graphs are useful in a number of branches of mathematics.

© Jeff Henry/Corbis

A geyser at Yellowstone.

Weighted Graph

A **weighted graph** is a graph for which each edge has a number called a **weight** associated to it.

A typical weighted graph is shown in Figure 15.31.

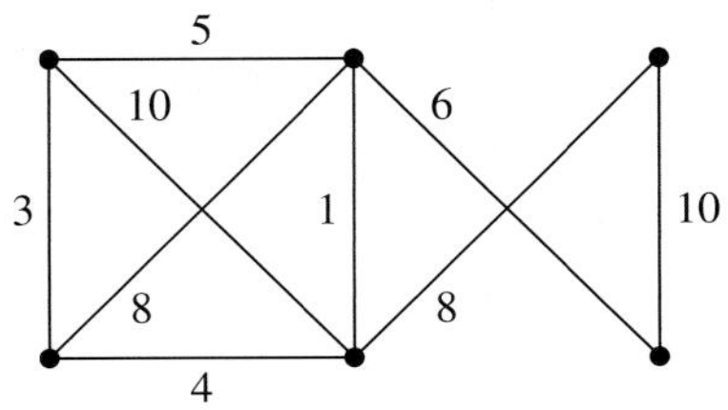

FIGURE 15.31

Given a path (or circuit) in a weighted graph, the **length** of the path is the sum of the weights of each of its edges. Notice that for any path, the path obtained by *reversing* the order of the edges has the same length as the original path. We shall therefore not distinguish between the two.

EXAMPLE 3 Finding the Length of a Path or Circuit

For each of the weighted graphs, Figures 15.32(a) and 15.32(b), find the length of the path or circuit indicated (note that for circuits you may choose any vertex as a starting point).

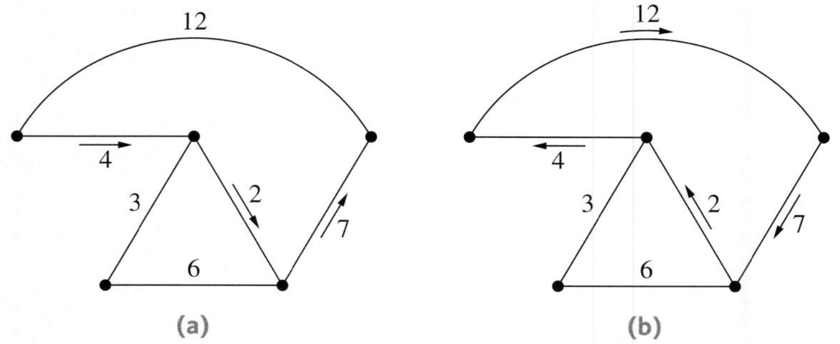

FIGURE 15.32

Solution

To accomplish the task, we need only add the weights of each of the edges indicated.

(a) The length is $4 + 2 + 7 = 13$. **(b)** The length is $12 + 7 + 2 + 4 = 25$.

When a mail carrier delivers mail, he or she would like to choose a route that involves the least amount of walking. When planning a vacation trip to multiple destinations, a travel agent will try to find the least expensive airline routes for a client. When a salesman plans a business trip to numerous cities, he would like to *minimize* the total distance he must travel. These are just a few examples of a famous (and quite difficult) problem in mathematics called the **traveling salesman problem.**

EXAMPLE 4 Finding an Efficient Route

Suppose a salesman lives in New York City. On his next business trip he would like to visit clients in Miami, Los Angeles, and Seattle in the most efficient manner. In particular, he would like to visit each city *once and only once.* He would also like to plan the most cost-effective trip. The airline that the salesman uses offers service between each pair of cities. The prices for a one-way ticket (in either direction) are indicated on the map in Figure 15.33.

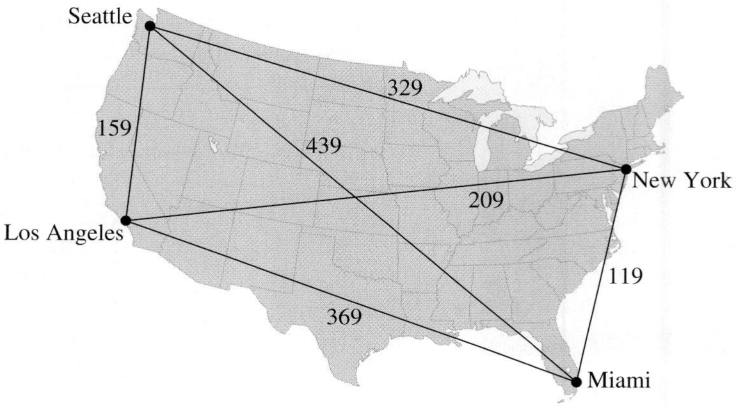

FIGURE 15.33

Solution

As you can see, this situation can be clearly illustrated using the techniques of graph theory. Each destination is represented by a vertex and each flight by an edge joining the corresponding vertices. The cost of a one-way ticket between a pair of cities is the *weight* of the corresponding edge.

Since the salesman would like to visit each destination once and only once before returning home, he will plan his trip by searching for a Hamilton circuit on the graph in Figure 15.34. In addition, he would like to choose the trip that costs the least. By tracing out each Hamilton circuit on the graph and calculating their lengths, we can deduce which route is optimal. As mentioned previously, reversing the order of any particular Hamilton circuit does not change the weight of the circuit. Thus, there are only three distinct Hamilton circuits to be considered.

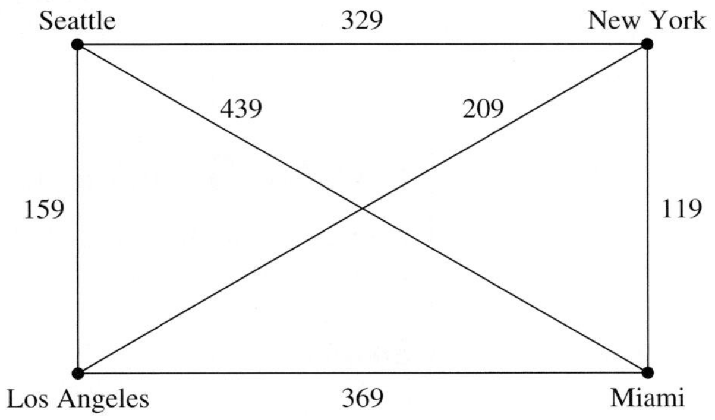

FIGURE 15.34

New York → Seattle → Miami → Los Angeles → New York
Weight = 329 + 439 + 369 + 209 = 1346

New York → Seattle → Los Angeles → Miami → New York
Weight = 329 + 159 + 369 + 119 = 976

New York → Los Angeles → Seattle → Miami → New York
Weight = 209 + 159 + 439 + 119 = 926

Since the third route has the least weight, $926, it is the *solution* to the traveling salesman problem.

C The Nearest-Neighbor Method

As mentioned previously, there is no efficient algorithm for finding Hamilton circuits in a graph. But we have seen that in traveling salesman problems, finding such circuits is the key to obtaining a solution. In simple cases, a **brute-force** approach can be successfully employed (as was done in Example 4), but for complicated weighted graphs, the number of Hamilton circuits based at a given vertex may become so large that even high-speed computers could not perform the necessary calculations in our lifetime!

Fortunately, in many cases there is an algorithm that will provide us with an **approximate** solution to a traveling salesman problem. This approximate solution, though not usually a circuit of shortest length, will have a length that is reasonably close to a Hamilton circuit of minimal length.

Recall that the complete graph K_n is the graph with n vertices in which each pair of vertices is joined by exactly one edge. It is obvious that for any n, the complete graph K_n has a Hamilton circuit. In fact, it can be shown that for any vertex in K_n, there are $\frac{(n-1)!}{2}$ different Hamilton circuits based at that vertex. Thus, for large values of n, the number of Hamilton circuits for K_n is incredibly large. For example, the graph K_{10} has 181,440 different Hamilton circuits based at any given vertex and K_8 has 2520 different Hamilton circuits based at A as shown in Figure 15.35! In such a situation, computing the lengths of all possible Hamilton circuits is not practical. This is precisely the reason that an efficient algorithm is desirable, even if the answer we obtain is only an approximate solution.

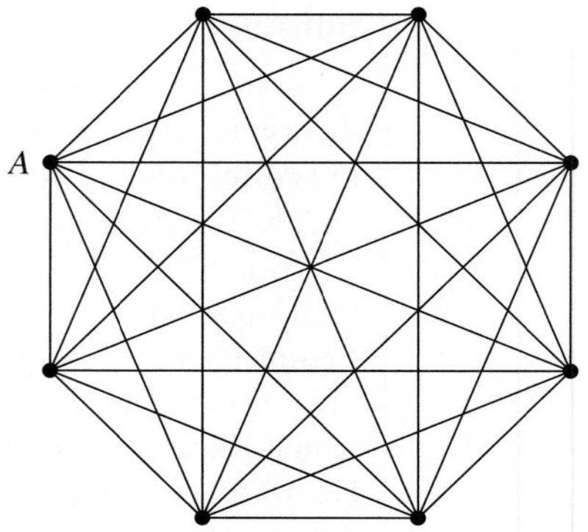

FIGURE 15.35 K_8 has 2520 different Hamilton circuits based at A.

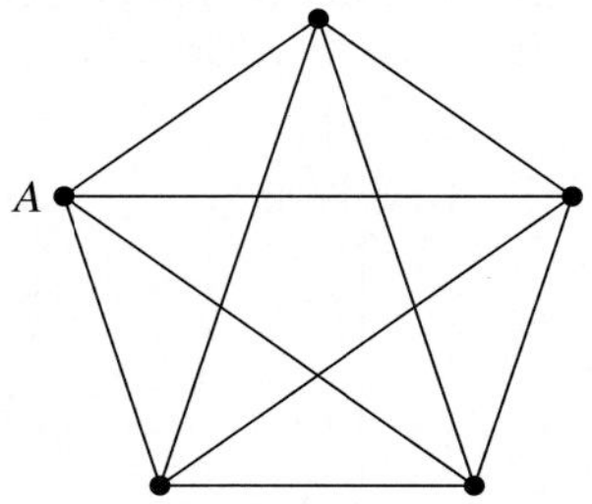

K_5

FIGURE 15.36

EXAMPLE 5 Finding Hamilton Circuits

Find all Hamilton circuits based at vertex A indicated in the complete graph K_5 in Figure 15.36.

Solution

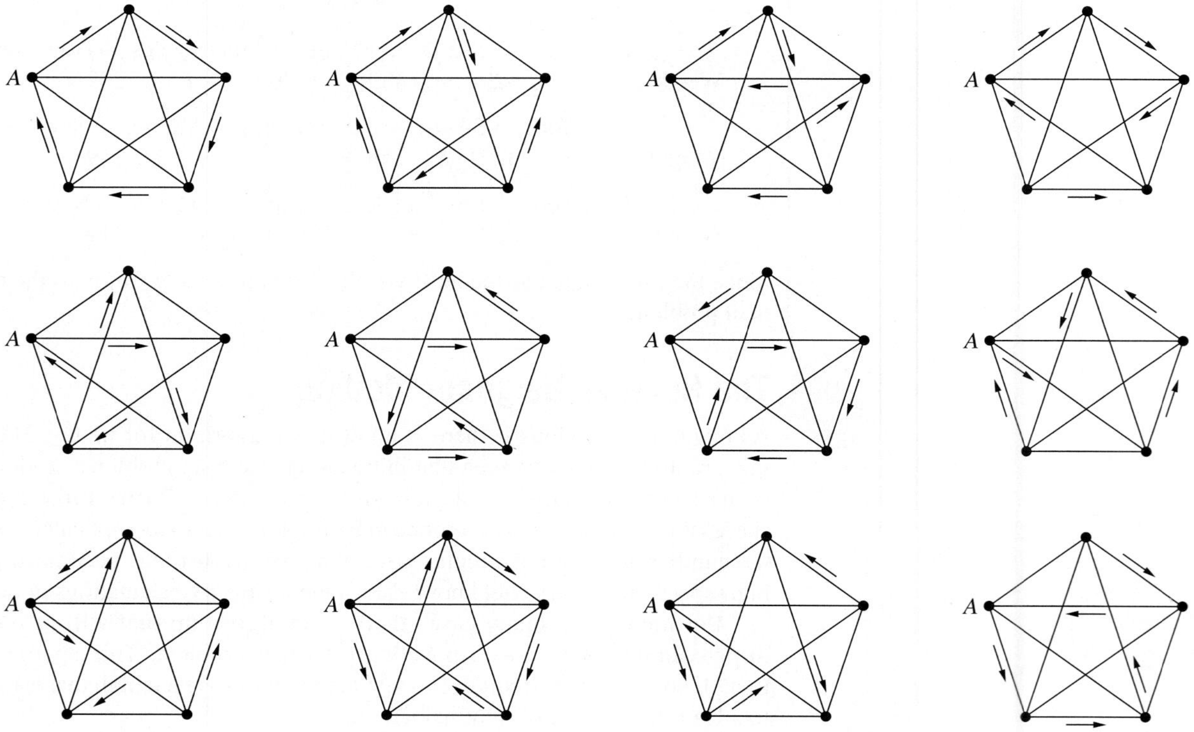

FIGURE 15.37

According to the formula given above, there will be $\frac{[(5-1)!]}{2} = 12$ different Hamilton circuits (remember that a circuit in the *reverse* order is not counted separately). Therefore, the circuits given in Figure 15.37 provide a complete listing of all distinct Hamilton circuits based at A.

Even though complete graphs have a large number of Hamilton circuits, these are precisely the graphs we are interested in. We will consider **complete weighted graphs** (i.e., complete graphs with weights associated with each edge). It turns out that for such graphs there is a simple algorithm for producing a **nearly minimal** Hamilton circuit, one that has a relatively short length. In applications, this nearly minimal Hamilton circuit will be used as an approximate solution to traveling salesman problems. The algorithm is called the **nearest-neighbor method.**

Nearest-Neighbor Method

1. Given a complete weighted graph, begin at the indicated starting point. If none is indicated, choose one at random.
2. In deciding which vertex to visit next, choose to travel along the edge with the *smallest* weight (the vertex at which we arrive is the "nearest" neighbor). If there is more than one edge of minimal weight, choose one at random.
3. From the new vertex, repeat this process: Choose to travel along the edge that has the *smallest* weight (don't return to the previous vertex; we want a *Hamilton* circuit). If there is more than one edge of minimal weight, choose one at random.
4. Continue in this fashion: From each new vertex, travel to an unvisited vertex along the edge of least weight, choosing an edge at random if there is more than one edge of minimal weight.
5. Once every vertex has been visited, return to the starting point along the edge with *smallest* weight. Once again, if there is more than one edge of minimal weight, choose one at random. The circuit that has been traced out is a **nearly minimal** Hamilton circuit.

EXAMPLE 6 Using the Nearest-Neighbor Method

For each of the graphs in Figures 15.38(a) and 15.38(b), use the nearest-neighbor method to find a nearly minimal Hamilton circuit based at vertex *A*. What is the weight of the circuit you found?

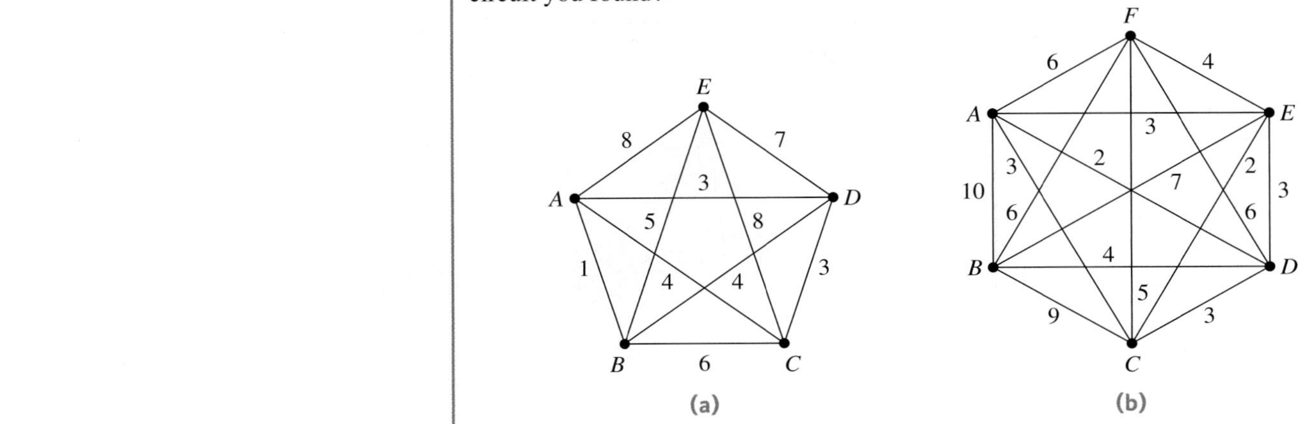

FIGURE 15.38

Solution

(a) (i) Among the edges emanating from vertex *A* in the graph on the left, the edge joining *A* and *B* has the least weight, so this will be the first edge of our circuit. Since we cannot return to vertex *A* at this point, we consider the other three edges that meet *B* and determine that the edge joining *B* and *D* has the least weight. This edge is the second of our circuit.

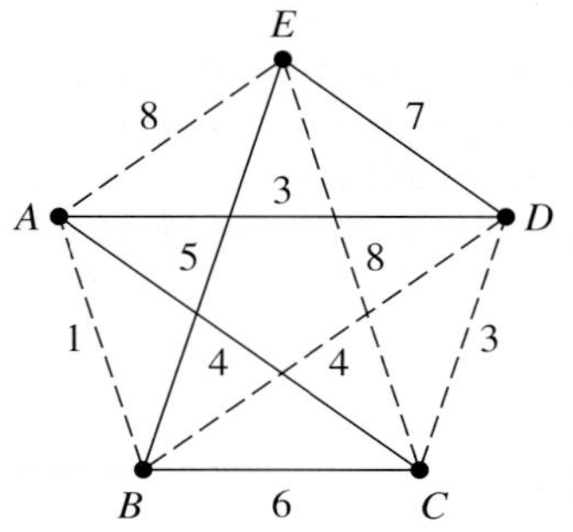

(a)

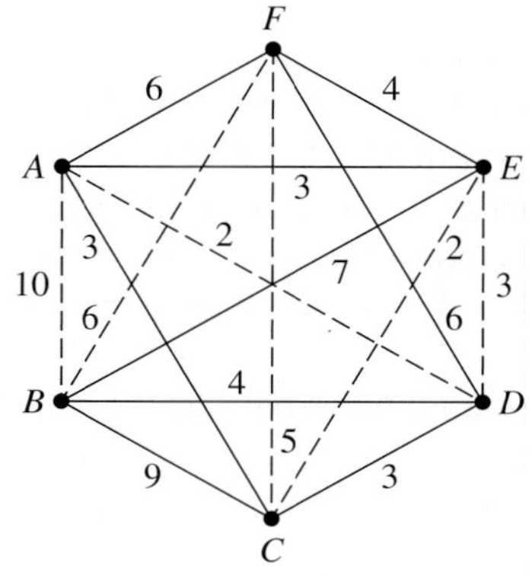

(b)

FIGURE 15.39

(ii) From D we need only consider the edges that proceed to *C* and *E* (the other edges would take us to vertices that we have already visited). Since the edge that joins *C* and *D* has the smaller weight, we use this as the third edge of our circuit.

(iii) At this point we have no choice but to continue on to vertex *E* and then complete our circuit along the edge joining *A* and *E*. The actual circuit is given in Figure 15.39(a). The weight of this circuit is

$$1 + 4 + 3 + 8 + 8 = 24$$

(b) (i) Among the edges emanating from *A* in Figure 15.39(b), the edge joining *A* and *D* has the least weight and will, therefore, become the first edge of our circuit.

(ii) From *D* there are two edges of least weight along which we may proceed (remember, we cannot return to *A*): the edge joining *C* and *D* and the edge joining *D* and *E*. We choose at random the edge joining *D* and *E* as the second edge of our circuit.

(iii) From *E* we will proceed to *C* because it is the edge of least weight emanating from *E*. From *C* we must proceed to *F* because the edge joining *C* and *F* has the least weight among edges along which we are allowed to travel. At this point there is no alternative: We continue on to vertex *B* and then return to starting point *A*. Figure 15.39b shows the circuit determined by the nearest-neighbor method. The weight of this circuit is

$$2 + 3 + 2 + 5 + 6 + 10 = 28$$

The nearest-neighbor method is an effective way to find an approximate solution to many traveling salesman problems, as shown in Example 7.

EXAMPLE 7 Using the Nearest-Neighbor Method

Suppose our salesman is based in Los Angeles. He needs to visit clients in Salt Lake City, Seattle, Denver, Dallas, Chicago, and New Orleans (Figure 15.40). We can assume, not unreasonably, that from any of the cities listed there is an airline flight to any of the other cities. We will also assume that the order in which he visits the cities does not matter. His only objective is to accomplish the trip as inexpensively as possible. The price of a one-way ticket between two cities (in either direction) is given in Figure 15.41.

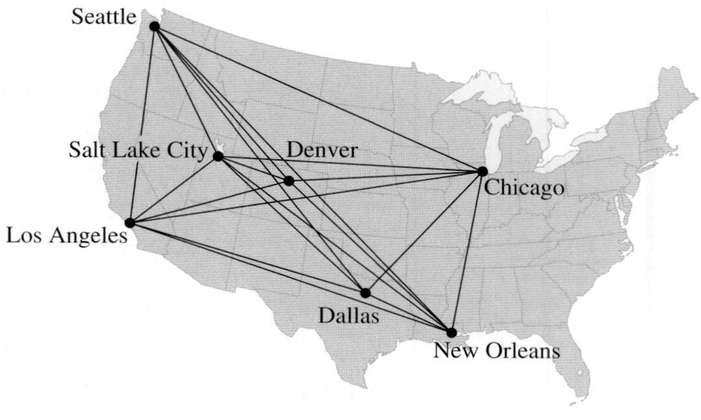

FIGURE 15.40

The first step is to represent this problem as a weighted graph. We have one vertex for each city and one edge for each pair of cities (representing the flight between two cities). Notice how the weight corresponding to an edge is the cost of a one-way ticket between the two cities. What we obtain is a complete weighted graph. Our goal now is to obtain an inexpensive travel itinerary for the salesman. We will use the *nearest-neighbor method* to accomplish this.

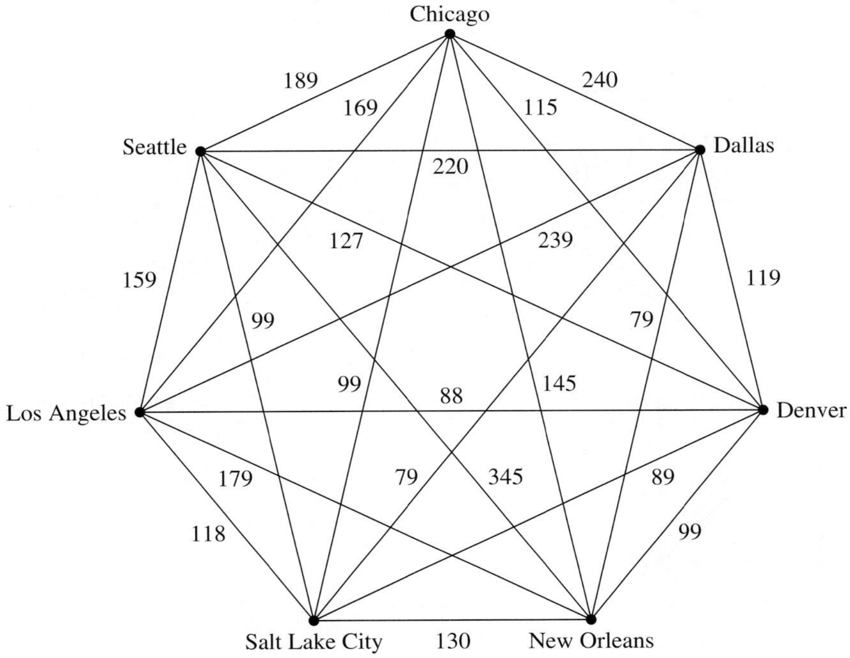

FIGURE 15.41

The salesman is based in Los Angeles, so this will be the initial vertex of our Hamilton circuit. The edge joining Los Angeles and Denver has the least weight and therefore, will be the first edge of the circuit. The next edge will be the one joining Salt Lake City and Denver because it has the least weight among edges that do not lead to Los Angeles. From Salt Lake City, the clear choice is to proceed to Dallas. The edge of least weight emanating from Dallas leads to the next destination: New Orleans. After a night on Bourbon Street, the salesman is ready for his next flight. Although the edges from New Orleans to Denver, Salt Lake City, and Los Angeles have smaller weight among the edges emanating from New Orleans, he goes to Chicago (remember, he wants to complete a *Hamilton* circuit). His final destination before returning to Los Angeles is Seattle—the only unvisited vertex.

	LA $\rightarrow$	Denver $\rightarrow$	SLC $\rightarrow$	Dallas $\rightarrow$	N.O. $\rightarrow$	Chi $\rightarrow$	Seattle $\rightarrow$	LA
Weight:	88 +	89 +	79 +	79 +	145 +	189 +	159	= 828

The itinerary is shown on the first line, and the cost is \$828.

15.3 EXERCISES

A Hamilton Paths and Circuits

In problems 1–4, determine whether the sequence of edges [a, b, c, d, e] represents a Hamilton path, a Hamilton circuit, or neither.

1.

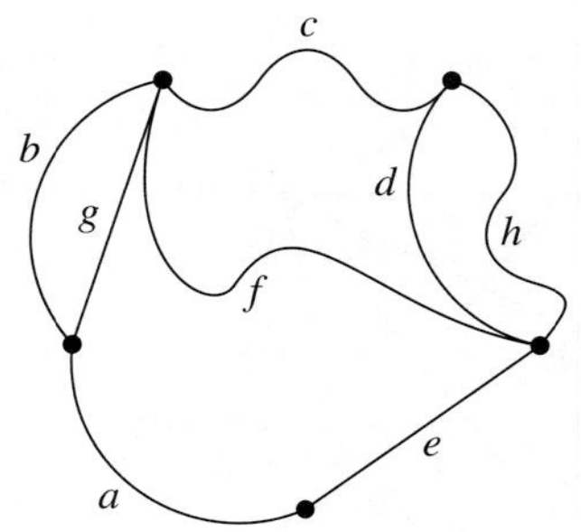

2.

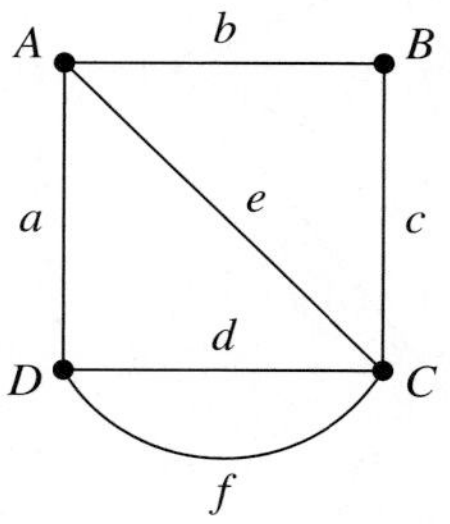

3.

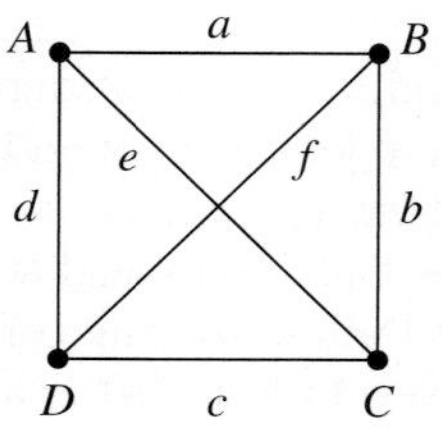

4.

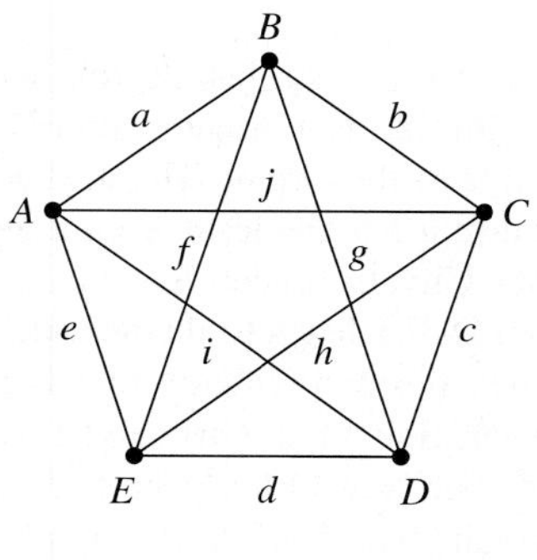

B Weighted Graphs

In problems 5–8, determine the length of the indicated path or circuit.

5.

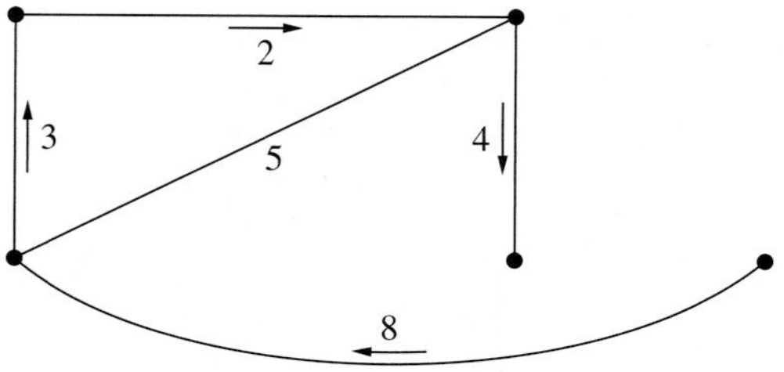

6.

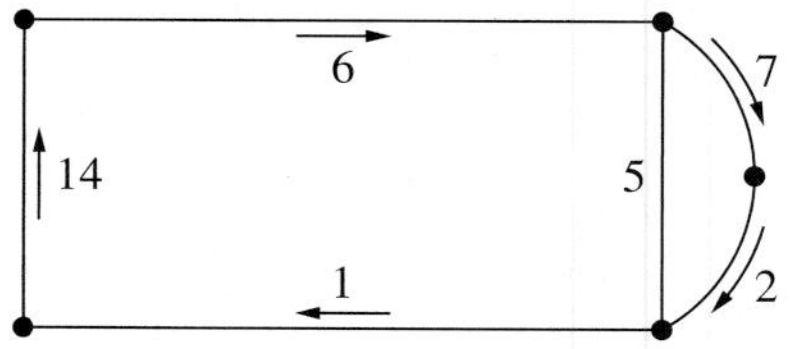

7.

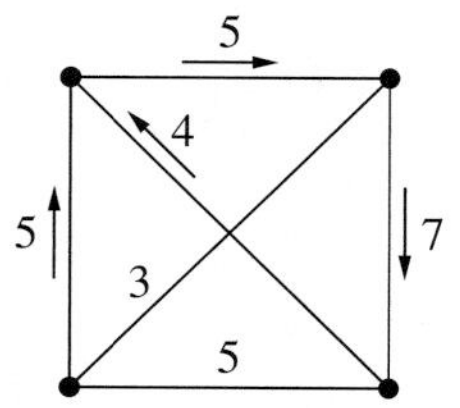

8.

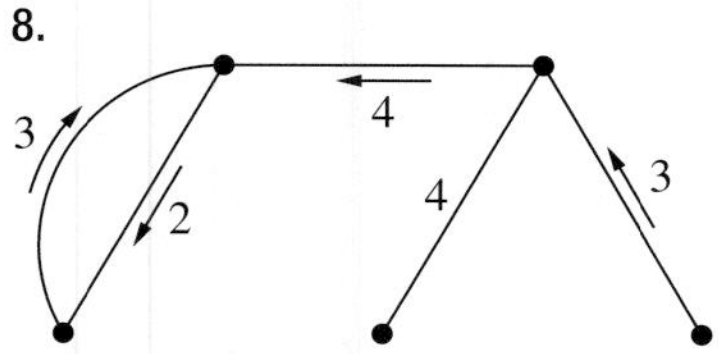

9. Find the lengths of all Hamilton circuits based at vertex A.

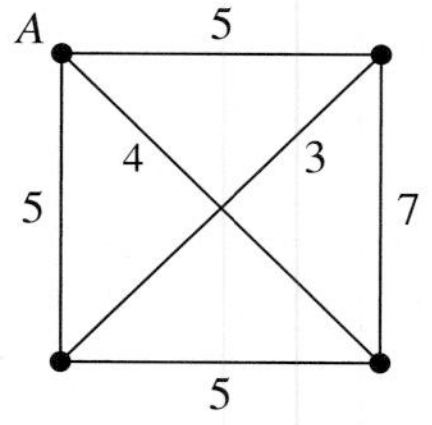

10. Find the lengths of all Hamilton circuits based at vertex B.

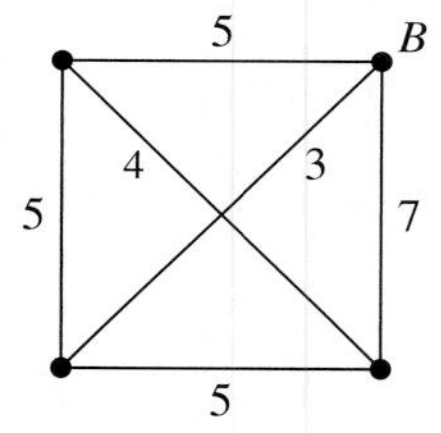

C The Nearest-Neighbor Method

In problems 11–16, use the nearest-neighbor method to find a nearly minimal Hamilton circuit based at the vertex A and find the length of the circuit (answers may vary).

11.

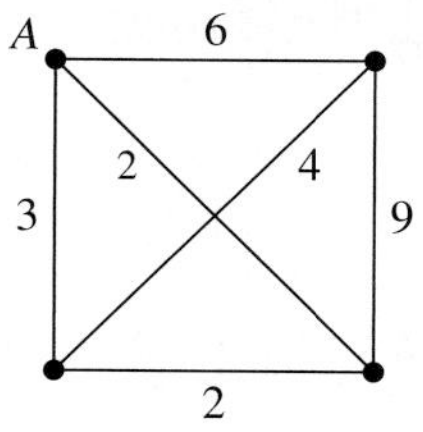

12.

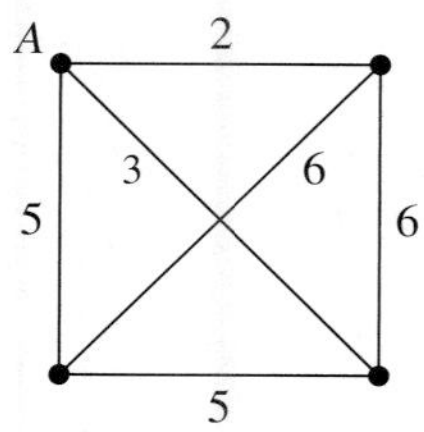

13.

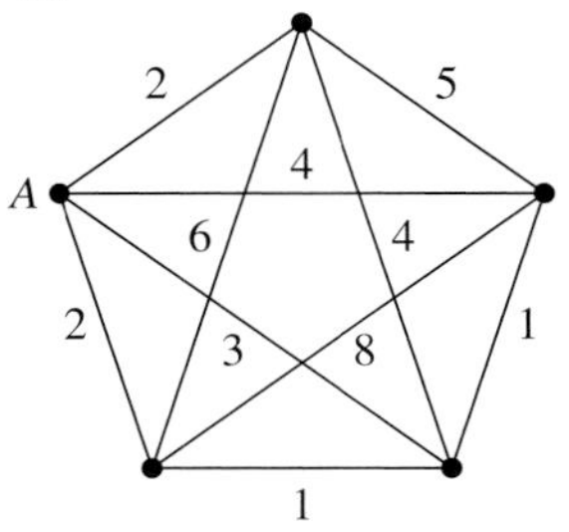

14.

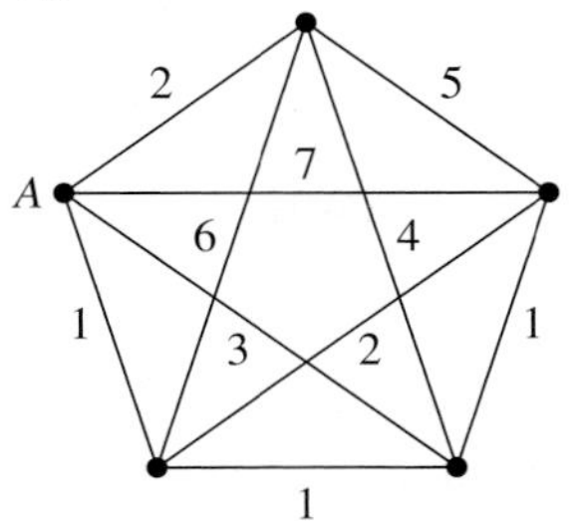

15.

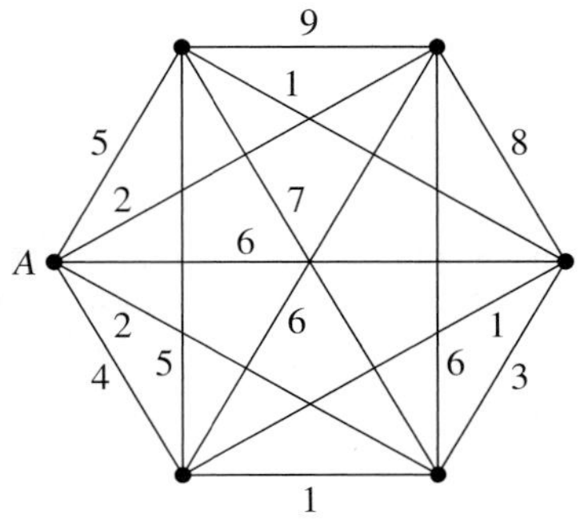

16.

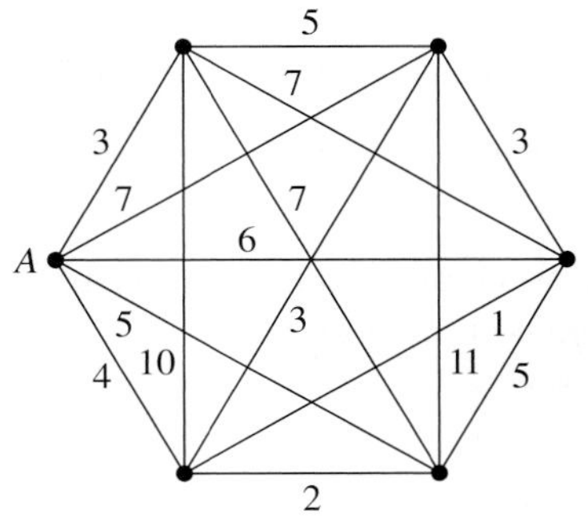

In problems 17–20, use the nearest-neighbor method to find a delivery route of minimal length starting and ending at the indicated vertex so that each of the vertices is visited once and only once.

17.

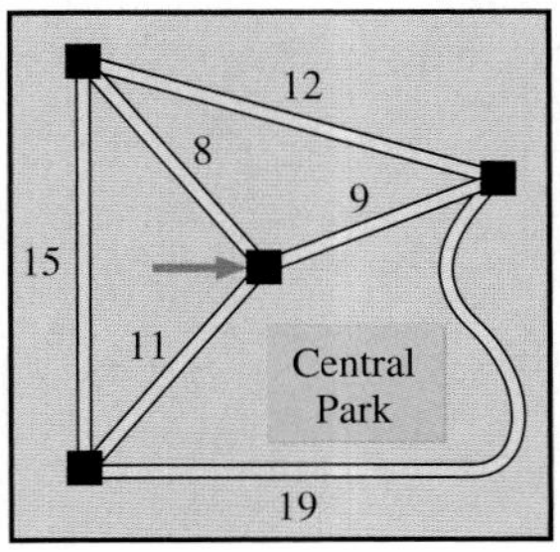

18.

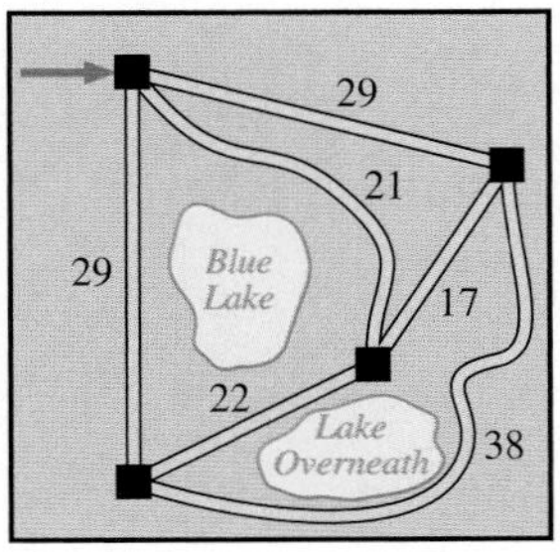

19.

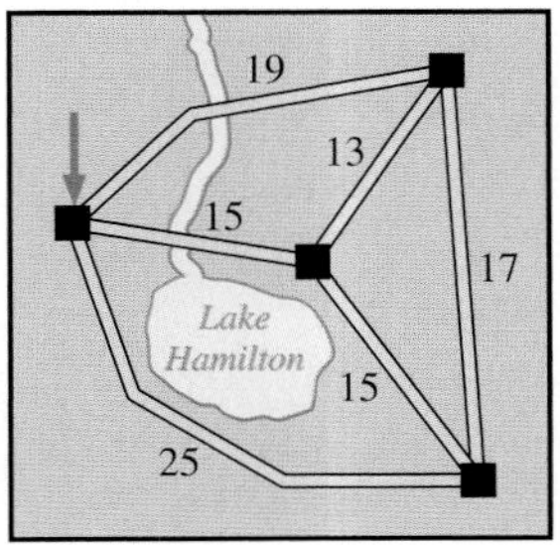

20.

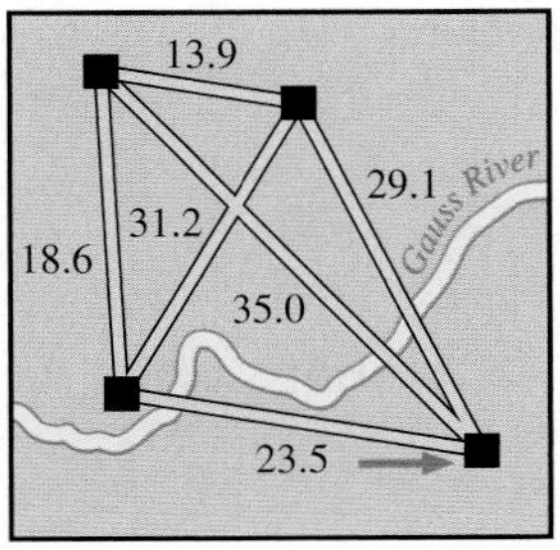

WEB IT EXERCISES

Did you know that there are three common styles for lacing shoes? The idea is to find the shortest path from the top eyelet (or lace hole) on one side to the top eyelet on the other side, passing through every eyelet just once. What are the three common styles for lacing shoes, and which style do you use? Which style requires the shortest and which the longest length of lace? What is the connection between lacing shoes and the traveling salesman problem? To answer these three questions, visit www.maa.org/mathland/mathtrek_2_8_99.html.

*In this section we studied the nearest-neighbor method, an algorithm for producing a nearly minimal Hamilton circuit. Find three other algorithms that produce a nearly minimal Hamilton circuit, and write the procedure used in each of them. (*Hint: *Go to http://www.ctl.ua.edu/math103/ for ideas.)*

IN OTHER WORDS

21. Describe the traveling salesman problem in your own words.

22. In your own words, explain what a Hamilton path is. What is the difference between a Hamilton path and a Hamilton circuit?

23. Describe the nearest-neighbor method in your own words.

24. Describe the difference between an Euler circuit and a Hamilton circuit.

USING YOUR KNOWLEDGE

In this chapter we used the nearest-neighbor method to solve the traveling salesman problem and other related problems. In these problems we always started at one particular vertex and proceeded to find a nearly minimal Hamilton circuit. What happens if we try starting at a different vertex? Might we find an even shorter Hamilton circuit? Let's find out!

25. Pick any vertex (other than A) on the graph in problem 11. Apply the nearest-neighbor method to find a nearly minimal Hamilton circuit based at the vertex you chose. Compare your answer with your result from problem 11.

26. Pick any vertex (other than A) on the graph in problem 12. Apply the nearest-neighbor method to find a nearly minimal Hamilton circuit based at the vertex you chose. Compare your answer with the result from problem 12.

27. Pick any vertex (other than A) on the graph in problem 13. Apply the nearest-neighbor method to find a nearly minimal Hamilton circuit based at the vertex you chose. Compare your answer with the result from problem 13.

28. Pick any vertex (other than A) on the graph in problem 14. Apply the nearest-neighbor method to find a nearly minimal Hamilton circuit based at the vertex you chose. Compare your answer with the result from problem 14.

15.4 Trees

GETTING STARTED

OBJECTIVES

A. Find spanning trees in a given graph.
B. Use Kruskal's algorithm to find a minimal spanning tree.

THE TREES AND THE BEES

Do you know your roots? Have you ever worked on your family tree? What about the family tree for a male bee? What about for a female bee? Are they always different? For an answer, go to Collaborative Learning in Exercises 1.1 in Chapter 1. For a lot of trees, visit www.maths.surrey.ac.uk/hosted-sites/R.Knott//Fibonacci/fibnat.html#Rabbits.

A Trees and Forests

Recall that a graph is *connected* if, for any pair of vertices, there is a path joining them.

Definition of a Tree

A **tree** is a *connected* graph in which there are no simple circuits. A graph that has no circuits but is not necessarily connected is called a **forest.**

The Auto Tree, Big Basin, California.

EXAMPLE 1 Determining Trees and Forests

Determine whether each of the graphs, (a), (b), and (c), in Figure 15.42 is a tree, a forest, or neither.

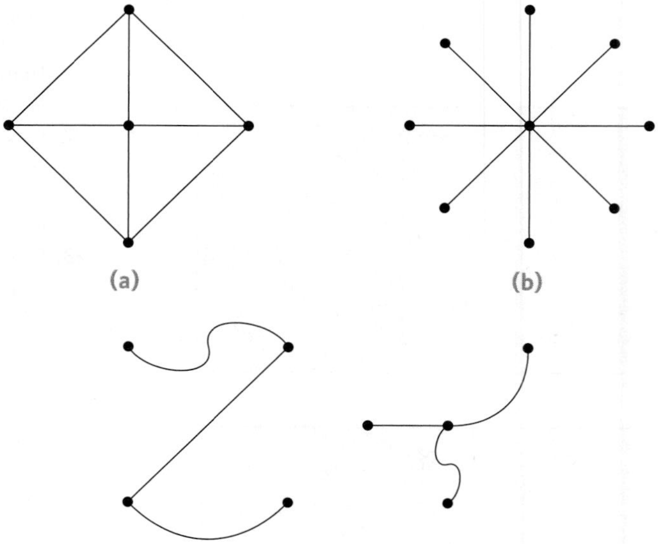

(a) (b) (c)

FIGURE 15.42

Solution

(a) Neither **(b)** Tree **(c)** Forest

The **unique path property** is an important property of all trees.

Theorem 15.1 Unique Path Property

For any two vertices in a tree, there is *exactly* one simple path joining them.

In Section 15.3 we discussed Hamilton circuits, which are circuits that meet every vertex of a graph.

Spanning Tree

A **spanning tree** (or **maximal tree**) in a graph is a *tree* that meets every vertex of the graph.

EXAMPLE 2 Finding a Spanning Tree

Find a spanning tree for each of Figure 15.43, parts (a) and (b).

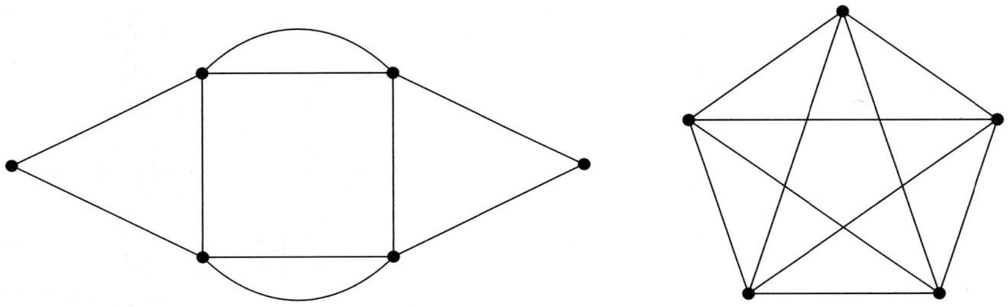

(a) (b)

FIGURE 15.43

Solution

There are numerous spanning trees for each of the graphs. We have indicated one for each of the graphs (a) and (b) in Figure 15.44.

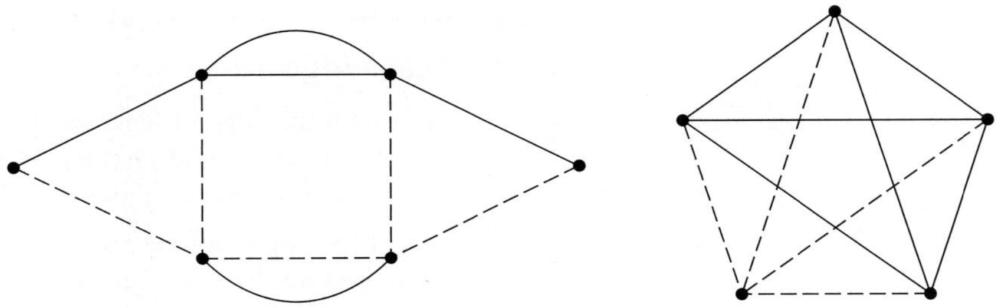

(a) (b)

FIGURE 15.44

We have seen examples of graphs and their spanning trees. Naturally, we might wonder whether it is possible for a (connected) graph to have *no* spanning trees. The following theorem tells us that this cannot happen:

Theorem 15.2 Existence of Spanning Trees

Every connected graph has *at least one* spanning tree.

B Weighted Graphs and Spanning Trees

Suppose that we have a weighted graph. We know from Theorem 15.2 that this graph has at least one spanning tree (and may have many). The *weight* of a spanning tree in a labeled graph is the sum of the weights of each of the edges in the tree. A **minimal spanning tree** is a spanning tree with the *least* weight.

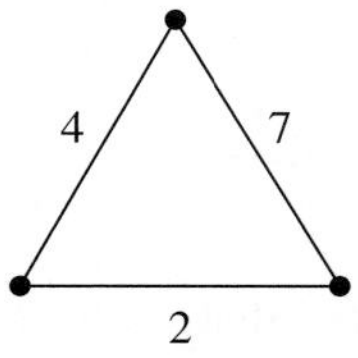

FIGURE 15.45

EXAMPLE 3 Finding a Minimal Spanning Tree

Find a minimal spanning tree in the complete weighted graph in Figure 15.45.

Solution

The graph in Figure 15.45 has three distinct spanning trees, which are shown in Figures 15.46(a) to (c). To find the minimal spanning tree, we simply compute the weight of each spanning tree and choose the one with minimal weight.

(a) $4 + 7 = 11$ (b) $4 + 2 = 6$ (c) $2 + 7 = 9$

Thus, the spanning tree in Figure 15.46(b) is minimal.

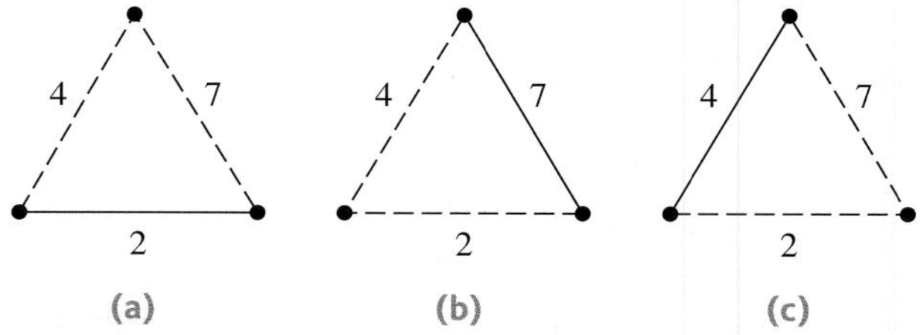

FIGURE 15.46

Typically, a graph has many spanning trees, so attempting to find a *minimal* spanning tree by brute force (as we did in Example 3) would be a tedious exercise when the graph is complicated. Thankfully, there is an algorithm for finding a *minimal* spanning tree.

Kruskal's Algorithm

1. Start with the edge of least weight in the graph. If there is more than one, choose one of them at random. This is the first edge of a subgraph that we will use to form our minimal spanning tree.
2. Out of the edges not yet selected, choose the edge of minimal weight (this edge does not have to share a vertex with the other edge). If there is more than one edge of minimal weight, choose one at random.
3. Out of the remaining edges, choose any edge of minimal weight as long as the subgraph of selected edges does not form a circuit. If there is more than one edge of minimal weight, choose one at random.
4. Repeat step 3 until the subgraph contains all vertices of the original graph.

We will now illustrate Kruskal's algorithm with an example.

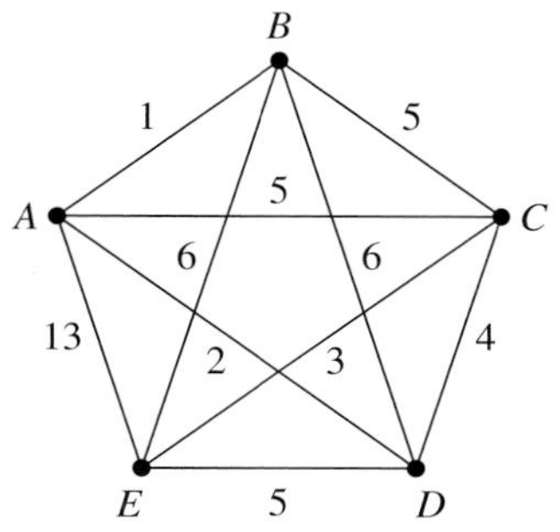

FIGURE 15.47

EXAMPLE 4 Finding a Minimal Spanning Tree

Find a *minimal* spanning tree in the complete weighted graph given in Figure 15.47.

Solution

We apply Kruskal's algorithm as follows:

1. The edge joining vertices A and B has weight 1, so we choose it as the first edge of our spanning tree.
2. The edge joining vertices A and D has weight 2 and will therefore be the next edge.
3. The edge joining vertices C and E has weight 3 and will therefore be the next edge.
4. Finally, the edge joining vertices C and D has weight 4 and will complete our spanning tree, in Figure 15.48.

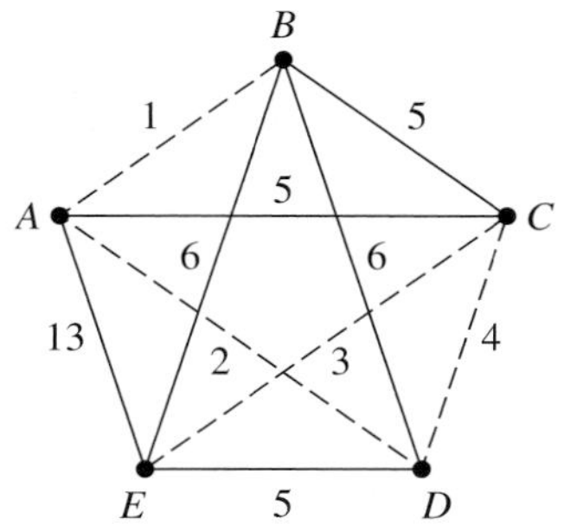

FIGURE 15.48

Like Euler circuits and Hamilton circuits, spanning trees have numerous applications. We now discuss how Kruskal's algorithm can be used to find efficient solutions to some real-world problems.

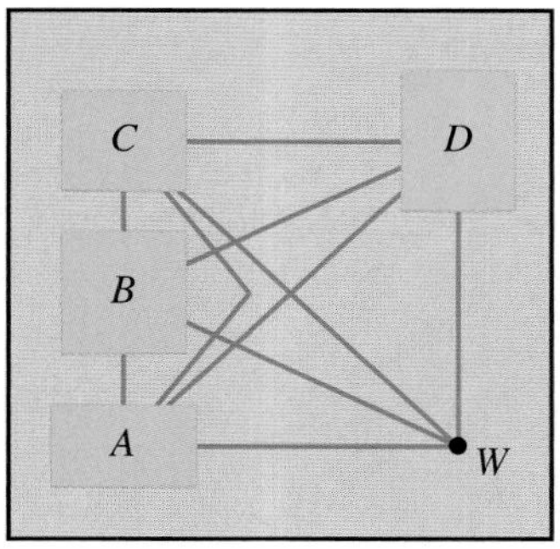

FIGURE 15.49

EXAMPLE 5 Finding a Subgraph

A farmer wants to install a new irrigation system for his farm, which is divided into four distinct plots of land as shown in Figure 15.49.

The water is to be drawn from a well and fed to each of the four sprinkler systems by pipes. It is possible to connect any two points on the farm by pipe. To illustrate this, the farmer draws a graph with vertices representing the sprinkler systems and the well, whereas the edges represent possible connecting pipes. He labels the vertices

Anton's farm.

A farming irrigation system.

corresponding to the sprinklers *A, B, C,* and *D* and the vertex corresponding to the well *W.* It should not be surprising that the graph the farmer draws will be a complete graph (see Figure 15.50).

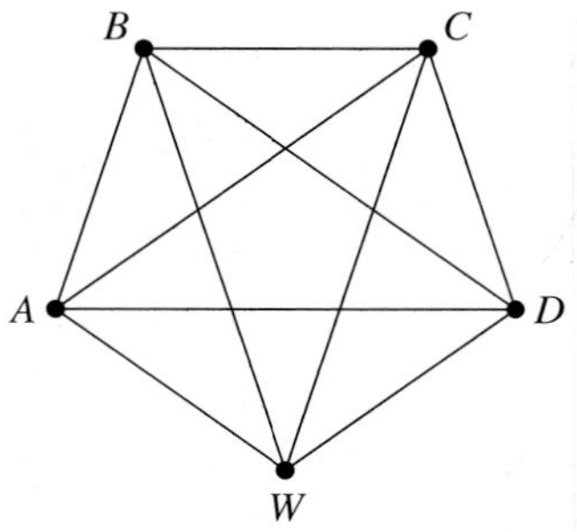

FIGURE 15.50

To ensure that water reaches each of the four sprinklers, the farmer needs to find a *subgraph* of the complete graph that is connected and meets each of the five vertices. For example, each of the subgraphs in Figure 15.51 would accomplish the task.

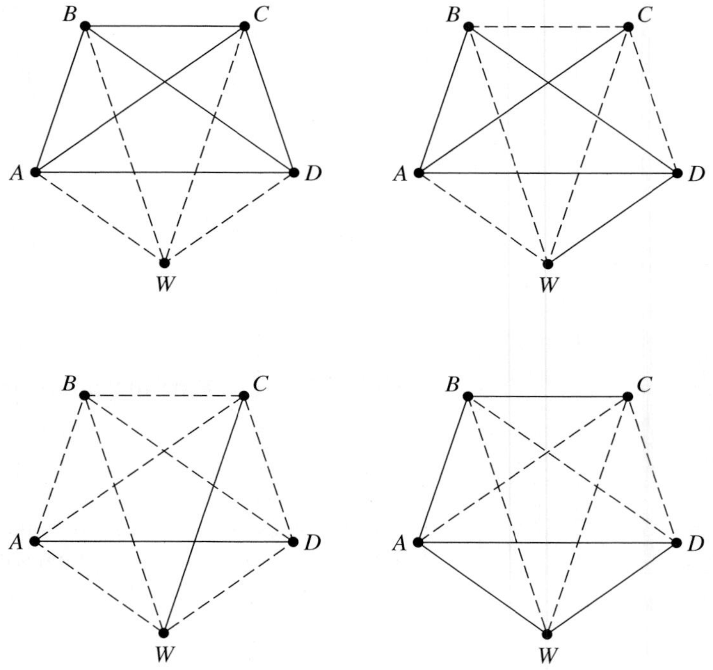

FIGURE 15.51

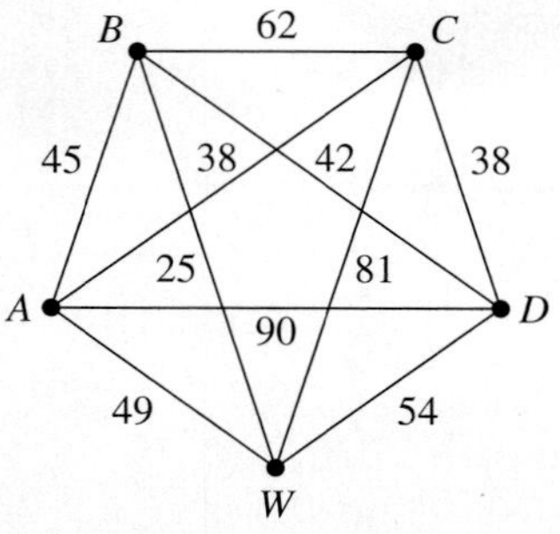

FIGURE 15.52

The farmer would like to design the irrigation system so that its cost is as *low* as possible, so he calculates the cost of connecting any two points with a pipe. The costs are indicated in Figure 15.52. Find the subgraph and the lowest possible cost for the irrigation system.

Solution

Since it is unnecessary to have more than one source of water feeding any particular sprinkler, there need be only one path in the subgraph starting at vertex *W* and ending at any of the other vertices. In other words, the subgraph will be a tree, and since the tree will meet each of the vertices, it will be a *spanning* tree. Possible spanning trees are indicated in Figure 15.53.

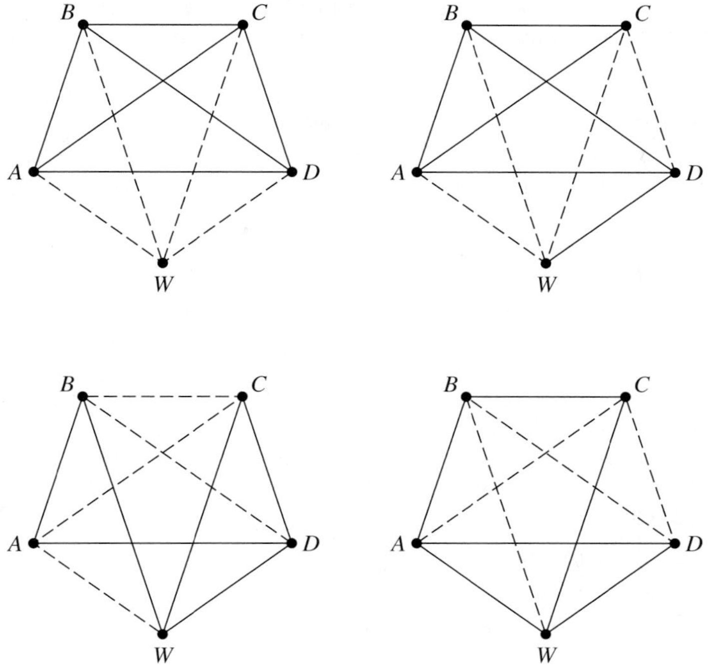

FIGURE 15.53

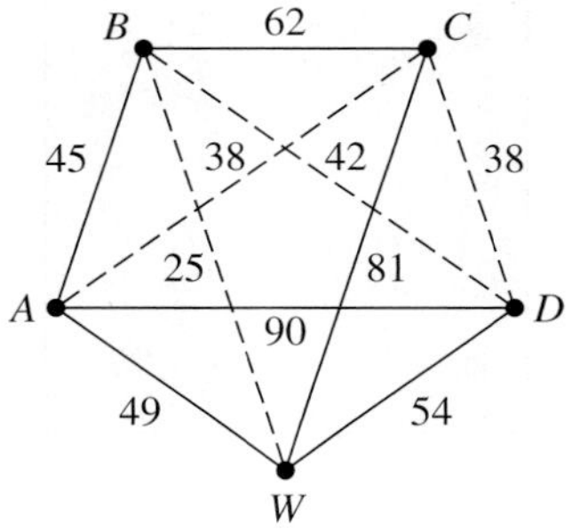

FIGURE 15.54

To design the irrigation system with the lowest possible cost, the farmer needs to find a *minimal spanning tree.* To find the desired result, he applies Kruskal's algorithm.

1. The edge joining vertices B and W has minimal weight (25) and, therefore, will be the first edge of the spanning tree.
2. The edge joining vertices A and C and the edge joining vertices C and D both have minimal weight (38) among the remaining edges, and since no circuit is formed, each of these edges will be included in the spanning tree.
3. Adding the edge joining vertices B and D (42) completes the spanning tree in Figure 15.54.

The total cost of the irrigation system is the weight of the spanning tree, that is,

$$25 + 38 + 38 + 42 = \$143.$$

15.4 EXERCISES

A Trees and Forests

In problems 1–4, determine whether or not the given graph is a tree.

1.

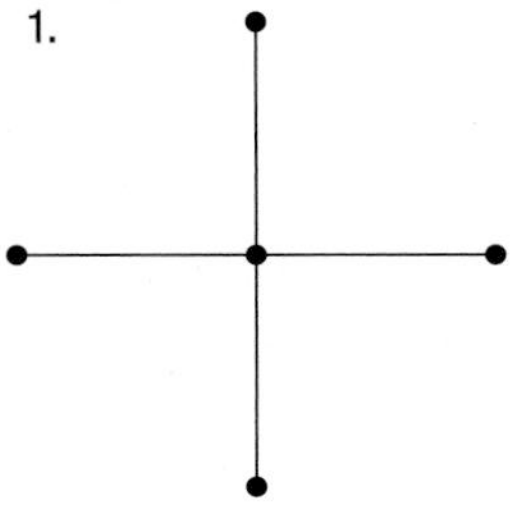

2.

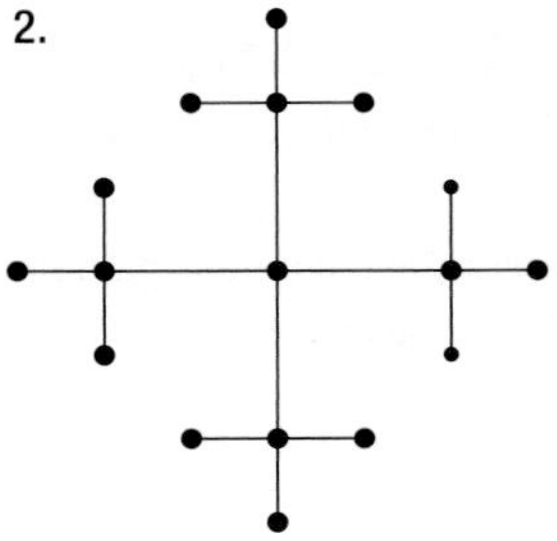

3.

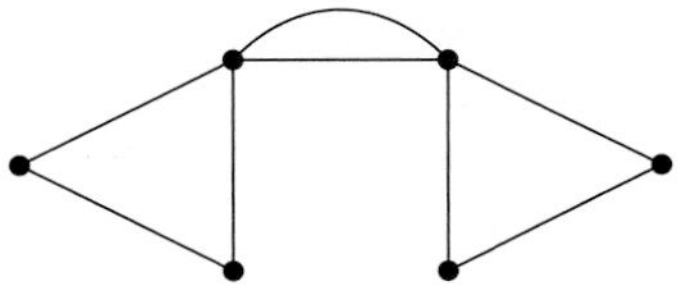

4.

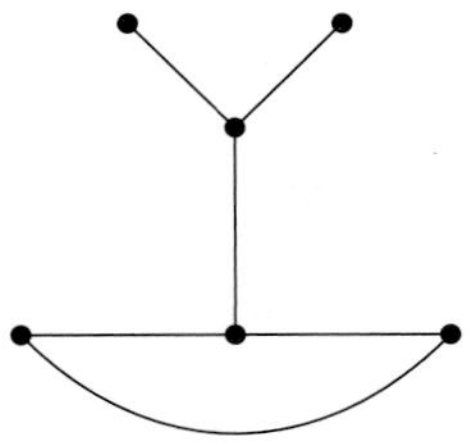

In problems 5–10, specify the edges needed to determine a spanning tree in the given graph. (Answers may vary.)

5.

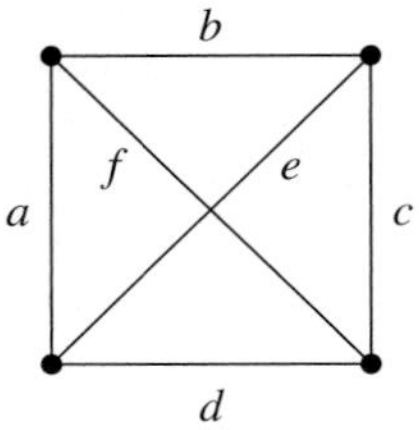

6.

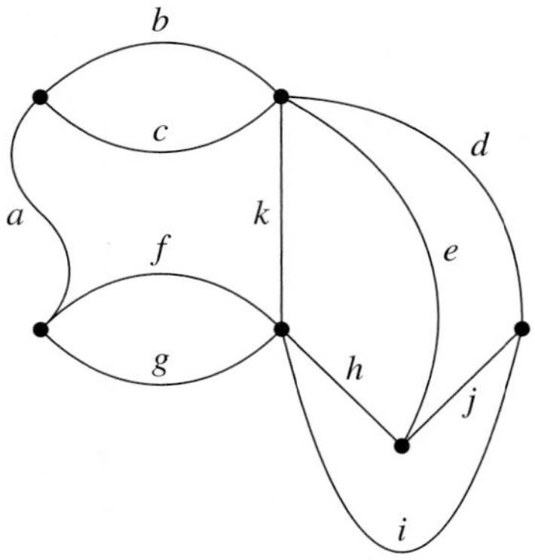

7.

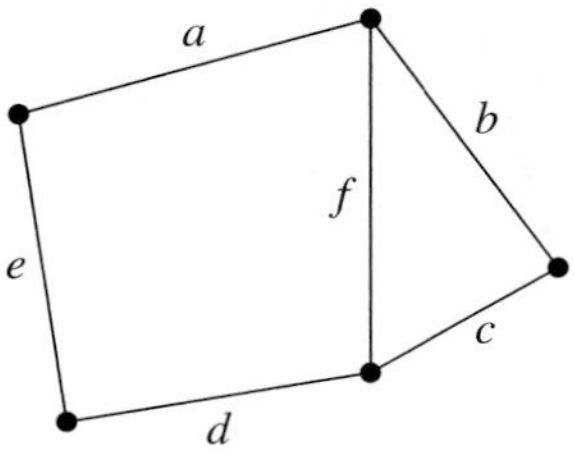

8.

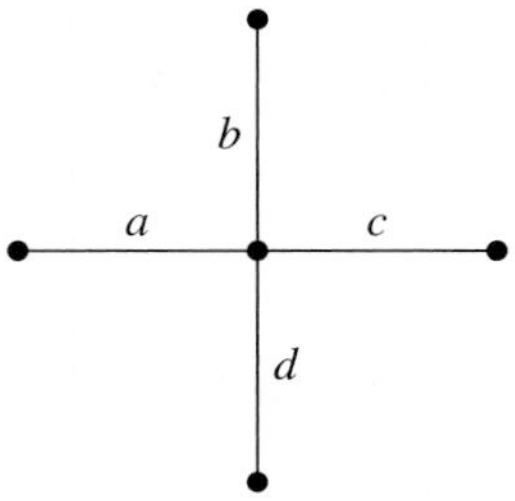

9.

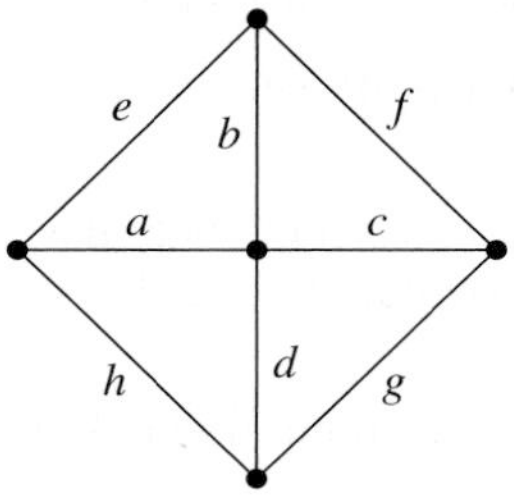

10.

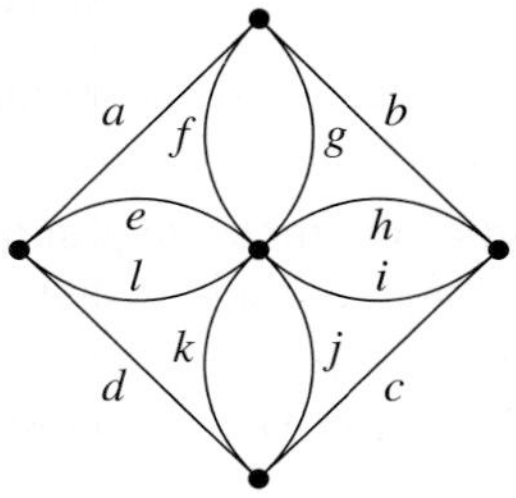

B Labeled Graphs and Spanning Trees

In problems 11–16, use Kruskal's algorithm to find a minimal spanning tree, and then find its weight.

11.

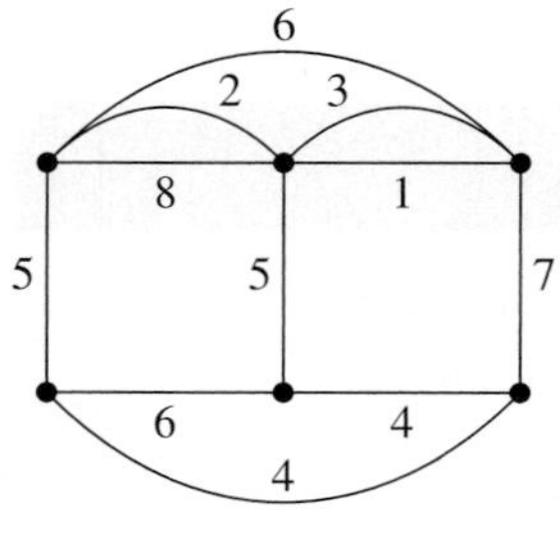

12.

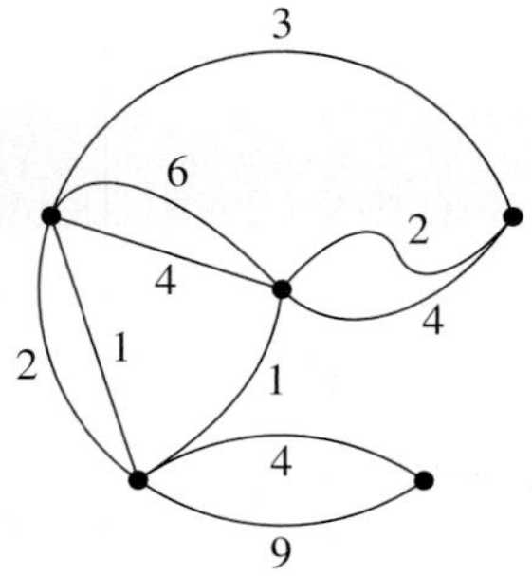

13.

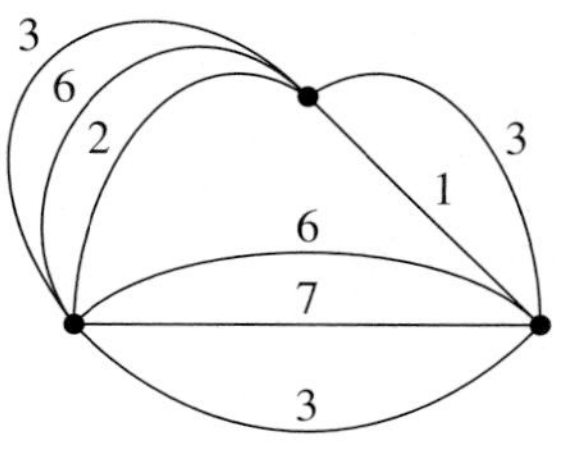

14.

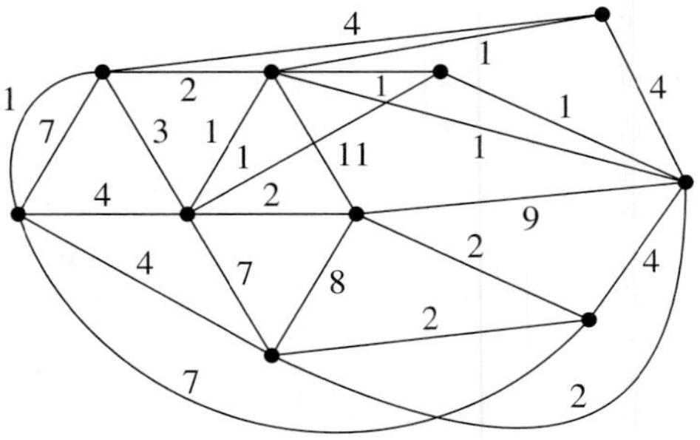

15.

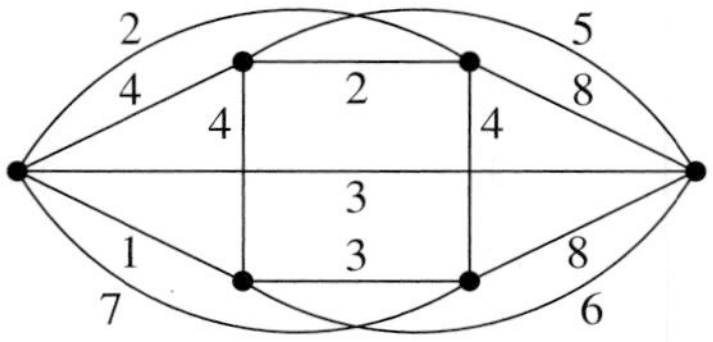

16.

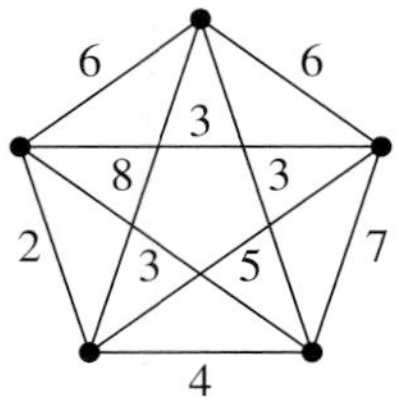

In problems 17–18, use Kruskal's algorithm to find a minimal spanning tree representing the most economical way to link the towns shown as vertices. The cost (in millions) of linking two towns is indicated by the number on the corresponding edge.

17.

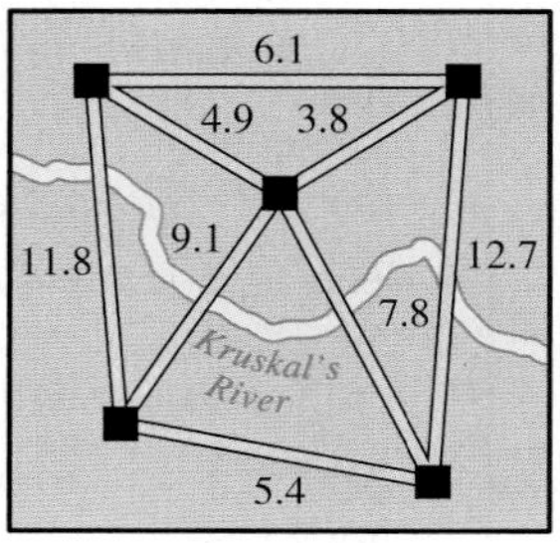

18.

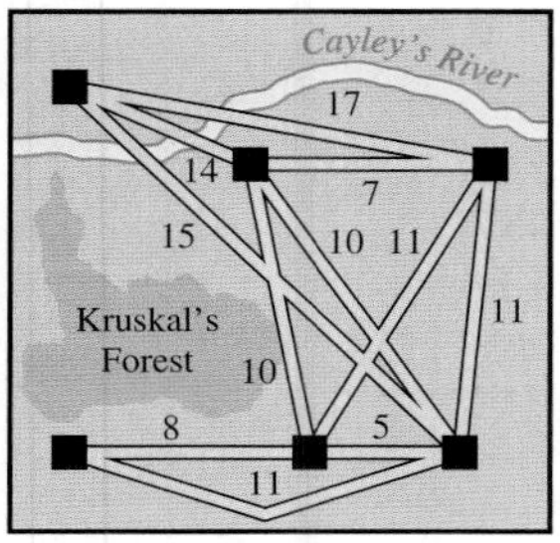

In problems 19–20, use the procedure of Example 5 to design an irrigation system of minimal cost.

19.

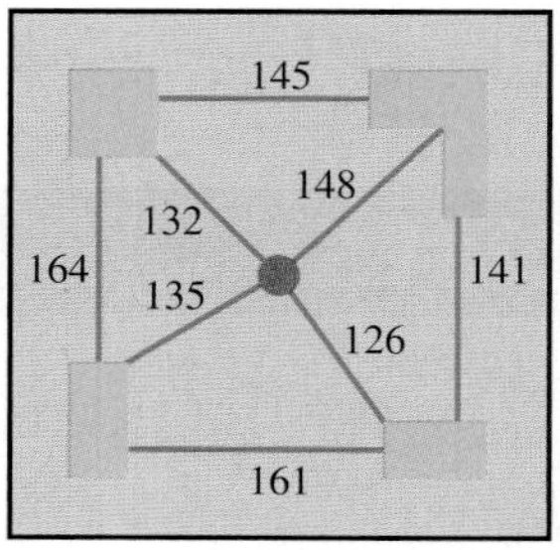

20.

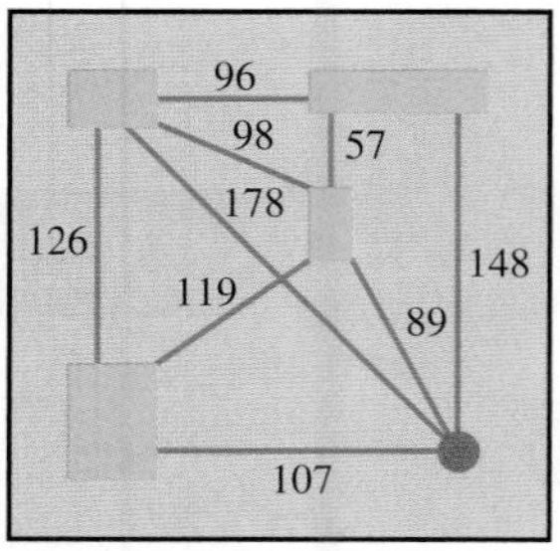

IN OTHER WORDS

21. In your own words, describe a spanning tree.
22. Describe Kruskal's algorithm in your own words.
23. Describe the unique path property in your own words.
24. Describe in your own words the difference between a tree and a forest.

USING YOUR KNOWLEDGE

25. Amazon Telephone & Telegraph Company (AT&T) is beginning a project to bring telephone service to a remote area of the Amazon. The cost of laying line between towns is listed below (in millions), and the company wants to find the cheapest way to lay telephone line so that all the cities are connected. (The line must be run along the existing roads because of the huge cost and danger in running the line through the jungle.) *Would either Euler or Hamilton circuits or paths help the company find the cheapest way to do this? Why or why not?*

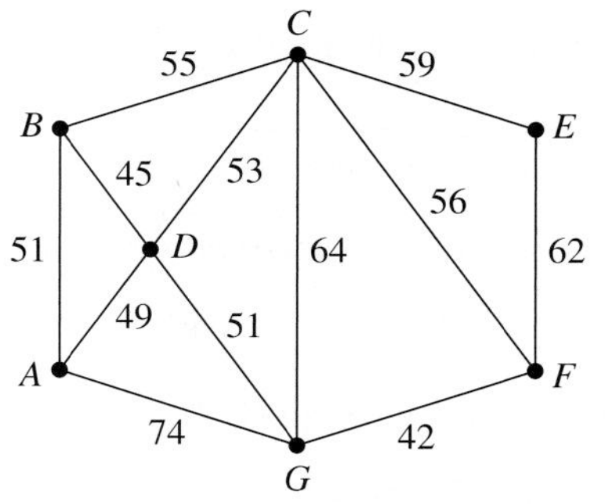

Source: Courtesy of Professor Larry Bowen, University of Alabama.

WEB IT EXERCISES

Recently, Center for Research and Parallel Computation (CRPC) researcher Bob Bixby (Rice University) and colleagues David Applegate (AT&T Bell Labs), Vasek Chvatal (Rutgers University), and William Cook (Bellcore) using a network of a SPARC 2, DEC Station 5000, SGI workstation, and others (a total of 50 workstations) determined an optimal route for a traveling salesman going through 3038 cities, a dramatic step beyond the old record of 2392 cities set by M. Padberg and G. Rinaldi. Trace the origins of the traveling salesman problem starting with the work of Hamilton and continuing on into the present day. (Hint: Find some information at www.tsp.gatech.edu/history/index.html.)

CHAPTER 15 Summary

SECTION	ITEM	MEANING
15.1A	Graph	A collection of points, called *vertices,* and arcs or line segments, called *edges,* which join pairs of vertices
15.1	Vertex	A vertex may be an endpoint of any number of edges, or it may stand alone in a graph.
15.1	Degree of a vertex	The *number* of edges, which have the vertex as a common endpoint
15.1	Subgraph	A graph that consists of some of the vertices and edges of another graph
15.1	Path	A sequence of edges that can be traced along without lifting the pencil
15.1	Circuit based at A	A path that begins and ends at the vertex A
15.1	Connected graph	A graph for which any two vertices can be joined by a path
15.1	Complete graph	A graph in which every pair of vertices is joined by exactly *one* edge
15.1	K_n	A complete graph with n vertices
15.2A	Euler path	A path that uses *every* edge of a graph *once and only once*
15.2	Euler circuit	An Euler path that begins and ends at the *same* vertex
15.2	Traversable graph	A graph that has an Euler path (or circuit)
15.2B	Bridge	An edge in a graph that, when removed, creates a *disconnected* graph
15.2	Untraveled subgraph	The edges that have not been used when building an Euler circuit

continued

CHAPTER 15 Summary – *continued*

SECTION	ITEM	MEANING
15.2A	Fleury's algorithm	An algorithm used to find Euler circuits
15.3A	Hamilton path	A path that meets each *vertex once and only once*
15.3	Hamilton circuit	A path that meets every vertex *once* and then returns to the starting point
15.3B	Weighted graph	A graph for which each edge has a number called a *weight* associated to it
15.3C	Nearest-neighbor method	An algorithm used to find an approximate solution to a traveling salesman problem
15.4A	Tree	A *connected* graph in which there are no simple circuits
15.4	Forest	A graph that has *no* circuits but is *not* necessarily *connected*
15.4	Unique path property	For any two vertices in a tree, there is *exactly* one simple path joining them.
15.4	Spanning tree	A subgraph that is a tree and contains every vertex of the original graph
15.4	Existence of spanning trees	Every connected graph has at least one spanning tree.
15.4B	Minimal spanning tree	A spanning tree with the *least* weight
15.4	Kruskal's algorithm	An algorithm used to find a minimal spanning tree

CHAPTER 15 Practice Test

For problems 1 and 2, find the degree of each of the vertices in the graph.

1.

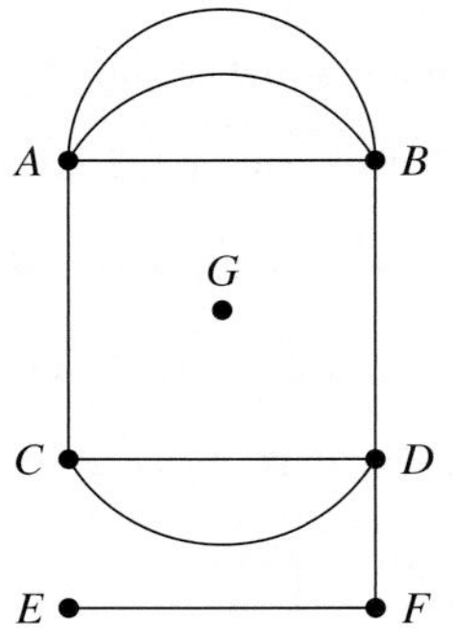

2.

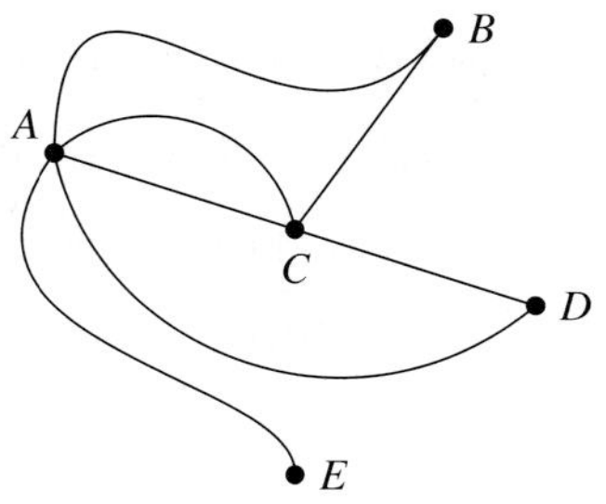

CHAPTER 15 Practice Test – *continued*

Use the following graph for problems 3–6:

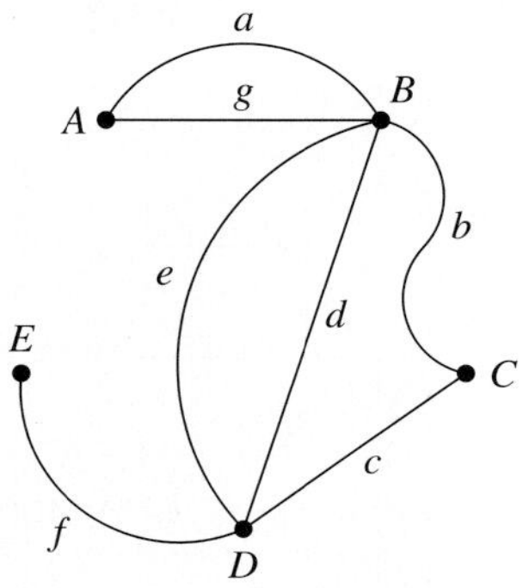

3. Does the sequence of edges $[a, b, c, d]$ represent a path, a circuit, or neither?

4. Does the sequence of edges $[g, a, e, d]$ represent a path, a circuit, or neither?

5. Does the sequence of edges $[b, c, f]$ represent a path, a circuit, or neither?

6. Does the sequence of edges $[g, d, b, c, f]$ represent a path, a circuit, or neither?

In problems 7–10, determine whether the graph has an Euler path, an Euler circuit, or neither. If the graph has an Euler path, which vertices must form its beginning and ending points? If the graph has an Euler circuit, use Fleury's algorithm to find one.

7.

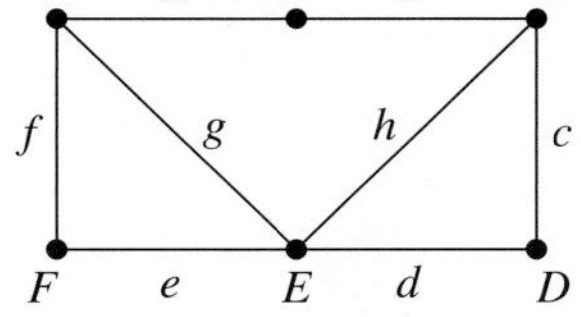

8.

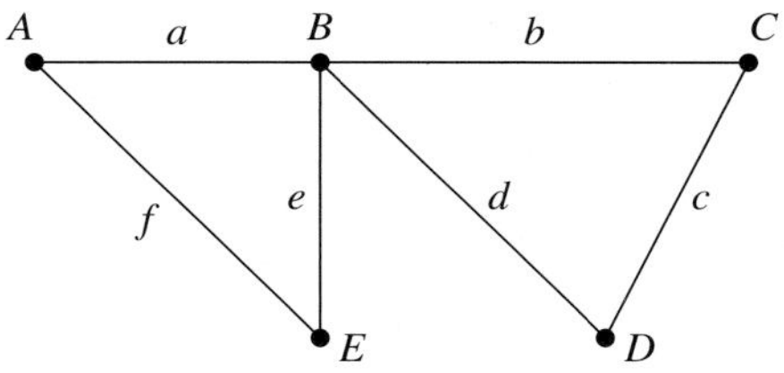

9.

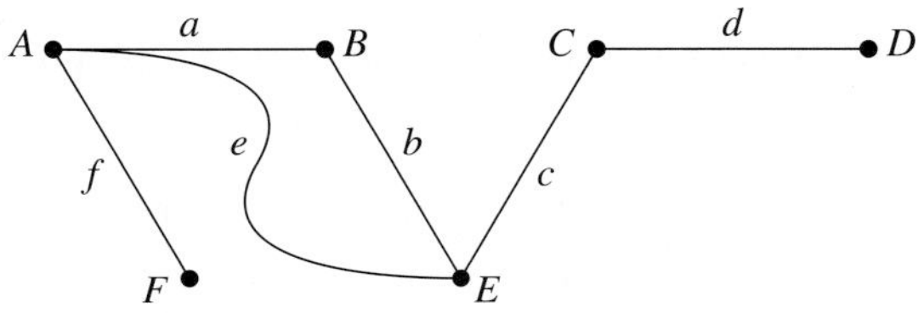

10.

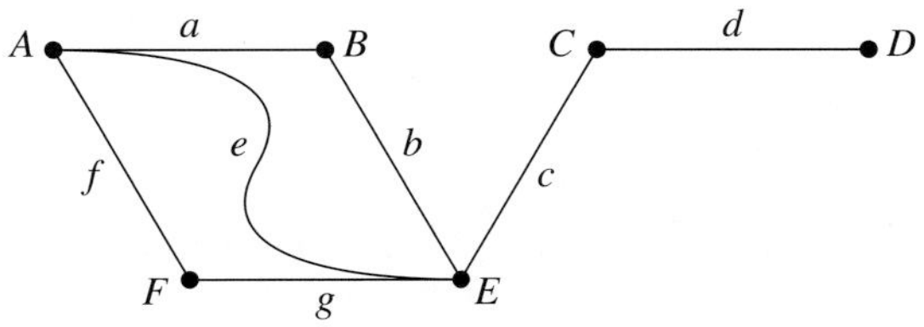

continued

CHAPTER 15 Practice Test – *continued*

11. A Tampa mail carrier's territory is shown in the following map. Is it possible for the mail carrier to walk along each street shown once and only once?

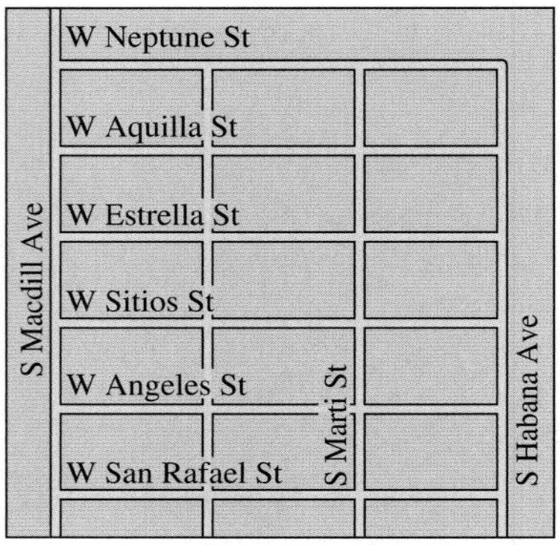

12. A Sacramento County employee must inspect the roads indicated on the map below. His job is to report any major potholes in the roads. Is it possible for the employee to drive along each of the roads once and only once?

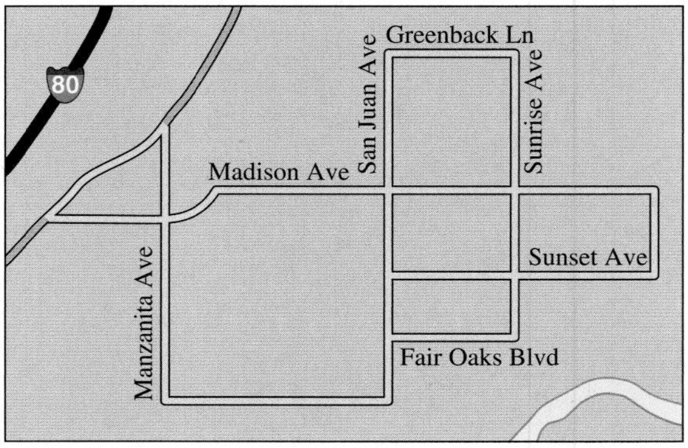

In problems 13 *and* 14, *determine which edges are bridges.*

13.

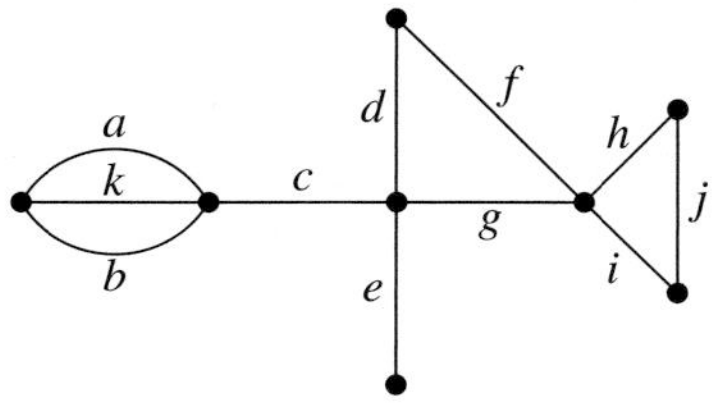

14.

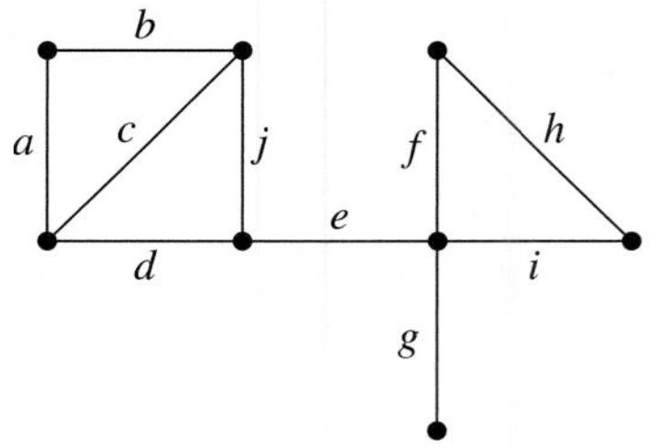

In problems 15 *and* 16, *use the nearest-neighbor method to find a nearly minimal Hamilton circuit based at the vertex A. Calculate the length of the path you find.*

15.

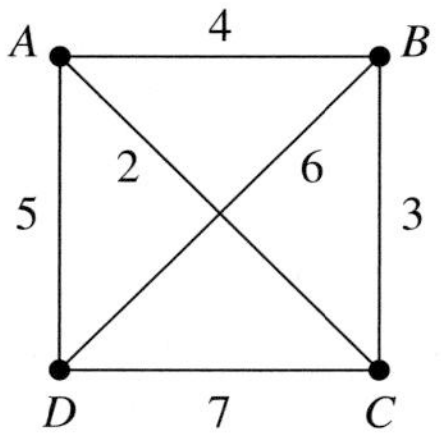

16.

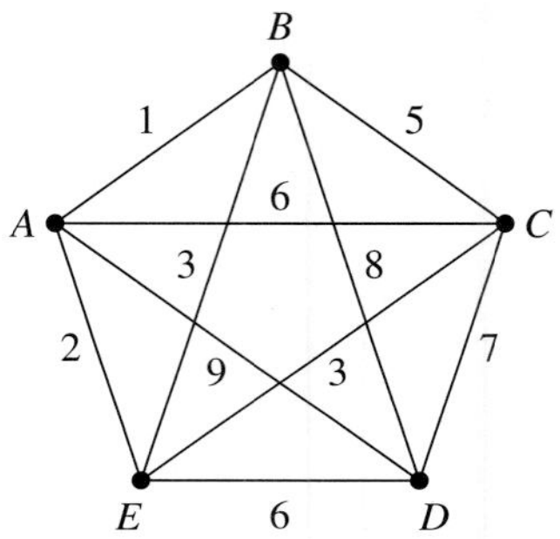

CHAPTER 15 Practice Test – *continued*

17. A pilot wants to visit the four state capitals indicated on the following map. The distance between each of the cities is included on the map. Using the nearest-neighbor method, find the nearly minimal route for the pilot if he begins his journey in Sacramento.

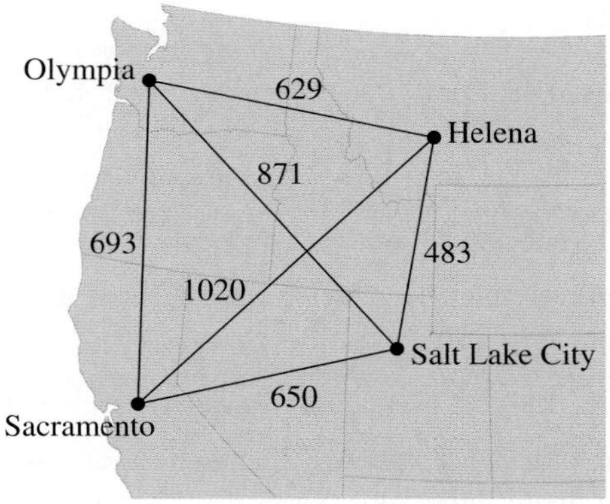

18. The Mexican government would like to build a new highway system so that each of the cities indicated on the following map may be reached via the highway. The cost (in millions of U.S. dollars) is given on the map. Find the highway system that costs the least to build.

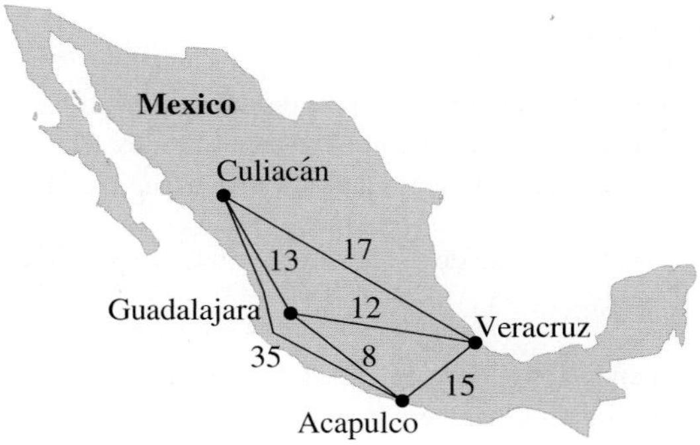

In problems 19 and 20, use Kruskal's algorithm to find a minimal spanning tree in the graph.

19.

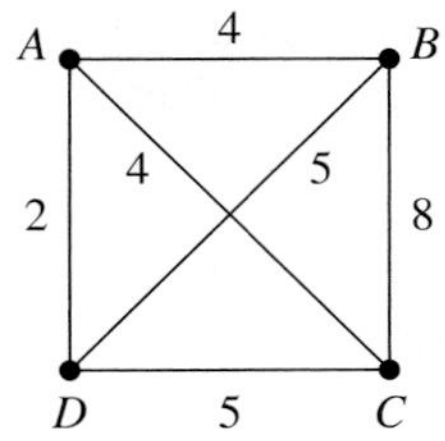

20.

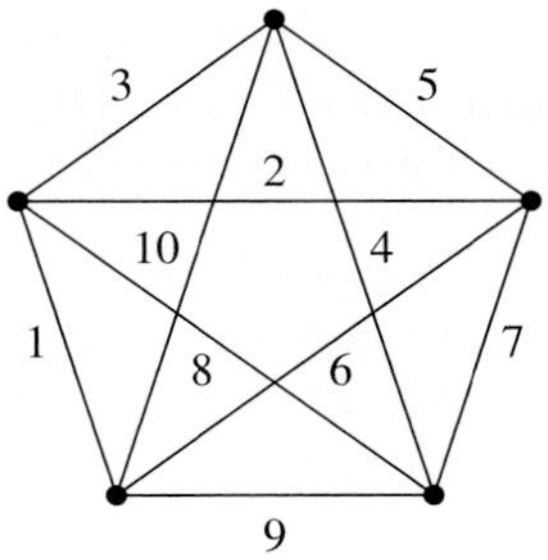

ANSWERS TO PRACTICE TEST

CHAPTER 15		What to Review *If You Missed It*		
QUESTION	**ANSWER**	**SECTION**	**EXAMPLE(S)**	**PAGE(S)**
1	The degrees of vertices *A, B, C, D, E, F,* and *G* are 4, 4, 3, 4, 1, 2, and 0, respectively.	15.1	1	873
2	The degrees of vertices *A, B, C, D,* and *E* are 5, 2, 4, 2, and 1, respectively.	15.1	1	873
3	The sequence $[a, b, c, d]$ represents a path from *A* to *B*.	15.1	2	874
4	The sequence $[g, a, e, d]$ represents a circuit based at *B*.	15.1	2	874
5	The sequence $[b, c, f]$ represents a path from *B* to *E*.	15.1	2	874
6	The sequence $[g, d, b, c, f]$ does not represent a path (and so cannot represent a circuit either), since edges *b* and *d* do not share the endpoint *D*.	15.1	2	874
7	Since vertices *A* and *C* have odd degree, while all the rest have even degree, there is an Euler path in the graph beginning at *A* and ending at *C* (or vice versa).	15.2	3	879
8	Each vertex in the graph has even degree. According to the traversability rules, there is an Euler circuit based at any vertex. For example, the sequence $[a, b, c, d, e, f]$ represents an Euler circuit based at *A*.	15.2	3, 7	879, 882–883
9	*A, D, E,* and *F* have odd degree, therefore no Euler path or circuit exists.	15.2	3	879
10	Vertices *A* and *D* have odd degree, while all other vertices have even degree. This implies that there is an Euler path beginning at *A* and ending at *D* (or vice versa).	15.2	3	879
11	By representing the streets that the mail carrier must cover by edges and each intersection as a vertex, we see that there are more than two vertices with odd degree. Thus, it is impossible to find an Euler path or circuit; the mail carrier will have to retrace his steps at some point.	15.2	2, 3, 4	878, 879, 879–880
12	By representing each of the roads by an edge and each intersection as a vertex, we see that there are two vertices with odd degree. Thus, there is an Euler path in the graph; the pothole inspector will not have to retrace her steps.	15.2	2, 3, 4	878, 879, 879–880
13	Edges *c* and *e* are bridges.	15.2	5	880
14	Edges *e* and *g* are bridges.	15.2	5	880
15	By visiting the vertices in the order *A-C-B-D-A,* one obtains a Hamilton circuit of length $2 + 3 + 6 + 5 = 16$.	15.3	6	893–894
16	By visiting the vertices in the order *A-B-E-C-D-A,* one obtains a Hamilton circuit of length $1 + 3 + 3 + 7 + 9 = 23$.	15.3	6	893–894

ANSWERS TO PRACTICE TEST — *continued*

CHAPTER 15		What to Review *If You Missed It*		
QUESTION	**ANSWER**	**SECTION**	**EXAMPLE(S)**	**PAGE(S)**
17	Applying the nearest-neighbor method, the pilot travels from Sacramento to Salt Lake City, then to Helena, next to Olympia, and then returns to Sacramento. Total mileage: 650 + 483 + 629 + 693 = 2455	**15.3**	**7**	**894–895**
18	Applying Kruskal's algorithm, the spanning tree will be composed of each of the three highways, extending from Guadalajara. Total cost: 8 + 12 + 13 = $33 million	**15.4**	**4, 5**	**901–903**
19	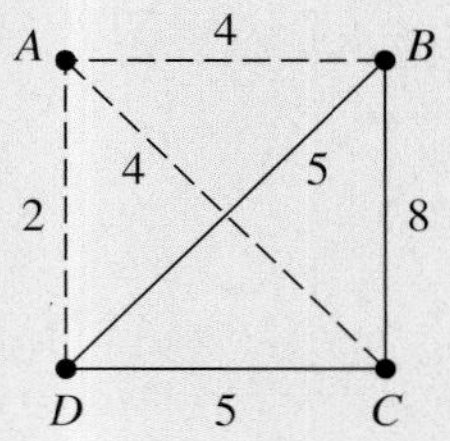	**15.4**	**4**	**901**
20	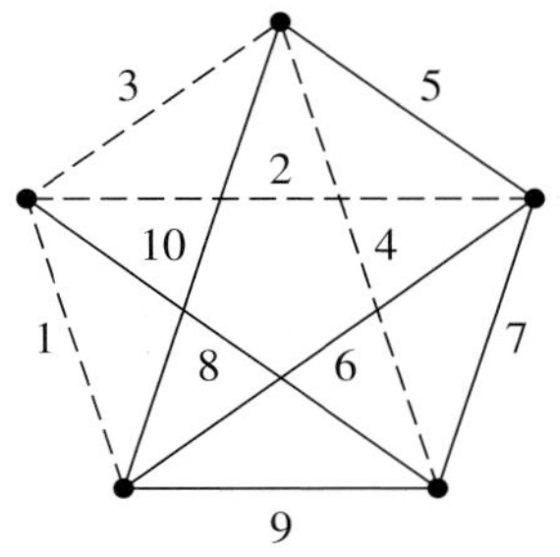	**15.4**	**4**	**901**

Answers to All Numbered Exercises

CHAPTER 1

Exercises 1.1

1. Step 1. Understand the problem.
   Step 2. Devise a plan.
   Step 3. Carry out the plan.
   Step 4. Look back.
2. 1. **R**ead the problem.
   2. **S**elect the unknown.
   3. **T**hink of a plan.
   4. **U**se the techniques you are studying to carry out the plan.
   5. **V**erify your answer.
3. What does the problem ask for? What is the unknown?
4. Sprint (you get 300 messages for $5.00)
5. AT&T
6. AT&T ($15.00)
7. Sprint; $10.00
8. AT&T ($15.00)
9. Either
10. The cost for males or females is $20.00 per month.
11. Add n to the nth term. The next three terms are 11, 16, and 22.
12. 26, 37, 50 (Add the next odd number.)
13. The odd-numbered terms are 1s. The even-numbered terms start with 5 and add 5 for each additional such term. The next three terms are 1, 20, and 1.
14. 3^{16}, 3^{32}, 3^{64} Double the exponent.
15. Going clockwise, move the shaded region one place, then two places, then three places, and so on.

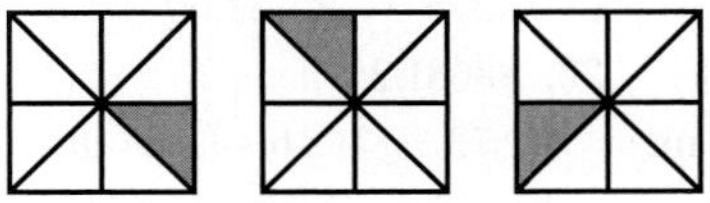

16. Going clockwise, move the shaded region 2, 3, and 3 places, then repeat. (Answers will vary.)

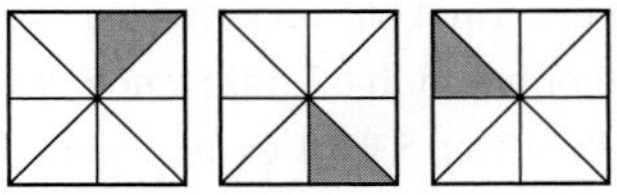

17. Each term is half the preceding term. The next three terms are $\frac{1}{16}$, $\frac{1}{32}$, and $\frac{1}{64}$.
18. $\frac{1}{5}, \frac{1}{8}, \frac{1}{3}$ Decrease the denominator of the odd terms by 2; decrease the denominator of the even terms by 2.
19. The odd-numbered terms are 1, 2, 3, 4, 5, 6, ... The even-numbered terms are 5, 6, 7, 8, 9, ... The next three terms are 7, 4, and 8.
20. 13, 18, 17 Add 3 to the odd terms, 4 to the even terms.
21. a.

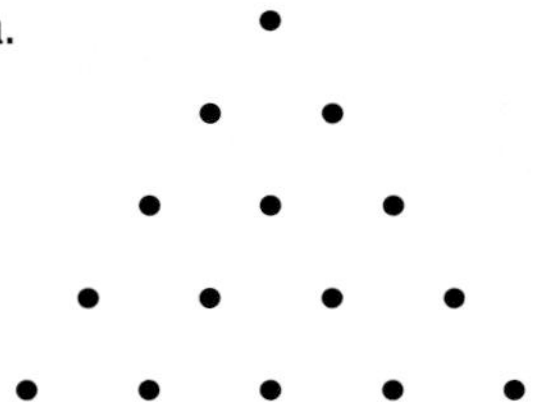

15

b. At each step add one row, one dot longer, at the bottom. The next three triangular numbers are 15, 21, and 28.
c. The tenth triangular number is 55.

22. a. 2, 3, 4, 5, 6, 7, 8, 9, 10
b. 4, 9, 16, 25, 36, 49, 64, 81, 100
c. 100
d. $15^2 = 225$

23. a. 36
b. $1 + 2 + 3 + 4 + 5 + 6 + 7 + 8 = \boxed{36}$
c. 78
d. $1 + 2 + 3 + \cdots + 12 = \boxed{78}$
e. $1 + 2 + 3 + \cdots + (n - 1) + n = \dfrac{n(n + 1)}{2}$
f. $50 \cdot 101 = 5050$

24. a.

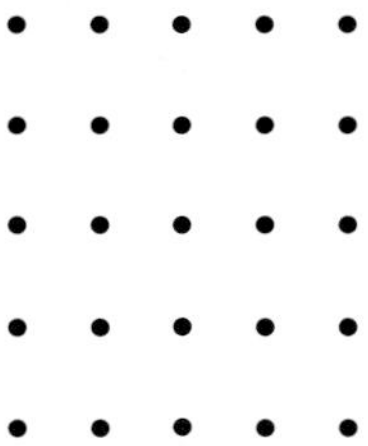

25

b. The nth square number is n^2; 25, 36, 49
c. $12^2 = 144$

25. a.

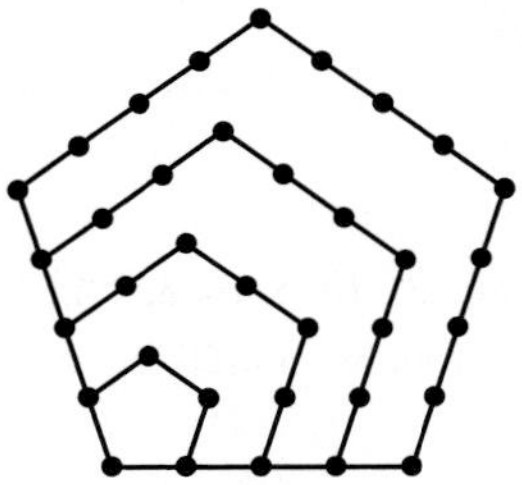

35

b. At each step, increase the length of the bottom and the left lower side of the pentagon by 1 unit. The number of dots on each side is increased by 1 unit.
c. The sixth pentagonal number is 51.

26. a. For 6; $5 + 4 + 3 + 2 + 1 = 15$
b. For 9; $8 + 7 + 6 + 5 + 4 + 3 + 2 + 1 = 36$

27. The number of diagonals is three less than the number of sides of the polygon. Thus, seven diagonals can be drawn from one vertex of a decagon.

28. a.

5	10	20	100
12	17	27	107
36	51	81	321
30	45	75	315
10	15	25	105
5	10	20	100

The final result and the original number are the same.

b. n
$n + 7$
$3n + 21$
$3n + 15$
$n + 5$
n

29. a.

5	10	20	100
12	17	27	107
36	51	81	321
30	45	75	315
10	15	25	105
5	5	5	5

The final result is always 5.

b. n
$n + 7$
$3n + 21$
$3n + 15$
$n + 5$
5

30. a.

5	10	20	100
10	15	25	105
40	60	100	420
20	30	50	210
10	20	40	200

The final result is twice the original number.

b. n
$n + 5$
$4n + 20$
$2n + 10$
$2n$
The final result is twice the original number.

31. a.

5	10	20	100
10	15	25	105
40	60	100	420
20	30	50	210
10	10	10	10

The final result is always 10.

b. n
$n + 5$
$4n + 20$
$2n + 10$
10

32. a. 22, 11, 34, 17, 52, 26, 13, 40, 20, 10, 5, 16, 8, 4, 2, 1
b. 15, 46, 23, 70, 35, 106, 53, 160, 80, 40, 20, 10, 5, 16, 8, 4, 2, 1
c. 4, 2, 1 **d.** No

33. a. 4
b. *Hint:* Try the numbers from 0 to 10 to see what happens.

34. a.
$$1 + 3 + 5 + 7 + 9 = 5^2$$
$$1 + 3 + 5 + 7 + 9 + 11 = 6^2$$
$$1 + 3 + 5 + 7 + 9 + 11 + 13 = 7^2$$
b. 10^2

35. a.
$$(1 + 2 + 3 + 4)^2 = 1^3 + 2^3 + 3^3 + 4^3$$
$$(1 + 2 + 3 + 4 + 5)^2 = 1^3 + 2^3 + 3^3 + 4^3 + 5^3$$
$$(1 + 2 + 3 + 4 + 5 + 6)^2 = 1^3 + 2^3 + 3^3 + 4^3 + 5^3 + 6^3$$
b. The square of the sum of the first n counting numbers equals the sum of the cubes of these numbers.

36. a. $3^4 + 4^4 + 5^4 + 6^4 = 7^4$ **b.** No

37. The number of units of length of the pendulum is the square of the number of seconds in the time of the swing.

38. a. 14, 17, 20 **b.** 32

39. a. 12, 15, 18 **b.** $9\frac{2}{3}$ in.

40. a. \$382, \$467, \$552, \$637 **b.** \$85 increase each period
c. Probably not. (Answers will vary.)

42. Answers will vary. **44.** Deductive **45.** Deductive

46. Inductive **47.** Deductive

Collaborative Learning

1. Many topics (including bees) about the Fibonacci sequence can be found at: http://www.maths.surrey.ac.uk/hosted-sites/R.Knott/Fibonacci/fibnat.html

2. Answers will vary.

3. The results correspond to the terms in the Fibonacci sequence.

4. a. Yes. Every fourth Fibonacci number (3, 21, 144) is a multiple of 3.
b. Every fifth Fibonacci number (5, 55, 610) is a multiple of 5.
c. Every sixth Fibonacci number (8, 144) is a multiple of 8.
d. Every k^{th} Fibonacci number is a multiple of $F(k)$, where $F(k)$ denotes the kth Fibonacci number. *Note*: $F(1) = 1$, $F(2) = 1$, $F(3) = 2$, $F(4) = 3$, and so on.

Exercises 1.2

1. \$12,000 **2.** \$100

3. \$8 + \$2 + \$4 + \$2 + \$3 = \$19 **4.** \$36

5. 900 gal **6.** 300 acres

7. a. $\frac{4256}{14,053} \approx 0.303$ **b.** $\frac{4300}{14,100} \approx 0.305$

8. a. $\frac{236}{539} \approx 0.438$ **b.** $\frac{240}{540} \approx 0.444$

9. ERA $= \frac{9 \times 14}{140} = 0.900$ **10.** $\frac{9 \cdot 25}{222\frac{2}{3}} \approx 1.010$

11. 400 to 800 **12.** 100 cups; 7 gal of soup **13.** 33 lb

14. 33 lb **15.** 25 lb **16.** 25 cups; 2 gal of gravy

17. a. 5182 **b.** 80 kWh **c.** \$6.40 **d.** \$192

18. a. 5540 **b.** 39 kwh **c.** \$3.12 **d.** \$93.60

19. a. 7001 **b.** 50 kWh **c.** \$4 **d.** \$120

20. a. 6145 **b.** 45 kwh **c.** \$3.60 **d.** \$108

21. 11,181.25 **22.** \$8681.25

23. a. 71.16 in. **b.** 73 − 71.16 = 1.84 in.

24. a. 69.39 in **b.** (73 − 69.39) in. ≈ 3.61 in.

25. About 22.87. The person's BMI is normal.

26. 24.46. To be overweight, the BMI has to be 25–29, so technically, 24.46 is normal but very close to overweight!

27. 980 lb, 10 lb of hay, 5 lb of grain, and 6 gal of water

28. 1039 lb; 10 lb of hay, 5 lb of grain, 6 gallons of water

29. \$1655 **30.** \$1763

31. a. 24 + 12 = 36 years old **b.** 24 + 32 = 56 years old

32. a. 37 years old **b.** 57 years old

33. 15 mi **34.** 22.5 mi **35.** 15 mi **36.** 18.75 mi

37. $22\frac{1}{2}$ mi **38.** \$3 **39.** \$4.50 **40.** \$3 **41.** \$3.75

42. \$4.50 **43.** 8933.33 lb **44.** About 35,733,333

45. 466.67 lb **46.** About 2333 **47.** 1800 **48.** 1320

50. Answers will vary. **51.** 1,335,840 ft^2 **52.** 667,920

Exercises 1.3

1. a. Paper; 41% **b.** Plastic; 7%
c. 410 and 70, respectively

2. a. 8% **b.** 80 tons **c.** 330 tons

3. a. Cheddar **b.** Swiss **c.** Mozzarella

4. **a.** Fish **b.** 7 lb **c.** 14 lb **d.** 30 lb
e. 31.5 lb **f.** 1.05 lb **g.** 1.5 lb
5. **a.** Bathing **b.** 150 gal **c.** Toilet leak **d.** 20 gal
6. **a.** $\frac{1}{2}$ **b.** $\frac{1}{4}$ **c.** Mushrooms
d. 2 lb crust; 1 lb cheese **e.** 100 lb
7. **a.** Paper **b.** Yard trimmings **c.** 20 lb; 9 lb
8. **a.** 0.7 hr **b.** 1.1 hr **c.** Same
9. **a.** Oil **b.** Nuclear **c.** Natural gas
10. **a.** Military and defense, 30% **b.** 20.3% **c.** \$2030
d. Job training, 0.4% **e.** \$370 **f.** \$2630
11. **a.** 114.4 **b.** 114 **c.** 111.2
d. 2–<3/day; 110 **e.** >3/day; almost 120
12. **a.** 1.0 **b.** 2.7 **c.** 2.7 **d.** 1.0 **e.** 3.1
f. 3.1 **g.** Abstaining women
13. **a.** 39 **b.** 29 **c.** 0.20–0.29; 14
14. **a.** 23 **b.** 8 **c.** 6:01 P.M.–9:00 P.M.
d. 3:01 A.M.–6:00 A.M.
15. **a.** 20–29 **b.** 13–15; answers will vary
c. Less than 50 years old **d.** 90^+; answers vary.
16. **a.** Cell phone **b.** 47% **c.** 7%
17. **a.** 2250 **b.** 1770 **c.** 1560 **d.** 210
18. **a.** 240 **b.** 200 **c.** 260 **d.** 180
e. Chocolate fudge yogurt **f.** Chocolate fudge ice cream
19. **a.** $520 - 360 = 160$ cal **b.** $1040 - 720 = 320$ cal
20. **a.** Marathon; HS baseball, Ekiden about 30%
b. Martial arts; about 10%
c. Marathon, HS baseball, Ekiden
d. About 35% of 3000 or 1050
21. **a.** Cuban toast **b.** Cheese toast
c. 105; about 27 (rounded from $26\frac{1}{4}$)
22. **a.** Cuban **b.** Cuban Special
c. 150 sandwiches; 37.5 or 38 loaves
23. **a.** 3100 **b.** 250 **c.** 700
24. **a.** 0.2% **b.** About 377 **c.** 0.10% **d.** About 188
25. **a.** About 175,000,000 **b.** About 200,000,000
c. About 250,000,000 **b.** About 300,000,000
e. About 325,000,000
26. **a.** About 12,500,000 **b.** About 25,000,000
c. About 50,000,000 **d.** About 75,000,000
e. About 80,000,000
27. **a.** 2040 **b.** 2100
28. **a.** $I = 0.025x$ **b.** $I = 0.025(40) = 1°C$
c. Yes, both are 1°C
29. **a.** 60 **b.** About 10 **c.** About 2
30. **a.** 40 **b.** 12 **c.** 2 **d.** A dog
31. **a.** 3 kg **b.** 8 kg **c.** 9 mo
32. About \$950 **33.** About \$570 **34.** \$800 **35.** \$300
36. 0 **38.** Answers will vary. **39.** Answers will vary.
40. **a.** 139 **b.** 99 **c.** 40
d. Less colorectal cancer and hip fractures when taking the medicine. Take the difference of incidences between colorectal cancer and hip fractures
e. Endometrial cancer and deaths
41. **a.** Years 1–7 **b.** Years 2–7
c. Years 1–7 **d.** Years 4–7
e. Year 7 of either the breast cancer group or the stroke group; about 0.005
f. Breast cancer; years 0–4

CHAPTER 2

Exercises 2.1

1. Not a set **2.** Not a set. **3.** A set **4.** A set.
5. A set **6.** A set. **7.** Not a set **8.** Not a set.
9. **a.** Incorrect **b.** Correct **c.** Incorrect
d. Correct **e.** Incorrect
10. $a \in X$ **11.** $\in$ **12.** $X \notin X$ **13.** $\notin$
14. $\{bay\} \notin X$ **15.** T **16.** F **17.** F
18. T **19.** T **20.** F
21. The set consisting of the first and the last letters of the English alphabet
22. The set of letters in the word "man."
23. The set consisting of the names of the first biblical man and woman
24. The set consisting of the name of the man usually assumed to be the discoverer of America.
25. The set of counting numbers from 1 to 7
26. The set of products of the pairs of consecutive counting numbers from $1 \cdot 2$ to $5 \cdot 6$.
27. The set of odd counting numbers from 1 to 51
28. The set of hours slept per day by 15–19-year-old men
29. The set of hours slept per day by 15–19-year-old women
30. The set of hours slept per day by 20–24-year-old men and women
31. {Dioxin, Xylene} **32.** {Chloroform, Heptachlor}
33. $\{1, 2, 3, 4, 5, 6, 7\}$ **34.** $\{1\}$
35. $\{0, 1, 2, 3, 4, 5, 6, 7\}$ **36.** $\{0, 1, 2, 3, 4, 5, 6, 7\}$
37. $\{4, 5, 6, 7\}$ **38.** $\{3, 4, 5, 6\}$ **39.** $\{M, Y, X\}$
40. $\{O, S, G.I.\}$ **41.** $\{O, Y, X, M\}$ **42.** $\{S, G.I.\}$ **43.** $\{4, 6\}$
44. $(1, 2, 3, 5, 7, 8\}$ **45.** $\{4, 6, 9, 10\}$ **46.** $\{2\}$
47. $\{1\}$ **48.** $\{6, 7\}$ **49.** $\{1\}$
50. $A \neq B$. (The smallest number in A is 3 and in B is 1.)
51. Sets A and B are not equal.
52. $A = B$. (The repetitions in A do not affect the equality.)
53. Sets A and B are equal. They are both the empty set.
54. **a.** D **b.** C **c.** B or C
55. **a.** $=$ **b.** $\neq$ **c.** $\neq$
56. **a.** $=$ **b.** $\neq$ **c.** $\neq$
57. $\emptyset, \{a\}, \{b\}, \{a, b\}$. The first three are proper subsets.
58. $\emptyset, \{1\}, \{2\}, \{3\}, \{1, 2\}, \{1, 3\}, \{2, 3\}, \{1, 2, 3\}$. All but the last one are proper subsets.
59. $\emptyset, \{1\}, \{2\}, \{3\}, \{4\}, \{1, 2\}, \{1, 3\}, \{1, 4\}, \{2, 3\}, \{2, 4\}, \{3, 4\}, \{1, 2, 3\}, \{1, 2, 4\}, \{1, 3, 4\}, \{2, 3, 4\}, \{1, 2, 3, 4\}$. All but the last of these are proper subsets.
60. $\emptyset, \{\emptyset\}$ Only $\emptyset$ is a proper subset.
61. $\emptyset, \{1\}, \{2\}, \{1, 2\}$. The first three are proper subsets.
62. $\emptyset, \{x\}, \{y\}, \{z\}, \{x, y\}, \{x, z\}, \{y, z\}, \{x, y, z\}$. The first seven are proper subsets.

63. 2^4, or 16 64. 15 65. 2^{10}, or 1024 66. 15

67. 5 68. 5 69. 6 70. 6

71. Yes. Every set is a subset of itself.

72. No. $\varnothing$ contains no elements that are not elements of $\varnothing$.

73. $B \subseteq A$

74. $P = \{a, b\}$, $Q = \{a, b, \{a, b\}\}$ Answers will vary.

75. a. 5 b. 10 c. 10

76. 31 77. 8 78. 9

80. The set of all good students is not well defined because not everyone agrees on the meaning of the word "good." (Answers to the second question vary.) One example is: the set of students who scored above 80 on the test.

82. a. Every set is a subset of itself.
b. No set is a proper subset of itself.
c. The empty set is a proper subset of every nonempty set.
d. The empty set is a subset of every set.
e. Every set is a subset of the corresponding universal set.

83. a. If $g \in S$, then Gepetto shaves himself; this contradicts the statement that Gepetto shaves all those men and only those men who do not shave themselves. Therefore, $g \notin S$.
b. If $g \in D$, then Gepetto does not shave himself, and so by the same statement he does shave himself. Thus, there is a contradiction and $g \notin D$.

84. a. No, if $N \in M$, then $N \in N$, which contradicts the definition of N.
b. No, if $N \in N$, it contradicts the definition of N.

85. The word *non-self-descriptive* cannot be classified either way without having a contradiction.

86. If Paradox.html has a link to itself, by definition it does not link to itself. But if it does not link to itself, then it has to have a link to itself. In either case, it is a paradox.

Collaborative Learning

1. $\varnothing, \{a\}, \{b\}, \{a, b\}$
2. two; $\varnothing \subseteq \{a\}$ The empty set is a subset of any of the other sets.
3. two; $\varnothing \subseteq \{a\}$ The empty set is a subset of any of the other sets.
4. two; $\varnothing \subseteq \{a\}$ The empty set is a subset of any of the other sets.
5.

Number of Elements in the Set	Number of Subsets	Number of Subsets Selected to Meet #2
1	2	2
2	4	2
3	8	2
4	16	2

Exercises 2.2

1. a. $\{1, 3, 4\}$ b. $\{1\}$ c. $\{1, 6\}$
2. a. $\{1, 2, 3, 4, 5, 6\}$ b. $\{1, 2, 3, 4, 5, 6, 7\}$
c. $\{1, 3, 4, 6, 7\}$
3. a. $\{1, 3, 4\}$ b. $\{1, 2, 3, 4, 5, 6\}$
4. a. $\{1, 3, 4, 6, 7\}$ b. $\{1, 3, 4\}$
5. $\{1, 2, 3, 4, 5, 6, 7\}$ 6. $\{1, 2, 3, 4, 5, 6\}$
7. $\{1\}$ 8. $\{1, 6\}$ 9. a. $\{c\}$ b. $\varnothing$
10. a. $\{\{a, b\}, a, b, c\}$ b. $\{\{a, b\}, a, b, c\}$
11. a. Correct b. Incorrect
12. (a) and (b) correct.
13. a. Correct b. Correct
14. (a) and (b) incorrect.
15. a. $\{b, d, f\}$ b. $\{a, c\}$
16. a. $\varnothing$ b. $\{a, b, c, d, f\}$
17. a. $\varnothing$ b. $\{a, b, c, d, f\}$
18. a. $\{c, e\}$ b. $\varnothing$
19. a. $\{c, e\}$ b. $\{a, b, c, d, f\}$
20. a. $\{b, d, e, f\}$ b. $\{a, c, e\}$
21. a. $\{b, d, f\}$ b. $\{a, c\}$
22. a. $\varnothing$ b. $\{a, c, e\}$
23. a. $\{a, b, c, d, e, f\}$ b. $\{c, e\}$
24. a. $\{c\}$ b. $\{b, d, f\}$
25. a. $\{b, d, f\}$ b. $\{a, c\}$
26. a. $\{a, c\}$ b. $\{b, d, f\}$
27. a. $\{2, 3\}$ b. $\{2, 3\}$
28. a. $\{2, 3\}$ b. $\{1, 5\}$
29. $\mathcal{U}$ 30. $\varnothing$ 31. $\varnothing$ 32. A 33. A
34. A 35. $\varnothing$ 36. U 37. A 38. A
39. $\{1, 2, 3, 4, 5\}$
40. {Beauty, Intelligence, Cheerfulness, Congeniality, Consideration, Friendliness, Helpfulness, Kindliness, Loyalty}
41. {Beauty, Consideration, Kindliness, Friendliness, Helpfulness, Loyalty}
42. {Intelligence, Cheerfulness}
43. {Intelligence, Cheerfulness, Congeniality}
44. {Intelligence, Cheerfulness, Congeniality}
45. {Intelligence, Cheerfulness}
46. {Encourages suggestions, Sets goals with me, Gets me to have high goals, Listens carefully, Is self-aware}
47. {Is aware of others, Follows up on action}
48. {Encourages suggestions, Sets goals with me, Gets me to have high goals, Listens carefully, Is self-aware, Is aware of others, Follows up on action}
49. {Follows up on action} 50. {Is aware of others}
51. $\{p, n, a, t, l\}$ 52. $\{n, t, l\}$ 53. $\{p, a\}$ 54. $\{p\}$
55. $\{p\}$ 56. $\{n, t\}$ 57. $\{n, a, t, l\}$ 58. $\{p, n, t, l\}$
59. $\{a\}$ 60. $\varnothing$ 61. $\{p, n, a, t, l\}$ 62. $\{p, n, a, t, l\}$
63. {Blogspot.com, Baidu.com, Qq.com, MSN.com, MySpace.com, Blogger.com}
64. {Wikipedia.org}
65. {Blogger.com, MSN.com, MySpace.com}
66. {Blogspot.com, Baidu.com, Qq.com} 67. {Toyota}
68. {Lincoln, Mercury, Ford} 69. {Toyota (Prius)}
70. {BMW} 71. {Toyota (Prius)} 72. {Lexus}
73. {Toyota (Prius)} 74. {Toyota (Prius)}
75. {BMW, Lexus} 76. {Ford, Lincoln, Mercury}
77. A and B have no elements in common.
78. All the elements of A are elements of B. A could be the set of all bloodhounds and B the set of all dogs. (Answers will vary.)
79. All the elements of A are elements of B, and all the elements of B are elements of A ($A = B$).

80. A and B have some elements in common. A could be the set of bulldogs and B the set of dogs who will bite people. (Answers will vary.)

81. a.–b. The set of characteristics that are in both columns of the table {long tongue, skin-covered horns, native to Africa}

c. The set of characteristics that appear in either column of the table

d. $G' =$ {short, short neck}

e. $O' =$ {tall, long neck}

82. 3,293,000 **83.** 685,000

84. 3,978,000 (3,293,000 + 685,000)

85. 12- to 17-year-old females; $F \cap A$

86. This is the Universal set of both males and females.

87. This set is empty. There are no persons who are both male and female.

88. \$94,206 **89.** \$60,293 **90.** \$54,830

91. \$39,935 **92.** F ∩ H

93. Males with a high school degree

94. Males or females

Collaborative Learning

Comets only: Made of frozen ice, gas, or dust; Halley is one; Have a long gas tail; Have a long dust tail; Have a long ion tail; Highly elliptical orbit; Surrounded by hydrogen cloud; Sungrazers are ones that crash into the Sun.

Asteroids only: Made of rock and/or metal; Ceres is the biggest; Have no tail; Most orbit between Jupiter and Mars; Also known as planetoids; Have no atmosphere.

Intergalactics: Orbit the Sun; Some come close to the Earth; Part of our solar system; Some have hit the Earth.

Exercises 2.3

1.

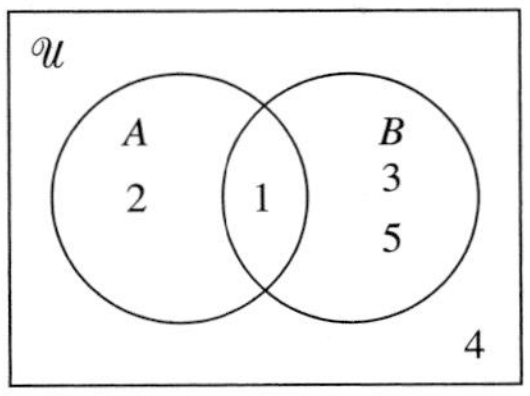

2.

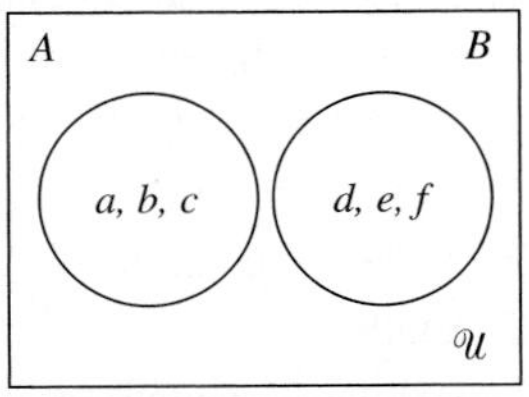

3.

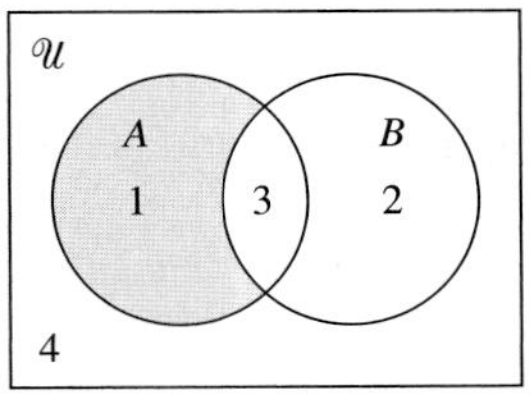

4.

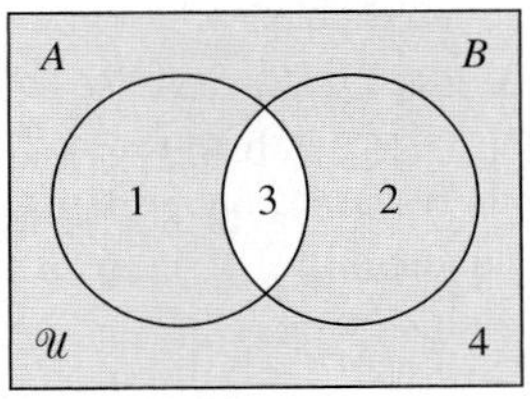

5.

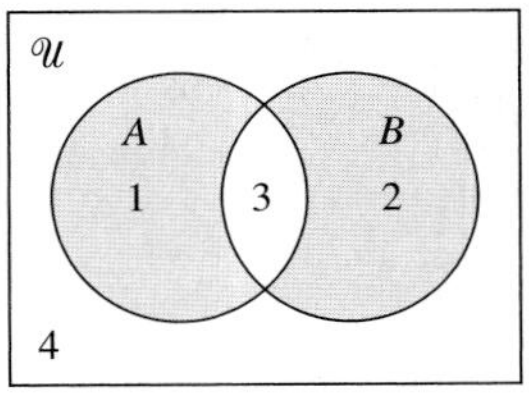

6.

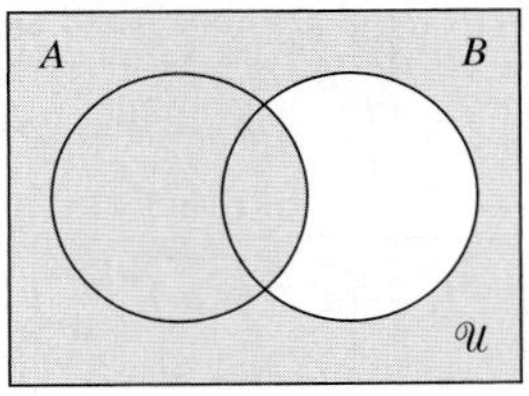

7.

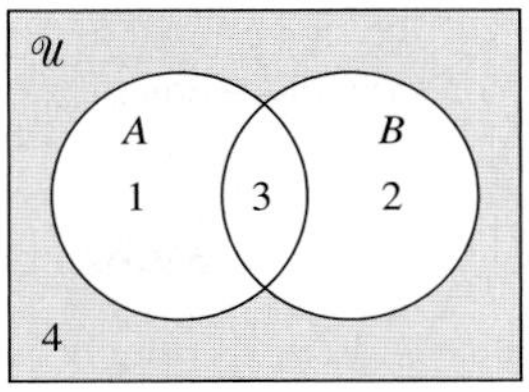

8.

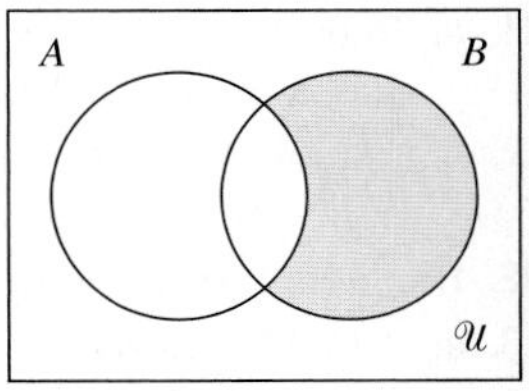

9. Region 1 **10.** Regions 5, 6, 7 **11.** ∅

12. Regions 1, 3, 5 **13.** Regions 4, 5, and 7

14. Regions 1, 2, 3 **15.** Regions 1, 4, 5, 6, and 7

16. Region 3 **17.** Region 8

18.

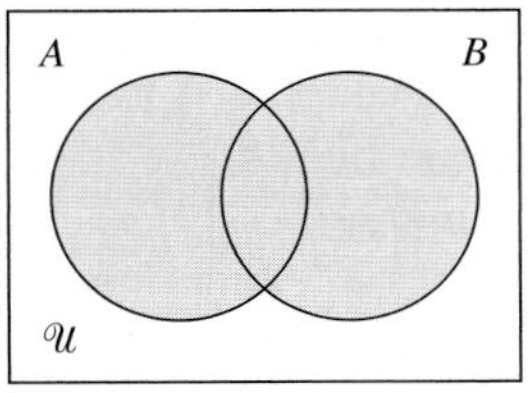

19.

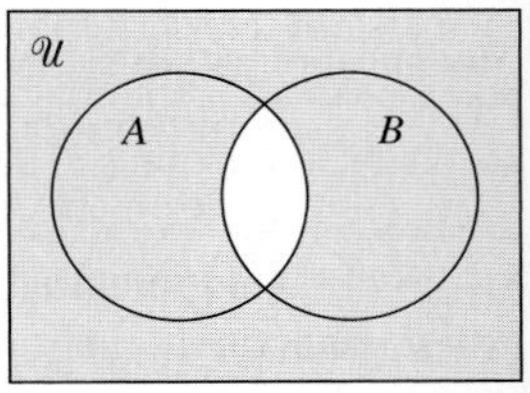

20.

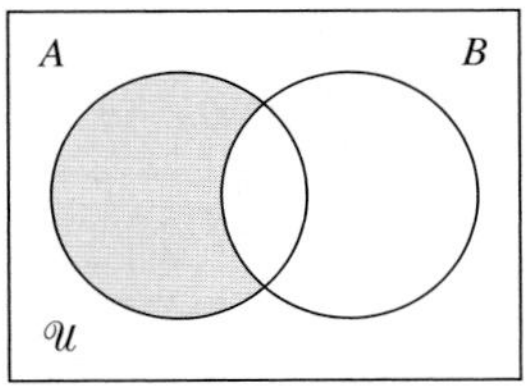

21.

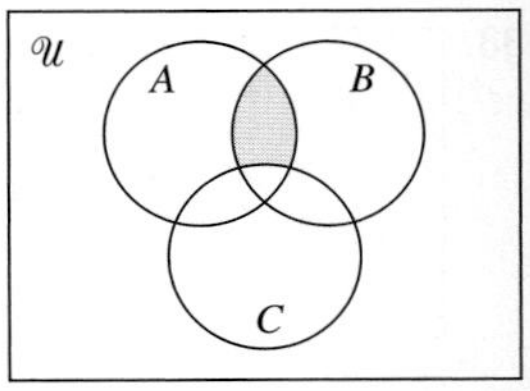

22.

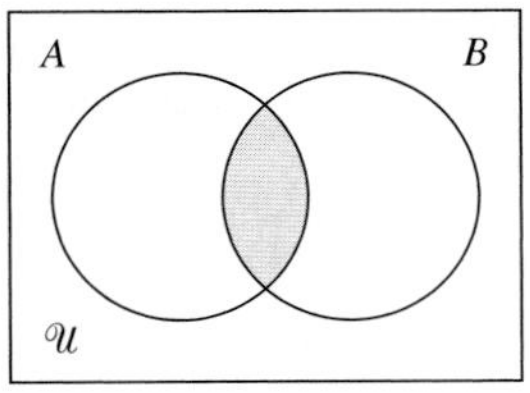

23.

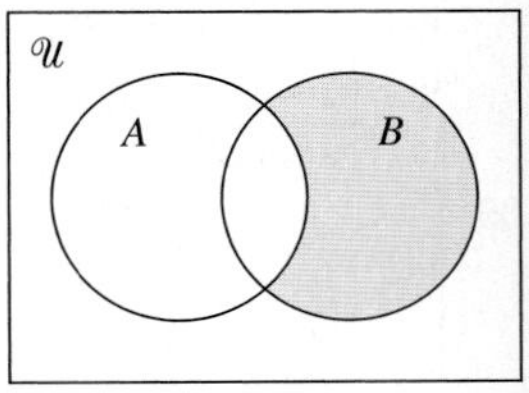

24.

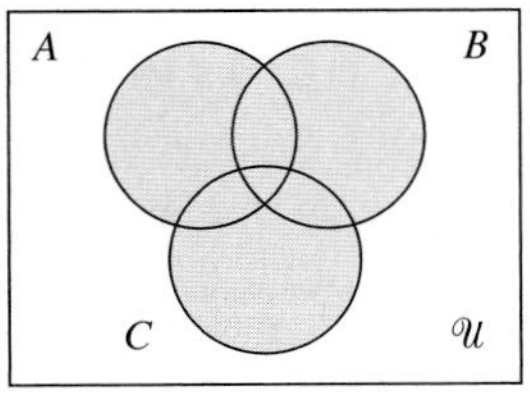

25.

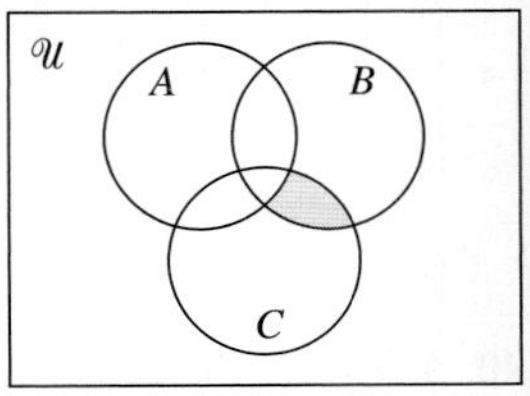

26.

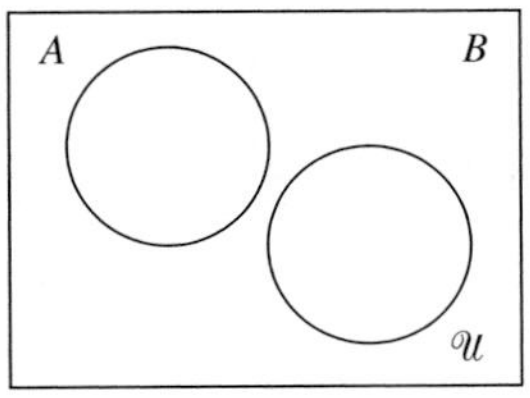

27.

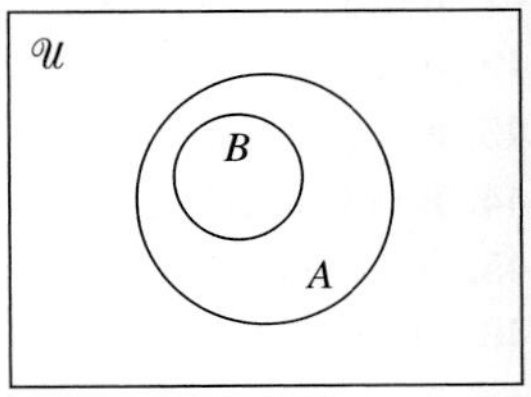

28.

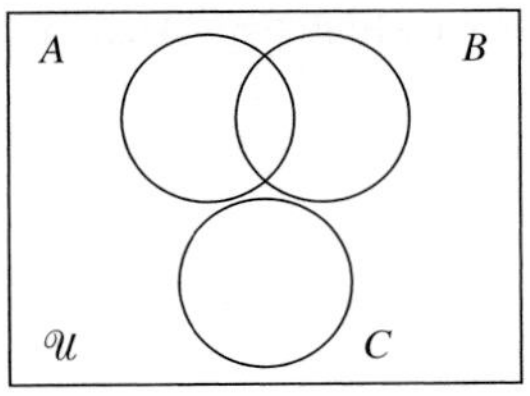

29.

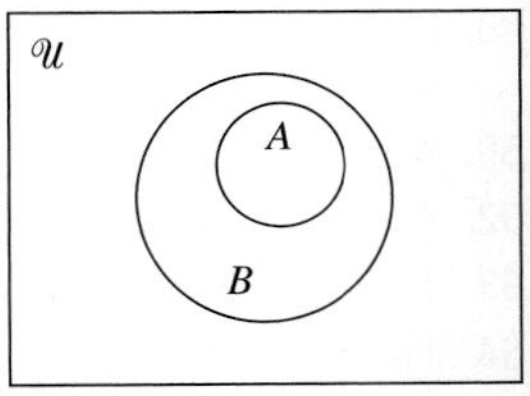

30. a. Both sets correspond to regions 1, 2, 3, 5, 6, 7.

b. Both sets correspond to regions 3, 7.

31. a. Both $A \cup (B \cup C)$ and $(A \cup B) \cup C$ correspond to regions 1, 2, 3, 4, 5, 6, and 7. This verifies the given equality.
b. Both $A \cap (B \cap C)$ and $(A \cap B) \cap C$ correspond to region 7. This verifies the given equality.
32. Both sets correspond to regions 1, 3, 5, 6, 7.
33. a. $A \cup A'$ corresponds to regions 1, 2, 3, 4, 5, 6, 7, and 8. Therefore, $A \cup A' = \mathcal{U}$.
b. Since A and A' have no region in common, $A \cap A' = \varnothing$.
c. $A - B$ corresponds to regions 1 and 5, and $A \cap B'$ also corresponds to regions 1 and 5. Thus, $A - B = A \cap B'$.
34. a. Both sets correspond to regions 4, 8.
b. Both sets correspond to regions 1, 2, 4, 5, 6, 8.
35. a. $A \cap B$ is represented by regions 3 and 7.
36. The set of regions $\{1, 2, 3\}$ represents $(A \cup B) \cap C'$ or (b).
37. a. $A = \{a, b, c, e\}$, $B = \{a, b, g, h\}$, and $\mathcal{U} = \{a, b, c, d, e, f, g, h\}$
b. $A \cup B = \{a, b, c, e, g, h\}$
c. $(A \cap B)' = \{c, d, e, f, g, h\}$
38.
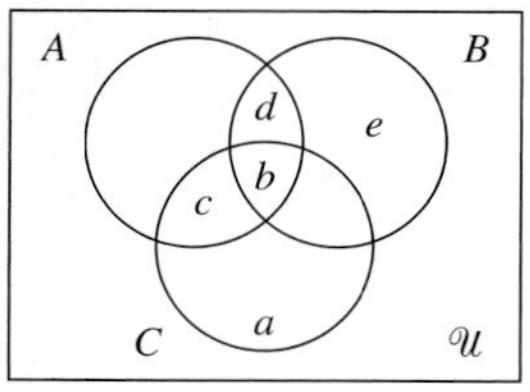

a. $A = \{b, c, d\}$, $B = \{b, d, e\}$, $C = \{a, b, c\}$
b. $\{b\}$
c. $\{a, b, c, d, e\}$
39.
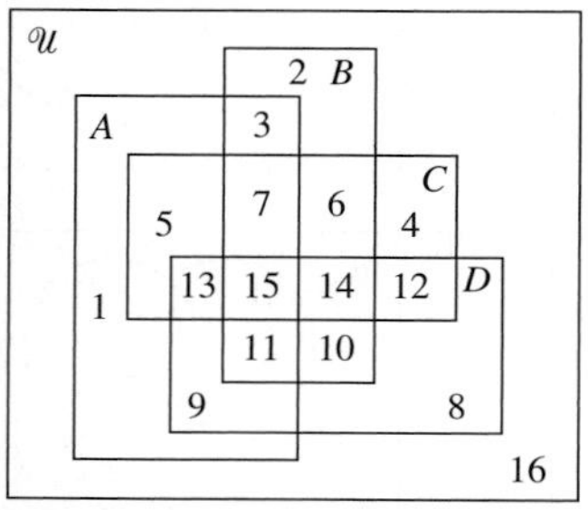

40. a. 6% b. 2%
41. a. 16% b. 14%
42. a. 67% b. 25%
43. a. 7% b. 1%
44. E ∪ O ∪ H′
45. (E ∪ O ∪ H′)′
46. {Facebook, MySpace}
47. Facebook
48. Facebook. (They rank number one on both lists. Answers may vary.)
50. Answers will vary.
52. Answers will vary.
53. The set of elements common to A and B
54. The set of elements in B but not in A.
55. The set of elements in $\mathcal{U}$ and not in either A or C
56. The set of elements common to B and C, but not in A.
57. $A = \{S, F\}$, $B = \{S, C\}$
58. $A \cap B = \{S\}$; expenditure \$4417
59. $A = \{U, M\}$, $B = \{U, L\}$
60. $A \cap B = \{U\}$; expenditure \$7285
61. AB^+, the blood type of a person who has all three antigens and thus may receive blood from any person
62. O^-
63. No, because the B^- person does not have the A antigen
64. Yes
65. No, because the O^- person does not have the Rh antigen
66. Yes 67. 44% 68. 15% 69. 45%
70. O is most common. 71. 16, or 2^4 72. 2^n
73. a. Region 11 b. Regions 8 and 16

Collaborative Learning

1. White 2. Black 3. Yellow, Magenta, Cyan
4. None 5. Yellow 6. Magenta 7. Cyan

Exercises 2.4

1. 30 2. 4 3. 20
4. a. 50 b. 30 c. 80 d. 70
5. 40 families subscribe to both.
6. 7 families
7. a. None b. 10 c. 10
8. a. 20% b. 10%
9. a. Room and board: \$7259; \$14,637
b. Room and board: \$8535; \$20,339
c. Tuition and fees: \$19,595; \$32,329
10. a. \$5702 b. \$17,692 c. \$11,990
11. a. Books and supplies: \$1133
b. Transportation: \$1073
c. Transportation: \$1073
12. a. \$4892 b. \$16,882 c. \$11,990
13. a. 95 b. 69 c. 49 d. 56 e. 38
14. a. $D \cap X$ b. $D \cap Y$ c. $M \cap I$ d. $X \cap I$
15. a. 5 b. 30 c. 20
16. a. 75 b. 220
17. \$450
18. His data accounts for only 28 persons; hence his figures are unreliable.
19. 28
20. a. 16 b. 58 c. 15 d. 42
21. a. 120 b. 80 c. 50
22. 150
23. a. 80 b. 120 c. 50
24. a. 130 b. 170
25. a. 73 b. 55 c. 91 d. 38 e. 5
26. a. 17 b. 12 c. 48 d. 51 e. 85
27. 31%
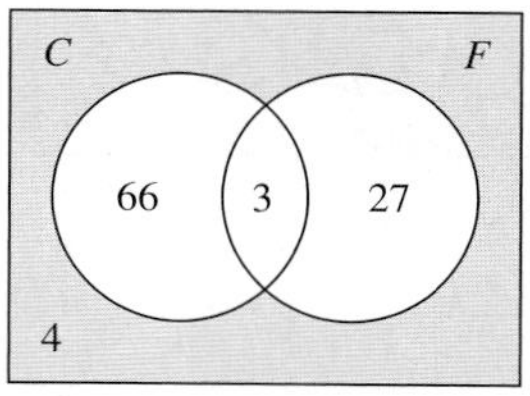

28. 4%

29.

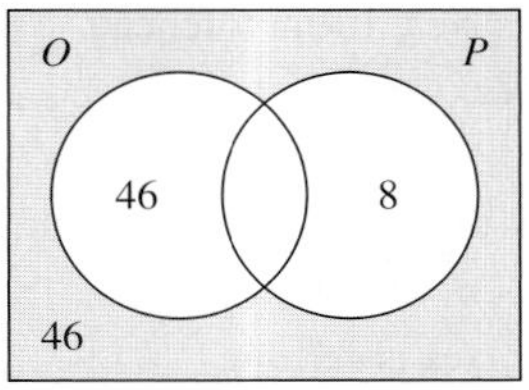

30. 37%

31. False. A counterexample is $A = \{1, 2\}$, $B = \{m, n\}$.

32. True. If $A = B$, then the number of elements in A must be equal to the number of elements in B since A and B are identical.

33. False. A counterexample is $A = \{1, 2\}$, $B = \{1, 2, 3\}$.

34. False. Let $A = \{1, 2\}$ and $B = \{a, b\}$. Then $n(A) = 2 = n(B)$, but $A - B =$ A since no elements of B are in A.

35. The Venn diagram shows that with the added information, the statistics in the cartoon are possible.

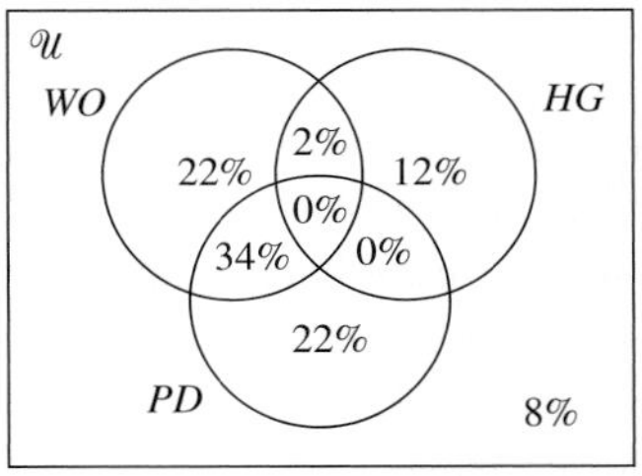

36.

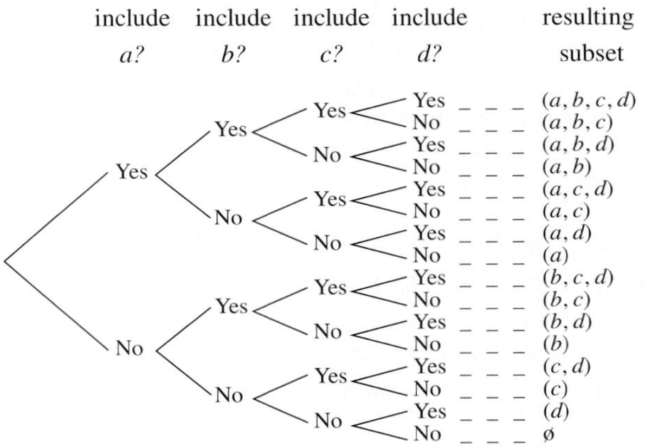

37. $2^4 = 16$ different subsets

38. If there are n elements and each element can be either included or not included (2 choices for each element), then there is a total of $2 \cdot 2 \cdot 2 \cdot \ldots \cdot 2 = 2^n$ different subsets.

Exercises 2.5

1. $n(A) = 26$ **2.** 10 **3.** $n(C) = 50$

4. $\aleph_0$ **5.** $n(E) = \aleph_0$

6.
$$\begin{array}{ccccc} 1 & 2 & 3 & 4 & 5 \\ \downarrow & \downarrow & \downarrow & \downarrow & \downarrow \\ a & b & c & d & e \end{array}$$
This shows that $A \sim B$.

7. The following correspondence shows that sets P and Q are equivalent:
$$\begin{array}{cccc} 2 & 4 & 8 & 12 \\ \updownarrow & \updownarrow & \updownarrow & \updownarrow \\ 6 & 12 & 24 & 36 \end{array}$$

8.
$$\begin{array}{cccccccc} 0 & 1 & 2 & 3 & \ldots & n & \ldots \\ \downarrow & \downarrow & \downarrow & \downarrow & & \downarrow & \\ 1 & 2 & 3 & 4 & \ldots & n+1 & \ldots \end{array}$$
This shows that $W \sim N$.

9. The following correspondence shows that sets I^- and N are equivalent:
$$\begin{array}{cccccc} -1 & -2 & -3 & \ldots & -n & \ldots \\ \updownarrow & \updownarrow & \updownarrow & & \updownarrow & \\ 1 & 2 & 3 & \ldots & n & \ldots \end{array}$$

10.
$$\begin{array}{cccccc} 1 & 2 & 3 & \ldots & n & \ldots \\ \downarrow & \downarrow & \downarrow & & \downarrow & \\ \frac{1}{1} & \frac{1}{2} & \frac{1}{3} & \ldots & \frac{1}{n} & \ldots \end{array}$$
This shows that $N \sim F$.

11. The following correspondence shows that sets N and O are equivalent:
$$\begin{array}{cccccc} 1 & 2 & 3 & \ldots & n & \ldots \\ \updownarrow & \updownarrow & \updownarrow & & \updownarrow & \\ 1 & 3 & 5 & \ldots & 2n-1 & \ldots \end{array}$$

12.
$$\begin{array}{cccccc} 1 & 2 & 3 & \ldots & n & \ldots \\ \downarrow & \downarrow & \downarrow & & \downarrow & \\ 5 & 10 & 15 & \ldots & 5n & \ldots \end{array}$$
This shows that $N \sim F$.

13. The following correspondence shows that sets E and G are equivalent:
$$\begin{array}{cccccc} 2 & 4 & 6 & \ldots & 2n & \ldots \\ \updownarrow & \updownarrow & \updownarrow & & \updownarrow & \\ 102 & 104 & 106 & \ldots & 100+2n & \ldots \end{array}$$

14.
$$\begin{array}{cccccc} 1 & 3 & 5 & \ldots & 2n-1 & \ldots \\ \downarrow & \downarrow & \downarrow & & \downarrow & \\ 2 & 4 & 6 & \ldots & 2n & \ldots \end{array}$$
This shows that $O \sim E$.

15. The following correspondence shows that sets G and T are equivalent:
$$\begin{array}{cccccc} 202 & 204 & 206 & \ldots & 200+2n & \ldots \\ \updownarrow & \updownarrow & \updownarrow & & \updownarrow & \\ 302 & 304 & 306 & \ldots & 300+2n & \ldots \end{array}$$

16. Finite

17. The set $\{100, 200, 300, \ldots\}$ can be put into a one-to-one correspondence with a subset of itself, $\{200, 300, 400, \ldots\}$. This shows that the set is infinite.

18. Infinite

19. The set $\{\frac{1}{3}, \frac{2}{3}, \frac{3}{3}, \ldots\}$ can be put into a one-to-one correspondence with a subset of itself, $\{\frac{2}{3}, \frac{3}{3}, \frac{4}{3}, \ldots\}$. This shows that the set is infinite.

20. Finite

21. Sets B and D are equal and equivalent.

22. B and C, C and D, B and D

23. Set A is neither equal nor equivalent to any of the other sets.

24. $\aleph_0$. The set $\{0, 1, 2, 3, \ldots\}$ can be put into one-to-one correspondence with the set $\{1, 2, 3, \ldots\}$.

25. $\aleph_0$

26. $\aleph_0$. The sets $\{1, 2, 3, \ldots\}$ and $\{2, 4, 6, \ldots\}$ can be combined to form the set $\{1, 2, 3, 4, 5, 6, \ldots\}$. All three of these sets have the same cardinal number which shows that $2 \times \aleph_0 = \aleph_0$.

27. $\aleph_0$
28. $n\{1, 2, 3, 4, 5, 6, \ldots\} = n\{1, 3, 5, \ldots\} + n\{2, 4, 6, \ldots\}$
The cardinal number of the set of all counting numbers is the sum of the cardinal numbers of the set of all odd counting numbers and the set of all even counting numbers.
29. a. $\frac{7}{9}$ and $\frac{8}{9}$
b. $\frac{1}{3} + \frac{2}{9} + \frac{4}{27} + \frac{8}{81} + \cdots$; the sum gets closer and closer to 1.
30. Yes. It can be shown that there are as many points in the Cantor set as there are points in the unit interval.
31. To room 223
32. Into Room 1.
33. Rooms 1, 3, 5, . . . , $2n + 1$, . . .
34. Into Room 2.
35. To room 666
36. a. $A = \{\text{London, Paris}\}$, $B = \{\text{San Francisco, Toronto}\}$
b. Yes. A and B can be placed into a one-to-one correspondence.
c. No.
d. Both sets are finite.

CHAPTER 3

Exercises 3.1

1. Not a statement
2. Compound. Lemons are citrus fruits. Oranges are citrus fruits.
3. A compound statement with the following components: Jane is taking an English course. She has four themes to write.
4. Simple
5. Not a statement
6. Not a statement
7. A compound statement with the following components: Students at Ohio State University are required to take a course in history. Students at Ohio State University are required to take a course in economics.
8. Compound. Today is Sunday. Tomorrow is Monday.
9. $a \wedge f$ 10. $r \wedge \sim e$ 11. $d \vee f$ 12. $\sim a \vee p$
13. $b \wedge p$ 14. $u \wedge d$ 15. $a \vee m$ 16. $\sim d \wedge (t \vee p)$
17. $p \wedge q$ 18. $q \wedge \sim p$ 19. $\sim(p \vee q)$ 20. $\sim(q \wedge p)$
21. Ricky loves Lucy, or Lucy does not love Ricky.
22. It is not the case that Ricky loves Lucy or Lucy loves Ricky.
23. Ricky loves Lucy, but Lucy does not love Ricky.
24. Ricky does not love Lucy, and Lucy does not love Ricky.
25. It is not the case that Ricky and Lucy love each other.
26. It is not a long time before the end of the term.
27. Bill's store is not making a good profit.
28. The number ten is not a round number.
29. My dog is not a spaniel.
30. Your cat is a Siamese.
31. I like to work overtime.
32. These are not negations of each other.
33. These two are negations of each other.
34. These are negations of each other.
35. Some men are not mortal.
36. No women are engineers.
37. All basketball players are 6 ft tall.
38. All things are what they appear to be.
39. He is not bald, and he does not have a 10-in. forehead.
40. Somebody does not like Sara Lee.
41. No circles are round.
42. No men earn less than $8 an hour or more than $50 an hour.
43. Nobody up there loves me.
44. Something other than death or taxes is certain.
45. Somebody does not like to go on a trip.
46. Someone can sue us under this coverage.
47. Some persons occupying your covered auto are not insured.
48. Some of your contributions are deductible.
49. All expenses are subject to the 2% limit.
50. Statement c
51. Statement d
52. $(m \vee d) \wedge e$
53. $(d \wedge p) \vee r$
54. $(c \vee n) \wedge e$
55. $r \wedge (t \vee g)$
56. a. Today is not Friday or tomorrow is not Saturday.
b. Today is not Friday or tomorrow is Saturday.
c. Today is not Friday and tomorrow is not Saturday.
57. a. The diagram is neither a rectangle nor a square.
b. The diagram is a square or not a rectangle.
c. The diagram is a square and a rectangle.
58. If (1) is true, then (2) is true. But if (2) is true, then (1) has to be false, a contradiction!
59. Sentence (1) is true. Sentence (2) is false. If we assume that sentence (3) is true, there will be two sentences, (1) and (3), that are true; thus, sentence (3) is false!
60. No. A statement is a sentence that can be classified as true or false.
61. F 62. F 63. F 64. F 65. T
66. T 67. F 68. T
69. a. (Hispanics and females and not high school graduates) or (white and females and not high school graduates): $16,500
b. Males and Hispanics and not high school graduates: $22,200
70. a. Females and Asian and Advanced Degrees ($67,200)
b. Asians

Exercises 3.2

1. Today is Friday or Monday.
2. Today is Friday and Monday.
3. Today is not Friday.
4. The statement in Problem 2 is always false.
5. He is a gentleman or a scholar.
6. He is not a gentleman.
7. He is a gentleman and a scholar.
8. $\sim(g \vee s)$ 9. $g \wedge s$ 10. $\sim g \wedge \sim s$
11. a. $p \wedge q$ b. $p \vee q$
c. Statement in (**a**) is false.
Statement in (**b**) is true.
12. $p \wedge \sim q$ 13. $\sim q \wedge p$ or $\sim(q \vee \sim p)$
14. $\sim(\sim p \wedge q)$ 15. $p \vee q$

16. With the given assumptions, the statements in Problems 14 and 15 are both true.

17. $p \vee q$, true **18.** $p \vee \sim q$, true **19.** $\sim p \wedge \sim q$, false.

20. $(p \vee q) \wedge \sim(p \wedge q)$, true **21.** $\sim q \wedge \sim p$, false

22. $g \vee j$, true **23.** $g \vee \sim j$, false **24.** $\sim g \wedge \sim j$, false

25. $(g \vee j) \wedge \sim (g \wedge j)$, true **26.** $\sim g \wedge \sim j$, false

27.

1	2	4	3
p	q	$p \vee$	$\sim q$
T	T	**T**	F
T	F	**T**	T
F	T	**F**	F
F	F	**T**	T

28.

1	2	3	4
p	q	$p \vee q$	$\sim(p \vee q)$
T	T	T	F
T	F	T	F
F	T	T	F
F	F	F	T

29.

1	2	3	4
p	q	$\sim p$	$\wedge q$
T	T	F	**F**
T	F	F	**F**
F	T	T	**T**
F	F	T	**F**

30.

1	2	3	4	5
p	q	$\sim p$	$\sim q$	$\sim p \vee \sim q$
T	T	F	F	F
T	F	F	T	T
F	T	T	F	T
F	F	T	T	T

31.

1	2	5	4	3
p	q	$\sim$	$(p \vee$	$\sim q)$
T	T	**F**	T	F
T	F	**F**	T	T
F	T	**T**	F	F
F	F	**F**	T	T

32.

1	2	3	4	5	6
p	q	$\sim p$	$\sim q$	$\sim p \vee \sim q$	$\sim(5)$
T	T	F	F	F	T
T	F	F	T	T	F
F	T	T	F	T	F
F	F	T	T	T	F

33.

1	2	6	3	5	4
p	q	$\sim$	$(\sim p$	$\wedge$	$\sim q)$
T	T	**T**	F	F	F
T	F	**T**	F	F	T
F	T	**T**	T	F	F
F	F	**F**	T	T	T

34.

1	2	3	4	5	6
p	q	$p \vee q$	$p \wedge q$	~ 4	$3 \wedge 5$
T	T	T	T	F	F
T	F	T	F	T	T
F	T	T	F	T	T
F	F	F	F	T	F

35.

1	2	3	6	4	5
p	q	$(p \wedge q)$	$\vee$	$(\sim p$	$\wedge q)$
T	T	T	**T**	F	F
T	F	F	**F**	F	F
F	T	F	**T**	T	T
F	F	F	**F**	T	F

36.

1	2	3	4	5	6	7
p	q	$\sim p$	$\sim q$	$p \wedge 4$	$3 \wedge q$	$5 \wedge 6$
T	T	F	F	F	F	F
T	F	F	T	T	F	F
F	T	T	F	F	T	F
F	F	T	T	F	F	F

37.

1	2	3	5	4
p	q	r	$p \wedge$	$(q \vee r)$
T	T	T	**T**	T
T	T	F	**T**	T
T	F	T	**T**	T
T	F	F	**F**	F
F	T	T	**F**	T
F	T	F	**F**	T
F	F	T	**F**	T
F	F	F	**F**	F

38.

1	2	3	4	5
p	q	r	$q \wedge r$	$p \vee (q \wedge r)$
T	T	T	T	T
T	T	F	F	T
T	F	T	F	T
T	F	F	F	T
F	T	T	T	T
F	T	F	F	F
F	F	T	F	F
F	F	F	F	F

39.

1	2	3	4	7	6	5
p	q	r	$(p \vee q)$	$\vee$	$(r \wedge$	$\sim q)$
T	T	T	T	**T**	F	F
T	T	F	T	**T**	F	F
T	F	T	T	**T**	T	T
T	F	F	T	**T**	F	T
F	T	T	T	**T**	F	F
F	T	F	T	**T**	F	F
F	F	T	F	**T**	T	T
F	F	F	F	**F**	F	T

40.

1	2	3	4	5	6	7	8	9	10	11
p	q	r	s	$\sim r$	$\sim s$	$p \wedge q$	$q \wedge 5$	$r \wedge 6$	$7 \vee 8$	$10 \vee 9$
T	T	T	T	F	F	T	F	F	T	T
T	T	T	F	F	T	T	F	T	T	T
T	T	F	T	T	F	T	T	F	T	T
T	T	F	F	T	T	T	T	F	T	T
T	F	T	T	F	F	F	F	F	F	F
T	F	T	F	F	T	F	F	T	F	T
T	F	F	T	T	F	F	F	F	F	F
T	F	F	F	T	T	F	F	F	F	F
F	T	T	T	F	F	F	F	F	F	F
F	T	T	F	F	T	F	F	T	F	T
F	T	F	T	T	F	F	T	F	T	T
F	T	F	F	T	T	F	T	F	T	T
F	F	T	T	F	F	F	F	F	F	F
F	F	T	F	F	T	F	F	T	F	T
F	F	F	T	T	F	F	F	F	F	F
F	F	F	F	T	T	F	F	F	F	F

41. **a.** When j and h are both true **b.** Either j or h is false
c. Either j or h is true **d.** When j and h are both false

42. **a.** Answers will vary. **b.** When u and p are both false
c. When either u or p is true
d. When both u and p are false

43.

1	2	3	5	4	6	8	7
p	q	r	$p \vee$	$(q \wedge r)$	$(p \vee q)$	$\wedge$	$(p \vee r)$
T	T	T	**T**	T	T	**T**	T
T	T	F	**T**	F	T	**T**	T
T	F	T	**T**	F	T	**T**	T
T	F	F	**T**	F	T	**T**	T
F	T	T	**T**	T	T	**T**	T
F	T	F	**F**	F	T	**F**	F
F	F	T	**F**	F	F	**F**	T
F	F	F	**F**	F	F	**F**	F

Columns 5 and 8 of the above truth table show that the two statements have the same truth values, so they are equivalent.

44.

1	2	3	4	5	6	7	8
p	q	r	$q \vee r$	$p \wedge 4$	$p \wedge q$	$p \wedge r$	$6 \vee 7$
T	T	T	T	T	T	T	T
T	T	F	T	T	T	F	T
T	F	T	T	T	F	T	T
T	F	F	F	F	F	F	F
F	T	T	T	F	F	F	F
F	T	F	T	F	F	F	F
F	F	T	T	F	F	F	F
F	F	F	F	F	F	F	F

Columns 5 and 8 are identical. Thus, the two statements are equivalent.

45.

1	2	4	3	5	7	6
p	q	$\sim$	$(p \vee q)$	$\sim p$	$\wedge$	$\sim q$
T	T	**F**	T	F	**F**	F
T	F	**F**	T	F	**F**	T
F	T	**F**	T	T	**F**	F
F	F	**T**	F	T	**T**	T

Columns 4 and 7 of the above table show that the two statements have the same truth values, so they are equivalent.

46.

1	2	3	4	5	6	7
p	q	$\sim p$	$\sim q$	$p \wedge q$	~ 5	$3 \vee 4$
T	T	F	F	T	F	F
T	F	F	T	F	T	T
F	T	T	F	F	T	T
F	F	T	T	F	T	T

Columns 6 and 7 are identical. Thus, the two statements are equivalent.

47.

1	2	3	5	4	6
p	q	$(p \wedge q)$	$\vee$	$\sim p$	$q \vee \sim p$
T	T	T	**T**	F	**T**
T	F	F	**F**	F	**F**
F	T	F	**T**	T	**T**
F	F	F	**T**	T	**T**

Columns 5 and 6 of the preceding table show that the two statements have the same truth values, so they are equivalent.

48.

1	2	3	4	5	6	7	8	9	10
p	q	$\sim p$	$\sim q$	$p \vee q$	$3 \vee 4$	$5 \wedge 6$	$1 \wedge 4$	$3 \wedge 2$	$8 \vee 9$
T	T	F	F	T	F	F	F	F	F
T	F	F	T	T	T	T	T	F	T
F	T	T	F	T	T	T	F	T	T
F	F	T	T	F	T	F	F	F	F

Since columns 7 and 10 are identical, the statement is true.

49. **a.** $p \wedge q$ is true only when both p and q are true; this gives the truth values *TFFF*. $p \wedge \sim q$ is true only when p is true and q is false; this gives the truth values *FTFF*. $\sim p \wedge q$ is true only when p is false and q is true; this gives the truth values *FFTF*. $\sim p \wedge \sim q$ is true only when p and q are both false; this gives the truth values *FFFT*. This verifies the table.

b. $p \wedge q$ is true only in the first row, and $\sim p \wedge \sim q$ is true only in the last row. So $(p \wedge q) \vee (\sim p \wedge \sim q)$ has the truth values *TFFT*.

c. $(p \wedge \sim q) \vee (\sim p \wedge q)$ has truth values *FTTF*. $(p \wedge \sim q) \vee (\sim p \wedge q) \vee (\sim p \wedge \sim q)$ has truth values *FTTT*. $\sim(p \wedge q)$ is a simpler statement with truth values *FTTT*.

50. It would be true when p is true, q is false, and r is true, or when p, q, r are all false. It would be false in all other cases.

51. None are eligible.

52. None of the three qualifies.

53. 7 is greater than or equal to 5.

54. 8 is less than or equal to 9.

55. 0 is less than or equal to 3.

56. $\frac{1}{3}$ is less than 1.

57. $\frac{1}{2}$ is greater than $\frac{1}{8}$.

58. **a.** I will go fishing and the sun is shining.

b. The sun is not shining.

c. I will go fishing or the sun is shining.

59. I will not go fishing or the sun is not shining. This would be true if either or both of the components,"I will not go fishing" and "The sun is not shining,"were true.

60. **1.** $(e \wedge g) \vee a$ **2.** h **3.** $(c \vee n) \vee \sim t$

61. $[(e \wedge g) \vee a] \wedge h \wedge (c \vee n \vee \sim t)$

62. $a \wedge h \wedge n$, $a \wedge h \wedge \sim t$

63. Mr. Baker is the carpenter.

Exercises 3.3

1.

1	2	3	5	4	6
p	q	$\sim q$	$\rightarrow$	$\sim p$	$p \rightarrow q$
T	T	F	**T**	F	**T**
T	F	T	**F**	F	**F**
F	T	F	**T**	T	**T**
F	F	T	**T**	T	**T**

Columns 5 and 6 are identical, so $\sim q \rightarrow \sim p$ is equivalent to $p \rightarrow q$.

2.

1	2	3	4	5	6	7
p	q	$\sim q$	$p \rightarrow 3$	$p \wedge q$	~ 5	$4 \Leftrightarrow 6$
T	T	F	F	**T**	F	**T**
T	F	T	T	**F**	T	**T**
F	T	F	T	**F**	T	**T**
F	F	T	T	**F**	T	**T**

3.

1	2	3	4	5
p	q	$\sim p$	$\sim p \rightarrow q$	$p \vee q$
T	T	F	**T**	**T**
T	F	F	**T**	**T**
F	T	T	**T**	**T**
F	F	T	**F**	**F**

Since columns 4 and 5 are identical, $\sim p \rightarrow q$ and $p \vee q$ are equivalent.

4. *T* **5.** *F* **6.** *T* **7.** *T* **8.** 7

9. x can be any number. **10.** x may be any number.

11. x can be any number except 4.

12. **a.** When p is true and q is false

b. When o is false, n is true and b is false

13. **a.** When o is false

b. When n is true and b is false

c. o false, n true, b false

14.

1	2	3	4	5
p	q	$p \rightarrow q$	$3 \rightarrow p$	$4 \rightarrow q$
T	T	T	T	T
T	F	F	T	F
F	T	T	F	T
F	F	T	F	T

15.

1	2	3	4	6	5
p	q	r	$(p \rightarrow q)$	$\Leftrightarrow$	$(p \vee r)$
T	T	T	T	T	T
T	T	F	T	T	T
T	F	T	F	F	T
T	F	F	F	F	T
F	T	T	T	T	T
F	T	F	T	F	F
F	F	T	T	T	T
F	F	F	T	F	F

16.

1	2	3	4	5	6
p	q	$\sim q$	$p \rightarrow q$	$p \wedge \sim q$	$4 \Leftrightarrow 5$
T	T	F	T	F	F
T	F	T	F	T	F
F	T	F	T	T	T
F	F	T	T	T	T

17.

1	2	3	5	4
p	q	r	$p \rightarrow$	$(q \wedge r)$
T	T	T	T	T
T	T	F	F	F
T	F	T	F	F
T	F	F	F	F
F	T	T	T	T
F	T	F	T	F
F	F	T	T	F
F	F	F	T	F

18.

1	2	3	4	5	6
p	q	r	$p \rightarrow q$	$p \rightarrow r$	$4 \wedge 5$
T	T	T	T	T	T
T	T	F	T	F	F
T	F	T	F	T	F
T	F	F	F	F	F
F	T	T	T	T	T
F	T	F	T	T	T
F	F	T	T	T	T
F	F	F	T	T	T

19. The final columns in the tables in problems 17 and 18 are identical, so the two statements are equivalent.

20. $q \rightarrow p$ 21. $p \rightarrow q$ 22. $q \leftrightarrow p$ 23. $\sim q \rightarrow \sim p$

24. $\sim p \rightarrow \sim q$ 25. $q \rightarrow \sim p$ 26. $\sim s \rightarrow \sim b$

27. $\sim b \rightarrow \sim s$ 28. $b \leftrightarrow s$

29. $\sim a \vee b$; the temperature is not above 80°, or I would go to the beach.

30. $\sim h \vee r$ Mida is not home by 5 or dinner would be ready by 6.

31. $\sim a \vee g$; Eva does not have a day off, or she would go to the beach.

32. You do not work or you have to pay taxes.

33. You do not have the time, or we've got the beer.

34. You do not find a better one or you buy it.

35. If it is a dog, then it is a mammal.

36. If it is a cat, then it is a feline.

37. If it is a man, then it is created equal.

38. If it is a prime number greater than 2, then it is an odd number.

39. If it is a rectangle with perpendicular diagonals, then it is a square.

40.

1	2	3	4	5	6	7
p	q	$\sim p$	$\sim q$	$3 \vee q$	~ 5	$p \wedge 4$
T	T	F	F	T	F	F
T	F	F	T	F	T	T
F	T	T	F	T	F	F
F	F	T	T	T	F	F

Columns 6 and 7 are identical. Thus, the two statements are equivalent.

41.

1	2	4	3	6	5
p	q	$\sim$	$(p \rightarrow q)$	$p \wedge$	$\sim q$
T	T	**F**	T	**F**	F
T	F	**T**	F	**T**	T
F	T	**F**	T	**F**	F
F	F	**F**	T	**F**	T

Since columns 4 and 6 are identical, $\sim(p \rightarrow q)$ and $p \wedge \sim q$ are equivalent.

42. You earn a lot of money, but you do not pay heavy taxes.

43. Johnny does not play quarterback, and his team does not lose.

44. Alice passes the test but does not get the job.

45. I kiss you once, but I do not kiss you again.

46. Saturday is a hot day and I will not go to the beach.

47. Evel Knievel is careless, but he will not lose his life.

48. $TFTT$

49. If Johnny plays quarterback, then his team wins.

50. If Alice does not fail the test, then she gets the job.

51. If Joe had not had an accident, then he would be able to get car insurance.

52. a. Definition 1 shows truth values $TFFF$, which is the truth table for $p \wedge q$.
 b. Definition 2 shows truth values $TFFT$, which is the truth table for $p \leftrightarrow q$.
 c. Definition 3 shows truth values $TFTF$, which is the truth table for q.

53. No 54. Yes 55. Statement d 56. Statement b.

57. Statement d 58. Statement d.

59. No. $p \rightarrow q$ is true if p is false and q is either true or false.

60. The statement "if p then q" is false only when p is true and q is false. If p is false, then q can be either true or false. Thus, based only on the given excerpt, the insurance company can pay or not pay.

61. The student has to take the placement examination only if the student has satisfied the freshman requirements (perhaps by advanced courses in high school) and is being admitted to sophomore standing, but is entering college for the first time.

62. Answers will vary.

64. Answers will vary.

66. $d \rightarrow r$ 67. $r \rightarrow a$ 68. $d \rightarrow (r \wedge a)$

69. No. It only says that an adjustment will be made if a report is made in 10 days.

70. Does the first road lead to freedom and are you telling the truth, or does the first road lead to freedom and are you lying?

71. A must see at least one black hat, or she would know that her hat is black since they are not all white. B also must see at least one black hat, and further, that hat had to be on C; otherwise she would know that her hat was black (since she knows A saw at least one black hat). So C knows that her hat is black, without even seeing the others' hats.

72. The fact that there are two is a red herring—you only need one of either type. You ask him the following question: "If I were to ask you if the left fork leads to Someplaceorother, would you say 'yes'?"

73. The one who fell silent, presumably the quickest of the three, reasoned that his head must be painted also. The argument goes as follows. Let's call the quick logician Q, and the other two D and S. Let's assume Q's head is untouched. Then D is laughing because S's head is painted, and vice versa. But eventually, D and S will realize that their head must be painted, because the other is laughing. So they will quit laughing as soon as they realize this. Q waits what he thinks is a reasonable amount of time for them to figure this out, and when they don't stop laughing, his worst fears are confirmed. He concludes that his assumption is invalid and he must be crowned in crimson too.

Skill Checker 3.3

p	q	$\sim p$	$p \vee q$	$p \wedge q$
T	T	F	T	T
T	F	F	T	F
F	T	T	T	F
F	F	T	F	F

Collaborative Learning

1. $[(w \vee s \vee t \vee ts \vee g \vee c \vee d) \wedge \sim o] \rightarrow u$
2. Answers will vary.
3. Yes, provided you meet one of the other seven conditions.
4. No. Did not satisfy one of the seven conditions.
5. The IRS wants you to believe that $\sim w \rightarrow r$ is a tautology.

Exercises 3.4

1. If n is divisible by 2, then n is an even number.
2. Converse: If you have no cavities, then you brush your teeth with Clean. Contrapositive: If you have cavities, then you do not brush your teeth with Clean. Inverse: If you do not brush your teeth with Clean, then you have cavities.
3. $q \rightarrow p$ 4. $q \rightarrow p$ 5. $q \rightarrow p$
6. If I kissed you once, then I will kiss you again.
7. If one is a mathematics major, then one takes calculus.
8. If Eva is convinced, then the argument is a good one.
9. If the measure gets a two-thirds vote, then it carries.
10. If we have rain, then we have clouds.
11. If we have a stable economy, then we have low unemployment.
12. If a person is a woman, then the person will join a women's club.
13. If birds are of a feather, then they flock together.
14. If it is a dog, then it is a canine.
15.

			Converse	*Inverse*
p	q	$p \rightarrow q$	$q \rightarrow p$	$\sim p \rightarrow \sim q$
T	T	T	**T**	**T**
T	F	F	**T**	**T**
F	T	T	**F**	**F**
F	F	T	**T**	**T**

The converse, $q \rightarrow p$, is true except when q is true and p is false (third row). The inverse, $\sim p \rightarrow \sim q$, is true except when $\sim p$ is true and $\sim q$ is false (third row). The converse and the inverse have the same truth values and, hence, are equivalent.

16. $u \rightarrow h$ 17. $u \rightarrow h$ 18. $h \rightarrow u$ 19. $u \rightarrow h$
20. $h \rightarrow u$ 21. $u \rightarrow h$ 22. $u \rightarrow h$ 23. $u \leftrightarrow h$
24. $h \rightarrow u$; $\sim u \rightarrow \sim h$; $\sim h \rightarrow \sim u$
25. $u \rightarrow h$; $\sim h \rightarrow \sim u$; $\sim u \rightarrow \sim h$
26. $p \rightarrow s$ 27. $p \leftrightarrow s$ 28. $p \leftrightarrow s$
29. a. Converse: If you are not strong, then you do not eat your spinach.
   Inverse: If you eat your spinach, then you are strong.
   Contrapositive: If you are strong, then you eat your spinach.
   b. Converse: If you are strong, then you eat your spinach.
   Inverse: If you do not eat your spinach, then you are not strong.
   Contrapositive: If you are not strong, then you do not eat your spinach.
   c. Converse: If you eat your spinach, then you are strong.
   Inverse: If you are not strong, then you do not eat your spinach.
   Contrapositive: If you do not eat your spinach, then you are not strong.
30. Statements a and c.
31. If the square of an integer is divisible by 4, the integer is even. True.
32. If there are clouds in the sky, then it is raining. Not always true.
33. If I am neat and well dressed, then I can get a date. False.
34. If all our problems are over, then M is elected to office. Not always true.
35. If you pass this course, then you get passing grades on all the tests. False.
36. If the three angles of a triangle are not equal, then the triangle is not equilateral.
37. If we cannot find a cure for cancer, then the research is inadequately funded.
38. If it is not beautiful, then it is not black.
39. If a person does not want to improve the world, then the person is not a radical.
40. If everyone does not want to buy it, then it is not a smartphone.
41. Equivalence c.
42. Equivalence b.
43. Statement b.
44. Statement c.
45.

1	2	3	4
p	q	$(p \wedge q) \rightarrow p$	
T	T	T	**T**
T	F	F	**T**
F	T	F	**T**
F	F	F	**T**

Column 3 is the conjunction of columns 1 and 2, and so has T only in the first row, where both p and q are true. Therefore, column 4 is all T's; this shows that $(p \wedge q) \rightarrow p$ is a tautology.

46.

1	2	3	4	5	6	7	8
p	q	r	$p \to q$	$q \to r$	$4 \wedge 5$	$p \to r$	$6 \to 7$
T	T	T	T	T	T	T	T
T	T	F	T	F	F	F	T
T	F	T	F	T	F	T	T
T	F	F	F	T	F	F	T
F	T	T	T	T	T	T	T
F	T	F	T	F	F	T	T
F	F	T	T	T	T	T	T
F	F	F	T	T	T	T	T

Since column 8 is all T's, the statement is a tautology.

47.

1	3	2
p	$p \leftrightarrow$	$\sim p$
T	$\boldsymbol{F}$	F
F	$\boldsymbol{F}$	T

Since column 3 is all F's, the statement $p \leftrightarrow \sim p$ is a contradiction.

48. Equivalent

49.

1	2	3	4	6	5
p	q	$(\sim p$	$\wedge\, q)$	$\to$	$(p \to q)$
T	T	F	F	$\boldsymbol{T}$	T
T	F	F	F	$\boldsymbol{T}$	F
F	T	T	T	$\boldsymbol{T}$	T
F	F	T	F	$\boldsymbol{T}$	T

Since column 6 is all T's, the first statement, $\sim p \wedge q$, implies the second, $p \to q$.

50. Neither implies the other.

51. Equivalent **52.** Equivalent

53. $p \wedge \sim q$ implies $\sim p \vee \sim q$.

54. Equivalent

56. **(1)** For q to be true, it is sufficient that p be true.
(2) A sufficient condition for q to be true is that p be true.

58. **(1)** p is true only if q is true.
(2) q is false only if p is false.

60. The conditional $p \to q$ is true whenever the consequent q is true. Thus, if q is true, then $p \to q$ is a tautology and q implies q whether p is true or false.

62.

Statement	*Set*
$\sim q$	Q'
$p \vee q$	$P \cup Q$
$p \wedge q$	$P \cap Q$
$p \Rightarrow q$	$P \subseteq Q$
$p \Leftrightarrow q$	$P = Q$
t, a tautology	U
C, a contradiction	$\varnothing$

63. a. $Q \cap R'$ **b.** $(P \cap Q) \cap R'$

64. a. $P \cap (Q \cup R)'$ **b.** $(P \cup Q) \cap (Q \cup R)'$

65. The contrapositive of $\sim q \to \sim p$ is $p \to q$.

66. The inverse $\sim p \to \sim q$ is

$\sim(\sim p) \to \sim(\sim q)$, that is $p \to q$.

67. The inverse of $p \to q$ is $\sim p \to \sim q$, and the contrapositive of $\sim p \to \sim q$ is $q \to p$.

68. $r \vee s \vee \sim p \vee \sim q \Leftrightarrow [\sim(r \vee s) \to \sim(p \wedge q)]$

This is true because:

$$[\sim(r \vee s) \to \sim(p \wedge q)] \Leftrightarrow [(r \vee s) \vee \sim(p \wedge q)]$$
$$\Leftrightarrow [(r \vee s) \vee (\sim p \vee \sim q)]$$
$$\Leftrightarrow r \vee s \vee \sim p \vee \sim q$$

69. $(\sim r \wedge \sim s) \vee (p \vee q) \Leftrightarrow (r \vee s) \to (p \vee q)$; it is true because $(r \vee s) \to (p \vee q) \Leftrightarrow \sim(r \vee s) \vee (p \vee q) \Leftrightarrow (\sim r \wedge \sim s) \vee (p \vee q)$, and the converse of $(r \vee s) \to (p \vee q)$ is $(p \vee q) \to (r \vee s)$.

70. The direct statement **71.** The direct statement

72. The inverse **73.** The contrapositive **74.** The converse

Collaborative Learning

4. a. $t \to b$ **b.** $i \to p$ **c.** $m \to \sim l$
d. $w \to p$ **e.** $r \to (p \wedge m)$

Exercises 3.5

1. Premises: "No misers are generous" and "Some old persons are not generous."
Conclusion: "Some old persons are misers."

2. Premises: "No thieves are honest," and "Some dishonest people are convicted."
Conclusion: "Some thieves are convicted."

3. Premises: "All diligent students get A's" and "All lazy students are not successful."
Conclusion: "All diligent students are lazy."

4. Premises: "All students like logic," and "Robin likes logic."
Conclusion: "Robin is a student."

5. Premises: "No kitten that loves fish is unteachable" and "No kitten without a tail will play with a gorilla."
Conclusion: "No unteachable kitten will play with a gorilla."

6. Premises: "No birds are proud of their tails," and "Some birds cannot sing."
Conclusion: "Peacocks cannot sing."

7. Valid

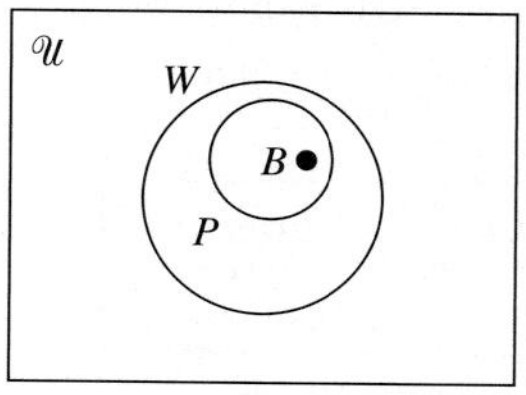

8. Invalid

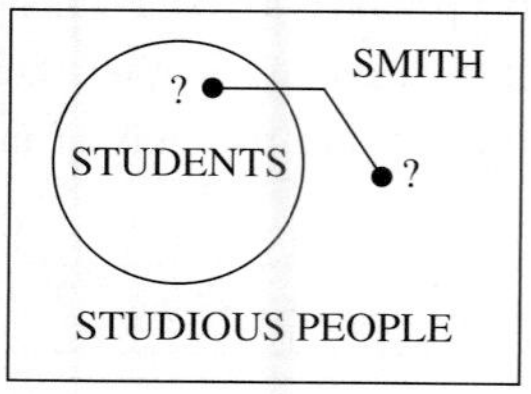

9. Invalid

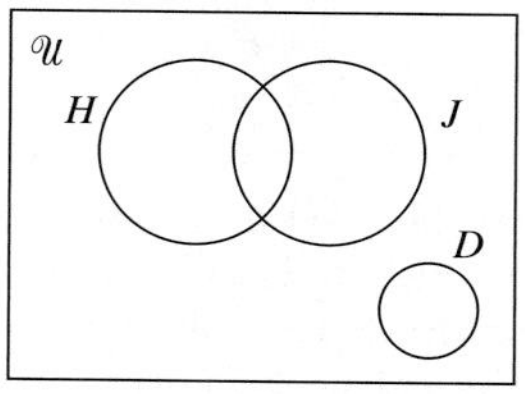

10. Valid

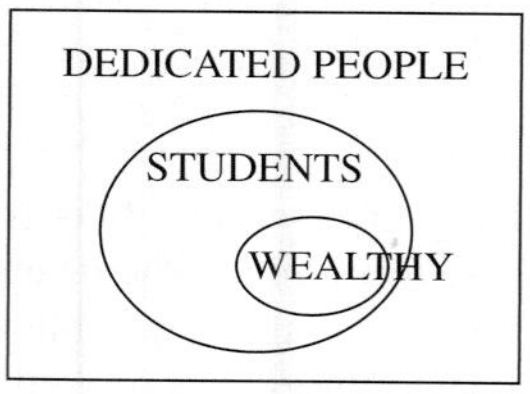

11. Valid

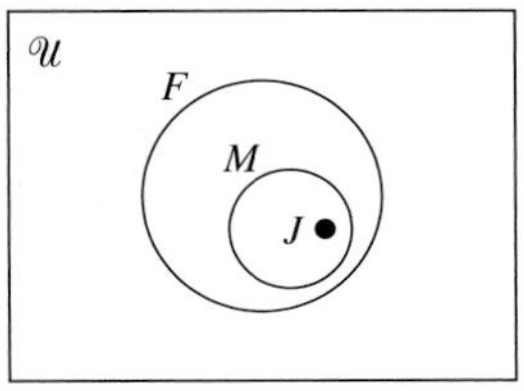

12. Invalid

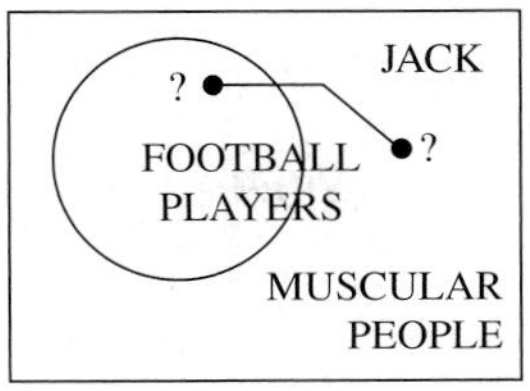

13. Invalid

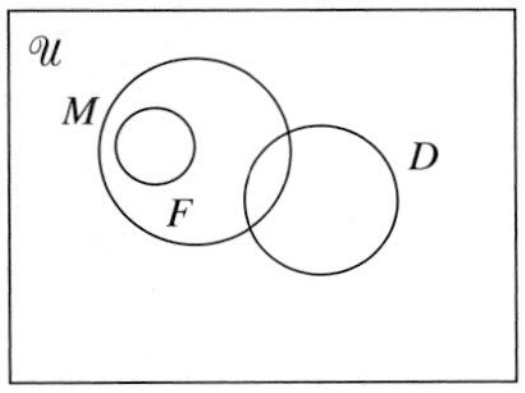

14. Invalid

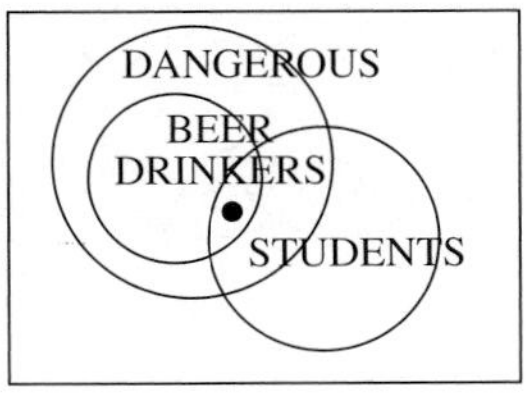

15. Invalid

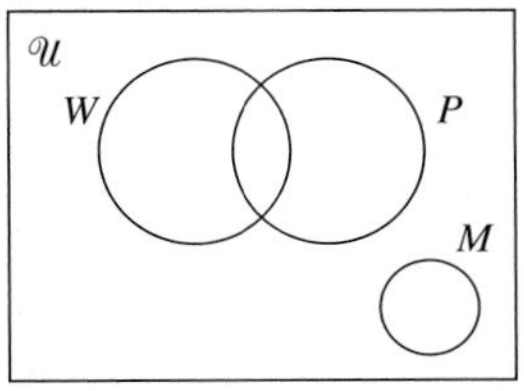

16. Valid

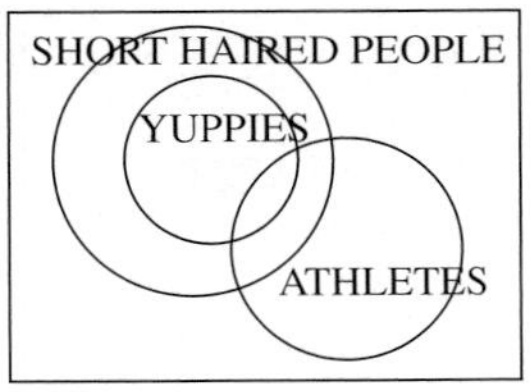

17. Invalid

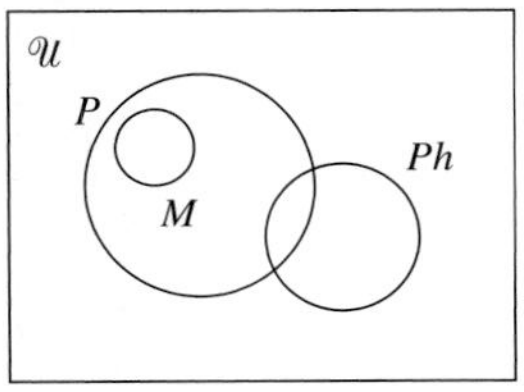

18. Valid

19. Valid

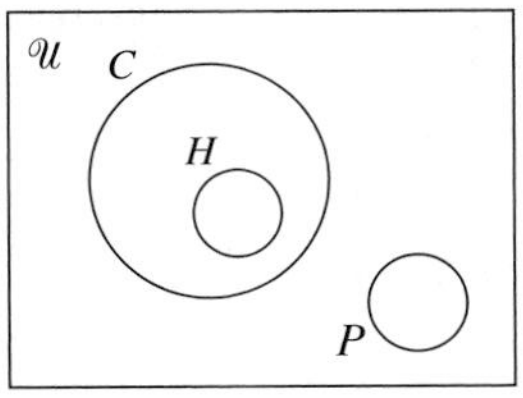

20. Invalid

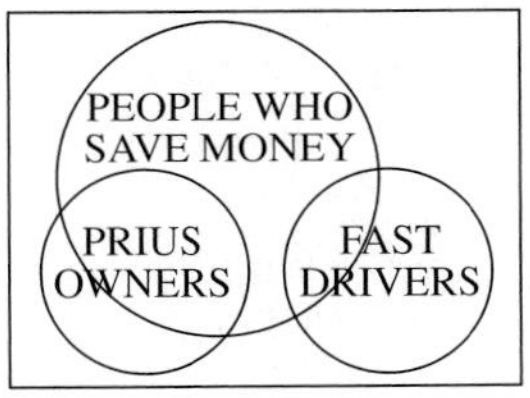

21. Invalid

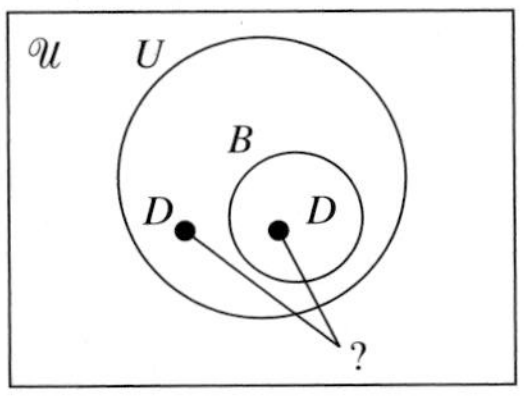

22. Valid

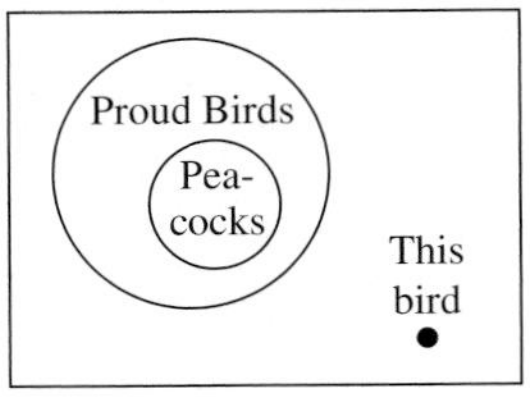

23. Invalid

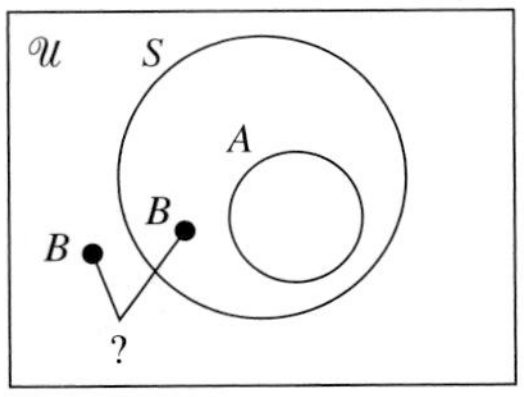

24. Valid

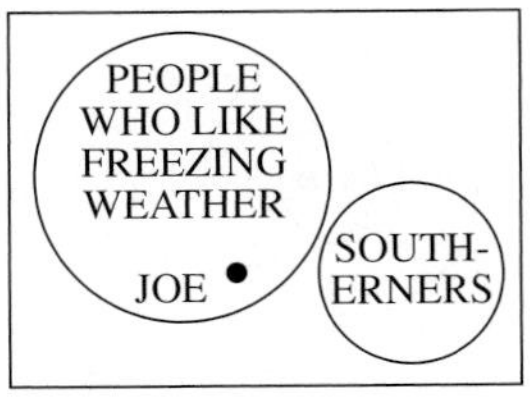

25. Invalid

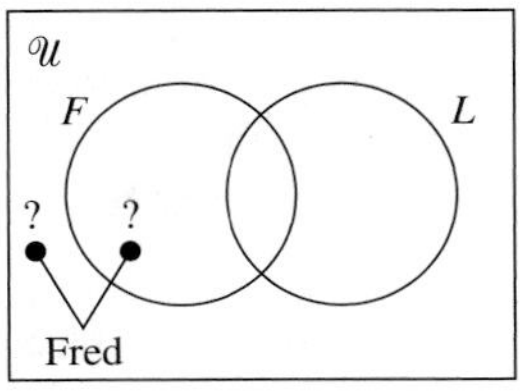

26. Invalid

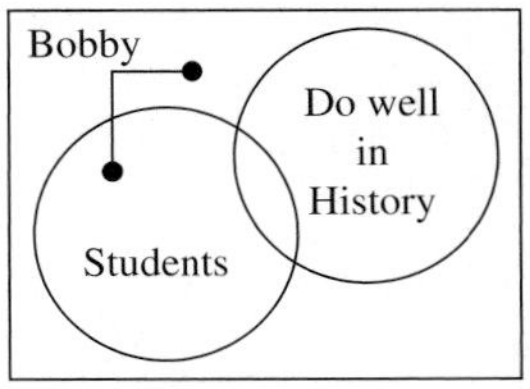

27. b.

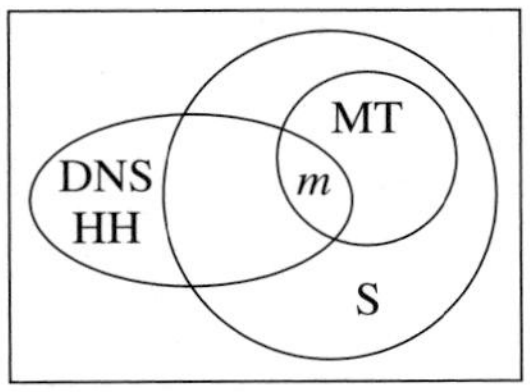

m is a salsero and does not sing hip-hop, so (**b**) is the correct conclusion.

28. Answer is a.

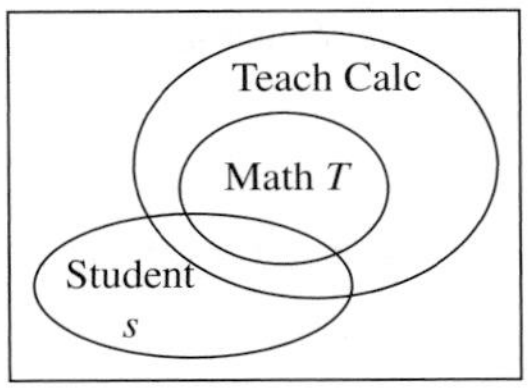

s is a student that is not a math teacher, so (**a**) is the correct conclusion.

29. a.

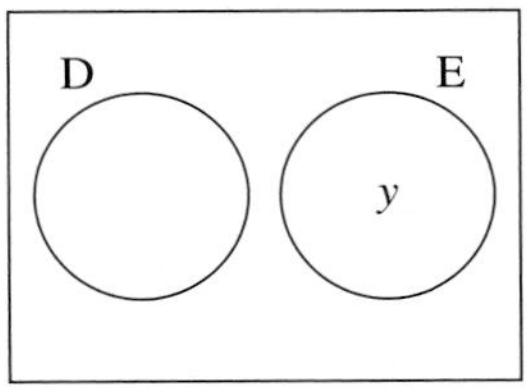

y (you) are inside Enthusiastic and outside Doctors, so you are not a doctor and the correct conclusion is (**a**).

30. Answer is b.

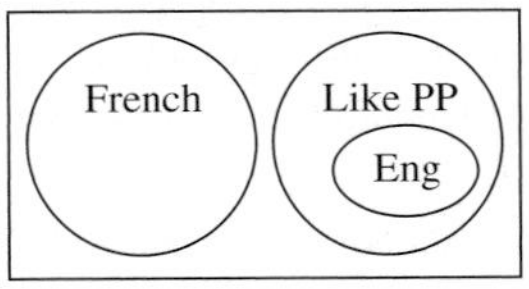

The set of Englishmen *E* does not intersect with the set of Frenchmen *F*, so (**b**) is the correct conclusion.

31. b.

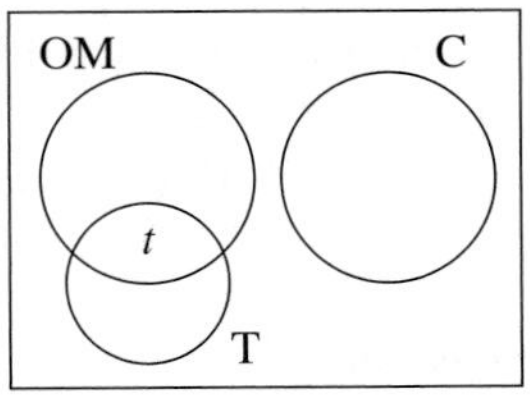

t is a thin person who is not cheerful, so (**b**) is the correct conclusion.

32. Answer is a.

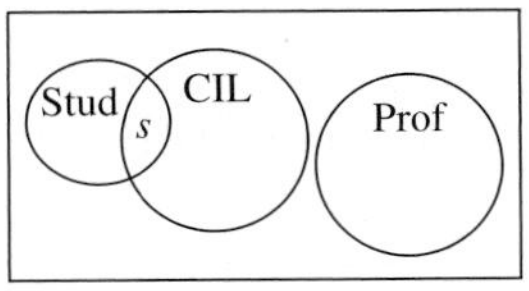

s is a student and not a professor, so (**a**) is the correct conclusion.

33. a.

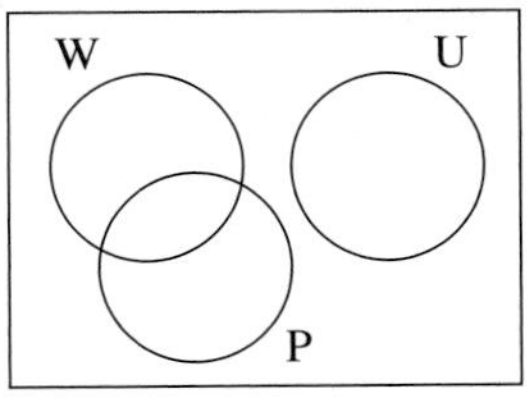

The intersection of the set of puppies *P* and the set of wasps, *W* is not necessarily empty, so no conclusion can be drawn.

34. Answer is a.

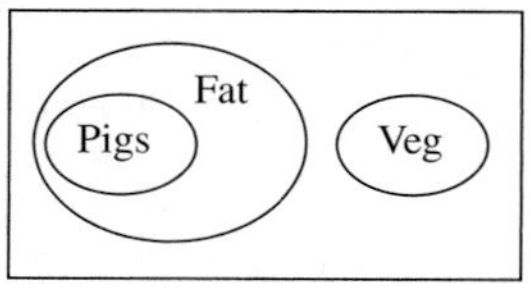

The sets F and V do not intersect, so the correct conclusion is (**a**).

35. a.

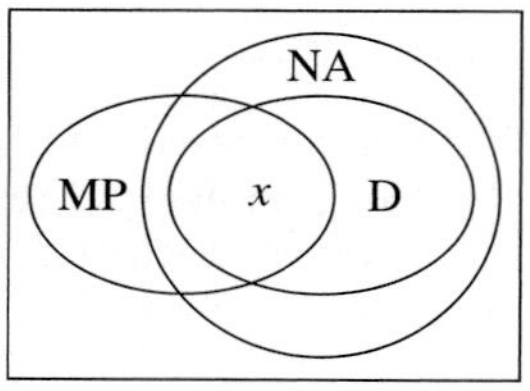

x is a difficult problem that needs attention, so the correct conclusion is (**a**).

36. Answer is a.

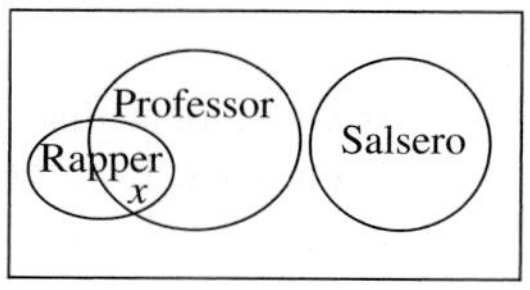

x is a rapper that is not a salsero, so (**a**) is the correct conclusion.

37. b. Statement (b) can be logically deduced from the diagram.

38.

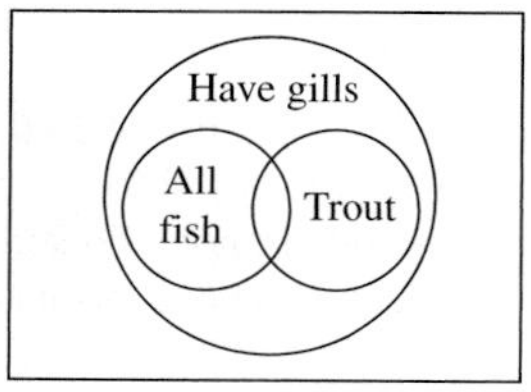

(b) is invalid

39. a. Yes, an argument is valid if and only if the conclusion is true whenever all the premises are true.

b. No. By the preceding statement, if the premises are all true and the conclusion is false, then the argument is invalid.

40. a. No. If all the premises are true and the conclusion is true, then the argument is valid.

b. Yes. If all the premises are true and the conclusion is false, then the argument is invalid.

41. No. It may be that the conclusion does not follow from the premises. See Example 2 of this section.

42. a. This is not necessarily true. Some of the premises might be true, but if the argument is valid, then at least one of the premises must be false.

b. This is true if the argument is valid.

c. If all the premises are true and the conclusion is false, then the argument must be invalid.

43. The conclusion is true.

44. Nothing. False premises can lead to any conclusion.

45. Valid

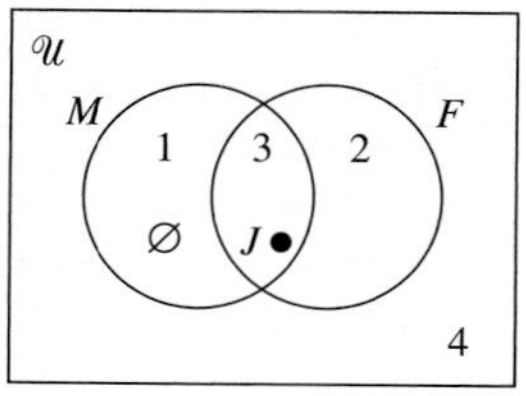

46. Invalid

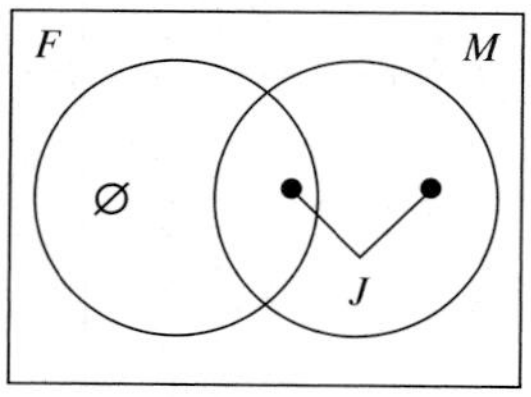

47. Invalid

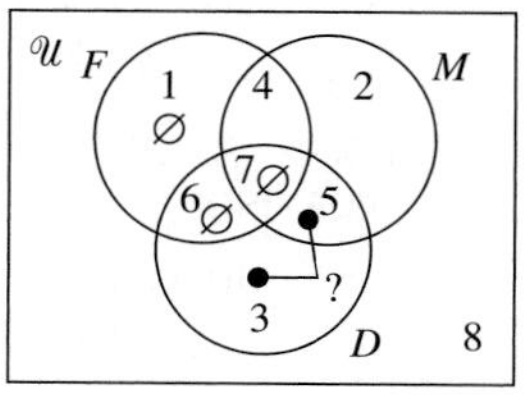

48. Invalid

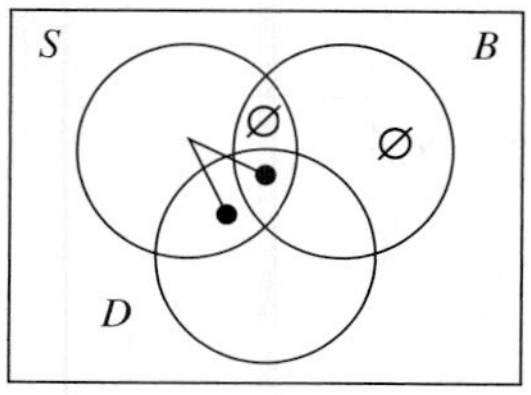

49. Invalid

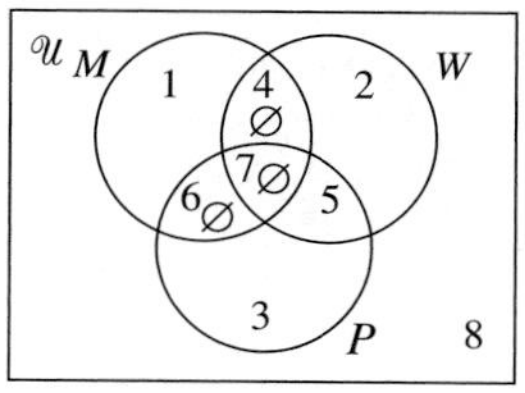

50. Valid

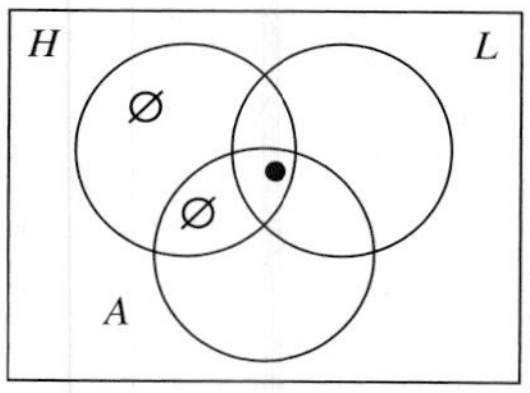

51. Invalid

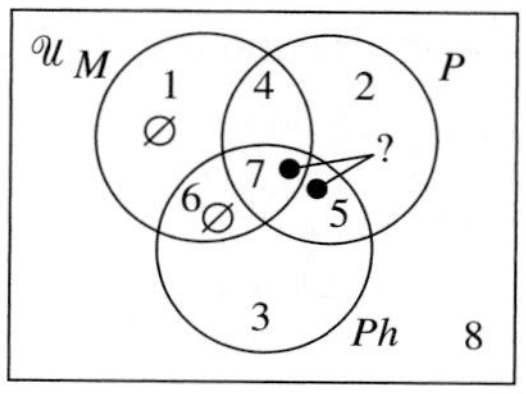

52. Valid

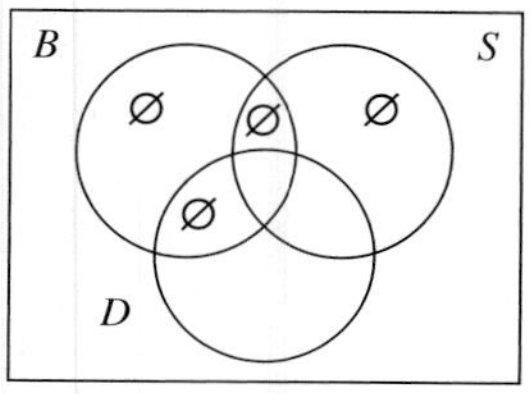

53. Valid

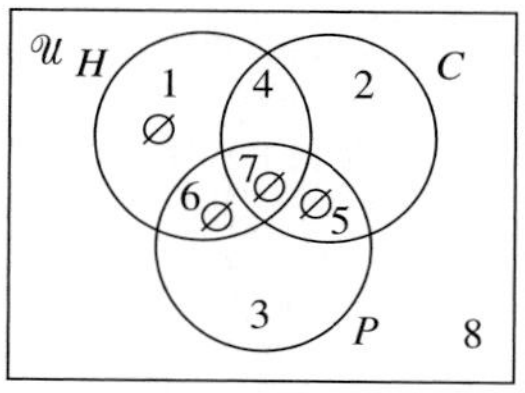

54. Invalid

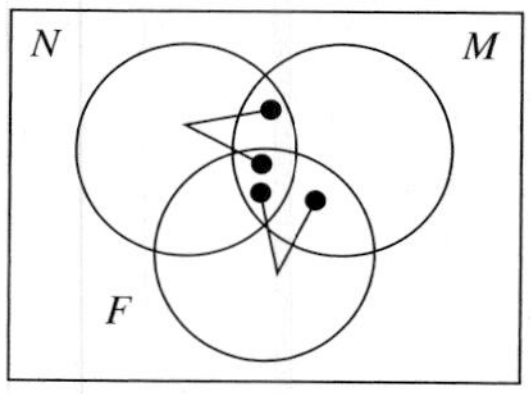

55. Only conclusion (**a**) is valid.

56.

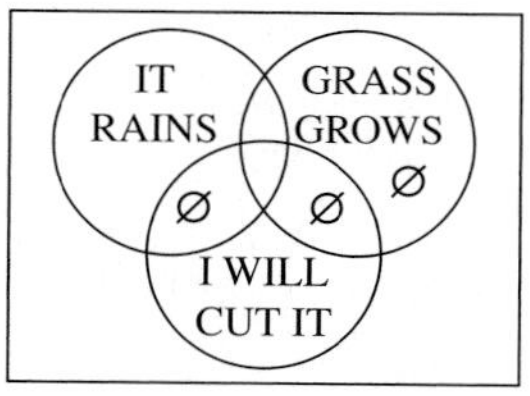

None of the conclusions are valid.

57. Yes. See the diagram.

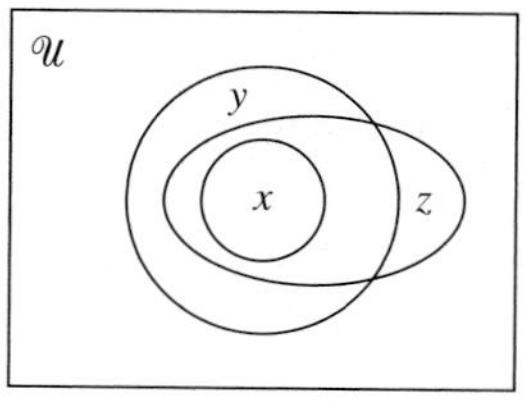

58. No z is x.

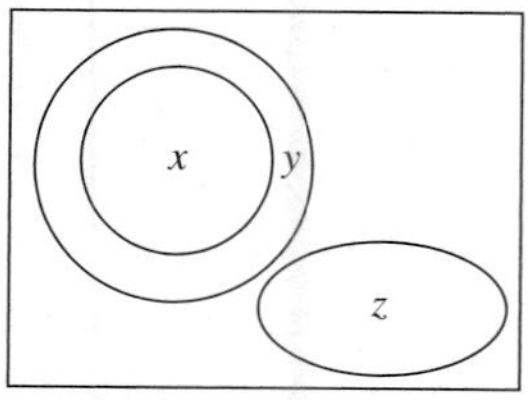

59. Some z's are y's. See the diagram.

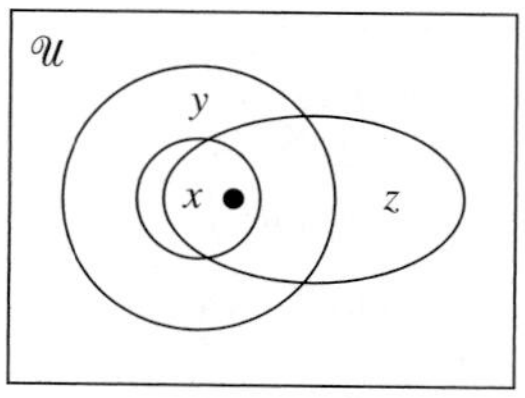

60. Yes. See Exercises 57 and 59.

Skill Checker

1.

p	q	$\sim p$	$\sim q$	$p \rightarrow \sim q$	$p \vee \sim q$	$\sim p \wedge q$
T	T	F	F	F	T	F
T	F	F	T	T	T	F
F	T	T	F	T	F	T
F	F	T	T	T	T	F

2. **a.** $\sim q \rightarrow \sim p$ **b.** $\sim p \rightarrow q$
c. $p \rightarrow q$ **d.** $q \rightarrow \sim p$

Exercises 3.6

1. $e \rightarrow p$; $\sim e$; $\therefore \sim p$ — Invalid

2. $e \rightarrow p$; $\sim p$; $\therefore \sim e$ — Valid

3. $s \rightarrow e$; $\sim e$; $\therefore \sim s$ — Valid

4. $m \vee e$; $\sim e$; $\therefore m$ — Valid

5. g; $\therefore g \wedge r$ — Invalid

6. $u \rightarrow s$; $s \rightarrow t$; $\therefore u \rightarrow t$ — Valid

7. $w \rightarrow m$; $\sim w \rightarrow g$; $\therefore m \vee g$ — Valid

8. $b \rightarrow i$; $m \rightarrow \sim d$; $i \rightarrow d$; $\therefore b \rightarrow \sim m$ — Valid

9. $t \rightarrow b$; t; $\therefore b$ — Valid

10. r; $r \rightarrow \sim g$; $\therefore \sim g$ — Valid

11. $s \rightarrow f$; s; $\therefore f$ — Valid

12. $(e \vee h) \rightarrow a$; $\sim h$; $\therefore \sim a$ — Invalid

13. $m \rightarrow e$; $\sim m$; $\therefore \sim e$ — Invalid

14. $p \rightarrow a$; $\sim a$; $\therefore \sim p$ — Valid

15. $f \rightarrow s$; $\sim f$; $\therefore \sim s$ — Invalid

16. $a \rightarrow m$; m; $\therefore a$ — Invalid

17. Valid **18.** Valid **19.** Invalid **20.** Valid
21. Valid **22.** $p \rightarrow \sim s$ **23.** $p \rightarrow r$ **24.** $p \rightarrow \sim s$
25. s **26.** $\sim p$ **27.** q
28. No supervisors are lovable.
29. No politicians are reliable.
30. Some employees will not be promoted.
31. Some students are snobs.
32. If it rains, then the grass is higher than 8 inches.
33. All romances are well written.
34. No land bird is a duck.
35. Aardvarks do not vote.
36. **a.** Some music students won't learn to play well.
37. **c.** Some college students will not pass the course.
38. **c.** No supervisors are party animals.
39. **b.** No teacher is dumb.
40. Problem 2, modus tollens;
Problem 4, disjunctive syllogism;
Problem 6, hypothetical syllogism;
Problem 11, modus ponens.
41. **c.** **42.** Conclusion d **43.** **b.** **44.** Conclusion d
45. **b.** **46.** None of these. **47.** You read *X* magazine.
48. You will be popular.
49. "Affirming the consequent" means that the "then" statement is affirmed and the "if" statement is taken as a valid conclusion. This is a fallacy because $p \rightarrow q$ is true if p is false and q is either true or false.
50. In the statement, "If p then q," p is the antecedent and q is the consequent. "Denying the antecedent" assumes "If $\sim p$ then $\sim q$" is true.
51. Kittens that will play with a gorilla do not have green eyes. (Or the equivalent: No kitten with green eyes will play with a gorilla.)

Collaborative Learning

1. The Megarian logician Eubulides of Miletus.
2. Three.
3. Answers will vary.
4. Answers will vary.
5. Answers will vary.

You can read more about sorites and see the three different types at:
http://plato.stanford.edu/entries/sorites-paradox/#Hist

CHAPTER 4

Exercises 4.1

1.  **2.** 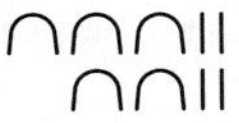 **3.** 

4.  **5.** 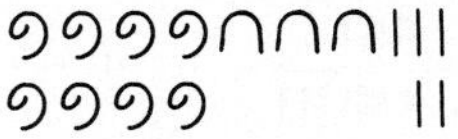

6. 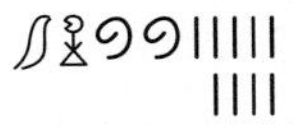 **7.** 113 **8.** 1904 **9.** 322 **10.** 45

11. 11,232 **12.** 655

13. 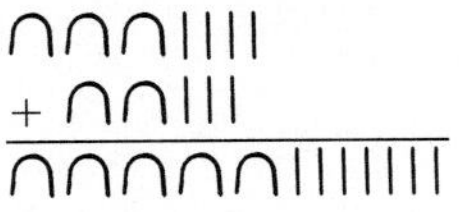 **14.** 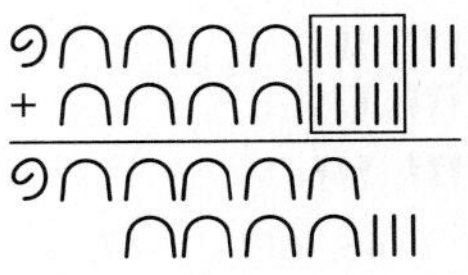

15. 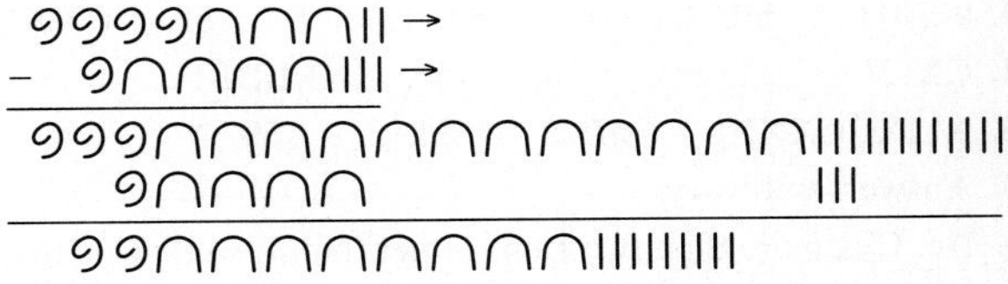

16. 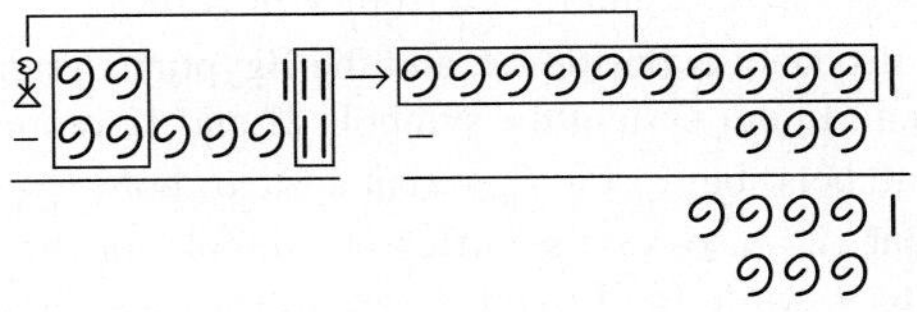

17.

\1	40
\2	80
\4	160
\8	320
15	600

18.

\1	15
2	30
4	60
\8	120
\16	240
25	375

19.

1	51
\2	102
\4	204
8	408
\16	816
22	1122

20.

\1	63
2	126
\4	252
8	504
\16	1008
21	1323

21.

18	32
9	64*
4	128
2	256
1	512*
	576*

22.

15	[32]
7	[64]
3	[128]
1	[256]
	480

23.

12	51
6	102
3	204*
1	408*
	612*

24.

40	61
20	122
10	244
5	[488]
2	976
1	[1952]
	2440

25. 𒁹𒁹𒁹𒁹𒁹𒁹 **26.** 𒌋𒌋𒁹𒁹𒁹𒁹 **27.** 𒌋𒌋𒌋𒁹𒁹 **28.** 𒁹 𒁹𒁹𒁹𒁹

29. 𒁹𒁹 𒁹𒁹𒁹 **30.** 𒁹𒁹 𒌋𒌋𒁹𒁹𒁹𒁹 **31.** 𒁹𒁹𒁹𒁹 𒌋𒁹𒁹𒁹𒁹𒁹𒁹𒁹𒁹𒁹

32. 𒁹𒁹𒁹 𒌋𒁹𒁹 **33.** 𒁹 𒁹𒁹 𒌋𒁹𒁹𒁹 **34.** 𒁹 𒁹𒁹𒁹𒁹 𒌋𒌋𒌋𒌋𒁹𒁹𒁹

35. 92 **36.** 792 **37.** 192 **38.** 843 **39.** 4322

40. 7864

41.
  𒌋𒌋𒌋𒁹𒁹
+ 𒌋𒌋𒌋𒌋𒁹𒁹𒁹
𒌋𒌋𒌋𒌋𒌋𒌋𒌋𒁹𒁹𒁹𒁹𒁹 = 𒁹 𒌋𒁹𒁹𒁹𒁹𒁹

42.
𒁹 𒁹𒁹𒁹
+ 𒁹 𒌋𒌋𒁹
𒁹𒁹 𒌋𒌋𒁹𒁹𒁹𒁹

43.
𒁹𒁹 𒌋𒁹𒁹𒁹
+ 𒁹 𒁹𒁹𒁹𒁹𒁹𒁹𒁹𒁹𒁹
𒁹𒁹𒁹 𒌋𒁹𒁹𒁹𒁹𒁹𒁹𒁹𒁹𒁹𒁹𒁹𒁹 = 𒁹𒁹𒁹 𒌋𒌋𒁹

44.
𒁹𒁹𒁹𒁹 𒁹𒁹
+ 𒁹𒁹𒁹 𒁹
𒁹𒁹𒁹𒁹𒁹𒁹𒁹 𒁹𒁹𒁹

45. 126 **46.** 617 **47.** 42,000 **48.** 30,601

49. 90,405 **50.** 450,600 **51.** LXXII **52.** DCXXXI

53. CXLV **54.** MDCCIX **55.** $\overline{\text{XXXII}}$DIII

56. $\overline{\text{XLIX}}$CCXXXI **57.** 8 **58.** 3 **59.** 4

60. Answers will vary.

61. No. C is more than two steps larger than I, so this subtraction is not allowed. I may be subtracted from V or X only.

62. Our decimal system is positional, and the Egyptian system is not positional. In our system the symbols 21 and 12 represent different numbers, but in the Egyptian system, both ∩|| and ||∩ represent 12. Also, we use different symbols for the digits from 1 to 9, while the Egyptian system uses just the corresponding number of vertical strokes. Finally, the Egyptians had no symbol for 0.

63. The Babylonian system is a base 60 system, and our decimal system is a base 10 system. Another important difference is the lack of a symbol for zero in the Babylonian system. The Babylonian system was not a good place system; it depended on spacing. The symbol for 1 was the same as that for 60, and only the spacing could show which was intended.

64. The Roman system of numeration uses both an addition and a subtraction principle to write numbers. For example, XI means $10 + 1$, while IX means $10 - 1$. Our decimal system uses the addition principle (for instance, 12 means $10 + 2$), but we do not use a subtraction principle. For large numbers, the Roman system uses an overbar. We do not use a corresponding symbol.

65. The Egyptian system was based on 10 and the Babylonian on 60. The Egyptian system was not a positional system; it depended essentially on the addition of the symbol values. The Babylonian system used spacing to change symbol values.

66. The spacing between the symbol for 10 and the five wedges for 5 is the only difference between 605 and 15. Unless this spacing is very distinct, the number would be read as 15 rather than 605.

67. Assume the answer is 6. $6 + (\frac{1}{6})(6) = 7$ and $21 \div 7 = 3$. Hence, the correct answer is $3 \times 6 = 18$.

68. Assume that the answer is 8. $8 + \frac{1}{2} \cdot 8 + \frac{1}{4} \cdot 8 = 14$ and $28 \div 14 = 2$. Therefore, the correct answer is $2 \cdot 8 = 16$.

69. Assume the answer is 3. $3 + (\frac{2}{3})(3) = 5$. $5 - (\frac{1}{3})(5) = \frac{10}{3}$ and $10 \div \frac{10}{3} = 3$. Therefore, the correct answer is $3 \times 3 = 9$.

70. $n = 9$ **71.** $n = 8$ **72.** $n = 14$

Exercises 4.2

1. $(4 \times 10^2) + (3 \times 10) + (2 \times 10^0)$

2. $(5 \times 10^2) + (4 \times 10) + (9 \times 10^0)$

3. $(2 \times 10^3) + (3 \times 10^2) + (7 \times 10^0)$

4. $(3 \times 10^3) + (4 \times 10) + (7 \times 10^0)$

5. $(1 \times 10^4) + (2 \times 10^3) + (3 \times 10^2) + (4 \times 10) + (9 \times 10^0)$

6. $(1 \times 10^4) + (9 \times 10^2) + (5 \times 10)$

7. 1 **8.** 34 **9.** 45 **10.** 432 **11.** 9071

12. 70,002 **13.** 748,308 **14.** 8,000,300,204

15. 4,000,031

16.

32	$(3 \times 10) + (2 \times 10^0)$
+ 15	$+ (1 \times 10) + (5 \times 10^0)$
47	$(4 \times 10) + (7 \times 10^0)$

17.

23	$(2 \times 10) + (3 \times 10^0)$
+ 13	$(1 \times 10) + (3 \times 10^0)$
36	$(3 \times 10) + (6 \times 10^0)$

18.

21	$(2 \times 10) + (1 \times 10^0)$
+ 34	$+ (3 \times 10) + (4 \times 10^0)$
55	$(5 \times 10) + (5 \times 10^0)$

19.

71	$(7 \times 10) + (1 \times 10^0)$
+ 23	$(2 \times 10) + (3 \times 10^0)$
94	$(9 \times 10) + (4 \times 10^0)$

20.

34	$(3 \times 10) + (4 \times 10^0)$
− 21	$- (2 \times 10) + (1 \times 10^0)$
13	$(1 \times 10) + (3 \times 10^0)$

21.

76	$(7 \times 10) + (6 \times 10^0)$
− 54	$(-)(5 \times 10) + (4 \times 10^0)$
22	$(2 \times 10) + (2 \times 10^0)$

22. $\begin{array}{r} 45 \\ -\ 22 \\ \hline 23 \end{array}$ $\quad \begin{array}{r} (4 \times 10) + (5 \times 10^0) \\ -\ (2 \times 10) + (2 \times 10^0) \\ \hline (2 \times 10) + (3 \times 10^0) \end{array}$

23. $\begin{array}{r} 84 \\ -\ 31 \\ \hline 53 \end{array}$ $\quad \begin{array}{r} (8 \times 10) + (4 \times 10^0) \\ (-)(3 \times 10) + (1 \times 10^0) \\ \hline (5 \times 10) + (3 \times 10^0) \end{array}$

24. 3^{14} **25.** 7^{11} **26.** 4^7 **27.** 6^{40} **28.** 5^5

29. 6^7 **30.** 7^{12} **31.** 6^{12} **32.** 3^8 **33.** 5^{12}

34. 7^{15} **35.** 10^{30}

36. $\begin{array}{r} 41 \\ \times\ 23 \\ \hline 123 \\ 82 \\ \hline 943 \end{array}$ $\quad \begin{array}{r} (4 \times 10) + (1 \times 10^0) \\ \times\ (2 \times 10) + (3 \times 10^0) \\ \hline (1 \times 10^2) + (2 \times 10) + (3 \times 10^0) \\ (8 \times 10^2) + (2 \times 10) \\ \hline (9 \times 10^2) + (4 \times 10) + (3 \times 10^0) \end{array}$

37. $\begin{array}{r} 25 \\ \times\ 51 \\ \hline 25 \\ 125 \\ \hline 1275 \end{array}$ $\quad \begin{array}{r} (2 \times 10) + (5 \times 10^0) \\ \times\ (5 \times 10) + (1 \times 10^0) \\ \hline (2 \times 10) + (5 \times 10^0) \\ (10 \times 10^2) + (25 \times 10) \\ \hline 10^3 + (27 \times 10) + (5 \times 10^0) \end{array}$

$= (1 \times 10^3) + (2 \times 10^2) + (7 \times 10) + (5 \times 10^0)$
$= 1275$

38. $\begin{array}{r} 91 \\ \times\ 24 \\ \hline 364 \\ 182 \\ \hline 2184 \end{array}$ $\quad \begin{array}{r} (9 \times 10) + (1 \times 10^0) \\ \times\ (2 \times 10) + (4 \times 10^0) \\ \hline (3 \times 10^2) + (6 \times 10) + (4 \times 10^0) \\ (18 \times 10^2) + (2 \times 10) \\ \hline (21 \times 10^2) + (8 \times 10) + (4 \times 10^0) \end{array}$

$= (2 \times 10^3) + (1 \times 10^2) + (8 \times 10) + (4 \times 10^0)$

39. $\begin{array}{r} 62 \\ \times\ 25 \\ \hline 310 \\ 124 \\ \hline 1550 \end{array}$ $\quad \begin{array}{r} (6 \times 10) + (2 \times 10^0) \\ \times\ (2 \times 10) + (5 \times 10^0) \\ \hline (30 \times 10) + (10 \times 10^0) \\ (12 \times 10^2) + (\ 4 \times 10) \\ \hline (12 \times 10^2) + (34 \times 10) + (10 \times 10^0) \end{array}$

$= (1 \times 10^3) + (5 \times 10^2) + (5 \times 10)$
$= 1550$

40. $\begin{array}{r} 12 \\ 4\overline{)48} \\ \underline{4} \\ 8 \\ \underline{8} \\ 0 \end{array}$ $\quad \begin{array}{r} (1 \times 10) + (2 \times 10^0) \\ 4 \times 10^0\overline{)(4 \times 10) + (8 \times 10^0)} \\ \underline{(4 \times 10)} \\ (8 \times 10^0) \\ \underline{(8 \times 10^0)} \\ 0 \end{array}$

41. $\begin{array}{r} 8 \\ 8\overline{)64} \\ \underline{64} \\ 0 \end{array}$ $\quad \begin{array}{r} (8 \times 10^0) \\ 8 \times 10^0\overline{)(6 \times 10) + (4 \times 10^0)} \\ \underline{(6 \times 10) + (4 \times 10^0)} \\ 0 \end{array}$

42. $\begin{array}{r} 31 \\ 3\overline{)93} \\ \underline{9} \\ 3 \\ \underline{3} \\ 0 \end{array}$ $\quad \begin{array}{r} (3 \times 10) + (1 \times 10^0) \\ 3 \times 10^0\overline{)(9 \times 10) + (3 \times 10^0)} \\ \underline{(9 \times 10)} \\ (3 \times 10^0) \\ \underline{(3 \times 10^0)} \\ 0 \end{array}$

43. $\begin{array}{r} 12 \\ 6\overline{)72} \\ \underline{6} \\ 12 \\ \underline{12} \\ 0 \end{array}$ $\quad \begin{array}{r} (1 \times 10) + (2 \times 10^0) \\ (6 \times 10^0)\overline{)(7 \times 10) + (2 \times 10^0)} \\ \underline{(6 \times 10)} \\ \underline{(1 \times 10) + (2 \times 10^0)} \\ \underline{(1 \times 10) + (2 \times 10^0)} \\ 0 \end{array}$

44. 1.5×10^9 lb **45.** 3×10^5 **46.** 1.1×10^7 pet reptiles

47. 7.735×10^7 dogs **48.** 2.4×10^6 searches/day

49. 1.6×10^6 searches **50.** 1.28×10^{11} lb

51. 6.4×10^{10} lb **52.** 6.464×10^9 lb **53.** 1.8816×10^{10} lb

54. 4.448×10^9 lb **55.** 7.68×10^9 gal **56.** 1.6×10^{10} gal

57. 5 lb **58.** $8.46 \times 10^9 = 8{,}460{,}000{,}000$ lb

59. $7.56 \times 10^9 = 7{,}560{,}000{,}000$ lb **60.** 2

61. You must add the exponents; you obtain a^{m+n}.

62. Write a with the exponent $m - n$.

63. You must multiply the exponent m by the exponent n; you obtain a^{mn}.

64. The answer should be 1 if $a \neq 0$. Thus, if we write $\frac{a^m}{a^n} = a^{m-n} = a^0$, then we should define a^0 to be 1.

65. There were 137,256 in all on the road to Rome.

66. There was only one going to St. Ives (if the traveler meets the others going in the opposite direction). If all travelers were going to St. Ives, the total would be 1 + 1 + 2800 = 2802. If only the kits, cats, sacks, and wives are counted, 2800 were going to St. Ives.

Exercises 4.3

1. 22_{three} **2.** 33_{five} **3.** 31_{four} **4.** 36_{ten}

5. [********] *******; 17_{eight}

6. [*****] [*****] [*****] = 30_{five}

7. [*******] [*******] *; 21_{seven}

8. [************] *** = 13_{twelve}

9. 22 **10.** 16 **11.** 139 **12.** 371 **13.** 27

14. 41 **15.** 291 **16.** 2766 **17.** 30_{five} **18.** 102_{five}

19. 11100_{two} **20.** 101011_{two} **21.** 19_{sixteen}

22. 79_{sixteen} **23.** 41_{six} **24.** 102_{six} **25.** 121_{seven}

26. 234_{seven} **27.** 46_{eight} **28.** 207_{eight} **29.** $5BB_{\text{sixteen}}$

30. $2376F_{\text{sixteen}}$ **31.** $73 = 1001001_{\text{two}} = 111_{\text{eight}}$

32. $87 = 127_{\text{eight}} = 57_{\text{sixteen}}$

33.

00110	01010	00101	00011	01100
3	5	2	1	6

34. 01010 00110 01001 00011 01010, 53415

35.

01001	00101	00011	00110	01010
4	2	1	3	5

36. 10010 11000 10001 01001 00110, 80743

37. **38.**

39. **40.**

41. Yes. The zip code has nine digits, but the tenth digit is the checking number.

42. **(a)** 6 **(b)** 3 + 3 + 6 + 7 + 5 = 24
2 + 4 = 6 ← Check digit

43. One of the meanings of *binary* is "based on two." The prefix *bi-* means "two."

44. Octal means related to or being a number in the base 8 number system. The prefix oct means eight.

45. *Hexadecimal* means "based on 16." The prefix *hexa-* means "six."

46. We can't use more than one decimal digit because in the base 16 system, $10_{16} = 16$, $11_{16} = 16 + 1 = 17$, and so on. Thus, we use letters to correspond to the base 10 numbers 10, 11, 12, 13, 14, and 15.

47. The trick works because the columns correspond to the binary digits in the number. For instance, $6 = 110_{\text{two}}$ and this corresponds to the number $6 = 2 + 4$, the numbers that head columns B and C. Note that 6 occurs in columns B and C, but not in A.

48. Four

49. Use the same procedure as for the numbers from 1 to 7 but with five columns instead of three.

Calculator Corner

1. 13 **2.** 45 **3.** 113 **4.** 490 **5.** 1914 **6.** 714

Collaborative Learning

1. 36 (Base 1, Base 2... Base 10, Base 11 (using A), Base 12 (using A, B), etc).

2. Answers will vary. **3.** Answers will vary.

4. Answers will vary.

You can read more about prime words by visiting http://www.cut-the-knot.org/recurrence/word_primes.shtml

Exercises 4.4

1. 1001_2 **2.** 1100_2 **3.** 10011_2 **4.** 11100_2
5. 10010_2 **6.** 100000_2 **7.** 600_8 **8.** 1011_8
9. 10112_8 **10.** 6701_8 **11.** 417_{16} **12.** 533_{16}
13. $9B8_{16}$ **14.** $D6C_{16}$ **15.** 101_2 **16.** 11_2 **17.** 1_2
18. 110_2 **19.** 1010_2 **20.** 101_2 **21.** 507_8 **22.** 550_8
23. 2306_8 **24.** 4107_8 **25.** 10010_2 **26.** 1010_2
27. 101101_2 **28.** 1100010_2 **29.** 110111_2
30. 1001101_2 **31.** 432_8 **32.** 403_8 **33.** 7154_8
34. 24722_8 **35.** $A367_{16}$ **36.** $579C_{16}$ **37.** $4A451_{16}$
38. 249306_{16} **39.** 110_2 R 1_2 **40.** 100_2 R 1_2
41. 100_2 R 10_2 **42.** 1001_2 **43.** 1011_2 R 100_2
44. 10001_2 **45.** 35_8 R 4_8 **46.** 711_8 **47.** 250_8 R 5_8
48. 230 R 12_8
51. Answers will vary depending on the number chosen.
52. 7 **53.** 55 **54.** Closer to black **55.** 000001_2
56. 111110_2

Collaborative Learning

1. Yes. No. **2.** Yes. Answers will vary. **3.** 272

CHAPTER 5

Exercises 5.1

1. For identification only **2.** Ordinal number

3. A cardinal number **4.** Cardinal numbers

5. The "First" is for identification; the "one" is an ordinal number.

6. 14, an ordinal number; 5696, a cardinal number; 0166, for identification.

7.

51	52	53	54	55	56	57	58	59	60
61	62	63	64	65	66	67	68	69	70
71	72	73	74	75	76	77	78	79	80
81	82	83	84	85	86	87	88	89	90
91	92	93	94	95	96	97	98	99	100

The primes in the table are circled.

8. 9 **9.** 6 **10.** 6 **11.** 4 **12. a.** 2 **b.** 2

13. a. 2 and 3

b. No. If any pair of consecutive counting numbers greater than 2 is selected, one of the pair must be an even number (divisible by 2) and, hence, not a prime.

14. 5 and 7, 11 and 13, 17 and 19, 29 and 31, 41 and 43

15. a. The product part of m is exactly divisible by 2, so that m divided by 2 would have a remainder of 1.

b. The product part of m is exactly divisible by 3, so that m divided by 3 would have a remainder of 1.

c.–d. Exactly the same reasoning as in parts **(a)** and **(b)** applies here. If m is divided by any prime from 2 to P, there is a remainder of 1.

e. Because P was assumed to be the largest prime.

f. Because m is not divisible by any of the primes from 2 to P.

16. 1, 2, 4, 7, 14, 28 **17.** 1, 2, 5, 10, 25, 50

18. 1, 7, 17, 119 **19.** 1, 2, 4, 8, 16, 32, 64, 128

20. 1, 3, 5, 7, 13, 15, 21, 35, 39, 65, 91, 105, 195, 273, 455, 1365

21. 1, 7, 11, 13, 77, 91, 143, 1001 **22.** $2^3 \cdot 3$

23. 41 is a prime. **24.** $2 \cdot 41$ **25.** $91 = 7 \times 13$

26. 191 is a prime **27.** $148 = 2^2 \times 37$ **28.** 450

29. 490 **30.** 330 **31.** 1200

32. a. Divisible by 2 and by 3

b. Divisible by 2 and by 5

c. Divisible by 3 and by 5

d. Divisible by 2 and by 3

33. a. Divisible by 3 and by 5

b. Divisible by 2, by 3, and by 5

c. Divisible by 2, by 3, and by 5

34. $\boxed{36} = 9 \cdot 4 = 5 \cdot 7 + 1 = 7 \cdot 5 + 1$

35. Three: 2, 11, and 22 **36.** GCF $(14, 210) = 14$

37. 27 **38.** GCF $(315, 350) = 35$ **39.** Relatively prime

40. GCF $(368, 80) = 16$ **41.** 47

42. GCF $(12, 18, 30) = 6$ **43.** Relatively prime

44. GCF $(285, 315, 588) = 3$ **45.** 20 **46.** $\frac{20}{23}$

47. $\frac{31}{44}$ **48.** $\frac{1}{2}$ **49.** $\frac{3}{14}$ **50.** $\frac{3}{4}$ **51.** $\frac{1}{4}$

52. $\frac{716}{4235}$ is already in lowest terms. **53.** LCM $= 165$; $\frac{14}{165}$

54. LCM $(17, 136) = 136$; $\frac{9}{136}$ **55.** LCM $= 992$; $\frac{101}{992}$

56. LCM $(124, 155) = 620$; $\frac{19}{620}$ **57.** LCM $= 720$; $\frac{7}{720}$

58. LCM $(284, 568) = 568$; $\frac{7}{568}$ **59.** LCM $= 180$; $\frac{31}{180}$

60. LCM $(12, 15, 20) = 60$; $\frac{1}{5}$ **61.** LCM $= 167{,}580$; $\frac{281}{33{,}516}$

62. LCM $(100, 200, 320) = 1600$; $\frac{29}{1600}$

63. LCM $= 4200$; $\frac{3}{280}$ **64.** 12 hr **65.** 12 hr

66. 20 days **67.** 20 days **68.** $\frac{13}{40}$ **69.** $\frac{3}{10}$

70. a. 53 **b.** 61 **c.** 1681 **d.** No. $1681 = 41^2$

71. a. $100 = 3 + 97 = 11 + 89 = 17 + 83$
$= 29 + 71 = 41 + 59 = 47 + 53$

b. $200 = 3 + 197 = 7 + 193 = 19 + 181$
$= 37 + 163 = 43 + 157 = 61 + 139$
$= 73 + 127 = 97 + 103$

72. a. $20 = 2 + 7 + 11$ or $20 = 2 + 5 + 13$

b. $43 = 2 + 7 + 11 + 23$ or $43 = 2 + 2 + 2 + 37$

73. The number 1 has only one divisor: itself. It is not a prime because a prime must have exactly *two distinct* divisors, 1 and itself. It is not a composite number because it has only one divisor.

74. The number 1 is neither prime nor composite.

75. The largest prime that you need to try is 13, because the next prime is 17 and $17^2 = 289$, which is greater than 211.

76. If there were only a finite number of primes, we could select the largest. Since Euclid proved that there is no largest prime, the number of primes must be infinite.

77. All the other digits are multiples of 3, so their sum is divisible by 3. Thus, only the sum of 2 and 7 needs to be checked.

78. No. $5 + 7 + 1 = 13$, not divisible by 3.

79. Since 999 and 99 and 9 are all divisible by 9, only the sum

$$2 \times 1 + 8 \times 1 + 5 \times 1 + 3$$

which is exactly the sum of the digits, needs to be checked. If this sum is divisible by 9, the original number is divisible by 9, and not otherwise.

80. **a.** Divisible by 9, not by 6
b. Not divisible by either 6 or 9
c. Divisible by 9 and by 6
d. Divisible by 6, not by 9

81. **a.** Divisible by 4, not by 8
b. Divisible by 4 and by 8
c. Divisible by 4 and by 8
d. Divisible by 4, not by 8

82. **a.** Divisible by 10 and by 12
b. Not divisible by 10 or by 12
c. Divisible by 10 and by 12
d. Divisible by 10, not by 12

83. None of the numbers 1, 2, 3, 4, or 5 is the sum of its proper divisors. Therefore, 6 is the smallest perfect number.

84. 28

85. $496 = 1 + 2 + 4 + 8 + 16 + 31 + 62 + 124 + 248$. so 496 is a perfect number.

86. 8 is not a perfect number because $1 + 2 + 4 = 7 < 8$.

87. All primes are deficient because they have only 1 as a proper divisor.

88. Yes. This is so because all primes are deficient.

89. They end in 6 or 28. Also, they are sums of powers of 2; $6 = 2 + 2^2$, $28 = 2^4 + 2^3 + 2^2$, and so on.

90. 1111111111100000000. No.

Collaborative Learning

1. $2^{17} - 1$ and $2^{19} - 1$ are prime.

2. 23, 29, and 37 do not produce primes in $2^n - 1$.

3. In 1644 Mersenne claimed that $2^n - 1$ is prime if $n = 2, 3, 5, 7, 13, 17, 19, 31, 67, 127$ and 257 but composite for the other 44 primes smaller than 257.

Over the years it has been found that Mersenne was wrong about 5 of the primes less than or equal to 257 (he claimed two that didn't lead to a prime (67 and 257) and missed 3 that did: 61, 89, 107).

4. Answers will vary.

Exercises 5.2

1. -9 **2.** -11 **3.** 10 **4.** 17 **5.** 0 **6.** 14
7. 27 **8.** 24 **9.** 16 **10.** 19 **11.** 2 **12.** 3
13. 7 **14.** 13 **15.** 5 **16.** 2 **17.** -13 **18.** -9
19. 8 **20.** -11 **21.** $3 + (-8) = -5$
22. $8 + (-3) = 5$ **23.** $3 + (-4) = -1$
24. $-3 + (-4) = -7$ **25.** $-5 + (-2) = -7$
26. $-3 + (-5) = -8$ **27.** $5 + (+6) = 11$
28. $6 + (+3) = 9$ **29.** $-3 + (+4) = 1$
30. $-5 + (+6) = 1$ **31.** 32 **32.** 36 **33.** -56
34. -40 **35.** -10 **36.** -81 **37.** 20 **38.** 18
39. 70 **40.** 18 **41.** 5 **42.** 7 **43.** -4
44. -5 **45.** -5 **46.** -3 **47.** -10 **48.** -16
49. -20 **50.** -7 **51.** 7 **52.** 4 **53.** 14 **54.** 23
55. Not defined **56.** 0 **57.** 0 **58.** Not defined
59. Not defined **60.** 0 **61.** 64 **62.** -64
63. -36 **64.** 36 **65.** -216 **66.** -216
67. 81 **68.** -81 **69.** -64 **70.** -64
71. **a.** -27 **b.** 4 **72.** **a.** 4 **b.** 10
73. **a.** -9 **b.** -5 **74.** **a.** -1 **b.** -5
75. 10 **76.** 32 **77.** -5 **78.** 12
79. 11,800 **80.** 0 **81.** 10 **82.** 7
83. 20 **84.** 20 **85.** -14; 492 **86.** -23; 491
87. $+19$; 525 **88.** $+19$; 533 **89.** $+53$; 559
90. -19 **91.** $5(-4)$; -20°F **92.** $10(-4)$; -40°F
93. $15(-4)$; -60°F **94.** $3(-7)$; -21°C
95. $5(-7)$; -35°F **96.** $6(-7)$; -42°C
97. $50 + 7(-4)$; 22°F **98.** $50 + 13(-4) = -2$°F
99. $10 + 4(-7)$; -18°C **100.** $5 + 4(-7) = -23$°C
104. -3 **105.** 0 **106.** 0

Collaborative Learning

1. 1089

2. No

Exercises 5.3

1. Numerator 3, denominator 4
2. Numerator 4, denominator 5
3. Numerator 3, denominator -5
4. Numerator -4, denominator 5
5. $\frac{17}{41} = \frac{289}{697}$ **6.** $\frac{19}{23} = \frac{323}{391}$ **7.** $\frac{11}{91} = \frac{253}{2093}$ **8.** $\frac{2}{3}$
9. $\frac{5}{2}$ **10.** $\frac{21}{43}$ **11.** $\frac{7}{16}$ **12.** $\frac{5}{4}$ **13.** $\frac{15}{14}$ **14.** $\frac{2}{3}$
15. $\frac{2}{3}$ **16.** $\frac{8}{3}$ **17.** $\frac{14}{18}$ **18.** $\frac{42}{18} + \frac{14}{18} + \frac{15}{18} = \frac{71}{18}$
19. $\frac{11}{18}$ **20.** $\frac{10}{21}$ **21.** $\frac{16}{63}$ **22.** $\frac{43}{77}$ **23.** $\frac{19}{12}$ **24.** $\frac{17}{36}$
25. $\frac{176}{323}$ **26.** $\frac{4}{21}$ **27.** $\frac{2}{63}$ **28.** $\frac{1}{77}$ **29.** $-\frac{1}{12}$
30. $\frac{11}{36}$ **31.** $\frac{62}{323}$ **32.** $\frac{3}{14}$ **33.** $\frac{2}{3}$ **34.** $\frac{7}{24}$ **35.** $\frac{21}{8}$
36. $\frac{6}{25}$ **37.** $\frac{56}{27}$ **38.** $-\frac{8}{45}$ **39.** $\frac{18}{77}$ **40.** $-\frac{36}{35}$
41. $\frac{9}{14}$ **42.** $-\frac{15}{4}$ **43.** $-\frac{1}{6}$ **44.** $-\frac{11}{28}$ **45.** $\frac{1}{8}$
46. $\frac{35}{24}$ **47.** $\frac{1}{4}$ **48.** $\frac{3}{140}$ **49.** $\frac{49}{80}$ **50.** 1 **51.** 16
52. $\frac{13}{8}$ **53.** $\frac{3}{2}$ **54.** $\frac{1}{24}$ **55.** $\frac{2}{5}$ **56.** $\frac{2}{3}$
57. $1\frac{9}{14}$ 58. $3\frac{2}{3}$ **59.** $\frac{2}{7}$ **60.** -2 **61.** $3\frac{5}{12}$
62. $1\frac{3}{4}$ **63.** $\frac{3}{7}$ **64.** -5 **65.** $-\frac{3}{4}$ **66.** $1\frac{1}{3}$
67. -18 **68.** -3 **69.** $-\frac{4}{5}$ **70.** $2\frac{1}{4}$
71. -30 **72.** $\frac{7}{30}$ **73.** $7\frac{1}{8}$ **74.** $-1\frac{1}{8}$ **75.** $2\frac{5}{8}$
76. $\frac{1}{2}$ **77.** 0 **78.** $-\frac{3}{8}$ **79.** $-\frac{2}{9}$ **80.** $1\frac{1}{4}$
81. $-5\frac{3}{4}$ **82.** $-2\frac{3}{5}$ **83.** $1\frac{1}{6}$ **84.** $1\frac{7}{12}$ **85.** $\frac{1}{2}$
86. $\frac{37}{90}$ **87.** $\frac{7}{36}$ **88.** $\frac{13}{60}$ **89.** $3\frac{7}{15}$ **90.** $1\frac{7}{15}$
91. $(6 \times 10^2) + (9 \times 10) + (2 \times 10^0) + (8 \times 10^{-2}) + (7 \times 10^{-3})$

92. $(3 \times 10) + (2 \times 10^{-1}) + (9 \times 10^{-2}) + (5 \times 10^{-3}) + (9 \times 10^{-4})$

93. $(1 \times 10^{-3}) + (7 \times 10^{-5})$

94. $(4 \times 10^{0}) + (3 \times 10^{-1}) + (8 \times 10^{-5})$

95. 5020.39 **96.** 405.0609 **97.** 0.004702

98. 0.2504 **99.** 9.35×10^{2} **100.** 3.72×10^{-1}

101. 1.2×10^{-3} **102.** 3.453×10^{6} **103.** 86,400

104. 90,100,000 **105.** 0.00671 **106.** 0.000000402

107. 2×10^{-8} **108.** 1.667×10^{3}

109. 6.82×10^{-1} **110.** 1.715×10^{-2}

111. 3×10^{-2} **112.** 1×10^{3}

113. a. 4.74 **b.** -4.74

114. a. 17.657 **b.** -19.623

115. a. -4.158 **b.** -5.864

116. a. 6.696 **b.** 6.696

117. a. 0.045 **b.** 0.128

118. a. 205 **b.** 36

119. a. -0.05 **b.** 0.02

120. a. -20 **b.** -300

121. $\frac{1}{12}$ **122.** $\frac{1}{6}$ **123.** $\frac{1}{12}$

124. a. 8.0592×10^{9} **b.** 8,059,200,000

125. a. 9.8112×10^{9} **b.** 9,811,200,000

126. 87

127. a. 144 **b.** 126

128. a. $99.99 **b.** $77.99

129. 62.26 **130.** 62.92 **131.** 64.17 **132.** Yes; Yes

135. 0.06 **136.** 0.07 **137.** 0.10

Exercises 5.4

1. 0.9 **2.** 0.3 **3.** 1.1 **4.** 2.7 **5.** 0.17

6. 0.38 **7.** 1.21 **8.** 35.20 **9.** 0.003 **10.** 0.143

11. 1.243 **12.** 25.360 **13.** 0.6 **14.** 0.875

15. 0.5625 **16.** 0.46875 **17.** 0.625

18. 1.25 **19.** 0.714285 · · · **20.** 1.1666 · · ·

21. 0.266 · · · **22.** 6.25 **23.** 7.142857 · · ·

24. 3.666 · · · **25.** 0.1875

26. No terminating decimal expansion.

27. 0.015625

28. No terminating decimal expansion.

29. 0.00992 **30.** 0.036 **31.** $0.\overline{5}$ **32.** $0.\overline{7}$

33. $0.\overline{64}$ **34.** $0.\overline{73}$ **35.** $0.\overline{235}$ **36.** $0.\overline{930}$

37. $0.21\overline{5}$ **38.** $0.713\overline{2}$ **39.** $0.079\overline{35}$ **40.** $0.23\overline{51}$

41. $5.\overline{07}$ **42.** $9.23\overline{37}$ **43.** $\frac{8}{9}$ **44.** $\frac{2}{3}$ **45.** $\frac{31}{99}$

46. $\frac{7}{33}$ **47.** $\frac{38}{333}$ **48.** $\frac{34}{333}$ **49.** $\frac{229}{99}$ **50.** $\frac{1889}{333}$

51. $\frac{137}{111}$ **52.** $\frac{17}{999}$ **53.** $\frac{14}{11}$ **54.** $\frac{112}{45}$ **55.** $\frac{151}{330}$

56. $\frac{191}{825}$ **57.** $\frac{224}{1111}$ **58.** $\frac{121}{600}$ **59.** 0.29 **60.** 0.234

61. 0.009 **62.** 0.569 **63.** 0.4569 **64.** 0.00008

65. 0.3415 **66.** 0.9356 **67.** 0.000234 **68.** 38%

69. 345% **70.** 999.8% **71.** 56.7% **72.** 0.452%

73. 900.3% **74.** 0.04% **75.** 0.45% **76.** 0.08%

77. 60% **78.** 57.1% **79.** 83.3% **80.** 87.5%

81. Irrational **82.** Rational **83.** Irrational

84. Rational **85.** Rational **86.** Irrational

87. Rational **88.** Rational **89.** Rational

90. Rational **91.** Rational **92.** Irrational

93. Irrational **94.** Rational **95.** Rational

96. Rational **97.** Irrational **98.** Irrational

99. Rational **100.** Rational **101.** Irrational

102. $<$ **103.** $>$ **104.** $<$ **105.** $<$ **106.** $=$

107. $>$ **108.** $<$ **109.** $<$ **110.** $<$ **111.** $<$

112. $=$ **113.** $=$ **114.** $=$ **115.** $>$

116. 0.315 (Other answers are possible.)

117. 0.2825 (Other answers are possible.)

118. 0.311212345 · · · (Other answers are possible.)

119. 0.28101001000 · · · (Other answers are possible.)

120. 0.1011 (Other answers are possible.)

121. 0.3031 (Other answers are possible.)

122. 0.101101001000 · · · (Other answers are possible.)

123. 0.303103003000 · · · (Other answers are possible.)

124. $\frac{7}{22}$ (Other answers are possible)

125. $\frac{79}{99}$ (Other answers are possible)

126. 0.5101001000 · · · (Other answers are possible.)

127. 0.2273101001000 · · · (Other answers are possible.)

128. $\frac{11}{18}$ (Other answers are possible.)

129. $\frac{19}{180}$ (Other answers are possible)

130. a. F **b.** T **c.** F **d.** F **e.** T **131.** -1.35

132. -0.928 **133.** 2.016 **134.** 3.875 **135.** $\frac{4}{9}$ **136.** $\frac{4321}{9999}$

Exercises 5.5

1. $3\sqrt{10}$ **2.** $6\sqrt{2}$ **3.** Simplest form

4. $5\sqrt{7}$ **5.** $6\sqrt{5}$ **6.** $9\sqrt{2}$ **7.** $10\sqrt{2}$

8. $\sqrt{191}$ is in simplest form. **9.** $8\sqrt{6}$ **10.** $9\sqrt{6}$

11. $14\sqrt{3}$ **12.** $50\sqrt{2}$ **13.** $\frac{3\sqrt{7}}{7}$ **14.** $\frac{6\sqrt{5}}{5}$

15. $-\frac{\sqrt{10}}{5}$ **16.** $-\frac{\sqrt{21}}{7}$ **17.** $\sqrt{2}$ **18.** $\frac{\sqrt{3}}{3}$ **19.** $\frac{\sqrt{3}}{7}$

20. $\frac{\sqrt{7}}{4}$ **21.** $\frac{2\sqrt{3}}{3}$ **22.** $\frac{5\sqrt{11}}{11}$ **23.** $\frac{2\sqrt{2}}{7}$ **24.** $\frac{3\sqrt{2}}{5}$

25. $\frac{3}{5}$ **26.** $\frac{2\sqrt{2}}{5}$ **27.** $\frac{4\sqrt{10}}{25}$ **28.** $2\sqrt{14}$ **29.** $5\sqrt{10}$

30. $5\sqrt{2}$ **31.** $\sqrt{14}$ **32.** $\sqrt{11}$ **33.** $\frac{1}{5}$ **34.** $\frac{1}{7}$

35. $\frac{\sqrt{6}}{2}$ **36.** $\frac{\sqrt{6}}{2}$ **37.** $3\sqrt{3}$ **38.** $2\sqrt{2}$ **39.** $9\sqrt{5}$

40. $-3\sqrt{6}$ **41.** 5 **42.** 13 **43.** 5 **44.** 7

45. $5\sqrt{7}$ **46.** $9\sqrt{3}$ **47.** $-7\sqrt{7}$ **48.** $-10\sqrt{7}$

49. $-8\sqrt{5}$ **50.** $-33\sqrt{3}$

51. a. 1 hr **b.** $\frac{5\sqrt{15}}{9} \approx 2.15$ hr

52. a. $\frac{\sqrt{2}}{4}$ hr **b.** Resumed; storm lasts 0.35 hr.

53. a. 20 m/sec **b.** 207 m/sec

54. $\sqrt{300} = 10\sqrt{3}$ m/sec **55.** 20%

56. a. $10\sqrt{1857}$ mi

b. About 430 mi

57. 15 m/sec **58.** 30 m/sec **59.** 28 ft/sec

60. 40 ft/sec **61.** 3 **62.** 1 **63.** 13

64. $\frac{17}{12}$ **65.** $\frac{2}{3}$ **66.** $\frac{1}{6}$

67. Check rational numbers and real numbers.

68. Rational; real

69. Check whole numbers, integers, rational numbers, and real numbers.

70. Irrational; real

71. Check natural numbers, whole numbers, integers, rational numbers, and real numbers.

72. Natural; whole; integer; rational; real

73. Check rational numbers and real numbers.

74. Rational; real

75. Check irrational numbers and real numbers.

76. Irrational; real

78. Every integer can be written in the form $\frac{a}{b}$ where $b = 1$.

79. $6\frac{4}{13}$, 6.31 (Calculator gives 6.32.)

80. $8\frac{4}{17} \approx 8.24$

81. $9\frac{4}{19}$, 9.21 (Calculator gives 9.22.)

82. $10\frac{8}{21} \approx 10.38$

Collaborative Learning

$\sqrt{10} \approx 3.16227766$

$\sqrt{867} \approx 29.44486373$

$\sqrt{900} \approx 30$

$\sqrt{40} \approx 6.32455532$

$\sqrt{68} \approx 8.246211251$

$\sqrt{85} \approx 9.219544457$

$\sqrt{108} \approx 10.39230485$

Exercises 5.6

1. **a.** $a_1 = 7$ **b.** $d = 6$ **c.** $a_{10} = 61$ **d.** $a_n = 6n + 1$

2. **a.** $a_1 = 3$ **b.** $d = 3$ **c.** $a_{10} = 30$ **d.** $a_n = 3n$

3. **a.** $a_1 = 43$ **b.** $d = -9$ **c.** $a_{10} = -38$ **d.** $a_n = 52 - 9n$

4. **a.** $a_1 = 3$ **b.** $d = -4$ **c.** $a_{10} = -33$ **d.** $a_n = 7 - 4n$

5. **a.** $a_1 = 2$ **b.** $d = -5$ **c.** $a_{10} = -43$ **d.** $a_n = 7 - 5n$

6. **a.** $a_1 = \frac{2}{3}$ **b.** $d = \frac{1}{6}$ **c.** $a_{10} = \frac{13}{6}$ **d.** $a_n = \frac{n+3}{6}$

7. **a.** $a_1 = -\frac{5}{6}$ **b.** $d = \frac{1}{2}$ **c.** $a_{10} = \frac{11}{3}$ **d.** $a_n = \frac{n}{2} - \frac{4}{3}$, or $\frac{3n-8}{6}$

8. **a.** $a_1 = -\frac{1}{4}$ **b.** $d = \frac{1}{2}$ **c.** $a_{10} = \frac{17}{4}$ **d.** $a_n = \frac{2n-3}{4}$

9. **a.** $a_1 = 0.6$ **b.** $d = -0.4$ **c.** $a_{10} = -3$ **d.** $a_n = 1 - 0.4n$

10. **a.** $a_1 = 0.7$ **b.** $d = -0.5$ **c.** $a_{10} = -3.8$ **d.** $a_n = 1.2 - 0.5n$

11. $S_{10} = 340$, $S_n = n(3n + 4)$

12. $S_{10} = 165$; $S_n = \frac{3}{2}n(n + 1)$

13. $S_{10} = 25$, $S_n = \frac{n}{2}(95 - 9n)$

14. $S_{10} = -150$; $S_n = n(5 - 2n)$

15. $S_{10} = -205$, $S_n = \frac{n}{2}(9 - 5n)$

16. $S_{10} = 14\frac{1}{6}$; $S_n = \frac{n}{12}(n + 7)$

17. $S_{10} = 14\frac{1}{6}$, $S_n = \frac{n}{12}(3n - 13)$

18. $S_{10} = 20$; $S_n = \frac{1}{4}n(n - 2)$

19. $S_{10} = -12$, $S_n = \frac{n}{5}(4 - n)$

20. $S_{10} = -15.5$; $S_n = \frac{1}{4}n(3.8 - n)$

21. **a.** $a_1 = 3$ **b.** $r = 2$ **c.** $a_{10} = 1536$ **d.** $a_n = 3 \cdot 2^{n-1}$

22. **a.** $a_1 = 5$ **b.** $r = 3$ **c.** $a_{10} = 98{,}415$ **d.** $a_n = 5 \cdot 3^{n-1}$

23. **a.** $a_1 = \frac{1}{3}$ **b.** $r = 3$ **c.** $a_{10} = 6561$ **d.** $a_n = 3^{n-2}$ or $\frac{1}{3}(3^{n-1})$

24. **a.** $a_1 = \frac{1}{5}$ **b.** $r = 5$ **c.** $a_{10} = 390{,}625$ **d.** $a_n = 5^{n-2}$

25. **a.** $a_1 = 16$ **b.** $r = -\frac{1}{4}$ **c.** $a_{10} = -\frac{1}{16{,}384}$ **d.** $a_n = \frac{(-1)^{n-1}}{4^{n-3}}$ or $(-1)^{n-1}\,4^{3-n}$

26. **a.** $a_1 = 3$ **b.** $r = -\frac{1}{3}$ **c.** $a_{10} = -\frac{1}{6561}$ **d.** $a_n = \frac{(-1)^{n-1}}{3^{n-2}}$

27. $S_{10} = 3(2^{10} - 1) = 3069$; $S_n = 3(2^{n-1})$

28. $S_{10} = \frac{5}{2}(3^{10} - 1)$; $S_n = \frac{5}{2}(3^n - 1)$

29. $S_{10} = \frac{1}{6}(3^{10} - 1) = 9841\frac{1}{3}$; $S_n = \frac{1}{6}(3^{n-1})$

30. $S_{10} = \frac{1}{20}(5^{10} - 1)$; $S_n = \frac{1}{20}(5^n - 1)$

31. $S_{10} = \frac{4^{10} - 1}{5 \cdot 4^7} = \frac{209{,}715}{16{,}384}$; $S_n = \frac{4^n - (-1)^n}{5 \cdot 4^{n-3}}$

32. $S_{10} = \frac{9}{4}(1 - \frac{1}{3^{10}})$; $S_n = \frac{9}{4}(1 - (-\frac{1}{3})^n)$

33. $S = 12$ **34.** $S = 18$ **35.** $S = -16$ **36.** $S = \frac{27}{4}$

37. $\frac{7}{9}$ **38.** $\frac{14}{9}$ **39.** $\frac{208}{99}$ **40.** $\frac{14}{11}$

41. **a.** \$1020 **b.** \$18,000

42. \$3250

43. **a.** \$95 **b.** \$8625

44. **a.** About 3.5 ft **b.** 190 ft

45. \$610.51

46. **a.** 4 **b.** 1 **c.** $a_n = 7 - n$ **d.** 21 **e.** $60(3) = 180$ **f.** $60(7 - n)$

47. If n is an even number, there are $n/2$ pairs and the sum of each pair is $(n + 1)$. The total sum is $n(n + 1)/2$. If n is an odd number, find the sum of the first $(n - 1)$ terms. The preceding formula gives $n(n - 1)/2$. Then adding n, the omitted term, gives the sum $n(n + 1)/2$, as before.

48. **a.** The sum of each pair is $2n + 2$ and there are $\frac{n}{2}$ pairs. Thus, the total sum is $n(n + 1)$.

b. Each term of the sequence here is double the corresponding term of the sequence in Problem 47.

49. In an arithmetic sequence, each term after the first is obtained by adding the constant difference d to the preceding term. In a geometric sequence, each term after the first is obtained by multiplying the preceding term by the constant ratio r.

50. In the Fibonacci sequence, the difference between successive terms is not constant, and the ratio of successive terms is not constant. Thus, the sequence is neither an arithmetic nor a geometric sequence.

51. $a_n = 0 + (n - 1)4.5 = 4.5n - 4.5$

52. $8(4.5)\% = 36\%$

53. $a_n = 45 + (n - 1)(-0.5) = -0.5n + 45.5$

54. 41%

CHAPTER 6

Exercises 6.1

1. -2 and 0 are solutions. 2. $\frac{1}{3}$ and 0
3. 3 and 1 are solutions. 4. 2 5. 2
6. 4 7. $x = 5$ 8. $x = 13$ 9. $x = 3$
10. $x = 1$ 11. $x = 2$ 12. $x = -2$
13. $x = 9$ 14. $x = 4$ 15. $x = 1$
16. $x = 5$ 17. $x = 2$ 18. $x = \frac{9}{5} = 1\frac{4}{5}$
19. $n = 6$ 20. $a = \frac{3}{2} = 1\frac{1}{2}$ 21. $x = \frac{3}{2}$
22. $x = \frac{5}{6}$ 23. $x = 12$ 24. $x = \frac{11}{10} = 1\frac{1}{10}$
25. $x = \frac{15}{4}$, or $3\frac{3}{4}$ 26. $y = -\frac{8}{5} = -1\frac{3}{5}$
27. $x = \frac{10}{7}$, or $1\frac{3}{7}$ 28. $x = \frac{12}{5} = 2\frac{2}{5}$
29. $x = 10$ 30. $x = 3$ 31. $p = 4$
32. $t = 4$ 33. $h = V/\pi r^2$ 34. $h = \frac{3V}{\pi r^2}$
35. $W = V/LH$ 36. $H = \frac{V}{LW}$
37. $b = P - s_1 - s_2$ 38. $s_2 = P - s_1 - b$
39. a. $T = D/R$ b. 4 hours
40. a. $H = \frac{W + 190}{5}$ b. 70 in.
41. a. $A = 34 - 2H$ b. 18 years
42. a. $b = \frac{2A - ah}{h}$ b. 5 units
43. $\{x \mid x < 4\}$ 44. $\{x \mid x < 4\}$
45. $\{x \mid x > 3\}$ 46. $\{x \mid x > -5\}$
47. $\{x \mid x > 3\}$ 48. $\{x \mid x > 4\}$
49. $\{x \mid x \ge -2\}$ 50. $\{x \mid x \le 9\}$
51. $\{x \mid x > -4\}$ 52. $\{x \mid x < 6\}$
53. $\{x \mid x \le -2\}$ 54. $\{x \mid x \ge -3\}$
55. $\{x \mid x \le -9\}$ 56. $\{x \mid x \ge 4\}$
57. $\{x \mid x > 3\}$ 58. $\{x \mid x > 4\}$
59. $\{x \mid x > -4\}$ 60. $\{x \mid x < 6\}$
61. $\{x \mid x \le -\frac{2}{3}\}$ 62. $\{x \mid x \ge -4\}$ 63. $\varnothing$
64. R, the set of all real numbers; $\{x \mid x \in R\}$
65. $\{x \mid x \le 2\}$ 66. $\{x \mid x \le 1\}$
67. $\{x \mid x > -2\}$ 68. $\{x \mid x < -1\}$
69. $\{x \mid x \le \frac{2}{5}\}$ 70. $\{x \mid x \le \frac{1}{2}\}$
71. $\{x \mid x \le -4\}$ 72. $\{x \mid x < 2\}$
73. 32 74. 9 75. 10% 76. 200%
77. 12.5% 78. $66\frac{2}{3}$% 79. 200 80. 25
81. a. 22 mpg b. 545 gal
82. a. 12 gal b. 588 gal
83. 67% 84. \$20 85. The \$100 price
86. $83\frac{1}{3}$% 87. 2.5 years
88. a. $x = -7.75$ $x = -7.75 \approx -8$
 b. $I = A$ about 8 years before the study started. They will not be equal in the future.
89. a. 9.72 million; within 0.18 million
 b. 11.52 million; within 0.02 million
 c. 10.92 million
90. a. 16.62 million students are enrolled. This is very close to the graph value.
 b. 19.5 million students are enrolled. This is exactly the graph value.
 c. 20.7 million students are projected for 2019.
91. 11 in. 92. $9\frac{1}{3}$ in. 93. 8 94. $21\frac{1}{3}$ in. 95. 12 in.
96. a. 11 in. b. $10\frac{1}{2}$ in.
97. a. 47 b. 48
98. More than 20,000 99. When $x < 23.8$ oz
100. When $h < 13$ hr
101. When $x > 2$, that is, after 1998
102. Answers will vary.
104. Answers will vary.
106. Answers will vary.
107. 250 cal
108. The total calories in the Big Mac are about 491 calories.
109. 710 cal 110. No. For $F = 80$, $N = 160$.
111. 150 chirps 112. 40°F 113. 1 cm/sec
114. 4°C; The cricket stops chirping before the ant stops crawling as the temperature drops.

Exercises 6.2

1.
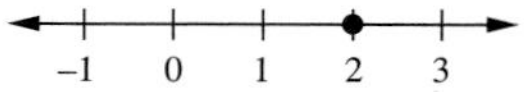

2.
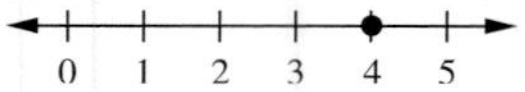

3.
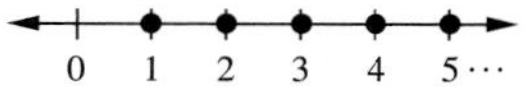

4.
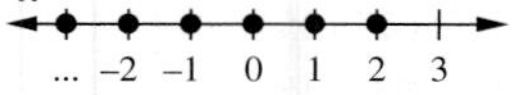

5.
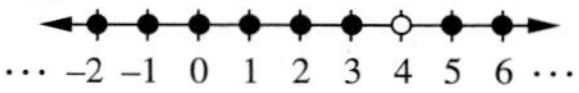

6.
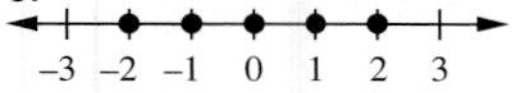

7.
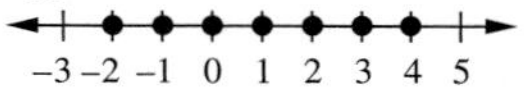

8.

9.
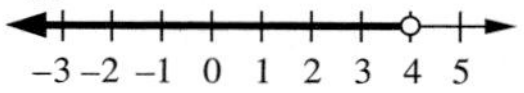

10.
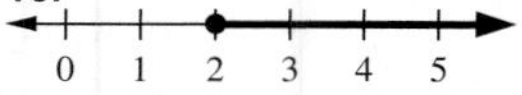

11.
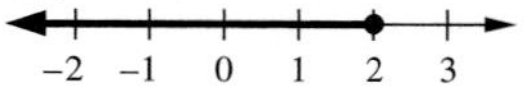

12.
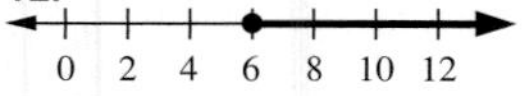

13.
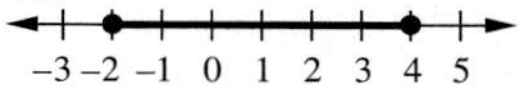

14.
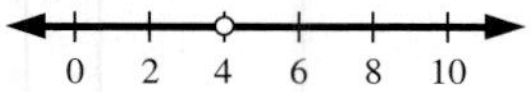

15.
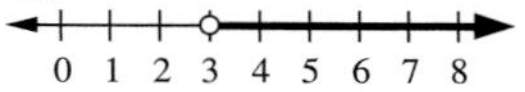

16.
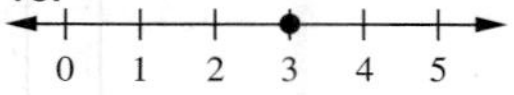

17.
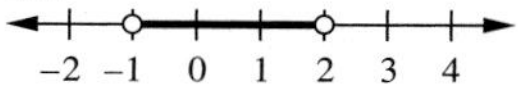

18.
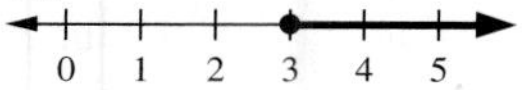

19.
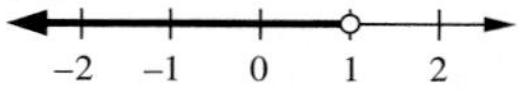

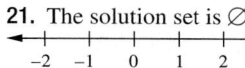

20.
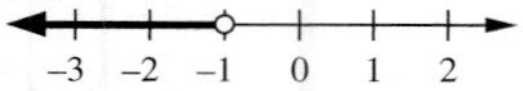

21. The solution set is $\varnothing$.
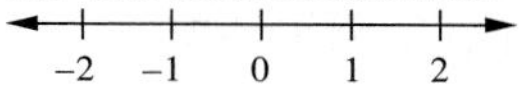

22. (all real numbers)
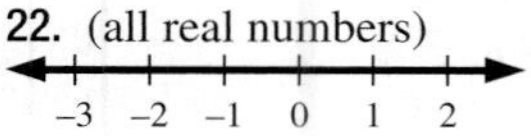

23.
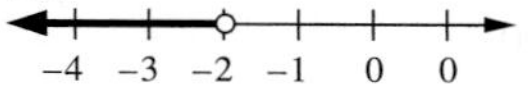

24.
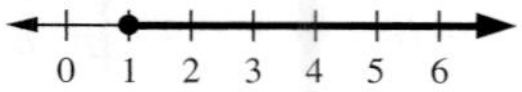

25.
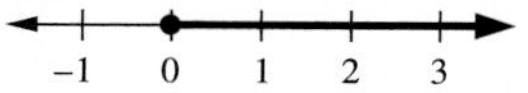

26.
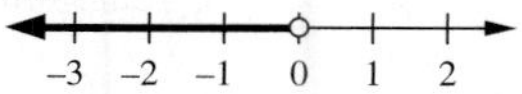

27. $\{-1, 0, 1, 2, 3, 4\}$ 28. $\{1, 2, 3, 4, 5\}$
29. $\{3, 4, 5, 6\}$ 30. $\{-4, -3, -2, -1, 0\}$
31. $\{2\}$
32. $\{\ldots, -2, -1, 0, 1, 5, 6, 7, \ldots\}$
33. $\{\ldots, -8, -7, -6, 6, 7, 8, \ldots\}$
34. $\{\ldots, -5, -4, -3, 0, 1, 2, \ldots\}$

35.
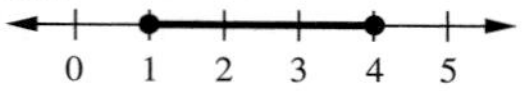

36.
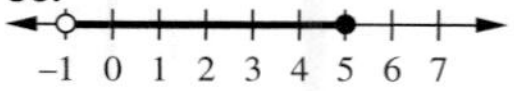

37. ∅

38.

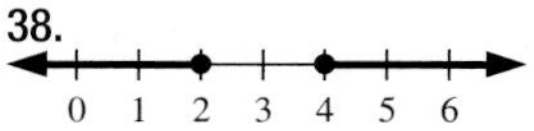

39.

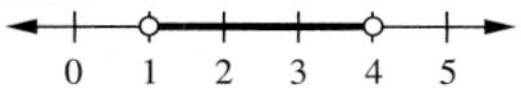

40.

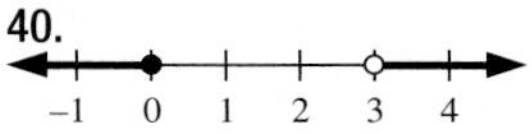

41.

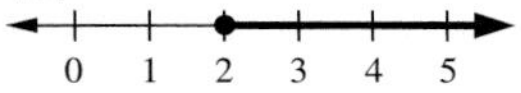

42. (all real numbers)

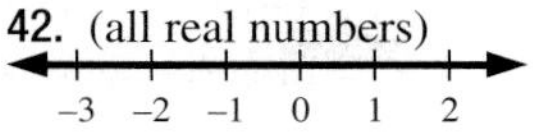

43. ∅

44.

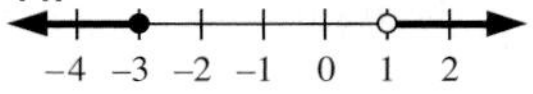

45.

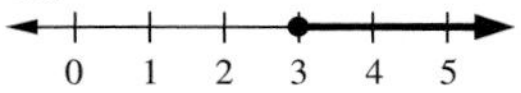

46.

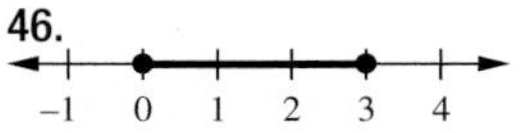

47.

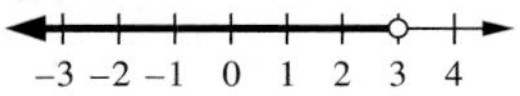

48. ∅

49.

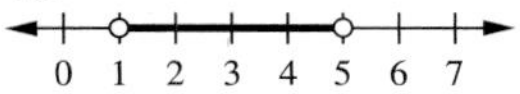

50.

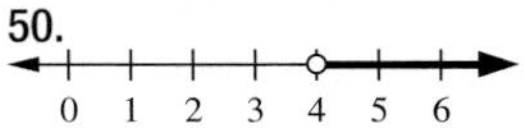

51. All real numbers

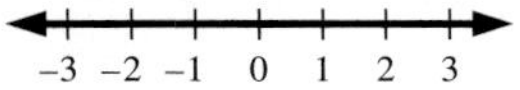

52. (all real numbers)

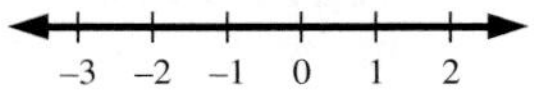

53. **a.** $C = 4953 + 0.12\,m$

b. $6000 < 4953 + 0.12\,m < 6500$

c. $8725 < m < 12{,}892$. Each car is budgeted to run between 8725 and 12,892 mi annually.

54. **a.** $C = 6689 + 0.15\,m$

b. $7000 < 6689 + 0.15m < 7500$

c. $2073 < m < 5406$. To stay within the budget, the car can be driven between 2073 and 5406 mi.

55. $N > 6$ years after 2010, that is, after 2016

56. $N > 10$ years after 2010, that is, after 2020

57. **a.** All the real numbers between -1 and $+2$ including the 2 but not the -1

b. All the real numbers between -1 and $+2$ including the -1 but not the 2

c. All the real numbers between -1 and $+2$ not including the endpoints

d. All the real numbers between -1 and $+2$ including the endpoints

58. **a.** The real numbers less than 1 or greater than 4

b. The real numbers less than or equal to 1 or greater than 4

c. The real numbers less than or equal to 1 or greater than or equal to 4

d. The real numbers less than 1 or greater than or equal to 4

59. **a.** The set of all the real numbers between -1 and 2

b. The set of all the real numbers between -1 and 2 including the 2

c. The set of all the real numbers between -1 and 2 including the -1

d. The set of all the real numbers between -1 and 2 including both the -1 and the 2

60. $[-4, \infty)$ **61.** $(-\infty, 5)$ **62.** $(-\infty, -6]$

63. $(9, \infty)$ **64.** $(3, 7)$ **65.** $[-4, -1)$ **66.** $(0, 8]$

67. $[-1, 10]$ **68.** $B > F > J$

69. Let J in. be Joe's height. Then $J = 60$ in. **70.** $B > F$

71. Let F in. be Frank's height and S in. be Sam's height. Then $F = S - 3$.

72. $F > J$ **73.** Let S be Sam's height. Then $S = 77$ in.

74. $B > F > J$

75. Let B be Bill's height. Then $B > 74$ in. (6 ft 2 in.).

Exercises 6.3

1. 10 **2.** 15 **3.** $\frac{1}{8}$ **4.** $\frac{3}{4}$ **5.** 3 **6.** 3

7. 2 **8.** -1 **9.** -8 **10.** 1

11. 2 and $\frac{5}{3}$ are solutions.

12. 1 is the only solution.

13. $\{0\}$

14. $\{\ldots, -2, -1, 0, 1, 2, \ldots\}$ **15.** $\{-5, 5\}$

16. $\{-3, -2, -1, 0, 1, 2, 3\}$

17. $\{\ldots, -3, -2, -1, 1, 2, 3, \ldots\}$

18. $\{-3, -2, -1, 0, 1, 2, 3\}$

19. No interval

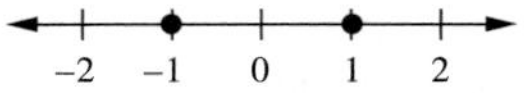

20.

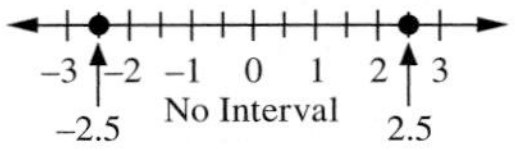

21. In interval notation, $[-4, 4]$

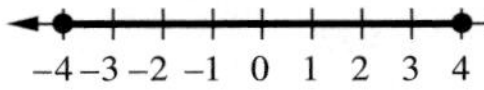

22.

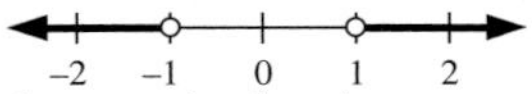

$(-\infty, -1) \cup (1, \infty)$

23. In interval notation, $(-4, 2)$

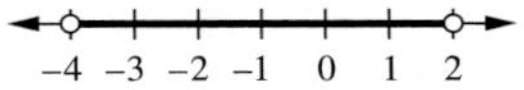

24.

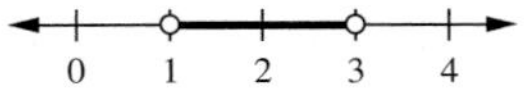

$(1, 3)$

25. In interval notation, $(-\infty, -1] \cup [1, \infty)$

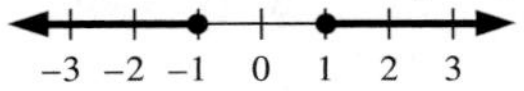

26. All real numbers

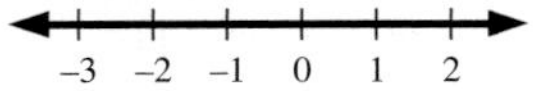

$(-\infty, \infty)$

27. In interval notation, $(-\infty, -1) \cup (3, \infty)$

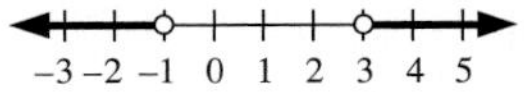

28.

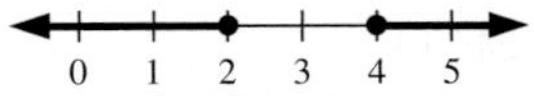

$(-\infty, 2] \cup [4, \infty)$

29. In interval notation, $(-2, 2)$

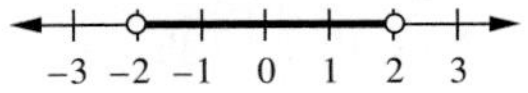

30.

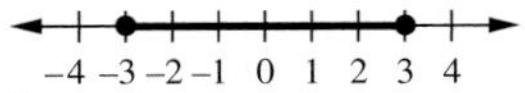

$(-3, 3)$

31. In interval notation, $(-\infty, -2] \cup [2, \infty)$

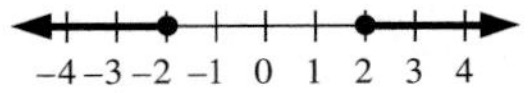

32.

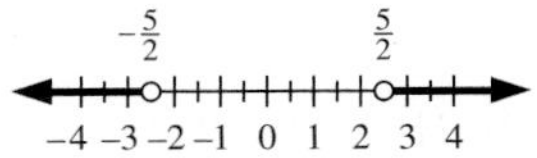

$\left(-\infty, -\frac{5}{2}\right) \cup \left(\frac{5}{2}, \infty\right)$

33. In interval notation, $[0, 3]$

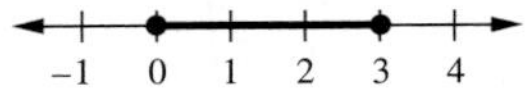

34. 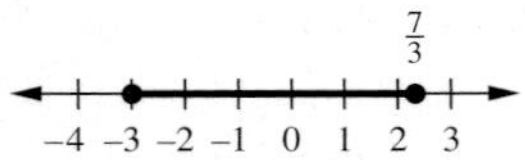
$\left[-3, \frac{7}{3}\right]$

35. In interval notation, $(-\infty, 0) \cup (3, \infty)$
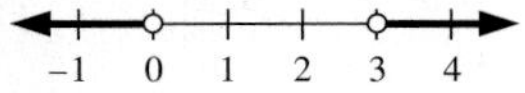

36. 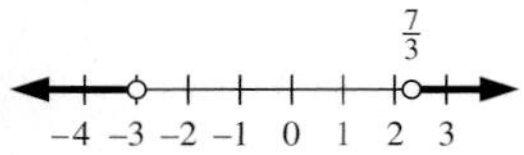
$(-\infty, -3) \cup \left(\frac{7}{3}, \infty\right)$

37. Any amount between \$450 and \$550, inclusive

38. Between \$760 and \$840, inclusive. **39.** Yes

40. a. $|x - \frac{5}{2}| > \frac{3}{2}$ **b.** $|x - \frac{5}{2}| \le \frac{3}{2}$
c. $x = 4$ or $|x - \frac{5}{2}| < \frac{3}{2}$ **d.** $x = 1$ or $|x - \frac{5}{2}| > \frac{3}{2}$

41. a. $|w - 137| \le 7$
b. $-7 \le w - 137 \le 7$, or $130 \le w \le 144$

42. a. $|w - 162| \le 10$ **b.** $152 \le w \le 172$

43. a. $|L - 12| \le 0.24$ **b.** $11.76 \le L \le 12.24$

44. a. $|L - 1| \le 0.01$ **b.** $0.99 \le L \le 1.01$

45. a. $|s - 505| \le 4$ **b.** $501 \le s \le 509$

46. a. $|c - 186| \le 27.9$ **b.** $158.1 \le c \le 213.9$

47. $\$450 \le a \le \$550$ **48.** $\$760 \le a \le 840$

49. Yes **50.** Yes

Skill Checker

1. $2\sqrt{2}$ **2.** $\sqrt{61}$ **3.** $2\sqrt{3}$ **4.** $\sqrt{17}$
5. 7 **6.** 9 **7.** $6\sqrt{3}$ **8.** $2\sqrt{6}$ **9.** 12 **10.** $2\sqrt{11}$

Exercises 6.4

1. $(x + 2)(x + 4)$ **2.** $(x + 2)(x + 5)$ **3.** $(x - 4)(x + 3)$
4. $(x - 5)(x + 2)$ **5.** $(x + 9)(x - 2)$
6. $(x - 11)(x - 1)$ **7.** $(x - 5)^2$ **8.** $(x - 4)^2$
9. $(x + 5)^2$ **10.** $(x + 8)^2$ **11.** $(2x + 3)(x - 1)$
12. $(3x + 1)(x + 3)$ **13.** $(2x - 1)(3x - 1)$
14. $(2x - 3)(3x - 1)$ **15.** $\{2, 4\}$ **16.** $\{-2, -3\}$
17. $\{-2, 3\}$ **18.** $\{-5, 6\}$ **19.** $\{-1, 0, 1\}$
20. $\{-1, -2, 3\}$ **21.** $\{-2, \frac{1}{2}\}$
22. $\{-\frac{5}{3}, -\frac{7}{4}\}$ **23.** $\{-4, 4\}$ **24.** $\{3, -3\}$
25. $\{-5, 5\}$ **26.** $\{-4, 4\}$ **27.** $\{-\frac{3}{2}, \frac{8}{5}, 2\}$
28. $\{-7, 0, \frac{3}{2}\}$ **29.** $\{-6, 6\}$ **30.** $\{-\frac{7}{2}, \frac{7}{2}\}$ **31.** $\{3, 9\}$
32. $\{2, 4\}$ **33.** $\{-2, 10\}$ **34.** $\{-3, 12\}$ **35.** $\{-\frac{1}{2}, -\frac{1}{5}\}$
36. $\{-\frac{5}{2}, -\frac{1}{3}\}$ **37.** $\{-\frac{5}{3}, 1\}$ **38.** $\{-\frac{3}{2}, 2\}$
39. $\{-\frac{5}{2}, 1\}$ **40.** $\{\frac{1}{3}, 2\}$ **41.** $\{-\frac{7}{2}, 1\}$ **42.** $\{-\frac{5}{4}, 3\}$

43. $\left\{\frac{-5 - \sqrt{13}}{2}, \frac{-5 + \sqrt{13}}{2}\right\}$ **44.** $\{-4, \frac{1}{2}\}$

45. $\left\{\frac{4 - \sqrt{6}}{5}, \frac{4 + \sqrt{6}}{5}\right\}$ **46.** $\left\{\frac{-5 - \sqrt{13}}{6}, \frac{-5 + \sqrt{13}}{6}\right\}$

47. $\left\{\frac{3 - \sqrt{2}}{7}, \frac{3 + \sqrt{2}}{7}\right\}$ **48.** $\{\frac{5}{7}, 1\}$

49. $\left\{\frac{1 + \sqrt{3}}{3}, \frac{1 - \sqrt{3}}{3}\right\}$ **50.** $\left\{\frac{4 - \sqrt{6}}{2}, \frac{4 + \sqrt{6}}{2}\right\}$

51. $\left\{\frac{-1 + \sqrt{3}}{2}, \frac{-1 - \sqrt{3}}{2}\right\}$ **52.** $\left\{\frac{3 - \sqrt{19}}{2}, \frac{3 + \sqrt{19}}{2}\right\}$

53. $\{-\frac{5}{2}, \frac{1}{2}\}$ **54.** $\left\{\frac{1 - \sqrt{11}}{2}, \frac{1 + \sqrt{11}}{2}\right\}$

55.
$$\begin{aligned}(2ax + b)^2 &= (2ax + b)(2ax + b)\\ &= 2ax(2ax + b) + b(2ax + b)\\ &= (4a^2x^2 + 2abx) + (2abx + b^2)\\ &= 4a^2x^2 + 4abx + b^2\end{aligned}$$
which is the left side of the equation, as stated. If we subtract b from both sides of
$$2ax + b = \pm\sqrt{b^2 - 4ac}$$
we get
$$2ax = -b \pm \sqrt{b^2 - 4ac}$$
If we divide both sides of this last equation by $2a$, we get the quadratic formula as given.

56. 6, 8, 10 **57.** 6 cm, 8 cm, and 10 cm **58.** 10, 24, 26

59. 5 in., 12 in., and 13 in.

60. a. $x^2 = 2y + 1$
b. 5, 12, 13; 7, 24, 25; 9, 40, 41; 11, 60, 61

61. 1 sec **62.** 2 sec **63.** 1 sec **64.** 5 sec

65. a. $(t + 13)^2$ **b.** 2809 **66. a.** $(t + 14)^2$ **b.** 2916

67. a. $P(1 - r)^2$ **b.** \$18,062.50

68. a. $25{,}000(r - 1)^2$ **b.** \$16,000

69. a. The \$9000 is lower
b. $H(15) = \$10{,}125$, lower than the \$13,100 in the graph

70. a. $250 + 10n$ **b.** $17{,}500 + 200n - 20n^2$ **c.** 4 or 6
d. \$290 (for 62 apartments)
\$310 (for 58 apartments)

72. Answers will vary. **74.** Answers will vary.

75. If $b^2 - 4ac = 0$, there is only one solution, $-\frac{b}{2a}$.

76. Two unequal real numbers.

77. If $b^2 - 4ac < 0$, there are no real number solutions.

78. $1 + 3.25 = 4.25$ sec **79.** About 211 ft

80. 400 ft **81.** 7225

Collaborative Learning

1. 1. $(x + 2)(x + 1)$; $-2, -1$
2. $(x + 3)(x + 2)$; $-3, -2$
3. $(x + 4)(x + 3)$; $-4, -3$
4. $(x - 1)(x - 2)$; 1, 2
5. $(x - 2)(x - 3)$; 2, 3
6. $(x - 3)(x - 4)$; 3, 4
7. $(x + 1)(x - 2)$; $-1, 2$
8. $(x + 2)(x - 3)$; $-2, 3$
9. $(x + 3)(x - 4)$; $-3, 4$

2. If the integers whose product is ac are m and n, the roots of $ax^2 + bx + c = 0$ are: $-\frac{c}{m}$ and $-\frac{c}{n}$.

Exercises 6.5

1. $4m = m + 18$ **2.** $2n(2n + 4) < (2n + 2)^2$

3. $n(n + 2) = 10(n + 2) - 20$

4. $x^2 - 2x = x + 10$ **5.** $4x + 5 = 29, x = 6$

6. $2x + 11 = 19; x = 4$ **7.** $3x + 8 = 29, x = 7$

8. $7x + 6 = 69; x = 9$ **9.** $3x - 2 = 16, x = 6$

10. $5x = 2x - 9; x = -3$

11. $2x^2 = 2x + 12, x = -2$ or 3

12. $\frac{1}{2}x^2 - 5 = x - 1$; $x = -2$ or $x = 4$

13. $\frac{1}{3}x^2 - 2 = 10$, $x = -6$ or 6

14. $\frac{1}{5}x^2 + 2x = 15$; $x = -15$ or $x = 5$ **15.** 2.71 million lb

16. External tank: 1.28 million lb; Boosters: 1.62 million lb

17. Pedro is 30, Maria is 15. **18.** 8 years **19.** 130 mi

20. 20 times at bat **21.** 2% per year **22.** 3%

23. a. 204 mi **b.** The mileage rate

24. The flat rate **25.** 2% **26.** 3% **27.** 30 mph

28. 0.5 sec **29.** 76.5 ft **30.** 50 mph **31.** 0.6 sec

32. $\frac{2}{3}$ sec **33.** 20 mph **34.** 40 mph **35.** 4 and 5

36. 14 fives; $76 **37.** 40

38. a. $2725 **b.** Answers will vary.

c. Answers will vary.

39. a. Revenue $= T + \frac{3N(2800)}{40} = T + 210N$ (dollars)

b. Cost = (40)($100) + (40)($150) + 40 ($1000) + $3000 = $53,000

c. $T + 210N = 53{,}000$ **d.** $N = \frac{53{,}000 - T}{210}$

e. $N = 161$ is the least number of students needed to incur no loss.

40. a. $C_A = 20{,}000 + \frac{4m}{20}$ **b.** $C_B = 25{,}000 + \frac{4m}{25}$

c. $m = 125{,}000$

d. Buy car *A* if you plan to drive less than 125,000 mi. Buy car *B* if you plan to drive more than 125,000 mi.

41. a. See the "Total" rows in the table.

b. Rent 5 size A units **c.** Rent 1 size C unit

d. Rent 1 size A unit and 1 size B unit.

Identical Row Alignment

	Unit		
	A	*B*	*C*
Cost per month	$ 25	$ 90	$128
Number per row	5	10	10
Rows	5	5	10
Layers	3	5	5
Total	75	250	500
Units needed	5	2	1
Cost for 2 months	$250	$360	$256

Staggered Row Alignment

	Unit		
	A	*B*	*C*
Cost per month	$ 25	$ 90	$128
Number per row	2–4s & 3–5s	3–10s & 2–9s	6–10s & 5–9s
Rows	5	5	11
Layers	3	5	5
Total	69	240	525
Units needed	6	2	1
Cost for 2 months	$300	$360	$256

42. Hours Spent And Grade Earned

MATH	SCIENCE	ENGLISH	GPA
6(A)	4(A)	0(C)	$\frac{30}{9}$
6(A)	2(B)	2(A)	$\frac{33}{9}$
3(B)	4(A)	3(A)	$\frac{33}{9}$

Either of the last two plans is best.

43. Spend 3 hr on mathematics, 6 hr on science, and 3 hr on English to get your best GPA.

44. a.

Overdue	1 day	2 days	3 days
Rock-Busters:			
New	3 + 2.50 = 5.50	3 + 5 = 8	3 + 7.50 = 10.50
Old	3 + 1.50 = 4.50	3 + 3 = 6	3 + 4.50 = 7.50
Video Renters:			
New	2.5 + 2 = 4.50	2.5 + 4 = 6.50	2.5 + 6 = 8.50
Old	2.5 + 2 = 4.50	2.5 + 4 = 6.50	2.5 + 6 = 8.50

b. $C_R = 6 + 6n$ (dollars)

$C_V = 5 + 4n$ (dollars)

c. $C_R = \$26$; $C_V = \$25$

45. a.

Returned After	*Blockbuster*	*Red Rabbit*
2 Days		
New	$3 + $2 = $5	$3 + $3 = $6
Old	$3 + $0 = $3	$1.60 + $0 = $1.60
3 Days		
New	$3 + $4 = $7	$3 + $6 = $9
Old	$3 + $2 = $5	$1.60 + $1.50 = $3.10
4 Days		
New	$3 + $6 = $9	$3 + $9 = $12
Old	$3 + $4 = $7	$1.60 + $3 = $4.60

b. Let C_B = cost at Blockbuster, and C_R = cost at Red Rabbit.

$C_B = 4n$; $C_R = 4.50n - 1.40$ (in dollars)

c. $C_B = \$11$; $C_R = \$15$

46. a.

Hrs of Pkg	1	2	3	4	5
P & S	5.00	5.50	6.00	6.50	7.00
SP	4.75	5.35	5.95	6.55	7.15

b. $C_{P\&S} = 4.50 + 0.50n$ (dollars)

$C_{SP} = 4.15 + 0.60n$ (dollars)

47. a. The average stopping distance (in feet) is $d = 0.9v + 0.06v^2$

b. 162 ft **c.** 242 ft **d.** 3.67 sec

48. 4.08 sec

49. You should try to determine what is the unknown, that is, what is wanted.

50. You must check to see that the conditions of the problem are met.

51. 4.48 **52.** $31,250

53. If *M* were greater than *G*, then *y* would be negative; this is unrealistic.

Exercises 6.6

1. 7000 to 2000; 7000 : 2000; $\frac{7000}{2000}$: or 7 to 2; 7 : 2; $\frac{7}{2}$

2. 700 to 800; 700 : 800; $\frac{700}{800}$

3. 70 to 4260; 70 : 4260; $\frac{70}{4260}$: or 7 to 426; 7:426; $\frac{7}{426}$

4. 28 to 34; 28:34; $\frac{28}{34}$ **5.** $\frac{10}{3}$ reduced trans. ratio
6. $\frac{6}{100}$ or 0.06 **7.** 17 mi/gal
8. a. 13.6¢ **b.** 13.3¢ **c.** The 4-oz generic can
d. The generic can here
9. a. 6 cents **b.** 5 cents **c.** White Magic
10. a. 5¢ **b.** 6¢ **c.** The A&P Liquid
11. $x = 12$ **12.** $x = 2.5$ **13.** $x = 6$
14. $x = \frac{7}{3}$ **15.** $x = 24$ **16.** $x = 15$ **17.** $\frac{9}{2} = \frac{n}{40}$
18. $\frac{L}{10} = \frac{3}{2}$ **19.** 6 **20.** 15 lb **21.** 66.5 in.
22. 111 tortillas **23.** $t/7600 = 1/48$; $158.\overline{3}$ or 159 trees
24. 8 in. **25.** 2650 fish
26. a. $I = km$ **b.** $k = 0.055$ **c.** \$41.25
27. a. $S = kn$ **b.** $k = 153{,}600$ bytes **c.** 3,072,000 bytes
28. a. $d = ks^2$ **b.** $k = 0.06$ **c.** 216 ft
29. a. $T = kh^3$ **b.** $k = \frac{1}{1750} \approx 0.0005714$ **c.** 241 lb
30. a. $s = \frac{k}{y}$ **b.** 30
31. a. $f = k/d$ **b.** $k = 4$ **c.** 16
32. 36 lb/in.^{2} **33.** 10.8 in.^{3}
34. a. $W = \frac{k}{d^2}$ **b.** $k = 121 \cdot 3960^2$ **c.** 81 lb
35. a. $w = \frac{k}{s}$ **b.** $k = 7200$ **c.** 720
36. a. $P = \frac{k}{s}$ **b.** 2500 **c.** \$96.15
37. a. $b = \frac{k}{a}$ **b.** $k = 2970$ **c.** 90
38. a. $m = kg$ **b.** $k = 44.3$ **c.** 44.3 mpg
39. a. $d = ks$ **b.** $k \approx 17.6$
c. The number of hours to travel the distance d at the speed s
40. a. $N = 0.4P$ **b.** 2000
41. a. BAC $= k(N - 1)$ **b.** 0.026 **c.** 0.104 **d.** 4
42. a. BAC $= k(N - 1)$ **b.** 0.03 **c.** 0.12 **d.** 3
43. a. $C = 4(F - 37)$ **b.** 212
44. 3600 hours or about 150 days
45. a. $T = k/n$ **b.** $k = 70$ **c.** $70/48 = 1.4583\ldots$ min
46. $\frac{1}{2}$°C **47.** $C = 102.9$
48. a. BAC $= \frac{k}{W} = \frac{7.8}{W}$ **b.** 0.03 **c.** 97.5 lb
d. Less than 0.08
49. a. $BAC = \frac{k}{w}$ **b.** 0.033 **c.** 107.25 lb
d. Less than 0.08
50. A ratio is a quotient of two numbers. A proportion is an equality between two ratios.
52. Answers will vary.
54. No. A sum must be performed first.
56. The faster you drive the car, the more gas you use. This is a direct proportion.
57. a. $T = 15S$ **b.** 4

CHAPTER 7

Exercises 7.1

1. Domain: {1, 2, 3}; range: {2, 3, 4}
2. Domain: {1, 2, 3}; range: {1}
3. Domain: {1, 2, 3}; range: {1, 2, 3}
4. Domain: {4, 5, 6}; range: {1, 2}
5. Domain: $\{x \mid x$ is a real number$\}$; range: $\{y \mid y$ is a real number$\}$
6. Domain: $\{x \mid x$ is a real number$\}$; range: $\{y \mid y$ is a real number$\}$
7. Domain: $\{x \mid x$ is a real number$\}$; range: $\{y \mid y$ is a real number$\}$
8. Domain: $\{x \mid x$ is a real number$\}$; range: $\{y \mid y$ is a real number$\}$
9. Domain: $\{x \mid x$ is a real number$\}$; range: $\{y \mid y \ge 0\}$
10. Domain: $\{x \mid x$ is a real number$\}$; range: $\{y \mid y$ is a real number and $y \ge 2\}$
11. Domain: $\{x \mid x \ge 0\}$; range: $\{y \mid y$ is a real number$\}$
12. Domain: $\{x \mid x$ is a real number and $x \ge 1\}$; range: $\{y \mid y$ is a real number$\}$
13. Domain: $\{x \mid x \ne 0\}$; range: $\{y \mid y \ne 0\}$
14. Domain: $\{x \mid x$ is a real number and $x \ne 2\}$; range: $\{y \mid y$ is a real number and $y \ne 0\}$
15. This is a function because only one real value of y corresponds to each real value of x.
16. A function. To each real x, there corresponds one real y.
17. This is not a function because two values of y correspond to each positive value of x.
18. Not a function. To each x greater than -1 in the domain, there correspond two values of y. For example, when $x = 3$, $y = \pm 2$.
19. This is a function because only one real y value corresponds to each x value in the domain.
20. A function. To each x in the domain, $\{x \mid x \ge 0\}$, there corresponds one value of y.
21. This is a function because only one real value of y corresponds to each real value of x.
22. A function. To each real x, there corresponds one real y.
23. a. 1 **b.** 7 **c.** -5 **24. a.** 1 **b.** -1 **c.** 3
25. a. 0 **b.** 2 **c.** 5 **26. a.** -1 **b.** 7 **c.** -1
27. a. $3x + 3h + 1$ **b.** $3h$ **c.** 3
28. $f(x) = \frac{1}{2}x$. The missing numbers are 15, 4.8, and $\frac{2}{7}$.
29. $g(x) = x^2$; $\frac{1}{16}$, 4.41, ± 8 **30. a.** -4 **b.** -42 **c.** 8
31. a. 1 **b.** -5 **c.** 15
32. a. 59° **b.** 212° **c.** 18 **d.** -459.4° F
33. a. 140 beats per minute **b.** 130 beats per minute
34. a. $130 \le R \le 160$ **b.** $120 \le R \le 145$
35. a. 160 lb **b.** 78 in. **36. a.** \$78 **b.** 203
37. a. 639 lb/ft^2 **b.** 6390 lb/ft^2
38. a. 19.6 m **b.** 122.5 m **39. a.** 144 ft **b.** 400 ft
40. 32.2 ft/sec^2

41.
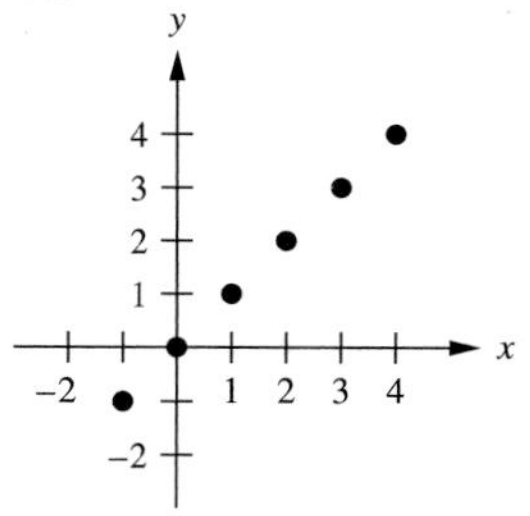

42.
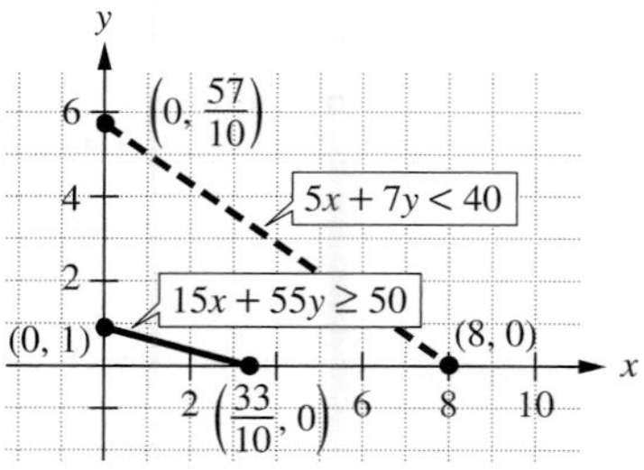

43.
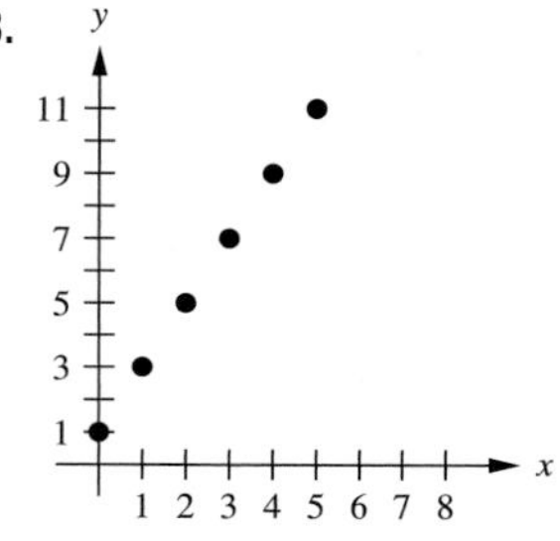

44.
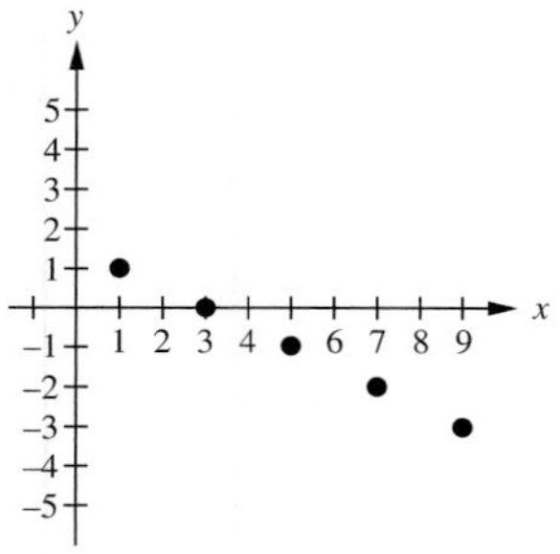

45.

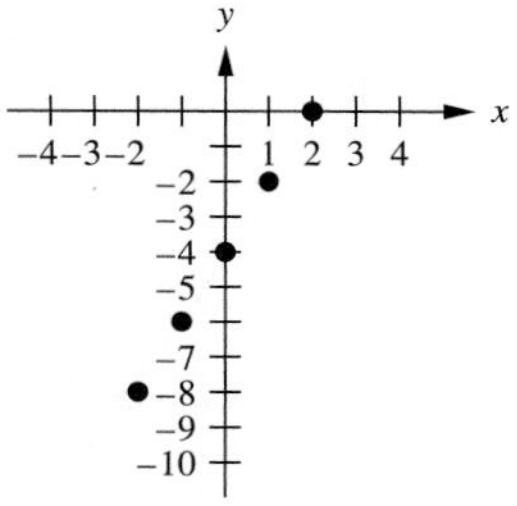

46.

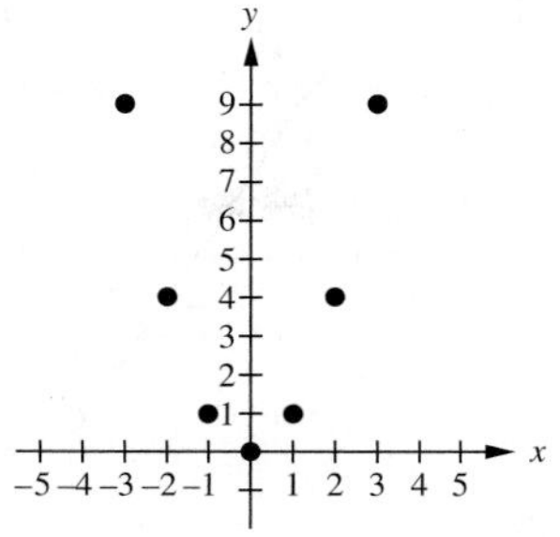

47.

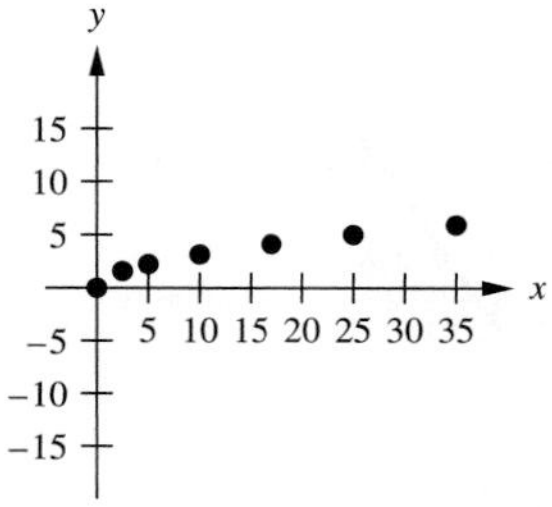

48.

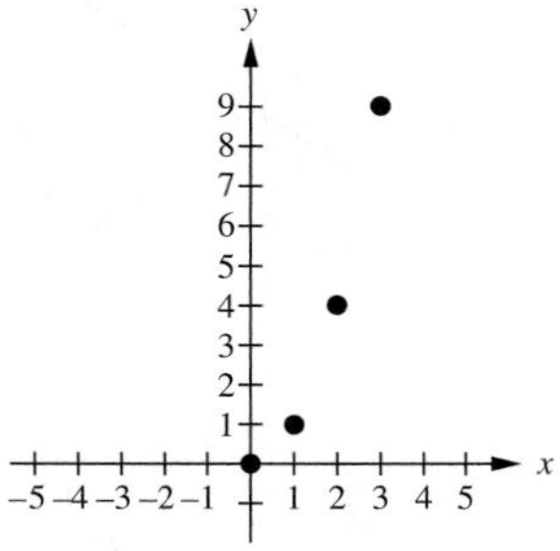

49.

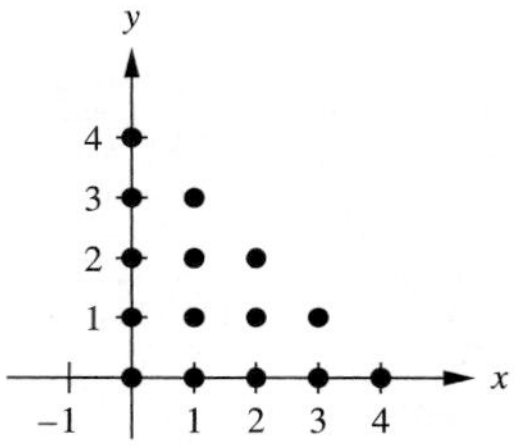

50.

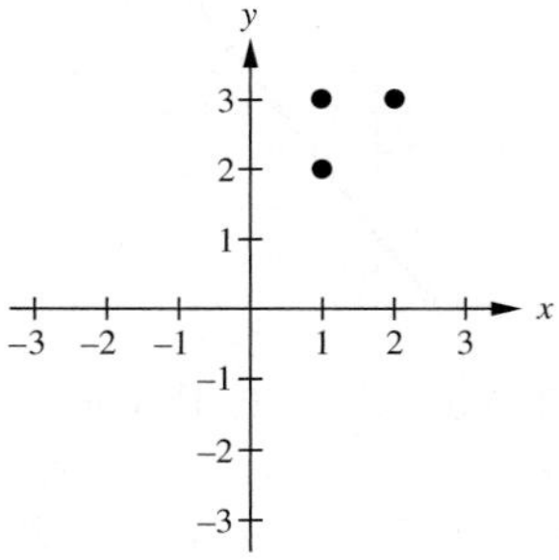

51.

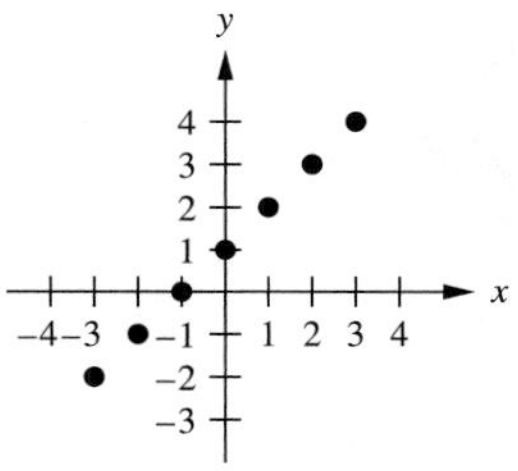

52.

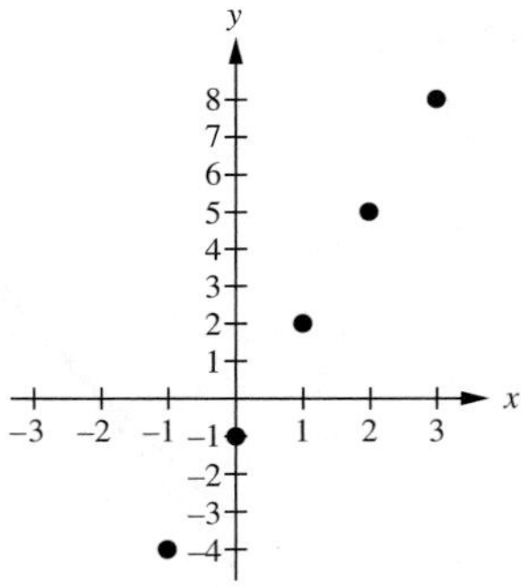

53.

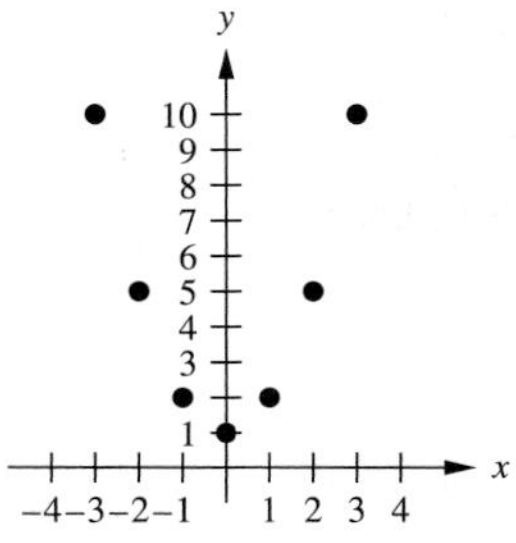

54.

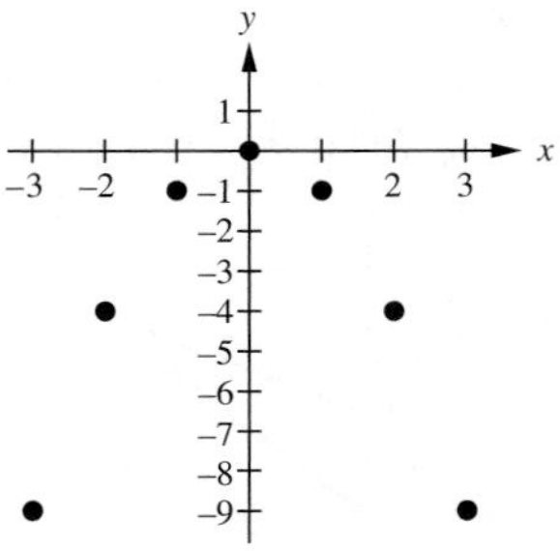

55. **a.** $h(x) = 2.89x + 70.64$

b. $h(34) = 168.9$ cm, or about 169 cm

56. **a.** $c(h) = 25h + 30$ **b.** \$80; \$105; \$130

c.

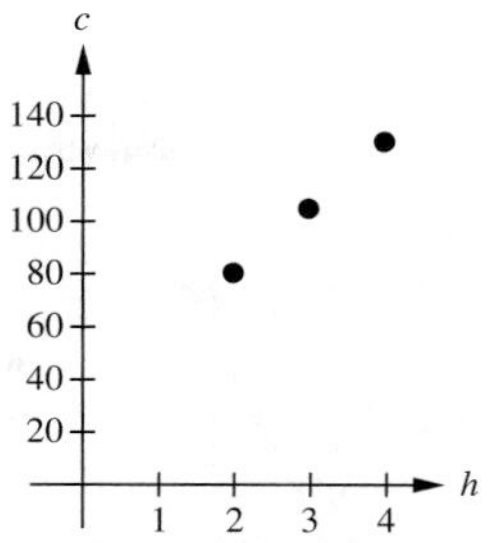

57. **a.** Not a step function **(see below)**

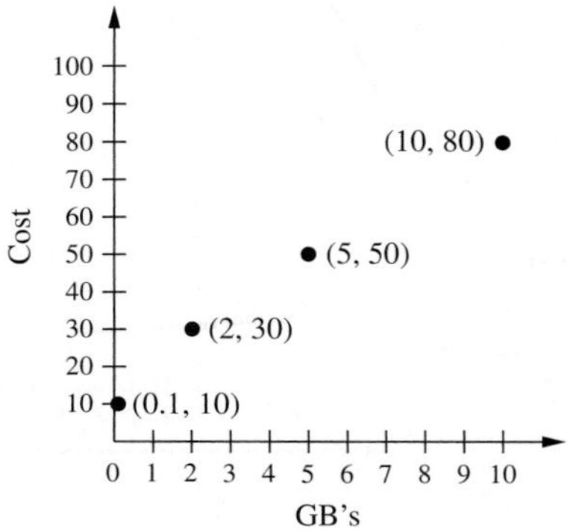

b. \$50 **c.** No **d.** \$80; \$90

58. **a.** 50,400,000 million gallons
b. $o(n) = 1.05n$ million gallons per day
c. 63 million gallons

59. **a.** 252,000,000 gallons
b. $e(n) = 4.2n$ million gallons/day
c. 252 million gallons

60. **a.** $r(n) = 441{,}000n$ gallons/day
b. 26,460,000 gallons

61. **a.** $a(n) = 2{,}079{,}000n$ gallons/day
b. 124,740,000 gallons

62. $x = -1$ and $x = 1$. These values would result in a zero denominator.

63. $g(x) = \sqrt{x - 1}$ is real if and only if $x \geq 1$. Thus, we would exclude all values of x less than 1 if g is to have real values.

64. Exclude $x \leq -1$. These values would not result in a real value for h.

65. The graph of a function $f(x)$ is a picture of the set of points $\{(x, y) \mid y = f(x), x \text{ an element of the domain of } f\}$.

66. No. A relation is any set of ordered pairs. A function is a set of ordered pairs such that for every element in the domain there is exactly one corresponding element in the range.

67. Yes. It is a relation for which there is exactly one value of y for each value of x in the domain.

68. Because if a vertical line intersects the graph at more than one point, it means that for particular x there is more than one y, and thus the graph is not the graph of a function.

69. $c = f(x) = 4(x - 40)$, x in °F

70. 160 chirps **71.** $f(t) = 16t^2$ **72.** 1600 ft

73. $f(x) = \sqrt{x}$ **74.** 36 units **75.** 10,000 units

76. 49 units

Collaborative Learning

Answers will vary

Exercises 7.2

1. 4 **2.** 5

3.

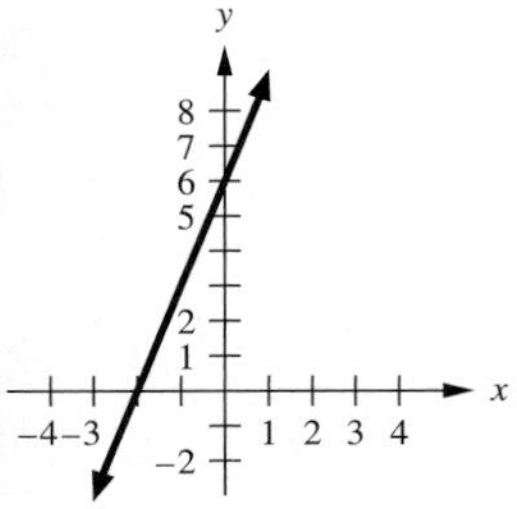

4.

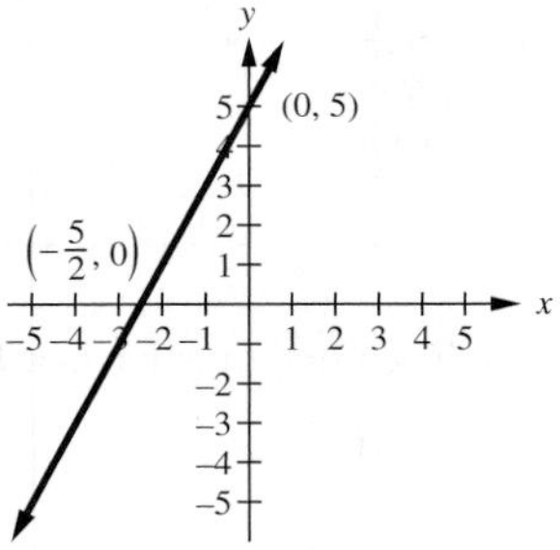

5.

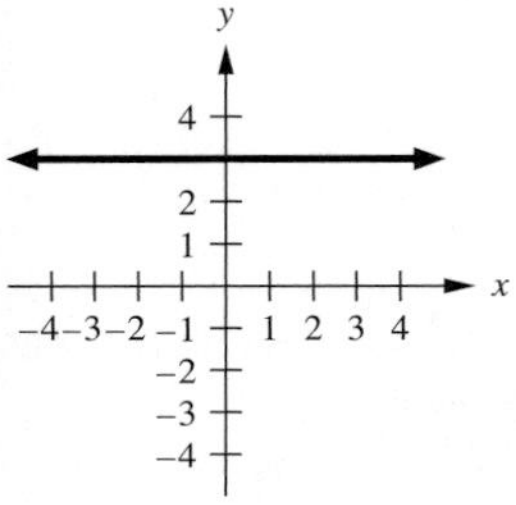

6.

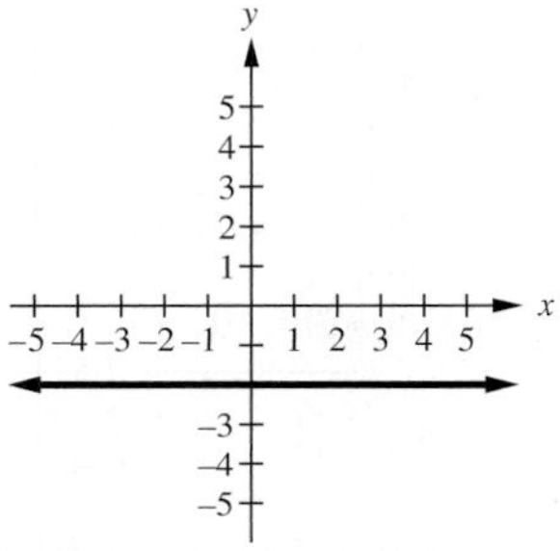

7.

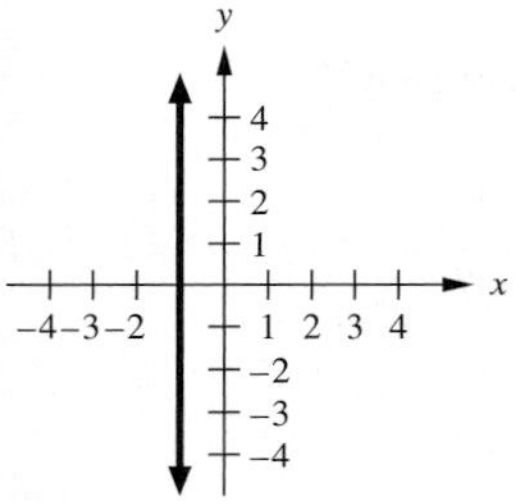

8.

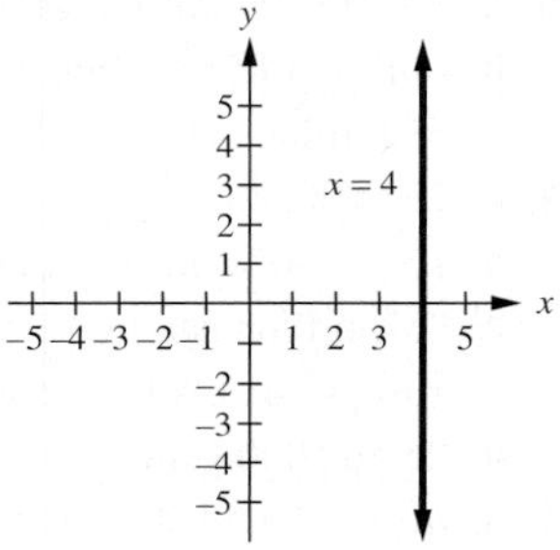

9.

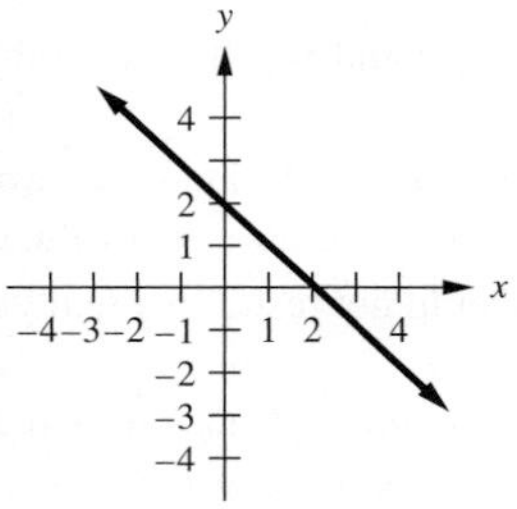

10.

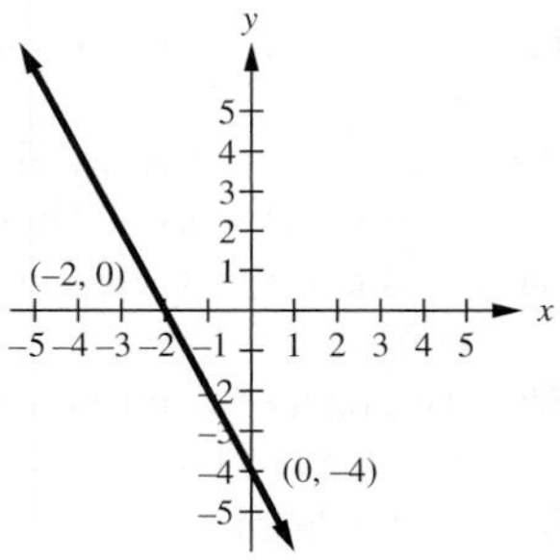

11.

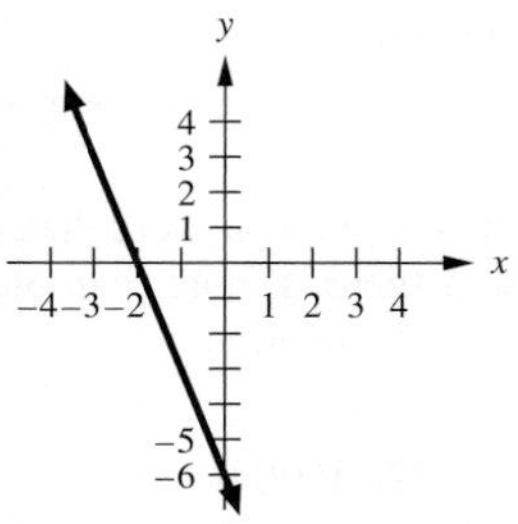

12.

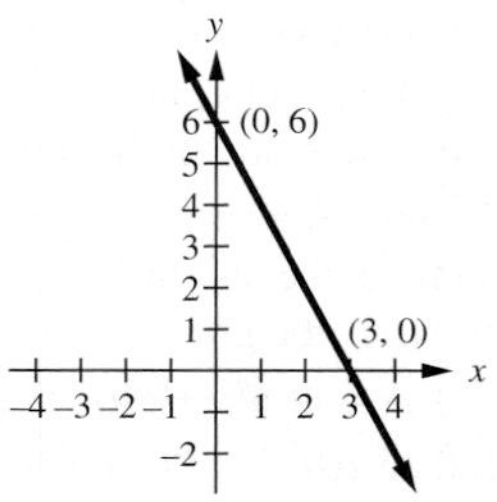

13.

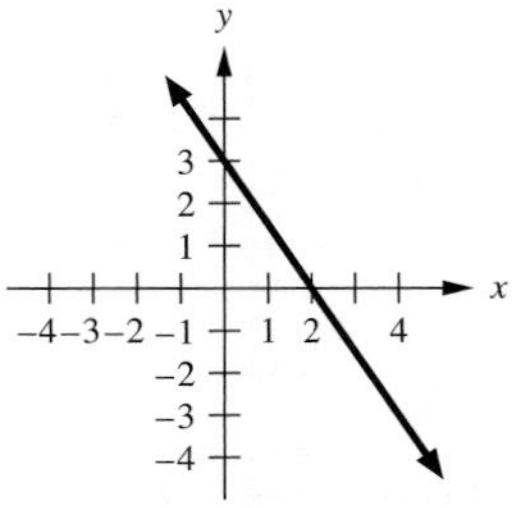

14.

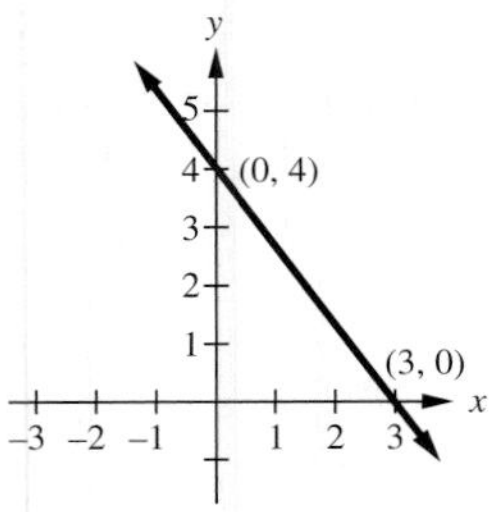

15.

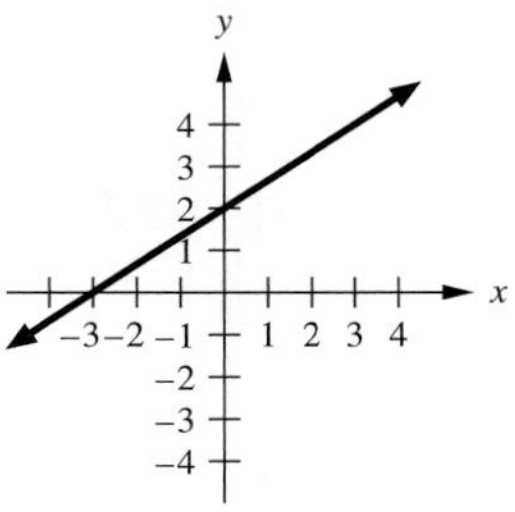

16.

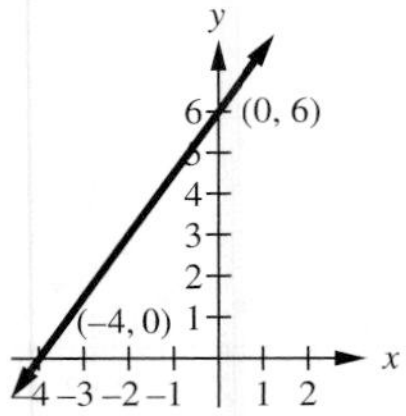

17.

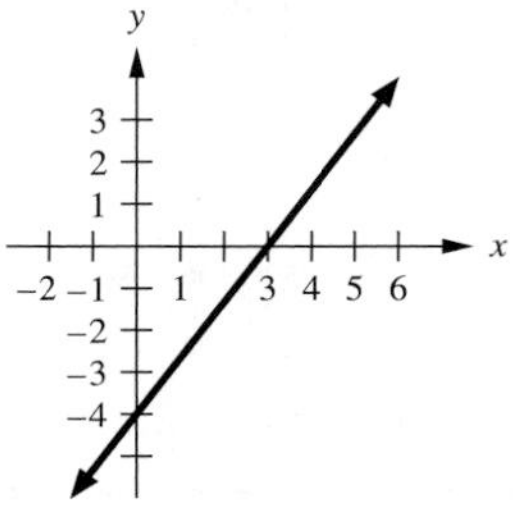

18.

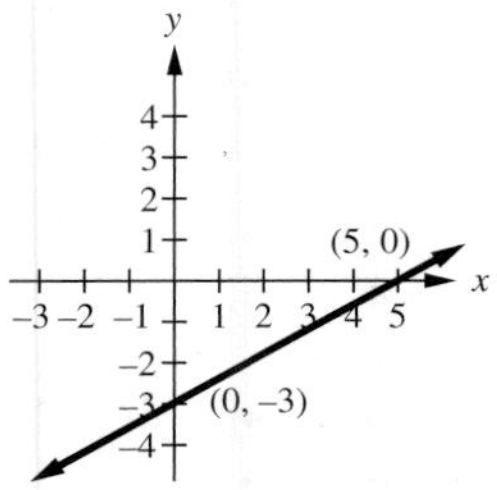

19. 5 units **20.** 13 units **21.** $\sqrt{73} \approx 8.54$ units

22. $\sqrt{65} \approx 8.06$ units **23.** $\sqrt{58} \approx 7.62$ units

24. $2\sqrt{17} \approx 8.25$ units **25.** 2 units

26. 2 units **27.** 4 units **28.** 7 units

29. a. $E(x) = 500 + 25x$; $S(x) = 1000 + 20x$

b.

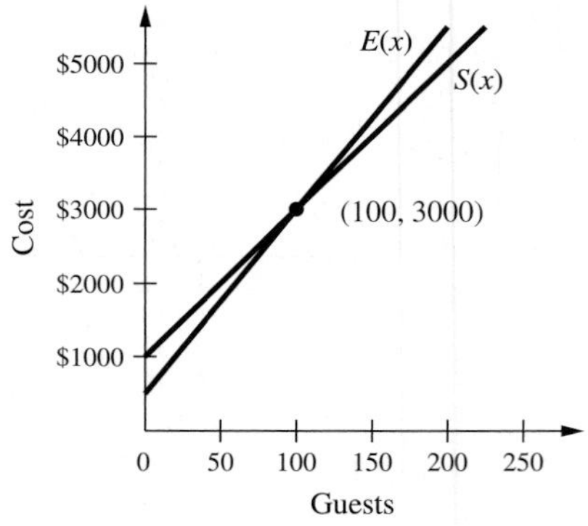

c. The cost is the same for 100 persons.

30. a.

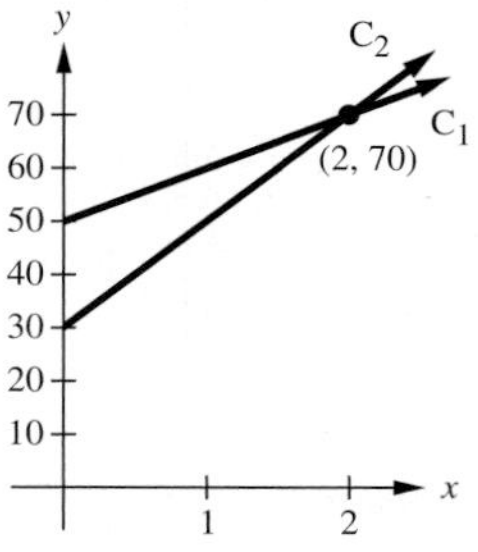

b. 2 hours

31. **a.** $m(2) = \$30, m(5) = \$50$
b. $m(d) = \$30 + \$10 = \$40$
c. $m(d) = \$30 + 2(\$10) = \$50$
d. $m(d) = \$30 + 3(\$10) = \$60$
e.

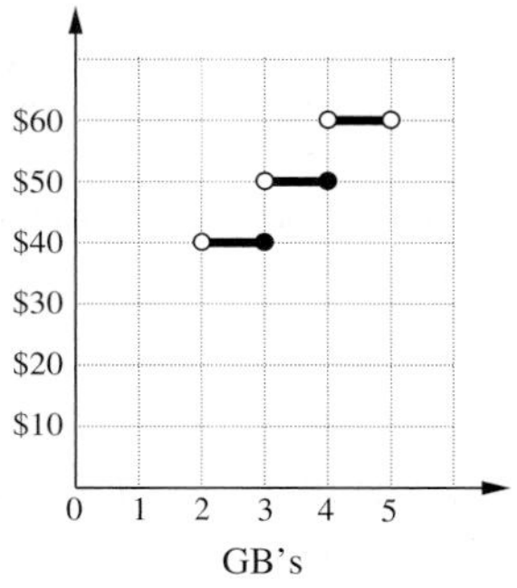

32. **a.** $m(10) = \$80$
b. $m(d) = \$50 + \$10 = \$60$
c. $m(d) = \$50 + 2(\$10) = \$70$
d. $m(d) = \$50 + 3(\$10) = \$80$
e. $m(d) = \$50 + 4(\$10) = \$90$
f. $m(d) = \$50 + 5(\$10) = \$100$
g.

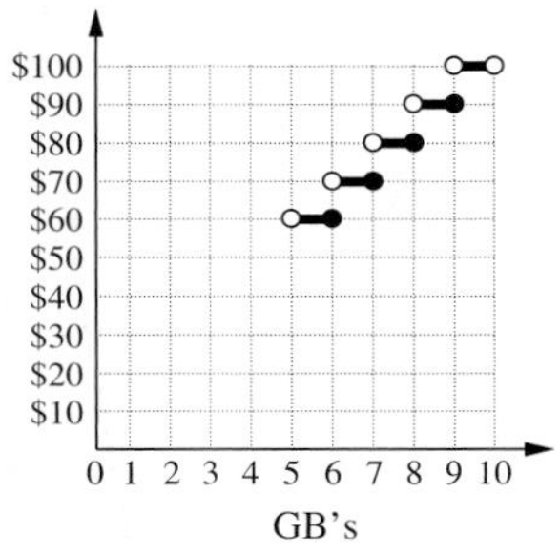

33. Yes. The distance d from $(2, -3)$ is $\sqrt{52} = 2\sqrt{13} < 10$ mi.
34. $\sqrt{29} > 5$, so you are not in the evacuation zone.
35. **a.** 30.4; 27.7 **b.** 30; 27.9 **c.** 27
d. When $t = 20$, that is, 20 years after 2002 in 2022
36. **a.** 63% **b.** 70% **c.** 7%
d. About 13%. It does not fit the pattern for this age group.
37. **a.**

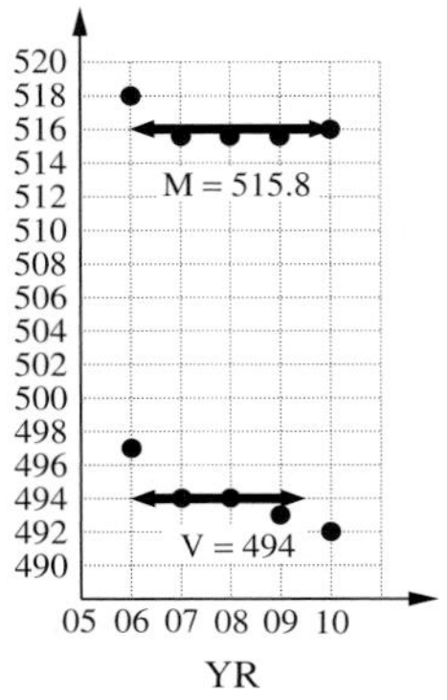

b. $V = 494, M = 515.8$
c. $y = V$ and $y = M$ model the data very well
d. Yes. By the vertical line test (Any vertical line touches the graph only once.)

38. **a. c.**

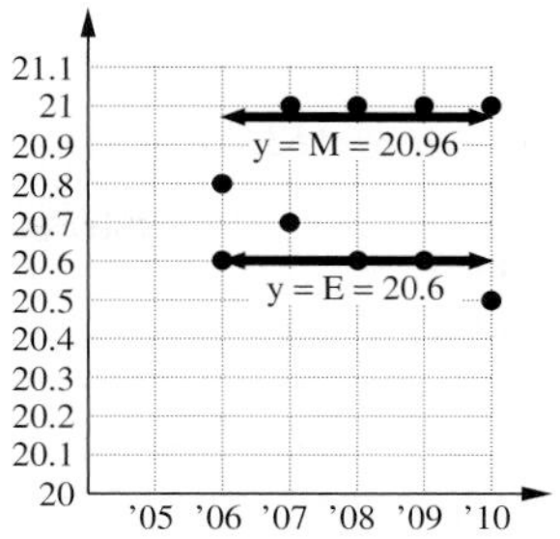

b. $E = 20.6, M = 20.96$
d. Yes. By the vertical line test (any vertical line touches the graph only once.)
39. Use the distance formula to find the square of the length of each side of the triangle.

$$(AB)^2 = (a_1 - b_1)^2 + (a_2 - b_2)^2$$
$$(AC)^2 = (a_1 - c_1)^2 + (a_2 - c_2)^2$$
$$(BC)^2 = (b_1 - c_1)^2 + (b_2 - c_2)^2$$

The triangle is a right triangle if and only if one of these squares equals the sum of the other two squares. You can check this.
40. We know that the graph is a horizontal line. Since $y = b$ for all values of x, we can plot the point $(0, b)$ and (a, b), where a is any convenient value of x. Then draw the straight line through $(0, b)$ and (a, b). The graph is a line parallel to the x axis and b units from that axis.
41. See the Problem Solving procedure following Example 1 and follow it step by step for $x = c$.
42. Let $x = 0$ to get the point $(0, b)$. Then let $f(x) = 0$ to get the point $(-\frac{b}{a}, 0)$. Plot these two points and draw the straight line through them for the desired graph.
43. About $940 **44.** About $600
45. About $800 **46.** About $300
For problems 47–58, see the corresponding answers for Exercise 7.2

Exercises 7.3

1. $m = 1$ **2.** $\frac{1}{2}$ **3.** $m = -1$ **4.** 0
5. $m = -\frac{1}{8}$ **6.** -1 **7.** $m = \frac{1}{4}$ **8.** 1
9. $m = 0$ **10.** 0 **11.** $y = \frac{1}{2}x + \frac{3}{2}$
12. $y = -2x - 4$ **13.** $y = -x + 6$
14. $y = \frac{3}{2}x + \frac{11}{2}$ **15.** $y = 5$
16. Has no slope-intercept form. ($x = 3$ is the simplest form.)
17. **a.** $m = 1$ **b.** $b = 2$
18. **a.** -2 **b.** 3
19. **a.** $m = \frac{4}{3}$ **b.** $b = 0$
20. **a.** $\frac{1}{2}$ **b.** 2
21. **a.** $m = -1$ **b.** $b = 14$
22. **a.** 4 **b.** 8
23. **a.** $m = 0$ **b.** $b = 6$
24. **a.** 0 **b.** 8
25. **a.** The slope is not defined.
b. The line does not intersect the y axis.
26. **a.** $-\frac{1}{2}$ **b.** $\frac{3}{2}$
27. $3x - y = 4$ **28.** $4x - y = -8$

29. $x + y = 5$ 30. $5x + 3y = 15$
31. $10x - y = 0$ 32. $x = -4$
33. $w = 5h - 176$ 34. $w = 4h - 150$
35. $w = 5h - 187$ 36. 6 ft 2 in.
37. $C = 1.70\,m + 0.30$; \$51.30
38. $C = 1.50\,m + 1.50$; \$16.50; This one.
39. 6 mi 40. $C = 1.50m + 2.00$; \$47
41. a. \$2 b. $(m - 1)$
c. \$1.70 d. $1.70(m - 1)$
e. $C = 1.70m + 0.30$; yes
42. $C = 1.50m + 2.00$; Yes
43. a. $C = 2m + 55$ b. \$55
44. a. $C = 7.8m$ b. About 22 min
45. Parallel 46. Parallel 47. Not parallel
48. Not parallel
49. Parallel
50. Not parallel
51. $4x - y = 6$
52. $3x + 2y = 6$
53. a. $5x - 2y = 10$ b. $x + 2y = 3$
c. $2x + y = 2$ d. $5x - 4y = 1$
54. If we write the equations in the general form, we have $m_1x - y = -b_1$ and $m_2x - y = -b_2$. The condition given in problem 53 becomes $m_1m_2 + 1 = 0$. Thus, $m_2 = -\frac{1}{m_1}$. We need the condition $m_1 \neq 0$, because we cannot divide by zero. Also, if $m_1 = 0$, the first line is parallel to the x axis and the perpendicular line is parallel to the y axis, so its slope is not defined.
55. For the first line, $m_1 = 2$, and for the second line, $m_2 = -\frac{415}{790}$. Since $m_2 \neq \frac{-1}{m_1}$, the lines are not perpendicular.
56. a. $m = \frac{15}{9}$ b. $y = \frac{15t}{9} + 9$
c. $P(t) = \frac{15t}{9} + 9$
d. Increase in wireless subscribers per year
e. 42.33 million wireless subscribers
57. a. 1.12. The number of friends F for every follower f.
b. 0 c. $F(f) = 1.12f$ d. 13.44 million friends
58. a. 0.8
b. Increase in the number of grams of fat consumed per year
59. a. Decreasing b. Decreasing
c. Fish and shellfish
60. a. 0.16 b. Increasing
c. The annual increase in life span for American women.
61. a. 0.19 b. Increasing
c. The annual increase in life span for American men.
62. a. -5 b. Decreasing
c. The rate at which the velocity of the ball is decreasing
63. a. 0.4 b. Increasing
c. The slope 0.4 represents the annual increase in fat consumption.
64. a. -0.2 b. Decreasing
c. The rate at which the consumption of milk is decreasing per year
65. a. 168.2 grams b. 177.6 grams c. 140
d. Increasing
66. a. 162 b. 64
c. -9.8. The annual decrease in deaths from heart disease
67. a. 2.5 b. The annual population increase
c. 312.5 or 313 d. Yes
68. The slope of a vertical line does not exist. (Let $x = a$ be the equation of the line. Then (a, b) and (a, c), $b \neq c$, are two distinct points on the line. The slope formula gives $\frac{b-c}{a-a} = \frac{b-c}{0}$, which is undefined.)
69. If (x_1, y_1) and (x_2, y_2) are any two distinct points on a horizontal line, $y_1 = y_2$ and $x_1 \neq x_2$. Thus, the slope is

$$m = \frac{y_2 - y_1}{x_2 - x_1} = \frac{0}{x_2 - x_1} = 0$$

70. The lines parallel to the y axis. (The lines $y = b$ are parallel to the x axis, so the perpendicular lines must be parallel to the y axis.) The equations are of the form $x = a$.
71. a. 0.79 b. No 72. a. 0.32 b. No
73. a. 0.25 b. Yes 74. 64 ft
75. The slope is 0.25, which is not safe for parking. $x = 105$ ft will give the maximum allowable slope.
76. Parking: \$4; Admission: \$3
77. The fixed fee is \$35. The hourly rate is \$25.
78. Fee: \$30; Charge: \$0.25 per minute

Skill Checker

1.
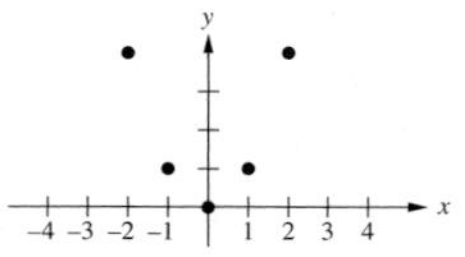

2.
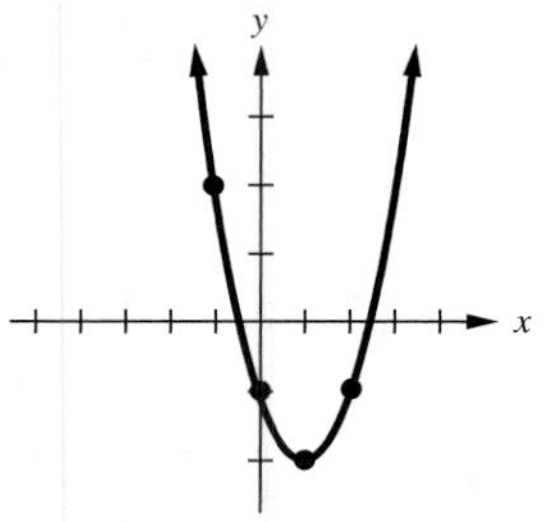

$f(0) = -1, f(1) = -2, f(-1) = 2,$
$f(2) = -1, f(-2) = 7$

Exercises 7.4

1.
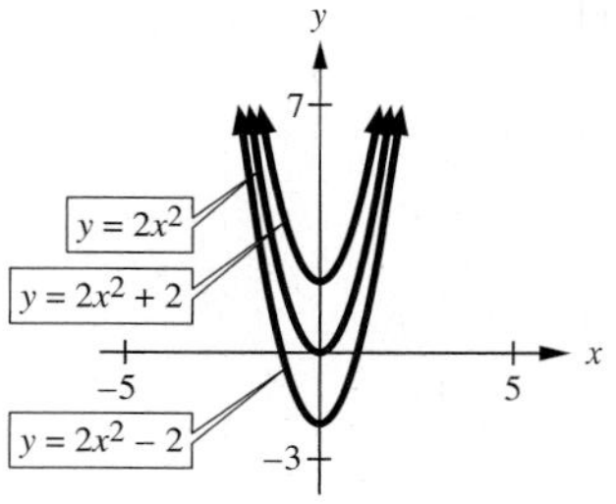

2.
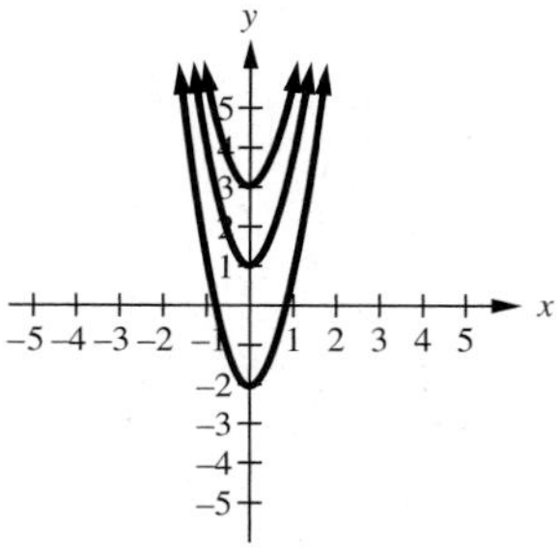

$y = 3x^2 + 3$
$y = 3x^2 + 1$
$y = 3x^2 - 2$

3.

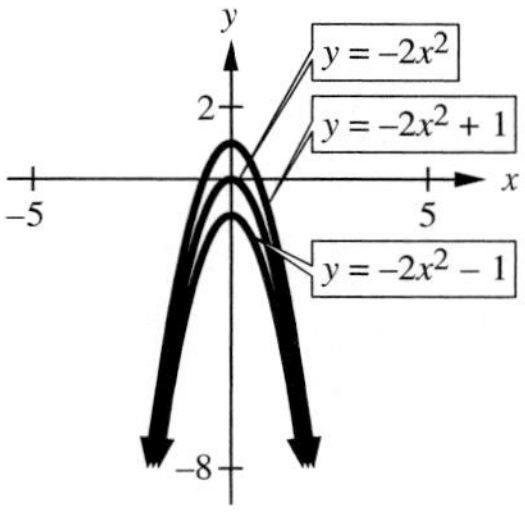

4.

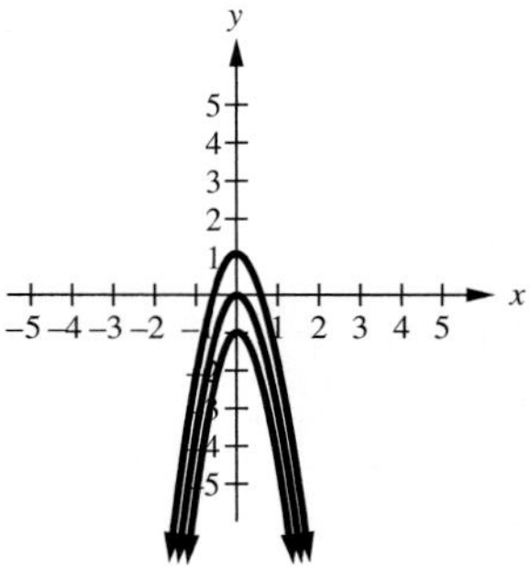

$y = -4x^2 + 1$
$y = -4x^2$
$y = -4x^2 - 1$

5.

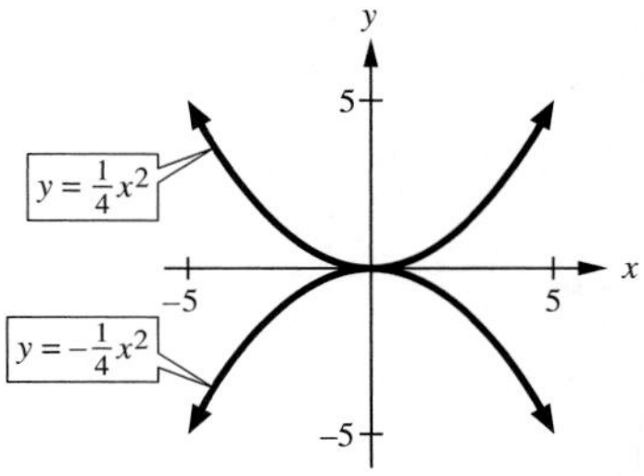

6.

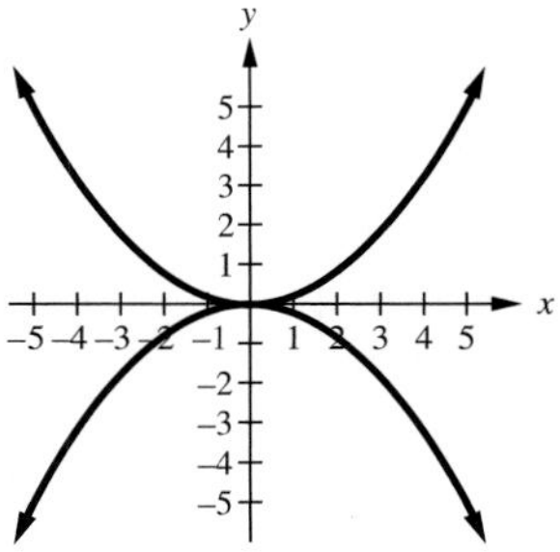

$y = \frac{1}{5}x^2$
$y = -\frac{1}{5}x^2$

7.

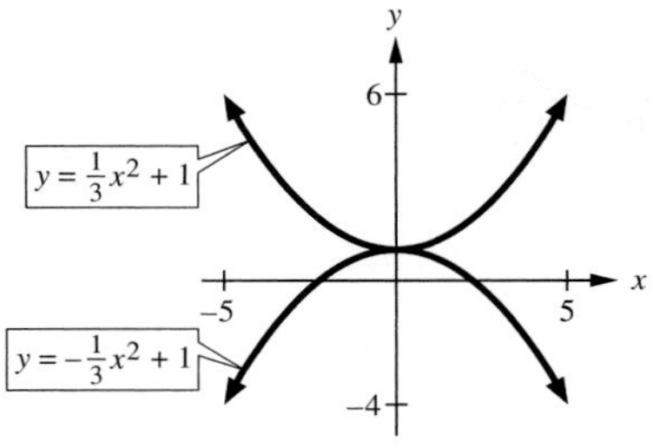

8.

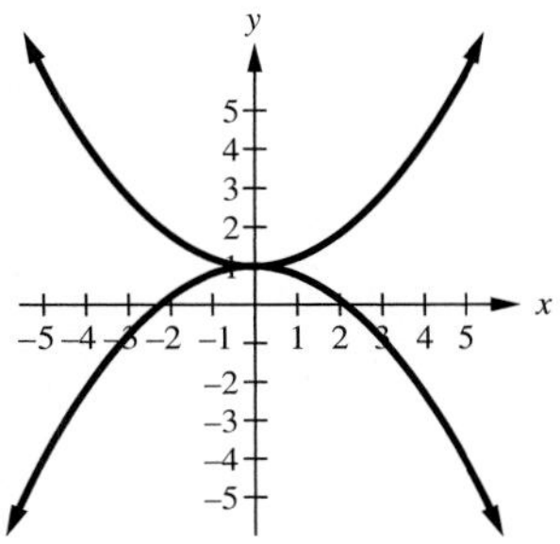

$y = \frac{1}{4}x^2 + 1$
$y = -\frac{1}{4}x^2 + 1$

9.

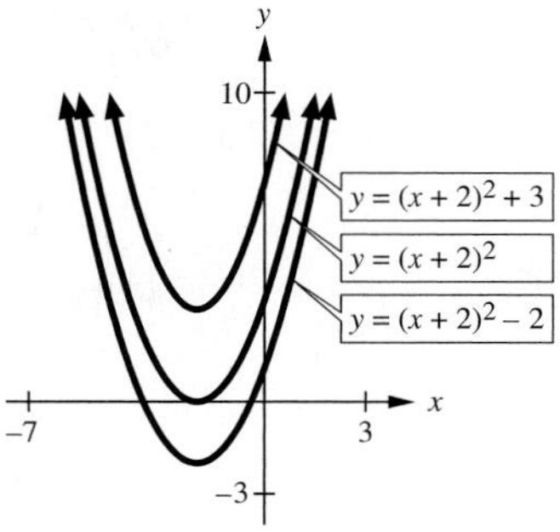

10.

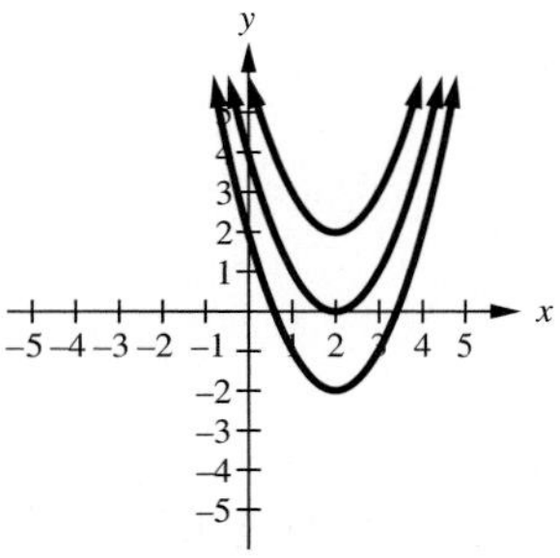

$y = (x - 2)^2 + 2$
$y = (x - 2)^2$
$y = (x - 2)^2 - 2$

11.

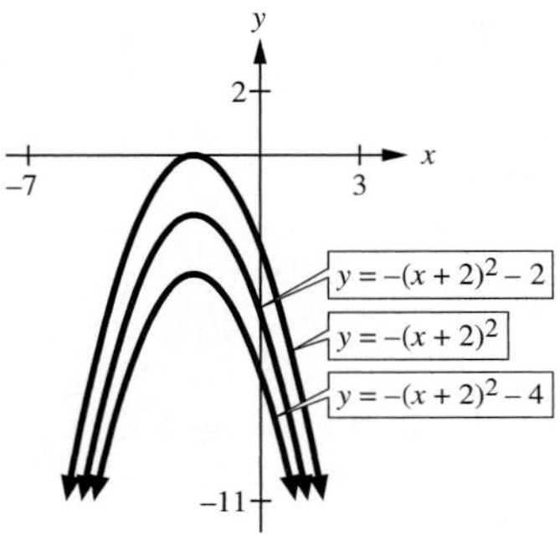

12.

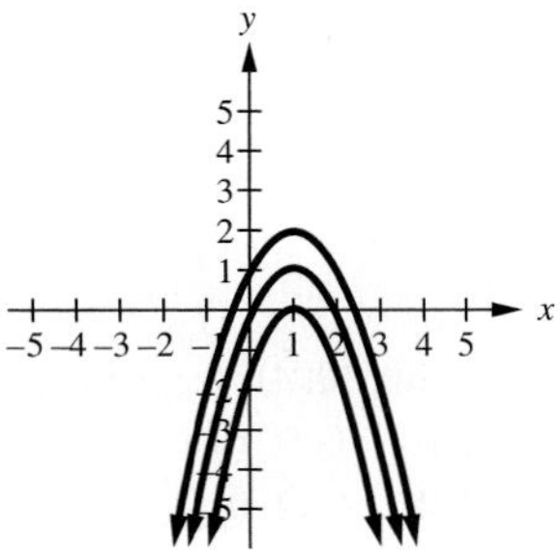

$y = -(x - 1)^2 + 2$
$y = -(x - 1)^2 + 1$
$y = -(x - 1)^2$

13.

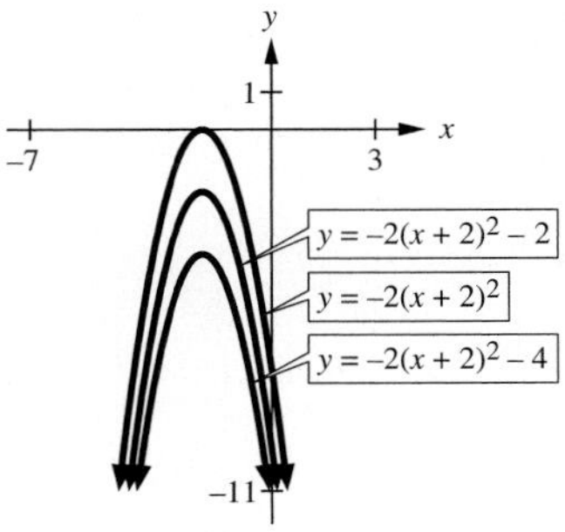

14.

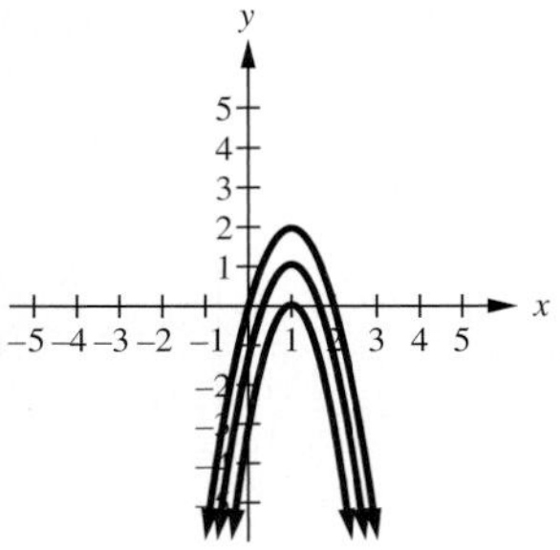

$y = -2(x - 1)^2 + 2$
$y = -2(x - 1)^2 + 1$
$y = -2(x - 1)^2$

15.

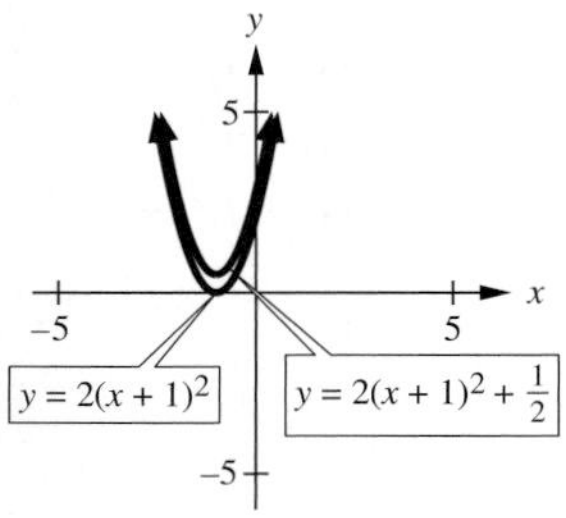

16.

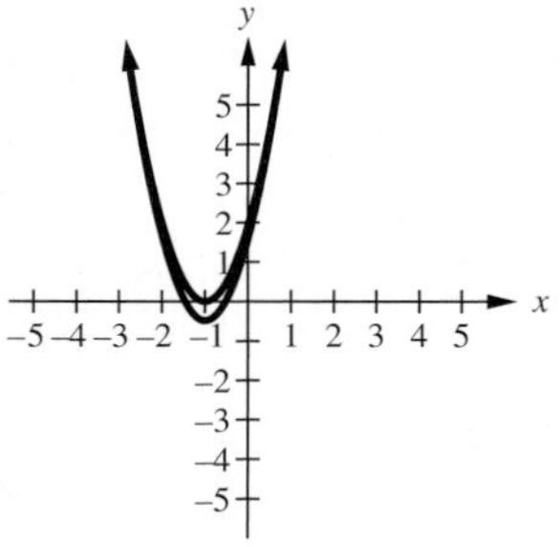

$y = 2(x + 1)^2$
$y = 2(x + 1)^2 - \frac{1}{2}$

17.

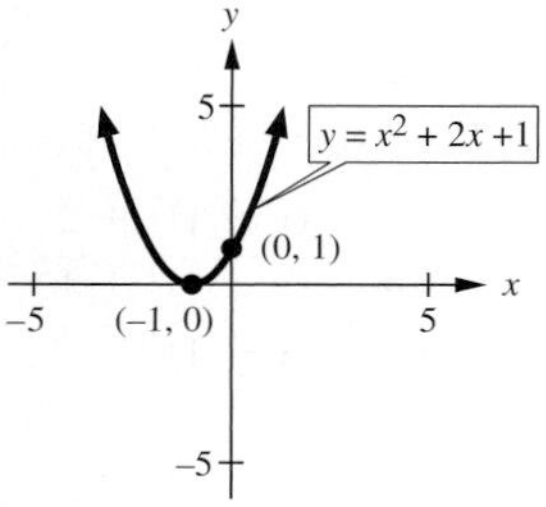

18.

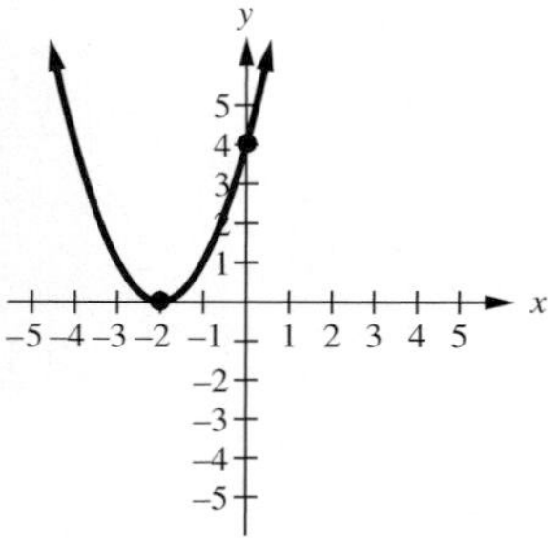

int: $(0, 4)$
$(-2, 0)$
V: $(-2, 0)$

19.

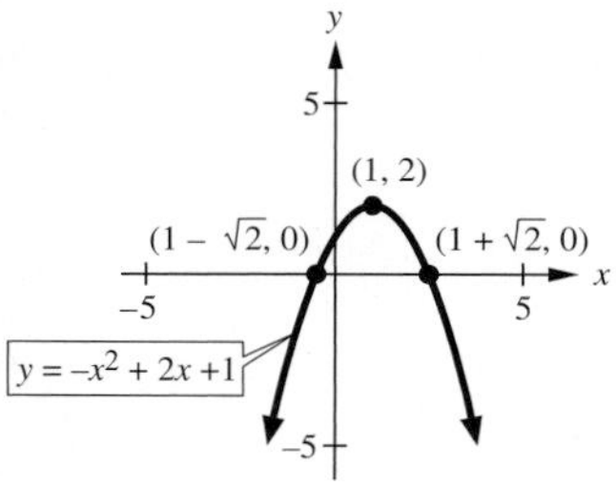

20.

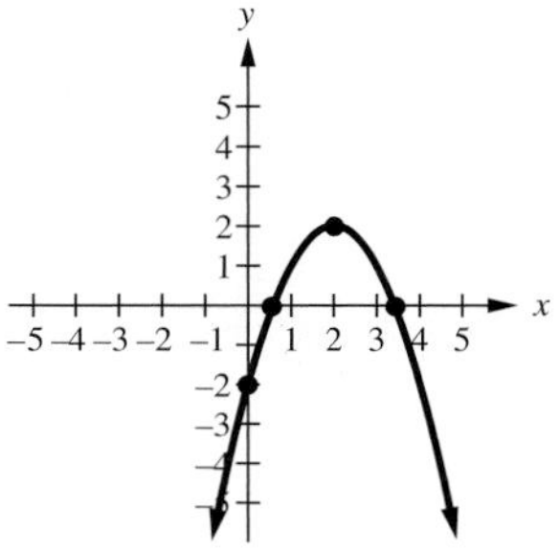

int: $(0, -2)$
$(0.6, 0)$
$(3.4, 0)$
V: $(2, 2)$

21.

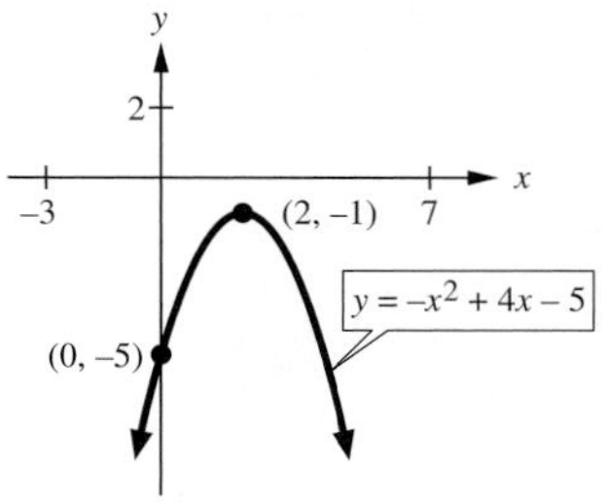

22.

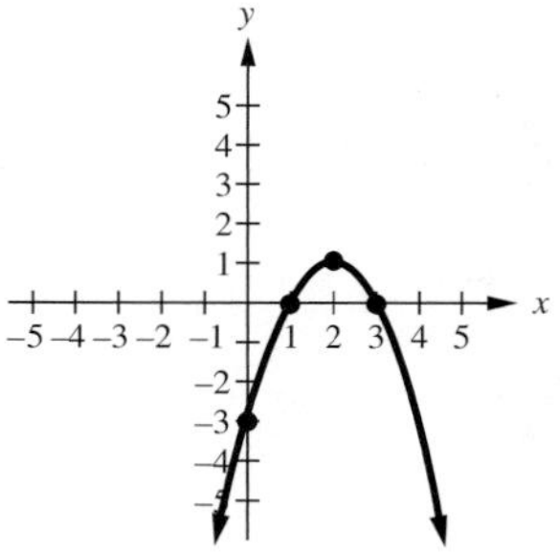

int: $(0, -3)$
$(1, 0)$
$(3, 0)$
V: $(2, 1)$

23.

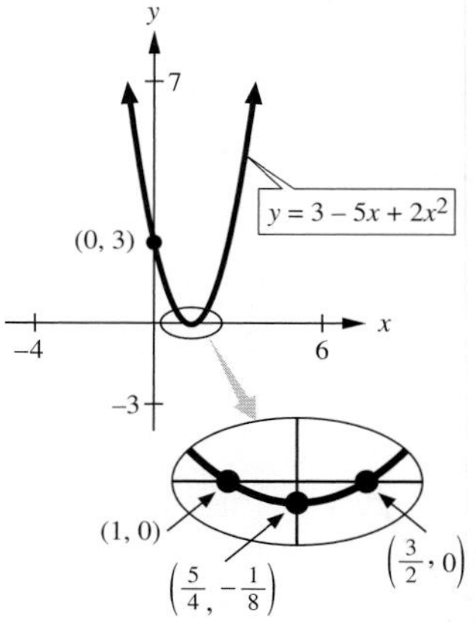

24.

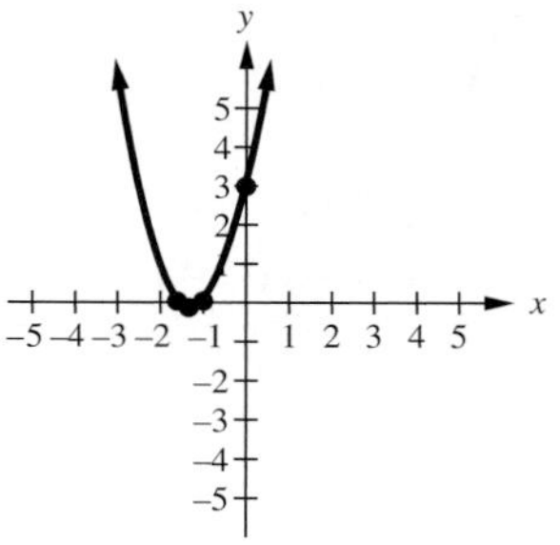

int: $(0, 3)$
$(-1, 0)$
$(-\frac{3}{2}, 0)$
V: $(-\frac{5}{4}, -\frac{1}{8})$

25.

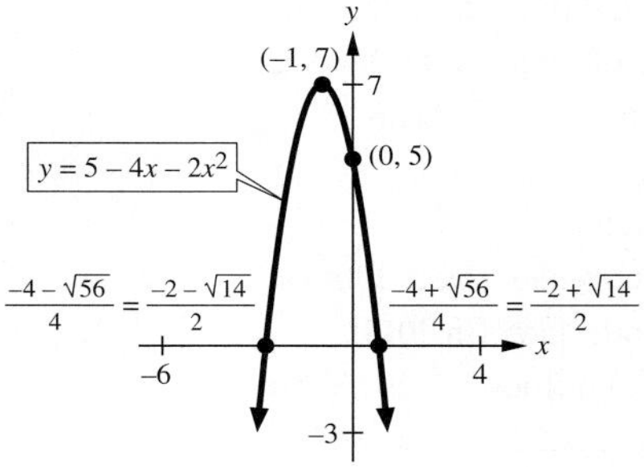

26.

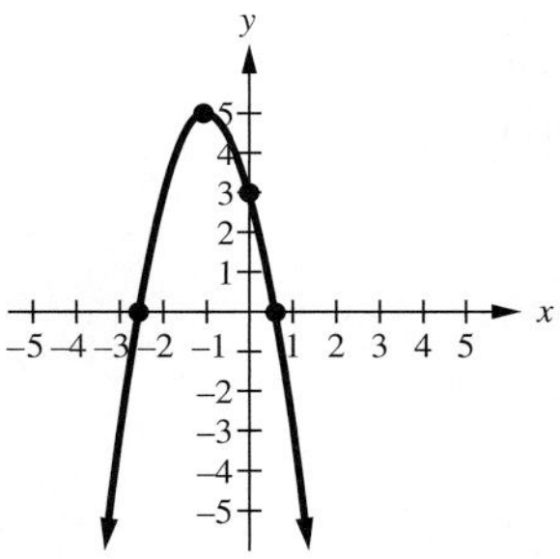

int: $(0, 3)$
$(-2.6, 0)$
$(0.6, 0)$
V: $(-1, 5)$

27.

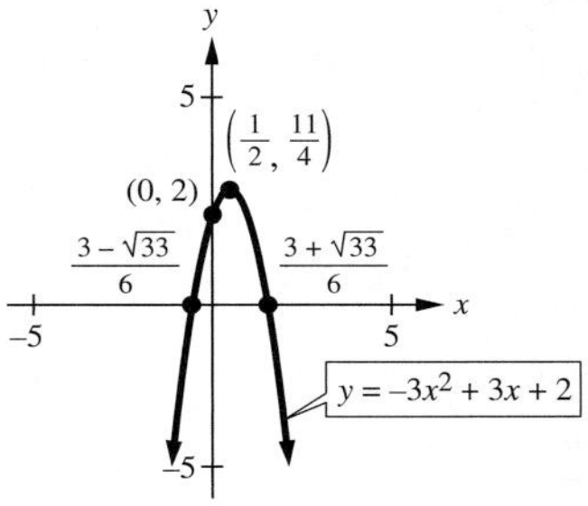

28.

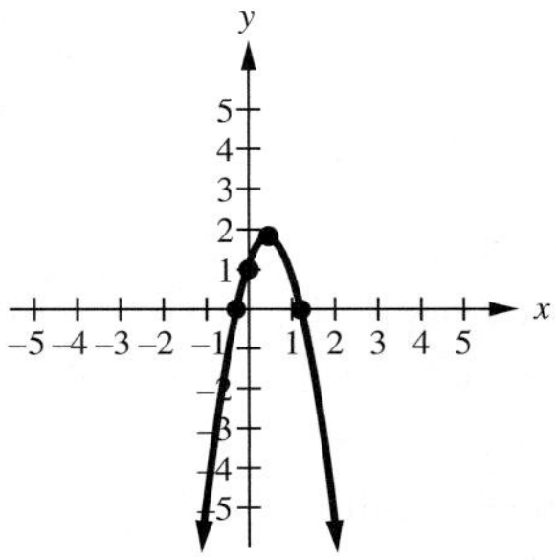

int: $(0, 1)$
$(-0.3, 0)$
$(1.3, 0)$
V: $\left(\frac{1}{2}, \frac{7}{4}\right)$

29. $x = 4000$; $P = \$11{,}000$ **30.** $P = 10$

31. \$25,000 **32.** \$20,000 **33.** 400 ft

34. It takes $\frac{5}{8}$ seconds to reach the maximum height of $6\frac{1}{4}$ ft.

35. $P = (600 + 100W)(1 - 0.10W)$; P = price, W = the weeks elapsed. The maximum for P occurs when $W = 2$ (at the end of 2 weeks).

36. 200 ft by 100 ft

37. **a.** (42, 18) **b.** 18 in. **c.** 84 in.

d.

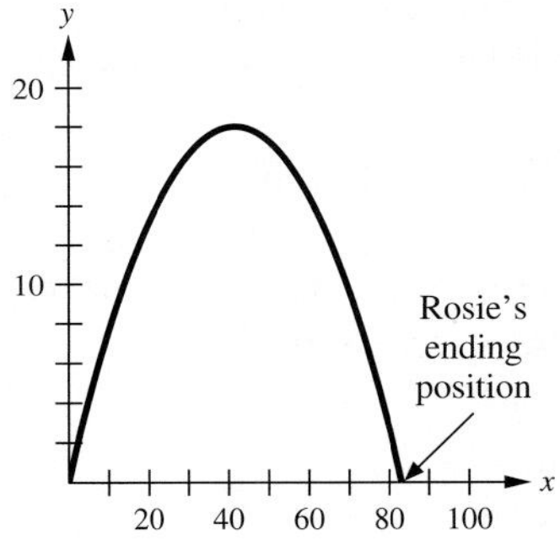

38. **a.** vertex: (70, 24.5)

b. 24.5 in.

c. 140 in.

d.

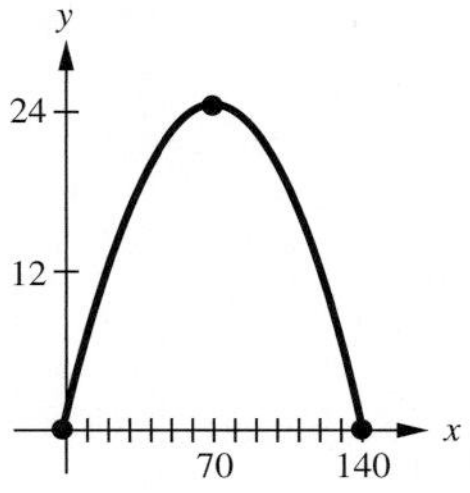

39. **a.** (200, 100) **b.** 100 ft **c.** 400 ft

d.

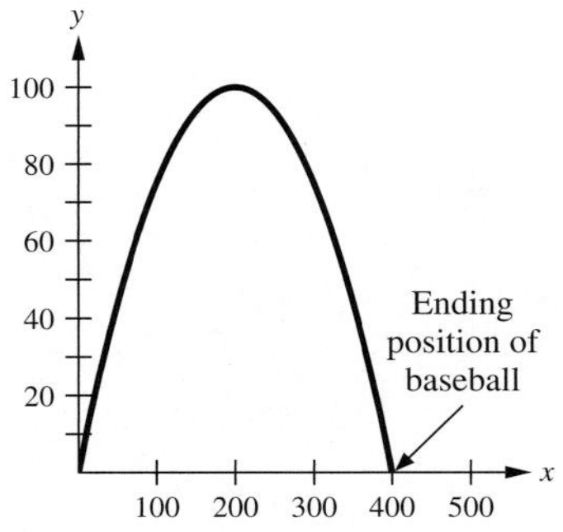

40. **a.** 10.5% occurs at about 22 years.

b. 19.5% occurs at about 48–49 years.

c. $a > 0$

41. **a.** 6.3%; 27 **b.** 10.5% **c.** 22 **d.** 16

42. If $a > 0$, it opens up.
If $a < 0$, it opens down.

43. If $a > 1$, it is narrower. If $a < 1$, it is wider.

44. k moves the graph of $y = ax^2$ k units up when k is positive or k units down when k is negative.

45. Down. If it opened up from (1, 1), it would have no x intercept.

46. Because if it had two y-intercepts, it would not be a function (two y values for one x value).

47. Negative

48. Approximately (1962, 510)

49. (1962, 520) (approximately)

50. Approximately 310 **51.** \$40

52.

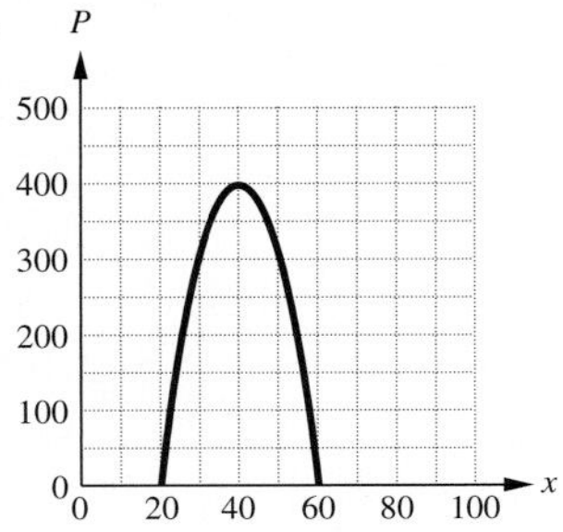

53. \$400

54. **a.** (0, 1) **b.** $y = -1$

56. $x^2 = 5000y$

Exercises 7.5

1. **a.** $\frac{1}{5}$ **b.** 1 **c.** 5
2. **a.** 5 **b.** 1 **c.** $\frac{1}{5}$
3. **a.** $\frac{1}{9}$ **b.** 1 **c.** 9
4. **a.** 9 **b.** 1 **c.** $\frac{1}{9}$
5. **a.** $\frac{1}{10}$ **b.** 1 **c.** 10
6. **a.** 10 **b.** 1 **c.** $\frac{1}{10}$
7.

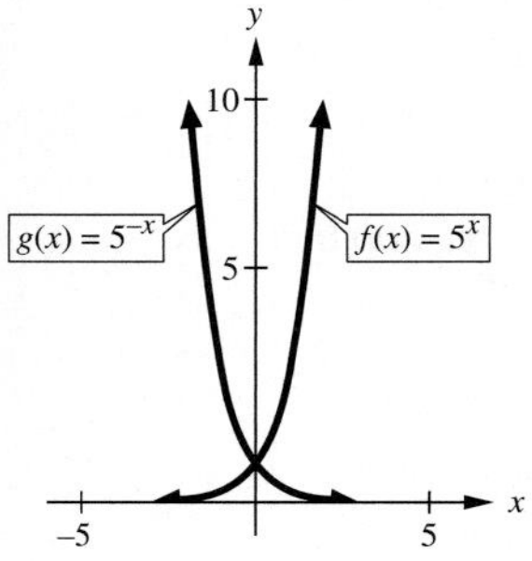

8. $g(t) = 3^{-t}$ $f(t) = 3^t$

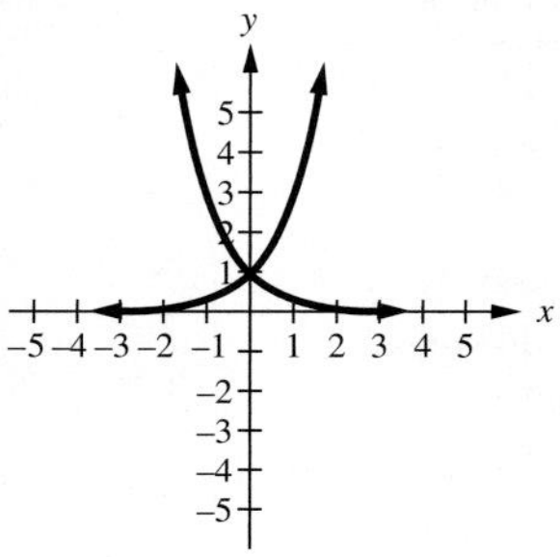

9.

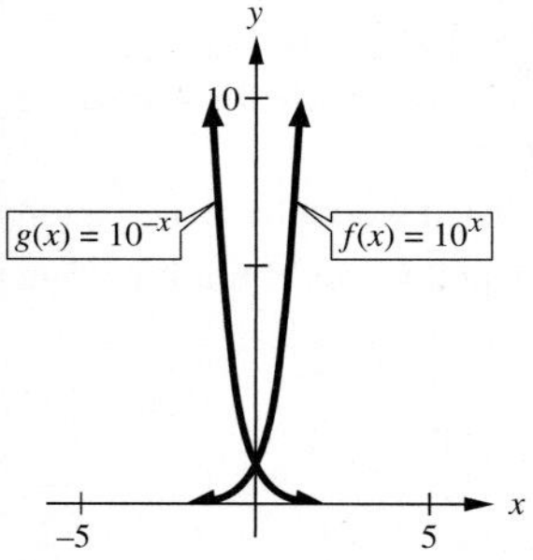

10. $g(t) = 10^{-t/2}$ $f(t) = 10^{t/2}$

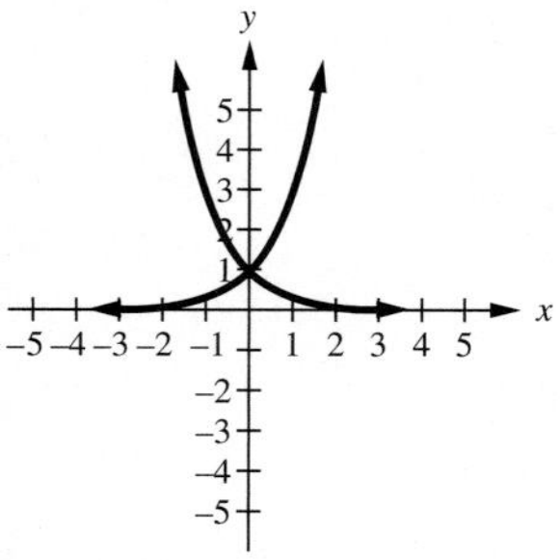

11. **a.** \$2459.60 **b.** \$2435.19
12. **a.** \$6049.65 **b.** \$5930.15
13. **a.** \$1822.12 **b.** \$1814.02
14. **a.** \$3320.12 **b.** \$3290.66
15. **a.** 4000 **b.** 8000 **c.** 16,000
16. **a.** 1200 **b.** 38,400 **c.** 1,228,800
17. **a.** 2000 g **b.** 699.9 g **c.** 244.9 g
18. **a.** 2000 **b.** 665.7 **c.** 221.6
19. 61.93 million
20. About 43.68 million
21. **a.** About $11\frac{1}{2}$ months later (Dec. 2008)
b. About 131 months later (in 2018)
22. **a.** 410 million, 989 million **b.** 50 million
23. **a.** 333,333 **b.** 222,222 **c.** 8671
24. **a.** \$6000 **b.** \$60.47
25. **a.** About 4.42 lb/in.^{2} **b.** About 6.42 lb/in.^{2}
26. **a.** 4.17 lb/in^2. **b.** 6.35 lb/in^2.
27. $f(x) = \log_5 x$

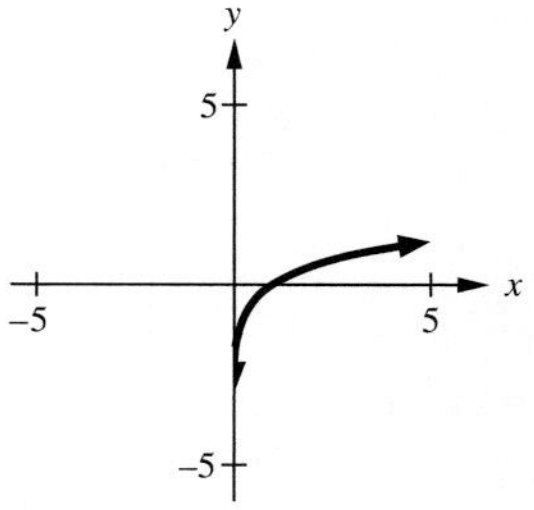

28.

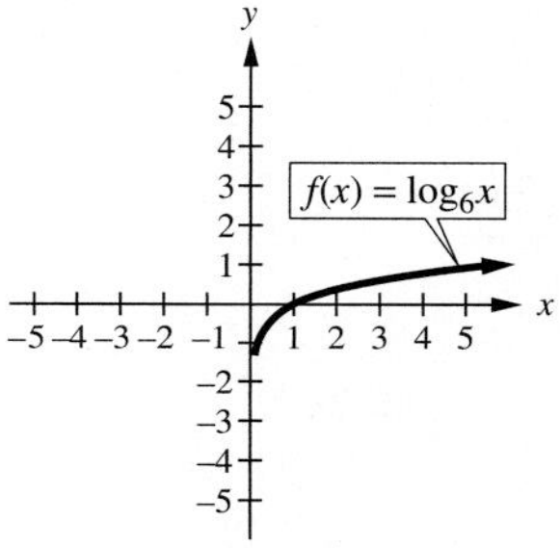

29. About 13.86 year **30.** 9.9 years
31. About 10.66 year **32.** 9.24 years
33. About 6.88 billion **34.** About 7.27 billion
35. About 17.3 min **36.** About 40.2 min
37. About 80.5 min **38.** About 97.8 min
39. **a.** 100,000 **b.** About 67,032
c. About 13,534 **d.** About 1832
40. 73 days **41.** About 23,105 years
42. 11 years **43.** About 13.3 years
44. 346.6 years
45. **a.** 14.7 lb/in.^{2} **b.** About 11.4 lb/in.^{2} **c.** 8.92 lb/in.^{2}
46. **a.** 30 in. of mercury at sea level
b. 10.66 in. of mercury at 5 mi
47. **a.** 13 years (in 2013) **b.** 70% **c.** 36.8%
d. Players but note that the year intervals are different.
48. 4 years
49. **a.** 5000 **b.** About 2247 **c.** 2010
50. 0.24 min
51. **a.** 50,000 **b.** About 74,591 **c.** About 166,006
52. **a.** 50,000 **b.** 45,242 **c.** 18,394
53. **a.** 1000 **b.** About 368

54. a. 1.9×10^{-20} dollars **b.** \$100

55. a. 0 **b.** 39.3

56. a. 50 people **b.** 50 people

57. a. -0.8055 **b.** -3.8968

58. a. 87% **b.** 99.995%

59. Continuous, \$1822.12; monthly, \$1819.40. Continuous compounding gives about \$2.72 more.

60. \$3320.12 continuous; \$3310.20 monthly. Continuous earns \$9.92 more.

61. a. $f(x) = 1$, a horizontal line **b.** Yes

62. Answers will vary.

63. Symmetric with respect to y axis

64. Answers will vary.

Skill Checker

1.

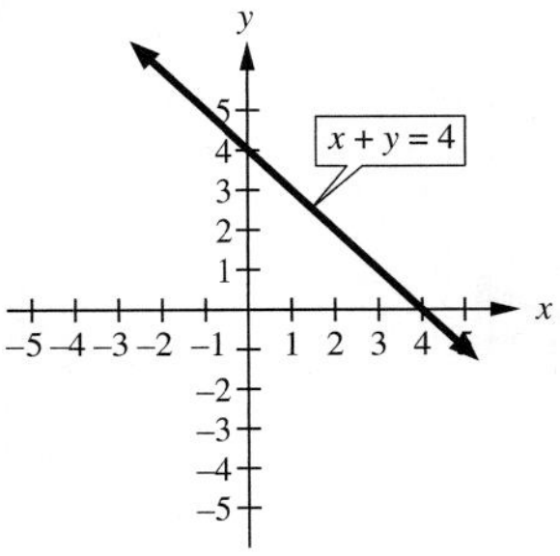

2 and 4.

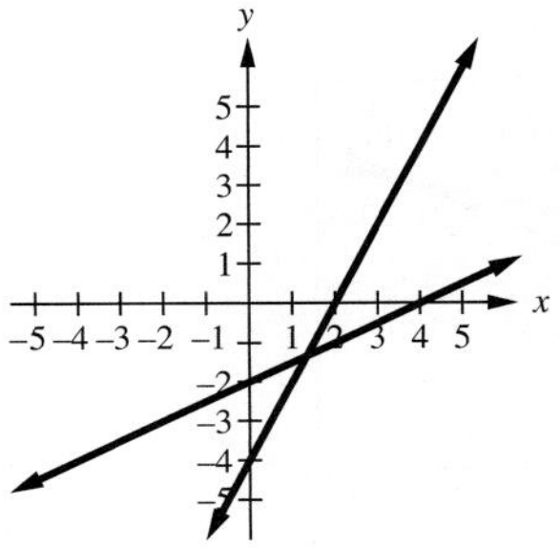

$2x - y = 4$
$x - 2y = 4$

3.

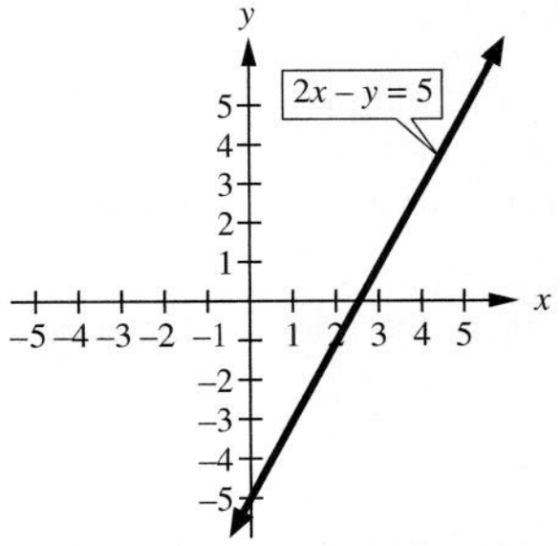

Exercises 7.6

1. (1, 2) **2.** (4, 1) **3.** (3, −4) **4.** (2, 1)

5. $(2, -\frac{1}{2})$ **6.** (2, −2) **7.** (1, 2) **8.** (4, 1)

9. (4, 2) **10.** (3, 1) **11.** (3, −4) **12.** (2, 1)

13. No solution

14. The lines coincide; if a is any real number, both equations are satisfied by the solution $(a, 2a + 5)$.

15. (1, 2) **16.** (−3, 5) **17.** $(2, -\frac{1}{2})$

18. (2, −2) **19.** (−3, 10)

20. No solution. The lines are parallel.

21. $(-2, \frac{1}{2})$ **22.** $(\frac{1}{4}, -1)$ **23.** (2, −5)

24. $(\frac{1}{2}, \frac{5}{2})$ **25.** $(\frac{2}{3}, \frac{5}{6})$ **26.** $(\frac{5}{2}, -\frac{3}{8})$

27. No solution **28.** $r = 5, s = 0$

29. $u = -\frac{5}{2}, v = 6$; or $(\frac{-5}{2}, 6)$

30. $w = -\frac{1}{2}, z = -\frac{1}{2}$

31. a. 100 **b.**

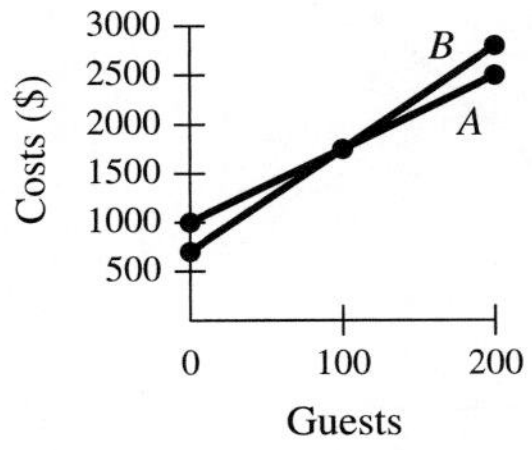

c. Company A

32. a. $y = 50x + 5400$ **b.** $y = 600x + 1000$

c.

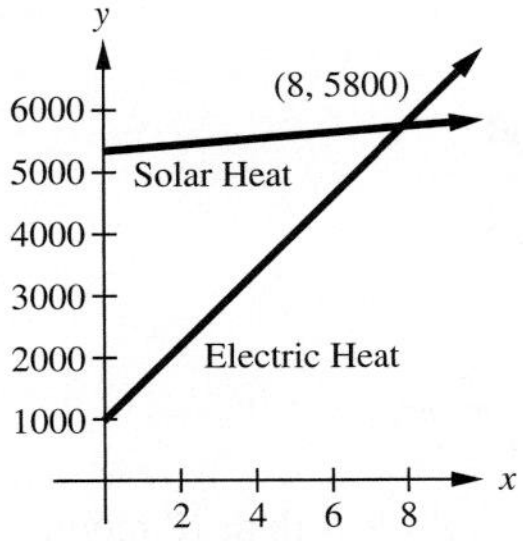

d. $x = 8, y = 5800$ **e.** 8 years

33. a. $x + y = 22$ **b.** $P_Q = 2x$
c. $P_F = y$ **d.** $2x + y = 30$
e. McDonald's 8; family restaurant 14

34. a. $x + y = 16$ **b.** $P_Q = 2x$
c. $P_W = y$ **d.** $2x + y = 24$
e. Both 8 grams

35. a. $x + y = 15$ **b.** $P_Q = 2x$
c. $P_B = y$ **d.** $2x + y = 23$
e. McDonald's 8; Wendy's 7 (less!)

36. a.

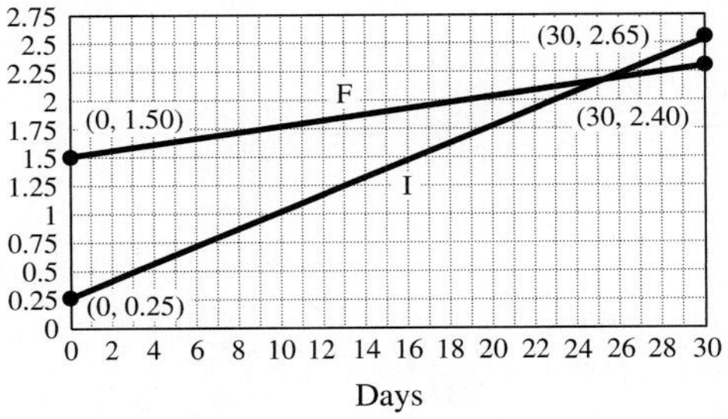

b. Incandescent **c.** 25 days

37. a. $C = 20 + 35m$

b.

m	C
6	230
12	440
18	650

c.

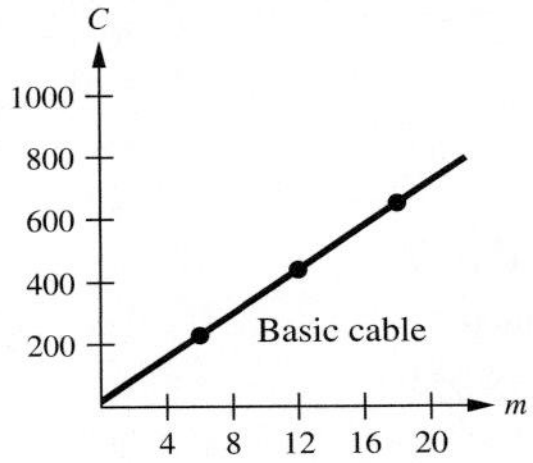

38. a. $C = 200 + 25m$

b.

m	6	12	18
C	350	500	650

c.

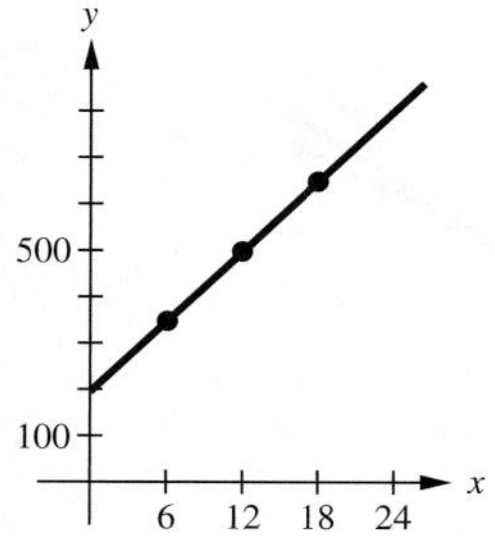

39.

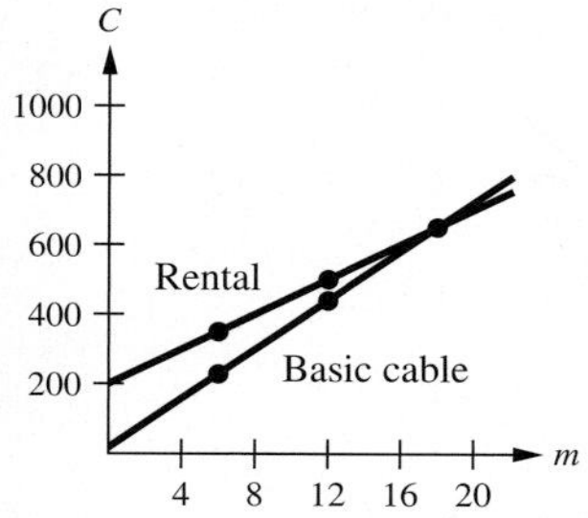

40. Cable service is cheaper if used less than 18 months.

41. When you use it for more than 18 months.

42. a. $W = 80 + 5t$

b.

t	5	10	15	20
W	105	130	155	180

c.

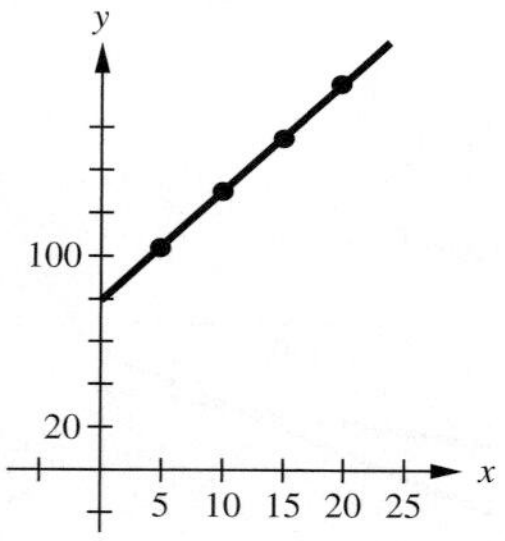

43. a. $W = 100 + 3t$

b.

t	W
5	115
10	130
15	145
20	160

c.

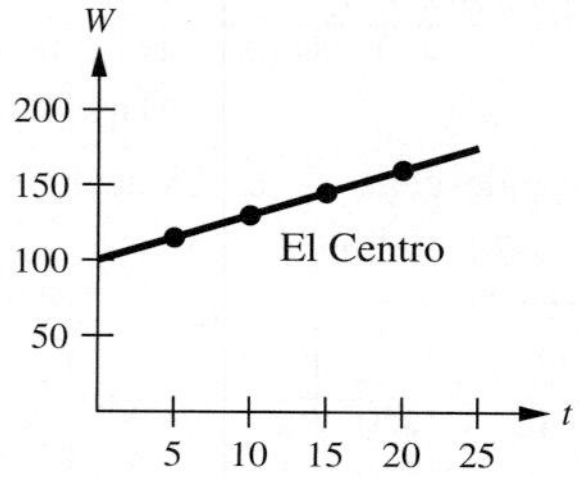

44. $(\frac{4}{7}, 145.71)$

45. $(3, 340)$

46. $(\frac{9}{8}, 228.75)$

47.

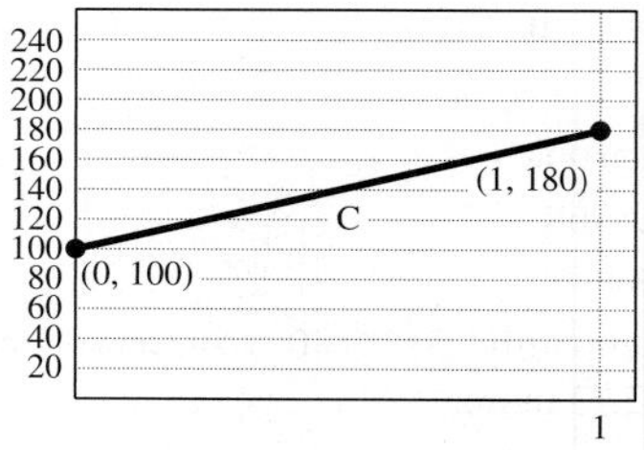

48.

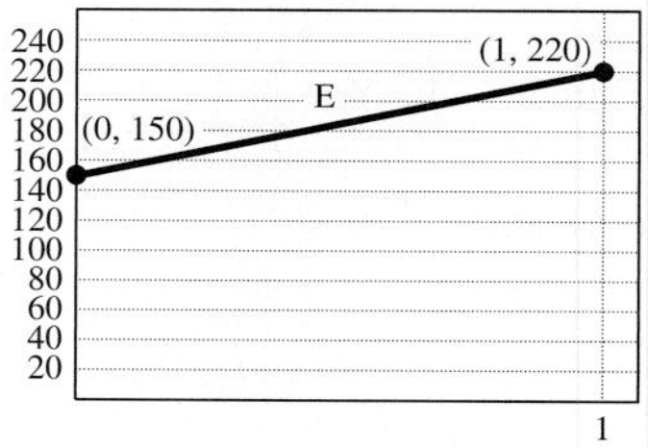

49. a. Canon **b.** C: \$180; E: \$220

c. \$40 if using the Canon

50.

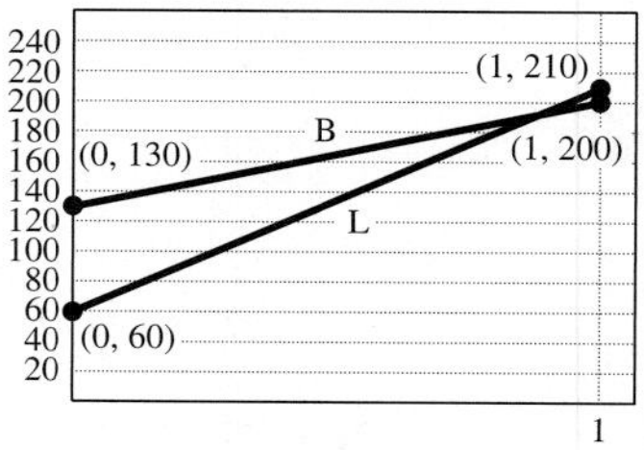

51.

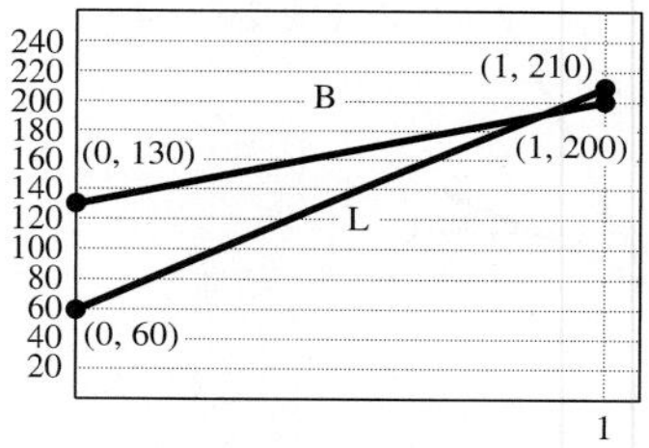

52. a. Lexmark **b.** B: \$200; L: \$210

c. \$ 10 if using the Brother

53. The Epson; \$220

54. The point that satisfies all the equations in the system

56. The lines intersect.

58. Infinitely many solutions, because the lines are the same

Collaborative Learning

1. The lines intersect at (66, 70.7).

2. The number of employed men and women is equal in the year 2021 at an employment rate of 70.7%.

Exercises 7.7

1.

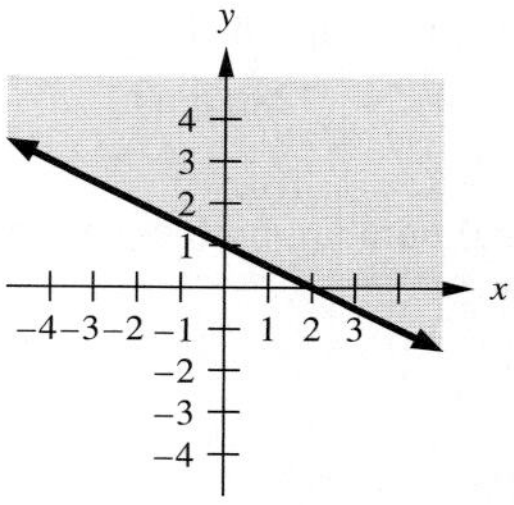

2.

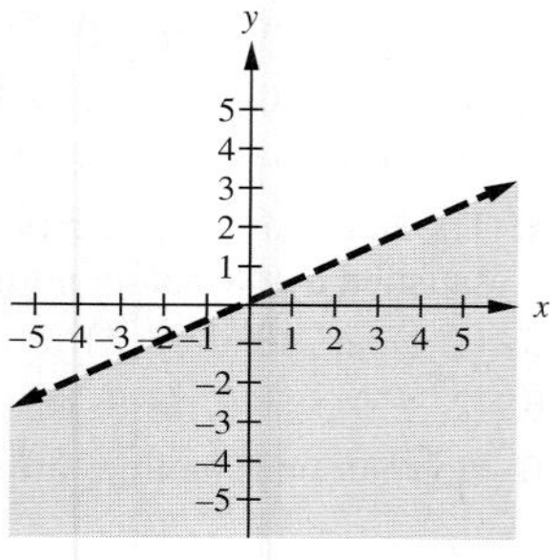

3.

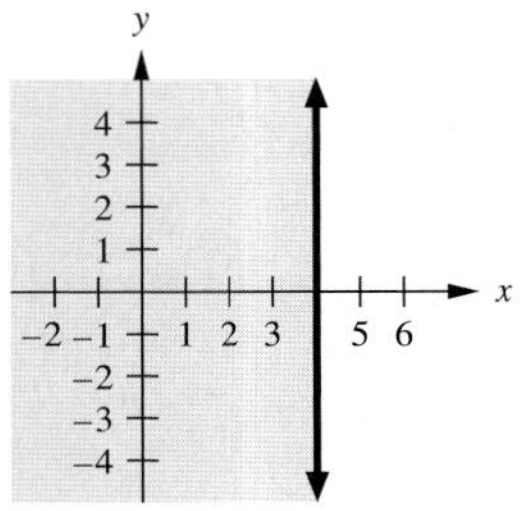

4.

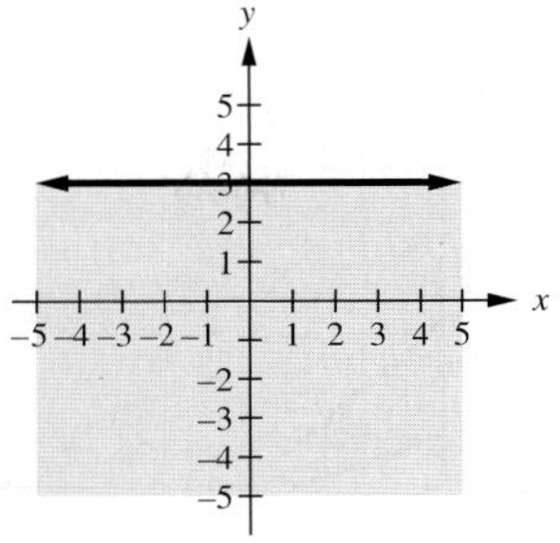

5.

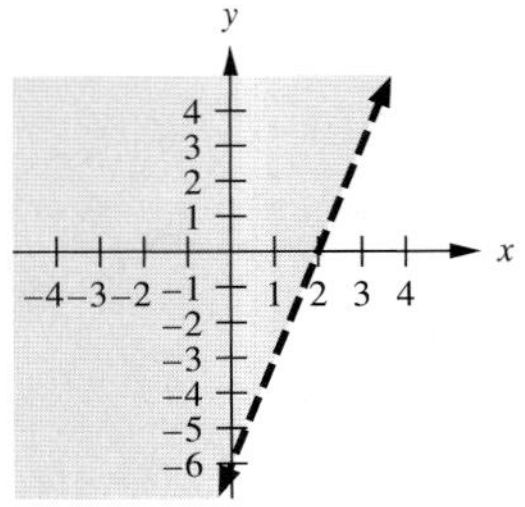

6.

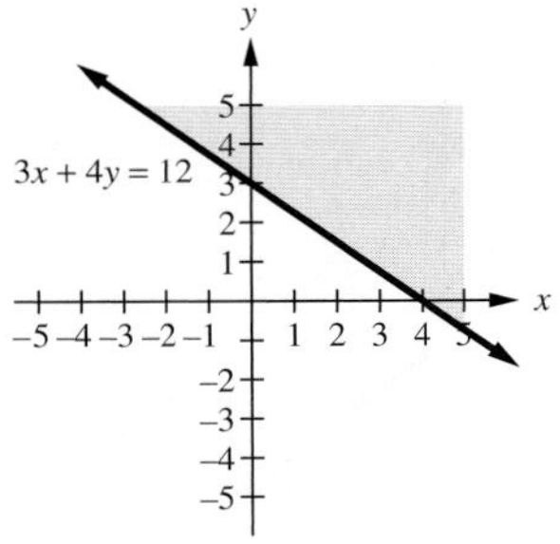

7.

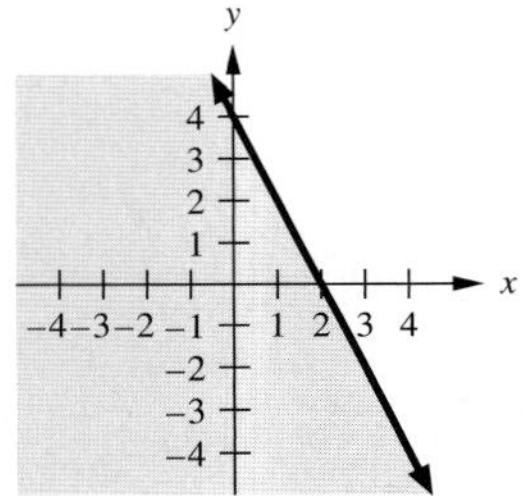

8.

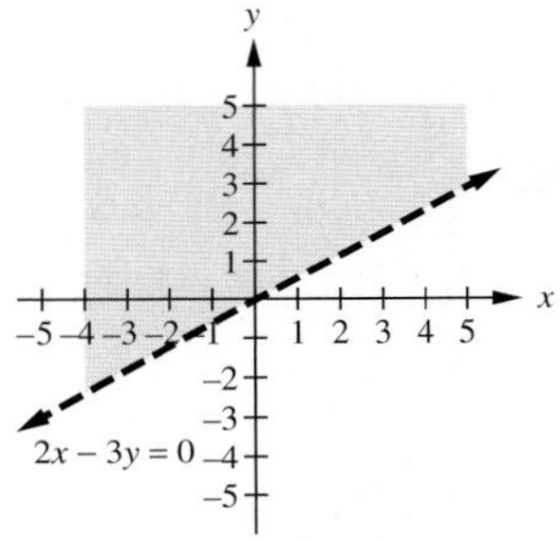

9.

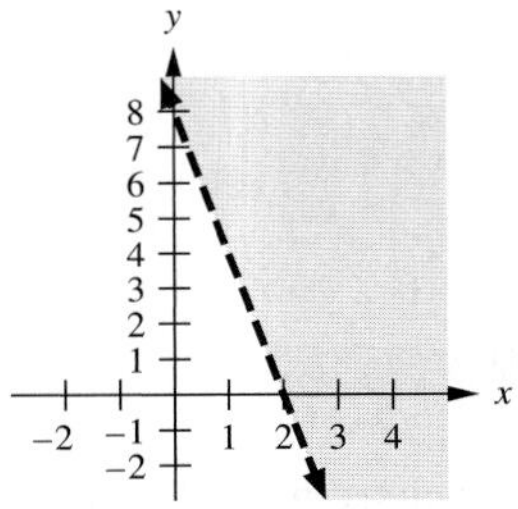

10.

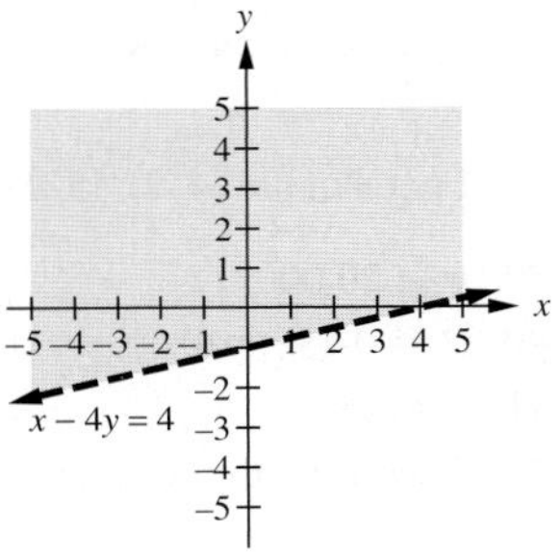

11.

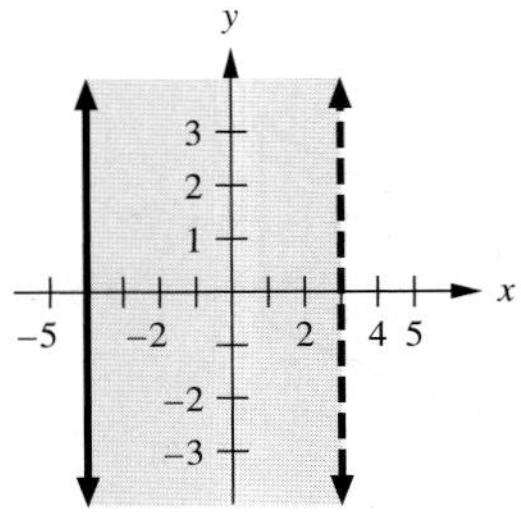

12.

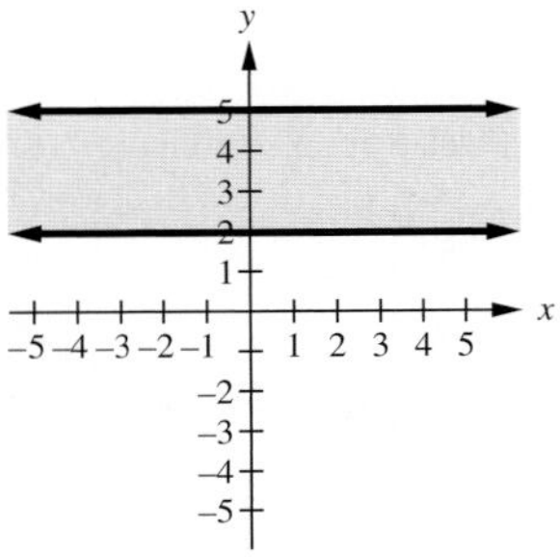

13.

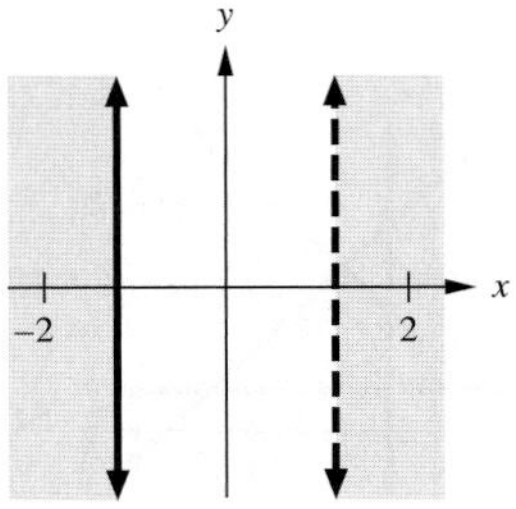

14.

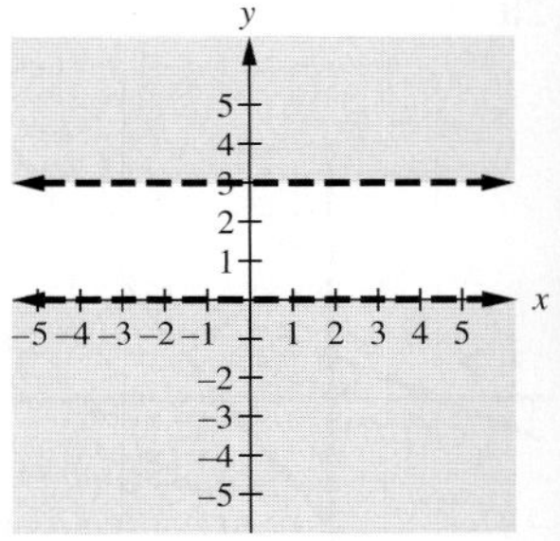

15.

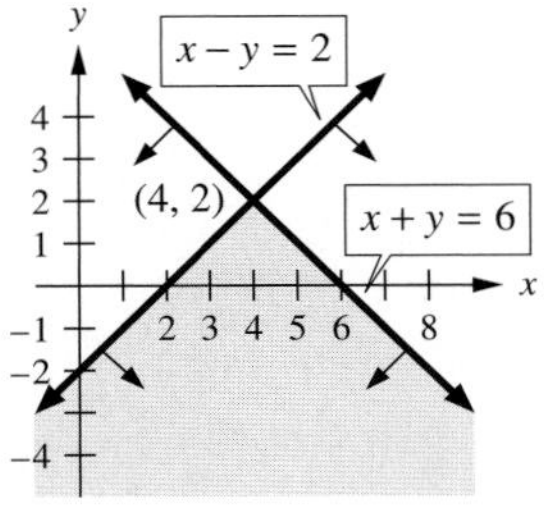

16.

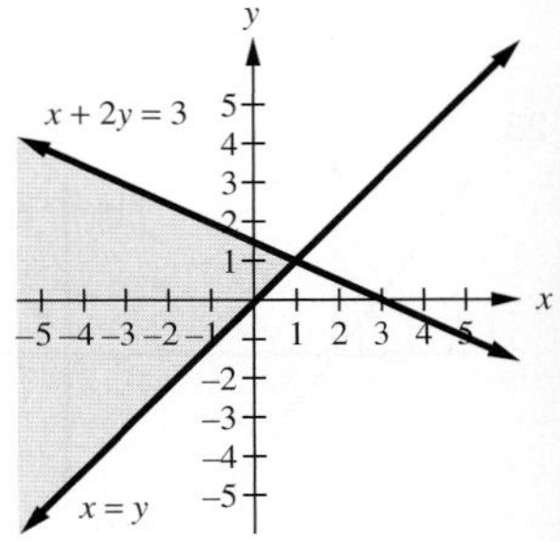

17.

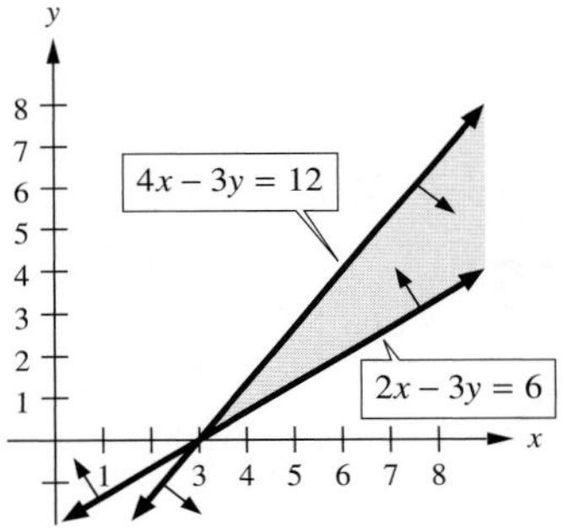

18.

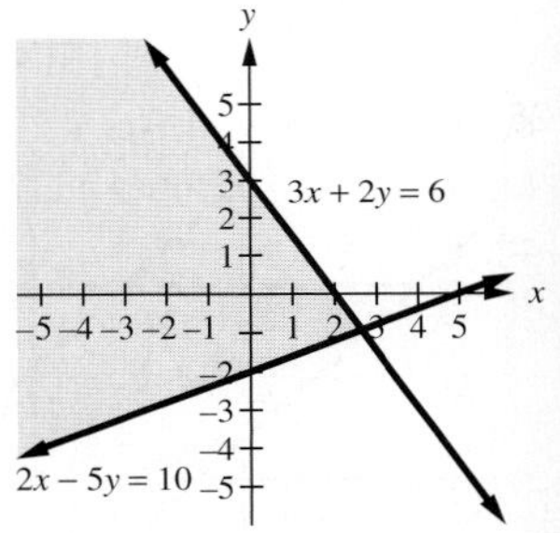

19.

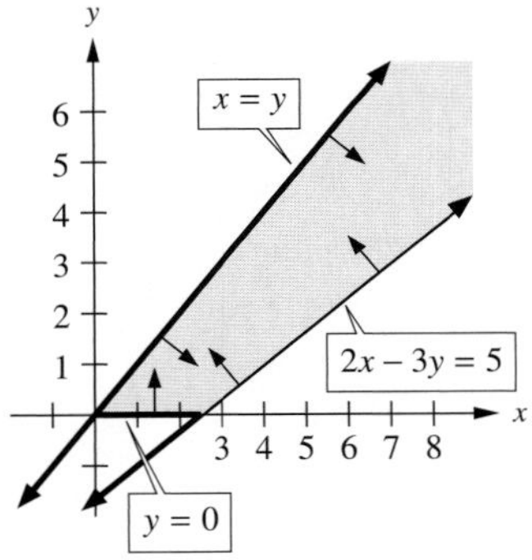

20.

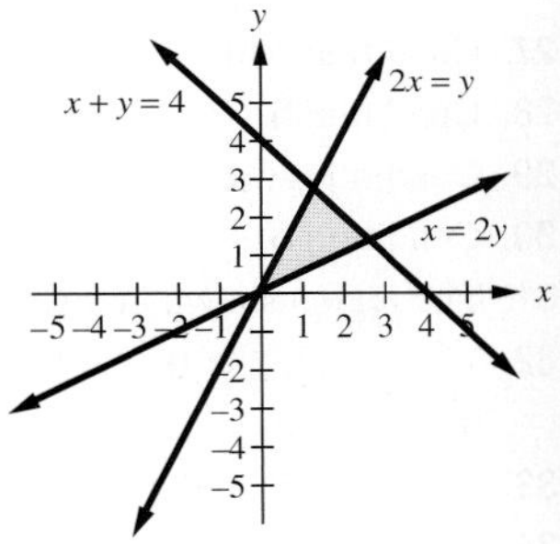

21.

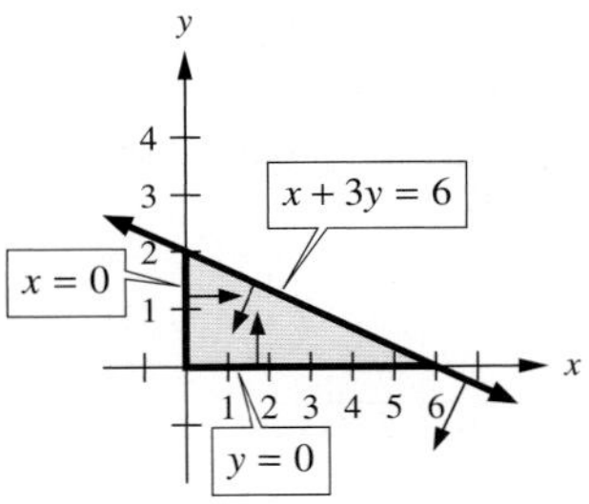

22.

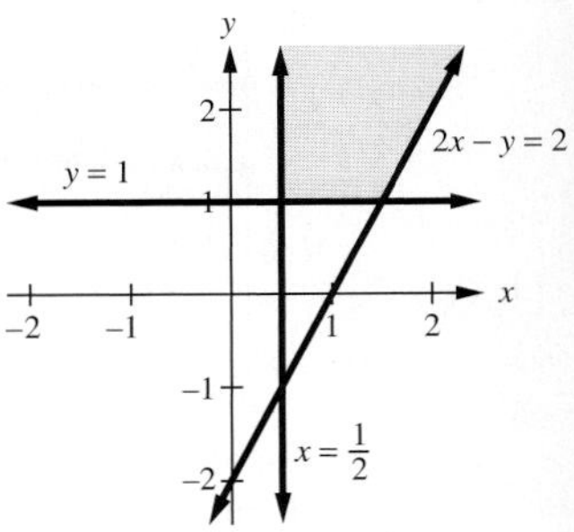

23.

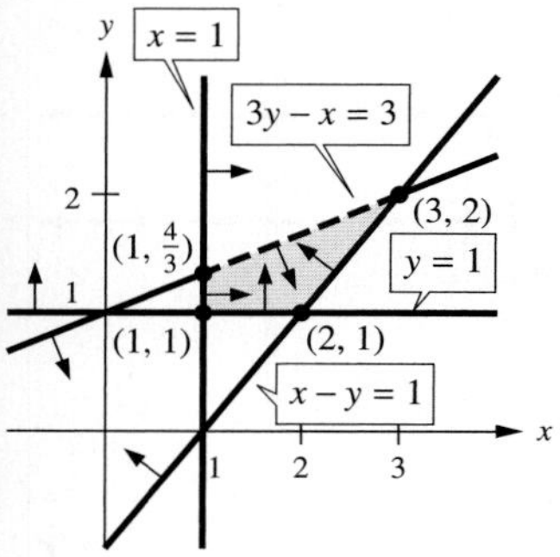

24.

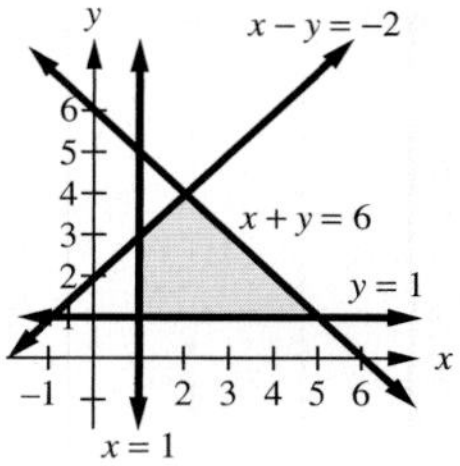

25.

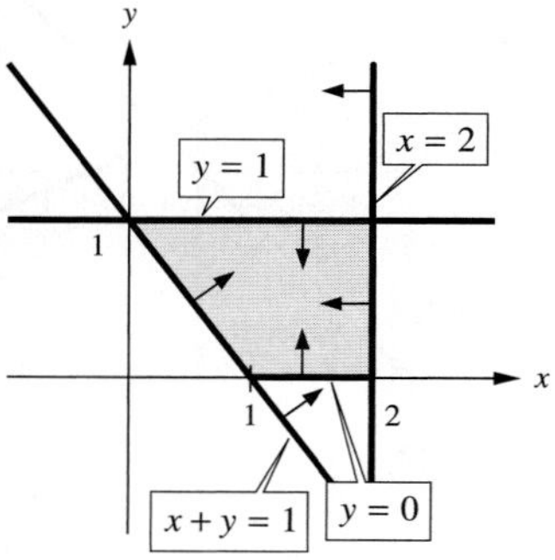

26.

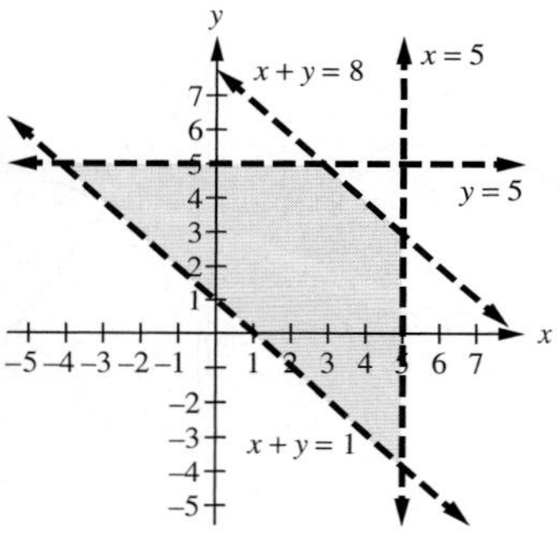

27. Conditions (**b**)

28. Condition **b**

29. Conditions (**a**)

30. Condition **b**

31. The region shown in (c)

32. $x + y \geq 2, x \geq 0, y \geq 0$
$0 \leq x \leq 15$

33. $0 \leq x \leq 15, y \leq 13x + 1700, y \geq 0$

34. $y \geq 13x + 1700$
$y \leq 30x + 180$

35. a. and b.

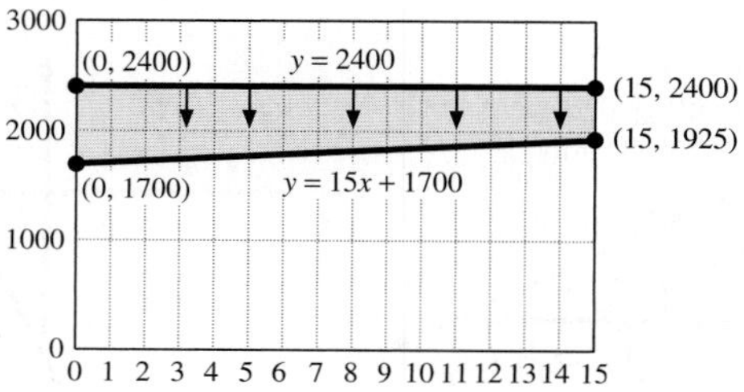

c. The region on and under the line $y = 2400$ and above and on the line $y = 15x - 1700$

36.

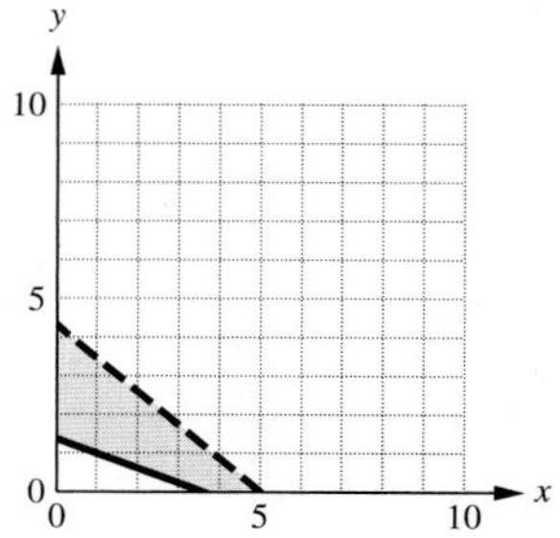

For example (1, 2), (2, 2)

37.

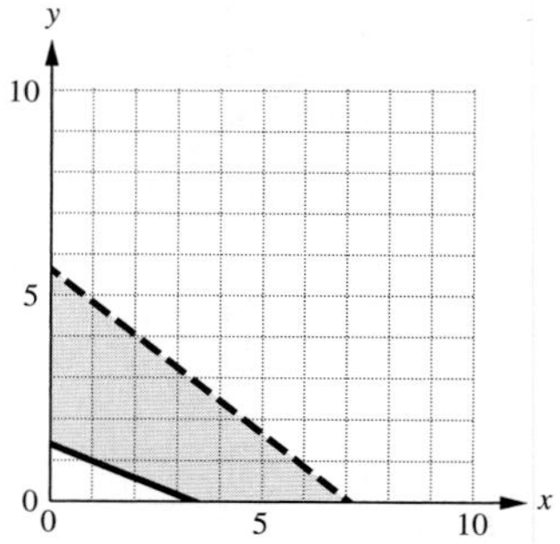

For example (1, 3), (2, 3)

38.

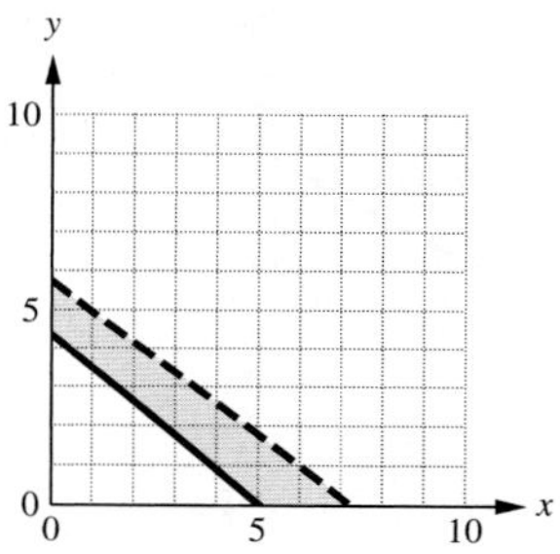

For example (4, 2), (5, 1)

39. $n > 20{,}000$

40. $P = 0.45 + 0.20(x - 1) < 6.00$; $x < 28.75$ oz

41. $h < 13$

42. According to this equation, this occurred in 1914.

43.

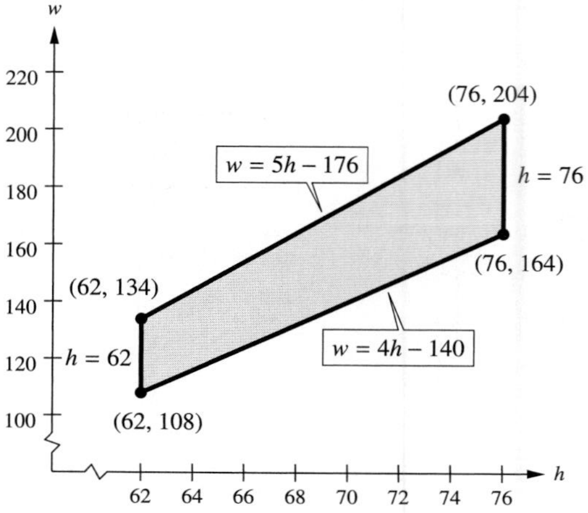

44.

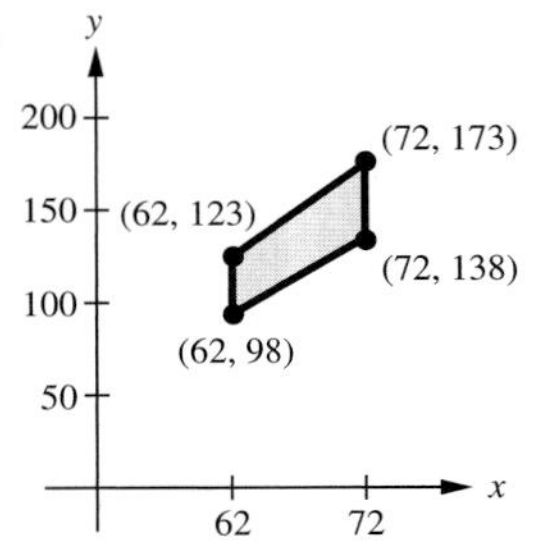

45. Suppose $c \neq 0$.

Step 1. Find the intercepts of the line $ax + by = c$.

Step 2. Draw a dashed line through these intercepts.

Step 3. Substitute (0, 0) into the equation. This gives zero for the left side.

Step 4. If $c > 0$, shade the region opposite the origin. If $c < 0$, shade the region on the origin side of the line.

46. Draw the line $y = mx + b$ dotted. On this line, the value of y is $mx + b$. If $y < mx + b$, the value of y must be less than its value on the line so the region below this line must be shaded.

47. The graph would show $x = k$ as a solid line with the region to the right of this line as the shaded region.

48.

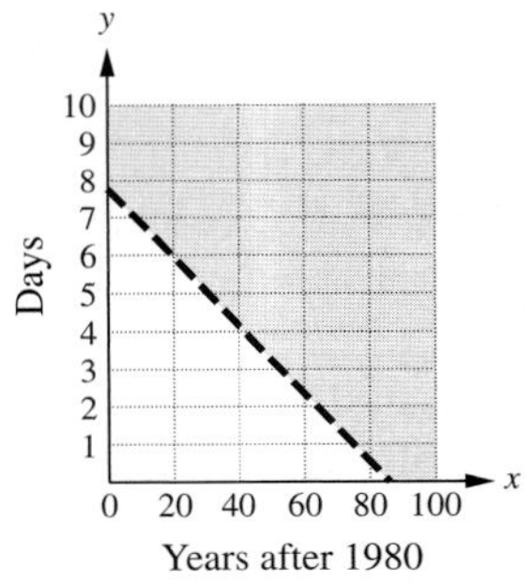

49.

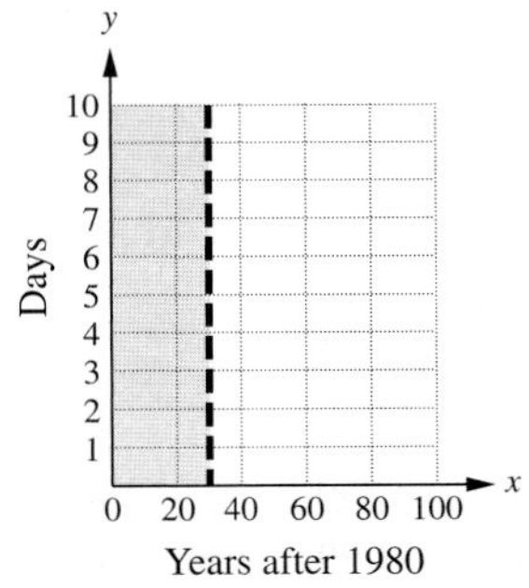

50.

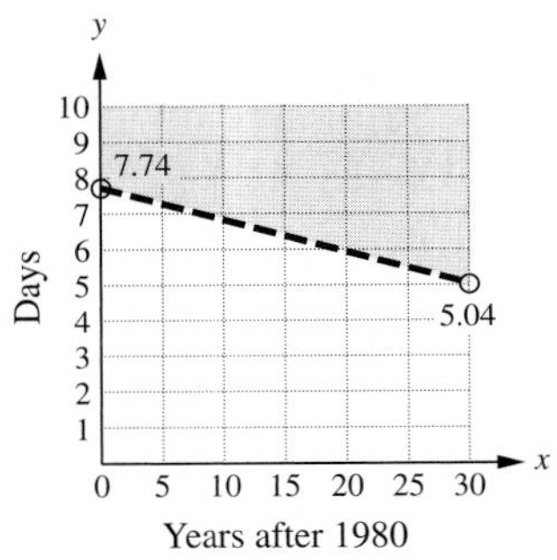

51. **a.** 33 mi **b.** Rental A (It's $10 cheaper.)

52. 40 mi

53. If you plan to drive more than 33 mi, rental A is the cheaper.

54. No. The closest you can get is when you drive 34 mi and the cost is $36 + 34(0.15) = \$41.10$.

The first part of the flowchart graphs the line. If $c > 0$, then (0, 0) is not in the desired region, so we shade the half-plane not containing the origin. If $c < 0$, then (0, 0) is in the desired region, so we shade the half-plane containing the origin.

55. Answers will vary.

57. Leave everything as in the given flowchart except for interchanging the shading instructions at the end, so that if the answer to "Is $c > 0$?" is no, the half-plane not containing the origin will be shaded, and if the answer is yes, then the half-plane containing the origin will be shaded.

58.

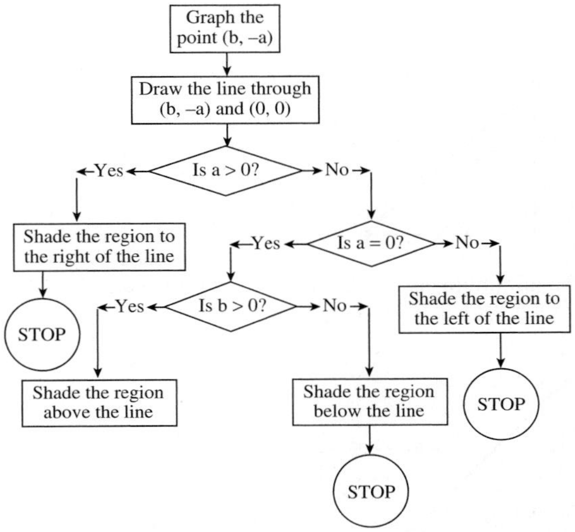

If the inequality is $ax + by < 0$, rewrite it as $-ax - by > 0$. Then use the $-a$ and the $-b$ for the a and the b in the flow chart.

Collaborative Learning

Team 1: $B = 0.0225D - 0.035$

$B > 0.0225D - 0.035$

Team 2: $m = 0.035$

$B = 0.035D - 0.04$

$B > 0.035D - 0.04$

Team 3: $0.00125W - 0.01875D > 0.1$

Exercises 7.8

1. Minimum value 3 at (1, 1)
2. Maximum value 10 at (2, 2)
3. Minimum value 2 at $\left(\frac{1}{3}, \frac{2}{3}\right)$
4. Minimum value 26 at (10, 2)
5. Minimum value 6 at (2, 2)
6. Maximum value 11 at (1, 3)
7. Maximum value 10 at (2, 4)
8. Maximum value 28 at (2, 4)
9. 80 cars and 20 trucks
10. 14 Zigs, 1 Zag
11. 50 tablets in each bottle
12. 80 g A, 40 g B
13. 3 oz of X and 2 oz of Y
14. Factory 1, 3 days; Factory 2, 2 days

15. 100 batches from I and 10 batches from II

16. Program A: 2 times; Program B: 4 times

17. 500 boxes of oranges, 100 boxes of grapefruit, and 200 boxes of tangerines.

18. \$10,000 in A, \$5000 in B

19. 3 trees and 2 shrubs

20. EMC No. 1, 14 days; EMC No. 2, 6 days

21. **a.** 6 oz of each juice

b. 42¢

c. 30 units A, 30 units C, 12 units D

22. Yes. Grapenuts, 8 oz; Product 19, 2 oz; Raisin Bran, 2 oz; 100 calories/oz; $\frac{5}{6}$ g fat/oz; 212.5 mg sodium/oz

23.

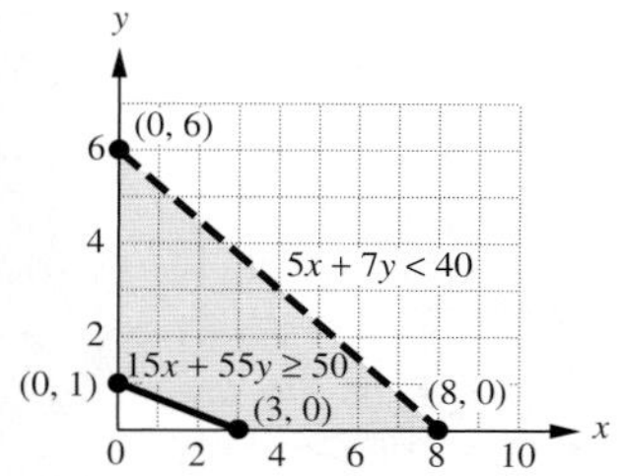

The minimum cost occurs at (0, 1). At this point $C = \$4$

24.

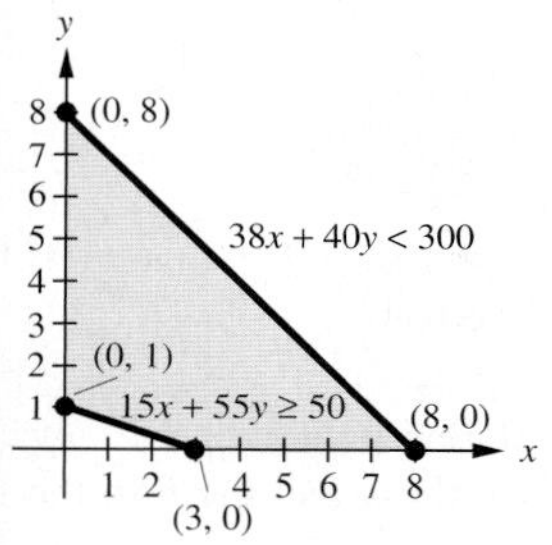

The maximum cost occurs at (0, 8). At this point $C = \$32$.

25.

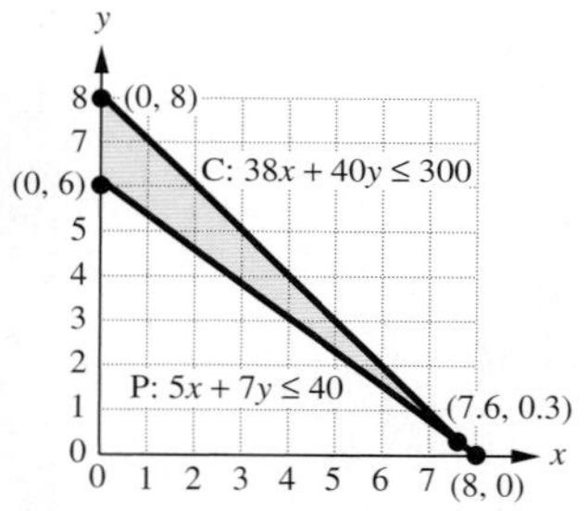

The maximum cost occurs at (0, 8). At this point $C = \$32$.

26. **a.** The specified conditions in a linear programming problem, usually defined by a set of linear inequalities.

b. The solution of the inequalities given in the constraints.

27. **a.** The requirement that the variables of the objective function be nonnegative.

b. A polygon such that the points of the line segment joining any two points on the boundary lie entirely inside the region.

28. A function specifying the quantities to be maximized or minimized.

29. **c.** The least amount that Gary can bet for a net gain of \$100 is \$1500 on the champion to win and \$800 on the challenger to win, for a total of \$2300.

30.

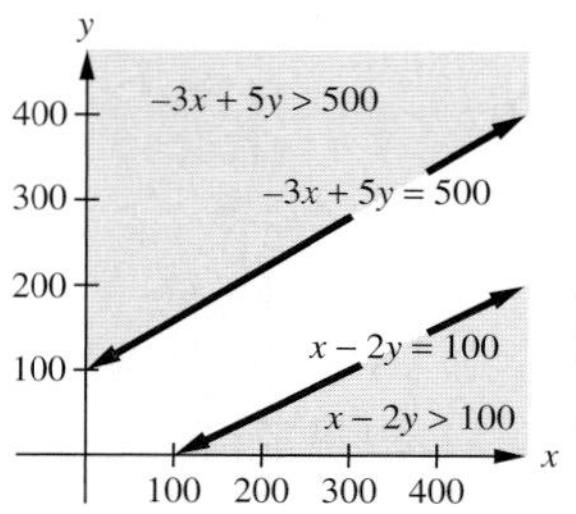

The diagram shows that there is no region where all four inequalities are true. Therefore, there is no feasible region.

CHAPTER 8

Exercises 8.1

1. **a.**  **b.** 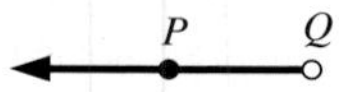 **c.** 

2. **a.**  **b.** 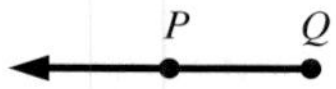

c. 

3. The segment $\overline{BC}$ **4.** The segment $\overline{BC}$

5. The ray $\overrightarrow{AD}$ (or $\overrightarrow{AC}$ or $\overrightarrow{AB}$) **6.** The ray $\overrightarrow{DA}$ or $\overrightarrow{DB}$ or $\overrightarrow{DC}$

7. The segment $\overline{AD}$ **8.** The segment $\overline{BD}$

9. The segment $\overline{AD}$ **10.** The segment $\overline{AD}$ **11.** $\varnothing$

12. $\varnothing$ **13.** The point C **14.** The point B

15. **a.** $\overleftrightarrow{AB}, \overleftrightarrow{AC}, \overleftrightarrow{AD}, \overleftrightarrow{BC}, \overleftrightarrow{BD}, \overleftrightarrow{CD}$

b. $\overleftrightarrow{AB}$ and $\overleftrightarrow{CD}$; $\overleftrightarrow{AC}$ and $\overleftrightarrow{BD}$; $\overleftrightarrow{AD}$ and $\overleftrightarrow{BC}$

c. No

16. **a.** $\overleftrightarrow{AB}, \overleftrightarrow{BC}, \overleftrightarrow{CD}, \overleftrightarrow{DA}, \overleftrightarrow{EA}, \overleftrightarrow{EB}, \overleftrightarrow{EC}, \overleftrightarrow{ED}$

b. Parallel: $\overleftrightarrow{AB}$ and $\overleftrightarrow{CD}$, $\overleftrightarrow{AD}$ and $\overleftrightarrow{BC}$

c. Skew: $\overleftrightarrow{AB}$ and $\overleftrightarrow{EC}$, $\overleftrightarrow{AB}$ and $\overleftrightarrow{ED}$, $\overleftrightarrow{BC}$ and $\overleftrightarrow{EA}$, $\overleftrightarrow{BC}$ and $\overleftrightarrow{ED}$, $\overleftrightarrow{CD}$ and $\overleftrightarrow{EA}$, $\overleftrightarrow{CD}$ and $\overleftrightarrow{EB}$, $\overleftrightarrow{DA}$ and $\overleftrightarrow{EB}$, $\overleftrightarrow{DA}$ and $\overleftrightarrow{EC}$

d. Intersecting: $\overleftrightarrow{EA}, \overleftrightarrow{EB}, \overleftrightarrow{EC}$ and $\overleftrightarrow{ED}$; $\overleftrightarrow{EB}, \overleftrightarrow{AB}$ and $\overleftrightarrow{CB}$; $\overleftrightarrow{EC}, \overleftrightarrow{BC}$ and $\overleftrightarrow{DC}$; and $\overleftrightarrow{AD}, \overleftrightarrow{CD}$ and $\overleftrightarrow{ED}$; $\overleftrightarrow{BA}, \overleftrightarrow{DA}$ and $\overleftrightarrow{EA}$

17. True **18.** False **19.** True **20.** True **21.** True

22. False **23.** False **24.** True **25.** False **26.** True

27. **a.** $\angle BAC$ (or $\angle CAB$) **b.** $\angle\beta$ (or $\angle FAE$)

28. **a.** $\angle\alpha$ **b.** $\angle EAF$

29. $\angle BAC, \angle CAD, \angle DAE, \angle EAF$ **30.** $\angle BAD, \angle DAF$

31. $\angle BAE, \angle CAE, \angle CAF$

32. **a.** $\angle CAD$ **b.** $\angle DAE$

33. **a.** $\angle DAE$ **b.** $\angle CAD$

34. **a.** $\angle CAF$ **b.** $\angle BAE$

35. **a.** $\angle DAF$ **b.** $\angle BAE$

36. 75° **37.** 35° **38.** 55° **39.** 15° **40.** 110°

41. $\angle B$ **42.** $\angle A$ and $\angle C$ **43.** 110° **44.** 70° **45.** 20°

46. 290° **47.** 220° **48.** $(180 - x)°$

49. **a.** 150° **b.** 30° **c.** 150°

50. **a.** $m\angle D = 30°$ **b.** $m\angle E = 150°$ **c.** $m\angle F = 30°$

51. $\angle C, \angle E, \angle A, \angle G$

52. a. $m\angle BOC = 40°$ b. $(50 - x)°$

53. a. 49° b. 139°

54. a. 71° b. 161° 55. $x = 16$ 56. 34

57. $x = 15$; 35° and 145° 58. $x = 15$; 30° and 60°

59. $x = 10$; 30° and 60° 60. $x = 14$; 82° and 98°

61. a. 30° b. 180°

62. a. 210° b. 360°

63. 90° 64. 8° 65. 25

66. $m\angle A = 40°$, $m\angle B = 50°$, $m\angle C = 90°$

67. a. $m\angle A + m\angle B = 180°$
Angles A and B form a straight angle.
b. $m\angle C + m\angle B = 180°$
Angles C and B form a straight angle.
c. $m\angle A + m\angle B = m\angle C + m\angle B$
Both sides equal 180° (substitution).
d. $m\angle A = m\angle C$
Subtract $m\angle B$ from both sides.

68. right angle 69. Acute 70. right angle 71. Obtuse

72. acute and right angles 73. Obtuse 74. about 150°

75. 0° 76. 45° 77. 100°

78. Technically speaking, a straight line has no distance. The distance between two points on a straight line is the measure of the segment between these points.

79. Point, line, and plane 80. Answers will vary.

81. The ray may have only its endpoint in common with the plane, it may have only some other single point in common with the plane, or it may lie entirely in the plane.

82. The ray can have its endpoint on the line or some other point of the ray can be a point on the line or the ray can be on the line.

83. a. One of the usual meanings of *acute* is "sharp" or "intense." Thus an *acute pain* means a "sharp or intense pain."
b. One of the ordinary meanings of *obtuse* is "dull." Thus, *obtuse intelligence* means "dull intelligence" or "stupidity."

84. (a)

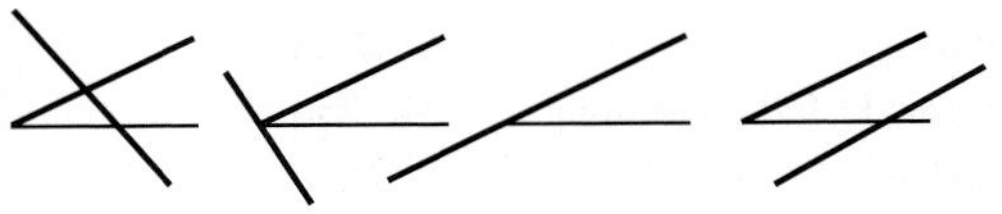

(b)

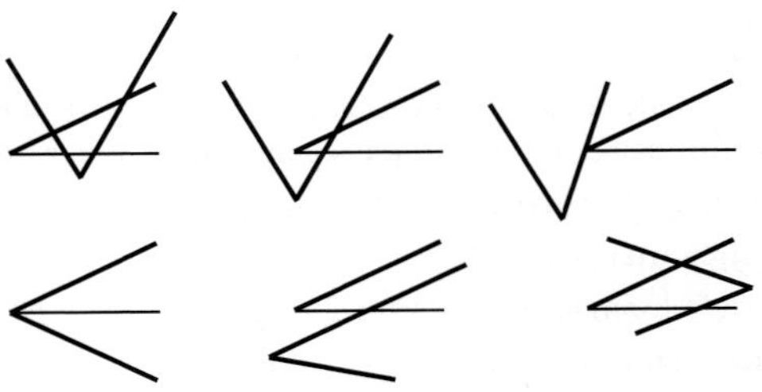

85. Obtuse, Acute 86. Right, obtuse 87. Isosceles, Acute

88. 56° 89. Acute angles

90. γ is an acute angle, β is an acute angle, and δ is a right angle.

91. a. Straight angle, 180° b. Acute angle, 79.2°
c. Acute angle, 68.4° d. Acute angle, 32.4°

92. a. Straight angle, 180° b. Acute angle, 28.8°
c. Acute angle, 32.4° d. Acute angle, 46.8°
e. Acute angle, 72°

Exercises 8.2

1. a.

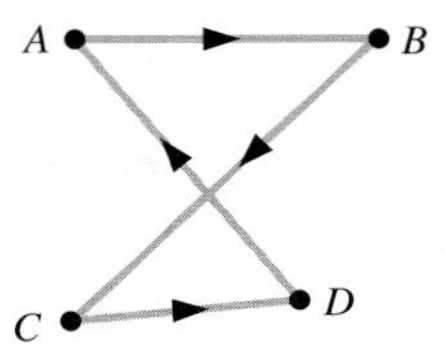

b.

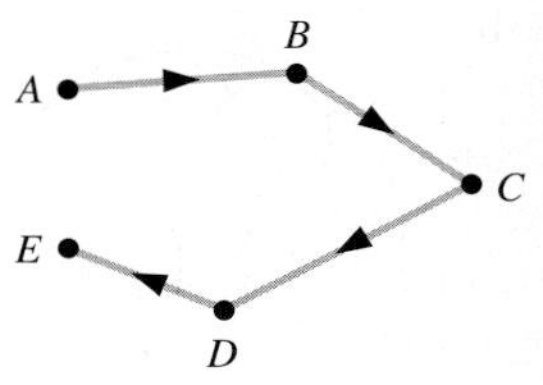

2. a.

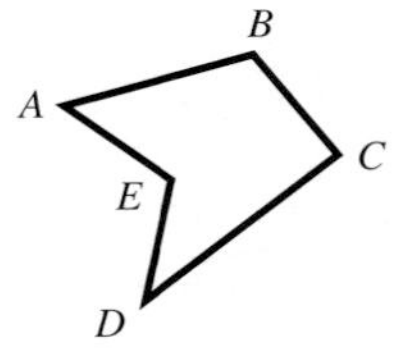

b.

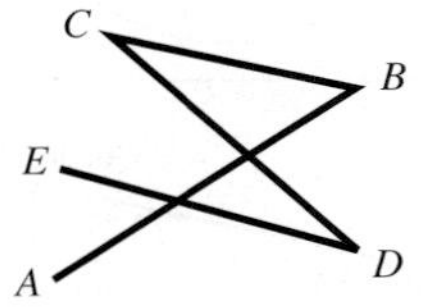

3. a. ***C, D, I, J, L, M, N, O, P, S, U, V, W, Z*** b. ***B, D, O***

4. a. B b. C, I, J, L, M, N, P, S, U, V, W, Z

5. a. ***D, O*** b. ***A, E, F, G, H, K, Q, R, T, X, Y***

6. Concave 7. Convex 8. a. Rectangle b. Triangle

9. Parallelogram 10. Parallelogram 11. Rectangle

12. Square 13. Trapezoid 14. Trapezoid

15. Parallelogram 16. Trapezoid 17. Scalene, right

18. Isosceles, right 19. Scalene, acute

20. Isosceles, obtuse 21. Isosceles, acute

22. Scalene, right 23. Scalene, obtuse

24. Isosceles, right 25. (a) and (c) 26. (a) and (c), $\frac{4}{5} = \frac{4.8}{6}$

27. $x = 5\frac{1}{3}$, $y = 6\frac{2}{3}$ 28. $12\frac{1}{2}$ 29. 14 30. $3\frac{1}{3}$ 31. $1\frac{1}{3}$

32. 4 33. $5\frac{1}{4}$ and $3\frac{1}{2}$ cm 34. $7\frac{1}{2}$ cm, 10 cm

35. 8, 12, and 16 in. 36. $4\frac{1}{2}$ in., 6 in., $7\frac{1}{2}$ in. 37. $18\frac{3}{4}$ ft

38. 22.5 ft

39. The two triangles are similar because the corresponding angles are equal. The tree is 25 ft tall.

40. 180 m 41. 600 m 42. 180 m

43. Recall that an isosceles triangle is one that has two sides of equal length. By SAS, $\triangle ABD \cong \triangle BCD$. This implies that $AB = BC$ and so $\triangle ABC$ is isosceles.

44. Note that $\overleftrightarrow{BD}$ is the included side of $\angle D$ and $\angle B$ in both triangles, so we can apply ASA to get $\Delta ABD \cong \Delta BCD$.

45. It is given that $\triangle ACD$ and $\triangle BCD$ have two pairs of sides with equal length. They also share the side CD. This means we can apply SSS to get $\triangle ACD \cong \triangle BCD$.

46. The two triangular plots have three pairs of sides with equal length. According to SSS, these plots are congruent and therefore, must have the same area. In other words, Old McBello is telling the truth.

47. a. $m\angle A = m\angle B = 50°$, $m\angle C = 80°$
b. $m\angle A = m\angle B = 40°$, $m\angle C = 100°$

48. 75° 49. 30° 50. $m\angle C = 75°$, isosceles

51. 2160° 52. 3240° 53. 108° 54. 120°

55. 135° 56. 140° 57. 144° 58. 150°

59. a. $(E \cup I \cup S) = T \subset P$

b.

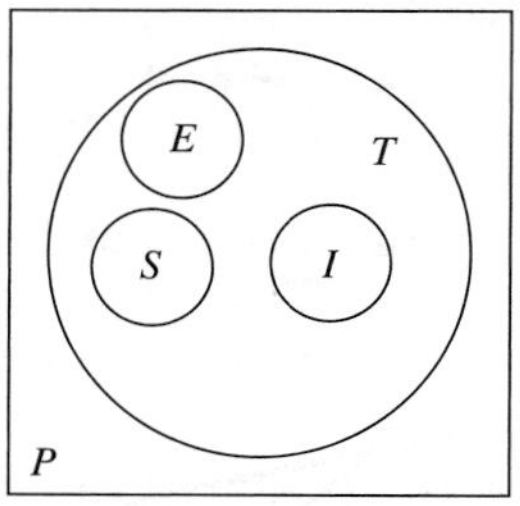

60.

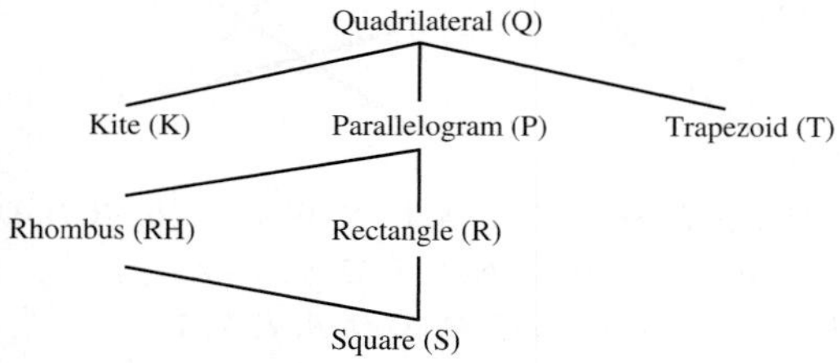

61.

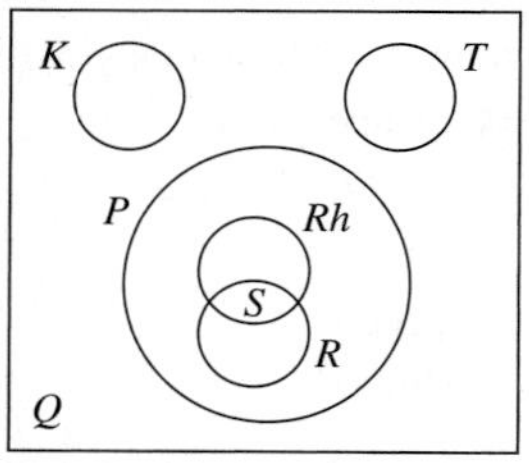

62. They are similar (same shape but different size).

64. $\frac{8}{4} = \frac{10}{5} \neq \frac{12}{7}$. Corresponding sides are not proportional, so the triangles are not similar.

65. a.

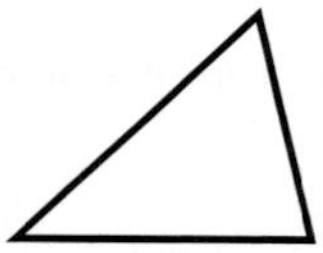

b.

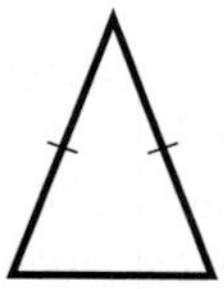

c.

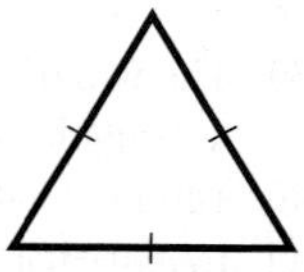

66. a.

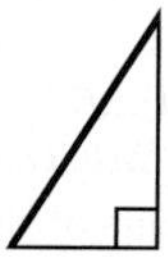

b.

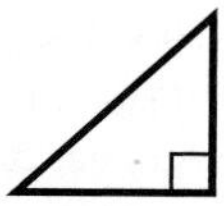

c. Impossible

67. a.

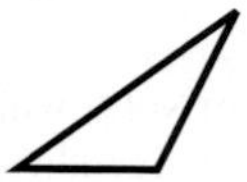

b.

c. Impossible

68. ER and EO

Exercises 8.3

1. 65 cm 2. 60 ft 3. 12.6 yd 4. 28.8 in. 5. 184.6 m
6. 14.1 m 7. 57.2 m 8. 24.4 km 9. 30 cm
10. 48 in. 11. 10 ft 12. 75 m 13. 90 ft 14. 53 yd
15. 716 by 518 ft 16. About 1.4 in. 17. $7\pi \approx 22.0$ m
18. 8π ft ≈ 25.1 ft 19. $20\pi \approx 62.8$ ft
20. 8.8π m ≈ 27.6 m 21. $3\pi \approx 9.42$ cm
22. 6π in. ≈ 18.8 in. 23. $9\pi \approx 28.3$ yd
24. 11π m ≈ 34.5 m 25. $61\pi \approx 192$ cm
26. 17π in. ≈ 53.4 in. 27. $16\pi \approx 50.2$ cm
28. 3π in. ≈ 9.42 in. 29. $8\pi \approx 25.1$ ft
30. 12π in. ≈ 37.7 in. 31. $d = 15$ cm, $r = 7.5$ cm
32. $\frac{48}{\pi}$ in. ≈ 15.3 in. 33. $7/\pi \approx 2.23$ cm
34. $\frac{251.2}{\pi}$ ft ≈ 80 ft 35. $\frac{4.125}{\pi} \approx 1.31$ in.
36. $\frac{31680}{13\pi} \approx 776$ rev/mi
37. About 15,500,000 (rounded from 15,520,000)
38. $\frac{70}{\pi}$ ft ≈ 22.3 ft, so we need a 23-ft pan.
39. $16\pi \approx 50.2$ yd 40. $\frac{15}{\pi}$ min $\approx$ 5 min
41. 490 mi 42. 669 mi 43. 564 mi 44. 241 mi
45. 260 in. 46. 220 in. 47. 94.20 in. 48. 150.72
49. A bicycle tire
50. Find the circumference of the finger where the ring is to fit. Substitute this number of inches for C in the formula and solve for s.
51. The worn tire has a smaller circumference, so will turn more times per mile.
52. Answers will vary, but to the nearest tenth, the rounded answers should agree.
53. $\frac{3}{4}$ in. 54. 1 in. 55. $\frac{3}{4}$ in. 56. 3/4; four

Exercises 8.4

1. 15 in.^{2} 2. 12 in.^{2} 3. 15 cm^2 4. 16 m^2 5. 24 ft^2
6. 28 ft^2 7. 30 ft^2 8. 5 in.^{2} 9. $800 + 50\pi \approx 957$ cm^2
10. $250 + 50\pi \approx 407$ m^2 11. $64 + 32\pi \approx 164$ cm^2
12. 37.5π in.$^2 \approx 118$ in.^{2} 13. $18 - \frac{9}{2}\pi \approx 3.87$ cm^2
14. 20π in.$^2 \approx 62.8$ in.^{2} 15. $\frac{25}{4}\pi \approx 19.6$ ft^2
16. 33 in.^{2} 17. 175 ft 18. 59 ft 19. 310 ft
20. 260 ft 21. 17.804 cm 22. 126 ft 23. 126 ft
24. 224 ft 25. 6400 yd^2 26. a. 51 b. \$714
27. 18 ft wide 28. 680 ft 29. 96 ft wide
30. About 80 ft 31. 16π cm^2 32. 7 in.
33. 12 in. wide and 18 in. long 34. 250 ft
35. 15,386 ft^2 36. 113.04 m^2 37. 803.84 mi^2
38. 45,216 mi^2 39. 725.34 mi^2 40. 1256 ft^2
41. 14.13 ft^2 42. 2289.06 ft^2 43. 14.13 in.^{2}
44. For a triangle to be a right triangle, the square of one of the sides must equal the sum of the squares of the other two sides.
a. Not a right triangle, $3^2 + 5^2 \neq 6^2$.
b. A right triangle, $5^2 + 12^2 = 13^2$.
c. A right triangle, $7^2 + 24^2 = 25^2$.
d. Not a right triangle, $9^2 + 10^2 \neq 15^2$.
45. a. in.^{2} and cm^2 b. mi^2 and km^2 c.–d. yd^2 and m^2
46. A 2-in. square is a square that is 2 in. on a side; its area is 4 in.^{2}. 2 in.^{2} is an area of 2 in.^{2}
47. a. $2\frac{2}{3}$ gal b. \$42 48. a. 2 b. \$34
49. a. 15 bags b. \$60
50. a. 95 in.^{2} b. 177 in.^{2} c. One large pizza
51. a. 2.49¢/in.^{2} b. 2.36¢/in.^{2} c. The 10-in. pie
52. $\frac{1 + \sqrt{5}}{2}$

53. The area of the rectangle taken away is Wx and the area of the rectangle added on is hy. Since $hy = Wx$, the area of the new rectangle is equal to the area of the original one.

54. The construction should look like the one in Exercise 53.

Collaborative Learning

Group 1:

1. $\sqrt{2r}$ 2. $2r^2$

Group 2:

1. $h = \frac{\sqrt{3}}{2}r$ 2. $\frac{3\sqrt{3}}{2}r^2$

Group 3:

1. The perimeter of the polygon.
2. $nb = 2\pi h$ (the circumference)
3. $A = \frac{1}{2}(nb)\,h = \frac{1}{2}(2\pi h)h = \pi h^2$

Exercises 8.5

1. a. A, B, C, D, E b. $\overleftrightarrow{AB}, \overleftrightarrow{AC}, \overleftrightarrow{AD}, \overleftrightarrow{AE}, \overleftrightarrow{BC}, \overleftrightarrow{BE}, \overleftrightarrow{CD}, \overleftrightarrow{CE}, \overleftrightarrow{DE}$

2. a. A, B, C, D, E, F b. $AB, BC, CA, DE, EF, FD, AD, BE, CF$

3. $ABCD$ 4. $ADHE$

5.

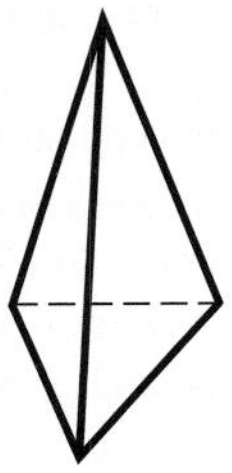

6.

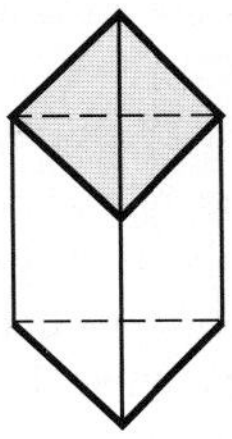

7.

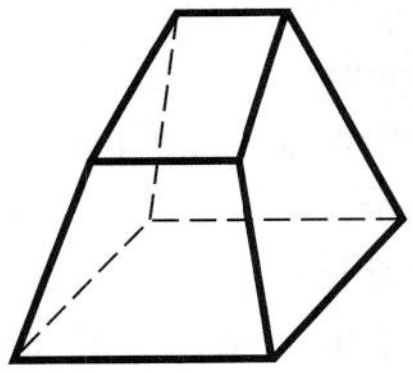

8.

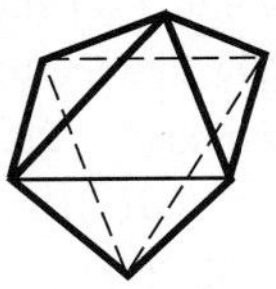

9. a. The volume is multiplied by 8.
 b. The volume is multiplied by 27.

10. 434,073.6 gal 11. 7234.6 sq ft

12. 1, 562,665.0 L 13. 651.1 sq m

14. 4.2 in.^{3} 15. 50 in.^{3} 16. 30 ft^3

17. 11,134,944 ft^3

18. $\frac{9\sqrt{3}}{2}$ in.^{3} 19. 1.5 liters 20. 2,353,158 m^3

21. a. $V = 225\pi \approx 707$ in.^{3}
 $S = 140\pi \approx 440$ in.^{2}
 b. $V = \frac{225}{3}\pi \approx 236$ in.^{3}
 $S = (25 + 5\sqrt{106})\pi \approx 240$ in.^{2}

22. a. $V = 600\pi \approx 1880$ cm^3
 $S = 320\pi \approx 1000$ cm^2
 b. $V = 200\pi \approx 628$ cm^3
 $S = (100 + 20\sqrt{34})\pi \approx 680$ cm^2

23. a. $V = 36\pi \approx 113$ ft^3
 $S = 42\pi \approx 132$ ft^2
 b. $V = 12\pi \approx 37.7$ ft^3
 $S = 24\pi \approx 75.4$ ft^2

24. a. $V = 432\pi \approx 1360$ cm^3
 $S = 216\pi \approx 678$ cm^2
 b. $V = 144\pi \approx 452$ cm^3
 $S = (36 + 36\sqrt{5})\pi \approx 366$ cm^2

25. $288\pi \approx 904$ in.^{3} 26. $2304\pi = 7235$ cm^3

27. $2{,}536{,}456\pi \approx 7{,}960{,}000$ ft^3 28. 117.2 cm^3

29. 523,333,333.3 ft^3 30. About 6,780,000 gal

31. $r = 3.81$ cm, $h = 10.16$ cm, $V \approx 147.5\pi \approx 463$ cm^3
 The can holds about 463 g.

32. About 109 grams

33. a. Baseball: $S_1 = \frac{81}{\pi} \approx 25.8$ in.^{2}
 $V_1 = \frac{243}{2\pi^2} \approx 12.3$ in.^{3}
 Soccer ball: $S_2 = \frac{729}{\pi} \approx 232$ in.^{2}
 $V_2 = \frac{6561}{2\pi^2} \approx 333$ in.^{3}
 Basketball: $S_3 = \frac{900}{\pi} \approx 287$ in.^{2}
 $V_3 = \frac{4500}{\pi^2} \approx 456$ in.^{3}
 b. $\frac{S_1}{S_3} \approx \frac{9}{100}$ c. $\frac{V_1}{V_2} = \frac{1}{27}$

34. a. About 106 million gals b. About 1300 gals

35. a. $\frac{6561}{2\pi^2} \approx 333$ in.^{3} b. About 15.66 lb

36. a. About 456 in.^{3} b. About 872 in.^{3}
 c. About 52%

37. a. 1428 in.^{3} b. 730 in.^{2} c. 32,000 bags

38. 7904 in.^{3} 39. 1760 in.^{3} 40. 440 in.^{3} 41. 2288 in.^{3}

42. 3.14 ft^3 43. 35.33 in.^{3} 44. 1.57 ft^3 45. 88 in.^{3}

46. a. 2304 in.$^3 \approx 1.33$ ft^3 b. 5184 in.$^3 \approx 3.0$ ft^3
 c. 7776 in.$^3 \approx 4.5$ ft^3 d. b and c

47. a. 1232 ft^3 b. 63 ft^3 c. No, $1300 > 1295$

48. a. 1120 ft^3 b. 63 ft^3 c. No. You have only 1183 ft^3

49. About 1.41π ft$^3 \approx 4.43$ ft^3 50. About 0.88 ft^3

51. About 5.31 ft^3 52. About 63.6 ft^3

53. About 94.16, or 94

54. 7.86 buildings, so about 7 buildings

56. The volume. The circumference and area can be made very large by flattening the burger.

58. For the McDonald burger, $C = 2\pi$. For the Burger King burger, $C = 3.5\pi$. The ratio of Burger King to McDonald is $\frac{3.5\pi}{2\pi} = 1.75 = 175\%$, so you can claim (erroneously) that the Burger King burger has 75% more meat than the McDonald burger.

60. For a sphere, if the diameter is doubled, the volume is 8 times as large and the surface area is 4 times as large.

62. The volume is doubled.

63. Since the sum of the face angles at a vertex must be less than 360°, three, four, or five equilateral triangles, three squares, or three pentagons can be put together at any vertex. There are no other possibilities, so only the five regular polyhedrons listed are possible.

64. Make the icosahedron.

65.

Figure	*F*	*V*	*E*	*F* + *V*
8.69B	6	8	12	$14 = E + 2$
8.69C	6	5	9	$11 = E + 2$
8.69D	7	10	15	$17 = E + 2$
8.70	5	6	9	$11 = E + 2$
8.71	6	6	10	$12 = E + 2$

Thus, Euler's formula is $F + V = E + 2$.

66. $F = 20, V = 12, E = 30$.

Thus, $F + V = 32 = E + 2$.

Exercises 8.6

1. a. 3 **b.** 0

c. Traversable; all three vertices are possible starting points.

2. a. 2 **b.** 2 **c.** Traversable. Start at *B* or *D*.

3. a. 3 (*B*, *D*, and *E*) **b.** 2 (*A* and *C*)

c. Traversable; start at either *A* or *C*.

4. a. 3 **b.** 4 **c.** Not traversable

5. a. 1 (*A* only) **b.** 4 (*B*, *C*, *D*, *E*)

c. Not traversable; it has more than two odd vertices.

6. a. 2 **b.** 2 **c.** Traversable. Start at *C* or *D*.

7. a. 5 (*A*, *C*, *D*, *E*, *G*) **b.** 2 (*B*, *F*)

c. Traversable; start at *B* or *F*.

8. a. 3 **b.** 4 **c.** Not traversable

9. a. 1, the vertex of the pyramid

b. 4, the vertices of the base

c. Not traversable; it has more than two odd vertices.

10. a. 0 **b.** 8 **c.** Not traversable

11. Think of each region as a vertex and the individual line segments in its boundary as the number of paths to the vertex. The boundary of region *A* has four segments, so the corresponding vertex would be even. The boundary of region *B* has five segments, so the corresponding vertex would be odd. The boundary of region *C* has four segments, so the corresponding vertex would be even. The boundary of region *D* has five segments, so the corresponding vertex would be odd. The boundary of region *E* has ten segments, so the corresponding vertex would be even. Thus, the network would have two odd vertices (*B* and *D*). By starting in region *B* or *D*, it is possible to draw a simple connected broken line that crosses each line segment exactly once.

12. It is not possible because the corresponding network has four odd vertices.

13. Region *A* has three doorways, so the corresponding vertex would be odd. Regions *B*, *C*, and *D* and the outside each has two doorways, so the corresponding vertices would be even. Region *F* has three doorways, so the corresponding vertex would be odd. There are two odd vertices, *A* and *F*. By starting in either of these rooms and ending in the other, it is possible for a walk to pass through each doorway exactly once. It is not possible to start and end outside.

14. Yes. The corresponding network has no odd vertices.

15. *A* and *D* have three doorways and the other rooms and the outside each have an even number of doorways. Thus, the corresponding network has two odd vertices. By starting in either *A* or *D* and ending in the other, it is possible for a walk to pass through each doorway exactly once. It is not possible to start and end outside.

16. No. The corresponding network has four odd vertices, *C*, *D*, *E*, and the outside.

17. All the rooms and the outside have an even number of doorways, so the corresponding network has no odd vertices. The walk can start in any room or outside and end in the same place and pass through each doorway exactly once.

18. Yes. The corresponding network has two odd vertices, *A* and *F*. Start in *A* and end in *F*, or vice versa.

19. Rooms *B* and *D* have three doorways, so the corresponding network has two odd vertices. The walk can start in either *B* or *D* and end in the other one, passing through each doorway exactly once. It is not possible to start and end outside.

20. No, The corresponding network has four odd vertices, *C*, *D*, *F*, and the outside.

21. Room *A* and the outside *D* each have three doorways. Thus, the corresponding network has two odd vertices. By starting in *A* and ending in *D* (or vice versa), a walk can pass through each doorway exactly once. It is not possible to start and end in *D*. (See the traversability rules.)

22. Yes. Start from *A* or *D*. It is not possible to start and end outside.

23. Given a line and any point not on that line, there is one and only one line through that point that is parallel to the given line.

24. Given a line and a point not on the line, there is no more than one line through the given point parallel to the given line.

25. Given a line and any point not on that line, there is no line through that point that is parallel to the given line.

26. Euclidean **27.** In hyperbolic geometry

28. Elliptic or Riemannian **29.** The surface of a rectangular box

30. A pseudosphere **31.** The surface of a sphere

32. Riemannian **33.** (a)–(e) are topologically equivalent.

34. a. True **b.** False **c.** False **d.** True **e.** True

35. (a)–(e) are of genus 2. (f) is of genus 1.

36. a. Zero **b.** Three

37. Topo is correct. If you cut through a loop of the left-hand figure, you can unwind it into a single strip as you can with the circular cord.

38. Yes. It takes only one cut to give two pieces of either clip.

39. a. 6 **b.** 2 **c.** Yes. No odd vertices **d.** 10,471 km

e. 108 hrs **f.** $\dfrac{10{,}471}{108} \approx 97$ km/hr. About 60 m /hr

40. a.

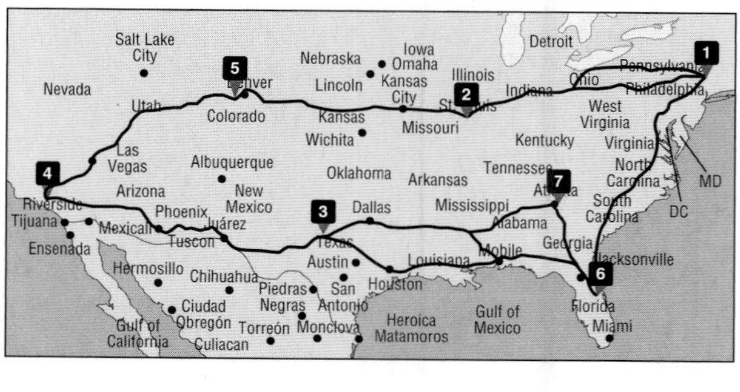

b. 1. 3 edges
2. 3 edges
3. 4 edges
4. 2 edges
5. 2 edges
6. 4 edges
7. 2 edges

41. a. Yes **b.** You have to start at one of the odd vertices
c. At the other odd vertex

42. a. Yes
b. No. Adding a bridge joining any two of the vertices makes it traversable.

45. Vertices 3; regions 2; arcs 3 **46.** V: 4; R: 3; A: 5

47. Vertices 5; regions 2; arcs 5 **48.** V: 4; R: 3; A: 5

49. Vertices 2; regions 3; arcs 3

50. V: 5; R: 3; A: 6

51. Vertices 6; regions 3; arcs 7

52. V: 9; R: 4; A: 11

You can check that the results in problems 46–52 all fit the formula $V + R = A + 2$.

Exercises 8.7

1. $c = 5$ **2.** 13 **3.** $c = 17$ **4.** 10 **5.** $b = 12$

6. 16 **7.** $a = 10$ **8.** 15

9. a. $\cos A = \frac{3}{5}$ **b.** $\sin A = \frac{4}{5}$ **c.** $\tan A = \frac{4}{3}$

10. a. $\frac{5}{13}$ **b.** $\frac{12}{13}$ **c.** $\frac{12}{5}$

11. a. $\cos A = \frac{8}{17}$ **b.** $\sin A = \frac{15}{17}$ **c.** $\tan A = \frac{15}{8}$

12. a. $\frac{5}{13}$ **b.** $\frac{12}{13}$ **c.** $\frac{12}{5}$

13. a. $c = 15$ **b.** $\cos A = \frac{3}{5}$, $\sin A = \frac{4}{5}$, $\tan A = \frac{4}{3}$

14. a. 41 **b.** $\frac{9}{41}, \frac{40}{41}, \frac{40}{9}$

15. a. $c = 37$ **b.** $\cos A = \frac{12}{37}$, $\sin A = \frac{35}{37}$, $\tan A = \frac{35}{12}$

16. a. 35 **b.** $\frac{3}{5}, \frac{4}{5}, \frac{4}{3}$

17. a. $a = 23$ in. **b.** $c = 28$ in.

18. a. 17.5 ft **b.** 30.5 ft

19. a. $b = 67$ in. **b.** $c = 71$ in.

20. a. 14 ft **b.** 43 ft

21. 96 ft **22.** 278 ft **23.** 13 mi **24.** 230 mi

25. 294 ft **26.** 7 mi **27.** 222 ft **28.** 302 ft

29. 118 ft, 236 ft **30.** 145 ft

32. Find the missing sides and angles of the triangle.

34. An angle of elevation is an angle above the horizontal. An angle of depression is an angle below the horizontal.

35. $a = \sqrt{3}, b = 1$ **36.** $a = 4\sqrt{3}; c = 8$

37. $b = 1, c = 2$ **38.** $b = \frac{5}{2}; a = \frac{5}{2}\sqrt{3}$

39. $\tan 30° = \frac{\sqrt{3}}{3}$ **40.** $\sqrt{3}$

41. $\tan 30° = \frac{\sqrt{3}}{3}$ **42.** $\sin 45° = \frac{\sqrt{2}}{2}$; $\tan 45° = 1$

43. $\sin 15° \approx 0.24$, $\tan 15° \approx 0.25$

44. $\cos 23° = 0.92$; $\tan 23° = 0.42$

Exercises 8.8

Note: Answers may vary because of rounding.

1.

x	0.2	0.862	0.850	0.865	0.846	0.868	0.841	0.871
y	0.56	0.416	0.446	0.409	0.456	0.401	0.468	0.393

x	0.835	0.874	0.829	**0.875**	**0.827**	**0.875**	**0.827**
y	0.482	0.385	0.496	**0.383**	**0.501**	**0.383**	**0.501**

There are four attractors: **0.383, 0.501, 0.827, and 0.875.**

2.

x	0.7	0.682	0.640	0.547	0.404	0.463	0.396	0.478
y	0.735	0.759	0.806	0.867	0.843	0.870	0.837	0.873

After about 20 steps you will fiind one attractor: 0.383.

3.

x	0.4	0.605	0.609	0.613	0.615	0.618	0.620	0.621	0.623
y	0.72	0.717	0.714	0.712	0.710	0.708	0.707	0.706	0.705

x	0.624	0.625	0.626	0.628	0.629	0.630	**0.631**	**0.631**
y	0.704	0.703	0.702	0.701	0.700	**0.699**	**0.699**	**0.699**

There are four attractors: **0.631, and 0.699.**

4.

x	0.800	0.435	0.500
y	0.320	0.492	0.500

After about 4 steps you will find one attractor: 0.500.

5. Take s as the length of one side of the original triangle.

a. $4s$ **b.** $\frac{16}{3}s$

6.

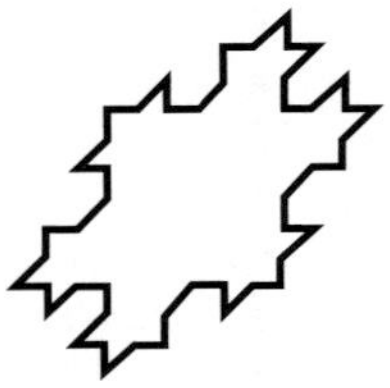

7. On completing the second step, the fractal appears like this.

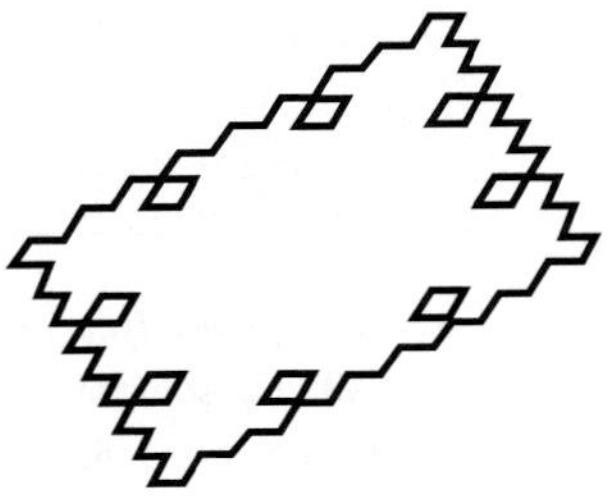

8. 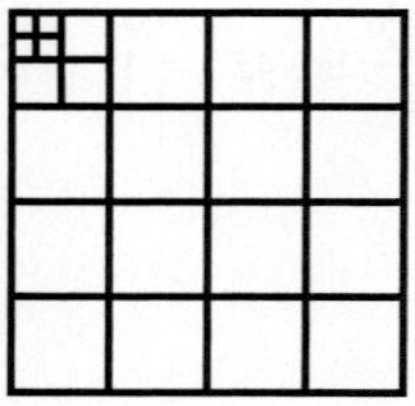

9. $\frac{1}{1024}$ in.^{2}

10. a. 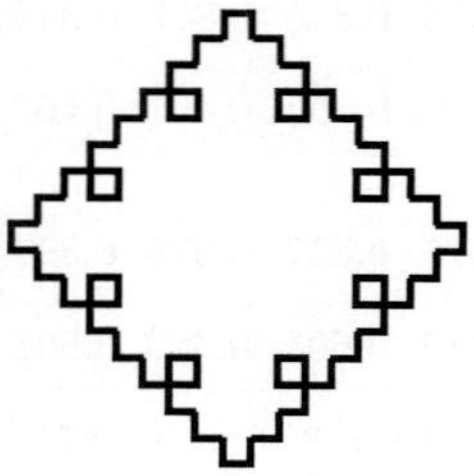

b. No, the length increases indefinitely.

c. Yes, if the side of the original square is S, the figure will always lie inside a square of side $2S$.

11. On completing the second step, the fractal appears like this.

12. $\frac{5}{9}s^2$ 13. $\frac{25}{81}s^2$

14. The perimeter becomes longer and longer. Yes.

15. The remaining area approaches zero.

16. 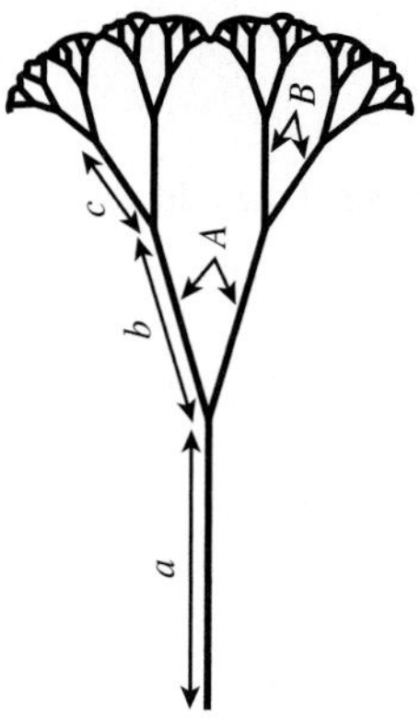

17. a. 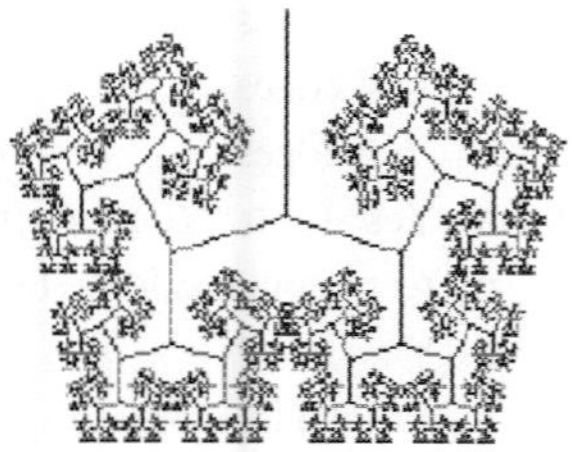

b. About 1/2 in., about 1/4 in., 2

c. Yes

d. About 165°

e. Yes

18. See the figure in the text.

19. $\frac{\sqrt{3}}{6}s^2$ 20. $A = \frac{7s^2\sqrt{3}}{54}$

21. The perimeter increases without limit.

22. The area tends to zero as more and more triangles are taken away.

CHAPTER 9

Exercises 9.1

1. 4 2. 10 3. 11 4. 12 5. 3 6. 6 7. 7 8. 3 9. 5 10. 9 11. 9 12. 9
13. 1 14. 1 15. 2 16. 6 17. 11 18. 8 19. 10 20. 10 21. 1 22. 8 23. 12
24. 12 25. 6 26. 3 27. 4 28. 12

29.

⊗	1	2	3	4	5	6	7	8	9	10	11	12
1	1	2	3	4	5	6	7	8	9	10	11	12
2	2	4	6	8	10	12	2	4	6	8	10	12
3	3	6	9	12	3	6	9	12	3	6	9	12
4	4	8	12	4	8	12	4	8	12	4	8	12
5	5	10	3	8	1	6	11	4	9	2	7	12
6	6	12	6	12	6	12	6	12	6	12	6	12
7	7	2	9	4	11	6	1	8	3	10	5	12
8	8	4	12	8	4	12	8	4	12	8	4	12
9	9	6	3	12	9	6	3	12	9	6	3	12
10	10	8	6	4	2	12	10	8	6	4	2	12
11	11	10	9	8	7	6	5	4	3	2	1	12
12	12	12	12	12	12	12	12	12	12	12	12	12

30. 3 31. 3 32. 3, 7, 11 33. 11 34. Impossible
35. 4 36. 8 37. 8 38. 3 39. No solution
40. 1, 2, 3, 4, 5, 6, 7, 8, 9, 10, 11, 12 41. False 42. True
43. False 44. True 45. False 46. True
47. 2 (mod 5) 48. 1 (mod 10) 49. 4 (mod 5)
50. 2 (mod 7) 51. 3 (mod 5) 52. 2 (mod 5)
53. 1 (mod 5) 54. 4 (mod 5) 55. 3 (mod 5)
56. 4 (mod 5) 57. 3 (mod 5) 58. 3 (mod 5)
59. 0 60. 2 61. 0 62. 2 63. 1 64. 3
65. 2 66. 4 67. 2 68. 3 69. 2

70. 3 **71.** 3 **72.** 1 **73.** 2 **74.** 3 **75.** Yes

76. Yes **77.** Yes, 1

78. **a.** No inverse **b.** 1 **c.** 3 **d.** 2 **e.** 4

79. Ox **80.** Dragon **81.** No; yes

82. Answers will vary.

83. It is in the 20s or 30s, and so on.

84. Yes

85. 1948, 1960, 1972, 1984, 1996, 2008, . . .

86. 1950, 1962, 1974, 1986, 1998, 2010, . . .

87. 24. It avoids confusion between A.M. and P.M.

88. Wednesday

90. The 0005234983 is correct. Dividing 523498 by 7 leaves a remainder of 3, not 1

91. 5 **92.** X **93.** 2 **94.** 4 **95.** 1 **96.** 7

97. 4 **98.** 2 **99.** 7 **100.** 5 **101.** 3 **102.** 8

103. 1 **104.** 2 **105.** 7

106. Not Valid–Change 5 to 6 **107.** Yes

108. Not Valid–Change 3 to 4 **109.** No; 2

110. Not Valid–Change 7 to 0 **111.** No; 4

112. Not Valid–Change 4 to 7 **113.** Yes

114. Not Valid–Change 8 to 5 **115.** No; 8

116. Error (Sum 184) **117.** Valid

118. Valid **119.** Error (Sum is 189)

120. Valid

To read a neat project concerning checking numbers under different schemes, go to: http://www.missioncollege.org/depts/math/sanitate/lynn.htm.

Collaborative Learning

1.

1
1 1
1 2 1
1 3 3 1
1 4 6 4 1
1 5 10 10 5 1
1 6 15 20 15 6 1

2.

1
1 1
1 0 1
1 1 1 1
1 0 0 0 1
1 1 0 0 1 1
1 0 1 0 1 0 1

3. Here are the first 8 rows:

Exercises 9.2

1. **a.** a **b.** c **c.** b

2. **a.** b **b.** b **c.** Yes

3. **a.** a **b.** a **c.** Yes

4. **a.** c **b.** c **c.** Yes

5. **a.** c **b.** c **c.** Yes

6. Yes. The table is symmetric with respect to the diagonal from upper left to lower right.

7. Yes. If $x \in S$ and $y \in S$, then $x \mathbin{@} y \in S$.

8. **a.**

F	1	2	3
1	1	1	1
2	2	2	2
3	3	3	3

b. Yes **c.** No

d. $a \text{ F}(b \text{ F } c) = a \text{ F } b = a$

$(a \text{ F } b)\text{F } c = a \text{ F } c = a$

Therefore, $a \text{ F}(b \text{ F } c) = (a \text{ F } b) \text{ F } c$

9. **a.** Yes. If a and b are natural numbers, then $a \text{ F } b = a$, which is a natural number.

b. Yes. $a \text{ F } (b \text{ F } c) = a \text{ F } b = a$ and $(a \text{ F } b) \text{ F } c = a \text{ F } c = a$. Thus, $a \text{ F } (b \text{ F } c) = (a \text{ F } b) \text{ F } c$.

c. No. If $a \neq b$, then $a \text{ F } b = a$ and $b \text{ F } a = b$, so $a \text{ F } b \neq b \text{ F } a$.

10. **a.** Yes. The product of two multiples of 5 is a multiple of 5.

b. Yes. This is a property of ordinary multiplication of numbers.

c. Yes. This is a property of ordinary multiplication of numbers.

11. **a.** No. For example, $3 + 5 = 8$, which is not an odd number

b. Yes. The product of two odd numbers is an odd number.

c. Yes. The sum of two even numbers is an even number.

d. Yes. The product of two even numbers is an even number.

12. **a.** Ordinary addition. $1 + 1 = 2 \notin S$

b. Subtraction: $1 - (0 - 1) = 2$ but $(1 - 0) - 1 = 0$.

c. Subtraction: $1 - 0 \neq 0 - 1$

13.

$\cap$	$\varnothing$	$\{a\}$	$\{b\}$	$\{a, b\}$
$\varnothing$	$\varnothing$	$\varnothing$	$\varnothing$	$\varnothing$
$\{a\}$	$\varnothing$	$\{a\}$	$\varnothing$	$\{a\}$
$\{b\}$	$\varnothing$	$\varnothing$	$\{b\}$	$\{b\}$
$\{a, b\}$	$\varnothing$	$\{a\}$	$\{b\}$	$\{a, b\}$

14. **a.** $\varnothing$ **b.** $\varnothing$ **c.** Yes

15. **a.** $\varnothing$ **b.** $\varnothing$ **c.** Yes

16. Yes

17. Yes. All elements in the table are elements of S.

18. Yes. The table is symmetric across the diagonal from upper left to lower right.

19. **a.**

L	1	2	3	4
1	1	2	3	4
2	2	2	3	4
3	3	3	3	4
4	4	4	4	4

b. 1

20. Yes. 4

21. **a.** No inverse **b.** No inverse

c. No inverse **d.** 4

22.

$\times$	-1	0	1
-1	1	0	-1
0	0	0	0
1	-1	0	1

23. Yes; 1

24. **a.** 1 **b.** -1 **c.** No inverse

25. **a.** The identity element is A, because for every B that is a subset of A, $A \cap B = B \cap A = B$.

b. No, there is no other identity element.

26. Yes. All elements in the table are elements of S.

27. Yes. The identity element is 0.

28. **a.** 0 **b.** 3 **c.** 2 **d.** 1

29. **a.** 3 **b.** 4

30. **a.** 4 **b.** 6

31. The distributive property holds. If a, b, and c are real numbers, then $a \text{ F } (b \text{ L } c) = a$ and $(a \text{ F } b) \text{ L } (a \text{ F } c) = a \text{ L } a = a$.

32. If a, b, c are real numbers, then $a \text{ L } (b \text{ F } c) = a \text{ L } b$ and $(a \text{ L } b) \text{ F } (a \text{ L } c) = a \text{ L } b$. Therefore, this distributive property holds.

33. Yes

34. $a \div (b - c) \neq (a \div b) - (a \div c)$. For example, $20 \div (4 - 2) = 20 \div 2 = 10$, but $(20 \div 4) - (20 \div 2) = 5 - 10 = -5$.
However, $(a - b) \div c = (a - b) \cdot \frac{1}{c} = \frac{a-b}{c} = \frac{a}{c} - \frac{b}{c} = (a \div c) - (b \div c)$. Thus, one of the distributive laws holds for division: $(a - b) \div c = (a \div c) - (b \div c)$.

35. Yes **36.** No

37. Yes (actually, a commutative group)

38. No. Not closed because odd + odd = even.

39. No; no multiplicative inverses

40. Yes

41. No; no identity element

42. No. There is no identity element.

43. No; no multiplicative inverses

44. Yes

45. No; no multiplicative inverses

46. No. Zero has no multiplicative inverse. (You can't divide by zero.)

47. Yes

48. No. Not closed because $1 + 1 = 2$, which is not an element of the set.

49. No; no multiplicative inverse for 0

50.

#	a	a	a
a	c	a	b
b	a	b	c
c	b	c	a

51. No; no identity element

52. No. There are no multiplicative inverses.

53. No (no multiplicative inverses)

54. No. There are no multiplicative inverses.

55. No (no multiplicative inverses)

56. Yes

57. Check to see that $a \blacklozenge b$ is always an element of S.

58. Check to see if the table is symmetric to the diagonal from upper left to lower right. If it is, then the operation has the commutative property; otherwise, it does not have this property.

59. Check the table to see whether there is an element e in S such that the column under e is identical to the column at the far left and the row opposite e is identical to the top row. If there is, then e is the identity element. If there is no such element, then there is no identity element.

60. If there is an identity element, say e, check to see if $a \blacklozenge b = b \blacklozenge a = e$.

61. You have to check that $x * (y * z) = (x * y) * z$ for all possible values of x, y, and z from the set $\{a, b, c\}$. If you had to check all possible cases, there would be 27 of these because each of the 3 places has 3 possible values. However, since the operation has the commutative property, the number of cases to be checked is greatly reduced. Think about it.

62. The operation $\cdot$ is associative, and the identity element is e. To use the theorem, we only have to check that a and b have inverses. The table shows that $a \cdot b = c$ and $b \cdot a = c$. This completes the check.

63. **a.** Yes **b.** Yes **c.** Yes **d.** 7

$\oplus$	1	2	3	4	5	6	7
1	1	1	1	1	1	1	1
2	1	2	2	2	2	2	2
3	1	2	3	3	3	3	3
4	1	2	3	4	4	4	4
5	1	2	3	4	5	5	5
6	1	2	3	4	5	6	6
7	1	2	3	4	5	6	7

64. **a.** No **b.** Yes **c.** Yes **d.** 0

$\otimes$	0	1	2	3	4	5	6
0	0	1	2	3	4	5	6
1	1	2	3	4	5	6	7
2	2	3	4	5	6	7	8
3	3	4	5	6	7	8	9
4	4	5	6	7	8	9	10
5	5	6	7	8	9	10	11
6	6	7	8	9	10	11	12

65. Yes. $3 \otimes (4 \oplus 5) = 3 \otimes 4 = 3 + 4 = 7$
and $(3 \otimes 4) \oplus (3 \otimes 5) = 7 \oplus 8 = 7$
Thus, $3 \otimes (4 \oplus 5) = (3 \otimes 4) \oplus (3 \otimes 5)$

66. **a.** $\min\{e, x\} = x$ **b.** $x \leq e$
c. 3 **d.** -5 **e.** x

67. $6 \times 9999 = 6(10{,}000 - 1) = 60{,}000 - 6 = 59{,}994$

68. $8 \cdot 99 = 8(100 - 1) = 800 - 8 = 792$

69. $7 \times 59 = 7(60 - 1) = 420 - 7 = 413$

70. $8 \cdot 999 = 8(1000 - 1) = 8000 - 8 = 7992$

71. $4 \times 9995 = 4(10{,}000 - 5) = 40{,}000 - 20 = 39{,}980$

72. $3 \cdot 9998 = 3(10{,}000 - 2) = 30{,}000 - 6 = 29{,}994$

73. The following steps show why the puzzle works:

Think of a number.	x
Add 3 to it.	$x + 3$
Triple the result.	$3x + 9$
Subtract 9.	$3x$
Divide by the number x with which you started.	3

74. 2

Collaborative Learning

1. Yes. Answers are elements of C.

2. *At* **3.** *At* **4.** *L* **5.** *R* **6.** *A* **7.** Yes

8. Yes. Satisfies Definition 8.18.

9. Yes. The reflection of the bottom half of the table along the diagonal is identical to the top half.

Exercises 9.3

1. Strictly determined. Optimal pure strategy: Row player should play row 1, column player should play column 1. Value = 4.

2. Strictly determined. Optimum strategy: Row player should play row 1, column player column 2. Value = 1.

3. Not strictly determined

4. Not strictly determined.

5. Strictly determined. Optimal pure strategy: Row player should play row 1, column player should play column 3. Value = 4.

6. Strictly determined. Optimum strategy: Row player should play row 3, column player column 2. Value = 0.

7. Strictly determined. Optimal pure strategy: Row player should play row 3, column player should play column 1 or column 3. Value = 4.

8. Strictly determined. Optimum strategy: Row player should play row 1 or row 3, column player column 2. Value = 1.

9. a. No saddle point

b. Row player should play row 1 five-sixths of the time and row 2 one-sixth of the time.

10. a. No saddle point.

b. Row player should play row 1 two-thirds of the time and row 2 one-third of the time.

11. a. No saddle point

b. Row player should play row 1 one-sixth of the time and row 2 five-sixths of the time.

12. a. No saddle point.

b. Row player should play row 1 six-elevenths of the time and row 2 five-elevenths of the time.

13. Optimal row strategy: Play row 1 one-fourth of the time, row 2 three-fourths of the time, and do not play row 3. Value = 3.

14. a. Row player should select row 1 two-sevenths of the time and row 3 five-sevenths of the time. He should not select row 2. Value $= \frac{135}{7} = 19\frac{2}{7}$.

15. Study 2 hr half the time, and 4 hr half the time.

16. Study English 2 hr, Math 3 hr three-fourths of the time and English 3 hr, Math 2 hr one-fourth of the time.

17. Ann's optimal strategy: Buy no bonds, buy stocks with five-sevenths and money market funds with two-sevenths of her investment. Her expected return will be $11\frac{3}{7}\%$.

18. $p = \frac{1}{4}$

19. Station R should price its gasoline at $1 four-fifths of the time.

20. 45%

21. a.

$$\begin{array}{lcc} & \text{Younger} & \text{Older} \\ \text{Performance} & 70\% & 20\% \\ \text{Safety} & 40\% & 80\% \end{array}$$

b. $\frac{4}{9}$ performance, $\frac{5}{9}$ safety

22.

$$\begin{array}{ll} & \text{Friend} \\ & \quad P \quad\; N \\ \text{You } P & \begin{bmatrix} +1 & -1 \\ -5 & +5 \end{bmatrix} \\ N & \end{array}$$

Your optimal strategy is to put down your penny five-sixths of the time and your nickel one-sixth of the time. The expected value of the game is 0.

23.

$$\begin{array}{lcc} & \multicolumn{2}{c}{\text{Freeze}} \\ & \text{Yes} & \text{No} \\ \text{Water Yes} & 6000 & -400 \\ \text{No} & -4000 & 4000 \end{array}$$

Optimal strategy: water $\frac{5}{9}$ of the time; don't water $\frac{4}{9}$ of the time.
Expected payoff $= \frac{\$14{,}000}{9} \approx \$1556$.

24. Because it is a minimum in its row and a maximum in its column

25. If row i dominates row j, this means that in the long run playing row i is more profitable than playing row j. Thus, row j can be eliminated from the row player's options.

26. Because in the long run, column i is more profitable than column j for the column player

27. Row 1.

28. Row 1.

29. Send poems $\frac{5}{8}$ of the time and candy $\frac{3}{8}$ of the time. Do not send flowers.

30. $2\frac{3}{8}$

Collaborative Learning

1.

$$\begin{array}{lcc} & \multicolumn{2}{c}{\text{Clyde}} \\ & \text{Confess} & \text{Don't} \\ \text{Bonnie Confess} & (10, 10) & (0, 20) \\ \text{Don't} & (20, 0) & (1, 1) \end{array}$$

2. Bonnie should confess since only two things can happen: Clyde can confess or not.

If Clyde confesses, Bonnie gets 20 years if she doesn't, 10 years if she does, so she should confess.

If Clyde does not confess, Bonnie goes free if she confesses or gets 1 year if she doesn't, so she should confess.

3. Same strategy as Bonnie: confess

4. Each gets 10 years.

5. Each gets 1 year.

6. The "dilemma" is that when they both confess each goes to prison for 10 years, but if they both had kept silent (not confess) each would have gotten only 1 year.

For more reading on prisoners' dilemma try:
http://faculty.lebow.drexel.edu/McCainR/top/eco/game/dilemma.html
http://plato.stanford.edu/entries/prisoner-dilemma/
http:/www.constitution.org/pd/pd.htm

CHAPTER 10

Exercises 10.1

1. 8 different outfits

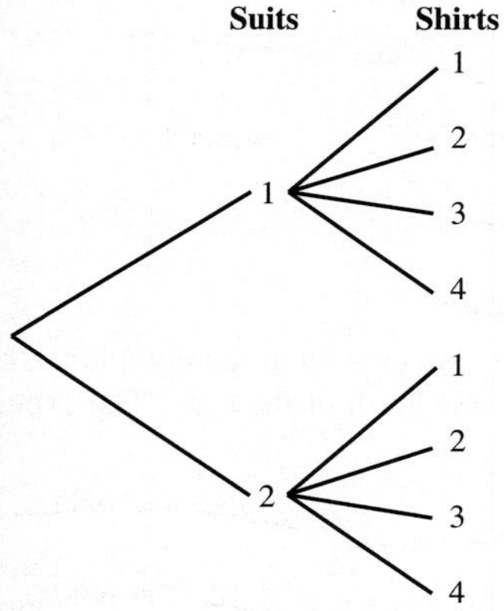

2.

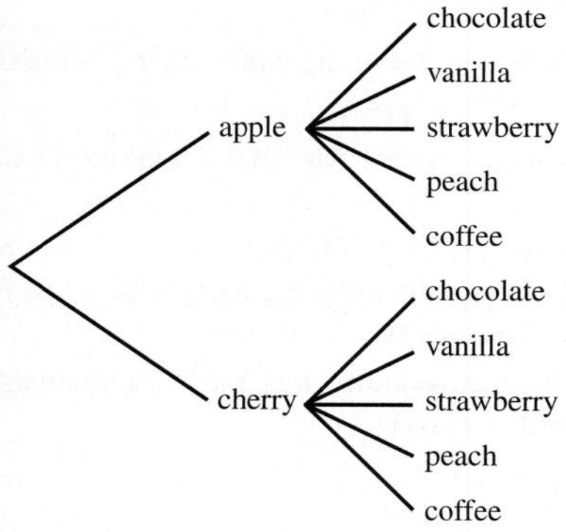

3. $4 \times 3 = 12$ outcomes

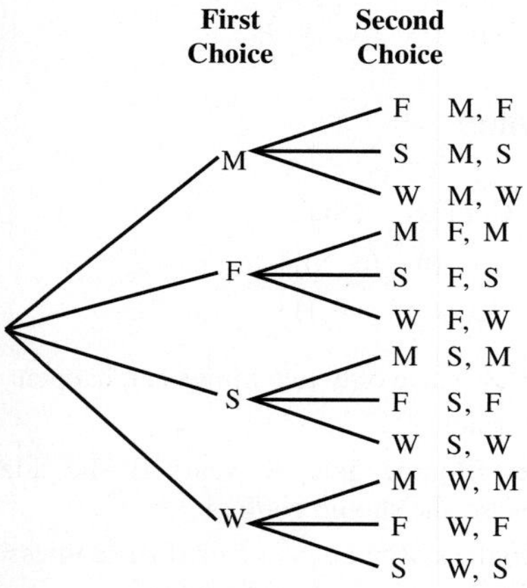

4. a. 3905 b. \$312.50
5. a. 9 b. 126 c. 25
6. a. 650 b. 650 c. 1352
7. a. 12 b. 144
8. a. 20 b. 5
9. 30 10. 676 11. 17,576 12. 6
13. 378 14. 24 15. a. 720 b. 24
16. a. 17,576 b. 1000 c. 17,576,000
17. 90 18. 900
19. a. 900,000,000 b. 10^9
20. $8 \times 10^6 = 8{,}000{,}000$
21. a. 59,280 b. $40^3 = 64{,}000$
22. 30
23. a. 10 b. 2 c. 4 d. 80
24. a. 9 b. 72
25. a. 19 b. 152
26. a. 90 b. 720
27. 720 28. 560 29. 480 30. 280
31. (*a*, @), (*a*, &), (*a*, %), (*b*, @), (*b*, &), (*b*, %), (*c*, @), (*c*, &), (*c*, %), (@, *a*), (&, *a*), (%, *a*), (@, *b*), (&, *b*),(%, *b*), (@, *c*), (&, *c*), (%, *c*)
32. 25,200 different couples 33. $2 \times 2 = 4$
34. 4 35. $3 \times 2 = 6$ 36. 9
37.

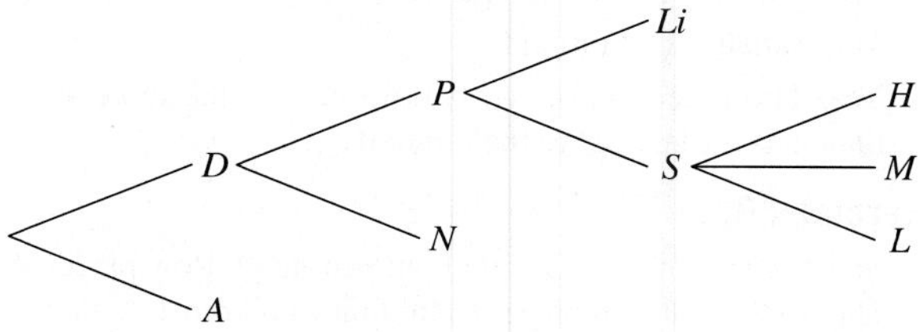

38.

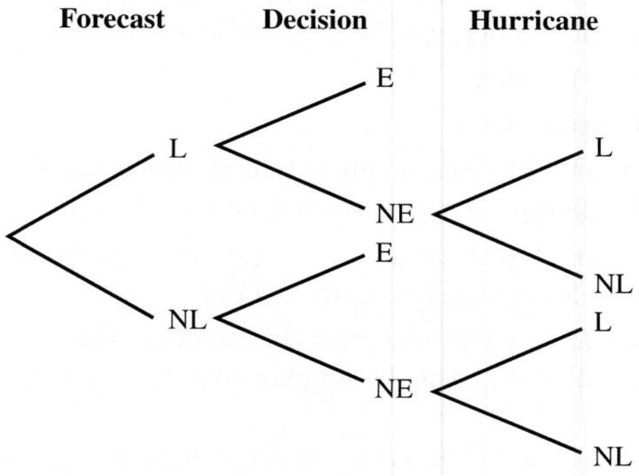

39.

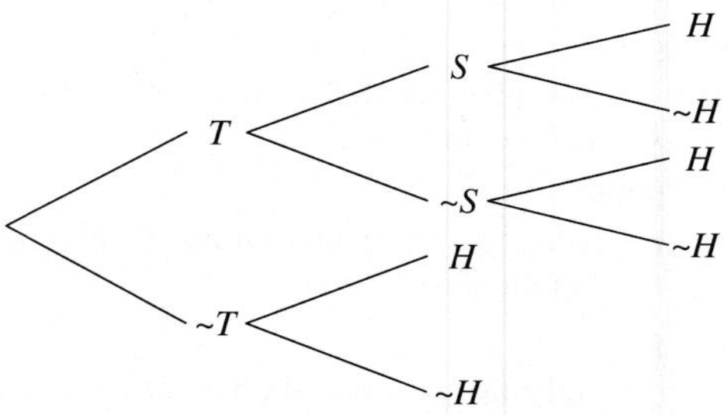

40.

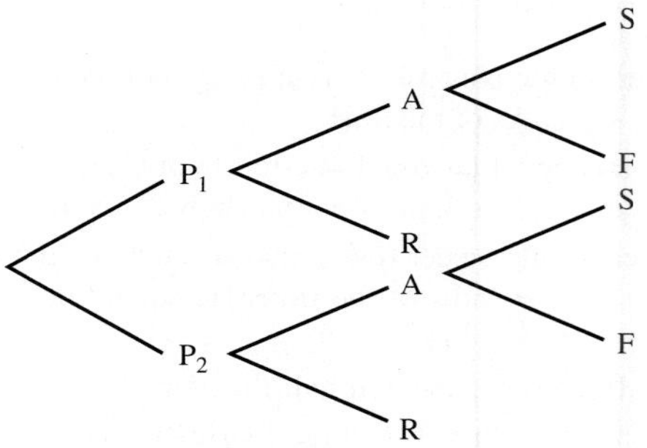

41. If a single event can occur in *m* ways or in *n* ways, then the total number of ways in which the event can occur is $m + n$ (assuming no duplications).
42. There are 26 different letters available, so the number of different plates available is much greater than with the use of digits.
43. 24 44. 24

45. There are not enough different sets of initials for 27,000 people, so at least 2 people must have the same set of initials.

46. 12 **47.** 144 **48.** 20,736

49. It will point to 3 if no slippage occurs. **50.** 12

Collaborative Learning

1. Conventional Therapy ($250)
2. New drug with side effects ($600)
3. New drug, no side effects
4. New drug with side effects
5. Make improvements, rent for $2100, start lease Sept. 1 ($24,000)
6. Make improvements, rent for $1950, start lease Nov. 1 ($18,300)

Exercises 10.2

1. 24 **2.** 24 **3.** 720 **4.** 5040 **5.** 120

6. 120 **7.** 40,320 **8.** 3,628,800 **9.** 362,880

10. 720 **11.** 990 **12.** 28 **13.** 126 **14.** 3024

15. 90 **16.** 5 **17.** 10 **18.** 672 **19.** 20,160

20. 24 **21.** 120 **22.** 720

23. a. 120 **b.** 60 **c.** Yes, Yes

24. 30,240 **25.** 1716 **26.** 12 **27.** 650 **28.** 17,160

29. 60 **30.** 24 **31.** 9 **32.** 18 **33.** 31 **34.** 11

35. 1 **36.** 63 **37.** 57 **38.** 7 **39.** 60 **40.** 67

41. a. $10^6 = 1{,}000{,}000$ **b.** $P(10, 6) = 151{,}200$

c. 151,200 are not enough for a population of 608,827.

42. a. 175,760,000 **b.** 78,624,000

43. $2 \cdot P(25, 3) = 27{,}600$

44. a. 10^9 **b.** 3,628,800 **c.** $10! - 9(8!) = 3{,}265{,}920$

45. $n! = n \times (n - 1)!$ for $n > 1$. This formula holds for $n = 1$ only if 0! is defined to be 1.

The formula $P(n, r) = \dfrac{n!}{(n - r)!}$ holds for $r = n$, only if 0! is defined to be 1.

46. $P(n, 0) = 1$, $P(n, 0) = \dfrac{n!}{(n - 0)!} = \dfrac{n!}{n!} = 1$

47. The number of elements in the union of two sets is the sum of the number of elements in each of the sets diminished by the number of elements common to the two sets.

48. If the events are independent and the number of ways that each event can occur is known, then it is easier to use the additive counting principle.

49. 120 **50.** 6 (Assuming there are no other ties)

51. 3, including a possible tie for fourth place

52. 3 **53.** $(n - 1)!$ **54.** 2 **55.** 4 **56.** 4

Collaborative Learning

1. 60

3. Yes. *abc* is a different selection from *cba*.

4. 60 **6.** Yes **7.** 10

9. No. *abc* is the same choice as *cba*.

Exercises 10.3

1. $C(5, 2) = 10$, $P(5, 2) = 20$

2. $C(6, 4) = 15$, $P(6, 4) = 360$

3. $C(7, 3) = 35$, $P(7, 3) = 210$

4. $C(5, 0) = P(5, 0) = 1$

5. $C(9, 6) = 84$, $P(9, 6) = 60{,}480$

6. $C(7, 0) = P(7, 0) = 1$ **7.** $C(5, 4) = 5$

8. 10 **9.** $C(5, 3) = 10$ **10.** 10 **11.** $C(8, 2) = 28$

12. 21 **13.** $C(12, 8) = 495$ **14.** 3003

15. a. 220 **b.** 79 **c.** 1 **d.** 79

16. 10 **17.** $C(5, 4) = 5$ **18.** 26

19. a. $C(5, 3) = 10$ **b.** 26

20. 190 **21.** $C(24, 3) = 2024$ **22.** 252

23. $C(10, 3) = 120$ **24.** 9880 **25.** $C(52, 5) = 2{,}598{,}960$

26. 28 **27.** $C(100, 5) = 75{,}287{,}520$ **28.** 792 **29.** 15

30. 15 **31.** 63 **32.** 219 **33.** $C(8, 4) = 70$

34. a. 20 **b.** $\dfrac{n(n - 3)}{2}$

35. Answers will vary; the important difference is that permutations take account of order and combinations do not.

36. a. No. It might need some other permutation of the numbers 1, 2, 3.

b. 1, 2, 3; 2, 3, 1; 3, 1, 2; 1, 3, 2; 3, 2, 1; 2, 1, 3. Yes, one of these would open the lock because these are the only possible permutations.

37. The order of the numbers is important, so a permutation is being used.

38. a. Since $C(n, r) = \dfrac{P(n, r)}{r!}$, $C(n, r) = P(n, r)$ if and only if $r! = 1$, that is, $r = 0$ or $r = 1$.

b. The same formula as in (a) shows that $P(n, r) = r! \cdot C(n, r)$. Hence, $P(n, r) > C(n, r)$ if $r > 1$.

39. $n = 6$: 1 6 15 20 15 6 1

$n = 7$: 1 7 21 35 35 21 7 1

40. a. 15 **b.** 35

41. a. $(a + b)^4 = a^4 + 4a^3b + 6a^2b^2 + 4ab^3 + b^4$

b. $(a + b)^5 = a^5 + 5a^4b + 10a^3b^2 + 10a^2b^3 + 5ab^4 + b^5$

42. $(a + b)^6 = a^6 + 6a^5b + 15a^4b^2 + 20a^3b^3 + 15a^2b^4 + 6ab^5 + b^6$

43. $C(5, 0) = 1$ **44.** $C(5, 1) = 5$ **45.** $C(5, 3) = 10$

46. $C(5, 4) = 5$ **47.** $C(5, 5) = 1$

48. The coin can fall in either of two ways. If it is flipped 5 times, the total number of possible outcomes is 2^5 or 32.

49. The left side is the sum of the number of ways in which there could be 0 heads and n tails, 1 head and $n - 1$ tails, 2 heads and $n - 2$ tails, and so on, to n heads and 0 tails. The right side is exactly the number of ways in which n coins can fall either heads or tails. Thus, the two sides are equal.

Collaborative Learning

1. 10^6

2. Answers will vary.

3. Probably not, because $2 \times 568{,}158 = 1{,}136{,}316$ which is greater than 10^6.

4. Answers will vary. **5.** Answers will vary.

6. a. 175,760,000; 17,576,000 **b.** First method

Exercises 10.4

1. a. $P(52, 3) = 132{,}600$ **b.** $C(52, 3) = 22{,}100$

2. a. $C(6, 4) = 15$ **b.** $P(6, 3) = 120$

3. a. $50 \times 50 \times 50 = 125{,}000$ **b.** $C(50, 3) = 19{,}600$

4. a. $P(6, 3) = 120$ **b.** $C(6, 3) = 20$ **5.** $C(5, 3) = 10$

6. a. $P(3, 3) = 6$ **b.** $P(2, 2) = 2$

7. a. $C(7, 3) = 35$ **b.** $P(7, 4) = 840$

8. a. $C(100, 3) = 161{,}700$

b. $C(40, 2)C(100, 2) = 3{,}861{,}000$

9. a. $P(10, 2)P(14, 2) = 16{,}380$

b. $P(10, 2)P(12, 2) = 11{,}880$

10. a. $C(6, 2)C(4, 2) = 90$ **b.** $C(6, 3)C(4, 1) = 80$

c. $C(6, 4) = 15$ **d.** $C(10, 4) = 210$

11. a. $C(7, 3)C(8, 1) = 280$ **b.** $C(5, 3)C(2, 1) = 20$

12. $C(6, 3)C(6, 2)C(5, 1) = 1500$ **13.** 831,600

14. $\dfrac{11!}{1!4!4!2!} = 34{,}650$ **15.** 22,680

16. $\dfrac{12!}{1!1!3!3!1!2!1!} = 6{,}652{,}800$

17. $C(7, 2)C(5, 3)C(2, 2) = 210$

18. $C(n, 3) = 20$ for $n = 6$, so six different ads are needed.

19. $C(n, 5) \geq 21$ for $n \geq 7$ **20.** $C(n, 5) = 56$ for $n = 8$

21. $C(4, 2)P(3, 2)C(2, 1) = 72$

22. $C(4, 1)C(3, 2) + C(4, 2)C(3, 1) = 30$

23. a.

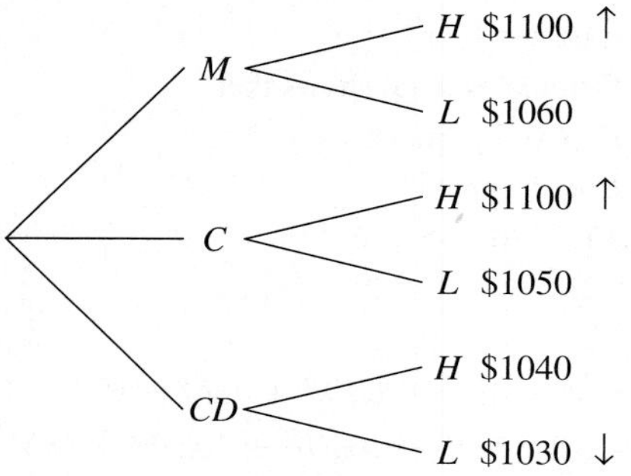

b. $1100, mutual fund (*M*), high (*H*) or management company (*C*), high (*H*)

c. $1030, *CD*, low (*L*)

24. a.

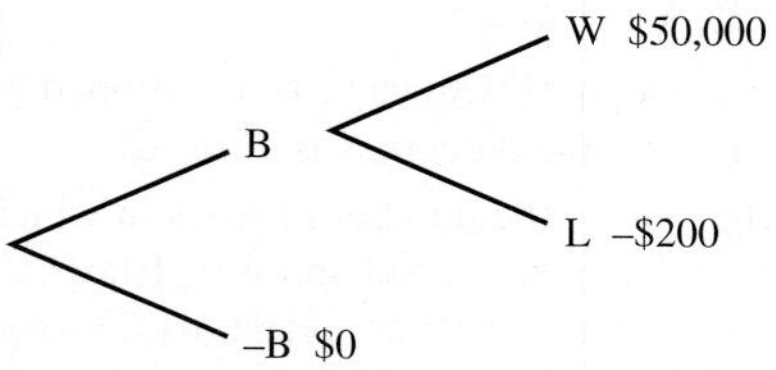

b. $50,000 **c.** −$200

25. a.

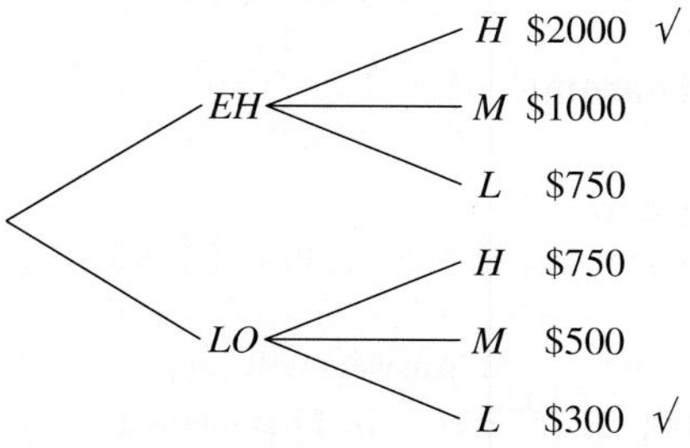

b. $2000, market size extremely high (*EH*), sales high (*H*)

c. $300, market size low (*LO*), sales low (*L*)

26. a.

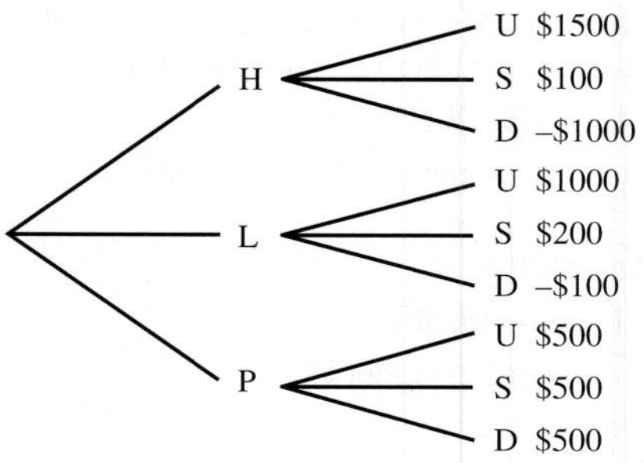

b. $1500. High-risk stocks that go up.

c. −$1000. High-risk stocks that go down.

27. Answers will vary.

28. If a set of n objects consists of r different types, with objects of the same type being indistinguishable, let n_k be the number of objects of type k for $k = 1, 2, 3, \ldots, r$. Then the total number of distinct permutations of the n objects is given by the formula $\dfrac{n!}{n_1!n_2! \ldots n_r!}$.

29. 15 **30.** 48

31. $(a + 1)(b + 1)(c + 1)(d + 1)$

32. 60

Collaborative Learning

1. 10. Vaccinate, no complications, no disease or don't vaccinate, no disease.

2. Answers will vary.

3. 0. There are 3 ways to get a score of 0. (See the diagram.)

4. Vaccinate, no complications, has disease, partial recovery or don't vaccinate, had disease, partial recovery.

CHAPTER 11

Exercises 11.1

1. $\frac{1}{6}$ **2.** $\frac{1}{2}$ **3.** $\frac{1}{3}$ **4.** $\frac{2}{3}$ **5.** $\frac{1}{10}$ **6.** $\frac{1}{2}$ **7.** $\frac{9}{10}$

8. $\frac{9}{10}$ **9.** 0 **10.** $\frac{7}{10}$ **11.** $\frac{1}{13}$ **12.** $\frac{1}{52}$ **13.** $\frac{1}{4}$

14. $\frac{3}{13}$ **15.** $\frac{11}{26}$ **16.** $\frac{8}{13}$ **17. a.** $\frac{1}{5}$ **b.** $\frac{3}{5}$ **c.** $\frac{4}{5}$

18. a.

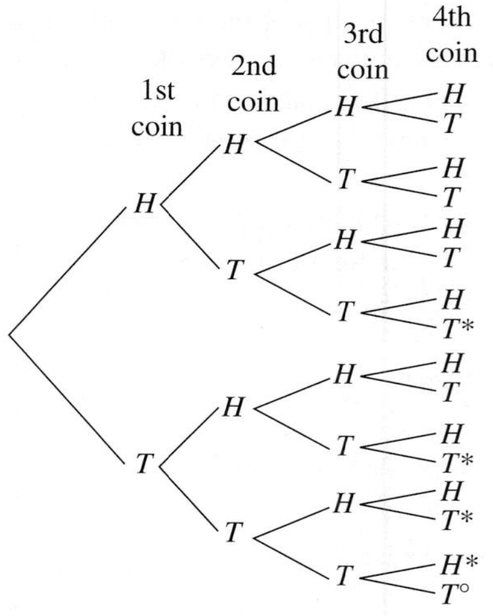

b. $\frac{11}{16}$ **c.** $\frac{1}{4}$

19. a. $\frac{1}{3}$ **b.** $\frac{1}{3}$ **20.** $\frac{1}{8}$ **21.** $\frac{1}{8}$ **22.** $\frac{7}{8}$ **23** $\frac{3}{8}$

24. a.

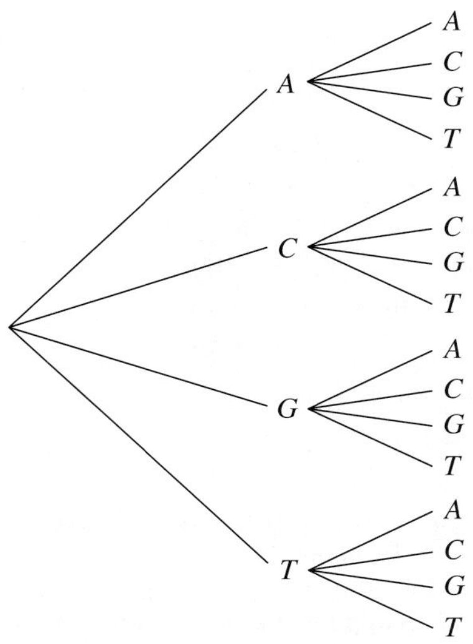

b. $\frac{1}{16}$ **c.** $\frac{1}{16}$ **d.** $\frac{1}{16}$

25. $\frac{1}{6}$ **26.** $\frac{1}{36}$ **27.** $\frac{1}{6}$ **28.** $\frac{5}{6}$ **29.** $\frac{1}{2}$ **30.** $\frac{1}{2}$

31. a. $\frac{1}{4}$ **b.** $\frac{7}{25}$ **c.** $\frac{6}{25}$ **d.** $\frac{23}{100}$ **e.** $\frac{1}{4}$ **f.** $P(B)$

32. a. $\frac{3}{20}$ **b.** $\frac{9}{50}$ **c.** $\frac{1}{5}$ **d.** $\frac{13}{100}$ **e.** $\frac{3}{20}$ **f.** $\frac{19}{100}$

33. a. $\frac{6}{25}; \frac{1}{6}$ **b.** $\frac{9}{100}; \frac{1}{9}$ **c.** $\frac{29}{100}; \frac{5}{18}$ **d.** $\frac{1}{5}; \frac{2}{9}$ **e.** $\frac{9}{50}; \frac{2}{9}$

34.

	Outcome	Empirical Probability	Theoretical Probability
a.	Sum = 2	0.03	$\frac{1}{36}$
b.	Sum = 5	0.12	$\frac{1}{9}$
c.	Sum = 7	0.17	$\frac{1}{6}$
d.	Sum = 9	0.13	$\frac{1}{9}$
e.	Sum = 12	0.02	$\frac{1}{36}$
f.	Sum > 10	0.08	$\frac{1}{12}$
g.	Sum < 4	0.07	$\frac{1}{12}$
h.	Sum > 2	0.97	$\frac{35}{36}$
i.	Sum < 12	0.98	$\frac{35}{36}$

35. a. $\frac{3}{25}$ **b.** $\frac{9}{50}$ **c.** $\frac{13}{25}$ **d.** $\frac{12}{25}$
e. Getting a sum of 8 **f.** Getting a sum of 2 (or 4 or 12)
g. Getting a sum of 2, 4, or 12 **h.** No

36. a. $\frac{1}{18}$ **b.** $\frac{7}{36}$ **c.** $\frac{1}{9}$ **d.** $\frac{35}{36}$ **e.** 0
f. 2, 3, 4, 7, 11, 12

37. a. $\frac{86}{251}$ **b.** $\frac{73}{502}$ **c.** Having exactly 4 credit cards
d. Having no credit cards **e.** $\frac{165}{251}$

38. a. $\frac{15}{302}$ **b.** $\frac{9}{302}$ **c.** $\frac{56}{151}$ **d.** $\frac{12}{151}$

39. a. $\frac{3}{20}$ **b.** $\frac{37}{50}$ **c.** $\frac{11}{100}$

40. a. 0.22 **b.** 0.25 **c.** TV viewing

41. a. $\frac{89}{239}$ **b.** $\frac{33}{239}$ **c.** $\frac{206}{239}$ **d.** $\frac{24}{239}$

42. a. $\frac{10}{27}$ **b.** $\frac{139}{441}$ **c.** $\frac{416}{1323}$

43. a. $\frac{140}{5543}$ **b.** $\frac{2804}{5543}$ **c.** $\frac{2739}{5543}$

44. a. $\frac{349}{1218}$ **b.** $\frac{2137}{8523}$ **c.** $\frac{1532}{8523}$

45. a. $\frac{13}{17}$ **b.** $\frac{4}{17}$

46. 55%

47. a. $\frac{50}{1831}$ **b.** $\frac{158}{5533}$

48. a. $\frac{54}{559}$ **b.** $\frac{42}{587}$

49. a. AL players; their probability of hitting a home run $\frac{158}{5533} = 0.028$ is higher than that of NL players $\frac{50}{1831} = 0.027$

50. Jose Bautista; his probability of hitting a home run is $\frac{54}{559} = 0.10$ against $\frac{42}{587} = 0.07$ for Pujols.

52. Answers will vary. Tossing a coin is a simple probability experiment. The sample space consists of all possible outcomes.

53. The probability formula does not apply if the events are not all equally likely to occur (see Belgian one-euro coin). If a die is weighted so that a 6 is twice as likely to come up as any other number, then to calculate the probability that an even number comes up, it would be wrong to use the fact that 3 of the 6 faces are even so the probability is $\frac{1}{2}$. Instead, the 6 face must be given a weight of 2 and the other faces weights of 1. Then the weight of the even faces is $1 + 1 + 2 = 4$ and the weight of all the faces is 7. Thus, the probability that an even number comes up is $\frac{4}{7}$.

54. a. Experiment
b. Experiment
c. Outcome
d. Experiment

56. Think of a red and a green die. Then, the possible outcomes will be: $7 = 1 + 6 = 2 + 5 = 3 + 4 = 4 + 3 = 5 + 2 = 6 + 1$

57. $\frac{4653}{4720}$, or about 0.986

58. $\frac{781}{784} \approx 0.996$

59. $\frac{253}{254}$, or about 0.996

Collaborative Learning

1. a. $\frac{1}{200}$
For (b), (c) and (d), go to: http:www.dartmouth.edu/~chance/chancenews/recent_news/chance_news_8.01.html #be robbed.

2. a. The sample space is {BB, BG, GB}, so the probability of two boys is $\frac{1}{3}$.
b. Answers will vary.

Exercises 11.2

1. $\frac{1}{18}$ **2.** $\frac{1}{10}$ **3.** $\frac{1}{8}$ **4.** $\frac{C(3,1)}{C(40,3)} = \frac{3}{9880}$

5. $\frac{C(2,2)C(23,2)}{C(25,4)} = \frac{1}{50}$ **6. a.** 4 **b.** $\frac{1}{663}$

7. a. $\frac{1}{5}$ **b.** $\frac{4}{5}$ **8.** $\frac{C(75,4)}{C(100,4)} = \frac{75 \cdot 74 \cdot 73 \cdot 72}{100 \cdot 99 \cdot 98 \cdot 97}$

9. a. $\frac{4}{21}$ **b.** $\frac{1}{21}$ **10.** $\frac{C(5,1)C(6,1)}{C(11,2)} = \frac{6}{11}$

11. $\frac{P(4,2)}{P(52,2)} = \frac{1}{221}$ **12.** $\frac{C(13,2)}{C(52,2)} = \frac{1}{17}$

13. $\frac{13 \times 3}{52 \times 51} = \frac{1}{68}$ **14.** $\frac{C(13,1)C(3,1)}{C(52,2)} = \frac{1}{34}$

15. $\frac{P(26,2)}{P(52,2)} = \frac{25}{102}$ **16. a.** 12 **b.** 210 **c.** $\frac{2}{35}$

17. a. 15 **b.** $\frac{5 \times 3}{15 \times 14} = \frac{1}{14}$ **c.** $\frac{1}{7}$

18. 0.9604 **19.** 0.0396 **20.** $\frac{1}{45}$

21. $\frac{6}{100} \cdot \frac{8}{10{,}000} = \frac{3}{62{,}500} = 0.000048$

22. a. $\frac{C(5,2)}{C(8,2)} = \frac{5}{14}$ **b.** $\frac{C(3,2)}{C(8,2)} = \frac{3}{28}$ **c.** $\frac{C(5,1)C(3,1)}{C(8,2)} = \frac{15}{28}$

23. a. $\frac{C(4,2)C(4,2)C(44,1)}{C(52,5)}$ **b.** $\frac{C(4,3)C(4,2)}{C(52,5)}$

24. $\frac{C(70,2)C(245,1)}{C(315,3)} = \frac{5635}{49{,}141} = 0.115$

25. $\frac{C(3,1)C(1,1)}{C(4,2)} = \frac{3}{6} = \frac{1}{2}$

26. a. $\frac{1}{C(10,3)} = \frac{1}{120}$ **b.** $\frac{C(3,2)C(7,1)}{C(10,3)} = \frac{7}{40}$

27. $\frac{4}{C(52,5)} = \frac{1}{649{,}740} \approx 0.0000015$

28. $\frac{40}{C(52,5)} = \frac{1}{64974} \approx 0.000015$

29. $\frac{13 \times 48}{C(52, 5)} = \frac{1}{4165} \approx 0.00024$

30. $\frac{13 \cdot C(4, 2) \cdot 12 \cdot C(4, 3)}{C(52, 5)} = \frac{6}{4165} \approx 0.0014$

31. $\frac{4 \times [C(13, 5) - 10]}{C(52, 5)} = \frac{5148 - 40}{C(52, 5)} = \frac{1277}{649{,}740} \approx 0.0020$

32. $\frac{10 \cdot 4^5 - 40}{C(52, 5)} = \frac{5}{1274} \approx 0.0039$

33. 0.2 **34.** 0.1

35. Dome structure, dry

36. a.

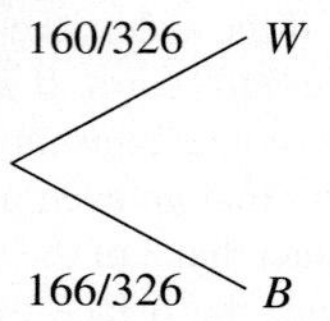

b. $\frac{160}{326}$ **c.** $\frac{166}{326}$

37.

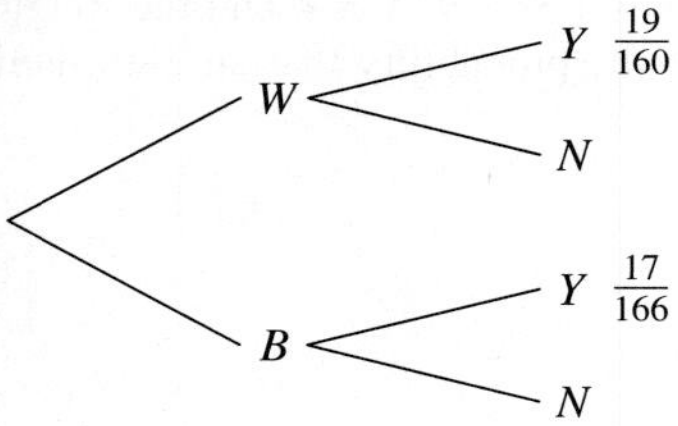

38.

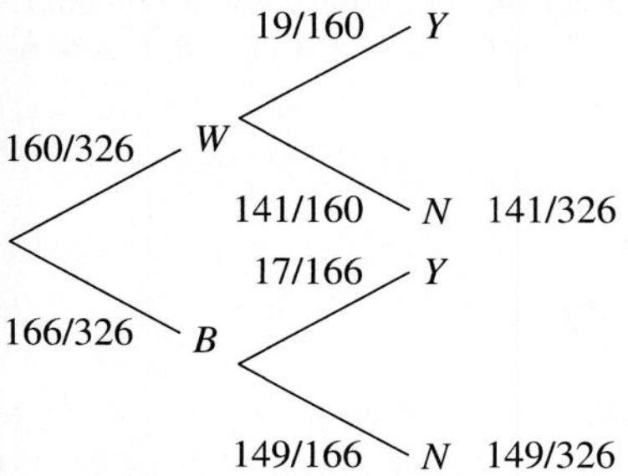

$\frac{290}{326} = \frac{145}{163}$

39. $\frac{141 + 149}{326} = \frac{290}{326} = \frac{145}{163}$ **40.** Yes

41. No. The coin is probably weighted to come up heads. Bet on heads.

42. Bet on heads. Coin is probably weighted to come up heads.

43. No. The coin is probably weighted to come up heads. Bet on heads.

44. a. Bet on heads. **b.** Don't bet. **c.** Bet on tails.

45. $\frac{C(40{,}000,150)\,C(36{,}000,150)}{C(76{,}000,300)}$ **46.** $\frac{C(160, 15)\,C(140, 15)}{C(300, 30)}$

47. $\frac{C(16, 6)\,C(14,6)}{C(30,12)}$

Collaborative Learning

Go to http://www.mste.uiuc.edu/reese/birthday/intro.html for some answers. If you assume N people are in a room, what is the smallest N such that there is at least probability 0.5 that M people have the same birthday? Assuming that the birthday distribution is uniform over 365 days, we have:

M	N	Probability
2	23	0.507297234324
2	22	0.475695307663
3	88	0.511065110625
3	87	0.499454850632
4	187	0.502685373189
4	186	0.495825706383

Exercises 11.3

1. 0; property 1

2. 1; property (4)

3. 1; property 2

4. 0; property (1)

5. $\frac{3}{5}$ **6.** $\frac{7}{10}$ **7.** 1 **8.** $\frac{7}{10}$ **9.** $\frac{7}{26}$ **10.** $\frac{1}{13}$

11. $\frac{1}{4}$ **12.** $\frac{1}{2}$ **13.** $\frac{3}{13}$ **14.** $\frac{8}{9}$ **15.** $\frac{41}{50}$ **16.** 0.20

17. 0.2 **18.** 0.90 **19.** 0.45 **20.** 1

21. a. $\frac{4438}{32{,}847}$ **b.** $\frac{7763}{98{,}983}$

22. a. $\frac{72{,}066}{97{,}147}$ **b.** $\frac{81{,}944}{98{,}466} = \frac{40{,}972}{49{,}233}$

23. a. $\frac{25{,}081}{97{,}147}$ **b.** $\frac{8261}{49{,}233}$

24. a. 0 **b.** 0 **25. a.** 1 **b.** 1

26. $\frac{17}{20}$ **27.** $\frac{11}{20}$ **28.** $\frac{13}{20}$ **29.** $\frac{4}{5}$ **30.** $\frac{1}{5}$ **31.** $\frac{13}{17}$

32. $\frac{59}{85}$

33. If the probability of an event is 0, then the event cannot occur.

34. If the probability of an event is 1, then the event is certain to occur.

35. If $P(A \cap B) = 0$, that is, A and B have no common elements, then $P(A \cup B) = P(A) + P(B)$.

36. An event is either possible or not possible. If the event is impossible, its probability is 0. If the event is possible, then the probability is a positive fraction not greater than 1. In any case, the probability cannot be negative.

37. About 0.83 **38.** About 0.84

39. Answers will vary.

40. $\frac{3}{5}$ **41.** $\frac{9}{10}$ **42.** $\frac{1}{10}$ **43.** $\frac{2}{5}$ **44.** $\frac{3}{10}$

45. $\frac{1}{5}$ **46.** $\frac{1}{20}$ **47.** $\frac{1}{20}$

Exercises 11.4

1. 0 **2.** 0 **3. a.** $\frac{1}{6}$ **b.** 0 **c.** 1 **d.** 0

4. a. 0 **b.** 1 **5.** $\frac{1}{2}$ **6. a.** $\frac{1}{4}$ **b.** 0 **7.** $\frac{1}{2}$

8. a. $\frac{20}{100000} = 0.0002$

b. $\frac{15}{100000} = 0.00015$

c. $\frac{150}{100000} = 0.0015$

9. a. $\frac{1}{5}$ **b.** $\frac{1}{3}$

10. a. 0.4 **b.** 0.2 **c.** 0.4

11. a. $\frac{17}{66}$ **b.** $\frac{49}{66}$ **c.** 17%

12. $\frac{1}{51}$ **13.** $\frac{1}{17}$ **14.** $\frac{4}{51}$ **15.** $\frac{1}{5}$ **16.** $\frac{3}{5}$

17. $\frac{P(A \cap B)}{P(A)} = \frac{2}{3}$ **18.** $\frac{2}{5}$

19. a. $\frac{3}{10}$ **b.** $\frac{39}{100}$

20. a. $\frac{168}{240} = \frac{7}{10}$ **b.** $\frac{244}{400} = \frac{61}{100}$

21. a. 44% **b.** 5%

22. a. $\frac{70}{108 + 144 + 124 + 110 + 95 + 70} = 11\%$

b. $\frac{108}{108 + 144 + 124 + 110 + 95 + 70} = 17\%$

23. a. $\frac{27}{40}$ **b.** $\frac{7}{10}$

24. a. 0.6 **b.** 0.1 **c.** $\frac{3}{7}$ **d.** $\frac{2}{3}$

25. $\frac{19}{160} \approx 0.119$ **26.** $\frac{17}{166} \approx 0.102$

27. No (only about 0.017)

28. $\frac{19}{151} \approx 0.126$ **29.** $\frac{11}{63} \approx 0.175$

30. $\frac{0}{9} = 0$ **31.** $\frac{6}{103} \approx 0.058$

32. Blacks get the death penalty more often, regardless of the race of the victim.

33. Answers will vary.

34. A: A die coming up an even number.
B: A die coming up 1, 2, 3, 4, 5, 6.
If A and B are independent events or if A is a subset of B and B is the universal set, then $P(A|B) = Pa$.

35. a. $\frac{75}{128}$ **b.** $\frac{53}{128}$ **c.** Male

36. a. $\frac{2}{3}$ **b.** $\frac{1}{3}$

37. $\frac{9}{53}$ **38.** $\frac{1}{15}$

Exercises 11.5

1. Yes

2. a. 0.25 **b.** 0.185 **c.** 0.0036 **d.** 0.0025 **e.** 0.022

3. a. $\frac{1}{96}$ **b.** $\frac{1}{48}$ **c.** $\frac{7}{16}$

4. a. 0.0833 **b.** 0.2646 **c.** $0.49 \cdot 0.54 + 0.17 \cdot 0.20 = 0.2986$

5. a. $\frac{1}{8}$ **b.** $\frac{1}{2}$ **c.** $\frac{7}{8}$

6. a. $\frac{1}{8}$ **b.** $\frac{1}{8}$ **c.** $\frac{1}{2}$

7. a. $\frac{1}{4}$ **b.** $\frac{1}{4}$ **c.** $\frac{1}{16}$ **d.** $\frac{9}{16}$

8. a. $\frac{1}{4}$ **b.** $\frac{1}{4}$ **c.** $\frac{1}{17}$ **d.** $\frac{19}{34}$

9. a. $\frac{1}{2}$ **b.** $\frac{3}{4}$ **c.** $\frac{3}{8}$ **d.** They are independent.

10. a. $\frac{4}{663}$ **b.** $\frac{1}{221}$ **c.** $\frac{188}{221}$ **d.** $\frac{32}{221}$

11. $\frac{5}{108}$ **12.** $\frac{2}{81}$ **13.** $\frac{25}{324}$ **14.** $\frac{7}{9}$ **15.** $\frac{25}{36}$

16. $\frac{1}{19}$ **17.** $\frac{9}{76}$ **18.** $\frac{21}{38}$ **19.** $\frac{9}{380}$ **20.** $\frac{26}{95}$

21. $\frac{28}{625}$ **22.** $\frac{16}{625}$ **23.** $\frac{289}{625}$ **24.** $\frac{33}{125}$ **25.** $\frac{301}{625}$

26. 0.068921 **27.** 0.205379 **28.** 0.017794

29. 0.636056 **30.** Health care

31. a. $\frac{1}{12}$ **b.** $\frac{1}{8}$ **32.** $\frac{5}{12}$

33. a. $\frac{1}{4}$ **b.** $\frac{1}{12}$ **c.** $\frac{1}{4}$

34. a. Yes **b.** Yes

35. About 0.86597 **36.** About 0.6988 **37.** About 0.59

38. A and B are independent.

39. a. $\frac{1}{8000}$ **b.** $\frac{57}{8000}$ **40.** 0.18

41. a. 0.2126; 0.2409 **b.** AL **c.** 0.00204; 0.00337

42. a. $\frac{2}{3}$ **b.** $\frac{2}{3}$ **c.** $\frac{8}{27}$ **43.** $\frac{1}{2}$

44. I(A, A), II(0, 0), III(A, 0)

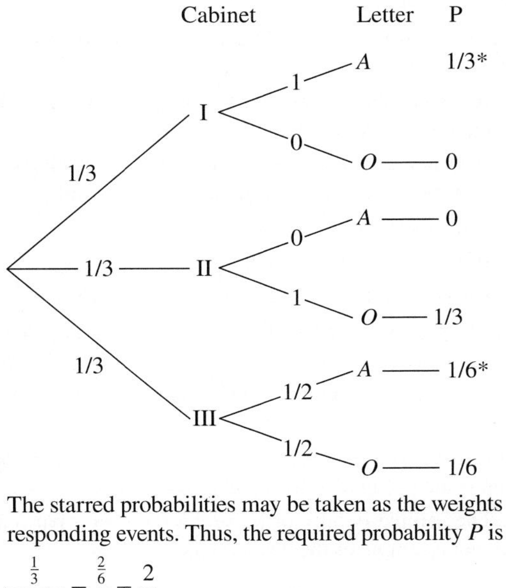

The starred probabilities may be taken as the weights for the corresponding events. Thus, the required probability P is given by:

$$\frac{\frac{1}{3}}{\frac{1}{3} + \frac{1}{6}} = \frac{\frac{2}{6}}{\frac{3}{6}} = \frac{2}{3}.$$

45. $\frac{3}{5}$ (*Hint:* Draw a tree and use the final probabilities as weights for the two possibilities.)

46.

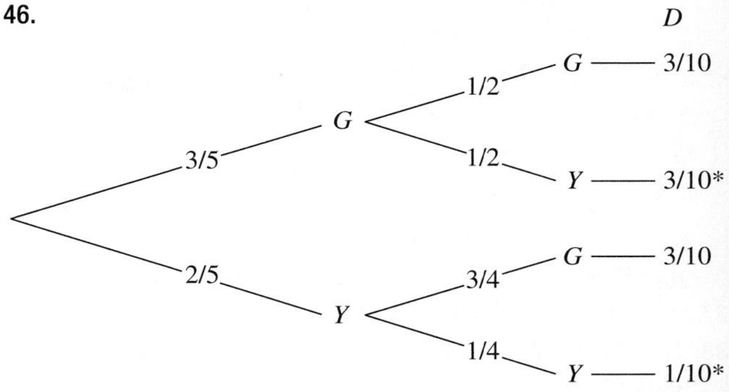

As in problem 44, the starred probabilities may be taken as the weights for the corresponding events. Thus, the probability P is;

$$\frac{\frac{3}{10}}{\frac{3}{10} + \frac{1}{10}} = \frac{\frac{3}{10}}{\frac{4}{10}} = \frac{3}{4}.$$

47. a. The probability of one of the events does not depend on the probability of the other event, or the occurrence of one of the events does not affect the occurrence of the other event.
b. Find the product $P(A)P(B)$.

48. Based on this information, the probability that a hurricane in the Atlantic basin hits the United States was $\frac{0}{12} = 0$. If you assume these probabilities hold for next year, the probability of at least one hurricane in the Atlantic basin hitting the United States is $1 -$ probability none hitting $= 1 - 0 = 1$

49. $\frac{C(50, 25)}{2^{50}}$

50. $\frac{C(6, 3)C(6, 4)C(6, 5)C(6, 6)}{2^6} = \frac{21}{32}$

51. $1 - [C(6, 0)(\frac{1}{3})^6 + C(6, 1)(\frac{1}{3})^5(\frac{2}{3}) + C(6, 2)(\frac{1}{3})^4(\frac{2}{3})^2] = \frac{656}{729}$

52. Probability gets less and less.

53. $C(5, 2)(\frac{1}{6})^2(\frac{5}{6})^3 = \frac{625}{3888}$

54. $1 - C(5, 1)(\frac{1}{6})(\frac{5}{6})^4 - C(5, 0)(\frac{5}{6})^5 = \frac{763}{3888} \approx 0.196$

55. 0.02 **56.** 0.0004 **57.** 0.000008

58. 99.9992% reliable

Exercises 11.6

1. 1 to 5 **2.** 1 to 1 **3.** 1 to 12 **4.** 1 to 1

5. 1 to 3 **6.** 3 to 1 **7.** 5 to 21 **8.** 5 to 1

9. 1 to 1 **10.** 51 to 1 **11.** 10 to 3 **12.** 1 to 3

13. $C(6, 3) \cdot C(47, 3)/C(53, 6) = \frac{32430}{2295748}$; 32,430 to 2,263,318

14. $\frac{C(6, 4)C(47, 2)}{C(53, 6)} = \frac{3243}{4, 591, 496}$
3243 : 4, 588, 253

15. $\frac{3}{5}$ **16.** 1 to 19 **17.** $\frac{63}{10,000}$; 63 to 9937 **18.** $\frac{1}{5}$

19. 1 to 1 **20.** 1 to 3 **21.** $\frac{10}{4877}$ **22.** $\frac{41}{50}$ **23.** $\frac{1}{8}$

24. 19 to 81 **25.** 33 to 67 **26.** 50 cents **27.** $-\$5$

28. \$3.50 **29. a.** \$495.30 **b.** \$495.30 **c.** \$41.28

30. a. \$2139.60 **b.** \$2139.60 **c.** \$260.40

31. 4.125 **32.** 5.8125

33. Build at the first location and make \$50,000.

34. a. \$14,000 **b.** \$25,000 **c.** Discontinue the campaign

35. a. $-\$4000$ **b.** \$10,000 **c.** Discontinue the campaign.

36.

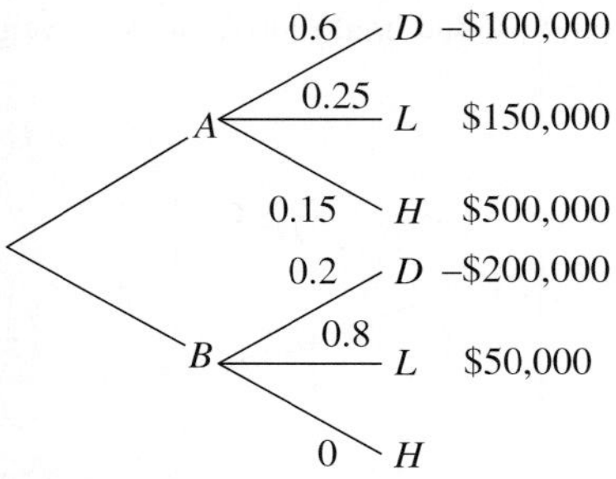

a. \$52,500 **b.** 0 **c.** Site A

37. a. \$200 **b.** \$450 **c.** B

38. If the odds in favor of an event are p to q, then the probability of the event is $\frac{p}{p+q}$.

39. The mathematical expectation is that you lose \$.58 per \$2 bet.

40. Need to know the gain or loss that depends on how the problem is decided and need to know the odds (or the probability) for the gain or loss.

41. a. About 0.81 **b.** About 0.19

42. a. 4 to 1 **b.** 1 to 4

43. Odds against you are 9 to 1, so put up \$1 for each \$9. Thus, you should bet $(\frac{1}{9})(\$10)$, or about \$1.11, to make the bet fair.

44. The probability of a black number is $\frac{18}{38}$, of a red number is $\frac{18}{38}$, and of either 0 or 00 is $\frac{2}{38}$. If 0 or 00 turns up, then the player gets his money back (but gains nothing) if a black number comes up next and loses his \$1 if a red number comes up next. Thus, the expected value is

$$E = 1 \cdot \tfrac{18}{38} - 1 \cdot \tfrac{18}{38} + 0 \cdot \tfrac{2}{38} \cdot \tfrac{18}{38} - 1 \cdot \tfrac{2}{38} \cdot \tfrac{18}{38}$$
$$= -\$1 \cdot \frac{9}{19 \cdot 19} \approx -0.025.$$

45. If the ball stops on red or black, you break even. If the ball stops on 0 or 00 and then on red or black, you lose 50¢. Thus, the expected value is $-(50)(\frac{2}{38})(\frac{36}{38}) = -\frac{\$9}{361} \approx -2.5¢$.

Collaborative Learning

1. 0 **2.** 0.29 **3.** Answers will vary.

4. 0.60 **5.** 0.40 **6.** Answers will vary.

7–10. Answers will vary (see below).

NOTE: The probability of winning the lottery varies, depending on the number of balls used in the drawing and how many balls you have to guess. For the sake of argument, suppose there are 40 balls (numbers) in your state and it takes 6 correct numbers to win. The probability that you win is $\frac{1}{C(40,6)} = \frac{1}{3,838,380} \approx 0.0000002605$. The probability that you win with 50 dollars is $\frac{50}{C(40,6)} = 0.0000130263288\ldots$

The probability of winning *at least once* in 50 tries is the same as the probability of *not losing* 50 times in a row.

The probability of *losing* is $1 - 0.0000002605\ldots = 0.9999997394\ldots$

The probability of *losing* 50 *times in a row* is 0.9999997394. . . to the 50th power or 0.99998697. . .

The probability of *not losing* 50 *times in a row* is $1 - 0.99998697\ldots = 0.0000130262457\ldots$

Note that this is the probability of winning at least once in 50 tries.

So, since the probability of winning at least once in 50 tries is 0.0000130262457. . . and the probability of winning one lottery with 50 dollars is 0.0000130263288. . ., the odds are very slightly more favorable by playing all 50 dollars in one lottery than spreading it out among 50 lotteries.

You can see the whole discussion at: http://members.cox.net/mathmistakes/rawdata.htm.

Author's Note. Is it possible that the small discrepancy is due to rounding? Does it matter what numbers you select? Discuss.

CHAPTER 12

Exercises 12.1

1. Descriptive statistics is the science of collecting, organizing, and summarizing data.

2. Inferential statistics is the science of drawing conclusions from an organized set of data.

3. A sample population usually consists of just a part of the target population.

4. a. The 116 million U.S. households with a TV set
b. The households that agree to use the NPM

5. a. All households in the United States
b. The 1006 households surveyed

6. a. All the colleges of the nation.
b. The 50 colleges in the sample from whom the students took information.

7. a. No
b. The sample includes only those viewers who are willing to pay for the call.

8. a. Adults in the United States
b. The 1015 adults interviewed **c.** No

9. a. Make a card for each student, number the cards, and mix them up. Then draw 10 cards at random and select the corresponding students. Answers may vary.
b. Make a card for each student, number the cards, and do any of the following:
i. Pick only even-numbered cards.
ii. Pick only odd-numbered cards.
iii. Don't mix the cards and pick the first 10.

10. a. The 50,000 households
b. The 120 million total households

11. a. All TV watchers
b. People who visit the Web site and are willing to participate in the survey
c. No. Respondents do not necessarily represent the target population (all TV watchers).

12. a. No. The sample surveys students at the bookstore and would probably not include those who bought books online.
b. The students at the school.
c. The students at the bookstore.
d. No. Some students may not go to the bookstore.

13. Although both surveys ultimately had 50 responses, the second survey should produce more accurate results because $\frac{50}{75} \approx 67\%$ of the people responded compared with only $\frac{50}{100} \approx 50\%$ for the first survey.

14. a. The target population is all Americans. The sample population is the group of constituents surveyed.
b. No. The sample is only of those who live in a particular area, not a sample of the whole United States.

15. a. Attended a football game last year?

Y	720
N	160
NR	120
Total	1000

b. So the total will add to 1000

16.

Y	72%
N	16%
NR	12%

17. a.

Number of Hours	*Tally Marks*	*Frequency*
0	|	1
1	|	1
2	|||	3
3	|||	3
4	|||	3
5	|||	3
6	||||	4
7	||	2

b. 6 **c.** 6; $\frac{6}{20} = 30\%$ **d.** 14; $\frac{14}{20} = 70\%$

18. a.

Number of Hours	*Tally Marks*	*Frequency*
0	|	1
1	|	1
2	|	1
3	||	2
4	|	1
5	|||	3
6	||	2
7	|	1
8	|	1
9	|	1
10	||	2
11	|||	3
12	||||	4
13	||||	4
14	||	2
15	|	1

b. 12 and 13 hours **c.** 11; $\frac{11}{30} = 36.7\%$ **d.** 9; 30%

19. a.

Outcome	*Tally Marks*	*Frequency*
1	卌 卌 |	11
2	||	2
3	卌 |	6
4	||	2
5	卌 |||	8
6	|	1

b. The 1; 11 **c.** The 6; 1

20. a.

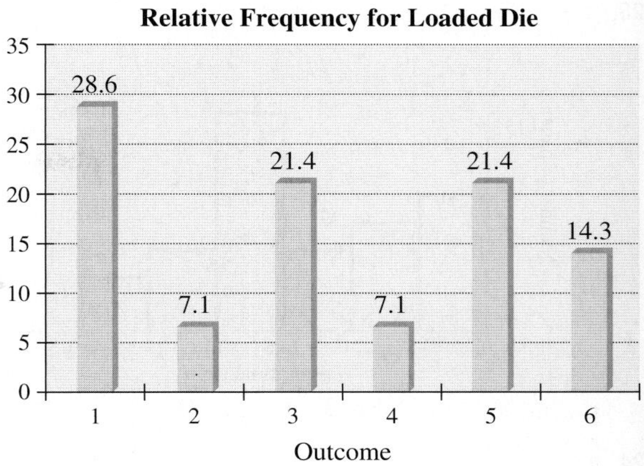

b. 28.6% **c.** 7.1%

d. You can only if you know the total number of outcomes.

21. a.

Number of Hours	*Tally Marks*	*Frequency*
0	||	2
1	|||	3
2	||	2
3	|||	3
4	|||	3
5	||	2
6	||	2
7	||	2
8	||||	4
9	|	1
10	||	2
11		0
12	||	2
13		0
14	|	1
15	|	1

b. 8 **c.** 4 **d.** 15 **e.** About 36.7%

22.

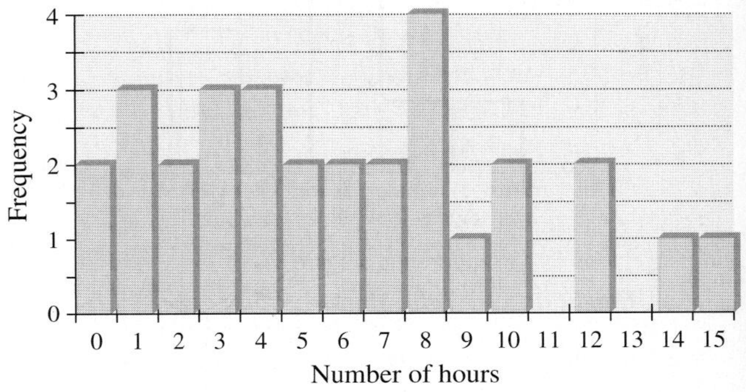

23. a.

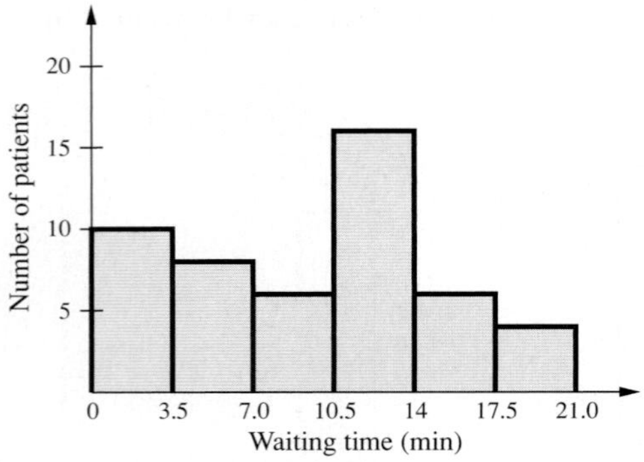

b. 36% **c.** 52%

24. a.

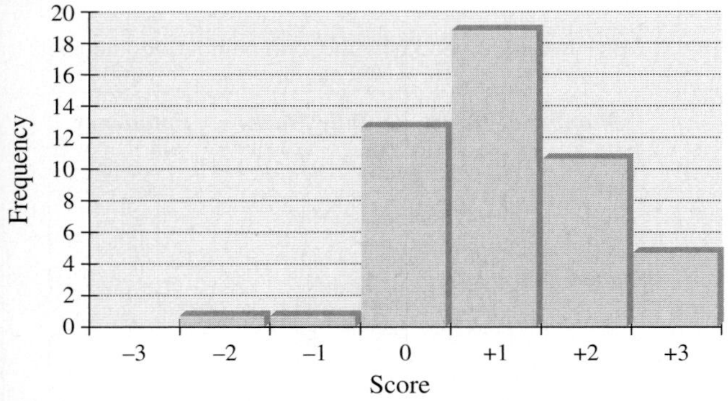

b. 70% **c.** 26%

25. a.

Age	*Tally Marks*	*Frequency*
6	|	1
7	|	1
8	|||	3
9	|||	3
10	||	2

b.

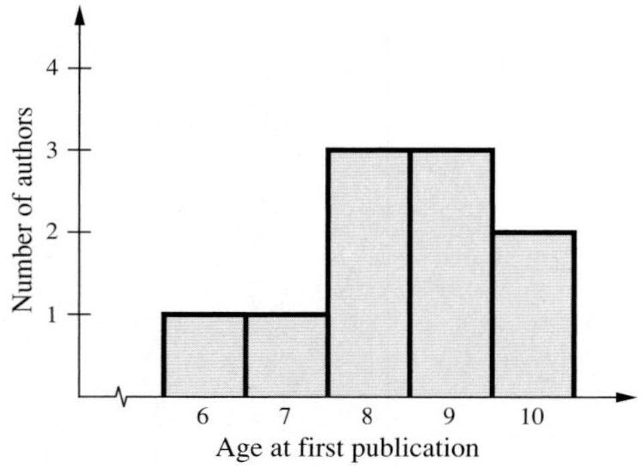

c. 20%

26. a.

Height (in.)	*Tally Marks*	*Frequency*
62	|||	3
63	||	2
64	||	2
65	|	1
66	||	2

b.

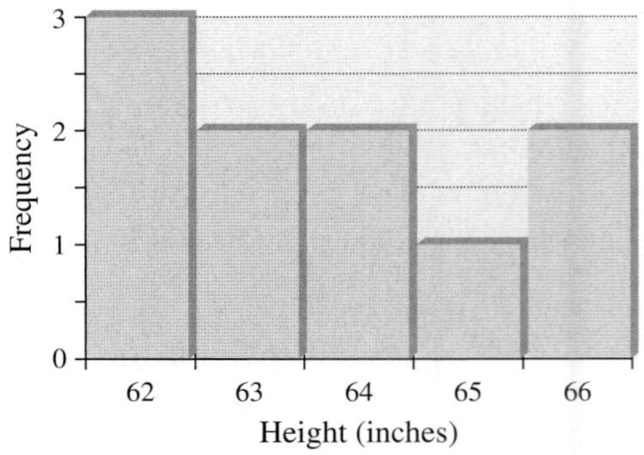

27. a.

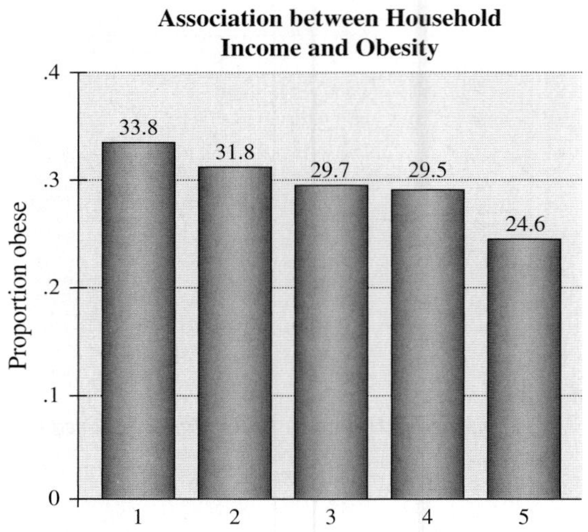

b. 1 **c.** 24.6%

d. As household income *increases*, the percent of obese people *decreases*.

28. a.

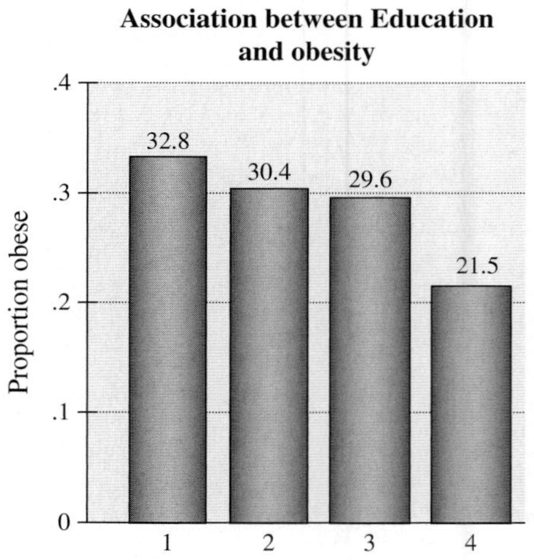

b. 1 **c.** 29.6%

d. As the level of schooling *increases*, the percent of obese people *decreases*.

29.

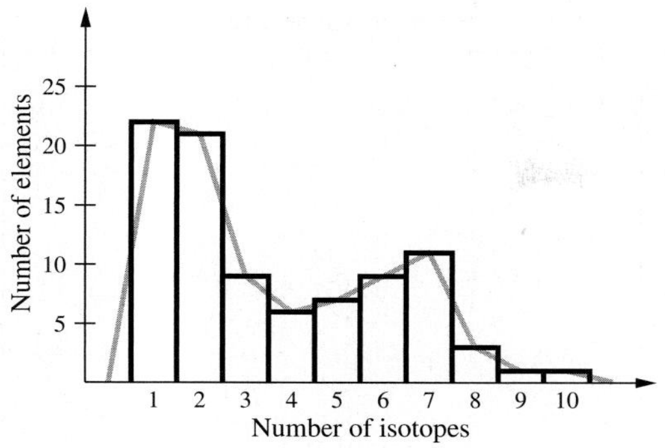

30. a.

Inches	*Tally Marks*	*Frequency*
0.245	|	1
0.246	|	1
0.247	||	2
0.248	|	1
0.249	||||	4
0.250	||	2
0.251	||||	4
0.252	||	2
0.253	||	2
0.254	|	1

b. 0.250 in. **c.** 50%

d. 0.250 because it is the median ("average").

31. a.

Letter	*Frequency*	*Letter*	*Frequency*
a	10	n	13
b	4	o	14
c	3	p	2
d	4	q	0
e	18	r	7
f	2	s	10
g	3	t	17
h	9	u	5
i	12	v	2
j	0	w	5
k	1	x	0
l	4	y	2
m	4	z	0

b. e **c.** About 39.1%

32.

No. of Heads	*Tally Marks*	*Frequency*
0	||	2
1	~~||||~~ |||	8
2	~~||||~~ ~~||||~~ ||	12
3	~~||||~~ |||	8
4	||	2

33.

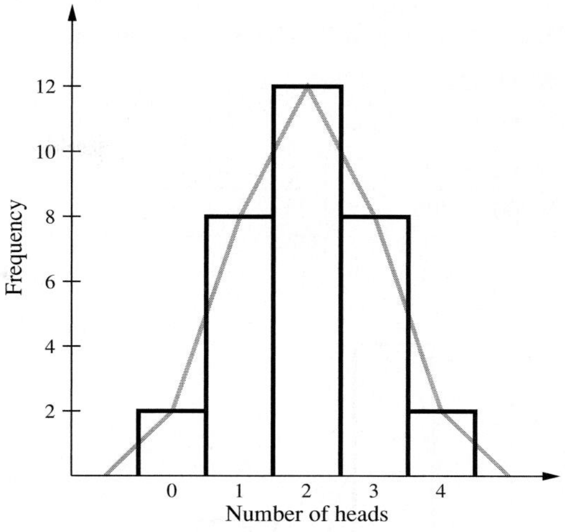

34.

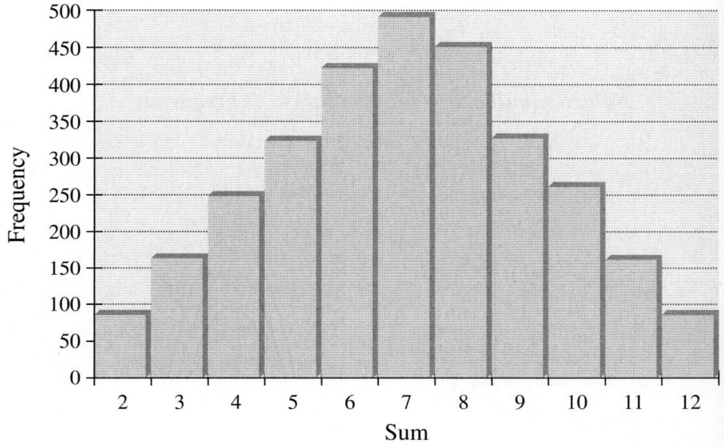

35. a.

Concentration	*Tally Marks*	*Frequency*
0.00–0.04	~~||||~~ |	6
0.05–0.09	~~||||~~ ~~||||~~ |||	13
0.10–0.14	~~||||~~	5
0.15–0.19	||||	4
0.20–0.24	||	2

b. 20% **c.** 56.7%

36.

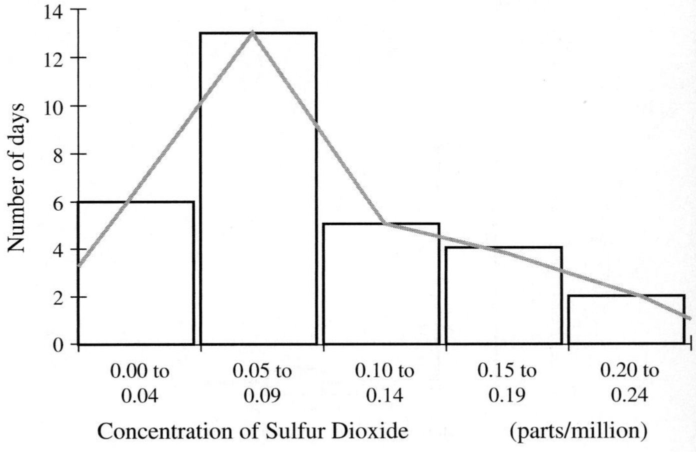

37. a.

Weekly Salary	*Tally Marks*	*Frequency*
$600–$2400	𝍸 𝍷𝍷𝍷𝍷	9
$2400–$4200		0
$4200–$6000	𝍷𝍷	2
$6000–$7800	𝍷	1

b.

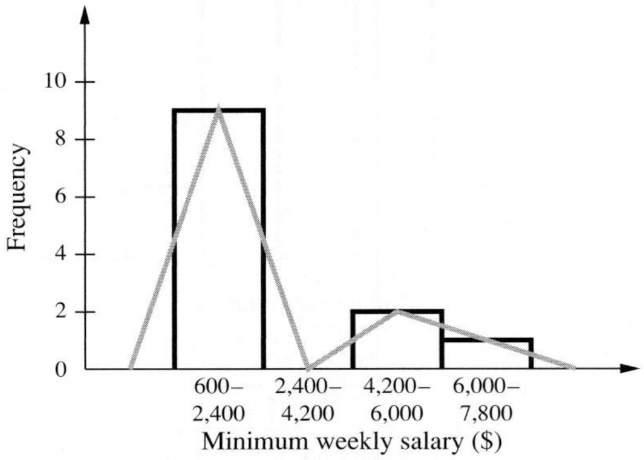

38. a.

Salaries (millions)	*Tally Marks*	*Frequency*
$7^+ - 8$	𝍸	5
$8^+ - 9$	𝍸	5
$9^+ - 10$	𝍷𝍷𝍷	3
$10^+ - 11$	𝍷𝍷	2

b.

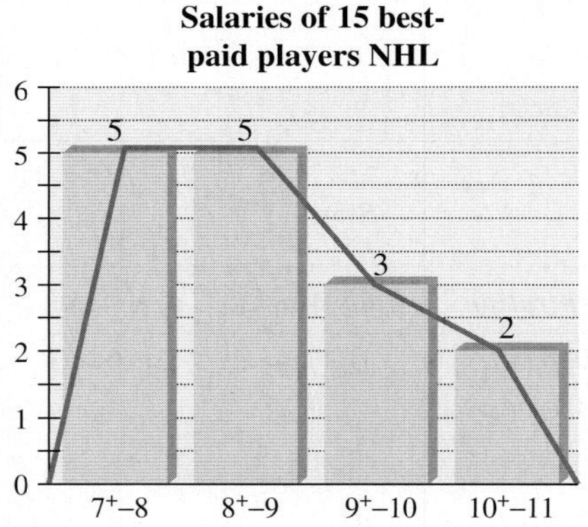

39. a.

Salary (X 1000)	*Tally Marks*	*Frequency*
$20–$34	𝍸 𝍸 𝍸 𝍸	20
$34–$48	𝍷	1
$48–$62	𝍷	1
$62–$76	𝍷𝍷	2
$76–$90	𝍷	1

b.

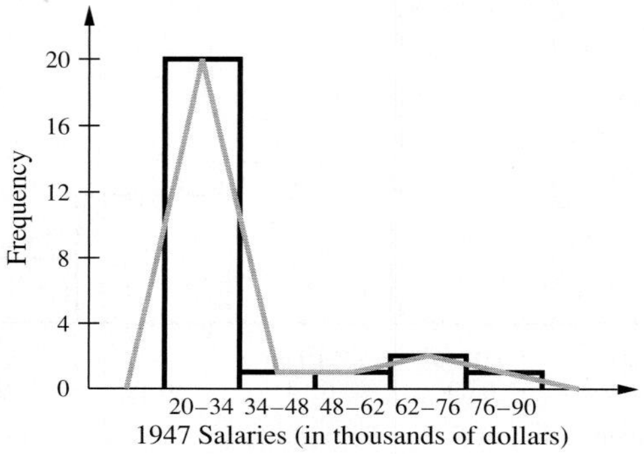

40. a.

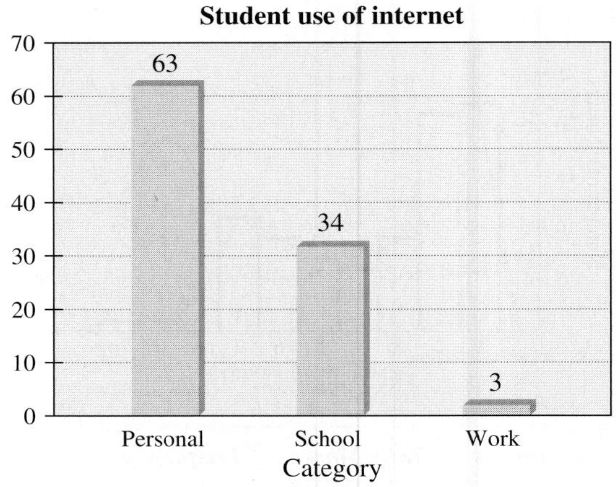

b.

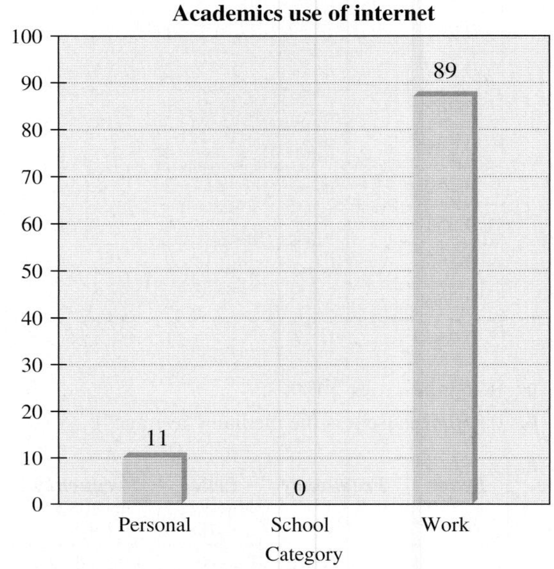

c. Work. Students rarely use the internet for work.

d. Work. Academics use the Internet mostly for work.

41. a. $74

b.

Price	*Tally Marks*	*Frequency*
$180–$254	𝍸	5
$254–$328	𝍸 𝍷𝍷	7
$328–$402		0
$402–$476	𝍷	1
$476–$550	𝍷𝍷	2

c.

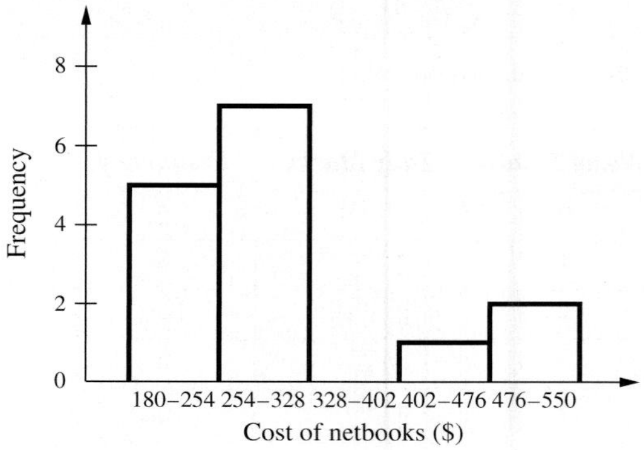

42. a. Class width is $7 million.

b.

Loss (millions)	*Tally Marks*	*Frequency*
14 – 21	𝍸 ||	7
21 – 28	||	2
28 – 35	|	1

c.

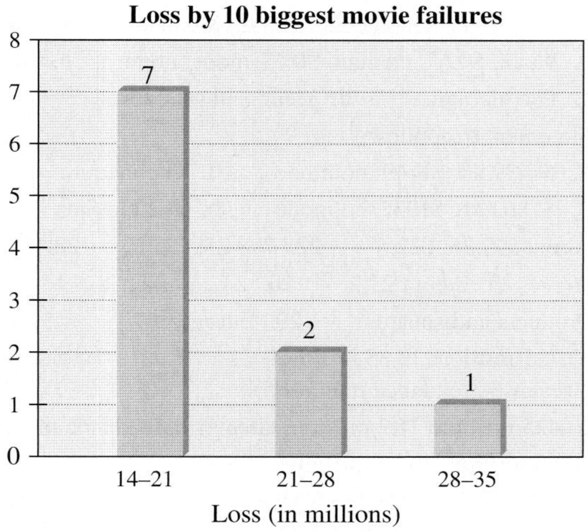

43. a. 2 years

b.

Age	*Tally Marks*	*Frequency*
115–117	𝍸 𝍸 𝍸 ||||	19
117–119	||||	4
119–121	|	1
121–123	|	1

c.

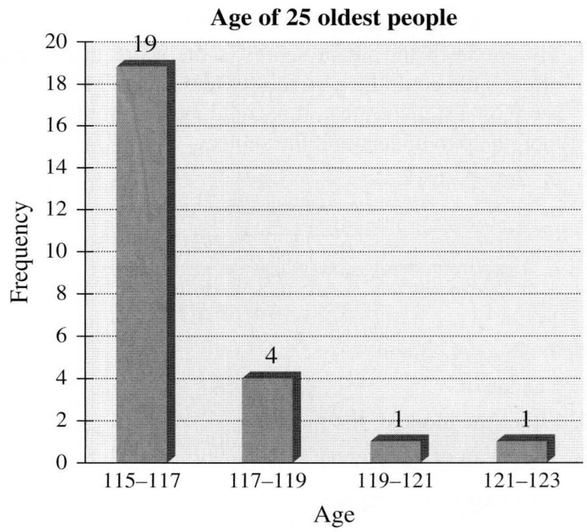

44. Tract 1305 **45.** Tract 1304

46. Tract 1304 **47.** Tract 1305

48. a. 200 **b.** 1 **c.** 0.5%

49. No. The women were not selected at random.

50. They only surveyed Midway travelers.

51. No. Not all members of the population had the same chance of being chosen.

52. This is done so that there will be no space between adjacent bars.

53. The upper and lower class limits, respectively, are the least and the greatest values in that class. Each class boundary is the midpoint between the upper limit of the respective class and the lower limit of the next class.

54. $130 + 123 = 253 \neq 200$ Somebody can't count!

55.

Digit	*Frequency*
0	1
1	4
2	5
3	6
4	4
5	4
6	3
7	3
8	5
9	5

56. Most frequent digit is 3. Least frequent digit is 0.

57. Yes. 100,271

58. About 3.2%

59. Yes. In each case, most of the bar is omitted.

60. a. It can be either frequencies or relative frequencies. The y-axis needs to start at 0, so that the bars are not distorted.

b. About 13%

c. They could be very close; the Democrats could be lower, and the Republicans could be higher.

d. Start the y-axis at zero, not 53.

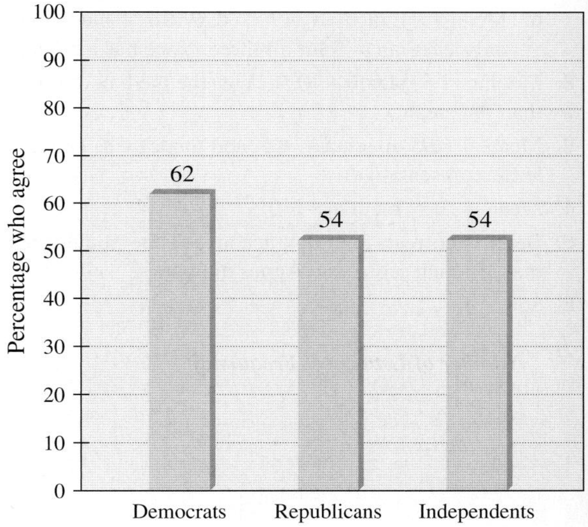

Collaborative Learning

1. Answers will vary.

2. Answers will vary.

3. Makeup and deodorant

4. No. There is space between bars. The figure is a bar graph. It makes no difference.

5.
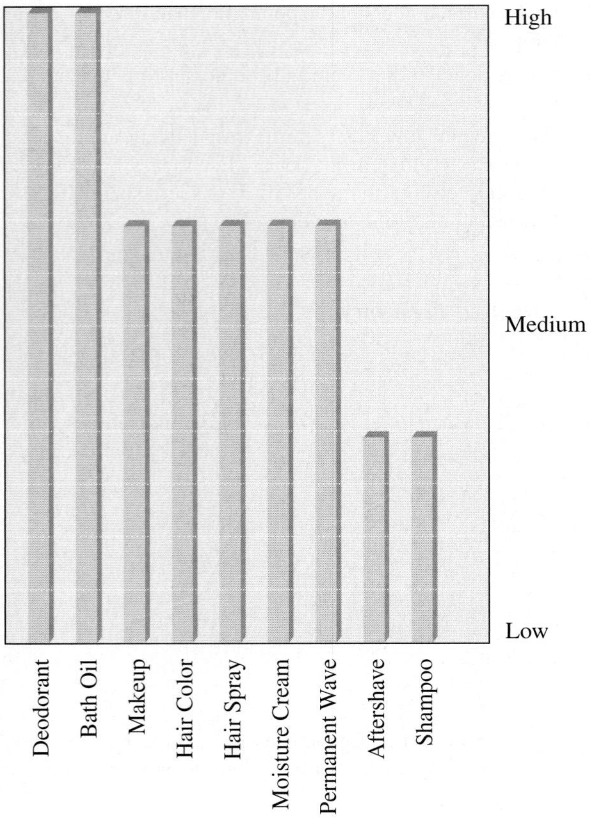

Exercises 12.2

1. **a.** Mean = 9; median = 9 **b.** Mean = 24.2; median = 9 **c.** Mean = 11; median = 9 **d.** Mean = median for part (**a**) only. Median = 9 for all three. None has a mode.
2. Median = 6. Mean = 10.5. Thus, the median of this set is less than the mean.
3. Mean = 6.05, median = 6.5, and mode = 8. The mode is the least representative.
4. Mean = 51.6, median = 60
5. Betty is correct. She took account of the number of students making each score, and Agnes did not.
6. $60
7.

Number of Letters	*Frequency*
2	1
3	5
4	4
5	5
6	0
7	3
8	2
9	0
10	0
11	1

a. 3 and 5 **b.** 5 **c.** 5.05
d. No. There is too much repetition.

8. **a.** $\bar{x} = 77.3$, median = 75 **b.** $\bar{x} = 87.9$, median = 90 **c.** $\bar{x} = 67.4$, median = 66
9. **b.–c.** Answers will vary, but should be approximately 8.
10. 1500 **11.** 60 **12.** 80 **13.** $84 per week **14.** 40
15. **a.** 0.34 **b.** $20,000–$24,999 **c.** $39,444 **d.** $20,000
16. **a.** Mean: $4.61; median: $4.41; mode: none **b.** No **c.** The median **d.** Mean and median
17. **a.** Mean: $0.67, median: $0.75, mode: none **b.** No **c.** The median **d.** Mean and Median
18. Statement **d.** applies.
19. **a.** $1439.80; $1449; no mode **b.** The median
20. **a.** $1862.40, $1935, no mode **b.** The median
21. About 577.25; 622.5 **22.** 798.25; 755.5 **23.** 20.6
24. 16 **25.** About 22.2 **26.** 24 **27.** 28
28. Products and spiritual **29.** Internet
30. 13.725 million; 13.35 million
Greater (Attendance increased)
31. 13.425 million; 14.2 million; Greater (attendance increased)
32. 10.85 million; 10.95 million
Smaller (Attendance decreased)
33. 9.5 million; 9.75 million; Greater (attendance increased)
34. 8.25 million; 8.2 million
Smaller (Attendance decreased)
35. 475 million **36.** 2.85 million
37. **a.** 43,216.40; $40,827; none **b.** Median
38. mean = $21,710.80; median = $21,611; no mode
39. The median of a set of scores is the middle number (if there is one) when the scores are arranged in order of magnitude. If there is no middle number, the median is the average of the two middle numbers. The median is not a good measure of a set of scores as it gives no indication of how the scores are spread.
40. The mode of the set of scores is the score that occurs most often. This could be a good measure. If the mode is a failing score on a statistics test, this could mean that the class needed more help to understand the subject.
41. **a.** 2.4 **b.** 2
42. **a.**

		E	*F*	
		D	*E*	*F*
A	*B*	*C*	*D*	*E*
1	2	3	4	5

b. 2 **c.** 3 and 4
43. The mean
44. Either the mode or the median
45. The mean of a secretary's and a worker's salaries

Collaborative Learning

	RACE	SEX
1.	29,764.6	24,900.2
2.	31,182.6	26,735.6
3.	$36.42 million	$46.26 million

Exercises 12.3

1. **a.** 18 **b.** 7.21 **2. a.** 24 **b.** About 9.67
3. **a.** 20 **b.** 7.91 **4. a.** 12 **b.** About 4.74
5. **a.** 4 **b.** 1.58 **6. a.** 8 **b.** About 3.16

7. a. 8 **b.** 3.11 **8. a.** 10 **b.** About 3.55
9. a. 6 **b.** 2.16 **10. a.** 12 **b.** About 4.32
11. a. 8 **b.** 6.5 **c.** 6 **d.** 3.23 **e.** 70% **f.** 100%
12. a. 8 **b.** 8 **c.** About 7.31
d. About 1.96 **e.** 68.75% **f.** 100%
13. a. 110 **b.** 110 **c.** 108
d. 3.71 **e.** 102, 103, 113; 30%
14. a. 110 **b.** 108 **c.** 107
d. About 3.42 **e.** 102, 103, 25%
15. Range 15, mean 7, standard deviation $\sqrt{30} \approx 5.48$
16. Range: 14; Mean: 37
Standard Deviation ≈ 5.03
17. Range 9, mean 7, standard deviation $\sqrt{10} \approx 3.16$
18. Range: 49: Mean ≈ 45.17;
Standard Deviation ≈ 13.60
19. \$80, \$390, 0, \$89, \$77
20. \$110; \$300; \$215; \$103.50; \$106.50
21. \$167 **22. a.** \$87.94 **b.** 80% **c.** 100%
23. \$14 **24.** About \$32.19 **25.** \$6.30
26. a. 80% **b.** 100%
27. The numbers are all the same. If zero is the standard deviation, then $(x - \bar{x})^2 = 0$ for all x in the set.
28. Answers will vary.
29. Choose the numbers 1, 1, 5, and 5 (remember, repetitions are allowed). The mean of these numbers is 3, and 1, 1, 5, and 5 are as far from the mean 3 (2 units) as possible.
30. For the first class, $x + s = 80$, $x + 2s = 85$, so the probability of scores ≥ 90 is very small. For the second class, $x + s = 85$, $x + 2s = 100$, so we would expect several scores ≥ 90.
31. 5 **32.** 2; more than 12 **33.** About 8.66
34. The standard deviation stays the same because the differences from the mean will remain the same.
35. If you multiply each data point by 1.1 (100% + 10% = 1.1), it increases the spread of the points by a factor of 1.1. For example, two employees making \$64,000 and \$44,000 are now \$20,000 apart. When each gets a 10% raise, they are $1.1 \times 64{,}000 - 1.1 \times 44{,}000 = 1.1 \times (64{,}000 - 44{,}000)$, or \$22,000, apart.

Collaborative Learning

1. 25%; 5.9%; 83.2% **2.** 40.5% (using 86, 7, 5, and 3)
3. 75% **4.** 100%

Exercises 12.4

1. a. \$19,310 **b.** \$574 **c.** 34%
2. a. 16% **b.** 2.5% **c.** 0.025 = 2.5%
d. No. If the distribution is normal, we would expect only 16% to have incomes over \$50,000.
3. a. 25 **b.** 25 **c.** 680
4. a. 680 **b.** 25 **c.** 180
5. A, 12 or 13; B, 67 or 68; C, 340; D, 67 or 68; F, 12 or 13
6. a. 16%; 3180 **b.** 2.5%; 497 **c.** 16% **d.** \$17,163
7. 5 **8.** From \$23,800 to \$26,200
9. 19 ft 10.5 in. and 20 ft 1.5 in.
10. a. 40 and 60 **b.** 68% **c.** More than 65
11. The purchasing director will decide to buy. If the lifetimes are normally distributed, $2\frac{1}{2}$% will last 40 or more days. Thus, of the 8000, about 200 will last 40 or more days.
12. a. 8 **b.** 42 **c.** 320 **d.** 380
13. The student who scored 635 on the S.A.T. has the higher score relative to the test.
14. 16.15 oz
15. a. 10 **b.** 5 **c.** 40 **d.** 65 **e.** 60; 30 **f.** 75; 60
16. a. 34% **b.** 71.5% **c.** 100%
17. 16.15 oz **18. a.** 160 lb **b.** 150 lb **19.** 90
20. 0 **21. a.** 0.8 **b.** 1.6 **c.** 2
22. 0.2996 rounded to 0.3 **23.** The German test score
24. The Spanish test score was the better. **25.** 47.7%
26. 0.34 = 34% **27.** 62.9% **28.** 9 minutes
29. a. 0.249 **b.** 0.477 **30.** About 0.816
31. a. 0.998 **b.** 0.004
32. a. About 0.452 **b.** About 0.909 **33.** 0.228
34. About 0.011 **35.** Taller than 69.4 in. or about 5 ft $9\frac{1}{2}$ in.
36. (10 + 2490) or 2500
37. 1 indicates that \$4400 is 1 standard deviation above the mean, \$4200.
38. −2; \$3800 is 2 standard deviations below the mean.
39. Between 7.25 and 8.75 oz
40. a. About 0.067 **b.** About 0.067 or 6.7% of the time
41. 44.5%
42. At least 50% of the students scored less than you did.
43. 100 and 120 gal **44.** 90 and 130; About 84.3 and 134.7
45. 50% **46.** 50% **47.** 34% **48.** 68%
49. 0.067, or 6.7% **50.** 50 − 49.9 = 0.01 or 1%
51. Yes. See Figure 12.14 on page 708. In this figure both curves have the mean 0. The standard deviation for A is $\frac{1}{3}$ unit, while that for B is 1 unit.
52. Yes. Each item of the second set could be some constant greater than the corresponding item of the first set. In this case, the mean for the second set would be greater than the mean for the first set, but the standard deviations would be equal.
53. No. If curve A in Figure 12.14 on page 708 is moved 2 units to the right, this would be an example. The standard deviation for A would be $\frac{1}{3}$ unit and that for B would be 1 unit, while the mean for A would be 2 and that for B would be 0.
54. A z-score is the number of standard deviations that the corresponding score is from the mean.
55. 80th **56.** 88.75
57. a. 20th **b.** 60th **c.** 90th **d.** 0th
58. 50% of the scores were less than 90, and 10% of the scores were less than 30. So 40% of the scores were between 30 and 90 (with the 30 included but not the 90).
59. a. 75 **b.** 89 **c.** 49
60. a. $h = 5$ **b.** $h = \frac{10}{3}$ **c.** $h = \frac{5}{3}$
61. $\bar{x} = 6$; $s \approx 4.77$. Three lie within 1 standard deviation from the mean, and all nine lie within 2 standard deviations from the mean. The theorem makes no prediction for 1 standard deviation; it predicts 75% for 2 standard deviations.

62. No. Suppose that $|x_n - \bar{x}|$ is the largest deviation and that $\sigma > |x_n - \bar{x}|$. Then,
$$n\sigma^2 > n|x_n - \bar{x}|^2 \geq |x_1 - \bar{x}|^2 + |x_2 - \bar{x}|^2 + \ldots + |x_n - \bar{x}|^2$$
which is the contradiction because $n\sigma^2$ is exactly this last sum.

63. No. It cannot exceed 25%.

Collaborative Learning

3. 100 **4.** 10 **5.** 2 **6.** −2 **7.** 68%; 50%; yes

8. 0.005 = 0.5%; 5%; Yes

Exercises 12.5

1.

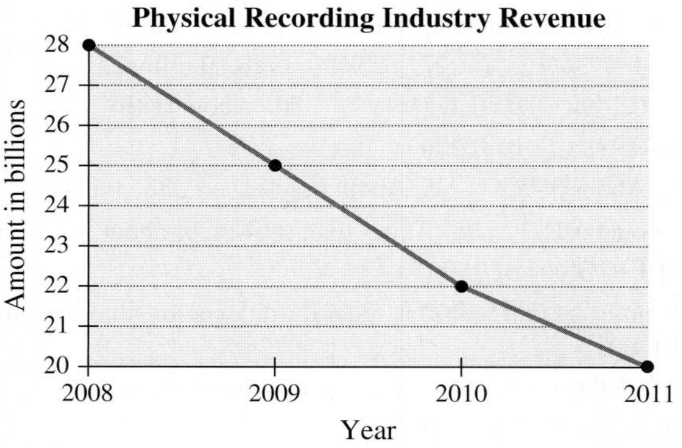

2.

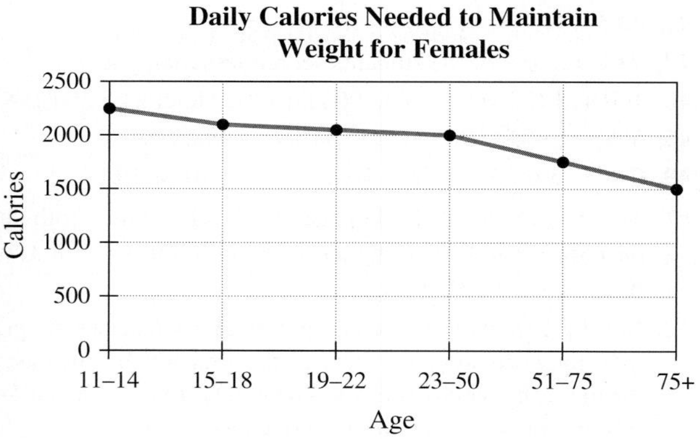

3.

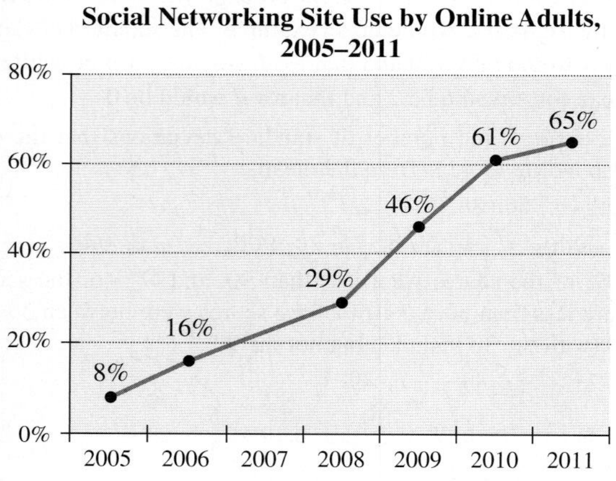

4.

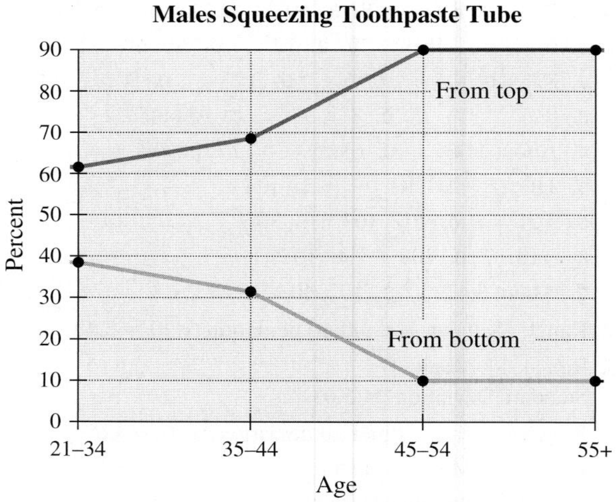

5.

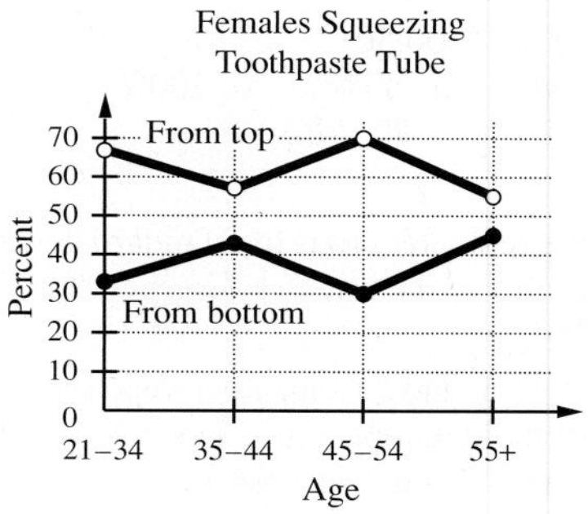

6.

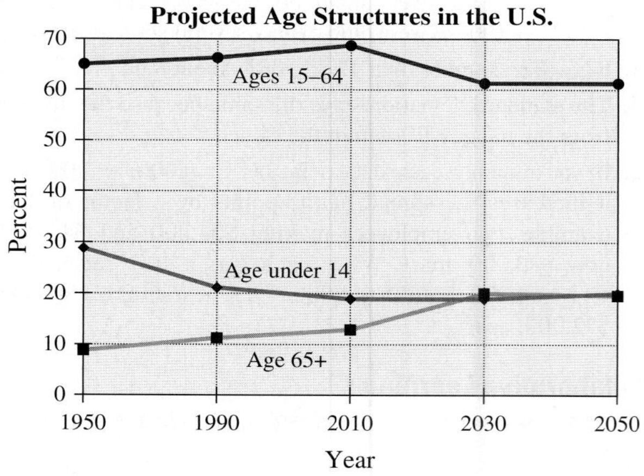

7.

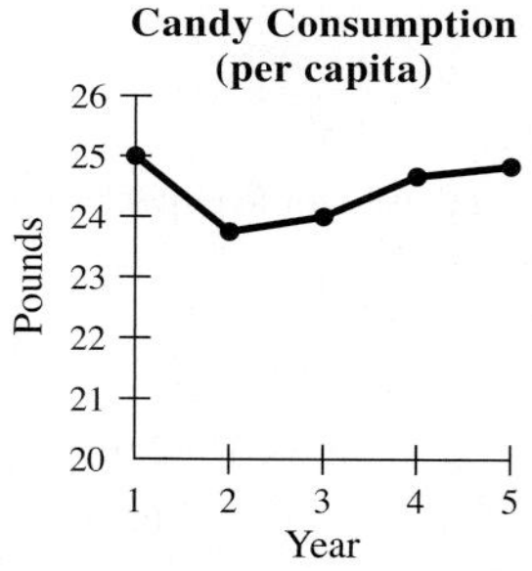

8.

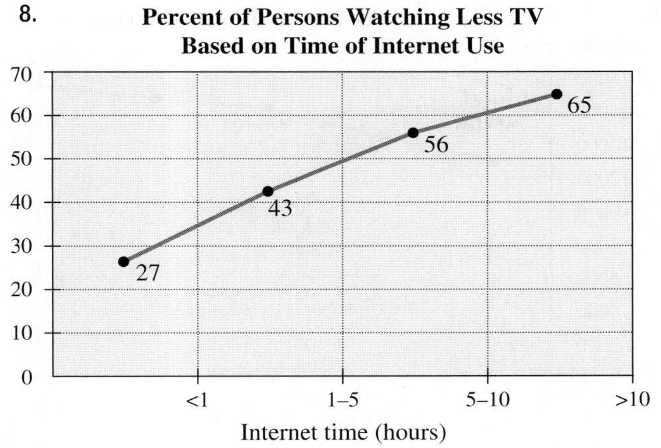

9.

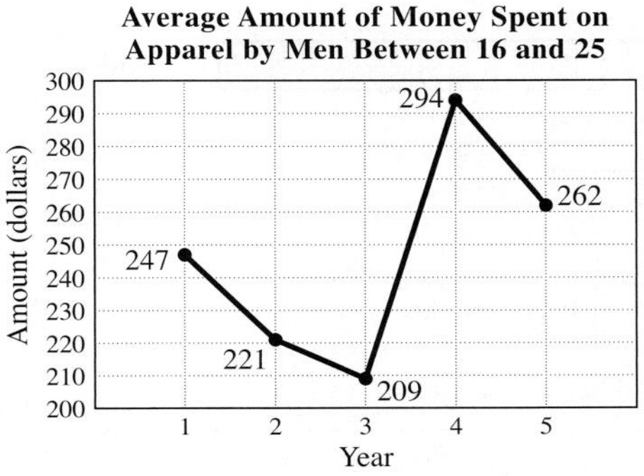

10.

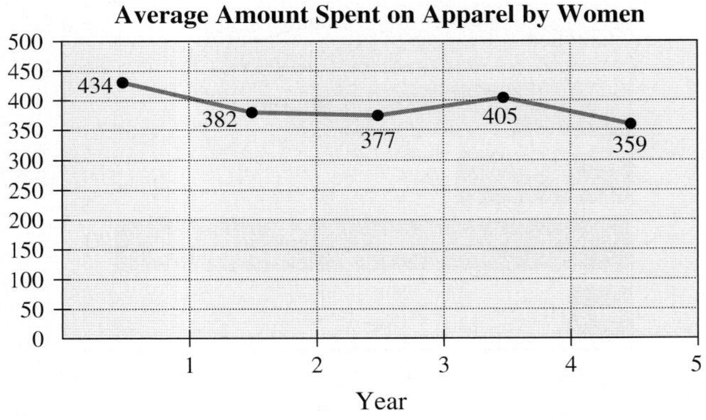

11.

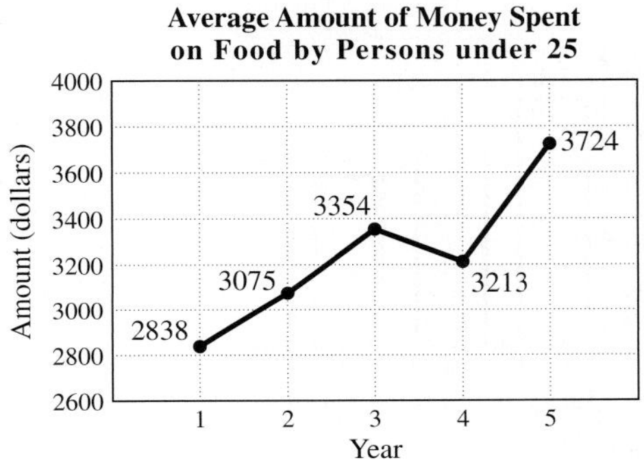

12.

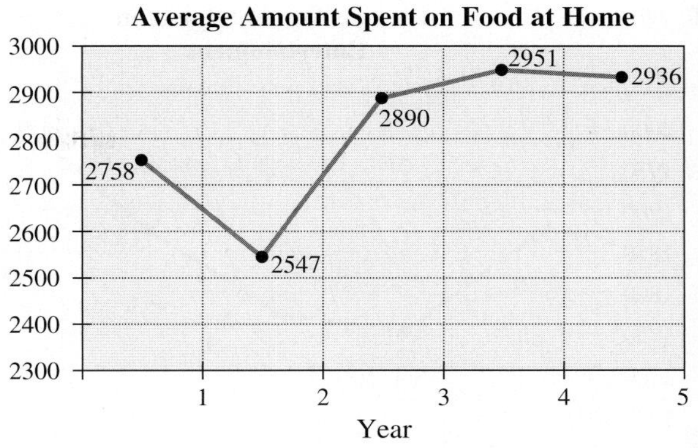

13.

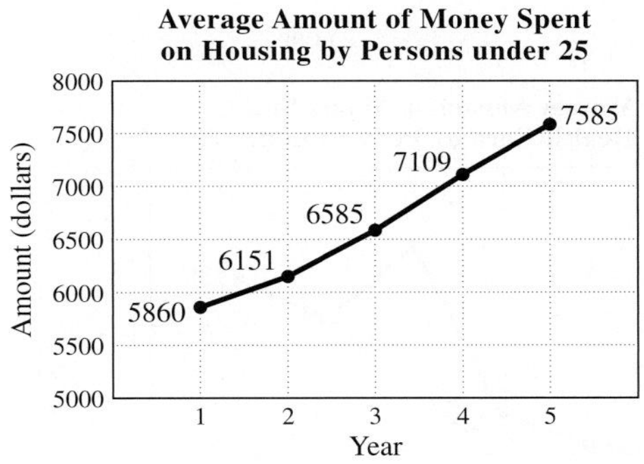

14.

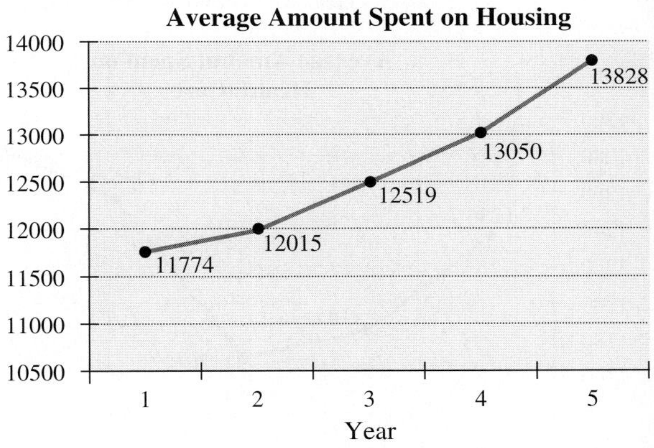

15.

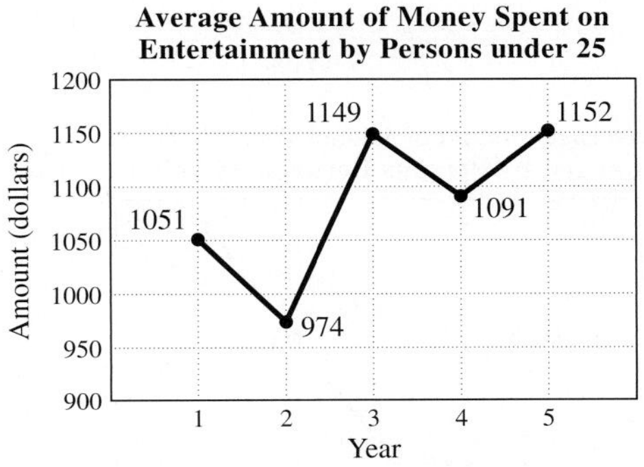

16.

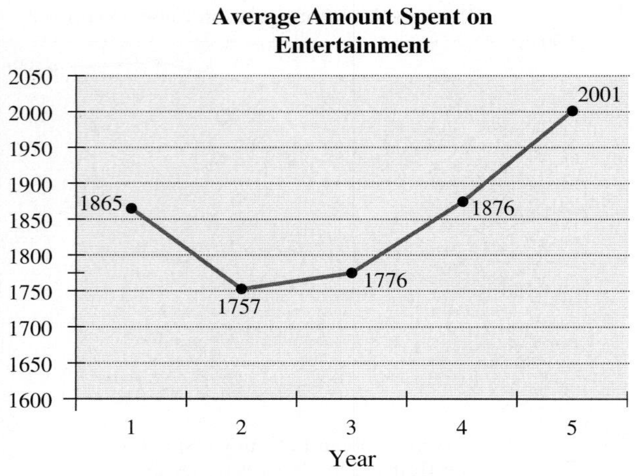

17.

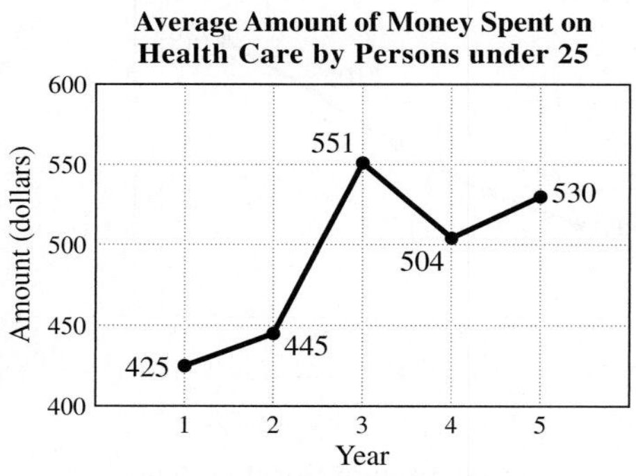

18.

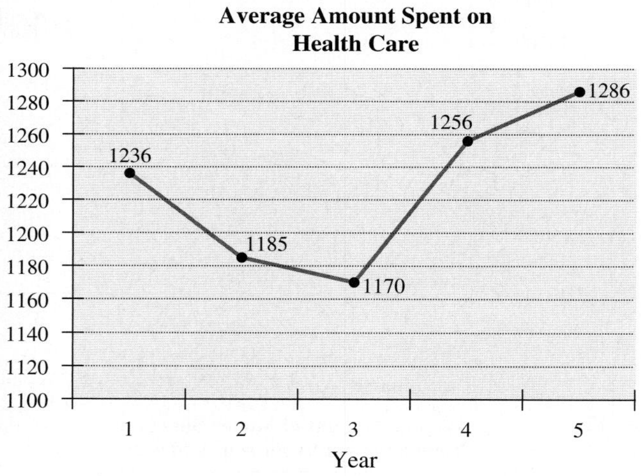

19.

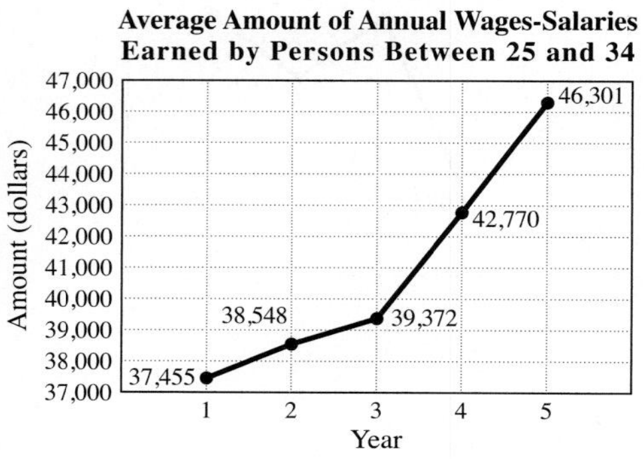

20.

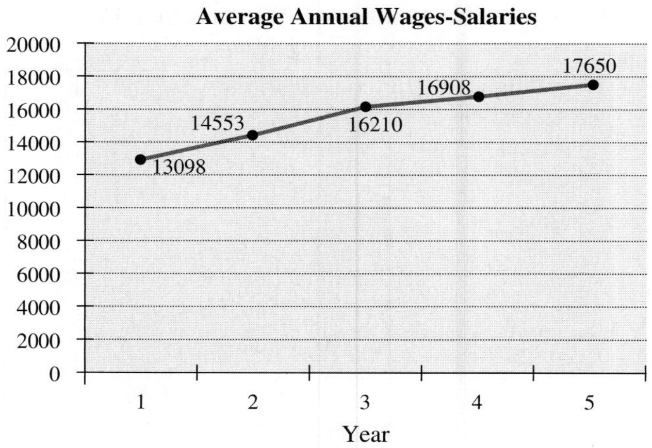

21.

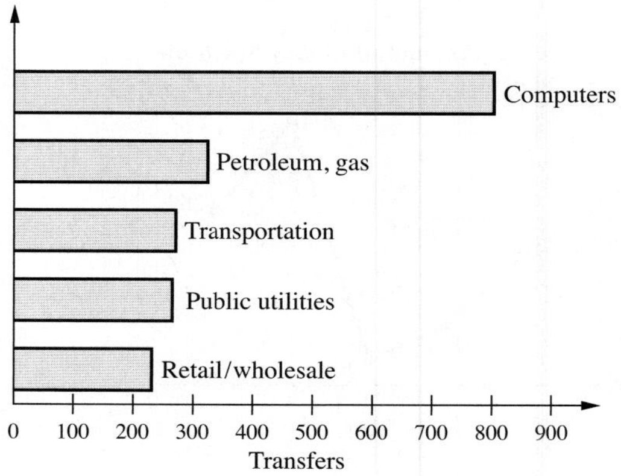

22. a.

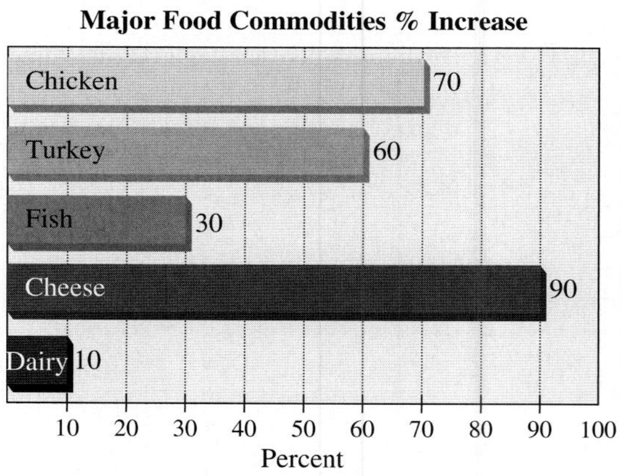

b. Cheese; Dairy

23. a.

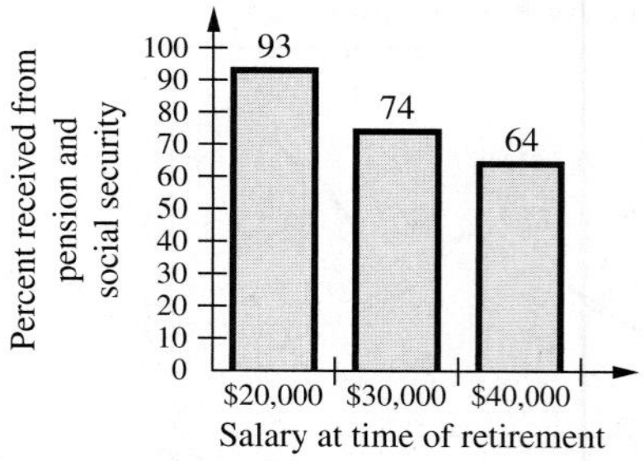

b. $18,600

24.

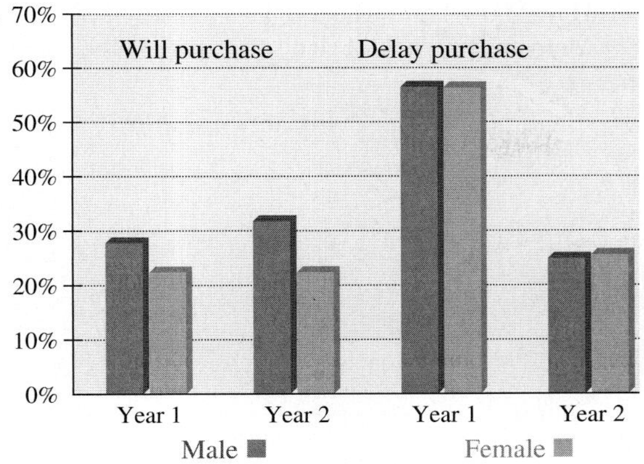

25. a.

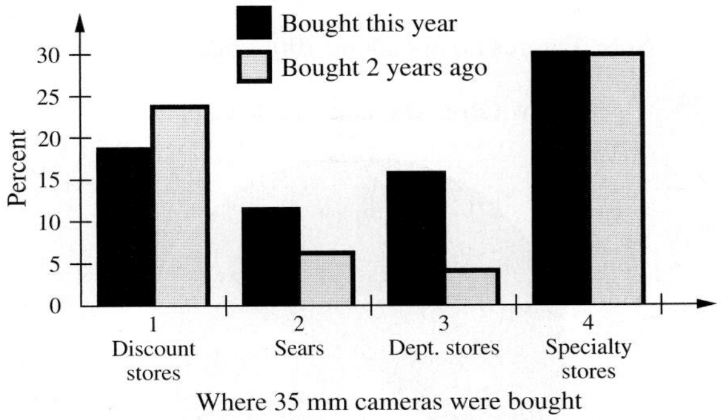

b. At specialty stores **c.** Department stores

d. Specialty stores

26. a.

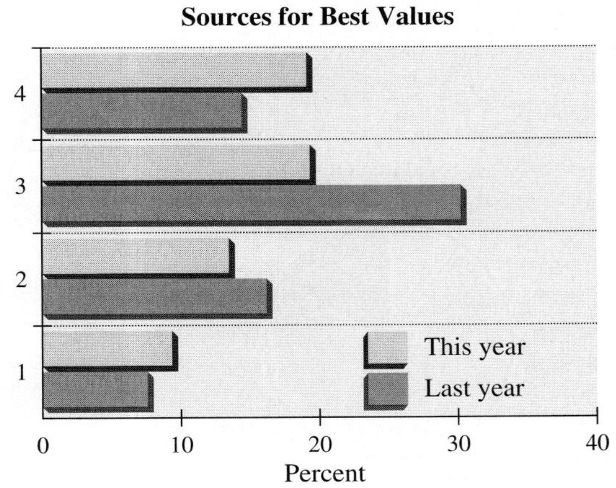

1. Discount stores **2.** Sears

3. Electronic stores **4.** Department stores

b. Electronic stores

27. a.

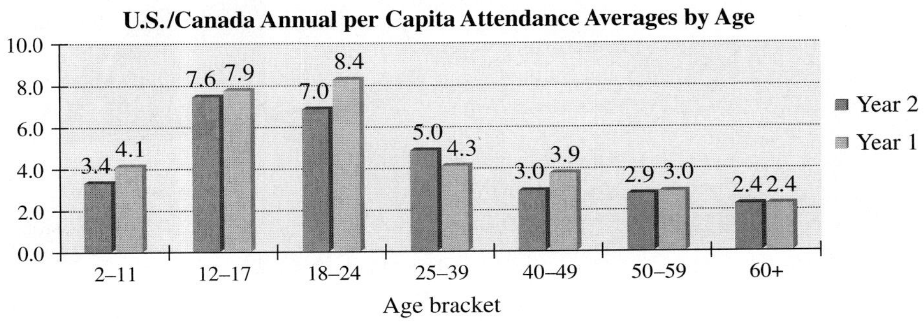

b. 18–24 in year 1 **c.** 60+ **d.** 25–39

28. a.

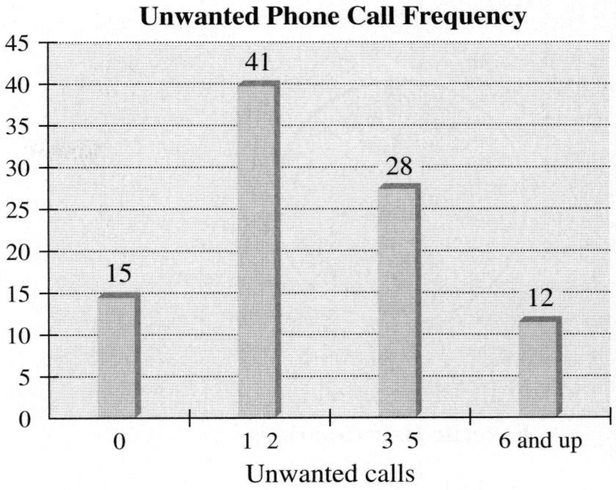

b. 1 – 2 **c.** 15%

29. a.

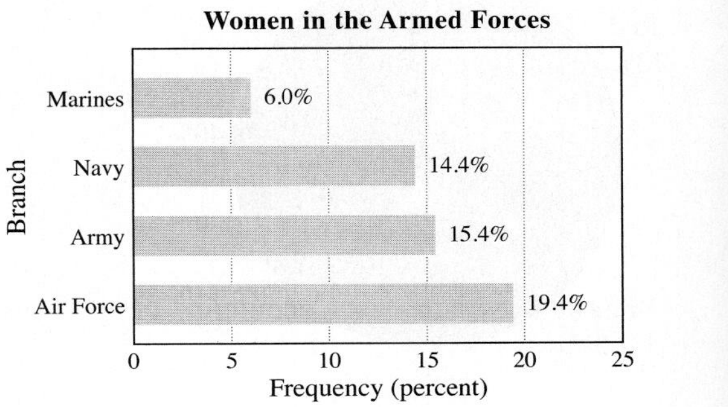

b. Air Force **c.** Marines

d. No; we need to know the total numbers, not just the percents

30. a.

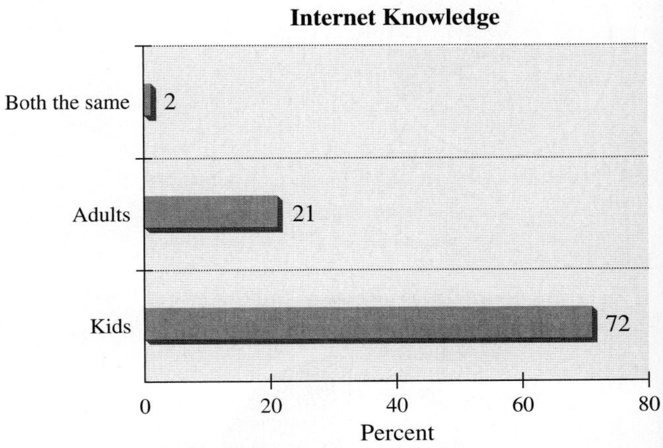

b. Kids **c.** 2%

31.

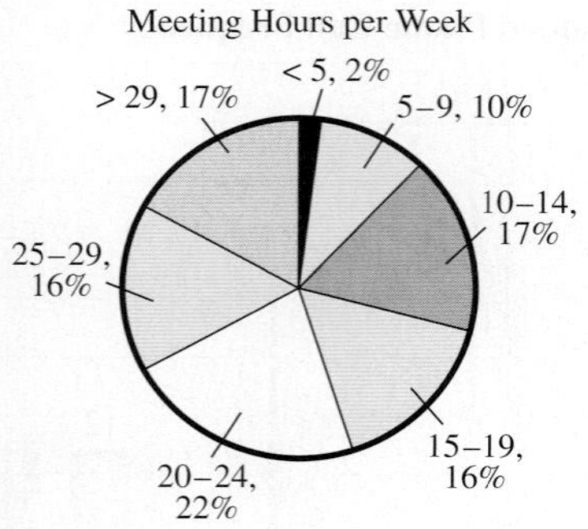

32. **Favorite Hair Colorings**

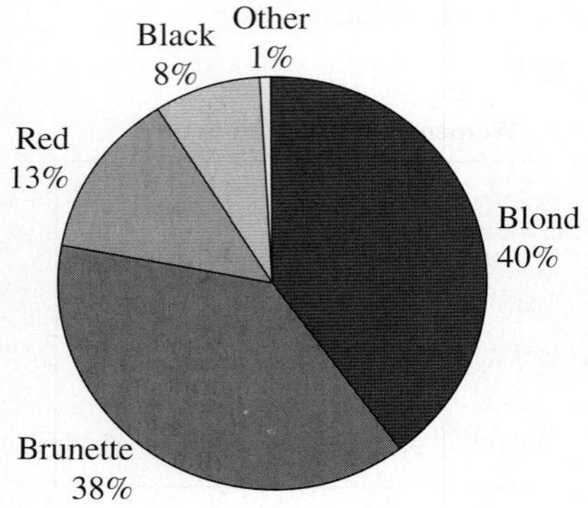

33.

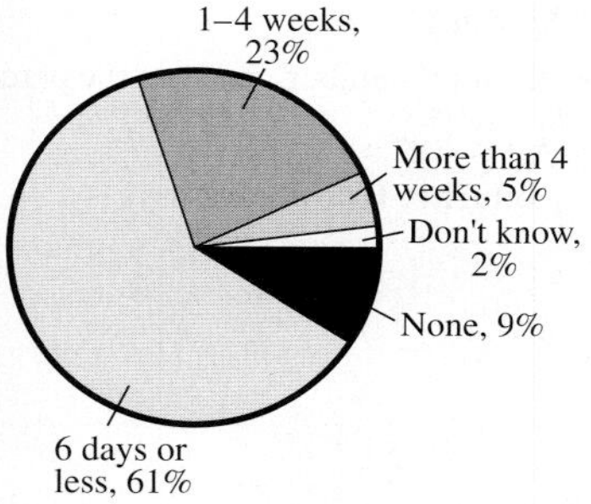

34. **Water Use in Home**

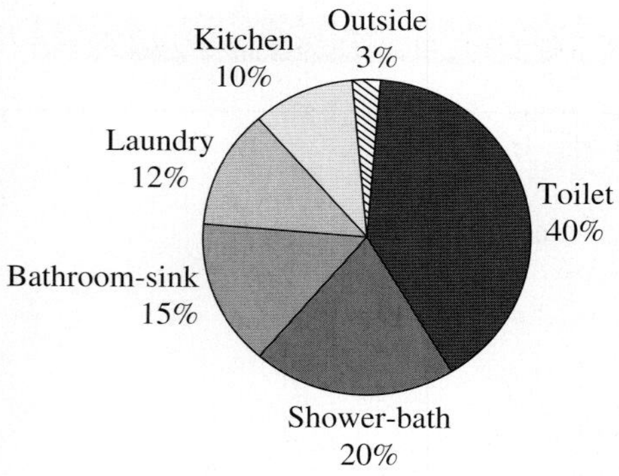

35. **How Many Times Have you Met your Facebook Friend?**

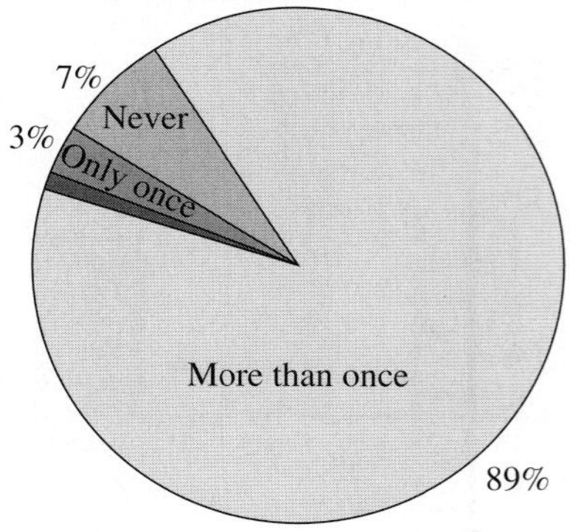

Note: Figures do not add to 100% due to rounding

36. **How Often do You Wash Your Car?**

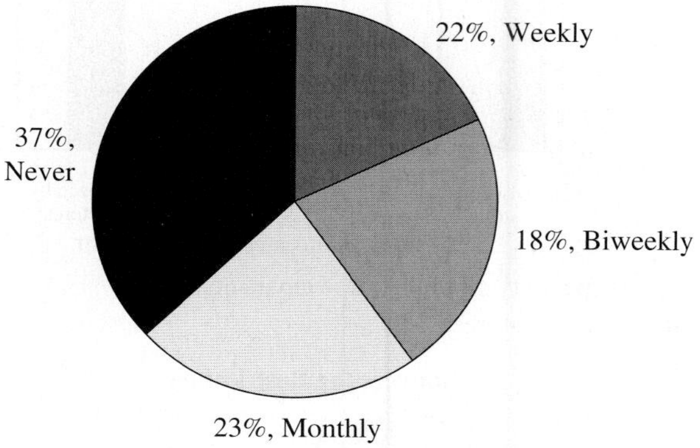

37. a. **Ages of 500 Eating Breakfast Out**

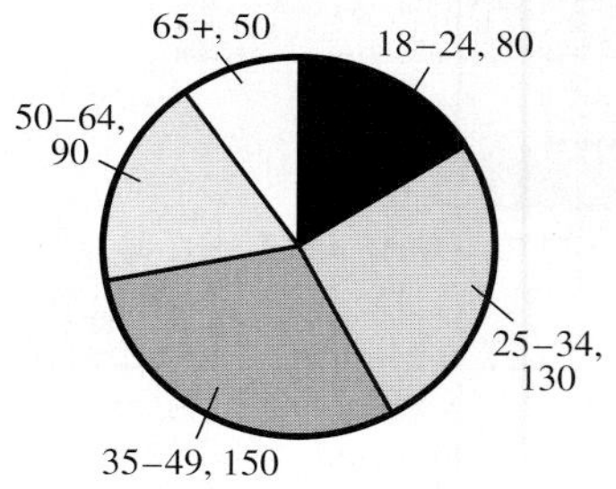

b. 35–49

38. **Where the Advertising Dollar Goes**

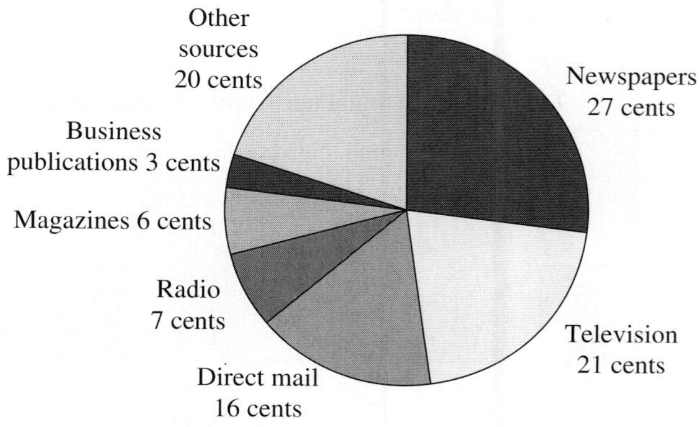

39. **Favorite Activities of 500 People**

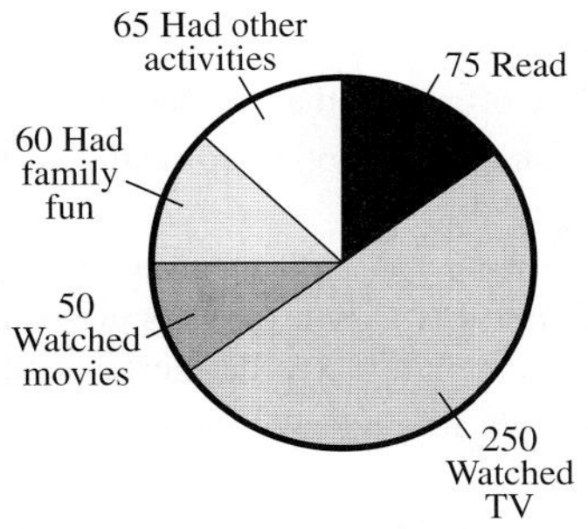

40. **Frozen Pizza Sales**

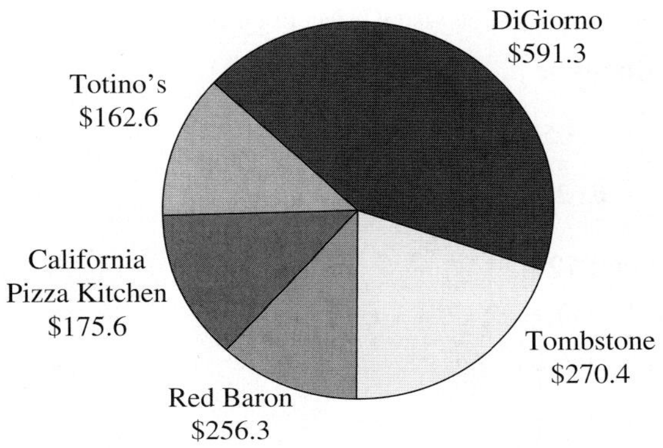

41. **Retired Couple's Budget**

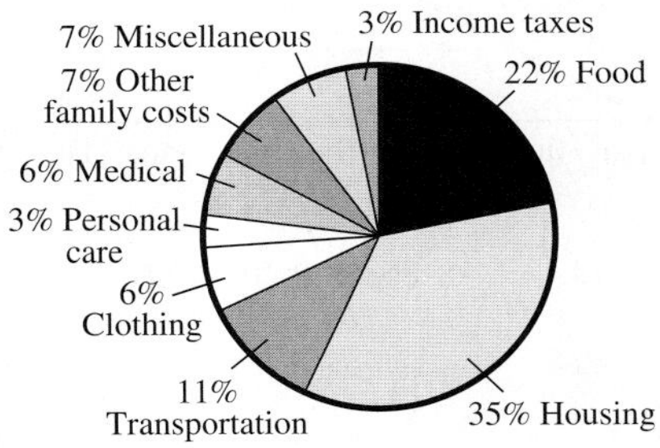

42.

Outlays

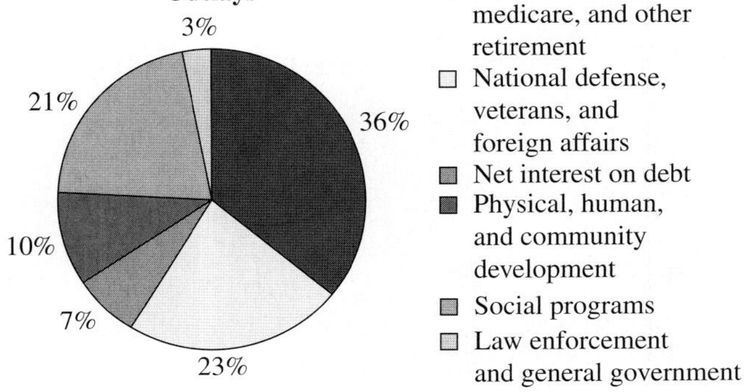

43. a. **Top Six TVs by Brand**

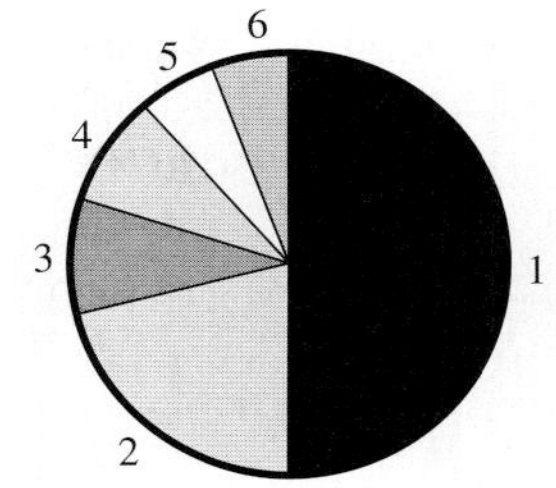

b.

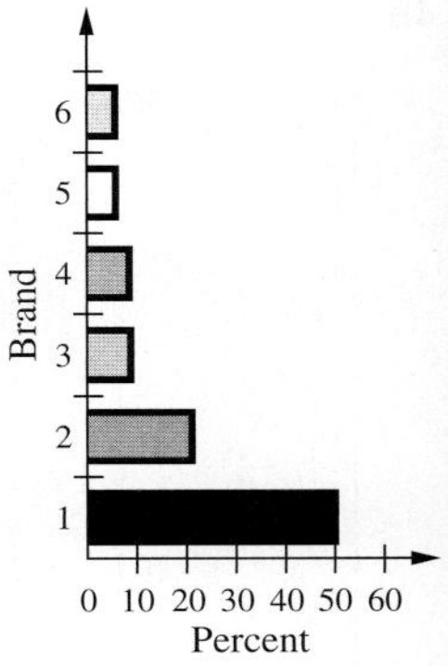

c. The circle graph. The area corresponding to brand 1 overshadows all the rest of the chart.

44. **Do Women Like Housework?**

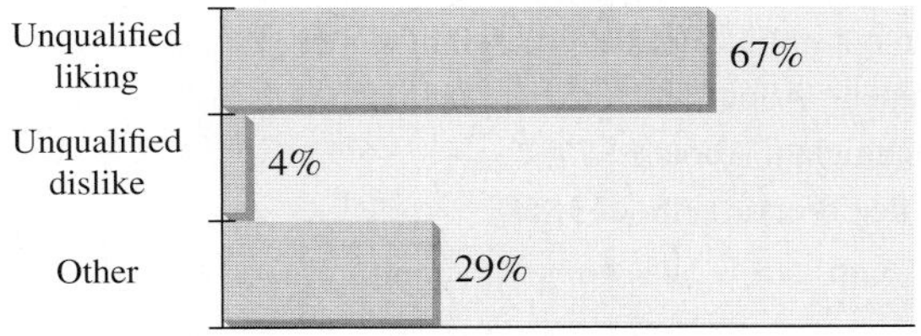

45. a. Yes. To give a correct visual impression, only the height should be doubled. If both the height and the radius are doubled, the volume is multiplied by 8.

b.

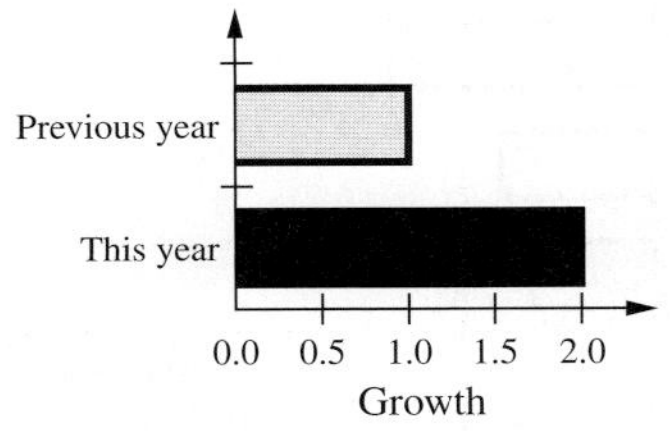

46.

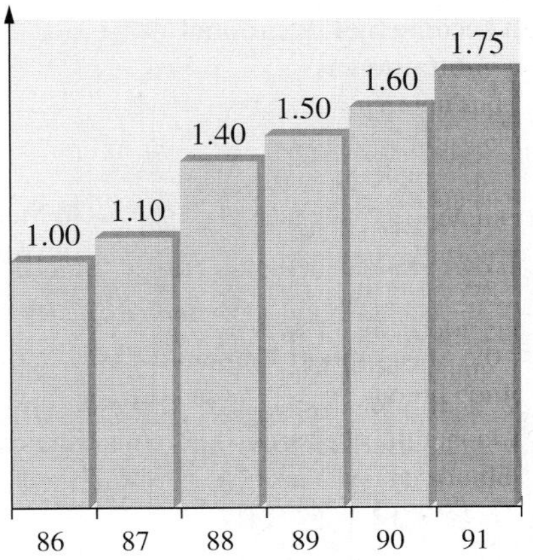

47.

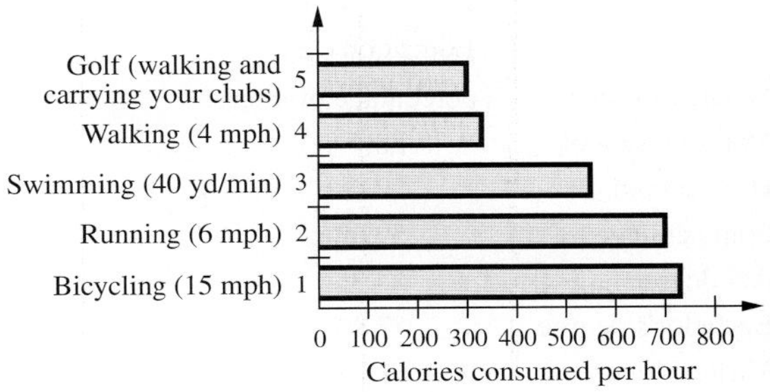

48.

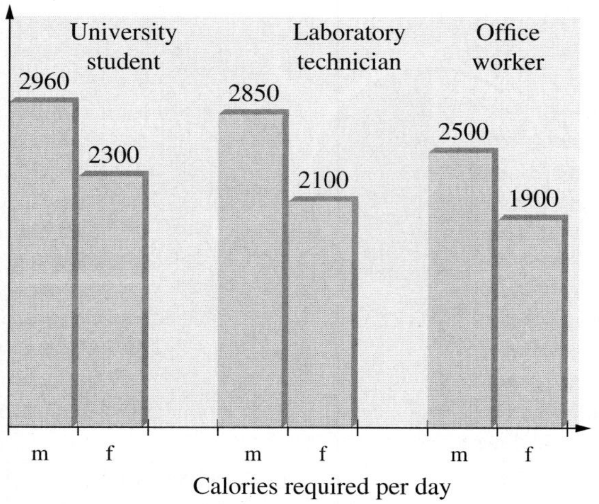

Percent more calories required by males

Student: About 28.7%

Technician: About 35.7%

Office Worker: About 31.6%

49.

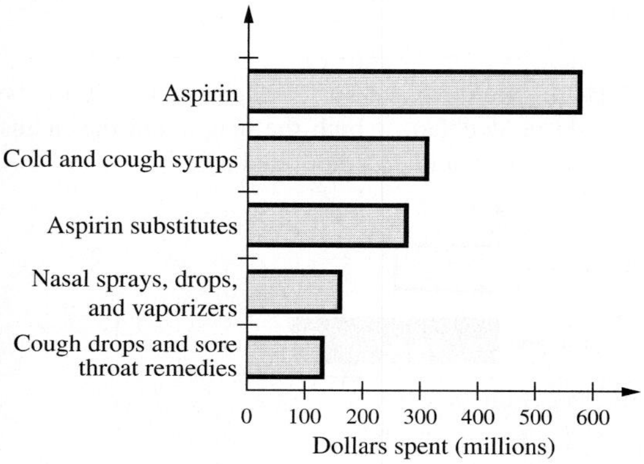

50.

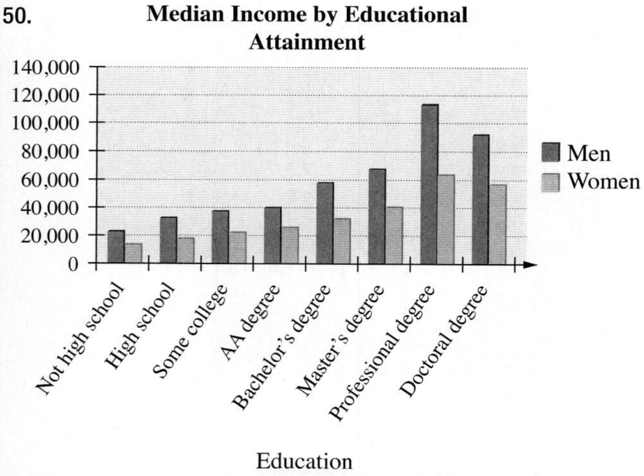

Women's income as a percentage of men's:

Not high school	58.4%
High school	59.8%
Some college	59.0%
AA degree	64.3%
Bachelor's degree	57.8%
Master's degree	61.4%
Professional degree	55.1%
Doctoral degree	61.8%

51. a. \$16,000,000 **b.** In year 6. **52.** 37.5%

53. a. Use a large scale on the vertical axis.

b. Use a very small scale on the vertical axis.

54. a. Use a large scale and cut off part of the zero end of each bar.

b. Use a small scale so that the bars appear to be about of the same length.

55. The area of the bar in a bar graph indicates the amount of the item that is graphed. For this reason the bars are usually shaded. In a histogram, the height of the bar corresponds to the frequency of the item in question and there is no space between the bars.

56. When we wish to compare at a glance the magnitudes of the categories involved.

57. The second graph has a very much compressed vertical scale that diminishes the visual effect of each increase or decrease.

Skill Checker

1. $-\frac{3}{2} = -1.5$ **2.** 3 **3.** $y = -1.5x + 3$

4. 1 **5.** 2 **6.** $y = x + 2$

Exercises 12.6

1. a.

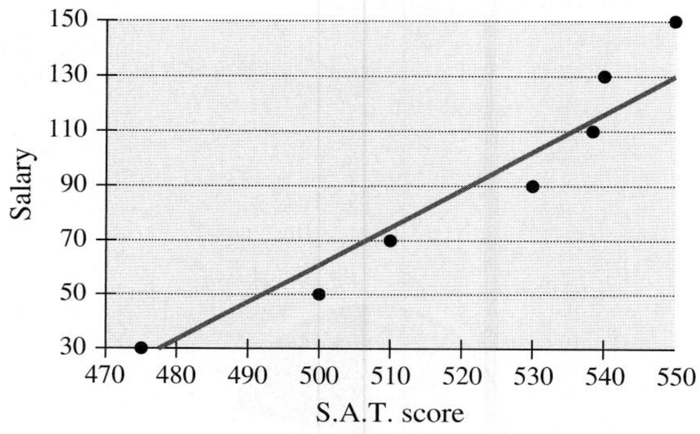

b. $y = 1.554x - 718.4$ **c.** \$58,600; \$120,760

2. a.

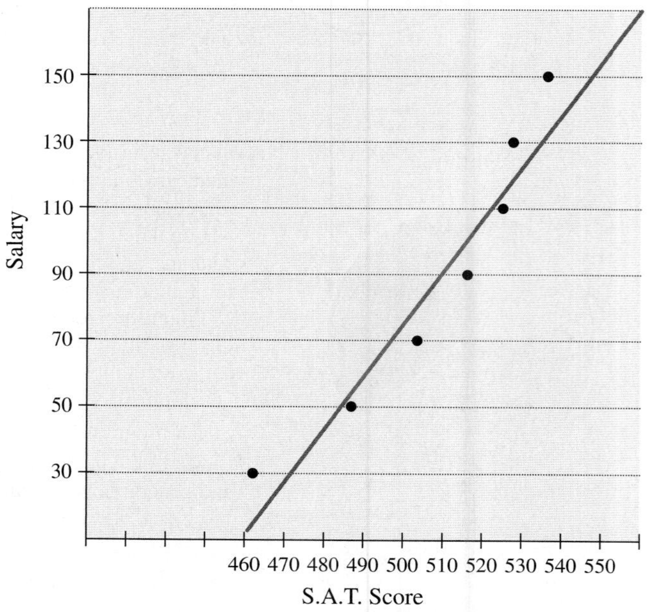

b. $y = 1.577x - 712.2$ **c.** \$76,300; \$139,380

3. a.

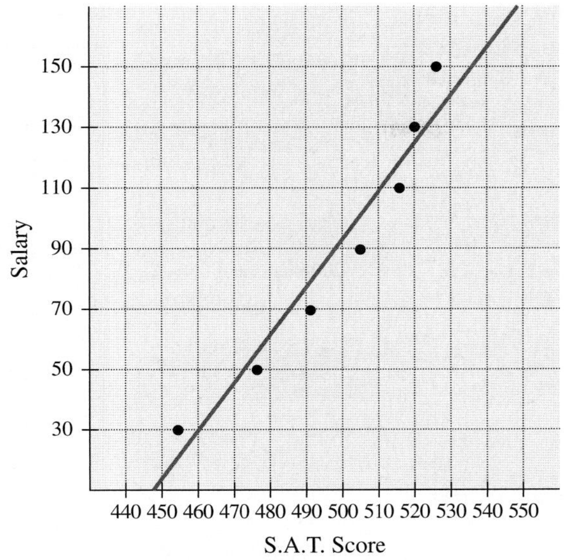

b. $y = 1.574x - 694.5$ **c.** \$92,500; \$155,460

4. a.

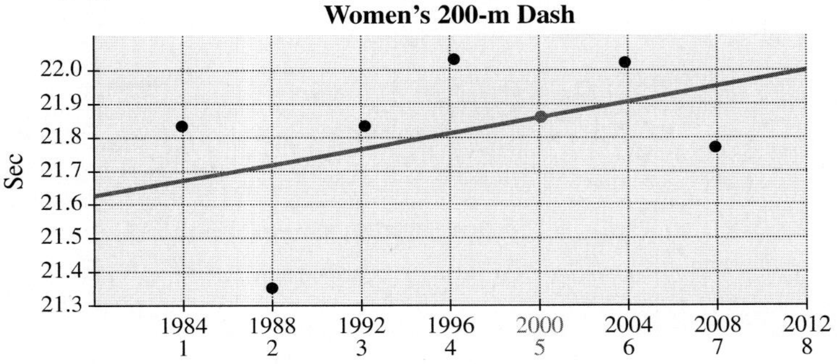

b. $y = 0.045x + 21.64$ **c.** 21.865 **d.** 22

5. a.

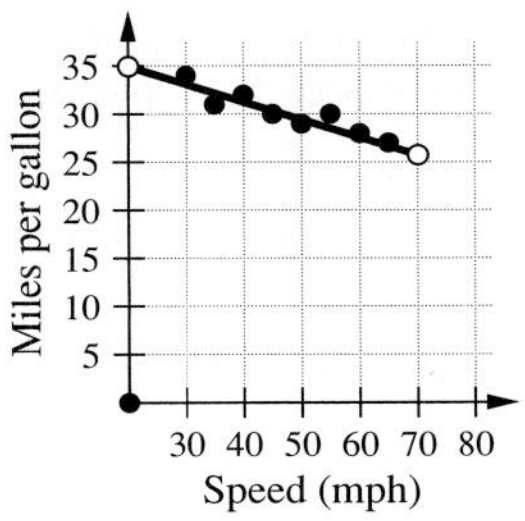

b. About 26 mi/gal (may vary) **c.** $y = -0.169x + 38.155$
Prediction: About 26.3 mi/gal

6. a.

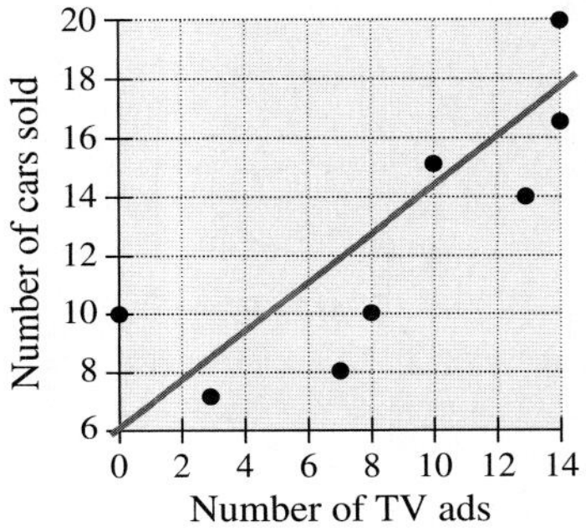

b. 10 or 11 (Answers will vary.) **c.** $y = 0.704x + 6.470$
Prediction: 10.7 cars (when $x = 6$)

7. a.

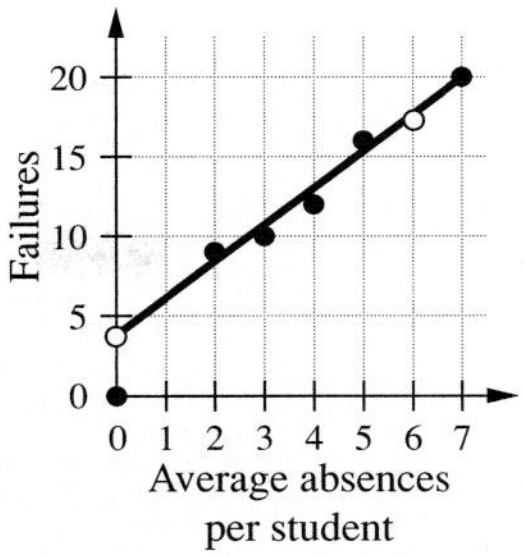

b. About 18 **c.** $y = 2.338x + 3.581$
Prediction: About 18 would fail.

8. a. $y = 0.735x - 0.088$
b. $y = 19.022$ hotdogs ($x = 26$)

9. a.

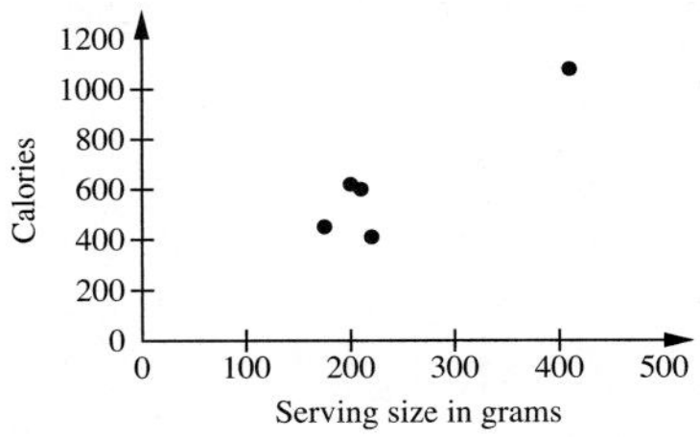

b. About $y = 2.706x - 32.5$ **c.** About 779 calories

10. a.

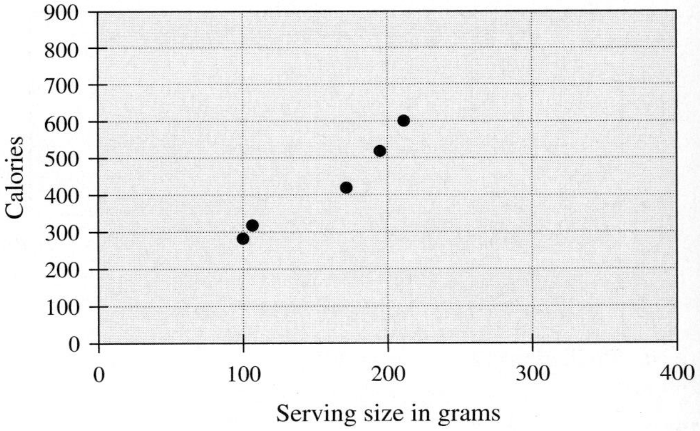

b. $y = 2.663x + 9.709$
c. Prediction: 808.61 calories ($x = 300$)

11. a.

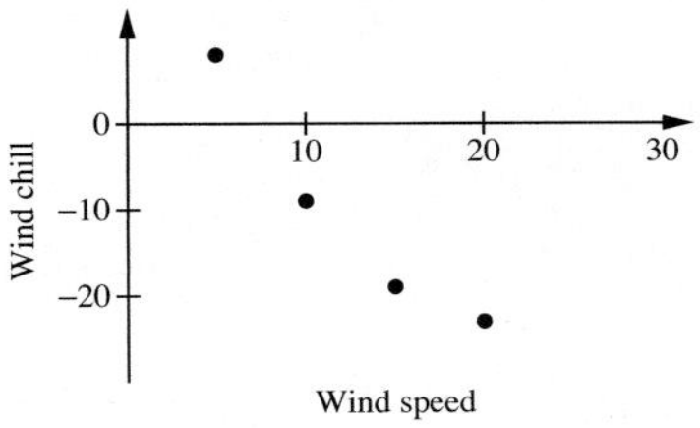

b. $y = -1.98x + 13.5$ **c.** −36

12. **a.**

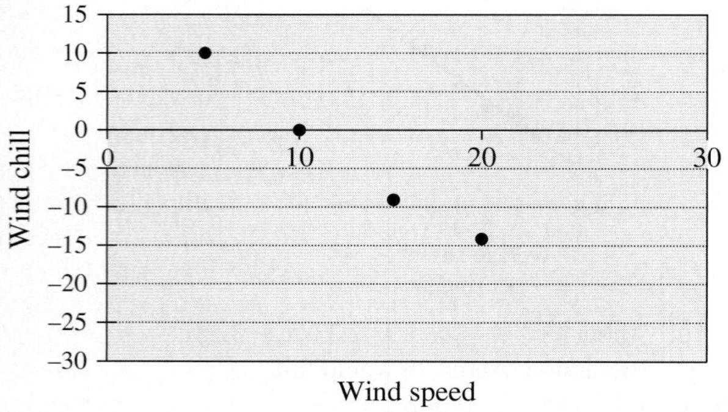

b. $y = -1.6x + 17$ **c.** Prediction: $-23 (x = 25)$

d. The current wind chill is -36, so -23 is higher.

13. **a.**

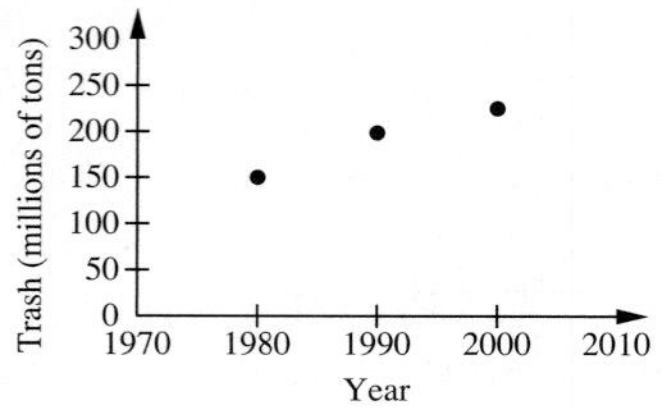

b. $y = 3.5x + 155$ **c.** 260 tons; 277.5 tons

14. **a.**

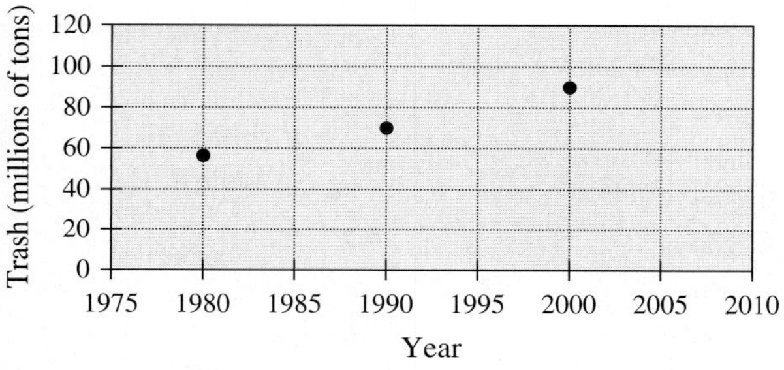

b. $y = 1.75x + 71.667$ (million tons)

c. Prediction: 124.167 $(x = 30)$

132.917 $(x = 35)$

15. **a.**

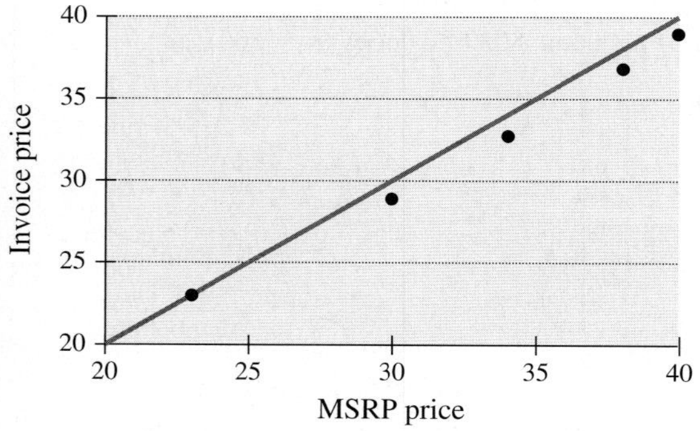

b. $y = 0.94x + 0.7$ **c.** \$28,900

16. **a.**

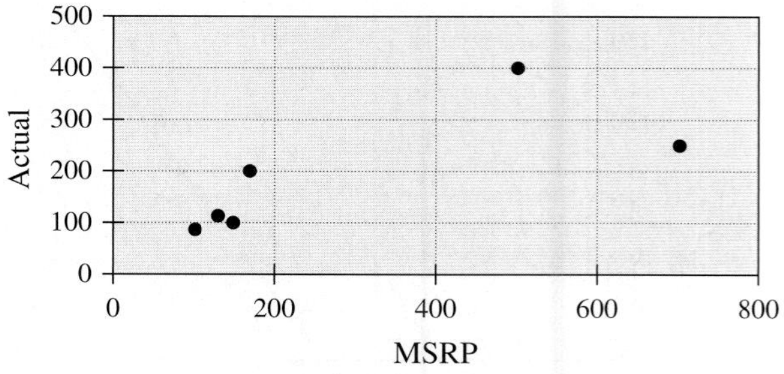

b. $y = 0.358x + 88.875$ **c.** Prediction: \$196.28$(x = 300)$

17. **a.**

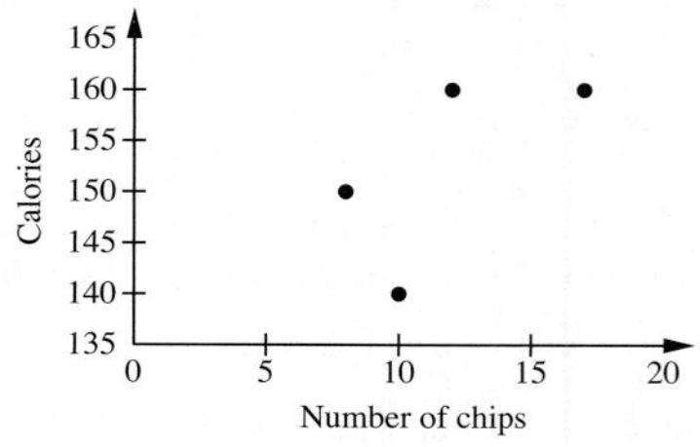

b. About $y = 2.184x + 124.66$ **c.** About 157 calories

18. **a.**

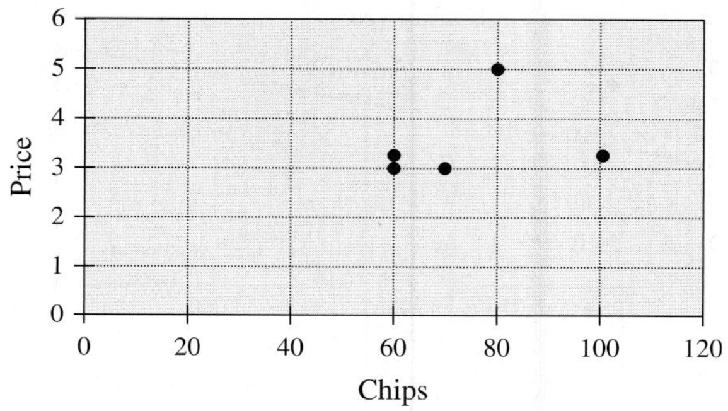

b. $y = 0.013x + 2.509$ **c.** Prediction: \$3.68$(x = 90)$

19. 720 **20.** 600 people **21.** 200 **22.** 166.67 cars

23. 426 **24.** 36 males and 76 females

25. **a.** About 13 **b.** About 9 **c.** About 9

d. About 3 **e.** About 3 **f.** About 3

26. 70 African American and 135 white students

27. 100; 160

28. **a.**

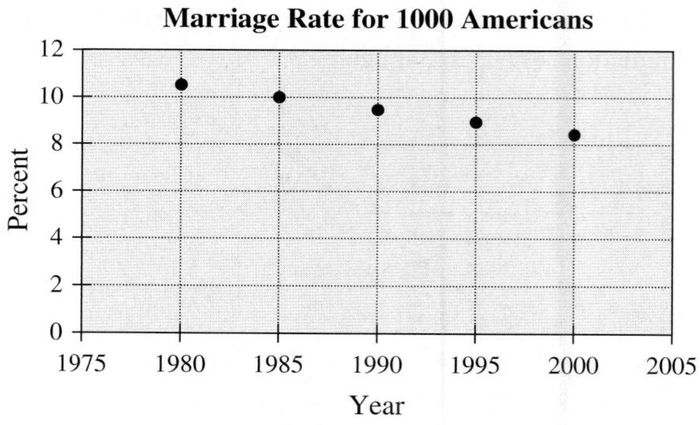

b. 7.5%; 7% **c.** 350

29. a.

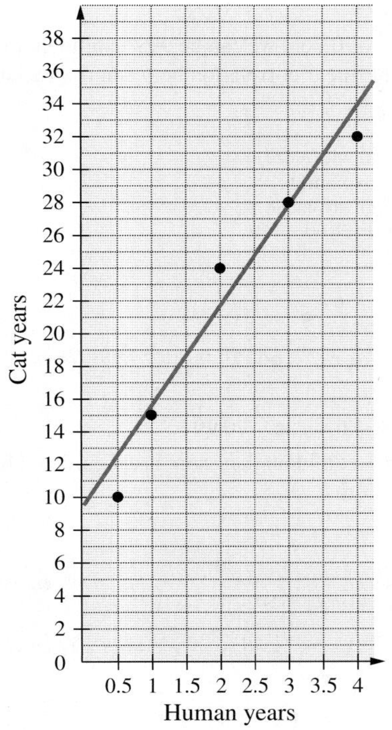

b. $y = 6.2x + 8.7$ **c.** 21.1

30. a. 60 **b.** 10 **31.** 2

32. $y = 5.4x + 12$

33. a. 93 **b.** 90

34.

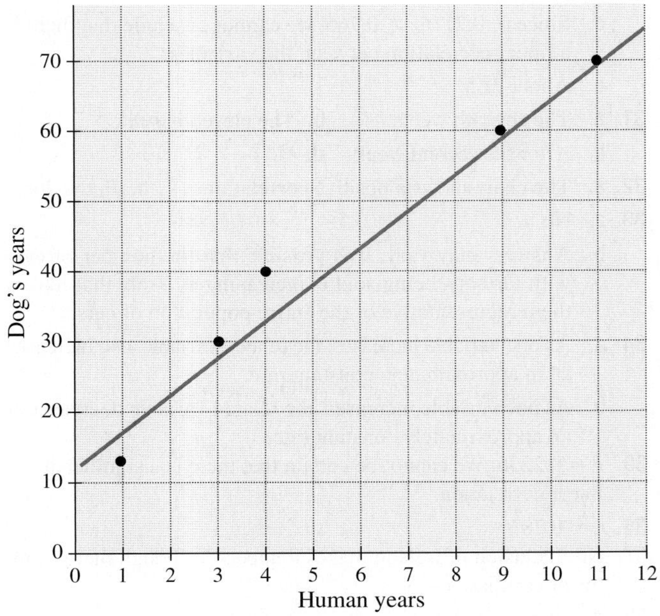

35. a. (9, 60) **b.** (9, 60.6)

36. a. 75 mph **b.** 48 to 72 hr **c.** Now to 48 hr

37. a. $y = -0.417x + 75$ **b.** $64.992 \approx 65$ mph **c.** 50 mph **d.** $y = 50$ **38.** About 23°

39. Procedure (d) **40. c.** is most appropriate.

41. a. The women who shop on Rodeo Drive are not necessarily a good representation of the entire population of California.
b. The same can be said of the male population of Berkeley.
c. The same can be said of the people attending an Oakland baseball game.

42. Assume that the sample is a random sample of the entire population that is being surveyed. If the population is not too large, use the entire population. Otherwise, put all the names in a box and draw a random sample as large as is feasible.

43. 19.9 **44.** $m = \dfrac{19.9 - 19.58}{-7} = -0.046$

45. $y = -0.046x + 19.9$ **46.** 19.532 sec

47. 19.53 sec **48.** 0.002 sec

Exercises 12.7

1. No. Too many data points below the line.
2. Good. As many points above as below the line.
3. Good **4.** Not good. Too many points above the line.
5. Positive **6.** Positive **7.** None **8.** Positive
9. Negative **10.** Negative **11.** Positive **12.** Negative
13. (c) **14.** (d) **15.** (c) **16.** (b) **17.** (a) **18.** (a)
19. (c) **20.** (c) **21.** (c) **22.** (d)

23. a.

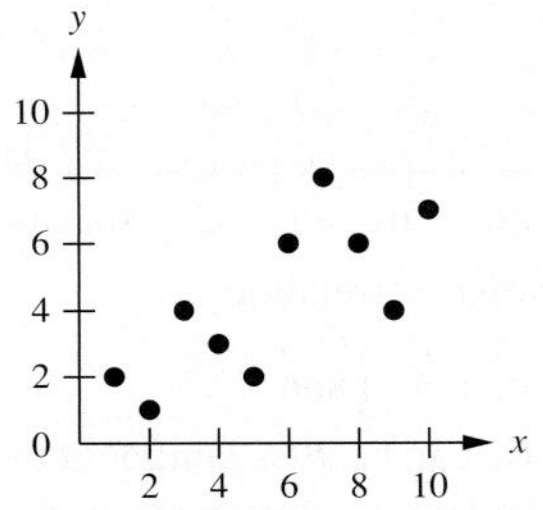

b. $y = 0.58x + 1.133$ **c.** 0.7388
d. We can be 95% confident that there is a significant positive linear correlation.

24. a.

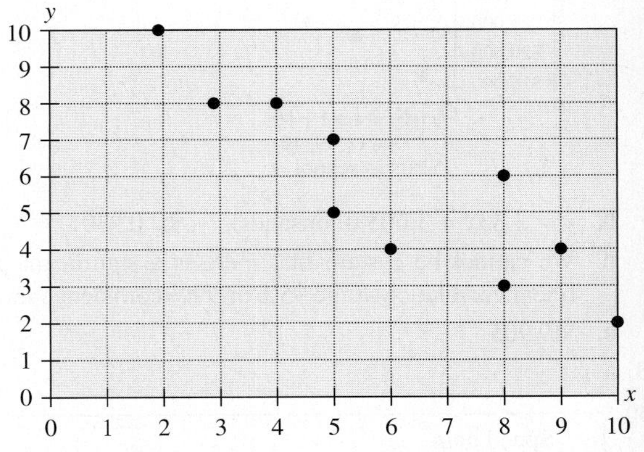

Negative correlation

b. $y = -0.84 + 10.76$ **c.** $r \approx -0.886$
d. Since $|-0.886| > 0.765$, we can be 99% confident that there is a significant linear correlation between the variables.

25. **a.**

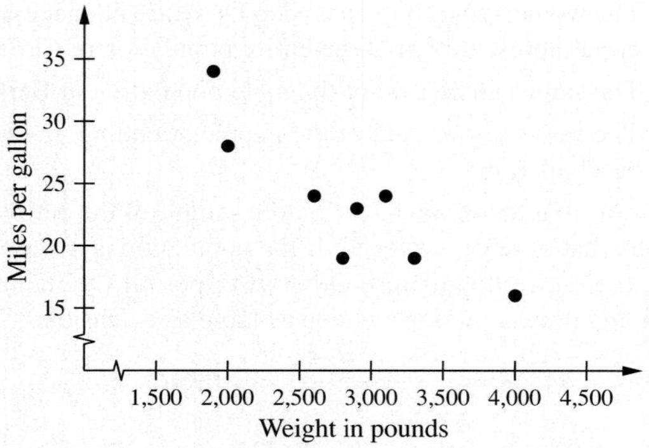

b. $y = -0.01x + 44.315$ **c.** -0.889

d. We can be 99% confident that there is a significant negative linear correlation.

26. **a.**

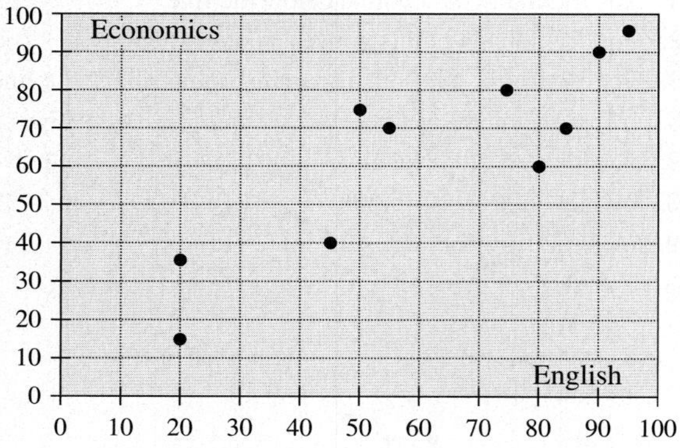

Positive correlation

b. $y = 0.80x + 13.73$ **c.** $r \approx 0.866$

d. Since $|0.866| > 0.765$, we can be 99% confident that there is a significant linear correlation between the variables.

e. About 70.

27. **a.**

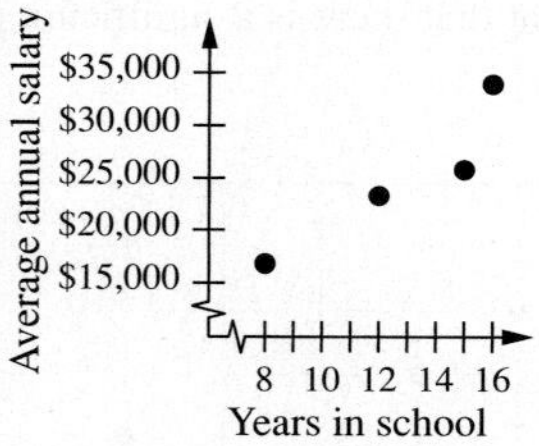

b. $y = 1.83x + 1.605$ (thousands) **c.** 0.9307

d. We cannot be certain that there is a significant positive linear correlation at the 95% or 99% confidence level.

e. $19,905

28. **a.**

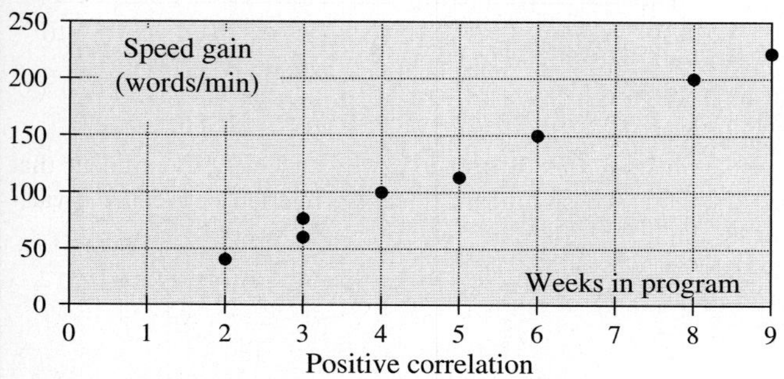

Positive correlation

b. $y = 25x - 6.25$ **c.** $r \approx 0.993$

d. Since $|0.993| > 0.765$, we can be 99% confident that there is a significant linear correlation between the variables.

e. About 169 wpm.

29. **a.**

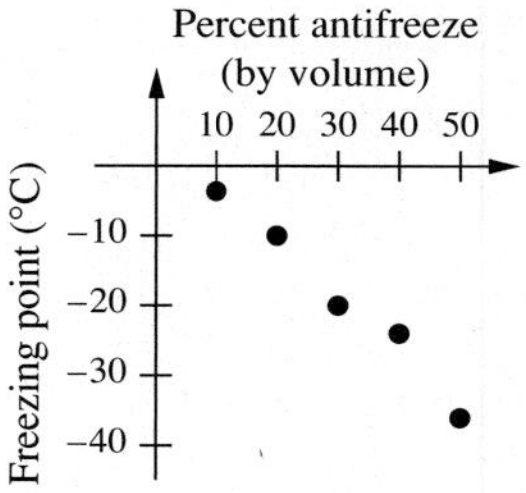

b. $y = -0.78x + 4.6$ **c.** -0.99

d. We can be 99% confident that there is a significant negative linear correlation.

e. About −14.9°C

30. **a.**

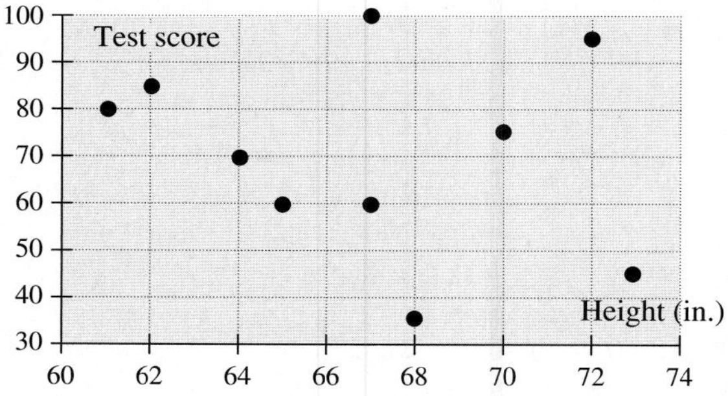

No correlation

b. $y = -1.10x + 144.14$ **c.** $r \approx -0.2116$

d. Since $|-0.2116| \not> 0.765$, we cannot conclude that there is a linear correlation between the variables.

e. About 71.5.

31. **a.** The seventh week **b.** The eleventh week

c. After the second week **d.** No

32. **a.** The chart shows a positive correlation. **b.** In the 70s

33. **a.** No

b. Answers may vary. It is possible that the number of cars with air bags being sold is increasing at a rate that makes them representative of the entire population of cars.

34. **a.** As one variable increases, the related variable also increases at an approximately constant rate.

b. As one variable increases, the related variable decreases at an approximately constant rate.

35. $r = 0.2236$. We cannot be certain that there is a significant linear correlation.

36. $r \approx 0.78$

37. No. Inclusion of Ireland makes it appear as though there is no linear correlation.

38. Answers will vary.

CHAPTER 13

Exercises 13.1

1. **a.** $240 **b.** $120 **2.** $315 **b.** $157.50

3. **a.** $540 **b.** $270 **4.** **a.** $1984 **b.** $992

5. **a.** $200 **b.** $70 **6.** **a.** $240 **b.** $30

7. **a.** \$62.50 **b.** \$15.63 **8.** **a.** \$90 **b.** \$20
9. **a.** \$466.67 **b.** \$200 **10.** **a.** \$400 **b.** \$75
11. **a.** \$2.41 **b.** \$42.61 **12.** **a.** \$26.64 **b.** \$692.64
13. **a.** \$1356 **b.** \$1836 **14.** \$2295
15. \$850 + 0.15(\$25,850 − \$8500) = \$850 + \$2602.50
= \$3452.50
16. \$850 + 0.15(\$9500 − \$8500) = \$850 + \$150 = \$1000
17. **a.** \$40 **b.** \$160 **c.** \$168
18. **a.** \$450 **b.** \$450 **c.** \$477
19. **a.** \$125 **b.** \$375
20. **a.** \$162 **b.** \$18 **c.** \$171.72
21. **a.** \$1.42 **b.** \$26.98
22. **a.** \$252 **b.** It makes no difference.
Calculator answers may vary; see solutions manual.
23. **a.** \$159.38; \$59.38 **b.** \$136.86; \$36.86
24. **a.** \$2580.40; \$1580.40 **b.** \$1384.20; \$384.20
25. **a.** \$7154.60; \$4574.60 **b.** \$3083.30; \$503.30
26. **a.** \$21,796; \$15,566 **b.** \$7901.10; \$1671.10
27. **a.** \$26,195; \$14,195 **b.** \$16,473.43; \$4473.43
28. **a.** \$58,046; \$43,046 **b.** \$22,289.21; \$7289.21
29. **a.** \$25,364; \$5364 **b.** \$21,230.40; \$1230.40
30. **a.** \$48,141; \$18,141 **b.** \$35,177.36; \$5177.36
31. **a.** \$3,880,688; \$3,840,688 **b.** \$103,482.82; \$63,482.82
32. **a.** \$503,135; \$453,135 **b.** \$121,363.12; \$71,363.12
33. **a.** \$2854.30 **b.** \$2898.30
34. **a.** \$179.08 **b.** \$390.91
35. **a.** \$3993 **b.** \$993
36. **a.** \$1485.90 **b.** \$1628.90 **c.** Bank B
37. \$15.30
38.

n	*6% Compounded*	*6.5% Simple*
1	\$60	\$65
2	\$123.60	\$130
3	\$191.02	\$195
4	\$262.48	\$260

The table shows that at the end of four years, the 6% compounded interest exceeds the accumulated 6.5% simple interest by \$2.48. Because interest is being paid on the accumulated interest, the compounded interest will continue to exceed the simple interest by an increasing amount after this time.

39. \$2081.62 **40.** \$4475.47
41. 11% semiannually yields about \$51.47 more.
42. \$0.0018; \$3.56 **43.** 2.020% **44.** 3.045%
45. 6.09% **46.** 6.17% **47.** 8.24% **48.** 12.68%
49. 9.31% **50.** 15.56% **51.** 19.56% **52.** 16.08%
53. Simple interest means that the interest itself does not earn additional interest. Compound interest means that the interest earns interest at the same rate. For instance, \$100 at 10% simple interest would earn \$20 in 2 years, while \$100 at 10% compounded annually would earn \$21 in 2 years.
54. No. If the price P is increased by 10%, the new price is 1.10P. If this new price is decreased by 10% the final price is (0.90)(1.10P) or 0.99P. Thus, the final price is 1% less than the starting price.
56. 4.00% **58.** 3.96%

Collaborative Learning

1. $t = \frac{\ln 2}{r}$ **2.** $t = \frac{0.069315}{r}$
3. **a.** 17.3 yr. **b.** 8.7 yr. **c.** 5.8 yr.

Exercises 13.2

1. \$15,000 per year **2.** \$20,000 **3.** \$141.35
4. \$136.65 **5.** \$185.01
6. \$137.29 **7.** \$557.48
8. **a.** \$0.76 **b.** \$224.16 **c.** \$11.21
9. **a.** \$1.28 **b.** \$236.28 **c.** \$11.81
10. **a.** \$2.31 **b.** \$231.31 **c.** \$11.57
11. **a.** \$5.16 **b.** \$409.16 **c.** \$20.46
12. **a.** \$6.67 **b.** \$726.96 **c.** \$36.35
13. **a.** \$1.21 **b.** \$180.39 **c.** \$10
14. **a.** \$0.52 **b.** \$85.49 **c.** \$10.00
15. **a.** \$.84 **b.** \$92.73 **c.** \$10
16. **a.** \$1.48 **b.** \$145.05 **c.** \$10.00
17. **a.** \$.52 **b.** \$122.81 **c.** \$10
18. \$8.35 **19.** \$2.85 **20.** $1\frac{1}{2}$%
21. \$1.35 **22.** \$1.13
23. **a.** \$1998 **b.** \$261 **c.** \$1071.45; \$235.32
24. **a.** \$36 **b.** \$33 **25.** **a.** \$450 **b.** \$136
26. **a.** \$3780 **b.** \$299 **27.** **a.** \$60 **b.** \$26
28.

n	*Int*	*Bal Due*	*Payment*	*New Bal*
1	15.00	1015.00	200.00	815.00
2	12.23	827.23	200.00	627.23
3	9.41	636.64	200.00	436.64
4	6.55	443.19	200.00	243.19
5	3.65	246.84	200.00	46.84
6	0.70	47.54	47.54	0.00

Total interest paid \$47.54

n	*Int*	*Bal Due*	*Payment*	*New Bal*
1	15.00	1015.00	215.00	800.00
2	12.00	812.00	212.00	600.00
3	9.00	609.00	209.00	400.00
4	6.00	406.00	206.00	200.00
5	3.00	203.00	203.00	0.00

Total interest paid \$45.00
Cissie would save \$2.54 because she would not have to pay interest on the accumulated interest.
29. This procedure gives the longest possible time between the purchase date and the date when payment must be made to avoid a finance charge.
30. This would make the unpaid balance as small as possible and thus would avoid some of the finance charge.
31. 6.4% **32.** 10.1% **33.** 10% **34.** 7.6%

Exercises 13.3

1. 14% **2.** 15% **3.** 16% **4.** $17\frac{1}{2}$%
5. 17% **6.** 18% **7.** $15\frac{1}{2}$% **8.** $14\frac{1}{2}$%
9. 16% **10.** $16\frac{1}{2}$% **11.** **a.** \$2 **b.** \$98
12. **a.** \$4.50 **b.** \$170.50 **13.** **a.** \$8.40 **b.** \$261.60

14. a. $13.68 b. $76.32 15. a. $4.18 b. $45.82
16. a. $52.23 b. $53.30 c. $1294.77 d. $1293.66
17. a. $18.48 b. $19.88 c. $422.52 d. 421.13
18. a. $95.79 b. $98.43 c. $1044.21 d. $1041.61
19. a. $104.13 b. $120.04 c. $1413.39 d. $1397.43
20. a. $2304 b. 17% 21. a. $24 b. $14\frac{1}{2}$%
22. a. $2132 b. 17% 23. a. $134 b. $16\frac{1}{2}$%
24. $17\frac{1}{2}$% 25. a. $4 b. $196
26. a. $9 b. $341
27. a. $72 b. $66 c. $9.23 d. $254.77
28. a. $225 b. $68.06 c. $59.21 d. $553.33
29. a. $120 b. $51.11 c. $4.21 d. $149.12
30. a. $23,532 b. $570 c. $18,184
31. a. $562 b. $554 32. a. $8 b. 4% ($537 pmt)
33. a. $22,344 b. $22,637
c. $22,933 d. About $300
34. $367.47; $14,228.80 35. $632.99; $10,423.67
36. Answers will vary. If the loan required n payments and the debtor wishes to pay off the loan with r payments remaining, the debtor may feel that he is due a refund of r/n of the finance charge. The Rule of 78 would give the debtor a refund of only $\frac{r(r+1)}{n(n+1)}$ of the finance charge. Thus, the Rule of 78 charges the debtor the additional fraction $\frac{n-r}{n+1}$ of the finance charge as a penalty for the early payoff.
37. 14.3% (0.3% more than answer to problem 1)
38. 15.3% (0.3% more than answer to problem 2)
39. 16.9% (0.9% more than answer to problem 3)
40. 18.5% (1% more than answer to problem 4)
41. 17.7% (0.7% more than answer to problem 5)
42. 19.7% (1.7% more than answer to problem 6)
43. 17.1% (1.6% more than answer to problem 7)
44. 14.6% (0.1 % more than answer to problem 8)
45. 17.6% (1.6% more than answer to problem 9)
46. 17.6% (1.1% more than answer to problem 10)

Web It Exercises

3. a. $2167 for the lease; $2250 for the loan
b. $10,283 c. $7633 d. Buying is cheaper.

Exercises 13.4

1. a. Yes b. Yes c. Yes
2. a. No. They qualify up to $90,000 only.
b. Yes. They qualify up to $692.31.
c. Yes. They qualify up to $840.
3. a. $61,600 b. $15,400 c. $2310
4. a. $57,000 b. $3000 c. $1800
5. $526.27 6. $637.27 7. $935.10 8. $923.93
9. $1282.64 10. $999.83
11. a. $1350 b. $44,437.50
12. a. $4500 b. $146,625
13. a. $2250 b. $73,237.50
14. a. $2850 b. $92,862.50
15. a. $46,200 b. $44,437.50 c. $374.99
16. a. $156,000 b. $146,625 c. $879.09
17. a. $75,100 b. $72,850 c. $538.36
18. a. $95,500 b. $92,862.50 c. $1176.38
19. a. $3000 b. $667.64
20. a. $18,000 b. $721.98
21. a. $3000 b. $813.04
22. a. $20,000 b. $799.00
23. a. $439 b. 360 c. $158,040
d. $108,040 e. Less
24. a. $281.75 b. 360
c. $101,430 d. The price is less than the interest.
25. a. $11,185 b. $549 c. $563.04
26. a. $9032.50 b. $613.58 c. $627.51
27. a. $25,630 b. $872.80 c. $885.92
28. a. $39,977.50 b. $1064.38 c. $1085.06
29. a. $10,467 b. $812.70
30. a. $4720 b. $596.43
31. Answers will vary. 32. Answers will vary.
33. On a loan of $100,000 at 9% for 30 years, the total interest will be $189,800, which is more than the price of the house. On a $50,000 loan under the same terms, the total interest will be $94,900, which is more than the price of the house.
34. Answers will vary.

Web It Exercises

If possible, try to visit
http://www.mortgagecalc.com
Then select
http://www.mortgagecalc.com/mortgage/biweekly.html

2. a. Your monthly payment will be $733.76.
b. The total interest will be $164,155.25.
c. If you use a biweekly schedule, you will make two extra principal payments a year of $386.88 and the loan will terminate in 276 months (23 years)
3. Same
4. For a loan of $100,000 at an interest rate of 3.8815% for 15 years, the standard payment (principal and interest) will be $733.76.

Exercises 13.5

1. a. $3528 b. $106 c. $73.56
d. $76.44 e. 182.44 f. 5.07%
2. a. $1740 b. 0 c. $36.80
d. $63.20 e. $63.20 f. 3.56%
3. a. $5754 b. $144 c. $120
d. $126 e. $270 f. 4.60%
4. a. $12,830 b. $80 c. $256
d. −$286 e. −$206 f. −1.57%
5. a. $616.08 b. 0 c. $50
d. −$66.08 e. −$66.08 f. −9.92%
6. a. $11,862.60 b. $220 c. $50
d. $1687.40 e. $1907.40 f. 16.01%
7. a. $2235 b. $340 c. 15.04%
8. a. $41,195 b. $3400 c. 8.25%
9. a. $3035 b. $190 c. 6.21%
10. a. $3525 b. $150 c. 4.23%
11. a. $18,985 b. $890 c. 4.68%

12. a. $3635 b. $120 c. 3.28%
13. a. $180 b. $1800 14. a. $153.13 b. $1531.25
15. a. $337.50 b. $1350 16. a. $187.50 b. $750
17. a. $575 b. $5750 18. a. $660 b. $6600
19. a. $29.025 b. 1722 20. a. $7.01 b. 5706 shares
21. a. $29.06 b. 3441 22. a. $29.02 b. 861 shares
23. a. $29.05 b. 3442
24. a. $36,575 b. 2050 shares
25. a. 10% b. 3.75% c. 18.57%
26. a. 5% b. 2.5% c. 13.89%
27. a. 1.67% b. 1.56% c. 8.33%
28. a. 2% b. 1.25% c. 35%
29. a. 2.5% b. 8% c. 35%
30. a. 0.5% b. 3% c. 28.75%
32. Answers will vary. 34. Answers will vary.
35. 7.89% 36. 5.61% 37. 6.05%
38. 3.83% 39. 5.31% 40. 5.93%
41. $1428.57 42. $1666,67 43. $2000
44. $909.09 45. $833.33 46. $769.23

CHAPTER 14

Exercises 14.1

1. a. 131,257,328 b. 46%; 53% c. Yes, Obama won 53%
2. a. 122,295,345 b. 51%; 48% c. Yes, Bush won 51%.
3. a. 5,937,705 b. 930 c. 0.016% d. Yes
4. Bush
5. a. 20 b. 11 c. No d. C (7 votes)
6. a. 251 b. No c. T (220 votes)
7. a. S and T
   b. S has 280 votes; T has 220. Thus, S is the winner.
8. a. 35 b. 18 c. No d. A (13 votes)
9. a. A and C
   b. 23 prefer A over C; 12 prefer C over A. Thus, A is the winner.
10. Busch Gardens: 90 points
    Disney World: 85 points
11. Disney World wins.
12. Busch Gardens wins: 3 points
13. O (orange) wins with 11 first-place votes.
14. 19 people prefer G (2 green peppers) over O (orange); G (2 green peppers) wins.
15. J ($\frac{1}{2}$ cup fresh orange juice) wins with 66 points.
16. J ($\frac{1}{2}$ cup fresh orange juice) is the winner.
17. J wins with 3 points.
18. Adams 19. Adams 20. Coca-Cola
21. a. 12 b. 40 c. 15 d. 18 e. Cappuccino
22. a. 6 b. 7 c. 6 d. 8 e. Mr. Davis
23. No 24. Beijing (32) 25. Beijing 26. Sydney
27. Berlin (277 points) 28. Berlin (189 points)
29. Manchester
30. Berlin (189), Manchester (187), Sydney (171), Beijing (169), Istanbul (164)
31. Sydney (45 votes)
32. Sydney (45), Beijing, (43), Manchester and Istanbul (tie, 41), Berlin (9)
33. Rio de Janeiro 34. No 35. No
36. Madrid and Rio de Janeiro 37. Madrid
38. a. Paris b. London
39. Coala Cola (15) 40. Best 41. Best Cola (93)
42. Assign 5-4-1-0 points to first, second, third and last place. The results are:
    A: 157 B: 153 C: 85 D: 105
    Assigning 10-9-1-0 yields:
    A: 332 B: 303 C: 160 D: 205

Exercises 14.2

1. a. W b. P (65 votes) c. Yes d. W
2. a. L (La Septima) b. L (La Septima)
   c. No d. L (La Septima)
3. a. C
   b. No. L wins under the plurality method, but C wins under the Borda count method.
4. a. Yes, Cats is preferred. b. Yes, Cats wins under plurality.
5. a. Yes. Staples (S) is preferred.
   b. Yes. S wins under the plurality method, too.
6. No. L (Los Angeles) is the winner of the first election but does not win the second election after obtaining additional support.
7. Yes. Washington, DC (D), is the winner of the first election and also the winner of the second election with H removed.
8. No. D (Washington, DC) wins the first election, but H wins the second election when A is removed.
9. a. A b. Yes. A c. A d. Yes. A e. C
   f. The majority criterion g. No. A wins.
   h. Majority criterion (C wins under Borda, but A has a majority); Condorcet (C wins under Borda, but A wins head-to-head); irrelevant alternatives (C wins under Borda, but B's dropping out causes C to lose to A).
10. a. B b. Yes. B c. A
    d. Condorcet (A wins under plurality, but B wins under head-to-head).
    e. No. B wins.
    f. Irrelevant alternatives (A wins under plurality, but C dropping out causes A to lose to B).
    g. B h. Yes, B i. None
11. a. D b. C c. Yes. C
    d. Condorcet (D wins under the plurality with elimination method, but C wins under the head-to-head method).
12. a. C b. B
    c. Monotonicity (C wins under plurality with elimination, gains additional support, but loses to B).
13. a. B b. Yes c. None
14. a. A b. No. B
    c. Irrelevant (A wins under comparison, but C dropping out causes A to lose to B).
15. a. three b. six c. ten d. $n(n - 1)/2$
16. a. 2 b. 3 c. 4 d. $n - 1$
17. See the discussion on page 835. Answers will vary.
18. See the discussion on page 835. Answers will vary.

19. See the discussion on page 836. Answers will vary.
20. See the discussion on page 838. Answers will vary.
21. See the discussion on page 838. Answers will vary.
22. See the discussion on page 836. Answers will vary.
23. See Table 14.22, page 838. Answers will vary.
24. See the discussion on page 840. Answers will vary.

Exercises 14.3

1. a. $200,110,285 b. $9255 c. $14,675
2. UF: $385,484,926; FGC: $26,774,414
3. USF: $266,729,578; UWF: $66,858,492
4. a. 1081.105 b. FAU: 17.716; UCF: 27.758
5. a. 681.815 b. FAU: 15.730; UCF: 26.858
6.

	Students	*Quota*	*Initial*	*Extra*	*Final*
UF	41.652	38.4739	38		38
FSU	30.689	28.3474	28		28
FAMU	11.324	10.46	10		10
USF	31.555	29.1473	29		29
FAU	19.153	17.6916	17	1	18
UWF	7.790	7.1956	7		7
UCF	30.009	27.7193	27	1	28
FIU	30.096	27.7996	27	1	28
UNF	11.360	10.4932	10	1	11
FGC	2.893	2.6723	2	1	3
Total	**216.521**		**195**	**5**	**200**

7.

	FTE	*Quota*	*Initial*	*Extra*	*Final*
UF	29,646	43.4810	43		43
FSU	21,195	31.0861	31		31
FAMU	8064	11.8273	11	1	12
USF	18,176	26.6583	26	1	27
FAU	10,725	15.7301	15	1	16
UWF	4556	6.6822	6	1	7
UCF	18,312	26.8577	26	1	27
FIU	17,434	25.5700	25		25
UNF	6697	9.8223	9	1	10
FGC	1558	2.2851	2		2
Total	**136,363**		**194**	**6**	**200**

No

8.

SQ	*R-Down*	*Actual*
15/1.2 = 12.5	12	12
30/1.2 = 25	25	25
12/1.2 = 10	10	10
8/1.2 = 6.67	6	6 + 1 = 7
25/1.2 = 20.83	20	20 + 1 = 21
	73	**75**

9.

State	*Cases*	*Quota*	*Initial*	*Extra*	*Final*
CAL	5637	22.7748	22	1	23
FL	5683	22.9607	22	1	23
NY	7655	30.9280	30	1	31
TEX	3715	15.0095	15		15
NJ	2061	8.3269	8		8
Total	**24,751**		**97**	**3**	**100**

10.

College	*Students*	*SQ*	*Rounded Down*	*Delegates*
Agriculture	2500	19.23	19	19
Arts	500	3.85	3	4
Business	3000	23.08	23	23
Engineering	4000	30.77	30	31
Science	3000	23.08	23	23

11.

Activity	*Participants*	*Quota 5.35*	*Modified 5.25*	*Final*
Exercise	150	28.0374	28.5714	28
Sports	90	16.8224	17.1429	17
Charity	85	15.8879	16.1905	16
Home repair	130	24.2991	24.7619	24
Computer hobbies	80	14.9533	15.2381	15
Total	**535**			**100**

12.

Charity	*Donation*	*Quota 23.5333*	*Modified 23.3*	*Final*
Salvation Amy	1,230	52.2663	52.7897	52
YMCA	630	26.7705	27.0386	27
Fidelity Inv.	570	24.221	24.4635	24
Amer. Cancer	560	23.796	24.0343	24
Amer. Red C	540	22.9462	23.1760	23
Total	**3,530**			**150**

13.

Pet	*Cost*	*Quota 1.08*	*Modified 1.08*	*Final*
Dogs	190	175.9259	175.9259	176
Cats	110	101.8519	101.8519	102
Birds	10	9.2593	9.2593	9
Horses	230	212.9630	212.9630	213
Total	**540**			**500**

14.

Continent	*Immigration*	*Quota 0.9286*	*Modified 0.928*	*Final*
Europe	90	96.9231	96.9828	97
Asia	220	236.9231	237.0690	237
North America	255	274.6154	274.7845	275
South America	45	48.4615	48.4914	48
Africa	40	43.0769	43.1034	43
Total	**650**			**700**

15.

Park	*Acreage*	*Quota 20*	*Modified 20.5*	*Final*
Lake Park	600	30	29.2683	30
E. G. Simmons	470	23.5	22.9268	23
Lettuce Lake	240	12	11.7073	12
Lithia Springs	160	8	7.8049	8
Eureka Springs	30	1.5	1.4634	2
Total	**1500**			**75**

16.

State	*Area Codes*	*Quota 2.8*	*Modified 3.08*	*Final*
Texas	21	7.5	6.8182	7
California	20	7.1429	6.4935	7
Florida	12	4.2857	3.8961	4
Ohio	10	3.5714	3.2468	4
Colorado	7	2.5	2.2727	3
Total	**70**			**25**

		Dade	*Broward*	*Hills*	*Orange*	*Pinellas*
17. a.	SD = 930					
b.	Standard Quota	35.48	22.58	18.28	11.83	11.83
c.	Hamilton's Method	35	23	18	12	12
18. a.	Modified Quota	36.02	22.92	18.56	12.01	12.01
b.	Jefferson's Method	36	22	18	12	12
19. a.	Modified Quota	34.79	22.14	17.92	11.60	11.60
b.	Adam's Method	35	23	18	12	12
20.	Webster's Method	35	23	18	12	12

		SF Gen	*JH*	*Mass*	*UCSF*	*Sloan*
21. a.	SD = 1.7					
b.	Standard Quota	58.82	42.35	36.47	32.94	29.41
c.	Hamilton's Method	59	42	37	33	29
22. a.	Modified Quota	59.719	42.998	37.026	33.443	29.860
b.	Jefferson's Method	59	42	37	33	29
23. a.	Modified Quota	58.011	41.768	35.967	32.486	29.006
b.	Adams's Method	59	42	36	33	30
24.	Webster's Method	59	42	37	33	29

25. a. A: $20,000 B: $40,000 C: $60,000 D: $80,000
b. They get the same amounts as in part (**a**). **c.** Yes
26. Answers will vary. **27.** Answers will vary.
28. a. Adams **b.** Hamilton and Jefferson **c.** Webster

Exercises 14.4

1. a. Yes. With 30 seats, α, β, and δ get 6, 8, and 16 seats, respectively. With 31 seats, α, β, and δ get 5, 9, and 17 seats, respectively. So, α *loses* one seat (from 6 to 5) when seats are *increased* from 30 to 31.
b. No
2. a. No
b. Yes. With 114 seats A, B, C, and D get 21, 42, 27, and 24 seats, respectively. With 115 seats A, B, C, and D get 20, 43, 27, and 25 seats, respectively. So, A loses one seat (from 21 to 20) when seats are increased to 115.
3. Yes. Six Flags Magic Mountain goes from 8 to 7 tickets.
4. Yes.
a. Hispanics **b.** Whites and Asians **c.** Blacks
5. a. 1, 4, and 6 million, respectively
b. 2, 4, and 5 million, respectively
c. Kansas (12.63%)
d. Yes. Kansas's population increased by 12.63%, but contributions decreased from $6 to $5 million, while Delaware, with a smaller 10.91% increase, got an extra million.
6. a. 72,10, and 18, respectively
b. 71, 11, and 18
c. No. Even though A lost one seat and B gained one, the percent growth for A was 8.99% while that for B was 16%. (B deserved it more!)
7. a. 2, 4, and 7, respectively
b. 3, 4, and 6, respectively
c. Yes. Even though C's growth rate was 9.78% and A's was 8.99%, C lost a seat and A gained one.
d. C will be unhappy.

8. a. 8, 4, 10, 11, and 17, respectively.
   b. 8, 5, 10, 11, and 16, respectively.
   c. Yes. Even though state B did not grow at all (0%), it gained one seat. On the other hand, E grew at a modest 0.34% rate but lost one seat.
   d. E would be unhappy.
9. a. 30 for P and 11 for S
   b. Yes. The new apportionment is 29 for P, 12 for S, and 8 for A, so P lost one manager and S gained one.
10. a. 22 for A and 8 for B.
    b. No. A and B still get 22 and 8 seats, respectively.
11. a. 90 for A and 10 for B
    b. Yes. The new apportionment is 89 for A and 11 for B, so A lost one seat and B gained one.

CHAPTER 15

Exercises 15.1

1. The degrees of vertices *A*, *B*, *C*, *D*, and *E* are 1, 1, 1, 0 and 3, respectively.
2. The degrees of vertices *A*, *B*, *C*, *D*, *E*, and *F* are 3, 3, 1, 2, 4, and 1, respectively.
3. The degrees of vertices *A*, *B*, *C*, and *D* are 5, 3, 4, and 6, respectively.
4. The degree of each vertex is 7.
5. Not a subgraph (Each edge needs two endpoints.)
6. Subgraph 7. Subgraph
8. Not a subgraph (Edge *c* needs 2 endpoints.)
9. Path from *A* to *D* 10. Not a path
11. Circuit based at *A* 12. Not a path
13. Path from *A* to *G* 14. Circuit based at *G*
15. Not a path 16. Circuit based at *F* 17. Connected
18. Disconnected 19. Disconnected 20. Connected
21. Complete 22. Complete 23. Not complete
24. Not complete 25. Complete 26. Not complete
27. Simple 28. Not simple 29. Simple
30. Not simple
32. A circuit is a path with one extra condition: the starting and ending point is the same.
33. Represent each computer as a *vertex* and the connecting wires as *edges* as shown in the diagram below.

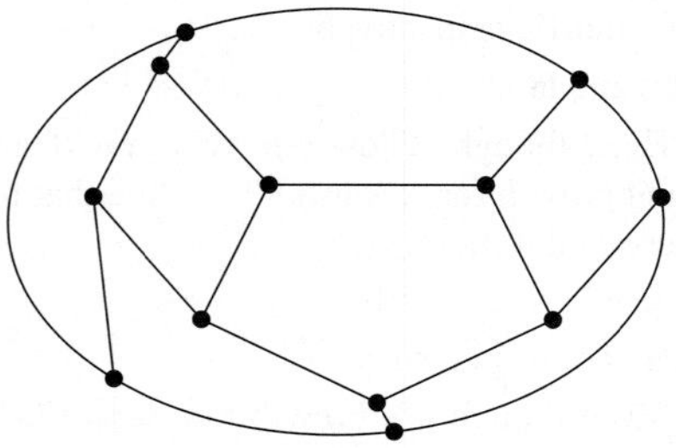

Exercises 15.2

1. Euler path from *D* to *B*
2. Neither (This sequence of edges does not even represent a path.)
3. Euler circuit based at *A*
4. Neither (This sequence of edges represents a circuit based at *A*, but is not an Euler circuit because edge *f* is not used.)
5. Each vertex has even degree, so the graph has an Euler circuit based at each vertex.
6. The graph has two vertices of odd degree; thus there is an Euler path from either odd vertex to the other.
7. Each vertex has even degree, so the graph has an Euler circuit based at each vertex.
8. The graph has 4 vertices of odd degree, so it is not traversable.
9. Each vertex has even degree, so the graph has an Euler circuit based at each vertex.
10. The graph has 6 vertices of odd degree, so it is not traversable.
11. There are many correct solutions; for example, [*a*, *b*, *c*, *d*, *e*, *f*, *g*, *i*, *j*, *h*] is an Euler circuit.
12. There are many correct solutions; for example, [*a*, *b*, *c*, *d*, *e*, *f*, *g*] is an Euler circuit.
13. There are many correct solutions; for example, [*a*, *b*, *e*, *f*, *h*, *g*, *d*, *c*] is an Euler circuit.
14. There are many correct solutions: for example, [*a*, *b*, *c*, *f*, *e*, *d*, *g*, *l*, *k*, *m*, *h*, *i*, *j*] is an Euler circuit.
15. There are many correct solutions; for example, [*a*, *b*, *c*, *d*, *e*, *f*, *g*, *h*, *i*] is an Euler circuit.
16. There are many correct solutions: for example, [*a*, *b*, *c*, *d*, *e*, *f*, *g*, *h*, *i*, *j*, *k*, *l*, *m*, *n*, *o*] is an Euler circuit.
17. There are many correct solutions; for example, [*a*, *b*, *c*, *d*, *e*, *f*, *g*, *h*, *i*, *j*, *k*, *l*] is an Euler circuit.
18. There are many correct solutions; for example, [*a*, *b*, *d*, *c*, *e*, *f*] is an Euler circuit.
19. We represent the streets as labeled edges and the intersections as vertices. The result is shown.

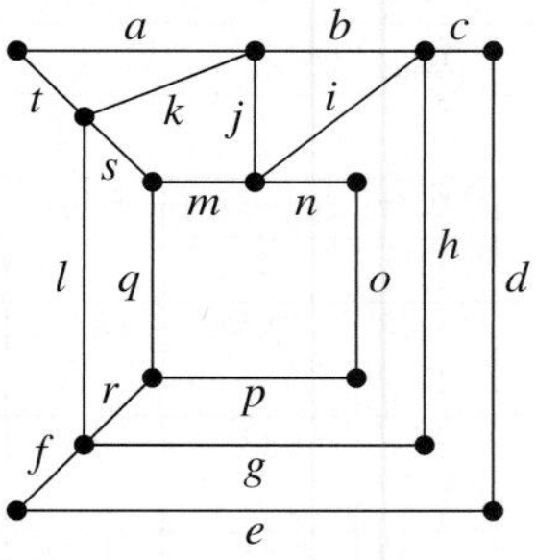

There are many correct solutions that start at either vertex of odd degree. For example, [*s*, *t*, *a*, *b*, *c*, *d*, *e*, *f*, *g*, *h*, *i*, *j*, *k*, *l*, *r*, *p*, *o*, *n*, *m*, *q*] is a possible Euler path.

20. We represent the streets as labeled edges and the intersections as vertices. The result is as follows.

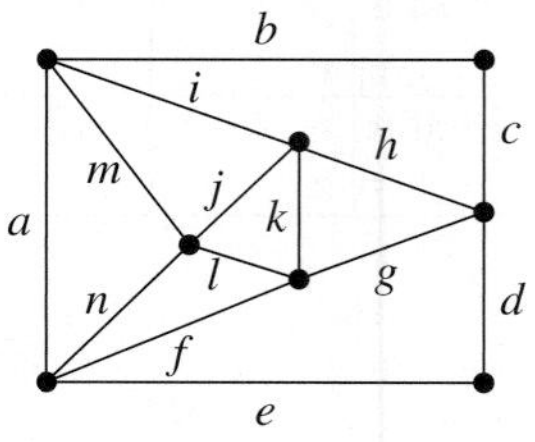

There are many correct solutions, and you can start at any vertex. For example, [*a*, *b*, *c*, *d*, *e*, *f*, *g*, *h*, *i*, *m*, *j*, *k*, *l*, *n*] is an Euler circuit.

21. We represent the streets as labeled edges and the intersections as vertices. The result is shown.

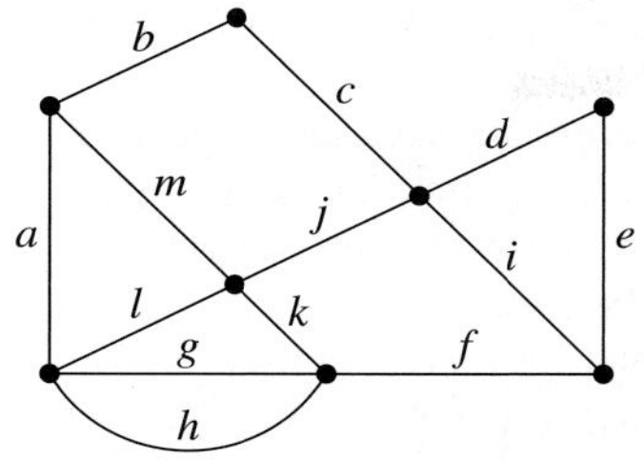

There are many correct solutions that start at either vertex of odd degree. For example, [*a*, *l*, *m*, *b*, *c*, *j*, *k*, *g*, *h*, *f*, *i*, *d*, *e*] is a possible Euler path.

22. We represent the streets as labeled edges and the intersections as vertices. The result is as follows.

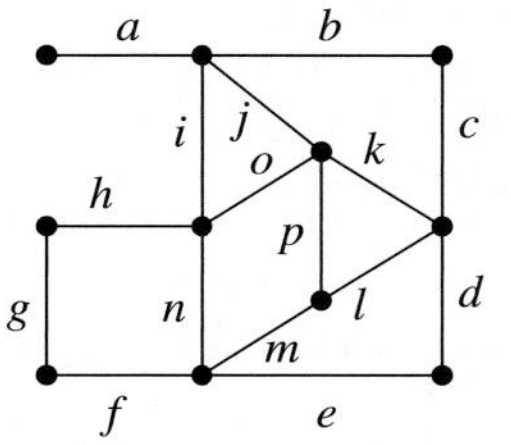

There are many correct solutions that start at either vertex of odd degree. For example, [*a*, *b*, *c*, *d*, *e*, *f*, *g*, *h*, *i*, *j*, *k*, *l*, *m*, *n*, *o*, *p*] is a possible Euler path.

24. The problem asks whether it is possible to travel over each of the seven bridges of Königsberg once (and only once) and arrive back at the original starting point.

25. There are 3 regions, 5 edges, and 4 vertices. Thus, $X(G) = 3 - 5 + 4 = 2$.

26. $X(G) = 4 - 6 + 4 = 2$

27. There are 9 regions, 12 edges, and 5 vertices. Thus, $X(G) = 9 - 12 + 5 = 2$.

28. $X(G) = 5 - 9 + 6 = 2$

29. There are 6 regions, 8 edges, and 4 vertices. Thus, $X(G) = 4 - 8 + 6 = 2$

30. $X(G) = 2$ for every graph

Exercises 15.3

1. Hamilton circuit

2. Neither (The sequence does not even represent a path.)

3. Neither **4.** Hamilton circuit

5. The length of the path is $8 + 3 + 2 + 4 = 17$.

6. The length of the circuit is 30.

7. The length of the path is $5 + 5 + 7 + 4 = 21$.

8. The length of the path is 12.

9. Recall that the graph K_4 has $(4 - 1)!/2 = 3$ distinct Hamilton circuits based at vertex *A*. Their lengths are $5 + 7 + 5 + 5 = 22$, $5 + 3 + 5 + 4 = 17$, and $5 + 3 + 7 + 4 = 19$.

10. Recall that the graph K_4 has $(4 - 1)!/2 = 3$ distinct Hamilton circuits based at vertex *B*. Their lengths are: $7 + 5 + 5 + 5 = 22$, $7 + 4 + 5 + 3 = 19$, and $5 + 4 + 5 + 3 = 17$.

11. The nearest neighbor method determines the circuit with length $2 + 2 + 4 + 6 = 14$.

12. There is more than one answer. One possibility is the circuit with length $2 + 6 + 5 + 3 = 16$.

13. There is more than one answer. One possibility is the circuit with length $2 + 1 + 1 + 5 + 2 = 11$.

14. The nearest neighbor method determines the circuit with length $1 + 1 + 1 + 5 + 2 = 10$.

15. There is more than one answer. One possibility is the circuit with length $2 + 1 + 1 + 1 + 9 + 2 = 16$.

16. There is more than one answer. One possibility is the circuit with length $3 + 7 + 2 + 1 + 3 + 7 = 23$.

17. The most efficient delivery route has length $8 + 12 + 19 + 11 = 50$.

18. The most efficient delivery route has length $21 + 17 + 38 + 29 = 105$ miles.

19. Using the nearest-neighbor method, we get $15 + 13 + 17 + 25 = 70$.

20. The most efficient delivery route has length $23.5 + 18.6 + 13.9 + 29.1 = 85.1$ miles.

22. A Hamilton path is a path that meets every vertex of the graph exactly one time. A Hamilton circuit is a circuit that meets every vertex of the graph exactly one time (except for the base, of course).

24. An Euler circuit traverses every edge exactly one time, while a Hamilton circuit meets every vertex exactly one time before returning to the base.

25. There are numerous answers depending on your choice of starting point.

26. There are numerous answers, depending on your choice of starting point.

27. There are numerous answers depending on your choice of starting point.

28. There are numerous answers, depending on your choice of starting point.

Exercises 15.4

1. Tree **2.** Tree

3. Not a tree **4.** Not a tree

5. There are many correct answers. One possibility is $\{a, b, c\}$.

6. There are many correct answers. One possibility is $\{a, b, d, i, j\}$.

7. There are many correct answers. One possibility is $\{a, b, c, d\}$.

8. This graph is already a tree, so there is only one correct solution: $\{a, b, c, d\}$.

9. There are many correct answers. One possibility is $\{a, b, c, d\}$.

10. There are many correct answers. One possibility is $\{a, b, c, j\}$.

11. The following graph indicates a minimal spanning tree (there is more than one). Its weight is $1 + 2 + 4 + 4 + 5 = 16$.

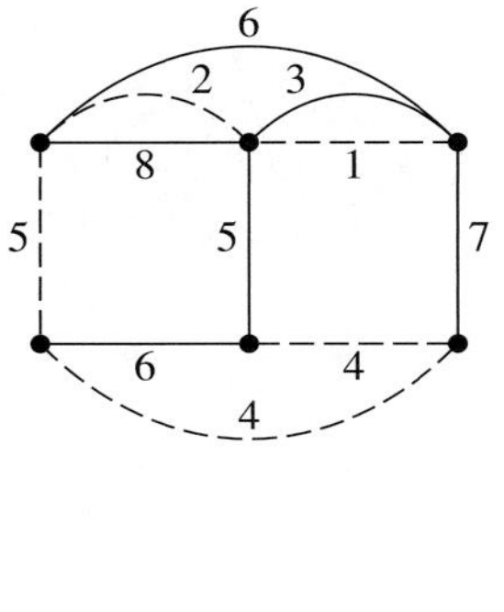

12. Applying Kruskal's algorithm provides the solution indicated below. Its weight is $1 + 1 + 2 + 4 = 8$.

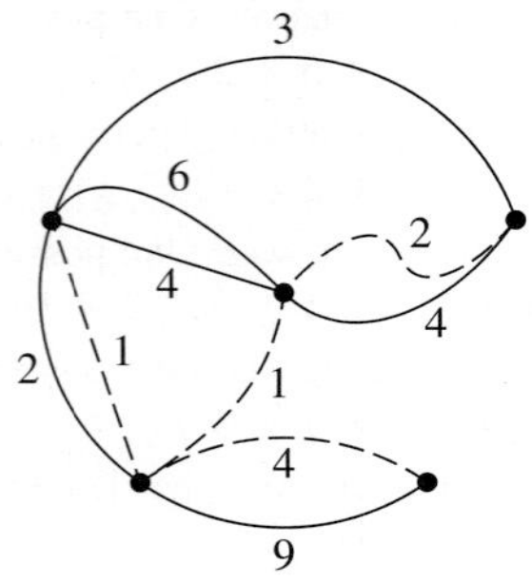

13. Applying Kruskal's algorithm provides the solution indicated in the graph. Its weight is $1 + 2 = 3$.

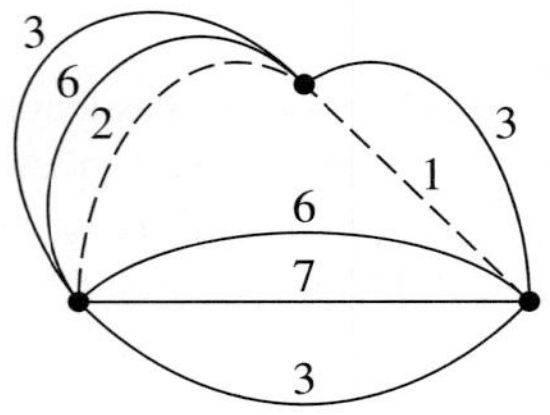

14. The graph below indicates a minimal spanning tree (there is more than one). Its weight is $1 + 1 + 1 + 1 + 1 + 2 + 2 + 2 + 2 = 13$.

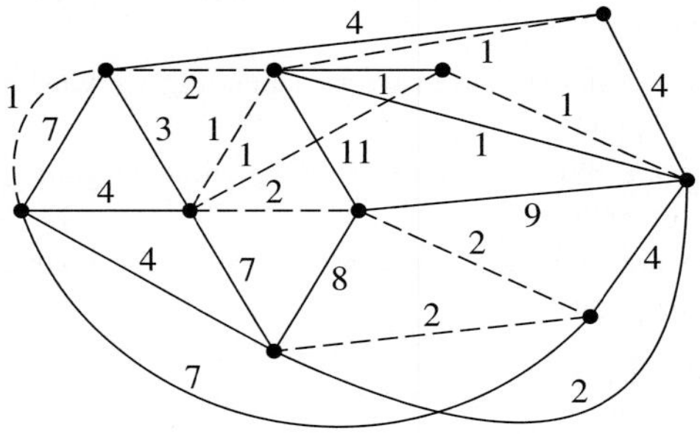

15. Applying Kruskal's algorithm provides the solution indicated in the graph. Its weight is $1 + 2 + 2 + 3 + 3 = 11$.

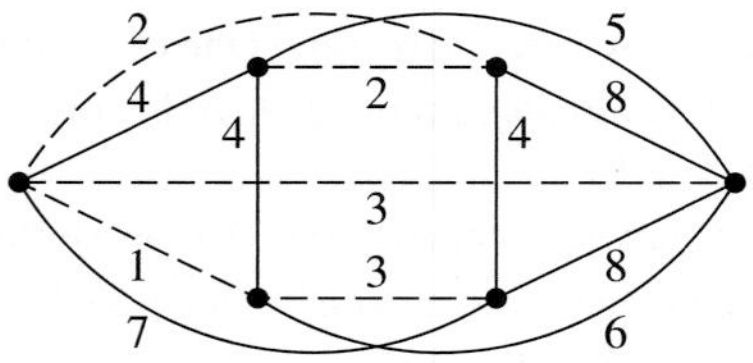

16. Applying Kruskal's algorithm provides the solution indicated below. Its weight is $2 + 3 + 3 + 3 = 11$.

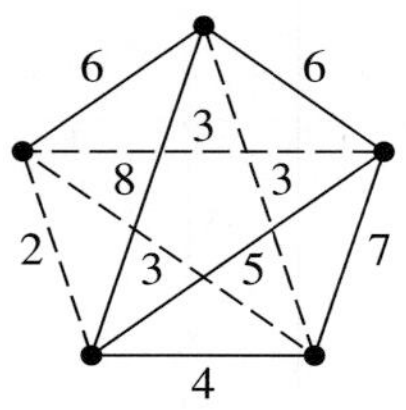

17. Applying Kruskal's algorithm, we find that the most economical way to link all the cities is a network of length $3.8 + 4.9 + 5.4 + 7.8 = 21.9$, representing a cost of \$21.9 million.

18. Applying Kruskal's algorithm, we find that the most economical way to link all cities is a network of length $5 + 7 + 8 + 10 + 14 = 44$ representing a cost of \$44 million. (Answers may vary.)

19. The minimal cost is $126 + 132 + 135 + 141 = \$534$.

20. The minimal cost is: $57 + 89 + 96 + 107 = \$349$.

22. A spanning tree is a subgraph that is connected, has no simple circuits, and contains all of the vertices of the original graph.

24. A tree is a connected forest.

25. Neither Euler or Hamilton circuits nor paths would be appropriate here because both require that every edge be used. For this problem, we are not concerned about edges. In fact, if we can leave out an edge and still connect all the cities, it will be cheaper and, thus, more desirable. The tree shown is a possible answer! Is it the cheapest way? Can you find a better way?

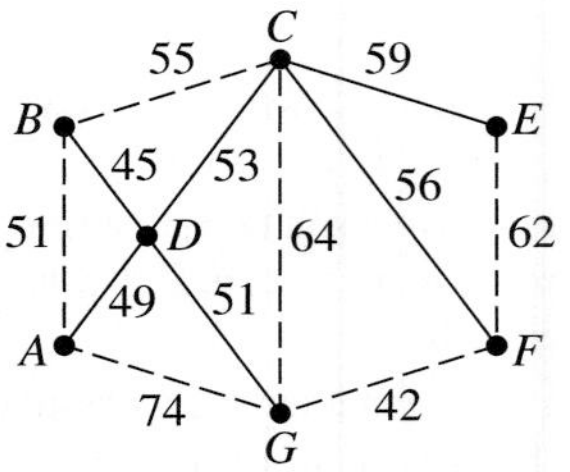

APPENDIX

Exercises A.1

1. a. 1000 **b.** 0.001 **c.** 100 **d.** 1000
2. a. Liters **b.** Kilograms **c.** Millimeters **d.** Centimeters **e.** Grams
3. (c) **4. a.** 4 m by 5 m **5.** (a) **6. c.** 100 m
7. (a) **8. b.** 19 cm
9. a. 8000 **b.** 400 **c.** 34.09 **d.** 4.94
10. a. 8.413 **b.** 7300 **c.** 0.319 **d.** 0.758
11. 2.1 m **12.** 0.6 **13.** 1500 m **14.** 160
15. a. 157.5 m **b.** 26.25 m **c.** 15.75 m
16. a. 6300 **b.** 0.0723 **c.** 1300 **d.** 0.003479
17. 1000 liters **18.** Less **19.** 3.5 g **20.** 0.1 g
21. 10 liters **22.** 76 **23.** 250 milliliters
24. a. 10,000 **b.** 2640
25. a. 14,000 **b.** 4800 **c.** 0.0028 **d.** 3900
26. a. 0.037 **b.** 0.000049 **c.** 0.041 **d.** 3.978
27. 1000 g **28. b.** 1 liter **29.** (b) **30. c.** 3.5 kg
31. 15 **32.** 45 **33.** 30 **34.** −20 **35.** −30
36. −18 approx **37.** 50 **38.** 77 **39.** 14 **40.** 5
41. 260°C **42.** 55 **43.** 105.8°F **44.** 158
45. 37°C **46.** 6170 **47. a.** 5°C **b.** 100°C
48. −50° C **49.** −108.4°F **50.** Answers will vary.
51. About 157 cm

52. (i) and (d), (ii) and (e), (iii) and (b), (iv) and (c), (v) and (a)
53. (i) and (d), (ii) and (c), (iii) and (e), (iv) and (a), (v) and (b)
54. $C = K - 273.15$

Exercises A.2

1. 20.32 **2.** 13.208 (Both 5.2 and 2.54 are exact.)
3. 4.73 **4.** 9.85 **5.** 46.61 **6.** 1.10 **7.** 4.03
8. 4.91 **9.** 6.44 **10.** 9.82 **11.** 2.30 **12.** 8.69
13. 2.72 **14.** 3.63 **15.** 11.00 **16.** 2.64 **17.** 4.73
18. 5.77 **19.** 8.59 **20.** 11.7 **21.** 2.46 **22.** 2620
23. 16.39 **24.** 0.06 **25.** 182.80 **26.** 274 **27.** 0.85
28. 1.09 **29.** 64 km/hr **30.** **a.** 35 km **b.** 150 km
31. About 56.7 m **32.** 271 **33.** 28,900 ft **34.** 61.0
35. 560 kg **36.** 18.9 **37.** 48.3 km **38.** 77.6
39. About 114 lb **40.** 13.5 **41.** About 298 m **42.** 33.0
43. 12.7 metric tons **44.** 13.6 **45.** 17.0 km/liter
46. Answers will vary. Important items are that the metric system is a simple decimal system while the U. S. customary system is a mixed up batch of units such as the inch, the foot, the yard, and the mile.
47. 1.18 mi **48.** 160 **49.** 96.5 m **50.** 4.24
51. About 102-66.0-96.5 **52.** $1.24 **53.** About 24 km
54. 235 **55.** About 19 liters **56.** About 277,000
57. About 560,000 g

ENHANCED WebAssign

If you elect to use Enhanced WebAssign with this course, you will find problems in Enhanced WebAssign based on exercises from the textbook that are listed below. Visit www.webassign.net/cengage for the most up-to-date list of Enhanced WebAssign problems.

1.1 Inductive and Deductive Reasoning
11, 12, 13, 15, 17, 19, 21, 25, 26, 29, 35, 36, 37, 39

1.2 Estimation: A Problem-Solving Tool
1, 2, 3, 5, 7, 8, 13, 17, 23, 25, 31, 35, 46, 47

1.3 Graph Interpretation: A Problem-Solving Tool
5, 6, 7, 9, 11, 12, 13, 15, 29, 31, 32

2.1 Sets: A Problem-Solving Tool
1, 3, 7, 9, 16, 23, 25, 33, 38, 45, 51, 57, 64, 67, 70, 73, 77

2.2 Set Operations
1, 3, 7, 13, 14, 17, 21, 22, 27, 28, 35, 40, 45, 59, 67, 70, 75

2.3 Venn Diagrams
1, 7, 9, 12, 13, 16, 21, 31, 35, 37, 40, 45, 47, 72

2.4 The Number of Elements in a Set: A Problem-Solving Tool
1, 3, 5, 7, 16, 17, 19, 20, 23, 25, 28

2.5 Infinite Sets
1, 3, 5, 6, 9, 13, 17, 19, 20, 21, 22, 23

3.1 Statements
1, 7, 9, 11, 13, 19, 25, 31, 33, 37, 47, 53

3.2 Truth Tables: A Problem-Solving Tool
1, 7, 9, 10, 13, 14, 17, 20, 23, 31, 35, 47, 55, 60

3.3 The Conditional and the Biconditional
3, 6, 7, 9, 13, 21, 27, 29, 33, 37, 43, 51, 54, 55

3.4 Variations of the Conditional and Implications
1, 5, 9, 13, 17, 20, 25, 27, 30, 33, 39, 45, 51, 54

3.5 Euler Diagrams: A Problem-Solving Tool
5, 7, 14, 15, 19, 21, 25, 31, 34, 35, 37, 38

3.6 Truth Tables and Validity of Arguments
3, 4, 7, 8, 13, 21, 23, 24, 29, 33, 37, 41, 44, 45

4.1 Egyptian, Babylonian, and Roman Numeration Systems
8, 12, 17, 22, 27, 36, 40, 46, 48, 50, 52, 54, 57

4.2 The Hindu-Arabic (Decimal) System
5, 8, 11, 24, 28, 32, 44, 46, 48, 54

4.3 Number Systems with Bases Other Than 10
2, 10, 12, 14, 16, 18, 20, 22, 29, 32, 34, 36

4.4 Binary, Octal, and Hexadecimal Arithmetic
2, 6, 8, 12, 14, 16, 18, 22, 26, 28, 32, 35, 37, 39, 42, 47, 53

5.1 Number Theory: Primes and Composites
16, 24, 26, 28, 32, 34, 36, 41, 46, 50, 54, 60, 65, 67, 69, 71

5.2 Whole Numbers, Integers, and Order of Operations
4, 7, 105, 15, 19, 24, 35, 36, 41, 45, 53, 69, 72, 75, 78, 80, 84, 86, 91, 95, 97, 99

5.3 Operations with Rational Numbers, Expanded and Scientific Notation
7, 9, 100, 102, 105, 107, 108, 110, 112, 118, 15, 18, 24, 29, 32, 37, 41, 45, 50, 56, 63, 76, 86, 95, 125, 127

5.4 Rationals and Irrationals as Decimals: Percents
16, 21, 28, 35, 44, 52, 57, 64, 69, 78, 86, 88, 92, 99, 105, 107, 109, 111, 113, 119, 125

5.5 Radicals and Real Numbers
2, 12, 14, 16, 20, 26, 28, 36, 38, 42, 47, 53, 55, 58, 65

5.6 Number Sequences
1, 5, 8, 19, 22, 24, 26, 27, 31, 34, 36, 38, 41, 42, 44

6.1 Solutions of First-Degree (Linear) Sentences
2, 10, 14, 19, 24, 32, 34, 40, 45, 51, 58, 68, 73, 77, 84, 89, 91, 96, 98, 101, 113

6.2 Graphs of Algebraic Sentences
2, 4, 6, 10, 14, 20, 24, 28, 30, 38, 42, 48, 54, 55, 62

6.3 Sentences Involving Absolute Values
5, 8, 10, 13, 17, 19, 21, 24, 30, 35, 38, 40, 42, 44

6.4 Quadratic Equations
2, 6, 8, 11, 17, 19, 23, 30, 40, 48, 50, 58, 65, 69

6.5 Modeling and Problem Solving
1, 2, 5, 9, 11, 14, 18, 20, 25, 29, 33, 40, 48, 51

6.6 Ratio, Proportion, and Variation
2, 6, 7, 9, 18, 20, 25, 26, 30, 32, 34, 40, 41, 48

7.1 Graphing Relations and Functions
3, 10, 13, 17, 19, 23, 29, 35, 39, 45, 55, 61

7.2 Linear Functions, Relations, and Applications
3, 4, 7, 10, 14, 17, 19, 21, 25, 29, 30, 33

7.3 Slopes and Equations of a Line
1, 5, 11, 13, 17, 19, 25, 29, 37, 43, 45, 51, 59, 63, 67

7.4 Quadratic Functions and Their Graphs
1, 3, 6, 7, 9, 12, 13, 17, 20, 25, 29, 33, 36, 41

7.5 Exponential and Logarithmic Functions
1, 3, 5, 7, 9, 12, 15, 18, 27, 30, 33, 40, 44, 45

7.6 Two Linear Equations in Two Variables
1, 6, 8, 11, 15, 20, 21, 30, 32, 37, 43

7.7 Linear Inequalities
1, 3, 5, 11, 13, 15, 16, 25, 27, 29, 32, 39, 41

7.8 Linear Programming
1, 5, 13, 17, 21, 25

8.1 Points, Lines, Planes, and Angles
1, 3, 5, 7, 13, 15, 19, 29, 35, 43, 50, 56, 59, 71, 73, 77, 91

8.2 Triangles and Other Polygons
1, 5, 6, 9, 13, 19, 21, 25, 27, 30, 39, 40, 47, 55

8.3 Perimeter and Circumference
1, 5, 11, 12, 15, 16, 21, 25, 28, 32, 33, 36, 41, 43

8.4 Area Measure and the Pythagorean Theorem
3, 5, 7, 10, 11, 14, 25, 27, 52

8.5 Volume and Surface Area
1, 5, 16, 21, 27, 30, 36, 37, 49, 51, 53

8.6 Networks, Non-Euclidean Geometry, and Topology
1, 3, 4, 6, 7, 10, 11, 13, 17, 21, 22, 23, 29, 33, 41

8.7 Right Triangle Trigonometry
5, 6, 11, 15, 21, 27, 29, 43

9.1 Clock and Modular Arithmetic
6, 10, 16, 20, 24, 30, 37, 44, 48, 52, 56, 60, 66, 71, 74, 79, 81, 85, 95, 98, 103, 111

9.2 Abstract Mathematical Systems: Groups and Fields
1, 2, 4, 6, 10, 14, 20, 21, 26, 28, 50, 52, 54, 56

9.3 Game Theory
2, 4, 6, 8, 10, 12, 14, 18, 22, 28, 29

10.1 The Sequential Counting Principle (SCP): A Problem-Solving Tool
1, 4, 5, 6, 11, 16, 17, 23, 31, 33, 35, 39, 44

10.2 Permutations
3, 6, 7, 13, 15, 21, 22, 25, 27, 30, 31, 33, 34, 41

10.3 Combinations
3, 6, 13, 16, 17, 19, 20, 21, 24, 27, 29, 32, 33

10.4 Miscellaneous Counting Methods
1, 2, 6, 7, 9, 10, 11, 12, 13, 15, 19, 22, 23, 25

11.1 Sample Spaces and Probability
3, 7, 9, 10, 14, 16, 17, 27, 28, 31, 35, 41, 43, 46

11.2 Counting Techniques and Probability
1, 2, 5, 6, 7, 9, 10, 13, 16, 37, 39

11.3 Computation of Probabilities
1, 3, 7, 9, 12, 14, 15, 19, 23, 26, 27, 31, 32

11.4 Conditional Probability
1, 3, 4, 5, 9, 10, 11, 13, 15, 17, 18, 24

11.5 Independent Events
1, 3, 5, 7, 14, 15, 17, 27, 32, 37, 43, 45, 46

11.6 Odds and Mathematical Expectation
3, 5, 6, 7, 11, 15, 21, 25, 26, 27, 36

12.1 Sampling, Frequency Distributions, and Graphs
1, 5, 15, 16, 45, 47, 48, 51

12.2 Measures of Central Tendency: The Mean, Median, and Mode
1, 4, 5, 7, 11, 13, 22, 24, 25, 27, 31

12.3 Measures of Dispersion: The Range and Standard Deviation
1, 2, 4, 9, 11, 15, 19, 21, 22, 23, 25, 30

12.4 The Normal Distribution: A Problem-Solving Tool
3, 4, 5, 10, 11, 15, 19, 23, 25, 31, 35, 40

12.5 Statistical Graphs: A Problem-Solving Tool
5, 8, 9, 19, 23, 29, 31, 45, 51, 52

12.6 Making Predictions: Linear Regression
8, 9, 11, 13, 14, 17, 21, 23, 24, 39

12.7 Scattergrams and Correlation
1, 5, 7, 13, 14, 15, 21, 24, 25, 26, 27, 29, 30, 31

13.1 Interest, Taxes, and Discounts
12, 16, 17, 01a, 20, 023a, 027a, 030a, 33, 37, 39, 41, 49, 07a

13.2 Credit Cards and Consumer Credit
3, 5, 7, 11, 12, 15, 17, 19, 20, 21, 25, 26, 28

13.3 Annual Percentage Rate (APR) and the Rule of 78
1, 9, 11, 15, 16, 17, 21, 22, 25, 26, 29, 37, 38, 45

13.4 Buying a House
2, 3, 5, 7, 9, 11, 13, 15, 17, 19, 20, 22, 23, 26

13.5 Investing in Stocks, Bonds, and Mutual Funds
1, 5, 7, 11, 13, 16, 17, 20, 23, 27, 28, 36, 41, 45

14.1 Voting Systems
1, 6, 9, 20, 22, 27, 32, 38

14.2 Voting Objections
1, 5, 7, 11, 16

14.3 Apportionment Methods
1, 5, 11, 15, 21

14.4 Apportionment Objections
1, 7, 11

15.1 Introduction to Graph Theory
3, 5, 9, 21, 29

15.2 Euler Paths and Euler Circuits
2, 11, 15, 19, 21

15.3 Hamilton Paths and Hamilton Circuits
1, 7, 13, 17

INDEX

APPLICATIONS INDEX